EIGHTH EDITION

SCHROEDER'S
ANTIQUES
PRICE GUIDE

Edited By Sharon & Bob Huxford

COLLECTOR BOOKS
A Division of Schroeder Publishing Co., Inc.

On the cover::
  14" composition character doll, $395.00; 16" celluloid toddler, $365.00. Courtesy of *Patricia Smith's Doll Values, Antique to Modern, Sixth Series*.

  Cambridge Hunt Scene amber, gold-encrusted decanter, $300.00-350.00. Courtesy of *Very Rare Glassware of the Depression Years*, by Gene Florence.

  Windsor-type chair made by Quaint American Furniture, Stickly Brothers Company, $350.00. Courtesy of *Furniture of The Depression Era*, by Bob and Harriett Swedberg.

  Hall China star-shaped teapot with World's Fair Decoration, $285.00-300.00. Courtesy of *The Collector's Encyclopedia of Hall China*, by Margaret and Kenn Whitmyer.

  Whig Rose quilt ca. 1850, Greenfield, Massachusetts. Courtesy of *American Beauties: Rose & Tulip Quilts*, by Gwen Marston and Joe Cunningham. (No price available.)

Additional copies of this book may be ordered from:

COLLECTOR BOOKS
P.O. Box 3009
Paducah, Kentucky 42002-3009

@$12.95. Add $2.00 for postage and handling.

Copyright: Schroeder Publishing Co., Inc. 1990

Introduction

As the editors and staff of *Schroeder's*, our goal is to compile the most useful, comprehensive, and accurate background and pricing information possible. Our guide encompasses nearly 700 categories, many of which you will not find in other price guides. Our sources are varied; we use auction results, dealer lists, trade paper ads, and we consult with national collectors' clubs, recognized authorities, researchers, and appraisers. We have by far the largest Advisory Board of any similar publication on the market. Each year we add several new advisors and now have more than 240 who cover almost 500 categories. They go over our computer print-outs line by line, deleting listings that are misleading or too vague to be of merit; they often send background information and photos. We appreciate their assistance very much -- only through their expertise and experience in their special fields are we able to offer with confidence what we feel are useful, accurate evaluations that provide a sound understanding of the dealings in the market place today. Correspondence with so large an advisory panel adds months of extra work to an already monumental task, but we feel that to a very large extent this is the foundation that makes *Schroeder's* the success that it has become.

Our Directory, which you will find in the back of the book, lists each contributor by state. These are people who have allowed us to photograph various examples of merchandise from their show booths, sent us pricing information, or in any way have contributed to this year's book. Feel free to contact them; many will be glad to ship you the merchandise you need. If you happen to be traveling, consult the Directory for shops along your way. We also list clubs who have worked with us and auction houses who have agreed to permit us the use of photographs from their catalogs. Our Advisory Board lists only names and home states, so check the Directory for addresses and telephone numbers should you want to correspond with one of our experts. Remember that when you do, if you expect an answer from either an advisor or a contributor, please send a stamped, self-addressed envelope.

To be used to your best advantage, this guide should be regarded as a basic tool, a rule of thumb, only one source of the information you need to digest in order to become a knowledgeable dealer or collector. Antique shows, trade papers, collectors' books, and association with others sharing the same interests all contribute toward making you more keenly aware of market trends and thus educate you toward becoming a wise and confident buyer.

We have organized our topics alphabetically, following the most simple logic, usually either by manufacturer or by type of product. If you have difficulty in locating your subject, consult the index. Our guide is unique in that much more space has been allotted to background information than any other publication of this type, and it is easier to read due to the larger-than-average print. Our readers tell us that these are features they enjoy. To be able to do this, we have adopted a format of one-line listings wherein we describe the items to the fullest extent possible by using several common-sense abbreviations; they will be easy to read and understand if you will first take the time to quickly scan through them.

The Editors

Listing of Standard Abbreviations

The following is a list of abbreviations that have been used throughout this book in order to provide you with the most detailed descriptions possible in the limited space available. No periods are used after initials or abbreviations. When two dimensions are given, height is noted first. If only one dimension is listed, it will be height, except in the case of bowls, dishes, plates, or platters, when it will be diameter. The standard two-letter state abbreviations apply.

For glassware, if no color is noted, the glass is clear. Hyphenated colors, for example blue-green, olive-amber, etc., describe a single color tone; colors divided by a slash mark indicate two or more colors, i.e. blue/white. A number following the last comma in a listing indicates how many items are included in the lot price. Teapots, sugar bowls, and butter dishes are assumed to be 'with cover.' Condition is extremely important in determining market value. This year, in order to conserve space, the condition line has been left out of the narrative, except when our advisors requested that it remain, or when the category contained items of such a varied nature that we felt it advantageous to leave the line in to avoid confusion. Common sense suggests that art pottery, china, and glassware values would be given for examples in pristine, mint condition, while suggested prices for utility wares such as Redware, Mocha, and Blue and White Stoneware, for example, reflect the the probability that since such items were subjected to everyday use in the home they may show minor wear (which is acceptable) but no notable damage. Values for other categories reflect the best average condition in which the particular collectible is apt to be offered for sale without the dealer feeling it necessary to mention wear or damage. For instance, advertising items are assumed to be in excellent condition since mint items are scarce enough that when one is offered for sale the dealer will most likely make mention of that fact. The same holds true for Toys, Banks, Coin-Operated Machines, and the like. Paper ephemera is evaluated as if in very good to excellent condition unless otherwise noted. A basic rule of thumb is that an item listed as VG (very good) will bring 40% to 60% of its mint price (a first-hand, personal evaluation will enable you to make the final judgement); EX (excellent) is a condition midway between mint and very good, and values would correspond.

Am .... American	dvtl .... dovetail	lt .... light
appl .... applied	drw .... drawer	litho .... lithograph
att .... attributed to	ea .... each	mahog .... mahogany
bk .... back	emb ...... embossed, embossing	mk .... mark
bsk .... bisque	embr .... embroidered	MIG .... Made in Germany
b3m .... blown 3-mold	eng ...... engraved, engraving	M .... mint
bl .... blue	EX .... excellent	MIB .... mint in box
brn .... brown	ext .... exterior	MOP .... mother-of-pearl
bulb .... bulbous	ft. ftd ...... foot, feet, footed	mt, mtd ...... mount, mounted
cb .... cardboard	fr .... frame, framed	mc .... multicolor
CI .... cast iron	Fr .... French	NE .... New England
C .... century	G .... good	NM .... near mint
ca .... circa	grad .... graduated	NP .... nickel plated
compo .... composition	grpt .... grain painted	opal .... opalescent
c .... copyright	gr .... green	orig .... original
cr/sug ...... creamer and sugar	HP .... hand painted	o/w .... otherwise
X,Xd .... cross, crossed	hdl, hdld ...... handle, handled	pnt .... paint
c/s .... cup and saucer	imp .... impressed	pr .... pair
cvd .... carved	ind .... individual	pat .... patented
cvg .... carving	int .... interior	ped .... pedestal
dk .... dark	irid .... iridescent	pc .... piece
dtd .... dated	Invt T'print ...... Inverted Thumbprint	pk .... pink
decor .... decoration	lg .... large	pt .... pint
dia .... diameter	lav .... lavender	prof .... professional
Dia Quilt ...... Diamond Quilted	ldgl .... leaded glass	porc .... porcelain
dbl .... double	L .... length	rfn .... refinished

re .... regarding	
rpt .... repainted	
rpr .... repaired	
rpl .... replaced	
rstr .... restored	
rtcl .... reticulated	
rvpt ...... reverse painted	
rnd .... round	
s&p ...... salt and pepper	
sgn .... signed	
SP .... silverplated	
sz .... size	
sm .... small	
sq .... square	
std .... standard	
str .... straight	
trn ...... turned, turning	
turq .... turquoise	
uphl .... upholstered	
VG .... very good	
Vict .... Victorian	
wht .... white	
W .... width	
w/ .... with	
w/o .... without	
yel .... yellow	

A B C Plates

Children's plates featuring the alphabet as part of the design were popular from as early as 1820 until after the turn of the century. The earliest English creamware plates were decorated with embossed letters and prim moralistic verses; but the later Staffordshire products were conducive to a more relaxed mealtime atmosphere — often depicting playful animals and riddles or scenes of pleasant leisure-time activities. They were made around the turn of the century by American potters as well. All featured transfer prints, but color was sometimes brushed on by hand to add interest to the design. Braille plates were made for the blind, but these are rather scarce and therefore usually more valuable. You may also find an occasional bowl or mug. . . a matching set is rare.

In the Garden, Elsmore & Son, England, 8", $95.00.

Ceramic

Artist at easel in diamond center, 4 other scenes 135.00
Bear w/cubs, brn transfer, ABC rim, Staffordshire, 7⅜" 68.00
Bird on branch, cattails, ferns, Shaw, Burslem, 7¼" 48.00
Bowl, Dutch motif, Germany 60.00
Bowl, Ride a Stick Horse...Banbury Cross, Wood, Burslem, 6½" .25.00
Bowl, 2 kids in early car, ABC/animal rim, Germany, 7⅝" 48.00
Buffalo Hunt, mc transfer, Staffordshire, 7¼" 65.00
Canary, bullfinch, goldfinch, mc transfer, 6¾" 55.00
Candle Fish, Indian in canoe, Staffordshire, 7" 125.00
Children playing skip rope, Germany, 7" 45.00
Cricket Game, Staffordshire, 7½" 125.00
Donkey, gr transfer, 6" 50.00
Drive, couple in horse-drawn carriage, mc, Staffordshire, 6" ...110.00
Dutch children, group of 3, deaf signs, transfer, 6¼" 150.00
Dutch children w/goose, deaf signs, mc transfer, 8¼" 150.00
Elephant & tiger, Meakin, 6" 95.00
Elephant w/3 passengers, 6" 65.00
Evening Bathing Scene at Manhattan Beach, 7½" 85.00
Fox & Geese, polychrome, 8" 85.00
Gathering Cotton, mc transfer, Staffordshire, 5½" 195.00
General Grant, ABC rim, Staffordshire, 5" 150.00
General NP Banks, ABC rim, Staffordshire, rpr, 5⅛" 65.00
Harvest Home, Meakin, 5½" 65.00
Highland Dance, blk transfer, Staffordshire, 5¼" 85.00

Hush My Dear..., mother, baby, angels, Staffordshire, 5" 125.00
Indian Cinonca watches wagons/cavalcade..., 7½" 75.00
Lost, girl holds doll & cries, adults behind, unmk, 5⅜" 75.00
Matrimonial Ladder, couple in park, Staffordshire 200.00
Milk maid w/cows, ABC rim, Staffordshire, 5" 110.00
Mr & Mrs Rabbit, deaf signs, Aynsley & Co, 6¼" 150.00
Mug, gold trim, ABC rim, Germany 25.00
Mug, Jack in the Corner, brn transfer, Staffordshire, 2¾" 90.00
Mug, K&L w/illus, mc 80.00
Mug, W is for whipping, 4 children & switch, Staffordshire ...110.00
Niagara From Edge of American Falls, mc, 7½" 85.00
Organ Grinder, Staffordshire, 7½" 88.00
Playing Cricket, Staffordshire, 7" 95.00
Pretty Child...Stands to Reach Piano..., Staffordshire, 6" ...125.00
Punch & Judy, Staffordshire, 7½" 45.00
Set, bunny w/mouse scene, Lord Nelson Pottery, 4-pc 75.00
Set, colorful animals, German porc, bowl+mug+plate 70.00
Silks & Satins..., Franklin's Proverbs, mc transfer, 6¼" 75.00
Sioux Indian Chief, brn transfer, English, 6¾" 85.00
Spaniels, flow bl, rare, 5½" 150.00
Stable Yard, horse, pony & barn, 8" 135.00
Stag & Fawn, ironstone, blk transfer w/mc enameling, 7" 75.00
Their First Day, hotel china 50.00
Victorian children at play, mc, Staffordshire, 6¾" 65.00
What Fruit Does Our..., Blks in center, Staffordshire, 5" 225.00
Why Is the Gentleman..., Blks in center, Staffordshire, 5" ...225.00
3 Removes Are As Bad..., A Rolling Stone Gathers..., 7" 105.00

Glass

Amber, Clay Cristal Works, 8" 25.00
Centennial Expo 1876, 6¾" 120.00
Clock face, months of yr/days of wk, 7" 50.00
Dog, ABC rim 15.00
Garfield, Lindsey-301, 6" 60.00
Little Bo-Peep, #s 1-9, ABC rim 55.00
Mug, EX gold trim, old 40.00
Rabbit in grass, house behind, stippled ABC rim 75.00
Stork, marigold 45.00
1000 Eye, clock in center, ABC rim, 6" 65.00

Tin

Boy & girl roll hoops, 3" 45.00
Girl swinging, 6¼" 45.00
Hey Diddle Diddle, 8" 50.00
Jumbo, elephant, 6" 55.00
Washington & 3 stars, 5½", EX 85.00
Who Killed Cock Robin, 7¾" 60.00

Abingdon

From 1934 until 1950, the Abingdon Pottery Co. of Abingdon, Ill., made a line of art pottery with a white vitrified body decorated with various types of glazes in many lovely colors. Novelties, cookie jars, utility ware, and lamps were made in addition to several lines of simple yet striking art ware. Fern Leaf, introduced in 1937, featured molded vertical feathering. La Fleur, in 1939, consisted of flowerpots and flower-arranger bowls with rows of vertical ribbing. Classic, 1939-40, was a line of vases, many with evidence of Chinese influence. Several marks were used, most of which employed the company name. In 1950 the company reverted to the manufacture of sanitary ware that had been their mainstay before the Art

Ware Division was formed.

　　Highly decorated examples and those with black, bronze, or red glaze usually command at least 25% higher prices.

#A1, vase, red, 3½" 75.00
#C2, vase, wht, 4½" 65.00
#G3, vase, Rope, yel, 18" 180.00
#102, vase, Beta, 10" 20.00
#104, vase, Delta, turq matt, 10" 28.00
#104, vase, Delta, yel, 10" .25.00
#109, vase, Alpha, wht, 6" .18.00
#110, vase, Classic, bl, sm .10.00
#114, vase, Classic, wht, 10" 25.00
#118, vase, Classic, 10" 20.00
#126, candle holder, Classic, wht gloss, pr 32.00
#142, vase, Classic, gr, sm .16.00
#150D, flowerpot, Columbine, decorated 12.00
#150D, flowerpot, yel gloss 12.00

Cookie jar, Mother Goose, $95.00.

#200, pitcher, ice lip, all other colors, 2-qt 20.00
#200, pitcher, ice lip, red matt 25.00
#202, pitcher, chartreuse, 1-pt 38.00
#302L, lamp base, Lunge, wht brass fittings 225.00
#305, bookend, sea gull, turq matt, 6", pr 40.00
#306, ash tray 12.00
#310, jar, Chang, undecorated, w/lid, 10½" 50.00
#314, vase, Swedish, bronze blk 115.00
#319, vase, Modern, turq, 7" 40.00
#321, bookend, cossack 65.00
#351, vase, Capri, Regency gr, 5¾" 40.00
#351, vase, Capri, turq matt 40.00
#363, bookend, colt, 5¾", pr 62.50
#377, wall pocket, morning-glory, pk matt 12.00
#379, wall pocket, daisy, undecorated, 9" 20.00
#3906, figurine, shepherdess & fawn 230.00
#400, tea tile, geisha, turq gloss 80.00
#401, tea tile, coolie, turq gloss 80.00
#402, vase, Art Deco, box form, bronze blk 76.00
#404, candle holder, triple, Chain, beige 42.00
#409, bowl, Volute, turq matt, 6" 45.00
#416, figurine, peacock, gr .20.00
#420, vase, Fern Leaf, undecorated, 7¼" 15.00
#432, bowl, Fern Leaf, red matt, 15" 40.00

#441, bookend, horse's head, blk gloss, pr 50.00
#442, vase, Laurel, turq matt, 5½" 33.00
#444, bookend, dolphin, pr 45.00
#444, vase, dolphin, pk, 5½" 16.00
#445, vase, lace cuff, wht matt, 8" 40.00
#457, wall pocket, Ionic, undecorated, 9" 15.00
#466, vase, wheel hdl, wht matt, 6" 22.00
#469, figurine, Dutch boy, wht matt 25.00
#490, planter, Dutch Girl, wall mt, 10" 17.50
#496, vase, decorated, 7½" 25.00
#510, ash tray, donkey, blk, 5½" 60.00
#516, vase, Acadia 20.00
#520, vase, wht, undecorated 22.00
#525, bowl, flared, gray or blk, oblong 20.00
#525, bowl, flared, yel, oblong 8.00
#527, bowl, hibiscus, pk, 10" 28.00
#528, bowl, hibiscus, yel, 15" 30.00
#529, bowl, Tai Leaf, bl, 16" 30.00
#543, bowl, geranium 30.00
#563, vase, bl, decorated, urn shape 18.00
#565, cornucopia, blk 32.00
#569D, cornucopia, bl, decorated 25.00
#581, cornucopia, dbl, pk 20.00
#583, cornucopia, triple, yel 15.00
#586D, wall pocket, calla lily, decorated, 9" 30.00
#590, wall pocket, ivy, decorated 40.00
#591, vase, pk 10.00
#593, vase, bow knot, bl, 9" 25.00
#596, vase, sea horse, decorated 25.00
#615, ash tray, blk gloss 15.00
#637, vase, bl, oblong, 9" 35.00
#645, bowl, Contour, wht 15.00
#661, figurine, swan, bl 25.00
#668, planter, daffodil, decorated 20.00
#669, planter, donkey, bl 25.00
#676D, wall pocket, cookbook 30.00
#699, wall pocket, Apron, decorated 35.00
#714, candle holder, Star, gr, ea 8.00
#716, candle holder, Bamboo, decorated, pr 25.00
#9701, dish, 2 geese: 1 upright/1 feeding, pk, oblong 20.00
Cookie jar, #471, Black Lady, decorated 100.00
Cookie jar, #471, Old Lady, decorated 60.00
Cookie jar, #495, Fat Boy, beige 60.00
Cookie jar, #549, Hippo, undecorated, 8" 50.00
Cookie jar, #561, Baby 55.00
Cookie jar, #588, Money Sack 40.00
Cookie jar, #611, Jack-in-the-Box, undecorated, 11" 40.00
Cookie jar, #651, Locomotive, cream w/red & blk . . .50.00
Cookie jar, #653D, Cookie Time 35.00
Cookie jar, #662, Little Miss Muffet 60.00
Cookie jar, #663, Humpty Dumpty, decorated 45.00
Cookie jar, #663, Humpty Dumpty, undecorated, 10¼" 35.00
Cookie jar, #664, Pineapple, decorated 40.00
Cookie jar, #664, Pineapple, undecorated 30.00
Cookie jar, #674, Pumpkin .45.00
Cookie jar, #677D, Daisy, brn 25.00
Cookie jar, #694, Little Bo Peep 65.00
Cookie jar, #695D, Mother Goose, bl ruffles, goose by side 95.00

Adams

　　Wm. Adams, whose potting skills were developed under the tutelage of Josiah Wedgwood, founded the Greengates Pottery at Tunstall, England, in 1769. Many types of wares including basalt, ironstone, parian, and jasper were produced; and various impressed or printed marks were employed. Until 1800 'Adams Co.' or 'Adams' impressed in block letters identified the company's earthenwares and a fine type of jasper similar in color and decoration to Wedgwood's. The latter mark was used again from 1845 to 1864 on parian figures. Most examples of their product found on today's market are transfer-printed dinnerwares with ornate backstamps which often include the pattern name and the initials 'W.A. & S.' This type of product was made from 1820 until about 1920. After 1890 the word 'England' was included in the mark; 'Tunstall' was added after 1896. From 1914 through 1940, a printed crown with 'Adams, Estbd 1657, England' identified their products. From 1900 to 1965, they produced souvenir plates with transfers of American scenes, many of which were marketed in this country by Roth Importers of Peoria, Illinois. In 1965 the company affiliated with Wedgwood. Although there were other Adams potteries in Staffordshire, their marks incorporate either the first name initial or a partner's name and so are easily distinguished from those of this company. See also Spatter; Staffordshire; Adam's Rose.

Blue and white Jasperware bowl, marked/signed J.C., 9", $200.00; Pitcher, dome lid, marked, 8", $150.00.

Bowl, Cries of London, 10" 75.00
Bowl, Cries of London, 7½" 45.00
Bowl, Dr Syntax-Stopt by Highwaymen, 10¼" 65.00
Bowl, Jasper, bl/wht, hunters/hounds, 9" 150.00
Candlestick, Cries of London, 3½", pr 65.00
Cheese dish, cherubs/fleur-de-lis, wht on maroon, 10" dia 400.00
Cup & saucer, handleless; stick spatter w/gaudy floral, EX 45.00
Cup plate, man/dog in winter, transfer, Staffordshire, 4" 85.00
Pitcher, Jasper, bl/wht, hunters/hounds, w/lid, 8" 200.00
Plate, Currier & Ives scene, pk/yel rose on gray, 10½" 25.00
Plate, Dr Syntax Bound to Tree, 9" 45.00
Plate, My Old KY Home, dk bl transfer 30.00
Plate, roses, red brushstrokes w/gr leaves, 1825, 8½" 45.00
Platter, 2 stags/3 does, bl transfer, 1850s, 16" 275.00
Soup plate, fishing/cottage scene, dk bl transfer, 10", NM 75.00

Adams' Rose, Early and Late

In the second quarter of the 19th century, the Adams and Son Pottery produced a line of hand-painted dinnerware decorated in large, red brush-stroke roses with green leaves on whiteware, which collectors call 'Adams' Rose. Later, G. Jones and Son (and possibly others) made a similar ware with less brilliant colors on a gray-white surface.

Bowl, early, rare size, 9", M 450.00
Bowl, vegetable; late, 10¾" 75.00
Creamer, early, 5¾", M 285.00

Pitcher, early, stains/minor flakes, 7" 205.00
Pitcher, late, 6¾" 145.00
Plate, early, emb scalloped rim, 10½", NM 100.00
Plate, early, 9" 190.00
Plate, late, 8¾", EX 95.00
Plate, late, 9½", EX 45.00
Platter, late, 12", EX 85.00
Soup plate, early, wear/minor stains/glaze flakes, 9" 80.00
Soup plate, early, 10" 150.00
Soup plate, mk Adams, early, 11" 120.00
Sugar bowl, late 135.00
Sugar bowl, w/lid, early, M 350.00
Tea bowl & saucer, early 195.00
Tea bowl & saucer, late, M 60.00
Teapot, early, dome lid, rpr, 11½" 550.00
Teapot, late 200.00

Advertising

The advertising world has always been a fiercely competitive field. In an effort to present their product to the customer, every imaginable gimmick was put into play. Colorful and artfully decorated signs and posters, thermometers, tape measures, fans, hand mirrors, and attractive tin containers — all with catchy slogans, familiar logos, and often-bogus claims — are only a few of the many examples of early advertising memorabilia that are of interest to today's collectors.

Porcelain signs were made as early as 1890 and are highly prized for their artistic portrayal of life as it was then . . . often allowing amusing insights into the tastes, humor, and way of life of a bygone era. As a general rule, older signs are made from a heavier gauge metal. Those with three or more fired-on colors are especially desirable.

Tin containers were used to package consumer goods ranging from crackers and coffee to tobacco and talcum. After 1880 can companies began to decorate their containers by the method of lithography. Though colors were still subdued, intricate designs were used to attract the eye of the consumer. False labeling and unfounded claims were curtailed by the Pure Food and Drug Administration in 1906, and the name of the manufacturer as well as the brand name of the product had to be printed on the label. By 1910 color was rampant with more than a dozen hues printed on the tin or on paper labels. The tins themselves were often designed with a second use in mind — as canisters, lunch boxes, even toy trains. As a general rule, tobacco-related tins are the most desirable, though personal preference may direct the interest of the collector to peanut butter pails with illustrations of children, or talcum tins with irresistible babies or beautiful ladies. Coffee tins are popular, as are those made to contain a particularly successful or well-known product.

Perhaps the most visual of the early advertising gimmicks were the character logos — the Fairbank Company's Gold Dust Twins, the goose trademark of the Red Goose Shoe Company, Nabisco's ZuZu Clown and Uneeda Kid, the Campbell Kids, the RCA dog Nipper, and Mr. Peanut, to name only a few. Any example of these brings high prices on the market today.

Our listings are alphabetized by company name or, in lieu of that information, by word content or other pertinent description. When no condition is indicated, the items listed below are assumed to be in excellent condition, except glass and ceramic items, which are assumed mint. Remember that condition greatly effects value. For instance, a sign in excellent or mint condition may bring twice as much as the same one in only very good condition.

We have several advertising advisors; Allen Smith specializes in Buster Brown, Pepsi-Cola, Planters Peanuts, and Red Goose Shoes. He is listed in the Directory under Texas. See also Advertising Dolls; Advertising Cards; Coca-Cola; Banks; Calendars; Cookbooks; Paperweights; Posters; Sewing Items.

Key:
cb — cardboard
cl — celluloid
lcs — litho on canvas sign
pre-pro — pre-prohibition

ps — porcelain sign
sf — self-framed
tc — tin container
ts — tin sign

Adams Pepsin Tutti-Frutti hanging poster, ca 1900, 26x14", $2,500.00.

A&W Root Beer, coffee mug, porc, EX 22.00
ABC Bohemian Beer, ts, lion on mtn, ornate fr, 31x43" 2,000.00
Adams Pepsin Tutti-Frutti Gum, case, wood/glass, 17x12" 600.00
Adams Pepsin Tutti-Frutti Gum, display tin, 1917, 6x6½x5" . .150.00
Alaga Syrup, cb sign, Willie Mays, 1960s, 18x9" 15.00
Allen's Red Tame Cherry, emb cutout, kids at table, 40x28" .6,500.00
Allen's Root Beer Extract, paper sign, lady/cherubs, 22x15" .1,000.00
American Express Co, ts, lettered, fr, 31x23", VG 225.00
Anderson's Soups, pocket mirror 30.00
Anderson's Sour Mash, rvpt, sign, nudes/bath, 1900, 32x41" .2,000.00
Anheuser-Busch, sf ts, Dutch girl/bottle, Shonk, 38x26" 1,900.00
Anheuser-Busch, tray, lady holds 'A'/eagle, VG 400.00
Anheuser-Busch, tray, levee scene, 1914, VG 100.00
Anheuser-Busch Budweiser, sign, wood fr, 1914, 45x34" 325.00
Apollinaris, tip tray, Phil May cartoon w/lady, 1920, NM 70.00
Arden Buttermilk, dispenser, porc, boy/bottles, 22" 300.00
Arm & Hammer Soda, poster, bees/hunters, 1910, 25x17" . . .225.00
August Flower German Syrup, clock, rvpt, sq, 20" 850.00
Aunt Jemima Pancakes, paper plate, M 20.00
Aunt Jemima Pancakes, sheet music, 1925 . . . . .25.00
Babbitt's Soap, poster, Little Lord Fauntleroy, 1890, 30x15" 95.00
Baker's Breakfast Cocoa, tray, lady/homestead, 1915, 6½" 180.00
Baker's Chocolate, pencil sharpener, CI, lady figural, 2" 30.00
Baker's Cocoa, tc, lady litho, sq, Walter Baker Co 65.00
Ballantine Brewery, sf ts, Meek litho, c 1909, 23x31" 700.00
Ballistite DuPont Powder, paper sign, hunter, 1915, 33x22" .1,500.00
Belding's Spool Silk, enclosed-cylinder cabinet, 23x31" 1,100.00
Bendix Washers, soap model, machine form, 1940s, MIB 35.00
Benson & Hedges Parliament Cigarettes, ts, mc, 12x24", EX . .25.00
Berina Malted Milk, porc sign, Scotsman, mc, 24x60", EX 385.00

Bethesda Water of Quality, tray, litho tin, 10", NM 175.00
Black Cat Shoe Dressing, match holder, Shoes/Stoves, VG . . .275.00
Black Sheep Cigar, tin container, 1915, 5½x3¼x½" 75.00
Blanke's Faust Coffee, sf ts, Blk w/watermelon, 22x23", NM .1,500.00
Blatz Lager Brewery, token, copper, Civil War era, 1863 . . . . . .30.00
Bliss Native Herbs, match holder, capitol bldg, VG 425.00
Borden's Ice Cream, dbl-sided ts, Elsie the Cow, EX 365.00
Boschee's German Syrup, ts, lady, Wells & Hope, 30x22", VG .650.00
Bottl' O Grape, emb tin sign, Call for a..., 1940s, 12x20" 30.00
Boye Needles/Shuttles, cabinet, metal, 1920s, +some contents .100.00
Brazil Beer, sign, porc on steel, curved, Brazil IN, 20x11" 475.00
Brillo, sample box, lady using pan for mirror, early, EX 22.00
Britain's Best, tc, NITA, red/gold/blk, NM 7.50
Bromo Quinine Cold Medicine, rnd 3-color cl sign, 1930s 45.00
Bromo Quinine Laxative, cb sign, ca 1915, 44x53" 225.00
Brown Beauty Tobacco, tin lunch box, Aunt Jemima litho, EX. . .150.00
Brown's Bread, die-cut ts, ca 1920s, 12x14", M 100.00
Buck's Stoves/Furnaces, cb sign, Blk girl w/pie, 1910, 11x6" . . .85.00
Buckeye Incubators, emb sign, man/machine, 1920s, 11x35" . .150.00
Buckeye Root Beer, stand-up cb diecut, 3 satyrs, 24", VG 600.00
Buckeye Root Beer, tin sign, Refreshing, 1950s, 24x18" 25.00
Buckingham Tobacco, pushbar, porc, yel/blk, 3x30", EX 32.00
Budweiser Beer, belt buckle, brass, 1968, 2¼x3½" 10.00
Budweiser Beer, menu board, rvpt glass section, VG 425.00
Bull Durham, cb sign, Blks kiss through umbrella, early, EX .1,800.00
Bull Durham Smoking Tobacco, tin charger, orig fr, 36", EX. .2,300.00
Bull Durham Tobacco, angle sign, cut-out bull, 29" 1,600.00
Bull Durham Tobacco, cb cutout, Blks on fence, 6", VG 375.00
Bull Durham Tobacco, cb sign, bull by fence, 30x24" 850.00
Bull Durham Tobacco, emb ts, bull by fence, fr, 13x14", EX . . .350.00
Bull Durham Tobacco, emb ts, bull by fence, fr, 17x13" 1,200.00
Bull Durham Tobacco, plaster bull, ...3 Generations, 21" L . .3,700.00
Bull Durham Tobacco, tc, Forbs illus, 1890, 21x27" 500.00
Bullock Ward & Co, match holder, bldg, VG 200.00

Buster Brown

Buster Brown was the creation of cartoonist Richard Felton; his comic strip first appeared in the *New York Herald* on May 4, 1902. Since then Buster and his dog Tige (short for Tiger) have adorned sundry commercial products but are probably best known as the trademark for the Brown Shoe Company established early in this century. Today hundreds of Buster Brown premiums, store articles, and advertising items bring substantial prices from many serious collectors.

Bank, CI, BB & Tige w/horse & Good Luck, EX pnt, Arcade . .200.00
Bank, CI, horse & horseshoe, orig decal, Arcade, 4½", EX 200.00
Bank, plastic, red w/BB & Tige, EX .25.00
Bill hook, 1940s 10.00
Book, comic; 1946 . . . . .17.50
Book, dictionary, 1927, pocket size .20.00
Bowl, cereal; aluminum, BB & Tige .40.00
Bowl, cereal; porc, BB transfer, 2x4" 10.00
Camera, Anthony Scovill, early, EX in orig box 200.00
Camping set, 5-pc, ea w/logo on bottom, EX 85.00
Cigar band 8.50
Clock, electric, BB & Tige, wall type, Pam Clocks 175.00
Cup, ceramic, early 1900s, EX 95.00
Display figure, dressed in BB T-shirt & shorts 200.00
Flyer, shows 4 BB cl items, Whitehead/Hoag, sq, 6" 30.00
Hatchet, BB logo, 13" 40.00
Knife, hunting; etched blade, mk hdl, EX 50.00
Knife, pocket; high-top shoe-form hdl, good graphics, 3" 18.00
Mannequin, BB, plastic, 41" 100.00

Mask, BB Shoes, cb, NM 25.00
Mug, porc, BB & Tige transfer, gold trim, 3½" 50.00
Patch, felt, 1950s, EX 5.00
Pencil case, pencil form, 1930s, EX 65.00
Pin-bk button, BB Walking Club, oval, 1½" 20.00
Pin-bk button, for BB Bread, lg, early 30.00
Plate, BB w/Tige doing trick, 4¾" 15.00
Plate, porc, BB & Tige at tea, 6", +4" creamer 40.00
Playing cards, BB & Tige, 52 cards, 1906, EX in box 65.00
Playing cards, ea card a different scene, ca 1913, complete 28.00
Pocket mirror, Brunner's BB Bread, BB/Tige as bakers, 1907 ...100.00
Post card, BB valentine, Outcault, 1903, EX 10.00
Poster, linen, BB & Tige, Outcault illus, Selchow, 17x24" 40.00
Rug, BB & Tige on yel w/bl trim, 54" dia, EX 200.00
Shoe brush, brn w/cream bristles, wood hdl, 8½" 20.00
Sign, BB & Tige, 1940s, 18x18½", EX 45.00
Sign, emb tin, BB Bread, BB/Tige/wheat sheaf, 1920, 22x30" ...350.00
Sign, 2-pc tin cutout: dog pulls BB in shoe, 25x40", NM ...13,000.00
Socks, orig labels, pr 25.00
Stationery, BB letterhead, 5 pgs 10.00
Statue, compo, BB w/Tige at feet, 28" 145.00
Statue, mtd on wht marble base, dated 1904-1964, 3½" 20.00
String holder, BB/Tige/windmill top, CI base, ca 1900, 15" 550.00
Waffle iron, BB & Tige on bk, sm 75.00
Whistle, tin litho, flat 20.00
Whistle, wood, paper label 20.00

C.D. Kenny

C.D. Kenny was determined to be a successful man, and he was. Between 1890 and 1934, he owned seventy-five groceries in fifteen states. He realized his success in two ways: fair business dealings and premium giveaways. These ranged from trade cards and advertising mirrors to tin commemorative plates and kitchen items. There were banks and toys, clocks and tins. Today's collectors are finding scores of these items, all carrying Kenny's name.

Ad, Brundage Dutch girl, 1913, unfr 15.00
Box, tin, heart form w/angel decor, sm 50.00
Coffee bag 5.00
Coffee tin, Mammy's Favorite, Mammy w/coffee, 4-lb, VG 170.00
Fan, Kenny's Tea 4.00
Figurine, Indian in canoe, EX 15.00
Mirror, Dutch family drinks coffee w/in cup & saucer, oval 250.00
Plate, boy w/dog, holly trim, tin, Vienna Art 120.00
Plate, Santa & sleeping child, tin, 9½", M 150.00
Plate, Santa Claus, tin, lg 155.00
Portrait, George Washington, tin litho, 5x7" 100.00
Print, unfr, 1913, 10x13", EX 15.00
Tip tray, George Washington, 1920s, NM 85.00
Tip tray, lady in woods, w/flowers, M 65.00
Tip tray, Star Spangled Banner, EX 85.00
Tip tray, Thanksgiving, 1910, NM 145.00
Tip tray, Victorian lady, seated, 4" 100.00
Toothpick holder 35.00

CA Champagne, ts, mc litho, ca 1910, 19x13", EX 195.00
Calloway Gas Engines, booklet, mc, 1919, EX 12.00
Calumet, thermometer, wood, can/Trade Here Save, 22", VG .350.00
Calumet Baking Powder, clock, oak/rvpt, Sessions, 36", NM .800.00
Camel Cigarettes, tin sign, Need Cigarettes?, 1940s, 12x19" ...25.00
Campfire Marshmallows, booklet, ca 1920 ....5.00
Canada Dry, wood stand-up sign, 1940s, 12x10", EX 40.00

Campbell & Woods Co. coffee bin, 17 x 18", $395.00.

Canada Dry Hi-Spot, tin sign, 1946, 14x7" 20.00
Canada Sap Maple Syrup, emb tin sign, product, 14x10" 1,050.00
Canadian Club Cigars, 2-sided hanging cb sign, mc, 7", EX 10.00
Carhartt Brand Pants & Overalls, paper sign, 105x82", EX 220.00
Carhartt Overalls, pushbar, Buy Carhartt, EX 150.00
Cattaraugus Cutlery, frosted light globe w/Indian, 9", EX 500.00
CE Hiltz Shoes, match holder, emb tin, shoe/dagger, VG 550.00
Central Union Tobacco, lunch box, tall, VG 85.00
Ceresota, match holder, die-cut boy on barrel, VG 475.00
Champ Pomade, tin container, boxer on lid, oval, 4", VG 40.00
Chanticleer Cigarette Papers, dispenser, tin, NM 14.00
Chesterfield Cigarettes, cb sign, lady/pack, 1940s, 24x24" 32.00
Chicken Cock Whiskey, ts, cock/flowers, H Beach, 23x29" ..2,100.00
Clabber Girl Baking Powder, tin sign, 1952, 12x30" 25.00
Cleo Cola, thermometer, rvpt on convex glass, 10" dia, EX ...600.00
Coleman Lanterns & Stoves, cb standup, scout, 1930s, 19x12" ..75.00
Colts to the Front, gun litho, patriotic, 1915, 18x24" ...425.00
Columbia Flour, match holder, die-cut Miss Columbia, EX 750.00
Columbian Bottle Beer, ts, TN Brewing, ca 1930, 9½x13½" ...100.00
Continental Cubes, pocket tin, man in cape, 5", VG 110.00
Continental Cubes, tc, man in cape, orig closure, 8" 1,200.00
Continental Fire Ins Co of NY, paper sign, 1895, 32x37", VG .425.00
Cook's Beer, sign, gambler on dock w/kegs, 1930s, 28x20" ...250.00
Cortez Cigars, ts, lady w/box of cigars, 1915 ....425.00
Cottolene Shortening, tip tray, Blks in cotton field, 1910 ...110.00
Cow Ease, 2-part ts, man/cow in 10" disk at bottom, M 950.00
Cream of Wheat, recipe booklet, ca 1900, EX 10.00
Creme De Menthe Cola, sign, cb cut-out standup, early, 7x9" ..45.00
Crescent Beverages, ts, emb moon & star, 1940, 20x13", NM ...25.00
Crown Baking Powder, tray, lady's portrait, 10", NM 250.00
Crusade Tobacco, paper sign, knight w/sword, 1900, 13½x7" ...25.00
Crush, 2-sided cb sign, yel/blk/gr/wht, old, 15x15", EX ...115.00
Cuestra Rey Cigars, litho on canvas, ca 1905, 32x40" 450.00
Daisy Air Rifles, poster, Don't Cry Little Bro..., 27x19" ..2,700.00
Davenport Paper, paper sign, Indian/geese, 1937, 18x26" 110.00
Davy Crockett Cigars, emb ts, Davy w/gun, rare, 27x19" ...8,500.00
DeLaval Separators, cabinet, wood/tin, separator, 28", VG .400.00
DeLaval Separators, match holder, die-cut machine 225.00
DeLaval Separators, sf ts, lady/child, 1905, 26" dia 1,600.00
DeLaval Separators, tip tray, mother/child, 1915, NM 130.00
DeLaval Separators, ts, maid w/cow, ca 1915, 40x29" 1,300.00
Devoe Paints & Varnishes, dbl-sided angle sign, Indian, 25" .1,300.00
Devoe Varnish, decal on wood sign, native/tree, 11x19", EX ...90.00
Diamond Dyes, cabinet, wood/tin, Ages of Women, 30", VG ..600.00

Diamond Dyes, cabinet, wood/tin, baby reserve, 19x15", EX . .1,800.00
Diamond Dyes, cabinet, wood/tin, balloon scene, 24", VG 750.00
Diamond Dyes, cabinet, wood/tin, fairy in reserve, 24", EX . .1,300.00
Diamond Dyes, cabinet, wood/tin, jumping rope, 24", VG 500.00
Diamond Edge Tools, tin sign, Liberty MO, 1940s, 11x27" . . .25.00
Dixie Kid, lunch box, Black, EX 450.00
Dixie Kid, lunch box, blonde, EX .1,000.00
Dixie Queen Plug Tobacco, lunch box, basket style 70.00
Dixie Queen Plug Tobacco, lunch box, portrait, EX 240.00
Doe Wah Jack Rnd Oak Stoves, spoon, stove figural 70.00
Dominion Express, porc sign, purple/wht, 3x24", EX 65.00
Dorn's Carnation Chewing Gum, tip tray, pack/flowers, NM . .800.00
Dr A Reed Cushion Shoe, porc thermometer, 26", NM 110.00
Dr Caldwell's Syrup, pushbar, You Can Depend..., EX 175.00
Dr Chase's Catarrh Powder, tc, rnd portrait, yel/blk, MIB 15.00
Dr Chase's Nerve Food, porc thermometer, litho, 39x8", NM . .185.00
Dr LeGear Stock Remedies, ts, giant horse, 1911, 14x18" 275.00

Dr Pepper

A young pharmacist, Charles C. Alderton, was hired by W. B. Morrison, owner of Morrison's Old Corner Drug Store in Waco, Texas, around 1884. Alderton, an observant sort, noticed that the drugstore's patrons could never quite make up their minds as to which flavor of extract to order. He concocted a formula that combined many flavors, and Dr. Pepper was born. The name was chosen by Morrison in honor of a beautiful young girl with whom he had once been in love. The girl's father, a Virginia doctor by the name of Pepper, had discouraged the relationship due to their youth, but Morrison had never forgotten her. On December 1, 1885, a U.S. patent was issued to the creators of Dr. Pepper.

Booklet, 1899 . . . . .125.00
Bottle, clear, AM&B Co, circle A, EX 25.00
Bottle, seltzer; Cheerio-Memphis 150.00
Bottle, syrup; King of Beverages, EX 200.00
Calendar, 1935, complete, EX 200.00
Calendar, 1938, lady in yel gown, NM 250.00
Calendar, 1949, complete, NM 50.00
Calendar, 1950, girl w/half-mask, complete, NM 50.00
Calendar, 1960, brunette in strapless gown, complete, NM 25.00
Clock, brick wall effect, blk on beige, lt gr fr, rnd, 15" 100.00
Door pull, metal, bottle form, VG 45.00
Fountain glass, Dr Pepper etched in wht rectangle, M 10.00
Plate, roses, Vienna Art 175.00
Post card 10¢ coupon, M . . . ; 5.00
Poster, cb, girl w/bottle, 25x15", M in envelope 50.00
Radio, AM, cooler form, wood case, gr pnt, 1940, 12x7x7" 250.00
Sign, paper, bottle on gold, early, 9x11½", EX 25.00
Sign, tin, cut-out cap, 28", NM 50.00
Sign, tin, Drink..., 7x20", VG 17.50
Syrup dispenser, china w/metal legs, cylindrical, 18", VG 800.00
Syrup dispenser, Phos-Ferrates, sq ceramic, marble base, 21" .7,500.00
Tray, oval, 2 women, 13½x16½", EX 750.00
Tray, roses, King of Beverages, Vienna 250.00
Truck, 1970s, NM 15.00
Watch fob, Billiken, brass, EX 100.00
Watch fob, St Louis World's Fair, silvered brass, 1904 . . . . . . .125.00

Dr Saymnan's, cb container, tin top/bottom, 1917, 5", M 150.00
Dr Scholl's, pedograph, Silent Foot Analyst, 1917, EX 145.00
Drewry's Beer, plaster Mountie w/glass bottle, 7" 20.00
Duluth Brewing, ts, ornate fr, factory/moose, 33x43", VG . . .1,400.00
Duluth Imperial Flour, sign, high relief, Blk chef, 20x16" 1,400.00

DuPont Powders, paper sign, dead game, dtd 1904, fr, 38x28" . .950.00
DuPont Powders, sf tin sign, hunters/dog/boy, 33x23", VG 800.00
DuPont Powders, sf tin sign, 2 dogs, dtd 1903, 28x22", VG . . .300.00
Dutch Boy Paint, cb standup, painters/Dutch Boy, '30s, 51x45". 150.00
Dutch Boy Paint, match holder, die-cut boy & bucket, VG . . .650.00
Dy-O-La Dye, cabinet, wood w/tin sides, 15½x12x7½", EX 85.00
Eagle Lye, match holder, can of product, VG 110.00
Ebbert Wagon, sf ts, Shade of Old Apple Tree, 26x38", NM .1,900.00
EC or Schultze Shot, paper sign, Hunt illus: geese, 28x20" 650.00
Eilert's Patent Medicines, ts, lists products, 38x28", EX 2,500.00
El Verso Cigars, tip tray, man in chair/lady in smoke, M 150.00
Elgin Watches, rvpt sign, Father Time, gold/blk, fr, 30x23" . . .350.00
Ell-Ell Whiskey, sf ts, lg boat at dock, Lemle Levy, 22x28" 500.00
Etonia Spices, tc, Wht Pepper, man on camel, mc, NM 22.00
Eupion Oil, poster, lady, fancy home int, fr, 32x17", VG 425.00
Ex-Lax, porc thermometer, 5-color, minor chips, 36x8", EX . . .145.00
Fairmont Creamery, pot scraper, You Cannot Lose, EX 100.00
Falstaff, charger, tin, Home of.../tavern scene, 24" 450.00
Falstaff Bottled Beer, sf ts, Peacemaker/old car, 23x31" 4,500.00
Fern Glen Rye Whiskey, sf ts, Blk w/melon, 33x23", NM . . .1,800.00
Fire Chief, porc pump sign, fireman's helmet, mc, 12x8", NM . . .48.00
Five Roses Whiskey, pushbar, red/wht/blk, 3x30", EX 40.00
Forest & Stream, pocket tin, fisherman, EX 40.00
Foster Hose Supporters, celluloid sign, product/lady, 17x9" 350.00
Four Roses Whiskey, ts, fox/birds/rifle, 1900, 48x32", M 1,000.00
Francisco Auto Heater, sf ts, family in old car, 18x40", EX 850.00
Frozen Gold, menu board, wood, 11x14", EX 20.00
Gail & Ax Navy Tobacco, paper sign, sailor, fr, 41x32" 1,200.00
Game Fine Cut Tobacco, store bin, birds, 1920, 7x11x8", VG .150.00

I.W. Harper Whiskey sign, painted milk glass, signed Bernheim, dated 1909, 27x21", $850.00.

Ganong's Chocolates, cb sign, couple on picnic, '20s, 22x13" . . .95.00
Gem Ever Ready Blades, ts, man w/razor, 1919, 11" L, M 750.00
Gem Razors, window sign, die-cut animated man, 27", VG 250.00
General Electric, bulb display, tin/wood, lady in bulb, 27" 425.00
Gibson's Pure Old Rye Whiskey, ts, nudes/bottle, fr, 20x14" .2,200.00
Glendora Coffee, tin container, Bertels litho, 1930, 8" 200.00
Goblin Orangeade, porc sign, bright colors, 1920s, 12x18" 150.00
Gold Lion Tonic, clock, pendulum, rvpt, printed dial, Howe . .600.00
Golden Pyramid, needle tin, pyramid shape, NM 22.00
Goldyrock Birch Beer, tin sign, mc, 1930s, 11x22", EX 25.00
Grand Council Cigars, cb sign, 1870s, 17x14", EX 185.00
Grape Nuts, sf ts, There's a Reason, St Bernard/girl, 30x20" .1,000.00
Grapette, tin thermometer, Thirsty or Not!, EX 22.00
Green River Whiskey, cb sign, Blk/mule, fr, 27x22", VG 100.00

Green River Whiskey, charger, tin litho, Blk/mule, 24", EX . .1,000.00
Green River Whiskey, tin sgn, oak fr, c 1899, EX 1,250.00
Heidelberg Beer, chalk figurine, Student Prince, 1940s, EX 85.00
Heineken's Beer, tin emb w/cb bk, early, 11x14", EX 7.50
Henkle's Flour, pot scraper, Bread & Pastry, EX 250.00
Henry George Cigars, sf ts, bald man, Standard Co, 14" dia . . .650.00
Hepitol Splits, tray, bucking bronco, 12", VG 325.00
Hill's Bros Brewery, paper sign, Western scene/auto, 23x32" . . .850.00
Hill's Bros Coffee, porc thermometer, nightshirted man, 21" . . .300.00

Hires

    Charles E. Hires, a drugstore owner in Philadelphia, became interested in natural teas. He began experimenting with roots and herbs and soon developed his own special formula. Hires introduced his product to his own patrons and soon began selling concentrated syrup to other soda fountains and grocery stores. Samples of his 'root beer' were offered for the public's approval at the 1876 Philadelphia Centennial. Today's collectors are often able to date their advertising items by observing the Hires boy on the logo. From 1891 to 1906 he wore a dress; until 1914 he was shown in a bathrobe. From 1915 until 1926, he was depicted in a dinner jacket. The apostrophe may or may not appear in the Hires name; this seems to have no bearing on dating an item.

Almond Smash, ts, emb bottle, fr, early, 14x7", NM 115.00
Booklet, advertizing, 1894 . . . . .10.00
Booklet, How Hires Animals Helped the USA, EX 18.00
Booklet, Merry Rhymes for Thirsty Times 25.00
Bottle, wire/ceramic stopper, early, NM 15.00
Buckle, belt; Drink Hires Root Beer 5.00
Can, blob top, ca 1880, rare 30.00
Coaster, ceramic, Mettlach, rare, 4¾", EX 110.00
Dispenser, aluminum top w/porc stand, counter type, EX 150.00
Dispenser, Drink...It's Pure, nickel lid, spigot, ca 1920 . . . . . . .800.00
Dispenser, syrup; Muniemaker, brass/marble/glass, 35½" 2,300.00
Glass, Nature's Delicious Drink, syrup line, NM 45.00
Glass, soda; Enjoy Nature's..., syrup line, thin 22.00
Menu board, shows bottle, EX colors, 1940s, NM 35.00
Mug, blk or gray stoneware, block letters, EX 40.00
Mug, ceramic, boy lifts mug, Mettlach, EX 150.00
Mug, frosted glass, Drink Hires Root Beer, lg 6.00
Mug, pottery, blk letters, 7x4" 75.00
Opener, over-the-top, NM 12.00
Palm press, tin, 5-color, 4x14", NM .37.50
Pocket mirror, Put Roses in Your Cheeks, NM 175.00
Push plate, sf tin, 5-color, 4x14", EX 40.00
Sign, celluloid on metal, Drink Hires/girl, 10x7", EX 375.00
Sign, paper, c 1914, fr, 11x6½", EX .75.00
Sign, paper, German peasant/Colonial man, 1890s, 18x21" . . .475.00
Sign, paper, pop-eyed soda jerk, 5x13" 125.00
Sign, sf tin, Hires boy, Say Hires, Beach Art Co, oval, 24" . . .3,700.00
Sign, tin, Drink Hires in Bottles/girl, 9x6½", EX 150.00
Sign, tin, Hires Refreshes Right, 1930s, 10x30", EX 45.00
Sign, tin, It's High Time for..., 1930s, 42x14", NM 65.00
Sign, window; paper, Thirsts...Suffocated..., 7x11", M 75.00
Straw dispenser 750.00
Tire cover, canvas, for spare, 29" dia, EX 200.00
Trade card, Haskell Coffin, NM 45.00
Tray, Just What the Doctor..., 1914, EX 400.00

Hohner Harmonicas, display rack, wood, clockwork 200.00
Holly Brand Chocolate, tray, kids/dog/boat, 1900, 13½" 175.00

Honest Scrap, store bin, 2 dogs/product, 12x18", VG 225.00
Hood's Sarsaparilla, booklet, 1890, 16-pg 10.00
Hood's Sarsaparilla, paper doll, 1903, M 25.00
Hood's Sarsaparilla, puzzle, ballooning, 2 in box 145.00
Hoosier Drill Co, celluloid sign, man/horses/drill, 23x26" . . .3,200.00
Horlick's Malted Milk, paper sign, 3 girls, 1906, 37x12" 130.00
Howel's Root Beer, mc ts, ca 1920s, 57x16", EX 150.00
Hunter Cigars, tin sign, fox hunter/horse, 1915, 27x19" 250.00
Indian Crown Cigars, ts, 1912, 13x19", EX 400.00
Indian Motorcycle, paper sgn, blk/wht, 1940, 38x50", EX 550.00
Indian Motorcycle, ts, mc mtn litho, 1928, 29x42", NM 1,800.00
International Harness Soap, cb sign, Blk man, 32x25", VG 500.00
Iroquois Beer, shopping bag, Indian, 1920s, sm, M 20.00
Iroquois Beer, tip tray, Indian in headdress, 1910, NM 120.00
J&P Coats, oak swivel-base spool cabinet w/thread, '10, 23" .1,200.00
J&P Coats, wagon, wood w/spoked wheels, 43" L 825.00
J&P Coats, walnut spool cabinet, 2 drawers, VG 100.00
Jam Boy Coffee, tc, Continenta! Can Co, 1930, VG 130.00
Jap Rose Soap, fr cb sign, kids bathe doll, 1910, 38x28½" 275.00
Japp's Hair Rejuvenator, ts, actual hair samples, 10x13" 650.00
Jas E Patton Paints, match holder, palette form, VG 150.00
JB Coffee, porc sign, bag of coffee figural, mc, 24", EX 250.00
Jewel Stove Works, match holder, CI/mc beetle form, 5", EX . .425.00
Jewel Stoves & Ranges, porc sign, curved, lettered, 20x18" . . .500.00
JH Cutter Whiskey, tray, sailing ship, 1915, 17x14", NM 325.00
Jim Dandy Horse Collars, tin sign, mc, 13x19", VG 400.00
Johnson's Log Cabin Coffee, store bin, cabin figural, 29" 750.00
Joy Walker Corn Plaster, tin container, lady w/dog, 1890s 25.00
Junket Powder, pot scraper, different image on bk, VG 140.00
Kahn's American Beauty, porc clock/sign, butcher/ham, 30" . .450.00
Keen's Mustard, box, paper over wood, 12x22x4½", EX 50.00
Kelly Springfield Tires, vitrolite sign, electric, 21x17" 4,700.00
Kendall's Spavin Cure, stone litho, lady w/horse, 26x20" 400.00
Kent Cigarettes, cup & saucer, demitasse; Royal Crown China . .35.00
Kentucky Wagons, match holder, farm wagon, VG 550.00
Keystone Mincemeat, bucket, ca 1918, 9½x13x13" 100.00
King Cole Coffee, tin container, King, 1920, 6", EX 275.00
King Midas Flour, pot scraper, little girl, EX 250.00
Kis-Me Gum, light, milk glass globe, girl/crescent moon, 18" .1,300.00
Kist Soft Drink, tray, sailor girl, 1930s, 13" 150.00
Kitchen Queen Extracts, cabinet, wood/glass, Blk lady decal .2,200.00
Knight's Candy, thermometer, wood, pnt wear, VG 30.00
La Raphaelle Liqueur, stone litho, man/plane, 1908, 42x30" . . .250.00
LaBelle Chocolatiere, ts, lady w/tray, ca 1910, 39x27" 400.00
Laflin/Rand Powder, fr poster, hunting scene, 1870s, 26x20" . .750.00
Laurier Cigars, sf ts, man w/in horseshoe fr, ca 1915, EX 450.00
Lawrence Barrett Cigar, sign, porc on steel, curved, 21x20" . . .450.00
Lee Overalls, sheet metal sign, men of all sizes, 37x72" 450.00
Libbey's Corned Beef, sample tin 25.00
Lighthouse Cleanser, ts, box of product, 1920s, 13x9", M 550.00
Lion Coffee, store bin, wood, angel/chariot/lion, 1900, 27" 550.00
Lion Collars, display case, glass/copper/decal, full, 50x8" 800.00

Log Cabin Syrup

    Log Cabin Syrup tins have been made since the 1890s in variations of design that can be attributed to specific years of production. Until about 1914, they were made with paper labels. These are quite rare and highly prized by today's collectors. Tins with colored lithographed designs were made after 1914. When General Foods purchased the Towle Company in 1927, the letters 'GF' were added.

    A cartoon series, illustrated with a mother flipping pancakes in the cabin window and various children and animals declaring their appreciation of the syrup in voice balloons, was introduced in the 1930s. A Frontier

Village series followed in the late 1940s. A schoolhouse, jail, trading post, doctor's office, blacksmith shop, inn, and private homes were also available. Examples of either series today often command prices of $75.00 to $200.00 and up.

Bank, glass cabin figural, EX 32.00
Syrup tin, bear in door, cartoon ends, Towle's, 5-lb 100.00
Syrup tin, cartoon all sides, sm 110.00
Syrup tin, child in door, Towle's, NM 150.00
Syrup tin, children, man by pump, Towle's, 33-oz 150.00
Syrup tin, Dr RU Well, cartoon style, rare 120.00
Syrup tin, Express Office, coach, Towle's, 33-oz 150.00
Syrup tin, Frontier Inn, cowboys & horse, 5-lb 220.00
Syrup tin, Frontier Jail, 12-oz .68.00
Syrup tin, hand w/finger pointing on top, Towle's, med sz 165.00
Syrup tin, Home Sweet Home, 12-oz 75.00
Syrup tin, red, 5-lb 50.00
Syrup tin, Stockade School, Towle's, 33-oz 150.00
Syrup tin, Wigwam, 1-lb, 4x3¼x3½" 175.00
Teaspoon 17.50

Log Cabin Brownies, cb sign, little men/cabin, 13x23", EX 550.00
Long Tom Smoking Tobacco, tc, Blk litho, 5x3", VG 32.00
Longwy's Chocolate, mc tin sign, 3-pc diecut, 1908, EX . . .1,750.00
Lucas Paints, leaflet holder, 1920s, 8x24" 28.00
Lucky Lager Beer, ts, 2 for a quarter, 1930s, 13½x7", EX 65.00
Lucky Strike Cigarettes, cb sign, Bob Lefty Grove, 23x13" . .1,000.00
Lucky Strike Cigarettes, cb sign, Tony Lazzeri, 23x13", EX 700.00
Luden's Cough Drops, tip tray, 5¢ box, 1920s, NM 80.00
M Born Tailoring, stone litho, 1870s, 15x17" 225.00
Majors Cement, pushbar, Mends Everything, EX 130.00
Marathon Angle Tread Tires, ts, touring car, fr, 29x23" . . .5,500.00
Marlin Repeaters Rifles & Shotguns, emb ts, factory, 5x38" . .700.00
Mason's Challenge Blacking, mc litho, fr, ca 1880, 12x15" . . .250.00
McClary's Stoves & Ranges, porc flange sign, 12x15½", EX 75.00
McVit-Price's Biscuits, ts, mother/2 children, '30s, 19x14" 275.00
Merrick's Spool Cotton, clock, short-drop regulator, 25" 500.00
Merrick's Spool Cotton, display case, tag: pat 1897, 22" 850.00
Merrigan's Ice Cream, tray, girl/boy eating ice cream, 1923 . . . .225.00
Mesinger Bicycle Seats, paper sign, Spaniard/seat, 31x17" 210.00
Michelin, poster, Indian bites tire, 1908, 30x39" 425.00
Milady Toilet Soap, sf ts, lady w/soap at bowl, EX 650.00
Millburn Wagons, sf ts, emb, robbery attempt, 25x33", VG . .3,700.00
Miller Beer, sf ts, lobster/bottles on table, 1907, 19x15" 450.00
Miller Brewing, paper sign, girl lifts drink, 34x26" 1,100.00
Milward's Needles, cabinet, 2-drw oak, gold letters, 18" W 200.00
Min-Lax Tonic, sign, 1930s, 14x19" 30.00
Morrell's...Pride Hams & Bacon, paper sign, mc, fr, 20x24" . . .275.00
Mother Goose Pillows, paper sign, 1920s, 21x27½" 110.00
Mother's Worm Syrup, match holder, mother & child, VG . . .425.00
Mountain Dew, sf ts, hillbillies, Yahoo!, 1950s, 12x36" 50.00

Moxie

The Moxie Company was organized in 1884 by George Archer of Boston, Massachusetts. It was at first touted as a 'nerve food' to improve the appetite, promote restful sleep, and in general to make one 'feel better!' Emphasis was soon shifted, however, to the good taste of the brew, and extensive advertising campaigns rivaling those of such giant competitors as Hires and Coca-Cola resulted in successful marketing through the 1930s. Today the term Moxie has become synonymous with courage and audacity, traits displayed by the company who dared compete with such well-established rivals. For more information we recommend *The Book of Moxie*, by Frank N. Potter, available at your local bookstore or from Collector Books.

Bottle, aqua, wire stopper, 1-qt .12.50
Bottle, King Size, paper label, orig, 16-oz 10.00
Bottle, Moxie Nerve Food, amber, Denver CO, 26-oz 65.00
Bottle, Moxie Nerve Food, Lowell MA, paper seal over cork . .100.00
Bottle hanger, campfire scene, 2 7-oz bottles 15.00
Carrying bag, paper, Frank Archer, c 1932 . . . . .25.00
Coaster, tin litho, rare, 3½" dia, NM 130.00
Crate, wood, yel w/red lettering, 1950s, EX 45.00
Display, die-cut, man sits on case, 1920, 41x20", VG 125.00
Fan, Eileen Percy (actress), 1923, EX 38.00
Fan, girl & soda jerk, sm 37.00
Fan, Lillian MacKenzie, 1919, 8½" 30.00
Fan, Muriel Ostriche, 1916 . . . . .45.00
Grocery bag, 1931, EX 15.00
Horse car, tin litho, part horse/part car w/driver, 9", NM . . .1,500.00
Match holder, die-cut bottle, VG 300.00
Photo, closeup of horse mobile in parade, orig, 7x9" 70.00
Pin-bk, die-cut Moxie man, EX 80.00
Purse, pnt metal links, boy/dog/Moxie bag, 4x6½" 450.00
Sign, cb diecut, Moxieland, home of Moxie, 28x38", EX 225.00
Sign, metal, Braces First-Chases Thirst, med sz 65.00
Sign, metal, diecut, Old Moxie-New Moxie, 19x27" 65.00
Sign, metal diecut, Try a Moxie High Ball, 13x19" 100.00
Sign, Ted Williams w/Moxie 125.00
Sign, tin, Feeds the Nerves, Kauffman/Strauss, 1890s, 20x28" . .550.00
Sign, tin, Moxie horse car, fr, 24x33", EX 1,800.00
Smock, Moxie man 27.50
Thermometer, Remember Those Days, orange, rnd 20.00
Tip tray, girl drinking Moxie, I Like It, bl rim, 6" 175.00
Tip tray, girl holds glass, 4½" dia, VG 110.00
Tip tray, lady w/glass, I Just Love Moxie, rnd, EX 155.00
Tip tray, Moxie Nerve Food, Moxie girl w/purple sash, 6" . .1,100.00
Token, horse-drawn bottle wagon, Good for One Drink, 1900 . .45.00
Tray, copper, eng w/1907 Moxie logo, 13" 175.00

Mt Penn Stove Works, pot scraper, cloverleaf, NM 25.00
Munsingwear, display, free-standing man in union suit, 43" . .1,700.00
Munyon's Remedies, pushbar, They Prove..., oval, VG 150.00
Nature's Remedy, porc thermometer, 26", NM 225.00
Nesbitt's Soda, emb ts, Made...Real Oranges, 1940s, 24x24" 30.00
New Process Gas Ranges, match holder, ½-cylinder pocket . . .110.00
Niagara Punch, tin sign, bottle at left, 9x19", EX 40.00
Nigger Hair Smoking Tobacco, tin pail w/lid, 1890s, 6½" 145.00
Nova Scotia Insurance, porc sign, purple/wht, 12x19", NM . . .60.00
Nu Grape Soda, ts, yel & bl, Mar 9, 1920, EX 125.00
O'Keef's Pilsener Lager, ts, girl/crescent moon, fr, 25x19" . .4,700.00
OFC Bourbon, ts, deer drinks from barrel, 1900, 38x26" 385.00
OFC Rye, sign, wood fr, hunters, 1900, 22x23½" 395.00
Ohio Blue Tip Matches, pocket mirror, EX 40.00
Old Dutch Beer, rvpt sign, couple drinking, 1930s, 12" 110.00
Old Dutch Cleanser, porc sign, 32x22", EX 275.00
Old English Pipe Tobacco, paper sign, mc, fr, 1900s, 31x24" . .200.00
Old English Tobacco, paper sign, man & dog, 1910, 25x20" . . .185.00
Old Hill Side Cut Tobacco, fr paperboard sign, 1915, 26x22" . .100.00
Old Master Coffee, tin container, Meyers litho, 1930, 6" 170.00
Old Overholt Whiskey, ts, hunting, fr, 1900, 34½x26" 650.00
Old VA Cheroots, hanging sign, paper/metal strips, 20", EX . . .25.00

Nehi cardboard sign, ca 1920, 22x15", $150.00.

Clock, glass face w/convex cover, rnd, NM 200.00
Clock, plastic, logo & Please Pay Here, counter type, NM 45.00
Dispenser, napkin; early, M 350.00
Fan, Pepsi & Pete, NM 30.00
Glasses, 1930s, set of 12 in orig box 85.00
Jug, syrup; emb glass, ca 1910, 1-gal 300.00
Pencil, mechanical, EX 30.00
Radio, vendor, 3 sections across, EX 80.00
Sign, bottle hangs from thread, war label on bk, 16x9", NM 55.00
Sign, cb, for top of register, ca 1941, 6x9", MIB 75.00
Sign, cb cutout, Pepsi & Pete, beach girl, 12x8½", EX 175.00
Sign, plastic 3-D cap, easel bk, minor crack, EX 20.00
Sign, porc, Enjoy..., mc, 1950s, 30x12", NM 45.00
Sign, tin, Blk couple, oval, 1960s, M 70.00
Sign, tin, early carton & bottles w/paper labels, 1920 ......295.00
Sign, tin, gr bkground/wht letters, very early, 23x59" 150.00
Tip tray, 1890, Victorian lady in soda fountain, EX 200.00
Tip tray, 1909, lovely lady, oval, VG 175.00
Tray, 1906 ....450.00
Trolley card, 1941, cartoon by Whitney Darrow 65.00
Watch fob, New Bern NC 90.00

Oliver Chilled Plows, emb ts, 2 men/store, fr, 36x27", VG 700.00
Omar Cigarettes, cb sign, 2 men in tuxedos, fr, '10, 24x18" 185.00
Opera Cola, mc ts, tall bottle, C'est Si Bon!, 35x17", NM 55.00
Orange Crush, calendar, girl in swimsuit, 1932, EX 75.00
Orange Crush, clock, ornate oak, rvpt, printed dial, 36" 1,600.00
Orange Crush, clock, rvpt, electric, Art Deco 500.00
Orange Crush, display, cb bottle, 1927, VG 12.00
Orange Crush, menu board, rvpt, 6¾x19½", EX 55.00
Orange Crush, poster, lady in beach clothes, 1937, 14x21" 27.50
Orange Crush, tin sign, bottle figural, 1939, 18x4½" 70.00
Orange Julep, rvpt sign, lg orange, 9½" L, EX 700.00
Orinoco, tc, fisherman, 2¾x3½", EX 22.00
Osborne Threshers, hanging card, couple in rain, 1905, 7x8" ...25.00
Oscar Mayer Meats, plastic whistle, red/yel, weiner form 10.00
Oscar Mayer Meats, tie tack, 50 Years in Meats, brass 10.00
Ottawa Dairy, porc sign, red/wht/bl, 2-sided, 19x29", EX 75.00
Pacific Beer, porc sign, mc pnt, ca 1904, 22x15½" 200.00
Pacific Beer, tray, Mt Ranier, Tacoma WA, ca 1910, NM 50.00
Parcel Lockers, porc flange sign, bl/wht, 9x16½", EX 85.00
Paul Jones Whiskey, sf ts, farmer w/drink, 1900, 28x22", NM ..950.00
Pearl Beer, clock, bl neon, 8-sided, 19" 500.00
Pears' Dusting Powder, cb container, nurse/baby, 3x3", EX 17.50
Penzoil, tin sign, Supreme PA Quality, mc, 11x35", NM 45.00

Pepsi-Cola

Pepsi-Cola was first served in the early 1890s to customers of Caleb D. Bradham, a young pharmacist who touted his concoction to be medicinal as well as delicious. It was first called 'Brad's Drink' but was renamed Pepsi-Cola in 1898.

Ad, newspaper; Chinese lantern, early bottle, 1907, NM 35.00
Ad, newspaper; Pepsi & Pete, 1939, NM 20.00
Bank, miniature cooler, scarce 120.00
Bank, vending machine w/6 bottles & cb carrier, Marx, MIB ...40.00
Bottle, amber, w/both complete paper labels, 1930s, M 65.00
Bottle, dbl-dot logo at top, 1st no return, 1948 ....25.00
Bottle, gr, beer-bottle shape, wartime neck, w/cap, EX 35.00
Bottle, orig paper label, ca 1910 ....30.00
Bottle opener, bottle form, metal 15.00
Calendar, 1944, lady in rocker, 2 men, EX 60.00

Pepsodent, Goldberg's puzzle, premium 35.00
Perfection Cigarettes, sf ts, lady's hand w/pack, 1915, EX 550.00
Perstone, porc thermometer, red/wht/bl, 10" dia, NM 85.00
Peter Schuttler Wagons, cb sign, wagon train, fr, 25x31" 250.00
Peter's Weatherbird Shoes, porc thermometer, 27", VG 150.00
Piedmont Cigarettes, porc sign, bl/wht, ca 1920, 9x18", EX 95.00
Piedmont Tobacco, folding wooden chair, 1920s, 31", NM 120.00
Pillsbury, paper sign, Young Cavalier, 1893, fr, 29x22", EX 225.00

Planters Peanuts

Mr. Peanut, the dashing peanut man with the top hat, spats, monocle, and cane, has represented the Planters Peanut Company from 1916 to 1961 when the company was purchased by Standard Brands. He promoted the company's product by appearing on premium giveaways, store displays, jars, scales, and in special promotional events. Among the favored treasures of collectors today are the glass display jars. They come in a variety of styles — some are square, some hexagonal, some barrel-shaped, and others are round. The earliest, issued in 1926, was octagonal and is usually referred to as the 'pennant' jar. Although later reproduced, these are marked 'Made in Italy' on the bottom. The original is embossed on the back panel 'Sold Only in Printed Planters Red Pennant Bags.' In a second octagonal style, this embossed message was replaced with a paper label.

In 1930 a 'fishbowl' jar was introduced, and in 1932 a 'four-corner peanut' jar was issued. The rarest jar of all, the 'football' jar, was also used during the early 1930s. The Planters' square jar followed in the 1930s and was replaced by the 'barrel' jar. The six-sided jar with Mr. Peanut decals and the 'pickle' jar were later. All in all, more than fifteen different styles were developed.

In the late 1930s, premiums such as glass and metal figural paperweights, pens, and pencils were distributed. Post-war items were often made of plastic — Mr. Peanut salt and pepper shakers, mugs, and banks were popular. Today's collectors find a treasure trove of advertising memorabilia depicting that debonair gentleman, Mr. Peanut.

Ash tray, ceramic 60.00
Ball, beach; plastic blow-up, Mr Peanut 22.00
Bank, plastic, Mr Peanut 12.00
Book, color; Presidents, Mr Peanut 8.00

Book, comic; Mr Peanut on cover, 1956, NM 10.00
Book, Dedication, 1933, EX 20.00
Book, paint; Entertaining & Educational, 1950, M 16.00
Book, paint; Famous Men, 1935, M in envelope 25.00
Booklet, Your Victory Garden, 1943, EX 28.00
Bookmark, cb, Mr Peanut, 7¾x3" 8.00
Bookmark, paper litho, Mr Peanut, EX 10.00
Champagne glass, gr plastic 10.00
Charm bracelet, celluloid 15.00
Container, papier-mache, Mr Peanut, 12" 250.00
Costume, Mr Peanut Parade Man, rare 950.00
Counter bucket, Mr Peanut, lg head w/bl hat, 10" dia 25.00
Coupon, for Planters figural lighter, 1940s 8.00
Dish, die-cast 3-D Mr Peanut, EX 45.00
Doll, cloth, yel & blk, 19", NM 20.00
Game, paper board, EX colors, 1930s, complete, NM 75.00
Hat, knitted, early, EX 12.50
Hat, vendor's; early graphics, unused 45.00
Jar, Barrel, running Mr Peanut, paper label 225.00
Jar, chocolate-coverered cashews, paper label, 1944, 4½-oz 25.00
Jar, Clipper, orig lid 75.00
Jar, Fish Bowl, rectangular label 100.00
Jar, Fish Bowl, sq paper label 125.00
Jar, Football, peanut finial 300.00
Jar, frosted label, big knob, rnd 45.00
Jar, Leap Year, orig lid 50.00
Jar, mixed nuts, paper label, orig lid, 1950s, 4½-oz 15.00
Jar, octagon, Pennant 5¢, 7 sides emb 125.00
Jar, octagon, Pennant 5¢, 8 sides emb 200.00
Jar, peanut butter, early Mr Peanut on tin lid, scarce 25.00
Jar, Pennant 5¢, T paper label 175.00
Jar, sq, peanut finial, Planters emb ea side, 1934 ....150.00
Jar, Streamline, tin lid 50.00
Jar, 4-corner, lg blown-out peanut ea corner, M 300.00
Jar, 6-sided, printed yel label 60.00
Marbles in bag, 1940s 25.00
Nut chopper 22.00
Peanut-butter maker, Mr Peanut 30.00
Pencil, old Mr Peanut, M 15.00
Pin-bk button, colorful plastic, set of 5 ....15.00
Post card, Jacksonville FL 6.00
Profit chart, old Mr Peanut 25.00
Shakers, ceramic, Mr Peanut, pr 85.00
Shakers, plastic, Mr Peanut, 4½", MIB 15.00
Spoon, Mr Peanut hdl, gold finish 22.00
Tin container, Chopped Peanuts, red, 1952, scarce 90.00
Tin container, 5-lb sz, 9x6", EX 25.00
Wagon, plastic Mr Peanut, 1950s, M 165.00
Whistle, gr & red, 3½" 10.00

Poll Parrot Shoes, chalk parrot statue, 7" 45.00
Poll Parrot Shoes, neon sign, porc on steel, parrot, 25" 2,200.00
Poll Parrot Shoes, scissors 10.00
Poll Parrot Shoes, thermometer, rnd w/celluloid parrot 150.00
Popper's Ace Cigars, tc, biplane, ca 1910, oval, 5½" 160.00
Pratt's Veterinary Remedies, cabinet, wood/tin, w/list, 33" ..1,300.00
Prince Albert Pipe Tobacco, tin charger, man smoking, 24" ...600.00
Prince Albert Tobacco, pocket tin, Now King, rare, EX 250.00
Purity Ice Cream, pushbar, porc, red/wht/bl/blk, 3x30", M 40.00
Putnam Dye, cabinet, tin, 1931, +booklet 150.00
Quaker Oats, Dick Daring puzzle, w/orig mailer 30.00
Quick Meal Ranges, match holder, tin litho, VG 130.00

RCA Victor

Nipper, the RCA Victor trademark, was the creation of Francis Barraud, an English artist. His pet's intent fascination with the music of the phonograph seemed to him a worthy subject for his canvas. Although he failed to find a publishing house who would buy his work, the Gramaphone Co. saw its potential and adopted Nipper to advertise their product. The company eventually became the Victor Talking Machine Co. and was purchased by RCA in 1929. Nipper's image appeared on packaged accessories, in ads and brochures. If you are very lucky you may find a life-size statue of him — but all are not old, they have been reproduced! Except for the years between 1971 and 1981, Nipper has seen active duty; and, with his image spruced up only a bit for the present day, the ageless symbol for RCA still listens intently to 'His Master's Voice.'

Sign, lithographed textured paper, 29x25", $650.00.

Clock, His Master's Voice, rotating, 1950s 80.00
Nipper, chalk, 4½" 35.00
Nipper, papier-mache, glass eyes, early, 42" 1,250.00
Nipper, papier-mache, glass eyes, 44", EX 1,500.00
Nipper, papier-mache, 11", VG 80.00
Nipper, stuffed plush, mk collar, 1950s 145.00
Post card, hold-to-light, 1907 ....10.00
Puzzle, Victrola Talking Machine, 1908 ....85.00
Record brush, Nipper 30.00
Shakers, plastic, Nipper figural, 1950s, MIB, pr 15.00
Sign, paper, His Master's Voice, textured, fr, 25x29", EX 650.00
Sign, wooden, phonograph & dog 185.00
Snow dome, Nipper 50.00
Watch fob, EX 20.00

Rainier Beer, tray, girl rests arm on bear's head, 13", EX 250.00
Raleigh Cigarettes, cb sign, Jane Russell, EX color, 1940s 10.00
Ramon's Pills, wooden thermometer, 21", NM 275.00
Ramon's Tonic Liver Pills, cb sign, lady, ornate fr, 28x22" 500.00
Ramsay's Biscuits, cb sign, matted in fr, rare, 24x36", EX 250.00
Randolph Macon Cigars, sf ts, couple in reserve, 24x20" 550.00
Red Cross Cotton, paper sign, Blks in field, fr, 24x33", VG 200.00

Red Goose Shoes

Realizing that his last name was difficult to pronounce, Herman Giesceke, a shoe company owner, determined to give the public a modified, shortened version that would be better suited to the business world. The results suggested the use of the goose trademark, with the last two letters, 'ke,' represented by the key that this early goose held in his mouth. Upon observing an employee casually coloring in the goose trademark with a red pencil, Giesceke saw new advertising potential and renamed the company Red Goose Shoes. Although the company has changed hands down through the years, the Red Goose emblem has remained. Collectors of this desirable fowl increase in number yearly, as do prices. Beware of reproductions — new chalkware figures are prevalent.

Address book, EX 6.00
Bank, goose, CI w/red pnt, Red Goose School Shoes, 3¾" 225.00
Bank, M-1585, Save w/Shoes...Kid, tin/worn pnt, 5⅝" 45.00
Bank, M-463, CI/worn red & gold pnt, 4½" 125.00
Bank, M-610, CI/worn red & gold pnt, 3¾" 165.00
Bank, M-612, CI/worn red & orange pnt, 3⅞" 300.00
Bell, Ring for Red Goose Shoes 25.00
Bill spindle, old 15.00
Clicker, yel, Red Goose logo, 1950s, M 12.00
Clock, papier-mache, German, 23", EX 1,200.00
Goose, red vinyl, atop wood box, gives free eggs 150.00
Hood ornament, CI Arcade goose bank mtd on cap, 6", NM . .600.00
Marbles, early logo, cb box of 5, EX 50.00
Pencil box, wood, sliding top, 1920s, rare, EX 110.00
Pencil holder, pencil shape, early, EX 50.00
Shoe bench, seats 3 . . . . .650.00
Shoe horn 12.00
Sign, display; cb, 9x12" 25.00
Sign, neon on porcelainized steel, goose, 25" 1,400.00
Sign, wood, lights up, goose shape, EX color, NM 650.00
String holder, CI 1,400.00
Tablet, school; Red Goose Rodeo, ca 1935, VG 12.50
Watch fob, metal, oval, emb Red Goose, rare, 2" 145.00
Whistle, tin, red/bl/yel 15.00

Red Indian Cut Plug, paper sign, Indian w/bow, 31x25" 400.00
Red Jacket Tobacco, cb sign, baseball scene, 22x28", NM 125.00
Red Man Tobacco, sign, die-cut Indian, Chief of Chews, early . .150.00
Red Raven, tray, girl w/arms around lg raven, 12", VG 250.00
Red Rose Tea, pushbar, ...Is Good Tea, VG 120.00
Red Rose Tea, pushbar, tin, red/wht/bl, 3x30", NM 48.00
Red Rose Tea, tin sign, red/gr/wht, 4x23", NM 32.00
Red Tiger Tobacco, lunch box 60.00
Red Wing Milling Co, pot scraper, flour sack w/red wing, NM . .275.00
Remington Game Load, paper sign, game/birds, 1923, 28x20" . .95.00
Rice's Seeds, poster, man w/huge cabbage, fr, 30x24", EX 800.00
Richmond Cigarettes, sf ts, 1800s man, mc, 1900, 28x22", EX . .950.00
Rit Dye, cabinet, tin, late 1930s, EX 100.00
Robert Burns 10¢ Cigar, vitrolite curved sign, 23x16" 800.00
Robin Hood Flour, mirror, Made...Washed Wheat, 14x10", EX . .32.00
Robin Hood Flour, porc flange sign, 2-sided, EX 85.00

Roly Poly

The Roly Poly tobacco tins were patented on November 5, 1912, by Washington Tuttle and produced by Tindeco of Baltimore, Maryland. There were six characters in all—Satisfied Customer, Storekeeper, Mammy, Dutchman, Singing Waiter, and Inspector. Four brands of tobacco were packaged in selected characters; some tins carry a printed tobacco box on the back to identify their contents. Mayo and Dixie Queen Tobacco were packed in all six; Red Indian and U.S. Marine Tobacco in only Mammy, Singing Waiter, and Storekeeper. Of the set, the Inspector is considered the rarest and in mint condition may fetch as much as $1,000 on today's market.

Dutchman, Mayo, EX 550.00
Dutchman, Mayo, NM 750.00
Inspector from Scotland Yard, Mayo, NM 1,000.00

Mammy, Mayo, EX 600.00
Satisfied Customer, EX 550.00
Singing Waiter, Mayo, EX 575.00
Singing Waiter, US Marine, VG 400.00
Storekeeper, Mayo, NM 650.00

Rnd Oak Stoves, copper ash tray, emb Indian, 1905 . . . . .25.00
Rnd Oak Stoves, vitrolite curved sign, Indian, 23x16", NM . . . 6,000.00
Royal Crown Cola, cb sign, Santa & bottle, 1950s, 30x10", EX .45.00
Royal Crown Cola, pushbar, die-cut tin, 1936 . . . . .45.00
Royal Crown Cola, scales, CI w/40" plastic bottle bk, 1940 . .1,300.00
Ruby Grand Coal Burner, pot scraper, VG 150.00
Russell's Ales, sf ts, workers unload kegs, 1930s, 29x21" 195.00
Salada Tea, porc pushbar, bl/yel/blk, French, 3x30", EX 30.00
Salada Tea, porc sign, bl/wht, 10x19", EX 55.00
Salada Tea, porc sign, Delicious Flavor, mc, 3x30", EX 25.00
Sauer's Extracts, diecut, pretty girl, fr, 12x20", NM 210.00
Sauer's Extracts, wood thermometer, None Better, 23", VG . . .325.00
Schlitz Beer, match holder, litho cb, bottle, NM 325.00
Schoenhofen Brewery, cb sign, midget on keg, 1900, 23x18" . .385.00
Sedgwick Rye, fr cb sign, Blks gamble, 1900, 22x13" 250.00
Senaca Spices, tc, sailing ship, NM 12.00
Senator Smoking tobacco, tc, fr portrait, 5x3", EX 37.50
Senour's Floor Paint, ts, room interior, 1915, 20x14" 125.00
Sergeant's Dog Medicine, booklet, 1927, 48-pg 17.50
Sharples' Separator, match holder, man/product, VG 200.00
Sharples' Separator, pot scraper, lady/product, EX 110.00
Sharples' Separator, sf ts, girl/child/calf, 31x28", NM 2,800.00
Singer, emb diecut, in Yiddish, ca 1920, 26x38" 500.00
Sir Walter Raleigh, ts, mc on gr, ...Can't Bite!, 29x17", NM 30.00
Smart True Blue Gum, display box, w/20 packs of gum, M 55.00
Snow King Baking Powder, die-cut sign, Santa, 1900, 24x36" . .350.00
Snow King Baking Powder, mc cb sign, 1930s, 10x14", EX 40.00
Spark's Perfect Health, ceramic platter w/Mrs Cleveland, 20" . .600.00
St Lawrence Flour, porc thermometer, red/wht/gr, 30x8", EX . . .88.00
Standard Oil, post card, horse-drawn sled, early 1900s, EX 12.00
Star Weekly, porc sign, Read...on Sale Here, mc, 24x8", EX 75.00
Star Weekly, pushbar, porc, red/wht, 3x30", EX 30.00
Stephenson Union Suits, metal die-cut sign, 3-D, 1910, 37" .1,150.00
Stephenson Union Suits, pin-bk button, 1920s 15.00

Scottie Cigars humidor tin, 4x4x5", $225.00.

Stevens Old Judson Whiskey, match holder, VG 100.00
Stubby Cola, thermometer, plastic, bottle-cap form, 15", EX 45.00
Studebaker Bros Mfg, paper sign, 20 wagons/carriages, 29x39" .550.00
Sunbeam Bread, stand-up sign, 3-D cutout, girl, 22", NM 65.00
Suncrest, sf ts, tall bottle, mc, 22x8", NM 50.00
Sunny Brook Bourbon, match holder, bottle, EX 350.00
Sure Shot Chewing Tobacco, store tin, Indian/bow, 11x16" . . .375.00
Sweet & Pure Flour, thermometer, porc, 27", NM 275.00
Sweet Caporal, canvas banner, red/wht/gr/blk, 5x60", EX 27.50
Swift's Pride Soap, porc sign, curved, wood support, 14x9" 400.00
Tannhauser Tropfen Bitters, match holder, Englishman, NM . .200.00
Tasteless Perfect Purgative, tray, bluejay/bottle, 13", VG 250.00
Thomson's Corsets, paper sign, fr under glass, 1902, 10x14" . . .325.00
Tiger Chewing Tobacco, canister, gold/blk on red, 12x8½" . . .100.00
Tiger Head Brand Ales & Stouts, sf ts, tiger, oval, 23" 1,600.00
Toyland Peanut Butter, pail, ca 1920s, 2-lb, VG 130.00
Turkey Coffee, tin container, Am Can Co, ca 1910, 3-lb 550.00
UMC Shot Shells, paper sign, covey of quail, fr, 30x16" 450.00
Uneeda, cut-out boy display, litho cb, 1926, 50x21", EX 550.00
Union Leader Cut Plug, paper sign, Uncle Sam, 29x21" 6,500.00
Usher's Scotch, counter display, man in kilts, 17" 30.00
Valentino's Florida Fruit Chewing Gum, rvpt sign, 8" dia, VG .100.00

Van Mellis Toffee Biscuit Drops, Holland, 11", $75.00.

Vaseline, cb sign, Toonerville Town characters, '30s, 19x12" . .125.00
Vegederma, ts, topless lady, Chas Shonk illus, fr, 16x12" 4,500.00
Velvet Pipe Tobacco, ts, 2 men/child/dog, fr, 32x26", VG 650.00
Venus Pencils, display, tin revolving pencil figural, 36" 400.00
Viceroy Cigarettes, ts, Filtered Smoke, mc, 29x17", NM 24.00
Vision Baking Powder, clock, short-drop regulator, 25", VG . . .225.00
Walkover Shoes, dbl-sided angle sign, man, bk: lady, 27x17" 4,000.00
Ward's Extracts, pot scraper, Remedies/Extracts, VG 120.00
Wayne Knitting Mills, cb sign, ...Woman of '19, 21x14", VG . .300.00
Western Assurance, palm press, tin, 3x12", EX 40.00
Westinghouse Fan, thermometer, wood fan, no tube, 27", VG .200.00
White Rock Beverages, 6-pack carrier, wood nymph, M 10.00
White Rose, porc flange sign, 2-sided, sq, 18x18", NM 40.00
Winchester, paper sign, For Sale Here/2 dogs, 46x37", VG . .1,100.00
Winchester...Shotguns, paper sign, 2 dogs, fr, 33x20" 450.00
Winnipeg Tribune, porc thermometer, yel/blk, 39x8", VG 175.00
Woonsocket Rubber Boots & Shoes, emb ts, 1920s, 6x18" 30.00

Wrigley's Gum, glass jar w/lid, unmk, #3, EX in orig box 22.00
Yankee Girl, cb stand-up sign, 1930s, 7x10" 22.00
Yellow Kid Chewing Gum, 5-stick pack, 3" L 140.00
Zeno Chewing Gum, bookmark, paper, bldg/flowers, 5", NM . .100.00
Zeno Chewing Gum, case, glass/wood, 17", EX 550.00
20 Mule Team Borax, puzzle, w/orig mailer 35.00
7-Up, chalkboard, hand w/bottle, 27x19", EX 45.00
7-Up, menu cover, 1950s 30.00
7-Up, pin-bk button, concave, brass w/enamel, 1x1½", NM 7.50
7-Up, tin thermometer, Fresh Up Family Drink, 15x6", NM . . .45.00
7-Up, ts, Fresh Up w/7-Up, 1930s, 11x18", EX 32.00
7-Up, ts, You're Fresh Up, hand/bottle, 27x19", EX 55.00
7-Up, ts, 1954, 25x9½" 36.00

Advertising Cards

Advertising trade cards enjoyed a heyday during the last quarter of the nineteenth century when the printing process known as chromolithography was refined and put into popular use. The purpose of the trade card was to acquaint the public with a place of business, a product, or a service. Most trade cards range in size from 2" x 3" to 3" x 5"; however, some are found in both smaller and larger sizes. Four categories of particular interest to collectors are:

Mechanical — those which achieve movement through the use of a pull tab, fold-out side, or rotating disk.

Metamorphic — cards that transform a person or a thing from a 'before' to an 'after' condition, which of course represents a marked improvement immediately upon use of the featured product.

Hold-to-light — cards that reveal their design only when viewed before a strong light.

Diecuts — cards in figural forms such as the Heinz pickle series. Diecuts are usually in the shape of the advertised product or a theme-related object. For a more thorough study of the subject, we recommend *The Advertising Trade Card* by Kit Barry; his address can be found in the Directory under Vermont. When no condition is indicated, the items listed below are assumed to be in near-mint condition.

Allen's Root Beer Extract, girl stands in doorway w/product 12.00
Allen's Root Beer Extract, girl w/apron full of flowers 6.00
Anglo-Swiss Condensed Milk, baby in walker beating drum 4.00
Anglo-Swiss Condensed Milk, baby in walker w/doll 4.00
Anglo-Swiss Condensed Milk, baby in walker w/nurser 6.00
Anglo-Swiss Condensed Milk, 2 boys opening lg can, 3 w/spoons .6.00
Anglo-Swiss Condensed Milk, 2 girls & baby around lg can 6.00
Atmore's Mince Meat, boy at table holding knife & fork 5.00
Atmore's Mince Meat, chef holding pie .5.00
Ayer's Cherry Pectoral, girl w/basket of cherries 5.00
Ayer's Hair Vigor, girl w/horse & 2 dogs .7.00
Ayer's Sarsaparilla, girl w/pk bow facing right 7.00
Baker's Chocolates, lady in bl by table w/box 8.00
Baker's Chocolates, lady in red dress, w/box 12.00
Borden's Condensed Milk, baby asleep, puppy at nursing bottle . .8.00
Borden's Condensed Milk, 3 children, 1 holding can 6.00
Borden's Evaporated Milk, child w/witch's hat & 3 kittens 8.00
Borden's Evaporated Milk, 2 babies holding spoons 6.00
Briggs Pianos, baby at window 3.00
Capadura Cigar, lady on roller skates 7.00
Capadura Cigar, man falling on boy while roller skating 7.00
Carboline for the Hair, lady leaning over balcony 5.00
Carter's Backache Master, child & Grandpa 3.00
Carter's Little Liver Pills, baby playing guitar 3.00
Carter's Little Liver Pills, crow in tree holding sign 8.00
Carter's Little Liver Pills, girl looking out window 5.00

Carter's Little Liver Pills, lady standing w/flowers 5.00
Dalley's Magical Pain Extractor, lady w/sheep & 2 lambs 4.00
Dougherty's New England Mince Meat, girl in bl dress w/pie 4.00
Dr Morses Indian Root Pills, girl & boy under umbrella 4.00
Dr Morses Indian Root Pills, girl having tea w/doll 4.00
Duke Tobacco, metamorphic, 2 babies crying 14.00
Emerson Piano Co, couple & cupid at piano 4.00
Emerson's Albumenoid Food, lady in pk 5.00
Favorite Cream Root Beer, girl sits & reads newspaper 8.00
German Corn Remover, blk/wht metamorphic, 2 men/product ..15.00
Hagan's Magnolia Balm, 2 bottles, reclining lady, cherub 15.00
Halls Hair Renewer, bottle surrounded by 8 children's heads 6.00
Halls Hair Renewer, girl & boy w/bottle behind his back 5.00
Hartshorn's Root Beer Extract, girl w/umbrella 6.00

J&P Coats Best Six Cord, 3x4½", $5.00.

Highland Evaporated Cream, 9 babies at table w/nanny 15.00
Hood's Olive Ointment, 2 children w/top, Greenaway style 5.00
Hood's Sarsaparilla, metamorphic, lady/horse break window 15.00
Hood's Sarsaparilla, 3 crawling babies 5.00
Huyler's Cocoa, girl w/basket & doll 6.00
Imperial Granum, 2 children sitting, holding open book 6.00
Ithaca Organ, organ, floral border 5.00
Ivers & Pond Piano Co, girl & boy by apple tree 4.00
Limerick Plug Tobacco, man holding beer stein 4.00
Lone Fisherman Cigarettes, man fishing in wash tub 6.00
Mack's Milk Chocolate, lady paints at easel w/man 4.00
Mellins Food, Good Morning, Mamma 5.00
Mellins Food, The Family Doctor 6.00
Menier Chocolate, baby in lg shoe 5.00
Mennen's Corn Killer, lady & man holding his foot 6.00
Merchant's Gargling Oil, comic ballplayer, 'Put It There' 8.00
Merchant's Gargling Oil, horse's head in horseshoe 6.00
Merchant's Gargling Oil, lady's head in horseshoe 6.00
Merchant's Gargling Oil, 3 horses at water trough 5.00
Phenyo-Caffein Co, puzzle, My Girl & Her Mother 5.00
Phillips Digestible Cocoa, girl drinking cocoa w/cat 12.00
Pond's Extract, single maple leaf 2.00
Pond's Extract, The Obelisk 6.00
Quakeress Cigar, Quaker lady 8.00
Ridges Food, baby in goat cart 10.00
Ridges Food, lady holding can up, 4 children 6.00
St Jacobs Oil, butterfly diecut, lt stock paper 4.00
Tansill's Punch Cigar, man shooting his hat, 3 dogs 4.00
Thomas' Electric Oil, girl opening door for another 3.00

Turkish Trophies, lady in riding habit 7.00
Van Houten's Cocoa, The Skylark 4.00
Venables Tobacco, chariot drawn by 4 horses 8.00
Vose & Sons Pianos, 7 cherubs playing music 8.00
Warner's Safe Cure, child & St Bernard dog 5.00
Warner's Safe Yeast, girl & grandmother 6.00
Warner's Safe yeast, girl smelling lilies 6.00
Wheelock Piano, lady at piano, stained glass window 8.00
Whites Red Robin Gum, robin on fence 6.00

Advertising Dolls

Whether your interest in ad dolls is fueled by nostalgia or strictly because of their amusing, often clever advertising impact, there are several points that should be considered before making your purchases. Condition is of utmost importance; never pay book price for dolls in poor condition, whether they are cloth or of another material. Restoring fabric dolls is usually unsatisfactory and involves a good deal of work — seams must be opened, stuffing removed, the doll washed and dried, and then reassembled. Washing old fabrics may prove to be disastrous — colors may fade or run, and most stains are totally resistant to washing. It's usually best to leave the fabric doll as it is.

Watch for new dolls as they become available. Save related advertising literature, extra coupons, etc., and keep these along with the doll to further enhance your collection. Old dolls with no marks are sometimes challenging to identify. While some products may use the same familiar trademark figures for a number of years — the Jolly Green Giant, Pillsbury's Poppin' Fresh, and the Keebler Elf, for example — others appear on the market for a short time only and may be difficult to trace. Most libraries have reference books with trademarks and logos that might provide a clue in tracking down your doll's identity. Children see advertising figures on Saturday morning cartoons that are often unfamiliar to adults, or other ad doll collectors may have the information you seek.

Advertising dolls are still easy to find and relatively inexpensive, ranging in cost from $1.00 to $100.00, with the average price at about $10.00. They are popular with children as well as adults. For a more thorough study of the subject, we recommend *Advertising Dolls*, by Joleen Robison and Kay Sellers. Joleen is our advisor; she is listed in the Directory under Kansas.

A&W Restaurant, teddy bear, 1975, 13" 9.00

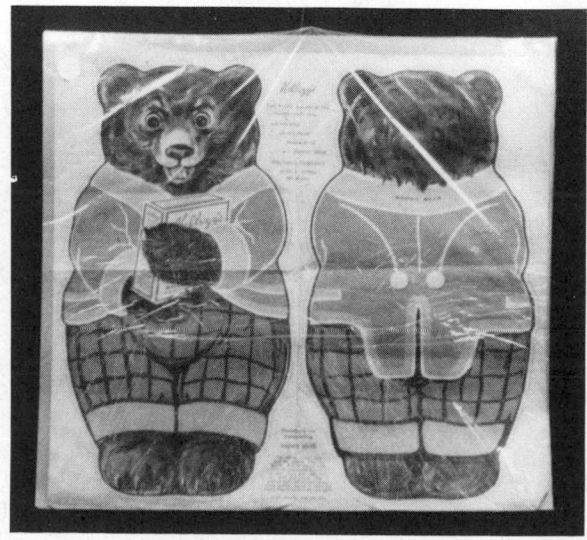

Daddy Bear, marked Kellogg's, ca 1925, 15", $125.00.

Allied Van Lines, girl, orange jumper, brn hair, 1970s, 17" 12.00
American Airlines, Mary Make Up, plastic, 1967, 12" 12.00
Aunt Jemima, Diana, cloth, ca 1905, 12" 65.00
Aunt Jemima, Wade, cloth, ca 1924 ....60.00
Aunt Sarah's Pancake House, Aunt Sarah, cloth, 1973, 15" ...18.00
Bear Brand Hosiery Co, Boy Bear, cloth, red shirt, 9" 100.00
Big Boy Restaurant, Big Boy, plastic, 1974-1978, 10" 5.00
Big Boy Restaurant, Dolly, cloth, red dress, mk, 1978, 14" 8.00
Borden, Elsie Cow, vinyl head, plush body, 1950s, 15" 12.00
Brunswick Corp, Itylyti, cloth, mk, 1968, 16" 15.00
Buddy Lee, compo, dungaree trousers, plaid shirt, 12½" 160.00
Buddy Lee, Minute Men, station uniform, plastic, 12" 180.00
Bumble Bee Tuna, Yum Yum Bumble Bee, inflatable plastic, 24" .5.00
Burger King, Magician, MIB 10.00
Buster Brown Shoes, Buster Brown, cloth, ca 1905, 13" 135.00
Campbell Kids, compo, Horseman, 1947, 14", pr, M 350.00
Campbell's Cheerleader, vinyl, 1957-1961, 9½" 20.00
Coast-to-Coast Hardware, Elfy, 20" 8.00
Cream of Wheat, Blk chef, cloth, 1-pc legs, 1949, 18" 55.00
Cream of Wheat, man, cloth, hat/apron, 1920s premium 75.00
Dan River, Buttons, cloth body, mask face, 1947, 12" 55.00
Esskay Meats, Baron Von Esskay, cloth, 11" 20.00
Exxon, tiger, plush, 1959, 16" 10.00
General Electric, Bandy, Maxfield Parrish, Cameo Doll Co, M .450.00
Gerber, baby, vinyl, yel hair, 1972, 11" 22.00
Green Giant, Little Sprout, plastic, 1982, 5" 6.00
Hostess Bakery, Happy Ho Ho, inflatable, 1970s, 48" 8.00
Just Rite Restaurant, Li'l Miss Rite, vinyl, jtd, 1965, 8" 15.00
Kellogg's, Jack Spratt, cloth litho, early 1900s, 14" 80.00
Kellogg's, Johnny Bear, printed cloth, uncut, 1925, 11" 125.00
Kellogg's, Tom the Piper's Son, stuffed 80.00
Kellogg's, Tony the Tiger, plastic, 1974, 8" 10.00
Levi Strauss, Levi Denim Rag Doll, yarn hair, 1974, 10" 8.00
McDonald's Corp, Grimace, purple plush fabric, 1976, 8", M ...8.00
McDonald's Corp, Hamburger Cop, knob moves head, jtd, 7" ...25.00
MD Bathroom Tissue, Cheshire Cat, cloth litho, unmk, 11" 15.00
Michelin Man, plastic, 15" 35.00
Mohawk Carpet, Mohawk Tommy, Indian, cloth, 16" 15.00
Nestle, Rabbit, brn/tan plush, vinyl eyes/teeth, 1976 ....10.00
Old Crow Whiskey, hard plastic, unmk, 1950, 4½" 12.00
Peter Pan Ice Cream, Peter Pan, cloth, unmk, 1972, 18" 10.00
Pillsbury, Dough Boy, rubber, mk, 1971, 7", EX 8.00
Quaker Crackle, boy, dtd 1930, uncut, rare 125.00
Ralston Purina, Shaggy DA, wht plush w/felt features, 21" 12.00
Shamrock Oil Co, Leprechaun, cloth litho, unmk, 15" 10.00
Sweets Candy, Peppermint Pattie, bean bag, 1973, 10" 12.00
Vlasic Pickles, Vlasic Stork, inflatable, 1977, 53" 10.00

African Art

These artifacts of the African nation are a unique form of folk art, of interest not only in relation to the craftsmanship evident in their making, but because of the culture they represent.

Chair, Asante, asipim, blk pnt on hide seat, decor, 31" 880.00
Cup, Kuba, compressed globular form w/geometrics, 5" dia ...990.00
Doll, Bechuana or Basuto, mc geometric beadwork, 7¼" 450.00
Doll, ceremonial; Cameroon, namdji, typical form, 10" 2,200.00
Doll, Fanti, akuaba, stylized form, incised, 13" 770.00
Doll, fertility; Asante, akuaba, naturalistic form, 10⅝" 1,500.00
Doll, Zulu, articulated limbs, feather inserts, beads, 9" 650.00
Figure, Bembe, female fetish stands on sq base, 9⅜" 935.00
Figure, Benin, bronze, leopard w/curved tail, pnt traces, 7" ..1,200.00

Figure, Kamba, male in uniform w/fez, brass inlay, 8" 660.00
Figure, Nanji, cvd & incised scarification, 11¼" 450.00
Figure, Nigerian, attenuated abstract female, 26¾" 880.00
Figure, Senufo, female w/conical breasts, crested hair, 9" 550.00
Figure, Senufo, male stands, pierced ears w/hoops, 17½" 175.00
Figure, staff; Wurkun, 21" abstract form on iron stake 660.00
Fly whisk, Ashanti, gilded wood, cvd animals/lineation, 10" ...375.00
Gameboard, abstract animal form, 12 cvd sections on bk, 35" ..660.00
Head, Leaga, Bwami Society, ivory, shell inlay eyes, 4½" 1,200.00
Headdress, ceremonial; Bamun, tunggunga, deep-set eyes, 19" .935.00
Headdress, dance; Yoruba, gelede, pierced eyes, mc pnt, 14" ...550.00

Fang mask, Gabon, raffia grass trim, used by NGI Society, 23", $900.00.

Headdress, Tschokwe, cloth/fiber, pelts at sides, 12½" 770.00
Headrest, Shona, openwork geometrics, brass rings, 5⅝" 935.00
Mask, cvd wood, yel/blk beaded face, cowrie shells, 13" 80.00
Mask, Dan, animal w/snout, teeth bared, pierced eyes, 12" 660.00
Mask, Ibibio, Ekpo Society, lozenge mouth, bared teeth, 6" ..3,000.00
Mask, Kuba/Chokwe, polychrome wood, incised features, 10" ..500.00
Mask, Senufo, Kpelie, geometric projections, slit eyes, 12" ..2,000.00
Sculpture, Bambara, iron, staff w/4 bell suspensions, 19" 75.00
Spoon, Senufo, cvd bird hdl, notched decor, deep bowl, 9½" ..880.00
Walking stick, Maori, spiralling geometrics, dtd 1889, 36" 880.00

Agata

Agata is New England peachblow with an applied metallic stain which produces gold tracery and dark blue mottling. The stain is subject to wear, and the amount of remaining stain greatly affects the value. It is especially valuable (and rare) when found on peachblow of intense color. Caution — be sure to use only gentle cleaning methods. See also Green Opaque.

Celery vase, scalloped sq top, glossy, vivid color, 6½" 895.00
Cruet, tricorn, 5½" 1,000.00
Pitcher, water; sq mouth, reeded hdl 3,900.00
Plate, ribbon candy fluted rim, EX color & decor, 6½" 850.00
Spittoon, lady's, ruffled/scalloped flared rim, 2¾x5½" 600.00
Spooner, sq crimped top, EX mottling, 4½" 800.00
Spooner, sq top, 4½" 450.00
Toothpick holder, bulbous w/pinched-in scalloped rim, rare ...795.00
Toothpick holder, tricorn top, paper label, EX mottle 550.00

Tumbler, allover mottle, M 785.00
Tumbler, lemonade; 5⅛x2½" 1,300.00
Vase, bulbous w/stick neck, 8½" 700.00
Vase, Morgan, orig glass griffin base, 8", EX 3,000.00

Akro Agate

The Akro Agate Co. founded in 1914 primarily as a marble maker, operated in Clarksburg, West Virginia, until 1951. Their popular wares included children's dishes, powder jars, flowerpots, and novelty items along with the famous 'Akro Aggies.' Much of their glass was produced in the distinctive marbleized colors they called Red Onyx, Blue Onyx, etc.; solid opaque and transparent colors were also produced. Most of the wares are marked with their trademark, a crow flying through the letter 'A' holding an Aggie in its beak and one in each claw. Other marks include 'J.P.' on children's pieces, 'J.V. Co., Inc,' 'Braun & Corwin,' 'N.Y.C. Vogue Merc Co. U.S.A,' 'Hamilton Match Co.,' and 'Mexicali Pickwick Cosmetic Corp.' on novelty items. In 1936 Akro obtained the moulds from the Balmer-Westite Co. of Weston, West Virginia. Westite produced a similar line of products for several years. Their ware is drab in color when compared to Akro and is generally unmarked. The embossed Westite logo does appear occasionally on the bottom of some pieces. Westite is commonly accepted as a companion collectible of Akro.

Chiquita

Creamer, baked-on colors, 1½" 8.00
Creamer, opaque gr, 1½" 5.00
Creamer, transparent cobalt, 1½" 10.00
Cup, baked-on colors, 1½" 5.00
Cup, opaque gr, 1½" 4.00
Cup, opaque turq, lav, or caramel, 1½" 15.00
Cup, transparent cobalt, 1½" 7.00
Plate, baked-on colors, 3¾" 4.00
Plate, transparent cobalt, 3¾" 6.00
Saucer, baked-on colors, 3⅛" 1.50
Saucer, opaque lav, caramel, or yel, 3¼" 7.00
Saucer, transparent cobalt, 3⅛" 2.00
Set, 16-pc, baked-on colors 70.00
Set, 16-pc, opaque colors other than gr 125.00
Set, 16-pc, opaque gr 47.00
Set, 16-pc, transparent cobalt 105.00
Sugar bowl, baked-on colors, open, 1½" 8.00
Sugar bowl, opaque turq, lav, or caramel, open, 1½" 10.00
Sugar bowl, transparent cobalt, open, 1½" 10.00
Teapot, baked-on colors, 3" 12.00
Teapot, opaque gr, 3" 9.00
Teapot, opaque turq or lav, 3" 35.00
Teapot, transparent cobalt, 3" 25.00

Concentric Rib

Creamer, opaque colors other than gr or wht, 1¼" 7.50
Creamer, opaque gr or wht, 1¼" 5.00
Cup, opaque colors other than gr or wht, 1¼" 5.00
Cup, opaque gr or wht, 1¼" 3.00
Plate, opaque colors other than gr or wht, 3¼" 3.00
Plate, opaque gr or wht, 3¼" 2.00
Saucer, opaque gr or wht, 2¾" 1.50
Sugar bowl, opaque colors other than gr or wht, 1¼" 7.50
Sugar bowl, opaque gr or wht, 1¼" 4.50
Teapot, opaque colors other than gr or wht, 3⅜" 10.00

Teapot, opaque gr or wht, 3½" 9.00

Concentric Ring

Cereal, lg, solid opaque colors, 3⅜" 18.00
Cereal, lg, transparent cobalt, 3⅜" 28.00
Creamer, lg, transparent cobalt, 1⅜" 25.00
Creamer, sm, solid opaque colors, 1¼" 12.00
Creamer, sm, transparent cobalt, 1¼" 20.00
Cup, lg, opaque lav or yel, 1⅜" 30.00
Cup, lg, opaque marbleized colors 30.00
Cup, lg, opaque pumpkin, 1⅜" 20.00
Cup, sm, transparent cobalt, 1¼" 26.00
Plate, lg, solid opaque colors, 4¼" 6.00
Plate, lg, transparent cobalt, 4¼" 12.00
Plate, sm, transparent cobalt, 3¼" 12.00
Saucer, lg, solid opaque colors, 3⅛" 4.00
Saucer, lg, transparent cobalt, 3⅛" 6.00
Saucer, sm, transparent cobalt, 2¾" 6.00
Set, 16-pc, solid opaque colors, sm 105.00
Set, 21-pc, transparent cobalt, lg 375.00
Sugar bowl, lg, marbleized bl, w/lid, 1⅞" 45.00
Sugar bowl, sm, transparent cobalt, 1¼" 25.00
Teapot, lg, solid opaque colors, 3⅜" 35.00
Teapot, lg, transparent cobalt, 3¾" 50.00

Interior Panel

Cereal, lg, azure bl or yel, 3⅜" 25.00
Cereal, lg, marbleized gr/wht, 3⅜" 22.00
Creamer, lg, marbleized bl/wht, 1⅜" 22.00

Set, large, in box; see listings below for values.

Creamer, sm, azure bl or yel, 1¼" 27.00
Creamer, sm, marbleized red/wht, 1¼" 25.00
Cup, lg, marbleized red/wht, 1⅜" 25.00
Cup, sm, marbleized red/wht, 1¼" 20.00
Cup, sm, pk or gr lustre, 1¼" 8.00
Cup, sm, pumpkin, 1¼" 20.00
Pitcher, sm, transparent gr or topaz, 2⅞" 11.00
Plate, lg, azure bl or yel, 4¼" 12.00
Plate, sm, marbleized bl/wht, 3¾" 7.00
Plate, sm, pk or gr lustre, 3¾" 5.00

Saucer, sm, azure bl or yel, 2⅜" 5.50
Saucer, sm, marbleized red/wht, 2⅜" 5.00
Set, lg, 21-pc, marbleized bl/wht .325.00
Set, sm, 16-pc, marbleized red/wht, MIB 220.00
Set, sm, 16-pc, pk or gr lustre, MIB 125.00
Set, sm, 8-pc, marbleized bl/wht, MIB 105.00
Set, sm, 8-pc, transparent gr or topaz 40.00
Sugar bowl, lg, lemonade/oxblood, w/lid, 1⅞" 25.00
Sugar bowl, lg, transparent gr or topaz, w/lid, 1¼" 20.00
Sugar bowl, sm, azure bl or yel, 1¼" 27.00
Sugar bowl, sm, marbleized bl/wht, 1¼" 25.00
Teapot, lg, lemonade/oxblood, 3¾" 47.00
Teapot, sm, azure bl or yel, 3⅜" 40.00
Teapot, sm, marbleized bl/wht, 3⅜" 35.00
Tumbler, sm, opaque, 2" 40.00
Tumbler, sm, transparent gr or topaz, 2" 6.00

J.P. (Made for J. Pressman Company)

Cup, baked-on colors, 1½" 4.00
Cup, transparent cobalt w/ribs, 1½" 4.00
Cup, transparent gr, 1½" 25.00
Cup, transparent red or brn, 1½" 30.00
Plate, transparent red or brn, 4¼" .20.00
Saucer, crystal, 3¼" 5.00
Saucer, transparent red or brn, 3¼" 8.00
Set, 17-pc, transparent red or brn 320.00
Set, 21-pc, baked-on colors 105.00
Sugar bowl, baked-on colors, w/lid, 1½" 10.00
Sugar bowl, transparent gr, w/lid, 1½" 25.00
Sugar bowl, transparent red or brn, w/lid, 1½" 38.00
Teapot, transparent red or brn, 1½" 50.00

Miss America

Creamer, wht 35.00
Cup, forest gr or marbleized orange/wht 32.00
Cup, wht 27.00
Plate, forest gr or marbleized orange/wht 20.00
Plate, wht 15.00
Saucer, forest gr or marbleized orange/wht 11.00
Saucer, wht 10.00
Sugar bowl, wht, w/lid 45.00
Teapot, forest gr or marbleized orange/wht 90.00
Teapot, wht 80.00

Octagonal

Cereal, lg, dk gr, bl, or wht, 3⅜" 6.00
Cereal, lg, lemonade/oxblood, 3⅜" 20.00
Cereal, lg, pk, other opaques, 3⅜" .6.00
Creamer, lg, beige, pumpkin, or lt bl, closed hdl, 1½" 12.00
Creamer, sm, dk gr, bl, or wht, 1¼" 10.00
Plate, sm, dk gr, bl, or wht, 3⅜" 4.00
Saucer, sm, yel or lime gr, 3⅜" 5.00
Set, lg, 21-pc, gr, wht, or dk bl 90.00
Set, lg, 21-pc, lemonade/oxblood, closed hdls, MIB 300.00
Sugar bowl, sm, dk gr, bl, or wht, 1¼" 8.00
Teapot, lg, bl or gr 14.00
Tumbler, sm, pumpkin, yel, or lime gr, 2" 12.00

Raised Daisy

Creamer, yel, 1¾" 35.00

Cup, bl, 1¾" 35.00
Plate, bl, 3" 8.00
Saucer, beige, 2½" 6.00
Sugar bowl, yel, 1¾" 35.00
Teapot, bl, w/lid, 2⅜" 57.00
Teapot, bl or gr, open, 2⅜" 25.00
Teapot, yel, 2⅜" 40.00
Tumbler, bl (no embossed pattern), 2" 55.00
Tumbler, yel or beige, 2" 18.00

Stacked Disc

Creamer, opaque colors other than gr or wht, 1¼" 7.50
Creamer, pumpkin, 1¼" 12.00
Cup, opaque gr or wht, 1¼" 5.00
Pitcher, opaque colors other than gr or wht, 2⅞" 12.00
Pitcher, opaque gr, 2⅞" 8.00
Set, 21-pc, opaque colors other than gr or wht 90.00
Set, 21-pc, opaque gr or wht 60.00
Sugar bowl, opaque colors other than gr or wht, 1¼" 7.50
Sugar bowl, opaque gr or wht, 1¼" 3.00
Sugar bowl, pumpkin, 1¼" 14.00
Teapot, opaque colors other than gr or wht, 3⅜" 10.00
Teapot, opaque gr or wht, 3⅜" 9.00
Teapot, pumpkin, 3⅜" 20.00
Tumbler, pumpkin, 2" 25.00

Stacked Disc and Interior Panel

Cereal, lg, marbleized bl, 3⅜" 35.00
Cereal, lg, opaque solid colors, 3⅜" 20.00
Creamer, lg, marbleized bl, 1⅜" 30.00
Creamer, lg, transparent cobalt, 1⅜" 25.00
Creamer, lg, transparent gr, 1⅜" 25.00
Creamer, sm, opaque solid colors, 1¼" 10.00
Cup, lg, transparent gr, 1⅜" 17.00
Cup, sm, marbleized bl, 1¼" 26.00
Cup, sm, transparent cobalt, 1¼" 18.00
Pitcher, sm, transparent gr, 2⅞" 12.00
Plate, lg, marbleized bl, 4¾" 18.00
Set, lg, 21-pc, opaque solid colors, MIB 225.00
Set, lg, 21-pc, transparent cobalt, MIB 350.00
Set, sm, 8-pc, opaque solid colors, MIB 65.00
Set, sm, 8-pc, transparent cobalt, MIB 115.00
Sugar bowl, lg, transparent cobalt, w/lid, 1⅞" 35.00
Sugar bowl, sm, marbleized bl, 1¼" 30.00
Sugar bowl, sm, transparent gr, 1¼" 20.00
Teapot, lg, marbleized bl, 3¾" 60.00
Teapot, sm, opaque solid colors, 3⅜" 25.00
Tumbler, sm, transparent cobalt, 2" 8.00
Tumbler, sm, transparent gr, 2" 7.00

Stippled Band

Creamer, lg, transparent amber, 1½" 20.00
Creamer, sm, transparent gr, 1¼" .22.00
Cup, lg, transparent amber, 1½" 6.00
Cup, sm, transparent gr, 1¼" 5.00
Pitcher, sm, transparent gr, 2⅞" 12.00
Plate, lg, transparent gr, 4¼" 4.50
Saucer, lg, transparent amber, 3¼" .3.00
Set, lg, 17-pc, transparent azure 260.00
Set, sm, 8-pc, transparent amber, MIB 35.00
Sugar bowl, lg, transparent amber, w/lid, 1⅞" 27.00

Sugar bowl, lg, transparent azure, w/lid, 1⅞" 35.00
Tumbler, sm, transparent amber, 1¾" 6.00
Tumbler, sm, transparent gr, 1¾" 7.00

Miscellaneous

Ash tray, bl, sq, emb AKROITE, 3" 45.00
Ash tray, marbleized bl/wht, leaf form 5.00
Ash tray, marbleized gr/wht, hexagonal 10.00
Ash tray, pumpkin, Hotel Edison 30.00
Ash tray, marbleized red/wht, sq, 3" 5.00
Basket, marbleized bl/wht, 2 hdls 25.00
Basket, marbleized orange/wht, 1 hdl 110.00
Bell, crystal 10.00
Bell, custard 45.00
Bell, gr 65.00
Bowl, fruit; cobalt, ftd 95.00

Fruit bowl, cobalt, no mark, 6x8", $95.00.

Bowl, marbleized bl/wht, ivy design, #323 ....8.00
Bowl, pumpkin, 3-ftd, #340 ....12.00
Flowerpot, blk, banded dart, #300 ....15.00
Flowerpot, custard, mk Made in USA, #1309 ....45.00
Flowerpot, gr/wht ribs & flutes, #296 ....6.00
Flowerpot, marbleized bl/wht, Stacked Disc, 4" 8.00
Flowerpot, marbleized orange/wht, ribbed top, #300F 6.00
Flowerpot, pumpkin, graduated darts, #307 ....12.00
Flowerpot, pumpkin, ribbed top w/darts, #295 ....45.00
Lamp, boudoir; custard, sm 15.00
Lamp, desk; custard 25.00
Lamp, orange/wht w/orange/wht shade 125.00
Powder jar, apple, pumpkin 95.00
Powder jar, blk, ribbed 16.00
Powder jar, Colonial lady, gr 85.00
Powder jar, Colonial lady, pk 35.00
Powder jar, marbleized gr/wht, Concentric Ring 16.00
Powder jar, orange/wht Mexicali, w/lid 18.00
Powder jar, scotty dog, crystal 110.00
Powder jar, scotty dog, wht 45.00
Vase, gr/wht, graduated dart, #312 ....45.00
Vase, pumpkin, tab hdls, #317 ....18.00
Vase, yel, ribs & flutes, #311, 8" 65.00
Westite, ash tray, hexagonal, base emb Westite 15.00
Westite, bowl, brn/wht, base emb Westite 10.00
Westite, jardiniere, mk W in diamond 12.00

Westite, sugar bowl, gr/wht, hexagonal 15.00

Alexandrite

Alexandrite is a type of art glass introduced around the turn of the century by Thomas Webb and Sons of England. It is recognized by its characteristic shading — pale yellow to rose and blue. Although it was also produced by other companies, only examples made by Webb command premium prices.

Custard, moire motif, w/underplate, Webb 975.00
Finger bowl, Honeycomb, scalloped, w/underplate, att Webb ..875.00
Finger bowl, swirled, scalloped, w/underplate 800.00
Goblet, floriform, irreg stem/ribbed petal bowl, Webb, 9" ...1,750.00
Pitcher, flower-form top, 5½" 1,700.00
Toothpick holder, ruffled edge, Webb 1,000.00
Vase, jack-in-pulpit; Honeycomb, crimped, 3¼x4" 925.00
Vase, star-shaped top, bulbous, 3⅛x2½" 600.00
Wine, Honeycomb, Webb, 4½x2⅜" 750.00

Almanacs

The earliest evidence indicates that almanacs were used as long ago as Ancient Egypt. Throughout the Dark Ages they were circulated in great volume and were referred to by more people than any other book except the Bible. *The Old Farmer's Almanac* first appeared in 1793 and has been issued annually since that time. Usually more of a pamphlet than a book (only a few have hard covers), the almanac provided planting and harvesting information to farmers, weather forecasts for seamen, medical advice, household hints, mathematical tutoring, postal rates, railroad schedules, weights and measures, 'receipts,' and jokes. Before 1800 the information was unscientific and based entirely on astrology and folklore. The first almanac in America was printed in 1639 by William Pierce Mariner; it contained data of this nature. One of the best-known editions, Ben Franklin's *Poor Richard's Almanac*, was introduced in 1732 and continued to be printed for twenty-five years.

By the nineteenth century, merchants saw the advertising potential in a publication so widely distributed, and the advertising almanac evolved. These were distributed free of charge by drug stores and mercantiles, and were usually somewhat lacking in information, containing simply a calendar, a few jokes, and a variety of ads for quick remedies and quack cures.

Today their concept and informative, often amusing text make almanacs popular collectibles that may usually be had at reasonable prices. Because they were printed in such large numbers and often saved from year to year, their prices are still low — most fall within a range of $4 to $15. Those printed before 1860 are especially collectible. Quite rare and highly prized are the Kate Greenaway 'Almanacks,' printed in London from 1883 to 1897. These are illustrated with her drawings of children, one for each calendar month.

1851, Pictorial Cultivator, illus, 32-pg 3.00
1868, Scovill's Farmers/Mechanics, EX 10.00
1870, Herrick's, EX 8.00
1871, Elgin Watches, color cover, 32-pg, EX 18.00
1881, Green's 10.00
1882, Case Threshing Machines, color cover, 32-pg, EX 22.00
1883, Kate Greenaway, George Rutledge & Sons, EX 98.00
1884, Dr Carey's Guide to Health 15.00
1892, Shaker, NY, 32-pg, in pictorial wrapper 30.00
1894, Kate Greenaway 50.00
1905, Armour's Farmer's Almanac, EX 15.00
1913, Ayer's American 7.50
1913, Watkins, VG 5.00

1915, Watkins, EX	15.00
1916, Pisco Pocket Book, EX	6.00
1925, Kate Greenaway, VG	35.00
1928, Foley's Family Almanac, VG	3.00
1932, Spalding Official Athletic, EX	10.00
1935, Dr Miles', G	8.00
1936, Dr Morse's, VG	5.00
1937, Kellogg's Housewife Yearbook, VG	4.00
1940, Illinois Herb Co, Indians/trapper on cover	4.00

Aluminum

Aluminum, though being the most abundant metal in the earth's crust, always occurs in combination with other elements. Before a practical method for its refinement was developed in the late nineteenth century, articles made of aluminum were very expensive. After the process for commercial smelting was perfected in 1916, it became profitable to adapt the ductile, non-tarnishing material to many uses.

By the late thirties, novelties, trays, pitchers, and many other tableware items were being produced. They were often handcrafted with elaborate decoration. Russel Wright designed a line of lovely pieces such as lamps, vases, and desk accessories that are becoming very collectible. Many who crafted the ware marked it with their company logo, and these signed pieces are attracting the most interest. In general, 'spun' aluminum is from the thirties or early forties, and 'hammered' aluminum is from the fifties. See also Russel Wright.

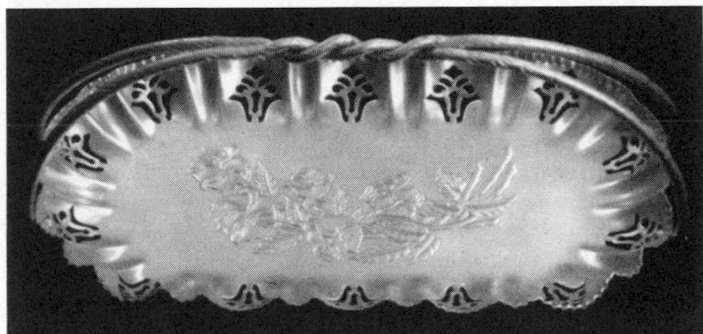

Tray, embossed roses, 12½" long, $10.00.

Bowl, fruit; floral/fruit in relief, hdls, 11"	12.00
Bowl, peapod hdl, Everlast, w/lid	12.00
Coaster, floral, mk Everlast Forged Alum, set of 8+tray	14.00
Console set, bowl w/porc insert+2 candlesticks, Farber	25.00
Crumber & brush, hammered, Rodney Kent, #444	15.00
Garden ornament, rabbit, cast, 12"	55.00
Platter, hammered, hdls, Cromwell, 16"	25.00
Tray, tulips relief, fancy hdls, hammered, w/lid, Kent, #440	20.00

AMACO, American Art Clay Co

AMACO is the logo of the American Art Clay Co. Inc., founded in Indianapolis, Indiana, in 1919, by Ted O. Philpot. They produced a line of art pottery from 1931 through 1938 that is today beginning to interest collectors. The company is still in business, but now produces only supplies, implements, and tools for the ceramic trade.

Box, #172, bright turq, w/lid, 5"	60.00
Candy dish, #183, bright bl, w/lid, 8"	50.00
Figural head, #130, bright bl, 7"	90.00

Figural head, #140, wht, 7"	95.00
Figural head, #152, wht, 6"	75.00
Figurine, kneeling geisha girl, #199, wht, 6½"	175.00
Vase, #131, orange matt, wht int, 6½"	50.00
Vase, #132, tan, 4½"	40.00
Vase, #31, gray crystalline, 7½"	65.00
Vase, #46, bright mulberry, 6½"	40.00
Vase, #48, matt gr w/Deco hdls, 9"	55.00

Amberina

Amberina, one of the earliest types of art glass, was developed in 1883 by Joseph Locke, of the New England Glass Company. The trademark was registered by W.L. Libbey, who often signed his name in script within the pontil.

Amberina was made by adding gold powder to the batch, which produced glass in the basic amber hue. Part of the item, usually the top, was simply reheated to develop the characteristic deep red or fuchsia shading. Early amberina was mold-blown, but cut and pressed amberina was also produced. The rarest type is plated amberina, made by New England for a short time after 1886. Other companies, among them Hobbs and Brockunier, Mt. Washington Glass Company, and Sowerby's Ellison Glassworks of England, made their own versions, being careful to change the name of their product to avoid infringing on Libbey's patent. See also Libbey.

Basket, appl flowers & leaves, reverse color, ribbed, 11½"	180.00
Bowl, Baby T'print, reverse color, ruffled, 3½"	100.00
Bowl, Daisy & Button, sq, Hobbs & Brockunier, 5½"	115.00
Bowl, Dia Quilt, slightly scalloped, 7½"	275.00
Bowl, gold flowers, amber lid finial & hdls, 4½x6"	365.00
Bowl, gold flowers, amber wafer ft, fluted, 8x11"	365.00
Bowl, gold flowers, swirled, amber ft/rigaree/hdls, 4½"	265.00
Bowl, triangle top, Mt WA, 2¼x5" dia	200.00
Celery vase, Dia Quilt, sq top, att NE Glass, 6½"	325.00
Celery vase, mc flowers/leaves, swirled mold, 7"	130.00
Celery vase, Venetian Dia, scalloped, NE Glass, 6¼"	335.00
Cruet, Venetian Dia, Mt WA	275.00
Decanter, Coin Spot, floral, mushroom stopper, sq, 8½"	750.00
Decanter, floral, reverse color, clear faceted stopper, 10"	275.00
Decanter, wine cruet; floral, amber stopper, 9x5"	265.00
Finger bowl, Dia Quilt, fuchsia, tricorn, NE, 3¾"	175.00
Jam jar, Invt T'print, EX floral	200.00
Pitcher, Dia Quilt, reeded amber hdl, 4"	130.00
Pitcher, Invt T'print, amber hdl, tapered top, 10½"	200.00
Pitcher, Invt T'print, clear rope hdl loops around neck, 7½"	175.00

Pitcher, Inverted Thumbprint, applied green handle, 8", $250.00.

Pitcher, Invt T'print, sq top, reeded hdl, NE Glass, 7½" 375.00
Pitcher, pk/wht florals, amber hdl, 11½", +5 tumblers 495.00
Sherbet, sgn Libbey, 5x5" 265.00
Toothpick holder, Venetian Dia, tricorn 210.00
Tumble-up, Dia Quilt, reverse color, 8½" 550.00
Tumbler, Dia Quilt, att Sandwich 100.00
Tumbler, Dia Quilt, NE Glass, 3¾" 165.00
Tumbler, Invt T'print 95.00
Vase, Baby T'print, conical on wide ft, Mt WA, 6" 275.00
Vase, Dia Quilt, pinched sides, rigaree at neck, 6" 300.00
Vase, fluted trefoil rim on trumpet form, att NE Glass, 12" 400.00
Vase, fuchsia, ribbed lily form, 8¾" 225.00
Vase, gold flowers, amber spiral trim/ft, 10¼" 195.00
Vase, gold flowers, lily form, 13¾x3¾" 245.00
Vase, gold flowers, rigaree at neck, swirled, 3¾x4" 175.00
Vase, Honeycomb, unusual form, 5" 115.00
Vase, Invt T'print, 3-petal top, leaf ft, 5½x3½" 145.00
Vase, lily form, att Sandwich or Mt WA, 12" 250.00
Vase, rigaree, floral/'World's Fair 1893,' ribbed, 8½" 220.00
Vase, swirled, ruffled rim, 21" 550.00
Vase, trumpet form, SP figural base, 9¼" 200.00
Wine, fuchsia, ribbed, 4¼" 250.00

Plated Amberina

Bowl, incurvate pinched top, ribbed, 7½" 4,750.00
Butter dish, ribbed, SP base w/unicorn in center, 4¾" 3,400.00
Condiment, ribbed, 4" shakers in SP fr mk Toronto 1,800.00
Cruet, ribbed, trefoil top, amber hdl, faceted stopper, 6" 3,600.00
Mug, fine color, ribbed, amber hdl 2,100.00
Shaker, salt; fine color, distinct ribbing 900.00
Tumbler, ribbed, EX color 1,800.00
Underplate, ribbed, ruffled, 6⅝" 1,150.00

American Encaustic Tiling Co.

A.E. Tile was organized in 1879 in Zanesville, Ohio. Until its closing in 1935, they produced beautiful ornamental and architectural tile equal to the best European imports. They also made vases, figurines, and novelty items with exceptionally fine modeling and glazes.

Bookends, cupid w/rabbit, mk, 1926, 5x5", pr 40.00
Paperweight, ram on pedestal, brn/bl crystalline, mk, 5½" 50.00

Tiles, peacock and parrot, 3-color, in wooden frame, tiles only: 12x6", $165.00.

Plaque, Dutch couple herd geese, 9x9" 170.00
Tile, bat/moon relief, lt bl w/blk & yel, 6" 200.00
Tile, cherub shields eyes from fire, brn, 6" 65.00
Tile, horseman rides through brush, blk on wht, 4¼" 30.00
Tile, peacock or parrot, gr/yel on cobalt gloss, 11½x6", pr 165.00
Tile, standing nude lady, bl w/brn & gr splotches, 7x4" 225.00
Tile, 16th century woman, bl gloss, 3-pc, fr, 18x6" 135.00
Vase, gray w/pk gloss, Oriental form, w/base mk & dtd, 7" 225.00
Vase, lt gr, buttress-style arms, 8" 145.00

American Indian Art

That time when the American Indian was free to practice the crafts and culture that was his heritage has always held a fascination for many. They were a people who appreciated beauty of design and colorful decoration in their furnishings and clothing; and because instruction in their crafts was a routine part of their rearing, they were well accomplished. Several tribes developed areas in which they excelled. The Navajo were weavers and silversmiths; the Zuni, lapidaries. Examples of their craftsmanship are very valuable. Today even the work of contemporary Indian artists — weavers, silversmiths, carvers, and others — is highly collectible. For a more thorough study we recommend *North American Indian Artifacts* by Lar Hothem; you will find his address in the Directory under Ohio.

Key:
bw — beadwork   NE — Northeastern
dmn — diamond   S — Southern
E — Eastern   W — Western

Apparel and Accessories

Before the white traders brought the Indian women cloth from which to sew their garments and beads to use for decorating them, clothing was made from skins sewn together with sinew, usually made of buffalo tendon. Porcupine quills were dyed bright colors and woven into bags and armbands and used to decorate clothing and moccasins. Examples of early quillwork are scarce today and highly collectible.

Early in the nineteenth century, beads were being transported via pony pack trains. These 'pony' beads were irregular shapes of opaque glass imported from Venice. Nearly always blue or white, they were twice as large as the later 'seed' beads. By 1870 translucent beads in many sizes and colors had been made available, and Indian beadwork had become commercialized. Each tribe developed its own distinctive methods and preferred decorations, making it possible for collectors today to determine the origin of many items. Soon after the turn of the century, the craft of beadworking began to diminish.

Arm bands, Nez Perce, red star/bl arrow bw on wht, 1900, 3½" .115.00
Belt, Woodlands, loom bw, 1910, 4x43" 100.00
Bonnet, Sioux, baby's, sinew-sewn buffalo w/full bw, 1880 ....500.00
Bonnet, Sioux, baby's, star/X bw, sinew sewn, 1890, 8x6" 500.00
Breastplate, Crow, hair pipe w/beads & teeth, 1940s, 35" 175.00
Breastplate, Crow, woman's, hair pipe/hawk bells, 1920, 19" 75.00
Breastplate, Crow, 4 rows hair pipe/brass beads, 1890, 16" 350.00
Breechcloth, Oto, trade cloth/contour bw/tin cones, 1800 ....125.00
Breechcloth, red flannel w/loom bw strips on satin, 57" 20.00
Buffalo robe, S Plains, blk bonnet motif, red/blk, 92x67" 800.00
Cape, Cree, tanned moose hide, bw front/bk, fringe, '20, 22" ..100.00
Coat, Athabascan, chief's, trade cloth/bw/ermine drops, 1880 .500.00
Cuffs, Crow, mc floral spot stitch on wht, EX work, 8" 175.00
Cuffs, Ute, floral bw on hide, 1890, 9x14" 175.00
Dress, Assiniboine, trade cloth, bw/thimbles/bells, 1870 .....575.00
Dress, Assiniboine, velvet, brass snaps/bw on yoke, 1870 .....350.00

Dress, Assiniboine, wine cloth/full bw yoke, 1870, 52" 400.00
Dress, N Plains, buckskin w/mc elk bw front & bk, '10, 50" ..1,300.00
Dress, Nez Perce, buckskin w/fringe, full bw yoke, 1890 ......800.00
Dress, Plains, wht smoked elk hide w/bw bands & elk teeth ...725.00
Dress, Shoshone, 2-pc buckskin, bw yoke, fringe, 1935, 42" ...500.00
Dress, Sioux, girl's, buckskin w/full bw yoke, fringe, 1890 ...1,100.00
Dress, Sioux, girl's, trade cloth/cowrie shells, 1890, 28" 400.00
Gauntlets, Nez Perce, full bw tops, fringe, 1890, 18x12" 150.00
Hair ornament, Cheyenne, buffalo, bw/cones/suspensions, 17" .150.00

Sioux beaded and fringed hide child's dress, 16" long, $900.00.

Hat, Nez Perce, lady's, twined corn husk, mc Vs, 1880s, 7" 575.00
Hat, rain; Haida, twined cedar bark, 1880, 13x6" 75.00
Jacket, Chimayo, lady's, bw motif, 1935, 21x25" 65.00
Leggings, Blackfoot, buffalo w/geometric bw strips, 1888 ......400.00
Leggings, Cheyenne, lady's, buckskin w/bw strips, 1930, 17" ...175.00
Leggings, Nez Perce, buckskin, bw on trade cloth trim, 30" 65.00
Mittens, Cree, moose hide w/floral bw, wool lined, 1890, 11" ..150.00
Moccasins, Arapaho, buffalo w/geometric bw toes, 1880, 9" ...210.00
Moccasins, Blackfoot, high top, buffalo, bw/trade buttons 500.00
Moccasins, burial, Sioux, buffalo/full bw in cobalt, 1880 ......550.00
Moccasins, Cheyenne, hide w/full bw geometrics, 1920, 11" ...125.00
Moccasins, Comanche, high top, silver buttons/bw, 1900 ...1,300.00
Moccasins, Cree, puckered toes, floral embr, 1880, 9½" 85.00
Moccasins, Plains, bw, sinew sewn, ca 1900, 9½" 100.00
Moccasins, Plains, infant's burial/ceremonial, allover bw 375.00
Moccasins, Sioux, child's, hide w/full bw uppers, 1940, 6" 75.00
Moccasins, Sioux, red/wht/bl bw w/gr vamp, minor wear, 11" ..125.00
Moccasins, Sioux, wht deerskin w/mc floral bw, 1900, 10" 110.00
Neckpiece, Sioux, 5½" mc bw medallion on 2" neck strip 85.00
Roach, Cree, cotton w/porcupine/horse & deer hair, 1910, 16" .250.00
Roach, Crow, deer/porcupine, bw band, shaping stick, 22" 140.00
Snowshoes, Cree, wood w/rawhide lacing, 43", pr 65.00
Vest, bw front w/florals & stars, VG 600.00
Vest, E Sioux, floral bw on yel-pnt buckskin, 1900, EX 700.00
Vest, Ojibway, floral bw on blk velvet both sides, 1930 ....370.00
Vest, Sioux, child's, bw Am flags/geometrics, 12", NM 900.00
Vest, Sioux, full bw flags/geometrics, quilled bottom, 1890 ..2,000.00
War shirt, Blackfoot, perforated/pnt buckskin w/bw, 1880 ...2,750.00

Arrowheads and Points

Relics of this type usually display characteristics of a general area, time period, or a particular location. With study, those made by the Plains Indians are easily discerned from those of the West Coast. Because modern man has imitated the art of the Indian by reproducing these artifacts through modern means, use caution before investing your money in 'too good to be authentic' specimens.

Agate Basin, gray/tan stone, IL, 6¼", NM 190.00
Angostura, gray stone, TX, 3⅜", NM 110.00
Angostura, gray/tan stone, Smith Co KS, 3" 110.00
Breckenridge Dalton, gray stone, AK, 3⅛", NM 110.00
Breckenridge Dalton, gray/tan stone, MO, 4¼", NM 85.00
Breckenridge Dalton, tan stone, AK, 2⅝", VG 25.00
Breckenridge Dalton, tan stone, AK, 3¼", NM 145.00
Bulverde, tan/pk stone, Brewster Co TX, 2" 10.00
Dalton, gray stone, AR, 2⅜", M 45.00
Dalton, gray stone, AR, 4¾", NM 275.00
Dalton, gray stone, IL, 3⅝", NM 75.00
Dalton, tan stone, AR, 3¼", NM 110.00
Dalton, tan stone, IL, 3½", NM 60.00
Dickson, wht/gray stone, Scott Co IA, 2¾", VG 35.00
Hardin, gray stone, IL, 2⅛", VG 30.00
Hardin, gray stone, IL, 2⅝", M 70.00
Hardin, gray/tan stone, IL, 3⅛", NM 45.00
Hardin, gray/tan stone, MO, 2⅞", EX 35.00
Hardin, tan stone, IL, 2¾", EX 40.00
Matamoros, red stone, McCurtain Co OK, 2" 6.00
Meserve, off-wht stone, MO, 2⅞", EX 75.00
Midland, gray/tan stone, TX, 2" 165.00
Montell, blk stone, McCulloch Co TX, 4" 50.00
Motley, wht stone, Hale Co AL, pre-historic, 2¼" 10.00
Pedernales, gray stone, TX, 2", EX 12.00
Pedernales, gray stone, TX, 3¾", EX 35.00
Pedernales, gray/wht stone, Bowie Co TX, 3", NM 35.00
Randolph, gray stone, TN, 4", EX 35.00
Trinity, blk stone, Cass Co TX, 3¼" 25.00
Wells, wine stone, 2", EX 25.00

Arts and Crafts

Blanket, Haida, pearl-button totemic motif, 1920, 76x60" 500.00
Blanket, Kwakiutl, buttons form totemic motif, 1940, 24x44" ..175.00
Box, NW Coast, curved cedar w/HP totems, 1955, 15x14x15" .250.00
Canoe, Algonquin, birch bark on wood fr, +paddles, 50" 850.00
Carving, Haida, beaver w/tail in mouth, cedar, 1955, 9x3½" ...175.00
Gouache, Pueblo, Santo Domingo corn dancer, sgn MaHaRe ..105.00
Painting on hide, Sitting Bull, by Shipshee, 37x26" 150.00
Pillow, Sioux, buffalo hide, bw/fringe, 1880, 18x18" 175.00
Sand-pnt tapestry, Navajo, 80 wefts to inch, 43x52", M 2,600.00
Tapestry, Navajo, 2 Yei ea side cornstalk+rainbow, 23x24" 175.00
Watercolor, Buffalo Dancer, sgn Thos Vigil, 1920s, 7x11" 200.00
Weaving, Chimayo, Germantown yarn, 1920s, worn, 39x75" ..115.00
Weaving, Navajo, Eye Dazzler, central lozenges, 1895, 70x44" .300.00
Weaving, Navajo, mtns/Shiprock New Mexico, 1965, 51x42" .250.00
Weaving, Navajo, 4-figure Yei on wht, 1940, 39x45" 175.00

Bags and Cases

The Indians used bags for many purposes, and most display excellent form and workmanship. Of the types listed below, many collectors consider the pipe bag to be the most desirable form. Pipe bags were long, narrow, leather and bead or quillwork creations made to hold tobacco in a compartment at the bottom and the pipe, with the bowl removed from the stem, in the top. Long buckskin fringe was used as trim and complemented the quilled and beaded design to make the bag a masterpiece of Indian Art.

Arapaho, pnt antelope hide/bw/quills/fringe, 1870, 42x43" . . **1,650.00**
Arapaho, pouch, bw horse, stripe borders, no fringe, 6x8" **205.00**
Assiniboine, scabbard, buckskin/bw/quills, 45", +1860 sword . . **800.00**
Athabascan, buckskin, silk floral embr, 1910, 6x8½" **95.00**
Blackfoot, hide w/bl & wht pony beads, fringe, 1860, 9x2½" . . . **100.00**
Cheyenne, awl case, bw/beaded drops, 1920, 5x2" **100.00**
Cheyenne, awl case, bw/trade beads, tin cones, 1870s, 12" **325.00**
Cheyenne, pipe, hide, bw/quills/fringe, 1880, 6½x17" **475.00**
Cheyenne, pipe, woman's, hide, fringe/bw, 1880, 12x4½" **95.00**
Cheyenne, possible, buffalo w/bw ends & flaps, 1870, 30x20" . . **500.00**
Cheyenne, scabbard, buffalo w/bw & brass beads, 1870, 12" . . . **350.00**
Cheyenne, scabbard, full bw/tin cones, 1890, 11", +knife **250.00**
Cheyenne, scabbard, rawhide, tin cones/bw/fringe, 1970s, 9" . . **125.00**

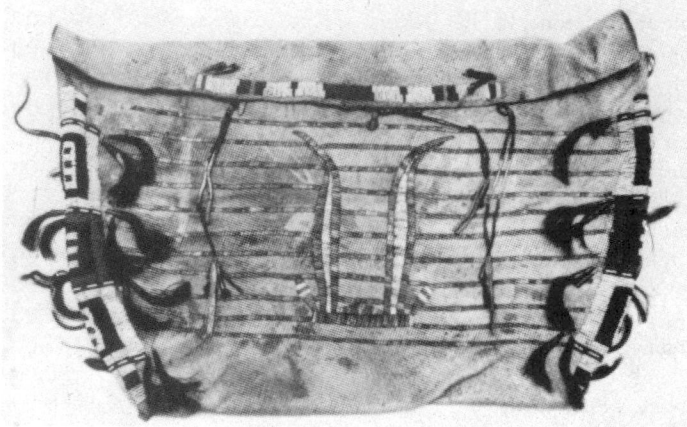

Plains beaded and quilled hide 'possible' bag, quillwork 'antelope prongs,' beadwork, tin cones, and horsehair suspensions, sinew sewn, 21" long, $1,500.00.

Cheyenne, scabbard, rawhide-lined buckskin/bw, 1870, 11" . . . **150.00**
Cheyenne, strike-a-lite, geometric bw/tin cones, 1890, 6½" . . . **300.00**
Cheyenne, throw-over saddlebags, buffalo/bw, 1880, 10x4" . . **1,450.00**
Chippewa, bandolier, floral bw, 1890, 11½x40" **450.00**
Chippewa, geometrics on hand-woven fabric, 1860, 16x14" **95.00**
Crow, awl case, bl/wht bw stripes on purple, 6", +awl **120.00**
Crow, belt pouch, bw, triangular, 1910 . . . . **175.00**
Crow, scabbard, pnt rawhide, bw/fringe, 1880, 34", +sword **425.00**
Crow, strike-a-lite, hide w/bw, tin cones, 1870, 5" **300.00**
Flathead, belt pouch, leather w/bw flap, 1910, 6x5½" **225.00**
Iroquois, velvet pouch w/flags & floral bw, 1890, 5x4" **45.00**
Mandan, medicine bag, porcupine quill decor, 1820, 7x4½" . . . **400.00**
Meti, scabbard, quilled hide w/fringe, 1880, 15", +knife **1,000.00**
Nez Perce, corn husk, geometrics ea side, 1880, 18x14" **300.00**
Nez Perce, corn husk, mc geometrics ea side, 1880, 24x18" **650.00**
Nez Perce, corn husk, twined, mc geometrics, 1880, 16½x13" . . **250.00**
Nez Perce, corn husk, w/flap, bw trim, 1880, 5x5" **70.00**
Nez Perce, powder flask, rawhide w/wooden stopper **55.00**
Nez Perce, saddlebags, buffalo/pony beads, 1870, 105x12" **850.00**
Pit River, ceremonial bag, stars/geometric bw, 1870, 6x5" **175.00**
Plains, saddlebags, pony beads on red stroud, 1840, 102x13" . **1,150.00**
Plains, wht bw, 2 old trade beads on drawstring, 1900, 7½" . . . **200.00**
Potowatomi, bandolier-type medicine man's, loom bw, 18x8" . . **350.00**
Shoshone, teepee, pnt parfleche, 3 flaps, 1880, 20x13" **200.00**
Sioux, pipe, bl-pnt hide w/sinew-sewn bw, no fringe, 16" **600.00**
Sioux, pipe, bw/quillwork Am Flags, sinew sewn, 18" **3,000.00**

Sioux, saddlebags, bw on buckskin, canvas bk, 44x12", NM . **2,100.00**
Sioux, teepee, bw/quillwork/tin cones/horsehair, 21x14", pr . **5,000.00**
Tlingit, pouch, seal skin w/pnt totemic motif, 1870, 6x10" **150.00**
Umatilla, mirror bag, floral contour bw, 1870, 27x6½" **1,700.00**
Ute, quiver, fringed/pnt leather, 1920, 22x5", +4 arrows **150.00**
Woodlands, deer hoof decor, gr cylinder beads, 1900, 6x6½" . . **200.00**
Woodlands, pouch, mc floral bw, 1880s, 3½x4¾" **20.00**
Yakima, contour bw: 2 deer/eagle/tree, 1925, 10x9" **175.00**
Yakima, full bw front w/stylized foliate motif, 1935, 13x14" . . . **100.00**
Yakima, heart shaped, full bw w/deer, 1910, 9x9" **100.00**
Yakima, purse, full bw, geometrics, bw strap, 1930, 7½x5½" **80.00**

Baskets

In the following listings, examples are basket form and coiled unless noted otherwise. The given dimension is diameter for bowls and round trays; for rectangular items, length is given.

Pima bowl, finely woven in cross and hooked meander pattern, 16" diameter, $850.00.

Anasazi, cave find, tray w/worn motif, 15½" dia **125.00**
Apache, bowl, star/animals, mc, 1930, 2x9½" **275.00**
Apache, burden type, twined, 2 motif bands, 1880, 16x13" **200.00**
Apache, plate, blk dbl-star motif, 1920, 9" dia **85.00**
Attu, wallet, silk thread geometric embr, 2-pc, 1900, 7x3½" . . **1,300.00**
Chippewa, splint storage basket w/lid, twist decor, 7x9" **45.00**
Choctaw, brn chevrons, dbl weave, 1925, 18x10" **125.00**
Choctaw, jar, plaited, natural color designs, 1910, 12x8" **130.00**
Haida, twined, blk line motif, w/lid, 1910, miniature, 3½" **220.00**
Hopi, red/yel/blk Yucca traditional motif, 6" dia **20.00**
Hupa, bowl, mc geometrics, reverse in bottom, 1910, 4x10½" . . **350.00**
Hupa, bowl, twined, zigzags on base & lid, 1920, 6x6½" **275.00**
Hupa, whiskey flask cover, twined, triangles, 1920, 7½" **90.00**
Jicarillo Apache, finely braided rim, worn mc, 1890s, 9x9" **235.00**
Klamath, hourglass design, finely twined, 1890, 2½x5" **70.00**
Klickitat, chevrons, rim loops, hard coiled, 1800, 9x8" **475.00**
Klickitat, quail top knots/dmns, conical/hard, 1890, 10x12" . . . **800.00**
Maidu, bowl, red meandering geometrics, 1900, 5½x11½" **650.00**
Maidu, gambling tray, radiating stars/etc, twined, 1880, 17" . . . **425.00**
Maidu, tray, 1-rod, red geometrics, 1915, 13½" dia **450.00**
Maricopa, dogs, connecting Vs, 1910, 5x9½" **525.00**
Mission, olla, mc geometrics, ca 1900, 6x7" **350.00**
Mission, tray, mc stepped devices, 1920, 4½x21x18" **1,000.00**
Navajo, wedding type, spirit release line, 1935, 13" dia **110.00**
Paiute, bowl, 1-rod, allover 3-color bw, 1935, 4½" **375.00**
Paiute, seed bottle, twined, hdls, 1910, 9½x5½" **150.00**
Panamint, bowl, eagles/hearts/arrowheads, 1910, 4½x8¾" **850.00**
Panamint, eagles/swastikas, finely coiled, 1910, 8½x10" **700.00**
Panamint, row ea of butterflies/outlined dmns, 1900, 9½x5" . . **850.00**
Papago, ascending stairsteps, 1930, 7x11" **160.00**

Papago, bowl, outlined squash blossom motif, 1945, 4x13" 125.00
Papago, storage type, geometrics, hdls, 1920, 16x12" 300.00
Papago, storage type, heron motif/frets on lid, 9x10" 300.00
Papago, tray, yucca w/Xs in martynia, ca 1950, 12" dia 105.00
Papago, tray, yucca/martynia, 8" dia 40.00
Pima, bowl, whirlwinds/spider webs, 1920, 2½x8½" 150.00
Pima, olla, stairsteps, 1890, 10x12" 200.00
Pima, plate, 3-petal squash blossom motif, 1940, 13" dia 400.00
Pima, willow/martynia star motif, flaring sides, 5x12" 225.00
Pima, willow/martynia stepped motif, slant sides, 4x6½" 105.00
Pima, 2 rows of humans, tightly coiled, 1910, 10x7" dia 325.00
Pomo, bowl, woven-in red/bl/gr beads, 1930s, 2x7" 750.00
Pomo, red stairsteps, 1900, 9x6" dia 650.00
Pomo, treasure type, allover feathers/beads/shells, 1940, 4" ...500.00
Pomo, 1-rod, step motif, 15 stitches per inch, 3x8", VG 165.00
Salish, berry basket, imbricated motif, ca 1840, rpr, 9" 175.00
Salish, carrying type, geometrics, 1920, 7x5x13" 75.00
Salish, cooking basket, imbricated motif/braid trim, 6x11" 150.00
Salish, imbricated geometrics, w/lid, 1910, 7x6" dia 100.00
Salish, tray, imbricated dmn motif, 1920, 14" dia 70.00
Seri, dog of jatropha shrub, 4½x15" 260.00
Seri, trees/deer of jatropha shrub, 4x17" 100.00
Shasta, burden type, twined, conical, 1890, 10x7" 150.00
Thompson River, imbricated motif, w/lid, 3½x4" 95.00
Tlingit, rattle top, brn/orange geometrics, twined, 6x5½" 190.00
Tlingit, rattle top, mc, ca 1900, 4x4¾", EX 300.00
Tlingit, twined, fret bands, w/lid, 7x7" dia 150.00
Tulare, bowl, rattlesnake motif/Xs, 1920, 6x11" 400.00
W Mono, blk lines/triangles, 1920, 6½x11½" 425.00
Wapato/Salish, sgn Richard, 6x7½", M 125.00
Washo, bowl, dmns/butterflies, 1920, 4x8" 400.00
Washo, winnower, twined, ca 1880, 13x16" 275.00
Wintun, bowl, key motif in red, braided rim, 1870, 3x12" 400.00
Yakima, hat, lady's, geometric bw, 1940, 9x7" 225.00

Blankets, Navajo

Pueblo Indians first made blankets centuries ago, but today most are made by Navajo Indians. Blankets were still made into the 1800s, when Pendleton and Hudson's Bay blankets became widely available. Around the turn of the century, rugs were developed because tourists were more likely to buy them as floor coverings and wall-hangings. Rugs or blankets are made in various regional styles; an expert can usually identify the area where it was made — sometimes even the individual who made it. The colors of wool are natural (gray-white, brown-black), vegetal (from plant dyes), or artificial (aniline, from synthetic chemicals.) Value factors include size, tightness of weave, artistry of design, and condition. Examples by artists whose names are well known command the higher prices.

Eye Dazzler, mc zigzag motif, 1910, 64x43" 400.00
Ganado Red, central lozenge/dmns, 1935, 52x36" 250.00
Germantown, handspun Eye Dazzler, dmn columns, 46x30" ...925.00
Germantown Chief's Moki type, 9-spot 3rd Phase, 63x70" ..1,500.00
Saddle, dbl, mc stripe w/fret corners, 30x59" 100.00
Saddle, dbl twill weave, contoured, heavy, 1930, 25x13" 25.00
Saddle, plain line design, 1890, 23x35" 45.00
Transitional, connecting key motif, 1910, 62x43" 150.00
Transitional, connecting triangles in red/wht, 1890, 59x41" ...150.00
Transitional, connecting X motif, 1900, 76x48" 700.00
2nd Phase Chief's, 1890, 77x66" 950.00

Ceremonial Items

Amulet, Arapaho, umbilical turtle, tin cones/hair drops, 7" 125.00

Amulet, Cheyenne, turtle form, mc bw, 3"+tail 45.00
Bowl, NW Coast, totem cvg ea bowed end, shells, 17" 1,200.00
Club, Mound Builder, crescent shaped, pre-historic, 8x2x4" 65.00
Dance club, Plains, beaded stone head, 1900, 12x3" 100.00
Dance club, Plains, buckskin covered, horsehair drop, 28" 120.00
Dance rattle, Peyote, cvd hdl w/heart & sqs, 1880s, 12" 50.00
Dance stick, buffalo horn, 16" 250.00
Dance wand, medicine man's, buffalo horn/rabbit skin on hdl ..150.00
Dish, Haida, cvd seal form w/abalone inlay, 1910, 20x8" 125.00
Drum, Arapaho, hide covered, cvd/pnt stand, 1955, 32x18" ...325.00

'Spider Woman' crosses in three white central diamonds, ceremonial feathers, 'Spirit Lines,' hand spun wools in early dyes, ca 1880s, repaired, $1,000.00.

Drum, Hopi, hand held, 1935, 4x2" 60.00
Drum beater, Plains, hide-covered head stuffed w/hair, 15" 200.00
Eccentric, chipped stone, pre-historic, 8x7" 35.00
Fetish, Blackfoot, umbilical turtle, bw/cowrie shells, 3" 50.00
Fetish, Cheyenne, turtle form, hide/bw, 1910, 2x1" 35.00
Fetish, Cheyenne, umbilical turtle, Xd flags bw, 1910, 7x4" ...135.00
Fetish, Plains, triangle w/pony beads & fringe, provenance 700.00
Fetish, Plains, turtle, hide w/bw geometrics, 6x3" 175.00
Fetish, Zuni, flying bird, shell w/turq inlay, 1940, 3½" 35.00
Fetish, Zuni, mtn sheep, cvd pk stone, 1940, 3½x1" 95.00
Fetish, Zuni, serpentine mtn lion/arrows, 1940, 4" 35.00
Fetish, Zuni, soapstone bear w/arrowhead on bk, 1965, 3½" 50.00
Fetish, Zuni, solid turq w/jet inlay eyes, 1940, 2½x2" 150.00
Fetish, Zuni, tan stone bear/arrows, 1935, 4x2" 75.00
Headdress, NW Coast, wolf's head w/hinged jaw, inlay/pnt 900.00
Ladle, Plains, buffalo horn, hide-wrap hdl, name/1890, 12" 400.00
Mask, Iroquois, False Face, hair/abalone eyes, 1900, 5" 65.00
Mask, Iroquois, False Face, tin eye plates/tobacco pouches ...2,900.00
Mask, Kwakiutl, deer w/antlers, pnt/cvd, att Seawed, 1935 ....225.00
Mask, NW Coast, pnt hide w/hair & inlaid eyes, 12x9" 250.00
Mask, NW Coast, skin covered, w/pnt & gray hair, 11½x7" 200.00
Medicine ball, Mandan, fully quilled w/drop, 1800, 2½x26" 800.00
Rattle, Blackfoot Society, hide disk w/fur-covered hdl, 15" 60.00
Rattle, Hopi, pnt gourd, 1930, 14x3" 85.00
Rattle, NW Coast, skin-covered head w/pnt & abalone, 21" 200.00
Rattle, Tlingit, cvd/pnt cedar, 1965, 12x5" 100.00
Shield, buffalo hide w/pnt symbols, sinew sewn, 18" dia 950.00
Soul catcher, Tlingit, cvd bone, 2 mystic figures, 1870, 3½" ...175.00
Spoon, Cheyenne, bent horn, beaded bird hdl, 1890, 12" 150.00

Spoon, Cheyenne, bent horn, bird head effigy, bw, 1870, 8½" . .300.00
Spoon, N Plains, effigy, buffalo horn, ½-dime suspensions 220.00
Spoon, Plains, bent horn, bead-wrap hdl, fringe, 27x5" 125.00
Spoon, Plains, cvd mtn sheep horn w/pnt motif, 1800, 2½x14" . .55.00
Spoon, Tlingit, horn, 3-figure totemic hdl w/inlay, '20, 10" . . .325.00
Totem pole, NW Coast, 5-figure, openwork edge, pnt, 36" . .1,050.00
Totem pole, Tlingit, 4-figure, cvd/pnt, 1920, 5x2½" 35.00
Whistle, Plains, bone, rawhide twist/feather attachment, 8" . . .650.00

Dolls

Cree, buckskin w/buckskin dress & moccasins, 1935, 11" 65.00
Kachina, Bajo, lg tableta, 1890s, 10x7" 200.00
Kachina, Imitator, cvd/pnt by Luther Honeyestewa, 1940, 13" .100.00

Plains doll wearing fringed hide dress over 'puffball'-stuffed muslin body, crochet-edged undergarmet, attached scalp, pigment and beaded facial decoration, earrings and necklace, dress yoke with seed attachments, quillwork on high-top leggings, sinew sewn, 1880s, 18½", $1,800.00.

Kachina, Ogre, dancing, cvd/pnt, 1940, 13" 225.00
Kachina, Shalako Mana, feathered tableta/sinew joined, 11" .2,800.00
Kachina, War God, by Walter Howato, 1970, 25x4" 125.00
Kachina, Warrior, w/helmet, cvd/pnt, 1950, 14" 75.00
Kachina, Wolf, feather fan/headdress, 1965, 14x8" 200.00
Navajo medicine man's, bl-head Yeibichi dancer, 1900, 7x2" . .350.00
Plains, bw leggings/breech cloth/mocs/vest, pipe/bag, 9" 250.00
Plains, formed leather face/fibre braids, bw/tin cones, 18" 175.00
Plains, smoked skin/bw dress, horsehair hair, 14" 975.00
S Plains, leather w/bw, horsehair braids, 11½" 225.00
Sioux, buckskin, bw dress & face, 1940, 8x4½" 65.00
Sioux, bw on elk skin, pnt/beaded features, 15", VG 1,300.00
Sioux, dress: fringe/EX bw, quill/bw hairpc, bw boots, 17" . . .1,400.00
Sioux, leather, fringe/bw yoke & bands, hair gone, 20" 900.00

Domestics

Cradle, Apache, willow/yellow cloth/pnt/bw, 1965, 24x12" . . .100.00
Cradle, Athabascan, birch bark w/florals, 1920, 24x15" 70.00

Cradle, Cheyenne, fully quilled/ribbonwork sides/bw, 1880 . .3,250.00
Cradle, Nez Perce, floral bw top, muslin bottom, 1880, 41" . .1,750.00
Cradle, Ute, pnt buckskin cover, bw on top, 1880, 42x17" . .1,100.00
Knife/fork set, Sioux, full bw hdls, 1800, ea: 9x1" 170.00
Spoon, utility; Crow, bw hdl, 1900, 2½x11" 60.00
Toy cradle, Apache, hide-covered willow w/bw trim, 1890, 9" . .45.00
Toy cradle, Cheyenne, hide w/bw & quilling, 1880s, 16x8" . . .550.00
Toy cradle, Crow, part bw, 9", +doll w/human hair 350.00
Toy cradle, Mandan, hide/boards/bw, 1865, 16x4½", +doll 425.00
Toy cradle, Nez Perce, hide w/bw top, 1930, 6x3", +doll 35.00
Toy cradle, Nez Perce, hide w/rnd bw top, 1901, 14" 375.00
Toy cradle, Shoshone, hide w/geometric bw, 1880, 16x7" 300.00

Jewelry

As early as 500 A.D., Indians in the Southwest drilled turquoise nuggets and strung them on cords made of sinew or braided hair. The Spanish introduced them to coral, and it became a popular item of jewelry; abalone and clam shells were favored by the Coastal Indians. Not until the last half of the nineteenth century did the Indians learn to work with silver. Each tribe developed its own distinctive style and preferred design, which until about 1920 made it possible to determine tribal origin with some degree of accuracy. Since that time, because of modern means of communication and travel, motifs have become less distinct.

Quality Indian silver jewelry may be antique or contemporary — age, though certainly to be considered, is not as important a factor as fine workmanship and good stones. Pre-1910 silver will show evidence of hammer marks, and designs are usually simple. Beads have sometimes been shaped from coins. Stones tend to be small; when silver wire was used, it is usually square. To insure your investment, choose a reputable dealer.

Arm bands, Sioux, stamped brass w/geometrics, 1820, 2½" 100.00
Belt, Navajo, lady's, 9 oval conchos+buckle, 1980, 2" W 125.00
Belt, Navajo, 17 conchos+buckle, ca 1930, 1½" W 275.00
Belt, Navajo, 5 oval conchos+6 butterflies w/turq, 1920 . . . . . .750.00
Belt, Navajo, 8 stamped/scalloped conchos+buckle, 1935 . . . . .700.00
Bola, Navajo, silver Kachina, 4 turq stones, 1940, 4½x1½" 125.00
Bracelet, child's, brass, 1880, 1" W .20.00
Bracelet, Navajo, sandcast, Yei figure, Bizbee stones, 1½" 70.00
Buckle, Zuni, silver w/mc inlaid dancer, 1975, 3½" 100.00
Choker, Potowatomi, side stitch bw w/dmn motif, 1890, 1x10" . .85.00
Gorget, trade pewter, eagle/13-star flags/motto, 6" W 100.00
Ketoh, Navajo, silver on leather w/5 lg turq, 1930, 4x3" 150.00
Necklace, amber beads, ca 1800, 19" 100.00
Necklace, Assiniboine, claws/brass & Padre beads/feathers 150.00
Necklace, Crow, bear claw/cornaline deleppo beads, '30, 26" . .150.00
Necklace, Navajo, coin silver T-bird on silver beads, 26" 150.00
Necklace, Navajo, stamped grad rnd silver beads, 17" 100.00
Necklace, Navajo, 12 squash blossoms w/bl turq, naja, 18" 350.00
Necklace, Navajo, 16 nickel silver squash blossoms, 1950 . . . . .375.00
Necklace, Navajo, 1935-36 nickels are squash blossoms, 28" 80.00
Necklace, Pima, rattlesnake vertebrae, 1920, 20" 35.00
Necklace, Santo Domingo, 2-strand branch coral/silver heishi . .80.00
Necklace, Santo Domingo, 3-strand grad turq heishi, 34" 100.00
Necklace, Sioux, lady's, trade bead breastplate, 37x8" 325.00
Necklace, squash blossom, 1500+ cts Morenci bl turq, 16" 650.00
Necklace, Yuma, girl's puberty, net/bw, 1900, 4½x27" 25.00
Pin, Zuni, bow form w/29 natural turq, 1935, 1½x4" 70.00
Trade beads, blk w/wht dot inlays, sm/rnd, 1800, 28" 35.00
Trade beads, cobalt/greasy yel, 1860, 28" 55.00
Trade beads, cobalt/wht Peking glass, lg, 1820, 22" 60.00
Trade beads, faceted vaseline glass, 1840, 24" 75.00
Trade beads, Venetian glass chevrons, barrel form, 1860, 30" . .35.00
Trade beads, Venetian inlaid blk disks, 1800, 28" 75.00

Trade beads, wht Venetians w/red & bl Xs, 1820, 28" 100.00
Trade beads, 10 beads from Lorenzo Hubble trade post, 1900 . .125.00

Knives and Chipped Blades

The knife was an indispensable tool to the Indian whether he was in battle, hunting game, or doing chores at the campsite. Before the white man's metal blades, all were made of copper, obsidian, flint, or chert. Knife cases, fashioned of leather with intricate decorations of quilling or beadwork, were first worn suspended from the neck; later they were attached to the belt.

Blade, Archaic, diagonal tang, chert, hafted, TX, 3¼" 100.00
Blade, Archaic, finely chipped, TN, 7½" 250.00
Blade, Archaic, flint, nodular, Harrison Co IN, 3" 18.00
Blade, Archaic, hafted, long stem, TN, 2⅞x1⅝" 30.00
Blade, Archaic, Woodlands, gray, ceremonial, 9½x2¼" 125.00
Blade, Archaic, Woodlands, pk, bevel on right, 2¼x1¼" 35.00
Blade, Benton, beveled/serrated, hafted, AR, 4¼x1½" 150.00
Blade, Harahey, Edwards Plateau chert, TX, 4¼" 100.00
Blade, Osceola, purple/gray Hixton quartzite, hafted, 3" 50.00
Blade, Paleo, banded agate, OR, 4" .40.00
Blade, Paleo, brn/tan mottled chert, 4⅞", VG 20.00
Blade, Paleo, tan flint, general purpose, 3¾" 35.00
Blade, Paleo, uni-face, 1 fine/1 coarse edge, AL, 4" 25.00
Blade, Paleo, yel-brn jasper, ground base/side, PA, 3¼" 50.00
Blade, Pedernales, Edwards Plateau flint, hafted, TX, 4¾" 400.00
Blade, Stilwell, mc glossy flint, hafted, AR, 5x1¾" 250.00
Blade, Waubesa, gray flint, hafted, 5x1⅞" 125.00
Blade, Woodlands, layered flint, strong hafting, 3½x2" 45.00
Blade, Woodlands-Mississippian, agate, 4" 45.00
Blade, Yorok, obsidian, cvd hdl, pnt traces, 10½x1½" 80.00
Crooked, E Woodland, bird effigy hdl, 1900, 11x1½" 45.00
Crooked, Woodlands, hearts/dmns/clubs cvd on hdl, 11" 200.00
Plains, Confederate AR toothpick, 1900, blade: 7"; hdl: 5" 100.00

Pipes

Pipe bowls were usually carved from soft stone, such as catlinite or pipestone, an argilaceous sedimentary rock composed mainly of clay. Granite was also used. Some ceremonial pipes were simply styled, while others were intricately designed naturalistic figurals, sometimes in bird or frog forms called effigies. Their stems, made of wood and often covered with leather, were sometimes nearly a yard in length.

Blackfoot, blk stone blade T-bowl, wood stem, 1840, 6x16" . . .175.00
Blk stone Cloud Blower w/3 snakes, pre-historic, 1½x5" 85.00
Blk/red pewter-inlaid T-bowl, tacked/bw puzzle stem, 4½x20" .410.00
Bowl only, catlinite, cvd horsehead, 3x7" 375.00
Eastern, red clay Cloud Blower tube w/alligator atop, 5x1" 60.00
Flathead, red T-bowl, sm wood stem, EX patina, 1860, 10" 55.00
NW Coast, Hudson Bay clay trade pipe bowl, seal stem, 1900 . . .45.00
Pipe tomahawk, all metal, red-pnt hdl, 1850, 5x14" 250.00
Pipe tomahawk, brass, 7" 160.00
Pipe tomahawk, Fr brass head, steel blade, cvd, 1870, 7½" . . .225.00
Pipe tomahawk, iron/brass axe, tacked stem, 1860, 9x22" 250.00
Pipe tomahawk head, iron, from Ft Wayne, 1870, 2½x8" 95.00
Plains, blk stone bowl w/lead inlay, wood stem, 15" 600.00
Plains, blk stone elbow, pewter inlay, wood twist stem, 23" 150.00
Plains, blk stone T-bowl, pewter inlay, EX puzzle stem, 33" 175.00
Plains, blk 5" T-bowl w/pipestone & pewter inlay, cvd stem 175.00
Plains, catlinite elbow-style pipe bowl & stem, 1890s, 13" 450.00
Plains, catlinite 8" bowl w/incised scallops, quilled stem 700.00
Plains, owl-form bowl, catlinite bowl & stem, 1890s, 14" 900.00

Plains, pipe tomahawk, brass tack/bw grip, 1880s, 21", VG . .1,600.00
Plains, pipe tomahawk, file-burnt/cvd stem, 1880, 8x15" 550.00
Plains, snake effigy, catlinite, cvd wood stem, 1900, 27" 550.00
Plains, woman's, catlinite bowl & stem, 1930s, 8" 55.00
Red pipestone T-bowl, flat/file-burnt stem, 1880, 6x27" 190.00
Sioux, catlinite bowl/stem, European shape, eng, 1870, 13" . . .300.00

Plains red catlinite pipe head, carved as eagle claw clutching an ovoid bowl, late 1800s, $275.00.

Sioux, catlinite bowl/9" stem, cvd heart/quilled stem, 1880 . . . .375.00
Sioux, lg red catlinite T-bowl, pewter inlay/buffalo cvg, '20 . . .175.00
Sioux, red catlinite T-bowl, file-burnt stem, 1860, 3x21" 275.00
Sioux, red catlinite 1½" T-bowl, plain wood stem, 1880 . . . . . .135.00
Tlingit, cvd wood bowl w/abalone inlay, 1880, 3½" 60.00

Pottery

Indian pottery is nearly always decorated in such a manner as to indicate the tribe which produced it or the pueblo in which it was made. For instance, the designs of Cochiti potters were usually scattered forms from nature or sacred symbols. The Zuni preferred an ornate repetitive decoration of a closer configuration. They often used stylized deer and bird forms, sometimes in dimensional applications.

Acoma, jar, umber on wht w/red ground, 7½x9" 150.00
Acoma, jar, umber/red on wht over red-orange, 1920, 8x10" . . .800.00
Acoma, olla, classic motif, convex base, 1910, 9x8" 275.00
Acoma, olla, rows of triangles, 'sq' bottom, 1890, 7½x6" 250.00
Acoma, seed jar, cvd plainware, sgn Lucy Lewis, 1968, 9" 250.00
Acoma, wedding vase, stylized bird motif, 1940, 6x4" 35.00
Anasazi, bowl, geometric int, blk on red, pre-historic, 9" 100.00
Casas Grandes, olla, mc fine lines/curves, sgn Baca, 9x9" 50.00
Casas Grandes, olla, pnt geometrics, pre-historic, 12x10" 105.00
Casas Grandes, parrot effigy pot, umber/red on buff, 8x7" 150.00
Casas Grandes, pot, umber/red on wht, contemporary, 15" 425.00
Chaco, foot form, blk on wht, pre-historic, 3½x5" 75.00
Cochiti, foot form, pnt motif, 1880, 4x6" 55.00
Cochiti, olla, blk-pnt foliate motif, 1880, 16x11" 350.00
Hopi, jar, 3-color on cream, sgn w/feather: Helen Naha, 5" 200.00
Hopi, umber/red on orange, minor wear, att Nampeyo, 4½x9" .500.00
Hopi, vase, stylized bird motif, mc, 1915, 9x4" 150.00
Jeddito, bowl, blk on orange, int geometrics, 5x8½" 60.00
Jeddito, bowl, buff w/blk-pnt motif w/in & w/out, 8x4" 75.00
Nampeyo, bowl, typical central design, ca 1875, 3¾x10" 255.00
Puerco, bowl, blk on red, AZ, pre-historic, 10x4" 80.00
Reserve Area, duck effigy, blk on wht, pre-historic, 10x7" 700.00
San Juan Pueblo, jar, cvd buff deer dancers on tan, sgn, 8" 105.00
Santa Clara, bear, blkware, sgn MI Naranjo, 4½" 245.00
Santa Clara, bowl, blk/blk, att Faustina, 3½x10½" 105.00
Santa Clara, bowl, blk/cvd, sgn Camilio Tofoya, 1960, 7x4" . . .450.00

Santa Clara, bowl, red, storm clouds pnt int, 1935, 8" 60.00
Santa Clara, owl, natural colors on buff, Luther & Van, 11" . . .190.00
Santa Clara, owl, sgn Margaret & Luther, 1920, 8½" 350.00
Santa Clara, plate, blk, hdls, sgn Chavaria, 1940, 7½x12" 110.00
Santa Clara, wedding vase, blk/blk, stylized bird, 1940, 7½" . . .60.00
Santo Domingo, bowl, floral, red/blk/buff, red bottom, 7" 35.00
Santo Domingo, dough bowl, blk motif on cream, 1900, 6x13" .310.00
Santo Domingo, jar, umber motif on gray over red clay, 5" 65.00
Santo Domingo, olla, blk/red lines, scalloped, 1920, 7x6" 90.00
Zia, jar, bird in red on wht w/umber tracing, sgn, 8x8" 255.00
Zia, olla, bird/rainbow motif, 1900, 10x10" 400.00
Zia, olla, looped top, birds/foliate motif, 1880s, 10x8" 800.00
Zuni, jar, deer in medallion, umber/red accents, 1910, 9½" 500.00
Zuni, owl, classic design, amber on cream, 5" 45.00

Pottery, San Ildefonso

The pottery of the San Ildefonso pueblo is especially sought after by collectors today. Under the leadership of Maria Martinez and her husband Julian, experiments began about 1918 which led to the development of the 'black-on-black' design achieved through exacting methods of firing the ware. They discovered that by smothering the fire at a specified temperature, the carbon in the smoke that ensued caused the pottery to blacken. Maria signed her work from the late teens to the 1960s; she died in 1980. Today a piece with her signature may bring a price in the $500 to $3,500 range.

Bowl, blk/blk, geometrics, sgn Maria & Julian, 4x9" 700.00
Bowl, blk/blk, terraces/feathers, 1935, 5x8" 60.00

Bowl vase, carved blackware, signed Tony and Juanita, 5½x9½", $400.00.

Bowl vase, blk/blk, pointed swags, Marie, 5" dia 425.00
Jar, blk lines on red, buff body, 1870, 6x7", EX 450.00
Olla, mc w/red-banded underbody design, 1890, 7½" 500.00
Plate, blk/blk, feathers, sgn Blue Corn, 7x8" 500.00
Plate, blk/blk, feathers on gun metal, Marie & Santana, 6" 425.00
Plate, blk/blk, Maria & Popovi, minor scratches, 5½" 375.00
Vase, blk/blk, avanyu at shoulder, Marie & Julian, 6½x10" . .2,700.00
Vase, wedding; blk/blk, geometrics, 2-spout, sgn PPB, 6" 125.00

Rugs, Navajo

Chinle, vegetal, fine weave, Joan Billie, 1950, 31x43" 175.00
Crystal, fishhooks/lg lozenge, fine weave, 1930, 45x70" 425.00
Crystal, lozenges, X w/swastikas, fine weave, 1935, 43x74" . . .425.00
Crystal, outlined dmns/'V' edges, soft weave, 1920, 66x126" . .750.00
Crystal, red/tan/gray on natural, minor stains, 1930, 33x56" . . .350.00
Crystal, serrated stripes, soft colors, 1920, 64x76", VG 325.00
Eye Dazzler, hand-carded long staple wool, 1890, 44x66", EX .625.00
Eye Dazzler, hand-spun wool/analine, fringe, 1890, 54x82" . .1,450.00
Ganado, classic, red/brn/natural, hand carded, 30x45" 325.00

Ganado, contemporary, red/blk/gray/natural, 26x48" 65.00
Ganado, gray/brn Xs on dk red, worn, 38x64" 175.00
Ganado, red/brn/natural terraces & Xs, 1920s, 39x58", EX . . .225.00
Ganado Red, series of 'T' designs, 1935, 41x70" 250.00
Klagetoh, classic, red/blk/wht/gray, ca 1960, 54x72" 625.00
Klagetoh, hand carded, red/wht/brn on tan, unused, 60x84" . . .650.00
Klagetoh, natural wool/vegetal dye, 1920, 43x78" 400.00
Pictorial, corn stalk/birds/swastikas/'CORN,' 1930, 45x76" . .1,550.00
Pictorial, tree/birds/animals/etc, 1950, 40x62" 450.00
Rows of dragonflies, wht/brn/blk, 1965, 35x56" 125.00
Storm, from The Gap trading post, 1965, 48x79" 500.00
Storm, soft weave, w/swastikas, 1910, 51x77" 125.00
Teec Nos Pos, elongated dmn/sm dmn ea end, heavy, 46x78" . .425.00
Teec Nos Pos, letters ea corner/outlined dmns, '20, 48x73" . .1,000.00
Teec Nos Pos, outlined dmn/terraces, 1935, 40x60" 200.00
Toadalena, hand carded, tan/brn/natural colors, 42x80" 325.00
Transitional, classic, outlined dmns/chevrons, 1905, 45x72" . . .300.00
Transitional, hand spun, red/tan/gray/blk, minor rpr, 40x74" . . .350.00
Twill weave, lg butterfly motif, ca 1960, 29x60" 60.00
W Reservation, arrowhead border/lg lozenge, 1910, 63x84" . . .500.00
W Reservation, banded serrated stars, 1940, 35x60" 250.00
W Reservation, central lozenge, 1935, 40x75" 225.00
W Reservation, rows of connecting triangles, 1940, 31x60" . . .125.00
W Reservation, sawtooth-outlined lozenge, 1935, 37x54" 150.00
W Reservation, Storm, hand carded, coarse, 1970, 52x78" 375.00
Yei, figure ea side mc central stripe, hand carded, 38x49" 250.00
Yei bi chai, 5 figures in red or orange kilts, 1930s, 36x64" 375.00
2 Grey Hills, natural wool, intricate, symbols, 1935, 42x61" . . .275.00
3rd Phase Chief's blanket design, 1940, 38x64" 250.00

Stone Artifacts

Banner stone, winged, drilled, pre-historic, 1½x9½" 40.00
Bird stone, Mound Builder, pop-eyed, gray mottle, 3x5" 75.00
Fish effigy, Wishram, Columbia River, 1750, 3x7" 90.00
Gunflint, chipped, 1" sq 5.00
Mortar, Wishram, cvd frog effigy, Columbia River, 1750, 7" . . .375.00
Mortar, Wishram, cvd owl effigy, basalt, 1600, 6½x9" 600.00
Pestle, gemstone, bell form, from Klickitat River, 4½" 75.00
Plummet, hematite, MO, 3" 85.00

Humpback gorget, slate, 4½" long, $500.00.

Tools

Axe, blk stone, fully grooved/crude, pre-historic, 6" 25.00
Axe, gray stone, ¾-grooved, Clayton Co IA, 6" 125.00
Axe, quartz crystal, from Black Hills, pre-historic, 5½" 325.00
Axe, trade; brass tacks on hdl, 24" 125.00
Axe, trade; wood hdl, 6¾x14" 50.00
Celt, blk stone, Madison Co IL, 7" 150.00
Celt, blk stone, TN, pre-historic, 3x7½" 55.00
Celt, wht flint, IA, 3¾" 8.00
Drill, bl/gray flint, well shaped, 2⅜" 22.00
Drill, gray stone, notched base, TN, 2" 10.00

Drill, late-Paleo basal form, 2½", EX 45.00
Drill, lt gray translucent Flintridge, flattened top, 2⅝" 25.00
Drill, off-wht semi-translucent Flintridge, 2⅛" 20.00
Drill, Pueblo, wood 'pump' for turq nuggets, 1965, 18x8" 155.00
Drill, short shaft, MI 6.00
End scraper, wht/bl-gray flint, well-worked tip 2.00
Engraver, blk stone, Brown Co IL, 1½" .8.00
Mace, Mound Builder, shaped gr stone, 6x19" 125.00
Scraper, elk antler, 1860, 12x2" 65.00
Scraper, gray/tan stone, rnd, notched, 2" 8.00
Scraper, mid-Archaic, brn/cream flint, classic form, 1⅞" 12.00
Scraper, Plains, metal blade, mk w/name, dtd 1890, 14" 125.00
Spud, excavated native copper, pre-historic, 13x6" 35.00
Spud, gray stone, curved, pre-historic, 7x3" 35.00
Spud, gray stone, Montgomery Co TN, pre-historic, 8x2½" 25.00

Trade Silver

Beaver, mk JM (Joseph Mailloux), 2⅛" L 400.00

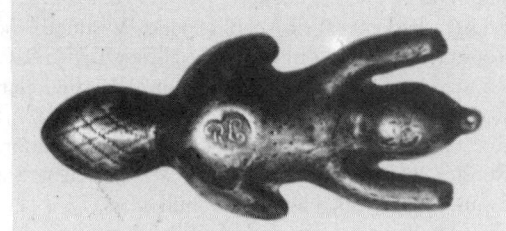

Beaver, signed, 2½", $250.00.

Brooch, Woodlands, crucifix, touchmk, 1780, 4" 400.00
Brooch, Woodlands, turtle, Quebec, 1700s, 2" 330.00
Council Sq brooch, German silver, stamped decor, sq, 1" 35.00
Earwheel, eng ea side, mk RC (Robert Cruickshank), 2⅜" . . .1,000.00
Gorget, concave, eng star/border, mk NV, 4" dia, VG 800.00
Masonic (Council Fire) brooch, eng, mk GR, 2⅛" 650.00
Masonic (Council Fire) brooch, Iroquois, German silver, 2" 80.00
Snake, eng, mk w/stamp of P Fox, 1790, ¾x1¼" 1,200.00
Turtle, loop under head, solid, mk XIII, 1¼" L 45.00
Wristband, ridged, edge eng, mk Montreal/RC, ⅞x5½", VG . . .525.00

Weapons

Blade for war club, Plains, cut-out designs, 1850, 10" 300.00
Bow, Modoc, pnt decor, 40" L 175.00
Club, Cheyenne, 5" gray stone head/buckskin & bw hdl, 1870 .200.00
Club, E Woodlands, 3" natural wood formation, 1870, 18" 70.00
Club, Plains, dbl, pnt stone, 2 areas w/quartz, 1880, 10x25" . . .100.00
Club, Plains, hide over 'flop knob,' bw hdl/suspensions, 12" . . .150.00
Club, Plains, 3" stone head, rawhide-covered 18" hdl, 1880 . . .150.00
Club, Plains, 3½" blk stone ball head, bw on wood hdl, 22" . . .125.00
Club, Plains, 5" stone head on bw hdl w/hair drop, 29" 250.00
Club, Plains, 9" blk egg-shape head w/pewter tips, bw hdl 300.00
Club, Sioux, red catlinite ovoid, hide/wood stem, 1870, 20" . . .75.00
Club, Sioux, stone w/cvd lines, bw hdl/tin cones/hair drops . . .200.00
Hatchet, MO, file-burnt hdl, metal head w/heart cutout, 17" . .400.00
Spear head, tan stone, OK, pre-historic, 10x13" 45.00
Tomahawk, iron head/wood hdl, rawhide suspension, 20" 700.00
Tomahawk, presentation, file burns/inlays, iron head, 21" . . .1,900.00
Tomahawk, swastika on 5" W metal head, wood hdl, 17" 100.00
War club, Plains, yel-pnt rawhide over wood hdl, 8x16" 50.00
War club, Sioux, braided horsehide around rnd stone, 19" 50.00
War club, stone head, hide-wrap hdl, 2 teeth decor, 4x13" 50.00

Miscellaneous

Blanket, Flathead, Hudson Bay cloth/floral bw, 1870, 47x37" . .225.00
Blanket, saddle; Crow, muslin/bw trim/buffalo tabs, 65x32" . . .350.00
Blanket, Saltillo, bl/wht stripes w/mc motif, 1925, 80x56" 100.00
Broadside, Indian Exhibition of relics/dances by N Glassion . . .380.00
Buckle, US Calvary, found on site of Custer's massacre 350.00
Gambling bones, Plateau, for Hand or Stick game, 1870, pr 45.00
Goldtone, Fire in Mtn Lion God, Curtis, orig fr, 11x13" 400.00
Peace medal, silver, Andrew Johnson, Pres of US, 1865, 3" 385.00
Photogravure, Flathead Camp..., sepia tone, 12x16" 190.00
Photogravure, Vanishing Race, ES Curtis, sgn, 7½x5½" 500.00
Quirt, Crow, antler, bw holder, cvd horse heads, 1880s, 9" 85.00
Quirt, Kootenai, incised/cvd antler, snake form, 1880, 14x1" . . .60.00
Quirt, Sioux, fully covered w/seed beads, 1880s, 13x1" 135.00
Quirt, Sioux, wood w/bw & rawhide whip, 1900, 14x1½" 75.00
Rope, Cheyenne, fine weave blk/wht horsehair, 1980, 20 ft 45.00
Saddle, Crow, child's, 1870, 8x18" 125.00
Saddle, Crow, woman's, rawhide w/brass tacks & bw, 33" 100.00
Saddle, Plains, hide covered, bird effigy horn, 1870, 20x7" 180.00
Saddle, Plains, rawhide, bird pommel, brass bells, 1920s 105.00
Saddle drape, Blackfoot, buffalo, bw/trade cloth, 10x82" 600.00
Scalp, horse's; Crow, 1880s, 18x2" 95.00
Teepee, Blackfoot child's, muslin, ochre/bl pnt, 1890, 11" 500.00

Amphora

The Amphora Porcelain Works in the Teplitz-Turn area of Bohemia produced Art Nouveau-styled vases and figurines during the latter part of the 1800s through the first few decades of the twentieth century. They marked their wares with various stamps, some incorporating the name and location of the pottery with a crown or a shield. Because Bohemia was part of the Austro-Hungarian empire prior to WWI, some examples are marked Austria; items marked with the Czechoslovakia designation were made after the war.

Our advisor for this category is Jack Gunsaulus; he is listed in the Directory under Michigan.

Vase, applied snowballs and leaves on basketweave, gilt handles, 6½", $195.00.

Bowl, floral, pk w/jewels, on tan & brn w/gold, mk, 6x8" 195.00
Bowl, shell form, water nymphs chase fish, 1900, 17", NM 625.00
Bust, maid in off-shoulder gown, upswept hair, RS&K, 21" 660.00
Ewer, trees on mottled lt & dk gr, gold hdl, fish form 165.00
Lamp, world globe base, rpl shade, 8½" 525.00
Planter, fruits & florals, mushroom form, 4 hdls, 9x9½" 195.00

Vase, bird, hdls, mk, 5¾" **65.00**
Vase, bl, molded gold snake in grass, 7½" **295.00**
Vase, blk birds in flight, forest in bkground, 9" **250.00**
Vase, Deco florals on gray, Czechoslovakia, 9x6¼" **175.00**
Vase, Deco parrots in relief, cobalt bands, hdls, mk, 6½" **175.00**
Vase, figural dog surprised by frog, ca 1900, 12" **285.00**
Vase, florals in raised cobweb, purple/bl irid, 13" **350.00**
Vase, florals in relief, urn form, dbl hdls, 6½" **145.00**
Vase, lady at work, in relief, 15" **375.00**
Vase, owl, bl w/cobalt, Czechoslovakia, 8½" **275.00**
Vase, panel: branch w/birds, cvd/HP, cream w/bl ft, 13", pr **350.00**
Vase, profile: maid on beige w/gold, RS&K, 7" **550.00**
Vase, profile: maid w/long hair, eagle-crest cap, RS&K, 9" ...**825.00**
Vase, Royal portrait, bk: church scene, HP, 16½" **300.00**

Animal Dishes with Covers

Covered animal dishes have been produced for nearly two centuries and are as varied as their manufacturers. They were made in many types of glass — slag, colored, clear, and milk glass — as well as china and pottery. On bases of nests and baskets, you will find animals and birds of every sort. The most common was the hen.

Some of the smaller versions made by McKee, Indiana Tumbler and Goblet Company, and Westmoreland Glass of Pittsburgh, Pennsylvania, were sold to food-processing companies who filled them with prepared mustard, baking powder, etc. Occasionally one will be found with the paper label identifying the product and processing company still intact.

Many of the glass versions produced during the latter part of the nineteenth century have been recently reproduced. As late as the 1960s, the Kemple Glass Company made the rooster, fox, lion, cat, lamb, hen, horse, turkey, duck, dove, and rabbit on split-ribbed or basketweave bases. They were made in amethyst, blue, amber, and milk glass, as well as a variegated slag. It is sometimes necessary to compare items in question to verified examples of older glass in order to recognize reproductions.

For more information, we recommend *Covered Animal Dishes* by our advisor, Everett Grist, whose address is in the Directory under Illinois. In the listings below, when only one dimension is given, it is length.

Bird w/berry, milk glass, Greentown **300.00**
Bird w/berry, split-ribbed base, chocolate, Greentown **350.00**
Cat, lacy base, gr eyes, milk glass, Atterbury, dtd lid **200.00**
Cat on drum, milk glass, mk Portieux **45.00**
Cat on hamper, chocolate, Greentown **350.00**
Chick & eggs, compote base, milk glass, Atterbury, dtd lid **195.00**
Chick & eggs, lacy base, milk glass, Atterbury, dtd, 7x7" **135.00**
Chick on basket, bl opaque **45.00**
Dog, bl opaque, milk glass head, Westmoreland, 5¼" **90.00**
Dog, Chow; split-ribbed base, milk glass, unmk McKee, 5½" ...**275.00**
Dog, Pekingese; milk glass, Sandwich, 4¾" **375.00**
Dog w/gun & ammunition pouch, milk glass, Vallerysthal **125.00**
Dove, split-ribbed base, milk glass, 2 McKee mks, 5½" **275.00**
Duck, bl opaque, Atterbury, dtd 1887, 11" **450.00**
Duck, cattail base, milk glass, 5½" **85.00**
Duck, Pintail; diamond-weave base, milk glass, 5½" **85.00**
Duck, swimming, yel, Vallerysthal, 5" **55.00**
Duck, wavy base, bl opaque, w/eyes **125.00**
Eagle mother, milk glass, WG mk **75.00**
Elephant, split-ribbed base, milk glass, mk McKee, 5½" ...**1,400.00**
Elephant, walking, milk glass, 4x8" **95.00**
Fighting cocks, clear or colored transparent, Greentown **600.00**
Fish, entwined, red eyes, milk glass, Atterbury, dtd, 6" **165.00**
Fish on skiff, milk glass, 7½" **65.00**
Fox, ribbed lid, lacy base, milk glass, 6¼" **165.00**

Fox, ribbed lid & base, milk glass, Atterbury, dtd, 6¼" **175.00**
Hand & dove, milk glass, Atterbury, pat date **110.00**
Hen, bl w/wht head, Wright **85.00**
Hen, cattail base, milk glass **65.00**
Hen, diamond-basketweave nest, Nile gr, Greentown **1,200.00**
Hen, lacy base, bl transparent head **275.00**
Hen, red eyes, milk glass, Challinor Taylor & Co, 8" **125.00**
Hen on sleigh, milk glass, Westmoreland Specialty **65.00**
Horse, split-ribbed base, milk glass, unmk McKee **145.00**
Horse on nest, purple slag, Wright **65.00**
Lamb, picket base, bl opaque/milk glass, Westmoreland **125.00**
Lion, British, milk glass **95.00**
Lion, picket fence base, milk glass, Westmoreland **85.00**
Quail, scroll base, milk glass **65.00**
Rabbit, Dome; clear or colored transparent, Greentown **150.00**
Rabbit, milk glass, Atterbury, dtd 1889, 9" **195.00**
Rabbit, molded eyes, milk glass, mk IG, 9" **88.00**
Rabbit, mule-eared, on picket fence base, milk glass **70.00**
Robin on nest, bl opaque, Vallerysthal, 5" **50.00**
Robin on ped base, bl opaque, Vallerysthal **125.00**
Robin on ped nest, milk glass **45.00**
Rooster, basketweave base, bl opaque, Westmoreland, lg **165.00**
Rooster, milk glass, pnt comb, Challinor Taylor & Co, 8" **135.00**
Rooster, standing, clear, red-pnt comb, Westmoreland **55.00**
Rooster, wide-rib base, dk bl opaque **65.00**
Rooster, wide-rib base, milk glass, bl head, Westmoreland, 5" ...**125.00**
Rooster, wide-rib base, milk glass, Westmoreland Specialty **65.00**
Swan, closed neck, basket base, milk glass, 5½" **85.00**
Swan, milk glass, Vallerysthal, 5½" **125.00**
Swan, raised wings, eye sockets, milk glass **125.00**
Turkey, split-ribbed base, milk glass, mk McKee, 5½" **200.00**
Turkey, standing, milk glass **85.00**

Scottie dogs, blue opaque, Akro Agate Co., 6½", $95.00.

Antiquities

The ancient Egyptians, Romans, and the early craftsmen of India and China have left us with exquisite treasures bearing mute witness of their esthetic convictions that even a water carrier, a knife, or a rug should be created a thing of beauty. Though time and the elements have taken their toll on the more fragile works of these ancient artisans, it is incredible that many remain intact to this day. The thin-walled tear and scent bottles, blown by Roman artisans from the first century A.D., and examples of the red or black predynastic potteries of Egypt — though understandably quite rare — can yet occasionally be found on the market today. Jewelry, often interred with the dead, has survived the centuries well; figurines of marble and terra cotta, ceremonial masks, earthenware vessels, and other relics such as these offer us of the twentieth century the only tangible link possible to the ancient world.

Bronze

Bacchus, Roman 200 AD, panther skin on shoulder, 3¼" **695.00**
Bell, animal; Roman 200-300 AD, 1½", G **25.00**
Brooch, Aucissa type, Fibula 100 AD, 1⅝", G **45.00**
Diety, Assyrian 700 BC, standing, cylindrical diadem, 3⅜" **485.00**
Dionysos head, Egyptian 50 AD, grapevine wreath, 3" **1,300.00**
Finial, Byzantine 1200 AD, archangel Michael, 5⅝" **2,400.00**
Hercules as infant, 100 BC, in lion skin, 4" **600.00**
Horse bit, Luristan 800 BC, cats flank base of spout, 12" **300.00**
Mirror, Roman, w/tang, EX patina **125.00**
Oil lamp, Roman 100-200 AD, lg horse-head finial, 7" L **500.00**
Pike head, Luristan 1200-800 BC, hollow quadrangle **90.00**
Plaque, Urartean 700 BC, goddesses w/gifts, 4x4" **300.00**
Ring, Roman 100-200 AD, oval bezel w/eng owner's seal **40.00**
Spearpoint, Greek Persian War period, 9½" **75.00**
Spout, Seljuk 1200 AD, cat's mouth forms spout, 4⅛" **400.00**
Strigil, Greek 500 BC, curving scraper, 9½" **500.00**

Glassware

Bottle, Islam 300 AD, bl-gr, high domed, folded rim, 8½" **250.00**
Bottle, Sidonia 200 AD, emerald gr/cobalt, 3¾", pr **425.00**
Dish, Egyptian 400 AD, olive gr, folded rim, 10" **675.00**
Ewer, 200-300 AD, aqua, bulbous w/strap hdl, folded lip, 5" ...**375.00**
Flask, Islam 200 AD, irid bl-gr, encrusted, globular, 8" **600.00**
Jar, 500 AD, olive gr, globular, aquamarine hdls/decor, 4" **425.00**
Pitcher, 400 AD, bl-gr, ribbed globular form, 6½" **345.00**
Vase, Egyptian 450 AD, amber, aquamarine hdls/collars, 6½" ..**450.00**

Hardstones

Axe, Danish Neolithic, stone, 1-hole, 4½" **165.00**
Beads, 100 BC, rock crystal w/4 wht/yel matrices, 14¼" **2,250.00**
Bust of youth, Cypriot 500 BC, limestone, incised, 6½" **800.00**
Fragment, capital; Roman 200-300 AD, limestone, 11¼" **800.00**
Head of Hadrianus, Roman 200 AD, marble base, 12" **3,000.00**
Libation vessel, Achaemenid 500 BC, rose granite, 8½" **1,200.00**
Makeup pallet, Egyptian, rectangular, red traces, 5½x3" **95.00**
Pitcher, Persian 300 BC, pouring spout, 5" **120.00**
Ring, Roman 100 AD, garnet cameo face, gold, 1" **1,500.00**
Seal, Egyptian early dynasty, cvd god Toth **75.00**
Seal, Proto-Elamite 3000 BC, marble, recumbent ibex, 1½" ...**775.00**

Pottery

Amphora, Campania 300 BC, red-figure, goose/female, 11" ...**450.00**
Amphorisk, Corinthian 600 BC, panthers/stags, 6¼" **675.00**
Bowl, Islamic Umiyed Culture, red stripes, 6" dia **90.00**
Dish, Ottoman 1600 AD, polychrome floral sprays, 12" **875.00**
Jar, Egypt, 3300 BC, buffware, pnt spirals, 4" dia **750.00**
Jar, Ilkhanid 1400 AD, pnt underglaze, seated dear, 12" **2,200.00**
Mug, 500-400 BC, blk, broad base, ring hdl, 3" **325.00**
Pitcher, Roman, plainware, 6" **65.00**
Tile, Ottoman 1500 AD, polychrome, 11¼x19¼" **2,995.00**
Vase, Egyptian 100 AD, bl faience, emb lotus, bulbous, 5" **325.00**

Terra Cotta

Eros on horsebk, Hellenistic 300 BC, much rstr, 3⅞" **300.00**
Girl, Boetian 200 BC, long chiton & himation, 4⅝" **675.00**
Goddess, Mycenaean 1350 BC, stands w/arms akimbo, 4⅝" ...**695.00**
Lamp, Greek 600 BC, semi-circular, head-form spout, 4¼" **775.00**
Plate, Apulian 350 BC, red-figure, lady's profile, 7" **300.00**
Pot, Greco-Roman, blk band decor, dbl hdls, 2¾" **35.00**
Vessel, Costa Rican, 3 scroll legs w/animal surmounts, 8" **200.00**
Vessel, storage; Roman 100 AD, 7" **15.00**

Miscellaneous

Amulet, dog form, Egyptian 300 BC, made of bone, ¾x3/4" **60.00**
Earrings, Roman 100 AD, gold, crescent w/appl bosses **500.00**
Head, Late Period 700 BC, lion, plaster, 3" **625.00**
Intaglio, Roman 100-300 AD, garnet, eng stylized dolphin **60.00**

Iranian terra cotta figures, 1st Millenium B.C.; Fertility, brown glaze, 14", $450.00; Ibex, red glaze, 9", $350.00.

Necklace, Egyptian 300 BC, mc beads, 1 sunburst bead **35.00**
Panel, Coptic 650 AD, tapestry woven linen, 8x9½" **695.00**
Pin, Hittite 2000 BC, gold, 4 joined semi-circles, 5¾" **895.00**
Venus, Roman 100 AD, cvd ivory, 2½" **400.00**

Appliances, Early Electric

Collectors of Americana enjoy vintage appliances such as those used in the kitchen — toasters, coffee makers, etc. — as well as early TV sets, vacuum cleaners, short-lived innovations, and examples with particularly distinctive Deco styling.

Coffee urn, chrome-plated Deco style, ca 1930s **30.00**
Coffee urn, Farberware, amber Lucite hdls, +cr/sug on tray **45.00**
Coffeepot, Drip-O-Lator, Deco aluminum w/Bakelite hdl, 12" ..**15.00**

Coffeepot, Farberware, percolator, Bakelite hdl, EX 35.00
Coffeepot, Universal, percolator, wood hdls, early 1900s, NM 50.00
Fan, Emerson, early 1900s, MIB 50.00
Fan, Master, CI base, gr pnt, 4 blades, orig cord, EX 45.00

'Petitpoint' chromed metal and plastic iron designed by Clifford Stevens and E.P. Schreyer, by Waverly Tools, ca 1941, 10", $350.00.

Iron, Chevron, fold-up, EX 30.00
Iron, Graybar Model 11, orig box 55.00
Light bulb, porc base, Edison, 5½" 18.00
Popcorn popper, Aladdin 30.00
Popcorn popper, Poppin' Pete, EX 35.00
Toaster, Bersted, #70 ....30.00
Toaster, Estate Electric, #177 ....100.00
Toaster, General Electric, D-12, EX 125.00
Toaster, Hotpoint, 115T1, EX 55.00
Toaster, Marion Giant Flip Flop, #67, EX 50.00
Toaster, Royal Rochester, D-30, EX 55.00
Toaster, Sunbeam, chrome w/blk trim 50.00
Toaster, Toastmaster, 1A1, EX 65.00
Toaster, Toastocator, EX 100.00
Toaster, Universal, early wire door, EX 50.00
Toaster, Universal, E7722, EX 55.00
Vacuum cleaner, Doty, early 1900s, EX 200.00
Waffle iron, Universal 28.00
Waffle iron, Universal, ceramic insert 65.00
Washing machine, Laundry Queen, copper tub 195.00

Arc-En-Ciel

The Arc-En-Ciel Pottery Company operated in Zanesville, Ohio, from 1903 until 1907. Artware was produced only until 1905, typically finished in a high lustre gold glaze. Though not always marked, those pieces that are carry the half-circle rainbow logo containing the company name.

Vase, Radford mold, gold glaze, 7½", $185.00.

Pitcher, gold w/pk highlights, swirled w/twisted hdl, 11½" 165.00
Vase, eagle & Washington, gold lustre, 7" 225.00
Vase, gold irid, bottle form, 6x2¼x2" 75.00
Vase, tree bark body, purple/gold lustre, 10½" 195.00

Argy-Rousseau, G.

Gabriel Argy-Rousseau produced both fine art glass and quality commercial ware in Paris, France, in 1918. He favored Art Nouveau as well as Art Deco and in the twenties produced a line of vases in the Egyptian manner, made popular by the discovery of King Tut's tomb. One of the most important types of glass he made was pate-de-verre. Most of his work is signed. Items listed below are pate-de-verre unless noted otherwise.

Ash tray, cameo of lady w/in, 4 rests, latticework, 6½" L 1,400.00
Bowl, lav roses w/gr centers on rim, mottled lav body, 2x3" ...700.00
Bowl, oak leaf band at rim, rose/pk on amber, 3½" 1,650.00
Bowl vase, starflower clusters, gray w/dk bl streaks, 3¾" 4,600.00
Compote, std w/gazelles chasing tiger, trumpet form, 5" 7,000.00
Lamp, bullet form w/rtcl circle-flowers; 3-leg iron ft, 8" 5,775.00
Lamp, 5" dome shade & vase std w/roses, gr/red/yel, 12" ...23,100.00
Lamp base, tiered fans at base, wine/red mottle on gray, 17" .1,300.00
Pendant, red berries/bl leaves on gray oval, sgn, 2¾" 1,600.00
Vase, lg faceted dmn lozenges, yel/amber/tan/orange, 6" 3,850.00
Vase, palm branches, ochre/gr/orange on gray/yel, 5¾" 3,300.00
Vase, pate-de-cristal, U-form, faceted lip, streaky, 5" 2,750.00
Vase, tiers of overlapping triangles, gray/dk bl/turq, 8½" 6,000.00
Vase, 3 rnd purple/maroon pine cone cartouches, 7" 3,850.00
Veilleuse, dome shade w/starflowers on 3-ftd iron disk, 5" ...7,700.00

Art Deco

To the uninformed observer, 'Art Deco' evokes images of chrome and glass, streamlined curves and aerodynamic shapes, mirrored prints of pink flamingos, and statues of slender nudes and greyhound dogs. Though the Deco movement began in 1925 at the Paris International Exposition and lasted to some extent into the 1950s, within that period of time the evolution of fashion and taste continued as it always has, resulting in subtle variations.

The French Deco look was one of opulence — exotic inlaid woods, rich material, lush fur and leather. Lines tended toward symmetrical curves. American designers adapted the concept to cover every aspect of fashion and home furnishings from small inexpensive picture frames, cigarette lighters, and costume jewelry to high-fashion designer clothing and exquisite massive furniture with squared or circular lines. Vinyl was a popular covering, and chrome-plated brass was used for chairs, cocktail shakers, lamps, and tables. Dinnerware, glassware, theaters, and train stations were designed to reflect the new 'Modernism.'

The Deco movement made itself apparent into the fifties in wrought iron lamps with stepped pink plastic shades and Venetian blinds. The sheer volume of production during those twenty-five years provides collectors today with fine examples of the period that can be bought for as little as $10 or $20 up to the thousands. Chrome items signed 'Chase' are prized by collectors, and blue glass radios and tables with blue glass tops are high on the list of desirability in many areas.

Those interested in learning more about this subject will want to read *Collectors Guide to Art Deco* by our advisor, Mary Frank Gaston. She is listed in the Directory under Texas. See also Bronzes; Chase; Frankart; Furniture; Jewelry; Lalique; Radios; etc.

Ash tray, ceramic w/cobalt glaze, 4½" 28.00
Belt buckle, mc Bakelite 14.00

Bottle, scent; Opening Night, Lucien Lelong, pyramidal, 6" ...**700.00**
Bowl, serving; blk/mc leaves on orange, gold trim, Japan, 10½" ..**35.00**
Box, jewel; porc w/HP abstract, octagonal, French **170.00**
Candle holder, chrome, stylized fish-form hdls, 4", pr **35.00**
Ceiling fan, chrome, airplane form **550.00**
Cigarette lighter/paperweight, elephant figural, chrome **75.00**
Clock, desk; bronze w/blk enamel trim, mk JAZ, 1930s, 5½" ...**225.00**
Clock, digital, bronze, Silvercrest, ca 1930s, 19" L **165.00**
Clock, NP, shaped/lobed, lightning-bolt hands, Cheuret, 5" .**6,000.00**
Clock, reclining musician, metal/compo ivory, French, 27½" ..**600.00**
Cocktail shaker, chrome zeppelin form, DRGM Germany, 12" .**500.00**
Cocktail shaker, chrome-plated penguin form, 11½x8" **185.00**
Coffeepot, copper, brass hdl/finial, 11½" **250.00**
Coffeepot, copper, wooden hdl/finial, American, 13" **130.00**
Compact, navy plastic, HP silver bar/wavy lines, mk France **95.00**
Compote, porc, HP butterflies on dk gr, French, 9¼" **70.00**
Figurine, draped nude, opal glass/chrome base, Etling, 9" **1,300.00**
Figurine, flamingo, pk, porc, 10½", pr **85.00**
Figurine, wolfhounds, ceramic, ca 1940s, German, 13" **250.00**

Wine decanter with nude inside, 9"; wine glasses with nude stems, Germany, $495.00 for the set.

Grooming set, plastic, 10-pc in leather case **20.00**
Hors d'oeuvres server, chrome w/Bakelite hdl, 11½" **70.00**
Ice bucket, glass w/chrome hdl, 6" **35.00**
Incense burner, cast metal, Egyptian motif, France **265.00**
Incense burner, ceramic, Egyptian figural, sgn Lisne, 6½" **375.00**
Jar, powder; pk frosted, Egyptian head finial **45.00**
Lamp, blk-lacquered wood w/rhinestones, pr **55.00**
Lamp, earth globe supported by Atlas figures, '30s, 18" **200.00**
Lamp, Harlequin plays lute, gr crackle globe, M **70.00**
Lamp, nude w/greyhound, wht metal, lg **175.00**
Lamp, patinated bronze 13" lady dancer, alabaster base **250.00**
Lamp, vanity; stylized nudes, wht metal w/bronze finish, pr **375.00**
Lawn sprinkler, CI, mermaid grasps post, worn pnt, 14" **1,300.00**
Magazine rack, nude/greyhound, bronze w/silver finish, 11" ...**450.00**
Mirror, cheval; silvered, arched/ribbed legs, Ruhlmann, 18" .**3,000.00**
Mirror, vanity; pot metal nude figure on faux marble base **140.00**
Mirror globe, ballroom; 1" sq mirrors, rotating, lg **400.00**
Picture frame, beveled glass, etched floral/leaf, 14½x17" **80.00**
Punch bowl, ruby glass w/chrome trim, +6 ruby glasses **155.00**
Radio, bl glass/wood, chrome trim, mk Spartan, 17" L **1,100.00**
Radio, wood/chrome, mk Fada, 8x11" **175.00**
Sconce, gold irid shade w/molded geometrics in 9" holder, pr ...**85.00**
Soda dispenser, chrome, mk Soda King made in USA, 9½" **20.00**
Tray, chrome/cobalt glass, att Norman Bel Geddes, 16" L **115.00**
Tumbler, chrome holder w/cobalt glass insert, 2½" **25.00**
Vase, bl mirror glass, graduated rings, 7" **65.00**

Vase, porc, HP Egyptian motif, 8½" **140.00**
Wall pocket, woman's head/hat, pottery, wht glaze **60.00**

Art Glass Baskets

A popular novelty and gift item during the Victorian era, these one-of-a-kind works of art were produced in just about any type of art glass in use at that time. They were never marked, since these were not true production pieces but 'whimsies' made by glassworkers to relieve the tedium of the long work day. Some were made as special gifts. The more decorative and imaginative the design, the more valuable the basket.

Amberina swirl, amber hdl, 7¾x6½x5" **245.00**
Bl, HP roses/gold Xs, clear wishbone hdl, 9" **125.00**
Bl opal, indented 'hobs,' thorn hdl, oblong, 1920s, 7x6" **125.00**
Bl overlay, amber ruffled rim, Xd hdl, 8¼x6" **165.00**
Bl overlay, wht int, ruffled, clear hdl, wafer ft, 6¾x6" **115.00**
Bl satin, appl satin Matsu-No-Ke, trilobed/3-hdl, 4½" **325.00**
Bl shaded, wht int, Herringbone, frosted wishbone ft, 6x4" **210.00**
Bl to clear w/wht rim, HP decor, thorn hdl, 7½x7½" **350.00**
Brn/orange mottle on wht w/mica flecks, 10¾x6½" **58.00**
Cranberry, clear edge/hdl, wishbone ft, 12x8⅜x6⅛" **265.00**
Cranberry, Dia Quilt, clear ruffled edge, 7½x4½" **225.00**
Cranberry to clear, threaded decor, twist hdl, 5½x3½" **118.00**
Cream opaque, appl mc florals, amber rim, 7x4¼" **148.00**
Cream w/rose int, appl gr & amber leaves & ft, S&W, 9x5" ...**365.00**
Gr w/cranberry opal ruffle, appl flowers, Sandwich, 11" **250.00**
MOP Herringbone, pk, floral tapestry, thorn hdl, 4 wht ft ...**1,250.00**
Orange, wht int, 8-crimp, clear ft/thorny hdl, 8¼x5¼" **165.00**
Pk, wht opal int, clear flowers/ft/hdl, 9¼x5⅝" **365.00**
Pk candy stripe overlay, ruffled/swirled, thorn hdl, 6½" **195.00**
Pk cased, appl florals, amber hdl, 7½x4½" **175.00**
Pk opal cased, appl leaves, 8-crimp, clear hdl, 7¼x4¼" **165.00**
Pk opal ruffle on vaseline opal, emb circles, twist hdl, 10" **375.00**
Pk overlay, wht int, clear edge/hdl/leaf ft, 7½x3⅝" **165.00**
Pk shaded, wht int, ruffled, clear hdl, 6¾x6½x8⅛" **110.00**
Pk spangle, crimped, reeded/thorny twist hdl, 5½" dia **185.00**
Pk/wht spatter, wht int, clear hdl, dimpled sides, 7x4⅝" **125.00**
Rubena threads on cranberry to clear, twist hdl, 5½x3½" **118.00**

Satin glass, blue with white interior, twisted briar handle, 9", $175.00.

Vaseline opal, Dia Quilt, appl florals, twist hdl, 7x6x7" **185.00**
Wht opal to vaseline w/thorny nubs, clear hdl/ft, 8¾x5⅛" **175.00**
Wht opaque, appl red cherries, amber stems/hdl, 6x4¼" **175.00**
Wht opaque, rose int, sq, folded, clear hdl/ft, 5¾x5⅝" **145.00**

Wht w/bl satin int, T'print, frosted twist thorn hdl, 11" 250.00

Art Nouveau

From the famous 'L'Art Nouveau' shop in the rue de Provence in Paris, 'New Art' spread across the continent and belatedly arrived in America in time to add its curvilineal elements and asymmetrical ornamentation to the ostentatious remains of the Rococo revival of the 1880s. Nouveau manifested itself in every facet of decorative art. In glassware, Tiffany turned the concept into a commercial success that lasted well into the second decade of this century and created a style that inspired other American glassmakers for decades. Furniture, lamps, bronzes, jewelry, and automobiles were designed within the realm of its dictates. Today's market abounds with lovely examples of Art Nouveau, allowing the collector to choose one or several areas that hold a special interest. See also Bronzes; Jewelry; Tiffany; Silver; specific manufacturers; etc.

Balustrade, CI, openwork shield/emb scrolls, Guimard, 30" ..4,000.00
Candelabra, SP, 5-light, 2 maids form stem, 1900s, 20", pr ..5,000.00
Candelabrum, wrought iron, 2 scroll arms/leafage, Brant, 14" ..400.00
Candlestick, bronze, sq/ftd leaf-cast base/std, Gorham, 49" ..4,400.00
Clock, bronze, draped maid, 4 scroll ft, Louis Chalon, 23" ...7,400.00
Crumber, SP, floral relief, mk Gallia, +8" L tray 220.00
Hook, brass, figural dragonfly/lotus leaves, Fr, 10", pr 1,650.00
Inkwell, metal, bust of youth relief, att de Feure, 9" L 220.00
Jardiniere, bronze/gilt, head of lady/lilies figural, 20" 2,200.00
Lamp, bronze, lady/forked support; irid shade, C Kuba, 23" ..3,800.00
Lamp, bronzed, Egyptian nude/columns, irid lily shade, 20" ...400.00
Lamp, lg bronze frog holds opal-set shade in extended arms ..7,250.00
Lamp, patinated metal, figural wood nymph, French, 52" ...1,300.00
Lamp, 2 nudes/tree support millefiori ball, Nordin, 21" 2,750.00
Mirror, hand; silver, marine motif, Whitting Mfg, 9½" 600.00
Note pad, SP, emb florals, ring for chatelaine, German mk 45.00
Panel, tin, stamped Nouveau ladies decor, 1890s, 36x25" 200.00
Plaque, pottery, emb maid in gr/lav robe, Pietzner, 10x8" 400.00

Table lamp, bronze, opaline cabachons in shade, France, 14½", $7,250.00.

Tray, tin litho, lady in long dress w/flowers, 1910, 10" dia 60.00
Urn, bronze, nude atop, relief cherub, Charpentier, 27" 5,000.00
Vase, metal/mc patina, floriform, lg orchid/etc, Regual, 25" ...550.00

Vase, Tudric pewter, floriform w/lg leafy hdls, #029, 10" 500.00

Arts and Crafts

The Arts and Crafts movement began in England during the last quarter of the nineteenth century, and its influence was soon felt in this country. Among its proponents in America were Elbert Hubbard (see Roycroft) and Gustav Stickley (see Furniture). They rebelled against the mechanized mass production of the Industrial Revolution and against the cumulative influence of hundreds of years of man's changing taste. They subscribed to the theory of purification of the styles — that designs be geared strictly to necessity. At the same time they sought to elevate these basic ideals to the level of accepted 'art.' Simplicity was their virtue; to their critics it was a fault.

The type of furniture they promoted was squarely built of heavy oak, and so simple was its appearance that as a result many began to copy the style which became known as 'Mission.' Soon factories had geared production toward making cheap copies of their designs. In 1915 Stickley's own operation failed, forced into bankruptcy by the machinery he so despised. Hubbard lost his life that same year on the ill-fated *Lusitania*. Within the decade the style had lost its popularity. See also Furniture; Roycroft; Silver; and specific manufacturers.

Andirons, wrought iron, spiraled openwork flame-shaped top ..850.00
Ash tray, L&JG Stickley #21, wood w/copper insert, 22" 400.00
Book rack, G Stickley #74, V-form shelf, unmk, rfn, 31x30" ...950.00
Bookends, ET Hurley, bronze, sea horse w/turq eyes, 6½" 700.00
Bookends, metal w/brn tile w/birds, Potter Studio-E102, 5" ...200.00
Bowl, G Stickley, hammered copper w/brass ft, no mk, 6" 250.00
Bowl, Kalo, hammered copper w/silver-wash int, M-323S, 7" ..400.00
Candle holder, Harry Dixon, copper, twist shaft, 11½", pr 750.00
Candlestick, ET Hurley, 3-arm, curved tubes join cups, 15" ..1,400.00
Candlestick, Jarvie, disk ft/slim std/bulbous cup, 13", pr 6,000.00
Candlestick, Stickley Bros, copper, trumpet std, 12", pr 600.00
Chamberstick, Jarvie, spun brass, angle hdl, rare, 6" 1,100.00
Coat tree, G Stickley #52, single post/4 ft, branded, 72" 800.00
Creamer, Kalo, sterling, hexagonal, angled hdl, 3¼" 400.00
Inkwell, G Stickley, hand-wrought copper w/rivets, 5½x2½" ..750.00
Lamp, G Stickley #504, wicker shade, copper/wood base 2,200.00
Lamp, hammered copper, mica inserts in shade, 15" 1,700.00
Lamp, Limbert #376, copper canister base, rpl mica in shade .4,500.00
Lamp, Prairie School, sq wood fr, slag glass, cutouts, 20" 1,300.00
Letter opener, ET Hurley, sea horse hdl, orig patina, 6" L 325.00
Letter opener, Handicraft Guild, hand-wrought copper, 7" L ..180.00
Log basket, Mission Oak, 2-slat sides, EX 125.00
Magazine rack, Limbert #302, 3-tier, brand, 28x28x11" 700.00
Magazine stand, L&JG Stickley, 4-tier, Handicraft, 45" 2,100.00
Magazine stand, L&JG Stickley #47, 4-tier, rfn, 42x15x18" ..1,000.00
Mirror, G Stickley #66, arched top/4 hooks, decal, 28x46" ..2,300.00
Mirror, G Stickley #68, 3-part, 4 copper hooks, 48 " L 2,400.00
Mirror, L&JG Stickley #66, 4 copper hooks, label, 23x40" ...1,800.00
Mirror, Limbert, vertical slats, scooped top, mk, 23x38" 1,700.00
Nut dish, G Stickley, hammered copper, 3 ft, Turchin mk, 3" ..325.00
Paperweight, ET Hurley, lobster form, orig patina, unmk, 6" ...300.00
Pedestal, Stickley Bros, 15" sq top on tapered sq base, mk 700.00
Pedestal, Stickley Bros, 4 ft extend through sq base, 27" 650.00
Pitcher, Stickley Bros, hammered copper, w/lid, label, 13½" ...525.00
Rug, Drugget, geometric, brn/blk/cream, fringed, 108x156" ..1,500.00
Rug, Drugget, geometric, wine/rust/tan/ivory, 136x154", EX .2,300.00
Rug, G Stickley Drugget, geometric, brn/ivory, 57x31", EX 275.00
Screen, G Stickley #83, tri-fold, wood/canvas, decal, 68" 1,800.00
Tray, Gorham, hammered copper, appl frog, polished, 8" L 150.00
Tray, Kalo, sterling, turned-up edge/appl 'H,' 10" dia 300.00

Table lamp, hammered copper with isenglass panels, 28", $1,100.00.

Vase, Dirk Van Erp, copper, bulbous, rolled rim, mk, 7x6" 800.00
Vase, Dirk Van Erp, copper, orig wine/rust patina, 5x5½" 950.00
Vase, Dirk Van Erp, copper shell casing mk UMC, 10x5" 800.00
Vase, Dirk Van Erp, hammered copper, new patina, 6x7" ... 1,000.00
Wastebasket, Mission Oak, sq w/corner posts, rfn, 15" 325.00

Aurene

Aurene, developed in 1904 by Frederick Carder of the Steuben Glass Works, is a metallic iridescent glassware similar to some of Tiffany's. Usually a rich lustrous gold or blue, green and red may also be found on rare occasion. It was used alone and in combination with calcite, a cream-colored glass with a calcium base also developed by Carder. Decorated examples are very rare. It is usually marked Aurene or Steuben, sometimes with the factory number added, etched into the glass by hand. Paper labels were also used. See also Steuben.

Ash tray, gold, sgn/#2725, 6" dia base 300.00
Basket, gold, sgn/#5069, 15" 1,200.00
Bowl, bl, petal base, sgn/#6058, 5½x11½" dia 800.00
Bowl, bl, spiral swirls, conical on ped ft, #6034, 12" 950.00
Bowl, bl, squatty, #2687, 6" 375.00
Bowl, gold, scalloped/flared, sgn/#1952, 8" H 550.00
Bowl, gold, sgn/#2775, 8" 800.00
Bowl, gold, 3-hdld, sgn/#2766, 9½" 750.00
Candlestick, bl, twist stem, sgn/#379, 10", pr 1,100.00
Candlestick, bl, twist stem, sgn/#686, 10", pr 925.00
Candlestick, gold, petal cups/bobeche, sgn/#6637, 5", pr 1,000.00
Candlestick, gold, twist stem, 10" 450.00
Compote, bl, sgn/#267, 6" 700.00
Cuspidor, gold, lady's, rare 500.00
Finger bowl & undertray, gold, gr vines/leaves, millefiori 1,150.00
Goblet, gold, twist stem, sgn/#2361 .... 400.00
Jar, bl, squat, sgn/#1458, 4¼" dia 650.00
Lemonade mug, gold, unsgn, 6½" 150.00

Plate, gold, unsgn, 6" 70.00
Salt cellar, gold, #2611 .... 175.00
Shade, gold, 2" fitting, 5½", pr 190.00
Toothpick holder, gold, pinched sides, 2¼" 300.00
Vase, bl, #2043, 6½" 425.00
Vase, bl, classic form, sgn/#2683, 11½" 1,100.00
Vase, bl, ftd, flared, silver Steuben label, 10" 725.00
Vase, bl, gold veining, fan form, sgn/#6297, 8½" 1,400.00
Vase, bl, gr leaves & veining, wht millefiori, sgn/#604, 3" 800.00
Vase, bl, ribbed, sgn/#1736, 5" 575.00
Vase, bl, ribbed, sgn/#7227, 5¾" 625.00
Vase, bl, 3 points pulled on rim, 3" 225.00
Vase, gold, classical form, sgn/#2647, mini, 2½" 350.00
Vase, gold, classical form, sgn/#2683, 6½" 500.00
Vase, gold, flared, ped ft, #312, 10" 550.00
Vase, gold, flat sided, triple-notch hdls, sgn/#8514, 13" 1,500.00
Vase, gold, lily form, sgn/#346, 6" 400.00
Vase, gold, ribbed, sgn/#568, 4½" 425.00
Vase, gold, ruffled, 5" 325.00
Vase, gold, slim trumpet form, sgn/#3844, 15" 700.00
Vase, gr, gold peacock feathers, sgn/#2196, 8½" 1,400.00
Vase, gr, silver veining, millefiori, sgn/#650, 4" 2,100.00
Vase, red, gold & wht feathers, scalloped trumpet form, 6" .. 3,900.00

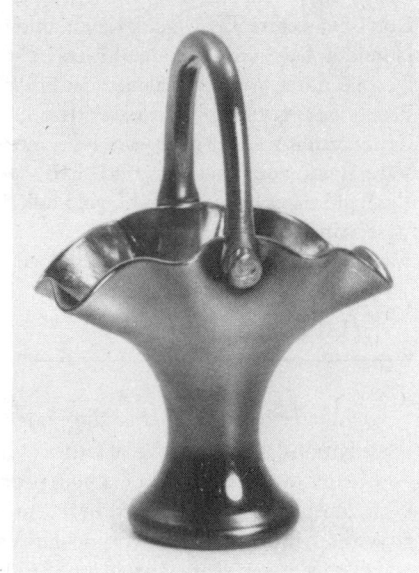

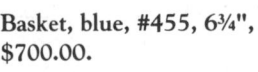
Basket, blue, #455, 6¾", $700.00.

Austrian Ware

From the late 1800s until the beginning of WWI, several companies were located in the area known at the turn of the century as Bohemia. They produced hard-paste porcelain dinnerware and decorative items primarily for the American trade. Today examples bearing the marks of these firms are usually referred to by collectors as Austrian ware, indicating simply the country of their origin. Of those various companies, these marks are best known: M.Z. Austria; Victoria, Carlsbad, Austria (Schmidt and Company); and O. & E.G. (Royal) Austria.

Though most of the decorations were transfer designs which were sometimes signed by the original artist, pieces marked Royal Austria were often hand painted and so indicated alongside the backstamp.

Of these three companies, Victoria, Carlsbad, Austria, is the most highly valued. Collectors should note that in our listings transfer decorations showing 'signatures' (sgn), such as 'Wagner,' 'Kauffmann,' 'LeBrun,' etc., were not actually painted by those artists but were merely based on their original paintings.

Bowl, Kaufmann scenes, 9½", $135.00.

Bowl, 3 maids/cupid, rose w/gold rim, Kauffmann, sq, 10" 120.00
Chocolate pot, apples on gr branches, pear shape, mk, 9" 75.00
Cup & saucer, teal gr w/gold, Kauffmann decor on ftd cup 50.00
Humidor, lady's head figural, flowers in hair 165.00
Pitcher, floral, gold rim, salamander hdl, mk, 13½" 255.00
Plate, ducks & flying birds, sq, Carlsbad, 7¾" 35.00
Urn, portrait transfer on cobalt, hdls, metal ft, 19½" 300.00
Vase, floral, lions' faces on tripod base, 7¾" 125.00
Vase, girl picks blossoms on bl, gold hdl, 8" 40.00
Vase, pansies, dbl hdls, 6½" 15.00
Vase, portrait on russet w/gold, scalloped, mk, 4¾x4¾" 30.00

Autographs

Philography is defined as the practice of collecting autographs or, literally translated, the 'love of writing.' It is estimated that two million Americans own autographs of famous people, and of these at least twenty thousand are serious collectors. In recent years, autograph collecting has grown both from a standpoint of popularity as well as investment. Examples which only fifteen years ago sold for $5 to $10 now command prices in the hundreds. For example, in 1970 a Clark Gable signature was valued at about $15; today it would bring approximately ten times that amount. Knowledgeable collectors watch the market for the opportunity of purchasing a rare item that within a few years can be turned over at a substantial gain. In one instance, a collector purchased a handwritten letter of James 'Wild Bill' Hickok for $2,500 — within five years he had turned down two different offers of $25,000 for the same letter.

The law of supply and demand is the foremost consideration in placing a value on an autograph. In most cases, age is not relevant. The greater the supply, the lower the value; when demand is great, the price goes up. Since the supply of signatures of persons no longer living is obviously stable, as more people become collectors, their values increase. Some celebrities are known to have signed their autographs thousands of times — others only a few, thus limiting their availablitiy. With fewer to go around, the cost to the collector would be higher.

The least desirable type of autograph is the simple signature signed on a card. The most desirable and valuable autograph is generally a handwritten letter signed in full. In between come signed photos, signed documents, signed typewritten letters, and various other types of autographs. In a letter, the content is important. Those conveying personal thoughts on or indicating involvement in issues relating to their participation in matters of public interest are more highly valued.

The beginning collector can add to his collection by corresponding with current celebrities. Most will respond to a letter when a self-addressed, stamped envelope is included. Because of their willingness to sign, the value of these autographs rarely exceed a few dollars. There are exceptions: Reagan's signature is worth around $50, Carter's about $40, Nixon's about $35, and Ford's around $25. Even more valuable — simply because they refuse to sign, or letters requesting signatures never reach them — are Greta Garbo, Idi Amin, Muhammar Khadafy, and the Ayatollah Khomeni, whose mere signature could easily bring $500 on today's autograph market. As a rule of thumb, signed glossy black and white photographs of recent movie stars sell in the range of $5.00 to $15.00.

Philography can be a fun and rewarding hobby — often all it takes to start is the address of someone you admire. In the listings below, photos are assumed black and white unless noted color.

Key:
    ADS — handwritten document signed
    ALS — handwritten letter signed
    ANS — handwritten note signed
    AQS — autograph quotation signed
    CS — counter signed
    DS — document signed
    ins — inscription
    ISP — inscribed signed photo
    LH — letterhead
    LS — signed letter, typed or written by someone else
    PLH — personal letterhead
    sig — signature
    SP — signed photo

Adams, John; ANS on bk of sheriff's notice, 1774 . . . . .600.00
Astaire, Fred; SP, glossy blk/wht, ca 1930, 8x10", NM 48.00
Bacall, Lauren; SP, color print, 8x10" 15.00
Bell, Alexander Graham; LS, sends requested sig, '04, 8x10" . .300.00
Bergen, Edgar; bold sig on check, 1967 .45.00
Berle, Milton; ISP, glossy blk/wht, early, 8x10" 10.00
Blanc, Mel; ISP, color, cartoonist w/characters, 8x10" 22.50
Bogart, Humphrey; bold sig on album pg w/photo, ca 1942 . . . .450.00
Bolger, Ray; SP, glossy blk/wht, as scarecrow, 8x10" 47.50
Braun, Wernher von; ISP, sits w/arms folded, 8x10" 245.00
Bronte, Charlotte; ALS, sending regrets, 1951, 1-pg 1,200.00
Buchanan, James; ALS as Sec of State, re correspondence 250.00
Burton, Richard; ISP, color, 1967, 8x10" 40.00
Carnegie, Andrew; sig on personal LH .38.00
Cather, Willa; sig on pg from book 24.00

Card signed and sold by Geronimo at the St. Louis Fair in 1904, $3,000.00.

Chevalier, Maurice; SP, 1920s 45.00
Clemens, Samuel; sgn personal calling card, SC/Mark Twain . .350.00
Clift, Montgomery; sig on album page w/photo, ca 1955 . . . . . .450.00
Clinton, De Witt; sig mtd on portrait, 1834, 10x6", EX 1,100.00
Cornwallis, Gen; LS, re health of Gen Patterson, 1780 . . . . .1,100.00
Crabbe, Buster; SP, glossy blk/wht, as Tarzan, 8x10" 28.00
Crawford, Joan; SP, w/ANS dtd 1954 .125.00

Criggs, Clare A; ALS, publication of cartoons, 1912 . . . . .42.50
Crosby, Bing; LS, LH, thanks for kind words, 1976 . . . . .32.00
Curtis, Tony; SP, matt blk/wht, ca 1955, 8x10" 17.50
Dahl, Arlene; ins & sig on sketch of lips, 5x3" 17.50
Dali, Salvador; sgn print, dbl matt, 10x8", M 175.00
Dalton, Emmett; sgn card, Compliments of..., 1923, 3x4" 550.00
Davis, Jefferson; DS as Sec of War, 1-pg, 8x10" 445.00
De Havilland, Olivia; SP, seated w/2 Oscars, 8x10" 27.50
Einstein, Albert; LS, German text, 1944, 1-pg 1,600.00
Eisenhower, Mamie D; LS White House LH, thank you, 1953 . .60.00
Fillmore, Millard; ALS, simple note to law partner, 1840 . . . . .600.00
Freemont, John Charles; ALS, re invitation, 1888, 2-pg 425.00
Gabor, Zsa Zsa; SP, glossy blk/wht, ca 1955, 8x10" 27.50
Geer, Will; sig on card, EX 17.50
Gibson, Charles Dana; sig on card, 3x5" 18.00
Goodman, Benny; SP, glossy blk/wht, 8x10" 65.00
Grant, Cary; sig on album page w/photo, ca 1940 . . . . .100.00
Grant, Ulysses S; sig on card, VG .145.00
Greeley, Horace; sig on note, busy/weary/etc, 1861, 5½x5" 70.00
Harding, Florence; sgn bank check, 1914 . . . . .45.00
Harding, Warren; handwritten speech on brn paper, 9-pg 750.00
Harrison, Benjamin; LS, re tobacco notes/destruction, 1783 . . .250.00
Harrison, Wm Henry; ADS, re issue of food to Indians, 1795 . .420.00
Hayes, RB; ADS as Gov of OH, re 15th Ammendment, 1870 .900.00
Hoover, Herbert; bold sig in book, 1st edition, 1922 . . . . .245.00
Hoover, Herbert; sig on plain card, EX 45.00
Hoover, J Edgar; LS, thanks for book, 1940, 8x10" 25.00
Hunter, Tab; ISP, glossy blk/wht, ca 1955, 8x10" 24.00
Irving, Washington; ALS, agrees to dine, 1718, 1-pg 95.00
Jackson, Andrew; DS, as president, 1-pg, EX 950.00
Johnson, Lyndon B; bold sig on bookplate w/presidential seal . .200.00
Johnson, Lyndon B; ISP, glossy blk/wht, ca 1940, 8x10" 425.00
Kaplan, Louis 'Kid'; sig on note, EX 18.00
Kelly, Emmett; sig on wht card, 3x5" 35.00
Kipling, Rudyard; sig clipped from letter 60.00
Kissinger, Henry; SP, glossy blk/wht, 8x10" 20.00
Knox, Henry; LS as Sec of War, re cavalry/rations, 1786 . . . . .300.00
Lafayette, Marquis de; sig on note, in French, EX 225.00
Landon, Alf M; ISP, color print, 1936, 10x13" 28.00
Longworth, Alice Roosevelt; ISP, wedding picture, 1906 . . . . . .30.00
Luther, Martin; DS, receipt for services, dtd 1784, EX 10,000.00
Mac Arthur, Douglas; SP, glossy blk/wht, 1943, 4½x6½" 400.00
Madison, James; ALS to Lafayette, re requested loan, 3-pg . .4,800.00
Mann, Thomas; sig on sm sheet of paper, mtd w/picture 32.00
Mead, Margaret; SP, blk/wht portrait, ca 1940, 8x10" 100.00
Mitchell, William D; LS as Attorney General, 1930, 2-pg 22.00
Montgomery, Robert; bold early sig on stationery 12.50
Nehru, Jawaharlai; SP, bold sig, 3½x5½" 88.00
O'Sullivan, Maureen; ISP, glossy blk/wht, bold sig, 8x10" 17.50
Palmer, Arnold; SP, color print, 8x10" 10.00
Peel, Sir Robert; ANS, setting appointment, 1832, ½-pg 24.00
Perminger, Otto; SP, glossy blk/wht, 8x10" 17.50
Pershing, John J; sig on card, EX .25.00
Pershing, John J; sig on WWI poster, ca 1917, 11½x15" 100.00
Pickford, Mary; SP, sepia tone, EX 125.00
Polk, James K; DS as Pres, endorses pardon, 1848 . . . . .450.00
Powell, Eleanor; ISP, glossy blk/wht, 8x10" 20.00
Powell, William; ALS, expressing sympathy, M 145.00
Presley, Elvis; sig on sm card, sealed, M 265.00
Reagan, Nancy; sig in her book, 1982, rare 75.00
Richelieu, Duc de; DS, bestows pension, 1916, 2-pg 30.00
Rickenbacker, Capt Eddie; ISP, 1967, 10x8", EX 95.00
Riley, James Whitcomb; ALS, literary topics, 1897, 1-pg 165.00
Robinson, Sugar Ray; SP, 8x10" 22.50

Rockefeller, John D Jr; LS, father's health, 1921 . . . . .85.00
Russell, Rosalind; SP, in fr w/sgn cancelled check, 1946 . . . . .115.00
Sherman, William T; full sig on album pg, 1876, 6½x8" 55.00
Sills, Beverly; SP, glossy blk/wht, 8x10" 22.00
Skelton, Red; sig on card, 3x5" 15.00
Snow, Hank; ISP, glossy blk/wht, 8x10" 17.50
Steinbeck, John; bold sig on card, 2½x4½" 180.00
Stephens, Alexander; ANS, House of Representatives LH, 1875..95.00
Stern, Isaac; SP, in concert, 8x10" .22.00
Stevenson, Adlai; LS, time for understanding, 1964, 1-pg 25.00
Sullivan, Ed; DS, re Eastman Kodak using name, 1959, 4-pg . . .95.00
Taft, William Howard; ALS, LH, re autograph, 1929, 1-pg 600.00
Taylor, Zachary, DS, as commander, requisition, 1834, EX 600.00
Temple, Shirley; ISP, glossy blk/wht, ca 1930s, 8x10" 27.50
Thomas, Lowell; LS, Winchell/Pearson problem, 1948 . . . . . . .22.00
Truman, Bess; SP, 1st Lady in garden, color, no date 80.00
Truman, Harry S; clipped sig from letter, bold style 90.00
Verdi, Giuseppe; ALS, warm greetings, French, 1894, 2-pg . .2,000.00
Warren, Earl; eng portrait w/sig, full face, 8x6", EX 50.00
Washington, Geo; DS, partly-printed 3-language sea letter . .4,800.00
Webster, Daniel; sig in booklet, 1850, 10-pg, EX 150.00
Wellington, Duke of; bold sig on book cover 25.00
Westmoreland, Wm C; SP, gr fatigues, 1966 . . . . .15.00
Whittier, John Greenleaf; sig w/portrait, dtd 1883 . . . . .25.00
Wilson, Woodrow; ALS, declines to speak, 1898, 2-pg 350.00
Wyman, Jane; SP, blk/wht, blonde hair, ca 1940s, 8x10" 37.50
Young, Brigham; sig on card, 2x3½" 245.00
Younger, Cole; sgn bank ck, 1904, EX 1,400.00

Automobilia

While some automobilia buffs are primarily concerned with restoring vintage cars, others concentrate on only one area of collecting. For instance, hood ornaments were often quite spectacular. Made of chrome or nickel plate on brass or bronze, they were designed to represent the 'winged maiden' Victory, flying bats, sleek greyhounds, soaring eagles, and a host of other creatures. Today they bring prices in the $75 to $200 range. R. Lalique glass ornaments go much higher!

Horns, radios, clocks, gear shift knobs, and key chains with company emblems are other areas of interest. Generally, items pertaining to the classics of the thirties are most in demand. Paper advertising material, manuals, and catalogs in excellent condition are also collectible.

License plate collectors search for early porcelain-on-cast-iron examples. First year plates — e.g., Massachusetts, 1903; Wisconsin, 1905; Indiana, 1913 — are especially valuable. The last of the states to issue regulation plates were South Carolina and Texas in 1917, and Florida in 1918. While many northeastern states had registered hundreds of thousands of vehicles by the 1920s making these plates relatively common, those from the southern and western states of that period are considered rare. Naturally, condition is important. While a pair in mint condition might sell for as much as $100 to $125, a pair with chipped or otherwise damaged porcelain may sometimes be had for as little as $25 to $30. See also Gas Globes and Panels.

Accelerator footrest, Stanwood, adjustable, orig box 15.00
Almanac, farm; Ford, 1936, 48-pg .12.00
Ash tray, Chevrolet, Silver Anniversary 1954-1979, logo 15.00
Ash tray, Graham Motor Cars, 3 helmeted men in center 40.00
Badge, employee; REO, diamond shape, lg logo 20.00
Badge, hat; Greyhound, Leave the Driving to Us, brass 40.00
Book, mechanic's, Audel's Automobile, 1949, lg, EX 10.00
Book, Model T Ford Price List of Parts, 1924, EX 25.00
Booklet, Buick, Marquette, 28-pg 20.00

Booklet, New Pontiac Big Six, 1930, 6x9", $38.00.

Booklet, General Motors 50 Million Cars, 1955, 40-pg 15.00
Burglar alarm, Devil Dog, automatic, ca 1950, orig box 50.00
Buyer's guide, General Motors, 1934, 80-pg 12.00
Calendar, Chrysler, brass, mc logo, 1962 ....20.00
Car bootjack, CI, Auto Theft Signal System, w/keys, 1914 .....85.00
Cigarette lighter, Goodyear Tires, cobalt bottle form, NM 35.00
Cigarette lighter, Victory, pull cord, electric, orig box 90.00
Coil box w/coils, K-W, 2-cylinder, wooden w/brass nameplate .130.00
Coin, General Motors Motorama, brass, oval, 1955 ....8.00
Emergency fuse kit, Ford w/script, holds 5 fuses 20.00
Gas tank straps, Ford, 1926-27, set of 2 ....25.00
Gauge, gasoline; Atwater Kent, 1909 ....15.00
Gauge, oil sight; Ford, brass 25.00
Gearshift knob, dice, simulated wht marble/red dots 30.00
Gearshift knob, photo, tan plastic, 1⅛" dia 12.00
Gearshift knob, wht w/brn center band, 2" dia 50.00
Grease gun, Model A Ford 15.00
Head lamps, Model T Ford, pr 50.00
Hood emblem, Graham, 3 helmeted heads, brass/chrome, pr 40.00
Hood ornament, Dodge Ram, 1937-38 ....45.00
Hood ornament, Old Dock Yak figure, wht metal/mc pnt, 5½" .500.00
Horn, brass, Model T Ford, EX 50.00
Horn, crank, 'ooga' type, brass bell, 1914 ....120.00
Ice scraper, Chevrolet bow tie, plastic 7.00
Ignition key, Ford script, A-841, 1928 ....10.00
Ignition/headlight switch, Buick, brass face, w/key, 3¾" dia ...35.00
Key chain medallion, Golden Anniversary 1903-1953, brass 20.00
Key chain/identification tag, Buick, script/logo, 1920s 30.00
Key chain/identification tag, Buick/Cadillac, brass, script 15.00
Key chain/identification tag, wht Chevrolet bow tie 25.00
Key chain/registration holder, Pontiac-Buick, tan/blk, 3" L 12.00
Key chain/tape measure, Ford, blk/wht script 10.00
Key rack, Model T Ford, EX 200.00
Letter opener, Cadillac, brass w/enameled logo, 9" L 100.00
License plate, MI, porc, 1914, EX 50.00
License plate add-on, Chevrolet bow tie, blk/wht metal 20.00
Lock, Ford, thief-proof, nickel plated, orig box 50.00
Luggage rack, Model T Ford, CI, EX 30.00
Manual, Ford, 1914 ....20.00
Matchbook, Plymouth, 1940 ....5.00
Medallion, Ford Chicago Expo, brass w/script, 1933 ....25.00
Medallion, nameplate; Hayes Body Corp, brass 35.00
Mirror, rear-view; ornate, 1921 ....40.00
Motometer, Hudson Super Six, wreath type 42.00

Motometer, Studebaker w/script, 3½" dia 70.00
Paperweight, C&D battery, lead battery figural, 1⅝" L 25.00
Paperweight, Firestone Supreme, emb rubber battery, 3½" L 37.50
Paperweight, Nash, logo on red insert, nickel-plated brass 100.00
Paperweight, Schrader Balloon Tires, figural gauge, pat '16 .....22.00
Paperweight, 1963 Henry Ford Centennial, Ford script, brass ...15.00
Pencil clip, Hupmobile, wht H in bl circle 25.00
Pennant, Buick w/script, yel felt, 6" L 10.00
Pin, employee; Studebaker, 5-yr 25.00
Pin, lapel; Chrysler, 10k gold w/diamond chip 35.00
Pin, trophy; Glidden, brass trophy shape, rare 50.00
Plate, dinner; stoneware, Buick, script/logo 48.00
Pliers, Ford w/script 10.00
Poster, Buick, Model 81 Limited Touring Sedan 45.00
Promotional car, Dodge Monaco, MIB 35.00
Promotional car, Ford Fairlane 500 Sports Coupe, 1964 ....50.00
Promotional car, Ford Galaxie 500, 1962 ....55.00
Radiator cap, Chevrolet Eagle, 1933 ....50.00
Radiator cap, Model T Ford, nickel-plated brass 45.00
Radiator cap ornament, Pierce-Arrow, brass, 1924-26 ....200.00
Radiator emblem, Chevrolet bow tie, bl/wht enamel 15.00
Radiator emblem, Essex, Super Six USA, hexagonal, EX 50.00
Radiator emblem, Nash, enameled, ca 1929 ....40.00
Record, promotional; Chevrolet, 1964, orig envelope 10.00
Screwdriver, advertising, REO-Dodge, metal hdl 25.00
Side light, Model T Ford, EX 45.00
Spark plugs, Champion X, Model T Ford, porc, set of 4 ....55.00
Spark plugs, Ford, Champion 3-X, set of 8, used 70.00
Spark plugs, Model T Ford, PAF non-foul, set of 4 ....30.00
Speedometer, Dodge, 0-60, #168444, beveled glass 70.00
Steering wheel knob, Bakelite, w/thermometer, EX 20.00
Stock certificate, Ford, 6 shares 25.00
Tin, Firestone Tube Repair, contents inside, EX 10.00
Tire breaker, CI, 1920s, rare 35.00
Tire gauge, Buick, Schrader, script/logo 50.00
Tire gauge, Model A Ford, brass nameplate, NM 130.00
Tool kit, Chevrolet, key form, brass w/logo 60.00
Trunk emblem, Plymouth, ship logo, chrome plated 35.00
Windshield scraper, Pontiac, plastic, 1957 ....35.00

Autumn Leaf

In 1933 the Hall China Company designed a line of dinnerware for the Jewel Tea Company, who offered it to their customers as premiums. Although you may hear the ware referred to as 'Jewel Tea,' it was officially named 'Autumn Leaf' in the 1940s. In addition to the dinnerware, frosted Libbey glass tumblers, stemware, and a melmac service with the orange and gold bittersweet pod were available over the years, as were tablecloths, plastic covers for bowls and mixers, and metal items such as cake safes, hot pads, coasters, wastebaskets, and canisters. Even shelf paper and playing cards were made to coordinate. In 1958 the International Silver Company designed silverplated flatware in a pattern called 'Autumn' which was to be used with dishes in the Autumn Leaf pattern. A year later, a line of stainless flatware was introduced. These accessory lines are prized by collectors today.

One of the most fascinating aspects of collecting the Autumn Leaf pattern has been the wonderful discoveries of previously unlisted pieces. Among these items are two different bud-ray lid one-pound butter dishes; most recently a one-pound butter dish in the 'Zepher' or 'Bingo' style; a miniature set of the 'Casper' salt and pepper shakers; coffee, tea, and sugar canisters; a pair of candlesticks; an experimental condiment jar; and a covered candy dish. All of these china pieces are attributed to the Hall China Company. Other unusual items have turned up in the accessory lines, as well, and include a Libbey frosted tumbler in a pilsner shape, a wooden serving bowl, and an apron made from the oilcloth (plastic) material that was used in the 1950s tablecloth. These latter items appear to be professionally done, and we can only speculate as to their origin. Collectors believe that the Hall items were sample pieces that were never meant to be distributed.

Hall discontinued the Autumn Leaf line in 1978. At that time the date was added to the backstamp to mark ware still in stock in the Jewel warehouse. A special promotion by Jewel saw the reintroduction of basic dinnerware and serving pieces with the 1978 backstamp. These pieces have made their way into many collections. Additionally, in 1979 Jewel released a line of enamel-clad cookware and a Vellux blanket made by Martex which were decorated with the Autumn Leaf pattern. They continued to offer these items for a few years only, then all distribution of Autumn Leaf items was discontinued.

It should be noted that the Hall China Company has produced three limited edition items for the National Autumn Leaf Collectors Club (NALCC): a New York-style teapot (1984), a vase (1987 — different than the original shape), and candlesticks (1988). All of these are plainly marked as having been made for the NALCC and are appropriately dated.

Baker, oval, Fort Pitt 70.00
Batter bowl, Saf-Hdl 1,200.00
Bean pot, 1-hdl 250.00
Bean pot, 2-hdl, 2¼-qt 85.00
Bowl, cereal; 6" 8.00
Bowl, coupe soup 10.00
Bowl, cream soup; 2-hdl 18.00
Bowl, fruit; 5½" 3.00
Bowl, metal, enamelware, set of 3 .... 75.00
Bowl, mixing; set of 3: 6¼", 7½", 9" 35.00
Bowl, Royal Glas-Bake, set of 4 .... 45.00
Bowl, salad 14.00
Bowl, stackette; set of 3: 18-oz, 24-oz, 34-oz, w/lid ..60.00
Bowl, vegetable; divided, 10½" 55.00
Bowl, vegetable; oval, w/lid, 10" 35.00
Bowl, vegetable; oval, 10½" 12.00
Bowl, vegetable; rnd, 9" 60.00
Bowl cover set, plastic, 8-pc: 7 assorted covers in pouch 50.00
Bread box, metal 125.00
Butter dish, 1-lb 165.00
Butter dish, ¼-lb 125.00
Butter dish, ¼-lb, Square Top 400.00
Butter dish, ¼-lb, Wings 400.00
Cake plate, 9½" 10.00
Cake safe, metal, motif on top & sides, 5" 25.00
Cake safe, metal, side decor only, 4½x10½" 22.00
Cake stand, metal base, orig box 125.00
Candy dish 300.00
Canister, metal, rnd, w/coppertone lid, set of 4 .... 125.00
Canister, metal, rnd, w/ivory plastic lid 10.00
Canister, metal, rnd, w/matching lid, 6" 15.00
Canister, metal, rnd, w/matching lid, 7" 25.00
Canister, metal, rnd, w/matching lid, 8¼" 35.00
Canister, metal, sq, set of 4: 8½" & 4½" 115.00
Casserole, Royal Glas-Bake, deep, w/clear glass lid ...25.00
Casserole, Royal Glas-Bake, shallow, w/clear glass lid 20.00
Casserole, Tootsie-Hdl, w/lid 18.00
Casserole/souffle, swirl, 3-pt 12.00
Casserole/souffle, 10-oz 8.00
Casserole/souffle, 2-pt 55.00
Cleanser can, metal, sq, 6" 250.00
Clock, orig works 350.00
Coaster, metal, 3⅛" 4.00

Coffee dispenser/canister, metal, wall type, 10½x19" dia 125.00
Coffee maker, 5-cup, all china, w/china insert 175.00
Coffee maker, 9-cup, w/metal dripper, 8" 35.00
Coffee percolator, electric, all china 225.00
Coffee percolator/carafe, Douglas, w/warmer base, MIB 200.00
Cookie jar, Tootsie 95.00
Creamer, New Style 8.00
Creamer, Old Style, 4¼" 15.00
Cup & saucer 8.00
Cup & saucer, St Denis 18.00
Custard cup 4.00
Flatware, silverplate, ea 15.00
Flatware, stainless, ea 10.00
Fruit cake tin, metal 10.00
Golden Ray base, to be used w/candy dish or cake plate, pr 50.00
Granulator, metal, no decal 35.00
Gravy boat 15.00
Hot pad, metal, red or gr felt-like backing, rnd 12.00
Hot pad, oval 10.00
Hurricane lamp, Douglas, w/metal base, pr 400.00

Irish coffee mug, $85.00.

Kitchen utility chair, metal 450.00
Marmalade jar, 3-pc 45.00
Mixer cover, Mary Dunbar, plastic 25.00
Mug, beverage 45.00
Mug, Irish coffee 85.00
Mustard jar, 3½" 45.00
Napkin, ecru muslin 20.00
Pickle dish, oval, 9" 16.00
Picnic thermos, metal 250.00
Pie baker, 9½" 18.00
Pitcher, beverage jug; 5½-pt 18.00
Pitcher, utility; 2½-pt, 6" 12.00
Place mat, paper, scalloped 22.00
Place mat, set of 8, in orig package 195.00
Plate, 10" 10.00
Plate, 6" or 7", ea 4.00
Plate, 8" 8.00
Plate, 9" 7.00
Platter, 11½" 14.00
Platter, 13½" 16.00
Playing cards, regular or Pinochle 110.00

Range set, shakers & covered drippings jar 32.00
Sauce dish, serving; Douglas, Bakelite hdl 125.00
Shakers, Casper, pr 16.00
Shakers, range, hdl, pr 16.00
Sugar bowl, New Style 12.00
Sugar bowl, Old Style, 3½" 18.00
Tablecloth, cotton sailcloth w/gold stripe, 54x54" 60.00
Tablecloth, cotton sailcloth w/gold stripe, 54x72" 70.00
Tablecloth, ecru muslin, 56x81" 150.00
Tablecloth, plastic 125.00
Teakettle, metal enamelware 75.00
Teapot, Aladdin 38.00
Teapot, long spout, 7" 45.00
Teapot, Newport 115.00
Teapot, Newport, dtd 1978 . . . . .90.00
Toaster cover, plastic, fits 2-slice toaster 25.00
Towel, dish; pattern & clock motif 45.00
Towel, tea; cotton, 16x33" 35.00
Trash can, metal, red 65.00
Tray, glass, wood hdl, 19½x11¼" 85.00
Tray, metal, oval 55.00
Tray, red w/allover red & yel design, red border 65.00
Tray, tidbit; 2-tier 35.00
Tray, tidbit; 3-tier 45.00
Tumbler, Brockway, 13-oz 15.00
Tumbler, Brockway, 16-oz 18.00
Tumbler, Brockway, 9-oz 14.00
Tumbler, frosted, 14-oz, 5½" 11.00
Tumbler, frosted, 9-oz, 3¾" 18.00
Tumbler, gold frost etched, flat, 10-oz 30.00
Tumbler, gold frost etched, flat, 15-oz 45.00
Tumbler, gold frost etched, ftd, 10-oz 45.00
Tumbler, gold frost etched, ftd, 6½-oz 45.00
Vase, bud; 6" 150.00
Warmer base, oval 100.00
Warmer base, rnd 90.00
Warmer base, rnd, w/4 orig candles, orig mk box 110.00

Aviation

Aviation buffs are interested in any phase of flying — from early developments with gliders, balloons, airships and flying machines to more modern innovations. Books, catalogs, photos, patents, lithographs, ad cards, and posters are among the paper ephemera they treasure alongside models of unlikely flying contraptions, propellers and rudders, insignia and equipment from WWI and WWII, and memorabilia from the flights of the Wright Brothers, Lindbergh, Earhart, and the Zeppelins. See also Militaria.

Book, Historic Airships, Rupert Holland, Phila, 1928 . . . . .25.00
Book, The Zeppelins, 15 plates, Ernst Lehmann, NY, 1927, EX .40.00
Pin, Air Canada pilot, maple leaf, red-enameled metal, older . . .30.00
Pin, lapel; ALPA, gilt wing 10.00
Pin, lapel; Chinese Airlines, red/bl enamel 15.00
Pin, lapel; TWA silver 4-engine plane 12.00
Pin, tie; ANSETT (Australian), orange enamel w/gilt 12.00
Shot glass, bl, 4th Year of Progress, 1952 . . . . .35.00
Shot glass, gold, 10th Anniversary, ca 1949-1959 . . . . .30.00
Shot glass, yel/wht, Fly the Southern Aristocrat, 1962 . . . . .20.00
Timetable, Hindenburg, French, 3-fold, 3⅞x8⅜" 25.00
Wing, British Airways pilot, gold-washed metal 22.00
Wing, co-pilot, Air Atlanta, star-form, gold 35.00
Wing, Deputy Sheriff Fresno County Aero Squadron, metal 15.00
Wing, Federal Express pilot, metal 35.00

Wing, flight attendant, Presidential, gold w/bl enamel 25.00
Wing, hat badge; Air Atlanta, gold 50.00
Wing, hat badge; flight attendant, Delta, gold w/red enamel 75.00
Wing, hat badge; Hughes Air West, metal 35.00
Wing, hat badge; pilot's, Southern Airline, gold w/bl enamel . .100.00
Wing, hat badge; pilot's, Southern Airline, silver 75.00
Wing, JAL (Japan), cloth & silver wire, child's 3.00
Wing, Midway captain pilot, gold-washed metal 22.00
Wing, Northwest Airlines junior pilot, plastic 2.50
Wing, Tube Investments pilot, gold wire 8.00

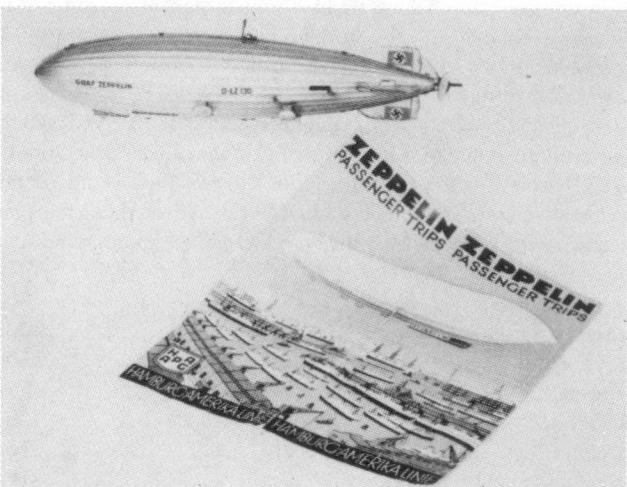

Graf Zeppelin, Tippco tinplate keywind 4-engine model in box, 11", $2,000.00; Hamburg-Amerika Line Zeppelin travel pamphlet, $100.00.

Avon

The California Perfume Company, the parent of the Avon Co., was founded in 1886. Although an 'Avon' line was introduced by the company in the mid-twenties, not until 1939 did it become known as Avon Products, Inc. Collectible Avon items include not only figural bottles and jars, but jewelry, awards, product samples, magazine ads, and catalogs as well. For more information concerning the Avon Collectors Club, see the Clubs, Newsletters, and Catalogs section of the Directory. See also California Perfume Company.

In the listings that follow, unless noted MIB, prices are for bottles only.

ABC Soap, 1915, 6 bars in floral box, MIB 100.00
Abigail Adams Plate, porcelain w/wooden stand, 1985, 9" 18.00
American Heirloom Porcelain Bowl, 1983-84, floral design, M . .15.00
Ariel Bath Salts, 1933-37, ribbed glass w/bl cap, 8½-oz 45.00
Baked w/Love Plate, porcelain, 1982-83, 9" 25.00
Bear Cookie Jar, ceramic, 1985, brn, M 20.00
Charmer Set, lipstick/mascara/rouge in satin-lined box, MIB . . .80.00
Clancy Clown Soap Holder, 1973-74 . . . . .5.00
Coconut Oil Shampoo, 1951-55, 6-oz .20.00
Collector's Stein Decanter, 1976-79, 8-oz 32.00
Country Christmas Plate, ceramic, 1980-82, 9" 20.00
Country Club Set, 1946-49, men's shaving cream/lotion/talc . . .95.00
Country Kitchen Trivet, ceramic, 1980-82, 7½" 12.00
Country Village Canister Set, 1985, Pfaltzgraff, M 42.00
Dew Kiss Decanter, 1974-75, glass jar/pk lid, 4-oz, MIB 4.00
Fashion Twins, 1965, 2 cameo lipsticks, mc box, MIB 15.00
For Beautiful Hands, 1956, floral box, 2 tubes, 2¾-oz, M 15.00
Forward Pass, 1958, brn football soap on a rope, 7½-oz 50.00

Garden Fresh Decanter, 1979-80, 10-oz, MIB 7.00
Going Steady Set, 1960, gray bag/lipstick/compact 20.00
Goldilocks Soap, yel, 5-oz, MIB 20.00
Imari Gift Set, 1986, cologne purse spray, red/gold earrings 15.00
Kitten Creamer, 1986, wht ceramic, 5¼" .5.00
Lady Bug Perfume, 1975-76, frosted glass/gold cap, ⅛-oz 25.00
Lilac Soap, Europe 1972, bl box w/bl ribbon, MIB 15.00
Mickey Mouse, 1969-71, holds bubble bath, 4½-oz, M 8.00
Perfection, 1941-48, Kwick metal polish, mc container 40.00
Persian Pitcher, 1974-76, holds bath oil, 6-oz, M 5.00
Pierre Decanter, 1984, wht glass pig, 8-oz, MIB 8.50
Pretty Notions, 1965, pk compact/cameo lipstick, set 6.00
Skin-So-Soft Decanter, 1966, 10-oz, MIB 10.00
Stage Coach Set, 1958, men's hair trainer/foamy bath, 2-oz 50.00
Summer Fun Figurine, porcelain, 1986, M 25.00
Tapestry Collection Picture Frame, porcelain, 1981, wht 15.00
Touch of Paris, 1958, lipstick/compact, MIB 20.00
Vita Moist Cream, 1959-61, yel glass jar .5.00
Watering Can, 1962-64, holds bubble bath, 8-oz, MIB 20.00
Whipped Cream Soap, 1968, box contains 4 mc soaps, MIB 12.00
Wright Brothers Mug, 1985, HP porcelain, 3", MIB 15.00
1936 MG Decanter, 1974-75, red, 5-oz, M 5.00

Baccarat

The Baccarat Glass company was founded in 1765 near Luneville, France, and continues to this day to produce quality crystal tableware, vases, perfume bottles, and figurines. The firm became famous for the high-quality millefiori and caned paperweights produced there from 1845 until about 1860. Examples of these range from $300 to as much as several thousand. Since 1953 they have resumed the production of paperweights on a limited edition basis. See also Paperweights.

Bottle, liqueur; lime gr w/floral, 3-petal top, label, 10" 125.00
Bottle, scent; Rose Tiente Swirl, 4¼x1½" 55.00
Bottle, scent; Rose Tiente Swirl, 5⅞x2⅜" 65.00
Bottle, scent; Rose Tiente Swirl, 7½x2⅞" 80.00
Bowl, Rose Tiente Swirl, 2x5" 45.00
Box, Rose Tiente Swirl, hinged lobed top, ball ft 140.00
Candlestick, Rose Tiente Swirl, ball form, mk, 1¼x1¾", pr 95.00
Candlestick, Swirl, mk, 6¼", pr 175.00
Decanter, St Remy, stencil sgn, 12", pr 325.00
Fairy lamp, Rose Tiente Sunburst, mk, 4x5¼" 235.00
Figurine, jumping horse, mk, 9" 175.00
Jar, powder; Rose Tiente Swirl, 4¼x3½" dia 95.00
Oil lamp base, Swirl, tall std, sq base, 1900, 22" 800.00
Paperweight, iceberg form, 2½" 75.00
Pitcher, St Remy, stencil sgn, 9½" 225.00
Sauce, Rose Tiente Swirl, ftd, 1½x3" 50.00
Tumbler, Rose Tiente Swirl, mk, 4½" .55.00
Vase, cut crystal, tapered octagon, mk, 8" 500.00
Vase, opal w/cvd entwined lav snake, mc beetle at top, 8" . . .1,400.00
Wine, Venice, mk, 5½", set of 12 . . . . .300.00

Badges

The breast badge came into general usage in this country about 1840. Since most are not marked and styles have changed very little to the present day, they are often difficult to date. The most reliable clue is the pin and catch. One of the earliest types, used primarily before the turn of the century, involved a 't-pin' and a 'shell' catch. In a second style, the pin was

hinged with a small square of sheet metal, and the clasp was cylindrical. From the late 1800s until about 1940, the pin and clasp were made from one continuous piece of thin metal wire. The same type, with the addition of a flat back plate, was used a little later. There are exceptions to these findings, and other types of clasps were also used. Hallmarks and inscriptions may also help pinpoint an approximate age.

Badges have been made from a variety of materials, usually brass or nickel silver; but even solid silver and gold were used for special orders. They are found in many basic shapes and variations — stars with five to seven points, shields, disks, ovals, and octagonals being most often encountered. Of prime importance to collectors, however, is that the title and/or location appear on the badge. Those with designations of positions no longer existing (City Constable, for example) and names of early western states and towns are most valuable.

Badges are among the most commonly-reproduced (and faked) types of antiques on the market. At any flea market, ten fakes can be found for every authentic example. Genuine law badges start at $30.00 to $40.00 for recent examples (1950-1970); earlier pieces (1910-1930) usually bring $50.00 to $90.00. Pre-1900 badges often sell for more than $100.00. Authentic gold badges are usually priced at a minimum of scrap value (carat, weight, spot price for gold); fine gold badges from before 1900 can sell for $400.00 to $800.00, and a few will bring even more. A fire badge is usually valued at about half the price of a law badge from the same circa and material.

Key: pt —— point

Building Inspector, Newburgh, silver color, 2¾", EX 30.00
Chief Deputy, Montgomery County TX, 5-pt ball-tipped star . . .40.00
Chief Police, Bellmead TX, state seal, silver w/eagle atop 30.00
Deputy Sheriff, CA, silver color w/blk enamel, 6-pt star 50.00
Deputy Sheriff, Tehama County, nickel star, 2½" 35.00
Deputy Sheriff, Tooele County UT, silver-color circle star 55.00

**Engineer, N.Y.F.D., silver, 3",
$250.00.**

Highway Patrolman, Arizona state seal, gold color, 7-pt star 45.00
Naval Police, Seabees emblem, 1940s 80.00
Penal Institution Commissioner, gold plate w/enamel, 1930s . .100.00
Police, Bibb County GA, gold color/blk enamel, eagle atop 35.00
Police, NC state seal, silver color/bl enamel, eagle atop 20.00
Police, Seattle, gold color, shield/cut-out star 25.00
Police, US Coast Guard, silver color, eagle/shield 30.00
Police Commissioner, gilded brass, state seal, wing top 15.00
Police Patrolman, Chicago, silver color, 5-pt star 75.00
Police Sergeant, Pecos TX, state seal, eagle atop 44.00
Railway Police, copper color, tiger in center, 5-pt star 29.00
Safety Officer, Temple Univ, silver w/blk enamel, eagle atop . . .30.00
Security Patrolman, TX, state seal, gold color w/bl enamel 18.00
Sheriff, Bowie County, gold color/blk enamel, 5-pt star 30.00
Sheriff's Assoc, TX, gold color w/red & bl enamel, 5-pt star 30.00

Special Police, Salt Lake City, silver color, rpl pin **64.00**
Special Police, Worchester, silver color w/blk enamel **40.00**

Banks

Collectors of mechanical and still banks have seen considerable change in the pricing picture in the past few years. An increasing number of banks are appearing in general auctions, and some auctions are now devoted entirely to banks and toys. Often the prices realized at auction varies greatly from advertised prices. This can sometimes be attributed to 'auction fever,' but it may also represent buyers with specific knowledge concerning the banks they are bidding on. Condition has become an important price-determining factor. A pristine bank will frequently sell for two to four times the price realized by the same bank in only 'good' condition. Always look for examples in the best-possible condition. They will cost more, but they will be the best investment for you. Banks should always be complete with all parts present, original, and in good working condition (if it is a mechanical). Replaced parts or retouched paint lessen a bank's value. Rarity is also an important factor in pricing banks — almost as important as condition.

Still banks are found in almost every shape and size; all types of material have been used in their making. Exactly how many styles were made is unknown; but about three thousand have been identified, and there are thousands more that are unlisted in any book. Cast iron examples are the most popular, but there is an increasing interest in the early tin and pottery banks made in the United States.

The category of mechanical banks is unique. Along with cast iron bell toys, they are among the most outstanding products of the Industrial Revolution and are recognized as some of the most successful of the mass-produced products of the nineteenth century. The earliest mechanicals were made of wood or lead; but when John Hall introduced Hall's Excelsior, a cast iron mechanical bank, it was an immediate success. J. and E. Stevens produced the bank for Hall and soon began to make their own designs. Several companies followed suit, most of which were already in the hardware business. They used newly-developed iron-molding techniques to produce these novelty savings devices for the emerging toy market. Mechanical banks reflect the social and political attitudes of the times, racial prejudices, the excitement of the circus, and humorous everyday events. Their designers made the most of simple mechanics to produce banks with captivating actions that served not only to amuse but to promote the concept of thrift to the children. The quality of detail in the castings are truly fine examples of industrial art. The most collectible examples were made during the period of 1870 to 1900; however, they continued to be made until the early days of World War II. J. and E. Stevens, Sheppard Hardware, and Kyser and Rex are some of the more well-known manufacturers — most made still banks as well.

While the cast iron banks dominate the market, there are examples made from many other materials. Combinations of tin and cardboard and banks made from tin alone are very collectible. Some of the European tin banks are quite rare; England made some fine cast iron mechanicals and many aluminum examples. The popularity of old mechanicals has created a market for reproductions and fakes. Reproductions may have minor value as such, but not as true collectibles. A few of the fakes have attained collectible status but are still not regarded as true mechanical banks.

As both value and interest continue on the increase, it becomes even more important to educate one's self to the fullest extent possible. We recommend these books for your library:*The Dictionary of Still Banks* by Long and Pitman, *The Penny Bank Book* by Moore, and *The Bank Book* by Norman. If you are primarily interested in mechanicals, *Penny Lane*, a new book by Davidson, is considered the most complete reference available. It contains a cross-reference listing of numbers from all other publications on mechanical banks.

In the listings that follow, banks are identified by L for Long, G for Griffith, M for Moore, N for Norman, D for Davisdon, and W for Whiting.

Key:
CI —— cast iron   NPCI —— nickel-plated cast iron
EPCI —— electroplated cast iron

Artillery, D-11, copper plated, $1,000.00.

Advertising

AC Spark Plug, horse in bathtub, rubber wheels, slush cast **115.00**
Atlantic Premium Motor oil, tin litho, 2⅞" **18.50**
Atlas Mason, M-1561, pressed glass/EX pnt, 3⅝" **35.00**
Bank on Republic Pig Iron, M-330, CI/worn rpt, recent, ...**720.00**
Betsy Ross Tea, tin & paper, EX **15.00**
Billiken Shoes Bring Luck, M-80, CI/worn gold pnt, 4⅛" **65.00**
Bl Sunoco Custom Blended, tin, M **16.00**
Buster Brown & Tige, M-241, CI/gold pnt, minor wear, 5" **145.00**
Calumet Baking Powder, L-1231, can figural **95.00**
Campbell Kids, M-163, CI/worn gold pnt, lt rust, 3¼" **185.00**
Dean's Dairy, rural mailbox, metal **20.00**
Decker's Iowan, M-603, pig, CI/worn gold pnt, 4⅜" L **90.00**
Fidelity Trust Vaults, M-903, CI/brn japanning, 6⅝" **275.00**
Gem Furnace, M-1364, CI/worn blk pnt, 4⅝" **105.00**
Gerber's Strained Orange Juice, tin, EX **10.00**
Grapette, clown **16.00**
Lifesavers, tin, pack figural, scarce, 10" **69.00**
Osborn Molding Machines, M-625, pig, You Can..., CI, 4" **255.00**
Parsley Brand Salmon, tin **45.00**
Roper Range, M-1341, Arcade, pnt CI, 4" **325.00**
Save Money w/Mellow Furnace, M-1363, CI/bronze finish, 3⅝" .**65.00**
Saver for Your Brunswick, M-825, wht metal/bronze finish, 5" . .**85.00**
Sinclair Power X, EX **12.00**
Stove, Save Your Money & Buy..., M-1349, CI/worn pnt, 5½" . .**75.00**
Utica Club Beer, tin, EX **12.00**
West Chemical Products, tin, NM **22.00**
Wht Rose, tin **35.00**

Mechanical

Always Did 'Spise a Mule, D-250, bench, EX **750.00**
Always Did 'Spise a Mule, D-251, jockey, pat 1897 . . . .**1,250.00**
Artillery, D-11, soldier fires coin into tower, pnt CI **1,000.00**
Bad Accident, D-20, mule pulls man/cart, child on ground . .**1,650.00**
Bamboula, D-21 . . . .**1,000.00**
Bird on Roof, D-36, CI **2,300.00**
Bismark, D-37, man sits w/in lg pig, 8", VG **3,000.00**

Boy on Trapeze, D-50, pnt CI, VG 1,600.00
Boys Stealing Watermelon, D-53, pnt CI, EX 950.00
Bulldog, D-69, standing, coin on tongue, CI/pnt traces, 3½" ...500.00
Butting Buffalo, D-90, NM 3,000.00
Cat & Mouse, D-104, CI/worn pnt, 8¼", G 850.00
Cat & Mouse, D-104, pnt CI, 8¼", VG 1,500.00
Chief Big Moon, D-108, pnt CI, EX 950.00
Clown Bust, D-104 ....5,500.00
Clown on Globe, D-127, pnt CI, 9", G 1,400.00
Crossed-legged Minstrel, D-142 ....2,500.00

Dark Town Battery, D-146, 10" long, $1,950.00.

Dark Town Battery, D-146, CI/worn pnt, 9⅞" 1,950.00
Dog on Turntable, D-159, NPCI, NM 350.00
Elephant & 3 Clowns, D-170, pnt CI 1,600.00
Freedman's Bureau, D-149 ....4,000.00
Fun Producing Savings Bank, D-205, tin 750.00
Gem Bank, D-206, NPCI, EX 525.00
Hall's Excelsior, D-228, pnt CI, 3¾", EX 275.00
Hall's Lilliput, D-230, CI, wht w/mc trim, no trap, 4¼" 475.00
Home Bank, D-243, no dormers, CI, EX 800.00
Horse Race, D-246, str base 2,700.00
Humpty Dumpty, D-248, pnt CI, EX 750.00
Indian & Bear, D-257, pnt CI, wht bear, orig feathers, VG ..1,600.00
Joe Socko, D-262 ....750.00
Jolly Nigger, D-275, pnt CI, Sheppard Hdw, Buffalo NY, 6½" .175.00
Jolly Nigger w/High Hat, D-272, aluminum, EX 275.00
Jumbo the Elephant, D-248, on wheels, NM 900.00
Leap Frog, D-292, EX 2,100.00
Lion & 2 Monkeys, D-300, lion/trees/monkeys, pnt CI, EX 950.00
Little Red Riding Hood, D-412 ....22,000.00
Magic Bank, D-310, CI/yel pnt, rpt/rpl roof, 5" 8,000.00
Mason, D-321, pnt CI, 7½", EX 4,000.00
Monkey & Coconut, D-332, pnt CI, VG 1,700.00
New Creedmore, D-358 ....1,200.00
Organ Bank, D-368, boy/girl, monkey w/red jacket, 7⅝" 725.00
Organ Bank, D-370, pnt CI, miniature 750.00
Owl Turns Head, D-375, pnt CI, Stevens, 4", VG 350.00
Pelican w/Arab, D-381, pnt CI, EX 2,800.00
Political Feud, pnt cast aluminum, modern, 9¾" 125.00
Punch & Judy, D-404, CI/mc pnt, minor wear, 7⅜" 1,400.00
Rabbit in Cabbage, D-408, 4½", NM 350.00
Rooster, D-419, crowing, CI, EX 275.00
Safety Locomotive, D-422 ....2,000.00
Southern Comfort, Confederate shoots coins, modern, 8x6" ...75.00
Speaking Dog, D-447, CI/worn pnt, w/key, 7" 925.00

St Bernard, I Hear a Call, D-156, semi-mechanical, NM 120.00
Strike, CI/polychrome pnt, modern, 11½" 95.00

Stump Speaker, Shepard Hdw. Co., 9¾", $2,000.00.

Tank & Cannon, N-5430, aluminum 270.00
Teddy & the Bear, pnt CI, D-459, Stevens, rpr, 10", VG 800.00
Tommy, D-477 ....5,500.00
Trick Pony, D-484, pnt CI, Sheppard, pat 1885, 7½", VG 850.00
Uncle Sam, D-493, CI/worn mc pnt, 11½" 850.00
Uncle Tom, pnt CI, star base plate, EX 400.00
Watchdog Safe, D-560, pnt CI, EX 550.00
William Tell, D-565, pnt CI, VG 600.00
Zoo, D-576, bldg w/animals in windows, EX 900.00
2 Frogs, D-200, CI/VG pnt, J&E Stevens/pat 1822, rpr, 8¾" ...625.00

Registering

Astronaut Daily Dime 20.00
B&R Mfg, NY, 10¢ register 10.00
Beehive Savings, M-681, CI/nickel finish w/pnt traces, 5¼" ...125.00
Daily Dime Clown 16.00
Junior Cash, M-930, worn NPCI, lt rust, 4¼" 65.00
Kettle, pnt NPCI, 5¢ register, 3½" 20.00
Prudential, NPCI, pat Feb 25, 1890, 7", VG 45.00
Spinning Wheel, tin litho w/2 scenes, sq, W Germany, 4¼" 25.00
Statue of Liberty 10.00
Trunk, Phoenix, M-947, 10¢ register, NPCI/worn blk pnt, 5" ..95.00
Wee Folks Money Box, tin litho, sq, English, 5" 50.00

Still

Admiral Dewey Bullet 70.00
Air Mail, M-848, CI/mc pnt, minor wear, 6⅜" 350.00
Amish Boy, holds pig, sits on hay bale 65.00
Apple, L-904, CI, yel pnt, 5½" 750.00
Armoured Truck, Brinks; combination lock, steel, 8½", MIB ..195.00
Aunt Jemima, M-175, w/basket, wht metal/EX pnt, 5¼" 65.00
Aunt Jemima, M-176, CI/worn polychrome pnt, 5¼" 70.00

Auto, Chevrolet, 1953 . . . . .65.00
Auto, Red; W-157, EX 495.00
Baby Emerging from Eggshell, C-535, EX 35.00
Bank Building, M-1007, 6-sided, CI/worn pnt, 2½" 105.00
Bank Building, M-1125, CI/worn dk japanning, 5½" L 65.00
Barrel, M-916, Puzzle...#3, NPCI, worn, 5⅛" 85.00
Barrel, Sunny Future, NY NY, 3½" 8.00
Baseball Player, L-640, CI/pnt traces, 5¾" 135.00
Basset Hound, M-380, CI/worn gold pnt, 3⅛" 775.00
Battleship Maine, M-1439, CI/mc pnt, minor wear, 10¼" 350.00
Battleship Oregon, L-1583, lg, 6" L .250.00
Bear, M-699, hinged head, metal/worn pnt, Germany, 2⅝" 100.00
Bear, M-713, standing, CI/worn brn pnt, 6⅜" 65.00
Bear, M-715, begging, CI/gold & red pnt, minor wear, 5⅜" 65.00
Bear Stealing Pig, W-246 . . . . .975.00
Beggar Boy, L-643, boy kneels, holds hat, 7", EX 65.00
Bicentennial Bank 1776-1976, M-1108, 6x6", M 40.00
Billiken, M-74, Good Luck, CI/worn gold, 4⅛" 50.00
Billiken, M-81, Good Luck, CI/old red & gold rpt, 6½" 35.00
Billiken on Throne, L-649, Good Luck, CI/EX pnt 130.00
Bird, M-644, CI/worn gold pnt, 4¾" 270.00
Blackpool Tower, M-984, CI/worn dk japanning, 7½", VG 85.00
Blk Boy, M-84, 2-faced, worn blk/gold pnt, 3⅛" 65.00
Blk Boy on Pot, chalkware, 13", M 30.00
Book, Lincoln Mutual, Lincoln NE, CI, pat 1923 . . . . .12.00
Boston Bulldog, M-421, CI/polychrome pnt, 5¼", EX 125.00
Boy Scout, L-654, CI, 8" 600.00
Boy Scout, M-45, CI/pnt traces, 5⅞" .80.00
Buffalo, M-556, Amherst Stones, CI/blk pnt, 8" 265.00
Buffalo, M-560, CI/gold rpt, 4⅜" 50.00
Building, Gothic style w/2 towers, CI/blk & red pnt, 3" 125.00
Bulldog, L-72, CI, 4¼" 35.00
Bulldog, M-405, CI/realistic pnt, worn, 3½" 125.00
Bulldog, M-413, CI/polychrome, minor wear, 4⅜" 85.00
Bungalow, M-999, CI/old rpt, minor wear, 3¾" 175.00
Camel, M-768, CI, worn gold/red/orange pnt, 4¾" 45.00
Camel, M-769, Oriental, on rockers, CI/worn pnt & gold, 4" . .700.00
Camel, W-201, lg 325.00
Camel, W-202, sm 235.00
Captain Kidd, M-38, CI/worn pnt, 5¾" 435.00
Carpet Bag, C-352, bronze, 3½", EX .45.00
Castle, M-954, CI/EX brn japanning, gold trim, 3" 250.00
Cat, C-146, stands, tail up, bow at neck, 4½" 75.00
Cat, L-48, seated, CI/gold pnt, 4⅜", EX 80.00
Cat, M-366, seated, CI, worn blk/red/gold pnt, 4⅛" 145.00
Cat, W-248, seated, CI 175.00
Cat w/Ball, M-352, CI/gray & gold pnt, minor wear, 5⅝" L . . .150.00
Champion Thrift, CI/worn red & bl pnt, 4" 30.00
Clock, L-1509, Time Is Money, CI w/blk & gold traces, 3½" . . .70.00
Clock, M-1537, CI/blk rpt, 1 hand missing, 4½" 85.00
Clown, M-211, CI/worn gold & red pnt, 6⅛" 75.00
Clown, M-217, CI/gold pnt & red trim, minor wear, 6" 65.00
Clown Head, L-687, w/pointed nose, pot metal, 3⅝" 75.00
Colonial House, M-992, CI/EX polychrome pnt, 4" 185.00
Colonial House, M-993, CI/EX gold & gr pnt, 3" 95.00
Columbia Bank, M-1073, nickeled steel, mk Kenton, 8¾" 425.00
Columbia Bank, M-1077, CI/worn wht pnt, trap missing, 7" . .225.00
Columbian Safe Deposit 175.00
Cow, M-544, CI/blk & wht pnt, 4⅝" 135.00
Cow, M-553, brass, 5⅜" L 15.00
Crown Bank, M-1227, CI/gray pnt, worn red trim, 3½" 45.00
Cupola Bank, M-1145, CI/worn pnt, 5½" 125.00
Daikoku, M-67, Japanese God of Wealth, lead/gold pnt, 3⅓" . . .85.00
Deer, L-59, 6¼" 75.00

Derby, Pass 'Round the Hat, CI/worn brn pnt, 3⅛" 135.00
Devil, M-31, 2-faced, CI/worn polychrome pnt, 4¼" 245.00
Do You Know Me, M-75, CI/worn gold & mc pnt, 6¼" 160.00
Doc Yak, L-692, CI, 4⅝" 220.00
Dog on Pillow, M-443, CI/blk & wht pnt traces, 5½" 90.00
Dome Bank, M-1177, CI/gold pnt, lt rust, 4¼" 55.00
Dome Bank, M-1181, CI/EX gold pnt, 3⅝" 115.00
Donkey, M-498, hinged saddle & padlock, CI/worn pnt, 3½" . . .45.00
Donkey, M-499, CI/gr pnt, average wear, 4½" L 50.00
Donkey, M-500, CI, gold/red/orange pnt, minor wear, 7" 215.00
Donkey, W-197, lg, EX 165.00
Duck on Tub, L-354, CI, Hubley, 5⅜" 115.00
Dutch Boy, M-180, CI/pastels & yel pnt, minor wear, 5½" 50.00
Dutch Girl, M-181, CI/EX mc pnt, 5⅜" 75.00
Eagle, L-358, w/shield, 4" 600.00
Eiffel Tower, M-1074, CI/bronze & gold finish, 9" 650.00
Elephant, M-447, CI/worn gr pnt, 4" L 315.00
Elephant, M-449, CI/EX bl pnt, 4" 75.00
Elephant, M-450, GOP, CI/EX red & gold pnt, 4" 155.00
Elephant, M-455, swivel trunk, CI/blk & gold pnt, 3½", EX . . .200.00
Elephant, M-455, swivel trunk, CI/pnt traces, 3½" 60.00
Elephant, M-461, wht metal/worn blk pnt, 5" 20.00
Elephant, M-462, circus, CI/EX polychrome pnt, 3⅞" 125.00
Elephant, M-472, CI/worn gray pnt, 4⅛" L 15.00
Elephant, M-477, CI, pnt traces, 5⅛" L 40.00
Elephant on Bench on Tub, L-160, CI, 3⅞", EX 95.00
Elephant on Tub, M-486, CI/gold pnt, rpl screw, 4" 165.00
Elephant w/Howdah, M-457, CI/gold pnt, 2⅜", EX 55.00
Elephant w/Howdah, M-457, CI/worn gold pnt, 2⅜" 35.00
Elephant w/Howdah, M-474, CI/gold pnt, minor wear, 4⅞" 65.00
Empire State Bank Bldg, NPCI, orig drw/key, pat 1891 . . . . . .600.00
Fido, M-193, CI/polychrome pnt, modern, 4⅞" 45.00
Fido on Pillow, L-105, CI/worn mc pnt, Hubley, 5½" 140.00
Flat-Iron Building, M-1160, CI/silver pnt, no trap, 5¾" 65.00
Fort Dearborn, L-507, CI, 5¾" 175.00
Foxy Grandpa, M-320, CI/worn pnt, 5½" 295.00
Frog, M-692, Iron Art, CI/gr pnt, 7" L 55.00
Garage, M-1009, 1-car, CI/worn gold & red pnt, 2½" 65.00
Garage, M-1010, 2-car, CI/worn silver & bl pnt, 2½" 85.00
General Pershing, L-815, CI, 7¾" 195.00
General Sheridan on Horse, M-50, CI/worn gold pnt, 6" 450.00
German Helmet, M-1405, tin/worn olive drab pnt, 4⅞" L 175.00
Give Billy a Penny, M-15, CI/pnt, minor wear, 4¾" 275.00
Give Me a Penny, L-733, CI, Wing Mfg, 5¾" 175.00
Globe, M-812, CI/worn striped bronze finish, 5⅜" 110.00
Globe on Wire Arc, L-923, CI, Arcade, 4⅝" 120.00
Goose, M-615, CI/gold pnt, 5", NM .150.00
Hall Clock, M-1540, w/pendulum, CI/blk pnt, worn gold, 5¾" .285.00
High Rise, M-1219, CI/EX silver & gold pnt, 5½" 65.00
Hippopotamus, M-721, CI/worn gold pnt, 5" L 200.00
Home Savings, M-1201, NPCI, worn, 10½" 425.00
Home Savings, M-1236, CI/worn gr & red pnt, 3½" 105.00
Home Savings, M-1237, CI/very worn pnt, 5¾" 75.00
Horse, Buster Brown, Tige, M-508, Good Luck, CI/EX pnt, 4" .115.00
Horse, M-506, prancing, CI/EX gold pnt, 4⅝" 165.00
Horse, M-512, on wheels, CI/EX gold & silver pnt, 5⅛" 265.00
Horse, M-513, rearing, CI/VG blk pnt, 5¼" 75.00
Horse, M-520, rearing, CI/gold rpt, 7¼" 25.00
Horse, M-523, CI/gold pnt, minor wear, 2⅞" 135.00
Horse, M-532, CI/gold pnt, 3" 115.00
Horse, M-533, CI/worn bronze finish, 4⅞" L 35.00
Horse, W-86, sm 225.00
Horse Beauty, L-207, CI/blk pnt, Arcade, 4⅛" 75.00
Horse on Tub, M-510, CI/worn silver pnt, 5½" 175.00

House, W-408, 2-story, CI 85.00
Humpty Dumpty, L-747, CI, 6", VG 350.00
I Hear a Call, M-438, CI/worn blk & silver pnt, 5¼" 45.00
Independence Hall, M-1211, CI/gold & bronze pnt, 11¼" ...750.00
Independence Hall, M-1244, CI/worn bronze finish, 9⅜" 275.00
Indian, L-751, CI, 6" 150.00
Jackie Robinson, metal 150.00
Japanese Safe, M-883, NPCI, worn, lt rust, 5⅜" 65.00
Jumbo, CI/gold & red pnt, NP wheels, 3⅞" 155.00
Kitty, M-349, CI/worn mc pnt, 4¾" 50.00
Lamb, M-595, CI/worn wht pnt, 3⅛" 95.00
Liberty Bell, M-809, CI/bronze finish, 3½" 20.00
Lindbergh Bust, L-779, aluminum, 6¼" 50.00
Lion, M-742, CI/gold pnt, sm hole in side, 2½" 40.00
Lion, M-754, CI/worn bl pnt, 5" 60.00
Lion, M-755, CI/EX gold pnt, red trim, 5⅛" 35.00
Lion, M-759, CI/worn silver rpt, 4⅜" L 15.00
Lion, M-764, CI/worn pnt, 5⅜" L 35.00
Lion, W-94, sm 225.00
Lion on Tub, M-746, CI/EX gold pnt, 5½" 65.00
Lion on Tub, M-746, CI/mc pnt, minor wear, 5½" 80.00
Lion on Tub, M-747, CI/gold pnt, casting hole, 4⅛" 65.00
Log Cabin, M-1023, CI, worn brn japanning w/red pnt, 2⅝" ..165.00
Lucky Joe, glass 15.00
Main Street Trolly, L-1603, w/people, pnt CI, Wms, 6½" L ...220.00
Main Street Trolly, M-1469, no people, CI/worn pnt, 6⅝" 175.00
Main Street Trolly, M-1474, NPCI, worn, 5⅛" 285.00
Mary & Lamb, C-6, 4½" 750.00
Mary & Lamb, M-164, CI/worn polychrome pnt, 4⅜" 285.00
Mourner's Purse, L-1481, lead, 1902, 5" 50.00
Mutt & Jeff, M-157, CI/worn gold pnt, 5⅛" 85.00
Newfoundland Dog, M-440, CI/worn blk pnt, 3⅝" 40.00
North Pole Ice Cream Freezer, L-959, CI, 4" 375.00
Officer, M-8, CI, worn bl/gold/wht pnt, 5¾" 225.00
Old South Church, M-988, roof variation, CI/gold rpt, 9½" ...600.00
Our Kitchener, M-1313, CI, 6½" 145.00
Owl on Stump, L-375, CI, Williams, 4⅞" 165.00
Palace, M-1116, CI/blk pnt & gold trim, minor damage, 7½" ..175.00
People's Bank, hinged door 160.00
Pig, M-582, seated, CI, worn gold w/red trim, 4¾" L 45.00
Pig, M-606, on haunches, CI, worn pnt w/gold traces, 5⅛" ...95.00
Pig, M-629, I Made Chicago Famous, CI/worn blk pnt, 4⅛" ..225.00
Pig, M-680, CI/EX wht & pk pnt, 5¼" L 75.00
Pirate Chest, tin 32.00
Pocahontas Bust, M-226, lead/worn bronze finish, Germany, 3" .45.00
Policeman, L-820, CI/worn pnt, Arcade, 5⅝" 255.00
Porky Pig by Barrel, L-826, pot metal, 4½" 60.00
Professor Pug Frog, M-311, CI/metallic gr & gold pnt, 5¼" ...350.00
Puppy, M-416, CI/EX polychrome pnt, 4⅝" 65.00
Rabbit, L-291, lying down, ears laid back, CI, 2¼" 350.00
Rabbit, L-292, on oval base, CI/gr & wht pnt, 2¼", EX 825.00
Rabbit, M-567, w/carrot, CI, wht w/mc details, 3⅜", EX 75.00
Rabbit, M-568, CI/rpt traces, 3¾" 65.00
Rabbit, M-570, CI/gray & wht pnt, minor wear, 4¾" 100.00
Rabbit, M-574, CI/EX gold pnt, 6½" 175.00
Radio, M-821, CI/bl pnt & gold traces, 3¼" 95.00
Radio, M-829, CI/red/gold pnt, nickel door, Kenton Toyo, 4¾" .85.00
Recording Bank, M-1062, NPCI, worn, 6⅝" 170.00
Retriever w/Pack, M-436, CI/worn orig pnt, 3¾" 45.00
Roof Bank, M-1124, CI, dk brn japanning/worn gold trim, 5¼" .75.00
Rooster, L-384, CI/gold & red pnt, minor wear, 4¾" 120.00
Rumplestiltskin, L-832, CI, 6", VG 325.00
Sailor, M-27, CI/worn pnt, 5¼" 105.00
Sailor, M-29, CI/worn wht pnt, 5¾" 45.00

Santa, L-843, standing, holding tree, rpt CI, Hubley, 6" 75.00
Santa at Chimney, M-104, lead w/polychrome pnt, 4½", EX ..125.00
Save for a Rainy Day, M-615, CI/EX polychrome pnt, 5⅜" 85.00
Save...to Make Dollars, M-1545, eagle clock, CI, 3½" 125.00
Scotty, L-118, CI, 3¼", EX 65.00
Scotty, M-419, seated, CI, blk w/red collar, 5", M 75.00
Scotty, M-430, coin slot in tin trap, worn wht pnt, 2⅞" 40.00
Security Safe Deposit, combination lock 35.00
Sharecropper, W-18 ....195.00
Sheep, M-595, CI/no pnt, 4¼" L 55.00
Shell Out, L-1178, CI, 2½" 350.00
Sidewheeler, M-1459, CI/bl & red pnt, minor wear, 7½" L ...150.00
Snoopy, ceramic 25.00
Soldier, M-45, CI/gold & red pnt, minor wear, 6" 145.00
Spirit of Savings, airplane, cast aluminum, 8" L, VG 165.00
Spitz Dog, M-409, CI/layers of worn gold pnt, 5" L 210.00
St Bernard, L-117, keg at neck, CI, 7⅝" 125.00
St Bernard, M-437, CI, blk pnt w/silver & gold, 5½" 55.00
Stag, M-737, CI/EX gold pnt, 9½" 95.00
Stag, M-737, NPCI/worn pnt, 9½", EX 65.00
State Bank, M-1080, CI/dk brn pnt & metallic trim, 5¾" ...115.00
State Bank, M-1085, CI/metallic japanning/bronze trim, 3⅛" ...90.00
Statue of Liberty, L-865, CI, 6½" 65.00
Statue of Liberty, M-1164, CI/worn gold pnt, 6" 115.00
Stork, L-389, CI, Harper, 5⅜" 650.00
Stove, Parlor; L-1004, CI, 7" 75.00
Stove, Radiation; L-1019 ....65.00
Tally-Ho, L-1190, CI/brn pnt, silver & gold trim, 4½", EX 100.00
Tammany, D-455, CI/EX polychrome pnt, 5¾" 265.00
Tank, L-1610, CI/gold pnt, USA, 1918, 5¾" 105.00
Tank, M-1437, CI/worn gold pnt, 4½" L 85.00
Tank, W-161 ....285.00
Teddy Roosevelt, W-309 ....425.00
Temple Bar, M-1163, CI/dk brn japanning, 4" 300.00
Time Around World, L-1506, japanned CI, cb inserts, 4", VG .250.00
Top Hat, L-1627, Pass Around the Hat, CI/worn blk pnt, 2⅜" ..65.00
Treasure Chest, M-928, CI/worn red pnt & gold trim, 2¾" ...155.00
Trolley Car, L-1605, CI, no wheels, 2½" 250.00
US Air Mail, CI/gr & gold pnt, 5⅝" 65.00
US Mail, M-835, CI/silver & red pnt, minor wear, 4¾" 55.00
US Mail, M-839, CI/worn red pnt, 3½" 25.00
US Mail, M-856, CI/worn red & gold pnt, lt rust, 5¼" 45.00
US Treasury, M-1053, CI/EX wht & red pnt, 3" 80.00
Villa, M-1179, CI/brn japanning, gold trim/red finial, 5½" ...185.00
Villa, M-959, CI/dk japanning, red & gold trim, 5½", EX 155.00
Whale, M-724, Whale of a Bank, CI/dk gr pnt, 5" 35.00
Wise Pig, M-609, CI, EX wht pnt w/polychrome trim, 6¾" ...85.00
Woolworth Building, M-1042, CI/worn gold pnt, 5¾" 55.00
Woolworth Building, M-1045, lead/worn silvering, 4" 35.00
Yel Cab, L-1570, CI, 4", VG 400.00
1-Pounder, M-1416, artillery shell form, pnt CI, 8" 45.00
100th Anniv, Battle of Gettysburg, M-1194, pnt CI, 7¼" 75.00
1876 Bank, M-1012, CI/pnt traces, 2⅞" 100.00
3 Monkeys, L-244, Hear/See/Speak No Evil, pnt CI, 5", EX ...175.00

Barber Shop Collectibles

Even for the stranger in town, the local barber shop was easy to find, its location vividly marked with the traditional red and white striped barber pole that for centuries identified such establishments. As far back as the twelfth century, the barber has had a place in recorded history. At one time he not only groomed the beards and cut the hair of his gentlemen clients, but was known as the 'blood-letter' as well — hence the red stripe for blood and the white for the bandages. Many early barbers even pulled teeth! Later, laws were enacted that divided the practices of barbering and surgery.

The Victorian barber shop reflected the charm of that era with fancy barber chairs upholstered in rich wine-colored velvet; rows of bottles made from colored art glass held hair tonics and shaving lotion. Backbars of richly carved oak with beveled mirrors lined the wall behind the barber's station. During the late nineteenth century, the barber pole with a blue stripe added to the standard red and white as a patriotic gesture came into vogue.

Today the barber shop has all but disappeared from the American scene, replaced by modern unisex salons. Collectors search for the barber poles, the fancy chairs, and the tonic bottles of an era gone but not forgotten. See also Bottles; Razors; Shaving Mugs.

Barber's bowl, attributed to Sampson, 14", $350.00.

Blade bank, Donkey & Elephant, Listerine giveaways, pr 25.00
Blade bank, pole figural, red/blk stripes, mk Blades, EX 50.00
Book, Once Over Lightly, C De Zemler, 1st ed, 1939, EX 40.00
Catalog, Gillette Safety Razors, 30-pg, ca 1920s, EX 120.00
Catalog, Koch's Barber Chairs & Poles, 1912, EX 90.00
Catalog, Koken Barbers' Supply, 240-pg, 16th edition, EX 220.00
Catalog, Maher & Grosh, Toledo OH, full line, ca 1896, EX ...45.00
Chair, child's, elephant, wood carousel type, EX rstr 5,500.00
Chair, child's, horse's head, mk Paidar, 43", NM 1,200.00
Chair, child's fire engine w/ladders, rstr 1,800.00
Chair, ornate CI legs w/horse's hoofs, Koken, EX 900.00
Chair, wood & brass, gr mohair, Koch's, 1898, rstr 1,775.00
Pole, folk art, red/wht old rpt, EX cvg, early, 24½" 110.00
Pole, ldgl/illuminated, free-standing, Koken, 90", EX 2,300.00
Pole, ldgl/illuminated, wall mt, porc-on-iron brackets, 32" 600.00
Pole, trn acorn ends, worn spiral stripes, 23" 140.00
Pole, trn wood, iron mt arm, worn 3-color pnt, 1900s, 18" ...200.00
Pole, trn wood, red/wht/gold & silver leaf, 1880s, 71x4" 425.00
Pole, trn wood, 3-color pnt, crown w/ball top, 1900s, 44x4" ...495.00
Rack, hat; wht porc ft, Koken, EX orig 450.00
Rack, shaving mug; oak w/glass front, holds 35, 49x28½x7" ...500.00
Showcase, Boker Razors, glass/wood slant front, 15x19x6" 85.00
Showcase, Remington/Dupont Cutlery, wood/glass, 20x14x9" .135.00
Showcase, wood & glass, Weiss Est 1848, 19x16x8", EX 25.00
Sign, tin over cb standup, Enders...Razor, 1914, 13x9", EX 70.00
Spittoon, brass, Elite Works, 7" dia 50.00
Sterilizer, Dewit Steri-Tool, E Liverpool OH, 5x9½x5½" 25.00
Sterilizer jar, lime gr, HP flower & scroll w/gold, 10x3" 150.00
Thermometer, porc over steel on wood, mc pole form, 17x5" ..125.00
Tintype, 2 men at table w/bottles & razors, 2¼x3½", VG 42.00

Barometers

Barometers are instruments designed to measure the weight or pres-

sure of the atmosphere in order to anticipate approaching weather changes. Those made around the turn of the century — earlier in England and on the continent — were beautifully housed in period cases of mahogany, rosewood, walnut, or cherry, often with brass trim. These quality pieces bring high prices on today's market.

Blatt, w/thermometer, orig mercury, 39" 250.00
English, banjo, level/mirror/thermometer/hydrometer, 40" 300.00
English, mahog banjo w/inlay, hygrometer, rpl bubble, 37" 275.00
F Molton, mahog-inlay satinwood Geo style banjo+temp 600.00
German, house, children/old lady at doors, 1900s, 7x6x4" 36.00
Negretti & Zambra, oak Geo III, dbl ivory indicator, 39" 850.00

Nicolas Andre, reverse painted, with thermometer, 36", $275.00.

Ortelli & Co, mahog banjo w/inlay, EX & working, 38½" 375.00
P Catanio, cvd crest, bevelled glass face, stick type, 42" 500.00
Smith & Sons, inlaid mahog case & dial+thermometer, 39" ...500.00
Somalvico, mahog-cased banjo w/satinwood inlay, 1820s, 42" .550.00

Baskets

Basket weaving is a craft as old as ancient history. Baskets have been used to harvest crops, for domestic chores, and to contain the catch of fishermen. Materials at hand were utilized, and baskets from a specific region are often distinguishable simply by analyzing the natural fibers used in their construction. Early Indian baskets were made of corn husks or woven grasses. Willow splint, straw, rope, and paper are only a few of the materials that have been used. Until the invention of the veneering machine in the late 1800s, splint was made by water-soaking a split log until the fibers were softened and flexible. Long strips were pulled out by hand and, while still wet and pliable, woven into baskets in either a cross-hatch or hexagonal weave.

Most handcrafted baskets on the market today were made between 1860 and the early 1900s. Factory baskets with a thick, wide splint cut by machine are of little interest to collectors. The more popular baskets are those designed for a specific purpose, rather than the more commonly-found utility baskets that had multiple uses. Among the most costly forms are the Nantucket Lighthouse baskets, which were basically copied from those made there for centuries by aboriginal Indians. They were designed in the style of whale oil barrels and named for the South Shoal Nantucket Lightship where many were made during the last half of the nineteenth century. Cheese baskets (used to separate curds from whey), herb-gathering baskets, and finely woven Shaker miniatures are other highly-prized examples of the basket weaver's art.

In the listings that follow, assume that each has a center bentwood handle (unless handles of another type are noted) that is not included in the height. Unless another type of material is indicated, assume that each is made of splint. See also American Indian; Eskimo; Sewing; Shaker.

From Albany Co., NY, ca 1850s, left to right: Loom basket, 2-tier, in original red paint, NM, 20", $1,100.00; Apple basket, swing handle, worn blue paint exposes originial red in some areas, 12" diameter, $1,200.00.

Apple, oak splint, concave bottom, ca 1900, 12x12", EX 98.00
Ash burl, cut-out semicircular hdls, NY, 1700s, 4½x9x11" . . .2,700.00
Bentwood fr, wide splint, VG age/color, oval, 12" W, VG 95.00
Berry, oak splint, flared w/sq base, 1900s, 7x6½", M 75.00
Berry, oak splint, tall oak hdl, MD, 6x7", 14" H w/hdl, M 55.00
Berry, oak splint, wrapped rim, ca 1900, 7x6", M 45.00
Buttocks, Eye of God hdl, 1800s, 6½x8x6", EX 245.00
Buttocks, oak splint, dbl raised rim, 1890s, 12x13x11" 195.00
Buttocks, oak splint, melon shape, VA, 1880s, 12x12x12", EX .135.00
Buttocks, oak splint, 1½" W hdl, ca 1900, 19x24x21", NM 185.00
Buttocks, oak splint, 36-rib, 1900, 15x18x14", NM 165.00
Buttocks, old red pnt, 1860s, 9½x12", 9" opening, M 550.00
Buttocks, orig gr pnt, ca 1900, 8x8", 7½" opening, EX 550.00
Buttocks, w/dome lid, 1800s, miniature, 5½" W 600.00
Buttocks, well made, EX age/color, bentwood hdl, 12x17" 300.00
Cheese, bentwood fr w/finger construction, 25" dia, VG 100.00
Cheese, minor damage, 10" dia 150.00
Cheese, wrapped rim & hdl, hanging, 1800s, 6x5" dia 450.00
Cotton field, oak splint, raised rim, 1880s, 15x26x19", EX 145.00
Egg, ash splint, sq base, rnd top, cvd hdl, 1880s, 14x11", EX . . .125.00
Egg, extruded wht oak, tapered, cvd hdl, 1880s, 12x12½" 85.00
Egg, initials cvd inside hdl, 10½" L 275.00
Egg, oak splint, concave base, 1860s, 3x10½" dia, NM 100.00
Egg, oak splint, sq base, rnd top, ca 1910, 12x11" 88.00
Egg, radiating ribs, EX age/color, minor damage, 14x17" 175.00
Egg, radiating ribs, Eye of God hdl, yel pnt, 13" L, EX 95.00
Egg, radiating ribs, minor damage, 5½x10" dia 55.00
Egg, radiating ribs, minor wear/damage, 13x14" 95.00

Egg, wide melon ribs in center, narrow in side, 14x14", EX 195.00
Egg, willow, wrapped hdl, PA, 1900s, 13½x13x11½", NM 35.00
Egg, 4-color, folding lids, 6x10x11" 155.00
Fruit, blk ash splint, cvd/notched hdl, 1890s, 11x13½" 85.00
Garden, oak splint, dbl hdl, MD, ca 1900, 16½x16½x8", M 60.00
Garden, oak splint, dbl-wrap rim, VA, 1900s 16x20x15", EX . .80.00
Garden, oak splint, hdl appl outside, ca 1900, 12x19½x12½" . . .88.00
Garden, oak splint, melon type, 1890s, 11½x11½", NM 150.00
Garden, oak splint, nailed hdl, PA, 1900s, 16x12x9", EX 58.00
Garden, oak splint, sq base, oval top, 1880s, 14x14x13", EX . . .120.00
Garden, oak splint, 7" sq base, ca 1900, 14½x11", NM 85.00
Hamper, feather storage; orig apple gr pnt, 1875, 24" 350.00
House, ash splint, tapered, cvd hdl, 1880s, 14½x13" dia 85.00
Kitchen, wht oak splint, extruded rods, 1890s, PA, 6x9½" 65.00
Loom, stepped sides on bk plate, 7½" 165.00
Loom, wide splint w/orig red pnt, 2-tier, 1840s, NY, 20x12" .1,100.00
Melon rib, Eye of God hdl, checkerboard weave, 9½x9x8", M .125.00
Melon rib, Eye of God hdl, miniature, 3½x6¼" dia 195.00
Melon rib, Eye of God hdl, 6x12" dia .95.00
Melon rib, Eye of God hdl, 6x6" 75.00
Melon rib, oak splint, ca 1900, 12¾x13x16", EX 100.00
Melon rib, oak splint, wrapped rim, 1870s, 15x16x14", EX . . .245.00
Melon rib, rim hdls, 11½x23x25", EX .75.00
Miniature, radiating ribs, woven hdl, pnt traces, 5½" dia 300.00
Miniature, 2¼x2½" 65.00
Mussel-gathering, melon rib, oak splint, 1880s, 11x14x12" 65.00
Nantucket, swing hdls on brass ears, MA, 1800s, 5¾x10½" 650.00
Nantucket, swivel hdl, label: Wm Appleton, 6" dia 850.00
Picnic, oak splint, tacked rim, factory made, '10, 16x19x13" . . .25.00
Pigeon, ash splint, center hinged lid, 1900, 11x16x10" 95.00
Provender, oak splint, 2 cleats on bottom, 1880s, 13x26x18" . . .55.00
Splint, bentwood hdl, 9x17" dia 65.00
Splint, bentwood rim hdls, EX age/color, 8x13" dia 250.00
Splint, bentwood rim hdls, minor damage, 7½x21x13½" 95.00
Splint, bentwood rim hdls, 12½x18" dia 225.00
Splint, faded colors, lift-out compartment, +lid, 13" H 65.00
Splint, finely woven, EX age/color, 5½" dia 275.00
Splint, loose weave, bentwood hdl, 14x28x15½" 195.00
Splint, pk/bl pnt, minor damage, 8x12½" dia 135.00
Splint, plaited rim, bentwood hdl, oval, 15x27x19" 115.00
Splint, radiating ribs, finely woven, bentwood hdl, 4x6" dia . . .135.00
Splint, red/gr/blk pnt decor, 4x8x6" .300.00
Splint, sq base, rnd top, 4 rim hdls, 16x33" dia 175.00
Splint, varnished, 6½x18½x12", EX 80.00
Splint, wide strips, plywood-reinforced base, 7x38x14" 105.00
Splint, worn red-brn stain, rim hdls, 12x21" dia 135.00
Store, oak splint, dbl-wrap rim, cvd hdl, 1880s, 11x19x14", EX .60.00
Swing hdl, graduated weaving, dbl-wrap rim, 9x12" 385.00
Swing hdl, old bl over orig red, NY, 1850, 12" dia 1,200.00
Table, extruded wht oak, 2 hdls, PA, 1880s, 7x19x11", EX 85.00
Table, twine, heavy tight weave, bowl form, gr pnt, 3½x11" 65.00
Wall, oak splint, tapered form, VA, 1910s, 11½x7x6", M 55.00
Weaver's, divided int, orange/bl watercolor designs, 10x18" . . .175.00
Willow & vine, mc pnt stripes, hinged lid, 10x19x13" 75.00

Batchelder

Ernest A. Batchelder was a leading exponent of the Arts and Crafts movement in the United States. His influential book, *Design in Theory and Practice*, was originally published in 1910. He is best known, however, for his artistic tiles which he first produced in Pasedena, California, from 1909 to 1916. In 1906 the business was relocated to Los Angeles where it continued until 1932, closing because of the Depression.

In 1938 Batchelder resumed production in Pasedena under the name of 'Kinneola Kiln.' Output of the new pottery consisted of delicately cast bowls and vases in an Oriental style. This business closed in 1951. Tiles carry a die-stamped mark; vases and bowls are hand incised.

Our advisor for this category is Jack Chipman; he is listed in the Directory under California.

Bookend, 2¾" tiles set in Potter Studio brass mts, pr 220.00
Bowl, blk/brn irid, 8" 85.00
Bowl, flared, Pasadena, #217, 8" 65.00

Tile, landscape with oak tree, brown englobe, impressed mark, 7¾", $175.00.

Tile, architectural, grapes, bl wash, 7x12" 95.00
Tile, castle, matt finish 125.00
Tile, Dutch boy w/water pails, sq, 5" 75.00
Tile, peacocks in high relief, bl wash, mk, 12" 200.00
Vase, lime gr, 6" 125.00

Battersea

Battersea is a term that refers to enameling on copper or other metal. Though originally produced at Battersea, England, in the mid-eighteenth century, the craft was later practiced throughout the Staffordshire district. Boxes are the most common examples — some are figurals, and many bear an inscription. Values are given for examples with only minimal damage, which is normal.

Bodkin case, 2 panels w/mottos, pk w/gr & blk lines, 4", VG ..330.00
Bonbonniere, apple shape, Bilston, ca 1770s, 1⅛" 1,500.00
Box, bird form, bird & fruit on lid, 1½", EX 800.00
Box, Esteem the Giver, oval, ca 1780, 1¼" 485.00
Box, floral, mc on wht lattice, rectangular, sm rpr, 2½" L 200.00
Box, hunt scene on lid, mc florals on wht, 5⅝" L, EX 500.00
Box, Trifle from London, floral garland, 1½" L, EX 200.00
Box, Virtue Fair/Manners Sweet..., sm, EX 350.00
Candlestick, florals in reserves, copper mts, rpr, 9", pr 900.00
Knob, Hope resting on anchor w/ship in bkground, EX 115.00
Knob, Thos Jefferson portrait 450.00
Locket, ship, bk: clock face, EX 220.00

Bauer

Originally founded in Paducah, Kentucky, in 1885, the J.A. Bauer Company moved to Los Angeles where it was re-established in 1909. Until the 1920s, their major products were terra cotta gardenware, flowerpots, and stoneware and yellowware bowls. During prohibition they produced crocks for home use. A more artful form of product began to develop with the addition of designer Louis Ipsen to the staff in 1915. Some of his work — a line of molded vases, flowerpots, bowls, etc. — was awarded a bronze medal at the Pacific International Exposition the following year.

In 1930 the first of many dinnerware lines was tested on the market. Their initial pattern, Plain Ware, was well accepted and led the way to the introduction of the most popular dinnerware in their history and with today's collectors — Ring Ware. It was produced from 1932 into the early 1960s in solid colors of jade green, royal blue, Chinese yellow, light blue, orange-red, and (in very limited quantities) black or white. Its simple pattern was a design of closely-spaced concentric ribs, either convex or concave. Over the years, more than one hundred shapes were available. Some were made in limited quantities, resulting in rare items to whet the appetites of Bauer buffs today. Other patterns were LaLinda, produced during the 1940s and 1950s, and Monterey Modern, introduced in 1948 and remaining popular into the 1950s, made in pink, black, gray, brown, and green.

After WWII a flood of foreign imports drastically curtailed their sales, and the pottery began a steady decline that ended in failure in 1962. Prices listed below reflect the California market. For more information, we recommend *The Complete Collector's Guide to Bauer Pottery* by Jack Chipman, our advisor for this category, and Judy Stangler. Mr Chipman's address may be found in the Directory under California.

Baking dish, Ring, cobalt, w/lid, 4" 30.00
Bean pot, plain, cobalt, hdls, 1-qt 40.00
Bottle, water; Ring, open, orange-red 45.00
Bowl, batter; Ring, gr or gray, 1-qt 40.00
Bowl, cereal; Monterey, burgundy, 4½" 15.00
Bowl, cereal; Ring, yel 15.00
Bowl, fruit; Ring, lt bl, 5" 13.00
Bowl, mixing; Al Fresco, Dubonnet or coffee brn, 4x5½" 7.50
Bowl, mixing; La Linda, #30, yel or gr, 1½-pt 12.00
Bowl, mixing; La Linda, #36, pk, gray, or ivory, 1-pt 9.00
Bowl, mixing; Ring, #12, blk 60.00
Bowl, mixing; Ring, #30, blk, 1½-pt 30.00
Bowl, mixing; Ring, #36, lt bl or yel, 1-pt 18.00
Bowl, mixing; Ring, #9, gr or turq, 1-gal 45.00
Bowl, nappy, Ring, lt bl, 9" 45.00
Bowl, pudding; plain, #6, yel, 10¼" 50.00
Bowl, punch; Ring, lt bl or red-brn, 14" 185.00
Bowl, salad; Ring, gr or turq, low, 12" .60.00
Bowl, salad; Ring, ivory or burgundy, 12" 75.00
Bowl, soup; Ring, lt bl, w/lid, 5½" 40.00
Bowl, soup/cereal; La Linda, burgundy or dk brn, 6" 12.00
Bowl, vegetable; Contempo, any color, 9½" 13.00
Butter dish, Al Fresco, speckled, gr, or gray 20.00
Butter dish, La Linda, lt brn or turq, oblong 30.00
Butter dish, Monterey, wht, oblong 45.00
Butter dish, Monterey Moderne, blk, oval 50.00
Butter dish, Ring, gr, rnd 38.00
Candlestick, Monterey, wht 30.00
Carafe, Ring, lt brn, w/lid, 7½" 40.00
Carafe, Ring, red, wood hdl 45.00
Casserole, Ring, lt bl or yel, w/lid, 7½" .40.00
Cigarette jar, Ring, cobalt, w/lid 125.00
Coffee server, Monterey, orange-red or burgundy, 8-cup 32.50

Coffee server, Ring, orange-red or cobalt, metal hdl, 6-cup 35.00
Coffeepot, ind; plain, burgundy, 2-cup 40.00
Cookie jar, Al Fresco, coffee brn 37.50
Cookie jar, Ring, blk 200.00
Creamer, La Linda, burgundy or dk brn 7.50
Creamer, plain, blk, midget 28.00
Creamer, Ring, gr, 12-oz 7.50
Creamer, Ring, orange, tall, 1-pt 45.00
Cup, coffee; La Linda, pk, gray, or ivory 12.00
Cup & saucer, El Chico, any color 20.00
Cup & saucer, Ring, cobalt or red 30.00
Goblet, plain, lt bl 50.00
Goblet, Ring, lt bl or yel 60.00
Lazy susan set, Al Fresco, gr or gray, complete 45.00
Mustard jar, Ring, gr, w/lid 100.00
Pie plate, Ring, gray, 9" 20.00
Pitcher, Contempo, any color, ice lip, 2-qt 18.00
Pitcher, La Linda, burgundy or dk brn, 1½-pt 24.00
Pitcher, Monterey, orange-red, ice lip, 2-qt 35.00
Pitcher, Ring, cobalt, 2-qt 40.00
Pitcher, Ring, lt bl or yel, 3-qt 40.00
Planter, swan, gr, 10" 30.00
Plate, bread & butter; plain, ivory or yel, 6" 9.00
Plate, chop; plain, orange-red, 12" 40.00
Plate, chop; Ring, red-brn, 14" 35.00
Plate, dinner; Ring, cobalt, 9" 15.00
Plate, dinner; Ring, lt bl, yel, or brn, 9" 15.00
Plate, divided relish; Ring, yel 50.00
Plate, salad; Ring, orange-red, 7½" 15.00
Plate, salad; Ring, turq, gray, or gr, 7½" 10.00
Platter, La Linda, burgundy or dk brn, 12" 20.00
Platter, Monterey, gr, yel, or turq, oval, 17" 25.00
Ramekin, plain, cobalt, 3½" 7.50

Ring Ware: See listings for specific values.

Sauce boat, Monterey, gr, yel, or turq, sm 22.50
Shaker, sugar; Ring, cobalt, 5" 60.00
Shakers, Contempo, any color, pr 5.00
Sherbet, Ring, yel 40.00
Soup plate, La Linda, pk, gray, or ivory, 7" 15.00
Soup plate, Ring, orange-red or cobalt, 7½" 25.00
Sugar bowl, Ring, yel, w/lid 15.00
Teapot, Contempo, any color, 6-cup 20.00

Teapot, Monterey, ivory or burgundy, 6-cup 45.00
Teapot, Ring, orange-red or cobalt, 2-cup 60.00
Tumbler, Al Fresco, speckled, gr, or gray, 8-oz 10.00
Tumbler, Monterey, gr, yel, or turq, 8-oz 15.00
Tumbler, Ring, blk, 12-oz 40.00
Tumbler, Ring, lt bl, 6-oz 10.00
Tumbler, Ring, wood hdl, cobalt, 6-oz 15.00

Bavaria

Bavaria, Germany, was long the center of that country's pottery industry; in the 1800s, many firms operated in and around the area. Chinaware vases, novelties, and table accessories were decorated with transfer prints as well as by hand by artists who sometimes signed their work. The examples here are marked with 'Bavaria' and the logos of some of the various companies which were located there. See also Children's Things, China.

Bowl, Chateau, ped ft, Schumann, 9" 42.00
Box, powder; portrait 42.00
Cake plate, floral, pk on wht w/gold medallions, sgn, 10" 18.00
Chocolate pot, gold decor on wht, +4 c/s 55.00
Chocolate pot, roses, artist sgn, +cr/sug 185.00
Cup & saucer, pk roses, pk lustre 38.00
Jam jar, vintage border, hdls, sgn/dtd 75.00
Nude, Deco style, reclines on flowered tray, mk, 6" 125.00
Pitcher, Grecian ladies, gold tracing, mk, 6x4" 95.00
Plate, lady's portrait, lacy gold rim, 6½" 30.00
Teapot, alternating panels w/gold, +6 c/s 175.00
Tray, poppies, orange on cream w/gold, mk, 11½x8½" 60.00
Vase, birds & florals, HP, dtd 1912, 5¼" 25.00

Beer Cans

When the flat-top can was first introduced in 1934, it came with printed instructions on how to use the triangular punch opener. Cone-top cans, which are rare today, were patented in 1935 by the Continental Can Company. By the 1960s, aluminum cans with pull tabs had made both types obsolete.

The hobby of collecting beer cans has been rapidly gaining momentum over the past ten years. Series types, such as South African Brewery, Lion, and the Cities Series by Schmit and Tucker, are especially popular.

Condition is an important consideration when evaluating market price. Grade 1 must be in like-new condition with no rust. However, the triangular punch hole is acceptable. Grade 2 cans may have slight scratches or dimples but must be free of rust. For Grade 3, light rust, minor scratching, and some fading may be acceptable. Grade 4 cans have the same defects but are in much worse condition. Cans in less-than-excellent condition devaluate sharply. In the listings that follow, cans are arranged alphabetically by brand name, not by brewery. Unless noted otherwise, values are for cans in Grade 1 condition.

Our advisor for this category is Lowell Owens; he is listed in the Directory under New York.

A-1 Pilsner, flat top, red & wht, 16-oz 180.00
ABC Extra Dry, cone top, red & blk, 12-oz 100.00
Alpine, flat top, 12-oz 42.00
American, flat top, red, wht, & gold, 12-oz 10.00
American Dry, flat top, 12-oz 10.00
Bartels, flat top, red, wht, & gold, 12-oz 50.00
Blatz, flat top, red & gold, 12-oz 6.00
Bonanza, pull top, red, wht, & bl, 12-oz 15.00

Brew 82, flat top, red & bl, 12-oz **78.00**
Brewer's Best, pull top, red & wht, 12-oz **16.00**
Buckaneer Stout, flat top, 8-oz **305.00**
Buckeye Sparkling Dry, cone top, red & wht, 12-oz **40.00**
Buckhorn, flat top, red, 12-oz **7.00**
Budweiser, flat top, gold & blk, 12-oz **22.00**
Budweiser, flat top, red & wht, 16-oz **9.00**
Budweiser, flat top, 10-oz **35.00**
Burger, pull top, wht, red, & gold, 16-oz **15.00**
Burgermeister, flat top, bl & wht, 12-oz **12.00**
Busch Bavarian, flat top, bl & wht, 12-oz **10.00**
Canadian Ace, cone top, 12-oz **27.00**
Cook's, pull top, red & wht, 12-oz **1.00**
Coors, flat top, gold & wht, 7-oz **5.00**
Copper Club, cone top, 12-oz **62.00**
Corona, flat top, blk & gold, 12-oz **77.00**
Dawson's Ale, cone top, 12-oz **42.00**
Drewry's, pull top, red & wht, 16-oz **6.00**
Drewry's Extra Dry, flat top, silver & red, 12-oz **12.00**
Drewry's Oldstock Ale, flat top, gr & gold, 12-oz **45.00**
Falstaff, cone top, blk & gold, 12-oz **27.00**
Fitzgerald's Pale Ale, cone top, red & wht, 12-oz **75.00**
Gablinger's, pull top, brn & wht, 12-oz **5.00**
Gold Brau, flat top, 12-oz **30.00**
Hamm's, flat top, bl & wht, 16-oz **5.00**
Heidelbrau, cone top, 12-oz **35.00**
Koehler's, cone top, red & wht, 12-oz **92.00**
Miller, flat top, gold & wht, 10-oz **10.00**
Miller, pull top, red & wht, 8-oz **3.00**
Muehlebach, cone top, gold & wht, 12-oz **72.00**
Reisch Gold Top, cone top, gold & wht, 12-oz **40.00**
Schlitz, pull top, 8-oz **3.00**

Belleek, American

From 1883 until 1930, several American potteries located in New Jersey and Ohio manufactured a type of china similar to the famous Irish Belleek soft-paste porcelain. The American manufacturers identified their porcelain by using 'Belleek' in their marks. American Belleek is considered the highest achievement of the American porcelain industry. Production centered around artistic cabinet pieces and luxury tablewares. Many examples emulated Irish shapes and decor with marine themes and other naturalistic styles. While all are highly collectible, some companies' products are rarer than others. The best-known manufacturers are Ott and Brewer, Willets, The Ceramic Art Company (CAC), and Lenox. You will find more detailed information in those specific categories. For a more thorough study of the subject, we recommend you refer to *American Belleek*, by our advisor Mary Frank Gaston; you will find her address in the Directory under Texas.

Key:
AAC — American Art China   CAP — Columbian Art Pottery
                                                  Works

Cup & saucer, demitasse; Tridacna, gold trim, CAP **165.00**
Cup & saucer, morning-glories, Morgan **120.00**
Ewer, grapes & vines, gold trim, unmk, 14" **200.00**
Mug, monk transfer in blk tones, CAP, blk mk, 5½" **235.00**
Pitcher, tankard; yel roses, artist sgn, fancy hdl, CAP, 13" **238.00**
Plate, Victoria, mk Morgan Belleek, 10" **165.00**
Plate, workers in wheat field, man at gate, AAC, 6¼" **155.00**
Sugar bowl, pk florals, AAC, 2½" **265.00**
Teapot, gold leaves on cream, dragon form, CAP, 7½x9" ... **1,100.00**

Vase, lg pastel florals on wht, AAC, 12" **650.00**

Belleek, Irish

Belleek is a very thin translucent porcelain that takes its name from the district in Ireland where it originated in 1857. The glaze is a creamy ivory color with a pearl-like lustre. Tablewares, baskets, figurines, and vases have been produced; Shamrock, Tridacna, Echinus, and Lotus are but a few of the many patterns.

It is possible to date an example to within twenty to thirty years of manufacture by the mark. Pieces with an early stamp often bring prices nearly triple that of a similar but current item. With some variation, the marks have always incorporated the wolfhound, castle, harp, and shamrock. The first three marks (usually in black) were used from 1863 to 1946. A series of green marks has been in use since 1946; the most current mark is gold.

Basket, appl floral rim & hdls, Belleek label, 9" L **325.00**
Basket, Henshall, 3-strand, appl buds/flowers, 8" **2,800.00**
Basket, 3-strand, appl buds/flowers, w/lid, early, 8½" L **4,800.00**
Bowl, Flying Fish; 1st blk mk, pearl, 5" L **650.00**
Bust, Clytie, 1st blk mk, 12" **1,995.00**
Bust, John Wesley, 1st blk mk, 8¼" **1,950.00**
Canterbury, creamer & sugar bowl, 3rd blk mk **175.00**
Chinese, teapot, 1st blk mk/registry mk, sm **900.00**
Cottage, butter dish, 1st gr mk, yel lustre, 2-pc **140.00**
Cottage, cheese dish, 1st gr mk, lustre trim, 6⅝" L **145.00**
Echinus, creamer, 1st blk mk, rose monogram, gold trim, 3⅝" .. **165.00**
Echinus, teapot, dejeuner; 1st blk mk, pk trim, 4", +5 pcs ... **1,750.00**
Fan, beaker, 3rd blk mk, cobalt trim, 4" **90.00**
Figurine, greyhound, 3rd blk mk, male **615.00**
Figurine, leprechaun on mushroom, 2nd blk mk, 5¼" **495.00**
Greek, plate, 1st blk mk, 9" **250.00**
Harp & Shamrock, creamer & sugar bowl, 3rd blk mk **125.00**
Harp & Shamrock, cup & saucer, demitasse; 3rd blk mk **125.00**
Harp & Shamrock, salt dish, 3rd blk mk **45.00**
Harp & Shamrock, tea set, 2nd blk mk, gr trim, 5-pc+tray ... **1,950.00**
Harp & Shamrock, teapot, 3rd blk mk **325.00**
Hexagon, cup & saucer, 2nd blk mk, wht **125.00**
Hexagon, teapot, 2nd blk mk, gr trim **365.00**
Institute, cup & saucer, 1st blk mk, pk trim **150.00**
Ivy, creamer & sugar bowl, 1st gr mk **70.00**
Ivy, sugar bowl, 3rd blk mk, w/lid **35.00**
Lily, basket, 3-strand, old, 11" **2,800.00**
Lily, creamer, 1st gr mk **32.00**
Lily, frame, 1st blk mk, beaded, oval, 6½" **1,750.00**
Lily, spill vase, 2nd blk mk, sm **85.00**
Limpet, coffeepot, 3rd blk mk **365.00**
Limpet, cup & saucer, 1st gr mk **45.00**
Limpet, cup & saucer, 3rd blk mk, cobalt lustre **125.00**
Limpet, plate, 3rd blk mk, cobalt lustre, 8½" **50.00**
Limpet, plate, 3rd blk mk, 6½" **45.00**
Marine, centerpiece, 1st blk mk, 3-lily, 2-shell base, 13" ... **1,900.00**
Mask, cup & saucer, demitasse; 3rd blk mk **110.00**
Mask, ewer, 3rd blk mk, gr trim, 8½" **795.00**
Mask, pitcher, 2nd blk mk, gr trim, ewer form, 8½x5" **895.00**
Neptune, cup & saucer, demitasse; 3rd blk mk **65.00**
Neptune, cup & saucer, 2nd blk mk, gr trim **135.00**
Neptune, teapot, 2nd blk mk, 4¾x4⅜" **245.00**
Neptune, teapot, 2nd gr mk, shell ft & finial **299.00**
Quilted Diamond, bowl, 1st gr mk **60.00**
Quilted Diamond, cache pot, 1st gr mk **75.00**
Shamrock, basket, 3-strand, old, 5" dia **750.00**

Shamrock, cup & saucer, demitasse; 3rd blk mk, twig hdl 68.00
Shamrock, cup & saucer, 1st gr mk 48.00
Shamrock, cup & saucer, 2nd blk mk, low, wide 56.00
Shamrock, cup & saucer, 3rd blk mk, twig hdl 80.00
Shamrock, marmalade, 3rd blk mk, barrel form, cobalt trim 85.00
Shamrock, plate, 2nd blk mk, 6½" 40.00
Shamrock, saucer, 1st blk mk 20.00
Shamrock, vase, 3rd blk mk, trunk form, 6½" 110.00
Shamrock Basketweave, bread plate, 2nd blk mk, hdls, 10½" ..135.00
Shamrock Basketweave, creamer, 2nd gr mk, brn twig hdl 45.00
Shamrock Basketweave, honey pot, 3rd blk mk 150.00
Shell, compote, 1st blk mk, 3-dolphin ped, 5x10" 645.00
Shell, sugar bowl, 1st blk mk, lg 575.00
Star, salt cellar, 2nd blk mk 45.00
Swan, yel/wht, gr mk 35.00
Sycamore, plate, 3rd blk mk, leaf form 50.00

Teapot, Shell and Seaweed, 3rd black mark, 5½", $350.00.

Thistle, cup, 1st blk mk, +saucer, 2nd blk mk 145.00
Thistle, plate, 2nd blk mk, pk trim, 6¾" 78.00
Thistle, wash jug & bowl, 1st production 1,050.00
Thorn, cup & saucer, 1st blk mk 95.00
Thorn, mug, 2nd blk mk, rare 140.00
Tridacna, creamer & sugar bowl, 3rd blk mk, boat form 100.00
Tridacna, cup & saucer, 1st blk mk, pk trim 125.00
Tridacna, cup & saucer, 2nd blk mk 75.00
Tridacna, cup & saucer, 3rd blk mk 45.00
Tridacna, plate, 2nd blk mk, 6" 60.00
Tridacna, teapot, 2nd blk mk, pk trim, lg 325.00
Vase, Bird's Nest & Tree Stump, gr mk, 12" 200.00
Vase, Corn, 1st blk mk, all wht, 6x3", pr 385.00
Vase, Double Fish, 1st blk mk, 12" 3,000.00
Vase, Frog, 2nd blk mk, blk eye, parian, 4¾" 850.00
Vase, Frog, 2nd blk mk, blk eye, 6" 1,375.00
Vase, Horse, 1st blk mk, trumpet form, 5" L 550.00
Vase, Lizard, 1st blk mk, pearl, 8¼" 1,500.00
Vase, Princess, 2nd blk mk, openwork hdls, mc florals, 9" 795.00
Vase, spill; Sea Horse, 2nd blk mk 180.00
Vase, spill; Typhia, 1st gr mk 40.00
Vase, 1st blk mk, tree trunk form, brn trim, 6¼x3¾" 165.00

Bells

The earliest form of bell, the crotal or closed-mouth, is most familiar to us today as the sleigh bell. Rattles, hollow forms containing stones or seed pods, are also of this type of construction. Gongs, most often associated with the Orient, have no clapper and must be struck to sound. The more common forms of bells are made with a flaring shape and a freely-moving interior clapper that causes the bell to ring as it is swung. Bells come in many shapes and serve many uses. They have been used throughout history to sound an alarm, call a congregation, announce dinnertime, or signal a victory. School bells called children in from recess, and cow bells made the herd easier to locate. Bells have been made in brass, glass, china, bronze, and cast iron; in simple as well as elaborately embossed forms; and in amusing figurals. See also Schoolhouse Collectibles.

**Brass, French lady with fan, 5½",
$75.00.**

Brass, braided cord clapper, on oval base, 7x6" 110.00
Church, mk Meneeley Bell Co/dtd 1911, w/bracket, 20" dia ...300.00
CI, Saignelecier, Ch'Antel Foundeur, dtd 1878, hand sz 36.00
Colonial maid figural, brass, 5x2½" 48.00
Cow, w/orig label, Sargent & Co, NY, 6½" 18.00
Crowned bear w/shield forms hdl, brass, Hemony, 5⅝x3⅜" 110.00
Door type, spring turns w/wht porc doorknob, Taylor, 1860 ....95.00
Dutch girl figural, bronze, 4½" 125.00
Elizabethan lady figural, brass, 4½" 65.00
Felix the Cat figural hdl, brass, 4¼x2½" 75.00
Glass, cranberry w/crystal hdl, England, 12" 150.00
Glass, custard, smocking pattern, orig clapper 145.00
Gong, brass, dome form on lamp-base std, 16" 75.00
Gong, wrought steel, curled ends, 1-pc triangle, 12" sides 60.00
Harness, Droschky, NP arched fr, clappers w/in & w/o, 12x12" .150.00
Lady in hoop dress & bonnet figural, brass, 5" 58.00
Napoleon figural hdl, brass, Waterloo scenes at base, 6¼" 70.00
Napoleon figural hdl, brass, 7x3⅜" 70.00
Neville Chamberlain head figural hdl, brass, 5¼x2½" 65.00
Powhatan Indian figural, brass 125.00
Roosevelt/Stalin/Churchill emb on metal, England, 5¾x4½" ...60.00
Sheep, brass, w/strap bar, 3½" dia 22.00
Sheep, brass, 3 on leather strap 40.00
Sheep, smooth heavy brass w/iron clapper, 3½x3½" 27.50
Sleigh, brass, 1¼" dia, 23 on orig leather strap, EX 165.00
Sleigh, brass, 1¼" dia, 30 on leather strap, EX 175.00
Sleigh, brass, 1⅛" dia, 23 on orig leather strap, 1890s 125.00
Sleigh, brass, 15 on leather strap, EX 70.00
Sleigh, brass, 32 graduated on old strap 225.00
Sleigh, brass, 4 on arched metal strap 40.00
Sleigh, brass, 42 single-throated on orig leather strap, EX 200.00
St Peter's or Vatican figures emb on brass, 7½" 185.00
Tap to ring, SP, mushroom, CI octagonal base, pat 1883, 6" 55.00
Tea, winged angel figural hdl, silver, mk 800 ....70.00

Turtle figural, CI, tap on head or tail to ring, 6½" 200.00
Victorian lady figural, brass, 4¼" 50.00
2 spaniels form hdl, brass, 4x2⅞" 70.00

Bennett, John

Bringing with him the knowledge and experience he had gained at the Doulton (Lambeth) Pottery in England, John Bennett built a kiln in New York City in the year 1876, where he continued his methods of decorating faience under the glaze. Early wares utilized imported English biscuit, though subsequently local clays (both white and cream-colored) were also used. His first kiln was on Lexington Avenue; he eventually erected others on East Twenty-Fourth Street. The earliest mark was 'J. Bennett, N.Y.'; 'West Orange, N.J.' was used later. The pottery was in operation for only six years.

Jar, mums, wht/teal on yel-brn, w/lid, 4" 400.00
Plaque, floral, lt gr/bl, sgn/101 Lex Ave NY 1877, 18" dia . . .7,500.00
Vase, floral, pk/wht on cobalt, sgn/412 E 24th NY, 10x8" 950.00
Vase, floral w/blk outlines on foliage ground, sgn, 13" 3,960.00
Vase, floral/butterflies, sm bulb neck, sgn/412 E 24, 8x6" 900.00

Vase, butterflies and dogwood branches, addressed '412 E. 24. NY,' 8½", $1,100.00.

Bennington

Although the term has become a generic one for the mottled brown ware produced there, Bennington is not a type of pottery, but rather a town in Vermont where two important potteries were located. The Norton Company, founded in 1793, produced mainly redware and salt-glazed stoneware; only during a brief partnership with Fenton (1845-47) was any Rockingham attempted. The Norton Company endured until 1894, operated by succeeding generations of the Norton family. Fenton organized his own pottery in 1847. There he manufactured not only redware and stoneware, but more artistic types as well — graniteware, scroddled ware, flint enamel, a fine parian, and vast amounts of their famous Rockingham. Though from an esthetic standpoint his work rated highly among the country's finest ceramic achievements, he was economically unsuccessful. His pottery closed in 1858.

It is estimated that only one in five Fenton pieces were marked; and although it has become a common practice to link any fine piece of Rockingham to this area, careful study is vital in order to be able to distinguish Bennington's from the similar wares of many other American and Staffordshire potteries. Although the practice was without the permission of the proprietor, it was nevertheless a common occurrence for a potter to take his molds with him when moving from one pottery to the next; so

particularly well-received designs were often reproduced at several locations. Of eight known Fenton marks, four are variations of the '1849' impressed stamp — 'Lyman Fenton Co., Fenton's Enamel Patented 1849, Bennington, Vermont.' These are generally found on examples of Rockingham and flint enamel. A raised, rectangular scroll with 'Fenton's Works, Bennington, Vermont,' was used on early examples of porcelain. From 1852 to 1858, the company operated under the title of the United States Pottery Company. Three marks — the ribbon mark with the initials USP, the oval with a scrollwork border and the name in full, and the plain oval with the name in full — were used during that period.

Among the more sought-after examples are the bird and animal figurines, novelty pitchers, figural bottles, and all of the more finely-modeled items. Recumbent deer, cows, standing lions with one forepaw on a ball, and opposing pairs of poodles with baskets in their mouths and 'coleslaw' fur were made in Rockingham, flint enamel, and occasionally in parian. Numbers in the listings below refer to the book *Bennington Pottery and Porcelain* by Barret.

Key: c/s —— cobalt on salt glaze

Baking dish, flint enamel, 1849 mk, minor staining, 7" dia 250.00
Baking dish, flint enamel, 1849 mk, 8-sided, 9" L 250.00
Banquet lamp, flint enamel, mk, cut globe/prisms, 27", EX . .8,500.00
Book flask, Bennington Companion, flint enamel, 10½", EX .2,600.00
Book flask, Departed Spirits, flint enamel, EX color, pt, NM . .700.00
Book flask, Departed Spirits, flint enamel, 2-qt, M 950.00
Book flask, flint enamel, very rare, 4-qt (largest sz), NM 2,000.00
Book flask, Hermit's Companion, flint enamel, mk, pt, EX 950.00
Book flask, LF&Co/Pat on spine, flint enamel, LF mk, pt, VG .500.00
Book flask, scroddled, minor chips/slight discolor, pt 400.00
Bottle, toby astride barrel, flint enamel, mk, 10¾", NM 1,400.00
Box, trinket; parian, florals/grapes, tinted, 5" L, NM 50.00
Candlestick, Rockingham, B 197-C, 8", M 500.00
Candlestick, Rockingham, minor kiln separations, 9", pr 725.00
Chamber pot, flint enamel, Scalloped Rib, 9" dia, M 600.00
Clinched fist, flint enamel, brn w/bl spots, rare, 4", VG 760.00
Coffeepot, flint enamel, Scalloped Rib, base crack, 12" 850.00
Creamer, B Franklin seated, flint enamel, grapevine hdl, rpr . . .500.00
Creamer, B Franklin toby, flint enamel w/gr, boot hdl, rpr 500.00
Creamer, cow form, flint enamel, w/lid, rpr on horn, 7" L 450.00
Creamer, cow form, Rockingham, w/lid, 7" L, NM 450.00
Creamer, cow form, yellowware, w/lid, USP Co, 7" L, NM . .1,600.00
Creamer, flint enamel, Tulip & Heart, 1849 mk, 6", EX 500.00
Creamer, Gen Stark, Rockingham, B 416-D, M 1,200.00
Creamer, porc, bl/wht, simple floral, bulbous, 3½", M 60.00
Creamer, seated toby, flint enamel, grapevine hdl, mk, rpr 500.00
Creamer, seated toby, Rockingham, 1849 mk, B IX-A, M 550.00
Creamer, toby, scroddled, brn, grapevine hdl, USP, rpr, 6" . .1,350.00
Cuspidor, flint enamel, Scalloped Rib, rare Fenton mk, 9", EX .450.00
Cuspidor, Rockingham, 1849 mk, 8" dia 200.00
Cuspidor, scroddled, bl, 8" dia, EX 550.00
Cuspidor, scroddled, tan, diamond motif, very rare, 9½", M . .1,200.00
Figure, poodle, flint enamel, extensive prof rpr, 9x10½" 4,250.00
Figure, poodle, flint enamel, prof rpr/flaw, 8x9½", pr 5,500.00
Figure, recumbent doe w/tree vase, flint enamel, rpr, 11" L . .4,000.00
Flowerpot, cattails emb, wht clay, attached saucer, 5⅜" 65.00
Foot warmer, Rockingham, rprs/age crack, B 183-C, 9" 100.00
Frame, flint enamel, Rococo form/embossing, 9¾x10¾", NM . .650.00
Frame, Rockingham, oval, 8x9½", M 750.00
Goblet, Rockingham, no hdl, 5½", M 525.00
Goblet, Rockingham, w/hdl, 4½", M 250.00
Inkwell, recumbent lion form, Rockingham, 4¾" L, EX 225.00
Miniature bowl, Rockingham, Turk's head, M 250.00
Miniature wash bowl & pitcher, Rockingham, rprs, bowl: 4" . . .950.00

Mixing bowl, Rockingham, 1849 mk, 16½" dia, M 1,800.00
Mold, flint enamel, Turk's head, B 145-C, 6½" dia, NM 150.00
Mug, flint enamel, 3" 130.00
Mug, Rockingham, att, 4", M 60.00
Mug, Rockingham, paneled, hairline, 3¼" 60.00
Nameplate, Rockingham, serpentine, no letters, 3½x8", M 125.00
Nameplate, Rockingham fr w/parian letters, 3½x8", M 400.00
Nameplate, wht porc, emb scrolls on scalloped form, 8" L, EX . 100.00
Paperweight, dog on dome base, Rockingham, mk, 4½" L, EX . 650.00
Paperweight, eagle form, graniteware, minor crazing, 4" L 300.00
Paperweight, flint enamel, hexagonal finial, mk, 5" L, EX 350.00
Paperweight, recumbent dog, graniteware, blk/gold, 4" L, NM . 300.00
Paperweight, recumbent dog, graniteware, no color, 4" L, NM . 250.00
Pipkin, flint enamel, w/lid, B 142, 9", M 2,600.00
Pitcher, flint enamel, Tulip & Heart, mk, 2 sm chips, 10" 600.00
Pitcher, parian, sheaf of wheat, B 101-C, 10¾" 75.00
Pitcher, parian, Wild Rose, glazed int, 10", M 200.00
Pitcher, Rockingham, Paneled Grapevine, 7¾", M 1,050.00

Rockingham pitchers, left to right: Pond Lily, U.S. ribbon mark,
10½", $700.00; Fox hunt relief, Norton & Fenton mark, 8", $800.00.

Pitcher, Rockingham, Pond Lily, US ribbon mk, 10½", M 700.00
Pitcher, scroddled, Alternate Rib, brn, oval USP mk, 6", EX . . 700.00
Plate, flint enamel, 9½" 135.00
Relish dish, Rockingham, leaf form, 10" L, M 350.00
Snuff jar, toby, flint enamel, gr-brn, mk, minor rpr, w/lid 600.00
Snuff jar, toby, Rockingham, 1849 mk, B IX-A, M 1,450.00
Sugar bowl, flint enamel, spherical body, B 126-C, 5¾", EX . . 850.00
Syrup pitcher, graniteware, Sheaf of Wheat, no lid, 6½", M . . . 50.00
Syrup pitcher, porc, bl/wht, Spinning Wheel, 5½", M 150.00
Teapot, Rockingham, Alternate Rib, sm firing mks, 6" 400.00
Tieback, flint enamel, 10-pointed form, 4½" dia, NM 30.00
Tile, flint enamel, sq w/diagonal gridwork, mk, 7", EX 400.00
Tobacco jar, flint enamel, cylindrical w/tab hdls, 7½", M 400.00
Toothbrush holder, flint enamel, Alternate Rib, w/lid, NM . . 500.00
Vase, majolica, grapevines, pointed rim, 4", M 275.00
Vase, parian, bl/wht, Poppy, appl grapes/hdls, 11", pr, NM . . 400.00
Vase, parian, bl/wht, putti/grape panels, twist hdls, 9", NM . . 350.00
Vase, parian, bl/wht, Songbird, B 280-E, 4", M 25.00
Vase, parian, boy w/sheaf of wheat figural, 7", NM 100.00
Vase, parian, swan form, 6¾", NM 200.00
Vase, tulip; flint enamel, 10", NM 600.00
Wash bowl, flint enamel, paneled, 1849 mk, 2 lg chips, 13½" . 475.00
Wash pitcher, flint enamel, Scalloped Rib, mk, rstr, 13" 750.00

Stoneware

Churn, floral spray (elaborate), c/s, E Norton, 5-gal 1,000.00

Churn, floral spray (simple), c/s, E Norton, ca 1890, 4-gal 600.00
Crock, chicken pecking corn, c/s, J Norton, 2-gal 800.00
Crock, floral, c/s, J&E, 1850-1859, 1½-gal 800.00
Crock, floral (bold/stylized), c/s, E&LP, 3-gal 150.00
Crock, floral & leaf spray, c/s, J&E, 1850-1859, 5-gal 575.00
Crock, flower basket (elaborate), c/s, J&E, 1850s, 4-gal 750.00
Crock, leaf (simple), c/s, E&LP, 1861-1881, 1-gal 165.00
Jug, bird on stump, c/s, J&E, 1850-1859, 1-gal 400.00
Jug, floral, c/s, E&LP, stains/minor firing crack, 16" 425.00

Jug, cobalt dog and fence on salt
glaze, strap handle, hairline, 17",
$1,200.00.

Beswick

In the early 1890s, James Wright Beswick operated a pottery in
Longston, England, where he produced fine dinnerware as well as ornamental ceramics. Today's collectors are most interested in the figurines
made since 1936 by a later generation Beswick firm, John Beswick, Ltd.
They specialize in reproducing accurately detailed bone china models of
authentic breeds of animals. Their Fireside Series includes dogs, cats,
elephants, horses, the Huntsman, and an Indian figure, which measure up
to 14" in height. The Connoisseur line is modeled after the likenesses of
famous racing horses. Beatrix Potter's characters and some of Walt Disney's
are charmingly recreated and appeal to children and adults alike. Other
items, such as character Tobys, have also been produced. The Beswick
name is stamped on each piece. The firm was absorbed by the Doulton
group in 1973.

Basket, blown-out palm trees, gold trim, 10½" 58.00
Cookie jar, horse & jockey figural, 10x9" 85.00
Figurine, cat, blk w/wht face, 3x3½" 20.00
Figurine, Clydesdale horse, 8½x10" 45.00
Figurine, hawk, orig gold sticker, #2316, 7" 38.00
Figurine, Hereford cow, brn/wht, 4½x7" 85.00
Figurine, monkey smokes pipe 38.00
Figurine, mouse, Beatrix Potter's Appley Dapply, 3¼" 18.00
Pitcher, character; Little Nell's Grandfather, sm 45.00
Platter, Romeo & Juliet 95.00
Vase, Naeda, floral w/gold, bl sponging, 8½" 35.00
Wall hangers, sea gulls flying, set of 3: 13½", 11", & 9" 85.00

Big Little Books

The first Big Little Book was published in 1933 and copyrighted in

1932 by the Whitman Publishing Company of Racine, Wisconsin. Its hero was Dick Tracy. The concept was so well accepted that others soon followed Whitman's example; and, though the 'Big Little Book' phrase became a trademark of the Whitman Company, the formats of his competitors — Saalfield, Goldsmith, Van Wiseman, Lynn, and World Syndicate — were exact copies. Today's Big Little Book buffs collect them all.

These hand-sized sagas of adventure were illustrated with full-page cartoons on the right-hand page and the story narration on the left. Colorful cardboard covers contained hundreds of pages, usually totaling over an inch in thickness. Big Little Books originally sold for 10¢ at the dime store; as late as the mid-1950s when the popularity of comic books caused sales to decline signaling an end to production, their price had risen to a mere 20¢. Their appeal was directed toward the pre-teens who bought, traded, and hoarded Big Little Books. Because so many were stored in attics and closets, many have survived. Among the super heroes are G-Men, Flash Gordon, Tarzan, the Lone Ranger, and Red Ryder; in a lighter vein, you'll find such lovable characters as Blondie and Dagwood, Mickey Mouse, Little Orphan Annie, and Felix the Cat.

In the early to mid-'30s, Whitman published several Big Little Books as advertising premiums for the Coco Malt Company, who packed them in boxes of their cereal. These are highly prized by today's collectors, as are Disney stories and super-hero adventures.

Our advisor for this category is Ron Donnelly; he is listed in the Directory under Florida.

Better Little Books, Blondie & Dagwood in Hot Water, #1410, 1946, EX, $20.00. (Photo courtesy Hake's Americana, York, PA)

Ace Drummond, 1935 . . . . .20.00
Boss of the Chisholm Trail, 1939, NM .22.00
Brave Little Tailor, 1939 . . . . .35.00
Buck Jones, Fighting Rangers, 1936 . . . . .30.00
Buck Rogers, City Below the Sea, 1934 .50.00
Buck Rogers, City of Floating Globes, Cocomalt, EX 100.00
Buck Rogers, Depth Men of Jupiter, 1935, VG 55.00

Buck Rogers, Planetoid Plot, 1936, NM 75.00
Buck Rogers, War w/Planet Venus, 1938, EX 65.00
Buck Rogers, 25th Century AD, 1933, VG 75.00
Dan Dunn, Secret Operative & Zeppelin of Doom, 1938, EX . . .60.00
Dan Dunn & Border Smugglers, 1938, NM 30.00
Dick Tracy, Boris Arson Gang, 1935 . . . . .40.00
Donald Duck, Herald for Trouble, 1942, G 35.00
Donald Duck & the Green Serpent, 1947 . . . . .50.00
Ella Cinders & the Mysterious House, 1934 . . . . .50.00
Farmyard Symphony, Disney, 1930 . . . . .25.00
Felix the Cat, 1943 . . . . .50.00
Flash Gordon, Ice World of Mongo, 1942, EX 50.00
Flash Gordon, Jungles of Mongo, 1947, EX 40.00
Flash Gordon, Perils of Mongo, 1940, VG 45.00
Flash Gordon, Power Men of Mongo, 1943, EX 50.00
Flash Gordon, Tournaments of Mongo, 1935, EX 65.00
G-Man Vs the Red X, 1936, EX 30.00
G-Men Alien, 1939 . . . . .20.00
Houdini's Big Little Book of Magic, 1927, EX 40.00
Inspector Wade Solves the Mystery of the Red Aces, 1937 . . . .20.00
Jack Armstrong, Mystery of Iron Key, EX 30.00
Jackie Cooper, Dinky, VG 25.00
Jackie Cooper, Skippy & Sooky, 1933, EX 35.00
Joe Lewis, Brown Bomber, 1936, VG 40.00
John Carter of Mars, 1941, EX 100.00
Just Kids, King Features, #1052, 1934, EX 65.00
Lil Abner Among the Millionaires, 1939, EX 50.00
Little Men, EX 25.00
Little Miss Muffet, EX 25.00
Little Orphan Annie, Ghost Gang, premium, 1935, EX 60.00
Little Orphan Annie, Thieves' Den, 1944, EX 25.00
Little Orphan Annie, 1933, VG 100.00
Mandrake & the Midnight Monster, EX 30.00
Mandrake the Magician, Flame Pearls, 1946, EX 25.00
Men w/Wings, 1938 . . . . .30.00
Mickey Mouse, Foreign Legion, EX 45.00
Mickey Mouse, Mail Pilot, 1933, EX .65.00
Mickey Mouse Runs His Own Newspaper, 1937, NM 45.00
Mr District Attorney on the Job, 1941 .25.00
Once Upon a Time, 1933, VG 50.00
Oswald the Lucky Rabbit, Whitman, 1934 . . . . .30.00
Plainsman, 1936 . . . . .35.00
Practical Pig, Disney, 1939 . . . . .30.00
Radio Patrol, Trailing the Safe Blowers 25.00
Roy Rogers at Crossed Feather Ranch, 1945, EX 25.00
Smitty, Golden Gloves Tournament, 1934 . . . . .35.00
Tailspin Tommy, Hunting for Gold, 1935, G 20.00
Tarzan, Beast of; 1937, NM 55.00
Tarzan, Golden Lion, VG 45.00
Tarzan, Lost Empire, 1933, EX 40.00
Tarzan, Twins, 1934, rare, NM 175.00
Terry & the Pirates, War in Jungle, 1944, G 25.00
Texas Kid, 1937, EX 20.00
Timid Elmer, Disney, 1939 . . . . .30.00
Tom Beatty, Ace of Service Scores Again, EX 20.00
Tom Mix, Fighting Cowboys, VG 50.00
Tom Mix & His Circus on Barbary Coast, 1940, EX 30.00
Wash Tubbs, Pandemonia, 1934, EX .30.00

Bing and Grondahl

In 1853 brothers M.H. and J.H. Bing formed a partnership with Frederick Vilhelm Grondahl in Copenhagen, Denmark. Their early wares were porcelain plaques and figurines designed by the noted sculptor Thorvaldsen of Denmark. Dinnerware production began in 1863, and by 1889 their underglaze color 'Copenhagen Blue' had earned them worldwide acclaim. They are perhaps most famous today for their Christmas plates, the first of which was made in 1895. The plate was titled 'Behind the Frozen Window,' and the series has continued to the present with annual editions. A second series commemorating Mother's Day was added in 1969.

Coffeepot, sea gull, lg 95.00
Figurine, boy w/sandals, #1671, pk 150.00
Figurine, boy w/trumpet, #1792, 6½" 175.00
Figurine, bullfinch, #1909, bl/tan on lt gr rock, 4¾" 95.00
Figurine, Come to Mom, #2324 .....140.00
Figurine, dachshund, #1755, 2¾" 110.00
Figurine, fisher boy, #2338, 7½" 250.00
Figurine, Friends, #2249, cat in basket, 3¾" 140.00
Figurine, girl & butterfly, #2125, 7½" 245.00
Figurine, girl talking to doll, #2191 .....150.00
Figurine, girl w/puppy, #2316 .....140.00
Figurine, guinea pig, #2479, sitting, 3½" 90.00
Figurine, Hans Christian Anderson, #2037, 9" 695.00
Figurine, kitten, #2506, standing, wht, 5" 70.00
Figurine, Little Match Girl, #1655, 5½" 210.00
Figurine, Love Refused, #1614 .....225.00
Figurine, mandolinist sitting on stool, #1600, gray/wht, 11" 325.00
Figurine, Marianne, #2373 .....190.00
Figurine, monkeys, #1581, 4 w/arms entwined, 4¾" 150.00
Figurine, newsboy, #2148 .....135.00
Figurine, nude man asleep on mule, #4026, 9¼" 660.00
Figurine, Pickie, #1636 .....135.00
Figurine, Prejudiced, #2175 .....240.00
Figurine, Siamese cat, #2464, wht, 5½" 85.00
Figurine, woodpecker, #1717, 4¾" 210.00
Figurine, young sailor holding rope, #2321 .....160.00
Figurine, 2 bears, #1825, fighting, 7" 295.00
Ginger jar, reticulated flowering trees, EHL, 9" 1,750.00
Paperweight, Christian X Silver Jubilee, pyramid shape, 5" 120.00
Plate, collector; 1907, Christmas, Little Match Girl 120.00
Plate, collector; 1908, Christmas, St Petri Church 88.00
Plate, collector; 1912, Christmas, Going to Church 88.00
Plate, collector; 1920, Christmas, Hare in Snow 88.00
Plate, collector; 1924, Christmas, Lighthouse 60.00
Plate, collector; 1935, Christmas, Lillebelt Bridge 65.00
Plate, collector; 1957, Christmas, Christmas Candles 150.00
Teapot, sea gull 75.00
Vase, bl bird on floral branch, sgn, #d/mk, 15½" 295.00
Vase, dandelions, 10" 60.00
Vase, sea gulls, gold wing tips, #682, 8" 95.00

Birdcages

Birdcages can be found in various architectural styles and in a range of materials — wood, wicker, brass, and gilt metal with ormolu mounts. Those that once belonged to the wealthy are sometimes inlaid with silver or jewels. In the 1800s, it became fashionable to keep birds, and some of the most beautiful examples found today date back to that era. Musical cages that contained automated bird figures became popular; today these command prices of several thousand dollars. In the latter 1800s, wicker styles came into vogue. Collectors still appreciate their graceful lines and find they adapt easily to modern homes.

Automaton, gilt metal wire dome, bird sings/nods, Fr, 12" 550.00
Brass, Hendrix, no stand 25.00
Brass, mk Leon All Brass, EX 60.00
Brass, rnd, Maxwell, w/glass & porc feeders 125.00
Iron & tin, 3 tiers, fancy corners, ca 1860, EX 975.00
Miner's, w/feed box, stoneware water jug, EX 40.00
Porc, rtcl roof/sides, scrolled borders, mk France, 15½" 425.00

Victorian-style wirework rectangular case with three doors on triple-hinged base, 54" long, $450.00.

Wire, Hendrix, w/stand, EX 50.00
Wire, sq w/peaked roof, acorn finial, G pnt, 1880s, 13x7x7" 80.00
Wire, 6-dome+gable roof, 3-door, 3-hinge base, Vict, 54" L 440.00

Bisque

Bisque is a term referring to unglazed earthenware or porcelain that has been fired only once. During the Victorian era, bisque figurines became very popular. Most were highly decorated in pastels and gilt and demonstrated a fine degree of workmanship in the quality of their modeling. Few were marked. See also Heubach; Nodders; and Dolls; Piano Babies.

Pair, boy with shovel, girl with watering can, no mark, 13", $175.00.

Baby w/hands in ink pot, gr tint/hands/body, 3%/8x2x3" 95.00
Blk man on cotton bale w/banjo, striped pants, 6¼x2¼" 95.00
Boy & girl in yel/floral attire, ped base, German, 10", pr 275.00
Boy & girl on swings, bl/pk/cream, 3½x1¾", pr 88.00
Boy carrying basket, bl shorts/lav shirt, German, 14" 225.00

Boy in lg hat holds gun; girl holds broken doll, 16", pr 300.00
Boy in nightshirt holds rabbit; girl holds dove, 13", pr 250.00
Boy lies w/football, mk G Kraus, 2⅞x7" 110.00
Bust, boy & girl w/blonde hair, German, 10", pr 275.00
Children on teeter-totter, X-feathers mk/Matino, 8x11" 60.00
Chimney sweep by egg-shaped vase, 5¼" 95.00
Couple, she seated asleep, he approaching w/flowers, 12" 150.00
Couple at well, pk & wht w/gold trim, 5¾x4½" 95.00
Couple under umbrella, pastel colors, EX details, 6x3½" 175.00
Grandmother w/3 sm children, mk Ernst Bohne, 6x2½x4" 225.00
Mamma Katzenjammer & Gloomy Gus, German, 1910, 5½", pr .65.00
Man, seated, offers bone to dog, kneeling shoeshiner, 8x9" 125.00
Night light, owl w/glass eyes, 4¼x3" 195.00
Persian harem dancer, wht w/gold trim, mk, 9½" 95.00
Romeo & Juliet, bright colors, EX details, unmk, 19" 450.00
Romeo & Juliet hold hands, unmk German, 13" 275.00
Shuttlecock players, boy/girl w/rackets, pastels, 13", pr 250.00
Urn, gold ormolu festoons/bows/mts, 24", pr 850.00
Young couple hold hands, floral attire, 13", pr 275.00
18th century couple, wht w/pk & gold, 17", pr 225.00
2 girls in wicker basket, 4¾x3¼" 135.00

Black Americana

Black memorabilia is without a doubt a field that encompasses the most widely-exploited ethnic group in our history. But within this field there are many levels of interest — arts and achievements such as folk music and literature, caricatures in advertising, souvenirs, toys, fine art, and legitimate research into the days of their enslavement and enduring struggle for equality. The list is endless.

In the listings below are some with a derogatory connotation. Thankfully, these are from a bygone era and represent the mores of a culture that existed nearly a century ago. They are included only to convey the fact that they are a part of this growing area of collecting interest. Black Americana catalogs featuring a wide variety of items for sale are published quarterly. See the Directory under Clubs, Newsletters, and Catalogs for more information. See also Post Cards; Posters, Minstrel; Sheet Music.

Ash tray, boy on potty, pot metal 75.00
Ash tray, Coon Chicken Inn, glass 32.00
Book, A Story of Our Gang, hard cover, Whitman, 1929, 20-pg .65.00
Book, Beloved Belindy, 2nd ed, Johnny Gruelle, 1926, 90-pg . . .45.00
Book, coloring; Little Blk Sambo, 1941, NM 65.00
Book, Janie-Bell, Abandoned Colored Baby, 1940, EX 60.00
Book, Little Blk Sambo, linen, lg 65.00
Book, Little Blk Sambo Magic Drawing, 1928, NM 50.00
Book, Little Brn Baby, P Dunbar, 1940, EX 45.00
Book, Little Nemo in Slumberland, 1945 reprint, EX 35.00
Book, New Story of Little Blk Sambo, CB Thurston, 1926, EX . .45.00
Book, Sambo & Twins, hard cover, H Bannerman, 91-pg, EX . .38.00
Book, Turkey Trott, hard cover, Kate G Dyer, 1942, NM 28.00
Book, 10 Little Niggers, McLoughlin, ca 1880, EX 185.00
Bookends, Mammy, wood, handmade, 7", EX, pr 55.00
Box, take-out; Coon Chicken Inn, colorful cb, 7x4x3" 15.00
Buttons, Mammy, maroon bandana, blk hair, pr 30.00
Cigarette holder, 3 Blk children on clothesline, ceramic 20.00
Cookbook, Aunt Jemima's Magical Recipes, 1952, 26-pg, NM . .35.00
Cookbook, New Orleans Recipes, Mammy cover, 86-pg, 6x8½" .18.00
Cookie jar, Blk chef's head, wht hat, pottery, 1930s, EX 65.00
Decanter, butler, full figure, ceramic, cork neck, 8", M 185.00
Doll, Mammy, appl felt facial features, cloth body, 16", EX 45.00
Doll, Topsy, blk compo, 3 pigtails, 10" 65.00

Doll, Topsy Turvy, cloth body, ca 1940s, 12½" 45.00
Figure, Blk boy w/hands in pocket, metal, 3", EX 65.00
Figure, Blk woman waving, CI/lead, England 32.00
Figure, bride & groom, chalkware, 1949, 3¾", M 65.00
Figure, porter, metal, 2½", EX 28.00
Figure, porter, papier-mache, 3½", EX 35.00
Figure, porter & cook, Grey Iron Co, Am Family series, pr 45.00
Figure, sleeping baby, chalkware, 4" 25.00
Flour sack, Aunt Jemima, 1940s, 25-lb, rare, M 65.00
Game, 10 Little Niggers, Parker Bros, EX in orig box 125.00
Laundry bag, Mammy, 24x16½", EX 48.00
Lawn ornament, Blk child w/watermelon, CI, 1930s, 24", pr . . .300.00
Match holder, Coon Chicken Inn, ca 1930, 4x6" 195.00
Menu, A&P, Mammy on cover, 1936, 8-pg, 8½x12", EX 25.00
Menu, Coon Chicken Inn, child's, 4½", EX 48.00
Night light base, boy praying, ceramic, 5½" 32.00
Note holder, Mammy holding broom, full figure, plastic, EX 38.00
Paperweight, alligator swallowing Blk boy, CI, EX pnt, 5½" 65.00
Paperweight, alligator w/Blk figural pencil in mouth, metal 40.00
Pin, Mammy on blk metal, rhinestone bandana, 1¾", M 28.00
Pin-bk button, Aunt Jemima Breakfast Club, Eat...Breakfast 15.00
Pincushion, Mammy, felt w/embr features, 8", EX 38.00
Pitcher, syrup; Aunt Jemima, F&F, EX 32.00
Pitcher, syrup; Little Blk Sambo HP on glass 125.00
Place mat, Coon Chicken Inn, paper 18.00
Plate, Coon Chicken Inn, 9¾", EX 150.00
Plate, golliwog/pig/clown in center, enamel on tin, 10" dia 95.00
Plate, pickaninny boy & goose, ceramic, 7", EX 35.00
Post card, Coontown Kids, Raphael Tuck, full color 12.00
Post card, Have a Smile w/Me?, 1910, EX 12.00
Post card, I Am Holding My Own, man holds crying baby, 1907 . .8.00
Post card, Le Negre Joueaux Dansard le Cakewalk, old 18.00
Post card, Watermelon Jake, silk emb, ca 1905, rare 35.00
Pot holder caddy, Mammy, wood w/HP features, M 35.00
Puzzle, Little Blk Sambo, sgn Fern Bisel Peat, 7½x9½" 38.00
Record album, Little Blk Sambo, 78rpm, ca 1940s, EX 28.00
Record set, Little Blk Sambo, Bluebird, 78rpm, 1930s, EX 45.00
Script, radio; Amos & Andy, Amos' Wedding, 1935 . . . . .20.00
Shakers, Aunt Jemima & Uncle Mose, plastic, 5", M, pr 30.00
Shakers, Blk boy on potty, ceramic, 4½", EX, pr 48.00
Shakers, Blk boy/watermelon, ceramic, EX, pr 45.00
Shakers, Mammy & Chef, china, 4½", M 38.00
Sheet music, Old Blk Joe, EX 15.00
Sheet music, 3 Little Words, 1930 . . . . .15.00
Shopping board, Mammy, We Needs?, 11x7", M 65.00
Soap holder, Mammy w/basket on head figural, CI, 5", EX 95.00
Spice set, Blk Chef, ceramic, on wood rack, EX 95.00
Spoon, demitasse; Sunny Jim, sterling, 4", M 95.00
String holder, Blk bellhop, pottery, ca 1930s, M 175.00
Tablecloth, Mammy serving pie, cotton, 52x48" 85.00
Teapot, Blk boy on elephant, ceramic, M 38.00
Toothpick holder, fancy-dressed Blk boy, milk glass, M 150.00
Towel, boy playing harmonica/children dancing, 26x15", EX . . .45.00
Trade card, We's Done Got Domestic, We Has!, litho, 4½x2¾" . .12.00
Tumbler, Coon Chicken Inn 30.00
Tumbler, 3 crap shooters on frosted glass, 7", M 25.00
Vase, lady figural, ceramic, 6", M 45.00
Wall plaque/spoon rest, Mammy, pottery 65.00

Black Cats

The main producer of the 'Black Cats' collectibles was the Shafford Company, although occasionally pieces will be found bearing the marks of other firms. Wood and Sons, Ltd., in Burslem, England, produced an 8" figural teapot as part of a novelty line marketed in this country by Fondeville of New York. Other items have been found marked 'Wales,' 'Empress,' and 'Napco Ceramics, Japan.' Black Cat collectors usually prefer to limit their 'litter' to those kittens with a shiny black glaze and styling similar to the Shafford cats.

    Our advisor for this category is Pam Ford; she is listed in the Directory under Missouri.

Ash tray, face only, flat, gr eyes, red bow/ears, 3"	12.00
Ash tray, face only, flat, gr eyes, 4½"	12.00
Bookends, seated on book, fluffy look, 5½", pr	30.00
Candy tray, face only, flat, wicker hdl, 5"	25.00
Creamer & sugar bowl, stacking	28.00
Cruet, head stopper, 7½", pr	33.00
Cruet, seated, kitten on bk as hdl, head removes, 8½"	18.00
Decanter, cordial; head stopper, paw spout, 8"	25.00
Decanter, stands, long body, bl tuxedo, 6 hooks on bk, 6⅝"	35.00
Desk caddy, pen forms tail, spring body holds letters, 6½"	10.00
Figurine, arched bk, on book by vase, yel eyes/red ears, 3"	12.00
Figurine, kitten, stands, lg head, 2½"	4.00
Napkin ring, ring forms body, 2⅜"	2.00
Pincushion, crouches, cushion on bk, tongue measure, 2x4¼"	18.00
Planter, stalking panther style, 11½" L	14.00
Shakers, on bk legs, paws folded, red bow, gold trim, 5", pr	12.00
Shakers, seated, gold bands/bows w/red dots, wht eyes, 3¾", pr	15.00
Shakers, strolling, dbl-ended, 10¼" L	12.00
Shakers, strolling, wht eyes, red ears, 1½x5", pr	16.00
Shakers, voice boxes in base, Souvenir of..., 3⅛", pr	10.00
Spice set, face on ea of 6 sq 3" jars, w/rack, Shafford	75.00
Sugar & creamer, cat-head lids are salt/pepper shakers, 5⅜"	35.00
Tea set, 5" pot +creamer & sugar bowl	35.00
Teapot, crouched, scarf/gold disk, spout through mouth, 3¾"	12.00
Teapot, paw spout, head forms lid, mk Shafford RD 95, 4"	26.00
Teapot, paw spout, 8½"	33.00

Teapot, individual, 5", $25.00.

Black Glass

Black glass is a type of colored glass that when held to strong light usually appears deep purple — though since each glasshouse had its own formula, tones may vary. It was sometimes etched or given a satin finish; and occasionally it was decorated with silver, gold, enamel, coralene, or any of these in combination. The decoration was done either by the glasshouse or by firms that specialized in decorating glassware. Crystal, jade, colored glass, or milk glass was sometimes used with the black as an accent. Black glass has been made by many companies since the seventeenth century. Contemporary glasshouses produced black glass during the Depression, seldom signing their product. It is still being made today.

Left to right: Aster bowl, 5", $30.00; Iris vase, 6", $30.00.

Bowl, crimped, 12", +flower frog	35.00
Bowl, ftd, 5", +flower frog	25.00
Box, lady in long gown HP on lid, florals on side, 3¾x5⅝"	245.00
Box, patch; butterfly HP on lid, 1¼x2¼"	125.00
Box, patch; mc HP flowers, wht dots, 1x2¼"	98.00
Box, patch; wht HP flowers/leaves, 1¼x2" dia	75.00
Cake plate, hdls, 10½"	45.00
Candle holder, 10¾", pr	35.00
Candle holder, 4", pr	10.00
Creamer, ftd	12.00
Planter box, emb nude dancers, mk LE Smith	45.00
Plate, 12-sided, 8"	12.00
Plate, 9½"	12.00
Tray, 12-sided, center hdl	25.00
Vase, dancers in relief, 7½"	35.00
Vase, HP florals, rnd w/flaring top, ringed neck, 15", pr	180.00
Vase, HP florals & bird, 13"	75.00
Vase, HP stork/aquatic plants, pilgrim flask form, 9x6½"	85.00
Vase, jack-in-the-pulpit	18.00
Vase, ped ft, hdls, 5¾"	20.00
Vase, silver florals, trophy shape, 8"	30.00

Blown Glass

    Blown glass is rather difficult to date; eighteenth and nineteenth century examples vary little as to technique or style — it ranges from the primitive to the sophisticated. But the metallic content of very early glass caused tiny imperfections that are obvious upon examination, and these are often indicative of age.

    In America, Stiegel introduced the English technique of using a patterned, part-size mold, a practice which was generally followed by many glasshouses after the Revolution. From 1820 to about 1850, glass was blown into full-size 3-part molds. In the listings below, glass is assumed clear unless color is mentioned.

    Numbers refer to a standard reference book, *American Glass* by

George S. and Helen McKearin. See also Bottles and specific manufacturers.

Key: b3m — blown three-mold

Bottle, gr, b3m, appl sloping lip, 12¾" .60.00
Bowl, appl ft, pouring spout, 12x9" dia 135.00
Bowl, aqua, str sides, gallery rim, worn, 6x11" 135.00
Creamer, pear form on ftd base, appl band/hdl, att NE, 6½" . . .375.00
Cuspidor, cobalt, appl hdl, 3½x3¾" .600.00
Decanter, appl 'chain,' orig stopper, att T Cain Boston, qt 650.00

**Blown 3-mold decanters, left to right: GI-18, pint, 7",
$250.00; GI-29, quart, 9⅝", $250.00.**

Flip, bird/tulip in sunburst eng, 4" 200.00
Flip, GIII-26, b3m, 5⅝", M 550.00
Flip, panel molded, 3⅜" 75.00
Flip, urn of flowers eng, 3½" 150.00
Fly catcher, bulbous, appl mouth, 8x6¾" 90.00
Glass, b3m, sheared rim, pontil, ca 1820, 2¾" 275.00
Inkwell, olive-amber, GII-18, b3m, 2x2⅝" 125.00
Lamp, fluid; onion font, tall std, no collar, NE type, 5¾" 85.00
Mug, facet cutting, eng crest w/'S,' German, 5½" 275.00
Pitcher, elaborate appl hdl, 2⅜" 150.00
Pitcher, GIII-12, b3m, 2" 350.00
Pitcher, GIII-21, b3m, 3" 325.00
Pitcher, GIII-5, b3m, appl hdl, 6½" 775.00
Pitcher, ogee sides, hollow appl hdl, 7¾" 250.00
Pitcher, pronounced swirl relief, ogee sides, 8½" 500.00
Plate, b3m, folded rim, 5⅝" 100.00
Salt cellar, GIII-6, b3m, M 200.00
Shot glass, GIII-16, b3m, M 250.00
Tumbler, floral, copper wheel eng, 7" .250.00
Tumbler, GI-20, b3m, 3", M 325.00
Tumbler, GII-14, b3m, M 500.00
Tumbler, GII-21, b3m, barrel shape, 3½" 475.00
Whiskey, GII-18, b3m, 2⅝" 175.00
Wine, cotton twist stem, 4½" 155.00
Wine, red/wht spiral stem w/wht latticinio, 6¾" 325.00

Blue and White Stoneware

Blue and white stoneware, much of which was decorated with such in-

mold designs as grazing cows and Dutch children, was made by practically every American pottery from the turn of the century until the mid-1930s. Crocks, pitchers, wash sets, rolling pins, and canisters are only a few of the items that may be found in this type of 'country' pottery that has become one of today's popular collectibles.

Roseville, Brush-McCoy, Uhl Co., and Burley Winter were among those who produced it; but very few pieces were ever signed. Naturally, condition must be a prime consideration, especially if one is buying for resale; pieces with good, strong color and fully-molded patterns bring premium prices. Normal wear and signs of age are to be expected since this was utility ware and received heavy use in busy households. In the listings that follow, crocks and jars are assumed without lids unless noted otherwise. See also specific manufacturers.

Bean pot, Boston Baked Beans, Flemish, w/lid 290.00
Beater jar, Bl Band 40.00
Bowl, berry; Flying Bird 95.00
Bowl, dough; dk bl, scalloped rim, lg 85.00
Bowl, mixing; feathers 125.00
Bowl, Wedding Ring, 10" 125.00
Bowl, Wedding Ring, 7" 85.00
Butter crock, Apple Blossom, orig lid .155.00
Butter crock, Apricot, orig lid & bail 200.00
Butter crock, Apricots w/Honeycomb, orig lid, bail, & hdl 225.00
Butter crock, Bl Band, orig lid & bail 110.00
Butter crock, Butterfly, orig lid & bail, 6½" 120.00
Butter crock, Colonial, scarce 130.00
Butter crock, Cow, printed, orig lid & bail, stenciled 120.00
Butter crock, Cows & Columns, orig lid 250.00
Butter crock, Daisy & Trellis, orig lid, 4½" 250.00
Butter crock, Dutch Couple, lg 155.00
Butter crock, Eagle, orig lid 450.00
Butter crock, HP flowers, ...150.00
Butter crock, Indian Good Luck Sign .125.00
Canister, Basketweave, Coffee, orig lid 185.00
Canister, Basketweave, Raisins, orig lid 225.00
Canister, Bl Band, Pepper, sm, w/lid 65.00
Canister, Diffused Bl, Tea, orig lid 125.00
Canister, Onion, w/lid, 9" 200.00
Canister, Snowflake, Rice 110.00
Canister, Wildflower, Crackers, orig lid 225.00
Canister, Wildflower, Farina 70.00
Coffeepot, Bl Band 275.00
Coffeepot, devil on body, emb Blanke's Coffeepot on lid, 9½" .350.00
Cookie jar, Basketweave, Put Your Fist In, orig lid, 7½" 325.00
Cookie jar, Brickers 245.00
Cookie jar, Flying Birds 350.00
Cup, Roses, decal 65.00
Cuspidor, Scrolls 85.00
Humidor, stippled w/bird dog on side, flower finial, w/lid 150.00
Milk crock, stove top, bailed, advertising 75.00
Mug, advertising 150.00
Mug, bands & rivets 75.00
Mug, Basketweave 95.00
Mug, Cattails 125.00
Mug, Diffused Bl 75.00
Mug, Flying Bird, ...135.00
Mug, golfer, bl/gray, Robinson Clay Products 150.00
Mug, plain 65.00
Mug, Windy City (Fannie Flagg), Robinson Clay Products 150.00
Pickle crock, Bl Bands 125.00
Pickle crock, Bl Bands, advertising, bail hdl, 5-gal 150.00
Pie plate, Star Mfg 145.00
Pitcher, American Beauty Rose, 10" 175.00

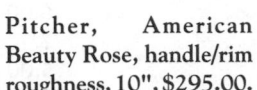
Pitcher, American Beauty Rose, handle/rim roughness, 10", $295.00.

Pitcher, Apricot, 8" 150.00
Pitcher, Avenue of Trees, 8" 145.00
Pitcher, Barrel, +6 mugs 395.00
Pitcher, Basketweave & Flowers 175.00
Pitcher, Bl Band, plain 80.00
Pitcher, Bl Band Scroll 160.00
Pitcher, Bl Sawtooth, Wht Hall 95.00
Pitcher, Bow Knot, cobalt decal 85.00
Pitcher, Butterfly, 4¾" 245.00
Pitcher, Butterfly, 9x7" 165.00
Pitcher, Castle & Fishscale, 8" 195.00
Pitcher, Cattails, 7½" 160.00
Pitcher, Cattails, 9" 155.00
Pitcher, Cattails & Butterfly 150.00
Pitcher, Cherry Cluster 225.00
Pitcher, Cosmos 195.00
Pitcher, Cow 175.00
Pitcher, Diffused Bl 150.00
Pitcher, Doe & Fawn 225.00
Pitcher, Dutch Boy & Girl 160.00
Pitcher, Dutch Children & Windmill 150.00
Pitcher, Dutch Farm Scene, stenciled, 9" 150.00
Pitcher, Dutch Landscape, stenciled, tall 150.00
Pitcher, Eagle 425.00

Pitcher, Flying Birds, rare, M, 8", $695.00.

Pitcher, Eagle & Shield & Arrows, rare 495.00
Pitcher, Edelweiss, no flower 175.00
Pitcher, Flat Iron bldg/girl, Robinson Clay Products, 8½" 185.00
Pitcher, Flowers, stenciled 100.00
Pitcher, Flying Bird 495.00
Pitcher, Grape Cluster on Trellis, 8½" 155.00
Pitcher, Grape w/Leaf Band, 9" 150.00
Pitcher, Grapes w/Rickrack, 8" 150.00
Pitcher, Hunting Scene, rare 300.00
Pitcher, Indian Boy & Girl 225.00
Pitcher, Indian Good Luck 140.00
Pitcher, Indian Head in War Bonnet, waffled body, 8", EX 250.00
Pitcher, Leaping Deer 200.00
Pitcher, Lincoln w/Log Cabin 450.00
Pitcher, Morning-Glory 150.00
Pitcher, Poinsettia, 6½" 250.00
Pitcher, Rose & Fishscale 155.00
Pitcher, Rose on Trellis, M 175.00
Pitcher, Scroll & Leaf, advertising 250.00
Pitcher, Swirl 155.00
Pitcher, Tulip 225.00
Pitcher, Wild Rose 275.00
Pitcher, Windmill & Bush, 7" 165.00
Salt crock, Apricot, orig lid 135.00
Salt crock, Bl Band, SALT in gold 85.00
Salt crock, Blackberry, orig lid 145.00
Salt crock, Butterfly, orig lid 185.00
Salt crock, Daisy on Snowflakes, orig lid 220.00
Salt crock, Eagle w/Arrow 325.00
Salt crock, Flying Bird, orig lid 300.00
Salt crock, Grape on Basketweave 150.00
Salt crock, Maple Leaf 90.00
Salt crock, Oak Leaf, orig lid 125.00
Salt crock, Peacock, orig lid 300.00
Soap dish, Beaded Panels w/Open Rose 125.00
Soap dish, Cat 165.00
Soap dish, Indian in War Bonnet 195.00
Soap dish, Lion 165.00
Soap dish, Rose & Fishscale 85.00
Spittoon, Leaf & Wreath 125.00
Spittoon, Peacock & Fountain 245.00
Toothbrush holder, Bowtie 55.00
Toothbrush holder, Bowtie, stenciled flower 50.00
Toothbrush holder, Rose & Fishscale 65.00
Umbrella stand, oak leaves/animals emb, 21", NM 350.00
Vase, Diffused Bl, ...125.00
Vase, Swirl, cone shape 300.00
Wash set, Rose & Fishscale, 2-pc 275.00
Wash set, Rose & Fishscale, 5-pc 600.00
Wash set, Rose on Trellis, 2-pc 300.00
Water cooler, Apple Blossom 500.00
Water cooler, Bl Band, orig lid 150.00
Water cooler, Cupid, orig lid 600.00
Water cooler, Polar Bear 500.00
Water cooler, Rachel at the Well 500.00

Blue Ridge

Blue Ridge dinnerware was produced by Southern Potteries of Erwin, Tennessee, from the late 1930s until 1956 in eight basic styles and eight hundred different patterns, all of which were hand decorated under the glaze. Vivid colors lit up floral arrangements of seemingly endless variation, fruit of every sort from simple clusters to lush assortments, barnyard fowl, peasant figures, and unpretentious textured patterns. Although it is these dinnerware lines for which they are best known, collectors prize the artist-signed plates from the forties and the limited line of character jugs made during the fifties most highly. Examples of the French Peasant pattern are valued at double the prices listed below; very simple patterns will bring 25% to 50% less.

Our advisors, Betty and Bill Newbound, have compiled a lovely book, *Blue Ridge Dinnerware*, Revised Third Edition, with beautiful color illustrations and current market values. They are listed in the Directory under Michigan. For information concerning the National Blue Ridge Newsletter, see the Clubs, Newsletters, and Catalogs section of the Directory.

Ash tray, advertising, w/rest	45.00
Ash tray, individual	10.00
Bonbon, divided, center hdl, china	38.00
Bowl, 10½" salad	40.00
Bowl, 11½" salad	40.00
Bowl, 5" fruit	3.50
Bowl, 6" cereal/soup	5.00
Bowl, 8" flat soup	9.00
Bowl, 8" round	9.00
Bowl, 8" round divided	12.00
Bowl, 8½" mixing	25.00
Bowl, 9" oval divided vegetable	15.00
Bowl, 9" oval vegetable	12.00
Box, cigarette	45.00
Box, cigarette; w/4 trays	80.00
Box, raised or sculptured designs	60.00
Box, round covered candy	75.00
Breakfast set	250.00
Butter dish, ¼-lb, w/lid	35.00
Butter pat/coaster	10.00
Cake lifter	20.00
Carafe, w/lid	45.00
Casserole, w/lid	25.00
Celery, leaf shape, china	30.00
Celery, Skyline shape	25.00
Child's cereal	12.00
Child's dish, deep feeding	17.50
Child's dish, divided feeding	17.50
Child's mug	12.00
Child's plate	15.00
Child's play set	190.00
Chocolate pot, pedestal, china	125.00
Coffeepot	70.00
Creamer, china	25.00
Creamer, demitasse	30.00
Creamer, regular	6.00
Cup & saucer, demitasse; china	25.00
Cup & saucer, jumbo	20.00
Cup & saucer, regular	7.00
Dish, 8x13" baking	24.00
Egg cup, dbl	15.00
Egg dish, deviled	22.00
Gravy boat	17.00
Gravy tray	15.00
Jug, character; china	350.00
Jug, covered batter	35.00
Jug, covered syrup	40.00
Lamp, china	85.00
Lazy susan, 6-pc, w/tray	85.00
Pitcher, fancy, china	85.00
Plate, artist sgn, china	285.00
Plate, Christmas or Turkey	55.00

Plate, party w/cup well	7.50
Plate, 10" dinner	12.00
Plate, 10½" cake	18.00
Plate, 11½"	20.00
Plate, 12", aluminum edge	17.50
Plate, 3-compartment snack	15.00
Plate, 6"	2.00
Plate, 7" pie	6.00
Plate, 7½" square	7.50
Plate, 8½" salad	5.00
Plate, 8½" salad; bird decor	30.00
Plate, 9½" dinner	7.00
Platter, Thanksgiving Turkey	150.00
Platter, Turkey w/Acorns	150.00
Platter, 11"	7.00
Platter, 12½"	15.00
Platter, 13"	12.00
Platter, 15"	17.00
Platter, 17½", artist sgn	500.00
Platter, 9"	7.00
Ramekin, 5", w/lid	15.00
Ramekin, 7½", w/lid	30.00
Relish, deep shell, china	45.00
Relish, loop hdl, china	45.00
Relish, Maple Leaf, china	30.00
Relish, Martha, 3-compartment, china	50.00
Relish, sm heart shape	25.00
Relish, T-hdl, china	27.00
Salad fork	25.00
Salad spoon	25.00
Server, center hdl	25.00
Shakers, Apple, pr	10.00
Shakers, Blossom Top, pr	30.00
Shakers, Bud Top, pr	30.00
Shakers, Chickens, pr	70.00
Shakers, Mallards, pr	85.00
Shakers, Moderne, pr	9.00
Shakers, Range, pr	25.00
Shakers, regular short, pr	12.00
Shakers, tall ftd, china, pr	35.00
Sugar bowl, demitasse	25.00
Sugar bowl, pedestal or flare, china	30.00
Sugar bowl, regular, w/lid	10.00
Tea tile, round or square	20.00
Teapot, china	50.00
Teapot, demitasse	65.00
Teapot, earthenware	65.00
Tidbit, 2-tier	25.00
Tidbit, 3-tier	30.00
Toast, covered	70.00
Tray, chocolate pot; china	275.00
Tray, flat shell, china	50.00
Vase, bud	45.00
Vase, tapered	75.00
Vase, 5½", round, china	45.00
Vase, 7¼", hdls, china	55.00
Vase, 8" boot	65.00
Vase, 9¼", ruffled top	70.00

Bluebird China

Made from 1910 to 1934, Bluebird china is lovely ware decorated with bluebirds flying among pink flowering branches. It was inexpensive dinnerware and reached the height of its popularity in the second decade of this century. Several potteries produced it; shapes differ from one manufacturer to another, but the decal remains basically the same. Among the backstamps you'll find W.S. George, Cleveland, Carrolton, Homer Laughlin, and Limoges China of Sebring, Ohio . . . and there are others.

Bowl, fruit; Deerwood, 5½"	12.50
Bowl, fruit; Hopewell China, 5"	10.00
Bowl, gravy; w/saucer, Hopewell China	50.00
Bowl, sauce; SP Co, 4½"	10.00
Bowl, soup; PMC Co, 8"	25.00
Bowl, w/lid, SP Clinchfield, 8½" dia	85.00
Butter dish, 4½" holder w/in 7" dia dish, Steubenville	85.00
Casserole, Ostro China, w/lid, 10½" dia	95.00
Casserole, w/lid, SP Clinchfield, 8½" dia	85.00
Creamer & sugar bowl, w/lid, Homer Laughlin	45.00
Cup, coffee, unmk, 3½"	25.00
Plate, dessert; Limoges, 6"	8.00
Plate, Homer Laughlin, 8½"	10.00
Plate, National China, 8"	10.00
Plate, reticulated, sq, unmk, 9"	35.00
Platter, Homer Laughlin, 15½x10½"	75.00
Platter, Hopewell China, 17½x13"	95.00
Platter, Steubenville, 12¾x9½"	55.00
Platter, unmk, 9x7"	35.00
Tea cup, unmk	15.00
Teapot, ELP Co, 8½x8½"	125.00

Boch Freres

Founded in the early 1840s in La Louviere, Boch Freres Keramos became the foremost producer of art pottery in Belgium. Though primarily they served a localized market, in 1844 they earned world-wide recognition for some of their sculptural works on display at the International Exposition in Paris.

In 1907 Charles Catteau of France was appointed head of the art department. Before that time, the firm had concentrated on developing glazes and perfecting elegant forms. The style they pursued was traditional, favoring the re-creation of established eighteenth-century ceramics. Catteau brought with him to Boch Freres the New Wave (or Art Nouveau) influence in form and decoration. His designs won him international acclaim at the Exhibition d'Art Decoratif in Paris in 1925, and it is for his work that Boch Freres is so highly regarded today. He occasionally signed his work as well as that of others who under his direct supervision carried out his preconceived designs. He was associated with the company until 1950 and lived the remainder of his life in Nice, France, where he died in 1966. The Boch Freres Keramos factory continues to operate today, producing bathroom fixtures and other utilitarian wares. A variety of marks have been used, all incorporating some combination of 'Boch Freres,' 'Keramos,' 'BFK,' or 'Ch Catteau.'

Plate, Voyage en Diligence, bl/wht transfer, #3	22.00
Vase, bl vines w/aqua & red flowers on yel, HP/cvd, 8"	330.00
Vase, deer grazing/geometrics, Catteau, bulbous, 15"	2,400.00
Vase, deer/geometric borders, Catteau, 14x8"	1,300.00
Vase, panels of yel leaves/brn rosettes on cream, ftd, 10"	250.00
Vase, triangle panels w/lime & bl abstract foliage, 9½"	300.00
Vase, wavy horizontal bands relief, crazed aqua, ftd, 8½"	80.00

Boehm

Boehm sculptures were the creation of Edward Marshall Boehm, a ceramic artist who coupled his love of the art with his love of nature to produce figurines of birds, animals, and flowers in lovely background settings accurate to the smallest detail. Sculptures of historical figures and those representing the fine arts were also made and along with many of the bird figurines have established secondary-market values many times their original prices. His first pieces were made in the very early 1950s in Trenton, New Jersey, under the name of Osso Ceramics. Mr. Boehm died in 1969, and the firm has since been managed by his wife. Today known as Edward Marshall Boehm, Inc., the private family-held corporation produces not only porcelain sculptures but collector plates as well. Both limited and non-limited editions of their works have been issued. Examples are marked with various backstamps, all of which have incorporated the Boehm name since 1951. 'Osso Ceramics' in upper case lettering was used in 1950 and 1951. Values listed below represent prices realized at auction.

Peregrine Falcon, 1973, 21x20", $1,300.00.

Alex Red Rose, #300-39	1,250.00
American Avocet, #40134	900.00
American Redstarts, #40138	800.00
Bob White Quail, #407	1,400.00
Bridled Tit, #200-24	550.00
Canada Geese	1,000.00
Cardinals, #415	3,000.00
Crested Flycatcher, #488	3,100.00
Daisies, #3002	750.00
Downy Woodpeckers, #427	1,500.00
English Nutcatch, #1001	750.00
Fledgling Blue Jay, 4½"	165.00

Fledgling Canada Warbler, #491 . . . . .1,900.00
Fledgling Kingfisher, 1960, 6" 175.00
Fledgling Magpie, 6" 225.00
Fledgling Western Bluebirds, 6" 185.00
Giant Panda, #5003 . . . . .4,000.00
Gold Rose w/Diamond, #G7 . . . . .625.00
Goldfinch on Thistle, #457 . . . . .1,100.00
Green Jays, #486 . . . . .4,100.00
Hooded Merganser, 1968, 10½", pr 1,700.00
Horned Lark on Grapes, #400-25 . . . . .2,800.00
Indigo Bunting, #429 . . . . .725.00
Kestrels, #492 . . . . .3,100.00
Lesser Prairie Chickens, #464 . . . . .1,250.00
Little Blue Heron, #200-19 . . . . .275.00
Madonna, La Pieta, 1950s, 10" 350.00
Mallard, #406, pr 1,500.00
Mountain Bluebirds, #470 . . . . .6,100.00
Otter, #5004 . . . . .850.00
Oven Bird, fern fronds, 1970, 10" 725.00
Parula Warblers, #484 . . . . .3,800.00
Prothonotary Warbler, #445 . . . . .575.00
Ptarmigans, 1962, 9½", 13¾", pr 1,100.00
Pussy Willows, #200-28, pr 175.00
Queen Elizabeth Rose, #30091 .1,400.00
Ring Neck Pheasants, #409 . . . . .1,100.00
Robin Nests, #10030 . . . . .850.00
Royal Blessings Rose, #300-99 .1,200.00
Song Sparrow, #400-59 . . . . .475.00
Tiger Lilies, #30077 . . . . .850.00
Tree Creepers, #1007 . . . . .2,500.00
Western Meadowlark, #400-15 .1,200.00
Woodcock, #413 . . . . .1,100.00
Young American Eagle, #498 . . . . .950.00

Bohemian Glass

The term 'Bohemian glass' has come to refer to a type of glass developed in Bohemia in the late sixth century at the Imperial Court of Rudolf II, the Hapsburg Emperor. The popular artistic pursuit of the day was stone carving, and it naturally followed to transfer familiar procedures to the glassmaking industry. During the next century, a formula was discovered that produced a glass with a fine crystal appearance which lent itself well to deep, intricate engraving, and the art was further advanced.

Although many other types of art glass were made there, collectors today use the term 'Bohemian glass' to most often indicate clear glass overlaid with color through which a design is cut or etched. Red on crystal is common, but other colors may also be found. Another type of Bohemian glass involves cutting through and exposing three layers of color in patterns that are often very intricate. Items such as these are sometimes further decorated with enamel work.

Bottle, scent; ruby/frosted, matching ruby stopper, 9" 75.00
Box, jewel; amber, animals/birds/trees, 3½x5" 350.00
Box, jewel; bl, cut star on top, oblong, 6" 175.00
Box, ruby, clipper ship intaglio, rectangular, 3¾" 175.00
Bread plate, bl, deer & pine tree, 13x8" 80.00
Compote, wht cut to gr, mc florals w/gold, faceted rim, 7x9" . . .125.00
Decanter, ruby, deer & castle, +4 sm stemmed goblets 165.00
Paperweight, gr, eng deer, 3⅜" dia 150.00
Rose bowl, ruby, deer & castle, lg .150.00
Urn, amber, vintage lid, pine trees/deer on body, 9½", pr 175.00
Vase, ruby, bird/trees/houses, 6" 85.00
Vase, ruby, deer & trees, ped ft, 7¾" 115.00

Vase, ruby, diamonds & ovals, flared, 5" 135.00
Vase, ruby, floral bouquets & swags, 10½" 80.00
Vase, ruby, triple dmn cutting, scalloped, 10" 75.00
Vase, ruby, X-loop/dmn cutting, faceted ped base, 9½x6", pr . . .250.00

Vases, ruby, etched florals, diamond-cut bands, 14½", $495.00 for the pair.

Bookends

Though a few were produced before 1880, bookends became a necessary library accessory and a popular commodity after the printing industry was revolutionized by Mergenthaler's invention, the linotype. Books became abundantly available at such affordable prices that almost every home suddenly had need for bookends. They were carved from wood, cast in iron, bronze, or brass, or cut from stone. Today's collectors may find such designs as ships, animals, flowers, and children. Patriotic themes, art reproductions, and those with Art Nouveau and Art Deco styling provide a basis for a diverse and interesting collection.

Abe Lincoln, bronzed metal, pr 22.50
Alonzo Stagg, bronze-washed iron, 7", pr 85.00
Blk man in loincloth w/panther, brass, pr 75.00
Charles Lindbergh, CI, pr 65.00
Charles Lindbergh, copper-finished metal, pr 65.00
Coach, brass, pr 22.00
Copper & brass, Mission style, pr 125.00
Dutch boy & girl by tree, bronze, Austria, 4", pr 175.00
Elephant, cast metal, 3x3¼", pr 35.00
End of Trail, bronze, pr 35.00
Golfer & caddy, metal, nice details, pr 65.00
History allegorical, bronze wash, Pompeiian Bronze, pr 145.00
Horse, head down, pot metal, pr 20.00
Horse, hollow, brass-plated CI, pr 30.00
Horse's head, clear glass, hollow, pr .18.00
In Time of Elizabeth, cast metal, mk Galleons, pr 30.00
Indian bust, CI, pr 30.00
Indian in high relief, brass, mk Reg App, 5½x5", pr 100.00
Knight on horse, bronze, sgn CS Allen, pr 100.00
Lady's head, Deco style, Frankart, pr 150.00
Last Ride, brass, pr 30.00
Liberty bell, bronze finish, pr 30.00
Lincoln, bronzed metal, Parson's Casket Hdwre, 5½", pr 50.00
Lion, bronzed metal, pr 30.00
Lion, Deco style, CI, orig gold pnt, EX, pr 20.00
Owl, CI, heavy, pr 18.00
Owl, cvd alabaster, pr 25.00
Puppies, Deco style, wht-pnt metal, pr 40.00

Roman bust, bronze, pr 38.00
Sailboats, Bronze Art, 7" 115.00
Scotty, CI, pr 40.00
Scotty, metal w/brass finish, Frankart, 7" 165.00
Squirrel, CI, red pnt, pr 35.00
Stag, bronze, Hartford Fire Ins, 1935, pr 100.00
Thinker, brass, pr 20.00
Thinker, bronzed spelter, pr 45.00

Bootjacks and Bootscrapers

Bootjacks were made from metal or wood — some were fancy figural shapes, others strictly business! Their purpose was to facilitate the otherwise awkward process of removing one's boots. Bootscrapers were handy gadgets that provided an effective way to clean the soles of mud and such.

Wrought iron, fox and hare, by Wilhelm Hunt Dieterich, 14" long, $1,200.00.

Bootjacks

Am Bull Dog, CI, pistol shaped, folding, blk pnt, 8" 75.00
Beetle, CI, VG orig mc pnt, ca 1890s, 10½x4x3" 70.00
Boot Jack in raised letters, CI, EX 75.00
Boss emb on shaft, lacy CI, 15" L 135.00
Dbl-ended, ornate CI, EX 75.00
Downs & Co, CI, EX 85.00
Lever action, wood/CI, EX 130.00
Lyre shape, CI, sm 55.00
Musselman's Boot-Jack Plug Tobacco, CI, sunflower decor 150.00
Naughty Nellie, CI, no pnt, 9½" 65.00
Naughty Nellie, CI w/worn mc pnt, 9½" 150.00
Raised heel holder, ornate CI, EX 65.00
Scissor action, CI, mk Pat 1877, EX .45.00
Shoe-shaped loop on end, spoked motif, CI, lg, EX 65.00
Try Me, CI, openwork, no pnt, ca 1890s, 12x4x1¾" 70.00
V-shape, ornate CI, VG 45.00
Whale bone, w/whale bone bracket pins, 17" L 650.00

Bootscrapers

Arched top, wrought iron, bronze finial, 14" 65.00
Baroque scrollwork, CI, set in marble block, 14" 80.00
Cat, open eye, long tail, CI, rectangular base, 17" L 225.00
Dachshund, CI, old dk gr pnt, 21" L 260.00
Deco fox/hare, hammered wrought iron, Dieterich, 7x14" 1,300.00

Duck, full bodied, scraper on bk, CI, 14½" L 350.00
Wrought iron, ram's horn finials, pitted, 12" W 75.00
Wrought iron, simple uprights w/scooped blade set in stone . . .150.00

Boru, Sorcha

Sorcha Boru was the professional name used by California ceramist Claire Stewart. She was a founding member of the Allied Arts Guild of Menlo Park (California) where she maintained a studio from 1932 to 1938. From 1938 until 1955, she operated Sorcha Boru Ceramics, a production studio in San Carlos. Her highly-acclaimed output consisted of colorful, slip-decorated figurines, salt and pepper shakers, vases, wall pockets, and flower bowls. Most production work was incised 'S.B.C.' by hand.

Our advisor for this category is Jack Chipman; he is listed in the Directory under California.

Penelope, fawn figurine, 6", $35.00.

Bowl, maroon, appl peony on lid, 6" 55.00
Figurine, bluejay, 6½" 175.00
Pitcher, robin's egg bl, w/underplate .175.00
Shakers, boy & girl, pr 50.00
Sugar shaker, lady figural, 6" 85.00

Bottles and Flasks

As far back as the first century B.C., the Romans preferred blown glass containers for their pills and potions. Though you're not apt to find many of those, you will find bottles of every size, shape, and color made to hold perfume, ink, medicine, soda, spirits, vinegar, and many other liquids. American business firms preferred glass bottles in which to package their commercial products and used them extensively from the late eighteenth century on. Bitters bottles contained 'medicine' (actually herb-flavored alcohol); and, judging from the number of these found today, their contents found favor with many! Because of a heavy tax imposed on the sale of liquor in seventeenth-century England by King George, who hoped to curtail alcohol abuse among his subjects, bottlers simply added 'curative' herbs to their brew and thus avoided taxation. Since gin was taxed in America as well, the practice continued in this country. Scores of brands were sold; among the most popular were Dr. H.S. Flint & Co. Quaker Bitters, Dr. Kaufman's Anti-Cholera Bitters, and Dr. J. Hostetter's Stomach Bitters. Most bitters bottles were made in shades of amber, brown, and aquamarine. Clear glass was used to a lesser extent, as were green tones. Blue, amethyst, red-brown, and milk glass examples are rare.

Perfume or scent bottles were produced abroad by companies all over Europe from the late sixteenth century on. Perfume making became such a prolific trade that as a result beautifully decorated bottles were fashionable. In America they were produced in great quantities by Stiegel in 1770 and by Boston and Sandwich in the early nineteenth century. Cologne bottles were first made in about 1830 and toilet-water bottles in the 1880s. Rene Lalique produced fine scent bottles from as early as the turn of the century. The earliest were one-of-a-kind creations with silver casings. He later designed bottles for the Coty Perfume Company with a different style for each Coty fragrance. (Our advisor for Cologne and Perfume Bottles is Madeleine France; she is listed in the Directory under Florida. See also Lalique.)

Spirit flasks from the nineteenth century were blown in specially designed molds with varied motifs including political subjects, railroad trains, and symbolic devices. The most commonly-used colors were amber, dark brown, and green.

From the twentieth century, early pop and beer bottles are very collectible, as are nearly every extinct commercial container.

Bottles may be dated by the methods used in their production. For instance, a rough pontil indicates a date before 1845. The iron pontil, used from then until about 1860, left a metallic residue on the base of the bottle, which is evident upon examination. A seam that reaches from base to lip marks a machine-made bottle from after 1903, while an applied or hand-finished lip points to an early mold-blown bottle. The Industrial Revolution saw keen competition between manufacturers; and, as a result, scores of patents were issued. Many concentrated on various types of closures; the crown bottle cap, for instance, was patented in 1892. If a manufacturer's name is present, consulting a book on marks may help you date your bottle.

Numbers refer to a standard reference book, *American Glass*, by George and Helen McKearin.

In the listings that follow, glass is assumed to be clear unless color is indicated.

See also Advertising, various companies; Avon; Barber Shop Collectibles; Blown Glass; California Perfume Company; Czechoslovakia; De Vilbiss; Fire Fighting; Lalique; Medical Collectibles; Steuben.

Key:

am — applied mouth	grd — ground pontil
bbl — barrel	GW — Glass Works
bt — blob top	ip — iron pontil
b3m — blown 3-mold	ps — pontil scar
cm — collared mouth	rm — rolled mouth
fm — flared mouth	sl — sloping
gm — ground mouth	sm — sheared mouth
gp — graphite pontil	tm — tooled mouth

Barber

Bulbous, Coin Spot, cranberry, 7" 70.00
Bulbous, Hobnail, bl opal, 7½" 85.00
Bulbous, Hobnail, cranberry, 7" 95.00
Bulbous, Mary Gregory, cottage on amethyst, 8½" 300.00
Bulbous, Mary Gregory, girl on amethyst, 8½" 250.00
Bulbous, milk glass, HP decor, Bay Rum, 8¾" 100.00
Bulbous, sm enamel flowers on amethyst, 7" 60.00
Bulbous, Stars & Stripes, cranberry & wht, 7" 250.00
Conical, clear/wht/bl opal variegated glass, 8" 100.00
Conical, clear/wht/cranberry variegated glass, 8" 100.00
Cylinder, Mary Gregory, boy on cobalt, 9" 265.00
Cylinder, milk glass, HP decor, 11" 110.00
Multi-sided, ftd; Mary Gregory, boy on amethyst, 8½" 295.00
Pear shape, bulb neck; enamel decor on lt gr, 9" 80.00
Sq, Spanish Lace, wht & bl, 8½" 80.00
Sq, swirled wht opal, 9" 90.00

Bitters Bottles

Left to right: Baker's Orange Grove Bitters, yellow-amber, smooth base, applied mouth, $150.00; Big Bill Best Bitters, decanter type, amber, smooth base, tooled lip, 11¾", $180.00.

Baker's Orange Grove, strawberry puce, sq w/emb rope, 9½" . . .220.00
Big Bill's Best, gold-amber, pyramid, tm, 12" 95.00
Brown's Celebrated Indian Herb, deep brn, pat 1867, rm, M . . .350.00
Brown's Celebrated Indian Herb, med amber, pat 1868, rm, M .275.00
Caldwell's, gold amber, triangular, sl-cm/ip, 12" 190.00
Damiana, aqua, rnd, sl-cm w/ring, 11½" 30.00
Dr AS Hopkins Union Stomach, lime gr, am, NM 325.00
Dr CW Roback's Stomach, yel-amber, bbl, sl-cm, 9½" 150.00
Dr Fisch's, gold-amber, fish form, sm cm, 11½" 110.00
Dr J Hostetter's Stomach, yel-gr, am, EX 60.00
Dr Manly Hardy's Jaundice, aqua, sl-cm/ps, 7" 100.00
Dr Renz's Herb, yel-amber w/olive, sq, sl-cm w/ring, 10" 125.00
Drake's Plantation, apricot puce, pat 1862, 6-log cabin, am . . .275.00
Drake's Plantation, ST; olive-amber, 4-log cabin, sl-cm, 10" . . .250.00
Drake's Plantation, ST; yel-amber, 5-log cabin, sl-cm, 10" 175.00
Drake's 1860 Plantation X, ST; deep puce, pat 1862, 6-log 150.00
Drake's 1860 Plantation X, ST; med puce, pat 1862, 6-log 80.00
Drake's 1860 Plantation X, ST; olive amber, pat 1862, 6-log 85.00
Drake's 1860 Plantation X, ST; yel, pat 1862, 6-log, am 130.00
Fish, WH Ware; bright yel-gr, pat 1866, fish form, mfg flaw . . .725.00
Fish, yel-amber, fish form, sm cm, light stain, 12" 130.00
Great Tonic Dr Caldwell's Herb, amber, am, minor stain 120.00
Greeley's Bourbon, bbl, med olive gr, am, rare color 400.00
Greeley's Bourbon, dk strawberry puce, bbl, sq cm, 10", EX 90.00
Hall's, EE Hall New Haven Est 1842, gold-amber, am, M 120.00
Hall's, yel-amber, bbl, sq cm, sm burst bubble, 9½" 95.00
Harzer Krauter, Herman G Asendorf, amber, tm, EX 60.00
Holtzerman's Pat Stomach, amber, 4-sided roof, tm, M 130.00
John Moffat Price $1.00 Phoenix, olive-amber, am/ps, M 260.00
Kelly's Old Cabin, amber, cabin form, am, M 575.00
Mack's Sarsaparilla, med amber, am, rare, NM 325.00
Morning (star), med amber, am, M 200.00

National, gold-amber, ear of corn, sl-cm w/ring, 12" 170.00
National, med amber, am, M 200.00
National, yel, am, M 300.00
Old Continental, amber, partial labels, sq cm, 10", EX 120.00
Old Homestead Wild Cherry, amber, pat, cabin form, am, M ..165.00
Old Sachem/Wigwam Tonic, amber, am, M 170.00
Only 25 C/Clarke's Sherry/Wine, aqua, am/ps, M 95.00
Suffolk, yel, pig form, dbl cm, minor stain/mfg flaw, 10" L 500.00

Blown Glass

Chestnut, olive gr, sm/ps, 1775-1830, minor wear, 5" 130.00
Chestnut, yel-olive, rolled cm/ps, Am, 1800-1830, 6" 200.00
Club, bright aqua, right swirl, cm/ps, Am, 8" 200.00
Decanter, GIII-16, b3m, olive gr, sm/ps, pt 375.00
Decanter, GIII-5, matching stopper, 8" 245.00
Demijohn, dk-gold amber, sl-cm/ps, New England, 17½" 170.00
Gemel, appl rigaree, copper wheel eng floral/monogram, 7½" ..100.00
Gin, yel-olive gr, mushroom mouth, ps, Netherlands, 11" 90.00
Ludlow, olive-amber, 4⅜" 105.00
Pitkin flask, lt bl-gr, 32-rib left swirl, sm/ps, Am, 6¾" 190.00
Pitkin flask, olive gr, 30-rib left swirl, sm/ps, 6½" 325.00
Pitkin flask, yel-gr, 24-rib right swirl, sm/ps, 1820s, 7" 310.00
Snuff, emerald, tm/ps, sq, Am, att Willington, 1820s, 6x3" 325.00
Snuff, olive-amber, freeblown/paddled, tm/ps, 1825, 4½" 260.00
Spirits, HP girl/buckets/flowers, European, 1700s, 6" 375.00

Cologne or Perfume Bottles

Sunburst, deep violet, pontiled, sheared lip, 3", $725.00.

Aventurine, mc w/gold spangles, lays down, hinged lid 245.00
Aqua, dancing Indian emb, sq, 4¾" 70.00
Bl opaline w/allover gold overlay, bulbous, 5½" 95.00
Canary yel, panel cut, gold metal top, 4" 170.00
Clear, heart w/emb motif, tm, 2¼" 170.00
Clear w/appl rigaree, sm/ps, 3" 180.00
Cobalt, b3m, Tam-o'-Shanter stopper, Sandwich, 6½" 500.00
Cobalt, fleur-de-lis/crowns/flaming hearts emb, Fr, 3½", pr 175.00
Cobalt, gold scrolls/foliage, HP floral, ornate top, 5¼" 75.00
French enamel, garden scene w/lady or gent, 4¼", pr 600.00
Lt aqua w/appl rigaree, sm/ps, att S Jersey, 3¼" 700.00
Med gr, dmn panels, pewter top, Sandwich, 3¼" 200.00
MOP, wht vertical stripes, sterling flip-top cap, 4" dia 485.00
Opalized robin's egg bl, rm/ps, 12" 70.00
Pk cased, HP gold scrolls, gold ball stopper, 4⅛x2⅝" 100.00

Salmon pk cased, gold florals, clear stopper, 4¼x2⅜" 100.00
Sea horse, lt aqua, wht loopings, appl rigaree, 3½" 150.00
Sea horse, wht/bl/puce loopings, appl rigaree, sm/ps, 2⅜" 235.00
Sunburst, med olive-gr, rm/ps, 2½" 725.00
Violet-bl w/wht & bl swirls, waisted octagon, 2½" 145.00

Figural Bottles

Blk waiter, hands in pockets, frosted w/blk head, 14", NM 140.00
Boys climbing tree, clear/frosted, tm/ps, emb Depose, 12" 130.00
Bust of Granger, emb Granger Pat June 2 1874, tm, 6½" 50.00
Ear of corn, clear w/yel pnt, orig cap, 6½" L 55.00
Fish, clear w/bl & wht pnt, gm, no cap, 8½" L 35.00
Girl standing on head, clear/frosted, tm, minor stain, 14" 65.00
Pig, emb CF Knapp Philada, tm, 3¾" L 30.00
Pistol, amber, orig cap, mfg flaw, 9½" L 25.00
Uncle Sam, ketchup, emb Pat Apld For, screw-on cap, 9¾" ...210.00
Woman holding urn, clear/frosted, tm/ps, 8" 170.00

Flasks

Adams/Jefferson, GI-114, gold-amber, sm/ps, ½-pt 135.00
Army Officer/Lg Flower, GXIII-15, lt bl-gr, calabash, qt 210.00
Ben Franklin/TW Dyott MD, GI-94, aqua, sm/ps, pt 125.00
Ben Franklin/TW Dyott MD, GI-96, aqua, sm/ps, qt 210.00
Cannon/Little More Grape...Braggs, GX-6, aqua, sm/ps, ½-pt ..250.00
Clasped Hands/Cannon, GXII-40, aqua, am w/ring, pt 100.00
Clasped Hands/Cannon, GXII-40, dk aqua, am w/ring, pt 120.00
Clasped Hands/Eagle, GXII-15, yel w/olive tone, cm, qt 450.00
Clasped Hands/Eagle, GXII-33, gold-amber, appl cm, ½-pt 125.00
Clasped Hands/Eagle, GXII-34, aqua, sm w/ring, ½-pt 40.00
Clasped Hands/Eagle, GXII-8, lt sapphire, am w/ring, qt 500.00
Clasped Hands/Masonic/Eagle, GIX-41, aqua, sq cm/ps, ½-pt ..160.00
Clasped Hands/Masonic/Eagle, GIX-42, aqua, sl-cm/ps, qt 160.00
Columbia/Eagle, GI-121, gr-aqua, sm/ps, pt 350.00
Concentric Ring Eagle, GII-76a, yel-gr, sm/ps, 1-pt+, EX ...2,000.00
Cornucopia/Urn, GIII-12, gold-amber w/olive, sm/ps, ½-pt 110.00
Cornucopia/Urn, GIII-13, aqua, sm/ps, Lancaster, ½-pt 120.00
Cornucopia/Urn, GIII-17, dk bl-gr, sm/ps, pt 190.00
Cornucopia/Urn, GIII-4, dk olive-amber, sm/ps, pt 60.00
Cornucopia/Urn, GIII-4, yel-olive, sm/ps, pt 65.00
Cornucopia/Urn, GIII-7, olive-amber, sm/ps, ½-pt 85.00
Dbl Eagle, GII-1, dk aqua, sm/ps, pt 200.00
Dbl Eagle, GII-108, dk forest gr, am w/ring, pt 150.00
Dbl Eagle, GII-108, olive-gr, am w/ring, pt 110.00
Dbl Eagle, GII-24, aqua, sm/ps, pontil chip/stain, pt 100.00
Dbl Eagle, GII-26, dk bright gr w/olive, sm/ip, qt 750.00
Dbl Eagle, GII-81, gold-amber w/olive, sm/ps, pt 120.00
Dbl Eagle, GII-83, gold-amber w/olive, sm/ps, pt 90.00
Dbl Eagle, GII-86, yel-amber, sm/ps, ½-pt 70.00
Dbl Eagle, GII-88, olive-gr, sm/ps, ½-pt, NM 90.00
Eagle/bk: plain, GII-143, bright gr, sl-cm/ip, calabash, qt 120.00
Eagle/Cornucopia, GII-73, olive-amber, sm/ps, pt 80.00
Eagle/Flag, GII-48, aqua, sm/ps, qt 125.00
Eagle/Flag, GII-52, aqua, sm/ps, pt, EX 70.00
Eagle/Flag, GII-52, gr-aqua, sm/ps, pt, NM 60.00
Eagle/Flag, GII-53, aqua, sm/ps, pt 150.00
Eagle/Flag, GII-54, striated olive-amber, sm/ps, pt 2,000.00
Eagle/Frigate, GII-42, aqua, sm/ps, minor stain, pt 160.00
Eagle/Lg Sunburst, GII-7, bright bl-gr, sm/ps, pt 2,700.00
Eagle/Morning-Glory, GII-19, dk aqua, sm/ps, pt, EX 300.00
Eagle/Oak Tree, GII-60, dk gold-amber, sm/ps, ½-pt 1,300.00
Eagle/Oak Tree, GII-60, dk gr-aqua, sm/ps, ½-pt 450.00
Eagle/Stag, GII-49, aqua, sm/ps, ½-pt 240.00

Eagle/Stag, GII-50, aqua, rm/ps, ½-pt .200.00
Eagle/Tree, GII-41, aqua, sm/ps, Kensington, pt, NM 110.00
Eagle/Tree, GII-47, aqua, sm/ps, faint stain, qt 425.00
Eagle/Willington Glass, GII-61, dk gr w/olive, cm, qt 170.00
Eagle/Willington Glass, GII-61, red-amber, dbl cm, qt 225.00
Eagle/Willington Glass, GII-63, yel-olive, dbl cm, ½-pt 150.00
Eagle/Willington Glass, GII-64, amber, rnd cm, pt, NM 80.00
For Pike's Peak Prospector/Eagle, GXI-27, yel-amber, pt 600.00
For Pike's Peak Prospector/Eagle, GXI-32, aqua, sm/ps, pt 110.00
For Pike's Peak Prospector/Hunter, GXI-52, aqua, cm, ½-pt . . .170.00
Gen Lafayette/Eagle, GI-90, aqua, sm/ps, pt 150.00
Gen Washington/Eagle, GI-1, lt bl-gr, sm/ps, minor wear, pt . .550.00
Gen Washington/Eagle, GI-14, aqua, sm/ps, minor stain, pt . . .120.00
Gen Washington/Eagle, GI-14, gr-aqua, sm/ps, Kensington, pt .200.00
Gen Washington/Eagle, GI-16, aqua, sm/ps, pt 110.00
Gen Washington/Eagle, GI-2, gr-aqua, sm/ps, pt 270.00
Gen Washington/Eagle, GI-3, aqua, sm/ps, minor wear, pt 600.00
Girl on Bicycle/bk: plain, GXIII-2, aqua, sm w/ring, pt, NM . . .100.00
Granite Glass Co/Stoddard NH, GXV-7, yel-amber, sm/ps, pt .160.00
Great Western Trapper/Stag, GX-20, aqua, am w/ring, pt, NM 375.00
Hearts & Flowers Scroll, GIX-51, gr-aqua, sm/ps, qt 2,100.00
Horse & Cart/Eagle, GV-7a, olive gr, sm/ps, pt 270.00
Hunter/Fisherman, GXIII-4, gold-amber, cm/ip, calabash, qt . .150.00
Hunter/Fisherman, GXIII-6, aqua, sl-cm/ps, calabash, qt, NM . .90.00
Jenny Lind/Glass Factory, GI-102, aqua, cm/ps, calabash, qt 50.00
Jenny Lind/Lyre, GI-110, lt bl-gr, sm/ps, qt, NM 750.00
Kossuth/Sloop, GI-111, aqua, sm/ps, minor stain, pt 175.00
Kossuth/Tree, GI-113, yel w/olive, sl-cm w/ring, ps, qt, EX 300.00
Lafayette/De Witt Clinton, GI-80, olive-amber, sm/ps, pt 475.00
Lafayette/Liberty Cap, GI-86, olive-amber, sm/ps, ½-pt 325.00
Louisville KY GW Scroll, GIX-8, gr-aqua, sm/ip, pt 110.00
Louisville KY GW Scroll, GIX-9, dk aqua, sm/ps, pt 140.00
M'Carty & Torreyson, sunburst scroll, bl-gr, sm/ps, qt 800.00
Masonic/Eagle, GIV-1, bl-gr, tm/ps, pt 340.00
Masonic/Eagle, GIV-19, olive-amber, sm/ps, Keene, pt 140.00
Masonic/Eagle, GIV-32, gold-amber, sm/ps, pt, NM 250.00
Masonic/Eagle, GIV-32, lt bl-gr, sm/ps, pt 210.00
Masonic/Eagle, GIV-32, shaded lt gold-amber, sm/ps, pt 600.00
Masonic/Eagle, GIV-37, aqua, sm/ps, pt 70.00
Masonic/Frigate, GIX-34, aqua, sm/ps, pt 225.00
R Knowles & Co/Union Factory Scroll, GIX-47, lt bl-gr, pt .1,800.00
Scroll, GIX-10, cornflower bl, sm/ps, pt 575.00
Scroll, GIX-11, dk gold-yel, sm/ip, pt, EX 125.00
Scroll, GIX-14, dk yel-gr w/olive tone, sm/ps, pt 700.00
Scroll, GIX-2, spruce gr, sm/ps, qt 700.00
Scroll, GIX-3, grass gr, sm/ps, faint stain, qt 225.00
Scroll, GIX-32, dk aqua, collared rm/ip, ½-pt 100.00
Scroll, GIX-36, gold-amber, sm/ip, ½-pt, NM 275.00
Scroll, GIX-45, dk gr-aqua, corset waisted, pt 950.00
Seeing Eye Masonic, GIV-43, olive-amber, sm/ps, pt 150.00
Sheaf of Wheat/Sheets & Duffy-Star, GXIII-41, aqua, qt 150.00
Sheaf of Wheat/Star, GXIII-39, bright yel-gr, dbl cm, pt 200.00
Sheaf of Wheat/Tree, GXIII-47, bright bl-gr, dbl cm/ip, qt 170.00
Sheaf of Wheat/Westford, GXIII-37, red-amber, dbl cm, ½-pt .150.00
Soldier/Ballet Dancer, GXIII-11, lt gr-bl, sm/ip, pt 150.00
Spring Garden/GW-Anchor-Cabin, GXIII-58, aqua, pt 120.00
Success to RR, GV-1, dk aqua, sm/ps, pt 220.00
Success to RR, GV-1b, bl-gr, dbl cm, smooth base, pt 750.00
Success to RR, GV-3, olive-amber, sm/ps, pt 190.00
Success to RR, GV-4, lt olive-amber, sm/ps, pt 310.00
Success to RR/Eagle, GV-8, olive-amber, sm/ps, pt 225.00
Summer Tree/Summer Tree, GX-17, dk aqua, sm/ps, pt, EX 50.00
Summer Tree/Winter Tree, GX-15, dk wine, dbl cm, pt 1,100.00
Sunburst, GVIII-1, lt aqua, tm/ps, base-ring chip, pt 350.00

Sunburst, GVIII-14, bright gr, sm/ps, ½-pt 1,300.00
Sunburst, GVIII-16, lt yel-olive, sm/ps, ½-pt, NM 220.00
Sunburst, GVIII-2, bright gr, sm/ps, pt, EX 300.00
Sunburst, GVIII-26, lt bright bl-gr, sm/ps, pt 500.00
Sunburst, GVIII-29, bl-gr, tm/ps, ½-pt 175.00
Sunburst, GVIII-3, lt yel-amber w/olive tone, sm/ps, pt 400.00
Sunburst, GVIII-7, olive-amber, sm/ps, pt 1,500.00
Sunburst, GVIII-8, olive-amber, sm/ps, pt 400.00
Taylor/Masterson Eagle, GI-77, lt gr-bl, sm/ps, qt, NM 700.00
Traveler's Companion/Ravenna Glass, GIV-3, gold-amber, pt .400.00
Traveler's Companion/Wheat Sheaf, GXIV-1, olive-amber, qt .160.00
Washington Monument/Corn...World, GVI-4, lt bl, sq cm, qt .150.00
Washington/Classical Bust, GI-22, gr-aqua, sm/ps, qt 200.00
Washington/Classical Bust, GI-22, lt yel-gr, sm/ps, qt 250.00
Washington/Jackson, GI-31, yel-olive, sm/ps, pt, EX 90.00
Washington/Sailing Ship, GI-28, gold-yel, dbl cm/ip, pt 900.00

Washington 'The Father of His Country'/Taylor 'Gen. Taylor Never Surrenders Dyottville Glassworks, Philada.,' GI-37, medium blue-green, open pontil, sheared mouth, $260.00.

Washington/Taylor, GI-38, aqua, sq cm, minor stain, pt 30.00
Washington/Taylor, GI-38, dk claret, sm, pt 500.00
Washington/Taylor, GI-43, aqua, sm/ps, qt 80.00
Washington/Taylor, GI-51, amethyst/striations, qt, NM 1,500.00
Washington/Taylor, GI-54, bright med gr, sm/ps, qt 200.00
Washington/Taylor, GI-54, cobalt, sl-cm, qt, EX 600.00
Washington/Taylor, GI-54, sea gr, dbl cm/ip, qt 210.00
Washington/Tree, GI-35, aqua, cm/ps, minor stain, qt 50.00
WC Eagle/Cornucopia, GII-12, gr-aqua, sm/ps, ½-pt 900.00
Will You Take a Drink/Will...Swim, GXIII-27, gr-aqua, pt 200.00
Wm Jennings Bryan/Eagle, GI-126, clear, coin form, tm, ½-pt .700.00
Zachary Taylor/Cornstalk, GI-74, apricot, sm/ps, pt, NM . . .4,500.00

Food Bottles and Jars

Berry, root beer, rnd w/10 shoulder panels, NE, 11" 200.00
Mustard, Giessen's Union (Am eagle), bbl, rm/ps, 5", M 85.00
Peppersauce, ERD & Co Feb 17 1874, aqua, partial label, 7½" . .20.00
Peppersauce, G Miller N-York, aqua, 20 vertical flutes, 10" . . .100.00
Pickle, aqua, MB Espy, ip/rm, int burst bubble, 9" 145.00
Pickle, cathedral arches, Altmore's, cm, 1870s, 11½" 150.00
Pickle, cathedral arches, bright bl-gr, r/cm, 1870, 11½" 170.00
Pickle, cathedral arches, bright gr, rm, 1860-1880, 11" 210.00
Pickle, cathedral arches, dk gr, rm, 9", M 375.00
Pickle, ribbed top & base, bright gr-yel, tm, bubbly, 9½" 65.00

Ink Bottles

Barrel, French's Violet Pat Oct 17 1865, clear, tm 170.00
Barrel, SI/Comp, clear, tm, lip chips, 2⅜" 65.00
Barrel, Tippecanoe Extract-Hard Cider, rm/grd p, 2" 210.00
Barrel, WE Bonney, aqua, 2½" 70.00
Cathedral, Carter, cobalt, 6-sided, ABM, 10", NM 60.00
Cathedral, Carter, cobalt, 6-sided, ABM, 8", M 95.00
Cone, base emb Carter's, aqua, 2½" 10.00
Cone, base emb Carter's, gr, 2⅝" 20.00
Cone, cobalt, 2¾" 25.00
Cone, olive-gr, ps, 2¼" 100.00
Cone, Wood's Black Ink, aqua, ps, 2¼" 150.00
Cottage, aqua, sq, 2½" 225.00
Figural, Ma & Pa Carter, mc/porc, Germany, 3½", pr 100.00
Figural, snail, clear, 1¾" 125.00
Franklin's head form, aqua, EX 125.00
Geometric, diamond & ribbed emb, olive gr, ps, 2" 95.00
Igloo, teal bl, 1¾" 160.00
Master, Harrison's Columbian, aqua, ps, 7½" 100.00
Master, Harrison's Columbian, cobalt, ps, 4⅛" 475.00
Pitkin, olive-gr, 36-rib, ps, 1¾" 450.00
Pitkin, olive-gr, 36-rib right swirl, 1½x2¾" dia, EX 550.00
Rnd, 12-sided, emerald gr, ps, 2" 300.00
Teakettle, Josiah Johnson's Japan...Fluid, pottery, 2½" 135.00
Turtle, J&IEM, lt amber, 1⅝" 100.00
Umbrella, 16-sided, olive-amber, ps, 2½" 200.00
Umbrella, 8-sided, aqua, ps, 2½" 35.00
Umbrella, 8-sided, orange-amber, rm/ps, 2¼" 85.00
Umbrella, 8-sided, yel-olive, ps, 2½" .175.00
12-sided, dk emerald, rm/ps, 1⅞" 350.00

Medicine Bottles

Allen's Lung Balsam, aqua, rectangular, 8⅛" 5.00
Davis, Vegetable Pain Killer, aqua, rectangular, ps, 5⅛" 35.00
Dr D Jayne's Expectorant, aqua, rectangular, ps, 6½" 30.00
Dr D Jayne's Expectorant, aqua, rectangular, 7" 5.00
Dr GW Phillips Cough Syrup Cincinnati, aqua, am/ip, rare, 7" 150.00
Dr Kilmer's Swamp Root, aqua, rectangular, 8½" 10.00
Dr Mile's New Heart Cure, aqua, rectangular, 8¼" 10.00
Dr Thomas' Eclectric Oil, aqua, rectangular, 5½" 5.00
Dr Wistar's Balsam of Wild Cherry, aqua, 8-sided, am/ps, 6½" . .65.00
Dr WS Lunt's Ague Killer, dk aqua, am/ps, rare, 7", M 150.00
Dr WS Lunt's Family, aqua, NM orig label, am/ps, 5" 350.00
Dr WS Lunt's Family, dk aqua, EX orig label, am/ps, 6½" 120.00
Hamlin's Wizard Oil, aqua, rectangular, 6⅜" 10.00
Houses Indian Tonic, dk aqua, full-figure Indian, rm/ps, 5½" . .700.00
I Covert's Balm of Life, olive-amber, am/ps, 6" 375.00
IL St John's Cough Syrup, aqua, 8-sided, am/ps, 5¼" 170.00
JL Hamilton Preparation, claret, 2 emb panels, sl-cm/ip, 7" . . .365.00
Keeley's Gold Cure for Drunkenness, clear, 5¾" 75.00
Kickapoo Indian Cough Cure, aqua, rnd, 6¼" 10.00
Kickapoo Indian Oil, aqua, rnd, 5½" 5.00
Kickapoo Indian Sagwa, aqua, rectangular, 9" 5.00
Laughlin's Bushfield Druggists VA, aqua, am/red ip, 9" 190.00
Laxol, cobalt, 7" 15.00
Lippitt's Unequalled Cough Syrup, aqua, am/ps, EX label, 6" . . .25.00
Lydia E Pinkham's Vegetable Compound, aqua, 8½" 5.00
Paine's Celery Compound, amber, rectangular, 10" 5.00
Swaim's Panacea Philada, dk olive gr, am/ps, 8" 120.00
Tippecanoe, HH Warner & Co, amber, rnd, 9¼" 75.00
Warner's Safe Cure, Rochester NY, amber, 9½" 15.00

Warner's Safe Cure London, embossed safe, bright yellow-green, smooth base, tooled lip, 4½", $750.00.

Wayne's Diuretic Elixir, amber, NM orig labels, tm, 8" 35.00
Wm Radam's Microbe Killer, amber, sq, 10½" 65.00
WM S Merrel & Co Druggist's Cincinnati, aqua, am/ip, 7½" . . .25.00

Mineral Water and Soda Bottles

Congress & Empire Spring Co, emerald, am, pt, NM 350.00
DL Ormsby NY Union Glassworks Phila, cobalt, am/ip 210.00
Dr CL Whitney's Pat Soda &..., med lb-gr, am/ip 375.00
E Roussel Philada Dyottville...Never Sold, cobalt, am/ip 375.00
F Sherwood Bridgeport & New Haven, bl-gr, cm/ip, ½-pt 200.00
Hathorn Spring Saratoga NY, orange-amber, am, qt 40.00
J Boardman NY, sapphire, squat/8-sided, cm/ip, wear, ½-pt 150.00
John Ryan 1866 Excelsior Savannah Geo, cobalt, am, NM 40.00
Luke Beard, med emerald, 10-pin form, am/ip 140.00
Pavilion & US Spring Co...Aperient, emerald, am, pt, NM . . .160.00
S Smith Auburn NY, cobalt, am/ip, rnd bottom 350.00
Superior, eagle on shield, cobalt, sl-cm/ip, ½-pt, NM 475.00
U & ID Clinton Woodbridge...Premium, emerald, am/ip, M . . .100.00

Sarsaparilla Bottles

Dr Guysott's Compound . . .Yel Dock, dk aqua, am/ps, 9½" . . .500.00
Dr Guysott's Yel Dock...JD Park, aqua, am/ip, 10", NM 130.00
Dr Russell's Balsam of Horehound..., aqua, am/ps, 9½" 160.00
Dr Townsend's Albany NY, dk gr, am/ip, stain, 9½" 110.00
Dr Townsend's Albany NY, lt bl-gr, am/ip, 9¾", NM 150.00
Dr Townsend's Albany NY IIII, olive-amber, am/ps, 9" 130.00
Gooch's, cornflower bl, tm, 9" 80.00
Hood's, aqua, rectangular, aqua, 8¾" 5.00
JL Kelley & Co, aqua, am/ps, 8", EX .100.00
John Bull Extract of, dk aqua, am/ps, 9" 130.00
Log Cabin, Rochester NY, amber, 9" 85.00

Spirits Bottles

AM Bininger. . .KY Bourbon, gold-amber, bbl, dbl cm/ps, 10" .130.00
AM Bininger whiskey, gold-amber, cannon bbl, tm, 12½", EX .325.00
Chicken Cock Bourbon decanter, mc enamel, 6⅜" 600.00
Drink While It Lasts From..., amethystine, hog form, 6½" 150.00
Duffy's Pure Malt Whiskey, amber, rnd, 10¼" 10.00
EG Booz's Old Cabin Whiskey, GVII-4 var, gold-amber, qt . . .600.00
Elk's Pride Whiskey, amber, rnd, paper label, cm, 10½" 15.00
Flask, emb Dia Quilt, 6" 10.00

Flask, lady under glass label, threaded cap, 5¾" **500.00**
Forest Grove Whiskey, decanter, wht-enamel emb, rnd **75.00**
Gordon's Gin, London, aqua, sq, cm **5.00**
Greeting Theodore Netter...Phila, cobalt, bbl, tm, 6" **200.00**
Hayner's, 4 city, amber, rnd, 11" **15.00**
Hayner's, 4 city, rnd, 11" **5.00**
Hunter Baltimore Rye, amber, paper label, rnd, cm, 11" **15.00**
JH Cutter Old Bourbon, amber, rnd, cm, 12" **40.00**
London Royal Imperial Gin, dk sapphire, sq/emb, sl-cm, 10" . .**165.00**
Mamouth Cave Whiskey, decanter, mc enamel, 6½" **325.00**
Mist of Morning Sole Agents Barnett/Lumley, amber, bbl, am .**110.00**
Monk's. . .Bourbon. . .Medicinal, olive-amber, am/ps **275.00**
Mt Vernon Rye, amber, sq, 8½" **15.00**
Old Prentice Whiskey, decanter, label under glass **850.00**
Puritan Rye, china canteen, red enamel letters, 6½" **250.00**
Reiger's, Kansas City, rnd, 11" **5.00**
Reiger's, sample sz, rnd, 4½" **15.00**
Slater's Pure Bourbon, San Francisco, amber, rnd, 12" **50.00**
Van Dunck's Genever...Ware/Schmitz, amber, coachman, 8¾" .**70.00**

Miscellaneous

Ackers Select Tea/Finley Acker & Co Tea Specialists Philadelphia U.S.A., embossed man on elephant and leaf and flower designs, bright yellow-green with gold-painted crown on lid, 11", $425.00.

Ambrosia, Heinze Inc, see California Perfume Co
Furniture polish, Gordon's-Chafala..., aqua, am/ps, 6" **140.00**
Hair restorative, CS Emberson's, aqua, am/ip, crude, 6" **130.00**
Hair tonic, Barker's Cheveux Tonique, aqua, am/ps, rare, 6" **30.00**
Hair tonic, Canitian for the Hair, Swan & Co, aqua, am/ps, 6" . .**45.00**
Lavender Salts, Goetting & Co, see California Perfume Co
Liniment, Dewitt's Stimulating, aqua, rm/ps, 2¼" **70.00**
Liniment, Loree's-Ohio, aqua, sm/ps, rare, 4" **100.00**
Liniment, Loree's-Ohio, dk aqua, rm/ps, 4", M **300.00**
Liniment, LP Dodge Rheumatic, med bl-gr, ps, 5", EX **375.00**
Snuff, E Roome Troy NY, olive-amber, sq w/beveled corners . .**150.00**
Snuff, JJ Mapes #61 Front St NY, dk olive-amber, tm/ps, 4½" . .**800.00**
Sweet 16, Goetting & Co, see California Perfume Co
System renovator, Dr Jas C Kerr's, amber, 1 orig label, 8" **60.00**

Boxes

Boxes have been used by civilized man since ancient Egypt and Rome. Down through the centuries, specifically designed containers have been made from every conceivable material. Precious metals, papier-mache, battersea, Oriental lacquer, and wood have held riches from the treasuries of kings, snuff for the fashionable set of the last century, China tea, and countless other commodities. See also Toleware; specific manufacturers.

Bentwood, floral/geometric woodburning, label/dtd 1900, 13" . .**300.00**
Bentwood, orig gr stain w/mc dots & zigzags, 6½" **55.00**

Bentwood, painted and decorated, oval with fitted lid, Germany, ca 1780, 7½x18¾x11¼", $1,750.00.

Brass, inlaid wood lid, mk Germany, 1920s, 4¾" **70.00**
Bride, couple/heart/German inscription, laced seams, 19" . . .**1,250.00**
Bride, couples/verse on lid, pine w/laced seams, mk, 18" **1,900.00**
Bride, figure/moon/inscription, pine, laced seams, 17", NM . .**2,800.00**
Bride's spice chest, flowers/name/1787, pine/veneer, 12x14" .**2,600.00**
Candle, pine, chamfered slide lid, ca 1800, 6x9x11" **260.00**
Candle, pine, slide lid, nailed, 1850s, 4x5½x12" **90.00**
Candle, pine, slide lid, old pnt, 1830s, 7x9x16" **150.00**
Candle, wood, dvtl, chamfered lid, 6½x4¼" **145.00**
Candle, wood, lollipop bk, 1 pocket, 1820s, 7½x11x12" **425.00**
Chip cvd, step-cut ft, sliding lid, 1-pc, 4½" **200.00**
Chip cvd, 2 sliding lids, brass-tack trim, 1-pc, 6" **150.00**
Curly maple, dvtl, trn ft, 14½", EX **375.00**
Curly maple, tambour lid w/brass knob, reeded sides, 10" **450.00**
Desk, walnut table-top, slant lid/ogee ft, 2-drw, 15x15x13" **700.00**
Document, dome top, yel w/ochre swirls & initials, 17", M **700.00**
Document, pine w/old brn pnt, dvtl, 1800s, 10x15" **150.00**
Flame mahog veneer, bevel edge lid, orig brass bail, 13½" **200.00**
Ivory, portrait, artist sgn, gold ormolu, French, sm **235.00**
Jewel, cranberry w/gold floral, brass mts/ring hdls, 5x5¾" **425.00**
Jewel, dk bl glass, floral on gold, brass mts/ft, 5x5" **400.00**
Jewel, red glass, gold birds/floral, brass ftd, 3½x10" **150.00**
Jewel, sapphire bl glass, roses/angel face, brass mts, 5x7" **400.00**
Jewel, sapphire bl glass w/floral & bird, brass hdls, 3½x7" **225.00**
Jewel, turq bl glass w/mc floral, ormolu ft/mts, 5½" dia **250.00**
Knife, ash, scrolled sides, high divider w/heart cutout, 10" **155.00**
Knife, walnut, dvtl, slant sides, center hdl, sq nails **110.00**
Leather-covered, brass-tack trim/bail, rpl lock, 12" **65.00**
Pantry, laced/tacked, papered, late 1800s, 4½x8½" **145.00**
Pantry, pinned wood lid & base, initialed, 6" dia **85.00**
Pantry, wood, pointed laps, dk mustard pnt, 7¼" dia **125.00**

Pantry, wood, pointed laps, taupe pnt, 8" dia 125.00
Pantry, wood, pointed laps, unpnt, 6½" dia 95.00
Pine, chip-cvd edges/crest, hex cutout, wall mt, 11¼" 350.00
Pine, dvtl, sliding bevel-edge lid, minor damage, 23" 82.50
Pine, old gr pnt, walnut trim, rpr, 18" 70.00
Pine/poplar, worn orig pnt w/striping, sliding lid, 10" 50.00
Pipe, cherry, front: scalloped w/heart cutout, drw, 8x22" . . .4,100.00
Pipe, pine, orig bl pnt, scalloped edges/crest, drw, 18x7" 300.00
Plique-a-jour, florals, flower finial lid, #925, 1¾x 2¼" 725.00
Poplar, cherry finish, dvtl, sliding lid, 2-part int, 7x9" 60.00
Poplar, orig brn grpt, dvtl, wrought end hdls, sgn, 27" 150.00
Poplar, red grpt & gold stencil, 12" 125.00
Poplar, rpt on orig brn grpt, added lid cvg, dome top, 24" 395.00
Poplar, stenciled rpt, dvtl, MOP escutcheon, 12" 165.00
Poplar, worn red pnt, dvtl, brass hdl, 14" 140.00
Poplar, yel pnt/blk striping, decoupage eng, wear, 15" L 55.00
Poplar w/brn sponging & red daubs, dvtl, minor wear, 18" 775.00
Salt, mahog, shaped crest, lift lid, drw, wall mt, 15x11" 425.00
Scouring, red pnt, sliding lid w/redware knob, 10x13" 200.00
Scouring, walnut/pine, star cutout, unfinished, hanging, 17" . . .500.00
Spice, poplar, dvtl, EX crest/lift lid, 4-part int, 14x10" 500.00
Spice, poplar, dvtl w/sliding lid, 3-part int, 10½" 135.00
Spice, poplar/red pnt traces, 6-section, dvtl, sgn lid, 8½" 200.00
Storage, bentwood w/bl rpt, 7x17" dia 300.00
Tortoise shell w/brass inlay, 3¼", EX 235.00
Wallpaper covered, floral, 8" 150.00
Walnut, inlaid rosewood/ebony/ivory, dvtl, age cracks, 12" 200.00
Walnut, star inlay lid, rpl bottom, 12" 75.00
Writing, mahog, curved tambour top, 1 dvtl drw, 9x12" 150.00
Writing, orig grpt imitates exotic wood, fitted int, 13" 45.00

Bradley and Hubbard

The Bradley and Hubbard Mfg. Company was a firm which produced metal accessories for the home. They operated from about 1860 until the early part of this century, and their products reflected both the Arts and Crafts and Art Nouveau influence. Their logo was a device with a triangular arrangement of the company name containing a smaller triangle and an Aladdin lamp.

Lamps

Brass & copper, appl metal designs, ball globe, mk, 21" 495.00
Domical 15" acid-cut orchid shade; strapwork base 700.00
Gr slag panels w/filigree border; 3-light base, 18" 385.00
Mottled glass 16" paneled shade w/floral overlay; sgn twice 700.00
Slag glass panels, cut-out leaf panels, base w/leaves, 20" 500.00

Miscellaneous

Andirons, mushroom finial, dmn vignettes on std, #3305, 20" .350.00
Book rack, sq end panels w/windswept pine trees, 5" closed 275.00
Candle lantern w/clock, pierced tin, faceted glass buttons . . .1,300.00
Card holder, Egyptian motif, brass .20.00
Cigar stand, brass, tray w/3 etched cups & cutter, 30" 175.00
Plaque, blown-out bust of lady in flowing gown, bronze, rare . . .395.00

Brass

Brass is an alloy consisting essentially of copper and zinc in variable proportions. It is a medium that has been used for both utilitarian items and objects of artistic merit. Today, with the inflated price of copper and the popular use of plastics, almost anything made of brass is collectible. Our advisor, Mary Frank Gaston, has compiled a lovely book, *Antique Brass*, with full-color photos; you will find her address in the Directory under Texas. See also Candlesticks.

Boot/shoe horn, seamed, tubular w/curl, 1700s, 9½" 260.00
Box lock, 5¼x9" 65.00

Brass kettle with trivet, riveted loop handle, hinged spout, wood handle and wrought iron legs, 27", $400.00.

Candle sconce, lyre bk, 3 removable scroll arms, late, 10" 65.00
Candlestick, crystal pendants, 11", pr 65.00
Candlestick, dolphin form, fine detail, early, 10½", pr 265.00
Candlestick, trn ped base, mid-1800s, 3", pr 120.00
Candlestick, trn ped base, 1800s, 4", pr 125.00
Desk sander, rpr, 2⅜" dia 55.00
Dishpan, 5x19" 55.00
Eagle on olive branch, 6¼" 75.00
Flintlock tinder lighter, English, mk Payne/Poolboro, EX 800.00
Hall tree, Victorian, simple styling, 64" 75.00
Horn, trumpet shape, slightly curved, late, 11" 55.00
Kettle shelf, EX detail, English registry mk, 12x12x15" 245.00
Ladle, shaped hdl w/rolled edges, hook end, ca 1840 . . . . .85.00
Letter holder, eagle, shield on breast, sgn/1875, 3½x3½x1¼" . . .55.00
Letter rack, horse by fence, rectangular base, 4x3x8⅛" 75.00
Mirror holder, emb eagle & shield, 1¾" dia, pr 70.00
Mug, copper rim/strap hdl, handmade, EX detail, 4" 90.00
Pail, cast, wide wrought iron hdl, 10" dia 50.00
Pail, cast, wrought iron bail w/copper rivets, 11½" dia 70.00
Pail, spun, Ansonia label, iron bail hdl, 9½x12½" 75.00
Pail, spun, HW Hayden's Pat, iron bail hdl, 7" dia 125.00
Pan, copper rivets in hdl, 1850s, 3½x7", 10" hdl 125.00
Piano lamp, 3-leg base, wht globe, 67" 325.00
Sconce, star shape, candle cup, pr 95.00
Spatula, forged iron flat hdl, hook end, mk, pat '86, 14½" 150.00

Tea strainer, pierced, slanted 6" tin hdl, ca 1850 . . . . .125.00
Teakettle, EX detail, mk Empress, late, 5½" 155.00
Tieback, pewter bk & iron shaft, 4x4", pr 45.00
Trammel, 14 adjustments, English, 1700s, extends to 22" 400.00
Wall bracket, elephant head figural, trunk is holder, 4x9" 85.00
Whistle, steamboat; Trident manifold, Lunkenheimer, NM . 1,750.00
Wick trimmers, scissors form, w/emb sheet brass tray, 8½" 65.00

Brastoff, Sascha

The son of immigrant parents, Sascha Brastoff was encouraged to develop his artistic talents to the fullest — encouragement that was well taken, as his achievements aptly attest. Though at various times he has been a dancer, sculptor, Hollywood costume designer, jeweler, and painter, it is his ceramics that are today becoming highly-regarded collectibles.

He began his career in the United States in the late 1940s. In a beautiful studio built for him by his friend and mentor, Winthrop Rockefeller, he designed innovative wares that even then were among the most expensive on the market. All designing was done personally by Brastoff; he also supervised the staff which at the height of production numbered approximately 150. Wares signed with his full signature were personally crafted by him and are valued much more highly than those signed 'Sascha B.,' indicating work done under his supervision. Sascha Brastoff still resides in Los Angeles, California, at present producing 'Sascha Holograms,' which are distributed by the Hummelwerk Company. In the listings below, all items are signed 'Sascha B.' unless otherwise indicated (full signature).

Our advisor for this category is Jack Chipman; he is listed in the Directory under California.

Ash tray, amber enameling, 6" 25.00
Ash tray, horse decor on gray 40.00
Ash tray, peacock decor, gold & silver on wht, 7" 25.00
Bowl, bl/silver, sm ft, full signature 65.00
Bowl, lav marbleized, 3-ftd, 6x3" 25.00
Bowl, nut; Huskie dog, lt gr, full signature 60.00
Box, cigarette; bird decor, wht/gold, full signature 80.00
Box, genie motif, egg shape, w/lid, #44-A, 7½" 45.00
Candle holder, amber resin, 8", pr 30.00

Figure of a horse, multicolor on white, signed Sascha B., $150.00.

Gravy boat, pk & silver, w/attached tray 25.00
Humidor, pipe; lid makes ash tray, full signature, lg 115.00
Obelisk, full signature, 22" 150.00

Plaque, enamel, leaves & jewels, 12" 45.00
Plaque, grapes decor, 14" 45.00
Tankard, gold, full signature 85.00
Tidbit tray, pk & silver 25.00
Vase, doves decor, 10½" 100.00
Vase, gold Deco overlay on gold, V-3, 12" 100.00

Brayton, Laguna

Durlin E. Brayton made hand-crafted vases, lamps, and dinnerware in a small kiln at his Laguna Beach, California, home in 1927. He soon married; and, with his wife, Ellen Webster Grieve, as his partner, the small business became a successful commercial venture. They are most famous for their amusing, well-detailed figurines, some of which were commissioned by Walt Disney Studios. Though very successful even through the Depression years, with the influx of imported novelties that deluged the country after WWII, business began to decline. By 1968 the pottery was closed.

Our advisor for this category is Jack Chipman; he is listed in the Directory under California.

Candle holder, sitting Blackamoor, pr .60.00
Cookie jar, puppy 125.00
Figurine, 'Ma' Horse/'Pa' Horse, ea 55.00
Figurine, cow, purple, 8" L 40.00
Figurine, crane, head down, blk matt, crackleware wings, 10" . . .45.00
Figurine, duck, gr/wht polka-dot hat, 9" 35.00
Figurine, Ellen, standing, arms out, children's series 25.00
Figurine, Eugene, children's series 25.00
Figurine, lady blues singer, long gown, necklace, 8" 36.00
Figurine, newlyweds in cab w/horse, Gay '90s series 95.00
Figurine, panther, stalking, red, 13" L 130.00
Figurine, peasant lady w/open baskets, 8" 40.00
Figurine, Pluto, head down, bk legs str, Disney, 6" L 100.00
Figurine, singing trio at bar, Gay '90s series 95.00
Flower frog, pouter pigeon, bl/wht/gr, incised, 5½x5¾" 30.00

From the circus series: Mr. Elephant, flower holder, scarce, $65.00; Circus Tent cookie jar, scarce, $125.00; Clown and dog shakers, $45.00 for the pair.

Shakers, peasant couple, wht & brn crackle, mk, 5½", pr 45.00
Vase, Blackamoor boy holds gold bowl-type vase, 8" 150.00

Bread Plates and Trays

Bread plates and trays have been produced not only in many types of glass but in metal and pottery as well. Those considered most collectible were made during the last quarter of the nineteenth century from pressed glass with well-detailed embossed designs, many of them portraying a particularly significant historical event. A great number of these plates were sold at the 1876 Philadelphia Centennial Exposition by various glass manufacturers who exhibited their wares on the grounds. Among the themes depicted are the Declaration of Independence, the Constitution, McKinley's memorial 'It Is God's Way,' Rememberance of Three Presidents, the Purchase of Alaska, and various presidential campaigns, to mention only a few. Numbers correspond with a reference book on glass by Lindsey.

American Flag, 38 stars, L-51, 11x8" 225.00
Be Industrious, 101 border, clear/frosted, 12" L 75.00
Blaine/Logan, clear/frosted, L-315, 11½x8½" 250.00
Bunker Hill, Prescott/1776/Stark, L-44, 13¼x9" 100.00
California Bear, 1894 Expo, L-104 . . . . .135.00
Carpenters Hall, L-28, 12x8½" 95.00
Classic, James Blaine, clear/frosted, L-312, 11½" dia 200.00
Cleveland/Hendricks, clear/frosted, L-314, 11½x8½" 250.00
Cleveland/Thurman busts, clear/frosted, L-325, 9½x8½" 200.00
Columbia, shield shape, bl, L-54, 11½x9½" 150.00
Columbia, shield shape, L-54, 11½x9½" 120.00
Constitution, L-43 . . . . .25.00
Continental, hand hdls, 12¾" L 75.00
Cupid & Venus, 10½" dia 45.00
Deer & Pine Tree, vaseline 75.00
Do Unto Others 45.00
Egyptian, Cleopatra center, 8¾x13" 50.00
Egyptian, Mormon Temple in center, rare 300.00
Eureka, w/motto, L-103 . . . . .28.00
GAR, L-505, 11" L 85.00
Garfield Memorial, L-302, 10" L 60.00
Give Us This Day, Eagle & Constitution 100.00
Give Us This Day, Sheaf of Wheat, 13" L 65.00
Grant Memorial, bl, maple leaf border, L-289, 10½" dia 65.00
Grapes, Pleasant to Labor 45.00
Heroes of Bunker Hill 45.00
Horseshoe, single horseshoe hdls, 9x13" 55.00
In Remembrance, 3 Presidents, clear/frosted, oval 75.00
Independence Hall, L-29, 12x8½" 95.00
Iowa City, Be Industrious, frosted beehive center 60.00
Jewel Band, Bread Is Staff of Life 40.00
John Bates, Minerva, L-375, scarce 60.00
Knights of Labor, amber, oval, L-512, 12" L 185.00
Knights of Labor, L-512 . . . . .125.00
Liberty & Freedom w/eagle, 12" L 75.00
Liberty Bell, Signers 125.00
Liberty Bell, 13 Colonies 45.00
Lion, lion hdls, motto, clear/frosted, 12" L 125.00
Lotus & Serpent 45.00
Martyrs, ornate hdls, L-271, 12½" L .100.00
McKinley, It Is God's Way, 10½" L 60.00
McKinley Gold Standard, L-332, 10½" L 350.00
Memorial Hall 60.00
Minerva, w/motto & portrait 70.00
Mitchell, Leader/Counsellor/Friend, L-448, scarce, 10¾" L 250.00
Nelly Bly, L-136, 12" L 170.00
Niagara Falls, clear/frosted, L-489, 16" L 125.00
Polar Bear & Ship, frosted, L-486, 16" L 150.00
Railroad w/Engine, L-134, 9x12" 85.00
Scroll w/Flowers, 12" dia 35.00
Teddy Roosevelt, dancing bears, L-357, 7¾x10¼" 135.00
US Grant, Let Us Have Peace, amber, 10½" dia 85.00

US Grant, Let Us Have Peace, vaseline, 10½" dia 85.00
Washington, First in War/First in Peace, L-27, 12x8½" 95.00
Westward Ho, w/deer hdls 150.00
3 Graces, Faith, Hope, Charity, pat & dtd 1875 . . . . .45.00

Bride's Baskets and Bowls

Victorian brides were showered with gifts, as brides have always been; one of the most popular gift items was the bride's basket. Art glass inserts from both European and American glasshouses, some in lovely transparent hues with dainty enameled florals, others of Peachblow, Vasa Murrhina, satin or cased glass were cradled in complementary silverplated holders. While many of these holders were simply engraved or delicately embossed, others such as those from Pairpoint and Wilcox were wonderfully ornate, often with figurals of cherubs or animals. The bride's basket was no longer in fashion after the turn of the century.

In the listings that follow, if no frame is described, the price is for a bowl only.

Apricot to pk to wht, HP florals w/gold; SP fr, 10" 275.00
Bl Invt T'print, gilt/florals, lg tiered ped, 9" cherub 750.00
Bl overlay, gold-traced scene; Meriden fr, 11½" 350.00
Bl satin, HP decor, fluted, crimped; SP fr, 11" dia 575.00
Burmese w/yel mums, ruffled; ornate SP std w/3 cherubs, 24" .1,600.00
Cranberry & clear stripes w/opal; mk Pairpoint fr, 7½x5½" 375.00
Cranberry overlay, pleated/fluted; Hartford fr (VG), 10" dia . . .185.00
Cream satin w/floral sprays, ruffled, trn-down side, 12x14" 450.00
Gr to rose, hobnails, pleated rim, New Martinsville 125.00
Lime-cased Coinspot, bl rim, ruffled; ormolu base, 14" 650.00
Lt to pk to fuchsia, gold decor, Webb, 15½x13½" 395.00
MOP Dia Quilt, bl, ruffled, tricorner; fancy SP fr, 9½" 735.00
MOP Herringbone, pk on lime w/mums; 3 cherubs/mirror . . .2,100.00
MOP Moire, bl; ornate Simpson Hall Miller fr w/strawberries . .450.00
Opal w/burgundy crimped rim; SP fr, 9" dia 125.00
Peach to apricot, fluted; ftd SP fr, 10" 155.00
Peachblow, gold florals, Mt WA; Pairpoint fr w/marine life . . .800.00
Pk satin, yel ext/lavish floral; Wilcox holder w/6" cherubs . . .1,500.00
Pk shaded, HP florals, ruffled/crimped; SP Barbour fr 365.00
Pk to bl overlay, mc florals; SP fr (VG), 9x10½" dia 195.00

Pink with gold trim and enameled florals, unmarked holder, 12", $400.00.

Pk to fuchsia w/raised gold, scalloped, mk Webb, 3½x13" 250.00
Pk to yel int, lav/bl florals; ftd fr w/birds, 10¼x12½" 450.00
Red to yel-gr overlay, HP florals, petaled rim, 3x12" 350.00
Robin's egg bl overlay, bust of lady/florals, 12" dia 250.00
Wht, cranberry int, circles, pleated/fluted rim; SP fr, 10" 250.00
Wht cased, bl int, morning-glories, Mt WA; orig SP fr, 1885 ..500.00
Yel satin, bl rim, 2 birds at side, S&W; orig SP fr 750.00

Bristol Glass

Bristol is a type of semi-opaque opaline glass whose name was derived from the area in England where it was first produced. Similar glass was made in France, Germany, and Italy. In this country, it was made by the New England Glass Company and to a lesser extent by its contemporaries. During the eighteenth and nineteenth centuries, Bristol glass was imported in large amounts and sold cheaply, thereby contributing to the demise of the earlier glasshouses here in America. It is very difficult to distinguish the English Bristol from other opaline types. Style, design, and decoration serve as clues to its origin; but often only those well versed in the field can spot these subtle variations.

Biscuit jar, beige w/pk & gold roses, SP top/rim/hdl, 6" 145.00
Biscuit jar, gray, mc floral w/gold, SP lid/rim/hdl, 6¼" 110.00
Bottle, scent; pk w/bl florals, w/stopper, 8¼" 100.00
Bottle, scent; turq w/florals & gold bands, 4x1¾" 70.00
Box, cream w/pk florals, egg form, ormolu ft, 6½x3⅛" 225.00
Box, wht, allover florals & leaves, ormolu mts, rnd, 5" H 175.00
Egg cup, cream, gold band on top & base, pr 30.00
Ewer, wht w/floral branch in gold, 11" 75.00
Pin dish, turq, gold floral/scallops/ft, 1¾x3¾" 50.00
Rose bowl, turq, gold floral/scallops, 4-crimp top, 4x3½" 100.00
Shot glass, turq, gold hearts, pk roses, HP trim, 2½x1⅝" 35.00
Tray, turq, yel florals & lacy gold band, 11x7¾" 120.00
Urn, cobalt, figures in landscape, paneled std, 9", pr 400.00
Urn, pk, gold reserve w/children & lamb, canister base, 18" ...595.00

Pair of vases, white with enameled birds and florals, 13¾", $125.00.

Vase, bl, gold florals & panels, ped ft, 4½x1½" 45.00
Vase, cream, stylized leaves, goat-head hdls, 8½" 60.00
Vase, pk, florals, ribbon reserve, urn form, 13", pr 150.00
Vase, tan, florals, gold trim, 16½", pr 270.00
Vase, turq, gold florals, much gold trim, 4⅝x2", pr 75.00
Vase, turq, gold florals, 3⅝x1⅞" 30.00

Vase, turq, gold florals/ft, calla lily shape, 5½x1¼" 45.00

British Royalty Commemoratives

While most modern-day commemorative collectors start their collections with souvenirs issued during Queen Victoria's reign, interest in royal commemorative collecting has been evident for centuries. A commemorative medal was issued for Edward VI's 1547 coronation. Ceramics are the most popular type of commemoratives. Food tins are gaining in popularity — so are glass, paper, and metal souvenirs. Since commemoratives have always been a commercial endeavor, nearly any item with room for a portrait and an inscription has been manufactured as a souvenir; thus a wide variety is available in all price ranges. Since royal events are an ongoing state of affairs, it is possible to choose almost any time in British history as a commemorative starting point. Even present-day souvenirs make a good, inexpensive beginning collection. Today's events will be tomorrow's history! For further study we recommend *British Royal Commemoratives*, by our advisor for this category, Audrey Zeder; she is listed in the Directory under California.

Key:
anniv — anniversary   LE — limited edition
com — commemorative   mem — memorial
cor — coronation   wed — wedding
Jub — Jubilee

Beaker, Edward VII 1901 King's Dinner w/printed program ...100.00
Beaker, Edward VIII, cor, w/relief portrait on pk 40.00
Beaker, Geo V cor, color portrait/decor, for Harrods 55.00
Beaker, Geo V cor, w/official mc portrait & design 45.00
Bell, Andrew/Sarah wed, Westminster Abbey 40.00
Bell, Charles/Diana engagement, bone china, wood hdl 45.00
Bell, Charles/Diana in wedding attire, china, 7½" 45.00
Bell, Elizabeth II Jub, SP, in orig box 50.00
Bell, Elizabeth II 1987 wed anniv, bone china 40.00
Cup & saucer, Charles/Diana wed, mc portraits & design 50.00
Cup & saucer, Queen Victoria 1887 Jub, picture on c/s 195.00
Cup & saucer, Victoria/Albert in 1851, pk lustre, china 225.00
Ephemera, Charles/Diana wed, miniature album/photos 20.00
Ephemera, Edward VII, advertising card, 3-fold 25.00
Ephemera, Edward VII memorial post card, unused 10.00
Ephemera, Edward VIII cor, calendar w/portrait & ad 30.00
Ephemera, Geo V cor, notepaper w/photo, unused 35.00
Ephemera, Geo V cor, post card, king, queen & family 10.00
Ephemera, Geo V Jub, fireworks display catalog 45.00
Ephemera, Geo V Jub, official program 25.00
Ephemera, Geo VI cor, family picture/unused calendar 25.00
Ephemera, Prince Albert 1868 color print, memorial 25.00
Ephemera, Prince of Wales (future Ed VII) photo 25.00
Ephemera, Princess Diana, unused 10-pg notepaper 20.00
Ephemera, Princess Elizabeth wed, ILN 30.00
Ephemera, Princess Margaret wed, ILN 30.00
Ephemera, Queen Caroline 1820 newspaper/divorce trial 100.00
Ephemera, Queen Elizabeth Jub, foil picture calendar 20.00
Ephemera, Queen Victoria 1860 blk/wht engravings, set of 3 ...45.00
Ephemera, Queen Victoria 1897 color print, 12x16" 25.00
Ephemera, Queen Victoria 1901 graphic 50.00
Ephemera, Queen Victoria 1901 ILN Record Number 125.00
Jug, Prince Albert/Royal Arms emb on salt glaze, 1862, 11" ...180.00
Loving cup, Charles/Diana wed, lion hdls, Paragon 75.00
Loving cup, Edward VII mem, HP, LE 100, Copeland, 7" ...1,000.00
Loving cup, Elizabeth II Jub, relief portrait, Burleigh 80.00
Loving cup, Elizabeth II 60th b'day, horsebk, Aynsley 40.00

Loving cup, Geo VI cor, family portrait, china 150.00
Loving cup, Prince William 1983 birthday, baby picture 35.00
Loving cup, Queen Mother, 80th birthday, Royal Doulton 50.00
Loving cup, Queen Victoria Transvall, 3-hdl, Copeland 1,500.00
Loving cup, Queen Victoria 1887 Jub, blk/wht 525.00
Mug, Andrew/Sarah wed, mc picture in wedding attire 35.00
Mug, Charles 1969 Investure, Guyatt design, Wedgewood 135.00
Mug, Charles/Diana, clear glass w/mc picture, ½-pt 25.00
Mug, Charles/Diana wed, mc picture/design, bone china 25.00
Mug, Charles/Diana wed, mc picture/design, stoneware 20.00
Mug, Charles/Diana 1st visit to Wales .35.00
Mug, Charles/Diana/William/Henry at Henry's christening 25.00
Mug, Duke/Duchess Windsor (Edward VIII) mem 85.00
Mug, Edward VII cor, sepia transfer on wht, Doulton 125.00
Mug, Elizabeth II Australian bi-centenary, #34, LE 500 . . . . . . .65.00
Mug, Elizabeth II cor portrait, 'E' hdl, Doulton 75.00
Mug, Elizabeth II 1987 ruby wed, portraits, Royal Crafton 25.00
Mug, Geo VI cor, king/queen/princesses, Copeland 100.00
Mug, Prince of Wales (Ed VIII) 1927 Canadian visit 75.00
Mug, Princess Anne wed, Guyatt design, Wedgwood 75.00
Mug, Princess Anne 1987 Princess Royal, Caverswall 75.00
Mug, Queen Alexander, cobalt w/color portrait 95.00
Mug, Queen Victoria 1887 Jub, brn transfer on wht 150.00
Novelty, Andrew/Sarah wed, bookmark, plastic, w/picture 10.00
Novelty, Andrew/Sarah wed, puzzle in tin box, unopened 30.00
Novelty, Charles/Diana, slippers w/sleeping heads 40.00
Novelty, Charles/Diana wed, coaster set, ceramic, 6 w/box 30.00
Novelty, Charles/Diana wed, playing cards, unused 20.00
Novelty, Charles/Diana wed, post card, record player 10.00
Novelty, Charles/Diana wed, wood slat wall hang, w/portrait . . .20.00
Novelty, Edward VII cor, match safe, relief portraits 45.00
Novelty, Elizabeth II China visit, peepshow telescope 20.00
Novelty, Elizabeth II cor, horse, brass, crown & date 15.00
Novelty, Elizabeth II cor, paperweight, crystal 50.00
Novelty, Elizabeth II cor, table lighter, Wedgewood jasper 75.00
Novelty, Elizabeth II Jub, perpetual calendar, tin 25.00
Novelty, Geo V Jub, cuff links, brass, mc portraits 35.00
Novelty, Princess Anne 1987 Pr Royal, thimble, peepshow 20.00
Novelty, Princess Bea 1988 birth, thimble, peepshow 20.00
Novelty, Queen Alexandra, inkwell, pearl lustre, mc portrait . .210.00
Pinback, Andrew/Sarah wed, mc portrait on wht 5.00
Pinback, Charles/Diana wed, blk/wht portrait on red/wht/bl 5.00
Pinback, Edward VIII, blk/wht portrait on red/wht/bl 15.00
Pinback, Geo VI cor, color portraits on buff 15.00
Pitcher, Edward VII 1863 wed, mc relief design 300.00
Pitcher, Edward VIII, relief design w/music box 400.00
Pitcher, Geo V cor, king in naval uniform 200.00
Pitcher, Queen Victoria 1840 wed, relief design on blk 275.00
Pitcher, Queen Victoria 1860 Royal Review, relief design 40.00
Pitcher, Queen Victoria 1897 Jub, brn stone, Doulton 275.00
Pitcher, Queen Victoria 1897 Jub, creamer, mc portrait 125.00
Plate, Charles/Diana honeymoon, silhouettes & Brittannia 150.00
Plate, Charles/Diana wed, mc design, relief edge, Rosina 50.00
Plate, Charles/Diana 650th anniv Duchy Cornwall, LE 500 . . .125.00
Plate, Edward VII cor, HP, fluted edge, Royal Doulton 225.00
Plate, Edward VIII cor, king in uniform, 6" 50.00
Plate, Elizabeth II Australian bi-centenary, #34, LE 500 . . . . . .85.00
Plate, Elizabeth II 1986 China visit, LE 250, Wilton 150.00
Plate, Elizabeth II 60th birthday, Aynsley, ftd, 5½" 40.00
Plate, Geo V cor, flow blue, Royal Doulton 225.00
Plate, Geo V cor, ribbon edge, mc portraits, 7" 150.00
Plate, Geo VI cor, med bl w/relief Art Deco design 75.00
Plate, Geo VI 1939 US visit, Royal Doulton, 4¼" 45.00
Plate, Prince Henry christening, w/family, 6" 30.00

Plate, Prince William birth, w/family & relatives, 10" 60.00
Plate, Queen Victoria 1897 Jub, elaborate design 225.00
Plate, Queen Victoria 1897 Jub, mc portrait, Doulton 195.00
Plate, Queen Victoria 1901 mem, mc transfer 175.00

Pot lid, Prince Albert's 1861 death, The Late Prince Consort, in wooden frame, 5¾", $165.00.

Textile, Charles/Diana wed, scarf, silk, mc portrait 50.00
Textile, Elizabeth II, handkerchief, cor scenes 20.00
Textile, Queen Victoria, handkerchief, special events 225.00
Textile, Queen Victoria, ribbon, mc portrait & design 75.00
Tin, Charles/Diana wed, mc portraits & design 35.00
Tin, Edward VII cor, mc portraits, Rowntree, 2½x5" 45.00
Tin, Elizabeth II Jub, w/matches, Cornish 25.00
Tin, Princess Mary, WWI gift for troops, brass 50.00
Tin, Queen Victoria, 1900 S Africa war gift for troops 75.00
Tin, Queen Victoria 1897 Jub, Ivory Starch, 10" 165.00

Broadsides

Webster defines a broadside as simply a large sheet of paper printed on one side. During the 1880s, they were the most practical means of mass-communication. By the middle of the century they had become elaborate and lengthy with information, illustrations, portraits, and fancy border designs.

Auburn and Moravia Stage, ca 1855, 13x10", $400.00.

Battle of Mobile Bay, general orders, Farragut, 1864, 10x8" . .2,000.00
Circus, Great India Elephant, 7000 lbs, NY, 1832, 36x24" . . .2,500.00
Death of Andrew Jackson, ca 1840s, 10x15" 75.00
Decret de la Convention Nationale, 1793, 20x16", EX 250.00
English Civil War, people's protests, 1642, 1-pg 280.00
Free Exhibition & Dollar Sale...JB Burleigh, 1875, 9x12" 60.00
Indian Exhibition, Penobscot tribe, 1851, 18x12" 375.00
Indian proclamation, sgn Henry Silverheels, 1864, 12x9" 145.00
Indians Take Notice, Ft Smith AR, 1893, 11x7½" 380.00
Massacre at Dartmoor Prison, Boston, 1812, 16x9½" 550.00
McClellan's address to troops, 1862, 1-pg, sm 200.00
Miner's Reply to ...Tuolumne County Water Co, 1855, 13x8" .650.00
Mortgage sale, Eldorado saloon, NM, 1873, 10x7½" 200.00
Proclamation by Gov J Trumbull of CT, 1783, 13½x8½" 380.00
Rates of toll on Santa Cruz Gap turnpike road, 1874, 18x12" . .350.00
Reward $500, conviction of lynching mob, CA, 1895 . . . . .175.00
RR passengers warned against playing cards, CA, 1874, EX . . .450.00
Sailing news of Alaska Gold Rush, ca 1899 . . . . .200.00
Sham Battle, July 4th, by 2000 soldiers, ca 1890s, 30x13" 500.00
Splendid Daguerreotype Miniatures, Hayden, 1850s, 10½x9" . .220.00
Spring fevers & malaria, ca 1880, 5½x8¾", VG 15.00
Status of Sutro Tunnel Co, VA City NV, 1869, 13½x7" 140.00
Steamboat New Hamburgh on Hudson, 1832, 17x11", VG 190.00
Steamboat trip to Annapolis, boat woodcut, 1845, 19x12", EX .780.00
Thanksgiving proclamation, lion/unicorn, 1703, 18x15" 775.00
TN proclamation, civilians obey military, 1862, 9x11½" 600.00
Two Orphans, Philadelphia play, silk, 1875, 10⅝x5", +fr 285.00
VA Instructs Senators/Reps on Amendments, 1795 . . . . .1,700.00

Bronzes

Thomas Ball, George Bessell, and Leonard Volk were some of the earliest American sculptors who produced figures in bronze for home decor during the 1840s. Pieces of historical significance were the most popular, but by the 1880s a more fanciful type of artwork took hold. Some of the fine sculptors of the day were Daniel Chester French, Augustus St. Gaudens, and John Quincy Adams Ward. Bronzes reached the height of their popularity at the turn of the century. The American West was portrayed to its fullest by Remington, Russell, James Frazier, Hermon MacNeil, and Solon Borglum. Animals of every species were modeled by A.P. Proctor, Paul Bartlett, and Albert Laellele, to name but a few.

Art Nouveau and Art Deco influenced the medium during the twenties, evidenced by the works of Allen Clark, Harriet Frismuth, E.F. Sanford, and Bessie P. Vonnoh.

Be aware that recasts abound. While often esthetically satisfactory, they are not original and should be priced accordingly. In much the same manner as prints are evaluated, the original castings made under the direction of the artist are the most valuable. Later castings from the original mold are worth less. A recast is not made from the original mold. Instead, a rubber-like substance is applied to the bronze, peeled away, and filled with wax. Then, using the same 'lost wax' procedure as the artist uses on completion of his original wax model, a clay-like substance is formed around the wax figure and the whole fired to vitrify the clay. The wax, of course, melts away — hence the term 'lost wax.' Recast bronzes lose detail and are somewhat smaller than the original due to the shrinkage of the clay mold.

Alpointe, Figure of Nymph, brn patina, 1904, 23" 850.00
Austrian School, eagle, polychrome, 1800s, 6" L 110.00
Austrian School, hunter standing over stag, mc, 19th C, 4" . . .300.00
Austrian School, lion, cold pnt, 20th C, 5½" L 300.00
Austrian School, Pierrot & Columbine, Altman mk, 6x12" . . .275.00
Austrian School, plaque of farmer, cold pnt, 1900, 26x17" 500.00

Barrault, Phryne, trn marble plinth, 1800s, 23" 400.00
Barye, AL; Half-Blood Horse, gr/brn patinae, 1800s, 5½x7" . .1,650.00
Bauer, figure of dancer, onyx plinth, ca 1925, 24½" 1,200.00
Bergmann, tiger, polychrome pnt, 4x8" 1,400.00
Blevon, Longhorn steer, American, 20th C, 8½x17½x8" . . .275.00
Bouraine, Amazon, nude kneels w/spear, gilt, 20th C, 24" L .2,200.00
Cartier, T; figure of lion, golden brn patina, 20th C, 21" 1,100.00
Chadwick, L; Maquette for Stranger, #340, 20th C, 12" 9,350.00
Chiparus, D; Hindu Dancer, pnt traces, 19th/20th C, 23½" . .6,600.00
Clemencin, FA; Woman & Ram, brn patina, 1900s, 13" 500.00
D'Aire, figure of witch, woman in cloak, ivory inlay, 6¼" 300.00
Davidson, Jo; Net Fishermen, American, 19th C, 4" 140.00
Delabassee, standing girl, marble base, 20th C, 18" 1,760.00
Dubucand, A; Arab boy & donkey, ca 1900, 13½" 1,400.00
Etrog, female torso, 20th C, 14¼" .1,320.00
Fayral (after), Dancer w/Cymbals, marble plinth, 19" 495.00

Ferdinand Preiss, Hoop Girl, cold-painted bronze and ivory, early 20th century, 8", $2,400.00.

French School, seated scholar, wood base, 19th C, 8½" 140.00
Frishmuth, HW; Thread of Life, nymph, 20th C, 12" 17,600.00
Fromme, bust of Lord Byron, marble socle, 19th C, 15" 300.00
Ghingre, figure of egret, circular base, 8" 137.00
Good, JW; horse, British, 19th C, 11x16x6" 350.00
Greenbaum, D; head of girl, dk brn patina, 20th C, 15" 220.00
Guyot, G; figure of hound, reclining, 20th C, 14" 450.00
Henry, B; untitled, kneeling nude, 12½x13½" 400.00
Houdon (after), Woman After the Bath, 19½" 500.00
Kauba, C (after); equestrian group, terrain base, 16½" 900.00
Kauba, C; Cheyenne, Indian/horse, granite base, 1800s, 5" . .2,250.00
Laessle, A; turtle on rock, 1900s, 2x2½" 85.00
Lavergne, figure of sailor boy, brn patina, ca 1900, 18" 500.00
Loutchansky, J; head of young woman, basalt base, 16½" 500.00
Mane-Katz, Violinist, blk patina, 1942, 13⅞" 3,300.00
Masulli, E; nude Roman/Greek male, 19th/20th C, 16" 275.00
Mene, PJ (after); figure of stallion, raised head, 13" 470.00
Moigniez, J (after); figure of pheasant, brn patina, 1900, 9" 400.00
Moore, Henry; Fat Torso, brn patina, sgn, 1981, 5⅞" 9,900.00
Moreau, A; figure of Diana, sq lighted base, 26" 1,100.00
Omerth, figure of skater, wht onyx base, 19th/20th C, 8" 528.00
Payer, H; animal group, silvered, marble base, 10½" 770.00

Picasso, Taureau, gilded, 1957, 5⅛" L 19,800.00
Pizzoni, I; Toro, gray-brn patina, 17¾" 4,950.00
Powell, A; Bronze Indian Head, sq walnut base, 20th C, 7¾" ..125.00
Remington, F (after); Indian on horsebk, Cheyenne, 18½" ...500.00
Remington, F (after); Norther, gr/brn patinae, 20½" 1,000.00
Remington, F (after); rodeo rider w/wide-brim hat, 22" 700.00
Rosin, H; Mother & Child, dk brn patina, Paris, 1933, 9" 330.00
Sandoz, EM; figure of parrot, gr patina, #7, 1925, 14¼" 5,500.00
Thomas, C; Wind, British, 20th C, 10" 140.00
Ventura, JP; bust of young girl, marble base, 11" 660.00
White, R; bust of Hercules, gr/brn patinae, 20th C, 19½" ...1,980.00
Yarnall, A; figure of man, sgn/inscribed, dtd 1953, 38" 700.00
Zuniga, F; standing woman, brn patina, #25, 1970, 15" 5,500.00

Brouwer

Theophlis A. Brouwer, an accomplished artist even before his interests turned to the medium of pottery, started a small one-man operation in 1894 in East Hampton, New York. Two years later he relocated in Westhampton, where he perfected the technique of fire-painting, learning to control the effects of the kiln to produce the best-possible results. In 1925 he founded the Ceramic Flame Company in New York, but it is for his earlier work that he is best known. Brouwer died in 1932.

Vase, brn irid/gr-gold gloss, bulbous w/long neck, mk, 9" 1,600.00
Vase, irid yel/brn/orange, cupped rim, mk Flame, 7¾x6" 2,700.00
Vase, orange/gold/gr, bulbous w/flare neck, 7½x11" 1,000.00
Vase, yel/orange irid, bulbous/sm neck, Flame/#12, 5x5½" ...2,500.00

Brownies by Palmer Cox

Created by Palmer Cox in 1883, the Brownies charmed children through the pages of books and magazines, as dolls on their dinnerware, in advertising material, and on souvenirs. Each had his own personality — among them The Bellhop, The London Bobby, The Chairman, and Uncle Sam. But the oversized, triangular face with the startled expression, the protruding tummy, and the spindlelegs were characteristics of them all. They were inspired by the Scottish legends related to Cox as a child by his parents, who were of English descent. His introduction of the Brownies to the world was accomplished by a poem called *The Brownies Ride*. Books followed in rapid succession — thirteen in the series, all written as well as illustrated by Palmer Cox.

By the late 1890s, the Brownies were active in advertising. They promoted such products as games, coffee, toys, patent medicines, and rubber boots. 'Greenies' were the Brownies' first cousins, created by Cox to charm and to woo through the pages of the advertising almanacs of the G.G. Green Company of New Jersey. Perhaps the best-known endorsement in the Brownies' career was for the Kodak Brownie, which became so popular and sold in such volume that their name became synonymous with this type of camera.

Almanac, G Green Woodbury, Palmer Cox illus, 1890 ....20.00
Basket, SP, Brownies w/chocolate advertising, Tufts 140.00
Book, Bomba the Merry Old King, 1903, EX 30.00
Book, Brownie Town, Palmer Cox illus, VG 85.00
Book, Brownie Yearbook, McLoughlin, 1895, VG 55.00
Book, Brownies in Fairyland, Century Co 35.00
Book, Jolly Chinee, 1903, VG 25.00
Book, Monk's Victory, 1911, EX 25.00
Book, Palmer Cox Brownie Primer, c 1909 & 1933, G 50.00
Book, Queer People, Palmer Cox illus, VG 25.00
Box, Log Cabin Brownies, cabin form, Nat'l Biscuit Co, '20s ..125.00

Candlestick, Uncle Sam & Brownies, majolica, ea 175.00
Crayons, in wood container w/Brownies, all orig 45.00
Cup & saucer, china 50.00
Cup & saucer, SP 100.00
Humidor, Brownie Sailor's head figural, Fr majolica, EX 150.00

Oval bowl, Dresden china, early 1900s, 7½" long, $48.00. (Photo courtesy of Hake's Americana, York, PA)

Paper doll, Russian Brownie, Lion Coffee, EX 15.00
Pitcher, china, 2 Brownies on front, 3 on bk, 4½" 65.00
Stickpin, Brownie policeman 20.00
Tin container, Brownie Ointment, 1924, MIB 40.00
Tray, pin; SP, Brownie crawling on edge, Pairpoint 130.00

Brush

George Brush began his career in the pottery industry in 1901 working for the J.B. Owens Pottery Co. in Zanesville, Ohio. He left the company in 1907 to go into business for himself, only to have fire completely destroy his pottery less than one year after it was founded. Brush became associated with J.W. McCoy in 1909 and for many years served in capacities ranging from General Manager to President. (From 1911 until 1925, the firm was known as The Brush-McCoy Pottery Co.; see that section for information.) After McCoy died, the family withdrew their interests, and in 1925 the name of the firm was changed to The Brush Pottery. The era of hand-decorated art pottery had passed for the most part and would soon be completely replaced by the production of commercial lines. Of all the wares bearing the later Brush script mark, their figural cookie jars are the most collectible. See also Brush-McCoy.

Cookie Jars

Antique Touring Car 75.00
Boy w/Balloons 110.00
Chick in Nest 75.00
Cinderella Pumpkin 55.00
Circus Horse 95.00
Clown, yel pants 85.00
Clown Head 75.00
Cookie House 45.00
Covered Wagon 125.00
Cow, w/cat on bk, brn 55.00
Cow, w/cat on bk, purple 300.00
Davey Crockett 85.00
Dog w/Basket 75.00

Donkey & Cart 85.00
Elephant, w/monkey on bk 200.00
Elephant w/Baby Bonnet 125.00
Fish 85.00
Formal Pig 75.00
Granny 75.00

Happy Bunny, $75.00.

Hen on Basket 45.00
Hill Billy Frog 250.00
Hobby Horse 95.00
Humpty Dumpty, w/beanie & bow tie 60.00
Humpty Dumpty, w/peaked hat 50.00
Lantern, brn/cream, mk K1 ....45.00
Laughing Hippo 75.00
Little Angel 125.00
Little Boy Blue 95.00
Little Girl 95.00
Little Red Riding Hood, basket in arm, mk K24 ....95.00
Nite Owl 55.00
Old Clock 55.00
Old Shoe 45.00
Panda 75.00
Peter Pan 110.00
Peter Peter Pumpkin Eater, boy/girl/pumpkin, mk W24 ..65.00
Puppy Police 85.00
Raggedy Ann 85.00
Sitting Hippo 75.00
Sitting Pig 65.00
Smiling Bear 85.00
Squirrel in Top Hat 65.00
Squirrel on Log 35.00
Stylized Owl 55.00
Stylized Siamese 65.00
Teddy Bear, feet apart 55.00
Teddy Bear, feet together 50.00
Treasure Chest 65.00

Brush-McCoy

The Brush-McCoy Pottery was formed in 1911 in Zanesville, Ohio, an alliance between George Brush and J.W. McCoy. Brush's original pottery had been destroyed by fire in 1907; McCoy had operated his own business there since 1899. After the merger, the company expanded and produced not only their staple commercial wares, but also fine artware. Lines such as Navarre, Venetian, Persian, Oriental, and Sylvan were of fine quality equal to that of their larger competitors. Because very little of the ware was marked, it is often mistaken for Weller, Roseville, or Peters and Reed.

In the twenties, after a fire in Zanesville had destroyed the manufacturing portion of that plant, all production was contained in their Roseville (Ohio) plant #2. A stoneware type of clay was used there; and as a result, the artware lines of Jewell, Zuniart, King Tut, Florastone, and Panel-Art are so distinctive that they are more easily recognizable. Examples of these lines are unique and very beautiful — also quite rare and highly prized!

The Brush-McCoy Pottery operated under that name until after J.W. McCoy's death when it became the Brush Pottery. The Brush-Barnett family retained their interest in the pottery until 1981 when it was purchased by the Dearborn Company. See also Brush.

Bowl, Navarre, gr w/wht Nouveau lady, 4½x8" 150.00
Candlestick, Zuniart, 10¼", pr 195.00
Clock, Jugtime, jug form, brn mottle, 7½" 85.00
Clock, Lux Sweetheart, pendulum 75.00
Jar, Nurock, emb peacocks, w/lid, sm flake, 5x6½" 150.00
Lamp, Wise Birds, owl figural, 8" 100.00
Salt box, Nurock, emb peacocks, brn-sponged yellowware, 6" ..125.00
Umbrella stand, Onyx, #74, 22½" 250.00
Vase, Jetwood, 10½" 375.00
Vase, Navarre, gr w/wht Nouveau lady, w/hdls, 8½" 245.00

Vase, Zuniart, 4", $125.00.

Buffalo Pottery

The founding of the Buffalo Pottery in Buffalo, New York, in 1901, was a direct result of the success achieved by John Larkin through his innovative methods of marketing 'Sweet Home Soap.' Choosing to omit 'middle-man' profits, Larkin preferred to deal directly with the consumer and offered premiums as an enticement for sales. The pottery soon proved a success in its own right and began producing advertising and commemorative items for other companies, as well as commercial tableware. In 1905 they introduced their Blue Willow line after extensive experimentation resulted in the development of the first successful underglaze cobalt achieved by an American company. Between 1905 and 1909, a line of pitchers and jugs were hand decorated in historical, literary, floral, and outdoor themes. Twenty-nine styles are known to have been made. These have been found in a wide array of color variations.

Their most famous line was Deldare Ware, the bulk of which was made from 1908 to 1909. It was hand decorated after illustrations by Cecil Aldin. Views of English life were portrayed in detail through unusual use of color against the natural olive-green cast of the body. Today the 'Fallowfield Hunt' scenes are more difficult to locate than 'Scenes of Village Life in Ye Olden Days.' A Deldare calendar plate was made in 1910. These are very rare and are highly valued by collectors. The line was revived in 1923 and dropped again in 1925. Every piece was marked 'Made at Ye Buffalo Pottery

— Deldare Ware Underglaze.' Most are dated, though date has no bearing on the value. Emerald Deldare, made with the same olive body and on standard Deldare Ware shapes, featured historical scenes and Art Nouveau decorations. Most pieces are found with a 1911 date stamp. Production was very limited due to the intricate, time-consuming detail. Needless to say, it is very rare and extremely desirable.

Abino Ware, most of which was made in 1912, also used standard Deldare shapes, but its colors were earthy and the decorations more delicately applied. Sailboats, windmills, and country scenes were favored motifs. These designs were achieved by overpainting transfer prints and were often signed by the artist. The ware is marked 'Abino' in hand-printed block letters. Production was limited; and as a result, examples of this line are scarce today. Prices only slightly trail those of Emerald Deldare Ware.

The many uncataloged items that have been found over the years indicate that Buffalo Pottery decorators were free to use their own ideas and talents to create many beautiful one-of-a-kind pieces.

Our advisors for this category are Ruth and Dale Van Kuren; they are listed in the Directory under New York. Assistance was also provided by Schrader Antiques; see California.

Calling card tray, Emerald, Dr Syntax Robbed of His Property, tab handles, 7¾", $450.00.

Abino

Bowl, fruit; 9"	825.00
Candlestick, 9"	500.00
Matchbox holder, 3¾"	675.00
Pitcher, lighthouse scene, 7"	825.00
Plaque, The Waning Day, 13½"	1,450.00
Plate, windmill or ships, 10", ea	625.00
Plate, windmill or ships, 6½", ea	285.00
Tankard, ship scene, 10½"	1,100.00
Tankard, ship scene, 7"	750.00
Vase, windmill, 6¾"	700.00

Deldare

Bowl, fruit; Fallowfield Hunt, 9"	465.00
Bowl, fruit; Ye Village Tavern, 9"	425.00
Bowl, nut; Ye Lion Inn, 8"	490.00
Bowl, sauce; Ye Olden Days, 6½"	150.00

Bowl, soup; Fallowfield Hunt, 9"	250.00
Candlestick, Emerald, 9"	400.00
Candlestick, Village Scenes, 9½"	325.00
Creamer, Fallowfield Hunt, Breaking Cover, 1908	200.00
Creamer & sugar bowl, Emerald, Dr Syntax, w/lid	650.00
Creamer & sugar bowl, Ye Olden Days, w/lid	365.00
Cup & saucer, Fallowfield Hunt	225.00
Cup & saucer, Ye Olden Days	185.00
Egg cup, untitled, no mk	200.00
Hair receiver, Emerald, w/lid	700.00
Hair receiver, Ye Village Street, w/lid	300.00
Humidor, Emerald, Dr Syntax, 7"	600.00
Humidor, Emerald, There Was an Old Sailor..., 8"	800.00
Humidor, Fallowfield Hunt, 7"	715.00
Humidor, Ye Lion Inn, 7"	525.00
Jardiniere, Ye Village Street, 6"	585.00
Matchbox holder & ash tray, Scenes of Village Life	415.00
Mug, Emerald, Dr Syntax, I Give the Law..., 2¼"	450.00
Mug, Emerald, Dr Syntax Made Free..., 4¼"	400.00
Mug, Fallowfield Hunt, Breakfast at 3 Pigeons, 4½"	325.00
Mug, Fallowfield Hunt, Breaking Cover, 3½"	300.00
Mug, Fallowfield Hunt, 2½"	300.00
Mug, Ye Lion Inn, 4¼"	285.00
Pitcher, Emerald, Dr Syntax Stopt By..., 6"	620.00
Pitcher, Fallowfield Hunt, Breaking Cover, 10"	625.00
Pitcher, Fallowfield Hunt, The Return, 8"	485.00
Pitcher, Fallowfield Hunt, 6"	400.00
Pitcher, tankard; Fallowfield, The Hunt Supper, 12½"	850.00
Pitcher, Village Scenes, Their Manner of..., 6"	385.00
Pitcher, Village Scenes, To Demand My Annual Rent, 8"	495.00
Pitcher, Village Scenes, To Spare an Old..., 7"	425.00
Pitcher, Village Scenes, Ye Olde English Village, 10"	650.00
Plaque, Emerald, Dr Syntax Sketching the Lake, 12"	1,050.00
Plaque, Fallowfield Hunt, Breakfast at 3 Pigeons, 12"	525.00
Plaque, Ye Lion Inn, 12"	475.00
Plate, An Evening at Ye Lion Inn, 14"	465.00
Plate, calendar, 1910, 9½"	1,285.00
Plate, Emerald, Dr Syntax Loses His Wig, 9¼"	700.00
Plate, Emerald, Dr Syntax Making a Discovery, 10"	650.00
Plate, Emerald, Dr Syntax Soliloquising, 7¼"	425.00
Plate, Fallowfield Hunt, Breaking Cover, 10"	235.00
Plate, Fallowfield Hunt, The Death, 8½"	175.00
Plate, Fallowfield Hunt, The Start, 14"	525.00
Plate, Fallowfield Hunt, The Start, 9¼"	190.00
Plate, Ye Lion Inn, 6¼"	85.00
Plate, Ye Olden Times, 9½"	165.00
Plate, Ye Town Crier, 8¼"	150.00
Plate, Ye Village Gossips, 10"	175.00
Plate, Ye Village Street, 7¼"	125.00
Powder dish, Ye Village Street, w/lid	300.00
Relish dish, Fallowfield Hunt, 6½x12"	435.00
Relish dish, Ye Olden Times, 6½x12"	375.00
Saucer, Ye Olden Days, 1908	50.00
Sugar bowl, Fallowfield Hunt, 6-sided, open, 3"	270.00
Tea tile, Emerald, Dr Syntax, 6"	500.00
Tea tile, Traveling in Ye Olden Days, 6"	275.00
Teapot, Emerald, Dr Syntax	550.00
Teapot, Scenes of Village Life, 3½"	350.00
Teapot, Scenes of Village Life, 5¾"	395.00
Tray, card; Ye Lion Inn, 7"	300.00
Tray, dresser; Dancing Ye Minuet, 9x12"	525.00
Tray, dresser; Heirlooms, 10½x12"	600.00
Tray, pin; Emerald, geometric, 3½x6¼"	450.00
Tray, pin; Ye Olden Days, 3½x6¼"	250.00

Vase, untitled Village Scene, 9" 365.00
Vase, Ye Village Parson, 8½" 750.00

Miscellaneous

Ash tray, 'Sea Cave' in Multifleure Lamelle, rnd, 4" 35.00
Bowl, Tom & Jerry, 11½" 75.00
Dish, child's feeding; Campbell Kids, 7¾" 75.00
Dish, child's feeding; Campbell Kids w/alphabet, 7¾" 110.00
Dish, child's feeding; Roosevelt Bears, 6¼" 95.00
Mug, Tom & Jerry, 4" 25.00
Mug, Vacation, 4½" 75.00
Pitcher, Buffalo Hunt, 6" 325.00
Pitcher, Cinderella, 6" 450.00
Pitcher, Dutch Jug, 6½" 310.00
Pitcher, Gaudy Willow, 5" 275.00
Pitcher, Gaudy Willow, 7½" 285.00
Pitcher, George Washington, 7½" 550.00
Pitcher, Geranium, bl-gr, 4" 150.00
Pitcher, Geranium, mc, 6½" 245.00
Pitcher, Gloriana, 9¼" 425.00
Pitcher, Holland, 6" 325.00
Pitcher, John Paul Jones, 9¼" 460.00
Pitcher, Pilgrim, mc, 9" 590.00
Pitcher, Robin Hood, 8¼" 390.00
Pitcher, Roosevelt Bears, 8" 850.00
Pitcher, Sailor, water sz 600.00
Plate, advertising; Advance, 7¼" 75.00
Plate, Ahwahnee, Yosemite Park, 1927, 9½" 45.00
Plate, Bluebird, 8" 18.00
Plate, Christmas, 1950-1960, 9½", ea 50.00
Plate, Christmas, 1962, 9½" 150.00
Plate, Commemorative; Faneuil Hall, 7¼" 50.00
Plate, Dr Syntax, bl/wht w/Clews-like floral border, 9" 200.00
Plate, game; wild turkey, 9" 75.00
Plate, Gaudy Willow, 6¼" 110.00
Plate, Gaudy Willow, 9¼" 165.00
Plate, historical; The White House, 10" 55.00
Plate, Roycroft Inn, 10" 150.00
Platter, Dr Syntax, bl/wht w/Clews-like floral border 285.00
Platter, turkey; 18½x13½" 185.00
Rose bowl, geranium decor, mc, 3¼" 85.00
Teapot, Argyle, w/orig infuser 185.00
Teapot, Gaudy Willow, 4½" 235.00
Vase, Geranium, mc, 4" 85.00

Burmese

Burmese glass is opaque, in soft shades of yellow shading to pink. It was patented in 1885 by Frederick Shirley of the Mt. Washington Glass Co. The formula he developed contained gold which reacted with the fire to produce the delicate pink blush. It was made in both a glossy and satin finish. Some pieces were decorated by hand or gilded. Similar glass was later produced by Webb in England; it was reissued by Gunderson-Pairpoint and in 1978 by Bryden at the Sagamore Pairpoint factory. The items below are assumed satin unless noted otherwise. See also Lamps.

Our advisors for this category are Betty and Clarence Maier; they are listed in the Directory under Pennsylvania.

Bell, shiny, clear hdl, Webb, 9½" 450.00
Bottle, scent; gold leaves/berries, silver cap, Webb, 3½" 695.00
Bowl, crimped, 10" 450.00
Bowl, pie crust rim, Webb, 2¼x2¾" 210.00

Bowl, ruffled rim, Webb, 2¾x4¼" 225.00
Candlestick, decor, Webb, 6" 950.00
Condiment set, ribbed, 4-pc, in FB Rogers SP holder 625.00
Cookie jar, oak leaves/acorns, SP rim/lid/hdl, Mt WA 600.00
Creamer & sugar bowl, grapes & leaves, SP holder, Webb 795.00
Creamer & sugar bowl, pine cones/buds/needles, Webb 800.00
Cruet, ribbed, Mt WA, 6½" 950.00
Fairy lamp, floral, Webb, 3-part, 5¾" 2,300.00
Fairy lamp, prunus blossom, pyramid, Webb 1,950.00
Finger bowl, Dia Quilt, ruffled, 4½" 225.00
Finger bowl, quilted, crimped top, Mt WA, 2x4⅜" 275.00
Finger bowl, ruffled, Webb, 4¾" 250.00
Pitcher, tankard; Longfellow verse, rural scene, florals 3,250.00
Plate, florals & leaves, ruffled, Webb, 7½" 450.00
Plate, stream w/stone bridge & house, Mt WA label, 7" 200.00
Rose bowl, florals, 2½" H 325.00
Rose bowl, scalloped rim, att Mt WA, 2½" dia 200.00
Rose bowl, 5-petal lav floral, 8-crimp top, Webb, 2½" 350.00
Shakers, ribbed, Mt WA, pr 240.00
Syrup, mums/shadow leaves, sq hdl, bugs/floral-emb SP lid ..2,500.00
Toothpick holder, shiny, bulbous, sq top, Mt WA, 2¾x2¼" ...275.00
Vase, berries/leaves, petal top, Webb, 3" 350.00
Vase, berries/leaves, ribbed, 4" 275.00
Vase, berries/leaves in gr & gold, Webb, 9" 1,100.00
Vase, bird/butterfly/florals, bottle form, Webb, 7⅝" 895.00
Vase, bulbous, fluted, 3 yel appl ft, unmk Webb, 3¼x2¾" 245.00

Vase, Chintz, 10½", $1,800.00.

Vase, flared w/ped base, 10" 600.00
Vase, florals, appl yel hdls, Webb, 5x3" 695.00
Vase, florals, crimped turned-in top, 3" 275.00
Vase, florals in bl/wht, star-shaped top, unmk Webb, 3x2½" ...495.00
Vase, florals in bl/yel, gr/brn stems, Webb, 3½" 250.00
Vase, florals in lav, flared, ruffled, att Webb, 4¼x2½" 325.00
Vase, florals in lav, ruffled ped ft/top, unmk, 3⅞x2¾" 300.00
Vase, florals/leaves, gold rim, bulbous w/stick neck, 8" 450.00
Vase, flower form, supported by Pairpoint cupid std, 9" 485.00
Vase, flower-petal top, squatty, Webb, 2¾x3¼" 225.00
Vase, flower-petal top, Webb, 3½x2⅞" 210.00
Vase, folded star-shaped top, Webb, 3¼x2⅝" 225.00
Vase, honeysuckle, Webb, 6½" 525.00
Vase, ivy, bottle form, Webb, 10x5½" 995.00
Vase, ivy, fluted scalloped top, ped ft, att Webb, 4½" 400.00

Vase, jack-in-pulpit; Mt WA, 7" 325.00
Vase, leaves, flared/ruffled top, ball base, unmk Webb, 3⅛" ...325.00
Vase, lily; Mt WA, 10" 550.00
Vase, lily; shiny, Mt WA, 6" 225.00
Vase, lily; shiny, Mt WA, 8" 350.00
Vase, petticoat shape, 3½" 225.00
Vase, Queen's, bulbous, Mt WA, 8" 1,250.00
Vase, shiny, 2 barn swallows, Mt WA, 4½" 300.00
Vase, shiny, 3 barn swallows, scalloped rim w/wht dots, 4½" ...585.00
Vase, stick neck, 9" 250.00
Vase, stylized floral, EX work, hdls, 12" 1,000.00
Vase, tapered, 10" 300.00
Vase, Thos Hood poem/roses, 12½" 3,500.00
Vase, trumpet form w/ped ft, Webb, 6x2¼" 250.00
Vase, yel coralene seaweed, 8" 400.00
Vase, 4 birds, gourd form w/narrow neck, 8" 600.00
Whiskey, Dia Quilt, Mt WA, 2¾x2¼" 195.00

Butter Molds and Stamps

The art of decorating butter began in Europe during the reign of Charles II. This practice was continued in America by the farmer's wife who sold her homemade butter at the weekly market to earn extra money during hard times. A mold or stamp with a special design, hand carved either by her husband or a local craftsman, not only made her product more attractive but also helped identify it as hers. The pattern became the trademark of Mrs. Smith, and all who saw it knew that this was her butter. It was usually the rule that no two farms used the same mold within a certain area, thus the many variations and patterns available to the collector today. The most valuable are those which have animals, birds, or odd shapes. The most sought-after motifs are the eagle, cow, fish, and rooster. These works of early folk art are quickly disappearing from the market.

Our advisor for this category is Rosella Tinsley; she is listed in the Directory under Kansas.

Molds

Beet & radish, EX cvg 45.00
Cherries, elliptical form, 5½x10" L 165.00
Cow, bell shape, pointed plunger, 3½" 215.00
Daisy, 2 leaves, geometric border, lg, EX 95.00
Eagle & shield, trn hdl, 3½" dia 160.00
Fleur-de-lis, precise/deep cvg, 4" dia 55.00
Flower, 8-petal, 3½" dia 65.00
Geometric floral, trn inserted hdl, 3½" dia 45.00
Heart, deep cvg, ca 1800, 3½" dia, EX 260.00
Melons, finely cvd, 1-lb 65.00
Parrot, scalloped edge, German, early 198.00
Pineapple, highly stylized, EX detail, 5x6½" L 195.00
Pineapple, trn inserted hdl, 3¾" dia 70.00
Rose, w/bud & leaves, 4" dia 95.00
Star, 8-point, machine made, very old, 3½" dia 40.00
Strawberry & leaves, deep cvg, 1840s 95.00
Tulip, stylized, dvtl, 5x6⅝" L, VG 185.00
Wheat, fine details, 1-lb 55.00
8 cvd designs, oblong/ftd, uncommon style, late 1800s, 2-lb ...225.00

Stamps

Cow, birch, cvd details, 1-pc, knob hdl, New England 395.00
Eagle, detailed cvg, ca 1820, 4½" dia 350.00
Eagle, knob hdl, ca 1820, 4" dia 395.00
Eagle & shield, bk: starflower, lollipop, 4¾" dia, 9" L 575.00

Eagle w/spread wings, pine, chip-cvd oval fr, 1850, 6x4" 275.00
Eagle w/star, filled-in crack, 4¼" dia 185.00
Flower, heart shaped w/foliage, 4⅞" dia 165.00
Flower w/bud & stem, maple, ca 1850, mini, 1¼" dia 115.00
Flowers, stylized, drilled holes, 1-pc, trn hdl, 4" dia 175.00
Flowers & ferns, birch, hewn hdl, 3½" 120.00
Foliage, stylized, lollipop form, 1900s, 7¾" 125.00

Maple butter stamps, left to right: Wheat sheaf, 3x4½", $70.00; Pineapple, 3x4½", $80.00; Leaf, 2¼x4", $80.00.

Pineapple, cross-hatched, 1-pc, knob hdl, 4½" dia 210.00
Pineapple, EX details, trn hdl, 3¾" dia 135.00
Pineapple, self trn hdl, scrubbed, 4¼" dia 145.00
Pineapple, 1-pc, mushroom knob hdl, ca 1800, 4¾" dia 235.00
Sheaf of wheat, dbl; EX cvg, rectangular, 1840s, 2¾x3½" 85.00
Sheaf of wheat, geometric border, ca 1800, 4½" 95.00
Starflower, star border, deep cvg, 1-pc, lg trn hdl, 5" dia 250.00
Starflower, 1-pc, long trn hdl, 2½" dia 135.00
Starflower (intricate), self trn hdl, 6" dia 95.00
Tree & leaves, deep cvg, oval, flat bk, 1700s, 1¼x4x4¾" 395.00
Tulip w/leaves & berries, elongated, w/hdl, 13¾" L 385.00
Tulip w/2 stars, deep cvg, 1-pc, lg trn hdl, 4" dia 225.00
2 birds in stylized tree, lollipop form, 5" dia, 8" L 350.00

Buttonhooks

Buttonhooks were made from around the mid-1800s when high-button shoes made of stiff leather became fashionable and continued to be used to some extent until 1935. They were made of bone, brass, iron, or silver — simple utilitarian no-nonsense styles, fold-up styles with jeweled gold handles, and combination styles with built-in gadgets — all designed to ease the struggle of buttoning high-top shoes, long kid gloves, and stiffly starched collars. While most do have a hook end, some were made with a wire loop instead. Study the construction; quality workmanship is an important worth-assesing factor in addition to the more obvious elements of material and design.

Brass, bird figural hdl 45.00
Brass, repousse, folding, 2 hooks 28.00
Bronze, emb design on hdl, 4¾" 7.50
Glove, pearl hdl, 2¼" 7.50
Gold-washed metal, 1" pearl hdl, 2½" 22.00
Lead, lady's-leg hdl, 7" 40.00
MOP quarter-moon hdl, 2½" 32.00
MOP teardrop hdl, 3½" 12.50
SP, repousse, hollow hdl, 7¼" 26.00
Sterling, head of long-haired lady forms hdl, 6½" 70.00
Sterling, repousse scrolls 35.00

Calendar Plates

Calendar plates were advertising giveaways most popular from about

1906 until the late twenties. They were decorated with colorful underglaze decals of lovely ladies, flowers, animals, birds — and, of course, the twelve months of the year of their issue. During the late thirties they came into vogue again, but never to the extent they were originally. Those with exceptional detailing, or those with scenes of a particular activity are most desirable — so are any from before 1906.

1904, Happy New Year, cupid & bell, 8" 32.00
1907, Santa in sleigh pulled by 4 reindeer, 9¼" 38.00
1909, bird holds ribbon in beak, 9½" 45.00
1909, Christmas theme, Four Corners IA 35.00
1909, house w/thatched roof by stream & stone bridge, 9½" ...24.00
1909, lady driving car, months border 35.00
1909, old building, water wheel by mill stream, 9½" 27.00
1909, sailboat on mountain lake, 8" 22.00
1909, violets in center, 6¼" 25.00
1910, druggist advertising, Ogden IA 35.00
1910, lighthouse, months on boats' sails, 8¼" 28.00
1910, Niagara Falls, 'Peter Cook...Oregon,' 8½" 24.00
1910, Star Union Brewing, tin, VG 75.00
1911, ducks in flight 28.00
1911, Victorian girl in horseshoe center, Republic MI 22.00
1912, eagle on shield, Liberty Bell, pen & paper, 7¼" 24.00
1912, Indian maiden sits by fire shucking corn, 8½" 36.00
1912, months form horseshoe, fruit/flower center, 8¼" 22.00
1914, hunting scene, 8" 22.00
1915, deer stand in woods, people in canoe 24.00
1915, owl on book, gold trim, 7½" 24.00
1920, Peace, globe & dove, 8¼" 20.00
1921, dove surrounded by 5 Allied flags, 7¼" 36.00
1922, dog by lake, mallards fly overhead, 9" 32.00
1924, hunting scene, NM 35.00

Calendars

Calendars are collected for their colorful prints, often attributed to a well-recognized artist of the period. Advertising calendars from the turn of the century often have a double appeal when representing a company whose products are themselves collectible. See also Parrish, Maxwell; Prints; and Rockwell, Norman.

1887, Fairy Soap, matted in fr, EX 40.00
1888, Clark's Thread, girl sewing, unused 35.00
1889, Hood's Sarsaparilla, VG 35.00
1890, Walter Wood Mowing & Reaping Machines, EX 75.00
1890, Walter Wood Mowing & Reaping Machines, post card sz ..25.00
1894, Walter A Wood Mowing & Reaping Machines, EX 65.00
1895, Hanford's Celery Cure, Syracuse NY, EX 50.00
1895, Hood's Sarsaparilla, heart shape, EX 50.00
1896, Hood's Sarsaparilla, complete pad, EX 30.00
1896, McKeehan Hiestand Grocery, boy/dog, complete, EX ...60.00
1898, Clark's, 13 babies, mc, full pad, 5x7", EX 85.00
1898, Hood's Sarsaparilla, full pad, M 45.00
1899, Ludwig Pianos, celluloid, for window, EX 20.00
1900, US Rubber, Victorian children, EX 32.00
1902, Life's Gibson calendar, EX 100.00
1902, Quaker Oats, Queen of Homes & Nation, EX 40.00
1903, Hood's Sarsaparilla, 4 Friends, complete, EX 40.00
1904, Plano Harvesting Machinery, girl w/cherries in hat, NM .275.00
1904, Val Blatz Brewing Co, Cincinnati OH, 30x22", VG 180.00
1906, Snag-Proof Rubber Footwear, 12x8", NM 125.00
1908, Antikamnia Tablets, heavy cb, Alfred E Newman, EX ..75.00
1908, Good Luck Baking Powder, Victorian pr in woods, M ...100.00

1909, Champion Harvesters, EX 85.00
1909, Osborne Machinery, EX 85.00
1911, Garr-Stott Threshers, EX 225.00
1911, Harness & Saddlery, EX 25.00
1917, Remington/UMC, EX 395.00
1918, Groceries, Niantic CT, 9x11" 30.00
1918, Remington/UMC, top only 350.00
1919, Hood's Sarsaparilla, Over There, 11x4½", NM 50.00
1919, Victor, shows Victrola player, EX 115.00
1923, Star Brand Shoes 35.00
1925, Lehigh Cement, Music Master by Rockwell, EX 45.00
1926, Jewel Tea, complete, NM 35.00
1926, Peters Cartridge Co, quail in tall grass, EX 250.00
1926, Round Oak Stoves, complete, EX 65.00
1927, Nehi Drink, lady in boat at beach, EX 165.00
1927, Wade Traver, girl w/roses, Am Art Wks, EX 65.00

1927, Peters Cartridge Co., in original packing tube, $300.00.

1931, Zula Kenyon, My Bluebird, orig wrapper 25.00
1936, Animal Lovers, Raphael Tuck 25.00
1937, Sundance, Weinold Reiss, 33x16", EX 40.00
1938, Atlantic Gas White Flash, Hintermeister print, EX 45.00
1939, Nature's Remedy, EX 35.00
1944, John Morrel, Flags in American History, M in envelope ..30.00
1947, Central Baking, Will Rogers, WI, 46x21", M 25.00
1947, Flowers of Our Land, Reindel, EX 15.00
1947, Petty, for True, 12-sheet, M 45.00
1947, Vargas, for Esquire, 12-sheet, M 45.00
1955, Marilyn Monroe, nude, 17x10", NM 25.00
1956, Petty, for Esquire, 12-sheet, M 35.00
1960, Girl Scouts of America, EX 20.00

California Faience

California Faience was the trade name used by William V. Bragdon and Chauncy R. Thomas on vases, bowls, and other artware produced at their pottery known as 'The Tile Shop' in Berkeley, California, from 1920 to 1930. Faience tile was the principal product of the business during these years and is the favorite with today's collectors. Items in a glossy glaze are rare and therefore more valuable. Tiles were marked 'California Faience' with a die stamp.

Our advisor for this category is Jack Chipman; you will find him listed in our Directory under California.

Bookends, eagle, bl matt, pr **700.00**
Bowl, bl, shell form, 12x15" **95.00**
Bowl, blk matt, turq int, ftd, w/frog, 10½" **150.00**
Bowl, dk bl w/turq int, scalloped, 3x6" **75.00**
Candle holder, bl gloss, 5", pr **125.00**
Flower holder, Oriental laundry woman, 6-color, 6" **75.00**

Paperweight, frog figural, $100.00.

Tile, fruit basket, 6-color, 5¼" dia **275.00**
Tile, stylized bluebells, turq/bl, 3¾" sq **65.00**
Tile, tea; mission, yel border, mk, 5" dia **350.00**
Vase, purple gloss, mk, 5" **150.00**
Vase, red gloss, stylized leaves, 6½" **175.00**

California Perfume Company

D.H. McConnell, Sr., founded the California Perfume Company (C.P. Company; C.P.C.) in 1886 in New York City. He had previously been a salesman for a book company, which he later purchased. His door-to-door sales usually involved the lady of the house, to whom he presented a complimentary bottle of inexpensive perfume. Upon determining his perfume to be more popular than his books, he decided that the manufacture of perfume might be more lucrative. He bottled toiletries under the name 'California Perfume Company' and a line of household products called 'Perfection' until 1929, when 'Avon Products, Inc.' appeared on the label. In 1939 the C.P.C. name was entirely removed from the product. The success of the company is attributed to the door-to-door sales approach and 'money back' guarantee offered by his first 'Depot Agent,' Mrs. P.F.E. Albee, known today as the 'Avon Lady.'

The company's containers are quite collectible today, especially the older, hard-to-find items. Advanced collectors seek bottles and other items labeled Goetting & Co., New York; Goetting's; or Savoi Et Cie, Paris. Such examples date from 1871 to 1896. The Goetting Company was at one time owned by D.H. McConnell; Savoi Et Cie was a line which they imported to sell through department stores. Also of special interest are packaging and advertising with the Ambrosia or Hinze Ambrosia Company label. This was a subsidiary company whose objective seems to have been to produce a line of face creams, etc., for sale through drugstores and other such commercial outlets. They operated in New York from about 1875 until 1954. Because very little is known about these companies, and since only

a few examples of their product containers and advertising material have been found, market values for such items have not yet been established. Other examples of rare items sought by the collector include products marked Gertrude Recordon; Marvel Electric Silver Cleaner; Easy Day Automatic Clothes Washer; pre-1930 catalogs; and California Perfume Company 1909 and 1910 calendars.

There are hundreds of local clubs throughout the world that are supported by the National Association of Avon Collectors Inc. Organization. Those wishing to join (as well as those seeking additional information concerning California Perfume Company and its products) may contact our advisor, Dick Pardini, who is listed in the Directory under California.

American Ideal Lipstick, 1929, CPC on tube, M **40.00**
American Ideal Perfume, in wood box, introductory sz, M **225.00**
American Ideal Perfume, 1929, gr satin box, 1-oz, MIB **140.00**
Ariel Perfume, 1930, glass stopper, 1-oz, MIB **125.00**
Ariel Toilet Water, 1930-1935, 2-oz **105.00**
Baby set, 1916, complete and mint **350.00**
Bandoline Hair Dressing, 1923, 4-oz **65.00**
Bay Rum, 4-oz, 1908, M **120.00**
Boudoir Manicure Set, 4-pc, w/booklet, 1929 . . . .**150.00**
California Tooth Tablet, metal lid, glass bottom, ca 1900 . . . . . .**90.00**
Carnation Sachet, bottle, 1915 . . . .**60.00**
Catalog, color, w/tabs, 1920s **90.00**
CPC Sample Case, basketweave w/label, 1915 . . . .**100.00**
Cut Glass Perfume, 1915, 2-oz **225.00**
Daphne Bath Salts, 1925, glass jar w/gold label, MIB **70.00**
Daphne Talcum Powder, tin container, 1923, 4-oz **65.00**
Depilatory, 1915, 1-oz **100.00**
Eau De Quinine, 1923, 6-oz **90.00**
Elite Powder, Perfect Foot Powder, oval can, 1923, sm **35.00**
Elite Powder, Perfect Foot Powder, tin can, 1923, 1-lb **75.00**
Gentleman's Shaving Set, 7-pc, w/box, 1917 . . . .**400.00**
Gertrude Recordon's Introductory Facial Treatment Set **300.00**
Juvenile Set, 1915 . . . .**435.00**
Lavender Salts, gr glass, 1910 . . . .**225.00**
Lemonal Cleansing Cream, jar, 1926 . . . .**65.00**
Lilac Vegetal, ribbed glass, 1925, 2-oz **65.00**
Liquid Shampoo, 1923, 6-oz **85.00**
Little Folks Set, 4 bottles, 1937 . . . .**175.00**
Lotus Cream, 1917, 12-oz **160.00**
Lotus Cream, 1925, 4-oz, MIB **90.00**
Massage Cream, jar, 1916 . . . .**125.00**
Mission Garden Compact, brass, 1922 . . . .**45.00**
Nail Cream, tin container, 1924 . . . .**15.00**
Narcissus Perfume, 1925, 1-oz **120.00**
Narcissus Perfume, 1929-30, mc box, 1-oz, MIB **160.00**
Natoma Rose Perfume, 1914-15, glass bottle w/stopper, ½-oz . .**160.00**
Natoma Rose Perfume, 1916, ½-oz, M **150.00**
Natoma Rose Talcum, squaw, triangular, tin container, 1914 . .**110.00**
Natoma Rose Talcum Powder, tin container, '11, 3½-oz MIB . .**160.00**
Perfection, Auto Lustre, can, 1930, 1-pt **80.00**
Perfection, Baking Powder, can, 1931, 1-lb **20.00**
Perfection, Coloring, bottle, 1934, ½-oz **15.00**
Perfection, Coloring Set, 5 bottles in wood box, 1920 . . . .**250.00**
Perfection, Furniture Polish, can, 1916, 12-oz **70.00**
Perfection, Kwick Cleaning Polish, can, 1922, 8-oz **50.00**
Perfection, Laundry Crystals, in box, 1931 . . . .**40.00**
Perfection, Liquid Shoe White, sample, 1935, ½-oz **40.00**
Perfection, Liquid Shoe White, 1931, 4-oz **20.00**
Perfection, Liquid Spots Out, 1925, 4-oz **45.00**
Perfection, Mending Cement, tube, 1933 . . . .**15.00**
Perfection, Mothicide, can, 1925, ½-lb **40.00**
Perfection, Olive Oil, can, 1931, 1-pt **40.00**

Perfection, Powdered Cleaner, can, 1934, 16-oz 12.00
Perfection, Prepared Starch, can, 1931, 6-oz 25.00
Perfection, Savoury Coloring, 1941, 4-oz 12.00
Perfection, Silver Cream Polish, can, 1931, ½-lb 20.00
Perfume Sample Set, 1931 . . . . 300.00
Powder Sachets, 1890s 90.00
Powder tin, 2 nude babies playing w/giant rose ea side, 1912 . . . 100.00
Radiant Nail Powder, tin container, 1923 . . . . 40.00
Rose Pomade, jar, milk glass, 1914 . . . . 65.00
Shampoo Cream, milk glass, 1908, 4-oz 75.00
Sweet Sixteen Face Powder, paper container, 1916 . . . . 50.00
Tooth Tablet, aluminum lid, clear or milk wht bottom, 1920s . . 50.00
Tooth Wash, emb bottle w/label, 1915 . . . . 105.00
Trailing Arbutus Face Powder, paper container, 1925 . . . . 40.00
Trailing Arbutus Talcum, tin container, 1914, sample sz 85.00
Trailing Arbutus Talcum, tin container, 1920, 1-lb 70.00
Verna Talc, 1928, mc container, MIB 95.00
Vernafleur Face Powder, tin container, 1925 . . . . 20.00
Vernafleur Perfume, 1923, 1-oz, MIB 140.00
Vernafleur Toilet Soap, 3 bars in turq/wht paper box, 1936 . . . . . 60.00
Violet Almond Meal, tin container, 1923, 4-oz, EX 70.00
Witch Hazel Cream, 1904, 2-oz tube, MIB 50.00

Calling Cards, Cases, and Receivers

The practice of announcing one's arrival with a calling card borne by the maid to the mistress of the house was a social grace of the Victorian era. Different messages — condolences, a personal visit, or a good-by — were related by turning down one corner or another. The custom was forgotten by WWI. Fashionable ladies and gents carried their personally engraved cards in elaborate cases made of such materials as embossed silver, mother-of-pearl with intricate inlay, tortoise shell, and ivory. Card receivers held cards left by visitors who called while the mistress was out or 'not receiving.' Calling cards with fringe, die-cut flaps that cover the name, or an unusual decoration are worth about $3.00 to $4.00, while plain cards usually sell for around $1.00.

Cases

Case, japanned metal with 24k gold Oriental scene, $35.00.

Filigree, appl butterflies/florals/beads, unmk, 3¾x2⅝" 110.00
Ivory, Chinese genre cvg in high relief, 4" L 165.00
Ivory, people/buildings/flowers cvg, 3⅜x1¾" 130.00
MOP, cvd cameo & monogram, 3⅝" 75.00
MOP, deer relief, grape & leaf cvg, hinged lid 50.00
MOP, Dia Quilt pattern, bl silk int, 3⅝" L 75.00
Silver, eng foliage scrolls & scene of Whitley Court, 4" 145.00
Silver, 4-petal floral & scroll decor, hinged lid, unmk 75.00
Sterling, eng name amid emb florals, hinged lid, 4x2½" 250.00
Sterling, repousse, Birmingham England, 1902 . . . . 325.00
Tortoise shell, fishing scene, canted corners, 4" L 75.00

Receivers

Brass tray w/Nouveau scrolled edge, 4¼x6¼" 45.00
CI, cupped hands w/grapes at wrist, 1865 . . . . 55.00
Gold-washed metal, swans hold shell-shaped dish 35.00
Pewter, lady & harp beside tray, Archibald Knox, EX 300.00
SP, mermaid brushes hair beside dish, 7½" W 65.00
SP, tray, quadruplated, Meriden, 6½" dia 80.00
Sterling, allover diapering w/monogram, c/b ft, Schultz, 6" 110.00
Sterling, woodland courtship scene, Nouveau style 250.00

Camark

The Camden Art and Tile Company of Camden, Arkansas, was organized in 1926. John Lessell and his wife were associated with the company only briefly before he died that same year. After his death, his wife stayed on and continued to decorate wares very similar to those he had made for Weller. Le-Camark closely resembled Weller LaSa; Lessell was almost a duplication of Marengo. Perhaps the most outstanding was a mirror black line with lustre decoration. Naturally, examples of these lines are very rare. The company eventually became known as Camark and began production of commercial ware of the type listed below.

In 1986 the pottery was purchased and reopened, but according to the new owners the old molds will not be used.

Bowl, console; +bird flower frog 15.00
Bowl, console; Iris 11.00
Candle holder, dbl, 7½", pr 15.00
Pitcher, Colonial man, chocolate, 5½" 25.00
Pitcher & bowl, #209, w/label 25.00
Shakers, S&P shapes, pr 6.00
Teapot & warmer, swirled, 8" 18.50
Vase, gr, florals, scalloped, 7¾" 22.50
Vase, gr, hdls, 8" 10.00

Vase with tazza insert, gun metal, 6x7", $15.00.

Cambridge Glass

The Cambridge Glass Company began operations in 1901 in Cambridge, Ohio. They made primarily crystal dinnerware and well-designed accessory pieces until the 1920s when they introduced the concept of color that was to become so popular on the American dinnerware market. Always maintaining high standards of quality and elegance, they produced many lines that became best-sellers; through the twenties and thirties they were recognized as the largest manufacturer of this type of glassware in the world.

Of the various marks the company used, the 'C in triangle' is the most familiar. Production stopped in 1958. For a more thorough study of the subject, we recommend *Colors in Cambridge Glass*, by the National Cambridge Collectors, Inc.; their address may be found in the Directory under Clubs. See also Carnival Glass.

Animals and Birds

Bluejay	125.00
Bluejay, peg base	100.00
Eagle, bookend	75.00
Heron, lg	125.00
Heron, sm	75.00
Lion, bookend	90.00
Pouter pigeon, bookend	30.00
Scottie	65.00
Scottie, bookend, pr	135.00
Scottie, frosted	75.00
Sea gull	45.00
Swan, candlestick, milk glass, 4½", pr	175.00
Swan, carmen, 3½"	75.00
Swan, carmen, 6½"	200.00
Swan, carmen, 8½"	250.00
Swan, Crown Tuscan, 3½"	35.00
Swan, Crown Tuscan, 8½"	150.00
Swan, ebony, 10½"	300.00
Swan, ebony, 12½"	350.00
Swan, ebony, 3½"	60.00
Swan, ebony, 4½"	85.00
Swan, ebony, 6½"	100.00
Swan, ebony, 8½"	125.00
Swan, emerald, 3½"	35.00
Swan, emerald, 6½"	95.00
Swan, emerald, 8½"	125.00
Swan, milk glass, 3½"	60.00
Swan, milk glass, 4½"	75.00
Swan, milk glass, 6½"	125.00
Swan, milk glass, 8½"	350.00
Turkey, amber, w/lid	450.00
Turkey, bl, w/lid	500.00
Turkey, gr, w/lid	450.00
Turkey, pk, w/lid	400.00

Apple Blossom, colors; bowl, cereal, 6"	18.00
Apple Blossom, colors; bowl, fruit; tab hdl, 11"	40.00
Apple Blossom, colors; bowl, relish; 4-part, 12"	40.00
Apple Blossom, colors; compote, fruit cocktail; 4"	20.00
Apple Blossom, colors; creamer, ftd	17.50
Apple Blossom, colors; pitcher, #3025, 64-oz	200.00
Apple Blossom, colors; pitcher, loop hdl, 67-oz	250.00
Apple Blossom, colors; plate, bread & butter; sq	9.00
Apple Blossom, colors; plate, bread & butter; 6"	9.00

Apple Blossom, colors; plate, 8½"	16.00
Apple Blossom, colors; platter, rectangular, tab hdl, 13½"	55.00
Apple Blossom, colors; platter, 11½"	50.00
Apple Blossom, colors; shakers, pr	95.00
Apple Blossom, colors; tray, sandwich; center hdl, 11"	37.00
Apple Blossom, colors; tumbler, #3130, ftd, 12-oz	30.00
Apple Blossom, colors; tumbler, #3400, ftd, 2½-oz	25.00
Apple Blossom, colors; tumbler, 6"	27.50
Apple Blossom, colors; vase, ripple sides, 6"	40.00
Apple Blossom, crystal; bowl, cereal; 6"	10.00
Apple Blossom, crystal; bowl, soup; w/liner plate	13.00
Apple Blossom, crystal; bowl, 4-ftd, oval, 12"	25.00
Apple Blossom, crystal; candy box, w/lid, 4-ftd	35.00
Apple Blossom, crystal; compote, 7"	20.00
Apple Blossom, crystal; pitcher, #3130, 64-oz	100.00
Apple Blossom, crystal; pitcher, #3135, w/lid, ftd, 76-oz	150.00
Apple Blossom, crystal; plate, dinner; 9½"	35.00
Apple Blossom, crystal; plate, grill; 10"	18.00
Apple Blossom, crystal; plate, sandwich; tab hdl, 11½"	20.00
Apple Blossom, crystal; tumbler, #3025, 4-oz	12.00
Apple Blossom, crystal; tumbler, #3130, ftd, 5-oz	11.00
Apple Blossom, crystal; tumbler, #3135, ftd, 10-oz	13.00
Caprice, blue; ash tray, #216, 5"	17.50
Caprice, blue; bonbon, #133, ftd, sq, 6"	35.00
Caprice, blue; bowl, #52, crimped, 4-ftd, 9½"	50.00
Caprice, blue; bowl, #60, crimped, 4-ftd, 11"	70.00
Caprice, blue; bowl, #66, crimped, 4-ftd, 13"	70.00
Caprice, blue; bowl, pickle; #102, 9"	32.50
Caprice, blue; bowl, relish; #125, 3-part, rectangular, 12"	90.00
Caprice, blue; candlestick, #646, 2-light, 5"	32.00
Caprice, blue; candlestick, #74, 3-light	42.50
Caprice, blue; candy dish, #165, w/lid, 3-ftd, 6"	85.00
Caprice, blue; coaster, #13, 3½"	20.00
Caprice, blue; compote, #130, low ft, 7"	50.00
Caprice, blue; cracker jar, #202, w/lid	225.00
Caprice, blue; creamer, #38, med	15.00
Caprice, blue; decanter, #187, w/stopper, 35-oz	200.00
Caprice, blue; ice bucket, #201	125.00
Caprice, blue; pitcher, #179, ball form, 32-oz	265.00
Caprice, blue; pitcher, #183, ball form, 80-oz	250.00
Caprice, blue; plate, dinner; #24, 9½"	115.00
Caprice, blue; plate, salad; #23, 7½"	18.00
Caprice, blue; shakers, #96, flat, pr	40.00
Caprice, blue; tumbler, #180, flat, 5-oz	40.00
Caprice, blue; tumbler, #188, flat, 2-oz	40.00
Caprice, blue; vase, #339, 8½"	45.00
Caprice, blue; vase, #345, 5½"	85.00
Caprice, crystal; ash tray, #214, 3"	6.00
Caprice, crystal; bonbon, #155, ftd, oval, 6"	15.00
Caprice, crystal; bowl, #52, crimped, 4-ftd, 9½"	27.50
Caprice, crystal; bowl, #61, crimped, 4-ftd, 12½"	32.50
Caprice, crystal; bowl, salad; #57, 4-ftd, 10"	32.50
Caprice, crystal; butter dish, #52, ¼-lb	195.00
Caprice, crystal; cake plate, #36, ftd, 13"	125.00
Caprice, crystal; candlestick, #646, 2-light, 5"	14.00
Caprice, crystal; candlestick, #70, w/prism, 7"	15.00
Caprice, crystal; cigarette box, #207, w/lid, 3½x2¼"	15.00
Caprice, crystal; compote, #130, 6"	22.00
Caprice, crystal; creamer, #41, lg	10.00
Caprice, crystal; pitcher, #183, ball form, 80-oz	90.00
Caprice, crystal; plate, #28, 4-ftd, 14"	27.50
Caprice, crystal; punch bowl, ftd	1,500.00
Caprice, crystal; shakers, #91, ball form, pr	37.50
Caprice, crystal; tumbler, #11, ftd, 5-oz	20.00

Caprice, crystal; tumbler, juice; #310, flat 15.00
Caprice, crystal; vase, #252, 4" 45.00
Caprice, crystal; vase, #346, 7½" .45.00
Chantilly, crystal; bowl, bonbon; hdls, ftd, 7" 16.00
Chantilly, crystal; bowl, tab hdl, ftd, 11½" 30.00
Chantilly, crystal; bowl, 3-part, 9" .22.00
Chantilly, crystal; bowl, 4-ftd, oval, 12" 32.50
Chantilly, crystal; butter dish, w/lid 125.00
Chantilly, crystal; candlestick, 3-light, 6" 110.00
Chantilly, crystal; compote, 5½" 30.00
Chantilly, crystal; creamer, #3900, scalloped edge 11.00
Chantilly, crystal; cruet, oil; w/stopper, 6-oz 45.00
Chantilly, crystal; ice bucket, chrome hdl 60.00
Chantilly, crystal; pitcher, ball form 110.00
Chantilly, crystal; pitcher, Doulton 190.00
Chantilly, crystal; plate, bonbon; tab hdl, ftd, 8" 15.00
Chantilly, crystal; plate, dinner; 10½" 42.00
Chantilly, crystal; plate, salad; 8" 12.50
Chantilly, crystal; plate, torte; 14" .32.00
Chantilly, crystal; shakers, pr 27.50
Chantilly, crystal; sugar bowl, #3900, scalloped edge 11.00
Chantilly, crystal; tumbler, juice; #3625, ftd, 5-oz 13.50
Chantilly, crystal; tumbler, juice; #3779, ftd, 5-oz 15.00
Chantilly, crystal; tumbler, tea; #3625, ftd, 12-oz 18.00
Chantilly, crystal; vase, ftd, 11" 35.00
Chantilly, crystal; vase, high ft, 6" .18.00
Chantilly, crystal; vase, keyhole base, 12" 35.00

Cherub candlestick, light emerald green, 6", $250.00.

Cleo, all colors; bowl, bonbon; Decagon, 5½" 20.00
Cleo, all colors; bowl, cereal; Decagon, 6" 20.00
Cleo, all colors; bowl, console; 12" .35.00
Cleo, all colors; bowl, fruit; 5½" 15.00
Cleo, all colors; bowl, hdls, Decagon, 10" 30.00
Cleo, all colors; bowl, soup; tab hdl, 7½" 30.00
Cleo, all colors; candlestick, 2-light 35.00
Cleo, all colors; candy box 65.00
Cleo, all colors; compote, #3115, tall, 7" 40.00
Cleo, all colors; creamer, Decagon .17.50
Cleo, all colors; decanter, w/stopper 100.00
Cleo, all colors; pitcher, #38, 3½-pt 150.00
Cleo, all colors; pitcher, #955, w/lid, 62-oz 225.00
Cleo, all colors; plate, dinner; Decagon, 9½" 40.00
Cleo, all colors; platter, 15" 55.00

Cleo, all colors; sherbet, #3115, low, 6-oz 13.00
Cleo, all colors; sherbet, #3115, tall, 6-oz 15.00
Cleo, all colors; tumbler, #3077, ftd, 2½-oz 20.00
Cleo, all colors; tumbler, #3077, ftd, 8-oz 22.00
Cleo, all colors; vase, 11" 100.00
Cleo, all colors; wine, #3077, 3½-oz 60.00
Crown Tuscan, bowl, flying nude, #3011/40 . . . . .195.00
Crown Tuscan, bowl, seashell, #18, 3-toed, 10" 75.00
Crown Tuscan, candlestick, dolphin, shell, ftd, 4", pr 100.00
Crown Tuscan, candy dish, #3500/57, 3-part, w/lid 65.00
Crown Tuscan, compote, nude stem, gold trim w/roses, 7" . . .150.00
Crown Tuscan, compote, nude stem, 7" 100.00
Crown Tuscan, compote, seashell, floral decor, 7" 125.00
Crown Tuscan, dish, shell, 3-ftd, 11" 75.00
Crown Tuscan, flower holder, seashell 58.00
Crown Tuscan, vase, centerpiece; shell, ftd, 8" 88.00
Crown Tuscan, vase, cornucopia; #3900/575, 10" 55.00
Decagon, cobalt; bowl, almond; ftd, 6" 35.00
Decagon, cobalt; bowl, cranberry; flat rim, 3¾" 14.00
Decagon, cobalt; compote, 5¾" 20.00
Decagon, cobalt; creamer, ftd 20.00
Decagon, cobalt; mayonnaise, w/liner & ladle 30.00
Decagon, cobalt; plate, bread & butter; 6¼" 5.00
Decagon, cobalt; plate, service; 12½" 17.50
Decagon, cobalt; sauce boat, w/plate 65.00
Decagon, cobalt; sherbet, high, 6-oz 20.00
Decagon, cobalt; sugar bowl, ftd 20.00
Decagon, cobalt; tray, service; oval, 12" 20.00
Decagon, cobalt; tumbler, ftd, 10-oz 22.00
Decagon, pastels; bowl, berry; 10" .12.00
Decagon, pastels; bowl, cereal; flat rim, 6" 8.00
Decagon, pastels; bowl, soup; w/liner 10.00
Decagon, pastels; compote, low ft, 6½" 15.00
Decagon, pastels; creamer, scalloped egde 8.00
Decagon, pastels; mayonnaise, w/liner & ladle 18.00
Decagon, pastels; plate, dinner; 9½" 15.00
Decagon, pastels; sugar bowl, scalloped edge 9.00
Decagon, pastels; tray, service; oval, 15" 15.00
Decagon, pastels; tumbler, ftd, 12-oz 15.00
Decagon, red; bowl, bonbon; hdls, 5½" 17.00
Decagon, red; bowl, vegetable; rnd, 11" 30.00
Decagon, red; bowl, vegetable; rnd, 9" 24.00
Decagon, red; compote, tall, 7" 30.00
Decagon, red; creamer, tall, lg ft 22.00
Decagon, red; plate, salad; 8½" 10.00
Decagon, red; salt dip, ftd, 1½" 20.00
Decagon, red; sherbet, low, 6-oz 15.00
Decagon, red; tray, celery; 11" 20.00
Decagon, red; tumbler, ftd, 8-oz 20.00
Diane, crystal; base, keyhole base, 9" 35.00
Diane, crystal; bowl, bonbon; hdls, ftd, 6" 17.00
Diane, crystal; bowl, flared, 4-ftd, 10" 40.00
Diane, crystal; bowl, flared, 4-ftd, 12" 40.00
Diane, crystal; bowl, soup; #3400, w/liner 23.00
Diane, crystal; butter dish, rnd 100.00
Diane, crystal; candelabrum, 3-light, keyhole base 30.00
Diane, crystal; candlestick, 3-light, 6" 35.00
Diane, crystal; compote, 5½" 25.00
Diane, crystal; creamer, #3900, scalloped edge 14.00
Diane, crystal; cup 14.00
Diane, crystal; ice bucket, chrome hdl 60.00
Diane, crystal; mayonnaise, w/liner & ladle 38.00
Diane, crystal; pitcher, Doulton 200.00
Diane, crystal; plate, dinner; 10½" .47.50

Diane, crystal; plate, salad; 8" .10.00
Diane, crystal; plate, torte; 14" 40.00
Diane, crystal; platter, 13½" .45.00
Diane, crystal; shakers, flat, pr 28.00
Diane, crystal; sherbet, #1066, tall, 7-oz 13.50
Diane, crystal; tumbler, juice; #3122, 5-oz 13.00
Diane, crystal; tumbler, sham bottom, 10-oz 27.00
Diane, crystal; tumbler, sham bottom, 2½-oz 27.00
Diane, crystal; tumbler, tea; #1066, 12-oz 14.00
Diane, crystal; vase, 13" 60.00
Diane, crystal; wine, #1066, 3-oz 22.00
Elaine, crystal; bowl, bonbon; tab hdl, ftd, 7" 27.00
Elaine, crystal; bowl, flared, 3-ftd, 10" 30.00
Elaine, crystal; candlestick, 2-light, 6" 25.00
Elaine, crystal; candy box, w/lid, rnd 60.00
Elaine, crystal; cocktail, #3121, 3-oz 22.00
Elaine, crystal; decanter, ftd, lg 140.00
Elaine, crystal; goblet, #1402 . . . . .20.00
Elaine, crystal; mayonnaise, w/liner & ladle 25.00
Elaine, crystal; pitcher, ball form 90.00
Elaine, crystal; plate, bonbon; tab hdl, 8" 15.00
Elaine, crystal; plate, dinner; 10½" 45.00
Elaine, crystal; plate, service; 4-ftd, 12" 25.00
Elaine, crystal; tumbler, juice; #3121, ftd, 5-oz 19.00
Elaine, crystal; tumbler, tea; #3121, ftd, 12-oz 22.00
Elaine, crystal; tumbler, water; #1402, ftd, 9-oz 17.00
Elaine, crystal; vase, ftd, keyhole, 9" 38.00
Elaine, crystal; vase, ftd, 6" 22.00
Elaine, crystal; wine, #1402, 3-oz 25.00
Everglades, blue; bowl, tulips, 12½" 65.00
Everglades, pink; bowl, 3-ftd, 10" 35.00

Flying Nude bowl, cobalt, only 2 known to exist, $3,000.00 to $4,000.00.

Flower Frog, Bashful Charlotte, amber, 13" 180.00
Flower Frog, Bashful Charlotte, crystal, 11½" 100.00
Flower Frog, Bashful Charlotte, lt gr, 11" 250.00
Flower Frog, Bashful Charlotte, midnight bl, 11" 550.00
Flower Frog, Bashful Charlotte, pk, 6½" 125.00
Flower Frog, Draped Lady, amber, 8½" 175.00
Flower Frog, Draped Lady, bl, 8½" 280.00
Flower Frog, Draped Lady, crystal, 12½" 150.00
Flower Frog, Draped Lady, crystal, 8½" 95.00
Flower Frog, Draped Lady, crystal frost, 13" 250.00
Flower Frog, Draped Lady, lt emerald, #513, 13" 250.00
Flower Frog, Draped Lady, mandarin gold, #518, 8½" 200.00

Flower Frog, Draped Lady, moonlight bl frost, 8½" 325.00
Flower Frog, Draped Lady, pk, 13" 250.00
Flower Frog, Draped Lady, pk, 8½" 100.00
Flower Frog, Geisha Girl, crystal, w/base 300.00
Flower Frog, Geisha Girl, pk, w/base 450.00
Flower Frog, Mandolin Lady, crystal 150.00
Flower Frog, Mandolin Lady, gr, bent 415.00
Flower Frog, Mandolin Lady, lt gr 225.00
Flower Frog, Mandolin Lady, pk 225.00
Flower Frog, Melon Boy, gr 400.00
Flower Frog, Melon Boy, pk 400.00
Flower Frog, Rose Lady, crystal 125.00
Flower Frog, Rose Lady, crystal, low base 190.00
Flower Frog, Rose Lady, gr frost 230.00
Flower Frog, Rose Lady, lt gr 165.00
Flower Frog, 2 Kids, mocha, 9" 250.00
Gloria, colors; bowl, bonbon; crimped edge, ftd, 5" 22.00
Gloria, colors; bowl, cereal; sq, 6" 16.00
Gloria, colors; bowl, flared rim, 13" 45.00
Gloria, colors; bowl, salad; tab hdl, 9" 40.00
Gloria, colors; cake plate, ftd, sq, 11" 100.00
Gloria, colors; candy box, w/lid, tab hdl, 4-ftd 75.00
Gloria, colors; compote, fruit cocktail; 4" 17.50
Gloria, colors; cup, rnd or sq 25.00
Gloria, colors; pitcher, w/lid, 64-oz 165.00
Gloria, colors; plate, dinner; sq 55.00
Gloria, colors; platter, 11½" 60.00
Gloria, colors; sherbet, #3035, low, 6-oz 15.00
Gloria, colors; syrup, tall, ftd 65.00
Gloria, colors; tray, relish; center hdl, 2-part 35.00
Gloria, colors; tumbler, #3115, ftd, 12-oz 22.00
Gloria, colors; tumbler, tea; #3135, 12-oz 22.00
Gloria, colors; vase, flared rim, keyhole base, 12" 85.00
Gloria, colors; wine, #3035, 2½-oz 30.00
Gloria, crystal; bowl, cereal; rnd, 6" 9.00
Gloria, crystal; bowl, console; 4-ftd, 12" 25.00
Gloria, crystal; bowl, nut; 4-ftd, 3" 22.00
Gloria, crystal; butter dish, w/lid, 2-hdl 90.00
Gloria, crystal; compote, 4-ftd, 6" 19.00
Gloria, crystal; goblet, #3115, 9-oz 13.00
Gloria, crystal; mayonnaise, w/liner & ladle, 4-ftd . . .35.00
Gloria, crystal; pitcher, ball form, 80-oz 100.00
Gloria, crystal; plate, bread & butter; 6" 6.00
Gloria, crystal; plate, salad; tab hdl, 10" 15.00
Gloria, crystal; sugar bowl, ftd 11.00
Gloria, crystal; tumbler, #3115, ftd, 10-oz 13.00
Gloria, crystal; tumbler, juice; #3115, ftd, 5-oz 12.00
Gloria, crystal; vase, flared rim, keyhole base, 14" . . .47.50
Gloria, crystal; wine, #3035, 2½-oz 17.50
Imperial Hunt Scene, colors; bowl, cereal; 6" 17.50
Imperial Hunt Scene, colors; candlestick, 3-light, keyhole 40.00
Imperial Hunt Scene, colors; cordial, #1402, 1-oz 95.00
Imperial Hunt Scene, colors; creamer, ftd 40.00
Imperial Hunt Scene, colors; ice bucket 57.50
Imperial Hunt Scene, colors; pitcher, #711, w/lid, 76-oz 175.00
Imperial Hunt Scene, colors; sherbet, #1402, 7½-oz 20.00
Imperial Hunt Scene, colors; sherbet, #3077, low, 6-oz 17.50
Imperial Hunt Scene, colors; sugar bowl, ftd 24.00
Imperial Hunt Scene, colors; tumbler, #1402, flat, 5-oz 16.00
Imperial Hunt Scene, colors; tumbler, #3077, ftd, 12-oz 27.00
Laurel Wreath, crystal; plate, #556, 8" 7.50
Laurel Wreath, crystal; sherbet, #3109, high, 6-oz 10.00
Martha Washington, crystal; sugar bowl, ftd 8.00
Martha Washington, green; bowl, flared, 9" 20.00

Mt Vernon, amber; ash tray, #71, oval, 6x4½" 11.00
Mt Vernon, amber; bowl, #44, flared, 12¼" 32.00
Mt Vernon, amber; bowl, fruit; #31, 4½" 6.00
Mt Vernon, amber; bowl, salad; #120, 10½" 25.00
Mt Vernon, amber; cake stand, #150, ftd, 10½" 35.00
Mt Vernon, amber; cigarette box, #69, w/lid, oval, 6" 25.00
Mt Vernon, amber; compote, #34, 6" 15.00
Mt Vernon, amber; creamer, #8, ftd 10.00
Mt Vernon, amber; decanter, #52, w/stopper, 40-oz 60.00
Mt Vernon, amber; ice bucket, #92, w/tongs 30.00
Mt Vernon, amber; pitcher, #90, 50-oz 75.00
Mt Vernon, amber; plate, #37, tab hdl, 11½" 20.00
Mt Vernon, amber; plate, salad; #5, 8½" 7.00
Mt Vernon, amber; sauce boat, #30-445, w/ladle, tab hdl 55.00
Mt Vernon, amber; shakers, #89, tall, pr 25.00
Mt Vernon, amber; sherbet, #42, low, 4½-oz 7.50
Mt Vernon, amber; sugar bowl, #8, ftd 10.00
Mt Vernon, amber; tumbler, water; #3, ftd, 10-oz 15.00
Mt Vernon, amber; vase, #119, crimped, 6" 20.00
Mt Vernon, amber; vase, #58, 7" .30.00
Mt Vernon, crystal; bottle, bitters; #62, 2½-oz 50.00
Mt Vernon, crystal; bowl, #129, flanged, rolled edge, 12" 30.00
Mt Vernon, crystal; bowl, cereal; #32, 6" 12.00
Mt Vernon, crystal; butter tub, #73, w/lid 60.00
Mt Vernon, crystal; candlestick, #35, 8" 20.00
Mt Vernon, crystal; coaster, #60, plain, 3" 5.00
Mt Vernon, crystal; compote, #81, 8" 25.00
Mt Vernon, crystal; honey jar, #74, w/lid 25.00
Mt Vernon, crystal; mustard, #28, w/lid, 2½-oz 22.00
Mt Vernon, crystal; pitcher, #91, 86-oz 100.00
Mt Vernon, crystal; plate, dinner; #40, 10½" 20.00
Mt Vernon, crystal; relish tray, #200, 3-part, 11" 22.50
Mt Vernon, crystal; sherbet, #2, tall, 6½-oz 9.00
Mt Vernon, crystal; tumbler, #14, barrel form, 14-oz 20.00
Mt Vernon, crystal; tumbler, juice; #22, ftd, 3-oz 9.00
Mt Vernon, crystal; vase, #46, ftd, 10" 50.00
Mt Vernon, crystal; wine, #27, 3-oz 12.50
Portia, crystal; bowl, bonbon; tab hdl, ftd, 7" 20.00
Portia, crystal; bowl, cranberry; 3½" 15.00
Portia, crystal; bowl, flared, 4-ftd, 10" 30.00
Portia, crystal; candlestick, 3-light, 6" 35.00
Portia, crystal; cigarette holder, urn form 37.50
Portia, crystal; cocktail, #3121, 3-oz 20.00
Portia, crystal; compote, blown, 5⅜" 35.00
Portia, crystal; cup, ftd, sq 18.00
Portia, crystal; decanter, w/stopper, ftd, 29-oz 125.00
Portia, crystal; goblet, #3126, 9-oz 18.00
Portia, crystal; ice bucket, chrome hdl 55.00
Portia, crystal; parfait, #3121, 5-oz 22.00
Portia, crystal; pitcher, Doulton 195.00
Portia, crystal; plate, bonbon; tab hdl, ftd, 8" 20.00
Portia, crystal; plate, dinner; 10½" 40.00
Portia, crystal; puff box, ball form, w/lid, 3½" 50.00
Portia, crystal; sherbet, #3121, tall, 6-oz 15.00
Portia, crystal; sugar bowl, w/hdl, ftd, ball form 14.00
Portia, crystal; tumbler, juice; #3121, ftd, 5-oz 16.00
Portia, crystal; tumbler, tea; #3121, ftd, 12-oz 20.00
Portia, crystal; tumbler, water; #3126, 10-oz 15.00
Portia, crystal; vase, ftd, 6" 30.00
Portia, crystal; vase, keyhole ft, 9" 47.50
Rosalie, colors; bowl, bonbon; hdls, 6¼" 17.50
Rosalie, colors; bowl, console; 13" 32.50
Rosalie, colors; bowl, flanged, oval, 15" 40.00
Rosalie, colors; bowl, fruit; 5½" 12.50

Rosalie, colors; bowl, soup 17.50
Rosalie, colors; candlestick, keyhole, 5" 25.00
Rosalie, colors; candy dish, w/lid, 6" 65.00
Rosalie, colors; compote, almond; ftd, 6" 35.00
Rosalie, colors; compote, high ft, 6½" 35.00
Rosalie, colors; creamer, ftd 12.50
Rosalie, colors; goblet, #801, 10-oz 22.50
Rosalie, colors; pitcher, #955, 62-oz 120.00
Rosalie, colors; plate, cheese & crackers; 11" 45.00
Rosalie, colors; plate, dinner; 9½" 35.00
Rosalie, colors; plate, salad; 7½" 8.50
Rosalie, colors; platter, 15" 50.00
Rosalie, colors; salt dip, ftd, 1½" 15.00
Rosalie, colors; sugar shaker 130.00
Rosalie, colors; tray, center hdl, 11" 30.00
Rosalie, colors; tumbler, #3077, ftd, 2½-oz 15.00
Rosalie, colors; vase, ftd, 6½" 45.00
Rose Point, crystal; ash tray, #721, sq, 2½" 35.00
Rose Point, crystal; bowl, #3400/4, flared, 4-ftd, 12" 65.00
Rose Point, crystal; bowl, bonbon; #3900/130, tab hdl, ftd, 7" . . .35.00
Rose Point, crystal; bowl, nappy, #3400/56, 5½" 32.50
Rose Point, crystal; bowl, nut; #2400/71, 4-ftd, 3" 55.00
Rose Point, crystal; candlestick, #3400/646, 1-lt keyhole, 5" 30.00
Rose Point, crystal; candy box, #1066, w/lid, 5⅜" 120.00
Rose Point, crystal; candy box, #3900/165, w/lid, rnd 95.00
Rose Point, crystal; cheese dish, #980, w/lid, 5" 375.00
Rose Point, crystal; cigarette box, #747, w/lid 92.50
Rose Point, crystal; cocktail, #3500, 3-oz 32.50
Rose Point, crystal; compote, #3900/136, scalloped edge, 5½" . . .47.50
Rose Point, crystal; creamer, flat 125.00
Rose Point, crystal; decanter, #1321, w/stopper, 28-oz 215.00
Rose Point, crystal; ice bucket, #3900/671, chrome hdl 125.00
Rose Point, crystal; mayonnaise, #3500/59, w/liner & ladle 65.00
Rose Point, crystal; pitcher, #3400/141, Doulton, 80-oz 255.00
Rose Point, crystal; pitcher, #3900/117, 20-oz 210.00
Rose Point, crystal; plate, #3900/33, rolled edge, ftd, 13" 70.00
Rose Point, crystal; plate, breakfast; #3400/62, 8½" 20.00
Rose Point, crystal; plate, dinner; #3900/24, 10½" 105.00
Rose Point, crystal; plate, torte; #3500/110, 4-ftd, 13" 72.50
Rose Point, crystal; punch bowl, Martha #478, 15" 1,500.00
Rose Point, crystal; shakers, #3900/1177, flat, pr 35.00
Rose Point, crystal; tumbler, #3900, 13-oz 42.50
Rose Point, crystal; tumbler, tea; #3500, low ft, 12-oz 23.50
Rose Point, crystal; urn, #3500/41, 10" 200.00
Rose Point, crystal; vase, #279, ftd, 13" 145.00
Rose Point, crystal; vase, #6004, ftd, 5" 50.00
Rose Point, crystal; vase, cornucopia; #3900/575, 10" 110.00
Rose Point, crystal; wine, #3121, 3½-oz 52.50
Valencia, crystal; ash tray, #3500/124, rnd, 3¼" 8.00
Valencia, crystal; bowl, #1402/82, 10" 32.50
Valencia, crystal; bowl, salad dressing; #1402/95 . . . . .40.00
Valencia, crystal; candy dish, #3500/103, w/lid 75.00
Valencia, crystal; cigarette holder, #1066, ftd 35.00
Valencia, crystal; compote, #3500/37, 7" 35.00
Valencia, crystal; cordial, #1402 . . . . .55.00
Valencia, crystal; creamer, #3500/14 . . . . .15.00
Valencia, crystal; cup, #3500/1 .17.50
Valencia, crystal; decanter, #3400/92, ball form, 32-oz 85.00
Valencia, crystal; mayonnaise, #3500/59, w/liner & ladle 40.00
Valencia, crystal; perfume, #3400/97, 2-oz 40.00
Valencia, crystal; plate, #3500/39, ftd, 12" 27.50
Valencia, crystal; plate, salad; #3500/167, 7½" 10.00
Valencia, crystal; shakers, #3400/18, pr 45.00
Valencia, crystal; sherbet, #1402, low 12.50

Valencia, crystal; sherbet, #3500, tall, 7-oz 15.00
Valencia, crystal; tray, relish; #3500/91, 3-part, 6½" 20.00
Valencia, crystal; tumbler, #3400/100, 13-oz 18.00
Valencia, crystal; tumbler, #3500, ftd, 16-oz 17.50
Wildflower, crystal; bowl, bonbon; 5¼" 16.00
Wildflower, crystal; bowl, flared, 4-ftd, 10" 30.00
Wildflower, crystal; bowl, tab hdl, ftd 35.00
Wildflower, crystal; candlestick, 3-light, ea 32.00
Wildflower, crystal; candy box, w/lid, rnd 50.00
Wildflower, crystal; compote, blown, 5⅜" 40.00
Wildflower, crystal; creamer 12.50
Wildflower, crystal; cup 16.50
Wildflower, crystal; ice bucket, chrome hdl 55.00
Wildflower, crystal; parfait, #3121, low, 5-oz 24.00
Wildflower, crystal; pitcher, ball form 95.00
Wildflower, crystal; pitcher, Doulton 155.00
Wildflower, crystal; plate, dinner; 10½" 42.00
Wildflower, crystal; shakers, pr 30.00
Wildflower, crystal; sherbet, #3121, low, 6-oz 15.00
Wildflower, crystal; tumbler, juice; #3121, 5-oz 13.50
Wildflower, crystal; tumbler, tea; #3121, 12-oz 17.50
Wildflower, crystal; vase, ftd, 13" 75.00
Wildflower, crystal; vase, ftd, 6" 30.00
Wildflower, crystal; vase, keyhole ft 40.00
Wildflower, crystal; wine, #3121, 3½-oz 25.00

Cameo

The technique of glass carving was perfected 2,000 years ago in ancient Rome and Greece. The most famous ancient example of cameo glass is the Portland Vase, made in Rome around 100 A.D. After glass blowing was developed, glassmakers devised a method of casing several layers of colored glass together, often with a light color over a darker base, to enhance the design. Skilled carvers meticulously worked the fragile glass to produce incredibly detailed classic scenes. In the eighteenth and nineteenth centuries, Oriental and Near-Eastern artisans used the technique more extensively. European glassmakers revived the art during the last quarter of the nineteenth century. In France, Galle and Daum produced some of the finest examples of modern times, using as many as five layers of glass to develop their designs, usually scenics or subjects from nature. Hand carving was supplemented by the use of a copper engraving wheel, and acid was used to cut away the layers more quickly.

In England, Thomas Webb and Sons used modern machinery and technology to eliminate many of the problems that plagued early glass carvers. One of Webb's best-known carvers, George Woodall, is credited with producing over four hundred pieces. Woodall was trained in the art by John Northwood, famous for reproducing the Portland Vase in 1876. Cameo glass became very popular during the late 1800s, resulting in a market that demanded more than could be produced, due to the tedious procedures involved. In an effort to produce greater volume, less elaborate pieces with simple floral or geometric designs were made, often entirely acid etched with little or no hand carving. While very little cameo glass was made in this country, a few pieces were produced by James Gillender, Tiffany, and the Libbey Glass Company. Though some continued to be made on a limited scale into the 1900s, for the most part, inferior products caused a marked reduction in its manufacture by the turn of the century. See also specific manufacturers.

Our advisor for this category is Don Williams; he is listed in the Directory under Iowa.

English

Biscuit jar, berries/leaves, wht on citron, SP top, 6½" 1,995.00

Biscuit jar, cyclamen/lg butterfly, wht on red, SP mts, 6½" ..2,000.00
Rose bowl, roses intaglio, 5-layer, 3¼" H 1,200.00
Sugar shaker, floral, wht on red, silver hallmk top, 3½" 1,200.00
Sweetmeat jar, floral, wht on red, SP top/rim/hdl, 3x3¾" 995.00
Vase, anemones, bl on wht, 4" 600.00
Vase, Christmas roses/2 lg butterflies, wht on bl, 9" 2,000.00
Vase, dahlias, bl on brn, 3½" 775.00
Vase, floral, wht on citron, unsgn, 4½x2" 795.00

Bottle, vining floral, white on citron, 5", $2,750.00.

Vase, floral, wht on cranberry frost, cylindrical, 5⅝x2½" 850.00
Vase, floral, 3-color, ovoid w/slim neck, 4x1¾" 1,075.00
Vase, morning-glories, bk: grain, pk/wht on citron, 9" 1,850.00
Vase, wide tropical leaves, wht on red, 7½" 1,600.00
Vase, wild roses/insect, wht on citron, 9" 1,050.00
Vase, wild roses/insects, red/wht on yel, stick neck, 12" 7,000.00

French

Cordial, floral, gr on wht, sgn Vesier, 5" 300.00
Pitcher, berries, cranberry on tan, sgn SP lid, 5" 600.00
Vase, floral, lav on frost, mini, 3" 195.00
Vase, lake/mtn, man/bridge, leaves at shoulder, Arsall, 9" 900.00
Vase, peacock in full plumage, enameled, St Denis, 8x7" 550.00
Vase, scenic, gray on lt mottled cream, 2 cuts, 8⅛" 475.00
Vase, stylized trees, brn/orange, 2 cuts, 4½x2¾" 165.00
Vase, trees/ships, brn on citron, flared, Michel, 10" 650.00

Canary Lustre

Canary lustre was produced from the late 1700s until about the mid-nineteenth century in the Staffordshire district of England. The body of the ware was of yellow clay with a yellow overglaze; more often than not, copper or silver lustre trim was added. Decorations were usually black-printed transfers, though occasionally hand-painted polychrome designs were also used.

Cradle, allover herringbone, lightweight/early, 4¾", EX 100.00
Creamer, blk house transfer, silver lustre rim, 4½", EX 95.00
Figurine, child holding rooster, hollow, yel glaze, 4", M 350.00
Flowerpot, bridge/man, rust transfer, lion hdls, 4", EX 110.00
Mug, Ann in rectangular panel, floral swags, 2⅝", EX 160.00

Mug, bull, rust transfer, copper lustre rim, 1¾", EX 160.00
Mug, floral/foliage in pk lustre, 2½", EX 95.00
Mug, For My Favorite, blk transfer/purple lustre, 2½", NM ...325.00
Mug, house/tree in pk lustre, pk lustre border, 3¾", M 325.00
Mug, man/woman/beehive, rust transfer, pk lustre rim, 2¾" ...275.00
Mug, Orientals in garden, mc, pk lustre rim, 2", M 150.00
Mug, 2 recumbent sheep, blk transfer, pk lustre rim, 2¼" 175.00
Pitcher, Mephistopheles, relief face, 1880s, 6", M 400.00
Pitcher, rural scene, bk: Masonic, 5¾", NM 700.00

Candle Holders

The earliest type of candlestick, called a pricket, was constructed with a sharp point on which the candle was impaled. The socket type, first used in the 16th century, consisted of the socket and a short stem with a wide drip pan and base. These were made from sheets of silver or other metal; not until late in the 17th century were candlesticks made by casting. By the 1700s, styles began to vary from the traditional fluted column or baluster form and became more elaborate. A Rococo style with scrolls, shellwork, and naturalistic leaves and flowers came into vogue that afforded the individual silversmith the opportunity to exhibit his skill and artistry. The last half of the 18th century brought a return to fluted columns with neoclassic motifs. Because they were made of thin sheet silver, weighted bases were used to add stability. The Rococo styles of the Regency period were heavily encrusted with applied figures and flowers. Candelabra with six to nine branches became popular. By the Victorian era when lamps came into general use, there was less innovation and more adaptation of the earlier styles. See also Silver; specific manufacturers.

Key: QA —— Queen Anne

Ash/hickory, dbl, ratchet type, CT, 1770s, extends to 30" 700.00
Brass, bulbous bobeche, simple stem/rnd ft, 1900s, 8½", pr 175.00
Brass, capastan base, Dutch, ca 1500s, 5½" dia, EX 1,100.00
Brass, Dia Quilt, beehive/push-up, mk England, 12", pr 100.00
Brass, Dia Quilt, beehive/push-up, 1800s, 12", pr 170.00
Brass, Geo II, removable bobeche, trn baluster std, 12", pr 350.00
Brass, QA, faceted petal base & knob, scalloped socket, 8" 350.00
Brass, QA, faceted petal base & knob, 7" 250.00
Brass, QA, polished, soldered ft rpr, 6¾" 200.00
Brass, QA, scalloped base, 7", EX, pr 700.00
Brass, QA, scrolled base, 7⅜", pr 1,600.00
Brass, saucer base, ejector, 1820s, 5" dia, pr 225.00
Brass, side push-up, English, 7" 80.00
Brass, spiral motif in knop, English, 1850s, 11", pr 300.00
Brass, sq base, push-up, Victorian, 9½", pr 170.00
Brass, wide scalloped plate-like base, 1500s, 7x7" 1,300.00
Brass, wide scalloped plate-like base, 1700s, 6" 700.00
Brass, Wm & Mary, faceted base, push-up, 1675, 7", pr 3,100.00
Brass w/traces of SP, chamberstick, polished, 3" 75.00
Bronze/marble, candelabra, putto holds 2 arms, 14", pr 700.00
Gilt brass, Empire style, emb leafage/fluted std, 10", pr 935.00
Glass, vaseline opal, dolphin std, Bakewell/Pears, 8½", pr 250.00
Iron, hogscraper, hanging tab, push-up 7" 145.00
Iron, hogscraper, sgn Hidson on ejector tab, 8½" 300.00
Iron, hogscraper, steel wedding band, sgn Shaw, 7¼" 250.00
Iron, hogscraper, wedding band, ejector, 1825, 8½", pr 900.00
Iron, hogscraper, wedding band, sgn E Clark, 8½" 350.00
Iron, open spiral w/push-up tab, rnd wood base, 8½" 225.00
Iron, rnd drip-pan base on 3 tall ft, twist std, 1770s, 11" 1,800.00
Iron, taper jack, EX detail, 5¼" 425.00
Iron w/brass base, coiled spiral, 6½" 250.00
Maple, trn, Wm & Mary, pricket type, 1700, 8", M, pr 850.00

Sheet brass, chamberstick, push-up, 4½", pr 160.00
Wrought iron, spiral w/push-up, worn trn base, primitive, 8" ..175.00
Wrought iron, sticking Tommy, 10½" 95.00
Wrought iron, torchiere, 4-socket, 1880s, 60" 170.00
Wrought iron, 4 legs, diamond-shaped ft, 12", pr 250.00
Wrought steel, spiral push-up, trn wood base, 8½", VG 165.00

**William and Mary, brass, late 17th Century, 7",
$3,100.00 for the pair.**

Candlewick

Candlewick crystal was made by the Imperial Glass Corporation, a division of Lenox Inc., Bellaire, Ohio. It was introduced in 1936; and, though never marked except for paper labels, it is easily recognized by the beaded crystal rims, stems, and handles inspired by the tufted needlework called candlewicking, practiced by our pioneer women. During its production, more than 741 items were designed and produced. In September 1982 when Imperial closed its doors, thirty-four pieces were still being made.

Identification numbers and mold numbers used by the company help collectors recognize the various styles and shapes. Most of the pieces are from the #400 series, though other series numbers were also used. Stemware was made in eight styles — five from the #400 series made from 1941 to 1962, one from #3400 series made in 1937, another from #3800 series made in 1941, and the eighth style from the #4000 series made in 1947. In the listings that follow, some #400 items lack the mold number because that information was not found in the company files.

A few pieces have been made in color or with a gold wash. At least two lines, Valley Lily and Floral, utilized Candlewick with floral patterns cut into the crystal. These are scarce today. Other rare items include gifts such as the desk calendar made by the company for its employees and customers; the dresser set comprised of a mirror, clock, puff jar, and cologne; and the chip and dip set.

Ash tray, eagle form, 6½" 35.00
Ash tray, heart form, 6½" 15.00
Ash tray, matchbook holder in center, 6" 47.50
Ash tray, oblong, 4½" 6.00
Ash tray, sq, 4½" 12.00
Ash tray set, sq, nesting, 3-pc 36.00

Basket, beaded hdl, 5" 110.00
Basket, hdld, 11" 95.00
Bell, 5" 35.00
Bowl, centerpiece; flared, 11" 35.00
Bowl, centerpiece; mushroom form, 13" 47.50
Bowl, cupped edge, 10" 40.00
Bowl, flared, oval, 14" 95.00
Bowl, fruit; beaded stem, 10" 70.00
Bowl, lily; 4-ftd, 7" 45.00
Bowl, nappy; 3-ftd, 4½" 25.00
Bowl, relish; 5-part, 13½" 32.50
Bowl, sauce; deep, 5½" 25.00
Bowl, shallow, 12" 40.00
Bowl, sq, fancy crimped edge, 4-ftd, 9" 45.00
Bowl, vegetable; w/lid, 8" 90.00
Bowl, 3-ftd, 8½" 55.00
Butter dish, beaded top,¼-lb 23.00
Butter dish, rnd, w/lid, 5½" 27.50
Cake stand, high ft, 11" 52.50
Cake stand, low ft, 10" 45.00
Candle holder, floral, beaded stem, 4½" 25.00
Candle holder, hdld, bowl base, 5" 35.00
Candle holder, heart form, 5" 25.00
Candle holder, mushroom form 17.50
Candle holder, rolled edge, 3½" 10.50
Candle holder, w/finger hole, 3½" 25.00
Candle holder, 3-way, beaded base 65.00
Candy box, beaded ft, w/lid 100.00
Candy box, sq, rnd lid, 6½" 95.00
Cigarette holder, beaded ft, 3" 20.00
Coaster, w/spoon rest 10.00
Coaster, 4" 5.00
Cocktail, #400/190, 4-oz 18.00
Compote, fruit; crimped, ftd, 10" 75.00
Compote, oval, ftd 95.00
Compote, 3 beaded stems, 5" 35.00
Cordial, #400/190, 1-oz 65.00
Creamer, beaded hdl, 6-oz 7.50
Creamer, domed ft 35.00
Cruet, oil; beaded base, 6-oz 37.50
Cruet, oil; hdl, bulbous base, 4-oz 42.00
Decanter, hdl, w/stopper 225.00

Double candle holders, 4", $30.00 for the pair.

Egg cup, beaded ft 30.00
Goblet, #4000, 11-oz 18.00
Goblet, water; #3800, 9-oz 18.00
Hurricane lamp, 3-pc, flared & crimped-edge globe 75.00
Ice tub, hdld, 7" 85.00
Jam set, oval tray w/2 marmalade jars & ladles 57.50
Ladle, marmalade; 3-bead stem 6.00
Ladle, mayonnaise; 6¼" 6.00
Ladle, punch 20.00

Mustard jar, w/spoon 30.00
Parfait, #3400, 6-oz 35.00
Pitcher, beaded ft, 80-oz 145.00
Pitcher, low ft, 16-oz 125.00
Pitcher, no ft, 16-oz 95.00
Plate, bread & butter; 6" 6.50
Plate, dinner; 10" 22.50
Plate, hdld, crimped, 6¾" 16.00
Plate, oval, 12½" 35.00
Plate, salad; oval, 9" 15.00
Plate, torte; cupped edge, 12½" 27.50
Platter, 13" 55.00
Punch set, 15-pc 200.00
Rose bowl, crimped edge, ftd, 7¼" 95.00
Salt dip, 2" 6.00
Shakers, bulbous, chrome top, beaded ft, pr 12.50
Shakers, bulbous w/beaded stem, plastic top, pr 25.00
Shakers, chrome top, beaded ft, pr 16.00
Sherbet, #3800, low 14.00
Sherbet, #4000, tall, 6-oz 14.00
Sugar bowl, domed ft 35.00
Sugar bowl, flat, beaded hdl 20.00
Tray, celery; hdld, oval, 13½" 27.50
Tray, fruit; center hdl, 10½" 25.00
Tray, lemon; center hdl, 5½" 13.50
Tray, up-turned hdls, 5½" 18.00
Tumbler, juice; #3400, ftd, 5-oz 15.00
Tumbler, sherbet; low, 5-oz 12.00
Tumbler, water; 9-oz 25.00
Vase, bud; beaded ft, 5¾" 45.00
Vase, crimped edge, flat, 6" 20.00
Vase, crimped edge, flat, 8" 55.00
Vase, flared rim, ftd, 6" 37.50
Vase, fluted rim, beaded hdls, 8" 27.50

Candy Containers

Figural glass candy containers have been made in many different styles since 1876 when the Liberty Bell and Independence Hall were created for our country's centennial celebration. The production of these glass toys launched an industry that lasted until the mid-1960s.

Candy containers include automobiles, animals, doll furniture, telephones and other household items, comic characters, guns, and hundreds of other intriguing designs. The oldest containers (prior to 1920) were usually handpainted and often contained extra metal parts in addition to the metal strip or screw closures. During the 1950s, these metal parts were replaced with plastic, a practice that continued until candy containers met their demise in the 1960s. While predominately clear, nearly all colors of glass can be found including milk glass, green, amber, pink, emerald, cobalt, ruby flashed, and light blue. Usually the color was intentional, but leftover glass was often used resulting in unplanned colors — light blue, for instance. Various examples are found in light or ice blue, and new finds are always being discovered. Production of the glass portion of candy containers was centered around the western Pennsylvania city of Jeannette. Major producers include Westmoreland Glass, West Bros., Victory Glass, J.H. Millstein, J.C. Crosetti, L.E. Smith, Jack Stough, and T.H. Stough. While 90% of all glass candies were made in the Jeannette area, other companies such as Eagle Glass, Play Toy, and Geo. Borgfeldt Co. have a few to their credit as well.

Buyer beware! Many candy containers have been reproduced. Some, for instance the Rabbit Pushing Wheelbarrow, come already painted from distributors. The following list should alert you to possible reproductions:

#12 — Chicken on Nest

#24 — Dog (clear and cobalt)

#38 — Mule and Waterwagon

#47 — Rabit Pushing Wheelbarrow (eggs are speckled on the repro; solid on the original.)

#55 — Peter Rabbit
       Rocking Horse

#76 — Independence Hall (original is rectangular; repro has offset base with red felt-lined closure.)

#89 — Happifats on Drum (no notches on repro for closure to hook into.)

#90 — Jackie Coogan (marked inside 'B.')

#91 — Kewpie (must have Geo. Borgfeldt on base to be original.)

#94 — Naked Child

#103 — Santa (original has plastic head; repro is all glass and opens at bottom.)

#114 — Mantel Clock

#144 — Amber Pistol (first sold full in the 1970s.)

#168 — Uncle Sam's Hat

#233 — Santa's Boot

#238 — Camera (original must say Pat Appld For; repro says B Shakman or could be ground off.)

#254 — Mailbox

#255 — Drum Mug

#268 — Safe

#289 — Piano

#352 — Auto

#377 — Auto

#378 — Station Wagon

#386 — Fire Engine

Others are possible.

Those who desire further information on candy containers may contact Candy Collectors of Americas Club listed in our Directory under Clubs, Newsletters, and Catalogs. A bimonthly newsletter offers insight on new finds, reproductions, updates, and articles from over two hundred collectors and members, including all authors of books on candy containers.

Numbers used in this category refer to a standard reference series, *An Album of Candy Containers*, Vols 1 and 2, by Jennie Long. Values are given for undamaged examples with original paint and metal parts when applicable. Repaired pieces (often repainted) are worth only a small fraction of one that is perfect.

Key: (+) — watch for reproduction

Acorn, #221 . . . . .600.00
Airplane, Army Bomber, w/paper label prop, #328 . . . . .25.00
Airplane, Musical Toy; #333 . . . . .25.00
Airplane, P-38, cb closure, #326 .100.00
Airplane, Spirit of St Louis, monoplane, complete, #321 . . . . .300.00
Airplane, Stough's, musical, #331, #332, or #333, ea 20.00
Airplane, US Army B-51, #591 . . . . .45.00
Barney Google, by Smith, G pnt, #79 . . . . .375.00
Barney Google on Pedestal, w/pnt, #78 . . . . .190.00
Basket, grape design, #223 . . . . .25.00
Basket, hanging; HP floral, w/wire hdl, #224 . . . . .20.00
Bear in Auto, #2 . . . . .135.00
Bear on Circus Tub, w/blades, orig tin, #1 . . . . .300.00
Bell, Hand; wood hdl, #494 . . . . .150.00
Bell, Liberty; #1, pewter top, paper label, #227 . . . . .75.00
Bell, Liberty; #3, complete, amber, #229 . . . . .65.00
Billiken, #82 . . . . .100.00

Black Cat for Luck, #4 . . . . .600.00
Black Cat Sitting, #5 . . . . .600.00
Boat, Submarine, #338 . . . . .350.00
Bottle, Apothecary; #62 or #63 . . . . .10.00
Bottle, Baby Nurser, closure, #65 . . . . .15.00
Bottle, Soda Pop; #500 . . . . .50.00
Bottle, Waisted Nurser, complete w/contents, #71 . . . . .15.00
Bus, Country Club; #341 . . . . .450.00
Bus, Greyhound #1, tin wheels .225.00
Bus, Jitney; closure, #340 . . . . .350.00
Bus, Rapid Transit, #345, VG 400.00
Bus, Victory Stages, #344 . . . . .350.00
Candelabrum, #202 . . . . .40.00
Candy Pump, gr plastic, #240 . . . . .125.00
Cane, #241 . . . . .30.00
Cannon, Quick Firer; #537 . . . . .1,000.00
Cannon #3, 4-wheel carriage, #139 . . . . .400.00
Car, #12 Racer, Victory Glass, #432 . . . . .150.00
Car, Electric Coupe #2, closure, #356 . . . . .50.00
Car, Limousine, West Bros Co, #350 . . . . .75.00
Car, Long Hood Coupe #1, complete, tin wheels, #357 . . . . .150.00
Car, Ribbed-Top Sedan, closure, #376 . . . . .25.00
Car, Taxi, 6-Vent; closure, orig pnt, #365 . . . . .75.00
Cash Register, #244 . . . . .375.00
Charlie Chaplin by Barrel, Borgfeldt, closure, orig pnt, #83 . . .125.00
Chick in Sagging Basket, closure, orig pnt, #8 . . . . .75.00
Chicken on Oblong Basket, closure, gr, #10 . . . . .75.00
Clock, Oval; pnt milk glass, closure, #114 . . . . .155.00
Coach, Angeline, #398 . . . . .225.00
Coach, No Couplers, complete, #399 . . . . .225.00
Coal Car, w/tender, #402 . . . . .170.00
Darner, Amster, #245 . . . . .55.00
Dirigible, Los Angeles, silver pnt, aluminum cap, #322 . . . . .175.00
Dog by Barrel, closure, orig pnt, #13 . . . . .200.00
Dog w/Umbrella, #19 . . . . .20.00
Donald Duck, #85 . . . . .150.00
Drum, milk glass w/emb cannon & flag, orig lid, 2⅞" dia 425.00
Duckling, closure, orig pnt, #30 .70.00
Fairy Pups, #23 . . . . .50.00
Fire Engine, bl glass, #381 . . . . .100.00
Fire Engine, complete, #384 . . . . .125.00
Fire Engine, Lg Boiler; closure, #380 . . . . .65.00
Fire Engine, Stough's 1914, closure, orig wheels, #379-A 100.00
Flatiron, #249 . . . . .375.00

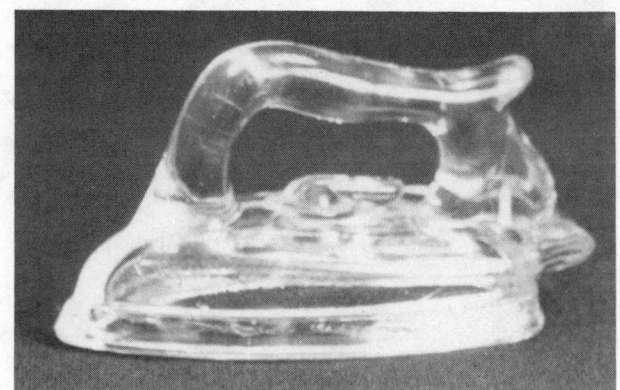

Flat Iron, 2½", $25.00.

Flossie Fisher, Bed, #127 . . . . .675.00
Gas Pump, #316 . . . . .180.00
Gun, Defense Field; metal tube, #142 . . . . .275.00

Gun, Lg #2; closure, #146 ....15.00
Gun, metal, #157 ....75.00
Gun, Victory Glass Co, #149 ....25.00
Gun, 3-Dot; Stough's, closure, #155 ....5.00
Happifats on Drum, orig pnt, #89, (+) 200.00
Horn, Millstein's, #282 ....20.00
Horn, 3-valve, w/mouthpc, #281 ....175.00
House, closure, orig pnt, #75 ....150.00
Jack-O'-Lantern, Blk Cat; #158 ....425.00
Kaleidoscope, #250 ....600.00
Kettle, closure, orig hdl, #251 ....30.00
Kewpie by Barrel, closure, orig pnt, #91 ....85.00
Lamp, Desk; mini, #213 ....225.00
Lamp, Hurricane; mini, #211 ....100.00
Lamp, Library; #207 ....400.00
Lamp, ringed base, #210 ....150.00
Lamp, Valentine; #556 ....325.00
Lantern, barn type #3, #179 ....40.00
Lantern, beaded trim, #180 ....20.00
Lantern, beveled glass globe, gilt/ruby-flashed, #175 ..55.00
Lantern, diamond mk, #183 ....25.00
Lantern, domed closure, #576 ....30.00
Lantern, glass reflector, #185 ....18.00
Lantern, Millstein's, plastic top/base, #197, lg 12.00
Lantern, ruby flashed, #575 ....30.00
Lantern, Stough's #3, lg, #196 ....12.00
Lantern, twins on anchor, #186 ....12.00
Learned Fox, #35 ....90.00
Locomotive, double rectangular windows, closure, #413 ....75.00
Locomotive, Little '23'; #409 ....120.00
Locomotive, Stough's #5, w/whistle, candy, #428 .....35.00
Mailbox, silver pnt, #254, (+) 115.00
Milk Bottle Carrier, 6 bottles, w/caps, #68 ....115.00
Mounted Policeman, closure, orig pnt, #551 ....1,300.00
Mug, Child's Tumbler; closure, #256 ....125.00
Mule Pulling Barrel, closure, orig pnt, #38 ....55.00
Owl, closure, glass eyes, #37 ....100.00
Owl, pewter head, #645 ....55.00
Pencil, labeled w/Ingred 50.00
Piano, #289, (+) 150.00
Play Nursing Set, #259 ....130.00
Pumpkin Head Policeman, G pnt, #163 ....500.00
Rabbit, Stough's, closure, #54, (+) 20.00

Rabbit pulling wooden cart, marked Germany, 12" long, $250.00.

Rabbit Begging, closure, orig pnt, #50 ....75.00
Rabbit in Egg Shell, closure, orig pnt, #48 ....85.00
Rabbit Nibbling Carrot, closure, #53 ....30.00
Rabbit on Dome, #46 ....275.00

Rabbit w/Basket on Arm, closure, no pnt, #49 ....70.00
Radio, #290 ....110.00
Rainbow Condiment Set, #503 ....115.00
Rocking Horse, variation A or B, #58 & #59, ea 275.00
Rolling Pin, #267 ....185.00
Rooster, crowing, orig pnt, #56, EX 175.00
Santa Claus, plastic head, #103 ....45.00
Santa Claus, sq chimney, closure, orig pnt, #99 ....175.00
Scotty Dog, #17 ....12.00
Soldier by Tent, perfect point 2,300.00
Spark Plug, #109 ....90.00
Suitcase, clear, #217 ....30.00
Tank w/Driver, #437 ....25.00
Telephone, Kiddie's Bank; tin, complete w/contents ..10.00
Telephone, Stough's #3, #308 ....20.00
Telephone, Victory #3, glass receiver, #300 ....40.00
Telephone, Victory #4, closure, receiver, #301 ......25.00
Telescope, #270 ....600.00
Toonerville Trolley, #111 ....550.00
Toy Town Dairy, #656 ....60.00
Train, Overland Limited, #394, 4-pc, EX 900.00
Truck, Express; orig tin 500.00
Truck, Laundry; orig tin, #459 ....500.00
Village Buildings, no glass inserts, #76, ea 20.00
Watch, hinged face, w/chain, #121 ....700.00
Watch w/Fob, #122 ....250.00
Windmill, pewter top, #443 ....400.00

Papier-Mache, Composition

Abe Lincoln, 4", NM 155.00
Billiken, orange/blk, 9", EX 250.00
Chick in fez, yel w/red & brn, glass eyes, 6" 185.00
Dachshund, brn w/blk nose & collar, Germany, 4x7", EX 125.00
Duck, bl cap, Germany, 1920s, EX 45.00
Egg, Germany, 5" 50.00
Football, Germany, ca 1910, 2½x3½", EX 50.00
George Washington on stump, metal axe, 4½", EX 175.00
Hen on tree stump, compo, Germany, 3½", NM 45.00
Hippo, tan/brn, neck closure, 4", EX 150.00
Humpty Dumpty, blk/wht/bl, 5" 225.00
Irish boy, gr, 4" 75.00
Irish girl, flesh face, gr hat/scarf/shoes, 4", EX 60.00
Irish hat, gr crepe w/Dresden trim, 2x4½" 55.00
Irishman, flesh face, blk hat/bl vest/gr coat, 4" 150.00
Irishman on mule, Germany, prof rpr on man, 1890s, 6" 400.00
Man in egg, red/wht/bl, 4½" 225.00
Pheasant on stump w/nest, Germany, 1900s, 3½x3½x2½" 65.00
Rabbit, brn/tan, glass eyes, Germany, 11½" 350.00
Rabbit, pressed cotton, wht w/orange carrot, glass eyes, 16" ...295.00
Rabbit, red pants/bl coat/orange shoes, 10" 295.00
Rabbit on log, tan/brn/gr, 4" 125.00
Ram, Germany, 3½" L, EX 175.00
Snowman's head, stovepipe hat w/noisemaker, US Zone, 6x3¼" ..75.00
Tricorner hat, blk flocking w/leaf & red berry, EX ...40.00
Turkey, gr/blk/gold/red/bl, 11" 250.00
Turkey, mc, Germany, ca 1900, 4x2½x2½" 45.00
Turkey, mc, Germany, 6" 95.00

Canes

    Fancy canes and walking sticks were once the mark of a gentleman. Hand-carved examples are collected and admired as folk art from the past, and the glass canes that never could have been practical as unique whimseys of the glass-blower's profession.

Canes

African wood, cvd Wire-Haired Terrier head hdl, 36" 275.00
Bamboo, plain brass tip, 36½" 8.00
Birch, intarsia floral & leaves inlay hdl, 35½" 30.00
Blackthorne, root end cvd in shape of ft, Scottish, 32½" 200.00
Blackthorne, thorns planed, curved hdl, sturdy 25.00
Cactus wood, incised vertically, root end, Austria, 36½" 25.00
French ivory, cvd Setter head hdl, brass ferrule/tip, 36" 50.00
Glass, amber w/appl wht spiral, Am, 1840-1880, 37" 170.00
Glass, aqua, spiral twist at hdl & tip, 30½" 75.00
Glass, aqua, vertical ribbing w/twisted hdl & tip, 42" 100.00
Glass, aqua w/lav spirals, hollow, shepherd's staff, 40" 90.00
Glass, aquamarine, appl mc spirals, baton type, 1860s, 44" 250.00
Gutta percha, dolphin hdl, ebony shaft, horn tip, 36" 110.00
Horn, curved hdl, inserts of amber, steel shaft, 36" 75.00
Horn, fox in tree hdl, thornwood shaft, metal tip, 36" 400.00
Mahogany, curved hdl, band of ebony inlay, 36" 75.00
Malacca, stag horn hdl, gold ferrule, horn tip, 36" 75.00
Ram's horn, horse's head hdl, walnut shaft, horn tip, 35½" 100.00
Softwood, shaft cvd w/seated monkey over gr lizard, Paris, 41" .350.00
Thornwood, thorns planed, curved hdl, 34½" 25.00
Zebra wood, curved hdl, 32" 55.00

Walking Sticks

African wood, giraffe head hdl, 36" 250.00
Bamboo, bas-relief cvg of rats/fruit, root-end hdl, Japan, 36" 95.00
Bamboo, silver hdl, metal tip, mk AA, 35¾" 55.00
Bamboo, SP hdl, opens to glass flask, horn tip, 33½" 60.00
Blackthorne, vines twisting around shaft, root hdl, 35½" 85.00
Bone, ivory fist hdl, horn segment divider, 35" 575.00
Bone, ivory knob, tapered paneled-to-rnd shaft, 35" 225.00

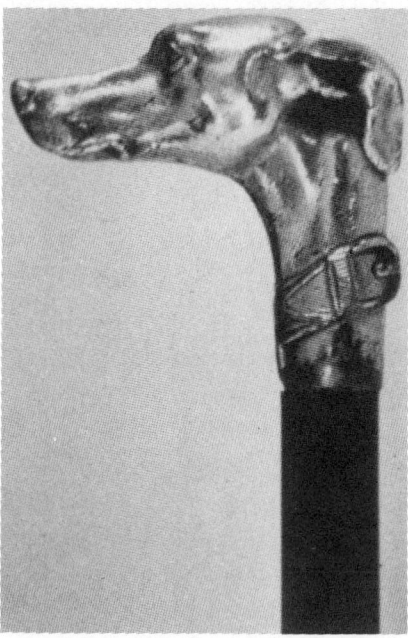

Ebony walking stick with chrome-plated cast brass dog head handle, bone tip, 36", $130.00.

Ebony, ivory pirate's head hdl, gold ferrule, 36½" 370.00
Ebony, ivory sphinx hdl, ivory tip, 37½" 410.00
Ebony, tooled gold-finish knob, eng presentation dtd 1885 .....90.00
Exotic wood, ivory knob, brass ferrule, 33" 100.00

Folk art, cvd wooden deer hoof, 35" 85.00
Folk art, mc bas-relief cvg of eagle/snake/turtle/lizard, 36" 60.00
Hickory, relief-cvd snake w/inlaid pearl eyes, 35½" 105.00
Mahogany, chip-cvd Scotty dog hdl, gold ferrule, 35" 250.00
Mahogany, ivory tip & paneled/bulbous knob, 33" 275.00
Mahogany, 3¼" Art Nouveau-patterned silver hdl, 35¾" 130.00
Malacca, brass hdl, 35½" 50.00
Malacca, silver hdl, horn tip, sturdy, 34" 100.00
Rhinoceros horn, 5½" inset of ivory under hdl, horn tip, 36" ..345.00
Root hdl w/grotesque animal head cvg, 31", VG 65.00
Rosewood, cvd cat's eye hdl, sterling ferrule, 35" 205.00
Rosewood, gr jadeite hdl w/faceted crystal bands, 39½" 400.00
Thornwood, cvd flowers/leaves, ivory tip, silver ferrule, 34" 85.00
Tiger maple, chrome repousse flashlight hdl, Austria, 35" 170.00
Tigerwood, natural stripes, bark hdl, 36" 30.00
Tortoise veneer, braided silver knob, 32¾" 100.00
Vertebrae on wooden dowel, horn segments & knob, 34", VG ..35.00
Zebra wood, steel hdl opens to monocular, 38½" 425.00

Canton

From the last part of the 18th century until the early 1900s, porcelain was made in and around Canton, China, expressly for western export. This pattern, whose name was borrowed from the city of its manufacture, is decorated in blue on a white ground with a scene containing a bridge, willow trees, birds, and a teahouse, all within a rain and cloud border. The popularity of Canton (porcelain) prompted potteries in England and the U.S. to adapt the pattern to earthenware dinner services which are referred to as Willow Ware today.

Bowl, quatrefoil, 9¾", NM 575.00
Bowl, salad; shaped 4-lobed border, 1850s, 9½" 850.00
Bowl, scalloped rim, lemon peel glaze, 5x10½" 525.00
Bowl, vegetable; w/lid, 1800s, 10½" L 400.00

Left to right: Box, divided interior, 19th century, 7½" long, $2,400.00; Cider jug, mid-19th century, $1,900.00.

Canister, tea; rectangular, 13½", mtd as lamp 1,100.00
Dish, entree; marquise form, fruit finial, 1880s, 10½" L 275.00
Dish, oval, 9" 250.00
Dish, w/pierced tray insert, 1800s, 12" L 425.00
Ginger jar, 1800s, w/lid, 7", NM 300.00
Mug, interlocking strap hdl, 1800s, 5½" 300.00
Pitcher, cane-shaped bamboo hdl, pear form, 1800s, 15" 700.00
Plate, ca 1920, 8½" 75.00
Platter, hexagonal, orange peel glaze, 16" 375.00
Platter, orange peel glaze, 18½" 550.00
Platter, oval, late, 21" 350.00
Platter, rain cloud border, mid-1800s, 13½" 300.00
Platter, well & tree, octagonal, 2 bar ft, 1800s, 15" 900.00

Platter, 1800s, 14½" **350.00**
Platter, 1820s, 12" **350.00**
Sauce boat, 7½" **275.00**
Teapot, canted corners, 9x12" L **550.00**
Tureen, boar's head hdls, canted corners, 1800s, 10" L **950.00**

Capo-Di-Monte

Established in 1743 near Naples and sponsored by Charles II, who was King of Naples at that time, Capo-Di-Monte produced soft-paste porcelain figurines and dinnerware usually marked with a 'crown over N' device, though a fleur-de-lis was used on occasion. The factory was closed throughout the 1760s but reopened in 1771 in the city of Naples. There both hard- and soft-paste porcelains were made, sometimes decorated with applied florals in high relief. Their technique as well as their marks were blatantly copied. As a result, this type of encrusted decoration is often referred to today as Capo-Di-Monte. The original factory closed in 1821. Some of their molds were purchased by the Docceia Porcelain factory in Florence which continues to operate to the present time. Most examples on the market today are of fairly recent manufacture. Capo-Di-Monte type wares have been made in Hungary and Germany, as well as France and Italy. Many of these pieces continue to bear the 'crown over N' gold stamp. As more collectors recognize and appreciate the quality of the older ware, buyer-demand drives prices higher.

Box, jewel; Roman & Biblical motif on lid, 3¼" H **125.00**
Cache pot, lady/putto/bldg, sq base/loop hdls, 1860s, 10x8" . . . **225.00**
Cup & saucer, birds/cherubs, gold trim, lg **75.00**

Demitasse set, sugar bowl, 6 cups and saucers on stand, $475.00.

Figurine, African Crowned Crane, 1 ft up, sgn Armani, 14" . . . **160.00**
Figurine, beautiful girl w/bouquet, 9½" **100.00**
Figurine, beggar w/umbrella mending coat, sgn, 12" **150.00**
Figurine, boy on stump w/fishing pole, 6x4½" **75.00**
Figurine, boy photographer, girl by wall, 9" **90.00**
Figurine, buccaneer draws sword, C Colle, 12x6" **125.00**
Figurine, coach+2 wht horses, man helps lady alight, 14" L **400.00**
Figurine, drunkards, old man pushes 2nd in wheelbarrow, 12" . **200.00**
Figurine, fisherman w/net, shells at base, Armani, 11" **150.00**

Figurine, pearl fisherman w/bag, Bonalberti, 9½" **165.00**
Figurine, pool hustler, priest/2 men/waiter, Armani, 21" L **360.00**
Figurine, woman roasts chestnuts, urchin at side, sgn, 10" **250.00**
Lamp, table; puffy tiers, cherubs, brass dolphin base, '20s **115.00**
Rose jar, figures sitting on rocks relief, mk, 4" **60.00**
Urn, cherubs/grapes relief, Bacchus-head hdls, 15", pr **375.00**

Carlton

Carlton Ware was the product of Wiltshaw and Robinson, who operated in the Staffordshire district of England from about 1890. During the 1920s, they produced ornamental ware with enameled and gilded decorations such as flowers and birds, often on a black background. In 1958 the firm was renamed Carlton Ware Ltd. Their trademark was a crown over a circular stamp with 'W & R, Stoke on Trent' surrounding a swallow. 'Carlton Ware' was sometimes added by hand.

Ash tray, Gordon's Dry Gin **16.00**
Ash tray, Rouge Royale, Oriental scene, sq, 4¾" **25.00**
Biscuit jar, floral, mc on cream w/gold, SP lid/rim/hdl, 7" **110.00**
Bookends, ladies w/shields & serpents, pr **165.00**
Bowl, Rouge Royal, storks & trees, 2-hdl, oval, 7" **40.00**
Box, wisteria/exotic bird, mc on cobalt **125.00**
Jar, bird/dragonfly/butterfly w/gold on mahogany, w/lid, 5" **55.00**
Sugar shaker, gr basket of mc fruit, 5¼" **48.00**
Vase, fruit on dk bl w/gold, MOP int, trumpet form, 10" **55.00**
Vase, Verte Royal, gr irid w/gold, fan form, 8½" **45.00**

Carnival Collectibles

Carnival items from the early part of this century represent the lighter side of an America that was alternately prospering and sophisticated or devastated by war and domestic conflict. But whatever the country's condition, the carnival's thrilling rides and shooting galleries were a sure way of letting it all go by . . . at least for an evening.

For further information on chalkware figures, we recommend *The Carnival Chalk Prize* by Thomas G. Morris, who is listed in the Directory under Oregon.

Chalkware figure, Beach Flirt, Carnival Supply, 1919, 9½" **75.00**
Chalkware figure, Betty Boop, HP, ca 1930-1940, 14½" **190.00**
Chalkware figure, Felix the Cat, unmk, 1922, 12½" **75.00**
Chalkware figure, Sailor Girl, Jenkins, 1934, 13½" **35.00**
Chalkware figure, Snow White, ca 1937-1950, 14" **45.00**
Chalkware figure, Uncle Sam, unmk, ca 1935-1945, 15" **40.00**
Knock-down figure, cat, seated, HP canvas, 1920s, 10" **65.00**
Knock-down figure, lady, HP canvas, wool hair, 10x4x2½" **55.00**
Knock-down figure, Puss 'N Boots, HP canvas, ca 1930, 20" . . . **85.00**
Knock-down game, 15 8x3" wooden milk bottles, EX **85.00**
Shooting gallery target, bird, CI, worn pnt, 6x4½" **50.00**
Shooting gallery target, bird & duck spinner, CI, 9½x5" **110.00**
Shooting gallery target, blk cat & seated dog, CI, 11x5" **125.00**
Shooting gallery target, duck, standing, CI, King, 8½x5½" **55.00**
Shooting gallery target, eagle, CI, bullet mks, 22" W **75.00**
Shooting gallery target, Indian w/tomahawk, Evans, 6½" **115.00**
Shooting gallery target, moose, CI, old wht pnt, 5½x6½" **70.00**
Shooting gallery target, mouse, CI, Evans, Chicago, 4x9x½" **80.00**
Shooting gallery target, mouse, CI, old pnt, 4½x8½" **65.00**
Shooting gallery target, rabbit, CI, old pnt, 7½x5½" **65.00**
Shooting gallery target, squirrel, CI, ca 1900, 6½x4" **50.00**
Shooting gallery target, 2 squirrels between target, CI, 11" **85.00**

Carnival Glass

Carnival glass is pressed glass that has been coated with a sodium solution and fired to give it an exterior lustre. First made in America in 1905, it was produced until the late 1920s and had great popularity in the average American household; for unlike the costly art glass produced by Tiffany, carnival glass could be mass-produced at a small cost. Colors most found are marigold, green, blue, and purple, but others exist in lesser quantities and include white, clear, red, aqua opalescent, peach opalescent, ice blue, ice green, amber, lavender, and smoke.

Companies mainly responsible for its production in America include the Fenton Art Glass Company, Williamstown, West Virginia; the Northwood Glass Company, Wheeling, West Virginia; the Imperial Glass Company, Bellaire, Ohio; the Millersburg Glass Company, Millersburg, Ohio; and the Dugan Glass Company (Diamond Glass), Indiana, Pennsylvania. In addition to these major manufacturers, lesser producers included the U.S. Glass Company, the Cambridge Glass Company, the Westmoreland Glass Company, and the McKee Glass Company.

Carnival glass has been highly collectible since the 1950s and has been reproduced for the last twenty-five years. Several national and state collectors' organizations exist, and many fine books are available on old carnival glass, including *The Standard Encyclopedia of Carnival Glass* by Bill Edwards.

Acanthus (Imperial), bowl, amethyst, 8"-9½", ea 90.00
Acanthus (Imperial), plate, marigold, 10" 155.00
Acorn (Fenton), bowl, bl, 7" 47.00
Acorn (Millersburg), compote, marigold, rare 1,800.00
Acorn Burrs (Northwood), bowl, gr, flat, 5" 55.00
Acorn Burrs (Northwood), creamer, amethyst 120.00
Acorn Burrs (Northwood), punch cup, marigold 28.00
Acorn Burrs (Northwood), sugar bowl, marigold 95.00
Acorn Burrs (Northwood), vase whimsey, marigold, rare 1,000.00
Age Herald (Fenton), bowl, amethyst, scarce, 9¼" 985.00
American (Fostoria), tumbler, marigold, rare 500.00
Apothecary Jar, marigold, sm 50.00
Apple & Pear Intaglio (Northwood), bowl, marigold, 10" 75.00
Apple & Pear Intaglio (Northwood), bowl, marigold, 5" 30.00
Apple Blossom Twigs (Dugan), plate, bl 225.00
Apple Blossoms (Dugan), bowl, peach opal, 7½" 150.00

Apple Blossoms (Dugan), plate, peach opal, 8¼" 165.00
Apple Panels (English), creamer, marigold 30.00
Apple Tree (Fenton), pitcher, water; bl 330.00
Apple Tree (Fenton), tumbler, bl 52.00
April Showers (Fenton), vase, gr 60.00
Arcadia Baskets, plate, marigold, 8" 50.00
Arched Fleur-De-Lis (Higbee), mug, marigold, rare 110.00
Arched Panels, tumbler, marigold 50.00
Arcs (Imperial), compote, amethyst 50.00
Art Deco (English), bowl, marigold, 4" 32.00
Astral, shade, marigold 45.00

August Flowers, shade, marigold 36.00
Aurora, bowl, marigold w/decor 150.00
Australian Swan (Crystal), bowl, amethyst, 9" 95.00
Australian Swan (Crystal), bowl, marigold, 5" 38.00
Autumn Acorns (Fenton), bowl, bl, 8¾" 40.00
Autumn Acorns (Fenton), plate, gr, rare 750.00
Aztec (McKee), pitcher, marigold, rare 1,300.00
Aztec (McKee), tumbler, marigold, rare 500.00
Baby Bathtub (US Glass), pastel, miniature 75.00
Baby's Bouquet, child's plate, marigold, scarce 90.00
Ball & Swirl, mug, marigold 90.00
Balloons (Imperial), cake plate, smoke 90.00
Balloons (Imperial), compote, marigold 55.00
Bambi, powder jar, marigold 25.00
Bamboo Bird, jar, amethyst, complete 725.00
Banded Diamonds (Crystal), bowl, marigold, 5" 50.00
Banded Diamonds (Crystal), pitcher, water; amethyst, rare . . .1,200.00

Banded Diamonds (Crystal), tumbler, marigold, rare 450.00
Banded Grape (Fenton), pitcher, water; bl 350.00
Banded Grape & Leaf (English), pitcher, water; marigold, rare . .500.00
Banded Grape & Leaf (English), tumbler, marigold, rare 90.00
Banded Rib, pitcher, marigold 120.00
Banded Rib, tumbler, marigold 20.00
Basketweave (Fenton), vase, whimsey; bl, rare 625.00
Basketweave & Cable (Westmoreland), sugar bowl, gr 85.00
Beaded Acanthus (Imperial), pitcher, milk; gr 210.00
Beaded Band & Octagon, lamp, kerosene; marigold 85.00
Beaded Bulls Eye (Imperial), vase, smoke, 14" 65.00
Beaded Cable (Northwood), candy dish, bl 70.00
Beaded Cable (Northwood), rose bowl, peach opal 750.00
Beaded Panels (Imperial), bowl, marigold, 8" 40.00
Beaded Panels (Imperial), powder jar, marigold 50.00
Beaded Panels (Westmoreland), compote, amethyst 50.00
Beaded Shell (Dugan), bowl, amethyst, ftd, 5" 38.00
Beaded Shell (Dugan), pitcher, water; marigold 360.00
Beaded Shell (Dugan), tumbler, amethyst 90.00
Beaded Spears (Crystal), tumbler, marigold, rare 75.00
Beaded Stars (Fenton), plate, marigold, 9" 90.00
Beaded Stars (Fenton), rose bowl, marigold 45.00
Beaded Stars & VTS, banana boat, marigold, 8¾" 90.00
Beaded Swirl (English) butter dish, bl 70.00
Bellaire Souvenir (Imperial), bowl, marigold, scarce 65.00
Bells & Beads (Dugan), bowl, peach opal, 7½" 85.00
Big Basketweave (Dugan), basket, amethyst, sm 40.00
Big Basketweave (Dugan), vase, amethyst, 6"-14", ea 40.00
Big Fish (Millersburg), banana bowl, gr, rare 1,800.00
Big Fish (Millersburg), rose bowl, vaseline, very rare 7,500.00
Big Thistle (Millersburg), punch bowl & base, amethyst 8,000.00
Bird of Paradise (Northwood), plate, amethyst, advertising 220.00
Birds & Cherries (Fenton), bonbon, gr 60.00
Birds & Cherries (Fenton), bonbon, marigold 40.00
Birds & Cherries (Fenton), bowl, marigold, rare, 5" 60.00

Birds & Cherries (Fenton), plate, bl or gr, rare, 10", ea 1,500.00
Blackberry, (Fenton), vase whimsey, bl, rare 325.00
Blackberry, Miniature (Fenton); compote, bl, sm 100.00
Blackberry (Northwood), bowl, amethyst, ftd, 9" 60.00
Blackberry Bark, vase, amethyst, rare 1,500.00

Blackberry Block (Fenton), tumbler, gr 75.00
Blackberry Bramble (Fenton), compote, bl 50.00
Blackberry Spray (Fenton), bonbon, gr 45.00
Blackberry Spray (Fenton), hat shape, aqua opal 195.00
Blackberry Wreath (Millersburg), bowl, ice cream; bl, 10" ...950.00
Blackberry Wreath (Millersburg), plate, amethyst, rare, 10" .4,700.00
Blocks & Arches (Crystal), creamer, marigold 38.00
Blocks & Arches (Crystal), pitcher, marigold, rare 150.00
Blossoms & Band (Imperial), bowl, marigold, 10" 35.00
Blossomtime (Northwood), compote, gr 250.00
Bo Peep (Westmoreland), mug, marigold, scarce 190.00
Border Plants (Dugan), bowl, amethyst, ftd, 8½" 70.00
Border Plants (Dugan), bowl, peach opal, flat, 8½" 170.00
Border Plants (Dugan), tumber, bl 50.00
Bow & English Hob (English), nut bowl, bl 55.00
Brocaded Summer Gardens, ice bucket, pastel 90.00
Brocaded Summer Gardens, vase, pastel 90.00
Broken Arches (Imperial), punch bowl & base, amethyst 475.00
Broken Arches (Imperial), punch cup, marigold 25.00
Brooklyn Bridge (Dugan), bowl, marigold, scarce 320.00
Bubbles, lamp chimney, amethyst 36.00
Bull Dog, paperweight, marigold 250.00
Bull's Eye (US Glass), oil lamp, marigold 185.00
Bull's Eye & Loop (Millersburg), vase, gr, 7"-11", ea 300.00
Bull's Eye & Spearhead, wine, marigold 48.00
Bunny, bank, marigold 30.00
Butterflies (Fenton), bonbon, bl 50.00
Butterflies (Fenton), card tray, bl 60.00
Butterflies & Bells (Crystal), compote, marigold 90.00
Butterfly (Northwood), bonbon, amethyst, ribbed exterior 260.00
Butterfly (Northwood), bonbon, bl 65.00
Butterfly & Berry (Fenton), bowl, bl, ftd, 10" 180.00
Butterfly & Berry (Fenton), hatpin holder, marigold, rare 750.00
Butterfly & Berry (Fenton), plate, bl, ftd 1,350.00
Butterfly & Berry (Fenton), sugar bowl, gr 190.00
Butterfly & Fern (Fenton), pitcher, amethyst 450.00
Butterfly & Tulip (Dugan), marigold, rare 850.00
Butterfly Bower (Crystal), compote, amethyst 115.00
Buttermilk, Plain (Fenton), goblet, gr 60.00
Buttons & Daisy (Imperial), slipper, clambroth, (old only) 70.00
Buzz Saw (Cambridge), cruet, gr, rare, 4" 375.00
Buzz Saw (Cambridge), cruet, marigold, rare, 6" 380.00
Buzz Saw (Cambridge), shade, marigold 40.00
Canada Dry, bottle, wht 28.00
Cane (Imperial), pickle dish, marigold 25.00
Cane (Imperial), wine, pastel 60.00
Cane & Daisy Cut (Jenkins), basket, pastel, w/hdl, rare 190.00

Cane & Daisy Cut (Jenkins), vase, marigold 90.00
Cannonball VT, pitcher, bl 285.00
Cannonball VT, tumbler, bl 70.00
Capitol (Westmoreland), mug, marigold, sm 75.00
Captive Rose (Fenton), bonbon, marigold 40.00
Captive Rose (Fenton), plate, gr, 9" 225.00
Carnation (New Martinsville), punch cup, marigold 45.00
Carnival Bell, marigold 350.00
Carnival Honeycomb (Imperial), bonbon, amethyst 45.00
Carnival Honeycomb (Imperial), plate, amethyst, 7" 80.00
Carolina Dogwood (Westmoreland), bowl, aqua opal, 8½" 290.00
Carolina Dogwood (Westmoreland), plate, milk glass opal 290.00
Caroline (Dugan), basket, peach opal, scarce 400.00
Cathedral (Sweden), pitcher, bl, rare 2,500.00
Cathedral Arches (English), flower holder, marigold 60.00
Cattails, hatpin, amethyst 26.00
Chain & Star (Fostoria), butter dish, marigold, rare 900.00
Chatham (US Glass), candlestick, marigold, pr 75.00
Chatham (US Glass), compote, marigold 65.00
Checkerboard (Westmoreland), cruet, clear, rare 600.00
Checkerboard (Westmoreland), pitcher, amethyst, rare 3,800.00
Checkerboard (Westmoreland), punch cup, marigold 75.00
Checkerboard (Westmoreland), tumbler, amethyst 450.00
Checkerboard (Westmoreland), wine, marigold, rare 250.00
Checkerboard Bouquet, plate, amethyst, 8" 50.00
Checkers, ash tray, marigold 30.00
Checkers, butter dish, marigold, 2 sizes, ea 140.00
Cherry (Dugan), cruet, wht, rare 500.00
Cherry (Millersburg), banana compote, bl, rare 2,400.00

Cherry (Millersburg), bowl, gr, scarce, 9" 100.00
Cherry (Millersburg), bowl, ice cream; bl, 10" 600.00
Cherry (Millersburg), bowl w/Hobnail exterior, bl, rare 750.00
Cherry (Millersburg), compote, gr, lg, rare 1,000.00
Cherry (Millersburg), powder jar, gr, rare 1,250.00
Cherry (Millersburg), sugar bowl, marigold 65.00
Cherry & Cable (Northwood), butter dish, marigold, rare 350.00
Cherry & Cable (Northwood), pitcher, marigold, rare 1,350.00
Cherry & Cable Intaglio (Northwood), bowl, marigold, 10" 36.00
Cherry Circles (Fenton), bonbon, bl 55.00
Cherry Circles (Fenton), compote, amethyst 62.00
Cherry Smash (US Glass), bowl, marigold, 8" 50.00
Cherub, lamp, pastel, rare 425.00
Chrysanthemum (Fenton), bowl, bl, ftd, 10" 80.00
Chrysanthemum (Fenton), bowl, gr, flat, 9" 85.00
Circle Scroll (Dugan), compote, amethyst, scarce 125.00
Circle Scroll (Dugan), creamer, amethyst 200.00
Circle Scroll (Dugan), hat shape, amethyst, rare 120.00
Circle Scroll (Dugan), pitcher, marigold, rare 1,500.00
Circle Scroll (Dugan), tumbler, marigold, rare 300.00
Circle Scroll (Dugan), vase whimsey, marigold, rare 120.00
Classic Arts (Czech), powder jar, marigold 275.00
Classic Arts (Czech), rose bowl, marigold 260.00

Classic Arts (Czech), vase, Egyptian; marigold, 7" 245.00
Classic Arts (Czech), vase, marigold, rare, 10" 300.00
Cleveland Memorial (Millersburg), ash tray, amethyst, rare . .1,700.00
Cobblestones (Imperial), bonbon, gr 55.00
Cobblestones (Imperial), bowl, gr, 8½" 75.00
Coin Dot (Fenton), basket whimsey, bl, rare 85.00
Coin Dot (Fenton), tumbler, amethyst, rare 125.00
Coin Dot VT (Westmoreland), compote, aqua opal 225.00
Colonial (Imperial), lemonade goblet, marigold 60.00
Colonial (Imperial), toothpick holder, amethyst 90.00
Colonial (Imperial), vase, gr 58.00
Columbia (Imperial), compote, amethyst 60.00
Concave Diamonds (Dugan), pitcher, vaseline, w/lid 550.00
Concave Diamonds (Northwood), pickle castor, marigold 450.00
Concave Diamonds (Northwood), tumble-up, aqua opal, rare .600.00
Concave Flute (Westmoreland), vase, gr 65.00
Concord (Fenton), plate, amethyst, rare, 10" 700.00
Constellation (Dugan), compote, peach opal 160.00
Coral (Fenton), compote, wht, rare 125.00
Corinth (Dugan), banana dish, amethyst 75.00
Corinth (Dugan), bowl, marigold, 9" 38.00
Corn Vase (Dugan), fancy husk, marigold, rare 800.00
Corn Vase (Northwood), pulled husk, gr, rare 6,000.00
Corn Vase (Northwood), regular mold, bl 1,200.00
Cosmos (Millersburg), plate, gr, 6" 65.00
Cosmos & Cane, bowl, marigold, 5" 36.00
Cosmos & Cane, butter dish, marigold 175.00

Cosmos & Cane, chop plate, marigold, rare 385.00
Cosmos & Cane, compote, marigold, tall, rare 300.00
Cosmos & Cane, rose bowl whimsey, marigold 700.00
Cosmos & Cane, spooner, marigold 95.00
Cosmos & Cane, sugar bowl, wht 225.00
Cosmos VT (Fenton), bowl, bl, 9"-10", ea 80.00
Cosmos VT (Fenton), plate, peach opal, rare, 10" 300.00
Country Kitchen (Millersburg), butter dish, amethyst, rare 600.00
Country Kitchen (Millersburg), butter dish, marigold 500.00
Country Kitchen (Millersburg), sugar bowl, gr 550.00
Covered Swan (English), marigold 150.00
Covered Turkey (Heisey), amethyst 385.00
Covered Turtle (Heisey), gr 300.00
Crab Claw (Imperial), bowl, gr, 10" 60.00
Crab Claw (Imperial), bowl, marigold, 5" 25.00
Crab Claw (Imperial), tumbler, marigold, scarce 95.00
Crackle (Imperial), auto vase, amethyst 35.00
Crackle (Imperial), candlestick, marigold, 3½" 25.00
Crackle (Imperial), candlestick, marigold, 7" 30.00
Crackle (Imperial), candy jar, gr, w/lid 35.00
Crackle (Imperial), pitcher, gr, dome base 140.00
Crackle (Imperial), plate, gr 45.00
Crackle (Imperial), punch bowl & base, gr 60.00
Crackle (Imperial), punch cup, marigold 10.00
Crystal Cut (Crystal), compote, marigold 50.00

Cut Arches (English), banana bowl, marigold 50.00
Cut Cosmos (Millersburg), tumbler, marigold, rare 295.00
Cut Crystal (US Glass), compote, marigold, 5½" 90.00
Cut Crystal (US Glass), water bottle, marigold 165.00
Cut Sprays, vase, marigold, 9" 35.00
Dahlia (Dugan), bowl, amethyst, ftd, 10" 130.00
Dahlia (Dugan), pitcher, amethyst, rare 750.00
Dahlia (Dugan), tumbler, amethyst, rare 135.00
Daisy (Fenton), bonbon, bl, scarce 95.00
Daisy & Cane (English), decanter, marigold, rare 75.00
Daisy & Cane (English), spittoon, bl, rare 185.00
Daisy & Drape (Northwood), vase, bl 395.00
Daisy & Plume (Northwood), candy dish, peach opal 100.00
Daisy Chain, shade, marigold 45.00
Daisy Squares, compote, amber, rare 500.00
Daisy Squares, goblet, amber, rare 350.00
Daisy Squares, rose bowl, amethyst 400.00
Daisy Wreath (Westmoreland), bowl, milk glass opal, 8"-10" . .340.00
Dandelion (Northwood), mug, gr 565.00
Dandelion (Northwood), tumbler, wht 190.00
Diamond & Daisy (US Glass), compote, amethyst 60.00
Diamond & Daisy (US Glass), tumbler, bl, rare 50.00
Diamond & Daisy (US Glass), vase, marigold, 10" 85.00
Diamond & Rib (Fenton), vase whimsey, gr 600.00
Diamond & Sunburst (Imperial), wine, gr 52.00
Diamond Band (Crystal), float set, amethyst 300.00
Diamond Band (Crystal), sugar bowl, marigold, open 38.00
Diamond Band & Fan (English), cordial set, marigold, rare . . .750.00
Diamond Checkerboard, bowl, marigold, 9" 35.00
Diamond Checkerboard, cracker jar, marigold 75.00
Diamond Checkerboard, tumbler, marigold 85.00
Diamond Flutes (US Glass), creamer, marigold 35.00
Diamond Fountain (Higbee), cruet, marigold, rare 675.00
Diamond Lace (Imperial), bowl, amethyst, 10"-11", ea 65.00
Diamond Lace (Imperial), tumbler, marigold 75.00
Diamond Point Columns (Imperial), bowl, marigold, 4½" 20.00
Diamond Point Columns (Imperial), butter dish, marigold 65.00
Diamond Point Columns (Imperial), plate, marigold, 7" 35.00

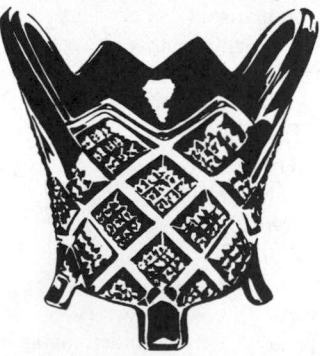

Diamond Point Columns (Imperial), spooner, marigold 40.00
Diamond Ring (Imperial), bowl, amethyst, 9" 45.00
Diamond Ring (Imperial), bowl, fruit; amethyst, 9½" 85.00
Diamonds (Millersburg), punch bowl & base, gr, rare 1,800.00
Dolphins (Millersburg), compote, bl, rare 3,200.00
Double Dolphins (Fenton), bowl, pastel, flat, 8"-10", ea 75.00
Double Dolphins (Fenton), bowl, pastel, ftd, 9"-11", ea 110.00
Double Dolphins (Fenton), candlestick, pastel, pr 85.00
Double Dolphins (Fenton), compote, pastel 65.00
Double Scroll (Imperial), punch cup, marigold 22.00
Double Star (Cambridge), bowl, gr, rare, 9" 195.00
Double Star (Cambridge), spittoon whimsey, gr, rare 1,500.00
Dragon & Lotus (Fenton), plate, peach opal, rare, 9½" 900.00
Dragon's Tongue (Fenton), bowl, marigold, scarce, 11" 285.00

Dragonfly, oil lamp, pastel, rare 650.00
Drape, oil lamp, pastel, rare 900.00
Drapery (Northwood), vase, bl 48.00
Dugan Fan (Dugan), sauce dish, amethyst, 5" 48.00
Duncan (National Glass), cruet, marigold 410.00
Durand (Fenton), bowl, bl, Grape & Cable 800.00
Dutch Mill, plate, marigold, 8" 35.00
Elegance, bowl, amethyst, 8¼" 90.00
Elks (Fenton), Atlantic City plate, bl, rare 975.00
Elks (Fenton), Detroit bowl, gr, scarce 350.00
Embroidered Mums (Northwood), bowl, aqua opal, 9" 975.00
Engraved Floral (Fenton), tumbler, gr 85.00
Engraved Grapes (Fenton), candy jar, marigold 45.00

Engraved Grapes (Fenton), pitcher, marigold, tall 85.00
Engraved Grapes (Fenton), tumbler, juice; marigold 20.00
Famous, puff box, marigold 75.00
Fancy Cut (English), pitcher, marigold, miniature, rare ...125.00
Fans (English), cracker jar, marigold, metal lid 118.00
Fantail (Fenton), bowl, bl, ftd, 5" 180.00
Fantail (Fenton), compote, bl 160.00
Fashion (Imperial), butter dish, amethyst 185.00
Fashion (Imperial), punch bowl & base, amethyst 165.00
Feather & Heart (Millersburg), tumbler, gr, scarce 105.00
Feathered Arrow (English), bowl, marigold, 8½" 40.00
Fentonia Fruit (Fenton), bowl, bl, ftd, 6" 55.00
Fentonia Fruit (Fenton), tumbler, marigold, rare 120.00
Field Thistle (US Glass), pitcher, marigold, scarce ...150.00
Field Thistle (US Glass), plate, marigold, rare, 9" ...350.00
File (Imperial & English), bowl, amethyst, 5" 40.00
File (Imperial & English), compote, marigold 40.00
Fine Cut Rings (English), vase, marigold 50.00
Fine Cuts & Roses (Northwood), rose bowl, gr, ftd 65.00
Flannel Flower (Crystal), cake stand, amethyst 175.00
Flannel Flower (Crystal), compote, marigold, lg 90.00
Flared Wide Panel, atomizer, marigold, 3½" 90.00
Fleur-De-Lis (Millersburg), bowl, gr, flat, 8½" 275.00
Flora (English), float boat, bl 75.00
Floral, hatpin, amber 50.00
Floral & Grape (Dugan), pitcher, amethyst 185.00
Floral & Grape VT (Fenton), pitcher, gr, 2 styles, ea .190.00
Floral & Grape VT (Fenton), tumbler, bl 30.00
Floral & Optic (Imperial), rose bowl, peach opal, ftd .190.00
Floral & Wheat (US Glass), bonbon, bl, stemmed 42.00
Floral Oval (Higbee), plate, marigold, rare, 7" 80.00
Flowering Vine (Millersburg), compote, gr, tall, very rare ...2,000.00
Flowers & Frames (Dugan), bowl, marigold, 8"-10", ea ...40.00
Flute (British), sherbert, marigold, mkd British 45.00
Flute (Millersburg), compote, marigold, clover base, rare, 6" ...450.00
Flute (Millersburg), punch bowl & base, marigold, rare ...150.00
Flute (Millersburg), punch cup, amethyst 30.00
Flute (Millersburg), vase, gr, rare 350.00
Flute (Northwood), bowl, amethyst, 5" 26.00

Flute (Northwood), ring tree, marigold, rare 175.00
Flute (Northwood), salt dip, marigold, ftd 30.00
Flute (Northwood), tumbler, gr, 3 varieties 70.00
Flute & Cane (Imperial), pitcher, milk; marigold 120.00
Flute #3 (Imperial), butter dish, gr 190.00
Flute #3 (Imperial), custard bowl, amethyst, 11" 285.00
Flute #3 (Imperial), punch bowl & base, gr 495.00
Flute #3 (Imperial), toothpick holder, marigold, regular ...55.00
Flying Bat, hatpin, amethyst, scarce 55.00
Forget-Me-Not (Fenton), pitcher, gr 375.00
Formal (Dugan), hatpin holder, marigold, rare 175.00
Fostoria, #1299 (Fostoria), tumbler, marigold 75.00
Fostoria #600 (Fostoria), napkin ring, marigold 75.00
Four Flowers (Finland), plate, peach opal, 6½" 190.00
Four Flowers VT (Westmoreland), bowl, gr, ftd, 8½" 75.00
Frosted Block (Imperial), compote, marigold 85.00
Frosted Block (Imperial), dish, pickle; marigold, hdld, rare ...40.00
Frosted Block (Imperial), rose bowl, marigold 45.00
Fruit & Flowers (Northwood), bonbon, bl, stemmed 65.00
Fruit & Flowers (Northwood), bowl, amethyst, 9" 60.00
Fruit Basket (Millersburg), compote, amethyst, hdld, rare ...1,200.00
Fruit Lustre, tumbler, marigold 28.00
Fruit Salad (Westmoreland), punch bowl & base, marigold ...750.00
Garden Path (Dugan), bowl, amethyst, 8½"-10", ea 70.00
Garden Path VT (Dugan), plate, peach opal, rare, 11" ...3,300.00
Gay '90s (Millersburg), pitcher, gr, rare 9,000.00
Goddess Athena, epergne, gr, rare 1,800.00
Gold Fish Bowl, marigold 70.00
Golden Cupids (Crystal), bowl, pastel, rare, 5" 95.00
Golden Honeycomb (Imperial), bonbon, amethyst 50.00
Golden Honeycomb (Imperial), bowl, marigold, 5" 25.00
Good Luck (Northwood), bowl, aqua opal, 8¾" 850.00
Grand Thistle (Finland), pitcher, bl, rare 1,800.00
Grape, Heavy (Imperial), bowl, fruit; w/base, marigold ...195.00
Grape, Heavy (Imperial), plate, marigold, 11" 140.00
Grape, Heavy (Imperial), plate, marigold, 8" 55.00
Grape, Heavy (Imperial), punch bowl & base, gr 240.00

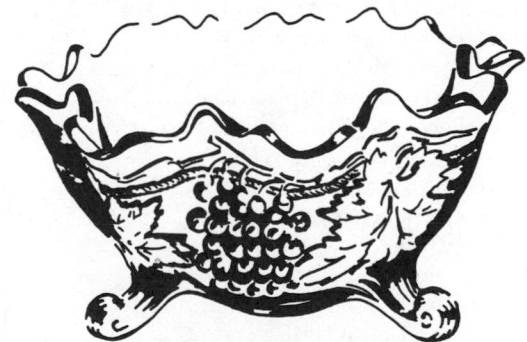

Grape (Fenton's Grape & Cable), orange bowl, bl, ftd ...175.00
Grape (Imperial), compote, gr 55.00
Grape (Imperial), decanter, marigold, w/stopper 95.00
Grape (Imperial), goblet, amethyst, rare 75.00
Grape (Imperial), nappy, marigold 26.00
Grape (Imperial), pitcher, milk; gr 200.00
Grape (Imperial), punch bowl & base, amber 400.00
Grape (Imperial), wine, amethyst 38.00
Grape (Northwood's Grape & Cable), bonbon, aqua opal ..500.00
Grape (Northwood's Grape & Cable), butter dish, gr 195.00
Grape (Northwood's Grape & Cable), compote, marigold ...2,650.00
Grape (Northwood's Grape & Cable), cookie jar, amethyst ...265.00
Grape (Northwood's Grape & Cable), cup & saucer, marigold ...400.00
Grape (Northwood's Grape & Cable), gr, ftd, 7"-9", ea ...65.00
Grape (Northwood's Grape & Cable), hatpin holder, gr ...170.00

Grape (Northwood's Grape & Cable), jar, tobacco; bl **1,200.00**
Grape (Northwood's Grape & Cable), nappy, marigold **45.00**
Grape (Northwood's Grape & Cable), plate, pastel, ftd **110.00**
Grape (Northwood's Grape & Cable), powder jar, bl **125.00**
Grape (Northwood's Grape & Cable), shot glass, marigold **225.00**

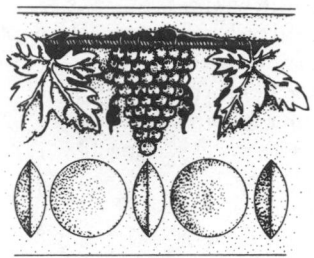

Grape (Northwood's Grape & Cable), sugar bowl, gr **115.00**
Grape (Northwood's Grape & Cable), sweetmeat, bl **1,400.00**
Grape (Northwood's Grape & Cable), tumbler, gr, jumbo **75.00**
Grape & Cherry (English), bowl, bl, rare, 8½" **150.00**
Grape & Cherry (English), bowl, marigold, rare, 8½" **65.00**
Grape & Gothic Arches (Northwood), bowl, amethyst, 5" **30.00**
Grape & Gothic Arches (Northwood), sugar bowl **80.00**
Grape Arbor (Northwood), tumbler, bl **260.00**
Grape Delight (Dugan), rose bowl, amethyst, ftd, 6" **65.00**
Grape Wreath (Millersburg), bowl, ice cream; marigold, 10" ...**125.00**
Grapevine Lattice (Dugan), plate, wht, 7"-9", ea **90.00**
Greek Key (Northwood), bowl, marigold, 7"-8½", ea **70.00**
Greek Key (Northwood), pitcher, amethyst, rare **900.00**
Greek Key (Northwood), pitcher, gr, rare **985.00**
Greek Key (Northwood), tumbler, gr, rare **210.00**
Hand Vase (English), amethyst, 5½"-8", ea **300.00**
Harvest Flower (Dugan), pitcher, marigold, rare **1,250.00**
Harvest Flower (Dugan), tumbler, gr **400.00**
Hattie (Imperial), rose bowl, marigold **90.00**
Hawaiian Lei (Higbee), creamer, marigold **65.00**
Headdress, compote, bl **46.00**
Heart & Vine (Fenton), plate, bl, rare, 9" **200.00**
Heart Band Souvenir (McKee), mug, gr, lg **110.00**
Hearts & Flowers (Northwood), plate, aqua opal, rare, 9" ...**1,450.00**
Heavy Heart (Higbee), tumbler, marigold **75.00**
Heavy Prisms (English), celery vase, bl, 6" **85.00**
Heavy Web (Dugan), plate, peach opal, rare, 11" **1,095.00**
Heisey #357, bottle, water; marigold **75.00**
Heisey Flute, punch cup, marigold **28.00**
Hobnail (Millersburg), rose bowl, marigold, scarce **175.00**
Hobnail (Millersburg), sugar bowl, bl, rare **780.00**
Hobnail (Millersburg), sugar bowl, gr, rare **570.00**
Hobnail (Millersburg), tumbler, gr, rare **1,000.00**
Hobnail Panels (McKee), vase, clambroth, 8¾" **65.00**
Hobnail VT (Millersburg), jardiniere, amethyst, rare **900.00**
Hobstar (Imperial), basket, marigold **90.00**
Hobstar (Imperial), bowl, berry; marigold, 10" **35.00**
Hobstar (Imperial), bowl, berry; marigold, 5" **24.00**
Hobstar (Imperial), cookie jar, gr **95.00**
Hobstar & Arches (Imperial), bowl, fruit; gr, w/base **70.00**
Hobstar & Feather (Millersburg), bowl, amethyst, rare, 5" **450.00**
Hobstar & Feather (Millersburg), butter dish, amethyst, rare .**1,500.00**
Hobstar & Feather (Millersburg), butter dish, gr, rare **1,500.00**
Hobstar & Feather (Millersburg), creamer, marigold, rare **700.00**
Hobstar & Feather (Millersburg), punch cup, bl, scarce **80.00**
Hobstar & Feather (Millersburg), sugar bowl, gr, rare **900.00**
Hobstar & File, tumbler, marigold, rare **170.00**

Hobstar & Fruit (Westmoreland), bowl, peach opal, rare, 10" ..**125.00**
Hobstar Band (Imperial), compote, marigold, rare **90.00**
Holly, Panelled (Northwood), bonbon, amethyst, ftd **60.00**
Holly, Panelled (Northwood), creamer, marigold **475.00**
Holly & Berry (Dugan), nappy, peach opal **65.00**
Holly Sprig or Whirl (Millersburg), bonbon, gr, plain **58.00**
Holly Sprig or Whirl (Millersburg), compote, pastel **900.00**
Honeycomb & Clover (Fenton), compote, bl **48.00**
Honeycomb & Hobstar (Millersburg), vase, bl, rare, 8¼" **6,100.00**
Honeycomb Ornament, hatpin, amethyst **70.00**
Horn of Plenty, bottle, marigold **56.00**
Hot Springs Souvenir, vase, marigold, rare, 9⅞" **115.00**
Humpty-Dumpty, jar, mustard; marigold **75.00**
Ice Crystals, bowl, pastel, ftd **85.00**
Idyll (Fenton), vase, bl, rare **650.00**
Illinois Daisy (English), cookie jar, marigold **55.00**
Imperial #5 (Imperial), vase, marigold, rare, 6" **90.00**
Imperial #9 (Imperial), compote, marigold **38.00**
Inca, vase, amethyst, rare, 7" **900.00**
Intaglio Feathers, cup, marigold **25.00**
Interior Panels, mug, marigold **75.00**
Interior Poinsettia (Northwood), tumbler, marigold, rare **465.00**
Interior Rays, sherbert, marigold **35.00**
Inverted Coin Dot (Northwood-Fenton), tumbler, amethyst ...**95.00**
Inverted Feather (Cambridge), cracker jar, gr **285.00**
Inverted Feather (Cambridge), punch bowl & base, gr, rare ..**3,800.00**
Inverted Feather (Cambridge), tumbler, gr, rare **600.00**
Inverted Feather (Cambridge), tumbler, marigold, rare **500.00**
Inverted Feather (Cambridge), wine, marigold, rare **90.00**
Inverted Strawberry, bowl, amethyst, 9"-10½", ea **190.00**
Inverted Strawberry, celery tray, bl, rare **1,350.00**

Inverted Strawberry, compote, gr, lg, rare **350.00**
Inverted Strawberry, pitcher, milk; amethyst, rare **1,100.00**
Inverted Thistle (Cambridge), bowl, gr, rare, 5" **95.00**
Inverted Thistle (Cambridge), chop plate, amethyst, rare ...**1,450.00**
Iris, Heavy (Dugan), pitcher, peach opal **1,250.00**
Iris, Heavy (Dugan), tumbler, marigold **85.00**
Iris (Fenton), compote, amethyst **60.00**
IW Harper, decanter, marigold, w/stopper **75.00**
Jacob's Ladder, perfume, marigold **47.00**
Jacob's Ladder VT (US Glass), rose bowl, marigold **52.00**
Jacobean Ranger (Czech & English), decanter, marigold **150.00**
Jacobean Ranger (Czech & English), pitcher, marigold **250.00**
Jacobean Ranger (Czech & English), tumbler, juice; marigold ..**70.00**
Jacobean Ranger (Czech & English), wine, marigold **28.00**
Jelly Jar, marigold, complete, rare **65.00**
Jewelled Heart (Dugan), bowl, peach opal, 10" **135.00**
Jewelled Heart (Dugan), pitcher, marigold, rare **775.00**
Jewelled Heart (Dugan), tumbler, pastel, rare **575.00**
Jewels (Imperial), vase, marigold **90.00**
Jockey Club (Northwood), bowl, amethyst, 7" **145.00**
Kingfisher & VT (Australian), bowl, amethyst, 9½" **90.00**

Kittens, bottle, pastel 52.00
Kittens (Fenton), bowl, bl, scarce, 4" 195.00
Kittens (Fenton), bowl, cereal; marigold, scarce 129.00
Kittens (Fenton), cup & saucer, bl, scarce 640.00
Kittens (Fenton), spooner, vaseline, rare, 2½" 210.00
Kookaburra & VTS (Australian), bowl, amethyst, 10" 92.00
Kookaburra & VTS (Australian), bowl, marigold, 5" 42.00
Lacy Dewdrop (Westmoreland), compote, pastel, w/lid 285.00
Lacy Dewdrop (Westmoreland), pitcher, pastel 585.00
Lacy Dewdrop (Westmoreland), tumbler, pastel 250.00
Large Kangaroo (Australian), bowl, amethyst, 10" 85.00
Large Kangaroo (Australian), bowl, amethyst, 5" 52.00
Lattice & Daisy (Dugan), bowl, marigold, 9" 60.00
Lattice & Daisy (Dugan), tumbler, bl 48.00
Lattice & Grape (Fenton), tumbler, peach opal 375.00
Lattice & Points (Dugan), vase, marigold 35.00
Lattice & Sprays, vase, marigold, 10½" 40.00
Lattice Heart (English), bowl, bl, 5" 40.00
Lattice Heart (English), compote, bl 85.00
Laurel Leaves (Imperial), plate, amethyst 55.00
Leaf & Beads (Northwood & Dugan), bowl, nut; aqua opal . . .550.00
Leaf Chain (Fenton), bonbon, gr 54.00
Leaf Chain (Fenton), plate, aqua opal, 9¼" 2,100.00
Leaf Chain (Fenton), plate, bl, 9¼" 85.00
Leaf Swirl (Westmoreland), compote, marigold 50.00
Leaf Tiers (Fenton), bowl, marigold, ftd, 10" 58.00
Leaf Tiers (Fenton), pitcher, gr, ftd, rare 630.00
Leaf Tiers (Fenton), sugar bowl, marigold, ftd 88.00
Leaf Tiers (Fenton), tumbler, bl, ftd, rare 95.00
Lily of the Valley (Fenton), pitcher, bl, rare 4,500.00
Lined Lattice (Dugan), vase, wht, 7"-14", ea 60.00
Lion (Fenton), bowl, bl, scarce, 7" 150.00
Lion (Fenton), plate, marigold, rare, 7½" 500.00
Little Beads, compote, peach opal, sm 48.00
Little Daisy, lamp, pastel, complete, 8" 395.00
Little Fishes (Fenton), bowl, bl, flat or ftd, 10", ea 165.00
Little Flowers (Fenton), bowl, amethyst, 9¼" 90.00
Little Flowers (Fenton), bowl, gr, 5½" 32.00

Little Flowers (Fenton), plate, marigold, rare, 10" 750.00
Little Owl, hatpin, gr, rare 150.00
Little Stars (Millersburg), bowl, amethyst, rare, 10½" 700.00
Little Stars (Millersburg), bowl, gr, scarce, 7" 90.00
Log, paperweight, marigold, rare, 3x1¼" 150.00
Long Hobstar, compote, marigold 65.00
Long Hobstar, punch bowl & base, marigold 125.00
Long Leaf (Dugan), bowl, peach opal, ftd 158.00
Long Thumbprint (Dugan), butter dish, marigold 60.00
Long Thumbprint (Dugan), compote, gr 39.00
Long Thumbprint (Dugan), vase, bl, 7"-11", ea 38.00
Lotus & Grape (Fenton), plate, bl, rare, 9½" 500.00
Lotus Land (Northwood), bonbon, amethyst 595.00
Louisa (Westmoreland), plate, amethyst, ftd, rare, 8" 150.00

Lovebirds, bottle, marigold, w/stopper 400.00
Lustre & Clear (Fenton), vase, fan; bl 50.00
Lustre & Clear (Imperial), butter dish, marigold 65.00
Lustre & Clear (Imperial), celery tray, marigold, 8" 35.00
Lustre & Clear (Imperial), pitcher, marigold 195.00
Lustre & Clear (Imperial), vase, gr, ftd, 8" 120.00
Lustre & Clear (Imperial), vase, marigold, ftd, 8" 85.00
Lustre Flute (Northwood), compote, amethyst 48.00
Lustre Flute (Northwood), punch bowl & base, gr 150.00
Lustre Rose (Imperial), bowl, berry; gr, 8"-9", ea 46.00
Lustre Rose (Imperial), bowl, gr, flat, 7"-11", ea 48.00

Lustre Rose (Imperial), fernery, amber 95.00
Lustre Rose (Imperial), pitcher, milk; marigold 57.00
Lustre Rose (Imperial), tumbler, amethyst 30.00
Maize (Libbey), celery vase, clear, rare 185.00
Many Prisms, perfume, marigold, w/stopper 65.00
Maple Leaf (Dugan), bowl, bl, stemmed, 4½" 30.00
Maple Leaf (Dugan), bowl, bl, stemmed, 9" 90.00
Maple Leaf (Dugan), pitcher, amethyst 325.00
Marilyn (Millersburg), pitcher, amethyst, rare 975.00
Marilyn (Millersburg), tumbler, gr, rare 400.00
Mary Ann (Dugan), loving cup, marigold, 3-hdld, rare 250.00
Massachusetts (US Glass), vase, marigold 150.00
Mayflower, compote, pastel 60.00
Melon Rib (Imperial), candy jar, marigold 30.00
Melon Rib (Imperial), pitcher, marigold 60.00
Melon Rib (Imperial), powder jar, marigold 35.00
Melon Rib (Imperial), tumbler, marigold 24.00
Memphis (Northwood), bowl, fruit; bl, w/base 2,250.00
Mikado (Fenton), compote, gr, lg 545.00
Milady (Fenton), pitcher, bl .500.00
Milady (Fenton), tumbler, amethyst 140.00
Milady (Fenton), tumbler, marigold 95.00
Mirrored Lotus (Fenton), bonbon, gr 60.00
Mirrored Lotus (Fenton), rose bowl, bl, rare 145.00
Mitered Diamond & Pleats (English), bowl, bl, 4½" 30.00
Mitered Diamond & Pleats (English), bowl, bl, 8½" 40.00
Mitered Ovals (Millersburg), vase, marigold, rare 2,600.00
Moonprint (English), bowl, marigold, 8¼" 45.00
Moonprint (English), compote, marigold 45.00
Moonprint (English), creamer, marigold 45.00
Moonprint (English), jar, bl, w/lid 85.00
Moonprint (English), jar, marigold, w/lid 60.00
Morning-Glory (Millersburg), pitcher, amethyst, rare 8,500.00
Morning-Glory (Millersburg), tumbler, gr, rare 1,000.00
Multi-Fruits & Flowers (Millersburg), cup, bl, rare 80.00
My Lady, powder jar, marigold 87.00
Mystic (Cambridge), vase, marigold, ftd, rare 120.00
Near Cut (Cambridge), decanter, gr, w/stopper, rare 2,200.00
Near Cut Souvenir (Cambridge), mug, marigold, rare 175.00
Near Cut Souvenir (Cambridge), tumbler, marigold, rare 210.00
Nesting Swan (Millersburg), bowl, bl, scarce, 10" 2,800.00

Nesting Swan (Millersburg), rose bowl, marigold, rare 2,100.00
Night Stars (Millersburg), bonbon, amethyst, rare 650.00
Night Stars (Millersburg), tray, card; amethyst, rare 700.00
Northwood's Nearcut, goblet, marigold, rare 110.00
Northwood's Nearcut, pitcher, marigold 1,500.00
Northwood's Poppy, pickle dish, bl, oval 65.00
Northwood's Poppy, tray, bl, oval, rare 225.00
Northwood's Poppy, tray, pastel, oval, rare 200.00
Number 2176 (Sowerby), lemon squeezer, marigold 50.00
Number 2351 (Cambridge), bowl, gr, rare, 9" 285.00
Number 4 (Imperial), compote, marigold 30.00
Octagon (Imperial), pitcher, milk; gr, scarce 170.00
Octagon (Imperial), toothpick holder, amethyst, rare 85.00
Octagon (Imperial), vase, amethyst, rare 130.00
Octagon (Imperial), vase, gr, rare 125.00
Ohio Star (Millersburg), compote, marigold, rare 950.00
Open Rose (Imperial), bowl, fruit; amethyst, 7"-10", ea 65.00
Open Rose (Imperial), bowl, fruit; pastel, 7"-10", ea 60.00
Open Rose (Imperial), bowl, gr, flat, 5½" 28.00
Optic & Buttons (Imperial), goblet, marigold 58.00
Optic & Buttons (Imperial), plate, marigold, 10½" 70.00
Optic Flute (Imperial), bowl, marigold, 5" 25.00
Orange Peel (Westmoreland), cup, amethyst 32.00
Orange Peel (Westmoreland), cup, custard; marigold, scarce 26.00
Orange Peel (Westmoreland), dessert, gr, stemmed, scarce 70.00
Orange Peel (Westmoreland), punch bowl & base, marigold ..125.00
Orange Tree (Fenton), bowl, bl, flat, 8"-10", ea 40.00

Orange Tree (Fenton), bowl, ice cream; bl, w/stem, ftd, 9"-11" ..28.00
Orange Tree (Fenton), bowl, marigold, flat, 8"-10", ea 28.00
Orange Tree (Fenton), cruet whimsey, bl, rare 1,200.00
Orange Tree (Fenton), pitcher, bl, 2 designs 300.00
Orange Tree (Fenton), punch bowl & base, gr 325.00
Orange Tree (Fenton), punch bowl & base, pastel 400.00
Orange Tree (Fenton), rose bowl, wht 250.00
Orange Tree (Fenton), wine, peach opal 60.00
Orange Tree & Scroll (Fenton), pitcher, gr 490.00
Ostrich (Australian), compote, marigold, rare, lg 125.00
Oval & Round (Imperial), bowl, amethyst, 4" 28.00
Oxford, mustard pot, marigold, w/lid 50.00
Palm Beach (US Glass), banana bowl, amethyst 220.00
Palm Beach (US Glass), bowl, marigold, 5" 30.00
Palm Beach (US Glass), tumbler, marigold 100.00
Palm Beach (US Glass), vase whimsey, amethyst 120.00
Panama (US Glass), goblet, marigold, rare 120.00
Panelled Diamond & Bows (Fenton), vase, bl, 7"-14", ea 35.00
Panelled Prism, jam jar, marigold 48.00
Panelled Thistle (Higbee), tumbler, marigold 95.00
Pansy (Imperial), pickle dish, gr, oval 45.00
Panther (Fenton), bowl, bl, ftd, 10" 150.00
Parlor, ash tray, bl 95.00
Pastel Panels (Imperial), mug, pastel, stemmed 85.00
Pastel Panels (Imperial), pitcher, pastel 320.00

Peach (Northwood), bowl, wht, 5" 60.00
Peach (Northwood), bowl, wht, 9" 210.00
Peach (Northwood), butter dish, wht 220.00
Peach (Northwood), tumbler, bl 80.00
Peaches, wine bottle, marigold 37.00
Peacock (Millersburg), banana bowl, amethyst, rare 2,000.00
Peacock (Millersburg), bowl, amethyst, 5" 55.00
Peacock (Millersburg), bowl, amethyst, 9" 275.00
Peacock (Millersburg), bowl, ice cream; bl, 5" 450.00

Peacock & Dahlia (Fenton), bowl, wht, 7½" 150.00
Peacock & Grape (Fenton), bowl, gr, flat or ftd, 7¾", ea 50.00
Peacock & Urn (Fenton), compote, vaseline 125.00
Peacock & Urn (Fenton), goblet, vaseline, rare 90.00
Peacock & Urn (Northwood), bowl, ice cream; aqua opal, 6"..1,600.00
Peacock & Urn (Northwood), bowl, ice cream; bl, 6" 275.00
Peacock & Urn & VTS (Millersburg), bowl, ice cream; gr, 10" .425.00
Peacock & Urn & VTS (Millersburg), plate, marigold, 10½"..2,600.00
Peacock at the Fountain (Northwood), bowl, bl, 5" 45.00
Peacock at the Fountain (Northwood), bowl, bl, 9" 98.00
Peacock at the Fountain (Northwood), cup, amethyst 35.00
Peacock Garden (Northwood), vase, marigold, rare, 8" 1,500.00
Peacock Lamp, carnival base, amethyst 300.00
Peacock Tail (Fenton), bonbon, bl 38.00
Peacock Tail (Fenton), bonbon, gr 40.00
Peacock Tail (Fenton), compote, bl 48.00
Peacock Tail (Fenton), plate, amethyst, 6" 70.00
Peacock Tail & Daisy, bowl, bl opal, rare 1,200.00
Peacock Tail VT (Millersburg), compote, gr, scarce 85.00
Pearl & Jewels (Fenton), basket, wht, 4" 190.00
Pearl Lady (Northwood), shade, wht 55.00
Penny, match holder, amethyst, rare 245.00
Perfection (Millersburg), pitcher, marigold, rare 3,800.00
Persian Garden (Dugan), bowl, ice cream; bl, 11" 290.00
Persian Garden (Dugan), bowl, ice cream; bl, 6" 90.00
Persian Garden (Dugan), chop plate, peach opal, rare, 13" ..4,750.00
Persian Garden (Dugan), chop plate, wht, rare, 13" 2,200.00
Persian Medallion (Fenton), bowl, amethyst, 8¼" 50.00
Persian Medallion (Fenton), rose bowl, pastel 90.00
Petal & Fan (Dugan), bowl, pastel, 5" 60.00
Petal & Fan (Dugan), bowl, peach opal, 10" 195.00
Peter Rabbit (Fenton), plate, gr, rare, 10" 2,200.00
Pin-Ups (Australian), bowl, marigold, rare, 8¾" 90.00
Pine Cone (Fenton), plate, gr, 6½" 58.00
Pineapple (English), compote, amethyst 65.00
Pinwheel (Dugan), bowl, marigold, 6" 38.00
Pinwheel (English), bowl, marigold, rare, 8" 65.00
Pinwheel (English), vase, marigold, 8" 50.00
Plaid (Fenton), bowl, gr, 8¾" 65.00
Plain Jane, paperweight, marigold 80.00
Plain Jane (Imperial), basket, marigold 60.00
Poinsettia (Imperial), pitcher, milk; amethyst 850.00
Pony (Dugan), plate, marigold, rare, 9" 450.00

Poodle, powder jar, marigold, w/lid 25.00
Poppy (Millersburg), salver, gr, rare 1,450.00
Poppy Show (Northwood), bowl, gr, 8½" 350.00
Potpourri (Millersburg), pitcher, milk; marigold, rare 1,150.00
Premium (Imperial), underplate, pastel, 14" 130.00
Pretty Panels (Northwood), pitcher, gr 160.00
Primrose (Millersburg), bowl, ice cream; gr, scarce, 9" 150.00
Primrose Panels (Imperial), shade, pastel 45.00
Princess (US Glass), lamp, amethyst, complete, rare 1,250.00
Prism & Daisy Band (Imperial), bowl, marigold, 8" 30.00
Proud Puss (Cambridge), bottle, marigold 80.00
Puzzle (Dugan), bonbon, wht, stemmed 65.00
Puzzle (Dugan), compote, peach opal 75.00
Quartered Block, butter, marigold 90.00
Question Marks (Dugan), bonbon, peach opal 70.00
Question Marks (Dugan), cake plate, amethyst, stemmed, rare .450.00
Quill (Dugan), pitcher, amethyst, rare 2,350.00
Ranger (Mexican), pitcher, marigold, rare 285.00
Ranger (Mexican), tumbler, marigold 270.00
Ranger Toothpick, toothpick holder, marigold 75.00
Raspberry (Northwood), bowl, gr, 9" 62.00
Raspberry (Northwood), compote, gr 58.00
Raspberry (Northwood), pitcher, gr 240.00
Raspberry (Northwood), pitcher, milk; amethyst 150.00
Rex, pitcher, marigold 365.00
Rex, tumbler, marigold 55.00
Ribbon & Block, lamp, marigold, complete 500.00
Ribbon Tie (Fenton), plate, bl, flat, 9½" 285.00
Rising Sun (US Glass), butter dish, marigold 150.00
Rock Crystal (McKee), punch bowl & base, amethyst 590.00
Roll, cordial set, marigold, complete 250.00
Rosalind (Millersburg), bowl, amethyst, scarce, 10" 245.00
Rosalind (Millersburg), bowl, gr, rare, 5" 400.00
Rose, bottle, pastel 120.00
Rose Garden (Sweden), bowl, amethyst, rare, 6" 75.00

Rose Garden (Sweden), butter dish, bl, rare 145.00
Rose Tree (Fenton), bowl, bl, rare, 10" 295.00
Rose Wreath (Northwood), bonbon, amethyst, rare 250.00
Roses & Fruit (Millersburg), bonbon, bl, ftd, rare 1,000.00
Round-Up (Dugan), bowl, peach opal, 8¾" 97.00
Royalty (Imperial), bowl, fruit; marigold, w/stand 100.00
Rustic (Fenton), vase, funeral; gr, 15"-20", ea 220.00
S-Repeat (Dugan), creamer, amethyst, sm 60.00
S-Repeat (Dugan), cup, amethyst, rare 110.00
S-Repeat (Dugan), sugar bowl, amethyst, rare 185.00
Sailboats (Fenton), bowl, gr, 6" 75.00
Saint (English), candlestick, marigold 275.00
Salamanders, hatpin, amethyst 45.00
Scale Band (Fenton), tumbler, bl .35.00
Scales (Westmoreland), bonbon, aqua opal 300.00
Scotch Thistle (Fenton), compote, bl 45.00
Scottie, powder jar, marigold 25.00

Scroll (Westmoreland), pin tray, marigold 45.00
Scroll Embossed (Imperial), bowl, marigold, 8½" 36.00
Seacoast (Millersburg), pin tray, gr, rare 275.00
Seaweed, lamp, marigold, 2 sizes, ea 195.00
Seaweed (Millersburg), bowl, ice cream; bl, rare, 10½" 450.00
Shrine (US Glass), champagne, clear 90.00
Singing Birds (Northwood), bowl, gr, 10" 75.00

Singing Birds (Northwood), sherbet, amethyst, rare 85.00
Singing Birds (Northwood), tumbler, marigold 45.00
Six Petals (Dugan), bowl, pastel, 8½" 60.00
Ski-Star (Dugan), basket, peach opal, w/hdl, rare 500.00
Small Rib (Dugan), rose bowl, amber, stemmed 48.00
Smooth Rays (Northwood-Dugan), compote, gr 52.00
Smooth Rays (Westmoreland), bowl, gr, dome base, 5"-7½", ea .50.00
Soda Gold (Imperial), pitcher, marigold 210.00
Sowerby Flower Block (English), flower frog, marigold 60.00
Spiderweb (Northwood), candy dish, smoke, w/lid 35.00
Split Diamond (English), creamer, marigold, sm 36.00
Spring Basket (Imperial), basket, smoke, w/hdl, 5" 48.00
Springtime (Northwood), pitcher, amethyst, rare 850.00
Springtime (Northwood), pitcher, gr, rare 1,050.00
Stag & Holly (Fenton), rose bowl, bl, ftd 950.00
Star & Fan (English), cordial set, marigold 750.00
Star & File (Imperial), custard cup, marigold 26.00
Star & File (Imperial), wine, iridized custard 102.00
Star & Rosette, hatpin, amethyst .38.00
Star Medallion (Imperial), celery tray, pastel 50.00
Star Medallion (Imperial), pitcher, milk; gr 75.00
Star Medallion (Imperial), vase, marigold 35.00
Starburst, perfume, marigold, w/stopper 50.00
Stars & Bars, wine, marigold 40.00
Stippled Acorns, candy dish, bl, w/lid, ftd 90.00
Stippled Rays (Northwood), compote, gr 60.00
Stork & Rushes (Dugan), basket, marigold, w/hdl 40.00
Stork & Rushes (Dugan), bowl, amethyst, 10" 29.00
Stork & Rushes (Dugan), cup, amethyst 35.00
Stork & Rushes (Dugan), punch bowl & base, bl, rare 235.00
Strawberry (Dugan), epergne, amethyst, rare 795.00
Strawberry Scroll (Fenton), pitcher, marigold, rare 1,800.00
Strawberry Spray, brooch, bl 170.00
Stream of Hearts (Fenton), bowl, bl, ftd, 10" 75.00
Summer Days (Dugan), vase, marigold, 6" 40.00
Sunflower (Millersburg), pin tray, gr, rare 275.00
Sunk Diamond Band (US Glass), pitcher, wht, rare 215.00
Sunk Diamond Band (US Glass), tumbler, marigold, rare 50.00
Sunray, compote, peach opal 45.00
Superb Drape (Northwood), vase, aqua opal, rare 2,000.00
Sweetheart (Cambridge), cookie jar, marigold, w/lid, rare . . .1,200.00
Swirl Hobnail (Millersburg), rose bowl, gr, rare 585.00
Swirl Variant (Imperial), cake plate, clear 75.00
Swirl Variant (Imperial), plate, gr, 6"-8¾", ea 50.00
Taffeta Lustre (Fostoria), candlestick, amethyst, rare, pr 300.00

Ten Mums (Fenton), tumbler, wht, scarce 280.00
Texas Headdress (Westmoreland), punch cup, marigold 40.00
Thin Rib & Drape (Fenton), vase, gr, 8"-14", ea 48.00
Thistle (Fenton), compote, bl 58.00
Thistle (Fenton), shade, marigold 40.00
Thistle & Thorn (English), bowl, marigold, ftd, 6" 46.00
Thistle & Thorn (English), plate, marigold, ftd, 8½" 130.00
Three Fruits (Northwood), bonbon, aqua opal, stemmed 700.00
Three Fruits (Northwood), bowl, aqua opal, 9" 500.00
Three Fruits (Northwood), plate, bl, 9" 135.00
Three-In-One (Imperial), rose bowl, marigold, rare 195.00
Tiny Hobnail, lamp, marigold 95.00
Toltec (McKee), pitcher, tankard; marigold, very rare 2,000.00
Top Hat, vase, pastel 45.00
Top O' the Morning, hatpin, amethyst 26.00
Tornado (Northwood), vase, gr, plain 395.00
Tree Bark (Imperial), candy jar, marigold 30.00
Tree Bark (Imperial), pickle jar, marigold, 7½" 35.00
Tree Bark (Imperial), pitcher, marigold, w/lid 70.00
Tree Bark (Imperial), tumbler, marigold, 2 sizes, ea 24.00
Tree of Life (Imperial), basket, marigold, w/hdl 30.00
Triands (English), celery vase, marigold 55.00
Tropicana (English), vase, marigold, rare 1,200.00
Twins (Imperial), bowl, pastel, 9" 42.00
Two Flowers (Fenton), bowl, gr, flat, 8" 48.00
Two Flowers (Fenton), plate, bl, ftd, 9" 550.00
Two Row (Imperial), vase, amethyst, rare 675.00
Umbrella Prisms, hatpin, amethyst, lg 30.00
Utility, lamp, marigold, complete, 8" 75.00
Vintage (Dugan), powder jar, amethyst 150.00
Vintage (Dugan), tray, dresser; marigold, 7x11" 78.00

Vintage (Fenton), bowl, bl, 6½" 42.00
Vintage (Fenton), punch bowl & base, gr 365.00
Virginia Blackberry (US Glass), pitcher, bl, rare, sm 225.00
Waffle Block (Imperial), basket, marigold, w/hdl, 10" 47.00
Water Lily (Fenton), bowl, pastel, ftd, 10" 67.00
Water Lily & Cattails (Fenton), bonbon, marigold 60.00
Water Lily & Cattails (Northwood), pitcher, marigold 285.00
Weeping Cherry (Dugan), bowl, peach opal, dome base 195.00
Western Thistle, tumbler, marigold, rare 235.00
Wheat (Northwood), bowl, amethyst, w/lid, rare 2,000.00
White Elephant, ornament, wht, rare 350.00
Wickerwork (English), bowl, marigold, w/base, complete 235.00
Wide Panel (Northwood-Fenton-Imperial), goblet, marigold . . .36.00
Wide Panel (Westmoreland), bowl, teal, 7½" 65.00
Wild Berry, jar, marigold, w/lid 75.00
Wild Loganberry (Westmoreland), goblet, peach opal 100.00
Wild Rose (Millersburg), lamp, gr, rare, sm 900.00
Wild Rose (Northwood), bowl, gr, flat, 8" 42.00
Wild Strawberry (Dugan), bowl, peach opal, rare, 6" 120.00
Windmill (Imperial), bowl, amethyst, 9" 37.00
Windmill (Imperial), pickle dish, gr .45.00

Windmill (Imperial), tumbler, gr 40.00
Wishbone (Imperial), flower arranger, marigold 85.00
Wishbone (Northwood), tumbler, amethyst, scarce 135.00
Wishbone & Spades (Dugan), bowl, amethyst, 5" 70.00
Woodpecker (Dugan), wall vase, vaseline 90.00
Wreath of Roses (Dugan), rose bowl, marigold 45.00
Wreath of Roses (Fenton), punch bowl & base, bl 375.00
Wreathed Cherry (Dugan), bowl, peach opal, oval, 10½" 375.00
Zig Zag (Millersburg), bowl, gr, 9½" 350.00
Zipper VT (English), Queen's vase, amethyst, rare 1,200.00
Zipper VT (English), sugar bowl, marigold 47.00
474 (Imperial), butter dish, amethyst 175.00
474 (Imperial), cup, gr 35.00
474 (Imperial), pitcher, milk; gr, scarce 475.00
474 (Imperial), punch bowl & base, gr 600.00
49'er (Imperial), decanter, marigold .125.00
49'er (Imperial), tumbler, marigold 75.00

Carousel Figures

Who can forget the dazzle of the merry-go-round — lights blinking, animals prancing proudly by to the waltzes that bellowed from the band organ . . .

Gustav Dentzel, a German woodworker, created one of the first carousels in America in 1867. By the turn of the century, his animals had evolved from horses with a military bearing to fanciful creatures in various postures with garlands of flowers, exotic saddles, and other adornment. Dentzel was followed in the business by his son William, and both are noted for the exacting perfection of their carving and painting. The Philadelphia Toboggan Company, established in 1903, is famous today for its superior chariot designs. In 1901 Marcus Charles Illions formed his company, M.C. Illions and Sons. Illions' carvings became more intricate with the growth of his company, and those from the twenties are generally valued more highly than those from between 1901 and 1910. The largest carousels were produced by the Artistic Carousel Manufacturers of Brooklyn, Harry Goldstein and Solomon Stein. Charles Carmel and Daniel Muller are both exquisite carvers whose work is today very highly regarded. Other builders whose works are also very valuable (though much less intricate) are The Herschell-Spillman Company; American Merry-Go-Round and Novelty Company; Charles Dare of the New York Carousel Manufacturing Company; and Charles Parker.

Until the 1930s, carousels were found in nearly every fair and amusement park in the country. One by one, as they fell into disrepair, many have been dismantled and junked or sold at auction. Today these hand-carved creatures are respected examples of American folk art and often bring prices well into the thousands. Price is based on a number of factors, the most important of which are: carver (with Dentzel, Looff, PTC, Carmel, Illions, and Muller the most valued), type of animal (some species are rarely encountered), and intricacy of carving. Also to be considered are size, wood and paint condition, where the figure was located on the carousel, whether it stands or jumps, and in some cases its age. Because there are so many factors to consider and since no two figures are identical, exact pricing is difficult. Condition can affect the price of an animal as much as $3,000 for the more elaborate pieces and up to 50% for the lower-priced animals.

Key:
IR — inside row
MR — middle row
OR — outside row
PP — park paint
SEC — Spillman Engineering Corp.
PR — paint removed
PTC — Philadelphia Tobaggan Company
MR — middle row
OR — outside row

Carmel/Borelli, outside row stander, tucked head, jewels, sword, and tassels, ca 1912, Coney Island Style, $11,000 at auction.

Allan Herschell, elephant OR stander, 1905, PP, 64x74" ..66,000.00
Anderson, dragon, 2-seater/mirror eye, early pnt 15,000.00
Armitage Herschell, IR jumper, jewels/Am shield, rstr 5,000.00
Bayol, jumper, folded mane/tail, 1900, PR 8,000.00
Carmel, jumper, bell at rear of saddle, PP, VG 10,000.00
Carmel, OR stander, ornate/jewels, 1908, PP, EX 11,000.00
Carmel, stander, head down, jeweled saddle, '08, PP, VG ..12,100.00
Carmel, stander, jeweled saddle, 1908, PP, EX 16,500.00
Carmel/Borelli, OR stander, allover jeweled/armor, PR 86,000.00
Carmel/Borelli, OR stander, armor/many jewels, 1908, rstr .61,000.00
Carmel/Borelli, OR stander, jewels/figure on side, PP 20,900.00
Carmel/Borelli, OR stander, jewels/sword on side, '08, PP ..16,000.00
Carmel/Borelli, OR stander, ornate/jewels, 1908, PP, VG ..22,500.00
Carmel/Borelli, stander, jewels, 1908, PP, rstr leg 14,000.00
Dare, elephant, orig had cloth saddle, ca 1870, early pnt 6,400.00
Dare, MR jumper, PP, 65" L, VG 4,000.00
Dentzel, goat, OR prancer, face on cantle, 1905, PP, VG ..34,000.00
Dentzel, jumper, 1908, PP, VG 8,500.00
Dentzel, lion, OR stander, leaf on side, 1905, PR 45,000.00
Dentzel, OR stander, jewels in brass rosettes, PP, EX 14,000.00
Dentzel, prancer, Indian head on saddle, 1905, VG 29,000.00
Dentzel, prancer, 1908, PP, 51x49", EX 9,500.00
Dentzel, reindeer, OR prancer, eagle cantle, 1905, PP, VG .25,000.00
Dentzel, tiger, OR stander, 1905, PP, VG 45,000.00
Dentzel, tiger, stander, ornate, pnt stripped to poor orig 76,000.00
Herschell-Spillman, MR jumper, jewels, rstr 6,000.00
Illions, IR stander, head down, ca 1908, PP, VG 7,000.00
Illions, MR stander, all 4 ft on ground, 1908, PP 6,600.00
Illions, OR stander, head down, tassels, 1908, PP, VG 14,000.00
Illions, OR stander, heavy armor, 1908, PP, VG 30,000.00
Loof, goat, OR prancer, tassels/rosettes/mirrors, 1895, EX ...9,000.00
Looff, att; lion, stander, frog on cantle, lg mane, PP, EX ...19,000.00
Looff, IR jumper, jeweled saddle, 1908, PP, EX 6,000.00
Looff, IR jumper, tassels/jewels, 1908, PP, EX 7,500.00
Looff, IR jumper, 1908, PP 6,600.00
Looff, MR jumper, jeweled saddle, 1908, PP, EX 7,000.00
Looff, OR prancer, dbl eagle saddle, PP, EX 6,500.00
Looff, OR stander, parrot saddle/checked blanket, PP, EX ..13,000.00

Looff/Borelli, lion, OR stander, 1908, PR, 81" L 40,000.00
Looff/Borelli, MR prancer, heavily jeweled, 1908, PP, EX ..11,000.00
Looff/Borelli, MR prancer, jeweled saddle/neck, 1908, PP ...7,500.00
Looff/Carmel, sea monster, PP, 1908, PP, EX 45,000.00
Muller, IR jumper, rosette cantle/flowing mane, PP, VG ...19,000.00
Muller, IR jumper, 1905, PP, VG 10,000.00
Muller, OR stander, saddle roll/canteen, 1905, PR 45,000.00
Muller, OR stander, saddle roll/gun, 1905, PR 55,000.00
Muller, OR stander, tassels/leaves, 1905, PP, 61x61", VG ..47,000.00
Muller, OR stander, 1905, PP, VG 39,000.00
Muller, OR stander, 1905, PP, 65x61", VG 46,000.00
Muller, OR stander, 1905, PR, 65x61" 49,000.00
Parker, MR jumper, armor/jewels/Am shield on front, rstr ..15,000.00
Parker, MR jumper, flag on side/rose cantle/jewels, rstr 11,000.00
Parker, MR jumper, jewels/genie cantle/glass eyes, rstr 7,000.00
Parker, MR jumper, mirror/jewels/dogs on cantle, rstr 10,000.00
PTC, camel, MR stander, EX detail, 1905, EX 4,000.00
PTC, cat, primitive, metal hdl, 1910, 17x36" 3,000.00
PTC, deer, OR stander, EX detail/genuine rack, 1905, PR ...15,000.00
PTC, IR jumper, intricate mane/layered trappings, 1905, EX .4,000.00
PTC, OR stander, EX trappings/layered mane, 1915, rstr ...15,000.00
PTC, OR stander, Muller style, 1905, rpl ears/PR 12,000.00
PTC, zebra, MR stander, layered trappings/tassel, 1905 .....6,000.00
Savage, cockerel, running, 2-seater, EX cvg, 1900, 45x64" ...4,250.00
Stein-Goldstein, IR jumper, feathers, hair tail, 1905, PR ...15,000.00
Stein-Goldstein, IR jumper, 1905, PP, G 8,200.00
Stein-Goldstein, IR jumper, 1905, PP, VG 10,500.00
Stein-Goldstein, IR jumper, 1905, PR 13,000.00
Stein-Goldstein, MR jumper, armored blanket, 1905, PR ..17,000.00
Stein-Goldstein, MR jumper, feathers, hair tail, PP, VG ...10,000.00
Stein-Goldstein, MR jumper, fine trappings, '05, PP, VG ..21,000.00
Stein-Goldstein, MR jumper, tassel/feathers, 1905, PR 17,000.00
Stein-Goldstein, MR jumper, 1905, PP, VG 11,500.00
Stein-Goldstein, MR jumper, 1905, PR 13,200.00

Carpet Balls

Carpet balls are glazed china spheres decorated with intersecting lines or other simple designs, that were used for indoor games in the British Isles during the early 1800s. Mint condition examples are rare; listings are for those with minimal damage.

Dk gr, emb Henselite Indoor 35.00
Pk, wht irregular ovals w/wht marks between, 3¼", NM 85.00
Purple w/wht polka dots, 3" NM 95.00
Wht w/gr & rose sponging, 3⅜", NM 120.00
Yel w/yel dots w/in wht circles, frilled rim, 3" 50.00

Cartoon Art

Collectors of cartoon art are interested in many forms of original art — animation cels, sports, political or editorial cartoons, syndicated comic strip panels, and caricature. To produce even a short animated cartoon strip, hundreds of original drawings are required, each showing the characters in slightly advancing positions. Called 'cels' because those made prior to the 1950s were made from a celluloid material, collectors often pay hundreds of dollars for a frame from a favorite movie. Prices of Disney cels with backgrounds vary widely. Background paintings, model sheets, storyboards, and preliminary sketches are also collectible — so are comic book drawings executed in India ink and signed by the artist. Daily 'funnies' originals, especially the earlier ones portraying super heroes, and Sunday comic strips, the early as well as the later ones, are collected. Cartoon art has become recognized and valued as a novel yet valid form of contemporary art.

Our advisor for this category is Bob Cook of Geppi's Comic World, Inc.; he is listed in our Directory under Maryland.

Betty Boop — Santa's Helper, airbrush and water-color, by Leslie Cabarga, 14x13", $1,300.00.

Animation Cel-Full Color

Dr Smuggles, witch w/blindfold, mouse in gown, 4x6" 75.00
First Aiders, Pluto in splints, Disney, 7x9" 500.00
Lady & the Tramp, pup pulls scotty's sweater, 1955, 9x12" ..1,100.00
Pete's Dragon, Elliot the Dragon in closeup, Disney, 11x15" . . .325.00
Snow White & 7 Dwarfs, Grumpy portrait, Disney, '39, 4½x4" ..900.00

Animation Drawing

Andy Gump w/champagne glass, Sydney Smith, 1913 . . . . .95.00
Autograph Hound, Donald Duck seated, pencil, 1939, 3x3½" . . .45.00
Bambi w/mother, heavy forest bkground, pencil, 1940, 12x35" .150.00
Felix the Cat, pen & ink for comic book, 1950s, full pg 125.00
Lady & Tramp, Tramp standing, mc pencil, 1955, 3½x5" 55.00
Pinocchio, sprouting donkey ears, pencil, 1940, 4½x4½" 700.00
Shattered Goddess, wizard/demons, ink, Fabian, 1983, 7x11" ..100.00
Snow White & 7 Dwarfs, Grumpy, pencil, 1937, 4½x5" 325.00
Steamboat Willie, Mickey w/drumsticks, 1928, 9x12" 950.00

Daily Newspaper Comic Strip

Happy Hooligan, Frederick Opper, 1924, 5¼x20¾" 250.00
Nancy & Slugo, Bushmiller, 1968, 6x20" 85.00
Peanuts, Lucy, & Snoopy; sgn Carl Schults, 1986, 5x21" 450.00
Ripley's Believe It or Not, King Features, 1961, 14x11" 75.00
Sam's Strip, Dumas, 1962, 6x20" 60.00
Toonerville Trolley, Fontaine Fox, fr, early, 12x10¼" 275.00

Storyboard

Bambi meets grasshopper, graphite, 1942, 9½x12" 800.00
Counterfeit Cat, Tex Avery, red/blk pencil, 1949, set of 3 . . . .60.00
Donald Duck as farmer, pastels, 1942, 8x8½" 550.00
Fantasia, dancing flower, mc pencils, 1940, 2½x6" 65.00
Fantasia, Mickey Mouse as sorcerer's apprentice, 1940, 4x6". 3,700.00

Mickey Mouse, 3 figures, Disney, 1930s, 9x11½" 85.00
Song of South, Brer Rabbit, crayon, 1946, 4x5½" 30.00
Three Little Pigs, practical pig, pencil, 1933, 2½x5" 95.00
Victory Through Air Power, aircraft, Disney, 1943, 5½x7" 45.00

Sunday Newspaper Comics

Blondie, Dagwood, & Baby Dumpling; CYoung, 1940, 14x17" ..275.00
Dick Tracy, Chester Gould, 1971, 23½x19½" 600.00
Hagar the Horrible, Dick Browne, 1983, 10x15" 225.00
Lil Abner, Daisy Mae working, Al Capp, 1950, full pg 175.00
Prince Valiant, Hal Foster, 1962, 33½x22½" 1,300.00
Terry & Pirates, George Wunder, 1970, 17x25" 165.00

Cartoon Books

'Books of cartoons' were printed during the first decade of the twentieth century and remained popular until the advent of the modern comic book in the late thirties. Cartoon books, printed in both color and black and white, were merely reprints of current newspaper comic strips. The books, ranging from thirty to seventy pages and in sizes from 3½" x 8" up to 11" x 17", were usually bound with cardboard covers and were often distributed as premiums in exchange for coupons saved from the daily paper. One of the largest of the companies who printed these books was Cupples and Leon, producer of nearly half of the two hundred titles on record. Among the most popular sellers were Mutt and Jeff, Bringing Up Father, and Little Orphan Annie.

Our advisor for this category is Bob Cook of Geppi's Comic World, Inc.; he is listed in our Directory under Maryland.

Barney Google & Spark Plug, Vol #2, 1924 . . . . .35.00
Bringing Up Father, 1st series, EX 60.00
Bringing Up Father, 2nd series, NM .60.00
Bringing Up Father, 3rd series, EX 45.00
Keeping Up w/Joneses, 1st series, NM 50.00
Keeping Up w/Joneses, 2nd series, EX 35.00
Moon Mullins, Willard, Cupples & Leon, 1925, EX 55.00
Mutt & Jeff, #4, EX 75.00

Mutt and Jeff, #6, EX, $45.00.

Peter Arno's Circus, 1931, in orig box 20.00
Toonerville Trolley, 1st series, Cupples & Leon, 1921, EX 25.00

When a Feller Needs a Friend, Clare Briggs, 1920s, 8x9", EX ...**25.00**

Cash Registers

Cash registers are being restored, rebuilt, and used as they were originally intended, in businesses ranging from eating establishments to antique stores. Their brass and marble construction has made them almost impervious to aging, and with just a bit of polish and shine they bring a bit of the grand Victorian era into modern times.

Antique cash registers are categorized as either restored or unrestored. A restored register is one where the cabinet has been stripped, polished, and lacquered; indicators are free of dust, dirt, and visible signs of wear; key stems are rust-free, plated or painted; and key checks and rings are new, used, or originals. The drawer has been stripped and revarnished, and the rails are in good condition. All mechanisms are completely reworked; broken parts are replaced, oiled, and working perfectly. Prices for registers in unrestored condition vary greatly. Unrestored registers are classed as either working or non-working. Values for those with missing major parts are much lower. In the listings that follow, M condition refers to fully-restored cash registers; VG condition is for registers in original unrestored working condition. For further information we recommend the highly-informative book *Antique Brass Cash Registers 1880 - 1920*, by Bartsch and Sanchez. Mr. Bartsch's address may be found in our Directory under Oregon.

American, 50-key register, copper plated, 212-lb, M **1,800.00**
American, 50-key register, copper plated, 212-lb, VG **900.00**
Michigan #1, 22-key, M **500.00**
Michigan #1, 22-key, VG **200.00**
Michigan #7, 9-key, M **750.00**
Michigan #7, 9-key, VG **450.00**
NCR #1000 class, autographic box attachment, 1910, M **1,200.00**
NCR #1000 class, autographic box attachment, 1910, VG **600.00**
NCR #13, nickeled CI, ionic pattern, continuous cap, M ...**1,000.00**

National Cash Register Co., Model #317, registers to $1.00, VG, $700.00.

NCR #13, nickeled CI, ionic pattern, continuous cap, VG **600.00**
NCR #210 or #211, 11-key, fleur-de-lis pattern, M, ea **1,400.00**
NCR #210 or #211, 11-key, fleur-de-lis pattern, VG, ea **800.00**
NCR #226, 5¢-$1.00 keys, unplated bronze, M **1,000.00**
NCR #226, 5¢-$1.00 keys, unplated bronze, VG **500.00**

NCR #312 or #313, dolphin pattern, 1902-1916, M, ea **1,000.00**
NCR #312 or #313, dolphin pattern, 1902-1916, VG, ea **700.00**
NCR #322, 15-key, extended base, M **1,600.00**
NCR #322, 15-key, extended base, VG **900.00**
NCR #332 or #333, dolphin pattern, M, ea **900.00**
NCR #332 or #333, dolphin pattern, VG, ea **400.00**
NCR #349-2-2, 2-counter, 2-drw, 1910, M **1,800.00**
NCR #349-2-2, 2-counter, 2-drw, 1910, VG **800.00**
NCR #360 to #367, 37-key, personalized top sign, M, ea **950.00**
NCR #360 to #367, 37-key, personalized top sign, VG, ea **600.00**
NCR #4, 40-key 'Signature Model,' 1892, M **2,500.00**
NCR #4, 40-key 'Signature Model,' 1892, VG **1,000.00**
NCR #444, check-numbering device, 1910, M **1,200.00**
NCR #444, check-numbering device, 1910, VG **700.00**
NCR #522 Class, 2-drw, requires electricity, 1906, M **2,400.00**
NCR #522 Class, 2-drw, requires electricity, 1906, VG **1,500.00**
NCR #593-E-L, 9-drw, floor cabinet, 460+ lbs, 67¾", M **5,000.00**
NCR #593-E-L, 9-drw, floor cabinet, 460+ lbs, 67¾", VG ...**2,500.00**
NCR #71 to #99½, 79 Principle, 1892 scroll pattern, M, ea ..**1,800.00**
NCR #71 to #99½, 79 Principle, 1892 scroll pattern, VG, ea ..**900.00**
Peninsula, Muren, nickel plated, ca 1912, M **500.00**
Peninsula, Muren, nickel plated, ca 1912, VG **200.00**

Cast Iron

In the mid-1800s, the cast iron industry was raging in the United States. It was recognized as a medium extremely adaptable for uses ranging from ornamental architectural filigree to actual building construction. It could be cast from a mold into any conceivable design that could be reproduced over and over at a relatively small cost. It could be painted to give an entirely versatile appearance. Furniture with openwork designs of grapevines and leaves and intricate lacy scrollwork was cast for gardens as well as inside use. Figural doorstops of every sort, bootjacks, trivets, and a host of other useful and decorative items were made before the 'ferromania' had run its course. See also Kitchen, Cast Iron Bakers and Kettles; and other specific categories.

Architectural pc, eagle, 3-pc casting, wood base, 31" W **375.00**
Architectural pc, eagle on branch, wings wide, 1890s, 10x25" .**225.00**
Architectural pc, eagle w/wings wide, EX details pnt, 16" W ...**185.00**
Architectural pc, lion's head, 1800s, 7x3x7" **110.00**
Birdbath, Victorian, int rust **400.00**
Birdhouse, wasp nest form, RC Reeves, c 1925, EX **185.00**
Bowl, 3 legs, 1700s, 8¾" dia **120.00**
Checkwriter, Royal Rouss, pat 1898, 5" dia **58.00**
Cork press, ornate, hinged, 2-part **60.00**
Dipper, wrought ferrule, wood hdl, mk S&T, 5" dia, 19" L **17.50**
Doe, standing, Whitman MA foundry, ca 1880, 54" **6,500.00**
Dove, 3-D, solid, hanging, 11" **1,600.00**
Foot rest, shoeshine; camel form, chrome plated, 8x8x3½" **85.00**
Foot rest, shoeshine; horse base, 6½" **50.00**
Hitching post, horse head, 3 lion's heads in post, 70", VG **280.00**
Hitching post, horse head silhouette, emb mane, 54", pr, EX .**1,300.00**
Hitching post, sm Blk boy stands on cotton bale, Fiske, 45" ..**1,400.00**
Lamppost finial, pineapple form, urn-form base, pnt, 20" **145.00**
Lawn sprinkler, alligator form, EX **135.00**
Lawn sprinkler, Nat'l Walking, EX **185.00**
Mailbox, pat 1909, EX **45.00**
Meat hook, w/2 pig figures, early, 5x2" **900.00**
Nail holder, cobbler's bench, lazy susan type, Griswold, EX ...**225.00**
Plate, pitted, 9½" **100.00**
Plate, 1700s, 7¾" **130.00**

Posnet pot, 6¼" dia, 6" hdl 50.00
Pot, twisted wrought bail, bulbous w/hdls & 3 tall ft, 14" 1,600.00
Rabbit, att Fiske, 11x10", pr 500.00
Rabbit, worn wht pnt, ca 1900, 12x11x6" 175.00
Rosette cookie maker, card suits, ca 1900, set of 4 . . . . .75.00
Settee, fern mold, rpt, minor breaks, 1850s, 56" 2,600.00
Settee, foliage scrolls/urn & garland detail, pnt, 38" 550.00
Settee, Gothic arch/floral, label: Kramer Bros, 44", VG 425.00
Shelf, openwork vines, wall hanging, pat 1868, 9x14x7" 110.00
Spittoon, Griswold 1,200.00
Stag, standing, mold by M Mansbach, ca 1880, 63" 7,250.00
Stag, worn orig pnt, welded rpr, vacant eye sockets, 18" 195.00
Stove plate, foliage/figures/words/1700s date, 23x21", VG 155.00
Stove-pipe plate, Adams, 1897, 15¾" dia 45.00
Teakettle, gooseneck spout, stationary bail, 7½x8½" 220.00
Umbrella stand, EX floral detail on center std, rpt, 27" 100.00
Umbrella stand, 3-D terrier on base, old rpt, 24½" 150.00
Urn, ftd, rpt, 12", pr 125.00

Urn on reticulated standard, ca 1875, 33", $300.00.

Wall pocket, hunters w/bag of game, ca 1890, 11x5x1½" 125.00
Wick trimmers, scissors shape, ca 1870 . . . . .35.00
Wig curler, scissors shape, ca 1800, 10" 75.00

Castor Sets

Castor sets became popular during the early years of the eighteenth century and continued to be used through the late Victorian era. Their purpose was to hold various condiments for table use. The most common type was a circular arrangement with a center handle on a revolving pedestal base that held three, four, five, or six bottles. Some had extras; a few were equipped with a bell for calling the servant. Frames were made of silverplate, glass, or pewter. Though most bottles were of pressed glass, some of the designs were cut; and occasionally colored glass with enameled decorations was used. To maintain authenticity and value, castor sets

should have matching bottles. Prices listed below are for those with matching bottles and in frames with plating that is in excellent condition (unless noted otherwise).

Watch for new frames and bottles in both clear and colored glass—these have recently been appearing on the market.

George III silver cruet stand by Paul Storr, London, 1810, with 6 cut crystal bottles, 12", $5,000.00.

3-bottle, Invt T'print, ruby stain; orig fr 175.00
4-bottle, Cape Cod, EX 47.00
4-bottle, Emblem; plated wht metal holder, miniature, 8½" . . .150.00
5-bottle, American Shield, pewter lids; orig 10" fr, child's 195.00
5-bottle, Bellflower; pewter fr, rpl period stoppers, 11" 275.00
5-bottle, Daisy & Button, clear/bl/amber bottles; glass fr 195.00
5-bottle, etched; Japanese-motif SP fr, bird at top 225.00
6-bottle, cut crystal; Paul Storr armorial fr, 1810, 12" 5,000.00
6-bottle, cut crystal; Victorian bamboo-emb SP fr, 17" 250.00
6-bottle, Daisy & Button, 19" rstr Meriden fr, w/florals 495.00
6-bottle, dmn/panel cutting; 3 ball ft, loop hdl, 11" 200.00
6-bottle, eng decor; tiered Simpson-Hall-Miller fr revolves 165.00
6-bottle, etched decor; Rogers rstr SP frame revolves, 19" 295.00
6-bottle, wreath cut/dots; rstr SP fr revolves, w/bell, 19" 395.00
7-bottle, wreath cut; 22" fr revolves, very ornate/openwork 600.00

Catalina Island

Catalina Island pottery was made on the island of the same name, which is about twenty-six miles off the coast of Los Angeles. The pottery was started in 1927 at Pebbly Beach, by Wm Wrigley, Jr., who was instrumental in developing and using the native clays. Its principal products were brick and tile to be used for construction on the island. Garden pieces were first produced, then vases, bookends, lamps, ash trays, novelty items, and finally dinnerware. The ware became very popular and was soon being shipped to the mainland as well.

Some of the pottery was hand thrown; some was made in molds. Most pieces are marked Catalina Island or Catalina with a printed incised stamp, or handwritten with a pointed tool. Cast items were sometimes marked in the mold; a paper label was also used.

The color of the clay can help to identify approximately when a piece was made: 1927 to 1932 — brown to red clay; 1931 to 1932 — an experimental period with various colors; 1932 to 1937 — mainly white clay, but tan to brown were also used on occasion.

After 1937 Catalina was sold to Gladding McBean (makers of Franciscan Ware) of Los Angeles, California. After the move to the mainland, all pieces were marked Catalina Pottery or Catalina Rancho. Although the clay, glazes, and ware in general are of much better quality, the Island ware still commands slightly higher prices because of its scarcity and method of production.

Dinnerware

Catalina Island, bowl, berry	18.00
Catalina Island, carafe, yel gloss	42.00
Catalina Island, cup & saucer	35.00
Catalina Island, custard cup	20.00
Catalina Island, plate, bread & butter; rimmed, 6½"	10.00
Catalina Island, plate, dinner; 10"	15.00
Catalina Island, plate, dinner; 11"	20.00
Catalina Island, plate, luncheon; 8"	10.00
Catalina Island, sugar bowl	18.00
Catalina Island, tumbler, lg	18.00
Catalina Island, wine cup, hdld	12.50
Rope Edge, cup	20.00
Rope Edge, plate, bread & butter	10.00
Rope Edge, plate, chop; 12"	60.00
Rope Edge, plate, dinner	20.00
Rope Edge, saucer	10.00
Rope Edge, service for 8	650.00

Miscellaneous

Ash tray, sq	35.00
Candelabrum, 3-holed, half-circle	95.00
Candelabrum, 3-holed, straight	100.00
Cigarette box, horse's head	105.00
Crane, flower frog	75.00
Vinegar bottle, gourd-shape	75.00

Catalogs

Catalogs are not only intriguing to collect on their own merit, but for the collector with a specific interest, they are often the only remaining source of background information available, and as such they offer a wealth of otherwise unrecorded data. The mail-order industry can be traced as far back as the mid-1800s. Even before Aaron Montgomery Ward began his career in 1872, Laacke and Joys of Wisconsin and the Orvis Company of Vermont, both dealers in sporting goods, had been well established for many years. The E.C. Allen Company sold household necessities and novelties by mail on a broad scale in the 1870s. By the end of the Civil War, sewing machines, garden seed, musical instruments — even medicine — were available from catalogs. In the 1880s, Macy's of New York issued a 127-page catalog; Sears and Spiegel followed suit in about 1890. Craft and art supply catalogs were first available about 1880 and covered such varied fields as china painting, stenciling, wood burning, brass embossing, hair weaving, and shellcraft. Today, some collectors confine their interests not only to craft catalogs in general, but often to one subject only. Examples may range from $1 to as much as $25 for the larger, color-illustrated versions.

Aladdin Homes, hardbound, 1916, 116-pg	30.00
American Radiators, 1920, 16-pg	7.00
Bannerman Military Goods, 1931, EX	65.00
Bugbees Minstrel Show Accessories, NY, 1930s, 24-pg, 5x7"	25.00
Burkhard's Guns, 1928, 54-pg	30.00
Butler Brothers, Spring, 1907, 372-pg	35.00
C Taylor, silverware, Philadelphia, 1922, 32-pg, 10x13"	20.00
Carlisle & Finch, toys/electric auto, 1901, 63-pg, VG	100.00
Charles & Co, food/tobacco/liqueur, hardbound, '30, 385-pg	40.00
Coleman Quicklite, lamps & lanterns, 63-pg, 8x10½"	50.00
Conn Musical Truth, 1934, EX	20.00
Conn Saxophones, ca 1925, EX	30.00
Crawford Bikes, 1897	50.00
Detroit Vet Supplies, 1912, 278-pg, 6x9"	35.00
Dietz-Ignatius, rolltop & cylinder desks, 1886, 22-pg, EX	40.00
Dodge Brothers, auto parts, bound, 1922, NM	35.00
Dunn, Foster, & Co; soda counter goods, 1908, 36-pg, M	40.00
Enterprise, coffee mills/meat grinders/etc, 1899, 109-pg	35.00
Eugene Dietzgen, drawing/surveying instruments, 1912, 555-pg	45.00
Felkner Bros Oil Equipment, 1932, 47-pg	13.00
Furst, ornamental clocks, Baltimore, 1893, 95-pg, 9x11"	50.00
Gilchrist, fountain equipment, 1916, EX	45.00
Goetze-Niemer Standard Surgical Instruments, 416-pg, 1922	110.00
Gregg-Seager, horseshoer's supplies, leather bound, '03	85.00
Grocer's Criterion, Hoyt Co, 53-pg	15.00
Harrington Arms #27, 1938, 28-pg	25.00
Harrison Wholesale Co, 1933, 100-pg	25.00
Heiser Holster #19, EX	55.00
Helin Tackle Co, The Flatfish, 24-pg, 1942, EX	10.00
Hepburn Boat & Oar Co, 1895, 72-pg	60.00
Hubley, automotive toys, w/prices, color, 1932, 40-pg, NM	600.00
Hundley Dry Goods, textiles, MO, 1910, EX	75.00
Hunt & Moffet, sporting goods/tools/supplies, 1926, 1004-pg	85.00
International Harvester Cream Separators, 1939	5.00
J&E Stevens, toy guns/banks/etc, w/prices, 1928, 20-pg, EX	160.00
Kalamazoo Stoves & Ranges, 1928-1929, 89-pg, VG	10.00
Karpen, fiber rush furniture, lg format, early 1900s, 75-pg	135.00
Keystone Ride-Em Toys, color, 1925, 31-pg, VG	350.00
Kipp Bros, children's vehicles, 1890, 11-pg, lg format, EX	85.00
Kipp Bros, toy jobber's, Christmas cover, 1927, 23-pg, VG	275.00
Lafayette Radio, 1940, 120-pg	20.00
Larkin Premium Products, toys & instruments, 1913, 159-pg	35.00
Lindeman Pianos, 1907, 16-pg, 3¼x6¼"	15.00
Lionel Trains, full color, 1921, 51-pg, VG	50.00
Lipscomb, hunting/fishing/tools, Nashville, 1913, 1019-pg	85.00
Lynn Illustrated Novelties, 1910, 10-pg, VG	12.50
Metz, millwork, color section, Dubuque IA, 1913-14, EX	75.00
Miller Toy Rubber Balls, 1920s, EX	27.50
MK Brody Carnival Goods, 1931, 192-pg, 6x9"	40.00
Montgomery Ward, fall/winter, 1881	40.00
Montgomery Ward, fall/winter, 1926-1927	30.00
Motorcycle Acessories #16, 1920s, 128-pg	20.00
Myers Farm Tools, OH, 1895, 120-pg, 6x9"	35.00
Nat'l Cloak, 1912, 200-pg, 7½x10"	25.00
Nat'l Cloak & Suit, 1911, 228-pg	30.00
Nickols, Shepard, & Co; vibrator threshers, 1877, 6½x9½"	60.00
Oregon Artificial Limbs, ca 1912, EX	15.00
Otto Young, watches & jewelry, 1902, 575-pg	100.00
Paine Doors, 1924, 55-pg	12.00
Peg Lock Block Co, model construction, 1917, EX	30.00
Radiant Home Stoves, 1920, 138-pg	18.00
Remington Firearms, 1941, 19-pg	25.00
Rhode-Spencer Wholesale Jewelry, 1925, 224-pg	50.00
Schott & Co, toys/games/dolls, 1898, 112-pg, EX	250.00
Schwabacher Hardware, Tacoma WA, 1924, 1246-pg, EX	100.00
Scott Radios, 1934, w/advertising booklet	60.00
Sears, 1910	75.00
Sears Tire & Auto Supply, ca 1922, EX	20.00
Sedgewick, elevators & dumbwaiters, 32-pg, 9x11"	25.00

Skinner & Steenman, sideboards & buffets, 1904, 48-pg 20.00
Steelcraft, pedal vehicles, full color, 1921, 40-pg, VG 425.00
Steelcraft, pedal vehicles, full color, 1933, 40-pg, EX 375.00
Stockman-Farmer, cowboy items, 1930s, EX 17.00
Sweet's Architectural, lists bldg catalogs, '30, 1278-pg 25.00
Sweet's Engineering, 2nd edition, hardbound, 1915, 823-pg ...125.00
Taylor, trapping supplies, St Louis MO, 1919 ....40.00
Thomas Register of American Manufacturers, 1937, 5200-pg ...50.00
Tootle-Campbell Dry Goods, household & clothing, 1910, EX ..85.00
Torrey Razors, Stichter Hardware of PA, 35-pg, EX 48.00
Union Fork & Hoe, 1928, 112-pg 5.00
Wedell, women's fashions, 1916, 102-pg 30.00
Wurlitzer Musical Instruments, color illus, #80, 1912 ....150.00

Caughley Ware

The Caughley Coalport Porcelain Manufactory operated from
about 1775 until 1799 in Caughley, near Salop, Shropshire, in England.
The owner was Thomas Turner, who gained his potting experience from
his association with the Worcester Pottery Company. The wares he
manufactured in Caughley are referred to as 'Salopian.' He is most
famous for his blue-printed earthenwares, particularly the Blue Willow
pattern, designed for him by Thomas Minton. For a more detailed
history, see Coalport.

Cup & saucer, acorns/leaves, mc/brn transfer, mk, NM 145.00
Cup & saucer, chinoiserie, 1750s, mk, M 170.00
Cup & saucer, man/cow/sheep, mc/brn transfer, mk 70.00
Cup & saucer, mc HP stylized flowers, vine band, mk 90.00
Cup & saucer, roses, mc/brn transfer, mk, EX 80.00
Sauce dish, house/people, mc/brn transfer, mk, 4½" 45.00
Sugar bowl, deer, w/lid, mk 375.00

Ceramic Art Company

Jonathan Coxon, Sr., and Walter Scott Lenox established the Ceramic Art Company in 1889 in Trenton, New Jersey, where they produced
fine belleek porcelain. Both were experienced in its production, having
previously worked for Ott and Brewer. They hired artists to hand paint their
wares with portraits, scenes, and lovely florals. Today, artist-signed examples bring the highest prices. Several marks were used, three of which
contain the 'CAC' monogram. A green wreath surrounding the company
name in full was used on special-order wares, but these are not often
encountered. Coxon eventually left the company, and it was later reorganized under the Lenox name. See also Lenox.

Our advisor for this category is Mary Frank Gaston; she is listed in the
Directory under Texas.

Box, floral, pk w/gold, rnd, mk 95.00
Box, trinket; lav Delft-style scene, artist sgn, mk, 5¼" 185.00
Creamer & sugar bowl, floral, gold on ivory, palette mk 120.00
Cup & saucer, demi; gr, flower garland int, in sterling fr, mk ...145.00
Mug, monk holds open box on brn, gr mk, 5¾" 85.00
Pitcher, cider; grapes, 3-color, palette mk 150.00
Pitcher, lemonade; roses, red on gr, sgn Durr, 5½" 135.00
Pitcher, tankard; grapes, 3-color, palette mk, 14" 275.00
Stein, monk scene, silver trim on lid, brn mk, 7½" 650.00
Vase, mums, purple/pk/yel on blended ground, CAC, 10x4" ...235.00
Vase, poppies, gold on gr, baluster form, mk, 12" 115.00
Vase, roses w/gold, ovoid w/ped base, hdls, 15" 365.00
Vase, spider mums, mc on shaded, bulbous, mk, ca 1889, 10" ..235.00
Vase, spider mums, pk & yel on purple, ca 1910, 10¼" 200.00

Vase, portrait of a lady, signed
Sandlers, 8", $145.00.

Ceramic Arts Studio, Madison

The Ceramic Arts Studio Company began operations sometime prior
to the 1940s; but it was about then that Betty Harrington started marketing
her goods through this company. Betty Harrington is the designer primarily
responsible for creating the line of figurines and knick-knacks that have
recently become so popular with collectors. There were two others — Ulli
Rebus, who designed several of the animals; and Ruth Planter, who worked
there for only a short time. About 65% of these items are marked, but even
unmarked items become easily recognizable after only a brief study of their
distinctive styling and glaze colors. Those that are marked carry either the
black ink stamp or the incised mark: 'Ceramic Arts Studio, Madison,
Wisc.'; a paper sticker was also used.

After the 1955 demise of the company in Madison, the owner (Ruben
Sand) went to Japan where he continued production under the same name
using many of the same molds. After a short time, the old molds were retired
and new and quite different items were produced. All of the Japan pieces
can be found with a Ceramic Arts Studio backstamp. The Japan identification was on a paper label and is often missing. Japan pieces are never
marked Madison, Wisc., but not all Madison pieces are either. Red or blue
backstamps are exclusively Japanese.

Another company that also produced figurines operated at about the
same time as the Madison studio. It was called Ceramic Art (no 's') Studio;
do not confuse the two.

A second and larger building in the C.A.S. complex in Madison was
for the exclusive production of metal accessories. The creator and designer
of this related line was Zona Liberace, Liberace's stepmother. These pieces
are rising fast in value and because they weren't marked can sometimes be
found at bargain prices. They were so popular that other ceramic companes
bought them to complement their lines as well, so they may also be found
with marks other than C.A.S.'s.

Our advisor for this category is Dan Fortney; he is listed in the
Directory under Wisconsin. For those seeking additional information, a
price guide and accompanying video tapes (Series 1 and 2) are available
from the author, BA Wellman, whose address can be found under Massachusetts. Mr. Wellman will also send a series of articles written for *The Daze*
to those who will include a large SASE with their requests.

Ash tray, hippo, 3½" 36.00
Bank, Paisley Pig, 3" 48.00
Bank, Tony, razor disposal, 4¾" 40.00

Bowl, Bonita	28.00
Bowl, scalloped, oval, 3½"	15.00
Candle holder, Bedtime Boy & Girl, 4¾", pr	45.00
Candle holder/vase, Hear/See/Speak No Evil, cherub, ea	25.00
Figurine, accordion boy, rare, 5"	35.00
Figurine, Alice, 4½"	65.00
Figurine, Archibald the Dragon, 8"	95.00
Figurine, Bali Gong, 5½"	35.00
Figurine, birchbark canoe, 8" L	32.00
Figurine, Black Sambo, 3½"	48.00
Figurine, cellist, pk, #478, 6½"	95.00
Figurine, Cinderella & Prince Charming, pr	125.00
Figurine, Col Jackson, Southern gentleman	35.00
Figurine, colts, Balky & Frisky, 3¾", pr	35.00
Figurine, Dawn, lav, #468, 6½"	48.00
Figurine, Dutch Love girl	45.00
Figurine, Egyptian man & woman, pr	120.00
Figurine, En Repose, gr dress, 4¾"	22.00
Figurine, Encore man & lady, 8¾" & 8¼", pr	75.00
Figurine, Lady Rowena on horsebk, 8¼"	75.00
Figurine, Little Bo Peep, 5¾"	22.00
Figurine, Little Boy Blue, 5¼"	25.00
Figurine, Lu Tang	25.00
Figurine, Madonna w/book, 9½"	50.00
Figurine, pekingese, 3"	20.00
Figurine, Peter Pan & Wendy, on base, pr	65.00
Figurine, Pixie on snail, 2¾"	17.50
Figurine, Polish boy & girl, 6¾" & 6", pr	35.00
Figurine, Rhumba couple, pr, ea	38.00
Figurine, rooster, pk & blk, B-481, 7"	45.00
Figurine, saxaphone boy, 5¼"	28.00
Figurine, Singing & Praying, angel group, ea	25.00
Figurine, Summer Bell, dinner bell, 5¼"	65.00
Figurine, Summer Sally, 3½"	45.00
Figurine, Swedish couple, dancing, lg, 7", pr	75.00
Figurine, Thunder, fighting stallion, 5½"	35.00
Figurine, violin lady, standing	45.00
Figurine, Winter Willie	28.00
Jug, ballerina, ewer form, 2"	20.00
Jug, Miss Forward, rare, 4"	35.00
Jug, rose motif, 2¾"	20.00
Lamp, Chinese lantern figure	125.00
Planter, Lorelei on seashell, 6"	45.00

Planter, rectangle, 3"	12.50
Planter, Svea & Sven, 6½", pr	65.00
Plaque, African man & woman, rare, 8", pr	165.00
Plaque, Attitude & Arabesque, red, pr	55.00
Plaque, Chinese Lantern man & woman, 8", pr	65.00
Plaque, Harlequin & Columbine, chartreuse, 8", pr	70.00
Plaque, Mary Contrary, rare, 5"	50.00
Plaque, Shadow Dancers, 7", pr	65.00
Plaque, Zor & Zorina, pr	45.00
Sauce boat, Jasperware, emb horse, miniature, 2"	20.00
Shakers, bear mother & baby, brn, pr	25.00
Shakers, chair & little boy, pr	25.00
Shakers, Chirp & Twirp, pr	28.00
Shakers, deer & doe, stylized, 3¾", pr	45.00
Shakers, Dem & Rep, donkey & elephant, rare, 4½", pr	25.00
Shakers, fighting cocks, pr	28.00
Shakers, fish stands on tail, 4", pr	22.00
Shakers, frog & toadstool, 2" & 3", pr	25.00
Shakers, kangaroo mother & baby, pr	35.00
Shakers, monkey mother & baby, pr	28.00
Shakers, Mr & Mrs Penquin, pr	25.00
Shakers, oxen & covered wagon, 3", pr	28.00
Shakers, polar bear & cub, pr	30.00
Shakers, rabbit mother & baby, pr	30.00
Shakers, skunk mother & baby, pr	35.00
Shelf sitter, Chinese boy & girl, pr	35.00
Shelf sitter, cowboy & cow girl, 4¾", pr	35.00
Shelf sitter, Cubist puma	20.00
Shelf sitter, En Pose & En Repose, ballerinas, 4½", pr	45.00
Shelf sitter, Fluffy & Tuffy, 4½", pr	30.00
Shelf sitter, Gay '90s couple, 6½ & 6¾", pr	45.00
Shelf sitter, girl w/cat, 4¼"	22.00
Shelf sitter, Gypsy couple w/wood bow, 6½ & 7", pr	65.00
Shelf sitter, Hans & Katrinka, on ped, 5½", pr	40.00
Shelf sitter, Indian Boy, 3"	25.00
Shelf sitter, Isaac, 12"	65.00
Shelf sitter, Mexican boy & girl, 6", pr	50.00
Shelf sitter, Nip & Tuck, 4¼" & 4", pr	25.00
Shelf sitter, Pudgie Parakeet, 5"	20.00
Shelf sitter, woman w/parasol, 6½"	35.00
Vase, bamboo bud; Wing-Sang, 5"	28.00
Vase, birds, rnd, 2"	15.00
Vase, man w/gong, 6¼"	15.00
Vase, roses, rnd, 2¼"	15.00

**Ophelia, plaque, 8½",
$35.00.**

Chalkware

Chalkware figures were a popular commodity from approximately 1860 until 1890. They were made from gypsum or plaster of Paris formed in a mold and then hand painted in oils or watercolors. Items such as animals and birds, figures, banks, toys, and religious ornaments modeled after more expensive Staffordshire wares were often sold door to door. Their origin is attributed to Italian immigrants. Today regarded as a form of folk art, nineteenth century American pieces bring prices in the hundreds of dollars. Carnival chalkware from this century is also collectible, especially figures that are personality related. For those, see Carnival Collectibles.

Bird on plinth, worn mc pnt, chips, 6½"	210.00
Cat, buff colored, gr eyes, rpr ft, 5"	125.00
Dog, freestanding front legs, worn mc pnt, hollow, 8"	185.00
Dog, seated, wistful face, NM blk/wht/yel pnt, 9½"	900.00
Dog, seated, worn blk/yel pnt w/red details, 5½", EX	250.00

Dove, orig gr/red/yel pnt, 11" 325.00
Dove bank, worn pnt, hole in bottom, 11" 225.00
Garniture, fruit/leafage, EX pnt, hollow, crack, 16" 900.00
Parrot perched on orb, yel/gr pnt, PA, 9" 700.00
Plaque, fawn head, yel/blk pnt, facing pr, 9", EX 470.00
Poodle, molded/stippled body, brn ears, red-dot collar, 7" 700.00
Ram, recumbent, red/blk trim, 1 horn rpr, 3⅜" 225.00
Squirrel on hind ft/nut to mouth, worn 3-color pnt, 6" 250.00
Squirrel w/nut, lt brn pnt w/blk markings, PA, 6¼" 600.00

Cat, painted features and collar, mid-19th century, small hole and crack, 16", $1,800.00.

Champleve

Champleve, enameling on brass, differs from cloisonne in that the design is depressed or incised into the metal, rather than being built up with wire dividers as in the cloisonne procedure. The cells, or depressions, are filled in with color, and the piece is then fired.

Box, arabesque decor, florals, ca 1900, 6" dia 550.00
Frame, w/mirror, mk France, 7x9" 175.00

Bronze urn on stand, China, 19th century, EX, 24", $650.00.

Incense burner, pierced cloud top, dragon hdls, ftd, 6½" 75.00
Inkwell, upraised pen-holder arms, on 3x4" onyx base 70.00
Umbrella stand, 2 reserves w/phoenix birds, Chinese, 23" 400.00
Urn, geometrics on bronze, Chinese, 12" 350.00
Vase, floral w/lappet bands & birds, dragon hdls, 12" 200.00
Vase, Tao mask, bronze, imp Oriental M King, 4¾", pr 125.00

Chase Brass & Copper Company

It was long after the 1925 'l'Exposition Internationale des Arts Decoratifs et Industriels Modernes' in Paris, France, that the Art Deco Movement reached American shores. This exhibition introduced the streamlined, prismatic, geometric styles which were to take America by storm. Sleek modernistic skyscrapers, diners, and movie houses replaced ponderous old-fashioned constructions allover the country. Products for daily use — glassware, pottery, jewelry, kitchenware, furniture, and lighting fixtures which bore the same unifying, streamlined characteristics — followed closely behind. Most early Art Deco pieces were handcrafted and expensive.

The Hollywood spectaculars of the 1930s exposed the population to the Art Deco style. They were, in fact, directly responsible for the introduction of Art Deco products into the average American home. Caught up in the grip of the worst depression in the country's history, buyers demanded alternatives to expensive 'designer' items and sought reasonably priced 'Hollywood-style' products to help relieve day-to-day economic hardships.

Chase Brass & Copper Company of Waterbury, Connecticut, recognized this demand and became the pioneer and major producer of machine-made, Art Deco-styled household accessories and lamps during the 1930s. The company engaged such famous designers as Russel Wright, Rockwell Kent, Walter von Nessen, and others to design Chase housewares which were made in the Hollywood style but which could be mass-produced and sold at reasonable prices. Emily Post, the highly-regarded home economist of the 1930s, strongly endorsed Chase products and used the mass media to encourage a nationwide movement toward informal, inexpensive entertaining using Chase chromium serving pieces such as hors d'oeuvre trays, warming dishes, coffee sets, etc. The Art Deco housewares line was discontinued by Chase with the advent of World War II and was not resumed after the war.

Products of the Chase Brass & Copper Company are gaining in popularity and are eagerly sought after by collectors. Thousands of pieces were sold during the 1930s, and most are still available in good condition at reasonable prices. However, the designers of many pieces are still unknown. Reasearch by collectors continues in an effort to identify 'designer pieces.' As the designer is identified, the demand (and hence the value) of these pieces may be expected to greatly increase.

For a more thorough study of this subject, we recommend that you refer to *Art Deco Chrome, The Chase Era,* by Richard J. Kilbride; you will find his address in the Directory under Connecticut. In the listings that follow, the finish is polished unless noted satin.

Ash tray, chrome or brass, plastic ship's wheel, #885 . . . . .23.00
Ash tray, chrome w/glass insert, #869, 6" dia 31.00
Ash tray, golfers, chrome or copper, #890, 4" dia 42.00
Bank, barrel, nickel, #405005, 2¼" dia .42.00
Bowl, flower, chrome or copper, plastic base, #15005, 10" 40.00
Bowl, Wright design, chrome or copper, #17108, 7" H 125.00
Butter dish, chrome, wht plastic knob, #17067 . . . . .65.00
Candlesticks, brass, #16008, 5" dia base, pr 40.00
Candy dish, brass/copper, wht plastic knob, #90011, 7" dia 18.00
Cheese knife, chrome, #17062, 7" L 32.00
Cigarette box, chrome top, wht plastic end, #17075, 5" L 38.00

Cocktail set, bl shaker/6 cups, chrome tray, #90077 . . . .**215.00**
Cocktail set, chrome w/blk, #90064, shaker+4 cups **250.00**
Coffeemaker service, #90120, 8⅛" pot+cr/sug+tray **330.00**
Coffeemaker service, chrome, #17054, 3-pc **225.00**

Coronet coffee urn service #90121. Urn: 12x8½" diameter; sugar bowl: 4½"; creamer: 3½"; tray: 16¾" long; 18 cups; polished chromium with white plastic handles and knobs, white tray bottom, complete set: $540.00 (coffee urn only: $195.00).

Cruet set, chrome, clear ribbed glass, #26008, 8" **83.00**
Ice crusher, chrome, #90135, 6" L **29.00**
Jam jar, chrome-plated, ribbed glass, #26005, 4", +spoon **25.00**
Lamp, brass, glass chimney, #6194, 11¾" **38.00**
Lamp, brass or silver, etched/frosted glass, #6311, 15½" **40.00**
Lamp, circle; chrome/brass or bronze, #01004, 14" **135.00**
Lamp, desk; chrome/brass or bronze, #01003, 14½" **110.00**
Lamp, glow; chrome or copper shade, #01001, 8¼" **55.00**
Napkin holder, chrome w/wht plastic hdl, #90148 . . . .**42.00**
Nut cracker, chrome or brass, #90150, 5⅞" **25.00**
Pitcher, water; chrome, wht plastic hdl, #90123, 2-qt **47.00**
Relish, 5-compartment glass in chrome tray, #90054, 12" dia . . .**33.00**
Shakers, chrome, spherical, #28004, pr **62.00**
Smoke stand, chrome or bronze, #877, 17¾" **395.00**
Smoke stand, chrome/bronze, #17076, 26" **390.00**
Snack server, chrome or copper, electric, 3-section, #90093 . . . .**95.00**
Tray, cocktail, chrome, #09013, 15⅞x5⅜" **22.00**
Tray, dbl, satin chrome or copper, #09025, open: 13x11" **43.00**
Tray, ring, chrome, #90058, 12" dia **30.00**
Tray, triple; satin, chrome, or copper, #09001, folded: 11x7" **95.00**
Vase, chrome or copper, #03011, 5½" dia **38.00**

Chelsea

The Chelsea Porcelain Works operated in London from the middle of the eighteenth century, making porcelain of the finest quality. In 1770 it was purchased by the owner of the Derby Pottery and for about twenty years operated as a decorating shop. Production periods are indicated by trademarks: 1745-1750 — incised triangle, sometimes with 'Chelsea' and the year added; early 1750s — raised anchor mark on oval pad; 1752-1756 — small painted red anchor, only rarely found in blue underglaze; 1756-1769 — gold anchor; 1769-84 — Chelsea Derby mark with the script 'D' containing a horizontal anchor. Many reproductions have been made; be suspicious of any anchor mark larger than ¼".

Bonbonniere, girl bends over doll in cradle, 1760, 2½" **3,800.00**

Bottle, scent; cupid at alter, appl florals, 1760s, 3", NM **2,400.00**
Bottle, scent; pug dog, gold mts, 1775, 2½", EX **4,000.00**
Bowl, floral sprays, oval, red anchor mk, 1760s, 11" L **850.00**
Dish, leaf form, HP veins, 1785, 11" **600.00**
Dish, leaf form w/HP veins & sunflower sprigs, 1760, 10" . . .**2,700.00**

Figure of a pheasant, anchor mark, 4", $175.00.

Figurine, lady w/purple hat/apron, gold anchor, 1760, 7" **375.00**
Plate, botanical plant, red anchor mk, 1775, 9½" **500.00**
Plate, garland/urn, swag border, dk bl/gilt, ca 1775, 9¾" **265.00**
Seal, dog, mtd w/carnelian intaglio of Aristotle, 1¼" **500.00**
Tureen, asparagus spears w/brn-raffia tie, w/lid, 7" L **8,000.00**

Chelsea Dinnerware

Made from about 1830 to 1880 in the Staffordshire district of England, this white dinnerware is decorated with lustre embossings in the grape, thistle, sprig, or fruit and cornucopia patterns. The relief designs vary from lavender to blue, and the body of the ware may be porcelain, ironstone, or earthenware. Because it was not produced in Chelsea as the name would suggest, dealers often prefer to call it 'Grandmother's Ware.'

Grape, coffeepot **140.00**
Grape, creamer **48.00**
Grape, cup & saucer **25.00**
Grape, egg cup **26.50**
Grape, pitcher, 6" **50.00**
Grape, plate, cake; 10" **38.00**
Grape, saucer, regular **8.00**
Grape, waste bowl **40.00**
Sprig, bowl, sauce **11.00**
Sprig, creamer **48.00**
Sprig, cup & saucer, ironstone **25.00**
Sprig, plate, cake; 9" **40.00**
Sprig, plate, dinner **25.00**
Sprig, plate, 7" **20.00**
Sprig, sugar bowl, w/lid **75.00**
Thistle, butter pat **12.00**
Thistle, cup & saucer **25.00**

Chelsea Keramic Art Works

Established in 1872 in Chelsea, Massachusetts, by several members of the Robertson family who later formed the Dedham Pottery, this firm is most noted for its experiments in attempting to re-create the ancient Oriental oxblood-red glaze. They succeeded in this in 1885 and also developed several other outstanding glazes as a result of their perseverance. One was their Oriental crackle glaze which they ultimately used in the manufacture of the very successful Dedham dinnerware. Though their very early artware utilized a redware body, by the late 1870s it was replaced with yellow- or buff-burning clay. A line called Bourgla-Reine (underglaze slip-decorated ware with primarily blue and green backgrounds) was produced, though not to any great extent. Other pieces were designed in imitation of metalware, even to the extent that surfaces were 'hammered' to further enhance the effect. Occasionally, live flora were pressed into the damp vessel walls to leave a decorative impression. The pottery closed in 1889. Early wares were not marked; those made from 1875 to 1880 were marked with either two or three lines containing 'Chelsea Keramic Art Works, Robertson and Son,' or the 'C-KA-W' cipher, which was used up to 1889. A paper label was used for a short time on the crackleware. See also Dedham.

Bowl, crackleware, plain, mk CPUS, 4½x5½" 500.00
Cake plate, clover decor rim, bisque fired, CPUS, 10½" 600.00
Jug, dk olive-gr gloss, bulbous, incised mk, 5x3½" 250.00
Vase, bl-gr, band of floral swags, petal base, hdls, 6" 200.00
Vase, bl-gr gloss, lion/ring hdls on flat oval form, 12½" 550.00
Vase, oxblood, smooth & orange peel areas, 8" 2,000.00
Vase, red/brn gloss, squat/wide body, mk, 2¾" 125.00

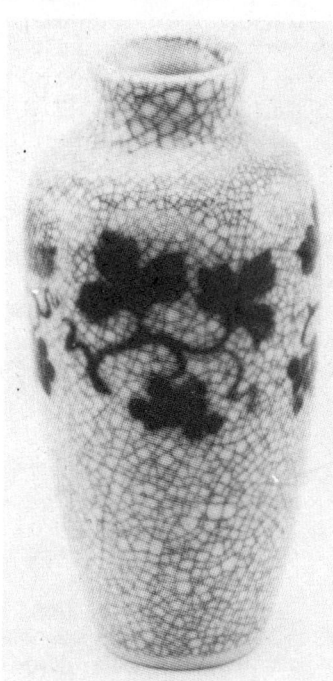

Vase, crackleware with vintage, marked CPUS, 7½", $2,000.00.

Children's Books

Children's books, especially those from the Victorian era, are charming collectibles. Colorful lithographic illustrations that once delighted little boys in long curls and tiny girls in long stockings and lots of ribbons and lace have lost none of their appeal. Some collectors limit themselves to a specific subject, while others may be far more interested in the illustrations. First editions are more valuable than later issues, and condition and rarity are very important factors to consider before making your purchase.

Bambi Meets His Forest Friends, NY Graphic Society, 1947 . . . .65.00

Blue Danube, The; Bemelmans, Viking, 1st ed, 1945 . . . . .25.00
Boat for Peppe, Politi, Scribner, 1950, 1st ed, EX 20.00
Book of Indians, The; C Holling, Platt & Munk 8.00
Bubble Book, w/3 records, Chase illus, Harper's, 1918, 7x6" 25.00
Calico Bush, Field, Macmillan, 1931, EX 35.00
Child's Garden of Verses, Stevenson, Saalfield, 1940, VG 35.00
Child's Stamp Book of Old Verses, J Wilcox Smith, 1915, VG . .75.00
Christmas ABC Book, McLoughlin, 1900, EX 32.00
Christmas Cheer, Donohue-Henneberry, 1894, EX 25.00
Daddy Turtle & the Well Sweep, McCandlish, NY, 1926 . . . . . .15.00
Desert Dan, Coatsworth, Viking, 1960, 1st ed, NM 15.00
Donald Duck, linen, #1, Whitman, Disney, 1935, EX 145.00

Dorothy and the Wizard of Oz, by Frank Baum, Reilly & Britton Co., Chicago, 1st Edition, 1st Issue, EX, $500.00.

Engines & Brass Bands, Miller, Book House/Doubleday, 1948 . . .30.00
Fables of Aesop, NY, Deluxe Editions, 1931, EX 20.00
Forest Pool, The; LA Armer, NY/Toronto, 1st ed, 1938 . . . . . . .40.00
Funny Animals, Palmer Cox, Donohue illus 18.00
Golden Windows, Richard, Little Brown, 1936, EX 12.50
Hill of Little Miracles, Angelo, Viking, 1942, EX 15.00
Jack the Giant Killer, shape book, McLoughlin, 1895, EX 15.00
Jungle People, Floethe, Scribner, 1971, 1st ed, NM 15.00
Knock at the Door, Coatsworth, Macmillan, 1st ed, 1931 . . . . . .35.00
Last of Great Scouts, Wetmore, Zane Gray illus, 1918, EX 15.00
Life of George Washington, McLoughlin Bros, 1893, EX 25.00
Little Days, Gill, Houghton Mifflin, 1917, 1st ed, EX 25.00
Little Knight's Dragon, The; Trez & others, World, 1963 . . . . . .20.00
Little Lord Fauntleroy, Burnett, Scribner's, 1892, EX 20.00
Lorna Doone, Blackmore, Dodd Mead, 1924, EX 20.00
Master Cornhill, McGraw, Atheneum, 1st ed, 1973 . . . . .12.00
Merry Time Stories, McLoughlin Bros, ca 1890, EX 30.00
Midnight Folk, Masefield, Macmillan, 1932, 1st ed, EX 40.00
Mother Goose Rhymes & Fairy Tails, Myers, Winston, 1917 . . .25.00
Nancy Owlett, Phillpotts, Macmillan, Brock color illus, 1933 . . .35.00
Night Before Christmas, Moore, Grosset & Dunlap, 1949, VG . .25.00
Nursery Songs, Russell color illus, Gabriel Sons, NY, 1916 . . . . .15.00
Orphan Annie Book, James Whitcomb Riley, 1908, EX 30.00
Ozma of Oz, Neill illus, Reilly Lee, 1907, EX 20.00
Pepper & Salt, Howard Pyle, illus, 1913 . . . . .12.00

Peter Rabbit & His Pa, Field & Albert, 1916, dust jacket, M ...25.00
Peter Rabbit & Little Boy, Almand, Platt & Munk, 1935, VG ..17.50
Pinocchio, Whitman, 1939, EX ...20.00
Pinto Horse, Perkins, Devin-Adaire, 1960, NM ...10.00
Raggedy Andy Stories, Gruelle, Donohue, 1920, EX 15.00
Red Eagle, Key, Volland, author color illus, 1st ed 30.00
Red Pony, Steinbeck, Viking Press, 1945, NM 20.00
Red Riding Hood, dtd 1899, VG ...25.00
Roller Skates, Sawyer, Viking & Jr Library Guild, 1936, VG 40.00
Servants of the Spring, Kreidold, La Jolla, 1979 ....15.00
Skitter Cat & Major, Youmans, Bobbs-Merrill, 1927, VG 15.00
Snow White's Last Call for Dinner, NY Graphic Society, 1947 .75.00
Suitable Child, Duncan, Revell, 1909, 8-volume set 40.00
Sword in the Stone, White, Putnam, 1939, VG 20.00
Tales of Timothy Turtle, Bailey, Smith illus, NM 25.00
Tanglewood Tales, Hawthorne, Crowell, Harper illus, 1897 ....15.00
Tarzan of the Apes, McClurg, 1913, 1st ed, VG 200.00
Thief in the Attic, The; Weise, Viking, 1st ed, 1965 ....12.00
Toby's Goblin, Atkins, Rand McNally, Trippe illus, 1st ed 30.00
Town & Country Cat, Hollyn, Workman, Goldstrom color illus 30.00
Twelve Months Make a Year, Coatsworth, Macmillan, 1943 ...25.00
Two Little Waifs, Molesworth, Macmillan, Crane illus, 1920 ...15.00
Uncle Wiggily on Farm, H Gates, Campbell illus, 1918, EX 25.00
Under the Lilacs, Alcott, Little Brown, 1928, 1st ed 25.00
Visit to the White Farm, H Alban, Nister & Dutton, 1st ed 35.00
Weathercock, The; Ratel, Mittelmann illus, NY/London 25.00
What the Moon Saw, Oxford University, 1978, 1st ed, M 15.00
Wise Little Hen, linen, 1937 ....75.00
Wizard of Oz, linen, 1939, EX 30.00

Children's Things

Nearly every item devised for adult furnishings has been reduced to child's size — furniture, dishes, sporting goods, even some tools. All are very collectible. During the late 17th and early 18th centuries, miniature china dinnerware sets were made both in China and in England. They were not intended primarily as children's playthings, however, but instead were made to furnish miniature rooms and cabinets that provided a popular diversion for the adults of that period. By the 19th century, the emphasis had shifted, and most of the small-scaled dinnerware and tea sets were made for children's play.

Late in the 19th century and well into the 20th, toy pressed glass dishes were made, many in the same pattern as full-scale glassware. Today these toy dishes often fetch prices in the same range as those for the 'grown-ups'!

One of our advisors for this category is Rosella Tinsley; she is listed in the Directory under Kansas. Authorities Margaret and Kenn Whitmyer have compiled a lovely book, *Children's Dishes*, with full-color photos and current market values; you will find their address in the Directory under Ohio. We also recommend *Children's Glass Dishes, China, and Furniture*, by Doris Anderson Letchler, available at your local bookstore or public library. See also A B C Plates; Canary Lustre; Willow Ware.

China

Beverage set, colorful children, mk Mitterteich, 5-pc 25.00
Bowl, Children Fishing, Noritake, 5⅞" 15.00
Cup & saucer, Mother Goose, Royal Doulton 55.00
Egg cup, Old Mother Hubbard 10.00
Mug, Boy & Pie, girl/boy in garden, 2½" 65.00
Mug, children playing, purple transfer w/mc, Staffordshire 75.00
Mug, Deer Stalking, hunters/dogs, 2⅝" 50.00
Mug, Dr Franklin's Poor Richard Illus, brn transfer, 2½" 105.00
Mug, Farm Yard, blk transfer of animals, Staffordshire, EX ...75.00

Mug, Fishing Party, 2¾" 65.00
Mug, Flowers of Literature, man w/tray on head, 2⅝" 55.00
Mug, Franklin's Maxims, blk transfer, Staffordshire, 2½" 95.00
Mug, gr stripes w/gold lustre, 2⅜" 75.00
Mug, Mary, rust/pk lustre bands, mfg flaw, 3" 110.00
Pitcher, Cock Horse, Royal Doulton, Schmoker, 4¼" 50.00
Plate, Kangaroo, 8-sided, polychrome borders 85.00
Plate, Little Bo Peep, Royal Doulton, Schmoker, 8" 45.00
Plate, Mischievous Cat, emb flower border, 8-sided, 7¼" 90.00
Plate, River Bank, children fishing, floral rim, 5⅝" 80.00
Plate, Three Children & Train, floral rim, 7" 100.00
Platter, Charles Dickens scenes, Ridgways, 6" 30.00
Tea set, Birthday Party, pastels w/gold trim, Japan, 15-pc 175.00
Tea set, Bl Willow, 6-place 100.00
Tea set, HP cherries on earthenware, England, 5-pc, rare 300.00
Tea set, scenic view in pk lustre, Czech, 5-pc, rare 140.00
Teapot, Punch & Judy, Staffordshire 70.00
Teapot, toby, twig hdl/spout, England, 3" 50.00
Teapot, Water Hen, bl/wht, Staffordshire, 5¼" 40.00
Tumbler, Hey Diddle Diddle, Royal Doulton, 3¾" 55.00

Furniture

Examples with no dimensions given are child's size unless noted doll size.

Side chair, painted and decorated paint, PA, ca 1845, $400.00.

Bed, wood, iron-bed look, doll size, EX 27.00
Blanket chest, orig bl-gr pnt, cut-out ends, 1725, 17x21" 1,600.00
Chair, arrow-bk side, VG pnt w/stencil, plank seat, 27" 190.00
Chair, bentwood arms/2-splat bk, bl pnt, worn splint seat 80.00
Chair, captain style, 1850s, rfn 175.00
Chair, ladderbk arm, 2-splat/trn posts/rush seat, 1800, 28" ...375.00
Chair, ladderbk arm, 3 arched splats, red pnt, NE, 1700s 550.00
Chair, made w/thick hickory dowels, rpl woven bk/seat, 22" 75.00
Chair, side, curly maple, saber leg, rpl cane seat, 27" 400.00
Cradle, cherry, heart cutouts on ends, dvtl, rfn, 38" L 260.00
Cradle, cherry w/walnut rockers, scroll/cut-out sides, 40" 130.00
Cradle, pine w/blk on red pnt decor, rpl hood, 20" L 80.00
Cradle, pine w/brn pnt, heart cutouts, handmade, 18" L 115.00
Cradle, pumpkin pine, hooded, 1800s, outstanding, 36" L 300.00
Cradle, walnut, arched bonnet, pierced hdls, PA, 1800, 42" ...500.00
Crib, trn posts/legs, lattice slats, rpt, 31x29x48" 65.00
Cupboard, openwork/chip cvg, trn posts, doors slide, 14" 125.00
Cupboard, poplar, 2 glass doors over step-bk base, 29" 275.00

Cupboard, walnut, scroll details, sq nails, porc knobs, 20" 375.00
Highchair, ladderbk, pnt, woven yew wood seat, 1825, 35" ..1,200.00
Highchair, ladderbk arm, lemon finials, NE, 1700s 2,000.00
Highchair, primitive, gr pnt, trn posts/ft/finials, 35" 200.00
Highchair, Windsor, EX detail, 2-color rpt/rpl arm, 30" 475.00
Highchair, 2-splat ladderbk w/rabbit ear posts, splay legs 650.00
Porch swing, wood, 2-seater, for 12" dolls 95.00
Rocker, Adirondack, oak splint seat, ca 1900, 22x19x16" 125.00
Rocker, G Stickley, 2 horizontal bk splats, armless, decal 425.00
Rocker, G Stickley, 3 horizontal splats, open arms, decal 500.00
Rocker, trn legs, bentwood bk, worn bl/yel pnt, 7" 110.00
Rocker, w/arms, trn posts/finials, slat seat/bk, 25" 125.00
Table, drop leaf; Country Sheraton, Southern pine, 19" L 200.00
Table & chair, hickory, primitive, splint seat, chair: 25" 250.00
Table & 2 chairs, G Stickley #342/658, 24" dia top, VG 1,300.00

Glass

Acorn, butter dish, 4" 185.00
Acorn, creamer, 3⅜" 85.00
Arched Panel, pitcher, cobalt or amber 85.00
Arched Panel, tumbler, cobalt 25.00
Austrian, butter dish, 2¼" 195.00
Austrian, creamer, canary, 3¼" 160.00
Austrian, sugar bowl, chocolate, w/lid, 3¾" 550.00
Baby Thumbprint, cake stand, 3" 75.00
Baby Thumbprint, compote, w/lid 130.00
Bead & Scroll, creamer, 3" 70.00
Bead & Scroll, table set, 4-pc 395.00
Beaded Hobnail, water set, bl 400.00
Beaded Swirl, sugar bowl, w/lid, 3¾" 48.00
Beaded Swirl, table set 165.00
Block, butter dish, amber 145.00
Block, spooner, amber or clear, 3" 65.00
Braided Belt, butter dish, 2¼" 125.00
Braided Belt, creamer, wht/decor, 2⅝" 110.00
Bucket, sugar bowl, w/lid, 3¾" 175.00
Button Panel, butter dish, 4" 85.00
Button Panel, creamer, 2½" 50.00
Buzz Saw, creamer, 2⅜" 20.00
Chimo, punch cup 15.00
Chimo, table set, 4-pc 225.00
Clear & Diamond Panels, butter dish, bl, 2⅞" 70.00
Clear & Diamond Panels, sugar bowl, bl, w/lid, 3½" 55.00
Cloud Band, spooner, 2⅜" 38.00
Colonial, pitcher, 3¼" 22.00
Colonial, punch cup, 1⅞" 13.00
Colonial #2630, butter dish, gr, 2½" 55.00
Colonial #2630, spooner, gr, 2⅛" 45.00
D&M #42, creamer, 2⅝" 42.00
D&M #42, honey jug, 2⅜" 70.00
Dewdrop, creamer, cobalt, 2¾" 60.00
Dewdrop, sugar bowl, cobalt, w/lid, 4⅛" 95.00
Diamond Ridge (D&M #48), butter dish 165.00
Diamond Ridge (D&M #48), spooner, 2¾" 65.00
Doyle #500, mug, 2" 25.00
Doyle #500, sugar bowl, w/lid, 3⅝" 50.00
Drum, mug, 2" 35.00
Drum, sugar bowl, w/lid 110.00
Dutch Kinder, pomade, bl milk glass, 1½" 95.00
Dutch Kinder, slop jar, milk glass, 2⅛" 80.00
Fancy Cut, sugar bowl, w/lid, 3⅛" 40.00
Fancy Cut, tumbler, 1⅝" 22.00
Fernland, creamer, cobalt, 2⅜" 45.00

Flattened Diamond & Sunburst, punch set, 7-pc 58.00
Flute, bowl, berry; sm 8.00
Frances Ware, pitcher, frosted w/amber or red, 4¾" 110.00
Frances Ware, tumbler, crystal w/amber/bl/or vaseline, 2¼" ...55.00
Galloway, tumbler, crystal w/gold, 2" 15.00
Grapevine w/Ovals, sugar bowl, w/lid, 2⅞" 45.00
Hawaiian Lei, butter dish, 2¼" 40.00
Hobnail w/Thumbprint, creamer, bl, 3⅜" 42.00
Hobnail w/Thumbprint, sugar bowl, bl, w/lid, 4" 85.00
Hobnail w/Thumbprint, tray, 7⅜" 35.00
Hunting Dogs, mug, bl 30.00
Inverted Strawberry, bowl, berry; sm 25.00
Kittens, banana dish, marigold 125.00
Lacy Dewdrop, cake stand, 3¼" 35.00
Lamb, butter dish, 3⅛" 115.00

Large Block table set: Butter dish, $75.00; Sugar bowl, $75.00; Creamer, $45.00.

Lazy Daisy, berry set, 5-pc 90.00
Leaf & Grape, decanter set, clear w/etching, 5-pc 325.00
Liberty Bell, creamer, 2½" 80.00
Lion, butter dish, frosted, 4¼" 145.00
Lion, cup, 1¾" 45.00
Long Diamond, butter dish, 2" 135.00
Long Diamond, spooner, 2½" 70.00
Mary Gregory, beverage set, amber, 5-pc 700.00
Menagerie, butter dish, amber, 2⅜" 850.00
Menagerie, spooner 90.00
Michigan, butter dish, 3½" 100.00
Michigan, creamer, clear w/gold, 2⅞" 60.00
Nearcut, pitcher, 3⅛" 30.00
Nursery Rhyme, bowl, berry; 1¼x2½" 25.00
Nursery Rhyme, punch bowl, bl milk glass, 3¼" 265.00
Nursery Rhyme, spooner, 2½" 45.00
Nursery Rhyme, table set, 4-pc 230.00
Oval Star, punch bowl 60.00
Pattee Cross, punch bowl, clear w/gold 110.00
Pattee Cross, punch cup, 1⅛" 25.00
Peacock Feather, creamer, 2" 55.00
Pennsylvania, creamer, gr, 2½" 80.00
Pennsylvania, spooner, 2½" 45.00
Pert, creamer, 3¼" 90.00
Pert, sugar bowl, w/lid, 5⅛" 145.00
Rolling pin, bl-gr 120.00
Rooster, butter dish, 2¾" 135.00
Sandwich Ivy, creamer, 2⅜" 85.00
Sawtooth, butter dish, 3" 55.00
Sawtooth, sugar bowl, w/lid, 4⅞" 45.00
Sawtooth Band, creamer, red flashed 75.00
Sawtooth Variation, table set 180.00

Standing Lamb, creamer, frosted, 3¼" 300.00
Standing Lamb, sugar bowl, w/lid, 5⅛" 285.00
Stippled Diamond, sugar bowl, w/lid, 3⅛" 80.00
Stippled Raindrop & Dewdrop, spooner, cobalt, 2⅛" 110.00
Stippled Vines & Beads, creamer, bl, 2⅜" 100.00
Stippled Vines & Beads, sugar bowl, teal, w/lid, 3⅛" 115.00
Sultan, sugar bowl, chocolate, w/lid, 4½" 340.00
Tappan, spooner, 2⅝" 18.00
Tappan, sugar bowl, w/lid, 4" 20.00
Tulip & Honeycomb, bowl, oval, 1¾" 60.00
Tulip & Honeycomb, punch cup, 1¼" 10.00
Twin Snowshoes, creamer, 2⅞" 45.00
Twist, sugar bowl, bl opal, w/lid, 3⅞" 110.00
Two Band, butter dish, 2" 65.00
Two Band, spooner, 2⅞" 40.00
Wheat Sheaf, bowl, berry; sm, 1" 10.00
Wheat Sheaf, punch bowl, 3½" 30.00
Wheat Sheaf, punch set, 7-pc 85.00
Wild Rose, candlestick 85.00
Wild Rose, creamer, milk glass, 1¾" 65.00
Wild Rose, punch cup, bl opaque, 1¼" 30.00
Wild Rose, spooner, milk glass, 1¾" 65.00
Wild Rose, sugar bowl, milk glass, open, 1¾" 65.00

Miscellaneous

Carriage, wicker, wood wheels/iron rims, becomes sled, 52" . . .325.00
Chair, wood retainer ring on plank w/CI horse head w/spring . .275.00
Doll stroller, wicker, wire wheels, wood hdl at bk, 1800s 120.00
Fork, tin, Peter Rabbit, ABCs 15.00
Rattle, elephant emb on sides, umk silver, 4½" 135.00
Rattle, ivory w/bl & amber glass beads, 4" 150.00
Rattle, SP comic cop form w/celluloid ring hdl, mk EPNS, 3¾" .65.00
Rattle & whistle, sterling top & bells, MOP hdl 135.00

Red Riding Hood tea set, lithographed tin, ca 1900, marked Germany, $175.00.

Rolling pin, oak, EX patina, New England, 1700s, 7" 175.00
Sled, horses/rider litho, Factory Girl, portrait, 44" 3,200.00
Sled, wood, lion/tiger litho, curled runners, 1900s, 27", EX 265.00
Sleigh, wood, bentwood runners, worn orig varnish/pnt, 35" . . .225.00
Sleigh, wood, curved iron-tipped runners, CI lion head, 33" . . .135.00
Sleigh, wood, curved iron-tipped runners, rpt, 27" L 110.00
Sleigh, wood, metal runners, stenciled horse head, 31" 160.00
Sleigh, wood, metal-tip runners w/CI swan ends, mc rpt, 33" . .375.00
Table, graniteware, ABC top/circus theme 165.00
Washboard, wood, grooved scrub surface, 9¼x6¼" 45.00
Washer, Columbia, wood w/CI gear agitator, rpr, 18" 450.00

Wheelbarrow, wood, John Deere, gr/yel pnt, 19x34x12" 240.00

Chocolate Glass

Jacob Rosenthal developed chocolate glass, a rich shaded opaque brown sometimes referred to as caramel slag, in 1900 at the Indiana Tumbler and Goblet Company of Greentown, Indiana. Later, other companies produced similar ware. Only the latter is listed here. See also Greentown.

Lamp base, Wild Rose with Festoons, 9½", $585.00.

Compote, jelly; Chrysanthemum Leaf, chocolate 325.00
Compote, jelly; Geneva, 3½x4½" .145.00
Compote, jelly; Melrose, 6" dia 135.00
Creamer, Chrysanthemum Leaf 475.00
Creamer, Rose Garland 950.00
Cruet, Chrysanthemum Leaf 850.00
Cruet, Geneva 1,000.00
Cruet, Wild Rose w/Bow Knot 300.00
Hatpin holder, Orange Tree 450.00
Lamp, Wild Rose w/Festoon, 9½" .585.00
Pitcher, Serenade, no spout 400.00
Pitcher, Serenade, w/spout, rare 525.00
Pitcher, Wild Rose w/Bow Knot, water sz 550.00
Plate, Serenade, lg 95.00
Sauce, Melrose, scalloped, 3¾" 125.00
Shakers, Geneva, pr 200.00
Sugar bowl, Chrysanthemum Leaf, w/lid 355.00
Syrup, Strigal 95.00
Toothpick holder, Geneva 125.00
Tray, dresser; Wild Rose w/Bow Knot 275.00
Tumbler, Serenade 150.00

Christmas Collectibles

Christmas past . . . lovely mementos from long ago attest to the ostentatious Victorian celebrations of the season.

St. Nicholas, better known as Santa, has changed much since 300 A.D. when the good Bishop Nicholas showered needy children with gifts and kindnesses. During the early eighteenth century, Santa was portrayed as the kind gift-giver to well-behaved children and the stern switch-bearing disciplinarian to those who were bad. In 1822 Clement Clark Moore, a New York poet, wrote his famous 'Night Before Christmas,' and the Santa he described was jolly and jovial — a lovable old elf who was stern with no one. Early Santas wore robes of yellow, brown, blue, green, red, or even purple. But Thomas Nast, who worked as an illustrator for Harper's Weekly, was the first to depict Santa in a red suit instead of the traditional robe, and to locate him the entire year at the North Pole headquarters.

Today's collectors prize early Santa figures, especially those in robes of fur or mohair or those dressed in an unusual color. Some early examples of Christmas memorabilia are the pre-1870 ornaments from Dresden, Germany. These cardboard figures — angels, gondolas, umbrellas, dirigibles, and countless others — sparkled with gold and silver trim. Late in the 1870s, blown glass ornaments were imported from Germany. There were over 6,000 recorded designs — all painted inside with silvery colors. From 1890 through 1910, blown glass spheres were often decorated with beads, tassels, and tinsel rope.

Christmas lights, made by Sandwich and some of their contemporaries, were either pressed or mold-blown glass shaped into a form similar to a water tumbler. They were filled with water and then hung from the tree by a wire handle; oil floating on the surface of the water served as fuel for the lighted wick.

Kugels are glass ornaments that were made as early as 1820 and as late as 1890. Ball-shaped examples are more common than the fruit and vegetable forms and have been found in sizes ranging from 1" to 14" in diameter. They were made of thick glass with heavy brass caps, in cobalt, green, gold, silver, and occasionally in amethyst.

Although experiments involving the use of electric lightbulbs for the Christmas tree occured before 1900, it was 1903 before the first manufactured socket set was marketed. These were very expensive and often proved a safety hazard. In 1921 safety regulations were established, and products were guaranteed safety approved. The early bulbs were smaller replicas of Edison's household bulb. By 1910 G.E. bulbs were rounded with a pointed end, and until 1919 all bulbs were hand blown. The first figural bulbs were made around 1910 in Austria. Japan soon followed, but their product was never of the high quality of Austrian wares. American manufacturers produced their first machine-made figurals after 1919. Today, figural bulbs — especially character-related examples — are very popular collectibles. Bubble lights were popular from about 1945 to 1960 when miniature lights were introduced. These tiny lamps dampened the public's enthusiasm for the bubblers, and manufacturers stopped providing replacement bulbs.

Feather trees were made from 1850 to 1950 — all are collectible. Watch for newly-manufactured feather trees that have lately been reintroduced.

Bulbs

Andy Gump, VG pnt, milk glass, working	85.00
Ape w/rifle, sitting on mound, brn/wht/blk, rare	120.00
Baby in red stocking, milk glass, EX	45.00
Ball w/stars, red	20.00
Bell w/3 Santa faces, VG pnt, milk glass, 3"	20.00
Betty Boop, pk/red dress, blk hair, milk glass, NM	70.00
Betty Boop, VG pnt, milk glass	40.00
Candy cane, red & wht, 3"	25.00
Cat, bright colors, 4"	35.00
Cat, wht in pk boot, 3"	40.00
Cat, 2-faced, wht w/red & yel dots, milk glass, 3½"	40.00
Chick in egg, yel/tan/red, milk glass, NM	125.00
Clown on ball, red suit w/yel ruffle, 3"	65.00
Cross, VG red pnt, clear glass	25.00
Cross, yel, 3"	25.00
Cross w/star, yel & pk, 2½"	30.00
Darla, girl in pk dress, orange hair, milk glass, NM	125.00

Dick Tracy, EX pnt, milk glass, 3"	135.00
Dick Tracy, VG pnt, milk glass, 3"	95.00
Dismal Desmond, sitting dog, mc pnt, milk glass, NM	45.00

Disney characters, $25.00 each.

Dog, brn & red, 4"	45.00
Dog in basket, milk glass	45.00
Donald Duck	65.00
Duckling, EX mc pnt, milk glass, NM	45.00
Ear of corn, gr & yel, 4"	50.00
Elephant w/trunk up, no pnt, milk glass	85.00
Frog, gr & yel, 3"	65.00
Girl, red rose, gr blouse, 4"	65.00
Grapes, orange/purple w/gr leaves, milk glass, 3¼"	20.00
Horsehead in shoe, pk horse, red halter, 3"	110.00
Hound dog, VG pnt, milk glass	40.00
Humpty Dumpty, standing, VG pnt, milk glass, 3"	65.00
Humpty Dumpty on wall, poor pnt, milk glass, non-working	25.00
Indian head, pk & orange, 1⅞"	250.00
Indians hunting, brn Indians/deer/birds w/wht & orange, 3"	37.50
Jack-O'-Lantern, EX pnt, milk glass	55.00
Kayo, squatting, milk glass, 1935	55.00
Lantern, milk glass, Japan, sm	16.00
Lantern, VG pnt, milk glass, Japan, lg	22.00
Lion w/tennis racket, red/yel/orange, milk glass, NM	50.00
Little Red Riding Hood, VG pnt, milk glass	40.00
Lucky Lindbergh, purple/pk/gold/blk, milk glass, EX	40.00
Man, pk head, yel tie, blk shirt, red/yel pants, 3"	60.00
Matchless Star, bl w/amber center, 2"	15.00
Matchless Star, clear w/gr center, 2"	10.00
Matchless Star, gr w/red center, 2"	10.00
Mickey Mouse	65.00
Moon Mullins, G pnt, milk glass, non-working	65.00
Orphan Annie, VG pnt, milk glass, mk c 1935, 3⅛"	50.00
Owl, blk hat & pants, pk tie, 4"	35.00
Owl, yel & gray, 3"	115.00
Peach, EX yel & peach pnt, 3"	40.00
Pear, VG yel & peach pnt, 3"	28.00
Pig, bl tie, gr jacket, yel pants, 3"	75.00
President bust	45.00
Rabbit, sitting, yel & red pnt, milk glass, NM	100.00
Rose, open, VG red pnt, milk glass	35.00
Sandy, G mc pnt, milk glass, 3"	50.00
Santa, bright colors, 5½"	75.00

Santa, bright colors, 9" 115.00
Santa, full figure w/pack, milk glass 20.00
Santa, red & gr w/pk bag, 3" 25.00
Santa, red & gray, flesh face, M pnt, Mazda, non-working 35.00
Santa, red w/gr tree, 2½" 25.00
Santa, 2-faced, mc pnt, milk glass, 4" 30.00
Santa, 2-faced, red, milk glass, 3" 28.00
Santa, 2-faced, red & blk, milk glass, 2" 25.00
Skull & Xbones on wht globe, Occupied Japan, 2" dia, M 15.00
Smitty, milk glass, VG 35.00
Snowman, red hat, bl bag, milk glass, 3" 25.00
Snowman w/pack on bk, milk glass, Japan 22.50
Star, Noma, 7", EX in orig box 20.00
Star w/face, EX pnt .30.00
Teddy bear, milk glass 75.00
Woman in shoe, mc pnt, milk glass, NM 75.00
Zeppelin, EX pnt, milk glass 45.00
3 Men in a Tub, bright colors, 3" 55.00

Candy Containers

Ball, papier-mache, bright colors, 3" 40.00
Candle, pressed paper, red w/wick & ribbon, 5½", EX 25.00
Cornucopia, crepe paper, die-cut decor 80.00
Donkey, compo, gray, detailed, head removes, Germany, 5" . . .125.00
Drum, Dresden, vertical gold strips, silver star, 2½x3" 70.00
Dwarf, cb, glitter, pnt face, 5" 25.00
Elf, compo, stands, detailed face, Germany, 8¼", EX 350.00
Elf, spun glass, Dresden horn, on compo snowball, German, 6" . .60.00
House, glass, red brick, gr roof, 3" 75.00
House w/cotton Santa on cotton roof, mk Japan 85.00
Irish heart, Dresden, gr w/opal stone, 2" 115.00
Jockey cap, Dresden, blk brim, mk MIG, 1¾x4x2⅜" 135.00
Lamb on egg, compo w/wood legs, cb egg, 4½", EX 70.00
Santa, cb/flannel, plastic face/cotton beard, Japan, 8", EX . . .100.00
Santa, papier-mache, red coat, bl pants, 4" 125.00
Santa, plaster face, cloth coat, 7" 155.00
Santa head on boot, mesh bag, Japan, 1930s, 3½" 60.00
Santa in basket, plaster hands, Japan, 5" 80.00
Santa in sleigh holds tree, felt suit/chalk face, Germany, 4½" . .150.00
Santa on deer, compo, metal horns, Dresden trim, Germany, . .600.00
Slipper, Dresden, pk crepe w/gold, 8" 255.00
Snowball, celluloid, 2" 25.00
Snowball, papier-mache, Germany, 1920s, EX 40.00
Snowman, compo, 7" .50.00
Star medallion, Dresden, cb/glitter, 3" 110.00
Wreath, Dresden, 4¼" 135.00

Ornaments

Al Jolson's head, blown, 1920s, 3¼" 300.00
Amelia Earhart w/gold bag, blown, ca 1920 . . . . .200.00
Angel, blown, pearly wht face, gold hair & wings, 3" . . .125.00
Apple, blown, pk & yel frost, 3" 55.00
Apple, blown, pk frost, 2½" 50.00
Apple, blown, silver w/blk leaves, 3½" 55.00
Apple w/face, blown, ca 1910, 2x2½" 230.00
Baby face ea side, blown, glass eyes, ca 1920 . . . . . .290.00
Baby w/pacifier, blown, pearly wht, 3" 185.00
Ballerina, blown, gold hair, pk blouse & slippers, 6" . . .95.00
Banana, blown, yel, unsilvered, 5" 95.00
Banjo, Dresden, orange & tan stripes, 3" 155.00
Basket, Dresden, tan, 2" 110.00
Bear, blown, gold w/blk features, 2½" 110.00

Bear, blown, standing, hump on bk, silvered, rare, 4½" 435.00
Bear w/stick, blown, gold w/blk points, 3" 85.00
Beetle, blown, pk w/gr wings, 3" 80.00
Bell w/crown top, blown, silvered, mid-1930s, 4" 60.00
Billy goat, Dresden, cream w/blk & red, 2½", M 225.00
Bird, blown, spun glass tail, on clip, ca 1920, 7¾" 35.00
Bird, blown, unsilvered, glass eyes, ca 1910, 5" 25.00
Birdcage, Dresden, red/gr/gold, flat, 5" 70.00
Birdcage w/wax baby, Sebnitz, 4", EX 450.00
Birds in nest, blown, pearly wht, yel nest, pk & bl birds, 3" . .100.00
Birds in nest, blown, spun glass tails, tinsel hanger, EX . . .70.00
Boy, blown, pearly wht, pk hat/scarf/belt, 3" 48.00
Brownie, blown, gr pants/pk tie/blk hat, unsilvered, 5" . .385.00
Bug, blown, pearly wht w/pk stripes, blk eyes, 3" 40.00
Butler, jtd compo, brn/bl/yel, hanger in head, Germany, 4" . .95.00
Butterfly, blown, red, 3" 70.00
Camel, Dresden, 3-D, tan & brn, 2" 65.00
Candle lantern, bl w/wht face, unsilvered, 5" 385.00
Car, blown, red & wht, 3" 185.00
Cat in slipper, blown, pearly wht/pk/yel, 3½" 145.00
Cat w/banjo, blown, yel hat & fiddle, 3½" 70.00
Charlie Chaplin, blown, pearly wht, blk hair, 3½" 285.00
Charlie Chaplin, bsk, spring legs, 1930s, 3", EX 40.00
Cherries on ovoid, blown, pearly wht & gr, red cherries, 4" . .25.00
Cherub, Dresden, pk & bl, flat, 6" 70.00
Child w/clown hat, blown, silver w/faded colors, 3¼" . . .45.00
Church, blown, pearly wht/gr/pk/bl, bright, 4" 65.00
Clock, wall; blown, paper face, detailed molding, early, EX . .80.00
Clown, blown, pearly yel, pk stripes, 6" 65.00
Clown, Dresden, blk & wht, 4" 300.00
Clown, pk hat, yel ruffle, pk & bl ball, 6" 185.00
Comic, blown, frosty wht face, turq hat, red mouth, 6" . . .80.00
Cornucopia, crepe paper, die-cut decor 80.00
Cross on heart, blown, gold on pearly wht, 2" 24.00
Dancer, cotton, paper clothes, compo face, 5", EX 200.00
Devil, blown, yel eyes, red mouth, blk features, 4½" . . .365.00
Dog, blown, red w/wht details, 4" 40.00
Dog, Dresden, brn w/blk features, 2½x2½" 275.00
Dog barking, Dresden, silver, 2½x3" 300.00
Dog begging, blown, pearly wht w/blk spots, 4" 55.00
Dog blowing horn, pearly pk & wht dog, brn ears & ft, 4" . .150.00
Doll's head, blown, glass eyes, silver hair, ca 1910, 2¾" . .100.00
Dwarf, blown, gr, 3½" 60.00
Eagle, blown, pearly wht w/pk/turq/gr, 3" 75.00
Eagle, flying, Dresden, tan & brn, 5½" wingspan, NM 285.00
Elephant, blown, gold, 2½" 40.00
Elephant, blown, wht w/red & gold, silvered, early, 3½" . .180.00
Elephant, circus; blown, silver/red/gold, 3" 145.00
Elephant, Dresden, tan & brn w/wht tusks, trunk up, 3½" . .255.00
Elf holding money bag, Dresden, 3-D 380.00
Elf on toadstool, blown, pearly wht/orange/red/gr, early . .135.00
Elk, Dresden, tan & brn, 3" 200.00
Elk, Dresden, tan & brn w/red mouth, 2" 150.00
Father Christmas, blown, pointed hat, red & wht, early, 4" . .55.00
Father Christmas, cotton, gold Dresden belt, die-cut face, 5" . .225.00
Father Christmas on pine cone, blown, pk on silver, 3½" . .40.00
Father Christmas' head, blown, bl-gr hat, ca 1900, 3" . . .140.00
Father Christmas' head, blown, wht w/red, silvered, early . .90.00
Fish, blown, pearly yel, pk fins & gills, 5" 100.00
Fish, blown, silver w/pk & gr fins, blk eyes, 3½" 45.00
Flapper, blown, pearly wht, yel hair, 3" 75.00
Flower, blown, pk/yel/turq, unsilvered, 3" 60.00
Flower girl, flesh face, gold hair, mc flowers, 4" 140.00
Flower w/girl's face, flesh w/gold, 3" 95.00

Fox, Dresden, brn & tan, 2½" 300.00
Foxy Grandpa, blown, extended legs, mc w/silver, 4½", NM . .250.00
Frog, blown, gr on pearly wht petal, 3" 50.00
Frog climbing mushroom, yel/gold/red, 4½" 150.00
Genie, blown, yel shirt, brn face, 3½" 130.00
Girl, cotton w/bsk face, in pk swan, 4x3", M 400.00
Girl in bag, blown, yel hair, pk bag, 3" 75.00
Girl on bicycle, Dresden, gr & red w/gold bike, 5x5" 185.00
Girl sucking thumb, blown, flesh face, pk & gr clothes, 4" 85.00
Goat, Dresden, blk & cream, 3¾", NM 300.00
Goat, Dresden, blk & wht, 3" 265.00
Goldilocks, blown pearly wht face, gold hair, pk ribbon 150.00
Goose, Dresden, wht w/orange, fat, EX 200.00
Graf Zeppelin, blown, red w/wht lettering, 5" 200.00
Grape cluster, blown, red, 4" 40.00
Grape cluster w/face & red tassel, blown, ca 1910, 4½" 150.00
Guard tower, Dresden, 1900s, 2¾", VG 325.00
Hag, blown, 2-faced, pearly pk, 2" .120.00
Happy Hooligan, blown, red coat & hat, EX pnt, on clip 250.00
Hatbox, Dresden, tan, 2" 130.00
Heart, Dresden, 1½" 60.00
Hedgehog, blown, pearly wht, blk stripe/eyes/ft, 5" 355.00
Horn, blown, turq, 6" 65.00
Hot air balloon, pk cotton w/colored scrap, 13" 120.00
Indian, head blown, pearly wht w/red & yel feathers, 3½" 385.00
Indian head, blown, copper, red & gray feathers, 3" 300.00
Indian head, blown, matt face, blk hair, feathers, 2½" 185.00
Jack-O'-Lantern, blown, dk red w/wht & blk, minor wear, 2½" . .65.00
Jesus on grape leaf, blown, flesh face, gold hair, 4" 445.00
Jockey, Dresden, flesh face, pk shirt, silver horse, 3" 355.00
Jockey cap, Dresden, bl w/gold, 1900s, ¾x1½", EX 200.00
Joey Lewis, blown, pk hat, yel ruffle, 6" 265.00
Keystone Cop, blown, extended legs, EX mc pnt, 4½" 295.00
Kittens in basket, blown, pearly wht, pk basket, 3" 85.00
Kugel, ball, cobalt, Baroque cap, 2½" 45.00
Kugel, ball, cobalt, swirl leaf-end brass hanger, 4" 95.00

Group of kugels, see listings for specific values.

Kugel, ball, cobalt, 8-petal hanger, 1½" 45.00
Kugel, ball, med gr, 2½" 65.00
Kugel, ball, red, Baroque hanger, 2" .90.00
Kugel, grapes, bl, 6", EX 200.00

Kugel, grapes, cobalt, brass hanger, 4" 250.00
Kugel, grapes, gr, brass hanger, 4½" 225.00
Kugel, grapes, silver, brass clip, 5" .225.00
Kugel, grapes, silver, emb brass hanger, 7" 285.00
Kugel, grapes, silver w/gr, 8-petal cap, ca 1890, 4" 235.00
Kugel, pear, emerald gr, Baroque brass hanger, 3¾" 250.00
Kugel, pear, silver, brass hanger, 9½" 250.00
Kugel, ribbed sphere, cobalt, common hanger, 1⅝" 250.00
Kugel, turnip, silver, metal holder, lg 250.00
Lamp, blown, gold base, pk shade, 3" 22.00
Lobster, Dresden, gold, dbl-sided, 5" 200.00
Lobster, Dresden, orange & beige, 4" 300.00
Los Angeles Zeppelin, blown, pearly wht/red/gr/gold, label . . .255.00
Mary Pickford, blown, extended legs, wht w/gold, 4½" 265.00
Mermaid, blown, flesh face, pk tail, 3x4" 200.00
Miss Liberty, blown, pearly gold, yel hair, pk hat, early 200.00
Mountain climber, blown, flesh face, mc clothes, 6" 40.00
Mrs Claus, blown, pearly wht, pk dress, 4½" 400.00
Mushroom head, blown, pearly wht, yel hat, 4" 115.00
Opera glasses, Dresden, dbl, old resilvering, 1¾x3" 245.00
Owl, Dresden, gold w/brn features, 6" 130.00
Owl, Dresden, tan & blk, silk candy bag in ft 255.00
Owl in top hat, blown, turq hat & belt, gold features, 3" 65.00
Paddlewheeler, Dresden, fine details, silvered, rare, NM 545.00
Parrot, blown, silver, gr wings, red stripe, 5" 65.00
Peacock, blown, gold w/pk/bl/silver feathers, 3½" 50.00
Pear, blown, yel & pk frost, 3" 30.00
Pear, blown, yel w/red blush, unsilvered, 3½" 55.00
Pear w/face, blown, wht w/pk, 1920s, 2½" 115.00
Pelican, pk wings & ft, red beak & eyes, 4" 65.00
Pickle, blown, gr, 5" 125.00
Pig, Dresden, fat/sitting, flesh color, rare, 3¼" 265.00
Pine cone, blown, gr, 3" 35.00
Pine cone w/Santa face, blown, silver w/sanded beard, 3" 35.00
Polar bear, Dresden, wht w/blk features, rare, 4", NM 400.00
Policeman, blown, flesh face, bl uniform, 4" 130.00
Policeman's head, flesh face, red hat, 1930s, 3¾" 145.00
Potato man, blown, pearly wht, orange arms, red mouth, 3" . . .165.00
Purse, Dresden, red, 1½" 95.00
Purse, Sebnitz, 4", EX 175.00
Reindeer, blown, Germany, ca 1930, 5¼" 45.00
Rhinoceros, Dresden, gray w/red mouth, rare 325.00
Rooster, blown, red, 3" 85.00
Rose, blown, frosty wht w/pk, 3" 55.00
Rose, blown, witch's face on 1 side, candle clip, EX pnt, 4" . . .350.00
Rose w/girl's face in center, blown, ca 1900, 2¾" 190.00
Sailor's head, blown, silver, bl cap, 3" 245.00
Santa, blown, flesh face, gold tree, chenille legs, 5½" 255.00
Santa, blown, gold w/pk bag, 3" 45.00
Santa, blown, pk hat & tree, bl sleeves, 2½" 35.00
Santa, blown, red & silver, 5" 50.00
Santa, bsk, Japan, ca 1930, 4" 40.00
Santa, cotton/papier-mache w/paper holly, mk Japan, 3¾" 65.00
Santa, red scrap on frosty wht ball, 3½" 65.00
Santa in airship, scrap Santa, blown pk airship, 7" 155.00
Santa in basket, blown, red w/gold, 3" 80.00
Santa in basket, spun glass, tinsel hanger, 1920s 65.00
Santa on ball, blown, orange suit, pearly aqua ball 85.00
Santa on swan, scrap Santa, blown turq bird, 7" 100.00
Santa rides below zeppelin, wht cb w/mica flakes, 4¾" 175.00
Scotty, blown, pk w/wht spots & collar, 3" 65.00
Scotty w/bow, blown, red/gr/blk, ca 1910, 3½" 75.00
Skeezix, blown, pearly wht, pk clothes w/gr tie, 4" 90.00
Snowman, red hat, candelabrum base, clear, European 50.00

Spaniel, blown, silver w/gr ears & legs, red bow, 3" 55.00
Squirrel, blown, pearly wht w/red nut, 3" 70.00
Star, Dresden, gold & gr, flat, 4" 65.00
Star, Dresden, silver, 4" 35.00
Stocking filled w/toys, blown, ca 1900, 4" 255.00
Strawberry, blown, yel/pk/wht frost, 5" 70.00
Teapot, blown, dainty spout & hdl, pearly w/gr & pk flowers ...25.00
Thumbelina, blown, flesh face, gold hair, yel blouse, 4" 65.00
Thumbelina on rose, milk glass, EX 40.00
Tomato, blown, red, unsilvered, 3" 150.00
Truck, blown, gold/silver/red, minor wear, 2¾" 150.00
Turtle, Dresden, gray, 3½" 180.00
Umbrella, closed, blown, unsilvered, ca 1890, 10" 85.00
Uncle Sam, blown, bl coat & hat, red striped pants, 3" 235.00
Uncle Sam, blown, grotesque, pearly w/gold hair, pk suit, 6" ...365.00
Vase, Dresden, w/2 paper flowers, ca 1890, 4" 110.00
Victorian bust, blown, pearly wht, 3" 165.00
Waiter, cotton, paper apron, compo face/wine bottles, 4½" 350.00
Walnut, blown, orange, unsilvered, 2½" 40.00
Watermelon, blown, silver/red/gr, 5" 140.00
Witch, blown, wht/bl/orange/blk, unsilvered, 5" 250.00
Witch, blown, wht/blk/red, on candle clip, 5" 275.00
Wreath, Dresden, gold w/red, Santa litho, 1900s, 4½" 75.00

Silvered glass Santa with tree, 3½",
$45.00.

Miscellaneous

Key: cndl —— candle holders

Box, cigar; wood w/paper litho: girl/holly/greeting, 5", VG 30.00
Candle holder, bird, tin w/some gold, 3x3" 80.00
Christmas light, amber, expanded diamond, Brooks, 4" 95.00
Christmas light, amber, expanded diamond, 3⅜" 75.00
Christmas light, aqua, swirl rib, folded rim, Stiegel type 175.00
Christmas light, bl-violet, expanded diamond, folded rim 75.00
Christmas light, cobalt, expanded diamond, 3½" 70.00
Christmas light, cranberry, expanded diamond, flared, 4½" 115.00
Christmas light, gr, expanded diamond, Brooks, 4" 95.00
Christmas light, sapphire bl, expanded diamond, folded rim, 3" .80.00
Cow, hide-covered, glass eyes, unmk, 1920s, 2½", EX 225.00
Deer, compo, red leather harness, Germany, 1920s, 4" 110.00
Father Christmas, cb, West Germany, 11½" 85.00
Father Christmas, compo face/hands/boots, Germany, 9¼" ...585.00
Father Christmas, spun glass, die-cut torso, Austria, 5½" 85.00

Fence, wood, gr w/red berries, 10½" sq 300.00
Fence, wood/wicker, tin posts, 9-section w/2 gates, 1910 ......250.00
Fireplace, cb, Santa/chimney, light makes fire, Noma, 40", M ..150.00
Holder, feather tree; CI, 1890s, EX 65.00
Horn, silver/gold foil-covered cb, brass bell, 12½" 70.00
Lantern, Santa, dbl-face, red & wht, 6", MIB 75.00
Lantern, snowman, wht, 6" 65.00
Lights, bells, plastic cups, EX in orig box 38.00
Lights, bubble, Noma, EX 35.00
Lights, colored glass panels in tin fr, 6 on string, 3½" 115.00
Lights, Disney's Silly Symphony, Noma, EX 325.00
Lights, Mickey Mouse, plastic cups, Noma, EX 150.00
Lights, Mother Goose characters, glass, Japan, MIB 125.00
Lights, Popeye, 1930s, NM 175.00
Lights, snowmen, working strand of 5, EX 35.00
Mask, molded paper, Santa w/hat/beard, Germany, 1900, EX ..150.00
Nativity, moss-covered cb, wax figures, France, early, 6" 175.00
Nativity, plaster of paris, EX color, Germany, 4½" 50.00
Reflectors, foil, varied colors, MIG, 1900s, EX in box 12.50
Reindeer, Dresden, prof rstr, 8½" 750.00
Santa, Belsnickel, holds switches, early heavy type, 10½" 200.00
Santa, Belsnickel, w/sm tree, heavy plaster, turq coat, 4" 110.00
Santa, cb/cloth/papier-mache/pipe cleaner hands, Japan, 5" ...75.00
Santa, celluloid, 2 dolls in pack, Irwin, 1930s, 7" 75.00
Santa, celluloid face, compo boots, red felt, 1930s, 6½" 25.00
Santa, celluloid face, mesh bag coat w/stars, compo ft, 8¾" 95.00
Santa, compo head, fur beard, wood hands, Germany, 5" 235.00
Santa, cotton w/compo face, blk boots, w/switches, 6½" 75.00
Santa, orange cotton, compo face, cotton beard, 4¾" 60.00
Santa, papier-mache, orange coat, mc pnt, 7¾", EX 350.00
Santa in cb sleigh, plaster over papier-mache, Germany, 7" ...250.00
Santa in sleigh w/deer, papier-mache, Germany, 1920s, EX ...145.00
Santa in sleigh w/1 deer, celluloid, mk Japan, 13" L, VG 45.00
Santa on skis, compo & wood, bag on bk, 3¾" 65.00
Sheep, compo, Germany, 1900s, 1¼" 65.00
Spring toy, Santa, papier-mache/felt/fur beard, 6¾" 75.00
Stocking, net w/paper angel bust, tinsel trim, 1920s, 6½" 65.00
Tree, feather, bl-gr, cndl, wht German base, 58" 565.00

Tree top, silver beads and tinsel,
Victorian, 7", $65.00.

•Tree, feather, gr, cndl, rnd wht German base, 23" 195.00
Tree, feather, gr, sq wht base w/poinsettia decals, 31" 235.00
Tree, feather, gr, 5 cndl, ivory base, MIG, 12", EX 135.00
Tree, feather, gr w/frosted tips, berries, German base, 55" 525.00

Tree, feather, gr w/red berries, cndl, Germany, 18" 225.00
Tree, feather, gr w/red berries, rpl base, 13" 250.00
Tree, feather, gr w/red berries, sq, 72" 750.00
Tree, feather, gr w/red berries, wood base, 2-pc, MIG, 96" ...1,500.00
Tree, feather, gr w/red berries & base, 7", EX 95.00
Tree, feather, wht, full, rnd red German base, 14" 145.00
Tree stand, CI, gold & blk, 1920s, EX 65.00
Tree stand, CI/VG pnt, 'Merry Xmas...', pat 1931 #1,' 7" 85.00
Tree stand, Santa form, cast cement, EX pnt, 11x11" 185.00
Tree stand, tin, gr w/manger litho, 1920s, 15" dia, EX 75.00

Chrysanthemum Sprig, Blue

This is the blue opaque version of Northwood's popular pattern, Chrysanthemum Sprig. Though collectors often refer to it as 'blue custard,' in the strictest sense it is not. It was made at the turn of the century and is today very rare, as its values indicate.

Our advisors for this category are Betty and Clarence Maier; they are listed in the Directory under Pennsylvania.

Butter dish 800.00
Celery vase, rare 800.00
Compote, jelly 475.00
Condiment tray, rare, VG gold 675.00
Creamer 350.00
Cruet 725.00
Pitcher, water 900.00
Sauce dish, EX gold 145.00
Shakers, pr 450.00
Spooner 250.00
Sugar bowl, open 300.00
Sugar bowl, w/lid 425.00
Toothpick holder 250.00
Tumbler 300.00

Circus Collectibles

The 1890s — the Golden Age of the circus. Barnum and Bailey's parades transformed mundane city streets into an exotic never-never land inhabited by trumpeting elephants with jeweled gold headgear strutting by to the strains of the calliope that issued from a fine red- and gilt-painted wagon extravagantly decorated with carved wooden animals of every description. It was an exciting experience — is it any wonder that collectors today treasure the mementos of that golden era?

See also posters.

Key:
B&B — Barnum & Bailey   RB — Ringling Bros.

Banner, charging tiger & lion, RB B&B, 1940s, 18-sheet 325.00
Book, Circus in America, CP Fox, 1969, 1st ed, EX 130.00
Book, Jungle Performers, Clyde Beatty, 1941, 1st ed, EX 80.00
Calliope, RB, mtd in fancy wagon, 1920s, 120" L, rstr 13,000.00
Drawings, parade wagon; blueprints w/artwork details, EX 675.00
Letterhead, B&B, circus vignette, 1913, EX 18.00
Map, B&B, tour of United Kingdom, hard cover, 1897-1898 ...90.00
Organ, band; B&B, in fancy case, ca 1908, rstr, 72x120x42" .1,100.00
Pennant, RB B&B, cloth, smaller sz, EX 25.00
Program, Adam Forepaugh & Sells Bros, 1905, EX 60.00
Program, B&B, 1904, EX 60.00
Route book, Tom Mix Circus, 1937, EX 35.00
Ticket, RB B&B, Greatest Show on Earth filming, 1950s 2.50

Clambroth

Clambroth is a term that refers to a type of glass popular during the Victorian period. It was semi-opaque and gray-white in color, said to resemble the broth of the clam.

Box, mc florals, cut panels, eng SP holder, tub form, 5" L 60.00
Candle holder, pewter insert, early, 9", pr 150.00
Candlestick, dolphin form w/petal socket 500.00
Dresser jar, rnd shoulders, orig octagonal stopper, 4½" 225.00
Egg cup, Diamond Point, w/lid, scarce 950.00
Pitcher, appl hdl, 10½" 70.00
Vase, leaf emb rim, 6" 12.50

Clarice Cliff

Between 1928 and 1935, in Burslem, England, as the director and part owner of Wilkinson and Newport Pottery Companies, Clarice Cliff and her 'paintresses' created a body of hand-painted pottery whose influence is felt to the present time.

The name for the oevre was Bizarre Ware, and the predominant sensibility, style, and appearance was Deco. Almost all pieces are signed and include the pattern names. There were over 160 patterns and more than 400 shapes, all of which are illustrated in *A Bizarre Affair — the Life and Work of Clarice Cliff*, published by Harry N. Abrams, Inc. written by Len Griffen and our advisors, Susan and Louis Meisel, whose address is listed in the Directory under New York.

Clarice Cliff died in 1972, shortly after the Victoria and Albert Museum showed her work in retrospect, and collectors (primarily in England) began seeking and admiring her work. In September of 1982, the Metropolitan Museum of Art in New York acquired and placed on view a selection of six pieces.

Ash tray, Crocus 60.00
Ash tray, Gay Day 75.00
Ash tray, Inspiration 400.00
Biscuit barrel, Geometric, 8" 900.00
Biscuit barrel, Oriental Garden, 8" 975.00
Bowl, Bizarre, Fantasque, landscape, octagonal, 8" 200.00
Bowl, Latona, 10" 750.00
Bowl, Secrets, 8" 300.00
Candlesticks, Geometric, 10", pr 1,800.00
Candlesticks, Geometric, 3", pr 475.00
Capital vase, Archaic, 10" 4,000.00
Capital vase, Archaic, 16" 5,500.00
Capital vase, Geometric, 10" 3,500.00
Capital vase, Latona, 16" 5,000.00
Charger, Floral, 18" 3,800.00
Charger, Forest Glen, 18" 3,500.00
Charger, Geometric, 18" 3,000.00
Coffee set, AD; Floral, serves 6 ....2,800.00
Conical bowl, Delecia 1,400.00
Conical bowl, Gay Day 800.00
Conical bowl, Inspiration 1,800.00
Lotus jug, Crocus, 12" 1,600.00
Lotus jug, Geometric, 12" 3,200.00
Lotus jug, Persian 7,700.00
Lotus jug, Sunray, 12" 6,500.00
Lotus jug, Tennis, 12" 3,800.00
Tea set, Geometric, serves 2 ....2,400.00
Tea set, Picasso, serves 1 ....1,800.00
Umbrella stand, Inspiration, 36" 9,000.00

Vase, Bizarre 'Delicia,' 7", $375.00.

Cleminson

A hobby turned to enterprise, Cleminson is one of several California potteries whose clever hand-decorated wares are attracting the attention of today's collectors. The Cleminsons started their business at their El Monte home in 1941 and were so successful that eventually they expanded to a modern plant that employed more than 150 workers. They produced not only dinnerware and kitchen items such as cookie jars, canisters and accessories, but novelty wall vases, small trays, plaques, etc., as well. Though nearly always marked, Cleminson wares are easy to spot as you become familiar with their distinctive glaze colors. Their grayed-down blue and green, berry red, and dusty pink say 'Cleminson' as clearly as their trademark. Unable to compete with foreign imports, the pottery closed in 1963.

Our advisor for this category is Jack Chipman; he is listed in the Directory under California.

Jar, 2-part figure of a girl, 7", $15.00.

Bowl, Distlefink, 4½x12½x6½" 20.00
Canister, cherries on tree branch 25.00
Darner, 5" 15.00
Gravy boat, Distlefink, 6x7½", +ladle 20.00
Hair receiver, girl w/hands folded, 2-pc 20.00
Match holder, cherries on tree branch, wall mt 12.50
Pitcher, Distlefink, 9½" 25.00
Plaque, fruit 8.50
Plaque, kitten in basket 12.00
Plaque, Let's Pay Off the Mortgage 8.00
Sprinkler bottle, girl, 6½" 18.00
Wall pocket, coffeepot 15.00
Wall pocket, row of 3 red Christmas bells, gr bow 15.00

Clewell

Charles Walter Clewell was a metal worker who perfected the technique of plating an entire ceramic vessel with a thin layer of copper or bronze treated with an oxidizing agent to produce a natural deterioration of the surface. Through trial and error, he was able to control the degree of patina achieved. In the early stages, the metal darkened and, if allowed to develop further, formed a natural turquoise-blue or green corrosion. He worked alone in his small Akron, Ohio, studio from about 1906, buying undecorated pottery from several Ohio firms, among them Weller, Owens, and Cambridge. His work is usually marked. Clewell died in 1965, having never revealed his secret process to others.

Bowl, orange/gr patinae, 2¼x7½" 220.00
Candlestick, gr patina, wide base, mk/#4115-2-6, 10", pr 475.00
Ewer, brn/gr patinae, archaic wine jug form, 10½x5½" 350.00
Jardiniere, gr/brn patinae, ovoid, 11x14" 3,000.00
Vase, brn/gr to dk brn & rust, bulbous w/collar neck, 8" 450.00
Vase, bud; EX patina, mk/#345-6, trumpet form, 6" 85.00
Vase, copper clad, elaborate decor, integral ring hdls, 5" 300.00
Vase, copper clad, F-2-6, 7½" 275.00

Vase, 7", $165.00.

Vase, copper-clad Indian design, flared top, 7½" 450.00
Vase, dk/lt gr patinae, mk/#d, hdls, 10" 425.00
Vase, EX orange/gr patinae, elongated gourd #260-26, 12" 600.00
Vase, EX patina, bulbous, #140-210, metal cracks, 5" 400.00
Vase, EX patina, mk/#467, slim form, 6¾" 185.00

Vase, EX patina, mk/#472, bulbous, 6" 275.00
Vase, EX patina & color, chalice shape, 6½" 350.00
Vase, golden patina, #525-5, 7" 250.00
Vase, gr patina, cylinder, 7" 105.00
Vase, rusty brn to gr patinae, #316-2-6, 8" 275.00
Vase, unusual gr/bl glossy patinae, #259-16, 10½" 800.00

Clews

Brothers Ralph and James Clews were potters who operated in Cobridge in the Staffordshire district from 1817 to 1835. They are best known for their blue and white transfer-printed earthenwares, which included American Views, Moral Maxims, Picturesque Views, and English Views. A series called *Three Tours of Dr. Syntax* contained nearly eighty different scenes with each piece bearing a descriptive title. Two other popular series were *Don Quixote* with twenty prints and *Pictures of Sir David Wilkie* with twelve. Both printed and impressed marks were used, often incorporating the pattern name as well as the pottery. See also Staffordshire, Historical.

Bowl, Meeting of Sancho & Dapple, dk bl transfer, 7¾" 175.00
Coffeepot, Christmas Eve, dk bl transfer, high dome, EX 425.00
Coffeepot, 2 Setters, dk bl transfer, rare, 11" 775.00
Gravy boat, Yangeusian Conflict, Don Quixote series, rare 350.00
Pitcher, Water Girl, dk bl transfer, 4½", EX 250.00
Pitcher, Welcome Lafayette Nation's..., dk bl transfer, 6" 750.00
Plate, Christmas Eve, dk bl transfer, mk, 9", EX 100.00
Plate, Don Quixote & Shepherdess, dk bl transfer, 10" 210.00
Plate, Knighthood Conferred on..., dk bl transfer, 10" 210.00
Plate, Mosaic Tracery, dk bl transfer, 8¼" 40.00
Plate, Valentine, Wilkie's Designs, dk bl transfer, mk, 9" 245.00
Waste bowl, Christmas Eve, dk bl transfer, 5½" 300.00

Clifton

Clifton Art Pottery of Clifton, New Jersey, was organized ca 1903. Until 1911 when they turned to the production of wall and floor tile, they made artware of several varieties. The founders were Fred Tschirner and William A. Long. Long had developed the method for underglaze slip painting that had been used at the Lonhuda Pottery in Steubenville, Ohio, in the 1890s. Crystal Patina, the first artware made by the small company, utilized a fine white body and flowing, blended colors, the earliest a green crystalline. Indian Ware, copied from the pottery of the American Indians, was decorated in black geometric designs on red clay. Robin's Egg Blue, pale blue on the white body, and Tirrube, a slip-decorated matt ware, were also produced.

Bowl, Indian Ware, squat/bulbous, 4 Mile Ruin AZ, 5x8" 125.00
Coffeepot, gold shades, molded, bulbous, 7½" 95.00
Vase, Crystal Patina, Nouveau floral silver overlay, 6½" 800.00
Vase, Crystal Patina flambe, ball w/slim yel neck, 1906, 8" 350.00
Vase, gr, waisted neck, bulbous, #136, 1906, 5½" 55.00
Vase, Indian Ware, bulbous bottom, 10x12" 300.00
Vase, Indian Ware, geometrics, 7x6½" 165.00
Vase, Tirrube, HP floral on red, bulbous bottom, 8½x6½" 150.00

Clocks

In the early days of our country's history, clock makers were influenced by styles imported from Europe and Germany. They copied their cabinets and re-constructed their movements. But needed materials were in short supply; modifications had to be made. Of necessity was born mainspring motive power and spring clocks. Wooden movements were made on a mass-production basis as early as 1808. Before the middle of the century, metal movements had been developed.

Today's collectors prefer clocks from the eighteenth and nineteenth centuries with pendulum-regulated movements. Bracket clocks made during this period utilized the shorter pendulum improvised in 1658 by Fromentiel, a prominent English clock maker. These smaller square-face clocks usually were made with a dome top fitted with a handle or a decorative finial. The case was usually walnut or ebony and was sometimes decorated with pierced brass mountings. Brackets were often mounted on the wall to accommodate the clock, hence the name. The banjo clock was patented in 1802 by Simon Willard. It derived its descriptive name from its banjo-like shape. A similar but more elaborate style was called the lyre clock. Twentieth century novelty clocks, such as the animated examples in the listings that follow, are becoming very popular collectibles, as their values indicate. Our novelty clock advisors are DLK Nostalgia and Collectibles; they are listed in the Directory under Pennsylvania.

Key:
esc — escapement   T&S — time and strike
mvt — movement   wt — weight
pnd — pendulum   2nds — seconds
reg — regulator

A Stowell, banjo shelf, mahog/brass/rvpt, spring works, 20" ...325.00
Am Clock Co, regulator, battery impulse, oak case 450.00
Anniversary, brass, glass dome, 11" 130.00
Ansonia, Arcadia, swing arm, bronze statue, rpr, 1890, 31½" .3,000.00
Ansonia, Bagdad, wall, crest w/finial, time only 775.00
Ansonia, Capitol, porc dial, time only, spring, mahog case 950.00
Ansonia, Crystal Palace, orig oval dome, #1 Extra 800.00
Ansonia, Envoy, crystal regulator 900.00
Ansonia, General, regulator, 8-day wt, 18" dial, mahog, 68" .3,200.00
Ansonia, Gilmore, kitchen, oak, 8-day/T&S, alarm 190.00
Ansonia, Jupiter, crystal regulator, glass columns 1,800.00
Ansonia, La Rata, porc, outside esc 600.00
Ansonia, Lucia, crystal regulator 900.00
Ansonia, mantel, blk marble, 4-pillar, Boston model 165.00
Ansonia, Queen Mary, 8-day/T&S, walnut case 750.00
Ansonia, Regis, crystal regulator 475.00
Ansonia, Royal Bonn case w/floral, porc dial, visible esc 650.00
Ansonia, siren statue, visible esc, porc dial, 1906 ....450.00
Ansonia, wall, mk Scott & Kikley, Ainwick, 8-day/T&S 220.00
Atkins & Downs for Geo Mitchell, pillar/scroll, wood face ..1,250.00
Aulding, carriage, brass, enamel face, 8-day, leather case, 6½" .450.00
Austrian, Vienna regulator, T&S, mirror bk, 37" 700.00
Banjo, gilt mahog w/HP florals, pnt iron dial, 8-day/T, 33" 900.00
Banjo, mahog Fed, brass eagle atop/rvpt, 8-day weight, 33" 900.00
Banjo, mahog/giltwood, rvpt badminton scene, 40" 1,350.00
Banjo, mahog/giltwood Fed presentation, 1820, rstr, 40" 1,800.00
Banjo, rnd mvt, T&S, New Haven, miniature, 18" 300.00
Barnes-Bartholomew, 3-part shelf, rvpt, acanthus cvg, 37" 700.00
Birge & Fuller, Empire, 8-day/T&S, 33" 425.00
Boston Clock Co, mantel, onyx w/bronze ormolu, porc dial ...450.00
Brewster & Ingraham, steeple, mahog, 8-day, T&S w/alarm ...375.00
C Jerome, shelf, gilt columns, rosewood case, 18¼" 150.00
Carriage, gilt brass, cylinder esc, 30-hour, 6" 175.00
Carriage, repeating, lever esc, 8-day/T&S, gilt, 7½" 900.00
Chelsea, banjo, rvpt: Perry's Victory at Lake Erie, 31", M 575.00
Chelsea, desk, brass, beveled glass, 4½" 500.00
Chelsea, ship's, brass case, hinged bezel, 6" dial 650.00
China, bracket, MOP moldings, crown-wheel esc, 1840s, 14". 1,550.00
Concord MA, banjo, eagle atop & in rvpt glass, 1830s, 34" 700.00

Cronier, mantel, alabaster, ormolu mtd, 8-day, 17" 1,900.00
Desbois, bracket, gilt/eng dial, ebony pagoda case, 10" 2,700.00
Drocourt, carriage, repeater, anglaise riche, 1880, 7" 800.00
Duverdry, carriage, pillars, filigree, gilt dial, 1880, 6" 450.00
E Downs, pillar & scroll, mahog, 30-hr, ca 1815-1840, 31" 800.00
E Howard, #5, banjo, dial sgn, numbered mvt, rosewood 1,800.00
Eli Terry, mahog veneer pillar/scroll, wood works/rvpt, 32" ..2,200.00
Elnathan Taber, mahog/brass urn, rectangular wall mt, 35" ..8,000.00
EN Welch, mantel, iron, side urns/statue atop, 8-day/T&S 550.00
EN Welch, steeple, rpl dial, mahog/rosewood, 8-day/T&S 225.00
English, bracket, mahog, appl cvd decor, ca 1820-1830, 16" ...975.00
English, gallery, brass bezel, brass fusee mvt, 21" 550.00
Fashion, #7, dbl blk dials, calendar, walnut case 2,400.00
Forestville, octagon wall, rosewood, 8-day/T&S, 25x16½" 325.00
French, brass, Rococo, urn finial, wht porc dial, T&S, 21" 400.00
French, china w/ormolu & HP cherubs, decor dial, 18", M 800.00
French, chinoiserie, pierced brass sheet, 1920, 10½" 115.00
French, mantel, bronze/ivory dancing figure, 17" 1,000.00
French, mantel, crystal regulator, gilt, 8-day, 11" 900.00
French, mantel, crystal regulator, mercury pnd, 6½" 700.00
French, mantel, gr onyx, putto atop, ornate gilt mts, 25" 1,200.00
French, mantel, onyx w/gilt-bronze garlands, mk JED, 17" ...375.00
French, marquetry w/ormolu mts, open brass face, T&S, 18½" .350.00
French, picture frame, MOP inlay, 8-day, spring drive, 24" 450.00
G Becker, key wind, fancy face, Germany, 8" dial, 48" 650.00
G Becker, walnut, 2-weight, fancy porthole style, pnd, 50" 950.00
G Becker, walnut, 2-weight, 44" 750.00
German, key wind, regulator, fancy oak case, 38" 275.00
German, wall, walnut, open pnd, spring, 8-day/T&S 475.00
Gilbert, #10, oak, 1-weight 2,000.00
Gilbert, #11, oak, 2-weight w/spring strike 1,800.00
Gilbert, #12, jeweler's wall regulator, porc dial/lyre pnd 5,500.00
Gilbert, #6, weight drive, wall type 1,100.00
Gilbert, #64, oak regulator, weight drive 800.00
Gilbert, Curfew, mantel, blk, top bell, mk mvt 300.00
Gilbert, Lake #4, kitchen, oak, 8-day/T&S 175.00
Gilbert, mantel, blk wood, ornate columns/mts, 8-day/T&S ...150.00
Gilbert, store reg/pelican model, 8-day/T&S, orig finish 450.00
H&H France, carriage, brass, wht enamel face, key, 4⅜" 375.00
Henry Allen Hinckley, Fed mahog lyre, rvpt eagle rstr, 38" ..2,000.00
Hingham, mahog Fed banjo, pnt metal dial/flat moldings, 32" .650.00
Horlogerie J, Paris, blk onyx w/ormolu, urn finial, 15½" 225.00
Ingraham, Admiral Dewey, kitchen, oak, 8-day/T&S 425.00
Ingraham, Gila, kitchen, calendar mvt, 8-day/T&S 275.00
Ingraham, Ionic, mosaic case, 8-day/T, w/label, rstr, 22" 400.00
Ingraham, Nyanza, banjo, time only, NM 600.00
Ingraham, store regulator, calendar, orig glass 475.00
Intermittent alarm, pat 1904, 2" dia 45.00
Ithaca, #11, dbl dial calendar, 8-day/T&S, walnut 600.00
Ithaca, calendar, mahog, cvd/ebonized architecture, 20" ...1,650.00
JC Brown, steeple, etched lower glass, walnut case, 8-day 325.00
JE Caldwell & Co, bracket, inlaid mahog, brass mts, T&S, 14" .200.00
John Birge, mahog Empire mantel, eagle/scroll/acanthus, 37" ..375.00
John Sawin, mahog banjo, 2 rvpt: floral/Father Time, 32" ...2,100.00
John Sawin, mahog/veneer banjo, pnd/brass works, rstr, 33" ...810.00
Junghans, bracket, inlaid mahog, w/chimes, brass face, 17" ...400.00
Kroeber Saxonia, CI, gladiator statue, gargoyle sides, 20" 450.00
Kundo, enamel dial, 1950s 140.00
Le-Coulture, mantel, brass/glass cased, French, 9", EX 300.00
Mark Leavenworth, pillar & scroll, wood works, rvpt, 30" ...1,050.00
New Haven, banjo, rvpt ship, 29", EX 150.00
New Haven, Elfrida, oak regulator, weight drive 1,250.00
New Haven, Tambour, 8-day/T&S 85.00
Seikosha, shelf, oak, Japan, 8-day/T&S 75.00

Sessions, banjo, rvpt Colonial scene, 27" 60.00
Sessions, store regulator, time only 325.00
Seth Thomas, #10, dbl dial calendar, walnut, office 3,000.00
Seth Thomas, #18, regulator 2,200.00
Seth Thomas, #50, Sonora, w/chimes, 5 bells 475.00
Seth Thomas, #64, Empire, crystal regulator, M 550.00
Seth Thomas, Gothic, rosewood, ripple front, 8-day/T&S 350.00
Seth Thomas, mahog shelf, gilt pilasters/rvpt/weights, 25" ...195.00
Seth Thomas, mantel, dbl dial calendar, walnut, 8-day, 20" ...850.00
Seth Thomas, mantel, ornate case, porc dial, bell strike 165.00
Seth Thomas, mantel, Sonora, chime, 4 rods 375.00
Seth Thomas, parlor shelf, burled walnut, 8-day/T&S 250.00
Seth Thomas, Queen Anne, walnut, time only 900.00
Seth Thomas, regulator, bl label, ca 1854, 34" 1,800.00
Seth Thomas, shelf, mahog, 8-day/T&S, alarm 160.00
Seth Thomas, time clock, oak, orig fancy case, 60", M 800.00
Seth Thomas, time clock, 30-day, nickel bob/mvt, ca 1900 ....650.00

Shelf clock, Hopkins & Alfred, Harwinton, CT, 30-hour weight-driven movement, ca 1820, 34", $700.00.

Sidney Ad Clock, rvpt panels/pnd, 3 ad cylinders rotate, 62" .6,000.00
Simon Willard, banjo, eagle atop/rvpt, 8-day/T, 34" 1,900.00
Standard, master, electric, oak, 2 bell ringers 575.00
Stennes, New Hampshire, mirror, 8-day, weight drive 800.00
Stromberg, cherry, master/street, rstr 550.00
Swiss, regulator, lyre pnd, walnut, sweep 2nds, 8-day/T 1,750.00
Terry & Andrews, steeple, brass springs, mahog, 30-hr 270.00
Tiffany, mantel, crystal regulator, brass, 8-day, 8¼" 900.00
Vermont Clock Co, crystal regulator, mercury pnt/porc dial ...250.00
Vienna, wall, gilt cast bezel, wht porc dial, ca 1850, 38" 2,575.00
W&H, bracket, inlaid mahog, brass ft/door/face, T&S, 15" 425.00
Wag on wall, brass works, pnt wood face, 13½" 275.00
Waltham, chronometer, up/down indicator, 8-day 650.00
Waterbury, #53, oak, rfn 1,600.00
Waterbury, #67, mahog, rfn 1,500.00
Waterbury, #9, jeweler's oak regulator, 8-day/T 2,800.00
Waterbury, kitchen, golden oak, ornate 150.00
Waterbury, mantel, wht onyx/ormolu, Jennings case, 15" 225.00
Waterbury, Rochester, walnut, rfn 450.00
Waterbury, shelf, Lenox, walnut, 8-day/T&S, alarm 180.00

Welch, #11, wall, oak, rstr dial, 60" 1,500.00
Welch, #5, regulator, dbl dial calendar 1,950.00
Westclox, Ironclad, CI, alarm 80.00
Westminster, wall type, walnut, 32" 350.00
Willard, banjo, mahog w/inlay, rvpt, brass works, 33" 3,000.00
Wilmer Stennes, mahog pillar & scroll, rvpt, 31" 900.00
WS Johnson, walnut, 8-day/T&S 160.00

Novelty

Art Nouveau, digital, NM 125.00
Blessing, cowboy w/6-shooter, gun rocks, 1970s 60.00
Blessing, duck w/rocking butterfly, sm letters 40.00
Blessing, teddy bear, eyes move 35.00
British Clock Co, bicycle rider, 1895, not running, 8" 650.00
Bugs Bunny, figural, talking clock, M 100.00
Cowboy waves hat, bronco rears, Deco, copper wash, 18" 95.00
Deer, eye moves, ceramic 45.00
Diamond, satellite acts as sweep 2nd hand 35.00

Figure of man with rolling eyes, marked T. Kennedy, patent applied for 1865, 17", M, $1,500.00.

German, blksmith elf lifts arm w/hammer, 1920s 300.00
German, boy & goose, goose pecks, 1970s 50.00
German, windmill, beveled glass, pre-WWII, 1920s 280.00
Haddon, Home Sweet Home, lady in rocker, 12", VG 45.00
Ingraham, Roy Rogers 100.00
Jerome, Squire, blinking eye, 30-hr lever mvt, rpt, 17" 450.00
Keebler, bulldog w/kitten, EX 30.00
Keebler, courthouse, 12½" 400.00
Keebler, quail cuckoo, 8-day mvt, 8x7½" 250.00
Lux, brass, 2 metal pillars, 3" ball, NM 55.00
Lux, clown w/seals, animated, NM 260.00
Lux, Fire Chief Petunia 20.00
Lux, mechanical bell, digital, G 35.00
Lux, Mississippi River steamboat, Robert Shaw Controls Co ...55.00

Lux, organ grinder w/monkey, arm turns, 1930s 150.00
Lux, showboat, paddle turns, 1950 ....90.00
Lux, spinning wheel, moving treadle, alarm on top 125.00
Lux, train, steam engine, 1970 ....50.00
Lux, Village Mill, figural, alarm, 1920, EX 49.50
Mastercrafters, mechanical swing, 1930, M 52.00
Mouse & bird, bird pecks, ceramic 45.00
Musical alarm w/ballerina, animated, NM 40.00
New Haven, 2 cats chase mice on stump, chalk, 12x10" 135.00
Powder box, musical, metal, WWI 130.00
Raggedy Anne talking clock 20.00
Smith, boxing dog & bear, arms move, 1960s 105.00
Smith, rooster pecks ground, sq case, late 1950s 210.00
Snoopy, figural, battery operated 22.00
Tiempo, horse race, horse rocks, Brazil 45.00
Tiempo, police, police car rocks, Brazil 45.00
UEC, Roosevelt Band Leader, 1934 ....90.00
UEC, Spirit of '76 Drummer 100.00
Waterbury, Sambo, blinking eyes, 30-hr lever mvt, 16" 1,700.00
Woodcutter, cuckoo, people saw & chop wood, music box, M .125.00
World, figural, 3" dia, NM 50.00

Cloisonne

Cloisonne is a method of decorating metal with enameling. Fine metal wires are soldered onto the metal body following the lines of a predetermined design. The resulting channels are filled in with enamels of various colors, and the item is fired. The final step is a smoothing process that assures even exposure of the wire pattern. The art is predominately Oriental and has been practiced continuously, except during war years, since the sixteenth century. The most excellent examples date from 1865 until the turn of the century. The early twentieth century export variety is usually lightweight and the workmanship inferior. Modern wares are of good quality and are produced in Taiwan as well as China.

Several variations of the basic art include plique-a-jour, achieved by removing the metal body after firing, leaving only the transparent enamel work; foil cloisonne, using transparent or semi-translucent enameling over a layer of embossed silver covering the metal body of the vessel; wireless cloisonne, made by removing the wire dividers prior to firing; and cloisonne executed on ceramic, wood, or lacquer rather than metal.

Apple box, floral, pk & red w/gr & bl leaves on tan, 5" 50.00
Basin, dragons on turq, gallery rim, faux Wanli mk, 17" 550.00
Bottle pendant, peonies, w/lid & chain, China, 1x1½" 25.00
Bowl, dragon w/flaming pearl, dragon inside, mk, 2½x8" 225.00
Bowl, peonies/birds on dk bl w/gold clouds, China, 10" 200.00
Bowl, peonies/butterfly, mc on dk bl, w/lid, 4x8" 350.00
Box, dbl T-fret/mc flowers on red, ball ft, 1¼x3¼x1¼" 55.00
Box, diapering & scrolls on red, ftd/hinged, 3x4½x3¼" 125.00
Box, floral, mc on bl, 4-ftd, China, 1¼x3⅞x3⅛" 85.00
Box, floral/butterfly/clouds, pk/gr/bl foil, 1¾x3⅛x2¼" 75.00
Charger, allover birds/flowers on turq, 11½" 375.00
Charger, butterflies on red, fan border on dk bl, 1920, 12" 400.00
Charger, flying bird & lily on royal bl, 10¾" 325.00
Charger, phoenix on aventurine, floral/medallion band, 18" ...550.00
Charger, phoenix on red, medallion/floral border, 1900, 18" ...500.00
Desk set, well/pen tray/stamp box, vines/palmettes on dk bl ...150.00
Figure, Gods of Good Fortune, ivory faces, 14", set of 3 ....1,800.00
Figure, Guanyin, mc/turq robe, sits on oval base, 12" 300.00
Figure, horse, zoomorphics/taotie masks, lid on bk, 27", pr ...1,750.00
Kogo, mc flowers/butterfly on cobalt, Japan, 2¼" dia 70.00
Plate, Imperial dragon over mc mtns/clouds on red, 8½" 200.00
Plate, iris/arabesques, bl/blk/orchid, copper, 1880s, 12" 350.00

Potpourri, butterflies/florals, mc, 3-ftd, Japan, 2½x2" 75.00
Shaker, floral, mc on wht, blk borders, copper top, 2¾" 60.00
Smoker set, 3-part, ea w/foo dog finials, on sq 11" tray 150.00
Stack boxes, thousand flowers, mc on cobalt, set of 3, 9x5" 225.00
Teapot, florals w/foil centers on cobalt, Japan, 5¾" 225.00
Teapot, vines/flowers/taotie masks on tan, 5x6½" 150.00
Teapot, 2 phoenix birds on cobalt, bulbous, 1900, 5" 250.00
Toothpick holder, dbl T-fret/mc on cobalt, no mk, 2" 35.00
Vase, animals in mtns on wht, ovoid w/trumpet neck, 12", pr . .200.00
Vase, banners w/dragons & phoenix birds, Japan, 15" 350.00
Vase, bats/leafy boughs on T-fret ground on yel, 10", pr 300.00
Vase, bird/foliage, yel/bl/gr, foil, Japan, 2⅜" 125.00
Vase, birds/florals on turq, abstract bands, Japan, 11" 250.00
Vase, dbl T-fret cloisons, mc florals on red, China, 9" 225.00
Vase, dbl T-frets, florals, teakwood base, China, 8¾", pr 350.00
Vase, dragon & phoenix bird on cobalt, unmk, 12" 385.00
Vase, florals, 1930, 5¼" 60.00
Vase, florals on brick red, teakwood base, 8¾" 250.00
Vase, florals/jewels w/gold, Drahtemail, 5" 115.00
Vase, Kakiemon-style, prunus, bird in flight on lt bl, 6" 250.00
Vase, lg mums/birds, elaborate neck/shoulder, 32", pr 1,650.00
Vase, peonies in pk/wht, yel duck on gr, bulbous, 10", pr 275.00
Vase, prunus, wht/pk/yel on royal bl, 12x6½", pr 360.00
Vase, roses, pk & gold on pigeon blood, bulbous, 7", pr 550.00
Vase, samurai on plain lt bl, silver/enamel rim, Meiji, 12" . . .1,600.00
Vase, temple; iris/pendant wisteria on cobalt, 1900, 36" 600.00
Vase, tiger lilies on gr, SP rim & base, Japan, 10" 600.00

Charger, enamel on copper, dragon and florals, late 19th century, 23½", $1,100.00.

Clothing and Accessories

'Second-hand' or 'vintage'? It's all a matter of opinion. But these days it's considered good taste — downright fashionable — to wear clothing from Victorian to World War II styles. Jackets with padded shoulders from the thirties are 'trendy.' Jewelry from the Art Deco era is just as beautiful and often less expensive than current copies. Victorian blouses on models with Gibson Girl hair styles are pictured in leading fashion magazines — but why settle for new when the genuine article can be bought for the same price with exquisite lace that no reproduction can rival! When once the 'style' of the day was so strictly obeyed, today — in New York and the larger cities of California and Texas, in particular — nothing well-designed and constructed is 'out of style.' And though in recent days costumes by such designers as Chanel, Fortuny, and Lanvin may bring four-figure prices at fine auction houses, as a general rule, prices are very modest considering the wonderful fabrics one may find in vintage clothing, many of which are no longer available. Cashmere coats, elegant furs, and sequined or beaded gowns can be bought for only a small fraction of today's retail. Though some are strictly collectors, many do buy their clothes to wear. Care must be given to alterations, and gentle cleaning methods employed to avoid damage that would detract from their value.

Our advisor for this category is Ruth Osborne; she is listed in the Directory under Ohio.

Key:
cap/s — cap sleeves	n/s — no sleeves
embr — embroidery	plt — pleated
hs — hand sewn	s/p — shoulder pads
lgth — length	s/s — short sleeves
l/s — long sleeves	/s — sleeves
ms — machine sewn	

Apron, child's full-body; cotton print, bk tie, 1930, EX 5.00
Apron, long farm style, red polka dots, 1950s, EX 14.00
Apron, smock; lilac print on wht, bk buttons, ca 1900, EX 35.00
Blouse, blk print on ivory satin, bow/collar, s/s, 1950s, EX 8.00
Blouse, child's inner; high neck, lace trim, ca 1900, EX 22.00
Blouse, ivory silk, mc pinstripes, l/s, high neck, 1920s 35.00
Blouse, maternity, cotton, jewel neck, ¾/s, 1920s, EX 35.00
Blouse, pk nylon, s/s, scalloped collar, button front, 1950s 12.00
Blouse, rayon, ¾/s, rnd neck, band at bottom, 1950s, EX 8.00
Blouse, silk chiffon, mc beads, sm collar, s/s, 1920s, VG 100.00
Blouse, wht cotton, collar w/lace, pinch pleats, s/s, 1940s 14.00
Blouse, wht linen, butterfly lace trim, s/s, 1950s 30.00
Blouse, wool blend, ¾/s, collar ties in front, 1950s, EX 7.50
Blouse, yel silk, s/s, pearl buttons, band at bottom, 1950s 12.00
Boa, red feathers, 3x100", EX 40.00
Bolero, ivory wool, ¾/s, ca 1920s, VG .35.00
Bonnet, gray/wht silk stripe, smocking, ruffled bk, Quaker 65.00
Bonnet, sleep; pk sateen w/machine lace front, pk bow 22.00
Bustle, 2-tiered, wire mesh, adjustable, EX 100.00
Cape, rose silk chiffon, silver beads, calf-lgth, 1920s, EX 200.00
Cape, velvet, blk w/cording & beads, satin lined, EX 150.00
Coat, blk velvet, high collar, celluloid buttons, 1920s, EX 45.00
Coat, child's, linen pique, scalloped collar, Victorian, EX 45.00
Coat, man's, beige linen, MOP buttons, Victorian, EX 75.00
Collar, blk ostrich plumes, boa style w/silk ties, 1890s 35.00
Dress, beige w/beads & sequins, n/s, mini, w/jacket, 1950s 35.00
Dress, blk crepe, V neck, ¾/s, s/p, rhinestones, 1940s, EX 35.00
Dress, blk crepe w/smocking, gold metallic insert, 1940s, EX 60.00
Dress, chemise, blk beaded net w/slip, 1920s, VG 250.00
Dress, child's, dotted swiss, embr collar, s/s, sash, 1920s 25.00
Dress, christening; wht w/eyelet trim, l/s, 31" L, EX 45.00
Dress, cotton, s/s, organdy overskirt w/net, 1950s, EX 12.00
Dress, cotton, spaghetti straps, plts, label, 1950s, EX 12.00
Dress, cotton, spaghetti straps, sash, bolero jacket, 1950s 20.00
Dress, cream lawn, raglan s/s, pk embr on linen apron, EX 15.00
Dress, crepe, blk w/beads & sequins, slit up front, 1940s, EX 40.00
Dress, crepe chiffon, drapes at hips, beaded, l/s, 1920s, EX 200.00
Dress, ecru crepe, Empire waist, low neck, ¾/s, 1910, EX 225.00
Dress, ecru lace net w/silver sequins & ribbon, 1890s, VG 100.00
Dress, evening; avocado crepe w/beaded belt/collar, 1940s, EX .100.00
Dress, evening; blk/wht lace w/silk slip, l/s, 1930s, EX 70.00
Dress, evening; gray silk satin, n/s, rhinestones, 1930s, EX 75.00

Dress, evening; silk shantung, drop waist/off-shoulder, 1940s ...75.00
Dress, evening; silver metallic lace, 2-pc, 1940s, EX 140.00
Dress, evening; wht crepe tunic w/rhinestones, 1940s, EX 175.00
Dress, flapper style w/rhinestones, 2-pc, Paris label, EX 300.00
Dress, gray & wht pinstripe silk w/lace, Quaker, 1860s, EX ...275.00
Dress, gray silk, full skirt, l/s, 1880s, EX 100.00
Dress, lace over foil silk, blk beaded bodice, ca 1900, EX 90.00
Dress, linen, much embr, peplum, ¾/s, Edwardian, EX 250.00
Dress, red silk, blk trim, drop waist, 1910, EX 65.00
Dress, satin, cream w/brn net front panel, Edwardian, EX 250.00
Dress, shift, navy satin w/crepe underdress, 2-pc, 1920s, EX ...150.00
Dress, silk, metallic gold/wht over red, 1920s, VG 150.00
Dress, silk & lace, blk w/tassels on bodice, ca 1918, EX 100.00
Dress, silk chiffon, w/flowers/lace bodice, 1930s, EX 70.00
Dress, silk print, s/s, fitted, ¾/s lined jacket, 1960s 15.00
Dress, silk taffeta, l/s, 3-tiered skirt, 1850s, EX 200.00
Dress, tea; mink-edged ecru lace, pk silk slip, NY label, EX 200.00
Dress, tea; silk cut velvet, fuchsia w/gold beads, 1920s, VG 150.00
Dress, tea; silk w/chiffon, lace & beads, Edwardian, EX 300.00
Dress, velvet & chiffon, s/s, V neck, 1920s, EX 130.00
Dress, walking; worsted w/velvet trim, mutton/s, 1900, VG ...250.00
Dress, wedding; gray silk w/blk velvet, 2-pc, 1862, EX 450.00
Dress, wedding; satin/lace, peplum, covered buttons, 1950s, EX .45.00
Dress, wht lawn, l/s, lace yoke/skirt, bustle, 2-pc, EX 400.00
Dress, wht wool challis, silk embr, sm train, 2-pc, 1900s, EX ...125.00
Dressing gown, cotton, l/s, gathered yoke, lace trim, 1890s 200.00
Fur cape, mink, slash pockets, silk lined, Dupler's, M 250.00
Fur cape, sable, brn, 78", EX 375.00
Fur capelet, red fox, short, satin lined, ca 1920, EX 65.00
Fur coat, beaver, full lgth, EX 250.00
Fur coat, buffalo, full lgth, EX 200.00
Fur coat, horse hair, Crosby Frisian Furs, NY, EX 200.00
Fur coat, man's, raccoon, wide collar, full lgth, EX 450.00
Fur coat, mink gill, calf lgth, bk belt, EX 450.00
Fur coat, monkey, blk, ¾-lgth, 1940s, EX, +hat 500.00
Fur muff, Hudson seal, blk, EX 30.00
Fur muff, natural lamb's wool, EX 25.00

Gloves, wht, knotted string type, 1920s, EX 22.00
Gloves, wht, nylon, opera length, 1950s 6.00
Hat, blk straw, med brim, Spanish style, 1930s, EX 22.00
Hat, blk-swirled straw w/silk bow & ties, 1880s 80.00
Hat, cloche, rose straw, velvet flowers/ribbon, 1920s, EX 30.00
Hat, garden; lt bl organdy, 4" wide brim, ca 1930s, VG 22.00
Hat, man's, Fidora, blk beaver, 1920s, VG 65.00
Hat, man's, top hat, beaver, MA label, EX in cb box 95.00
Hat, navy straw, blk bow w/navy net band, wide brim, 1930s ...22.00
Hat, tangerine velvet w/peacock feather band, wide brim, 1940s 24.00
Hat, toque, blk velvet w/jet beads, long ties, 1860s, VG 65.00
Hat, wht straw, velvet band/bow, silk flowers, netting, 1940s ...22.00
Head band, all rhinestone, 1920s, EX 50.00
Headpiece, rhinestones form bird w/wings out, 1920s, EX 100.00
Jacket, Battenburg lace, blk w/silk lining, bell/s, EX 100.00
Jacket, combing; silk crepe, lilac w/ecru lace, EX 35.00
Jacket, peach & wht satin, l/s, frogs, peplum, 1930s, EX 22.00
Jacket, smoking; mc on blk, blk velvet collar, lined, EX 75.00
Jacket, velvet w/jet-beaded tassels, silk collar, Victorian 175.00
Long johns, off-wht cotton, drop seat, 1930s, M 14.00
Pants, beige raw linen, belted bk, sm pockets, hs, early 65.00
Pants, capri style, lemon yel, side zipper, late 1950s, EX 10.00
Shawl, blk machine lace, leaf pattern, fringed, 60x60" 75.00
Shawl, paisley, EX rich colors, 65x93" 250.00
Shawl, paisley, red shades w/blk medallion, 62x65", EX 225.00
Shoes, high button; blk, toddler's, NM 55.00
Shoes, pumps, lav satin, T-strap, ca 1925, EX 15.00
Shoes, pumps, wht satin, 1950s, EX 10.00
Shoes, strollers w/mesh cap, open toe, Cuban heel, 1930s, EX ..15.00
Skirt, riding; culotte style, tan suede, fringed, 1800s, EX 100.00
Slip, crepe chiffon, beaded, lace, l/s, G 170.00
Stockings, wht cotton, beaded top, 1840s, 22", EX 85.00
Suit, gray wool, fitted jacket, s/p, slim skirt, 1940s, G 45.00
Suit, navy silk shantung, ¾/s jacket, A-line skirt, 1940s 35.00
Suit, wool, dbl-breasted, s/p, ¾/s, plt skirt, 1940s, EX 25.00
Sweater, gold metallic knit pullover w/collar, s/s, 1950s 45.00
Sweater, mohair, rnd neck, ¾/s, button front, embr, 1950s 45.00
Swim suit, blk lace, bk ties, Catalina, ca 1960, EX 8.00
Swim suit, gr faille, halter style, Cole of CA, 1940s, G 35.00
Waist, navy silk, puff l/s, stays, bustle bk, ca 1900, EX 45.00

Cluthra

The name Cluthra is derived from the Scottish word 'clutha,' meaning cloudy. Glassware by this name was first produced by J. Couper and Sons, England. Frederick Carder developed Cluthra while at the Steuben Glass Works, and similar types of glassware were also made by Durand and Kimball. It is found in both solid and shaded colors and is characterized by a spotty appearance resulting from small air pockets trapped between its two layers.

Bottle, scent; pk, sgn Steuben, 6¾" 425.00
Bowl, pomona gr, ribbed, oval, sgn Steuben, 2x6x3¼" 200.00
Candlestick, bl, Deco base mk Silver Crest, 8½", pr 900.00
Chalice, gr/wht, sgn Stanhope, 10½" 110.00
Rose bowl, mottled, rigaree, 8" 165.00
Rose bowl, orange/bl/brn, sgn Kimball/#d, 4" 185.00
Vase, bl, opal dbl S-hdls, Steuben/#8508, 10" 1,600.00
Vase, bl, ovoid, sgn Steuben, 9½" 1,500.00
Vase, pk, classic shape, att Steuben, 6" 900.00
Vase, plum, Steuben, sgn w/fleur-de-lis, #2683, 8½" 950.00
Vase, pomona gr, ovoid, sgn Steuben, 10½" 1,000.00
Vase, wht, sgn K for Kimball/#1968-6, 6" 175.00

Gentleman's velvet court coat with embroidered florals, French, late 18th century, $750.00.

Vase, wht to gr, step-down cylinder, sgn Steuben, 12" 950.00
Vase, yel, wht int, bulbous, sgn Kimball, 7" 200.00

Vase, pink, Steuben, 6½", $650.00.

Coalport

In 1745 in Caughley, England, Squire Brown began a modest business fashioning crude pots and jugs from clay mined in his own fields. Tom Turner, a young potter who had apprenticed his trade at Worcester, was hired in 1772 to plan and oversee the construction of a 'proper' factory. Three years later he bought the business, which he named Caughley Coalport Porcelain Manufactory. Though the dinnerware he produced was meant to be only everyday china, the hand-painted florals, birds, and landscapes used to decorate the ware were done in exquisite detail and in a wide range of colors. In 1780 Turner introduced the Willow pattern which he produced using a newly-perfected method of transfer printing. (Wares from the period between 1775 and 1799 are termed 'Caughley' or 'Salopian' — see section on Caughley.) John Rose purchased the Caughley factory from Thomas Turner in 1799, adding that holding to his own pottery which he had built two years before in Coalport. (It is from this point in the pottery's history that the wares are termed 'Coalport.') The porcelain produced there before 1814 was unmarked with very few exceptions. After 1820 some examples were marked with a '2' with an oversize top loop. The term 'Coalbrookdale' refers to a fine type of porcelain decorated in floral bas relief, similar to the work of Dresden.

After 1835 highly-decorated ware with rich ground colors imitated the work of Sevres and Chelsea, even going so far as to copy their marks. From about 1895 until the 1920s, the mark in use was 'Coalport' over a crown with 'England, A.D. 1750' indicating the date claimed as the founding, not the date of manufacture. From the 1920s until 1945, 'Made in England' over a crown and 'Coalport' below was used. Later, the mark was 'Coalport' over a smaller crown with 'Made in England' in a curve below. In 1926 the Coalport Company moved to Shelton in Staffordshire and today belongs to a group headed by the Wedgwood Company. See also Indian Tree.

Chocolate pot, birds/flowers HP on wht, 6" 65.00
Coffee can & saucer, landscapes on gilt, miniature, 1½" 160.00
Cup & saucer, Cairo, red 10.00
Cup & saucer, cobalt w/gold beading & trim, miniature, 1" 95.00
Ewer, Loch Earn gilt cartouch on lt gr, scroll hdls, 8", EX 200.00
Jar, appl florals, twig hdls, ftd, Coalbrookdale, 4½", EX 150.00
Plaque, cottage/castle ruins/man & sheep, 1838, 9x12" 600.00
Plate, Banks of Dee, musical symbols, 1820s, 8" 200.00
Soup tureen, appl florals, Coalbrookdale, 13" L, EX 280.00
Urn, floral/bird in wht reserve on pk, gilt, 1880, 18", pr 1,650.00
Vase, appl florals, ftd, scroll hdls, Coalbrookdale, 7", EX 220.00

Vase, HP/appl florals on base & dome lid, 12", +2 at 11" 880.00

Cobalt Glass

Cobalt glass is characterized by its deep transparent blue color obtained by mixing cobalt oxide and alumina to the batch. It may be found in free-blown, mold-blown, and pressed glassware. See Blown Glass.

Bottle, gold stopper, 9¾", +6 5" wines & 10½" dia tray 345.00
Bowl, HP florals, bird perched in center, gold trim, 9x10¼" . . .350.00
Bowl, swan figural, 10" L 125.00
Box, HP florals, gold scrolls, lift-off lid, 3¼x5¾" 110.00
Box, HP florals w/gold, lift-off lid, 2⅜x4⅜" 75.00
Box, HP wht lace on dome lid, gold bands at base, 2½x3¾" . . .140.00
Box, patch; HP gr leaves, wht dots, 1¾x2½" dia 85.00
Candlestick, lustred, early, 10½", pr 225.00
Communion set, server+5 glasses in brass-fr container, 9" 65.00
Tumble-up, floral etched through overlay, 7½" 50.00
Urn, HP florals w/gold, w/lid, 12½", pr 390.00
Vase, HP florals w/gold, 4-ftd, flattened oval, 3¼" 88.00
Vase, HP florals w/gold band & trim, 4⅝" 50.00

Coca-Cola

J.S. Pemberton, creator of Coca-Cola, originated his world-famous drink in 1886. From its inception the Coca-Cola Company began an incredible advertising campaign which has proven to be one of the most successful promotions in history. The quantity and diversity of advertising material put out by Coca-Cola in the last one hundred years is literally mind-boggling. From the beginning, the company has projected an image of wholesomeness and Americana. Beautiful women in Victorian costumes, teenagers and schoolchildren, blue and white collar workers, the men and women of the Armed Fouces — even Santa Claus — have appeared in advertisements with a Coke in their hands. Some of the earliest collectibles include trays, syrup dispensers, gum jars, pocket mirrors, and calendars. Many of these items fetch prices in the thousands of dollars. Later examples include radios, signs, lighters, thermometers, playing cards, clocks, and toys — particularly toy trucks.

In 1970 the Coca-Cola Company initialed a multi-million dollar 'image refurbishing campaign,' which introduced the new 'Dynamic Countour' logo, a twisting white ribbon under the Coca-Cola and Coke trademarks. The new logo often serves as a cut-off point to the purist collector. Newer and very ardent collectors, however, relish the myriad of items marketed since that date, as they often cannot afford the high prices that the vintage pieces command. For more information we recommend *Petretti's Coca-Cola Collectibles Price Guide;* you may order a copy from Nostalgia Publications, Inc., whose address is listed under Auction Houses in the Directory.

Beware of reproductions — prices are given for the genuine original articles, but the symbol (+) at the end of some of the following lines indicate items that have been reproduced. Watch for frauds: genuinely old celluloid items ranging from combs, mirrors, knives and forks to doorknobs that have been recently etched with a new double-lined trademark. Still another area of concern deals with reproduction and fantasy items. A fantasy item is a novelty made to appear authentic with inscriptions such as 'Tiffany Studios,' 'Trans Pan Expo,' 'World's Fair,' etc. In reality, these items never existed as originals. For instance, don't be fooled by a Coca-Cola cash register — no originals are known to exist! Large mirrors for bars are being reproduced and are often selling for $10.00 to $50.00.

Of the hundreds of reproductions (designated 'R' in the following examples) and fantasies (designated 'F') on the market today, these are the most deceiving.

Reproductions and Fantasies

The following items have been reproduced and are among the most deceptive of all:

Pocket mirrors from 1905, 1906, 1908, 1909, 1910, 1911, 1916, and 1920.

Trays from 1899, 1910, 1913, 1914, 1917, 1920, 1923, 1925, 1926, 1934, and 1937.

Tip trays from 1907, 1909, 1910, 1913, 1914, 1917, and 1920.

Knives: many versions of the German brass model.

Cartons: wood versions, yellow with logo.

Belt buckle, no originals thought to exist (F) up to 5.00
Bottle, dk amber, w/arrows, heavy, narrow spout (R) 10.00
Bottle carrier, wood, yel w/red logo, holds 6 bottles (R) 10.00
Clock, mantel; brass, battery-op, 1908, 6x9" (R) 100.00
Cooler, Glascock Jr, made by Coca-Cola USA (R) 200.00
Doorknob, glass w/etched trademark (F) 3.00
Knife, bottle shape, 1970s (F) 5.00
Knife, fork, or spoon w/celluloid hdl, newly-etched TM (F) 5.00
Knife, pocket; yel & red, 1933 World's Fair (F) 2.00
Letter opener, stamped metal, CC 5¢ (F) 3.00
Sign, cb, lady w/fur, dtd 1911, 9x11" (F) 3.00
Sign, oval, girl w/fur, 1970s (R) 10.00
Soda fountain glass holder, word 'Drink' not on orig (R) 5.00
Thermometer, bottle figural, DONASCO, 17" (R) 5.00
Trade card, copy of 1905 'Bathtub' foldout, emb 1978 (R) 3.00
Vanity pc (mirror/brush/etc), celluloid, newly-etched TM (F) 5.00
Watch, pocket; often old watch w/new face (R) 10.00

Centennial Items

1986 was the year for the Coca-Cola Company to celebrate her 100th birthday; and amidst all the fanfare comes many new collectible items, all sporting the 100th anniversary logo. These items are destined to become an important part of the total Coca-Cola Collectible spectrum. The following pieces are among the most popular centennial items.

Bottle, gold dipped, in velvet sleeve, 6½-oz 50.00
Bottle, Hutch, amber, Root Co, 6½-oz, 3 in case 125.00
Bottle, International, set of 9 in plexiglas case 150.00
Bottle, leaded crystal, 6½-oz, MIB 50.00
Medallion, bronze, w/box, 3" dia 50.00
Pin set, wood fr, 101 pins 250.00
Scarf, silk, 30x30" 35.00
Thermometer, glass cover, 14" dia, M 22.00

Coca-Cola Originals

Ad, 1903, str-sided bottle, CC Must Be Good, 2x4", NM 25.00
Ad, 1904, Nordica, color w/coupon, 6½x9¾", NM 100.00
Ad, 1910, full color, cover of Housewife Magazine, NM 110.00
Ad, 1915, Confederate soldiers' reunion, 9x13", M 50.00
Bank, 1960s, dispenser, plastic, VG 50.00
Banner, 1950, cloth (possibly linen), rare, 18½x56", EX 125.00
Banner, 1950s, canvas, Bergen w/McCarthy, 44x64", EX 175.00
Blotter, 1904, Drink...Refreshing, Deutsch & Heitmann, NM . .100.00
Blotter, 1905, Drink a Bottle..., NM .125.00
Blotter, 1906, Delicious...Invigorating, rare, NM 100.00
Blotter, 1912, Pure & Healthful, couple drinking, NM 125.00
Blotter, 1913, Pure & Healthful, EX 40.00
Blotter, 1916, Made to Chew, CC Pepsin gum, rare, NM 500.00
Blotter, 1920, Drink CC, Delicious..., NM 100.00
Blotter, 1924, Your Favorite Carbonated..., EX 100.00

Blotter, 1926, Refresh Yourself, 2 hobbleskirt bottles, NM 10.00
Blotter, 1927, couple leans on open icebox, NM 35.00
Blotter, 1930, Off to a Fresh Start, NM 65.00
Blotter, 1931, Natural Refreshment, girl in bathing suit, NM . . .65.00
Blotter, 1932, OK, boy w/Black waiter, M 50.00
Blotter, 1934, Thirst Come...Served, boy w/cap, M 75.00
Blotter, 1935, For Duty Ahead, trainman, NM 15.00
Blotter, 1940, clown, NM 40.00
Blotter, 1942, Wholesome Refreshment, Boy Scouts, NM 5.00
Blotter, 1951, Delicious & Refreshing, Sprite boy, NM 5.00
Blotter, 1956, Friendliest Drink, NM 5.00
Blotter, 1957, Sign of Good Taste, NM 5.00
Book, 1912, The Truth About Coca-Cola 20.00
Bookmark, 1900, celluloid, heart shape, 2¼x2", VG 285.00
Bookmark, 1903, Hilda Clark, cb, 6x2", NM 250.00
Bookmark, 1906, celluloid, owl, 1½x3⅛", NM 450.00
Bottle, amber, str sides, Canada, rare, EX 85.00
Bottle, Birmingham AL, Hutchinson script type, EX 600.00
Bottle, Chattanooga, Hutchinson block type, misspelled, VG . .350.00
Bottle, display; Dec 23, 1923, w/cap: 20", NM 200.00
Bottle, gold dipped, Los Angeles 50th anniv, w/ped, NM 40.00
Bottle, Indiana PA, lt amber, EX 40.00
Bottle, misprinted 'Coca-Coca' 30.00
Bottle, Newbern NC, ice bl w/air bubbles, EX 50.00
Bottle, olive gr, 'Prorety' misprint, str sides, Canada, EX 50.00
Bottle, Portland OR, dk amber, rare, EX 100.00
Bottle, Royal Wedding, United Kingdom, 1981, M 20.00
Bottle, seltzer; gr, etched logo, Winona MN, 1920s, 26-oz 195.00
Bottle, syrup; wreath, w/cap, minor wear, NM 300.00
Bottle carrier, 1940s, wood, wire hdl, 6-pack, EX 30.00
Bottle rack, 1930s, Drink...at Home, 60" 125.00
Bowl, 1930s, gr, ceramic, emb, NM .150.00
Calendar, 1903, Hilda Clark, top only, 7¾x15", NM 1,000.00
Calendar, 1913, lady in hat, H King, 13½x22½ ", NM 1,750.00
Calendar, 1914, Betty, complete, full pad, NM 700.00
Calendar, 1917, Constance w/glass, fr, 13x32", EX 950.00
Calendar, 1921, Autumn girl, glass, 1 pg on pad, 12x32", EX . .275.00
Calendar, 1924, view of seated girl w/Coke glass, 12x24", EX . .450.00
Calendar, 1925, girl at party, fr, 12x24", EX 425.00
Calendar, 1927, lady w/bottle, prof matted/fr, top only, EX . . .155.00
Calendar, 1931, seated boy, dog at ft, Rockwell, 12x24", EX . . .400.00
Calendar, 1933, gent/lady on porch, Rockwell, 12x24", EX . . .250.00
Calendar, 1933, Village Blacksmith, full pad, 12x24", NM . . .300.00
Calendar, 1937, boy fishing/dog, Wyeth illus, full pad, NM . . .350.00
Calendar, 1942, complete, 6-pg, NM .75.00
Calendar, 1945, lady in scarf, complete, 6-pg, NM 70.00
Calendar, 1951, girl & confetti, complete, NM 50.00
Calendar, 1957, girl on skates, Canada, 6-pg, 14x14", NM 30.00
Calendar, 1963, lady looks in mirror, complete w/6 sheets 20.00
Can opener, Have a Coke, red pnt/stamped logo, NM 5.00
Cap, baseball; 1940, child sz 6.50
Cb cutout, Olympic Games of 1932, complete, 10x15", NM 35.00
Cb cutout, Uncle Remus, complete, 10x15", NM 200.00
Checkers, 1930, Compliments of CC, red box, complete, NM . . .30.00
Chinese checkers board, 1940s, no marbles, NM 45.00
Cigar band, 1940s, pictures glass, M 75.00
Clock, dome style, windup, 'Trink,' Germany, 3x3", NM 165.00
Clock, 1901, Welch Schoolhouse, oak case, octagonal, EX . .1,800.00
Clock, 1905-1907, Regulator, printed dial, Ingraham 1,200.00
Clock, 1910, oak, glass w/decal of lady, Gilbert, NM 2,500.00
Clock, 1930, mantel, brass, windup, Germany, 6x9", NM 750.00
Clock, 1940s, silhouette girl, neon, rvpt, octagonal, NM 750.00
Clock, 1950s, Drink CC, light-up, w/bottle, 14" dia, NM 275.00
Coaster, 1939, Ice Cold, silhouette girl, NM 5.00

Coaster, 1950s, Have a Coke, octagonal, EX 2.00
Cooler, 1929, Glascock, single case, EX (+) 500.00
Cushion, stadium; bottle-cap form 50.00
Dispenser, ceramic w/chrome pump insert, block letters, NM . . .65.00
Display rack, 4 stackable shelves, folds, 1 of several 50.00
Earrings, 1960s, Coke can, metal 5.00
Fan, 1900, paper & bamboo, lg florals, NM 125.00
Fan, 1911, paper & bamboo, geisha, Drink..., 1911, edge wear .100.00
Fan, 1950s, cb foldout, flower basket, EX 20.00
Fan, 1950s, wicker, EX 20.00
Glass, bell, trademk in tail, acid etched, 1930s, 4-oz, NM 35.00
Glass, pewter, etched logo, 1930s, 6-oz, in leather case 300.00
Globe, milk glass, for hanging fixture, 9x12" dia, NM 500.00
Knife, 1950s, Compliments of CC Co, stainless steel, NM 35.00
Lighter, 1950s, bottle figural, Bakelite, 2-pc, NM (+) 15.00
Lock, safety; 1930s, Kam Indor, orig box 40.00
Match striker, 1939, porc, French, 4-color, 4½" sq, NM 150.00
Menu, 1903, Hilda Clark, 4⅛x6⅛", EX 350.00
Menu board, 1960s, plastic in chrome fr, decal, EX 50.00
Menu board, 1960s, plastic in metal fr, Good w/Food, 18x30" . . .25.00
Menu board, 1960s, tin, Sign of Good Taste, EX 35.00
Menu board, 1970s, plastic, M 7.50
Needle case, 1924 or 1925, NM, ea 40.00
Notebook, 1903, glass/syrup-use charts, leather, 2¾x5¾", VG .100.00
Opener, curved bottle shape, Germany, 1950s, EX 15.00
Opener, Drink 'Over the Top,' M 20.00
Palm press, Come In, porc, red/yel/wht, 4x11½", NM 75.00
Palm press, Thanks, red/yel/wht porc, 3½x13½", NM 75.00
Pencil, mechanical; w/bottle clip, ca 1950, M 15.00
Pillow, 1970s, race car form, Matador, 15", M 45.00
Playing cards, 1943, girl w/leaves, Coke bottle, MIB 45.00
Playing cards, 1943, girl w/terrier, complete, box, NM 85.00
Playing cards, 1959, Sign of Good Taste, girl in water, MIB 35.00
Playing cards, 1961, lady w/bowling ball, unopened, M 30.00
Pocket mirror, 1906, Juanita, Whitehead & Hoag, NM (+) . . .300.00
Pocket mirror, 1907, Relieves Fatigue, Wolf & Co, NM 300.00
Pocket mirror, 1910, H King, JB Carroll Co, NM (+) 200.00
Pocket mirror, 1911, H King, Whitehead & Hoag, NM (+) 200.00
Pocket mirror, 1916, Elaine, Whitehead & Hoag, NM (+) 225.00
Pocket mirror, 1920, Bastian Bros, NM (+) 300.00
Post card, 1906, Candler Building, NM 12.00
Post card, 1907, Atlantic City, EX 10.00
Post card, 1908, bridge on Potomac, Relieves Fatigue, NM 15.00
Post card, 1910, Hamilton King, CC girl, NM 400.00
Post card, 1912, Buffalo NY market scene, Coke sign, NM 10.00
Post card, 1913, train station, Coke sign, EX 5.00
Post card, 1935, IH truck, color, NM .15.00
Poster, cb, Roast Beef Sandwich w/Coke, 10x15", EX 20.00
Radio, Bakelite, bottle figural, 1930s, 30", NM 1,000.00
Radio, can figural, EX (+) 12.00
Radio, vending machine, AM/FM, 1982, 7¾x3¼", MIB 40.00
Record set, Coca-Cola/Harrison Jones, NM 20.00
Salesman's sample, 1928, cooler, steel/emb panels, 13"L . . .2,500.00
Salesman's sample, 1939, cooler/case/kit, 8x11x9", NM 2,000.00
Sheet music, The Coca-Cola Girl, in fr, ca 1927 . . . . .200.00
Sign, 1906, tin, sf, Relieves Fatigue, 27x18½", EX 3,000.00
Sign, 1908, tin, 2 str-sided bottles, 12x36", EX 600.00
Sign, 1920s, tin, arrow figural, 2-sided, 7¾x30", EX 375.00
Sign, 1926, cb cutout, 7 Million Drinks..., 32x18", EX 750.00
Sign, 1926, tin, girl holds out glass, oval, NM 1,000.00
Sign, 1927, tin, Drink Coca-Cola, 10½x31", NM 175.00
Sign, 1927, tin, girl w/bottle, 8½x11", EX/NM 650.00
Sign, 1930s, cb, Our CC is below 40 (degrees), 9x12", EX 200.00
Sign, 1930s, emb tin, Dasco, 6x18", EX 85.00

Sign, 1930s, porc, Fount-Serv, shield, 4-color, NM 350.00
Sign, 1930s, tin, Xmas bottle, Delicious..., 12x36", EX 150.00
Sign, 1931, emb tin w/1923 bottle, vertical, 12½x4½", NM . . .150.00
Sign, 1932, 3-D cb cutout, bottle/hot dog, 20x10", NM 185.00
Sign, 1933, tin, Ice Cold, w/bottle, vertical, 54x19", EX 175.00
Sign, 1936, cb, snowman w/2 bottles, Ice Cold, 30x14", M 110.00
Sign, 1940, wood, Ye Who Enter..., Kaye display, 11x39", NM .175.00
Sign, 1940s, cb, cheerleader w/Coke in hand, 20x36", EX 75.00
Sign, 1940s, tin, 2-sided, for store aisle, 8x10", EX 125.00
Sign, 1941, cb, Woman Flyer/Thirst...Wings, fr, 20x36", NM . .100.00
Sign, 1947, porc, red/yel/wht, 12x28", NM 100.00
Sign, 1950, cb, A Great Combination, 45x22", NM 70.00
Sign, 1950s, celluloid, Coca-Cola over bottle, disk, 9", M 75.00
Sign, 1950s, light-up, Pause & Refresh, waterfall, 9x20", NM . .375.00
Sign, 1950s, neon, Coke w/Ice, colorful, M 375.00
Sign, 1950s, tin, policeman, Slow School Zone, lt rust, VG . . .425.00
Sign, 1955, sf tin, red & wht, bottle on right, 18x54" 65.00
Sign, 1957, cb, Welcome Friend, 12x14", NM 30.00
Sign, 1957, Sign of Good Taste, cut-out bell form, NM 20.00
Sign, 1960, plastic & tin, light-up, lantern form 45.00
Sign, 1960s, Big King Size, tin, 20x28", NM 50.00
Sign, 1960s, electric, Enjoy..., 12x38", EX 50.00
Sign, 1968, cb, Santa, Stock-up...Holidays, EX 30.00
Syrup can, cylinder form, worn paper label, 1-gal, VG 65.00
Syrup keg, wood, great paper label, 10-gal, EX 250.00
Telephone, bottle form, M 135.00
Thermometer, 1905, wood, heavy wear, 15x4" 90.00
Thermometer, 1915, wood, minor scuffs, 21x5", NM 275.00
Thermometer, 1923, tin, bottle form, slight fading, EX 85.00
Thermometer, 1938, tin , red w/gold bottle, oval, NM 85.00
Thermometer, 1941, tin, twin bottles, 16x7", NM 100.00
Thermometer, 1950s, tin, red/wht, oval, 30", NM 65.00
Thermometer, 1950s, tin, Robertson, bottle form, EX 35.00
Thermometer, 1960s, rnd, glass front, 12" dia, NM 65.00
Thimble, 1930, aluminum, M 20.00
Tip tray, 1906, Juanita, Delicious, Refreshing, 4" dia, NM 400.00
Tip tray, 1907, Relieves Fatigue, 4¼x6", NM 385.00
Tip tray, 1909, St Louis Fair, 4¼x6", NM 275.00
Tip tray, 1910, girl in hat, Hamilton King, 4¼x6", NM 275.00
Tip tray, 1913, Hamilton King girl, 4¼x6", NM 250.00
Tip tray, 1914, Betty, Passaic litho, 4¼x6", NM 200.00
Tip tray, 1914, Betty, slight peeling, 4¼x6", EX 85.00
Tip tray, 1917, Elaine, oval, 4¼x6", NM 125.00
Tip tray, 1920, garden girl, 4¼x6", NM 250.00
Toy truck, 1930, Metalcraft, rubber tires, 10 bottles, EX 425.00
Toy truck, 1973, Big Wheel, 3 versions, battery operated 35.00
Toy truck, 1979, Smith Miller, red, 50 made, MIB 500.00
Tray, 1909, St Louis Fair girl, oval, 16½x13½", NM 1,400.00
Tray, 1910, Hamilton King girl, wide hat, 10½x13¼", EX 300.00
Tray, 1913, Hamilton King girl, oval, 12½x15¼", EX 300.00
Tray, 1913, Hamilton King girl w/Coke, 10½x13¼", EX (+) . . .225.00
Tray, 1914, Betty, 10½x13¼", EX 200.00
Tray, 1917, Elaine w/Coke, 8½x19", NM 200.00
Tray, 1920, garden girl, oval, 13¾x16½", EX 500.00
Tray, 1920, garden girl, 10½x13¼", EX 300.00
Tray, 1921, girl w/tam, 10½x13¼", EX 300.00
Tray, 1922, summer girl, 10½x13¼", EX 225.00
Tray, 1922, summer girl, 10½x13¼", NM 425.00
Tray, 1923, flapper girl, 10½x13¼", EX 125.00
Tray, 1924, smiling girl, 10½x13¼", EX 200.00
Tray, 1924, smiling girl, 10½x13¼", NM 375.00
Tray, 1925, girl w/fur, 10½x13¼", EX (+) 150.00
Tray, 1925, girl w/fur, 10½x13¼", NM(+) 250.00
Tray, 1926, golfers, 10½x13¼", NM 350.00

Tray, 1927, curb-side service, 10½x13¼", NM 325.00
Tray, 1927, girl sips from straw, 10½x13¼", VG 125.00
Tray, 1929, lady sitting w/bottle, 10½x13¼", EX 150.00
Tray, 1930, bathing beauty, 10½x13¼", NM 200.00
Tray, 1930, girl w/telephone, 10½x13¼", EX 145.00
Tray, 1931, Rockwell boy w/sandwich & dog, 10½x13¼", EX . .225.00
Tray, 1931, Rockwell boy w/sandwich & dog, 10½x13¼", NM .425.00
Tray, 1932, girl in yel swimsuit, 10½x13¼", EX 250.00
Tray, 1933, Frances Dee, 10½x13¼", NM 275.00
Tray, 1934, Weissmuller & O'Sullivan, 10½x13¼", NM (+) . .450.00
Tray, 1935, Madge Evans, 10½x13¼", NM 185.00
Tray, 1936, Hostess, bottom mk 1937, 10½x13¼", EX 95.00
Tray, 1937, running girl, 10½x13¼", NM (+) 100.00
Tray, 1938, girl in afternoon, 10½x13¼", EX 50.00
Tray, 1939, springboard girl, Fr Canadian, 10½x13¼", NM 90.00
Tray, 1940, sailor girl, 10½x13¼", VG .45.00
Tray, 1941, skater girl, 10½x13¼", NM 100.00
Tray, 1942, roadster girls, 10½x13¼", EX 60.00
Tray, 1948, girl w/wind in hair, 10½x13¼", NM 40.00
Tray, 1950, menu girl, 10½x13¼", NM 25.00
Tray, 1957, birdhouse, 10½x13¼", NM 75.00
Tray, 1957, rooster, French, 10½x13¼", NM 85.00
Tray, 1957, umbrella girl, French, 10½x13¼", NM 175.00
Tray, 1957, 6 sandwiches/6 cokes, 10½x13¼", EX 50.00
Tray, 1958, picnic basket, 10½x13¼", NM 25.00
Tray, 1960, fishtail, Drive In for Coke, EX 100.00
Tray, 1961, pansy garden, 10½x 13¼", NM 15.00
Tray, 1961, Thanksgiving, 13½x18¾", NM 15.00
Tray, 1970, Santa, orig, not Long John Silver, 10½x13¼", NM .20.00
Tray, 1976, Canadian Olympics, NM .10.00
Tray, 1978, Capt Cook, 10½x13¼", NM 6.00
Tray, 1982, calendar, rectangular, NM .8.00
Tray, 1982, Delicious/Refreshing, KEG label/5-gal, rnd, NM 8.00
Tray, 1982, Nashville Fair, rnd, NM 5.00
Watch fob, 1907, Relieves Fatigue, brass, NM 100.00
Watch fob, 1910, Gibson Girl, celluloid, bk: Drink CC, NM . .450.00
Watch fob, 1920s, Coke bulldogs, 1½x1", EX 85.00
Wooden nickel, 1942, Galesburg Bottlers, M 5.00
Yo-Yo, 1960, red/wht plastic, cap shape, Drink..., NM 10.00

Sheet music, 'The Palms,' full-color cover, published by Coca-Cola Co., 13x10½", NM condition, $500.00.

Coffee Grinders

The serious collector of kitchenwares and country store items rank coffee mills high on the list of desirable examples. A trend is developing toward preferring items whose manufacturers are easily identifiable. Names to look for include Adams, Arcade, Baldwin Bros., Daisy, Elgin National, Elma, Enterprise, Lane Bros., Parker, Regal, and Sun Mfg. Co.; there are many others. Any of these marks found on coffee mills represent companies who were in business at or before the turn of the century.

Side mills usually have a brass tag located on the tin hopper. If the hopper was made of cast iron, the name was usually cast into the metal. Some of the less expensive versions had no identification. Decals were often used on the front of lap mills and table styles, though sometimes you will find these decals on the inside of the drawer. Because decals are prone to flaking off and fading, and since they are often destroyed when the mill is being refinished, lap and table mills are the most difficult types to attribute to a specific manufacturer. Canister mills had names and patent dates molded into the cast iron housing or on the canister itself. Commercial mills used in country and general stores were made of cast iron. Important information such as manufacture and patent dates were usually cast into the wheels, housing, or base of the mill. Such identification helps determine date of manufacture and contributes considerably toward value.

Good examples of early coffee mills are rapidly becoming difficult to find. Beware of the many imported imposters that are on the market today.

Key: adj — adjustment

A Kendrick & Sons No 1, lap, CI w/brass hopper 95.00
American Beauty, canister, w/orig cup & papers 40.00
Arcade, Crystal No 3, canister, CI w/glass hopper, ca 1910 . . . .65.00
Arcade, Crystal No 44, CI w/glass hopper, orig lid & glass 75.00
Arcade, Favorite, lap, fancy CI top & hopper 90.00
Arcade, Favorite No 27, side, CI, orig CI lid 65.00
Arcade, Favorite No 7, side, CI, grind adj front 60.00
Arcade, Imperial, lap, wood & CI, 11" .75.00
Arcade, Imperial, table, 1-lb, wood & CI, 13" 75.00
Arcade, Imperial No 200, lap, oak, CI eagle, pat 1888-1889 . . . .90.00
Arcade, Jewel, canister, rectangular w/glass hopper 70.00
Arcade, Sunbeam, canister, CI w/glass hopper, tin lid 70.00
Arcade, table, 1-lb, w/decal, Pat 6/5/1884, 7x7x12½" 90.00
Arcade, Telephone, oak box, CI front & lid, Pat 1893 . . . . . . .325.00
Arcade IXL, table, fancy CI top, wood box, crank hdl, 10½" . . .125.00
Arcade No 147, lap, fancy CI closed top, wood box 85.00
Arcade No 700, lap, w/dust cover, Sears, ca 1908 . . . . .90.00
Blacksmith made, wall funnel hopper, ca 1790 . . . . .180.00
Brighton, Wrights Hdwe, table, 1-lb, 8" 75.00
Bronson Walton, canister, tin & CI, Pat 1911 . . . . .75.00
Canister, boy & girl decal, miniature, 5½x1½" 85.00
Caravan, canister, CI works, tin hopper, ca 1910 . . . . .55.00
Chas Parker No 350, side, CI, Pat 4/1876 . . . . .65.00

Chas Parker, countertop mill, patent March 9, 1897, 12½" wheels, 16", EX, $265.00.

Chas Parker No 5005, counter, CI, 12½" wheels, 17" 425.00
Clevis Walton, canister, orig cup, Pat 7/9/1901 . . . . .60.00
Coffee Bean Roaster, CI, rnd w/holder & trivet, ca 1840s 325.00
Coles Mfg No 7, counter, CI, Pat 1887, 16" wheels, 27" 475.00
Daisy No 867, table, w/decal, miniature, 4x2½x2½" 80.00
DeVe, Holland, lap, 1950s, 4¾x5⅛x8⅛" 45.00
Elgin National No 40, counter, CI, 2 wheels 275.00
Elgin National No 44, orig CI w/eagle, 15" wheels, 24" 325.00
Elgin National No 48, 2 wheels w/eagle, orig lily decal 375.00
Elma, counter, CI w/wooden drw, 10¾" single wheel, 17" 85.00
Enterprise, counter, CI, eagle on hopper, 2 wheels, Pat 1873 . .475.00
Enterprise, counter, closed hopper, blk hdl, Pat 1873, 12" 175.00
Enterprise, floor, eagle at top, Pat 1873, 39" wheels, 72" 3,400.00
Enterprise, table, CI, brass hopper, Pat 1873, 6" wheels 375.00
Enterprise, table, CI w/CI cup, orig gold decal 40.00
Enterprise No 1, counter, open hopper, Pat 1873, 11" hdl 175.00
Enterprise No 12, counter, 2 lg wheels w/eagle, Pat 1898 . . . . .595.00
Enterprise No 216, floor, CI hopper, decals, Pat 1898 . . . . . .2,500.00
Enterprise No 7, counter, CI, 17" wheels w/eagle 475.00
Enterprise No 9, CI, brass eagle, Pat 1898, 19" wheels, 28" 525.00
Euclid No 4, counter, CI w/aluminum hopper, 2 10" wheels . . .375.00
Fairbanks Morse, floor, CI, brass hopper, 72" 1,295.00
Golden Rule, canister, CI w/glass front, wood box 225.00
Grand Union Tea, canister, red, orig writing, Pat 1910 . . . . .85.00
Grand Union Tea, table, CI, sq base, rnd hopper 95.00
Ibach stamped on hdl, dvtl walnut, iron hopper 145.00
J Fisher, Warranted, lap, dvtl mahog, pewter hopper 145.00
J Fisher, Warranted, lap, dvtl walnut, brass hopper 145.00
K&M, lap, maple box, clips on drw, aluminum hopper 35.00
KM Geschmiedeetes und Gefrates Mahlwerk, brass hopper 55.00
L&S, side, CI, mtd on orig board 65.00
L'il Tot, orig drw, miniature, 4x2¾x2¾" 80.00
Landers, Frary & Clark, canister, tin & CI, Pat 1905 . . . . .65.00
Landers, Frary & Clark, counter, CI, #50 drw, 12" wheels 425.00
Landers, Frary & Clark, lap, fancy CI top, wood box 95.00
Landers, Frary & Clark, Regal No 44, canister, tin & CI 80.00
Landers, Frary & Clark, table, CI, Pat Feb 14, 1905 . . . . .45.00
Landers, Frary & Clark, Universal No 14, table, pat 1905 . . . . . .55.00
Lap, CI, octagon shape, open hopper, 4x4x4" 65.00
Lees, canister, CI works, rnd glass hopper 55.00
Lightning, canister, CI works, tin hopper 65.00
Logan & Strobridge, Franco American, lap, CI & wood 85.00
National, coffee & spice, counter, 12" wheels, 25" 350.00
National, coffee & spice, counter, 17" wheels, 28" 395.00
National Specialty Mfg, Philadelphia PA, CI, 25" wheels 575.00
New Home, table, 1-lb, CI top, enclosed hopper, wood box 75.00
New Model, lap, CI w/CI drw, 5½x4½x5½" 65.00
None Such, Bronson Co, Cleveland OH, table, tin 45.00
Parker, side, CI, grind adj on front, Pat 1876 . . . . .60.00
Parker Eagle No 144, canister, tin hopper 55.00
Parker No 2, counter, CI w/orig decals, 9" wheels 325.00
Parker No 449, canister, CI works, rnd w/glass hopper 65.00
Parker No 5000, counter, CI, Pat 1897, 12" wheels, 17" 325.00
Parker No 60, side, eagle on tin hopper, Parker lid 55.00
Persepolis, table, CI & brass 135.00
Peugeot Freres, lap, wood box, tin-covered hopper 30.00
Primitive, lap, brass/iron/dvtl walnut, handmade 160.00
Primitive, lap, cherry dvtl, brass hopper, 4x4" 155.00
Primitive, lap, red buttermilk pnt, pewter hopper, ca 1850 . . . .150.00
PS&W No 3500, side, CI 65.00
Putz stamped on hdl, lap, walnut, brass hopper 145.00
Rock Hard, Garant-Sewaarborge, lap, 4¾x4¾x5½" 35.00
Royal, side, CI w/CI cup, open hopper, Pat Apr 15, 1890 . . . . . .55.00
RR Kreiterr, Lewisberry, York County PA, dvtl, pewter hopper .155.00

Russer, canister, porc top 45.00
Starr, floor, CI, lg wheels, 72" 925.00
Sun Mfg, table, 1-lb, orig decal, screw lid, 12" 75.00
Sun Mfg, table, 1-lb, wood, 12" 75.00
Sun Mfg, No 1080, Challenge Fast Grind, Columbus OH, 1-lb . .75.00
Swift, side, CI, Pat 1845, Pat ext Aug 16, 1859 . . . . .75.00
Swift No 13, orig metal drw, Pat 1885, 12" wheels, 19" 325.00
Swift No 15, CI, orig decals, Pat 1875, 19" wheels 875.00
Telephone, canister, wood w/no CI, ca 1900-1910 . . . . .65.00
Turkish, table, primitive, 13x7½" sq box on 28" board 125.00
Universal No 12, canister, CI & tin, Pat 2/4/1905 . . . . .65.00
Unmk, lap, common, decals, box joints, CI hopper, 8x6½x6½" .55.00
W Cross & Sons, lap, CI w/orig CI drw, brass hopper 75.00
WW Weaver, lap, primitive, dvtl walnut, pewter hopper 155.00
X-Ray, canister, glass front, wood hopper, 1908 . . . . .60.00

Coin Operated Machines

Coin-operated machines may be the fastest-growing area of collector interest in today's market. Many machines are bought, restored, and used for home entertainment. Older examples from the turn of the century and those with especially elaborate decoration and innovative accessories are most desirable, often bringing prices in excess of $7,000.00.

Vending machines sold a product or a service. They were already in common usage by 1900 selling gum, cigars, matches, and a host of other commodities. Peanut and gumball machines are especially popular today. The most valuable are those with their original finish and decals. Older machines made of cast iron are especially desirable, while those with plastic globes have little or no collector value. When buying unrestored peanut machines, beware of salt damage.

The coin-operated phonograph of the early 1900s paved the way for the jukeboxes of the twenties. Seeburg was first on the market with an automatic 8-tune phonograph. By the 1930s, Wurlitzer was the top name in the industry with dealerships all over the country. As a result of the growing ranks of competitors, the forties produced the most beautiful machines made. Wurlitzers from this era are probably the most popularly sought-after models on the market today. The model 1015 of 1946 is considered the all-time classic, and often brings prices in excess of $7,000.

Coin-Op Newsletter; Jukebox Collectors' Newsletter; Chicagoland Antique Advertising, Slot Machine, and Jukebox Gazette; and *Loose Change Magazine* are all excellent publications for those interested in coin-operated machines; see the Clubs, Newsletters, and Catalogs section of the Directory for publishing information.

Our advisor for Jukeboxes is Rick Botts; he is listed in the Directory under Iowa. Jackie and Kenn Durham advise on the other sub-categories; they are listed under District of Columbia.

Jukeboxes

AMI JDJ-200, EX orig 75.00
AMI Model A, EX orig 3,000.00
AMI Model A, rstr 3,000.00
AMI Model C 800.00
AMI Model H-200, 1957, VG orig 750.00
Capehart Orchestrope #28-F, 1928, rstr 4,000.00
Cremona #3, rstr 6,500.00
Mills, novelty Ferris Wheel type, 78rpm, EX orig 2,000.00
Mills Carousel, 5¢ coin slot, 12-selection, 1933, VG orig 800.00
Mills Throne of Music, EX orig 750.00
Rock-Ola Lite-Up, EX orig 1,500.00
Rockola #1422, 1946, EX orig 1,700.00
Rockola #1426, EX orig 2,200.00
Rockola #1428, EX orig 2,000.00

Rockola #1428, rstr 3,250.00
Rockola #1434 ....600.00
Rockola #1464, wall mt, EX 950.00
Rockola Princess, EX orig 900.00
Rockola-Gabels, oak, early 1930s, EX orig 1,800.00
Seeburg #147, barrel style, rstr 2,700.00
Seeburg #220 ....1,375.00
Seeburg #222, EX orig 1,475.00
Seeburg B, pk, EX orig 1,950.00
Seeburg B, VG orig 700.00
Seeburg C, EX orig 2,675.00
Seeburg C, VG orig 850.00
Seeburg E, gilded harp, rfn case, non-working 3,350.00
Seeburg G, M 1,000.00
Seeburg HF-100R, M orig 2,000.00
Seeburg L, M rstr 6,500.00
Seeburg L Jr, full front doors, NM orig 3,900.00
Seeburg Q, EX orig 650.00
Seeburg R 2,250.00
Wurlitzer #10, rstr 2,400.00
Wurlitzer #1014, M 4,495.00
Wurlitzer #1015, 1946, NM 8,450.00

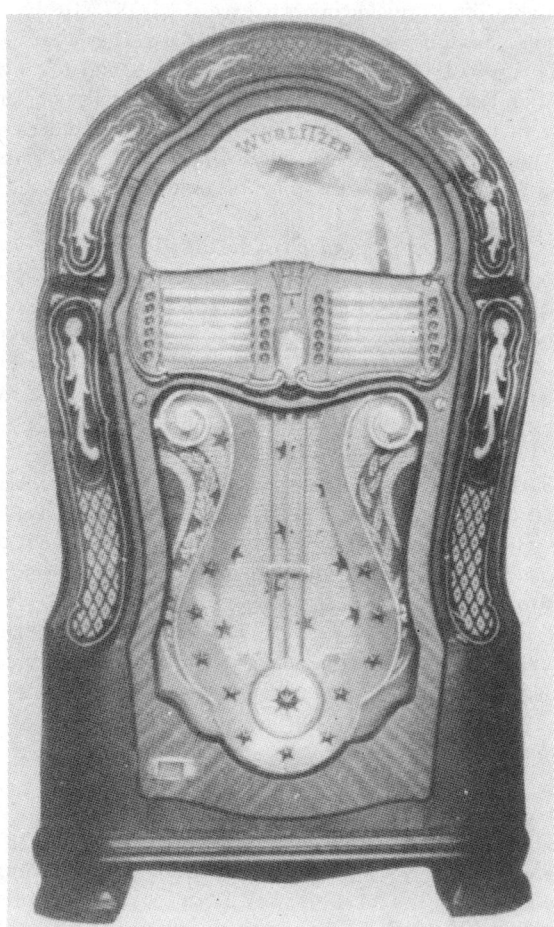

Wurlitzer Model #1080, EX original, $5,500.00.

Wurlitzer #1015, 1947, rstr 9,000.00
Wurlitzer #1100, 1948, EX orig 2,000.00
Wurlitzer #1450 ....850.00
Wurlitzer #1900 ....600.00
Wurlitzer #24, EX orig 1,750.00
Wurlitzer #24, VG orig 1,500.00

Wurlitzer #2810, EX orig 400.00
Wurlitzer #600, EX orig 1,450.00
Wurlitzer #750-E, EX orig 4,200.00
Wurlitzer #850, peacock front, VG orig 8,500.00
Wurlitzer Ambassador, 1949, EX orig 2,400.00
Wurlitzer X-7 ....900.00

Slot Machines

Bally Hold & Draw, EX orig 500.00
Bally Progressive, 1973 ....1,300.00
Bally 5¢ Draw Bell, console model, 1947, EX orig 475.00
Bally 5¢-25¢ Dbl Bell, EX orig 3,000.00
Buckley Long-Shot Horse Race, EX orig 595.00
Buckley Track Odds, EX orig 2,000.00
Buckley 5¢ '$7.50 Jackpot,' EX orig 1,400.00
Buckley 5¢ Bonanza, 1940s, NM rstr 1,500.00
Caille Blk Cat, musical cabinet, 1902, 66", EX rstr 18,000.00
Caille Jumbo Success 1,600.00
Caille 5¢ Bullfrog, floor model, 1903, EX orig 21,000.00
Caille 5¢ Bullfrog, floor model, 1903, NM orig 24,000.00
Genco 1¢ Buster Ball, EX orig 250.00
Horsehead Bonus 25¢, replated 220.00
Jennings Cigarola, rstr 3,300.00
Jennings Pace Front, VG orig 500.00
Jennings Victoria JP, 1931, EX orig, +vendor 1,500.00
Jennings Victoria Silent Bell, 1932, EX 1,750.00
Jennings 1¢ Little Duke, VG 1,800.00
Jennings 25¢ Dutch Boy, EX orig 1,500.00
Jennings 25¢ Dutch Boy-Dutch Girl, 1930s, VG orig 1,500.00
Jennings 25¢ Standard Chief, rstr 1,350.00
Jennings 25¢ Tic-Tac-Toe Sun Chief, 1949 ....1,800.00
Jennings 5¢ Duchess, rstr 1,600.00
Jennings 5¢ Lite-Up Sun Chief, 1940s, EX rstr 1,800.00
Jennings 5¢ Mints of Quality, w/side vendor & future pay ...1,600.00
Jennings 5¢ Victory Chief, ca 1941, NM rstr 1,500.00
Jennings 5¢-25¢ Challenger, rstr 3,200.00
Keeney 5¢ Super Bell, VG orig 500.00
Mill's 50¢ Hi-Top Deuces Wild, all orig, 28", VG 1,500.00
Mills Elf, EX orig 3,200.00
Mills Extraordinary Gold Award, 1933 ....1,500.00

Mills 10¢ Castle Blue Front, 3-wheel with jackpot, ca 1937, restored, 25", $1,600.00.

Mills 10¢ Castle Front 1,500.00
Mills 10¢ Lion's Head, EX orig 1,700.00
Mills 25¢ Futurity, EX orig 2,400.00
Mills 25¢ Golden Falls, EX orig 1,800.00
Mills 25¢ Roman Head, gold award, EX rstr 1,600.00
Mills 25¢ War Eagle, EX orig .1,600.00
Mills 5¢ Black Cherry, 1931, EX orig 1,500.00
Mills 5¢ Bursting Cherry, VG orig 1,500.00
Mills 5¢ Bursting Cherry, 1939, EX orig 1,750.00
Mills 5¢ Castle Front, rstr 1,600.00
Mills 5¢ Club, 4 bells/4 players, 1939, M 5,000.00
Mills 5¢ Dewey, floor model, 1898, EX orig 8,900.00
Mills 5¢ Dewey, quarter-sawn oak, anchor motif, rstr 7,500.00
Mills 5¢ Diamond Front, 1939, NM rstr 1,500.00
Mills 5¢ Golden Falls, EX orig 1,500.00
Mills 5¢ Hi-Top 1,400.00
Mills 5¢ Judge, 1899, rstr 6,900.00
Mills 5¢ Poinsettia, VG orig 1,500.00
Mills 5¢ Torch Front 1,500.00
Mills 5¢ War Eagle, NM orig .2,000.00
Pace Races, EX orig 4,500.00
Pace 1¢ Bantam, 1928, EX orig 1,200.00
Pace 5¢ Comet, EX orig 1,500.00
Pace 5¢ Deluxe Chrome, 1947 . . . . .1,500.00
Rockola 5¢ War Eagle, NM orig 1,900.00
Watling 5¢ Rol-A-Top, EX orig 2,600.00

Trade Stimulators

Ad-Lee 5¢ Try It, gumball, EX orig 400.00
Bar Boy 5¢, EX orig 395.00
Buckley Bang Tail, EX orig 395.00
Buckley Cent-A-Pack, EX 425.00
Caille Puritan Bell, CI, EX orig 750.00
Caille Puritan 3¢ Bell, 3-reel, aluminum, EX orig 595.00
Caille Royal Flush, EX orig 375.00
Caille 1¢ Ball Gum, all orig, 18x13½" 525.00
Churchill Downs, penny drop, EX orig 500.00
Columbus Bi-Mor 490.00
Daval's Poker, 5-reel, 1940s, EX 350.00
Exhibit Whom Shall You Marry, EX orig 395.00
Gee Whiz Horse Race, EX orig .350.00
Jennings Grand Stand, EX orig .395.00
Jennings 5¢ Poker, 5-reel, EX orig 375.00
Mercury 1¢, token pay out 265.00
Mercury 1¢ Pay Out, EX orig 225.00
Mills Little Perfection, cards, EX orig 650.00
Mills 5¢ Target Practice, CI, NM orig 425.00
Nat'l Penny Flip 275.00
Pick-A-Pak 1¢ Dice 450.00
Pok-O-Reel, 1940s, EX orig 345.00
Rockola Horse Race, gumball, EX orig 995.00
Shipman 1¢ Peanut Horse Race 175.00
Skilltest 1¢, oak cabinet 225.00
Smith Bros, oak penny drop, ca 1896, M orig 385.00
Stephens Magic Beer Barrel, pretzels, 3-reel, EX orig 595.00

Vendors

Abbey 3-Way, nuts 175.00
Acorn 5¢, gumball, glass top, EX orig 65.00
Ad-Lee E-Z, gumball, EX orig 450.00
Advance #11 Big Mouth, peanuts, 1923, rstr 175.00

Advance Model D, gumball, 1923, EX orig 145.00
Advance Model D, gumball, 1923, rstr 175.00
Asco Hot Nuts, 8-sided globe w/light on top, 1940s 175.00
Atlas Master, gumball, NM orig 50.00
Baker's Chocolate Chewing Gum, porc, wall type 175.00
Bartholomew, peanuts, EX orig .225.00
Beech-Nut Gum, cast metal/glass/tin, 7-column, 15" 600.00
Berkshire, gumball, orig decal 450.00
Bull's Head, perfume, CI/glass, orig pnt, 15" 3,200.00
Caille Fortune, gumball, ca 1928, NM orig 650.00
Challenger Hot Nut, 3-column, EX orig 350.00
Coast 1¢ Baseball Flip, gumball, 1950, EX orig 125.00
Coke #56, EX orig 400.00
Columbia, peanuts, rnd globe, 1921, EX 95.00
Columbia Model A 225.00
Columbus #14, gumball, aluminum 270.00
Columbus #14-X, gumball 375.00
Columbus A 1¢, peanuts, w/tray, EX 295.00
Columbus M Bulk, nuts, 1920s, EX orig 165.00
Columbus Triple, gumball, M 850.00
Coty, perfume dispenser 195.00
Exhibit Supply, cards, claw ft, EX orig 495.00
Exhibit Supply, post cards, 1937, EX 260.00
Ford 1¢, gumball, 1920s, EX orig .65.00
Hawkeye Novelty, peanuts, free portion, bell ringing, 1930s . . .275.00
Heinz Pickling Tester dispenser .495.00
Hershey's, chocolate bar, ca 1930, EX orig 175.00
Hit the Target Rocket Ship, gumball, 1950s, EX orig 125.00
Home Run, gumball, EX orig 250.00
Italian Balm 1¢, cologne, wall mt 130.00
Jacob's 5¢, cigars, holds 3 kinds, pat 1907, 36" W 1,400.00
Jennings In the Bag, puts nuts/candy in bag first, 20", NM 425.00
Kandy King, dbl-sided, EX 55.00
Lawrence 1¢, bulk, 1 column 85.00
Log Cabin, gum, EX orig 150.00
Mabe Eat 'Em Hot, nuts, 1934, EX orig 350.00
Mack 5¢, cigars, oak case, 1900-1910, EX orig 350.00
Masters 1¢, gumball, ca 1923, EX orig 165.00
Masters 1¢/5¢, low front, EX orig 195.00
Mills American Flag, stamps 175.00
Mills 1¢, perfume, orig bottles, rstr 3,800.00
Mutoscope, Old Mill, w/stand .2,250.00
Nat'l, peanuts, oak & CI, ca 1910, EX orig 675.00
Nat'l Hunter, gumball, EX orig .295.00
Nat'l Self-Service 5¢, mints & chewing gum 125.00
Northwestern #33, peanuts, CI & porc, EX orig 165.00
Northwestern #40 . . . . .95.00
Northwestern #60, peanuts, EX orig 60.00
Northwestern Rocket, gum, M orig 275.00
Northwestern Tab, gumball, EX orig 40.00
Orbit, peanuts, lg cylinder globe, EX orig 65.00
Perk-Up 5¢, peanuts, EX orig 75.00
Popperette 10¢, EX orig 1,275.00
Price Collar Button, glass/pnt CI, 11", EX orig 850.00
Pulver Gum, Clown, porc, 1899, NM 1,450.00
Pulver Gum, Foxy Grandpa, 4-panel 1,150.00
Pulver Gum, Policeman, clockwork, 1-pc, 20", EX orig 700.00
Pulver Gum, Traffic Cop, clockwork, 1-pc, 20", VG orig 450.00
Pulver Gum, Yel Kid, animated, 2-panel, 24", VG orig 350.00
Red Star 1¢, CI, ornate, SVM Co, EX orig 425.00
Regal 1¢, EX orig 65.00
Rex Gumball, CI/glass, 14", VG orig 550.00
Rex Silent Salesman, gumball, VG orig 1,000.00
Scoopy Gum, clockwork, man drops gum from scoop, 20" . . .1,500.00

Scup 1¢, matches, CI, w/cigar cutter, 13" 400.00
Select-O-Vend 1¢, gumball, EX 35.00
Selmor 1¢, peanuts, CI, EX 200.00
Silver King, w/ballerina music box .260.00
Simpson Log Cabin, CI & copper, EX orig 375.00
Soda Mint Gum, CI/wood, blinkey-eye face, 17", VG orig . . .5,200.00
Sovereign 1¢, perfume, CI steer head, 1900, EX 900.00
Toy-N-Joy, EX orig 20.00
U-Chew 1¢ 55.00
Victor Baby Grand, gumball, unusual decal, oak, 1954, M 100.00
Victor Baby Grand, gumball, VG orig 45.00

Victor Model V gumball vendor, ca 1940s, EX, $100.00

Victor Topper Deluxe, gumball, EX orig 95.00
Victor Vendorama, gumball, EX orig .35.00
Victor 1¢ Topper, gumball, glass top, 1950, EX orig 85.00
Victory Uncle Sam, stamps, enameled countertop, 1940s 85.00
Zeno, nuts, early, EX orig 575.00

Miscellaneous

Advance 1¢ Shock, w/marquee, EX orig 295.00
Automatic Games 50 Grand, pinball, 1920s, EX orig 400.00
Bally Classic Elton John Captain Fantastic, pinball 850.00
Booze Barometer, EX orig 195.00
Brantz Automatic Cashier, nickel/silver dollar/penny, EX 160.00
Buckley Digger, Deco style, EX orig 2,800.00
Caille Cailoscope 1¢ Peep Show, EX orig 1,350.00
Caille Cailoscope 1¢ Peep Show, rstr 1,850.00
Caille Hercules Strength Tester, rstr 3,500.00

Caille Mickey Finn Strength Tester, rstr 4,500.00
Challenger, pistol & ball-bearing arcade game, EX orig 225.00
Exhibit Farm Yard Shooting Gallery, floor model, EX orig . . .1,200.00
Exhibit Love Tester, light bulbs on 1 side, old, EX orig 750.00
Exhibit Supply First Striker, EX orig 650.00
Exhibit Supply Mystic Mirror, EX orig 1,400.00
Exhibit Supply Whom Shall You Marry, EX orig 1,500.00
Exhibit Supply 1¢ Photo-Scope, key wind 350.00
Exhibit Supply 3-D girlie viewer, floor model, 1940s, EX 295.00
Fireball, pinball, EX orig 1,300.00
Gatter Grip Tester, EX orig 1,500.00
Gottlieb Bank-A-Ball, pinball, 1960s, EX orig 350.00
Grandma Prophesies, fortune teller, EX orig 2,700.00
Gypsie Palmist, w/cards, EX orig 650.00
Happy Home, lg CI legs, EX orig 750.00
High Striker, strength machine, att Gatter, 1918, 96" 1,000.00
Mill's Perfect Muscle Developer, strength tester, rstr, 60" . . .2,100.00
Mills Autostereoscope, table model w/stand, EX orig 650.00
Mills Bowfront 1¢ Autostereoscope Peep Show, rstr 1,850.00
Mills Electricity Is Life, lg bow-front model, rstr 8,500.00
Mills Electricity Is Life, Silent Physician, oak, EX rstr 3,500.00
Miss America, pinball 550.00
Modern Peerless 1¢ Weighing Machine, Deco red/blk, EX orig .200.00
Monte Carlo 1¢ pinball, 1933, EX orig 250.00
Mutoscope Love Analyst, fancy cabinet, EX orig 650.00
Nat'l Automatic Weighing 1¢ Scale, ornate CI, 69", EX 1,000.00
Nat'l Shoeshine, 1914, rstr 2,100.00
Peerless 1¢ Honest Weight, NY, 68", EX orig 635.00
Peo Mini Baseball, EX orig 475.00
Rockola 10-Pin Bowler, EX orig 850.00
Scale, 1¢, CI, red/wht/bl, Am shield, 66", M rstr 1,000.00
Screwy, pinball, w/stand, EX orig .275.00
Seeburg Chicken Sam, arcade game, ca 1931, VG 850.00
Shipman Girlie Peep Show 265.00
Simpson Aristocrat, EX orig 230.00
Swami 1¢ Fortune Teller, cards 85.00
Watling 1¢ Fortune Scale 250.00
Watling 1¢ Scale, What Is Yur Wate..., porc/CI, 1920, 71" 550.00
Watling 1¢ Weight/Fortune, EX orig 275.00
Western Sweep Stakes, gambling machine, cash payout, 52" . .1,700.00
Williams Astrodome Shuffle Alley .525.00
Wizard 1¢ Fortune Teller, aluminum/wood, 19x14" 995.00
1¢ Crystal Gazer, fortune teller, EX orig 495.00

Comic Books

Public acceptance of the cartoon book as an enjoyable form of entertainment caused printing companies to experiment with size and format; by the early 1930s, the comic book as we know it today had evolved — 7" x 9" paper-back books stapled together and selling for 10¢. Each unfolded a new saga of adventure as experienced by detective extraordinare Dick Tracy; super-heroes like Batman and Robin, Superman and Wonderwoman, Tarzan, and The Lone Ranger; or the science fictional characters Flash Gordon and Captain Midnight.

Today first issues in excellent condition may bring prices as high as $300 or over. Though values on the majority of comic books are still modest, Marvel Comics #1, published in 1938, has sold for the astounding price of $35,000. Rarity, age, and quality of artwork are prime factors in determining comic book values. Condition is also important — prices below reflect examples in fine condition unless otherwise noted.

Our comic book advisor is Bob Cook of Geppi's Comic World; he is listed in the Directory under Maryland.

Action Comics #1, June 1938, EX, $20,000.00.

Abbott & Costello, #1, Feb 1948, VG+ 52.50
Adventure Comics, #282, DC, VG 18.00
Adventure Comics, #300, DC, NM 127.00
Adventure Comics, #370, DC, EX+ 5.50
Adventures of Jerry Lewis, #97, VG+ 4.00
Air Boy Comics, V8 #3, VG 11.00
Animal Comics, #23, VG 13.00
Archie's Girls, Betty & Veronica, #4, EC, VG 21.00
Archie's Pal Jughead, #25, VG 13.50
Archie's Pals & Gals, #16, EC Giant, VG 17.50
Atomic Rabbit, #6, 1957, VG 7.50
Baron Weir Wulf's Haunted Library, #21, NM 4.00
Best of Dennis the Menace, #3, 1960, NM 6.00
Betty & Veronica, #18, 1955, VG+ 25.00
Beverly Hillbillies, #1, Dell, Oct 1971, VG+ 14.50
Blackhawk, #44, VG 16.00
Blackhawk, #78, NM 43.50
Boy Comics, #46, EX 10.00
Buccaneers, #24, Quality, 1950, VG+ 22.00
Buccaneers, #25, Quality, VG+ 12.00
Bugs Bunny Christmas Funnies, #1, Dell Giant, 1950, VG 16.00
Buster Brown, #7, NM 15.00
Captain Marvel, #52, VG+ 23.00
Casper & Wendy, #1, Harvey, Sept 1972, M 7.00
Christmas in Disneyland, #1, 1957, EX 36.00
Christmas Parade, #26, Dell Giant, VG 19.00
Commander Battle, #3, EX+ 45.00
Crack Comics, #41, EX+ 31.50
Crime Suspense, #8, EC, EX+ 65.00
Davy Crockett, #8, Charlton, VG 4.00
Dennis the Menace, #8, Jan 1955, EX 18.50
Donald Duck, #29, 1953 . . . . 25.00
Donald Duck, #36, July/Aug 1954, EX 8.00
Donald Duck, Beach Party, #6, NM 15.00
Durango Kid, #12, G 33.00
Durango Kid, #9, EX+ 77.00
Famous Stories, #2, Tom Sawyer, VG 21.50
Feature Films, #2, Bing Crosby, EX 73.00
Felix The Cat, #39, Mar 1953, G 4.00
Fighting American, #1, 1960s version, VG+ 7.50
Fighting Yank, #14, NM 53.00
Four Color, #12, Gene Autry, scarce, VG 50.00
Four Color, #153, Roy Rogers, VG+ 20.00
Four Color, #16, 1st Porky Pig, Dell, 1942, VG+ 97.50
Four Color, #173, Flash Gordon, Dell, EX+ 50.00
Four Color, #207, King of the Royal Mounted, Dell, VG+ 36.00
Four Color, #214, Mickey Mouse & His Sky Adventure 30.00

Four Color, #223, Donald Duck in Lost in the Andes, EX 225.00
Four Color, #261, Mickey Mouse & the Missing Key 31.50
Four Color, #268, Mickey Mouse's Suprise Visitor, VG+ 26.00
Four Color, #31, Moon Mullins, Dell, 1943, M 71.00
Four Color, #4C-98, Lone Ranger, 1938-39, scarce, VG+ 59.00
Four Color, #422, Donald Duck & the Gilded Man, EX 75.00
Four Color, #438, Annie Oakley & Tag, Dell, photo cover, M . . 37.50
Four Color, #62, Donald Duck in Frozen Gold, ca 1945, EX . . . 300.00
GI Joe, #11, VG 7.00
GI Joe, #6, Marvel, NM 14.50
Haunt of Fear, #17, EC, 1950, G 65.00
Hi-Yo Silver, #13, EX 6.00
Hopalong Cassidy, #73, VG 7.50
House of Mystery, #185, NM 8.50
Howdy Doody, #15, early TV comic, VG 6.00
Howdy Doody, #29, 1954, NM 11.00
Huckleberry Hound, #10, Hanna Barbera cartoon, EX+ 4.00
Incredible Hulk, #1, Marvel, VG+ 250.00
It Really Happened, #8, Roy Rogers, VG 13.00
Jingle Jangle, #8, VG 16.50
Joe Palooka, #48, EX+ 13.50
Justice Traps the Guilty, #63, June 1954, EX+ 6.00
Kasco Komics, #2, Bill Woggin, 1949, VG 21.50
Legends of Daniel Boone, #1, DC, scarce, VG 30.00
Legends of Daniel Boone, #2, Oct/Nov 1955, scarce, VG+ 34.00
Little Lulu, #84, VG 9.00
Lone Ranger, #105, Dell, VG 6.00
Lone Ranger, #28, Dell, EX 31.00
Lone Ranger, #40, Dell, EX 17.00
Lone Ranger, #41, Dell, EX+ 21.00
Lone Ranger, #64, Dell, EX+ 18.00
Lone Ranger, #81, Dell, EX+ 14.50
Lone Ranger, #88, Dell, NM 18.00
Mad, #23, VG 18.00
Mad Comics, #10, EC, NM 106.50
Mad Comics, #19, EC, EX+ 51.00
Magic Comics, #33, EX+ 37.00
Manhunt, #2, VG 30.00
Marvel Family, #26, EX+ 39.00
Marvel Mystery Comics, #67, NM 220.00
Master Comics, #45, VG 32.50
Mickey Finn, #1, EX 37.50
Mickey Mouse, #36, EX 7.50
Mickey Mouse, #48, VG 3.50
Mickey Mouse, Summer Fun, #1, 1958, EX 46.00
Monte Hale, #43, VG+ 18.50
More Fun, #121, DC, EX 21.00
National Comics, #59, EX+ 49.00
New Comics, #1, DC, very rare, G 500.00
Nickel Comics, #6, VG+ 82.00
Out of the Shadows, #13, VG+ 14.00
Personal Love, #12, store stamp, VG 8.50
Peter Cotton Tail, #2, EX 11.00
Peter Rabbit, #24, Avon, 1954, VG 6.00
Piracy, #4, EC, VG+ 29.00
Plasticman, #1, Quality, G 115.00
Police Comics, #65, Quality, VG+ 37.50
Popeye, #14, wht pages, NM 36.00
Rangers Comics, #22, FH, VG 24.50
Rangers Comics, #34, FH, VG 23.00
Rangers Comics, #67, FH, EX 21.50
Red Ryder, #116, Dell, NM 12.00
Red Ryder, #137, Dell, NM 10.00
Red Ryder, #141, Dell, EX+ 9.00

Red Ryder, #95, Dell, VG 6.00
Return of the Outlaw, #2, VG 2.50
Rin Tin Tin, #15, M 4.00
Robin Hood Tales, #13, VG 10.00
Rocket to the Moon, #1, Avon, VG .95.00
Rocky Lane Western, #20, VG 8.50
Rocky Lane Western, #28, VG+ 14.00
Roy Rogers, #35, Dell, VG 11.00
Roy Rogers, #43, Dell, cover detached, G 6.00
Roy Rogers, #50, Dell, EX 17.50
Rulah, #22, Fox, VG+ 68.00
Sensation Comics, #57, DC, NM 85.00
Shock Suspenstories, #12, EC, EX .91.50
Shock Suspenstories, #6, EC, EX+ 112.00
Smash Comics, #55, Quality, VG 9.50
Space Squadron, #4, VG 20.00
Strange Worlds, #6, Avon, VG+ 64.00
Super Comics, #58, NM 42.00
Superboy, #78, DC, EX 17.50
Superman's Girlfriend, #21, EX 5.00
Sweet 16, The Phantom Postman, #6, 1947, VG 7.50
Sweethearts, #68, Robert Mitchum, Fawcett, photo cover, EX+ .16.00
Tales From the Crypt, #30, EC, VG .65.00
Tales From the Crypt, #39, VG, store stamp 31.50
Tarzan, #26, Dell, photo cover, EX .34.00
Tarzan, #71, Dell, Aug 1955, VG+ .6.50
The Texan, #10, oversize, VG+ 8.00
Tom & Jerry, #82, VG+ 5.00
Uncle Scrooge, #124, EX+ 5.00
Uncle Scrooge, #4, EX+ 125.00
Walt Disney's Silly Symphonies, #1, 1952 . . . . .36.00

Compasses

EM Sherman, Seattle, brass, liquid filled, EX in wood box 125.00
ES Ritchie & Sons, brass gimball, 9¾" dia, EX in box 100.00
J Hale, surveyor's, brass, pat Mar 10, 1886, EX orig 550.00
John Bliss, mahog, orig lamp, for sm boat 425.00
LE Gurley, engineer's, 1918, EX 55.00
Spear, surveyor's, brass, ca 1800, in display case 850.00
Star, ship's, brass, early, +dvtl wood box w/slide lid 50.00

Consolidated Lamp and Glass

The Consolidated Lamp and Glass Company of Coraopolis, Pennsylvania, was incorporated in 1894. For many years their primary business was the manufacture of lighting glass such as shades, globes, and table lamps. In the mid-1920s Consolidated introduced their Martele line, a type of 'sculptured' ware intended to resemble Lalique glassware of France. (Compare Consolidated's 'Lovebirds' vase with the Lalique 'Perruches' vase.) It is this line of vases, lamps, and tableware which is often mistaken for a very similar type of glassware produced by the Phoenix Glass Company, located nearby in Monaca, Pennsylvania. For example, the so-called Phoenix 'Grasshopper' vases are actually Consolidated's 'Katydid' vases.

Items in the Martele line were produced in blue, pink, green, crystal, white, or custard glass decorated with various fired-on color treatments or a satin finish. Their colors were distinctively different from those used by Phoenix. Although not foolproof, one of the ways of distinguishing Consolidated's wares from those of Phoenix is that perhaps 80% of the time Consolidated applied color to the raised portion of the design leaving the background plain, while Phoenix usually applied color to the background

leaving the raised surfaces undecorated. This is particularly true of those pieces in white or custard glass.

Consolidated closed its doors for good in 1964. Subsequently a few of the molds passed into the hands of other glass companies who later produced certain patterns in plain white milk glass or colors such as custard or green.

Key: MG —— milk glass

Bird & Flower, powder box, crystal, 7¼" dia 24.00
Candlesticks, birds on oval medallion, gr frost, ftd, pr 95.00
Catalonian, bowl, honey amber on crystal, 9" 40.00
Catalonian, fan vase, MG/HP pk flowers, Con-Cora label, 5" . . .18.00
Catalonian, plate, yel, 8" 10.00
Catalonian, tumbler, gr, flat, 4" 10.00
Dancing Nymph, bowl, crystal, 8" 55.00
Dancing Nymph, bowl, teal bl, 8" 80.00
Dancing Nymph, tumbler, clear crystal/satin bkground, 3½" . . .25.00
Dancing Nymph, tumbler, clear crystal/satin bkground, 5½" . . .35.00
Dogwood, vase, yel flowers/gr leaves/brn stems on wht, 10" . . .125.00
Dragonfly, vase, red w/brn cattails, tan leaves on wht, 6" 65.00
Fish, platter, w/water lilies, gr on crystal, 16" 200.00
Florette, biscuit jar, MG w/HP ivy, gold buttons, 8¾" 40.00
Florette, spooner, pk w/metal rim & hdls 70.00
Goldfish, vase, taupe on crystal, clear fish, 9¼" 135.00
Katydid, ash tray, amethyst on crystal, triangular, 5½x4" 35.00
Katydid, vase, 24k gold on MG, tumbler shape, 9" 65.00
Le Fleur, vase, salmon flowers on wht satin, 13" 135.00
Lovebird/Two-Bird, vase, pk on crystal, 6½" 65.00
Lovebirds, bowl, gr birds/pk flowers & vines on custard, 15" . . .160.00
Martele, Bird of Paradise, plate, amethyst on crystal, 8¼" 40.00
Martele, Flower & Leaf, console bowl, med bl, ftd, 11" 55.00
Martele, Fruit & Flower, sherbet, amethyst, ftd cone 15.00
Olive, vase, lt bl, ovoid, 8x4" 55.00

Martele, vase, birds in relief on transparent ruby, 6½", $40.00.

Owls, vase, honey amber on crystal, 6" 60.00
Peony, lamp, pk & aqua on custard, 13" 115.00
Ruba Rombic, whiskey decanter, smoke 190.00
Santa Maria, cigarette box, MG, w/lid 5.00
Wedding box, MG w/HP pk roses & ribbons 45.00

Cookbooks

Cookbooks from the nineteenth century, though often hard to find, are a delight to today's collectors both for their quaint formats and printing methods as well as for their outmoded, often humorous views on nutrition. Recipes required a 'pinch' of salt, butter 'the size of an egg' or a 'walnut,' or a 'handful' of flour. Collectors sometimes specialize in cookbooks issued as advertising premiums. Especially desirable are the figurals that were shaped like a jar, a slice of bread, or some other form relative to the product. Others with unique features such as illustrations by well-known artists or references to famous people or places are priced in accordance. Cookbooks written earlier than 1874 are the most valuable and when found command prices as high as $200; figurals usually sell in the $10 to $15 range.

Key: Cb — Cookbook

A World of Good Cooking, Ethel H Renwick, 1962, 270-pg 8.00
Amy Vanderbilt's Complete Cb, hardbound, 1961, 765-pg 9.00
Art of German Cooking & Baking, Mrs L Meir, 1944, 394-pg . .12.00
Aunt Jenny's Spry Shortening, 1940s 7.50
Betty Crocker's Good & Easy Cb, Golden Press, 1950s 5.00
Borden's World's Fair, 1939, EX 22.00
Calendar of Dinners-The Story of Crisco, 1915, 231-pg 10.00
Casserole, 4th ed, Olive M Hulse, 1914, 97-pg 9.50
Casual Meals, Anne Pierce, 1950, 265-pg 8.00
Colonial Recipes, Maude A Bomberger, 1907, 107-pg 10.00
Common Sense Cb, wood cover, Whitman, 1930s 15.00
Complete Round the World Meat, Myra Waldo, 1967, 457-pg . .10.00
Cooking for Compliments, Marion Young Taylor, 1954, 297-pg . .5.00
Cooking the Austrian Way, Ann Knox, 1960, 252-pg 6.00
Cuisine de France, Charlotte Turgeon, 1944, 709-pg 14.00
Dairy Cb, hardbound, Ruth Berolgheimer, 1941, 246-pg 9.00
Desserts Cb, hardbound, Southern Living, 1971, 188-pg 6.00
Easy Oven Meals, Betty Crocker, 1974, 74-pg 4.00
Family Home Cb, Melanie DeProft, 1956, 619-pg 12.00
Fish Cookery, Evelene Spencer & John N Cobb, 1921, 348-pg . .12.50
French Cooking for Everyone, Alfred Guerot, 1963, 204-pg 9.00
Good Food & How to Cook It, Ann Seranne's, 1972, 282-pg . . .10.00
Good Meals...Prepare Them, Fisher, Good Housekeeping, 1927 .15.00
Grandma's Cooking, Allen Keller, 1955, 232-pg 7.00
Guide of Good Cooking, Five Roses Flour Co, 1938 . . . . .15.00
Happy Eating, Frances Warfield Newell, autographed, 1952 . . . .10.00
Herbs for Urbans, 3rd ed, Katerine van der Veer, 1938, 95-pg 6.00
Jack Bailey's What's Cookin', hardbound, 1947, 180-pg 9.00
Jell-O, Jack Benny & Mary Livingston, 1937 . . . . .15.00
Joy of Chinese Cooking, Doreen Yen Hung Feng, 1974, 219-pg . .5.00
Lessons in Gourmet Cooking, Libby Hillman, 1963, 308-pg 7.00
Let's Cook It Right, Adelle Davis, 1947, 563-pg 7.00
Lowney's Cb, hardbound, Marie Willett Howard, 1907, 346-pg .36.00
Mary Blake's Carnation Milk Recipes, 1928 . . . . .7.50
Melrose Honey of Roses, Sterling Graham, 1942, 95-pg 17.00
Mexican Cb, Erna Fergusson, 1945, 118-pg 8.00
Mrs Allen on Cooking-Menu-Service, hardbound, '24, 929-pg . .16.00
New American Cb, Lily Wallace, 1945, 870-pg 9.00
New Cb of Favorite Breads, Ada Lou Roberts, 1970, 187-pg 7.00
New Winston Cb, Helen Cramp, 1922, 479-pg 17.00
One-Burner Cookery, Flara Harris, 1940, 177-pg 5.00
One-Piece Dinners, Mary D Chambers, 1925, 181-pg 6.00
Pearl's Kitchen, hardbound, Pearl Bailey, 1973, 206-pg 4.00
Peter Hunt's Cape Cod Cb, hardbound, 1954, 174-pg 7.50
Pillsbury Bake-Off Cake Cb, hardbound, 1969, 139-pg 6.00
Plan-Ahead Cb, Ceil Dyer, 1969, 233-pg 5.00

Practical Cooking & Dinner, Mrs M Henderson, 1877, 358-pg . .15.00
Science of Food & Cookery, HS Anderson, Pacific Press, 1921 . .18.00
Settlement Cb, 20th ed, Mrs Simon Kander, 1934, 624-pg 20.00
Seven Wonders of Cooking World, M Waldo, 1971, 415-pg . . .10.00
Sour Cream Cookery, Barbara Brown, 1947, 235-pg 10.00
Thoughts for Food-A Menu Aid, 1st ed, IPC, 1938, 312-pg 10.00
Toll House Recipes, Ruth Wakefield, 1940, 265-pg 5.00
Twelve Days of Christmas Cb, Susanne Huntley, 1965, 129-pg . . .6.00
Venus in the Kitchen, Pilaff Bey, 1953, 185-pg 6.50
Watkins Almanac Home Doctor & Cb, 1913 . . . . .15.00
West Coast Cb, hardbound, Helen Brown, 1952, 411-pg 5.00
White House Cb, H Ziemann & Mrs FL Gilette, 1923, 533-pg . .48.00
Woman's Favorite Cb, Ann R Gregory, 1902, 551-pg 45.00
You'll Eat It Up, 1st ed, Charlotte Adams, 1943, 295-pg 12.00

Cookie Cutters

Early hand-fashioned cookie cutters have recently been commanding stiff prices at country auctions, and the ranks of interested collectors are growing steadily. Especially valuable are the figural cutters; and the more complicated the design, the higher the price. A follow-up of the carved wooden cookie boards, the first cutters were probably made by itinerant tinkers from left-over or recycled pieces of tin. Though most of the eighteenth-century examples are now in museums or collections, it is still possible to find some good cutters from the late 1800s when changes in the manufacture of tin resulted in a thinner, less expensive material. The width of the cutting strip is often a good indicator of age — the wider the strip, the older the cutter. While the very early cutters were 1" to 1½" deep, by the twenties and thirties, many were less than ½" deep. Crude, spotty soldering indicates an older cutter, while a thin line of solder usually tends to suggest a much later manufacture. The shape of the backplate is another clue. Later cutters will have oval, round, or rectangular backs, while on the earlier type the back was cut to follow the lines of the design. Cookie cutters usually vary from 2" to 4" in size, but gingerbread men were often made as tall as 12". Birds, fish, hearts, and tulips are common; simple versions can be purchased for as little as $12.00 to $15.00. The larger figurals, especially those with more imaginative details, often bring $75.00 and up.

Boot, lady's, 3½" 30.00
Cello, flat bk, ca 1830, 6" 195.00
Dove, flat bk, 4½" 85.00
Heart, 1800s, 3x2½x2¼" 14.00
Horse, prancing, bobtail, flat bk, 6½x7½" 250.00
Lady w/sm arms & full skirt, late 1800s, 4x3x½" 18.00
Man in crescent moon, flat bk, 4" 29.00
Pony, 4½" 40.00
Rabbit, jumping, fat, 1800s, 6x4x¾" 25.00
Rooster, lg crimped tail, 6" 150.00
Violin, 5½" 55.00

Turkey, 3½x4½", $55.00; Bird, 3¼x5", $45.00.

Cookie Jars

The appeal of the cookie jar is universal; folks of all ages, both male and female, love to collect 'em! The early thirties' heavy stoneware jars of a rather nondescript nature quickly gave way to figurals of every type imaginable. Those from the mid to late thirties were often decorated over the glaze with 'cold paint,' but by the early forties underglaze decorating resulted in cheerful, bright, permanent colors and cookie jars that still have a new look forty years later.

Unmarked jars, unless properly identified and rare, bring the lowest prices, while cookie jars trimmed in gold are usually highly valued. The examples listed below were made by companies other than those found elsewhere in this book; see also specific manufacturers. For further study, we recommend *An Illustrated Guide to Cookie Jars* by Ermagene Westfall.

See specific manufactures such as Brush, Metlox, and McCoy.

After School Cookies, mk 741 USA, American Bisque	20.00
Albert Apple, Pee Dee Co	40.00
Animal Cookies, mk USA, American Bisque	15.00
Apple, mk USA, American Bisque	15.00
Atlantic Owl	10.00
Baseball Boy w/Bat, mk 875 USA	40.00
Bear, eyes closed, pnt indented dots, 130-USA, Am Bisque	22.00
Bear, eyes open, unmk American Bisque	20.00
Bear on Stump w/Sucker, brn, Twin Winton	35.00
Bear w/Cookie, American Bisque	30.00
Bell, Ring for Cookies, mk USA, American Bisque	15.00
Big Bird, Muppets Inc No 971, California Originals	55.00
Blackboard Bum, American Bisque	55.00
Blackboard Little Girl, mk USA, American Bisque	25.00
Blackboard Schoolboy, mk USA, American Bisque	25.00
Boots, mk USA, American Bisque	30.00
Boy, red hair, gr hat, Robinson Ransbottom	30.00
Brownie, Robinson Ransbottom	45.00
Buck Lamb, American Bisque	20.00
Bunny Rabbit Sheriff, Twin Winton	15.00
Bus, Disney characters in windows, Walt Disney	125.00

Campbell Kid, nodding head, marked DA — AR in oval with superimposed V, $65.00.

Captain, Robinson Ransbottom	45.00
Casper, cookie in hand, wht, Harvey Productions Inc	125.00

Cat, brn/yel, pk bow, unmk American Bisque	20.00
Cat, pnt indented dots, mk 131-A USA, American Bisque	25.00
Cat in Basket, unknown mfg	20.00
Cat on Beehive, American Bisque	25.00
Cheerleaders, mk 802 USA Corner Cookie Jar, Am Bisque	35.00
Chef, Nat'l Silver, M	150.00
Chef, Pearl China	150.00
Chef, Robinson Ransbottom	24.00
Chef w/Bowl of Eggs, Robinson Ransbottom	75.00
Chick w/Tam, American Bisque	35.00
Chicken, Twin Winton	18.50
Churn, American Bisque	15.00
Churn, red flowers, 24k gold trim, American Bisque	20.00
Circus Barker w/Bl Derby, lt bl/pk	75.00
Clown, indented pnt dots, mk 126-A USA, American Bisque	25.00
Clown, mk Design Patent 17119, American Bisque	20.00
Clown, pastel bl/red, mk USA, American Bisque	15.00
Clown Carousel, mk Made in Japan	30.00
Clown on Stage, mk 805 USA, American Bisque	30.00
Cockapoo, wht/orange head	15.00
Collegiate Owl, mk USA, American Bisque	20.00
Cookie Barrel, American Bisque	20.00
Cookie Cop, Pfaltzgraff	35.00
Cookie Truck, mk USA, American Bisque	30.00
Cottage, Twin Winton CA USA	35.00
Cow Jumped Over the Moon, no gold, Robinson Ransbottom	40.00
Cow Jumped Over the Moon, gold trim, Robinson Ransbottom	65.00
Cup & Cookies Coffeepot, American Bisque	30.00
Davy Crockett Head, Regal	95.00
Davy Crockett w/Rifle	125.00
Dog in Basket, G	25.00
Donkey w/Milk Wagon, American Bisque	30.00
Dove, gr or pk, Fapco	18.00
Dumbo, mk Pat Turnabout 4-in-1 Dumbo Walt Disney	95.00
Dutch Boy, American Bisque	30.00
Dutch Boy, Pottery Guild	20.00
Dutch Girl, Pottery Guild	20.00
Dutch Girl, Twin Winton	25.00
Ee-Yore, Disney	50.00
Elephant, brn, wht sailor hat, Twin Winton	25.00
Elephant, pastel bl/red, mk USA, American Bisque	20.00
Elephant, sailor, Treasure Craft	25.00
Elf Bakery Tree Stump, Keebler	20.00
Elsie the Cow	135.00
Elves & Schoolhouse	25.00
Farmer Pig, American Bisque	30.00
Fire Chief, hat w/#1 in front, Robinson Ransbottom	40.00
Flasher Clown, American Bisque	40.00
Flowers & dots on brn, Mar-Crest Oven Proof Stoneware USA	30.00
Frog, legs Xd, mk 106 USA	50.00
Gingerbread House	40.00
Glamour Boy Rooster, Artcraft of CA	40.00
Granny, American Bisque	30.00
Howdy Doody	200.00
Hubert Lion, Harris bank, Regal China	125.00
Irishman, Germany	175.00
Jack-in-the Box, American Bisque	35.00
Keystone Cop, mk GK1 USA	40.00
Kittens w/Ball of Yarn, American Bisque	25.00
Kraft Bear, Regal, lg	75.00
Lamb, brn, Twin Winton	25.00
Lamb, mk Design Patent Applied AB Co, American Bisque	20.00
Little Schoolhouse, red/wht/bl	65.00
Majorette, unmk American Bisque	35.00

Keystone Cop, Twin Wintons, $100.00.

Mammy, mk NS, Nat'l Silver Co 85.00
Mammy, Pearl China 200.00
Merry-Go-Round, mk USA 20.00
Mickey/Minnie Mouse, Turnabout, Disney 60.00
Milk Wagon, American Bisque 35.00
Monk, Thou Shalt Not Steal, Twin Winton 25.00
Monk, Treasure Craft 25.00
Monkey, Treasure Craft 15.00
Oscar, Robinson Ransbottom 20.00
Peter Peter Pumpkin Eater, Robinson Ransbottom ...48.00
Pig, American Bisque 35.00
Pig, boy or girl, unmk American Bisque 25.00
Pig, mk Design Patent...AB Co, American Bisque 25.00
Pig, pnt/indented dots, mk 128-A USA, American Bisque ..25.00
Pig w/Patch on Pants, mk USA, American Bisque 35.00
Pine Cones Coffeepot, mk USA, American Bisque 25.00
Poo Bear w/Bee, Disney 30.00
Poodle, behind counter, Twin Winton 25.00
Popeye, American Bisque 125.00
Porky Pig, Warner Bros 30.00
Preacher, blk hat, sq glasses, mk Robinson Ransbottom ...40.00
Puppy, in bl or yel pot, unmk American Bisque, ea 15.00
Puss N' Boots, mk Patent Puss N' Boots, M 100.00
Quaker Oats, Regal China 50.00
Rabbit, patches on clothes, mk USA, American Bisque ...25.00
Rabbit in Hat, American Bisque 30.00
Rabbit w/Baseball Bat, tie around neck 30.00
Ring for Cookies, American Bisque 20.00
Rooster, American Bisque 30.00
Rooster, brn w/red & yel, Robinson Ransbottom 35.00
Sandman Cookies, 2 kids watch TV, mk 801 USA, Am Bisque .30.00
Santa, 'Cookies' on front, plastic, mk Empire...USA 40.00
Santa, American Bisque 60.00
Schoolhouse w/Bell, American Bisque 25.00
Seal on Igloo, American Bisque 30.00
Sheriff Pig, Robinson Ransbottom 30.00
Shoe, unmk Doranne of CA, lg 45.00
Snacks, teapot shape, mk USA, American Bisque 15.00
Snowman, w/hat, scarf, & broom, Robinson Ransbottom ...30.00
Spaceship, American Bisque 50.00
Sugar Dairy, Twin Winton 25.00
Thumper, seated, paws folded, Walt Disney 50.00
Tigger, Walt Disney Productions 95.00

Timmy Tortoise 35.00
Tony Tiger, Kellogg 28.00
Train, Cookie RR, unmk American Bisque 25.00
Train, Pfaltzgraff 65.00
Train, Sierra Vista 45.00
Train, Twin Winton 35.00
Turtle, butterfly finial, mk GK5 USA 40.00
Umbrella Kids, American Bisque 55.00
White Rooster, American Bisque 40.00
Winking Farmer Pig, Robinson Ransbottom 40.00
Wise Bird, Robinson Ransbottom 28.00
Wooden Soldier, American Bisque 30.00
WWII Soldier, Robinson Ransbottom 35.00
Yarn Doll, American Bisque 25.00
Ye Olde Cookie Bucket, San Juan Capistrano, '59 ....22.00
Ye Olde Cookie Jar, San Juan Capistrano, dtd '59 ...15.00
Yogi Bear, Hanna Barbera Productions USA 1961 .....75.00
1946 Bubbler Jukebox, Treasure Craft 55.00

Coors

The firm that became known as Coors Porcelain Company in 1920 was founded in 1908 by John J. Herold, originally of the Roseville Pottery in Zanesville, Ohio. Though still in business today, they are best known for their artware vases and Rosebud dinnerware produced before 1939.

Ash tray, Rosebud, 3½" 50.00
Baking pan, Rosebud, 10¾x6¾" 17.50
Bowl, cereal; Rosebud, 6" 14.00
Bowl, fruit; Rosebud, 5" 7.50
Bowl, mixing; Rosebud, 6" 12.50
Bowl, pudding; Rosebud, 2-pt 12.50
Cake knife, Rosebud, 10" 22.50
Casserole, Dutch; Rosebud, 3½-cup 25.00
Casserole, Rosebud, str sides, 2-pt 20.00
Cookie jar, HP decor, lg 35.00
Cup, custard; Rosebud, 4" 7.50
Egg cup, Rosebud, 6-oz 15.00
Jar, utility; Rosebud, 2½-pt 25.00
Muffin set, Rosebud, 8" plate+5½" domed lid 40.00
Pitcher, Rosebud, open, 4-pt 22.50
Plate, dinner; Rosebud, 9" 10.00
Platter, Rosebud, 12x9" 15.00
Shaker, sugar; Rosebud, 5½" 14.00
Shakers, Rosebud, str sides, 4½", pr 12.50
Shakers, Rosebud, 2½", pr 24.00
Teapot, Rosebud, 2-cup 30.00
Tumbler, Rosebud, ftd, no hdl, 12-oz 22.50
Underplate, Rosebud, 7" 7.50
Water server, Rosebud, Commemorative, corked stopper, 3-pt ..88.00

Copper

Hand-crafted copper was made in America from early in the eighteenth century until about 1850, with the center of its production in Pennsylvania. Examples have been found signed by such notable coppersmiths as Kidd, Buchanan, Babb, Bently, and Harbeson. Of the many utilitarian items made, teakettles are the most desirable. Early examples from the eighteenth century were made with a dovetailed joint which was hammered and smoothed to a uniform thickness. Pots from the nineteenth century were seamed. Coffeepots were made in many shapes and sizes and along with mugs, kettles, warming pans, and measures are easiest to find.

Stills ranging in sizes of up to fifty-gallon are popular with collectors today.

Our advisor, Mary Frank Gaston, has compiled a lovely book, *Antique Copper*, with many full-color photos and current market values; you will find her address in the Directory under Texas.

Coal scuttle, helmet form, swing hdl, 16" W	275.00
Coffeepot, oval canister w/gooseneck, English, 1800s, 9"	175.00
Dipper, forged iron hdl, hook end, ca 1920, 21"	75.00
Dipper, iron hook hdl, ca 1830, 6" dia, 20½" L	160.00
Kettle, dvtl, heavy iron bail, rpr/polished, 16x26", EX	200.00
Kettle, dvtl, wrought iron bail, 20x30½"	220.00
Measure, haystack form w/pouring lip & hdl, 1860s, 1-gal	125.00
Pan, roasting; tinned, dvtl, oval, ca 1800, 3½x13x8½"	175.00
Pan, sauce; CI hdl, matching lid w/hdl, mk LED/HNY, 9" dia	65.00
Pitcher, dvtl, classic design, well made, 12"	110.00
Pot, dvtl, flat bottom, rim hdl, w/lid, 28" dia	65.00
Shoe buckle, tooled, worn SP, 2¾"	25.00
Skimmer, hammered, oval pierced spoon-shaped bowl, 17" L	130.00
Teakettle, brass finial, unsgn Jacob Gable, ca 1843, EX	450.00
Teakettle, dvtl, brass trim, 11½"	185.00
Teakettle, dvtl, oval, brass trim, milk glass hdl, 8"	125.00

19th Century English copper, left to right: 4-pint coffeepot, 9", $175.00; Maurice Cohen & Co. teakettle, 12", $250.00.

Copper Lustre

Copper lustre is a term referring to a type of pottery made in Staffordshire after the turn of the nineteenth century. It is finished in a metallic rusty-brown glaze resembling true copper. Pitchers are found in abundance, ranging from simple styles with dull bands of color to those with fancy handles and bands of embossed, polychromed flowers. Bowls are common; goblets, mugs, teapots, and sugar bowls much less so. It's easy to find, but not in good condition. Pieces with hand-painted decoration and those with historical transfers are the most valuable.

Our advisor for this category is Richard Marden; he is listed in the Directory under New Hampshire.

Bowl, bl band w/mc flower basket, 5½"	60.00
Coffeepot, ribbed & beaded, Georgian style, 10½"	375.00
Cup, satyr, w/frog inside, 5"	95.00
Cup & saucer, demitasse; mk Louis XV	15.00
Goblet, floral band in pk/gr/wht/yel, 4½"	75.00
Mug, Hope, mc transfer, ca 1800, 3⅛"	75.00
Mug, putty-colored band w/Eliza,' int stains, 2½"	50.00
Pitcher, allegorical scenic mc panels, 4⅞"	75.00
Pitcher, amber band, 1840, 6"	45.00

Pitcher, bl band w/emb floral, mask spout, 5¼"	85.00
Pitcher, bl band w/mc girl & dog, mask spout, 4¾"	75.00
Pitcher, Faith, 2-panel transfer, early 1800s, 4½"	75.00
Pitcher, gold band, 3"	38.00

Pitcher, House pattern, 7", $65.00.

Pitcher, roses relief, red/yel/gr pnt, 8½x4⅜"	125.00
Pitcher, yel band w/3 mc transfer reserves, 5¾"	45.00
Salt cellar, master; cobalt & tan band	75.00
Salt cellar & pepper shaker, cream band, NM, pr	80.00
Shaker, Toby, 4¾"	75.00
Teapot, beads/scrolls, eagle hdl, feathered spout, 1830s	145.00
Teapot, floral spray, bl trim, faceted sides, 7", NM	125.00
Tumbler, gr band, 3¼"	50.00
Waste bowl, emb mc girl & dog, 1840, 5½"	70.00

Coralene Glass

Coralene is a unique type of art glass easily recognized by the tiny grains of glass that form its decoration. Lacy allover patterns of seaweed, geometrics, and florals were used, as well as solid forms such as fish, plants, and single blossoms. It was made by several glasshouses both here and abroad.

Our advisors for this category are Betty and Clarence Maier; they are listed in the Directory under Pennsylvania.

Vase, blue with gold bands and pond lilies, marked patent, 4", $245.00.

Bowl, bl w/floral motif, 4½" dia, in SP holder 150.00
Vase, amethyst, lg water lily motif, amber ft, bowl form, 6" 325.00
Vase, bl, lg bird & floral motif, clear ribbed ft, 10", pr 250.00
Vase, bl w/yel seaweed motif, 7½" 250.00
Vase, Dia Quilt, pk MOP, star-in-diamond motif, 4¾x3" 475.00
Vase, Dia Quilt, pk MOP, star-in-diamond motif, 4x5½" 550.00
Vase, Dia Quilt, pk to fuchsia, bl florals, Webb, 8x5½" 235.00
Vase, peachblow w/yel seaweed motif, 7½" 375.00
Vase, Snowflake, golden-yel MOP, yel wheat motif, 5⅜x3¾" . .450.00
Vase, yel to wht w/yel seaweed motif, 7½" 250.00

Coralene, Oriental

Fine chinaware decorated in the same manner as coralene glass was produced in Japan during the early 1900s. Many items are marked 'Patent Pending' or with a specific patent date.

Biscuit jar, foliage/floral on bl, SP lid .365.00
Ewer, dragonfly/florals, cobalt & gold hdl, dtd 190?, 5¼" 200.00
Ewer, fruit, pk/gr on gr w/gold, 4x3½" 175.00
Plate, poppy, pk on gr w/gold-beaded rim, mk pat, 7¾" 100.00
Vase, floral, gr/brn/rust, bulbous, hdls, pat mk, 8" 195.00
Vase, floral on yel to sienna w/gold, 3-hdld, 5" 225.00
Vase, iris, purple on dk purple to lt gr, yel int, hdls, 8" 225.00
Vase, water lily, lav/pk on bl/pk mottle w/gold, hdls, 4" 250.00

Cordey

The Cordey China Company was founded in 1942 in Trenton, New Jersey, by Boleslaw Cybis. The operation was small with less than a dozen workers. They produced figurines, vases, lamps, and similar wares, much of which was marketed through gift shops both nationwide and abroad. Though the earlier wares were made of plaster, Cybis soon developed his own formula for a porcelain composition which he called 'Papka.' Cordey figurines and busts were characterized by old-world charm, Rococo scrolls, delicate floral appliques, ruffles, and real lace which was dipped in liquified clay to add dimension to the work.

Although on rare occasions some items were not numbered or signed, the 'basic' figure was cast both with numbers and the Cordey signature. The molded pieces were then individually decorated and each marked with its own impressed identification number, as well as a mark to indicate the artist-decorator. Their numbering system began with 200 and in later years progressed into the 8000s. As can best be established, Cordey continued production until sometime in the mid-1950s. Boleslaw Cybis died in 1957, his wife in 1958.

Key: ff — full figure

Ballerina, #4101, dancing position, lace trim, 10¾" 220.00
Bottle, scent; #7026, shades of bl, iris-form stopper, 8" 90.00
Box, #6038, roses on lid, 5x5", EX 50.00
Box, trinket; #7038, roses & mixed florals, ftd 33.00
Bust, #5007 . . . . .50.00
Bust, #5009 . . . . .50.00
Bust, #5012, lady w/ringlets, ivory w/gold flowers 45.00
Bust, #5027, Junior Miss, bl shawl, 7½" 65.00
Bust, #5051, lady w/flower basket, 10" 110.00
Cat, seated, wht w/bow, pk rose, 8¾" 200.00
Lady, #4184, ff, 17" 195.00
Lady, #5061, Madame Dubarry, rare, 14", NM 295.00
Lady, #5066, Carmen, ff, lav dress, long coat, high hat, 14" . . .165.00
Lady, #5089, ringlets, lace, big bustle, 10¾" 100.00

Lady, #5089A, bl eyes, upswept hair, 11¼" 140.00
Lady Harvester, #304 . . . . .135.00
Lamp, #6025, leaves & flowers on base 140.00
Lamp, Grape Harvesters, #304/#305, 16½", pr 300.00
Lamp, Oriental figures, 20", pr 260.00
Man & lady, #302/#303, ff, 16" 160.00
Man & lady, #305/#306, maroon/gr/wht/pk/peach, 16", pr 240.00
Man & lady, #4005/#4006, ff, pr 125.00
Man & lady, #4013/#4014, 7", pr 110.00
Man & lady, #5088/#5043, Colonial attire, 10½", pr 225.00
Neopolitan boy w/basket of breadsticks, #5045, 9½" 110.00
Pheasant, #343, vibrant mc, very early, scarce, 17" 225.00
Plaque, #902, lady's face 135.00
Tray, card; #8047, cherub w/pk roses & leaves, 8" 75.00
Vase, #7094, Oriental ladies in relief, appl flowers, 7" 125.00
Wall sconce, #7028, cherubs & flowers, pr 175.00
Wall shelf, #7029, Bow Knot, 7½", pr 120.00

Figure of a yellow canary with applied flowers, 8", $175.00.

Corkscrews

The history of the corkscrew dates back to the mid-1600s, when wine makers concluded that the best-aged wine was that stored in smaller containers, either stoneware or glass. Since plugs left unsealed were often damaged by rodents, corks were cut off flush with the bottle top and sealed with wax or a metal cover. Removing the cork cleanly with none left to grasp became a problem. The task was found to be relatively simple using the worm on the end of a flintlock gun rod — and the corkscrew evolved. Endless patents have been issued for mechanized models; handles range from figural ivories (lady's legs are popular) to repousse silver, carved bone, wood, and porcelain.

Our advisor for this category is Roger Baker; he is listed in the Directory under California.

Anheuser Busch, NP brass bottle w/label 65.00
Boar's tusk, cvd Nouveau hdl, sterling end cap, 7" 175.00
Brass w/ivory hdl, emb/gilt lion & unicorn label, 7", EX 200.00
Brass w/ivory-hdld brush end, 5¾" 200.00
Clough's Pat 1900, redwood sheath 10.00
Columbus, 1893 German Pat, wood hdl, center worm, unmk . .60.00
Daisy, Albert Pick Bar Supplies, bar mt, pat 1895 . . . . .295.00
English, Henshall type, trn wood hdl, brass shaft/button 100.00

English, NP roundlet, fluted helix worm 25.00
English, trn hdl, tapered helix, ca 1880 . . . . .20.00
Fish form, brass, w/opener & piercer 35.00
French, oval horn hdl, steel shaft, center worm, ca 1850 . . . . . .40.00
French, wood hdl, hand-cut steel shaft, helix worm, ca 1840 . . . .30.00
German, knob hdl, trn shaft, center worm 15.00
German, wood hdl, center worm, mk Hercules, ca 1880 . . . . . . .30.00
Hollweg Handy 85.00
Ivory hdl, mk English, late, 2⅜" 55.00
Monkey form, cast metal, NP shaft/center worm 20.00
Nude mermaid, celluloid, Geschutz .350.00
Rosewood hdl, thick tapered shaft, short helix worm 25.00
Sperry lever, single 450.00
Walker's Pat 1900, barrel-form wood hdl, nickel-plated shaft . . .20.00
Walker's Pat 1900, fruitwood hdl, bell cap, long center worm . . .40.00
Williamson's, rnd shaft, stag hdl, wire helix worm, 1900 . . . . . .25.00
Williamson's Pat 1897, rosewood hdl, bell cap 35.00

Cosmos

Cosmos, sometimes called Stemless Daisy, is a patterned glass table-ware produced from 1894 through 1915 by Consolidated Lamp and Glass Company. Relief-molded flowers on a fine cross-cut background were painted in soft colors of pink, blue, and yellow. Though nearly all were made of milk glass, a few items may be found in clear glass with the designs painted on. In addition to the tableware, lamps were also made.

Bottle, scent; pk & bl floral, orig stopper, M 135.00
Butter dish, 7½" dia 225.00
Condiment set, 3-pc on glass stand, complete 395.00
Creamer 150.00
Lamp, banquet; kerosene, 24" 475.00
Lamp, banquet; slender base, rnd globe, all orig, 16" 450.00
Lamp, mini, 7" 325.00
Lamp, 10" 400.00
Pickle castor, dbl, mk SP fr 500.00
Pickle castor, single, ftd SP fr 350.00
Pitcher, milk; 5" 170.00
Pitcher, 8¾" 250.00
Shakers, tall, orig lids, pr 135.00
Spooner 125.00
Sugar bowl, open 150.00
Sugar bowl, w/lid 185.00

Syrup pitcher, 7", $200.00.

Tumbler, 3¾" 65.00

Coverlets

The Jacquard loom, developed in France in the early 1800s, made possible the production of intricately woven coverlets in various motifs. They were made of wool, both dyed and natural, from patterns punched into paper cards that indicated the colors of woof and warp necessary to develop the design. Soon after 1820, the loom was brought to this country and by 1840 was standard equipment for every professional weaver. Pictorial designs once reserved for the wealthy became available at modest prices. The old geometrics were replaced by florals, eagles, and elaborate medallion patterns. The new process enabled the weaver to sign and date his work, though not all names refer to the artist; it was also a common practice to weave the new owner's name into the corner of the coverlet.

In America the earliest pattern-woven coverlets were made around 1820 at the Colonel Rutger's Works of Brunswick, New Jersey. Often used to cover the dead for burial, they became known as 'corpse coverlets.' Usually buried with the departed, true examples of this type of coverlet are rarely found today.

In the listings that follow, examples are blue and white unless noted otherwise.

Left to right: Floral with signed corners dated 1837, 4-color, $625.00; Rose medallion with eagle and tree borders, corners labeled 'Property of S.M.S. Orleans Co. NY,' 1839, $610.00.

Jacquard

Floral, bldg border, sgn/dtd 1836 corners, rpr, 81x86", VG 350.00
Floral, geometric borders, 3-color, 1865, 81x81"+4" fringe 325.00
Floral, gold/bl/wht/maroon, dtd 1854, 1-pc single, 72x87" 250.00
Floral, Liberty/spread eagle border, sgn Millstone/1835 . . . . . . .600.00
Floral, rose border, sgn/dtd corners, red/bl/gr/cream, EX 625.00
Floral, vintage border, 1-pc single, 76x84" 245.00
Floral, 2-pc dbl, some wear/stains, 82x94" 350.00
Floral, 3-color, corners dtd 1851, provenance, 79x86", VG 300.00
Floral medallions, floral/bird-in-tree border, 2-pc dbl, EX 200.00
Floral stripe, 2-pc dbl, edge/overall wear, 74x88" 250.00
Floral/dome bldgs, corners w/horses/eagle/motto, 5-color 400.00
Floral/foliage, fruit compote borders, 4-color, sgn/1846 . . . . . . .675.00
Floral/star medallions, bird/eagle borders, red/wht, 1845 . . . . . .650.00
Foliage/star/circle medallions, 5-color, sgn/1859, rpr 275.00
Medallions, dbl bldg border, 4-color, sgn corners/1856, VG . . .350.00
Medallions, vines/flowerpot borders, sgn/1841, red/bl, VG 400.00
Rose medallions, eagle/tree border, sgn/dtd 1839 . . . . .610.00
Snowflake, pine tree border, ca 1840, 82x82" 350.00
Starflower medallions, flowerpots/bird borders, 4-color, lg 375.00
Stars, 3-color, 2-pc single, 58x90", VG 250.00

Sunburst medallion, shield-bodied eagle corners, 3-color 400.00
Vintage/bird borders, 4-color, corners sgn/1848, 2-pc, EX 400.00
Washington portraits in corners, 4-color, dtd 1869, 82x76" ...695.00

Overshot

Geometrics, natural/gr/butternut, 1 end fringed, 70x76" 250.00
Optic rectangles & sqs, 2-pc, 62x89" 175.00
Optic sqs & lines, 3-color, 1-pc, minor wear/stains, 73x90" 150.00
Optic X-cut circles, positive/negative sqs, bl/wht, 77x90" 275.00
Plaid, 4-color, EX fringe, 2-pc, 66x95" 400.00

Cowan

Guy Cowan opened a small pottery near Cleveland, Ohio, ca 1912, where he made tile and artware on a small scale from the natural red clay available there. He developed distinctive glazes — necessary, he felt, to cover the dark red body. After the war and a temporary halt in production, Cowan moved his pottery to Rocky River, where he made a commercial line of artware utilizing a highly-fired white porcelain. Although he acquiesced to the necessity of mass-production, every effort was made to insure a product of highest quality. Fine artists, among them Waylande Gregory, Thelma Frazier Winter, and Viktor Schreckengost, molded figurines which were often produced in limited editions, some of which sell today for upwards of $1,000. Most of the ware was marked 'Cowan' or 'Lakewood Ware,' not to be confused with the name of the 1927 mass-produced line called 'Lakeware.' Falling under the crunch of the Great Depression, the pottery closed in 1931.

Bookend, horse, turq, 9½" 375.00
Bowl, pk on ivory, oval, ftd, #690, 16" L 24.00
Candle holder, ivory, sea horse base, 4", pr 26.00
Candle holder, leaping gazelle, caramel gloss, 5¾" 70.00
Candlestick, bl lustre, 2¼", pr 28.00
Candlestick, Rowfant Club, ground hog, gr, ltd ed, 9½" 800.00
Comport, ivory, sea horses base, oval, 6" 35.00
Creamer & sugar bowl, bl lustre, w/lids 45.00
Decanter, burnt orange, ribbed, w/stopper, 10½" 95.00
Decanter, King & Queen, Oriental red, pr 1,200.00
Figurine, Russian Peasant Dancer, tan crackle 450.00
Flower frog, single nude, ivory, #698, 6½" 120.00
Jar, ginger; purple, high lustre, w/lid, 5½" 48.00
Lamp & shade, mother deer & young emb, brn/gr matt, 19" ...230.00
Trivet, floral relief, 5-color, 6-sided, mks 325.00

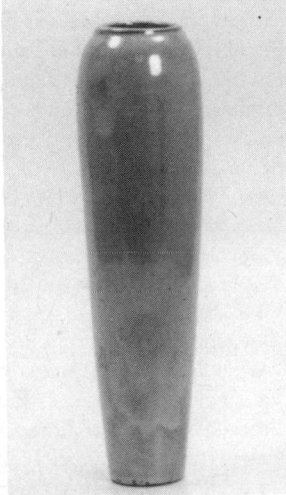

Vase, ochre lustre, signed Guy Cowan,
ca 1912, 10", $350.00 to $500.00.

Cracker Jack

Kids have been buying Cracker Jack since it was first introduced in the 1890s. By 1912 it was packaged with a free toy inside. Before the first kernel was crunched, eager fingers had retrieved the surprise from the depth of the box — actually no easy task, considering the care required to keep the contents so swiftly displaced from spilling over the side! Though a little older, perhaps, many of those same kids still are looking — just as eagerly — for the Cracker Jack prizes. Point of sale, company collectibles, and the prizes as well have over the years reflected America's changing culture. Grocer sales and incentives from around the turn of the century — paper dolls, post cards and song books — were often marked Rueckheim Brothers (the inventors of Cracker Jack) or Reliable Confections. The first loose-packed prizes were toys made of wood, clay, tin, metal, and lithographed paper. Plastic toys were introduced in 1948. Paper wrapped for safety purposes in 1933, subjects echo the 'hype' of the day — Yo-Yos, tops, whistles, and sports cards in the simple, peaceful days of our country, propaganda and war toys in the forties, games in the fifties, and space toys in the sixties. Few of the estimated 15 billion prizes were marked. Advertising items from Angelus Marshmallow and Checkers Confections (cousins of the Cracker Jack family) are also collectible. When no condition is indicated, the items listed below are assumed to be in excellent condition. 'CJ' indicates that the item is marked.

Our advisor for this category is Wes Johnson; he is listed in the Directory under Kentucky.

Cast Metal Prizes

Air corps wings, silver on blk, CJ, 3" 42.00
Badge, shield, CJ Jr Detective, silver, 1¼" 22.00
Badge, 6-point star, mk CJ Police, silver, 1¼" 22.00
Dollhouse items: lantern, mug, candlestick, etc; no mk, ea 6.50
Horse & wagon, Angelus & CJ, 3-D, silver or gold, 2½" 110.00
Man on horse, rocking, lg 20.00
Pistol, inked, rare, CJ along barrel 180.00
Stud button, Me for CJ, boy & dog 18.00
Stud button, Xd bats & ball, mk: Pitcher, etc; ea CJ 66.00
Tootsie Toy series: boats, cars, animals; 1-3", ea 7.00

Paper Prizes

Baseball cards, 1906 & 1907 series, CJ, ea on average 22.00
Baseball score counter, CJ 40.00
Book, Animals (or Birds), to color, CJ, ea 30.00
Book, drawing; w/tracing paper, early, CJ 40.00
Book, riddle; Jack & Bingo on cover, RWB, CJ 30.00
Book, riddle; jester on cover, CJ 33.00
Booklet, stickers, 'Borden,' recent, CJ 50
Hat, fold-out, More You Eat, More You Want, CJ 30.00
Hat, vendor cap, CJ 20.00
Magic Game Book, erasable slate, CJ, series of 13, ea 25.00
Movies, pull tab for 2nd picture, CJ, early, 3" 48.00
Post card, bear, 1907, CJ, series of 16, ea 14.00
Puzzle, dealer incentive, CJ or Checkers, orig envelope 18.00
Riddle cards, CJ, series of 20, ea 7.00
Top, Golf Game, CJ 25.00

Plastic Prizes

Animals, stand-up, alphabet letter on bk, ea 3.50
Animals, stand-up w/base, CJ, Nosco, etc 1.00
Badge, pretty lady pin-bk, mc, paper CJ label on bk, 1¼" 29.00
Dogs, 3-D figures, series of 10, ea 4.50

Figures on rocking base, semi-flat 2.00
Nosco boy w/balloons 1.50

Celluloid pencil clip, ca 1918, $150.00.

Ringmaster & other circus pcs, ea 1.50
Spinners, various designs, ea 2.00
Toy, 3-D, take apart & assemble, recent 2.00
Watch, CJ 12.00
Whistle, tube w/animals, CJ 12.50

Tin Prizes

American flag, oval standup, series of 4, no mk, ea 9.00
Bank, book form, red, gr, or blk, 3-D, CJ, 2" 48.00
Boy & dog, diecut, complete w/bend-over tabs, CJ 85.00
Cart w/wood hdl, CJ 28.00
Fortune Wheel 30.00
Harmonica, early premium, mk CJ 185.00
Horse & wagon, litho diecut, CJ, 2⅛" L 35.00
Model T Ford, NY 1916 #999, blk & wht, CJ, 2" 150.00
Pocket watch, silver or gold, CJ, 1½" 33.00
Radio, Tune in w/CJ 48.00
Sled, plated, CJ, 2" L 31.00
Stud pin, elephant 14.00
Top, aerial propellor; red/yel, wood axle, CJ 10.00
Tray, miniature, 2 sizes, CJ, ea 50.00
Wheelbarrow, plated, CJ, 2¼" 20.00
Whistle, plated, 2-tone, CJ, 2" L 13.00
Whistle, w/boy, litho, CJ 25.00

Miscellaneous

Ad, comic book 9.00
Ad, Saturday Evening Post, mc, 1919, 11x14" 18.00
Bat, wood, Hillerich & Bradsby, mk CJ 85.00
Box, store display, 1923, CJ, empty, unused 65.00
Crate, wooden, shipping, CJ, early, lg 150.00
Halloween mask, CJ, 10" or 12", ea 11.00
Medal, CJ Salesman 1939 Award, brass, rare 65.00

Popcorn box, ca 1920 ....85.00
Recipe book, Angelus, 1930s 22.00
Sign, Angelus Marshmallows, mc Santa/CJ, cb, 12" 110.00
Sign, bathing beauty, cb, 5-color, CJ, 17x22", EX 125.00
Sign, boy w/box, cb, 5-color, CJ, 17x22", EX 125.00
Sign, girl w/box, cb, 5-color, 17x22", CJ, EX 120.00
Sign, Jack & Bingo, cb diecut, easel bk, 7½x10½" 125.00
Tin canister, Candy Crisp, 10-oz 75.00

Crackle Glass

Crackle glass (or craquelle) was made during the 1800s in America as well as abroad. The name is derived from the crackled texture of the ware, achieved either by plunging the hot glass into cold water or by rolling it in small particles of broken glass which fuse to the surface upon reheating.

Cruet, cranberry, appl hdl, faceted stopper 150.00
Egg, on low std, 7-pc liqueur set w/in 100.00
Ewer, ruby, petal rim, appl vaseline hdl, 5" 25.00
Pitcher, amberina, reed hdl, 7½" 155.00
Pitcher, water; crystal, bulbous, w/lid 55.00
Tumbler, ruby, HP purple flowers, 3¾" 45.00
Vase, clear w/electric bl hdls, Deco style, 7½" 50.00

Cranberry

Cranberry glass is named for its resemblance to the color of cranberry juice. It was made by many companies both here and abroad, becoming popular in America soon after the Civil War. It was made in free-blown ware as well as mold-blown. Today, cranberry glass is being reproduced, and it is sometimes difficult to distinguish the old from the new. Ask a reputable dealer if you are unsure. See also Cruets; Salts; Sugar Shakers; Syrups.

Bottle, scent; gold-dot florals/band, orig stopper, 5⅜" 135.00
Bottle, scent; star cutting, faceted stopper, 5½" 110.00
Box, bl butterfly & florals, lift-off lid, 2½x4⅜" 135.00
Box, florals, hinged lid, ormolu ft, 3¼" dia 175.00
Box, jewel; wht roof w/doves, bl flowers, brass hdls, 6" H 400.00
Box, patch; gold metal filigree, 1¼x2¼" 135.00
Box, pk & wht floral, gr leaf, hinged lid, 3x3¾" dia 195.00
Cruet, HP decor w/gold bands, clear hdl & stopper, 9¼" 145.00
Decanter, swirled w/HP stylized flowers, heavy, early 215.00
Decanter, wine cruet; flat bulbous form, 3-petal top, 9½" 145.00
Decanter, wine cruet; pewter mts w/emb ladies' heads, Fr, 13" .375.00
Jam jar, Invt T'print, wild roses/ferns, SP top 165.00
Pitcher, appl clear Mat-Su-Noke motif/hdl/ft, 6¾" 550.00
Pitcher, Coin Spot, floral, milk sz 250.00
Pitcher, floral, bulbous w/long neck, amber hdl, 10" 325.00
Pitcher, Invt T'print, bulbous, clear ribbed hdl, 9" 225.00
Pitcher, wht florals, gold scrolling, clear hdl, 4" 70.00
Syrup, Guttate 230.00
Vase, bl forget-me-nots w/gold trim, flared top, 4½x3⅜" 75.00
Vase, bl/wht floral, gold scrolls, ped base, 10½" 225.00
Vase, clear appl leaves/rigaree/ped ft, 9½x4" 145.00
Vase, Dia Quilt, clear ruffled top, 4½x3½" 89.00
Vase, diamond cutting, clear stem, ped ft, 7¼x2¼" 175.00
Vase, eng bird & flowers, gold trim, clear hdls, ped ft, 5" 85.00
Vase, gold florals & leaves, bl dot trim, cylindrical, 7" 65.00
Vase, gold florals/insects, slim form, 8" 90.00
Vase, gold-traced/HP florals, 5¾x2¾" 75.00
Vase, HP florals, faint ribbing, 4⅛" 60.00
Vase, HP florals, gold scrolls, 3⅞" 55.00

Vase, HP florals, mini, 2¾x1½" 55.00
Vase, Invt T'print, long appl icicles hang from rim, 4½" 250.00
Vase, wht florals w/gold scrolls, clear ped ft, 5" 55.00

Vase, gold and enamel florals, 11", $225.00.

Creamware

Creamware was a type of earthenware developed by Wedgwood in the 1760s and produced by many other Staffordshire potteries, including Leeds. Since it could be potted cheaply and was light in weight, it became popular abroad as well as in England, due to the lower freight charges involved in its export. It was revived at Leeds in the late nineteenth century, and the type most often reproduced was heavily reticulated or molded in high relief. These later wares are easily distinguished from the originals since they are thicker and tend to craze heavily. See also Leeds.

Creamer, King of Prussia, blk transfer, bk: angel, 4" 200.00
Plate, emb feather edge, mk Adams, 10" 45.00
Platter, red-purple feather edge, 14", EX 325.00
Soup dish, mk Davenport, 9½" 45.00
Tea caddy, HP florals/geometrics, early, 4x4½", EX 80.00
Warming dish, twisted hdls w/appl florals, pierced, 13½" 275.00
Waste bowl, mc roses, 6", EX 100.00

Credit Cards and Charge Coins

Charge coins were first issued in 1890 with some stores continuing to use them as late as 1959. Coins were issued in various shapes and sizes. Some, from clothing stores, came in shapes such as shirts, socks, or hats. Coins were made of different materials such as copper, brass, German silver, steel, fiber, and celluloid. All coins have the store's name or monogram along with a number for indentification. None ever had the name of the individual to whom the coin was issued. When making a purchase, the salesperson would check a master list to compare the number of the coin and the name of the person presenting the coin to see if they matched. If they didn't, the coin would be confiscated until the rightful owner could be located. Most coins had holes so they could be put on a key chain. Often ladies wore their coins on necklaces to keep them from being mislaid.

In the 1930s, stores began using the metal charge plates. These plates looked like military dog tags. The front of the plate, in raised letters, contained the person's name, address, and account number. The back had a cardboard mount where the cardholder could sign his name. Metal plates were generally discontinued in the 1950s.

Paper credit cards were used in the early 1900s, but it was not until the 1940s that they began to be more common. By the early 1950s, they were being issued by many companies. Because paper was easily worn and damaged through everyday use, a clear plastic laminate was eventually added. By the late 1950s, companies began using the plastic credit card we know today.

Our advisor for this category is Greg Tunks; he is listed in the Directory under Texas.

Charge Coins

Filene's, Boston MA, wht metal, crown over name in wreath 8.00
Gimble Bros, Phila PA, wht metal, lion/shield w/GB, 31x23mm . .8.00
Horace Partridge Co, Boston MA, copper, w/bird, 32mm dia . . .10.00
Jordan Marsh, Boston MA, wht metal, J over M Co, 33x25mm . . .8.00

Charge coin, Neill, Philadelphia, PA, 1920s, square, 26mm, $10.00.

L Bamberger & Co, Newark NJ, celluloid 150.00
Strawbridge & Clothier, Phila PA, arrowhead shape 10.00

Credit Cards

American Express, red letters on purple-bl paperboard, 1958 . .300.00
American Express, violet on wht, centurion in corner, 1964 . . . .60.00
ARCO, Atlantic Richfield Co, 1975 . . . . .4.00
BankAmericard, no magnetic stripe, account # in tan area 8.00
Charga-Plate, metal, name of city on back 6.00
Eastern Airlines, couple seaside, 1970s 3.00
Gulf, laminated paper, 1950s 50.00
Gulf Travel Card, pictures auto, boat & plane 7.00
Hertz, drawing of 2-door Ford on back, 1969 . . . . .6.00
Lit Bros, metal Charga-Plate 6.00
Longchamps Restaurant, drawing of 2 women kissing 25.00
Master Charge, identification photo of cardholder on back 40.00
MasterCard, pre-hologram 3.00
Phillips Petroleum, Lifetime Executive Courtesy Card 7.00
Shell Oil, paper, 1940s 50.00

Sinclair, waving dinosaur 7.00
Skelly Oil Co, lady's credit card, 2 gloved hands w/symbol 12.00
Standard Oil, map of US, 1973 . . . . .8.00
TWA, swimsuited couple, 1972 . . . . .7.00
Visa, pre-hologram 2.50

Crown Milano

    Crown Milano was introduced in 1884 by the Mt. Washington Glass Company. When the company merged with Pairpoint in 1894, it continued to be one of their best sellers. It is an opaque, highly-decorated ware with gold or colored enamels in intricate designs on pale backgrounds. Many pieces were marked 'CM' with a crown. Since it is nearly always found in a satin finish, in the listings that follow, satin is assumed unless glossy is indicated.

    Our advisors for this category are Betty and Clarence Maier; they are listed in the Directory under Pennsylvania.

Biscuit jar, autumn leaves & roses, burmese color, 7½" 475.00
Biscuit jar, carnations, melon ribbed, no mk, SP mts, 8" 475.00
Biscuit jar, floral sprays w/gold on wht, SP lid/hdl, 8½x7" 585.00
Biscuit jar, florals, jewels, gold trim, SP mts, 8x6" 975.00
Biscuit jar, florals/gold scrolls, floral-emb lid, 7½" dia 950.00
Biscuit jar, gold-traced oak leaves, burmese color, 7½" 450.00
Biscuit jar, harbor scene, gold scrolls, paneled, #d, 9" 735.00
Biscuit jar, mums, burmese color, emb mk SP lid, #d, 6" 300.00
Bottle, atomizer; florals w/gold veins & dots, sgn 600.00
Bowl, autumn leaves w/gold tracing, 6x8" 525.00
Creamer & sugar bowl, florals, gold shell hdls, mk, 4" 525.00
Creamer & sugar bowl, violets w/gold, label, 3½" & 4½" 900.00
Cup, demitasse; florals, gold bands, curlicue hdl, mk 285.00
Ewer, ferns in gold, gold twist hdl, rpr, 10½" 500.00
Jar, mc pansies, SP lid/hdl, sgn/#d, 4" dia 300.00
Jardiniere, florals & gold scrolls, 5½x8" dia 250.00
Lamp, banquet; Garden of Allah, sq base, 31" 9,500.00
Pitcher, floral, gold/blk on gr shading, serpent hdl, 8½" 900.00
Rose bowl, pansies, mc w/gold tracing, 3½" H 300.00
Shakers, pansies on wht, ribbed, orig lids, 4", pr 100.00
Sweetmeat, floral, mc w/gold, melon ribs, SP lid/bail, 4x5" . . .400.00
Syrup, gold-traced water lilies, burmese color, ribbed, 5½" . . .985.00
Syrup, melon ribs, netting & florals alternate, SP mts, 5½" . .1,200.00
Syrup, swirls/scrolls in gold, mk/#d gold emb lid, 7" 900.00
Tray, 2 Guba ducks, gold scrolls, ruffled rim, red mk, 9½" . . .1,200.00
Vase, cherubs in ribbon reserve w/in wreath, shiny, unmk, 11" .585.00
Vase, chrysanthemums, bulbous body, thorn hdls, mk, 11½" .1,250.00

Vase, dragon head medallions and florals in gold on ivory, 8", $1,000.00.

Vase, gold mums w/shadow leaves in bkground, squatty, 6" 700.00
Vase, gold reserve w/HP floral, rim extends into hdls, 9½" 800.00
Vase, mallards in flight, bulbous, 6¾", NM 1,050.00
Vase, mc florals, gold scrolls, shadow leaves, 8" 600.00
Vase, petit-point florals, ball form, shoulder hdls, 8" 535.00

Cruets

    Cruets, containers made to hold oil or vinegar, are usually bulbous with tall narrow throats and a stopper. During the nineteenth century and for several years after, they were produced in abundance in virtually every type of glassware available. Those listed below are assumed to be with stopper and mint unless noted otherwise.

Alaska, bl opal, HP florals 275.00
Amber, bl hdl & stopper, 8¼x4" 135.00
Amberina, reed hdl, ftd, hollow stopper 300.00
Apollo, rose, scarce 95.00
Arched Fleur-de-Lis, ruby stain, rare, Higbee 395.00
Argonaut Shell, bl opal 350.00
Beaded Grape, gr 125.00
Beaded Loop 45.00
Beaded Swirl, gr 235.00
Beaded Swirl w/Lens, ruby stain 125.00
Bl, HP girl fishing, amber hdl, 7½" 375.00
Bl craquelle, HP decor, 5½" 145.00
Blazing Cornucopia, purple stain w/gold 65.00
Broken Column 65.00
Buckingham 55.00
Bull's Eye w/Point (Reverse Torpedo) .75.00
Burmese, melon rib, satin finish, Mt WA 1,200.00
Butterfly & Daisy, Pairpoint, 7" 135.00
Champion, amber stain 145.00
Christmas Bead & Panel, gr opal, very scarce 250.00
Coin Spot, amberina, HP florals, amber stopper, 4½" 350.00
Coin Spot, bl opal 200.00
Cranberry, clear rope hdl, clear faceted stopper, 8x3¼" 150.00
Cranberry, HP florals, clear hdl, bubble stopper, 7½" 195.00
Croesus, amethyst w/gold, lg 375.00
Croesus, gr w/gold, lg 275.00
Croesus, gr w/gold, 4" 195.00
Cut, Log 65.00
Daisy & Button w/Crossbars, vaseline, lg 160.00
Daisy & Fern, Apple Blossom mold, bl opal 175.00
Daisy & Fern, clear opal, rpl stopper 75.00
Dbl Circle, bl 175.00
Diamond & Fan, cut glass 95.00
Dice & Block, amber 100.00
Drape, amberina, Hobbs 325.00
Empress, emerald gr w/EX gold 275.00
Fancy Loop, Heisey 70.00
Fern, cranberry opal 300.00
Flattened Diamond & Sunburst 25.00
Flora, emerald gr, orig flower stopper .195.00
Flora, vaseline opal, 6½" 425.00
Fluted Scroll, bl opal 175.00
Fluted Scroll, vaseline opal, HP decor 175.00
Forget-Me-Not, butterscotch, Challinor, rare 275.00
Forget-Me-Not, gr opaque, Challinor .150.00
Forget-Me-Not, milk glass, Challinor .75.00
Forget-Me-Not, pk, Challinor 135.00
Georgia Gem, gr, scarce 175.00
Giant Sawtooth 30.00

Guttate, pk satin 325.00
Heart w/T'print 75.00
Herringbone, gr 110.00
Herringbone, lt bl opal, teardrop stopper, 7x3⅝" 275.00
Hobnail, rubena verde, Hobbs & Brockunier 565.00

Idyll, blue, with clear stopper, 6½", with good gold: $225.00; plain, no gold: $175.00.

Intaglio, clear opal 110.00
Invt Rib, vaseline w/gold 125.00
Invt T'print, amber & wht spatter 125.00
Invt T'print, amberina, HP florals, amber hdl, sq base, 7" 515.00
Invt T'print, cranberry, HP roses, ribbed, 7½" 195.00
Invt T'print, rubena verde, faceted stopper, att Hobbs, 6¾" ...395.00
Ivy Scroll, bl 135.00
Jewel & Flower, vaseline opal 375.00
Kokomo (Bar & Diamond), 3½" 45.00
Log & Star, amber, sm 50.00
Log & Star, sapphire bl, lg 90.00
Lone Star, gr 175.00
Manhattan, sm 60.00
Medallion Sprig, gr to clear 235.00
Moon & Star 95.00
MOP Swirl, pk shaded, frosted hdl/stopper, 5½x3" 435.00
Nestor, amethyst, Northwood 175.00
New Hampshire 50.00
Optic Diamond Quilted, HP florals, sq form 95.00
Panelled Daisy & Button 45.00
Pennsylvania (Late Balder), US Glass, 1898 ....45.00
Petticoat, vaseline, rare 275.00
Pillow Encircled (Hero), ruby stain, faceted stopper 120.00
Pressed Optic, vaseline w/gold, orig stopper w/inside rib 130.00
Prize, gr 175.00
Reversed Dia Quilt, amberina, clear faceted stopper, 6½" 250.00
Ribbed Pillar, pk & wht spatter 200.00
Riverside's Ranson, vaseline 175.00
Rosaline w/alabaster hdl, att Stevens & Williams, 6¼" 300.00
Royal Ivy, rubena 335.00
Scalloped Skirt, amethyst, no decor 50.00
Scalloped Skirt, amethyst w/decor 75.00
Scroll w/Acanthus, bl opal 160.00
Shoshone, gr 95.00
Shoshone, ruby stain 195.00
St Louis, cameo-etched stylized floral on frost 400.00
Starred Loop, ruby stain 195.00
Stars & Bars, amber 90.00
Stars & Bars, amber, +shakers & ped tray, M 165.00

Strawberry Diamond & Fan, faceted stopper 55.00
Stripe, bl opal, 3-petal top, cut faceted stopper, Hobbs, 6¾" ...225.00
Swag w/Brackets, bl opal 360.00
Swag w/Brackets, vaseline opal 385.00
Tarantum's Atlanta, ca 1894 ....95.00
Thousand Eye, amber, 3-knob stopper 100.00
Thousand Eye Variant, amber 175.00
Tiny Optic, amethyst, HP/gold decor 95.00
Tiny Optic, emerald w/decor 95.00
Tokyo, bl opal, clear stopper 250.00
Verre de soie, Hawkes eng, fancy hollow stopper, Steuben, 7" .335.00
Wild Bouquet, clear opal, scarce 200.00
Wild Rose & Bow Knot, chocolate 325.00
Wild Rose & Bow Knot, clear & frosted w/goofus decor, NM ..145.00
Wild Rose & Bow Knot, frosted 115.00
X-Ray, gr w/gold 195.00

Cup Plates, Glass

Before the middle 1850s, it was socially acceptable to pour hot tea into a deep saucer to cool. The tea was sipped from the saucer rather than the cup, which frequently was handleless and too hot to hold. The cup plate served as a coaster for the cup. It is generally agreed that the first examples of pressed glass cup plates were made about 1826 at the Boston and Sandwich Glass Co. in Sandwich, Cape Cod, Massachusetts. Other glassworks in three major areas — New England, Philadelphia, and the Midwest (especially Pittsburgh) — quickly followed suit.

Antique glass cup plates range in size from 2⅝" up to 4¼" in diameter. The earliest plates had simple designs inspired by cut glass patterns, but by 1829 they had become more complex. The span from then until about 1845 is known as the 'Lacy Period,' when cup plate designs and pressing techniques were at their peak. To cover pressing imperfections, the backgrounds of the plates were often covered with fine stippling which endowed them with a glittering brilliance called 'Laciness.' They were made in a multitude of designs — some purely decorative, others commemorative. Subjects include the American eagle, hearts, sunbursts, log cabins, ships, George Washington, the political candidates Clay and Harrison, plows, beehives, etc. Of all the patterns, the round George Washington plate is the rarest and most valuable — only three are known to exist today.

Authenticity is most important. Collectors must be aware that contemporary plates which have no antique counterparts and fakes modeled after antique patterns have had wide distribution. Condition is also important, though it is the exceptional plate that does not have some rim roughness. More important considerations are scarcity of design and color.

Our advisor for this category is John Blaine; he is listed in the Directory under New Jersey. The book *American Glass* by George and Helen McKearin has a section on glass cup plates. A more definitive book is *American Glass Cup Plates*, by Ruth Webb Lee and James H. Rose. Numbers in the listings that follow (computer sorted) refer to the latter. When no condition is indicated, the examples listed below are assumed to have only minor rim roughness as is normal. See also Staffordshire; Pairpoint.

R-101, scarce, G 45.00
R-102, scarce, VG 50.00
R-103, rare, G 55.00
R-104, G 28.00
R-11, VG 35.00
R-120, scarce, VG 55.00
R-124A, VG 36.00
R-127A, scarce, VG 47.00
R-13B, rare, VG 65.00

R-130, extremely rare, VG 180.00
R-136A, rare, VG 75.00
R-145C, VG 30.00
R-146, scarce, G 37.00
R-147A, scarce, VG 40.00
R-147B, rare, VG 53.00
R-148, VG 32.00
R-149, VG 29.00
R-15, rare, VG 69.00
R-151, VG 32.00
R-151A, VG 32.00
R-154B, EX 37.00
R-155, VG 30.00
R-156B, VG 34.00
R-158, very rare, VG 170.00
R-159B, VG 29.00
R-160B, VG 28.00
R-162B, EX 36.00
R-164A, EX 37.00
R-164B, EX 37.00
R-169B, EX 37.00
R-172A, G 26.00
R-172B, EX 37.00
R-176A, VG 30.00
R-176B, VG 32.00
R-177, EX 45.00
R-179A, rare, EX 77.00
R-180A, VG 33.00
R-181A, very rare, VG 200.00
R-188, very rare, VG 275.00
R-194, VG 22.00
R-197C, VG 34.00
R-20, VG 25.00
R-216, VG 65.00
R-217A, VG 67.00
R-22, VG 28.00
R-223, VG 35.00
R-226C, VG 28.00
R-228A, rare, VG 100.00
R-229B, scarce, G 41.00
R-233A, G 28.00
R-235, G 22.00
R-236, VG 30.00
R-24, VG 28.00
R-243, bl opal, scarce, VG 135.00
R-243, VG 36.00
R-245, VG 34.00
R-246, opal, very rare, G 200.00
R-25, VG 22.00
R-255, VG 23.00
R-255A, VG 34.00
R-262, dk bl, scarce, VG 130.00
R-268, VG 33.00
R-27, VG 29.00
R-271, VG 31.00
R-272, opal tint, VG 32.00
R-275, VG 32.00
R-277, scarce, VG 48.00
R-28, G 19.00
R-285, VG 34.00
R-29X1, EX 32.00
R-291, G 22.00
R-291X1, VG 28.00
R-292, VG 27.00

R-296A, VG 30.00
R-311, G 17.00
R-313, VG 21.00
R-32, EX 29.00
R-322, VG 19.00
R-323, bl opal, VG 38.00
R-324, bl opal, EX 36.00
R-331, VG 20.00
R-334, VG 19.00
R-334A, VG 21.00
R-339, VG 17.00
R-343B, scarce, VG 36.00
R-37, scarce, EX 42.00
R-373, VG 16.00
R-38, VG 28.00
R-391, EX 14.00
R-392, G 12.00
R-396, EX 15.00
R-40, G 22.00
R-402, EX 14.00
R-41, scarce, VG 42.00
R-412, VG 15.00
R-416, VG 15.00
R-436A, scarce, VG 36.00
R-439, G 21.00
R-441, VG 39.00
R-441A, VG 33.00
R-448, G 46.00
R-45, scarce, VG 61.00
R-455B, scarce, G 21.00
R-458, scarce, VG 28.00
R-459O, VG 24.00
R-46, VG 27.00
R-465J, bl opal, scarce, VG 60.00
R-465J, VG 22.00
R-465L, bl opal, scarce, VG 55.00
R-465L, VG 19.00
R-467A, VG 22.00
R-479, G 15.00
R-49, VG 32.00
R-495, VG 13.00
R-500, very rare, VG 48.00
R-508, G 11.00
R-520AX1, scarce, VG 28.00
R-522, bl opal, VG 25.00
R-53, scarce, VG 51.00
R-531, VG 25.00
R-561, Washington, octagonal, very rare, EX 2,900.00
R-562A, very rare, G 345.00
R-563, G 22.00
R-564, VG 28.00
R-565A, VG 30.00
R-565B, peacock bl, scarce, G 100.00
R-565B, VG 28.00
R-566A, scarce, VG 40.00
R-570, rare, EX 112.00
R-570, rare, VG 95.00
R-571, rare, VG 105.00
R-575, scarce, EX 75.00
R-576, scarce, VG 64.00
R-580B, very rare, VG 225.00
R-593, scarce, VG 47.00
R-601C, very rare, VG 500.00
R-605A, scarce, G 95.00

R-610, VG 40.00
R-610C, VG 39.00
R-612A, octagonal steamboat, rare, VG 255.00
R-619A, VG 42.00
R-619B, rare, VG 105.00
R-62A, scarce, EX 55.00
R-624A, scarce, VG 64.00
R-631, VG 43.00
R-632, VG 45.00
R-637, very rare, VG 260.00
R-641, VG 20.00
R-643, VG 23.00
R-643A, VG 23.00
R-65, scarce, EX 48.00
R-665A, VG 35.00
R-666, VG 36.00
R-666A, scarce, G 40.00
R-672, scarce, VG 52.00
R-676, scarce, G 50.00
R-676C, scarce, VG 54.00
R-679, VG 30.00
R-680B, VG 23.00
R-686, rare, G 95.00
R-695, scarce, VG 55.00
R-76, VG 50.00
R-78, scarce, EX 70.00
R-78, scarce, G 48.00
R-79, VG 35.00

R-842, sulfide bust of Napoleon, $250.00.

R-852, VG 18.00
R-866, VG 35.00
R-95, opal opaque, rare, VG 150.00
R-95, VG 36.00
R-96, VG 34.00
R-97, scarce, VG 48.00

Custard

As early as the 1880s, custard glass was produced in England. Migrating glassmakers brought the formula for the creamy ivory ware to America. One of them was Harry Northwood, who in 1898 founded his company in Indiana, Pennsylvania, and introduced the glassware to the American market. Soon other companies were producing custard, among them Heisey, Tarentum, Fenton, and McKee. Not only dinnerware patterns but souvenir items were made. Today, custard is the most expensive of the colored pressed glassware patterns. The formula for producing the luminous glass contains uranium salts which imparts the cream color to the batch and causes it to glow when it is examined under a black light.

Argonaut Shell, bowl, master berry; gold & decor, 10½" L 195.00
Argonaut Shell, butter dish, gold & decor 275.00
Argonaut Shell, compote, jelly; gold & decor, scarce 135.00
Argonaut Shell, creamer, gold & decor 110.00
Argonaut Shell, cruet, gold & decor 450.00
Argonaut Shell, pitcher, water; gold & decor 310.00
Argonaut Shell, sauce, ftd, gold & decor 65.00
Argonaut Shell, spooner, gold & decor 115.00
Argonaut Shell, sugar bowl, w/lid, gold & decor 160.00
Argonaut Shell, toothpick holder, gold & decor 275.00
Argonaut Shell, tumbler, gold & decor 85.00
Bead Swag, goblet, floral & gold 60.00
Bead Swag, sauce, floral & gold 45.00
Bead Swag, tray, pickle; floral & gold, rare 260.00
Bead Swag, wine, floral & gold 58.00
Beaded Circle, bowl, master berry; floral & gold 225.00
Beaded Circle, butter dish, floral & gold 325.00
Beaded Circle, creamer, floral & gold 120.00
Beaded Circle, cruet, floral & gold, rare 600.00
Beaded Circle, pitcher, water; floral & gold 450.00
Beaded Circle, shakers, floral & gold, pr 250.00
Beaded Circle, spooner, floral & gold 115.00
Beaded Circle, sugar bowl, w/lid, floral & gold 170.00
Beaded Circle, tumbler, floral & gold 75.00
Cane Insert, berry set, 7-pc 365.00
Cane Insert, table set, 4-pc 425.00
Cherry & Scales, bowl, master berry; nutmeg stain 130.00
Cherry & Scales, butter dish, nutmeg stain 225.00
Cherry & Scales, creamer, nutmeg stain 115.00
Cherry & Scales, pitcher, water; nutmeg stain 325.00
Cherry & Scales, spooner, nutmeg stain 85.00
Cherry & Scales, sugar bowl, w/lid, nutmeg stain 125.00
Cherry & Scales, tumbler, nutmeg stain 50.00
Chrysanthemum Sprig, bowl, master berry; gold & decor 185.00
Chrysanthemum Sprig, bowl, master berry; no gold 140.00
Chrysanthemum Sprig, butter dish, gold & decor 250.00
Chrysanthemum Sprig, celery vase, gold & decor, rare 600.00
Chrysanthemum Sprig, compote, jelly; gold & decor 115.00
Chrysanthemum Sprig, compote, jelly; no decor 60.00
Chrysanthemum Sprig, condiment tray, gold & decor 600.00
Chrysanthemum Sprig, creamer, gold & decor 105.00
Chrysanthemum Sprig, cruet, gold & decor, 6¾" 290.00
Chrysanthemum Sprig, pitcher, water; gold & decor 365.00
Chrysanthemum Sprig, sauce, gold & decor, ftd 50.00
Chrysanthemum Sprig, shakers, gold & decor, pr 225.00
Chrysanthemum Sprig, spooner, gold & decor 105.00
Chrysanthemum Sprig, toothpick holder, gold & decor 275.00
Chrysanthemum Sprig, toothpick holder, no decor 165.00
Chrysanthemum Sprig, tumbler, gold & decor 55.00
Dandelion, mug, nutmeg stain 165.00
Delaware, creamer, breakfast; pk stain 70.00
Delaware, sauce, pk stain 65.00
Delaware, tray, pin; gr stain 75.00
Delaware, tumbler, pk stain 55.00
Diamond w/Peg, bowl, master berry; roses & gold 215.00
Diamond w/Peg, butter dish, roses & gold 200.00
Diamond w/Peg, creamer, ind; souvenir 45.00
Diamond w/Peg, creamer, roses & gold 75.00
Diamond w/Peg, mug, souvenir 50.00
Diamond w/Peg, napkin ring, roses & gold, rare 150.00
Diamond w/Peg, pitcher, 5½" 140.00
Diamond w/Peg, sauce, roses & gold 40.00

Diamond w/Peg, shakers, souvenir, pr 95.00
Diamond w/Peg, sugar bowl, w/lid, roses & gold 160.00
Diamond w/Peg, toothpick holder, roses & gold 70.00
Diamond w/Peg, tumbler, roses & gold 40.00
Diamond w/Peg, water set, souvenir, 7-pc 500.00
Diamond w/Peg, wine, roses & gold 55.00
Diamond w/Peg, wine, souvenir 40.00
Everglades, bowl, master berry; gold & decor 215.00
Everglades, butter dish, gold & decor 365.00
Everglades, creamer, gold & decor 130.00
Everglades, sauce, gold & decor 60.00
Everglades, shakers, gold & decor, pr 325.00
Everglades, spooner, gold & decor 130.00
Everglades, sugar bowl, w/lid, gold & decor 175.00
Everglades, tumbler, gold & decor 100.00
Fan, bowl, master berry; good gold 185.00
Fan, butter dish, good gold 210.00
Fan, creamer, good gold 110.00
Fan, ice cream set, good gold, 7-pc 500.00
Fan, pitcher, water; good gold 275.00
Fan, sauce, good gold 55.00
Fan, spooner, good gold 85.00
Fan, sugar bowl, w/lid, good gold 125.00
Fan, tumbler, good gold 75.00
Fan, water set, good gold, 7-pc 700.00
Fine Cut & Roses, rose bowl, fancy int, nutmeg stain 100.00
Fine Cut & Roses, rose bowl, plain int 85.00
Geneva, bowl, master berry; floral decor, ftd, oval, 8½" L 90.00
Geneva, bowl, master berry; floral decor, rnd, 9" 120.00
Geneva, butter dish, floral decor 135.00
Geneva, butter dish, no decor 90.00
Geneva, compote, jelly; floral decor 85.00
Geneva, creamer, floral decor 70.00
Geneva, cruet, floral decor 265.00
Geneva, pitcher, water; floral decor 225.00
Geneva, sauce, floral decor, oval 45.00
Geneva, sauce, floral decor, rnd 45.00
Geneva, shakers, floral decor, pr 135.00
Geneva, spooner, floral decor 70.00
Geneva, sugar bowl, open, floral decor 65.00
Geneva, sugar bowl, w/lid, floral decor 120.00
Geneva, syrup, floral decor 300.00
Geneva, toothpick holder, floral w/M gold 135.00
Geneva, tumbler, floral decor 50.00
Georgia Gem, bowl, master berry; good gold 95.00
Georgia Gem, bowl, master berry; gr opaque 60.00
Georgia Gem, butter dish, good gold 190.00
Georgia Gem, celery vase, good gold 145.00
Georgia Gem, creamer, good gold 60.00
Georgia Gem, creamer, no gold 50.00
Georgia Gem, mug, good gold 45.00
Georgia Gem, powder jar, w/lid 60.00
Georgia Gem, shakers, good gold, pr 95.00
Georgia Gem, spooner, souvenir 55.00
Georgia Gem, sugar bowl, w/lid, no gold 60.00
Grape (& Cable), bottle, scent; nutmeg stain, orig stopper 525.00
Grape (& Cable), bowl, master berry; nutmeg stain, ftd, 11" ...265.00
Grape (& Cable), bowl, nutmeg stain, 7½" 50.00
Grape (& Cable), butter dish, nutmeg stain 235.00
Grape (& Cable), compote, jelly; nutmeg stain 75.00
Grape (& Cable), compote, nutmeg stain, 4½x8" 250.00
Grape (& Cable), cracker jar, nutmeg stain 525.00
Grape (& Cable), creamer, breakfast; nutmeg stain 75.00
Grape (& Cable), humidor, bl stain, rare 600.00

Grape (& Cable), humidor, nutmeg stain, rare 650.00
Grape (& Cable), nappy, nutmeg stain, hdls 45.00
Grape (& Cable), pitcher, water; nutmeg stain 375.00
Grape (& Cable), plate, nutmeg stain, 7" 45.00
Grape (& Cable), plate, nutmeg stain, 8" 55.00
Grape (& Cable), powder jar, nutmeg stain 300.00
Grape (& Cable), punch bowl, w/base, nutmeg stain 875.00
Grape (& Cable), sauce, nutmeg stain, ftd 45.00
Grape (& Cable), spooner, nutmeg stain 95.00
Grape (& Cable), sugar, breakfast; open, nutmeg stain 75.00
Grape (& Cable), sugar bowl, w/lid, nutmeg stain 150.00
Grape (& Cable), tray, dresser; nutmeg stain, scarce, lg 325.00
Grape (& Cable), tray, pin; nutmeg stain 125.00
Grape (& Cable), tumbler, nutmeg stain 75.00
Grape & Gothic Arches, bowl, master berry; pearl w/gold 200.00
Grape & Gothic Arches, butter dish, pearl w/gold 200.00
Grape & Gothic Arches, creamer, pearl w/gold, rare 90.00
Grape & Gothic Arches, favor vase, nutmeg stain 80.00
Grape & Gothic Arches, goblet, pearl w/gold 60.00
Grape & Gothic Arches, pitcher, water; pearl w/gold 275.00
Grape & Gothic Arches, sauce, pearl w/gold, rare 80.00
Grape & Gothic Arches, spooner, pearl w/gold 80.00
Grape & Gothic Arches, sugar bowl, w/lid, pearl w/gold 125.00
Grape & Gothic Arches, tumbler, pearl w/gold 65.00
Grape Arbor, vase, hat form 90.00
Heart w/T'print, creamer 80.00
Heart w/T'print, lamp, good pnt, scarce, 8" 275.00
Heart w/T'print, sugar bowl, ind 75.00
Honeycomb, wine 65.00
Horse Medallion, bowl, gr stain, 7" 70.00
Intaglio, bowl, master berry; gold & decor, ftd, 9" 250.00
Intaglio, butter dish, gold & decor, scarce 300.00
Intaglio, compote, jelly; gold & decor 125.00
Intaglio, creamer, gold & decor 100.00
Intaglio, cruet, gold & decor 350.00
Intaglio, pitcher, water; gold & decor 345.00
Intaglio, sauce, gold & decor 48.00
Intaglio, shakers, gold & decor, pr 200.00
Intaglio, spooner, gold & decor 110.00
Intaglio, sugar bowl, w/lid, gold & decor 145.00
Intaglio, tumbler, gold & decor 75.00
Inverted Fan & Feather, bowl, master berry; gold & decor 215.00
Inverted Fan & Feather, butter dish, gold & decor 295.00
Inverted Fan & Feather, compote, jelly; gold & decor, rare 410.00
Inverted Fan & Feather, creamer, gold & decor 130.00
Inverted Fan & Feather, cruet, gold & decor, scarce, 6½" 600.00
Inverted Fan & Feather, pitcher, water; gold & decor 450.00
Inverted Fan & Feather, punch cup, gold & decor 250.00
Inverted Fan & Feather, sauce, gold & decor 65.00
Inverted Fan & Feather, shakers, gold & decor, pr 450.00
Inverted Fan & Feather, spooner, gold & decor 130.00
Inverted Fan & Feather, sugar bowl, w/lid, gold & decor 185.00
Inverted Fan & Feather, tumbler, gold & decor 85.00
Jackson, bowl, master berry; good gold, ftd 125.00
Jackson, creamer, good gold 85.00
Jackson, pitcher, water; good gold 250.00
Jackson, pitcher, water; no decor 150.00
Jackson, sauce, good gold 45.00
Jackson, shakers, good gold, pr 135.00
Jackson, spooner, good gold 65.00
Jackson, sugar bowl, w/lid, good gold 135.00
Jackson, tumbler, good gold 45.00
Louis XV, berry set, w/nutmeg, 7-pc 375.00
Louis XV, bowl, master berry; good gold 165.00

Louis XV, butter dish, good gold 200.00
Louis XV, creamer, good gold 80.00
Louis XV, cruet, good gold 235.00
Louis XV, pitcher, water; good gold 225.00
Louis XV, sauce, good gold, ftd .47.00
Louis XV, spooner, good gold 80.00
Louis XV, sugar bowl, w/lid, good gold 150.00
Louis XV, tumbler, good gold 65.00
Maple Leaf, bowl, master berry; gold & decor, scarce 300.00
Maple Leaf, butter dish, gold & decor 255.00
Maple Leaf, compote, jelly; gold & decor, rare 455.00
Maple Leaf, creamer, gold & decor 90.00
Maple Leaf, cruet, gold & decor, rare 1,250.00
Maple Leaf, pitcher, water; gold & decor 345.00
Maple Leaf, sauce, gold & decor, scarce 95.00
Maple Leaf, shakers, gold & decor, pr 550.00
Maple Leaf, spooner, gold & decor 105.00
Maple Leaf, sugar bowl, w/lid, gold & decor 175.00
Maple Leaf, tumbler, gold & decor 85.00
Panelled Poppy, lamp shade, nutmeg stain, scarce 850.00
Peacock & Urn, bowl, ice cream; nutmeg stain, sm 80.00
Peacock & Urn, bowl, ice cream; nutmeg stain, 10" 310.00
Punty Band, shakers, pr 90.00
Punty Band, spooner, floral decor 60.00
Punty Band, tumbler, floral decor, souvenir 65.00
Ribbed Drape, butter dish, scalloped, roses & gold 280.00
Ribbed Drape, compote, jelly; roses & gold, rare 200.00
Ribbed Drape, creamer, roses & gold, scarce 115.00
Ribbed Drape, cruet, roses & gold, scarce 335.00
Ribbed Drape, pitcher, water; roses & gold, rare 345.00
Ribbed Drape, sauce, roses & gold 40.00
Ribbed Drape, shakers, roses & gold, pr, rare 200.00
Ribbed Drape, spooner, roses & gold 85.00
Ribbed Drape, toothpick holder, roses & gold 160.00
Ribbed Drape, tumbler, roses & gold 65.00
Ribbed Thumbprint, wine, floral decor 75.00
Ring Band, bowl, master berry; roses & gold 135.00
Ring Band, butter dish, roses & gold 200.00
Ring Band, compote, jelly; roses & gold, scarce 165.00
Ring Band, creamer, roses & gold 85.00
Ring Band, cruet, roses & gold 300.00
Ring Band, pitcher, roses & gold, 7½" 240.00
Ring Band, sauce, roses & gold 40.00
Ring Band, shakers, roses & gold, pr 115.00
Ring Band, spooner, roses & gold 85.00
Ring Band, syrup, roses & gold 335.00
Ring Band, toothpick holder, roses & gold 80.00
Ring Band, tray, condiment; roses & gold 175.00
Singing Birds, mug, nutmeg stain 85.00
Tarentum's Victoria, bowl, master berry; gold & decor 200.00
Tarentum's Victoria, butter dish, gold & decor, rare 275.00
Tarentum's Victoria, celery vase, gold & decor, rare 225.00
Tarentum's Victoria, creamer, gold & decor, scarce 90.00
Tarentum's Victoria, pitcher, water; gold & decor, rare 365.00
Tarentum's Victoria, spooner, gold & decor 95.00
Tarentum's Victoria, sugar bowl, w/lid, gold & decor 135.00
Tarentum's Victoria, tumbler, gold & decor 70.00
Vermont, butter dish, bl decor 185.00
Vermont, toothpick holder, bl decor 95.00
Vermont, vase, floral decor, jeweled 75.00
Wide Band, bell, roses 145.00
Wild Bouquet, butter dish, gold & decor, rare 400.00
Wild Bouquet, creamer, no gold .145.00
Wild Bouquet, cruet, no decor, w/clear stopper 300.00

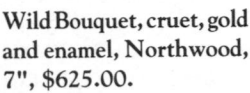

Wild Bouquet, cruet, gold and enamel, Northwood, 7", $625.00.

Wild Bouquet, sauce, gold & decor 60.00
Wild Bouquet, spooner, gold & decor 145.00
Wild Bouquet, tumbler, no decor 55.00
Winged Scroll, bowl, master berry; gold & decor, 11" L 140.00
Winged Scroll, butter dish, good gold 185.00
Winged Scroll, butter dish, no decor 150.00
Winged Scroll, celery vase, good gold, rare 400.00
Winged Scroll, cigarette jar, scarce 155.00
Winged Scroll, compote, ruffled, rare, 6¾x10¾" 495.00
Winged Scroll, cruet, good gold, clear stopper 235.00
Winged Scroll, hair receiver, good gold 120.00
Winged Scroll, pitcher, water; bulbous, good gold 300.00
Winged Scroll, sauce, good gold .35.00
Winged Scroll, shakers, bulbous, good gold, rare, pr 350.00
Winged Scroll, shakers, str sides, good gold, pr 165.00
Winged Scroll, sugar bowl, w/lid, good gold 150.00
Winged Scroll, tumbler, good gold 75.00

Cut Glass

The earliest documented evidence of commercial glass cutting in the United States was in 1810; the producers were Bakewell and Page of Pittsburgh. These first efforts resulted in simple patterns with only a moderate amount of cutting. By the middle of the century, glass cutters began experimenting with a thicker glass which enabled them to use deeper cuttings, though patterns remained much the same. This period is usually referred to as Rich Cut. Using three types of wheels — a flat edge, a mitered edge, and a convex edge — facets, miters, and depressions were combined to produce various designs. In the late 1870s, a curved miter was developed which greatly expanded design potential. Patterns became more elaborate, often covering the entire surface. The Brilliant Period of cut glass covered a span from about 1880 until 1915. Because of the pressure necessary to achieve the deeply cut patterns, only glass containing a high grade of metal could withstand the process. For this reason and the amount of handwork involved, cut glass has always been expensive.

Our advisors for this category are Jeanette and Marvin Stofft; they are listed in the Directory under Indiana. See also specific manufacturers.

Key:
dmn — diamonds   X-cut — cross-cut
straw — strawberry   X-hatch — crosshatch

Basket, dmn mitres, dmn points, star base, 6x4x6" 95.00
Bottle, dresser; pinwheel/flashed fan, Clark, 5" 140.00
Bottle, scent; amber to crystal, clear faceted stopper, 5" 118.00
Bottle, scent; X-hatching/fans, faceted stopper, 6" 135.00
Bowl, cane/hobstars/nailhead/dmn, scalloped/sawtooth, 9" 200.00
Bowl, Checkerboard, sq, 8½" .350.00
Bowl, chrysanthemum, shallow, 9" 125.00
Bowl, chrysanthemum/cane, sq, 7" 275.00
Bowl, flower; cane/dmn/pineapple blossom, sq/ftd, 7" 225.00
Bowl, fluted panels, chrysanthemum border, 10" 475.00
Bowl, fruit; hobstars/cane/etc, ped ft/dbl hdls, 7½x7" 1,100.00
Bowl, Harvard, deep, 8" 275.00
Bowl, Harvard, shallow, 9" 125.00
Bowl, hobstar chain around 6-point star, incurvate, 8" 275.00
Bowl, hobstars, scalloped/serrated, heavy, 10", NM 300.00
Bowl, hobstars, str sides, lobed rim, 11" 200.00
Bowl, hobstars/cane/daisy/button panels, serrated, 9" 125.00
Bowl, hobstars/dandelions/butterflies, sgn ST, 10" 375.00
Bowl, hobstars/prisms, scalloped cut rim, 8" 95.00
Bowl, hobstars/single stars/fern, scalloped/sawtooth, 10" 350.00
Bowl, Kohinoor & hobstars, 10" 650.00
Bowl, lg hobstar w/rays & cane border, serrated, 7" 80.00
Bowl, lg/sm hobstars, repousse silver Gorham rim, 9", NM 525.00
Bowl, Monarch, rayed ped base, notched rim, Hoare, 4⅛" H . . .165.00
Bowl, pinwheel/fan, serrated/scalloped, 8" 115.00
Bowl, pinwheel/fan & X-hatch, scalloped/sawtooth, 9" 150.00
Bowl, Rayed Points, deep cuts, 8" H 225.00
Bowl, star/daisy/button/cane, serrated 4-lobed rim, 9" 85.00
Bowl, Starflower, 3-ftd, 12" 140.00
Bowl, Wedding Ring, Hoare 2,000.00
Box, cigarette; fans/stars/dmns, lid is ash tray, 4½" 70.00
Box, dresser; blown-out, hobstars/fan, silver rim, 6x8½" 1,100.00
Box, glove; Harvard variation w/florals, lg 475.00
Candy dish, hobstar w/in hobstar, tricorn shape, ped ft 175.00
Carafe, Button, sq w/flared rim, faceted ball stopper, 8" 75.00
Carafe, buttons/t'prints, faceted ball stopper, 12", pr 200.00
Carafe, dmn & pineapple blossom, faceted stopper, 11" 75.00
Carafe, hobstar w/in hobstar, dmn points, 7¼x6½" 130.00
Carafe, hobstars/dmn fields/X-hatch/fans, 7¼x6¾" 135.00
Carafe, hobstars/fans/dmns, bulbous, 8" 95.00
Carafe, hobstars/ovals/triangles, heavy, 12", NM 400.00
Carafe, morning-glory vine cutting, pnt/cut stopper, 12" 125.00
Carafe, Pinwheel, 12", pr 250.00
Carafe, Russian, 7", pr 500.00
Carafe, strw & fan, notched panel neck, 8x5¾" 125.00
Carafe, t'print & dmn, faceted/flared rim, 12", pr 150.00
Champagne cooler, fluted panels, scroll hdls, 9" 200.00
Compote, Ambrosia, hobstars/fan/vesica variant/etc, 9x10" . . .650.00
Compote, chrysanthemum, 10" 350.00
Compote, floral etch, etched dmn ground w/floral panels, 4" . .125.00
Compote, hobstars, 6-sided, stemmed, heavy cuts, 9" 500.00
Creamer & sugar bowl, fan/cane, hobstar bottom, scalloped . . .140.00
Creamer & sugar bowl, pinwheel/fan, dbl-notched hdls 80.00
Creamer & sugar bowl, pinwheels, serrated, no lid 70.00
Creamer & sugar bowl, ribbons of cane/hobstar, EX 200.00
Creamer & sugar bowl, Trellis, sgn Hoare 700.00
Cruet, hobstar/fan, notched panel neck, tri-fold top 65.00
Cruet, petaled flowers/leaves, rayed base, faceted stopper 55.00
Cruet, wine; etched vine, faceted stopper, 8" 60.00
Ferner, hobstar in pinwheels, 3-ftd, metal liner, 4x7" L 125.00
Finger bowl, Lotus, Eggington, 4¾x2¾" 85.00
Goblet, X-hatch/fan on cut 6-sided stem, star base 50.00
Jar, chrysanthemum, bulbous, w/lid, 5" 125.00
Jar, sachet; panels w/horizontal cuts, repousse top, 3¼" 50.00

Jug, wine; thistle/leaf etching, rnd cut/etched stopper 110.00
Ladle, hobstars/fan, teardrop/notched hdl 575.00
Lamp, hobstars/cane/flashed fan, step-cut prism stem, 23" . . .2,800.00
Lamp, 11" dome shade w/pinwheels & daisies, prisms, 20" . . .1,500.00
Loving cup, Block, 3-hdld, ped ft, 10x9" 750.00
Mayonnaise set, cane borders, flowers/leaves, w/undertray 80.00
Mayonnaise set, strw band/cut rim, w/undertray 165.00
Mayonnaise set, strw dmns/spears/almonds, w/underplate 195.00
Muffineer, pinwheel/hobstar fans/dmn points, SP top, 6" 155.00
Nappy, intaglio tulips/butterflies, notched, ring hdl 55.00
Pitcher, cane, bulbous, faceted hdl, 7½" 400.00
Pitcher, chrysanthemum & cane, 12" 225.00
Pitcher, chrysanthemum & dmn, 8½" 225.00
Pitcher, Daisy & Alhambra, serrated, faceted hdl, 10" 550.00
Pitcher, dmn w/star band, hobnail/X-hatch top & base, 11" . . .275.00
Pitcher, hobstars, fans, multi-rayed base, t'print hdl, 9" 155.00
Pitcher, hobstars/vesicas/strw fields/fans, 9",+6 tumblers 325.00
Pitcher, milk; buzz stars, dbl-notched hdl, fluted spout 160.00
Pitcher, pinwheels/vesicas/fans, dbl hdl, 10½", +3 tumblers . . .270.00
Pitcher, strw dmn, bulbous, 7" .225.00
Pitcher, tankard; daisies/leaves intaglio, +6 tumblers 155.00
Pitcher, tankard; hobstars/etc, bull's eye facet hdl, 8" 140.00
Pitcher, water; hobstars/strw, rayed base, unmk 175.00
Plate, pinwheels/hobstars, scalloped/serrated, 12" 450.00
Plate, Russian-type center w/scalloped cut-out rim, 12" 925.00
Punch bowl, hobstars/cane/vesica/fan, sgn w/star, 13x14" . . .1,400.00
Punch bowl, compote base, ea pc sgn Hoare, 13x12½" . . .1,500.00
Sugar shaker, floral eng, pear shape, SP top/ft, 5¾" 60.00
Sugar shaker, hobstars in pinwheels w/dmn, SP lid, 6" 115.00
Syrup, hobstars & buttons in X-hatching w/fans, 5½" 195.00
Tazza, hobstars/fan/cane, 8-sided teardrop stem, Clark, 8" 250.00
Tazza, pinwheel/fan/hobstars, 6-sided scalloped base, 5" 95.00
Toothpick holder, dmn, flower shape, Deco style, 2¾" 55.00
Tray, celery; florals/butterflies, polished leaf sprays, 11" 70.00
Tray, celery; notched prism encircles oblong hobstar, 12" 195.00
Tray, hobstars/flashed fan/fringed starflowers, 12" 200.00
Tray, ice cream; florals, mitered cane/buzz stars, 14" 150.00
Tray, ice cream; florals/leaves, star/dmn chain border, 16" 225.00
Tray, ice cream; hobstars, ovoid w/lobed rim, 13½" 250.00
Tray, ice cream; hobstars/prism/nailhead, 7½x14" 375.00
Tray, mint; border: nailhead dmn/etched urn, ped ft, 5¾" 80.00
Tray, mint; pinwheel/fan, 5-panel std, serrated, 4½" dia 70.00
Tray, pin; split vesica/star/rays/floral, oval, 9" L 115.00
Tray, prisms/hobstars/etc cut in 6 joined circles, 13" dia 1,550.00

**Chrysanthemum, Diamond, and Pineapple Blossom vases, 14",
$500.00 for the pair; Chrysanthemum and Pineapple Blossom
vases, 10", $250.00 for the pair.**

Vase, bud; hobstar/fan, flashed hobstar base, sawtooth, 5½" 75.00
Vase, bud; strw dmn, 12" 125.00
Vase, chrysanthemum/facet banding, etched florals, 16" 150.00
Vase, daisy w/arched basket window, Clark, 10" 150.00
Vase, Harvard w/cut buttons, no mk, 15" 550.00
Vase, hobstars, trumpet form, 10" 325.00
Vase, hobstars/bull's eye, notched prism, serrated, 12" 200.00
Vase, purple/clear, grapes & leaves, 5⅜x4¾" 185.00
Vase, strw dmn/fan & star, prism-cut stem, star base, 12" 90.00

Cut Velvet

Cut Velvet glassware was made during the late 1800s. It is characterized by the effect achieved through the application of relief-molded patterns, often ribbing or diamond quilting, which allows its white inner casing to show through the outer pastel layer.

Cruet, Dia Quilt, shiny bl, clear hdl, bl stopper, 5½" 250.00
Pitcher, Dia Quilt, pk, frosted twist hdl w/rosettes, 9" 425.00
Pitcher, Dia Quilt, rose, wht hdl, 3¼x2¾" 225.00
Rose bowl, Dia Quilt, bl, wht int, 3⅛x3½" 175.00
Rose bowl, Dia Quilt, rose, egg form, 6-crimp, 3¾x3¼" 150.00
Tumbler, Dia Quilt, peachblow color 230.00
Tumbler, Ribbed, bl 125.00
Tumbler, Ribbed, med pk, 3¾" 125.00

Vase, Diamond Quilt, blue, signed Webb, 5½", $495.00.

Vase, Dia Quilt, lav, stick neck, 11" 200.00
Vase, Dia Quilt, pk, stick neck, 7" 150.00
Vase, Dia Quilt, rose, wht int, 9⅜x3½" 150.00
Vase, Ribbed, bl, ruffled top, 7x3¼" 145.00
Vase, Ribbed, bl, 6¼x3¼" 110.00
Vase, Ribbed, pk shaded, stick neck, 8¾" 145.00
Vase, Ribbed, rose, sq shape, 7¾x3" 145.00

Cybis

Boleslaw Cybis was a graduate of the Academy of Fine Arts in Warsaw, Poland, and was well recognized as a fine artist by the time he was commissioned by his government to paint murals in the Polish Pavillion's Hall of Honor at the 1939 World's Fair. Finding themselves stranded in America at the outbreak of WWII, the Cybises founded an artists' studio, first in Astoria, New York, and later in Trenton, New Jersey, where they

made fine figurines and plaques with exacting artistry and craftsmanship entailing extensive handwork. The studio still operates today producing exquisite porcelains on a limited edition basis.

Appaloosa Colt 300.00
Ariel, boy on grasshopper 375.00
Barnaby Bear 250.00
Beatrice 1,500.00
Calla Lily 1,000.00
Carmen 1,675.00
Chato, Apache Indian 2,675.00
Circus Elephant 250.00
Circus Rider, equestrienne 3,000.00
Cynthia Ballerina 625.00
Eleanor of Aquitaine 2,200.00
Elephant, wht porc, 18x25" 5,300.00
Figurine, Queen Esther, gold/gr/brn shades, mk, 1976, 13½" .1,250.00
Fitzgerald Donkey 160.00
Funny Face 250.00
Goldilocks 350.00
Hamlet 1,750.00
Jack & the Beanstalk 575.00
Jane Eyre 1,275.00
Jumbles Clown 675.00
Karina Ballerina 525.00
Kristina Ballerina 625.00
Little Red Riding Hood 195.00
Madame Butterfly 3,495.00
Marigold, girl on turtle 375.00
Maximilian Dormouse 285.00
Medicine Man, Beaver Head Indian 2,675.00
Oceania, Sea King's steed 1,450.00
Ophelia 2,000.00
Panda Bears 175.00
Pandora 135.00
Phineas Elephant 325.00

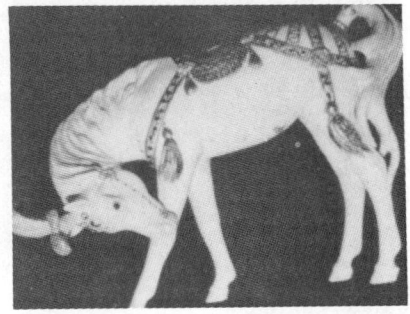

Figure of Polly, The Performing Circus Horse, 9" long, $400.00.

Pollyanna 350.00
Queen Esther 1,600.00
Raffles Racoon 350.00
Rapunzel, lilac 775.00
Red Riding Hood 325.00
Rumples Clown 525.00
Scarlett 2,200.00
Seal 150.00
Sleeping Beauty 695.00
Squirrel, fluffy tail 350.00
Unicorn & Lady 1,450.00
Wendy 150.00
White Buffalo 3,700.00
White Herons 2,500.00

Wood Wren w/Dogwood 260.00

Czechoslovakian Collectibles

Czechoslovakia came into being as a country in 1918. Located in the heart of Europe, it was a land with the natural resources necessary to support a glass industry that dates back to the mid-14th century. This ware has recently captured the attention of today's collectors, and for good reason. There are beautiful vases — cased, ruffled, applied with rigaree or silver overlay — fine enough to rival those of the best glasshouses. Czechoslovakian art glass baskets are quite as attractive as Victorian America's, and the elegant cut glass perfumes made in colors as well as crystal are unrivaled. There are also pressed glass perfumes, molded in lovely Deco shapes, of various types of art glass. Some are overlaid with gold filigree set with 'jewels.' Jewelry, lamps, porcelains and fine art pottery are also included in the field.

More than thirty-five marks have been recorded, including those in the mold, ink stamped, acid etched, or on a small metal name plate. The newer marks are incised, stamped 'Royal Dux made in Czechoslovakia' (see Royal Dux), or simply a paper label which reads 'Bohemian Glass made in Czechoslovakia.' For a more thorough study of the subject, we recommend you refer to the book *Made in Czechoslovakia*, by Ruth A. Forsythe; she is listed in the Directory under Ohio. In the listings that follow when one dimension is given, it refers to height; decoration is enamel unless noted otherwise. See also Erphila.

Scent bottle, clear with intaglio rose in stopper, 5", $125.00.

Candy Baskets

Bl mottle, yel ruffled top, blk hdl, 8" 110.00
Blk w/silver mica, bl int, blk hdl, 8" 85.00
Gr w/dk gr streaks, red opaque overlay, gr hdl, 8½" 110.00
Gr w/dk gr stripes, plain gr hdl, 8" 98.00
Red & gr mottle, clear twisted thorn hdl, 6½" 125.00
Red w/dk streaks, clear twisted thorn hdl, 5½" 145.00

Cased Art Glass

Box, mottled mc, bowl form, brn knob finial, 4½" 85.00
Candlestick, cameo vine on lt orange, 12½" 195.00
Candlestick, dk autumn mottle, 8½" 40.00
Candlestick, yel w/mottled mc base, 4" 27.50

Decanter, exotic bird, silver on lt orange, 12" 95.00
Mayonnaise, blk/bl mottled, 5½" 75.00
Pitcher, exotic bird on orange, blk hdl, 11½" 125.00
Vase, bud; floral, silver on orange, stick form, 6¼" 25.00
Vase, desert scene on shaded ground, classic form, 8½" 110.00
Vase, exotic bird & foliage on dk yel, classic form, 8½" 115.00
Vase, gr bullet form w/3 bl buttressed ft, 8¾" 60.00
Vase, jack-in-the-pulpit; yel w/blk trim, 13½" 50.00
Vase, lovebirds, silver on dk bl, classic form, 13" 125.00
Vase, mottled, metal flower arranger, 5½" 50.00
Vase, orange w/blk rim, ftd U-form, 7¼" 50.00
Vase, pk w/clear pk hdls, urn form, 7½" 60.00
Vase, purple/yel/wht mottle w/blk trim, fan form, 8¼" 85.00
Vase, red w/gr aventurine, fan form, 7½" 150.00
Vase, red w/gr aventurine at base, squash form, 7¼" 125.00
Vase, Roman lady, silver/blk on orange, classic form, 12" 125.00
Vase, scenic on dk yel, flared cylinder, 9½" 165.00
Vase, wht, appl bl leaf at waist, 8⅛" 65.00
Vase, wht, crystal rigaree on ruffled rim, 5½" 60.00
Vase, wht, dk amber rigaree at sides of ball form, 4⅝" 60.00

Cut Glass Perfume Bottles

Amber cut to clear, atomizer, 8½" 145.00
Amethyst, sloped sides to wide base, nude stopper, 6⅝" 350.00
Blk opaque, jeweled shoulders, clear floral stopper, 4⅛" 105.00
Crystal, diamond cuttings, gr lovebirds stopper, 5" 240.00
Crystal, overall cuttings, figure stopper, 6¼" 250.00
Crystal, twins, ringed decor, bl base & stoppers, 4⅛" 95.00
Crystal & frosted, fancy sq base, floral stopper, 6⅜" 90.00
Crystal & frosted, waffled cuts, butterfly stopper, 5½" 110.00
Gr, jeweled decor, canted corners, fancy gr stopper, 4¾" 110.00
Gr, overall florals on ball form, gr flower stopper, 5⅛" 125.00
Pk, sq cuttings, clear prism stopper, 7¼" 90.00
Red, sm neck, stepped shoulders, fancy clear stopper, 5⅞" 300.00

Lamps

Beaded crystal, basket filled w/bl flowers, 8½" 395.00
Dk bl lustre, classic form, rpl shade, 13¼" 110.00
Goebel girl in glass flower dress, 10¼" 585.00
Perfume lamp, HP florals, yel on clear frosted, 4" 135.00
Student lamp, acid-cut shade, slim brass std, 21" 395.00

Mold Blown and Pressed Bottles

Amethyst, gold decor, tall slim ft, atomizer, 7" 110.00
Amethyst & crystal, mc daisies, ped ft, atomizer, 7" 85.00
Blk w/gold decor at shoulder, atomizer, 9½" 110.00
Cranberry opal Hobnail, bulbous, wht opal stopper, 5½" 75.00
Crystal, gold & red jewels, lg jeweled stopper, 4¾" 95.00
Crystal, mc daisies, squat cylinder, crystal stopper, 3⅜" 50.00
Crystal, overall jeweled, ornamentation purse sz, 2¼" 70.00
Gr, appl blk serpentine decor, atomizer, 8" 90.00
Purple lustre, squat teardrop form, flower stopper, 4½" 70.00

Opaque, Crystal, Colored Transparent

Bowl, pk lustre, bl lustre King Tut decor, 3½" 350.00
Decanter, gr bubbly glass, HP decor, gr stopper, 9⅝" 125.00
Old Fashioned, gr bubbly glass, HP decor, 3⅜" 50.00
Pitcher, amber, yel overlay, 11½" 125.00
Shakers, talcum; pk, cut decor, rare, 4¾", pr 250.00

Vase, crystal w/red threading, ftd cylinder, 8¼" 85.00
Vase, orange/wht mottle, cylindrical, 5⅞" 27.50
Vase, wild horses in relief, frosted, 7" 60.00

Pottery, Porcelain, Semi-Porcelain

Clock, faux marble w/flower basket, German works, 7" 110.00
Creamer, cow figural, 6¼" 60.00
Creamer, parrot figural, 4½" 30.00
Cup & saucer, rooster, brn on tan w/gr, child's sz 32.50
Potato server, potato form w/butter pat finial, 5" 16.00
Shakers, Mexican couple, orange & yel, 2¾", pr 24.00
Teapot, pk lustre, 6⅛" 40.00
Teapot, rooster, brn on tan w/gr, 5¼" 60.00
Vase, portrait on shaded brn, hdls, 5¾" 40.00
Wall pocket, peacock, mc on dk bl, 7¼" 45.00

D'Argental

D'Argental cameo glass was produced in France from the 1870s until about 1920 in the Art Nouveau style. Browns and tans were favored colors used to complement florals and scenic designs developed through acid cuttings.

Our advisor for this category is Don Williams; he is listed in the Directory under Iowa.

Cameo

Lamp, perfume; forget-me-nots, bl on dk bl, 6" 1,250.00
Vase, bud; ferns, gr on beige, baluster w/wide ft, 5" 175.00
Vase, chateau & trees, brn/tan on gold, 3 cuts, 12⅛" 895.00
Vase, cottage/trees/castle, 3 cuts, 7" 700.00
Vase, floral, brn on gold frost, 2 cuts, mk, 4⅛x2⅜" 245.00
Vase, harbor/sailboats/city, brn/orange/yel, 3 cuts, 11¾" 1,650.00
Vase, lady doing wash by lake, bowl form, 3 cuts, 3½x3½" 550.00
Vase, poppies, red on amber, slim form, 6" 400.00
Vase, poppies/leaves, brn on lt rust, baluster form, 13" 935.00
Vase, rocky shore/lighthouse, 3 cuts, mk, 5" 675.00
Vase, wisteria, purple on gray, baluster form, 14" 1,000.00

Daum Nancy

Daum was an important producer of French cameo glass, operating from the late 1800s until after the turn of the century. They used various techniques — acid cutting, wheel engraving, and handwork — to create beautiful scenic designs and nature subjects in the Art Nouveau manner. Marked examples are much in demand and command very high prices.

Our advisor for this category is Don Williams; he is listed in the Directory under Iowa.

Cameo

Bottle, scent; floral, gold-traced on mottle, X mk, 4½" 1,400.00
Bowl, trees/water, gold/brn on gold frost, ped ft, 4¾x7" 950.00
Box, dresser; snow scene, brn on gold mottle, 3½" dia 350.00
Cruet, lily of valley/insects on opal texture, 7" 1,600.00
Lamp, rain scene on dome top/baluster base, HP detail, 14" . . .1,300.00
Pitcher, florals, HP/gold accents on wht opal, 1 cut, 3½" 500.00
Planter, florals, maroon/red on clear/yel mottle, X mk, 10½" .1,600.00
Rose bowl, rose hips/autumn leaves on cream & yel, 2¾" 650.00
Toothpick holder, gold/wht berries on lt yel, 2" 450.00

Tumbler, starflowers, red w/gr leaves on amber, X mk, 5" 775.00
Vase, appl dragonflies, gr/yel on bl to lav, slim, 22" 14,000.00
Vase, autumn forest, lav/red on gr, baluster, 20½" 4,900.00
Vase, autumn tree, purple/yel/brn/gr on translucent, 6" 2,000.00
Vase, berries, rose on frost, silver overlay rim, hdls, 9" 1,700.00
Vase, berry clusters, red w/gr leaves on frost, 13" 1,900.00
Vase, bird frieze, owls at rim, orange on clear, hdls, 6" 3,000.00
Vase, clematis, purple on gold, 1 cut/HP detail, 6" 850.00
Vase, daisies, 3-color on tan, foil lozenges, bowl form, 4½" . .2,900.00
Vase, dandelion leaves, gr on pk texture, 7" 1,600.00
Vase, floral, cranberry on cranberry frost w/gold, 5x2½" 500.00
Vase, grapes, purple w/gr leaves on gold frost, 5x2½" 1,500.00
Vase, ivy, brn on yel to lime, ovoid w/branch hdls, 8¾" 4,000.00
Vase, lake/field, pk/gr overlay, HP flowers, can form, 3¾" . . .1,900.00
Vase, lake/mtns, brn/amber on yel mottle, flask form, 16" . . .2,800.00
Vase, pine tree scene on gold, 3 cuts, 13x4⅛" 1,100.00
Vase, poppies, gr/pk/clear on martele ground, X mk, 12" 3,500.00
Vase, poppies, red/blk on wht, raised rnd ft, 7" 4,000.00
Vase, stark trees, brn on gr/amber streaked, slim, 10" 3,500.00
Vase, thistles, gold on amethyst texture, X mk, 7" 925.00
Vase, thistles, tan on red, 1 cut/HP detail, 4½" 750.00
Vase, trees along river, blk/gold frost, 3 cuts, mk, 14" 2,000.00
Vase, trees/islands, dk gr on pk/gr mottle frost, X mk, 14" . . .1,100.00
Vase, trees/lake, gr on bl to gr, slim canister, 6½" 1,900.00
Vase, trees/mts/water, plum/brn on gold frost, 11½" 2,500.00
Vase, trees/sailboats, brn on yel/amber streaks, 8" 1,500.00
Vase, winter trees, brn tones on gold frost, 14" 2,000.00

Inkwell, river scene, 4½", $3,500.00.

Enameled Glass

Vase, boy/windmill/boats, bl on wht, indented sides, 4½" 700.00
Vase, Dutch riverscape w/sailboats & windmills, 4½x10" 1,100.00
Vase, flowering vines on mottle, wide body, X mk, 3¾" 1,100.00
Vase, rampant lion on smoked glass, 4½" 975.00

Miscellaneous

Beetle, pate-de-verre, blk on free-form leaf socle, 4¼" 1,400.00
Bowl, gray w/bl & turq mottle, triangular, ped ft, X mk, 8" 450.00
Figure, pate-de-verre, classical lady, X mk, 10" 3,000.00
Lamp, 11½" shade/ball base acid-etched w/cirles & lines 6,600.00
Tray, pate-de-verre, fish amid waves, turq/gr, 7½" L 3,000.00

Tray, pate-de-verre, frog on lily pad aside, 7" L **5,500.00**
Vase, bl etched w/thin ribs & sm circles, oviform, 11" **990.00**
Vase, foil inclusions, in pierced iron base, Majorelle, 10" **700.00**
Vase, gray w/acid-etch lozenges & zigzags, X mk, 12¾" **1,200.00**
Vase, gray w/acid-etch panels, bulbous, 1930, 6" **400.00**
Vase, oval rim w/2 floral flanged hdls, ca 1935, 8½" **1,500.00**
Vase, raspberry stick neck on amber/lime ball bottom, 18" . . .**1,000.00**
Vase, thick brn etched w/wide zigzag lines, conical, 8½" **2,000.00**

Davenport

W. Davenport and Company were Staffordshire potters operating in that area from 1793 to 1887, producing earthenware, creamware, porcelain, and ironstone. Many different stamps, all with 'Davenport,' were used to mark the various types of ware. See also Blue Willow; Flow Blue; Mulberry.

Pitcher, tavern scene in relief, 4½" **150.00**
Plate, cattle & thatch hut, med-lt bl tranfer, 10" **65.00**
Plate, fence, underglaze bl transfer w/mc enamel, 9½", M **65.00**
Tazza, Imari pattern, 9½" dia **120.00**
Tureen, sauce; Flute Player, bl transfer, anchor mk, EX **95.00**

Davis, Lowell

Figurines, plates, bells, and ornaments painted by Lowell Davis and produced by Border Fine Arts, Schmid Sculptured Porcelain, capture the heritage of rural America.

Lowell Davis, known better as Mr. Lowell to his farm animals, is described by many as 'just a country farmer from Missouri' fulfilling his dreams of preserving rural America as he knew it in the 1930s.

A Secondary Market Price Guide is published by Rosie Wells Enterprises for his collectibles. She is listed in the Directory under Clubs, Newsletters, and Catalogs. Items below are assumed to be in mint condition with box.

Brer Bear, 6" **400.00**
Broken Dreams, 5" **725.00**
Country Road, 5" **385.00**
Idle Hours, 2" **125.00**
Lowell's Studio Mouse, 2" **225.00**
Mad As a Wet Hen, 6¾" **400.00**
Prairie Chorus, 4½" **500.00**
Punkin Seeds, 6½" **975.00**

De Vez

De Vez was a type of acid-cut French cameo glass produced by Cristallerie de Pantin in Paris around the turn of the century.

Our advisor for this category is Don Williams; he is listed in the Directory under Iowa.

Cameo

Bowl, flowers, dk gr/rose on gr, 3 cuts, 2¼x4⅛" **275.00**
Lamp, boudoir; island scenic, gr/coral/yel, 3 cuts, 6¾" **895.00**
Rose bowl, trees/water, blk on gold & pk satin, 3" H **500.00**
Vase, boat/house/mtns, bl/yel on pk, 3 cuts, mk, 8" **800.00**
Vase, harbor scenic, purple/aqua/wht, 3 cuts, mk, 9¼" **900.00**
Vase, lg bird on floral branch, orange/yel/bl on opal, 8" **1,200.00**

Vase, man fishing, bl/rose on gold, 3 cuts, mk, 4¼x4" **595.00**
Vase, meteor rock/village/mtns, bl/rose on gold, 3 cuts, 8½" . . .**895.00**
Vase, mtns/shepherds/animals, yel/bl on pk, flat sided, 12" . .**1,100.00**
Vase, panels of ships, leaf/vine border, purple on wht, 11" **660.00**
Vase, poppies, red on citron satin, 8½" **700.00**
Vase, river landscape, gold/gr/rose, 3 cuts, mk, 11½x3¾" **1,000.00**
Vase, river/tree/mtns, navy/yel on pk, 3 cuts, mk, 5¼" **495.00**
Vase, sailboat scene, maroon/rose/gr, 3 cuts, 8⅝x3⅜" **750.00**
Vase, sailboat/mtn, dk bl/coral on yel, 3 cuts, 9¾x2¾" **900.00**
Vase, trees/ship/mtn, dk gr/burgundy, 3½" **750.00**

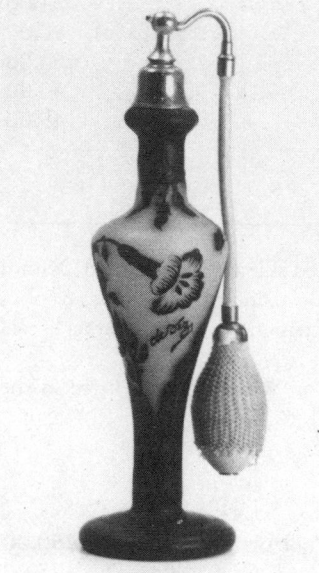

Atomizer, flower and insect, black on pink, 9", $850.00.

De Vilbiss

Perfume bottles, atomizers, and dresser accessories marketed by the De Vilbiss Company are appreciated by collectors today for the various types of lovely glassware used in their manufacture, as well as for their pleasing shapes. Various companies provided the glass, while De Vilbiss made only the metal tops. They marketed their merchandise not only here but in Paris, England, Canada, and Havana as well. Their marks were acid stamped, ink stamped, in gold script, molded in, or on paper labels. One is no more significant than another.

Atomizer, frosted peach squirrel supports wheel-engraved container, 7", $135.00.

Atomizer, bl, pineapple form, gilded bottom 75.00
Atomizer, bl aurene, Steuben, ca 1928, 7" 425.00
Atomizer, bl opal, Feathers 175.00
Atomizer, blk matt/gold, 9¼" 120.00
Atomizer, blk/clear, wheel etched, 4" 130.00
Atomizer, clear, threaded, 4" 85.00
Atomizer, gold aurene w/rare traces of pk, Steuben, 6" 300.00
Atomizer, gold crackle, beaded flower on top, mk, 4¾" 50.00
Atomizer, gold crackle & gold paste, paper label, 3" 30.00
Atomizer, irid w/gold trim, +lidded box & rnd tray 225.00
Atomizer, lt bl w/gold trim, mk, 5½", NM 70.00
Atomizer, lt gr, Opalescent Windows, 5" 75.00
Atomizer, penguin, felt wings, Lenox .90.00
Atomizer, pk w/blk dragonflies, ftd 100.00
Atomizer, silver crackle, w/label 35.00
Atomizer, yel w/blk decor, 4½" 115.00
Bottle, scent; irid, blk enamel top, stemmed ft, mk 75.00
Bottle, scent; 3 etched panels & ft, gold trim, mk, 5" 125.00
Box, powder: blk matt w/gold trim, mk 75.00
Ginger jar, Chinese red w/gold floral .75.00
Tray, pin; blk matt w/gold trim, unmk 25.00

Decanters

Ceramic whiskey decanters were brought into prominence in 1955 by the James Beam Distilling Company. Few other companies besides Beam produced these decanters during the next ten years or so; however, other companies did eventually follow suit, so that today there are at least twenty prominent companies and several on a lesser scale that make these decanters.

We have tried to list those brands that are the most popular with collectors. Likewise, individual decanters listed are the ones (or representative of the ones) most commonly found. These are a small fraction of the several thousand different decanters that have been produced. These decanters come from all over the world. While Jim Beam owns its own china factory in the U.S., some of the others import from Mexico, Taiwan, Japan and elsewhere. They vary in size from miniatures (approximately 2 oz.) to gallons. Values range from a few dollars to more than $3,000 per decanter. A mint condition decanter is one with no chips or cracks and all labels intact. Whether a decanter is full or not has no bearing on the value, nor does a missing federal tax stamp. It is advisable to empty the contents of a ceramic decanter, otherwise the thin inner glaze could crack, allowing the contents to seep through the porous body, thus ruining the decanter. An (m) behind a listing indicates a miniature. All others are fifth or 750 ml unless noted otherwise.

Animals, Domestic

Beam, Cats, Burmese, Siamese, or Tabby, ea 10.00
Beam, Dog, Great Dane 10.00
Beam, Dog, Poodle, gray or wht 10.00
Beam, Dog, St Bernard 28.00
Beam, Horse, Apaloosa 10.00
Beam, Horse, Mare & Foal 50.00
Beam, Horse, Stallion, rearing, blk/brn/or gray, '61 or '62, ea . . .20.00
Grenadier, Horse, Arabian 30.00
Hoffman, Cat, 6 different, ea 12.00
Hoffman, Dog, mini set #2 . . . . .12.00
Hoffman, Horse, 6 different, (m), ea 10.00
Old Bardstown, Dog, Bulldog 75.00
Old Bardstown, Horse, Citation 125.00
Old Commonwealth, Dog, Golden Retriever 30.00
Old Commonwealth, Horse, Tennessee Walking 28.00

Ski Country, Dog, Bassett Hound 50.00
Ski Country, Dog, Labrador w/pheasant 75.00

Animals, Wild

Beam, Doe 20.00
Brooks, Fox, Redtail 40.00
Brooks, Lion, African 30.00
Brooks, Raccoon 40.00
Brooks, Tiger, Bengal 30.00
Cyrus Noble, Elk, Bull 45.00
Cyrus Noble, Walrus 45.00
Famous Firsts, Panda 50.00
Hoffman, Doe & Fawn 30.00
Old Bardstown, Tiger 28.00
Old Bardstown, Wildcat #1 . . . . .60.00
Ski Country, Bobcat & Chipmunk 55.00
Ski Country, Deer, Wht Tail 85.00
Ski Country, Fox & Butterfly 55.00
Ski Country, Raccoons (wall plaque) .60.00
Ski Country, Sheep, Rocky Mountain 60.00
Ski Country, Sheep, Stone 55.00
Ski Country, Skunk Family 55.00
Ski Country, Squirrels (wall plaque) .70.00

Automotive

ASI, Cadillac, 1903, bl or wht 40.00
ASI, Chevrolet, 1914 . . . . .45.00
ASI, Oldsmobile 75.00
Beam, Chevy, 1957 Bel Air 60.00
Beam, Chevy, 1978 Corvette, red, yel, or wht 60.00
Beam, Duesenberg, Convertible Coupe 125.00
Beam, Duesenberg, 1934, lt or dk bl 110.00
Beam, Fire Engine, 1867 Mississippi Pumper 100.00
Beam, Ford, Woodie Station Wagon .50.00
Beam, Ford, 1903 Model A, blk or cream 40.00
Beam, Ford, 1913 Model T, blk or gr 45.00
Beam, Ford, 1928 Model A 65.00
Beam, Ford, 1929 Fire Chief's Car .100.00
Beam, Ford, 1929 Phaeton 48.00
Beam, Ford, 1929 Police Car 90.00
Beam, Ford, 1930 Fire Truck, Model A 90.00
Beam, Ford, 1964 Mustang, blk 110.00
Beam, Ford, 1964 Mustang, wht 30.00
Beam, Jewel Tea Wagon 78.00
Beam, Mack, 1917 Fire Truck 90.00
Beam, Mercedes 50.00
Beam, Oldsmobile, 1904 . . . . .50.00
Beam, Racecar, Unser Olsonite Eagle 60.00
Beam, Stutz Bearcat, 1914, gray or yel 50.00
Beam, Thomas Flyer, 1907, bl or cream 80.00
Beam, Volkswagen, red or bl 38.00
McCormick, Packard, 1937, blk or cream 40.00
Pacesetter, Fire Truck #1, LaFrance .45.00
Pacesetter, Fire Truck #2, Pirsch 60.00
Pacesetter, Fire Truck #3, Ahrens Fox 125.00
Pacesetter, Tractor #1, John Deere .125.00
Pacesetter, Tractor #2, Green Machine 75.00

Birds and Waterfowl

Beam, Blue Jay 9.00
Beam, Cardinal, female 12.00

Beam, Cardinal, male 30.00
Beam, Ducks Unlimited #1, Mallard 45.00
Beam, Ducks Unlimited #2, Wood Duck 45.00
Beam, Ducks Unlimited #3, Mallard Hen 40.00
Beam, Ducks Unlimited #4, Mallard Head 35.00
Beam, Owl, red or gray 12.00
Beam, Pheasant 15.00
Brooks, Baltimore Oriole 30.00
Brooks, Duck, Canadian Loon 35.00
Brooks, Macaw 35.00
Brooks, Owl #2, Eagle 60.00
Brooks, Snow Egret 30.00
Cyrus Noble, Penguin Family 45.00
Lionstone, Duck, Canvasback 40.00
Lionstone, Goose, Canadian 50.00
Lionstone, Goose, Snow 65.00
Lionstone, Pheasant 50.00
Ski Country, Dove 45.00
Ski Country, Duck, King Eider 50.00
Ski Country, Duck, Mallard, 1980 .... 50.00
Ski Country, Duck, Pintail 70.00
Ski Country, Duck, Widgeon 35.00
Ski Country, Eagle, Harpy 110.00
Ski Country, Eagle on Water 100.00
Ski Country, Falcon, Gyrafalcon 40.00
Ski Country, Falcon, Wht 60.00
Ski Country, Gamecocks, Fighting 125.00
Ski Country, Grouse, Ruffed 45.00
Ski Country, Hawk, Redtail 60.00
Ski Country, Owl, Barn 65.00
Ski Country, Owl, Horned 75.00
Ski Country, Owl, Saw-whet 50.00
Ski Country, Pheasant, Fighting 75.00
Ski Country, Pheasant in Corn 55.00
Wild Turkey, Series I, #1 .... 275.00
Wild Turkey, Series I, #2 .... 175.00
Wild Turkey, Series I, #3 .... 70.00
Wild Turkey, Series I, #4 .... 70.00
Wild Turkey, Series I, #5 .... 30.00
Wild Turkey, Series I, #6 .... 20.00
Wild Turkey, Series I, #7 .... 20.00
Wild Turkey, Series I, #8 .... 35.00

People

W.C. Fields Brand, ⅘-quart, $20.00.

McCormick, Elvis, Gold 195.00
McCormick, Elvis, Karate 125.00
McCormick, Elvis, Karate, (m) 50.00
McCormick, Elvis, Sergeant 200.00
McCormick, Elvis, Sergeant, (m) 35.00
McCormick, Elvis, Silver 110.00
McCormick, Elvis #1 .... 75.00
McCormick, Elvis #1, (m) 35.00
McCormick, Elvis #2 .... 40.00
McCormick, Elvis #2, (m) 20.00
McCormick, Elvis #3 .... 45.00
McCormick, Elvis #3, (m) 28.00
McCormick, Hank Williams, Jr 90.00
McCormick, Hank Williams, Sr 45.00

Vocations — Coalminers

Old Bardstown, Surface Miner 20.00
Old Commonwealth, Miner #1, (m) 20.00
Old Commonwealth, Miner #1, w/Shovel 100.00
Old Commonwealth, Miner #2, (m) 20.00
Old Commonwealth, Miner #2, w/Pick 50.00
Old Commonwealth, Miner #3, (m) 25.00
Old Commonwealth, Miner #3, w/Lump of Coal 35.00
Old Commonwealth, Miner #4, (m) 20.00
Old Commonwealth, Miner #4, Lunch Time 40.00
Old Commonwealth, Miner #5, (m) 20.00
Old Commonwealth, Miner #5, Coal Shooter 40.00

Vocations — Firefighters

Lionstone, #1, w/Hose 110.00
Lionstone, #2, w/Child 100.00
Lionstone, #3, Down Pole 80.00
Lionstone, #6, Hydrant 60.00
Lionstone, #7, Helmet 75.00
Lionstone, #8, Alarm Box 60.00
Lionstone, #9, Fire Extinguisher 55.00
Old Commonwealth, Professional #1, Modern Hero 35.00
Old Commonwealth, Professional #2, Nozzleman 40.00
Old Commonwealth, Professional #3, On Call 45.00
Old Commonwealth, Professional #4, Fallen Comrade 40.00
Old Commonwealth, Professional #5, Harmony 45.00
Old Commonwealth, Volunteer #2, Volunteer 50.00
Old Commonwealth, Volunteer #3, Valiant Volunteer 50.00
Old Commonwealth, Volunteer #4, Heroic Volunteer 55.00
Old Commonwealth, Volunteer #5, Lifesaver 45.00
Old Commonwealth, Volunteer #6, Breaking Through 45.00

Vocations — Railroad

Beam, Train, Baggage Car 55.00
Beam, Train, Boxcar, red or yel 50.00
Beam, Train, Caboose, red or yel 50.00
Beam, Train, Coal Tender 25.00
Beam, Train, Dining Car 60.00
Beam, Train, Grant Locomotive 70.00
Beam, Train, JB Turner Locomotive 75.00
Beam, Train, Log Car 40.00
Beam, Train, Lumber Car 30.00
Beam, Train, Observation Car 35.00
Beam, Train, Passenger Car 50.00
Beam, Train, Tank Car 30.00
Beam, Train, Wood Tender 30.00

Decoys

American colonists learned the craft of decoy making from the Indians who used them to lure birds out of the sky as an important food source. Early models were carved from wood such as pine, cedar, balsa, etc., and a few were made of canvas or papier-mache. There are two basic types of decoys: water floaters and shorebirds (also called 'stick-ups'). Within each type are many different species, ducks being the most plentiful since they migrated along all four of America's great waterways. Market hunting became big business around 1880, resulting in large-scale commercial production of decoys which continued until about 1910 when such hunting was outlawed by the Migratory Bird Treaty.

Today, decoys are one of the most collectible types of American folk art. The most valuable are those carved by such artists as Laing, Crowell, Ward, and Wheeler, to name only a few. Each area, such as Massachusetts, Connecticut, Maine, the Illinois River, and the Delaware River, produces decoys with distinctive regional characteristics. Examples of commercial decoys produced by well-known factories — among them Mason, Stevens, and Dodge — are also prized by collectors. Though mass-produced, these nevertheless required a certain amount of hand carving and decorating. Well-carved examples, especially those of rare species, are appreciating rapidly, and those with original paint are more desirable. Writer Carl F. Luckey has compiled a fully-illustrated identification and value guide, *Collecting Antique Bird Decoys*; you will find his address in the Directory under Alabama.

In the listings that follow, all decoys are solid-bodied unless noted hollow.

Key:
OP — original paint	RP — repaint
ORP — old repaint	WOP — worn original paint
OWP — original working paint	WRP — working repaint

Birch Swan, Charles Birch, hollow, OP, ca 1920, rare 500.00
Black Duck, A Elmer Crowell, oval brand, ca 1922, NM 6,000.00
Black Duck, Albert Laing, branded, RP by Charles Wheeler .2,100.00
Black Duck, Bill Cranmer, hollow, 1 eye broken 225.00
Black Duck, Dan English, low-head, stamped/branded, EX ..3,750.00
Black Duck, George Boyd, trn head, EX OP 1,025.00
Black Duck, George Ross Starr, branded, hollow, OP 525.00
Black Duck, Hayes, EX OP 230.00
Black Duck, Joel Barber, G OP, head reattached, rare 1,500.00
Black Duck, Ken Anger, hollow, OP, miniature, EX 575.00
Black Duck, Mason's Challenge, EX OP, head is loose 180.00
Black Duck, Ron Bonetti, sleeper, branded, EX OP, oversize ..200.00
Black Duck, Wildfowler, balsa body, OP, oversize 75.00
Black Duck, William Gibian, cvd primaries, M 700.00
Blackbellied Plover, Mason, tack eyes, NM pnt, lightly shot .1,500.00
Blue Jay, A Elmer Crowell, miniature, M 500.00
Bluebill, Mason's Standard, branded, tack eyes, M, pr 1,050.00
Bluebill, Paul Lipke, NM OP, weights missing, rare, pr 440.00
Bluebill drake, Billy Ellis, early, G OP, lightly shot 220.00
Bluebill drake, Bob McGaw, OP, EX 250.00
Bluebill drake, Charlie Joiner, OP, ca 1948, EX 230.00
Bluebill drake, Dodge, tack eyes, OP, neck filler missing 300.00
Bluebill drake, Ira Hudson, trn head/tail, G OP 500.00
Bluebill drake, Keyes Chadwick, branded CSA, ORP 250.00
Bluebill drake, Madison Mitchell, OP, ca 1950, EX 130.00
Bluebill drake, Mason's Challenge, high-head, OP, age lines ..450.00
Bluebill drake, Roy Conklin, OP, lightly shot 225.00
Bluebill drake, Stevens, humpbk, OP, lightly shot 275.00
Bluebill hen, Davey Nichols, relief cvg, OP, ca 1920s 400.00

Bluebill hen, Ernest Benway, tack eyes, OP, no flaws 90.00
Bluebill hen, Mason's Challenge, low-head, OP, rare 1,300.00
Bluewinged Teal, Grayson Chesser, EX, pr 450.00
Brant, Charles Birdsall, hollow, OP, EX 150.00
Brant, Delbert Daisey, branded, OP, slight crazing 275.00
Brant, Frank Gaskill, root-head, WRP, ca 1910 ....575.00
Brant, Joseph Lincoln, self-bailing, RP, EX 1,000.00
Brant, Mark McNair, Cobb Island style, EX 700.00
Brant, Mason's Challenge, NM OP, EX patina, rare 2,250.00
Brant, Nathan Cobb, hissing/hollow, OP, 1850s, rare, EX ..15,000.00
Broadbill, Reg Culver, branded, hollow, EX comb/feather pnt .800.00
Bufflehead, Dick Paulson, OP, pr 400.00
Bufflehead, Ward Bros, trn head, decorative, EX, pr 2,250.00
Bufflehead drake, Charles Allen, stamp, EX OP 200.00
Canada Goose, Clarence Bailey, old OP, rare 1,900.00
Canada Goose, Dipper Ortley, hollow, ORP 200.00
Canada Goose, Doug Jester, OP, EX 650.00
Canada Goose, Joe King, hollow, old pnt, tail chip 510.00
Canada Goose, Miles Hancock, floater/stick-up, OP 125.00
Canada Goose, Ralf Coykendall, preening, miniature, EX 175.00
Canvasback, WRP, age split in hen's neck, pr 300.00
Canvasback drake, John Rymal, feather cvg/wing detail, EX ...175.00
Canvasback drake, Sam Barnes, WRP, neck crack 175.00
Canvasback drake, William Beardsley, balsa body, RP 50.00
Coot, Evans, stamped, OP, lightly shot/age crack 522.00
Coot, Gus Nelo, high-neck, old WRP, tight checks in breast ..150.00
Coot, Tom Schroeder, branded Hy Dahlka, old OP 400.00
Crow, Charles Perdew, OP, age split at end of tail 350.00
Crow, Pratt, early gunning decoy, OP, bill chip 425.00
Curlew, Charles Clark, early, worn OP, rare 400.00
Curlew, David Ward, sickle bill, branded/dtd 1977, M 190.00
Curlew, Harry V Shourds, OP, bill is prof rpl 1,155.00
Curlew, John Dilley, full body, EX feather pnt, rare, NM 8,000.00
Curlew, W Ray Freden, sgn, EX pnt 250.00
Dove, Herters, OP, several hairline cracks 150.00
Dove, Lloyd Tyler, OP, decorative 130.00
Dowitcher, Mason, tack eyes/split tail, OP 400.00
Dowitcher, Bowman, cvd wings/glass eyes, EX OP, rare 9,500.00
Eider, Keith Mueller, trn heads, hollow, signed, pr 275.00
Golden Plover, Charles Coffin, trn head, NM OP, rare, EX ...825.00
Golden Plover, Mason, tack eyes, Fall plumage, OP, rare 600.00
Goldeneye, Roswell Bliss, hollow, branded, EX OP, pr 950.00
Goldeneye drake, Stevens, goiter neck, RP, age crack 325.00
Goldeneye hen, Frank Coombs, high-neck, EX OP 850.00
Goldeneye hen, Royal Perry, cork body, OP, lightly shot 100.00
Goldfinch, A Elmer Crowell, miniature, M 300.00
Greenwinged Teal, Cline McAlpine, branded, M pnt, pr 700.00
Greenwinged Teal drake, Anton Chiado, OP, EX 50.00
Gull, Russ Burr, stamped, flying, miniature, EX 50.00
Hutchins Goose, Roy Maxwell, hollow, OP, rare 900.00
Knot, Alvin Harris, OP, most of bill chipped away, rare 150.00
Mallard, Hurley Conklin, branded, cvd wing tips, EX pnt ...1,900.00
Mallard, William Quinn, raised cvd wing tips, EX OP, pr ...4,000.00
Mallard drake, Charles Althoff, G RP, neck crack 175.00
Mallard drake, Ken Anger, hollow, OP, rare 1,700.00
Mallard drake, Robert Elliston, EX RP, no structural flaws 330.00
Mallard hen, Charles Walker, early, NM OP 4,950.00
Mallard hen, Glen Cameron, branded, OP, sm bill chip 500.00
Old Squaw drake, Harry Rossiter, cvd initials, OP 90.00
Peep, Strater & Sohier, folding tin, OP, Pat Oct, rare 450.00
Pintail drake, John Baker, hollow, trn head, M 200.00
Pintail drake, Mike Frady, preening, NM OP, 2 sm cracks 250.00
Pintail hen, Charles Pice, hollow, OP 190.00
Pintail hen, Dick Janson, cvd primary feathers, NM 250.00

Pintail hen, John Dawson, hollow, cvd wing tips, OP, rare . .16,500.00
Pintail hen, Wildfowler, branded, EX pnt 150.00
Piping Plover, James Lapham, decorative, half-size, EX 50.00
Redhead drake, Clark Madara, hollow, OP, age split in neck . .700.00
Redhead drake, Lee Dudley, sgn, RP, lightly shot 5,000.00
Redhead drake, Norris Pratt, EX OP by Dick Dobbs 150.00
Redhead hen, Waylon Baum, WRP, lightly shot 250.00
Ringbill drake, Doug Clinton, preening, hollow, OP 200.00
Ringbill drake, Leon Somme, old pnt .90.00
Ringneck drake, Miles Pirnie, OP, working rpr to neck 120.00
Ruddy Duck, hollow, cvd wing tips, EX 70.00
Ruddy Turnstone, Daniel Leeds, OP, ca 1880, EX 3,750.00
Scoter, Wendell Gilley, hollow, G OP, well preserved 1,600.00
Scoter, Wildfowler, OP, pr 550.00
Sea Gull, Frank Kellum, OP, ca 1900, rare 1,000.00
Shoveler drake, Corb Reid, raised wing cvg, branded, EX 525.00
Shoveler drake, stamped Hayes #271, OP, tail cracks 550.00
Surf Scoter, Mark Holland, cork body, EX pnt, miniature 35.00
Swan, Dexter Snow, canvas over wire frame, old WRP 300.00
Swan, Herters, cvd wings, M 275.00
Turnstone, Horace Bearse, cvd wing tips, NM OP 500.00
Whitewinged Scoter, Gordon Mann, EX OP 200.00
Widgeon drake, Chet Reneson, hollow, EX OP 200.00
Widgeon drake, Willie Meaher, old pnt, sm bill chip 125.00

A.E. Crowell, decorative flying Wood Duck wall mount, signed, EX feather paint/EX condition, $2,500.00.

Yellowlegs, Dodge, Mackey stamp, old WRP, 1 eye missing . . .180.00
Yellowlegs, James Bourne, V-shaped breast, OP 300.00

Dedham Art Pottery

In 1895 the Chelsea Pottery moved to Dedham, changing its name to indicate the new locality and to avoid confusion with the Chelsea companies of England. Though their primary product was the blue-printed crackle-glazed dinnerware, two types of artware were also produced: crackle glaze and flambe. Their notable volcanic ware was a type of the

latter. The mark is incised and often accompanies the cipher of Hugh Robertson. See also Chelsea Keramic Art Works.

Crackleware vase, carved and incised with flowers and scrolls, early 20th century, 8½", $1,100.00.

Vase, brn/gr mottle, bulbous w/wide mouth, 7½", EX 275.00
Vase, crackleware, bl iris on wht, no mk, 7", NM 550.00
Vase, crackleware, wht iris on bl, 7½", NM 2,200.00
Vase, dk brn/bl/gr/cream flambe, Oriental form, Dedham, 9" . .600.00
Vase, drip glaze w/red, gr, bl, rust; incised HCR, rpr, 15" 4,250.00
Vase, gr drip, wide mouth, neck on ovoid, experimental, 8" . . .400.00
Vase, oxblood drip over olive, cylindrical, 7", NM 6,600.00
Vase, pk mottle, short neck on ovoid, sgn HR Jr, 9", EX 1,200.00
Vase, vegetation, bl/wht, wide mouth on cylinder, 9½" 2,200.00

Dedham Dinnerware

Originally founded in Morrisville, Pennsylvania, as the Chelsea Keramic Works, the name was changed to Dedham Pottery in 1895 after the firm relocated in Dedham, near Boston, Massachusetts. The move was effected to make use of the native clay deemed more suitable for the production of the popular dinnerware designed by Hugh Robinson, founder of the company. The ware utilized a gray stoneware body with a crackle glaze and simple cobalt border designs of flowers, birds, and animals. Decorations were brushed on by hand using an ancient Chinese method which suspended the cobalt within the overall glaze. There were thirteen standard patterns, among them Magnolia, Iris, Butterfly, Duck, Polar Bear, and the Rabbit, the latter of which was chosen to represent the company on their logo. On the very early pieces the rabbits face left; decorators soon found the reverse position easier to paint, and the rabbits were turned to the right. In addition to the standard patterns, other designs were produced for special orders. These and artist signed pieces are highly valued by collectors today.

The firm was operated by succeeding generations of the Robertson family until it closed in 1943. See also Chelsea Keramic Works.

Bouillon cup, Rabbit, hdls, ped ft, 3" .375.00
Bowl, Azalea, shallow, stamped, 9½" .250.00
Bowl, Azalea, w/lid, stamped, hairline, 9" 300.00
Bowl, Chestnut, stamped/registered, 4½" 175.00

Bowl, Rabbit, stamped, chip & hairline, 12" 300.00
Bowl, Rabbit, stamped, 3½x8¼" 495.00
Bowl, Rabbit, w/lid, 6x9½" 900.00
Bowl, stylized floral, notched/canted corners, stamped, 8" 950.00
Butterpat, Pansy, 5-petal flower form, stamped, 3½" 275.00
Butterpat, Primrose, stamped, 3½" dia 225.00
Candlestick, Azalea, squat can form, registered, 2", pr 300.00
Celery dish, Rabbit, stamped, 10" L .325.00
Chop plate, Rabbit, stamped, 12" 800.00
Creamer, Elephant, bulbous w/cylinder neck, mfg flaw, 3" 500.00
Cup & saucer, Rabbit, stamped, 2¾x6" 225.00
Cup & saucer, Snowtree, stamped, 4" dia 250.00
Dish, child's, Rabbit, central medallion, shallow, 8" 1,000.00
Dish, Rabbit, 5-sided, stamped, 7" 500.00

**Humidor, white elephants on blue, ca 1917,
8½", $2,700.00.**

Marmalade, Rabbit, spherical, stamped, 4½" 375.00
Mug, Rabbit, stamped, 2¾x3", NM 400.00
Paperweight, rabbit form, stamped/registered, 3" L 650.00
Paperweight, turtle form, stamped, 3½" L 550.00
Pitcher, Night & Morning, 5" 650.00
Pitcher, Oak Block, stamped/registered, 5½" 1,300.00
Plate, Azalea, stamped, 6" 150.00
Plate, Azalea, stamped/registered, 8" 185.00
Plate, Clover, stamped, 10", NM 650.00
Plate, Crab, stamped, 8½" 600.00
Plate, Crab, stamped/registered, 6" .475.00
Plate, Dolphin, imp/stamped, 7½" 450.00
Plate, Dolphin, stamped, 8½" 475.00
Plate, Duck, stamped/registered, 8" .300.00
Plate, Grape, stamped/registered, sgn MR, 8½" 250.00
Plate, Iris, stamped, 10" 250.00
Plate, Iris, stamped, 6" 185.00
Plate, Iris, stamped, 8½" 225.00
Plate, Lobster, stamped, 8½" 650.00
Plate, Magnolia, stamped, 8½" 200.00
Plate, Magnolia, stamped/registered, 6" 185.00
Plate, Moth, imp/stamped, 6", NM 175.00

Plate, Moth, stamped, sgn Maude Davenport, 8½" 475.00
Plate, Moth, stamped, 7" 300.00
Plate, Polar Bear, stamped, 6" 450.00
Plate, Polar Bear, stamped/registered, 7" 475.00
Plate, Pond Lily, stamped/incised, 8½" 250.00
Plate, Rabbit, imp/stamped, 6" 175.00
Plate, Rabbit, stamped, CPUS mk, 10" 375.00
Plate, Scottie Dog, stamped/registered, 8¾" 1,500.00
Plate, Snowtree, stamped, 10" 275.00
Plate, Turkey, stamped, 8½" 275.00
Plate, Turtle, stamped/dtd 2-17-16, 8½" 750.00
Plate, 2 lg lilies in center, stamped, 8½" 550.00
Platter, bacon; Butterfly, no mk, under-rim chip, 12" L 350.00
Platter, Rabbit, stamped/registered, 8½x14" 700.00
Tile, Rabbit, stamped, sq, 5½" 300.00
Tile, Rabbit, stamped, 6" dia 250.00

Degenhart

The Crystal Art Glass factory in Cambridge, Ohio, opened in 1947 under the private ownership of John and Elizabeth Degenhart. John had previously worked for the Cambridge Glass Company and was well known for his superior paperweights. After his death in 1964, Elizabeth took over management of the factory, hiring several workers from the defunct Cambridge Company, including Zack Boyd. Boyd was responsible for many unique colors, some of which were named for him. From 1964 to 1974, more than twenty-seven different moulds were created, most of them resulting from Elizabeth Degenhart's work and creativity, and over 145 official colors were developed. Elizabeth died in 1978, requesting that the ten moulds she had built while operating the factory were to be turned over to the Degenhart Museum. The remaining moulds were to be held by the Island Mould and Machine Company, who (complying with her request) removed the familiar 'D in heart' trademark. The factory was eventually bought by Zack's son, Bernard Boyd. He also acquired the remaining Degenhart moulds, to which he added his own logo.

In general, slags, jades, and opaques should be valued 15% to 20% higher than crystals in color.

Beaded Oval Toothpick, Bittersweet .35.00
Beaded Oval Toothpick, Fawn 18.00
Beaded Oval Toothpick, Sapphire 20.00
Bell, Amethyst 12.00
Bell, Lime Ice 16.00
Bell, Persimmon 12.00
Bird Salt & Pepper, Opalescent 35.00
Bow Slipper, Milk Blue 20.00
Buzz Saw Wine, Amethyst 15.00
Buzz Saw Wine, Cobalt 40.00
Buzz Saw Wine, Emerald Green 25.00
Buzz Saw Wine, Sapphire 20.00
Centennial Bell, Crystal 3.50
Centennial Bell, Ebony 5.00
Centennial Bell, Opal 15.00
Centennial Bell, Slag 15.00
Chick, Crown Tuscan, hand stamped, 2" 45.00
Chick, Crystal, 2" 15.00
Chick, Heliotrope, unsgn, 2" 40.00
Chick, Lemon Custard, 2" 50.00
Chick, Milk Blue, unsgn, 2" 20.00
Coaster, Persimmon 8.00
Colonial Drape Toothpick, Sapphire .15.00
Daisy & Button Salt, Milk Blue, unsgn 15.00
Daisy & Button Toothpick, Lime Ice 20.00

Daisy & Button Toothpick, Royal Crown Tuscan 25.00
Dog, April Green 15.00
Dog, Bittersweet Slag 66.00
Dog, Buttercup Slag 18.00
Dog, Charcoal 20.00
Dog, Fantastic 30.00
Dog, Gun Metal 20.00
Dog, Periwinkle 15.00
Dog, Smoky Blue 15.00
Dog, Tomato 85.00
Elephant Toothpick, Sapphire 25.00
Forget-Me-Not Toothpick, Amberina 15.00
Forget-Me-Not Toothpick, Bluebell 10.00
Forget-Me-Not Toothpick, Canary 15.00
Forget-Me-Not Toothpick, Crown Tuscan 20.00
Forget-Me-Not Toothpick, Crystal 8.00
Forget-Me-Not Toothpick, Ivorene 11.00
Forget-Me-Not Toothpick, Peach-Opaque 18.00
Forget-Me-Not Toothpick, Periwinkle 15.00
Forget-Me-Not Toothpick, Sapphire 8.00
Forget-Me-Not Toothpick, Spring Green 14.00
Forget-Me-Not Toothpick, Toffee 20.00
Gypsy Pot Toothpick, Honey Amber 20.00
Gypsy Pot Toothpick, Persimmon 20.00
Gypsy Pot Toothpick, Tomato 25.00
Hand, Canary 6.00
Hand, Crown Tuscan 15.00
Hand, Honey Amber 6.00
Hat, Sapphire 18.00
Heart & Lyre Cup Plate, Crown Tuscan 25.00

Heart Box, cobalt, 3½" wide, $35.00.

Heart Toothpick, Bernard Boyd's Ebony 35.00
Hen, Canary, 3" 25.00
Hen, Caramel Custard, 3" 45.00
Hen, Sapphire, 3" 20.00
High Boot, Crystal 15.00
Hobo Shoe, Caramel Custard Slag 20.00
Jewel Box, Crown Tuscan 30.00
Jewel Box, Light Chocolate Creme 35.00
Jewel Box, Royal Violet 25.00
Mini Pitcher, Opalescent 25.00
Mini Pitcher, Sapphire 15.00
Owl, Antique Blue 35.00
Owl, Bernard Boyd's Ebony 55.00
Owl, Bloody Mary 85.00
Owl, Blue & White Slag 50.00
Owl, Blue-Green 72.50
Owl, Bluebird #2 ....25.00

Owl, Chartreuse 40.00
Owl, Crystal 10.00
Owl, Dark Ruby 50.00
Owl, Degenhart Green 15.00
Owl, Fog Opaque 60.00
Owl, Forest Green 15.00
Owl, Heatherbloom 50.00
Owl, Heliotrope 75.00
Owl, Jade 50.00
Owl, January Blizzard 75.00
Owl, Lemon Chiffon 25.00
Owl, Lemon Opalescent 65.00
Owl, Mauve 35.00
Owl, Midnight Sun 25.00
Owl, Nile Green 40.00
Owl, Old Lavender 30.00
Owl, Pearl Gray 30.00
Owl, Persimmon 10.00
Owl, Red Carnival 75.00
Owl, Tangerine 100.00
Owl, Tiger 40.00
Owl, Wanda Blue 35.00
Pooche, Buttercup Slag 25.00
Pooche, Dark Amethyst 15.00
Pooche, Gray Marble Opal 30.00
Pooche, Tomato Slag 35.00
Priscilla, Bittersweet Slag 125.00
Priscilla, Blue Lady 95.00
Priscilla, Crystal 75.00
Priscilla, End of Day 120.00
Priscilla, Green Lavender Slag 78.50
Priscilla, Heather 100.00
Priscilla, Ice Blue Carnival 75.00
Priscilla, Ivory 85.00
Priscilla, Jade Green 100.00
Priscilla, Light Lavender 95.00
Priscilla, Milk Blue Opalescent 95.00
Priscilla, Orchid 85.00
Priscilla, Peach 75.00
Priscilla, Powder Blue 100.00
Priscilla, Smokey Blue 95.00
Seal of Ohio Cup Plate, Amberina 25.00
Seal of Ohio Cup Plate, Colored Crystals 10.00
Skate Shoe, Cobalt Carnival 40.00
Skate Shoe, Green, unsgn, decal 30.00
Tomahawk, Emerald Green 23.00
Turkey, Crown Tuscan 75.00
Turkey, Gray Slag, unsgn 80.00
Wildflower Candy Dish, Pink 25.00
Wildflower Candy Dish, Twilight Blue 35.00

Delatte

Delatte was a manufacturer of French cameo glass. Founded in 1921, their style reflected the influence of the Art Dra with strong color contrasts and bold design.

Cameo

Vase, floral, brn to orange, 2 cuts, mk, 9¼x3½" 750.00
Vase, floral, purple on wht, 2 cuts, 5⅝x3⅞" 365.00
Vase, landscape along river, maroon/rose on wht, hdls, 9" 900.00
Vase, trees at river, pk/mauve, 2 cuts, mk, 7½x4⅜" 595.00

Delft

Old Delftware, made as early as the 16th century, was originally a low-fired earthenware coated in a thin opaque tin glaze with painted-on polychrome designs. It was not until the last half of the 19th century, however, that the ware became commonly referred to as Delft, acquiring the name from the Dutch village that had become the major center of its production. English, German, and French potters also produced Delft, though with noticeable differences both in shape and decorative theme.

In the early part of the 18th century, the German potter, Bottger, developed a formula for porcelain; in England, Wedgwood began producing creamware — both of which were much more durable. Unable to compete, one by one the Delft potteries failed. Soon only one remained. In 1876 De Porcelyne Fles reintroduced Delftware on a hard white body with blue and white decorative themes reflecting the Dutch countryside, windmills by the sea, and Dutch children. This manufacturer is the most well known of several operating today. Their products are now produced under the Royal Delft label. See also specific manufacturers.

Bank, rabbit form, mc enameling, 4" L, EX 250.00
Charger, Dutch, florals/bird, 1800, 13½", EX 600.00
Charger, floral, bl/wht w/yel rim, mk, rim chips, 12¼" 600.00
Charger, Lambeth, floral, yel/lav/gr, 13½", NM 700.00
Dish, floral, bl/wht w/yel rim, mk, rim chips, 6½" 300.00
Ewer, floral/zigzag band in bl/purple/yel-ochre, 8½", EX 250.00
Ink pot, Lambeth, floral, mc w/bl hdl, 4¼" 300.00
Inkwell, floral, mc on wht, crazing/edge chips, 2x4x4" 175.00
Jar, apothecary; brn-blk enamel label, 9¾", EX 300.00
Jar, floral/'Maryland,' mc, edge chips, 8"+brass dome lid 875.00
Mug, bust/'In Memory of Lord Nelson,' bl/wht, 5½", NM 275.00
Planter, English, violin w/openwork front, floral, 15" L 95.00
Plate, Dutch, fronds/flowers, yel border, 1750s, 14", EX 440.00
Plate, floral, MPVD/1786 in center, bl/wht, rim chip, 9" 450.00
Platter, Oriental garden, bl/wht, rim chips, 20½" 1,300.00
Salt cellar, mc floral & dots, ped base, 1850s, 1½x3¼" 145.00
Tankard, floral, bl/wht, purple sponging, pewter lid, 7½" 450.00
Tankard, scenic, bl/wht, purple sponging, lid, 7¾", EX 700.00
Tile, Donkey in 3-band circle, medallions, mulberry/wht, 6" 50.00
Tile, Dutch, parrot perched on swing, 15½x10½" 135.00

Denver

The Denver China and Pottery Company began production in 1901 in Denver, Colorado. The founder, William A. Long, used materials native to Colorado and produced underglaze-decorated brownware as well as other artware lines. Several marks were used: an impressed 'Denver' (often with the Lonhuda Faience cipher inside a shield), an imprinted 'Denaura,' and an arrow mark. Pieces were sometimes dated.

Bowl vase, Denaura, emb violets/leaves, gr matt, 5½x2¼" 475.00
Jar, potpourri; bl w/cvd wht band, 5¼" 50.00
Vase, bl matt, hdls, 5" 125.00
Vase, gr matt, Arts & Crafts style, triple hdls, 5" 150.00

Depression Glass

Other than coins and stamps, colored glassware produced during the Depression era is probably the most sought-after collectible in the field today. There are literally thousands of collectors in the United States and Canada buying, selling, and trading 'Depression Glass' on today's market.

Depression Glass is defined by Gene Florence, author of several best-selling books on the subject, as 'the inexpensive glassware made primarily during the Depression era in the colors of amber, green, pink, blue, red, yellow, white, and crystal.' This glass was mass produced, sold through five-and-dime stores and mail-order catalogs, and given away as premiums with gas and food products.

The listings in this book are far from being complete. If you want a more thorough presentation of this fascinating glassware, we recommend *The Collector's Encyclopedia of Depression Glass* by Gene Florence, whose address is listed in the Directory under Kentucky.

Adam, ash tray, gr, 4¼" 16.50
Adam, bowl, cereal; gr, 5¾" 30.00
Adam, bowl, dessert; pk, 4¾" 10.00
Adam, bowl, gr, oval, 10" 18.00
Adam, bowl, gr, w/lid, 9" 60.00

Adam, bowl, gr, 9" 30.00
Adam, bowl, pk, oval, 10" 16.00
Adam, bowl, pk, w/lid, 9" 20.00
Adam, bowl, pk, 7¾" 15.00
Adam, butter dish, gr 245.00
Adam, butter dish, gr, bottom only 60.00
Adam, butter dish, pk 60.00
Adam, candlesticks, gr, 4", pr 75.00
Adam, candy jar, pk, 2½" 57.50
Adam, coaster, gr, 3¼" 12.50
Adam, creamer, pk 12.00
Adam, cup, gr 16.00
Adam, cup, pk 17.50
Adam, cup, yel 85.00
Adam, lamp, gr or pk 225.00
Adam, pitcher, gr, 32-oz, 8" 32.50
Adam, pitcher, pk, rnd base, 32-oz 40.00
Adam, plate, cake; gr, ftd, 10" 16.50
Adam, plate, cake; pk, ftd, 10" 13.00
Adam, plate, dinner; gr, sq, 9" 15.50
Adam, plate, dinner; pk, sq, 9" 16.50
Adam, plate, grill; pk, 9" 12.50
Adam, plate, salad; gr, sq, 7¾" 8.00
Adam, plate, sherbet; pk, 6" 4.00
Adam, platter, gr, 11¾" 14.00
Adam, shakers, gr, ftd, 4" 77.50
Adam, sherbet, gr, 3" 27.50
Adam, sugar bowl, pk 10.00
Adam, tray, relish; pk, divided, 8" 10.00
Adam, tumbler, iced tea; gr, 5½" 30.00
Adam, tumbler, pk, 4½" 17.00
Adam, vase, pk, 7½" 160.00
American Pioneer, bowl, console; gr, 10⅜" 50.00
American Pioneer, bowl, crystal, hdls, 5" 10.00
American Pioneer, bowl, crystal, w/lid, 9¼" 80.00

American Pioneer, bowl, gr, hdls, 9" 18.00
American Pioneer, bowl, pk, w/lid, 8¾" 70.00
American Pioneer, candlesticks, pk, 6½", pr 45.00
American Pioneer, candy jar, crystal, 1½-lb 70.00
American Pioneer, coaster, pk, 3½" 15.00
American Pioneer, creamer, crystal, 3½" 16.00
American Pioneer, cup, amber 21.00
American Pioneer, goblet, water; crystal, 8-oz, 6" 25.00
American Pioneer, goblet, wine; pk, 3-oz, 4" 30.00
American Pioneer, ice bucket, gr, 6" 42.50
American Pioneer, lamp, gr, 8½" 85.00
American Pioneer, lamp, pk, rnd, ball shape, 5½" 60.00
American Pioneer, mayonnaise, crystal, 4¼" 40.00
American Pioneer, pitcher, amber, covered urn, 5" 225.00
American Pioneer, pitcher, gr, covered urn, 7" 165.00
American Pioneer, plate, amber, 8" 18.00
American Pioneer, plate, crystal, hdls, 6" 8.00
American Pioneer, plate, gr, hdls, 11½" 14.00
American Pioneer, plate, pk, hdls, 6" 8.00
American Pioneer, sherbet, crystal, 3½" 12.00
American Pioneer, sherbet, pk, 4¾" 18.00
American Pioneer, sugar bowl, pk, 3½" 16.00
American Pioneer, tumbler, gr, 12-oz, 5" 35.00
American Pioneer, tumbler, juice; crystal, 5-oz 15.00
American Pioneer, tumbler, pk, 8-oz, 4" 20.00
American Pioneer, vase, gr, 4 styles, 7", ea 75.00
American Pioneer, whiskey, crystal, 2-oz, 2¼" 32.50
American Sweetheart, bowl, berry; monax, rnd, 9" 37.50
American Sweetheart, bowl, cereal; cremax, 6" 8.00
American Sweetheart, bowl, console; monax, 18" 265.00
American Sweetheart, cup, bl 80.00
American Sweetheart, cup, pk 9.50
American Sweetheart, pitcher, pk, 80-oz, 8" 360.00
American Sweetheart, plate, dinner; pk, 9¾" 15.00
American Sweetheart, plate, salad; red, 8" 40.00
American Sweetheart, tumbler, pk, 9-oz, 4¼" 45.00
Anniversary, bowl, fruit; crystal, 9" 7.00
Anniversary, bowl, soup; pk, 7⅜" 8.50
Anniversary, butter dish, crystal 22.50
Anniversary, creamer, pk, ftd 7.50
Anniversary, plate, dinner; crystal, 9" 3.50
Anniversary, plate, sandwich server; pk, 12½" 7.00

Anniversary, sherbet, pk, ftd 5.00
Anniversary, vase, pk, 6½" 17.50
Apple Blossom, see Dogwood
Aunt Polly, bowl, berry; gr, lg, 7⅞" 15.00
Aunt Polly, bowl, bl, oval, 8⅜" 45.00
Aunt Polly, creamer, gr 20.00
Aunt Polly, plate, luncheon; bl, 8" 12.00
Aunt Polly, tumbler, bl, 8-oz, 3⅝" 18.00
Aunt Polly, vase, gr, ftd, 6½" 20.00

Aurora, bowl, cereal; pk, 5⅜" 5.00
Aurora, creamer, cobalt, 4½" 9.00
Aurora, plate, pk, 6½" 4.00
Aurora, tumbler, cobalt, 10-oz, 4¾" 12.50
Avocado, bowl, gr, hdls, 5¼" 23.00
Avocado, bowl, salad; pk, 7½" 25.00
Avocado, creamer, pk, ftd 25.00
Avocado, pitcher, gr, 64-oz 650.00
Avocado, plate, sherbet; pk, 6¾" 9.50
Avocado, tumbler, gr 125.00
Ballerina, see Cameo
Banded Fine Rib, see Coronation
Banded Rings, see Ring
Basket, see Lorain
Beaded Block, bowl, gr, rnd, 6½" 6.50
Beaded Block, bowl, jelly; pk, hdls, 4½" 6.00

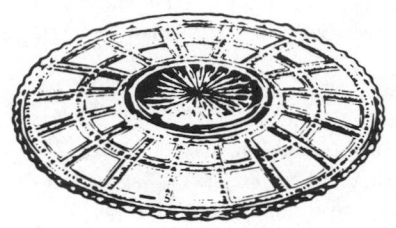

Beaded Block, plate, amber, rnd, 8¾" 10.00
Beaded Block, sugar bowl, gr 12.50
Block Optic, bowl, berry; pk, lg, 8½" 12.00
Block Optic, bowl, salad; gr, 7" 14.00
Block Optic, cup, yel, 4 styles, ea 6.00
Block Optic, goblet, cocktail; pk, 4" 20.00
Block Optic, goblet, wine; gr, 4½" 18.00
Block Optic, pitcher, gr, 80-oz, 8" 37.50
Block Optic, pitcher, pk, bulbous, 68-oz, 7⅝" 40.00
Block Optic, plate, dinner; yel, 9" 25.00
Block Optic, plate, grill; gr, 9" 6.50
Block Optic, sherbet, pk, 5½-oz, 3¼" 6.00
Block Optic, sherbet, yel, 6-oz, 4¾" 12.00
Block Optic, tumbler, gr, flat, 14-oz 20.00
Block Optic, tumbler, pk, ftd, 10-oz, 6" 14.00
Bouquet & Lattice, see Normandie
Bowknot, bowl, cereal; gr, 5½" 12.00
Bowknot, tumbler, gr, 10-oz, 5" 11.00
Bubble, bowl, berry; dk gr, lg, 8⅜" 7.50
Bubble, bowl, bl, flanged, 9" 75.00
Bubble, creamer, bl 20.00
Bubble, pitcher, red, ice lip, 64-oz 35.00
Bubble, plate, dinner; red, 9⅜" 5.50
Bubble, plate, grill; bl, 9⅜" 10.00
Bubble, sugar bowl, dk gr 6.50
Bubble, tumbler, juice; red, 6-oz 6.00
Butterflies & Roses, see Flower Garden w/Butterflies
Button & Bows, see Holiday
Cabbage Rose, see Sharon
Cameo, bowl, cereal; yel, 5½" 22.50
Cameo, bowl, console; pk, 3-legged, 11" 25.00
Cameo, bowl, cream soup; gr, 4¾" 45.00
Cameo, cookie jar, gr 37.50
Cameo, creamer, yel, 3¼" 12.50
Cameo, cup, pk, 2 styles, ea 55.00

Cameo, goblet, water; pk, 6" 125.00
Cameo, plate, cake; gr, flat, 10½" 75.00
Cameo, plate, grill; pk, 10½" 35.00
Cameo, plate, luncheon; yel, 8" 7.50
Cameo, plate, sandwich; gr, 10" .10.00

Cameo, platter, gr, closed hdls, 12" 14.00
Cameo, sherbet, gr, 4⅞" 24.00
Cameo, sugar bowl, pk, 4¼" 60.00
Cameo, tumbler, gr, 15-oz, 5¼" .45.00
Cameo, tumbler, yel, flat, 11-oz, 5" 37.50
Cameo, vase, gr, 5¾" 125.00
Cherry Blossom, bowl, berry; gr, rnd, 8½" 16.00
Cherry Blossom, bowl, soup; pk, flat, 7¾" 36.00
Cherry Blossom, bowl, vegetable; delphite, oval, 9" 40.00
Cherry Blossom, creamer, gr 12.50
Cherry Blossom, cup, pk 13.50
Cherry Blossom, plate, grill; pk, 9" 16.50
Cherry Blossom, plate, salad; gr, 7" 15.00
Cherry Blossom, platter, pk, oval, 11" 18.00
Cherry Blossom, sherbet, gr 12.50
Cherry Blossom, sugar bowl, pk 10.00
Cherry Blossom, tray, sandwich; gr, 10½" 12.00
Chinex Classic, bowl, castle decal, 11" 32.50
Chinex Classic, bowl, vegetable; ivory, 7" 12.50
Chinex Classic, plate, dinner; castle decal, 9¾" 12.00
Chinex Classic, plate, sandwich or cake; ivory, 11½" 6.50
Christmas Candy, bowl, soup; teal, 7⅜" 17.50
Christmas Candy, creamer, crystal 7.50
Christmas Candy, plate, sandwich; crystal, 11¼" 10.00
Christmas Candy, sugar bowl, teal 12.50
Circle, goblet, water; pk, 8-oz 8.50
Circle, pitcher, gr, 80-oz 16.50
Circle, plate, dinner; gr, 9½" 6.00
Circle, sugar bowl, pk 5.00
Cloverleaf, bowl, cereal; gr, 5" 20.00
Cloverleaf, bowl, dessert; pk, 4" 8.00
Cloverleaf, bowl, salad; yel, 7" H 35.00
Cloverleaf, creamer, blk, ftd, 3⅝" 12.50
Cloverleaf, creamer, gr, ftd, 3⅝" .7.50
Cloverleaf, cup, yel 8.00
Cloverleaf, plate, grill; yel, 10¼" 17.50
Cloverleaf, plate, luncheon; pk, 8" 5.00
Cloverleaf, plate, sherbet; blk, 6" 22.50
Cloverleaf, sherbet, blk, ftd, 3" .15.00
Cloverleaf, tumbler, gr, flat, 9-oz, 4" 30.00
Cloverleaf, tumbler, yel, ftd, 10-oz, 5¾" 20.00
Colonial, bowl, berry; pk, 3¾" 23.50
Colonial, bowl, cereal; gr, 5½" 40.00
Colonial, bowl, cream soup; gr, 4½" 40.00
Colonial, bowl, vegetable; crystal, oval, 10" 12.00
Colonial, cup, gr 9.00

Colonial, goblet, cocktail; crystal, 3-oz, 4" 10.00
Colonial, goblet, water; pk, 8½-oz, 5¾" 30.00
Colonial, mug, pk, 12-oz, 4½" .300.00
Colonial, plate, dinner; pk, 10" .27.50
Colonial, plate, grill; gr, 10" 20.00
Colonial, plate, sherbet; gr, 6" 4.00
Colonial, platter, crystal, oval, 12" 10.00
Colonial, shakers, crystal, pr 45.00
Colonial, sherbet, pk, 3" 12.50
Colonial, tumbler, gr, ftd, 3-oz, 3¼" 14.00
Colonial, tumbler, juice; pk, 5-oz, 3" 10.00
Colonial, tumbler, lemonade; crystal, 15-oz 23.00
Colonial, tumbler, pk, 10-oz 25.00
Colonial, whiskey, gr, 1½-oz, 2½" 9.00
Colonial Block, bowl, pk, 7" 12.50
Colonial Block, butter tub, gr 30.00
Colonial Block, creamer, wht 5.50
Colonial Block, goblet, gr 8.50
Colonial Block, pitcher, pk 25.00
Colonial Fluted, bowl, cereal; gr, 6" 6.00
Colonial Fluted, sherbet, gr 4.50
Columbia, bowl, salad; crystal, 8½" 11.00
Columbia, cup, pk 10.00
Columbia, plate, chop; crystal, 11" 6.00
Columbia, plate, luncheon; pk, 9½" 15.00
Columbia, tumbler, crystal 9.00
Coronation, bowl, nappy; pk, 6½" 3.50
Coronation, pitcher, pk, 68-oz, 7¾" 150.00
Coronation, plate, luncheon; royal ruby, 8½" 6.00
Coronation, sherbet, gr 35.00
Coronation, tumbler, gr, ftd, 10-oz, 5" 50.00
Cremax, bowl, cereal; ivory w/decor, 5¾" 6.00
Cremax, bowl, vegetable; ivory, 9" 5.50
Cremax, plate, dinner; ivory w/decor, 9¾" 6.00
Cube, bowl, dessert; gr, 4½" 5.00
Cube, bowl, salad; pk, 6½" 7.00
Cube, butter dish, pk 40.00
Cube, candy jar, gr, 6½" 25.00
Cube, creamer, pk, 3" 5.00
Cube, pitcher, gr, 45-oz, 8¾" 150.00
Cube, plate, luncheon; pk, 8" 3.00
Cube, shakers, gr, pr 27.50
Cube, sherbet, pk, ftd 4.50
Cube, sugar bowl, gr, 3" 6.00
Cube, tumbler, gr, 9-oz, 4" 40.00
Cubist, see Cube
Cupid, bowl, fruit; any color, ftd, 9¼" 50.00

Cupid, comport, any color, 6¼" .30.00
Cupid, fan vase, any color 75.00
Cupid, ice bucket, any color, 6" .65.00
Cupid, sugar bowl, any color, ftd, 5" 35.00

Daisy, bowl, cereal; gr, 6" 10.00
Daisy, bowl, vegetable; crystal, oval, 10" 6.00
Daisy, plate, dinner; amber, 9⅜" 6.00
Daisy, plate, luncheon; amber, 8⅜" 5.00
Daisy, platter, gr, 10¾" 5.00
Daisy, sherbet, amber, ftd 7.00
Daisy, tumbler, crystal, ftd, 12-oz 15.00
Dancing Girl, see Cameo
Diamond Quilted, bowl, blk, crimped edge, 7" 10.00
Diamond Quilted, bowl, cereal; bl, 5" 8.00
Diamond Quilted, bowl, cream soup; blk, 4¾" 15.00
Diamond Quilted, candlesticks, pk, 2 styles, pr 9.50

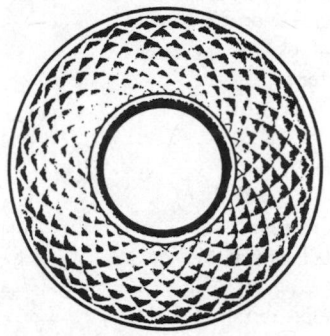

Diamond Quilted, goblet, cordial; gr, 1-oz 8.00
Diamond Quilted, goblet, wine; gr, 3-oz 8.00
Diamond Quilted, ice bucket, bl 55.00
Diamond Quilted, pitcher, pk, 64-oz 35.00
Diamond Quilted, plate, luncheon; gr, 8" 4.00
Diamond Quilted, sandwich server, bl, center hdl 35.00
Diamond Quilted, sugar bowl, blk 9.50
Diamond Quilted, tumbler, pk, ftd, 9-oz 9.50
Diamond Quilted, whiskey, gr, 1½-oz 6.50
Diana, bowl, cream soup; pk, 5½" 5.00
Diana, creamer, crystal, oval 2.00
Diana, plate, sandwich; pk, 11¾" 6.00
Diana, tumbler, amber, 9-oz, 4⅛" 15.00
Dogwood, bowl, berry; pk, 8½" 37.50
Dogwood, bowl, cereal; monax, 5½" 12.00
Dogwood, bowl, fruit; gr, 10¼" 100.00
Dogwood, pitcher, gr, decorated, 80-oz, 8" 400.00
Dogwood, plate, bread & butter; cremax, 6" 20.00
Dogwood, plate, dinner; pk, 9¼" 17.50
Dogwood, sherbet, gr, low, ftd 60.00
Dogwood, sugar bowl, pk, thin, 2½" 11.00
Dogwood, tumbler, pk, decorated, 11-oz, 4¾" 30.00
Doric, bowl, berry; delphite, lg, 8¼" 77.50
Doric, bowl, berry; pk, 4½" 5.00
Doric, bowl, cream soup; gr, 5" 160.00
Doric, bowl, vegetable; pk, oval, 9" 12.00
Doric, cake plate, gr, 3-legged, 10" 12.50
Doric, creamer, gr, 4" 8.50
Doric, cup, gr 6.50
Doric, pitcher, pk, ftd, 48-oz, 7½" 300.00
Doric, plate, salad; pk or gr, 7" 12.50
Doric, platter, gr, oval, 12" 13.50
Doric, sugar bowl, pk 9.00
Doric, tumbler, gr, 9-oz, 4½" 50.00
Doric, tumbler, pk, ftd, 12-oz, 5" 40.00
Doric & Pansy, bowl, berry; gr, 4½" 10.00
Doric & Pansy, bowl, pk, hdls, 9" 10.00
Doric & Pansy, bowl, teal, hdls, 9" 25.00
Doric & Pansy, creamer, gr 115.00

Doric & Pansy, cup, pk 7.50
Doric & Pansy, plate, dinner; teal, 9" 18.00
Doric & Pansy, plate, sherbet; crystal, 6" 6.00
Doric & Pansy, sugar bowl, gr, open 110.00
Doric & Pansy, tumbler, teal, 9-oz, 4½" 35.00
Double Shield, see Mt Pleasant
Dutch Rose, see Rosemary
Early American Rock Crystal, see Rock Crystal
English Hobnail, bowl, cream soup; amber 13.50
English Hobnail, bowl, relish; pk, oval, 12" 17.50
English Hobnail, candlesticks, gr, 8½", pr 50.00
English Hobnail, creamer, turq, ftd or flat 30.00
English Hobnail, cup, amber 15.00
English Hobnail, decanter, pk, w/stopper, 20-oz 75.00
English Hobnail, goblet, cordial; gr, 1-oz 22.50
English Hobnail, goblet, turq, 8-oz, 6¼" 30.00
English Hobnail, lamp, cobalt, 9¼" 100.00
English Hobnail, pitcher, amber, 39-oz 145.00
English Hobnail, plate, dinner; pk, 10" 20.00
English Hobnail, sherbet, gr 12.50
English Hobnail, tumbler, turq, ftd, 12½-oz 30.00
English Hobnail, vase, cobalt 100.00
Fine Rib, see Homespun
Fire-King Dinnerware, bowl, cereal; crystal, 5½" 15.00
Fire-King Dinnerware, bowl, salad; pk, 7¼" 40.00
Fire-King Dinnerware, cookie jar, gr 300.00
Fire-King Dinnerware, creamer, bl, ftd, 3¼" 75.00
Fire-King Dinnerware, plate, grill; pk, 10½" 30.00
Fire-King Dinnerware, plate, luncheon; crystal, 8" 18.00
Fire-King Dinnerware, plate, salver; gr, 10½" 35.00
Fire-King Dinnerware, tumbler, juice; bl, ftd, 3½" 125.00
Fire-King Oven Glass, baker, bl, 1-qt 4.50
Fire-King Oven Glass, bowl, utility; bl, 8⅜" 10.00
Fire-King Oven Glass, mug, coffee; bl, 2 styles, 7-oz, ea ...17.50
Fire-King Oven Glass, pie plate, bl, 9" 8.00
Fire-King Oven Glass, roaster, bl, 10⅜" 47.50
Fire-King Oven Ware, bowl, vegetable; bl, 8" 9.00
Fire-King Oven Ware, plate, bl, 7" 3.50
Fire-King Oven Ware, plate, dinner; jadite, 9⅛" 2.50
Fire-King Oven Ware, platter, jadite, 12" 7.50
Flat Diamond, see Diamond Quilted
Floragold, bowl, irid, sq, 8½" 12.00
Floragold, candy dish, irid, 1-hdl 6.50
Floragold, creamer, irid 6.00

Floragold, pitcher, irid, 64-oz 25.00
Floragold, plate, dinner; irid, 8½" 17.50
Floragold, sugar bowl, irid 5.00
Floragold, tumbler, irid, ftd, 10-oz 12.00
Floral, bowl, cream soup; pk, 5½" 600.00
Floral, bowl, vegetable; gr, oval, 9" 12.00
Floral, creamer, delphite, flat 60.00

Floral, plate, sherbet; gr, 6" 4.00
Floral, platter, pk, oval, 10¾" 11.00
Floral, shakers, gr, ftd, 4", pr 40.00
Floral, sherbet, pk 10.00
Floral, tumbler, gr, ftd, 3-oz, 3½" 90.00
Floral, tumbler, water; delphite, ftd, 7-oz, 4¾" 125.00
Floral, vase, rose bowl, gr, 3-legged 400.00
Floral & Diamond Band, bowl, nappy; pk, hdls, 5¾" 7.00
Floral & Diamond Band, butter dish, gr 85.00
Floral & Diamond Band, compote, pk, 5½" 9.50
Floral & Diamond Band, creamer, pk, 4¾" 12.00
Floral & Diamond Band, pitcher, gr, 42-oz, 8" 80.00
Floral & Diamond Band, sugar bowl, pk or gr, 5¼" 10.00
Floral & Diamond Band, tumbler, iced tea; gr, 5" 18.00
Florentine No 1, ash tray, gr, 5½" 17.50
Florentine No 1, bowl, cereal; yel, 6" 16.00
Florentine No 1, butter dish, pk 110.00
Florentine No 1, creamer, crystal 7.50
Florentine No 1, cup, bl 65.00
Florentine No 1, pitcher, gr, ftd, 36-oz, 6½" 32.50
Florentine No 1, plate, grill; yel, 10" 11.00
Florentine No 1, sugar bowl, yel or pk 10.00
Florentine No 1, tumbler, gr, ftd, 4-oz, 3¼" 10.00
Florentine No 1, tumbler, juice; yel, ftd, 5-oz, 3¾" 16.00
Florentine No 1, tumbler, water; pk, ftd, 10-oz, 4¾" . . .15.00
Florentine No 2, bowl, berry; crystal, 4½" 9.00
Florentine No 2, bowl, cereal; yel, 6" 25.00
Florentine No 2, bowl, gr, 5½" 25.00
Florentine No 2, comport, bl, ruffled, 3½" 45.00

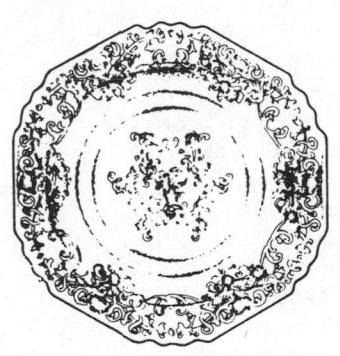

Florentine No 2, creamer, crystal 6.50
Florentine No 2, pitcher, pk, 48-oz, 7½" 97.50
Florentine No 2, plate, salad; yel, 8½" 7.00
Florentine No 2, platter, gr, oval, 11" 10.00
Florentine No 2, sherbet, crystal, ftd 6.00
Florentine No 2, tumbler, juice; gr, 5-oz, 3½" 9.00
Florentine No 2, tumbler, water; pk, 9-oz, 4" 7.00
Florentine No 2, tumbler, yel, ftd, 9-oz, 4½" 22.50
Florentine No 2, vase or parfait, yel, 6" 45.00
Flower & Leaf Band, see Indiana Custard
Flower Garden w/Butterflies, bonbon, blk, w/lid, 6⅝" dia 250.00
Flower Garden w/Butterflies, candlesticks, amber, 8", pr 75.00
Flower Garden w/Butterflies, comport, blk, ftd, 7" 175.00
Flower Garden w/Butterflies, creamer, gr 65.00
Flower Garden w/Butterflies, plate, pk, 10" 32.50
Flower Garden w/Butterflies, sandwich server, bl, center hdl 75.00
Flower Garden w/Butterflies, tumbler, crystal, 7½-oz 100.00
Flower Garden w/Butterflies, vase, blk, hdls, 10" 225.00
Flower Garden w/Butterflies, vase, yel, 10½" 150.00
Flower Rim, see Vitrock
Forest Green, bowl, soup; 6" .8.00
Forest Green, pitcher, 22-oz .12.50

Forest Green, plate, luncheon; 8⅜" 4.00
Forest Green, sugar bowl, flat .4.50
Forest Green, vase, 9" 5.00
Fortune, bowl, salad or lg berry; pk, 7¾" 8.00
Fortune, plate, luncheon; pk, 8" 5.00
Fortune, tumbler, water; crystal, 9-oz, 4" 4.50
Fruits, bowl, berry; gr, 8" 35.00
Fruits, cup, pk 4.00
Fruits, sherbet, pk 5.50
Fruits, tumbler, juice; gr, 3½" .7.50
Georgian, bowl, cereal; gr, 5¾" 14.00
Georgian, creamer, gr, ftd, 4" 10.00
Georgian, plate, dinner; gr, 9¼" 18.00
Georgian, sugar bowl, gr, ftd, 4" 8.50
Georgian, tumbler, gr, flat, 12-oz, 5¼" 67.50
Hairpin, see Newport
Harp, cup, crystal 5.50

Harp, vase, crystal, 6" 10.00
Heritage, bowl, berry; bl or gr, lg, 8½" 95.00
Heritage, bowl, berry; pk, 5" .25.00
Heritage, creamer, crystal, ftd 15.00
Heritage, plate, dinner; crystal, 9¼" 6.50
Heritage, sugar bowl, crystal, ftd, open 10.00
Hex Optic, bowl, mixing; pk, 8¼" 14.00
Hex Optic, ice bucket, gr, metal hdl 12.50
Hex Optic, shakers, pk, pr 17.50
Hex Optic, sugar shaker, pk .85.00
Hex Optic, tumbler, gr, ftd, 7" 7.50
Hobnail, bowl, salad; crystal, 7" 3.75
Hobnail, cup, pk 3.00
Hobnail, decanter, crystal, w/stopper, 32-oz 17.50
Hobnail, pitcher, crystal, 67-oz 20.00
Hobnail, sherbet, pk 2.50
Hobnail, tumbler, iced tea; crystal, 15-oz 6.00
Holiday, bowl, soup; pk, 7¾" 27.50
Holiday, bowl, vegetable; pk, oval, 9½" 12.00
Holiday, candlesticks, pk, 3", pr 55.00
Holiday, pitcher, pk, 52-oz, 6¾" 25.00
Holiday, plate, dinner; pk, 9" .9.50
Holiday, platter, pk, oval, 11⅜" 9.00
Holiday, sherbet, pk 5.00
Holiday, tumbler, pk, ftd, 4" .25.00
Homespun, bowl, cereal; pk, 5" 12.50
Homespun, pitcher, crystal, 96-oz 30.00
Homespun, plate, dinner; pk, 9¼" 9.50
Homespun, platter, crystal, closed hdls, 13" 8.50
Homespun, tumbler, iced tea; pk, 13-oz, 5¼" 18.00
Honeycomb, see Hex Optic
Indiana Custard, bowl, cereal; ivory, 5¾" 15.00
Indiana Custard, butter dish, ivory 52.50
Indiana Custard, cup, ivory 30.00

Indiana Custard, plate, dinner; ivory, 9¾" 13.50
Indiana Custard, saucer, ivory 6.00
Indiana Custard, sherbet, ivory 67.50
Iris, bowl, cereal; crystal, 5" 32.50
Iris, bowl, salad; irid, 9½" 8.00

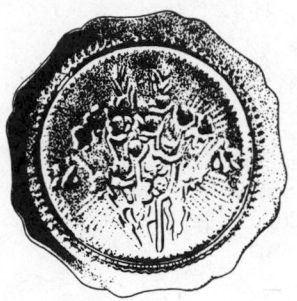

Iris, butter dish, crystal or irid 27.50
Iris, candlesticks, irid, pr 22.50
Iris, coaster, crystal 32.50
Iris, cup, irid 7.50
Iris, goblet, crystal, 4-oz, 5¾" 16.50
Iris, goblet, wine; irid, 4" 16.50
Iris, pitcher, irid, ftd, 9½" 27.50
Iris, plate, luncheon; crystal, 8" 35.00
Iris, sherbet, crystal, ftd, 2½" 15.00
Iris, sugar bowl, crystal 6.00
Iris, tumbler, irid, ftd, 6" 12.00
Iris, vase, pk or gr, 9" 50.00
Iris & Herringbone, see Iris
Jubilee, bowl, fruit; yel, hdls, 9" 45.00
Jubilee, creamer, yel 16.50
Jubilee, goblet, yel, 12½-oz, 6⅛" .65.00
Jubilee, plate, sandwich; yel, 13" 25.00
Jubilee, sugar bowl, yel 16.00
Jubilee, tray, sandwich; yel, center hdl 45.00
Knife & Fork, see Colonial
Lace Edge, bowl, salad; pk, 7¾" 15.00
Lace Edge, comport, pk, 7" 16.00
Lace Edge, creamer, pk 16.00
Lace Edge, plate, dinner; pk, 10½" 18.50
Lace Edge, plate, relish; pk, 3-part, 10½" 20.00
Lace Edge, platter, pk, 12¾" 19.00
Lace Edge, sherbet, pk, ftd 50.00
Lace Edge, sugar bowl, pk 15.00
Lace Edge, tumbler, pk, flat, 9-oz, 4½" 10.00
Laced Edge, bowl, bl, oval, 11" 45.00
Laced Edge, bowl, fruit; bl, 4½" 14.00
Laced Edge, creamer, bl 19.00
Laced Edge, plate, salad; bl, 8" 15.00
Laced Edge, platter, bl, 13" 55.00
Laced Edge, tumbler, bl, 9-oz 27.50
Laced Edge, vase, bl, 5½" 40.00
Lake Como, bowl, vegetable; wht, 9¾" 20.00
Lake Como, cup, wht, regular 15.00
Lake Como, cup, wht, St Denis 12.00
Lake Como, plate, dinner; wht, 9¼" 12.50
Lake Como, sugar bowl, wht, ftd .11.00
Laurel, bowl, berry; gr, lg, 9" 12.00
Laurel, bowl, cereal; bl, 6" 15.00
Laurel, bowl, soup; ivory, 8" 20.00
Laurel, bowl, wht opal, 11" 22.00
Laurel, candlesticks, gr, 4", pr 22.50

Laurel, cheese dish, ivory 50.00
Laurel, plate, salad; ivory, 7½" 8.00
Laurel, platter, bl, oval, 10¾" 27.50
Laurel, shakers, wht opal, pr 45.00
Laurel, sherbet, ivory 9.50
Laurel, tumbler, gr, flat, 9-oz, 4½" 35.00
Lincoln Inn, ash tray, bl or red 15.00
Lincoln Inn, bowl, bl, ftd, 10½" 35.00
Lincoln Inn, bowl, fruit; bl or red, 5" 9.50
Lincoln Inn, comport, red 20.00
Lincoln Inn, cup, bl 12.50
Lincoln Inn, goblet, wine; red 25.00
Lincoln Inn, pitcher, bl, 46-oz, 7¼" 750.00
Lincoln Inn, sherbet, red, 4¾" 15.00
Lincoln Inn, tumbler, bl or red, ftd, 9-oz 15.00
Lincoln Inn, vase, bl or red, ftd, 12" 95.00
Line 412, see Peacock Reverse
Lorain, bowl, cereal; gr, 6" 25.00
Lorain, bowl, vegetable; crystal, oval, 9¾" 27.50
Lorain, cup, yel 11.50
Lorain, plate, dinner; crystal, 10¼" 27.50
Lorain, plate, luncheon; yel, 8⅜" .20.00
Lorain, sherbet, gr, ftd 15.00
Lorain, sugar bowl, yel, ftd 15.00
Lorain, tumbler, gr, ftd, 9-oz, 4¾" 15.00
Louisa, see Floragold
Lovebirds, see Georgian
Lydia Ray, see New Century
Madrid, ash tray, amber, sq, 6" 150.00
Madrid, bowl, salad; gr, 8" 15.00
Madrid, bowl, sauce; bl, 5" 10.00
Madrid, bowl, vegetable; pk, oval, 10" 12.00
Madrid, butter dish, gr 70.00
Madrid, cup, bl 11.00
Madrid, pitcher, amber, 80-oz, 8½" 50.00
Madrid, pitcher, pk, sq, 60-oz, 8" .32.50
Madrid, plate, dinner; bl, 10½" 55.00
Madrid, plate, grill; gr, 10½" 13.50
Madrid, platter, pk, oval, 11½" 9.00
Madrid, tumbler, amber, ftd, 5-oz, 4" 20.00
Madrid, tumbler, gr, 9-oz, 4¼" 17.50
Manhattan, ash tray, crystal, sq, 4½" 15.00
Manhattan, bowl, cereal; crystal, 5½" 13.50
Manhattan, bowl, fruit; pk, 9½" .20.00
Manhattan, bowl, salad; pk, 9" 15.00
Manhattan, coaster, crystal, 3½" .5.00

Manhattan, comport, crystal or pk, 5¾" 15.00
Manhattan, cup, pk 95.00
Manhattan, pitcher, crystal, 42-oz 15.00
Manhattan, plate, dinner; pk, 10¼" 50.00
Manhattan, plate, salad; crystal, 8½" 7.50

Manhattan, sherbet, crystal **6.50**
Manhattan, tumbler, crystal or pk, ftd, 10-oz **10.00**
Manhattan, vase, crystal, 8" **11.50**
Many Windows, see Roulette
Mayfair, bowl, cereal; bl, 5½" **35.00**
Mayfair, bowl, cream soup; pk, 5" **34.00**
Mayfair, bowl, vegetable; gr, 7" **90.00**
Mayfair, cake plate, bl, ftd, 10" **40.00**
Mayfair, cake plate, bl, hdls, 12" **40.00**
Mayfair, candy dish, gr, w/lid **400.00**
Mayfair, creamer, bl, ftd **47.50**
Mayfair, cup, gr or yel **125.00**
Mayfair, decanter, pk, w/stopper, 32-oz **105.00**
Mayfair, goblet, cocktail; pk, 3½-oz, 4" **57.50**
Mayfair, goblet, water; gr, 9-oz, 5¾" **300.00**
Mayfair, pitcher, bl, 60-oz, 8" **105.00**
Mayfair, plate, grill; gr or yel, 9½" **55.00**
Mayfair, plate, luncheon; pk, 8½" **16.00**

Mayfair, plate, sherbet; pk, rnd, 6½" **9.00**
Mayfair, platter, pk, oval, open hdls, 12" **15.00**
Mayfair, sherbet, gr or yel, ftd, 4¾" **127.50**
Mayfair, sherbet, pk, flat, 2¼" **105.00**
Mayfair, sugar bowl, bl, ftd **47.50**
Mayfair, tray, celery; gr or yel, divided, 9" **110.00**
Mayfair, tray, celery; pk, divided, 10" **120.00**
Mayfair, tray, relish; bl, 4-part, 8⅜" **35.00**
Mayfair, tumbler, iced tea; pk, ftd, 15-oz, 6½" **27.50**
Mayfair, tumbler, juice; bl, 5-oz, 3½" **75.00**
Mayfair, tumbler, water; bl, 11-oz, 4¾" **85.00**
Mayfair, tumbler, yel, ftd, 10-oz, 5¼" **157.50**
Mayfair, whiskey, pk, 1½-oz, 2¼" **50.00**
Mayfair Federal, bowl, cream soup; amber, 5" **13.50**
Mayfair Federal, bowl, vegetable; gr, oval, 10" **17.50**
Mayfair Federal, plate, dinner; crystal, 9½" **7.00**
Mayfair Federal, sugar bowl, amber, ftd **10.00**
Mayfair Federal, tumbler, gr, 9-oz, 4½" **20.00**
Miss America, bowl, berry; gr, 4½" **7.00**
Miss America, bowl, berry; pk, 6¼" **12.50**
Miss America, bowl, vegetable; crystal, oval, 10" **10.00**
Miss America, butter dish, pk **375.00**
Miss America, cake plate, crystal, ftd, 12" **16.50**
Miss America, candy jar, pk, 11½" **95.00**
Miss America, coaster, crystal, 5¾" **12.50**
Miss America, comport, pk, 5" **16.00**
Miss America, cup, gr **8.00**
Miss America, goblet, juice; red, 5-oz, 4¾" **175.00**
Miss America, pitcher, pk, 65-oz, 8" **85.00**
Miss America, plate, dinner; crystal, 10¼" **10.00**
Miss America, plate, gr, 6¾" **6.00**
Miss America, plate, salad; pk, 8½" **14.00**
Miss America, shakers, gr, pr **275.00**

Miss America, tray, relish; pk, rnd, divided, 11¾" **350.00**
Miss America, tumbler, iced tea; crystal, 14-oz, 5¾" **20.00**
Miss America, tumbler, juice; pk, 5-oz, 4" **35.00**
Moderntone, bowl, berry; cobalt, lg, 8¾" **25.00**
Moderntone, bowl, cereal; cobalt, 6½" **40.00**
Moderntone, bowl, cream soup; cobalt, 4¾" **13.00**
Moderntone, bowl, soup; amethyst, 7½" **40.00**
Moderntone, cheese dish, cobalt, w/metal lid, 7" **175.00**
Moderntone, cup, amethyst **6.00**
Moderntone, plate, dinner; cobalt, 8⅞" **9.50**
Moderntone, plate, luncheon; cobalt or amethyst, 7¾" **6.00**
Moderntone, plate, salad; cobalt, 6¾" **6.50**
Moderntone, platter, amethyst, oval, 12" **25.00**
Moderntone, shakers, cobalt or amethyst, pr **27.50**
Moderntone, sherbet, cobalt **8.50**
Moderntone, tumbler, amethyst, 12-oz **40.00**
Moderntone, tumbler, cobalt, 5-oz **17.50**
Moderntone, whiskey, cobalt, 1½-oz **15.00**
Moondrops, ash tray, bl **30.00**
Moondrops, bowl, berry; red, 5¼" **10.00**
Moondrops, bowl, bl, hdls, oval, 9¾" **45.00**
Moondrops, bowl, soup; bl, 6¾" **12.00**
Moondrops, bowl, vegetable; red, oval, 9¾" **25.00**
Moondrops, butter dish, bl or red **360.00**
Moondrops, candy dish, red, ruffled, 8" **25.00**
Moondrops, comport, bl, 4" **17.50**
Moondrops, comport, red, 11½" **40.00**
Moondrops, cup, bl **9.00**
Moondrops, decanter, bl, lg, 11¼" **67.50**
Moondrops, decanter, red, sm, 7¾" **50.00**
Moondrops, goblet, bl, 5-oz, 4¾" **17.00**
Moondrops, goblet, wine; red, 4-oz, 4" **15.00**
Moondrops, mug, colors other than bl or red, 12-oz, 5⅛" **17.50**
Moondrops, pitcher, bl, med, 32-oz, 8⅛" **150.00**
Moondrops, pitcher, red, w/lip, lg, 50-oz, 8" **155.00**
Moondrops, plate, colors other than bl or red, 5⅞" **5.00**
Moondrops, plate, dinner; bl, 9½" **15.00**
Moondrops, plate, luncheon; red, 8½" **11.00**
Moondrops, platter, bl, oval, 12" **20.00**
Moondrops, sherbet, red, 4½" **20.00**
Moondrops, sugar bowl, red, 4" **11.50**
Moondrops, tumbler, bl, 8-oz, 4⅜" **12.00**
Moondrops, tumbler, juice; bl, ftd, 3-oz, 3¼" **12.50**
Moondrops, tumbler, red, 9-oz, 4⅞" **13.50**
Moondrops, vase, red, flat, ruffled top, 7¾" **45.00**
Moonstone, bowl, berry; opal, 5½" **9.00**
Moonstone, bowl, opal, flat, 7¾" **8.00**

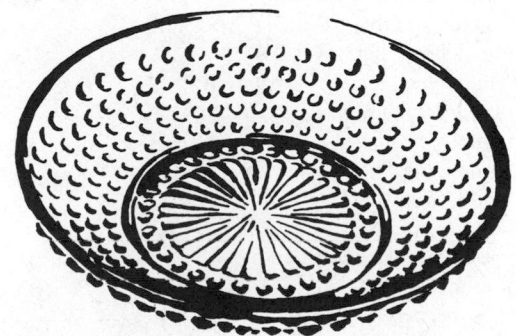

Moonstone, bud vase, opal, 5½" **8.50**
Moonstone, candle holder, opal, pr, candle holders **15.00**
Moonstone, creamer, opal **6.00**
Moonstone, goblet, opal, 10-oz **15.00**

Moonstone, plate, sandwich; opal, 10" 16.00
Moonstone, sugar bowl, opal, ftd .6.00
Moroccan Amethyst, bowl, cereal; 5¾" 4.50
Moroccan Amethyst, candy dish, w/lid 17.50
Moroccan Amethyst, plate, sandwich; 12" 6.00
Moroccan Amethyst, tumbler, water; 11-oz, 4½" 5.50
Moroccan Amethyst, vase, ruffled, 9" 27.50
Mt Pleasant, bowl, fruit; cobalt, scalloped, 10" 28.00
Mt Pleasant, bowl, fruit; pk, sq, ftd, 4" 10.00

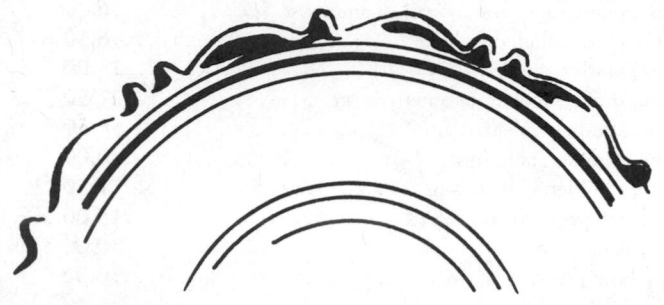

Mt Pleasant, creamer, gr 15.00
Mt Pleasant, plate, grill; amethyst, 9" 8.50
Mt Pleasant, sherbet, pk 6.50
Mt Pleasant, sugar bowl, gr 15.00
Mt Pleasant, vase, cobalt, 7¼" 20.00
New Century, bowl, berry; crystal, 4½" 5.00
New Century, bowl, cream soup; gr, 4¾" 9.00
New Century, cup, pk 15.00
New Century, decanter, gr, w/stopper 40.00
New Century, goblet, wine; crystal, 2½-oz 14.00
New Century, plate, dinner; gr, 10" 10.00
New Century, plate, grill; crystal, 10" 8.00
New Century, platter, gr, oval, 11" 11.00
New Century, saucer, cobalt 5.00
New Century, tumbler, amethyst, 12-oz, 5¼" 12.00
New Century, tumbler, cobalt, 5-oz, 3½" 7.50
New Century, tumbler, gr, 9-oz, 4¼" 10.00
New Century, tumbler, pk, 10-oz, 5" 10.00
New Century, whiskey, gr, 1½-oz, 2½" 12.00
Newport, bowl, cereal; cobalt, 5¼" 22.00
Newport, bowl, cream soup; amethyst, 4¾" 11.00
Newport, cup, cobalt 7.50
Newport, plate, luncheon; amethyst, 8½" 7.50
Newport, plate, sandwich; cobalt, 11½" 22.50
Newport, platter, amethyst, oval, 11¾" 22.50
Newport, sherbet, cobalt 9.00
Newport, tumbler, amethyst, 9-oz, 4½" 20.00
No 610 Pyramid, bowl, berry; yel, 4¾" 25.00
No 610 Pyramid, bowl, master berry; gr, 8½" 22.50
No 610 Pyramid, creamer, pk 16.50
No 610 Pyramid, ice tub, yel 175.00
No 610 Pyramid, pitcher, crystal 185.00
No 610 Pyramid, sugar bowl, yel 25.00
No 610 Pyramid, tumbler, gr, ftd, 11-oz 45.00
No 612 Horseshoe, bowl, cereal; gr, 6½" 15.00
No 612 Horseshoe, bowl, salad; yel, 7½" 16.00
No 612 Horseshoe, bowl, vegetable; gr, 8½" 17.00
No 612 Horseshoe, creamer, gr, ftd 11.50
No 612 Horseshoe, cup, yel 7.50
No 612 Horseshoe, pitcher, gr, 64-oz, 8½" 200.00
No 612 Horseshoe, plate, dinner; yel, 10⅜" 16.00
No 612 Horseshoe, plate, sandwich; gr, 11" 10.00

No 612 Horseshoe, sherbet, gr 10.00
No 612 Horseshoe, sugar bowl, yel, open 10.50
No 612 Horseshoe, tumbler, gr, 12-oz, 4¾" 85.00
No 612 Horseshoe, tumbler, gr, 9-oz, 4¼" 75.00
No 612 Horseshoe, tumbler, yel, ftd, 12-oz 85.00
No 616 Vernon, creamer, gr, ftd .20.00
No 616 Vernon, cup, crystal 5.00
No 616 Vernon, plate, luncheon; yel, 8" 6.50
No 616 Vernon, plate, sandwich; gr, 11" 18.00
No 616 Vernon, tumbler, crystal, ftd, 5" 10.00
No 618 Pineapple & Floral, ash tray, amber, 4½" 16.00
No 618 Pineapple & Floral, ash tray, crystal, 4½" 13.00
No 618 Pineapple & Floral, bowl, berry; amber, 4¾" 14.00
No 618 Pineapple & Floral, bowl, cereal; red, 6" 16.00
No 618 Pineapple & Floral, bowl, salad; crystal, 7" 5.00
No 618 Pineapple & Floral, cup, amber 7.00
No 618 Pineapple & Floral, plate, dinner; red, 9⅜" 12.50
No 618 Pineapple & Floral, plate, sandwich; crystal, 11½" 12.50
No 618 Pineapple & Floral, plate, sherbet; red, 6" 4.00
No 618 Pineapple & Floral, sherbet, red, ftd 15.00
No 618 Pineapple & Floral, tumbler, crystal, 12-oz, 5" 30.00
No 618 Pineapple & Floral, vase, crystal, cone shape 25.00
No 620, see Daisy
Nora Bird, cup, pk or gr 20.00
Nora Bird, mayonnaise, pk or gr, w/liner 50.00
Nora Bird, plate, pk or gr, 8" 15.00
Nora Bird, tumbler, pk or gr, ftd, 4¾" 32.50
Normandie, bowl, cereal; amber, 6½" 9.00
Normandie, bowl, vegetable; pk, oval, 10" 22.00
Normandie, creamer, irid, ftd 6.50
Normandie, pitcher, amber, 80-oz, 8" 50.00
Normandie, plate, dinner; pk, 11" 50.00
Normandie, plate, grill; irid, 11" 9.00
Normandie, plate, salad; irid, 8" 40.00
Normandie, platter, amber, 11¾" 11.00
Normandie, sugar bowl, pk 6.00
Normandie, tumbler, juice; amber, 5-oz, 4" 12.50
Normandie, tumbler, water; pk, 9-oz, 4¼" 28.50
Old Cafe, bowl, berry; pk, 3¾" 2.00
Old Cafe, bowl, cereal; crystal, 5½" 4.00
Old Cafe, cup, red 6.00
Old Cafe, pitcher, pk, 80-oz 75.00
Old Cafe, plate, dinner; crystal, 10" 15.50

Old Cafe, tumbler, juice; red, 3" .7.50
Old Cafe, tumbler, water; pk, 4" .6.00
Old Cafe, vase, red, 7¼" 13.50
Old English, bowl, fruit; pk, ftd, 9" 22.50
Old English, candlesticks, gr, 4", pr 22.50
Old English, creamer, amber 14.00
Old English, goblet, pk, 8-oz, 5¾" 22.50
Old English, pitcher, gr 50.00

Old English, sherbet, all colors, 2 styles .16.00
Old English, sugar bowl, gr .12.00
Old English, tumbler, amber, ftd, 5½" .25.00
Old English, vase, pk, ftd, 12" .40.00
Old Florentine, see Florentine No 1
Open Lace, see Lace Edge
Open Rose, see Mayfair
Optic Design, see Raindrops
Orchid, bowl, blk, hdls, 8½" .47.50
Orchid, bowl, cobalt, ftd, 10" .65.00
Orchid, bowl, red, sq, 4⅞" .22.50
Orchid, creamer, colors other than red, blk, or bl 20.00
Orchid, vase, colors other than red, blk, or bl, 10" 40.00
Ovide, bowl, cereal; wht decor, 5½" .10.00
Ovide, cocktail, fruit; blk, ftd .3.00
Ovide, creamer, wht decor .12.00
Ovide, cup, gr .2.00
Ovide, plate, dinner; wht decor, 9" .7.00

Ovide, shakers, blk, pr .20.00
Ovide, sugar bowl, gr, open .2.50
Ovide, tumbler, wht decor .15.00
Oyster & Pearl, bowl, crystal, heart shape, 1-hdl, 5¼" 5.00
Oyster & Pearl, bowl, fruit; red, deep, 10½" 32.50
Oyster & Pearl, bowl, pk, 1-hdl, 5½" .4.00
Oyster & Pearl, candle holders, crystal, 3½", pr 15.00
Oyster & Pearl, plate, sandwich; pk, 13½" 10.00
Parrot, bowl, berry; gr, 5" .12.50
Parrot, bowl, soup; amber, 7" .25.00
Parrot, bowl, vegetable; gr, oval, 10" .35.00
Parrot, creamer, amber, ftd .30.00
Parrot, pitcher, gr, 80-oz, 8½" .850.00
Parrot, plate, dinner; gr, 9" .30.00
Parrot, platter, amber, oblong, 11¼" .45.00
Parrot, shakers, gr, pr .177.50
Parrot, sugar bowl, gr or amber .20.00
Parrot, tumbler, gr or amber, 10-oz, 4¼" 95.00
Parrot, tumbler, gr or amber, 12-oz, 5½" 110.00
Patrician, bowl, berry; amber, 5" .7.50
Patrician, bowl, cereal; crystal, 6" .16.00
Patrician, bowl, cream soup; pk, 4¾" .15.00
Patrician, creamer, gr, ftd .9.50
Patrician, cup, amber .6.00
Patrician, plate, dinner; crystal, 10½" .5.50
Patrician, plate, grill; gr, 10½" .10.00
Patrician, plate, sherbet; crystal, 6" .6.75
Patrician, platter, pk, oval, 11½" .15.00
Patrician, shakers, pk, pr .70.00
Patrician, sherbet, gr .9.00
Patrician, tumbler, amber, 5-oz, 4" .22.50
Patrician, tumbler, crystal, 9-oz, 4½" .20.00
Patrician, tumbler, gr, ftd, 8-oz, 5¼" .37.50

Patrician, tumbler, pk, 14-oz, 5½" .22.00
Patrick, bowl, console; yel, 11" .25.00
Patrick, candlesticks, pk, pr .35.00
Patrick, creamer, yel .10.50
Patrick, goblet, juice; pk, 6-oz, 4¾" .15.00
Patrick, plate, luncheon; pk, 8" .6.50
Patrick, sugar bowl, yel .10.00
Patrick, tray, yel or pk, center hdl, 11" .25.00
Peacock & Wild Rose, bowl, all colors, ftd, 9½" 37.50
Peacock & Wild Rose, bowl, console; all colors, 14" 37.50
Peacock & Wild Rose, ice bucket, all colors, 6" 65.00
Peacock & Wild Rose, vase, all colors, 10" 67.50
Peacock Reverse, bowl, all colors, sq, 8¾" 50.00
Peacock Reverse, cup, all colors .37.50
Peacock Reverse, plate, luncheon; all colors, 8½" 25.00
Peacock Reverse, tumbler, all colors, flat, 10-oz, 4" 42.50
Peacock Reverse, vase, all colors, 10" .75.00
Petal Swirl, see Swirl
Petalware, bowl, cream soup; pk, 4½" .4.00
Petalware, bowl, soup; monax, 7" .15.00
Petalware, cup, florette .10.00
Petalware, plate, dinner; crystal, 9" .3.50
Petalware, plate, salver; monax, 11" .12.00
Petalware, platter, pk, oval, 13" .7.50
Petalware, sherbet, crystal, ftd, 4½" .3.00
Petalware, sugar bowl, florette, ftd .12.50
Philbe, see Fire-King Dinnerware
Pinwheel, see Sierra
Poinsettia, see Floral
Poppy No 1, see Florentine No 1
Poppy No 2, see Florentine No 2
Pretzel, bowl, soup; crystal, 7½" .7.50
Pretzel, creamer, crystal .4.50
Pretzel, pitcher, crystal, 39-oz .95.00
Pretzel, plate, sandwich; crystal, 11½" .7.00
Pretzel, tumbler, crystal, 9-oz, 4½" .12.00
Primo, bowl, yel, 7¾" .12.50
Primo, creamer, gr .7.50
Primo, cup, yel .6.50
Primo, plate, dinner; gr, 10" .10.00
Primo, sugar bowl, gr .7.50
Primo, tumbler, yel, 9-oz, 5¾" .12.00
Princess, ash tray, gr, 4½" .55.00
Princess, bowl, vegetable; pk, oval, 10" .15.00
Princess, coaster, yel .67.50
Princess, cup, gr .9.00
Princess, pitcher, gr, 60-oz, 8" .35.00

Princess, plate, dinner; pk, 9" .12.00
Princess, plate, grill; gr, 9" .10.00
Princess, plate, sandwich; pk, hdls, 11½" .7.50
Princess, platter, yel, closed hdls, 12" .37.50

Princess, shakers, gr, 4½", pr 40.00
Princess, sherbet, pk, ftd 11.00
Princess, tumbler, juice; pk, 5-oz, 3" 17.00
Princess, tumbler, water; gr, 9-oz, 4" 20.00
Princess, tumbler, yel, ftd, 10-oz, 5¼" 16.00
Princess, vase, gr, 8" 22.00
Provincial, see Bubble
Queen Mary, bowl, berry; pk, 5" 4.50
Queen Mary, bowl, cereal; crystal, 6" 4.00
Queen Mary, butter dish, pk 80.00

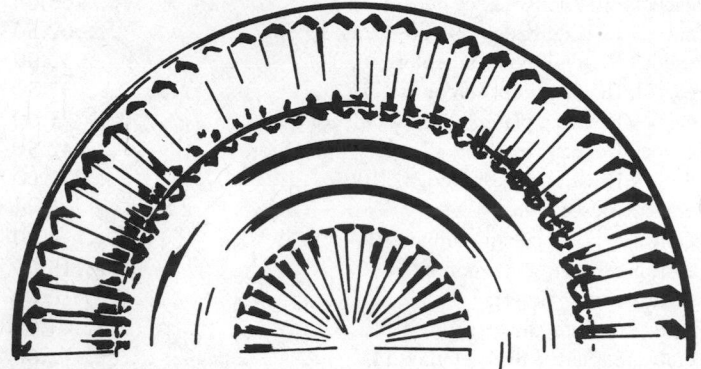

Queen Mary, comport, crystal, 5¾" 5.00
Queen Mary, creamer, pk, oval 5.00
Queen Mary, plate, crystal, serving tray, 14" 9.00
Queen Mary, plate, salad; pk, 8½" 4.50
Queen Mary, shakers, crystal, pr 15.00
Queen Mary, sugar bowl, crystal, oval 4.00
Queen Mary, tumbler, pk, ftd, 10-oz, 5" 20.00
Radiance, bowl, bonbon; red, ftd, 6" 15.00
Radiance, bowl, nut; amber, hdls, 5" 7.50
Radiance, bowl, pickle; red, 7" 12.50
Radiance, bowl, red, crimped, 12" 32.50
Radiance, candlesticks, red, 8", pr 50.00
Radiance, comport, amber, 6" 15.00
Radiance, creamer, red 15.00
Radiance, decanter, ice bl, w/stopper, hdld 65.00
Radiance, pitcher, red, 64-oz 175.00
Radiance, plate, luncheon; red, 8" 12.00
Radiance, tray, red, oval 25.00
Radiance, vase, amber, flared, 10" 22.50
Raindrops, bowl, berry; gr, 7½" 20.00
Raindrops, creamer, gr 5.00
Raindrops, plate, luncheon; gr, 8" 3.00
Raindrops, sherbet, gr 5.00
Raindrops, tumbler, gr, 10-oz, 5" 7.50
Raindrops, whiskey, gr, 1-oz, 1⅞" 4.00
Ribbon, candy dish, gr 27.50
Ribbon, creamer, gr, ftd 8.00
Ribbon, plate, luncheon; blk, 8" 10.00
Ribbon, tumbler, gr, 10-oz, 6" 16.50
Ring, bowl, soup; gr, 7" 10.00
Ring, cocktail shaker, crystal 10.00
Ring, ice tub, crystal w/mc rings 17.50
Ring, pitcher, crystal, 80-oz, 8½" 12.00
Ring, sandwich server, crystal, center hdl 12.00
Ring, shakers, crystal, 3", pr 15.00
Ring, tumbler, gr, 12-oz, 5⅛" 5.00
Ring, tumbler, water; crystal, ftd, 5½" 4.00
Ring, vase, crystal w/mc rings, 8" 27.50
Rock Crystal, bonbon, red, scalloped edge, 7½" 40.00
Rock Crystal, bowl, crystal, 4½" 9.00
Rock Crystal, bowl, salad; crystal, scalloped edge, 9" ...20.00

Rock Crystal, butter dish, crystal 250.00
Rock Crystal, candlesticks, red, 8½", pr 185.00
Rock Crystal, candy dish, crystal, rnd 27.50
Rock Crystal, comport, crystal, 7" 27.50
Rock Crystal, cup, red, 7-oz 45.00
Rock Crystal, pitcher, crystal, ½-gal, 7½" 85.00
Rock Crystal, sandwich server, red, center hdl 85.00
Rock Crystal, tumbler, juice; crystal, 5-oz 12.00
Rock Crystal, vase, crystal, cornucopia 50.00
Rock Crystal, vase, red, ftd, 11" 125.00
Rope, see Colonial Fluted
Rose Cameo, bowl, cereal; gr, 5" 8.00
Rose Cameo, plate, salad; gr, 7" 5.50
Rose Cameo, tumbler, gr, ftd, 2 styles, 5" 11.00
Rosemary, bowl, cereal; gr, 6" 20.00
Rosemary, bowl, cream soup; amber, 5" 8.00
Rosemary, creamer, gr, ftd 9.50
Rosemary, plate, dinner; pk 12.00
Rosemary, plate, salad; gr, 6¾" 6.00
Rosemary, sugar bowl, amber, ftd 6.50
Rosemary, tumbler, pk, 9-oz, 4¼" 25.00
Roulette, bowl, fruit; gr, 9" 10.00
Roulette, cup, crystal 3.50
Roulette, pitcher, pk, 64-oz, 8" 22.50
Roulette, plate, sandwich; pk, 12" 7.50
Roulette, tumbler, water; crystal, 9-oz, 4⅛" 10.00
Roulette, whiskey, gr, 1½-oz, 2½" 9.00
Round Robin, cup, irid, ftd 5.00
Round Robin, plate, sandwich; gr, 12" 5.00
Round Robin, sugar bowl, irid 5.00
Roxana, bowl, cereal; yel, 6" 6.50
Roxana, sherbet, yel, ftd 4.00
Roxana, tumbler, yel, 9-oz, 4" 10.00
Royal Lace, bowl, berry; pk, 5" 18.00
Royal Lace, bowl, cream soup; crystal, 4¾" 8.50
Royal Lace, bowl, vegetable; gr, oval, 11" 22.00
Royal Lace, butter dish, bl 385.00
Royal Lace, cup, crystal 5.50

Royal Lace, pitcher, gr, 96-oz, 8½" 120.00
Royal Lace, plate, dinner; pk, 9⅞" 12.00
Royal Lace, platter, bl, oval, 13" 37.50
Royal Lace, sherbet, gr, ftd 17.50
Royal Lace, tumbler, crystal, 9-oz, 4⅛" 8.50
Royal Lace, tumbler, pk, 10-oz, 4⅞" 27.50
Royal Ruby, bowl, salad; 11½" 20.00
Royal Ruby, bowl, soup; 7½" 9.50
Royal Ruby, pitcher, tilted, 3-qt 25.00
Royal Ruby, plate, dinner; 9¼" 7.50
Royal Ruby, sugar bowl, ftd 5.00
Royal Ruby, tumbler, juice; 5-oz, 2 styles 5.00
Royal Ruby, tumbler, water; 10-oz 5.00

Royal Ruby, vase, bulbous, 6½" 7.50
S Pattern, bowl, berry; crystal, 8½" 7.50
S Pattern, cake plate, crystal, heavy, 11" 30.00
S Pattern, plate, grill; yel or amber 32.50
S Pattern, sherbet, yel or amber, ftd, low 6.00
S Pattern, tumbler, crystal, 12-oz, 5" 7.50
Sandwich, bowl, cereal; crystal, 6½" 18.00
Sandwich, bowl, console; gr, 9" 15.00

Sandwich, bowl, console; pk, 10" 18.00
Sandwich, bowl, pk, scalloped, 8" 12.50
Sandwich, bowl, salad; crystal, 9¼" 17.50
Sandwich, cookie jar, gold 30.00
Sandwich, creamer, gr 17.50
Sandwich, creamer, red 40.00
Sandwich, cup, pk, gr, or bl 4.50
Sandwich, decanter, pk, w/stopper 85.00
Sandwich, goblet, gr, 9-oz 15.00
Sandwich, pitcher, gr, 68-oz 100.00
Sandwich, plate, dessert; gold, 7" 8.00
Sandwich, plate, dinner; gr, 10½" 12.50
Sandwich, plate, sandwich; crystal, 12" 9.00
Sandwich, sugar bowl, gr, open 15.00
Sandwich, tumbler, cocktail; pk, ftd, 3-oz 15.00
Sandwich, tumbler, water; crystal, 9-oz 6.50
Saxon, see Coronation
Sharon, bowl, berry; gr, 5" 8.50
Sharon, bowl, cereal; amber, 6" 11.00
Sharon, bowl, fruit; pk, 10½" 22.00
Sharon, cheese dish, amber 150.00
Sharon, creamer, pk, ftd 11.00
Sharon, pitcher, gr, w/ice lip, 80-oz 295.00
Sharon, plate, dinner; amber, 9½" 9.50
Sharon, platter, pk, oval, 12½" 13.50
Sharon, shakers, gr, pr 55.00
Sharon, tumbler, amber, ftd, 15-oz, 6½" 60.00
Sharon, tumbler, pk, thin, 12-oz, 5¼" 32.50
Sierra, bowl, vegetable; pk, oval, 9¼" 25.00
Sierra, butter dish, gr 50.00
Sierra, pitcher, pk, 32-oz, 6½" 45.00
Sierra, plate, dinner; pk, 9" 10.50
Sierra, platter, gr, oval, 11" 30.00
Sierra, tumbler, pk, ftd, 9-oz, 4½" 30.00
Spiral, bowl, berry; pk, 4¾" 4.00
Spiral, cup, gr 4.00
Spiral, plate, luncheon; pk, 8" 2.00
Spiral, sherbet, gr 3.00
Spiral, tumbler, water; gr, 9-oz, 5" 4.50
Spoke, see Patrician
Starlight, bowl, cereal; pk, 5½" 5.00
Starlight, bowl, pk, closed hdls, 8½" 9.00
Starlight, bowl, salad; crystal, 11½" 14.00

Starlight, plate, sandwich; wht, 13" 7.50
Starlight, sherbet, crystal 7.50
Stippled Rose Band, see S Pattern
Strawberry, bowl, berry; pk, 4" 7.00
Strawberry, comport, crystal, 5¾" 9.00
Strawberry, creamer, irid, lg, 4⅝" 12.50
Strawberry, pitcher, gr, 7¾" 130.00
Strawberry, plate, salad; irid, 7½" 6.50
Strawberry, plate, sherbet; pk or gr, 6" 5.00
Strawberry, sherbet, pk 6.50
Strawberry, tumbler, crystal, 9-oz, 3⅝" 14.00
Sunflower, cake plate, pk, 3-legged, 10" 9.00
Sunflower, plate, dinner; gr, 9" 12.00
Sunflower, sugar bowl, pk 12.00
Sunflower, tumbler, gr, ftd, 8-oz, 4¾" 20.00
Sweet Pear, see Avocado
Swirl, ash tray, pk, 5⅜" 6.00
Swirl, bowl, salad; ultramarine, 9" 15.00
Swirl, butter dish, pk 130.00
Swirl, creamer, ultramarine, ftd 9.50
Swirl, cup, pk 4.75
Swirl, pitcher, ultramarine, ftd, 48-oz 950.00
Swirl, plate, dinner; pk, 9¼" 7.00
Swirl, plate, sandwich; ultramarine, 12½" 13.50
Swirl, sugar bowl, pk, ftd 6.50
Swirl, tumbler, pk, 9-oz, 4⅝" 11.00
Swirl, tumbler, ultramarine, 9-oz, 4" 15.00
Swirl, vase, pk, ftd, 6½" 11.50
Swirl, vase, ultramarine, ftd, 8½" 17.50
Sylvan, see Parrot
Tea Room, bowl, vegetable; gr, oval, 9½" 45.00
Tea Room, candlesticks, gr, low, pr 35.00
Tea Room, creamer, pk, ftd, 4½" 12.00
Tea Room, goblet, gr, 9-oz 60.00
Tea Room, ice bucket, pk 35.00
Tea Room, parfait, pk 45.00
Tea Room, plate, luncheon; gr, 8¼" 25.00
Tea Room, plate, sherbet; gr, 6½" 20.00
Tea Room, saucer, gr or pk 15.00

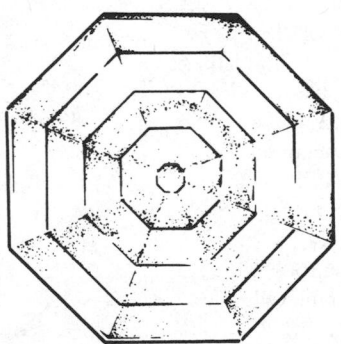

Tea Room, shakers, pk, pr 37.50
Tea Room, sherbet, gr, ftd, low 16.00
Tea Room, sugar bowl, pk, 4" 10.00
Tea Room, tumbler, gr, flat, 8½-oz 75.00
Tea Room, tumbler, gr, ftd, 11-oz 32.50
Tea Room, tumbler, pk, ftd, 12-oz 35.00
Tea Room, vase, gr, ruffled edge, 9" 75.00
Tea Room, vase, pk, ruffled edge, 11" 120.00
Thistle, bowl, cereal; gr, 5½" 15.00
Thistle, plate, grill; pk, 10¼" 12.50
Thistle, saucer, pk or gr 7.50
Threading, see Old English

Thumbprint, bowl, berry; gr, lg, 8" 6.00
Thumbprint, creamer, gr, ftd 10.00
Thumbprint, plate, dinner; gr, 9¼" 4.50
Thumbprint, shakers, gr, pr 20.00
Thumbprint, sugar bowl, gr, ftd 10.00
Thumbprint, tumbler, gr, 10-oz, 5" 4.00
Twisted Optic, bowl, cream soup; all colors, 4¾" 7.00
Twisted Optic, candy jar, all colors 10.00

Twisted Optic, pitcher, all colors, 64-oz 17.50
Twisted Optic, plate, luncheon; all colors, 8" 2.00
Twisted Optic, sugar bowl, all colors 5.00
Twisted Optic, tumbler, all colors, 12-oz, 5¼" 6.50
US Swirl, bowl, berry; pk, 4⅜" 5.00
US Swirl, bowl, oval, gr, 8¼" 16.00
US Swirl, butter dish, pk 67.50
US Swirl, creamer, gr 10.00
US Swirl, pitcher, gr or pk, 48-oz, 8" 30.00
US Swirl, plate, salad; pk, 7⅞" 5.00
US Swirl, shakers, gr, pr 32.50
US Swirl, tumbler, pk, 12-oz, 4⅝" 9.00
US Swirl, vase, gr, 6½" 12.50
Vertical Ribbed, see Queen Mary
Victory, bonbon, amber, 7" 9.00
Victory, bowl, cereal; blk, 6½" 18.00
Victory, bowl, console; gr, 12" 27.50
Victory, bowl, vegetable; pk, oval, 9" 25.00
Victory, creamer, bl 30.00
Victory, goblet, amber, 7-oz, 5" 17.50
Victory, gravy boat, bl, w/underplate 250.00
Victory, gravy boat, pk, w/underplate 125.00
Victory, plate, dinner; amber, 9" 15.00
Victory, plate, luncheon; blk, 8" 12.50
Victory, platter, gr, 12" 17.50
Victory, sherbet, pk, ftd 10.00
Victory, sugar bowl, bl 30.00
Vitrock, bowl, cream soup; wht, 5½" 8.00
Vitrock, bowl, vegetable; wht, 9½" 7.00
Vitrock, plate, soup; wht, 9" 7.00
Vitrock, platter, wht, 11½" 17.50
Waffle, see Waterford
Waterford, bowl, berry; pk, 4¾" 7.00
Waterford, bowl, cereal; crystal, 5½" 9.00
Waterford, creamer, crystal, oval 2.50
Waterford, cup, pk 10.00
Waterford, pitcher, juice; crystal, tilted, 42-oz 17.50
Waterford, pitcher, pk, w/ice lip, tilted, 80-oz 100.00
Waterford, plate, dinner; pk, 9⅝" 11.00
Waterford, plate, salad; pk, 7⅛" 4.50
Waterford, plate, sandwich; crystal, 13¾" 5.00
Waterford, sugar bowl, pk 6.50
Waterford, tray, relish; crystal, 5-part, 13¾" 13.00

Waterford, tumbler, pk, ftd, 10-oz, 4⅞" 12.00
Wild Rose, see Dogwood
Windsor, ash tray, pk, 5¾" 30.00
Windsor, bowl, berry; gr, 4¾" 7.00
Windsor, bowl, cream soup; crystal, 5" 4.50
Windsor, bowl, gr, hdls, 8" 14.00
Windsor, bowl, salad; crystal, 10½" 6.00
Windsor, bowl, vegetable; gr, oval, 9½" 15.00
Windsor, butter dish, gr 70.00
Windsor, cake plate, crystal, ftd, 10¾" 6.00
Windsor, candlesticks, pk, 3", pr 55.00
Windsor, candy jar, crystal 10.00
Windsor, comport, pk 12.00
Windsor, console bowl, fruit; pk, 12½" 65.00
Windsor, cup, gr 7.00
Windsor, pitcher, crystal, 20-oz, 5" 5.00
Windsor, pitcher, pk, 16-oz, 4½" 95.00
Windsor, plate, chop; pk, 13⅝" 20.00
Windsor, plate, salad; gr, 7" 10.00
Windsor, plate, sandwich; pk, hdls, 10¼" 9.00
Windsor, platter, crystal, oval, 11½" 4.50
Windsor, shakers, gr, pr 37.50
Windsor, sherbet, pk, ftd 6.00
Windsor, tray, gr, sq, 4" 6.50
Windsor, tumbler, crystal, ftd, 7¼" 9.00

Windsor, tumbler, gr, 5-oz, 3¼" 20.00
Windsor, tumbler, pk, 12-oz, 5" 20.00
Windsor Diamond, see Windsor

Derby

William Duesbury operated in Derby, England, from about 1755, purchasing a second establishment, The Chelsea Works, in 1769. During this period fine porcelains were produced which so impressed the King that in 1773 he issued the company the Crown Derby patent. In 1810, several years after Duesbury's death, the factory was bought by Robert Bloor. The quality of the ware suffered under the new management, and the main Derby pottery closed in 1848. Within a short time, the work was revived by a dedicated number of former employees who established their own works on King Street in Derby.

The earliest-known Derby mark was the crown over a script 'D'; however this mark is rarely found today. Soon after 1782, that mark was augmented with a device of crossed batons and six dots, usually applied in underglaze blue. During the Bloor period, the crown was centered within a ring containing the words 'Bloor' above and 'Derby' below the crown or with a red printed stamp — the crowned Gothic 'D.' The King Street plant produced figurines that may be distinguished from their earlier counterparts by the presence of an 'S' and 'H' on either side of the crown and crossed batons.

In 1876 a new pottery was constructed in Derby, and the owners revived the earlier company's former standard of excellence. The Queen bestowed the firm the title Royal Crown Derby in 1890; it still operates under that name today. See also Royal Crown Derby.

White bisque group of the 'Three Graces,' ca 1790, restored, 14", $1,000.00.

Basket, flower encrusted sides/hdls, oval, 1825, 8¾" L 770.00
Bowl, Sprig, mc/gilt florals on wht, dome lid, 1830s, 10" 175.00
Bowl, waste; exotic bird, Kakiemon palette, 6" 90.00
Bowl, waste; stylized roots/leaf border, bl/gilt, 1820, 6" 120.00
Cup & saucer, exotic bird, Kakiemon palette, 1815 . . . . 65.00
Cup & saucer, Mikado, bl 18.00
Figurine, allegorical Liberty & Matrimony, 1775, rstr, 6" 1,000.00
Figurine, ewe w/suckling lamb, 1770s, 5", EX 550.00
Figurine, Falstaff, floral shirt/red pants, ca 1768, 10½" 285.00
Figurine, Welsh Talyor & wife on goats' bks, 1810, 6", pr 350.00
Plate, exotic bird, Kakiemon palette, 7" 35.00
Plate, floral spray w/in gilt dot border, apricot rim, 9" 130.00
Plate, pheasant, flowers/grain rim, gold trim, mk, 9" 99.00
Sauce dish, bl/gilt border w/3 floral reserves, paw ft, 7" 200.00
Scurier w/lid & stand, gilt on cobalt/florals, 1820, 8" dia 200.00
Sugar basin, floral sprays, basketweave band, rstr, 4" 250.00
Vase, campana; View in Cumberland, snake hdls, 1820s, 6½" . . 240.00
Vase, floral, gold trim, bulbous w/slim neck, 11½x4½" 155.00
Vase, Imari, mk, 5" 220.00
Vase, scenic reserves on dk bl, gilt hdls, 1850s, 7", pr 400.00

Devon, Crown Devon

Devon and Crown Devon were trade names of S. Fielding and Company, Ltd., an English firm founded about 1879. They produced majolica, earthenware mugs, vases, and kitchenware. In the 1930s, they manufactured an exceptional line of Art Deco vases that have recently been much in demand.

Biscuit jar, florals on gr shaded, gold trim, SP rim/hdl, 8" 110.00
Box, cigarette/music; Scotsman & lass, H Lauder, 2¾x4x5½" . . 175.00
Jug, musical, Auld Lang Syne, emb figures, thistle hdl, 7" 175.00
Jug, musical, emb John Peel & hunt scene, fox hdl, 8x5¼" 195.00
Mug, musical, emb Irish jaunting cart, Killarney verse, 7" 150.00

Dickota

The Dickota Pottery, a name coined from Dickinson, North Dakota,

where it was founded as a brickyard, began operations in the early 1930s. In 1934 potters formerly associated with the North Dakota School of Mines and Charles Hyten from Niloak began their own operation there. Hyten developed a line of swirled ware which was marked 'Dickota Badlands.' Vases, bowls, and ash trays in a mottled glaze were also made. A variety of marks were used, all of which contain the Dickota name. The company closed in the late 1930s.

Advertising ash tray, 3", $38.00.

Ash tray, cowboy hat, advertising 45.00
Pitcher, bl mottled, fat, 5" 35.00
Vase, mauve, flat fan shape w/scallops, 4½" 33.00
Vase, Niloak type swirl, classic form, 6½" 65.00

Documents

Although the word 'document' is defined in the general sense as 'anything printed or written, etc., relied upon to record or prove something. . .,' in the collectible market, the term is more diversified with broadsides, billheads, checks, invoices, letters and letterheads, land grants, receipts, and waybills some of the most sought after. Some documents in demand are those related to a specific subject such as advertising, mining, railroads, military, politics, banking, slavery, nautical, or legal (deeds, mortgages, etc.). Other collectors look for examples representing a specific period of time such as colonial documents, Revolutionary, or Civil War documents, early western documents or those from a specific region, state, or city.

Aside from supply and demand, there are five major factors which determine the collector-value of a document. These are:

1) Age — Documents from the eastern half of the country can be found that date back to the 1700s or earlier. Most documents sought by collectors usually date from 1800 to 1900. Those with twentieth-century dates are still abundant and not in demand unless of special significance or beauty.

2) Region of origin — Depending on age, documents from rural and less-populated areas are harder to find than those from major cities and heavily populated states. The colonization of the West and Mid-West did not begin until after 1850, so while an 1870s billhead from New York or Chicago is common, one from Albuquerque or Phoenix is not, since most of the Southwest was still unsettled.

3) Attractiveness — Some documents are plain and unadorned, but collectors prefer colorful, profusely illustrated pieces. Additional artwork and engravings add to the value.

4) Historical content — Unusual or interesting content, such as a letter written by a Civil War soldier giving an eye-witness account of the Battle of Gettysburg or a western territorial billhead listing numerous animal hides purchased from a trapper, will sell for more than one with

mundane information.

5) Condition — Through neglect or environmental conditions, over many decades paper articles can become stained, torn, or deteriorated. Heavily damaged or stained documents are generally avoided altogether while those with minor problems are more acceptable, although their value will decrease anywhere from 20% to 50% depending upon the extent of damage. Avoid attempting to repair tears with scotch tape — sell 'as is' so that the collector can take proper steps toward restoration.

Foreign documents are plentiful; and, though some are very attractive, resale may be difficult. The listings that follow are generalized; prices are variable depending entirely upon the five points noted above. Values here are based upon examples with no major damage.

Our advisor for this category is Warren Anderson; he is listed in the Directory under Utah.

Key: illus —— illustrated

Billhead, CO, sale of carriage from livery stable, 1881 . . . . .12.00
Billhead, CO mining camp, sale of lumber, 1881 . . . . .10.00
Check, Capitol Nat'l Bank, Guthrie OK Territory, 1896 . . . . . . .25.00
Check, John Conley & Co, Bankers, Port Wine CA, 1865 . . . . .25.00
Check, Port of Portland, OR, 1892 . . . . .10.00
Check, WY Loan & Trust, Laramie WY, 1887 . . . . .45.00
Circular, Mormon, flour/gold pricing to emigrants, 1864 . . . . . .250.00
Contract, NY, ocean passage on La Lorraine, 1919 . . . . .10.00
Deed, Blkbird Mining District of ID, fully sgn, 1900, 2-pg 15.00
Deed, CA, property in town, sgn Thomas Larkin, 1849 . . . . . . .350.00
Deed, ID, sale of mine, fully sgn, legal sz, 2-pg 15.00
Invoice, Fort Cummings NM, supplies delivered, 1882 . . . . .25.00
Land grant, CO Territory, proxy signed US Grant, 1875 . . . . . . .50.00
Letter, CO, mining investment, ornate title, 1900, 2-pg 25.00
Letter, CO Territory, handwritten, mining life, 1864, 1-pg 75.00
Letter, OK Territory, AT&SF RR letterhead, 1889, 1-pg 18.00

Military discharge document, Harris' Light Cavalry, Custer's division, dated 1865, 16½x13½", $425.00.

Letter, PA, mother seeks leave for son, w/Dr's note, 1865 . . . . . .20.00
Letter, PA Cavalry, officer seeks return of horse, 1864 . . . . .15.00
Letter, S America, handwritten, mining concerns, 1893, 3-pg . . .30.00
Pay voucher, VA City NV, from county treasurer, 1870 . . . . . . .25.00
Receipt, CA, Wells Fargo, package received, 1906, 4x7" 10.00
Receipt, Quartermaster Gen's Office, of accounts, 1873, 3x8" . . .25.00
Receipt, San Andreas CA mining camp, script, 1868, 5x8" 17.00
Receipt, VA, Monroe County taxes, printed, 1856 . . . . .7.50
Receipt book, NV mining, red/blk print on pk, dtd 190? 25.00
Release, Camp Chase OH, Civil war prisoner, June 1865, G 30.00
Report, account of missing Union solider, handwritten, 1864 . . .20.00
Report, military; persons & articles hired, 1873, 17x22" 35.00
Reward notice, NJ, Lindbergh baby kidnapping, 1932, EX 300.00
School bond, CO Territory, state seal, ca 1870, 10x13" 40.00
Special order, investigate AWOL Union soldier, 1864 . . . . .15.00
Stagecoach waybill, OR, lists passengers & freight, 1891 . . . . . . .35.00
Voucher, SL City UT, sgn Henry Grow (Mormon leader), 1878 50.00
Warrant, MT Territory, $5 for animal burial, vignette, 1889 . . . .30.00
Warrant, Sierra County CA, court appearance, 1857, EX 150.00
Warrant, to arrest man, sgn Thomas Heyward, 1886, 1-pg 250.00
Waybill, PA, ship Ceasar, cargo of flour & Indian corn, 1790 . . .30.00

Dollhouses and Furnishings

Dollhouses were introduced commercially in this country late in the 1700s by Dutch craftsmen who settled in the East. By the mid-1800s, they had become meticulously detailed, divided into separate rooms, and lavishly furnished to reflect the opulence of the day. Originally intended for the amusement of adults of the household, by the latter 1800s their status had changed to that of a child's toy. Though many early dollhouses were lovingly hand-fashioned for a special little girl, those made commercially by such companies as Bliss and Schoenhut are highly valued.

Furniture and furnishings in the Biedermeier style featuring stenciled Victorian decorations often sell for several hundred dollars each. Other early pieces made of pewter, porcelain, or papier-mache are also quite valuable. Certainly less expensive but very collectible, nonetheless, is the quality, hallmarked plastic furniture produced during the forties by Renwal and Acme and the 1960s Petite Princess line produced by Ideal. In the listings that follow, dollhouses are litho paper on wood unless otherwise noted. When no manufacturer or country of origin is noted, examples are German, turn of the century.

Our advisor for this category is Barbara Rosen; she is listed in the Directory under New Jersey. See also Miniatures.

Furniture

Armoire, Rococo, mirror door, scrollwork, Biedermeier, 7" 150.00
Baby bed, gilt trim, Adrian Cook 38.00
Basket, fireside; w/mc flowers, Adrian Cook 30.00
Bathroom fixtures, Arcade, 1930s, 3-pc set 85.00
Bed, princess style, Petite Princess, MIB 25.00
Bedroom set, litho on wood, Bliss, 1895, 6-pc 350.00
Bedroom set, yel w/floral, sleigh bed+3 pcs, Tynietoy 200.00
Bird cage, w/bird, Adrian Cook 65.00
Buggy, Victorian, fancy, Adrian Cook .75.00
Candelabrum, Petite Princess, M 20.00
Chair, highbk; gilt trim, Adrian Cook .35.00
Chair, side; pnt tin w/3-loop wire bk, Rock-Graner, 6 for 700.00
Commode, pnt tin, front opens, Rock-Graner, 1850, 2½" 200.00
Desk, French style, gold japanning, Biedermeier, 5x4¾" 175.00
Dining room, Dream House, #170 . . . . .45.00
Fantasy room, Petite Princess, MIB 30.00

Bliss living and dining room set with complete alphabet, missing keys on piano, 10 pieces, $495.00.

Lawn swing, Kilgore	22.00
Living room, Dream House, #17	45.00
Living room suite, couch+chair+2 tables, red pnt, unmk, '30s	32.00
Loveseat, gilt trim, Adrian Cook	38.00
Refrigerator, Petite Princess	75.00
Sideboard, 2-shelf top, Rococo, scrollwork, Biedermeier, 7"	250.00
Sofa, Rococo, pnt tin, Rock-Graner, 1850s, 8" L	1,000.00
Sofa+5 side chairs, Rococo, gilt, satin uphl, Biedermeier	200.00
Table, dining; walnut, 6-leg, Strombecker, +3 chairs, EX	40.00
Table, drop leaf, red-pnt tin w/florals, Stevens-Brn, 3"	100.00
Table+chair, pnt tin, Rock-Graner, 1850, table: 3½" dia	450.00
Tea cart, Petite Princess, MIB	22.00

Houses

Bliss, att; paper on wood, 2-story, 2 doors open, 19x10x9"	700.00
Bliss, paper on wood, 2-story, orig int, ca 1910, 11x6x4"	650.00
European, paper/pnt on wood, 2-story, fr entrance, 16x9x6"	500.00
European, paper/pnt on wood, 2-story/4-room, 24x22x11", EX	650.00

Lancaster Country farm house, hand-split shingled roof, separate outhouse, ca 1890, 34x38x23", $8,250.00.

European, stable, paper on wood, faux brick, 15x17x9", EX	325.00
Railway station, pnt wood, red roof, paper label, 11x17x8"	150.00
Schoenhut, bungalo, emb cb/pnt wood, litho int, 15x19x16",	475.00
Schoenhut, emb cb/wood, 2-story/2-room, 12x14x12", EX	475.00
Schoenhut, railway station, emb cb/pnt wood, 11x17x13", EX	200.00
Stable, paper litho/pnt on wood, w/loft, 15x14x7", VG	300.00
Stable, paper on wood, 6 stalls, open loft, 20x30x11", EX	800.00
Stable, pnt wood, 2 doors in loft, 28 figures, 22x10x30", EX	2,800.00
Victorian, paper litho on wood, 2-story, 19x12x9", EX	950.00
Victorian, paper litho/pnt on wood, metal rails, 22x12x8"	325.00
Victorian, paper on wood, clapboard, dormers, 15½x13x9"	250.00

Dolls

Collecting dolls of any sort is one of the most rewarding hobbies in the United States. The rewards are in the fun, the search, and the finds — plus there is a built-in factor of investment. No hobby, be it dolls, glass, or anything else, should be based completely on investment; but any collector should ask: 'Can I get my money back out of this item if I should ever have to sell it?' Many times we buy on impulse rather than with logic, which is understandable; but by asking this question we can save ourselves a lot of 'buyer's remorse' which we have all experienced at one time or another.

Since we want to learn to invest our money wisely while we are having fun, we must become aware of defects which may devaluate a doll. In bisque, watch for eye chips, hairline cracks and chips, or breaks on any part of the head. Composition should be clean, not crazed or cracked. Vinyl and plastic should be clean with no pen or crayon marks. Though a quality replacement wig is acceptable for bisque dolls, composition and hard plastics should have their originals in uncut condition. Original clothing is a must except in bisque dolls, since it is unusual to find one in its original costume. However, they should be well dressed and ready for your collection.

A price guide is only that — a guide. It suggests the average price for each doll. Bargains can be found for less-than-suggested values, and 'unplayed-with' dolls in their original boxes may cost more. Dealers must become aware of condition so that they do not over-pay and therefore over-price their dolls — a common occurrence across the country. Quantity does not replace quality, as most find out in time. A faster turnover of sales with a smaller margin of profit is far better than being stuck with an item that does not sell because it is over-priced. It is important to remember that prices are based on condition and rarity. When no condition is noted, dolls are assumed to be in excellent condition with the exceptions of Armand Marseille, Madame Alexander, and Effanbee dolls, which are priced in mint condition. In relation to bisque dolls, excellent means having no cracks, chips, or hairlines, being nicely dressed, shoed, wigged, and ready to to be placed into a collection. For a more thorough study of the subject, we recommend you refer to the many lovely doll books written by authority Pat Smith, available at your favorite bookstore or public library.

Key:
bjtd — ball-jointed	OC — original clothes
blb — bent limb body	p/e — pierced ears
bsk — bisque	pnt — painted
c/m — closed mouth	pwt — paperweight eyes
hh — human hair	RpC — replaced clothes
hp — hard plastic	ShHd — shoulder head
jtd — jointed	ShPl — shoulder plate
MIG — Made In Germany	SkHd — socket head
NC — no clothes	str — straight
o/c — open closed	trn — turned

Armand Marseille

A 0½ M, 300n, Armand Marseille, adult, SkHd, 15½"	1,000.00
A 10/0 M, 324, Germany, Armand Marseille, pnt eyes, 7"	495.00

A 10/0 M, 390, SkHd, 1900, 18" .345.00
A 11 M, DRGM, Germany, SkHd, 26" 525.00
A 11 M, DRGM 276/1, Germany, SkHd, 26" 500.00
A 11 M, G 327 B, Germany, SkHd, 1914, 20" 425.00
A 11 M, 1894, ShPl, 26" 600.00
A 11/0 M, 255, DRGM, Germany, SkHd, intaglio eyes, 7½" . .425.00
A 11/0 M, 323, Germany, SkHd, glass eyes, 7½" 625.00
A 11/0 M, 395, Germany, SkHd, Heidi, 1920, 9" 225.00
A 11/0 M, 500, MIG, molded hair, Infant Berry, 1908, 5" 300.00
A 12 M, 390n, Germany, SkHd, Louisa, 1915, 27" 575.00
A 12/0 M, MIG, SkHd, o/c eyes, 7" 125.00
A 2/0 M, DRGM 201013, Germany, trn ShHd, talks, 16" 400.00
A 2/0 M, G 329 B, Germany, SkHd, girl, 9" 185.00
A 2/0 M, 500, DRGM, molded hair, Infant Berry, 1908, 10" . . .300.00
A 3/0 M, 990, SkHd, baby, 8" .145.00
A 30/0 M, MH, Germany, SkHd, c/m, lady, dimples, 1913, 10". 650.00
A 4 M, 347, Germany, SkHd, 1909, 16" 425.00
A 4/0 M, 320, Germany, SkHd, c/m, pnt eyes, 6½" 400.00
A 4/0 M, 323, Germany, SkHd, googly eyes, 11" 1,200.00
A 450 M, 1½, Germany, SkHd, c/m, provincial attire, 19" 850.00
A 5 M, 590, DRGM, o/c eyes & mouth, Hoopla Girl, 16" . . .1,500.00
A 5/0 M, 402, Germany, SkHd, pnt bsk, 14" 300.00
A 6 M, 550, DRGM, Germany, SkHd, c/m, 16" 1,800.00
A 6/0 M, G 327B, DRGM 259, Germany, SkHd, 1914, 12" . . .185.00
A 7 M, Germany, SkHd, 17" 295.00

**Armand Marseille, Florodora, A 77 M, socket head, marked MIG, 25",
$575.00.**

A 7 M, 257, Germany, SkHd, baby, 1914, 22" 450.00
A 7 M, 390, MIG, SkHd, 23" 425.00
A 7/0 M, MIG, ShHd, boy, 14" .385.00
A 7/0 M, 390, MIG, SkHd, 9½" .145.00
A 9 M, CM Bergmann, MIG, SkHd, 24" 475.00
A 985 M, 3, Germany, SkHd, baby, 13½" 375.00
Alma 10/0/Germany, ShHd, 26" 525.00
Alma 14/0, ShHd, 26" 525.00
Alma 3/0, ShHd, 12" 165.00
Alma 9/0, ShHd, 15" 250.00
AM Darling Baby, 1906, 12" 300.00
AM DEP, MIG, SkHd, 16" 225.00
AM DEP, 3/0, MIG, SkHd, 1894, 14" 300.00
AM DEP, 3200, ShHd, some trn, 1898, 16" 350.00
AM G 327 B, DRGM, SkHd, baby, fur hair, 1914, 12" 325.00
AM G 328 B, Germany, SkHd, closed dome, 1922, 14" 350.00
AM 0½ DEP, 3200, MIG, ShHd, 1898, 14" 250.00
AM 1½, DEP, SkHd, wht, 1894, 16½" 375.00
AM 11 DEP, 3200, ShHd, some trn, 26" 800.00
AM 12, Germany, flange neck, baby, 1907, 16" 475.00
AM 1894, DEP, Germany, SkHd, blk, 12" 425.00
AM 2½k, SkHd, o/m, blk, 12" 350.00
AM 2/0, DEP, 3500, MIG, ShHd, 17" 400.00
AM 2/0 DEP, 370, MIG, ShHd, 19½" 325.00
AM 20/0, Germany, SkHd, o/c, Indian, 1890s, 8" 400.00
AM 3 DEP, 370, MIG, ShHd, fur eyebrows, 22½" 425.00
AM 3k, 362, Germany, SkHd, closed dome, baby, wht, 15" . . .400.00
AM 341, Germany, flange, c/m, My Dream Baby, 1924, 7" . . .165.00
AM 341 7, Germany, flange, c/m, My Dream Baby, 18" 600.00
AM 341/Ok, Germany, SkHd, c/m, My Dream Baby, 16" 450.00
AM 341/10, Germany, flange, c/m, My Dream Baby, 21" 675.00
AM 341/3, Germany, socket & flange, c/m, baby, wht, 8" 165.00
AM 341/4, Germany, flange, c/m, My Dream Baby, 15" 450.00
AM 351 10/0, Germany, w/rubber body, Wee One, 7" 165.00
AM 351 17/0, Germany, socket & flange, o/m, 6" 145.00
AM 351/4k, Germany, socket & flange, o/m, wht, 22" 725.00
AM 351/6, Germany, socket & flange, o/m, 26" 1,200.00
AM 352 10, Germany, flange, Baby Love, 1914, 19" 675.00
AM 3524, 7, Germany, flange neck, baby, Baby Gloria, 18" . . .700.00
AM 390, MIG, SkHd, My Dearie, 1908-1922, 18½" 375.00
AM 4/0x DEP, 370, MIG, ShHd, 16½" 275.00
AM 5 DEP, 3200, ShHd, some trn, 15" 325.00
AM 5/0x, 370, MIG, ShHd, c/m, 15½" 225.00
AM 500, DRGM, Germany, Infant Berry, 1908, 8" 300.00
AM 6/0 DEP, 370, ShHd, 15" 250.00
AM 600, DRGM, Germany, flange, SkHd, c/m, 1910, 10" 700.00
AM 7/0 DEP, MIG, SkHd, 1894, 12" 250.00
AM 8 DEP, 3200, trn ShHd, 22" 500.00
AM 800, 'Mama,' talker in head, Baby Sunshine, 1925, 16" . .1,200.00
AM 83115, SkHd, 8" 165.00
AM 917, Germany, SkHd, baby, Mobi, 1921, 16" 350.00
AM 95 6 DEP, Armand Marseille, trn ShHd, 20" 425.00
AM 966 3, MIG, SkHd, baby, flirty eyes, 14" 450.00
AM 980, Germany, SkHd, baby, 14" 350.00
Armand Marseille, A 0½ M, 990, Germany, SkHd, 13" 350.00
Armand Marseille, A 1 M, 390, SkHd, 16" 425.00
Armand Marseille, A 11 M, 990, SkHd, Happy Tot, 1910, 21" .800.00
Armand Marseille, A 11/0 M, 390, Germany, o/c mouth, 7½" .125.00
Armand Marseille, A 2 M, 390n, Germany, Patrice, SkHd, 18". 500.00
Armand Marseille, A 2/0 M, 995, Germany, SkHd, 12" 250.00
Armand Marseille, A 2/0 M, 996, Germany, SkHd, baby, 15" . .425.00
Armand Marseille, A 4½ M, 990, Germany, SkHd, 1910, 16" .450.00
Armand Marseille, A 4/0x M, 390n, Germany, SkHd, 1915, 11".250.00
Armand Marseille, A 6 M, 390, MIG, SkHd, walks, 22" 525.00

Armand Marseille, A 6 M, 390, SkHd, 21" **425.00**
Armand Marseille, A 7 M, 390, Germany, SkHd, 22" **450.00**
Armand Marseille, A 7 M, 992, Germany, SkHd, 1914, 22" . . .**750.00**
Armand Marseille, A 9 M, 390, SkHd, pnt bsk, 9" **125.00**
Armand Marseille, A 975 M, 13, Germany, SkHd, 1914, 24" . .**700.00**
Armand Marseille, A 975 M, 2/0, Germany, SkHd, 1914, 9" . .**165.00**
Armand Marseille, AM 10/0 DEP, 370, MIG, ShHd, 12" **165.00**
Armand Marseille, AM 7/0 DEP, 370n, MIG, ShHd, 12" **165.00**
Armand Marseille, Germany, SkHd, c/m, 14" **600.00**
Armand Marseille, 390, MIG, SkHd, 24" **500.00**
Armand Marseille, 560a, DRGM 232, Dorothy, 1912, 15" . . .**475.00**
Columbia, MIG, ShHd, 1904, 24" **550.00**
Fany, A 11 M, 231, DRGM 248/1, baby, c/m, 1913, 25" **8,300.00**
Floradora, A 0 M, MIG, SkHd, 17" **325.00**
Floradora, A 1 M, MIG, SkHd, 20" **365.00**
Floradora, A 11 M, MIG, SkHd, 27" **575.00**
Floradora, A 3 M, MIG, ShHd, 23" **450.00**
Floradora, A 4 M, SkHd, 23" **450.00**
Floradora, A 5 M, Germany, ShHd, 24" **500.00**
Floradora, A 77 M, MIG, SkHd, 15" **300.00**
Floradora, A 9/0 M, MIG, SkHd, 12" **185.00**
Floradora, 1347, ShHd, fur eyebrows, 21" **425.00**
Floradora, 2/0x AM, ShHd, 21½" **400.00**
Floradora, 3740, 30, 1374, ShHd, 21" **425.00**
GB, A 5/0 M, DRGM 248/1, SkHd, o/m, 1912, 10" **165.00**
GB 250, A 1 M, Germany, SkHd, c/m, molded hair, 10½" . . .**350.00**
Googly, A 11/0 M, 254, SkHd, molded hair, 8" **550.00**
Googly, A 12/0 M, 210, Germany, SkHd, pnt eyes, 6" **500.00**
Googly, A 253 M, 5/0, DRGM, Germany, SkHd, 1915, 16" .**1,600.00**
Googly, A 3/0 M, G 252 B, DRGM, SkHd, 1915, 9½" **795.00**
Googly, A 3/0 M, 200, DRGM 213, SkHd, 11½" **2,200.00**
Googly, A 6/0 M, SB 252, DRGM, Germany, SkHd, 10" **795.00**
Googly, AM, 353, 5/0, SkHd, 6½" **600.00**
Googly, AOM, 253 SB, DRGM, Germany, SkHd, 8" **725.00**
Kiddiejoy, A 3 M, 997, Germany, SkHd, 14" **475.00**
Kiddiejoy, AM, 991, Germany, SkHd, 14" **375.00**
Kiddiejoy, AOM, Germany, ShHd, 9" **165.00**
Kiddiejoy, 3/0, Germany, ShHd, cloth body, c/m, girl, 20" . . .**1,600.00**
Kiddiejoy, 372, Germany, ShHd, molded hair, 1926, 9" **285.00**
Kiddiejoy, 375 6, Germany, c/m, molded hair, girl, 20" **1,800.00**
Lily, 4/0, MIG, ShHd, 1913, 17" **375.00**
Mabel, 131, Germany, ShHd, 1898, 17" **375.00**
Mabel, 3/0, Germany, ShHd, 1898, 15" **350.00**
My Dearie, A 2M, DRGM 246/1, SkHd, 1908, 14" **325.00**
My Playmate (Baby), AM Germany, closed dome, c/m, 18" . .**1,400.00**
Otto Gans, A 5 M, 970, Germany, Lady Marie, 1916, 20" **525.00**
Otto Gans, A 7 M, 975, Germany, SkHd, Sadie, 1914, 17" . . .**450.00**
Queen Louise, Germany, SkHd, 1910, 22" **525.00**
Queen Louise, 100, Germany, SkHd, 1910, 12" **300.00**
Queen Louise, 100, SkHd, 1910, 18½" **425.00**
Queen Louise, 315, Germany 12, SkHd, 27" **850.00**
Rosebud, A 4/0 M, MIG, ShHd, 1902, 15" **350.00**
Roseland, AOM, 1910, 18" **475.00**
Sunshine, 1910, Germany, ShHd, 24" **525.00**
Wonderful Alice, DRGM 377439, SkHd, fur eyebrows, 26" . . .**600.00**

Barbie Dolls and Related Dolls

Though the face has changed three times since 1959, Barbie is still as popular today as she was when she was first introduced. Named after the young daughter of the first owner of the Mattel Company, the original Barbie had a white iris but no eye color. These dolls are nearly impossible to find, but there is a myriad of her successors and related collectibles just waiting to be found. When no condition is indicated, the dolls listed below are assumed to be nude and in excellent condition unless otherwise specified. For further information, we recommend *An Illustrated Price Guide to Collectible Barbie Dolls* by Paris, Susan, and Carol Manos; and *The Collectors Encyclopedia of Barbie Dolls and Collectibles* by Sibyl DeWein and Joan Ashabraner.

Barbie, 1959, #1, blonde, swimsuit, holes in feet, MIB **1,500.00**
Barbie, 1960, #3, bl eyes, curved brows, ivory skin, MIB **1,500.00**
Barbie, 1960, #4, vinyl plastic, tan skin **150.00**
Barbie, 1961, Bubble Cut, MIB **125.00**
Barbie, 1963, Fashion Queen, w/3 wigs, swimsuit, MIB **165.00**
Barbie, 1964, Ponytail Swirl, no curly bangs **125.00**
Barbie, 1965, Color 'N Curl, 2 heads & accessories, MIB **300.00**
Barbie, 1967, standard, str legs, pnt lashes **65.00**
Barbie, 1968, Spanish Talking, MIB **150.00**
Barbie, 1969, Twist 'N Turn **60.00**
Barbie, 1972, Busy, long blonde hair **45.00**
Barbie, 1972, Ward's Anniversary, 100th Anniversary **150.00**
Barbie, 1973, Quick Curl, blonde, bendable knees **35.00**
Barbie, 1974, Sun Valley, w/ski accessories, MIB **60.00**
Barbie, 1974, Sweet Sixteen, Barbie's birthday, MIB **60.00**
Barbie, 1975, Free Moving, blonde, MIB **45.00**
Barbie, 1975, Funtime, bendable knees, twist waist, MIB **50.00**
Barbie, 1975, Gold Metal Skater, w/skates & stand **25.00**
Barbie, 1975, Hawaiian, str hair, grass skirt, MIB **60.00**
Barbie, 1976, Ballerina, blonde ponytail, wht tutu, MIB **40.00**
Barbie, 1976, Beautiful Bride, bendable knees, w/gown, MIB . . .**75.00**
Barbie, 1976, Plus 3, in package, M **50.00**
Barbie, 1977, Hawaiian Super Star, Canada, MIB **60.00**
Barbie, 1978, Beautiful Bride, MIB **30.00**
Barbie, 1978, Fashion Photo, remote control play camera, MIB .**45.00**
Barbie, 1978, Super Size Bridal, MIB **60.00**
Barbie, 1978, Super Star, In the Spotlight, w/3 outfits, MIB **75.00**
Barbie, 1979, Kissing, w/2 gowns, lipstick, & stand, MIB **40.00**
Barbie, 1979, Pretty Changes, w/lamp base **40.00**
Barbie, 1980, Beauty Secrets, MIB **20.00**
Barbie, 1981, Western, MIB **20.00**
Barbie, 1983, Twirly Curls **20.00**
Brad, 1970, Talking, Black, pnt hair, MIB **75.00**
Cara, 1975, Free Moving, Black, long hair w/bows, MIB **45.00**
Cara, 1976, Ballerina, Black, swivel head & arms, blk hair . . .**30.00**
Carla, 1965, Black, blk ponytail w/wht ribbon, MIB **45.00**
Casey, 1975, Baggie, blonde, str legs, swimsuit, MIB **30.00**
Christie, 1969, Talking, Black **55.00**
Christie, 1971, Live Action, Black, bendable knees, MIB **65.00**
Christie, 1979, Kissing, w/lipstick, MIB **45.00**
Christie, 1980, Golden Dream, 2nd issue, MIB **30.00**
Curtis, 1976, Free Moving, MIB **60.00**
Francie, 1966, bendable knees **60.00**
Francie, 1966, str legs, pnt lashes, swimsuit **50.00**
Francie, 1967, Black, 1st issue, brn eyes/red oxidized hair **300.00**
Francie, 1970, Hair Happenin's, 4 blonde hairpieces, MIB **125.00**
Francis, 1978, Malibu, MIB **20.00**
Ginger, 1976, Growing Up Ginger, brunette **30.00**
Guardian Goddess, Sun Spell, MIB **125.00**
Julia, 1969, Twist 'N Turn, 2-pc nurse's uniform, MIB **125.00**
Ken, 1961, Flocked Hair, movable head, arms, & legs **70.00**
Ken, 1969, Talking, bendable knees, jacket & shorts, MIB **125.00**
Ken, 1970, Spanish Talking, bl & orange outfit, MIB **150.00**
Ken, 1972, Walk Lively, pnt hair, MIB **85.00**
Ken, 1974, Ward's Dressed, bl & blk tuxedo, mod hair, MIB . .**125.00**
Ken, 1976, Funtime, bl trunks, MIB **40.00**
Ken, 1976, Gold Medal Skier, w/skis & ski poles, MIB **50.00**
Ken, 1977, Super Star, w/free gift, MIB **65.00**

Ken, 1978, Malibu, MIB 25.00
Ken, 1981, Western, MIB 25.00
Ken, 1982, All Star, MIB 20.00
Kitty O'Neil, MIB 35.00
Kristie McNichol, MIB 40.00
Midge, 1965, bendable legs, bouffant hair 100.00
Miss America, 1972, Kellogg's Walk Lively, wht gown, MIB ...125.00
Miss America, 1974, Kellogg's Blonde Quick Curl, MIB 85.00
PJ, 1970, Twist 'N Turn, blonde 45.00
PJ, 1971, Live Action PJ on Stage 95.00
PJ, 1975, Gold Medal Gymnast, w/balance beam 30.00
PJ, 1976, Free Moving, MIB 45.00
Ricky, 1965, red hair, str legs, freckles 45.00
Skipper, 1967, Funtime, blonde, bendable knees 40.00
Skipper, 1970, Pose 'N Play, MIB 40.00
Skipper, 1976, Growing Up, MIB 30.00
Skipper, 1979, Super Teen, MIB 25.00
Skipper, 1981, Western, MIB 20.00
Skooter, 1965, str legs, pigtails & freckles 40.00
Stacey, 1968, Talking, British accent, w/plastic box 75.00
Steffie, 1972, Busy Talking, blonde 75.00
Tiff, 1972, Pose 'N Play, swing-free arms 65.00
Truly Scrumptious, 1969, Talking, bendable legs 185.00
Tutti, 1966, Melody in Pink, set 65.00
Twiggy, 1967, blonde, bendable knees, mini dress, MIB 100.00

Barbie Gift Sets and Related Accessories

When no condition is indicated, the items listed below are assumed to be mint and in the original box.

Ballerina Barbie Stage, 1976-1986, MIB 40.00
Barbie, Skipper, & Ken McDonald outfits, 1976-1986, M, ea ...25.00
Barbie, Snow Princess Dog Sled, Sweden, MIB 200.00
Barbie & Ken Costume Trunk, #5070, by SSP, M 60.00
Barbie Baby-Sitting Room, Canada, 1976-1986, MIB 75.00
Barbie Beauty Kit, 1961, M 25.00
Barbie Diary, 1963, M 20.00
Barbie Heirloom Service, 1961 ....45.00
Barbie Make-Up Case, 1963, M 25.00
Barbie Motor Roller, w/Funtime Barbie, 1976-1986, MIB 125.00
Barbie Olympic Ski Village, MIB 35.00
Barbie Playhouse, Europe, 1976-1986, MIB 75.00
Barbie Record Player, Vanity Fair, 1961, M 50.00
Barbie Record Tote, 1961, M 20.00
Barbie Roller Gift Set, Spain 85.00
Barbie Snap Shot Album, 1963, M 25.00
Barbie Star Cycle, 1976-1986, MIB 20.00
Barbie Superstar Stage, 1976-1986, MIB 45.00
Barbie Thermos Bottle, 1961, M 15.00
Barbie Travel Case, 1961, M 10.00
Barbie Travelin' Trailor, 1976-1986, MIB 50.00
Barbie's Horse, Dancer 65.00
Beach Party Play Set, w/doll, 1976-1986, M 50.00
Clothes, Barbie Fur Collection, France, 1976-1986, MIB, ea ...35.00
Clothes, Bicentennial Dress, 1976-1986, M 40.00
Clothes, Blazing Fire, M 30.00
Clothes, Dreamtime, #1909, (1963 booklet) 20.00
Clothes, Drum Majorette, #0875, (1963 booklet) 45.00
Clothes, Enchanted Evening, #983, (#2 1958 booklet) 60.00
Clothes, Evening Gala, #1660, (1965 booklet) 60.00
Clothes, Fashion Fantasy, M 15.00
Clothes, Flower Girl, #1904, (1962 booklet), MIB 30.00
Clothes, Fun at the Fair, #1624, (1964 booklet) 45.00

Clothes, Garden Wedding, #1658, (1965 booklet) 30.00
Clothes, Golden Glory, #1645, (1965 booklet) 40.00
Clothes, Heavenly Holidays, Series I, 1976-1986, MIB 25.00
Clothes, Ice Empress, M 35.00
Clothes, Ken Suit Collection, MIB, ea 35.00
Clothes, Lace Pace, #1216, (1967 booklet) 40.00
Clothes, Orange Blossom, #987, (1962 booklet) 25.00
Clothes, Outdoor Life, #1637, (1964 booklet) 30.00
Clothes, Reception Line, #1654, (1965 booklet) 45.00
Clothes, Riding in the Park, #1668, (1965 booklet) 45.00
Clothes, Sheath Sensation, #986, (1961 booklet) 20.00
Clothes, Ship Ahoy, #1918, (1964 booklet) 30.00
Clothes, Springtime Magic, MIB 25.00
Clothes, Sugar Plum Fairy, 1976-1986, MIB 45.00
Clothes, Summer Job, #1422, (1965 booklet) 60.00
Dallas, Barbie's Horse, Germany, 1976-1986, MIB 60.00
Dance Sensation Barbie Gift Set, 1985, MIB 20.00
Francie Mod a Go-Go Bedroom Furniture, by Susy Goose, M ..200.00
Happy Birthday Barbie Gift Set, 1985, MIB 40.00
Honey, Skipper's Horse, 1976-1986, MIB 20.00
Living Barbie Action Accents Gift Set, #1585, 1970 ....350.00
Pink & Pretty Barbie Gift Set, England 100.00
Pretty Changes Barbie & Beauty Barbie's Dog Gift Set, MIB ..175.00
Skipper 'N Skooter Double Bunk Beds & Ladder 45.00
Skooter Cut 'N Button Gift Set, 1967 Sears X-mas catalog 150.00
Walking Jamie Strollin' in Style Gift Set, #1247, 1972 ....300.00
Wonderful World of Barbie Store Display, M 300.00

Belton

Concave head, 2 or 3 hole, EX bsk, o/c or c/m w/wig, 10" ...1,000.00
Concave head, 2 or 3 hole, EX bsk, o/c or c/m w/wig, 13" ...1,300.00
Concave head, 2 or 3 hole, EX bsk, o/c or c/m w/wig, 15" ...1,600.00
Concave head, 2 or 3 hole, EX bsk, o/c or c/m w/wig, 16" ...1,700.00
Concave head, 2 or 3 hole, EX bsk, o/c or c/m w/wig, 17" ...1,900.00
Concave head, 2 or 3 hole, EX bsk, o/c or c/m w/wig, 20" ..2,200.00
Concave head, 2 or 3 hole, EX bsk, o/c or c/m w/wig, 22" ..2,300.00
Concave head, 2 or 3 hole, EX bsk, o/c or c/m w/wig, 23" ..2,500.00
Concave head, 2 or 3 hole, EX bsk, o/c or c/m w/wig, 26" ...3,000.00
Concave head, 2 or 3 hole, EX bsk, o/c or c/m w/wig, 8" 625.00

Bru

Closed mouth, all kid body, bisque lower arms; Bru, 16" 6,800.00
Closed mouth, all kid body, bisque lower arms; Bru, 18" 7,600.00
Closed mouth, all kid body, bisque lower arms; Bru, 21" 8,500.00
Closed mouth, all kid body, bisque lower arms; Bru, 26" ...10,000.00
Closed mouth, kid/wood, bsk lower arms; Bru Jne, 12" 6,200.00
Closed mouth, kid/wood, bsk lower arms; Bru Jne, 14" 7,600.00
Closed mouth, kid/wood, bsk lower arms; Bru Jne, 16" 9,000.00
Closed mouth, kid/wood, bsk lower arms; Bru Jne, 20" 15,000.00
Closed mouth, kid/wood, bsk lower arms; Bru Jne, 25" 18,000.00
Closed mouth, kid/wood, bsk lower arms; Bru Jne, 28" 22,000.00
Closed mouth, kid/wood, bsk lower arms; Bru Jne, 32" 30,000.00
Closed mouth, mk Bru, circle dot, 16" 10,500.00
Closed mouth, mk Bru, circle dot, 19" 14,500.00
Closed mouth, mk Bru, circle dot, 23" 19,000.00
Closed mouth, mk Bru, circle dot, 26" 22,000.00
Open mouth, comp walker's body, throws kisses, 18" 3,800.00
Open mouth, comp walker's body, throws kisses, 22" 4,200.00
Open mouth, comp walker's body, throws kisses, 26" 5,600.00
Open mouth, nursing (Bebe), high color, late SFBJ, 12" ...1,400.00
Open mouth, nursing (Bebe), high color, late SFBJ, 15" ...2,400.00
Open mouth, nursing (Bebe), high color, late SFBJ, 18" 3,000.00

Open mouth, nursing Bru (Bebe), early, EX bsk, 12"	4,400.00
Open mouth, nursing Bru (Bebe), early, EX bsk, 15"	6,500.00
Open mouth, nursing Bru (Bebe), early, EX bsk, 18"	8,200.00
Open mouth, socket head on compo; Bru, R, 14", EX bsk	4,500.00
Open mouth, socket head on compo; Bru, R, 17", EX bsk	4,900.00
Open mouth, socket head on compo; Bru, R, 22", EX bsk	6,300.00
Open mouth, socket head on compo; Bru, R, 25", EX bsk	7,300.00
Open mouth, socket head on compo; Bru, R, 28", EX bsk	8,000.00

Japanese, blk or blonde hair, mk or unmk, RpC, 1910-20s, 17"	165.00
Man or Boy, glass eyes, side part, RpC, 14"	950.00
Man or Boy, pnt eyes, side part, RpC, 14", EX	700.00
Man or Boy, pnt eyes, side part, RpC, 16"	1,100.00
Peg wood body, early hairdo, 16", EX	2,800.00
Pet Name, molded shirtwaist w/name on front, RpC, '05, 19"	275.00
Pet Name, molded shirtwaist w/name on front, RpC, '05, 8"	115.00
Pierced Ears, various hairstyles, RpC, 14"	450.00
Pierced Ears, various hairstyles, RpC, 18"	700.00
Snood/Combs, any appl hair decor, RpC, 14"	450.00
Snood/Combs, any appl hair decor, RpC, 17"	650.00
Spill Curls, w/or w/out head band, RpC, 14"	300.00
Spill Curls, w/or w/out head band, RpC, 22"	650.00
Wood body, articulated/slim hips, RpC, 1840s-1850s, 12"	950.00
Wood body, articulated/slim hips, RpC, 1840s-1850s, 17"	2,100.00
Wood body, jtd hips, covered-wagon hairdo, 1840s-50s, 12"	950.00
Wood body, jtd hips, covered-wagon hairdo, 1840s-50s, 15"	1,900.00

Bru Brevete, swivel head with paperweight eyes, pierced ears, human hair wig, kid body, 16", $9,000.00.

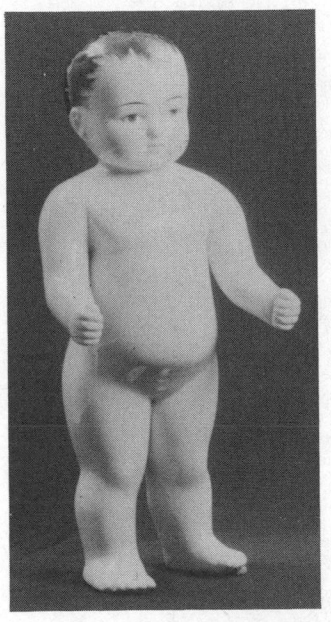

Frozen Charlie, 16", $595.00.

China, Unmarked

Adelina Patti, center part, curls at temples, 1860s, 14"	300.00
Adelina Patti, center part, curls at temples, 1860s, 18"	425.00
Adelina Patti, center part, curls at temples, 1860s, 22"	565.00
Biedermeier or Bald Head, takes wig, RpC, 14"	800.00
Biedermeier or Bald Head, takes wig, RpC, 20"	1,100.00
Brown Eyes (pnt), any hairstyle or date, 16"	700.00
Brown Eyes (pnt), any hairstyle or date, 20"	1,000.00
Common Hairdo, blonde or blk hair, RpC, after 1905, 12"	100.00
Common Hairdo, blonde or blk hair, RpC, after 1905, 23"	235.00
Common Hairdo, blonde or blk hair, RpC, after 1905, 8"	65.00
Covered Wagon style, sausage curls, RpC, 1840s-70s, 12"	325.00
Covered Wagon style, sausage curls, RpC, 1840s-70s, 24"	700.00
Curly Top, loose ringlet curls, RpC, 1845-1860s, 16"	550.00
Curly Top, loose ringlet curls, RpC, 1845-1860s, 20"	675.00
Dolly Madison, modeled ribbon/bow, RpC, 1870-1880s, 14"	250.00
Dolly Madison, modeled ribbon/bow, RpC, 1870-1880s, 18"	385.00
Dolly Madison, modeled ribbon/bow, RpC, 1870-1880s, 21"	450.00
Flat top, blk hair, mid-part/short curls, RpC, ca 1860, 17"	225.00
Flat top, blk hair, mid-part/short curls, RpC, ca 1860, 20"	285.00
Glass Eyes, various hairstyles, RpC, 1840s-1870s, 14"	1,500.00
Glass Eyes, various hairstyles, RpC, 1840s-1870s, 22"	2,800.00
Japanese, blk or blonde hair, mk or unmk, RpC, 1910-20s, 14"	125.00

Cloth

Amish, Swartzentrauber type, button eyes, 1880s, OC, 13"	400.00
Art Fabric Mills, pat Feb 13, 1886, OC, 24x11x4", EX	195.00
Blk baby, wooly hair, fingers, button eyes, OC, ca 1900, 21"	265.00
Blk lady, sock body, MOP button eyes, earrings, 1900s, 14"	125.00
Boy, knit, curly hair, fingers, OC, ca 1900, 20½"	150.00
Clown, yarn hair, stitched features, OC, 1900, 11"	185.00
Dodgio dancer, handmade, fancy costume/shoes, 1920s, 27"	400.00
Rag, cotton stuffed, pnt face, calico dress, 1880s, 18"	165.00
Rag, inked features, swim clothes, 1880s, 13", EX	100.00
Rag, old woman's face, button eyes, mohair wig, 1900, 11½"	185.00

Effanbee

Bernard Fleischaker and Hugo Baum became business partners in 1910; and, after two difficult years of finding toys to buy and a retail market to sell them in, they decided to manufacture dolls of their own. Their lovely dolls were a decided success largely because of their dedication to their work and the mutual trust and respect they held for each other. This is reflected in the Effanbee trademark — Eff stands for Fleischaker and bee for Baum. The company still exists today.

Alice, 1958, 15"	165.00

Amanda, 1982	55.00
America's Children, o/m, 1936-1940, 15", ea	650.00
Americana Collection, 1975-1977, ea	55.00
Antique Bride, 1979-1980	60.00
Baby Beauties, 1973, ea	55.00
Baby Bright Eyes, 1916, 11"	110.00
Baby Catherine, 1918, 12"	130.00
Baby Lisa by Astri, 1980-1983	80.00
Bedtime Story Collection, 1972, ea	55.00
Betty Ann, 1938, 15"	225.00
Betty Brite, 1933, 16"	145.00
Bicentennial Boy & Girl, 1976, ea	125.00
Bottle Tot, 1934, 16"	165.00
Brigette, 1980	70.00
Buckingham Palace, 1982-1983	60.00
Button Nose Betty, 1943, 8"	175.00
Candy Ann, 1954, 20"	100.00
Chantilly, 1981	70.00
Cinderella, 1952, 18"	250.00
Convent Garden, 1981	68.00
Cream Puff Collection, 1980, ea	55.00
Cuddle-up, 1953, 20"	65.00
Currier & Ives Collection, 1978-1980, ea	65.00
Daffy Dot Collection, 1972, ea	55.00
Dolly Dumpling, 1918, 14"	165.00
DyDee Ellen, 1940, 15"	135.00
DyDee Louise, 1940, 20"	195.00
Fairy Princess, 1935, 9"	250.00
Fall, 1976-1980, ea	70.00
Four Seasons, 1976-1980, ea	70.00
Gibson Girl, 1977-1979	75.00
Granny's Corner Collection, 1975-1976, ea	60.00
Half Pint Boy & Girl, 1980, ea	45.00
Happy Boy, 1959-1965, 11"	70.00
Honey Walker, 1949-1955, 16"	165.00
Honeybunch, 1923, 16"	185.00
Jan Carol, 1929, 24"	250.00
Laughing Marietta, 1912, 12"	175.00
Lil' Sweetie, 1967, 16"	100.00
Little Boy Blue, 1912, 12"	125.00
Little Lady Birthday Doll, 1941, 21"	285.00
Liza Lee, puppet, 1937, 14"	100.00
Lovums, 1928, 15"	275.00
Margie, 1921, 16"	150.00
Martha Washington, 1976-1977	80.00
Mary Jane, 1960-1962, 30"	130.00
Mint Julip, 1976	95.00
Miss Holland, in trunk, 1977	100.00
Most Happy Family, 1957-1961, set	150.00
My Baby, 1963-1965, 14"	40.00
My Fair Baby, 1958-1969, 14"	50.00
Nanette, 1981	68.00
Noma Electronic Talker, 1949-1951, 30"	150.00
Opal, 1981	95.00
Over the Rainbow, 1973, ea	55.00
Papa's Pet, 1979-1980	65.00
Patsy Ann, 1929, 19"	300.00
Patsy Jr, 1930, 11"	250.00
Patsykins, 1930, 11"	250.00
Peaches Baby, 1965-1966, 15"	55.00
Polka Dottie, 1954, 12"	185.00
Princess, 1976-1978	80.00
Regal Heirloom Collection, 1976-1978, ea	95.00
Robin Hood, 1978	80.00

Romper Babies, 1918, 15"	145.00
Rose Mary, 1927, 18"	225.00
Ruby, 1980	95.00
Saratoga, 1981	50.00
Ship Ahoy Collection, 1979, ea	60.00
Soft 'N Sweet Collection, 1979, ea	55.00
Spring in Yellow, 1976	100.00
Strolling in the Park, 1982-1983	55.00
Susan B Anthony, 1980, 15"	175.00
Sweetie Pie, 1938-1948, 14"	135.00
Tango Kitties, 1914, 12"	125.00
Teddy Bears, 1919, 12"	400.00
Tintair, 1951-1952, 14"	225.00
Trottie Trulife, 1921, 20"	185.00
Victorian Lady, 1976-1977, ea	95.00
Violette, 1977	80.00
Winkie, baby, 1963, 10"	45.00
Winter, 1976-1980, ea	70.00

Half Dolls

Half dolls, lovely porcelain figures awaiting attachment to secure bases, were never meant to be objects of play. Most of these lovely ladies were firmly sewn into pincushion bases that were beautifully decorated and served as the skirt of their gown. Other skirts were actually covers for items on milady's dressing table. Some were used for parasol or brush handles or for tops to candy containers or perfume bottles. Most popular from 1900 to about 1930, they will most often be found marked with the country of their origin — Bavaria, Germany, France, and Japan. You may also find some fine quality pieces marked Goebel, Dressel and Kester, and Heubach.

Numbers in the listings below refer to *The Collectors Encyclopedia of Half Dolls* by Frieda Marion and Norma Werner, available at your local bookstore or from Collector Books.

#A188 Germany, Empress Eugenie hat, gray curls, 4"	50.00
#0/6 France, movable arms, bsk, pnt eyes, orig wig, 5"	325.00
#10002/13273 Germany, Madame Pompadour, 6¼"	140.00
#1038, Theda Bara, att: Germany, 4"	185.00
#104 Japan, holds fans, pk dress, fancy hairdo, 3¾"	42.50
#11491, hands away, gray pompadour, 5¼x2½"	300.00
#1256, lady in turban, 1 arm near chest, 2nd near waist, 4"	85.00
#13273, arms away, fancy hairdo, 6x3½"	350.00
#13588, flapper, arms at neck, rose bodice, 3¾"	85.00
#14336 DEP, nude, arms away, blonde hair in bun w/rose, 4"	225.00
#14974 Germany, child, pk derby hat, w/bouquet, 1⅝"	85.00
#15009 MIG, nude, mohair wig over bald pate	75.00
#154, flapper, fur collar, bl hat, 5"	250.00
#15828, full figure, bl suit, 3½"	125.00
#16811 Germany, nude, arms extended above head, 4¼"	175.00
#21632 Germany, child w/side curls, red/bl dress, 2½"	100.00
#22672, maiden wearing golden crown, 3½"	125.00
#27411 E&R Germany, Madame Pompadour, yel dress, hat, 7"	300.00
#32, compo w/bsk arms, blonde hair, 3½"	85.00
#3305, pk glaze, long gray curls, detailed hands, 2⅝"	65.00
#4367½ Germany, arms away, mohair wig, lace shawl, 3½"	125.00
#5105, Princess de Lamballe, snuff box in hands	400.00
#5169 Germany, blonde mohair wig/red ribbon, bl eyes, 2½"	400.00
#5275 Germany, arms away, gray hair, 5⅛"	225.00
#5670, Germany, wht glaze, holds gr fan, sleeveless dress, 3"	80.00
#7800, tuxedo-type outfit, flower on lapel, hat, 5"	225.00
#9093 Germany, full figure in gr harem pajamas, 4⅜"	100.00
D-395, nude, porc, mauve flower in hand, brush marks	265.00
Dressel & Kister, child, both arms away, M/W-147-302	265.00
Dressel & Kister, hands out, holds pk rose, gray hair, 3⅞"	225.00

Flapper, w/beret, on fancy cushion 30.00
Germany, bsk bathing beauty, colorless, suit molded on, 3¼" . . .70.00
Germany, flapper, orange/wht hat, bl dress w/yel yoke, 4" 45.00
Germany, holds book at waist, lav/wht bodice, 1⅞" 30.00
Germany, nude, plaster, gold wig, 3½" 40.00
Germany B, perfume bottle, mirror in hand, bl, 6¾" 125.00
Goebel, nude, carries plate on head .350.00
Heubach, coquette, jtd arms, hair band, intaglio eyes, 2¾" 200.00
Japan, blonde hair, gr bodice, 3" 30.00
Japan, dog's head, 2¼" 22.00
Japan, yel hair, pk bodice, 3½" 32.00
Nippon, flapper, gr bodice/orange plumes, hat, 2⅝" 20.00
Nippon, Kewpie head on orig lamb's wool puff, 2" 50.00
Schneider, blk ribbon on neck, rose in hair, 5¼" 185.00
Schneider, nude, hands upraised, blonde hair, 3" 90.00
Unmk, arms away, auburn hair/dress, pincushion, 3½" 125.00
Unmk, arms away, flapper hairdo, orig pincushion & ft, 7½" . . .225.00
Unmk, blonde hair, teal dress/gold necklace, pnt features, 3½" . .50.00
Unmk, gr/wht bodice, gray hair/pk bow, pincushion, 3¼" 100.00
Unmk, lav bodice, holding flowers, pincushion, 3½" 100.00
Unmk, Mardi Gras girl, hands to waist, dbl ruffles, 5" 40.00
Unmk, Marie Antoinette style, nude, brn eyes, pnt face, 4½" . .100.00
Unmk, nude, holds fan, pk bow in hair, flared base, 2¼" 45.00

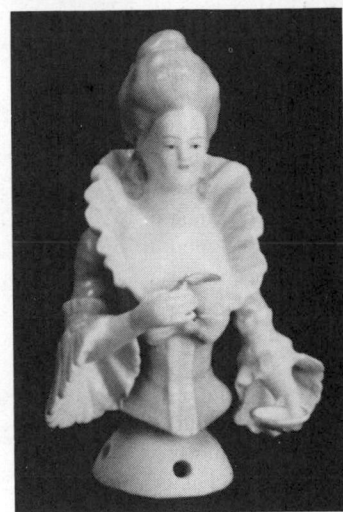

**Unmarked German half doll, 4½",
$125.00.**

Handwerck

#109, bjtd, orig wig, OC, 30" 900.00
#119, brn o/c eyes, RpC, 24" 600.00
#119-10½, o/c eyes, o/m w/6 teeth, jtd compo, 20" 450.00
#189, bl o/c eyes, RpC, 15" 575.00
#79-10, o/c eyes, p/e, jtd compo, OC, 17½" 500.00
Child, bsk, bjtd, o/c or set eyes, after 1885, RpC, 16" 325.00
Heinrich, bsk SkHd, bjtd, o/m, p/e, orig wig, 30" 900.00

Heubach

#10633, Dainty Dorothy, o/m, glass eyes, RpC, 16" 500.00
#5636, laughing child, compo, intaglio eyes, RpC, 10" 1,000.00
#5730, Santa, child body, o/c eyes, jtd, 20" 2,500.00
#6790, boy, intaglio eyes, c/m, OC, 12" 1,500.00
#7603, intaglio eyes, c/m, pnt hair, 12½" 425.00
#7604, laughing child, compo, glass eyes, 15" 1,200.00
#7604, laughing child, compo, intaglio eyes, 18" 1,600.00
#7622, pouty, bsk, molded hair, 16" 1,800.00
#7634, crying baby, o/c eyes, RpC, 15" 900.00

#7788, Coquette, tilted head, intaglio eyes, RpC, 12" 800.00
#7845, boy, bsk ShHd, kid body, 20" 700.00
#7977, Baby Stuart, bsk bonnet, glass eyes, RpC, 12" 1,500.00
#7977, Baby Stuart, bsk bonnet, intaglio eyes, RpC, 12" 1,000.00
#8192, o/c eyes, o/m, 5-pc body, 9" .450.00
#8774, Whistling Jim, eyes to side, puckered mouth, 16" 1,300.00
Boy, ShHd, o/c smiling mouth, cloth w/bsk hands & head, 15" .800.00
Pouty baby, bsk head, o/m, molded hair, 8" 350.00

Heubach-Koppelsdorf

#250, bl o/c eyes, o/m w/4 teeth, OC, 8" 165.00
Queen Louise, Germany, SkHd, 1910, 22" 525.00
Queen Louise, 100, Germany, SkHd, 1910, 12" 300.00
Queen Louise, 100, SkHd, 1910, 18½" 425.00
Queen Louise, 315, Germany 12, SkHd, 27" 850.00
Rosebud, A 4/0 M, MIG, ShHd, 1902, 15" 350.00
Roseland, AOM, 1910, 18" 475.00
Sunshine, 1910, Germany, ShHd, 24" 525.00
Wonderful Alice, DRGM 377439, SkHd, fur eyebrows, 26" . . .600.00

Horsman

Baby Bumps, compo w/cloth body, molded hair, unmk, 10" . . .165.00
Blink, compo w/cloth body, closed eyes, RpC, 13" 265.00
Jeanie, compo, o/c eyes, c/m, molded hair, RpC, 14" 185.00
Toddler, SkHd, glass eyes, orig wig, RpC, 16" 350.00
Tynie Baby, bsk head, o/c eyes, molded hair, RpC, 12" 675.00

Ideal

Baby Jane, compo, o/c eyes, o/m w/teeth, orig wig, RpC, 18" . . .225.00
Betsy Wetsy, compo w/rubber body, molded hair, 14" 120.00
Deanna Durbin, compo, o/c eyes, o/m w/teeth, OC, 14" 350.00
Jiminy Cricket, compo & wood, 9" 200.00
Princess Mary, plastic/vinyl, ballgown/wrist tags, 1952, 21" 200.00
Sara Ann, hp, o/c eyes, c/m, jtd, OC, 14" 150.00
Toni, Red Cross Nurse, hp, o/c eyes, orig wig, OC, 15" 225.00

Jumeau

Emile Jumeau took over his father's doll company sometime in the 1870s. He brought many new innovations and ideas to the business. One fascination Jumeau had concerned dolls' eyes and led to the patents for eyelids that dropped over the eye itself; a second type allowed the doll to 'sleep.' Jumeau's distaste for German dolls is apparent in the booklets that were packaged with his dolls. These booklets referred to the German dolls as cheap and ugly and and as having 'stupid' faces. In reality, these less-expensive dolls were the downfall of the French doll manufacturers, and in 1899 the Jumeau company had to combine with several others in an effort to save the French doll industry from the German competition.

Closed mouth, mk EJ (incised) Jumeau, 10" 4,800.00
Closed mouth, mk EJ (incised) Jumeau, 14" 5,200.00
Closed mouth, mk EJ (incised) Jumeau, 16" 5,800.00
Closed mouth, mk EJ (incised) Jumeau, 19" 6,200.00
Closed mouth, mk EJ (incised) Jumeau, 21" 6,700.00
Closed mouth, mk Tete Jumeau, 10" 3,200.00
Closed mouth, mk Tete Jumeau, 14" 2,300.00
Closed mouth, mk Tete Jumeau, 16" 2,600.00
Closed mouth, mk Tete Jumeau, 19" 3,000.00
Closed mouth, mk Tete Jumeau, 21" 3,400.00
Closed mouth, mk Tete Jumeau, 23" 3,800.00
Closed mouth, mk Tete Jumeau, 25" 3,900.00

Closed mouth, mk Tete Jumeau, 28" 4,500.00
Closed mouth, mk Tete Jumeau, 30" 5,500.00
Depose/Tete Jumeau, swivel head, p/e, long curls, 18" 5,000.00
Depose/Tete Jumeau, swivel head, p/e, long curls, 28" 6,400.00
E 6 J/Jumeau, swivel head, inset eyes, kid body, 16" 5,800.00
E 6 J/Jumeau, swivel head, inset eyes, kid body, 20" 6,600.00
EJ/Depose Brevete, swivel head/inset eyes, 'mama/papa,' 16" .5,800.00
Jumeau 1907, SkHd, appl ears, o/m, 18" 1,700.00
Jumeau 1907, swivel head, o/m, o/c eyes, p/e, 18" 1,700.00
Jumeau 1907, swivel head, o/m, o/c eyes, p/e, 23" 2,200.00
Jumeau 1909, swivel head, o/m, inset eyes, p/e, 21" 2,000.00

Jumeau/Medallie D'or/ Paris, paperweight eyes, pierced ears, closed mouth, 11", $2,200.00.

Long face, c/m, 21" 14,000.00
Long face, c/m, 30" 20,000.00
Mechanical/musical, cm, p/e, pwt eyes, hh, 12" on 4" box . . .3,800.00
Open mouth, mk Tete Jumeau, 10" 995.00
Open mouth, mk Tete Jumeau, 14" .1,400.00
Open mouth, mk Tete Jumeau, 16" .1,600.00
Open mouth, mk Tete Jumeau, 19" .1,900.00
Open mouth, mk Tete Jumeau, 21" .2,400.00
Open mouth, mk Tete Jumeau, 23" .2,800.00
Open mouth, mk Tete Jumeau, 25" .4,000.00
Open mouth, mk Tete Jumeau, 28" .4,800.00
Open mouth, mk Tete Jumeau, 30" .5,200.00
Open mouth, mk 1907 Jumeau, 14" .1,400.00
Open mouth, mk 1907 Jumeau, 17" .1,700.00
Open mouth, mk 1907 Jumeau, 20" .2,000.00
Open mouth, mk 1907 Jumeau, 25" .2,500.00
Open mouth, mk 1907 Jumeau, 28" .3,000.00
Open mouth, mk 1907 Jumeau, 32" .3,400.00
Phonograph in body, o/m, 20" 3,400.00
Phonograph in body, o/m, 25" 4,800.00
Portrait Jumeau, c/m, 16" 5,200.00
Portrait Jumeau, c/m, 20" 6,200.00

Kammer and Reinhardt

#101, boy or girl w/glass eyes, 12" .1,600.00
#101, boy or girl w/glass eyes, 16" .4,200.00
#101, boy or girl w/glass eyes, 20" .4,600.00
#101, boy or girl w/glass eyes, 9" 1,300.00
#101, boy or girl w/pnt eyes, 12" 1,200.00
#101, boy or girl w/pnt eyes, 16" 2,400.00
#101, boy or girl w/pnt eyes, 20" 3,200.00
#101, boy or girl w/pnt eyes, 9" 1,200.00
#109, rare, w/glass eyes, 15" 7,800.00
#109, rare, w/glass eyes, 18" 12,000.00
#109, rare, w/pnt eyes, 15" 6,600.00
#109, rare, w/pnt eyes, 18" 7,800.00
#112, rare, w/glass eyes, 15" 8,000.00
#112, rare, w/glass eyes, 18" 12,000.00
#112, rare, w/pnt eyes, 15" 5,500.00
#112, rare, w/pnt eyes, 18" 8,800.00
#114, rare, w/glass eyes, 15" 4,800.00
#114, rare, w/glass eyes, 18" 6,000.00
#114, rare, w/pnt eyes, 15" 2,800.00
#114, rare, w/pnt eyes, 18" 4,000.00
#115, closed mouth, 15" 2,500.00
#115, closed mouth, 18" 4,500.00
#115, closed mouth, 22" 5,000.00
#115, open mouth, 15" 1,300.00
#115, open mouth, 18" 1,900.00
#115, open mouth, 22" 2,500.00
#115a, closed mouth, 15" 2,500.00
#115a, closed mouth, 18" 4,500.00
#115a, closed mouth, 22" 5,000.00
#115a, open mouth, 15" 1,300.00
#115a, open mouth, 18" 1,900.00
#115a, open mouth, 22" 2,300.00
#116, closed mouth, 15" 2,000.00
#116, closed mouth, 18" 2,300.00
#116, closed mouth, 22" 2,900.00
#116, open mouth, 15" 1,300.00
#116, open mouth, 18" 1,900.00
#116, open mouth, 22" 2,300.00
#116a, closed mouth, 15" 2,000.00
#116a, closed mouth, 18" 2,300.00
#116a, closed mouth, 22" 2,900.00
#116a, open mouth, 15" 1,300.00
#116a, open mouth, 18" 1,900.00
#116a, open mouth, 22" 2,000.00
#117, closed mouth, 18" 4,200.00
#117, closed mouth, 24" 5,600.00
#117, closed mouth, 30" 6,800.00
#117a, closed mouth, 18" 4,200.00
#117a, closed mouth, 24" 5,600.00
#117a, closed mouth, 30" 6,800.00
Dolly face, open mouth, mold #400-403-109, etc, 16" 550.00
Dolly face, open mouth, mold #400-403-109, etc, 20" 650.00
Dolly face, open mouth, mold #400-403-109, etc, 24" 750.00
Dolly face, open mouth, mold #400-403-109, etc, 28" 875.00
Dolly face, open mouth, mold #400-403-109, etc, 38" 2,300.00
Dolly face, open mouth, mold #400-403-109, etc, 40" 2,500.00

Kestner

Johannes D. Kestner made buttons at a lathe in a Waltershausen factory in the early 1800s. When this line of work failed, he used the same lathe to turn doll bodies. Thus the Kestner company began. It was one of the few German manufacturers to make the complete doll. By 1860 with the purchase of a porcelain factory, Kestner made doll heads of china and bisque as well as wax, worked-in-leather, celluloid, and cardboard. In 1895 the Kestner trademark of a crown with streamers was registered in the U.S. and a year later in Germany. Kestner felt the mark was appropriate since he referred to himself as the 'king of German dollmakers.'

A, ShHd, o/m, MIG/Kestner, 19" 550.00
A/5, ShHd, o/c mouth, 23" 2,400.00
B/6, ShHd, kid w/bsk ½-arms, o/m w/teeth, o/c eyes, 19" 550.00
B/6, SkHd, jtd compo, o/m w/2 teeth, set eyes, 22" 600.00
Bergmann, SkHd, for CM Bergmann, o/m, JDK/CM, 14" 400.00
Bergmann, SkHd, for CM Bergmann, o/m, JDK/CM, 17" 475.00
Bergmann, SkHd, for CM Bergmann, o/m, JDK/CM, 20" 550.00
Century Doll Co, flanged closed dome, c/m, 15" 675.00
D/8, SkHd & ShHd, kid w/bsk ½-arms, c/m, 15" 950.00
E/9, ShHd, o/m, MIG, 26" 850.00
E/9, SkHd, o/m, 1892, 26" 850.00
G/11, SkHd, brn, o/m, 16" 500.00
G/8, trn ShHd, o/m, MI/JDK, 19" 500.00
Grace Putnam, bsk, 1-pc, pnt eyes, 10/10/COPR, 6" 650.00
Grace Putnam, bsk, 1-pc body & head, 1/COPR, 1923, 6" 650.00
Grace Putnam, Bye-Lo baby, 6 12/Copr, 1927, 16" 525.00
H1/2, ShHd, o/m, 23" 625.00
H/12, SkHd, o/c mouth, JDK, 1892, 23" 2,300.00
Handwerck, SkHd, made for Handwerck, o/m, JDK/H/12, 23" .625.00
Handwerck, SkHd, made for Handwerck, o/m, JDK/H/12, 27" .750.00
I/13, SkHd, o/m, JDK, 1892, 16" 450.00
I/13, SkHd, o/m, JDK, 1892, 26" 700.00
J/13, SkHd, o/m, 1896, 27" 750.00
JDK, bsk head on celluloid, R Gummi Co, turtlemark, 18" 600.00
K/12, SkHd, made for Century, o/c mouth, molded hair, 21" .2,000.00
Kewpie, bsk, Rose O'Neill/10 945G, 1913, 8" 350.00
KK/14 1/2d, o/m, 1896, 26" 700.00
L 1/2/15 1/2, SkHd, c/m, 14" 1,600.00
L/15, SkHd, c/m, 21" 2,100.00
L/15, SkHd, swivel, ShPl, c/m, 21" 2,100.00
L/3, ShHd, o/c mouth w/molded teeth, 23" 2,300.00
N/17, SkHd, o/m, 1892, 17" 475.00
SkHd, Oriental, o/m, JDK/Kestner, 14" 4,500.00
SkHd, pnt eyes, JDK/3 4/0, 8" 500.00
Trn ShHd, Kidoline w/bsk ½-arms, o/c eyes, G/MIG, 16" 650.00
10, SkHd, bsk ShPl, c/m, 21" 2,000.00
10, SkHd, o/c mouth w/2 teeth, JDK/MIG, 12" 600.00
10/G, SkHd, c/m, JDK, 1912, 12" 600.00
1070, SkHd, o/m, G11/237 15/JDK Jr 1914 HILDA/GES, 16".3,000.00
11, SkHd, o/c mouth, pnt eyes to side, JDK/MIG, 11" 600.00
12, SkHd, 5-pc baby, o/c eyes, o/m/2 teeth, JDK/MIG, 15" ...575.00
13, SkHd, o/m, JDK/MIG, 18" 500.00
143, ShHd, kid w/bsk ½-arms, o/m, 17" 675.00
145, ShHd, kid w/bsk ½-arms, o/c mouth, 15" 1,200.00
145, SkHd, c/m, MI/O/G/18, 14" 1,100.00
145, SkHd, c/m, 143/4/0/JDK, 11" 600.00
146, SkHd, swivel, on ShPl, o/m, JDK, 18" 550.00
147, trn ShHd, o/m, JDK, 25" 675.00
148, SkHd, kid w/bsk ½-arms, o/m, 7 1/2, 18" 450.00
148, ShHd, kid w/bsk ½-arms, o/m, 7 1/2, 21" 500.00
150.1, bsk, Kestner seal on body, 8" 350.00
151, SkHd, 5-pc baby, intaglio eyes, o/m/teeth, MIG/5, 12" ...425.00
151, SkHd, 5-pc baby, intaglio eyes, o/m/teeth, MIG/5, 16" ...575.00
151, SkHd, 5-pc baby, intaglio eyes, o/m/teeth, MIG/5, 20" ...675.00
152, SkHd, made for Wolf, o/m, LW & CO 12, 1916, 20" 675.00
154, SkHd/ShHd, kid w/bsk ½-arms, o/m/teeth, DEP, 14" 450.00
154, SkHd/ShHd, kid w/bsk ½-arms, o/m/teeth, DEP, 17" 600.00

154, SkHd/ShHd, kid w/bsk ½-arms, o/m/teeth, DEP, 20" 675.00
154, SkHd/ShHd, kid w/bsk ½-arms, o/m/teeth, DEP, 26" 850.00
16, SkHd, o/m, JDK/MIG, 21" 575.00
16/GES#1, ShHd, o/c mouth, molded boy's hair, 16" 1,800.00
167, SkHd, jtd compo, o/m, p/e, F 1/2/MI6 1/2 /G, 16" 450.00
167, SkHd, jtd compo, o/m, p/e, F 1/2/MI6 1/2/G, 20" 550.00
168, SkHd, o/m, MID/G7, 26" 700.00
169, SkHd, jtd compo, c/m, o/c eyes, B 1/2/BI6 1/2G, 16" ...1,800.00
169, SkHd, jtd compo, c/m, o/c eyes, B 1/2/BI6 1/2G, 18" ...2,500.00
171, SkHd, jtd compo, o/m, o/c eyes, 'Daisy,' F/M110, 15" ...425.00
171, SkHd, jtd compo, o/m, o/c eyes, 'Daisy,' F/M110, 18" ...550.00
171, SkHd, jtd compo, o/m, o/c eyes, 'Daisy,' F/M110, 22" ...600.00
172, ShHd, ball, kid fashion, bsk arms, c/m, p/e, 14" 1,600.00
180 12/Ox/Crown seal, SkHd, o/m, 16" 450.00
201, ShHd, celluloid on kid, o/m, set eyes/lashes, JDK, 19" ...425.00
211, SkHd, 5-pc baby, o/c mouth, o/c eyes, MI10/G/JDK, 12" ..500.00
211, SkHd, 5-pc baby, o/c mouth, o/c eyes, MI10/G/JDK, 15" ..675.00
215, SkHd, jtd compo, fur eyebrows, o/m, MI9/GJDK, 21" 575.00
217A/Kestner, bsk, c/m smile, googly pnt eyes, 12" 2,000.00
221/GES/GESCH, SkHd, c/m smile, googly eyes, G/JDK, 21".7,500.00
235, toddler, kid body, 16" 675.00
245, SkHd, 5-pc baby, G/MIG/11/JDK Jr/1914 Hilda, 14" ...2,600.00
245, SkHd, 5-pc baby, G/MIG/11/JDK Jr/1914 Hilda, 17" ...3,200.00
257, SkHd, 5-pc baby, o/m, G/JDK, 10" 400.00
257, SkHd, 5-pc baby, o/m, G/JDK, 16" 600.00
257, SkHd, 5-pc baby, o/m, G/JDK, 20" 800.00
257, SkHd, 5-pc baby, o/m, G/JDK, 24" 1,200.00
26, K&Co/JDK/MIG/81, 16" 425.00
270, SkHd, o/m, made for Carl Trautman, CP/39, 38" 2,400.00
639, trn ShHd, closed dome, c/m, G/6, 18" 700.00
7 1/2/B, ShHd, kid w/bsk ½-arms, o/m w/teeth, o/c eyes, 14" ...350.00

Lenci

Eleanora Scavani, separated from her husband who was in the service of Italy during WWI, found herself painfully alone after the death of her baby. With her brother as her partner, this talented artist began designing lovely felt-covered dolls with beautiful hand-painted features. These dolls became her children, and she regarded them as a tribute to her lost daughter.

Following the war, her husband returned and joined the firm as a partner. The Lenci firm (a name he used as a term of endearment for his wife) soon became well-known in the doll-making industry. Great care was taken in every detail. Characteristics of Lenci dolls include seamless, steam-molded felt heads, quality clothing, childishly plump bodies, and painted eyes that glance to the side. Fine mohair wigs were used, and the middle and fourth fingers were sewn together. Look for the factory stamp on the foot, though paper labels were also used. Dolls under 10" are known as mascots and usually sell for $125.00 to $150.00. The Lenci factory continues today, producing dolls of the same high quality.

Baby, jtd w/bent limbs, organdy dress/bonnet, 16", M 950.00
Boy & girl, molded/pnt features, leather oxfords, 17¼", pr ...850.00
Donald Duck Astronaut, holds wine bottle/map, 13¾", EX ..1,400.00
Girl, blonde hair/pnt features, red/brn/tan dress, 17" 850.00
Girl, brn glass eyes, no tag, all orig, 20½" 2,400.00
Girl in sailor dress, blonde wig, 1970s, boxed, 20", M 900.00
Glass eyes, braided bun, canvas-type body/limbs, 18" 1,200.00
Lady, blonde hair, mc dress, pk bonnet w/appl flowers, 37" ..2,000.00

Madame Alexander

Beatrice Alexander founded the Alexander Doll company in 1923 using a lovely doll that was designed after her daughter Mildred. With the help of her three sisters, the company prospered; and by the late 1950s there were three factories with over six hundred employees making Madame Alexander dolls. The company still produces these lovely dolls today.

Alice in Wonderland, compo, Little Betty, 9" 200.00
Amanda, Americana Group, hp, Wendy Ann, 1961, 8" 1,500.00
American Babies, cloth, 18" 500.00
Anna Ballerina, compo, Wendy Ann, 1940, 18" 700.00
Argentine Girl, hp, straight legs, 1976-1986, 8" 75.00
Aunt Betsy, cloth/felt, 1930s 600.00
Babs, hp, Maggie, 1949, 20" 475.00
Baby Betty, compo, 1935-1936, 10"-12" 175.00
Baby Clown, hp, pnt face, Wendy Ann, 1955, 8" 1,400.00
Baby Genius, all cloth, 1930s, 11" 300.00
Baby Jane, compo, 1935, 16" 700.00
Barbara Jane, cloth/vinyl, 1952, 29" 385.00
Betsy Ross, hp, bend knees, Wendy Ann, 1967-1972, 8" 125.00
Binnie Walker, hp, Cissy, 1954, 15" 175.00
Blue Boy, cloth, 16" 600.00
Brenda Starr, hp, 1964, 12" 200.00
Buck Rabbit, cloth/felt, 1930s 600.00
Butch, compo/cloth, 11"-12" 300.00
Camille, compo, Wendy Ann, 1938, 21" 1,600.00
Caroline, vinyl, w/dresses, 1961, 15" 350.00
Carrot Top, cloth, 1967, 21" 175.00
Chatterbox, plastic/vinyl, 1961, 24" 285.00
China, compo, Tiny Betty, 1936, 7" 175.00
Cinderella, compo, Tiny Betty, 1935, 7" 200.00
Civil War, hp, Margaret, 1953, 18" 800.00
Cleopatra, 1980-1985, 12" 70.00
Cookie, compo/cloth, 1938, 19" 275.00
Country Cousins, cloth, 10" 275.00
Cousin Grace, hp, bend knee walker, Wendy Ann, 1957, 8" .1,500.00
Curly Locks, hp, Wendy Ann, 1955, 8" 800.00
Davy Crockett Boy, hp, Wendy Ann, 1955, 8" 1,200.00
Debutant, hp, Maggie, 1953, 18" 800.00
Dicksie & Ducksie, cloth/felt, 1930s 475.00
Dilly Dally Sally, compo, Tiny Betty, 1937, 7" 175.00
Ding Dong Dell, compo, Tiny Betty, 1937, 7" 175.00
Elaine, hp, Cissy, 1954, 18" 800.00
Emily, cloth/felt, 1930s 550.00
Eva Lovelace, compo, Tiny Betty, 1935, 7" 200.00
Flowergirl, compo, Princess Elizabeth, 18" 400.00
France, compo, Tiny Betty, 1936, 7" 175.00
French Flowergirl, hp, Wendy Ann, 1956, 8" 600.00
Garden Party, hp, Margaret, 1953, 18" 800.00
Genius Baby, plastic/vinyl, flirty eyes, 1960-1961, 21" 150.00
Gidget, plastic/vinyl, Mary Ann, 1966, 14" 400.00
Girl on Flying Trapeze, cloth, pink satin tutu, 1951, 40" 550.00
Godey Bride, hp, Margaret, 14" 650.00
Godey Lady, hp, Margaret, 14" 750.00
Goldilocks, cloth, 1930s, 18" 550.00
Greek Girl, hp, bend knees, Wendy Ann, 1968-1972, 8" 125.00
Gretel, compo, Tiny Betty, 1937, 7" 175.00
Happy, cloth/vinyl, 1970, 20" .300.00
Hedy LaMarr, hp, Margaret, 1949, 17" 650.00
Hilda, Blk, compo, Margaret, 1946, 18" 750.00
Ice Skater, hp, Wendy Ann, 1954-1956, 8" 525.00
Irish, Cissette, 1963, 10" 1,200.00
Jack & Jill, compo, Tiny Betty, 1938-1939, 7" 175.00
Jane Withers, compo/cloth body, 1937, 17" 700.00
Janie, plastic/vinyl, 1960, 36" .400.00
Joanie, plastic/vinyl, 1960, 36" 425.00
Judy, hp/vinyl arms, Jacqueline, 1962, 21" 800.00

Kelly, hp, Lissy, 1959, 12" 425.00
Kitten, cloth/vinyl, 1962-1963, 14" 85.00
Kitty Baby, compo, 1941, 21" .265.00
Lady Churchill, hp, Margaret, 1953, 18" 750.00
Lazy Mary, compo, Tiny Betty, 1936, 7" 175.00
Little Bo Peep, compo, Tiny Betty, 1937, 7" 175.00
Little Emily, cloth, Dicken's character, 16" 600.00
Little Nell, cloth, Dicken's character, 16" 600.00
Littlest Kitten, vinyl, 1963, 8" .185.00
Lovey Dovey, vinyl baby, 1958, 19" 125.00
Lucy Bride, hp, Margaret, 14" .295.00

Madame Hendren, Whistling Rufus, ca 1926, 3½", $375.00.

Maggie Walker, hp, 1949, 15" .400.00
Marm Liza, compo, Wendy Ann, 1938, 21" 1,600.00
Mary Sunshine, plastic/vinyl, 1961, 15" 475.00
Melanie, hp/vinyl arms, Cissy, 1961, 21" 650.00
Mimi, in formal, 30" 750.00
Nancy Ann, hp, 17"-18" 550.00
Normandy, compo, Tiny Betty, 1935-1938, 7" 175.00
Old Fashioned Girl, compo, Betty, 13" 350.00
Parlour Maid, hp, Wendy Ann, 1956, 8" 1,500.00
Peruvian Boy, hp, Wendy Ann, 1965-1966, 8" 500.00
Peter Pan, hp, Margaret, 1953, 15" 500.00
Pitty Pat, cloth, 16" 350.00
Polly Pigtails, hp, Maggie, 14½" 450.00
Precious, compo/cloth baby, 1937, 12" 145.00
Prince Charles, hp, Wendy Ann, 1957, 8" 1,200.00
Princess Ann, hp, Wendy Ann, 1957, 8" 1,200.00
Priscilla, cloth, 18" 550.00
Puddin', cloth/vinyl, 1966-1975, 21" 125.00
Queen, hp, Margaret, 1953, 18" 700.00
Queen Alexandrine, compo, Wendy Ann, 1939, 21" 1,600.00
Red Cross Nurse, compo, Tiny Betty, 1937, 7" 175.00
Red Riding Hood, compo, Tiny Betty, 1936, 7" 175.00
Renoir, hp, Margaret, 1950, 14" 550.00
Riding Hood, cloth/felt, 1930s, 16" 550.00
Ringbearer, hp, Lovey Dovey, 1951, 14" 500.00
Roller Skating, hp, Wendy Ann, 1953-1955, 8" 500.00
Romeo, compo, Wendy Ann, 18" 725.00
Rose Fairy, hp, Wendy Ann, 8" 1,600.00
Ruffles Clown, 1954, 21" 400.00
Rusty, cloth/vinyl, 1967-1968, 20" 450.00

Sandy McHare, cloth/felt, 1930s 600.00
Scarlett O'Hara, compo, Little Betty, 9" 300.00
Scotch, compo, Tiny Betty, 7" 175.00
Seven Dwarfs, compo, 1937, ea 475.00
Sitting Pretty, foam body, 1965, 18" 450.00
Sleeping Beauty, compo, Little Betty, 1941, 9" 225.00
Snow White, compo, pnt eyes, Princess Elizabeth, 1937, 13" ..400.00
So Big, cloth/vinyl, pnt eyes, 1968-1975, 22" 185.00
Soldier, compo, Wendy Ann, 14" 475.00
Southern Belle, hp, Wendy Ann, 1954, 8" 1,200.00
Southern Girl, compo, Wendy Ann, 14" 450.00
Special Girl, cloth/compo, 1942, 23" 450.00
Sugar Tears, vinyl baby, Honey Bea, 1964, 12" 165.00
Susie Q, cloth, 1940 ....600.00
Sweet Baby, cloth/latex, 1948, 18½" 85.00
Sweet Tears, vinyl, 1965-1974, 9" 100.00
Sweet Violet, hp, Cissy, 1951-1954, 18" 550.00
Sweetie Baby, 1962, 22" 165.00
Sweetie Walker, 1962, 23" 275.00
Tinkerbelle, hp, Cissette, 1969, 11" 475.00
Tiny Betty, compo, 7" 175.00
Tippy Toe, cloth, 16" 600.00
Turkey, hp, bend knees, Wendy Ann, 1968-1972, 8" 145.00
Turkey, hp, bend knees, Wendy Ann, 1968-1972, 8" 250.00
Victorian, hp, Margaret, 1954, 18" 550.00
Wendy Ann, compo, 15" 450.00
Wendy Bride, compo, Wendy Ann, 14" 225.00
White Rabbit, cloth/felt 600.00
Winnie Walker, hp, Cissy, 1953, 15" 275.00
Yolanda, Brenda Starr, 1965, 12" 250.00

Papier-Mache

Papier-mache with molded and painted hair and features, EX, 14", $600.00; repaired, 12", $200.00.

Braided hair, cloth w/wood limbs, ca 1840s, 20" 1,200.00
Clown, pnt features, c/m, molded hair, cloth body, 16", EX ...650.00
Gentleman, molded/pnt head, cloth, wood arms, suit/hat, 10" .300.00
Gentleman, molded/pnt head, cloth, wood limbs, 1930, 13" ...450.00
Glass eyes, c/m, fully jtd/compo body, 20", EX 900.00
Molded blk curly hair, glass eyes, Germany, 1870-1900s, 16" ..500.00
Molded hair, pnt eyes, cloth w/kid arms, Greiner, 23" 1,100.00
Molded/pnt hair & features, cloth w/kid arms, 30" 1,600.00

Molded/pnt head, kid w/pnt wood limbs, Germany, 1845, 17" .400.00
Oriental boy, mohair, silk clothes, holds helmet/sword, 14" ...700.00
Oriental Warrior, cvd wood hands/feet, silk clothes, 11¼" 500.00
Poured, ShHd, glass eyes, appl wig, cloth wire body/limbs, 12" .200.00
Puff curls, cloth w/wood limbs, ca 1840s, 24" 2,300.00
ShHd, molded hair, pnt features, cloth w/kid limbs, 20" 275.00
ShHd, molded hair/features, cloth w/kid limbs, Grenier, 24" .1,100.00
ShHd, molded hairdo, kid w/wood limbs, red silk dress, 15" ...600.00
ShHd, pnt features, top knot/curls, linen/lace dress, 9" 350.00
ShHd, pnt hair, glass eyes, o/m, kid body, 26" 1,400.00
Trn ShHd, glass eyes, c/m, cloth/kid body, 22" 950.00

Parian

Blonde molded hair/kid hands, cloth body/legs, Germany, 23" .750.00
Blonde w/head band, ca 1860s, 24" 600.00
Bsk head, cloth body, all orig, 22", M 700.00
Cafe-au-lait hair w/snood, 10½" 485.00
Cloth/kid body, 27" 1,400.00
Glass eyes, orig cloth/kid body, silk dress, 20" 1,700.00
Man, orig corset body, old clothes, ca 1880, 17" 750.00
ShHd, molded brn hair, kid body, bl-striped silk dress, 18" ...600.00
ShHd, molded hair, cloth, pk/silver accents, bsk limbs, 9" 850.00

Schoenhut

Albert Schoenhut left Germany in 1866 to go to Pennsylvania to work as a repairman for toy pianos. He eventually applied his skills to wooden toys and later designed an all-wood doll which he patented on January 17, 1911. These uniquely jointed dolls were painted with enamels and came with a metal stand. Some of the later dolls had stuffed bodies, voice boxes, and hollow heads; some were made with heads of imitation bisque. These innovations influenced the development of the popular Bye-Lo Baby which was introduced in 1924. Due to the changing economy and fierce competition, the company closed in the mid-1930s.

Baby head, pnt hair & eyes, o/c mouth, jtd, 16" 600.00
Child, cvd hair w/comb mks/etc, c/m, spring jtd, OC, 16" ...1,800.00
Dolly face, decal eyes, pnt teeth, spring jtd, 21" 850.00
Dolly face, o/ or c/m, pnt eyes, wig, spring jtd, OC, 17" 675.00
Girl, brn o/c eyes, OC, 19", M 950.00
Girl, cvd hair w/comb mks, intaglio brn eyes, RpC, 19" 2,000.00
Girl, smiling o/m w/teeth, brn hair, pat Jan 17, 1911, 18" 750.00
Pouty, orig paper label, 1919, 11½" 550.00
Sailor boy, spring jtd, OC, 15", VG 550.00
Walker, bl pnt eyes, c/m, mohair wig, mk head/body, 16½" 725.00
Walker, pnt eyes, o/c mouth, OC, 17" 750.00

SFBJ

By 1895 Germany was producing dolls of good quality at much lower prices than the French dollmakers because of lower wages in German factories. This was a serious threat to the French companies; and, in a supreme effort to save the doll industry, several leading French manufacturers united to form one large company in the hope they could combine their strengths to save the French market. Bru, Raberry and Delphieu, Pintel and Godshaux, Fleischman and Bodel, and Jumeau united to form the company today known as SFBJ. Their dolls did well while Germany was otherwise occupied with WWII, but after the war German doll production proved to be too strongly competitive, and SFBJ closed in 1958.

Bebe Parisiana, bsk head, c/m, inset eyes, 1902, 16" 2,600.00
Celestine, bsk SkHd on papier-mache, o/m, inset eyes, 18" 800.00
SkHd, jtd papier-mache/wood body, o/m, o/c eyes, 30" 2,200.00

S.F.B.J., flirting eyes, human hair eyelashes, open mouth and teeth, pierced ears, unjointed legs, 22½", $1,600.00.

Tete Jumeau, p/e, o/m, o/c eyes/lashes, 18" 1,250.00
11, compo w/bsk swivel head, c/m, inset eyes, 16" 650.00
20, molded ptd shoes & eyes, 5-pc body, Paris/12, 10" 350.00
203, 1900 bsk head on compo, o/c mouth, inset eyes, 20" . . .2,500.00
215, bsk swivel on compo, c/m, inset eyes, 15" 1,800.00
223, bsk, closed dome, o/m/8 teeth, molded hair, 17" 2,000.00
227, brn swivel closed dome head, animal skin wig, 15" 1,800.00
227, brn swivel closed dome head, animal skin wig, 18" 2,000.00
227, closed dome, o/m, inset eyes, pnt hair, 15" 1,800.00
228, toddler, papier-mache body, c/m, inset eyes, 16" 1,800.00
229, compo w/swivel head, o/c mouth, inset eyes, 18" 2,400.00
229, wood walker, o/c mouth, inset eyes, 18" 2,000.00
230, compo walker, p/e, o/m, inset eyes, 16" 1,300.00
230, SkHd, p/e, o/m, o/c eyes, 23" 1,900.00
235, closed dome, molded hair, o/c mouth & eyes, 16" 1,800.00
235, closed dome, molded hair, o/c mouth & eyes, 8" 500.00
236, laughing Jumeau, o/m, o/c eyes, dbl chin, 12" 1,300.00
236, laughing Jumeau, o/m, o/c eyes, dbl chin, 20" 2,000.00
238, compo w/swivel head, o/m, inset eyes, Paris 6, 15" 2,500.00
239, Poulbot, c/m, street urchin, red wig, 14" 16,000.00
239, Poulbot, c/m, street urchin, red wig, 17" 19,000.00
245, boy, o/c mouth, lg glass eyes, googly, pnt shoes, 12" 2,600.00
245, boy, o/c mouth, lg glass eyes, googly, pnt shoes, 8" 1,000.00
247, toddler, o/c mouth/2 inset teeth, 16" 2,300.00
247, toddler, o/c mouth/2 inset teeth, 20" 2,700.00
247, toddler, o/c mouth/2 inset teeth, 24" 3,200.00
247, Twirp, SkHd, o/c mouth & eyes/2 teeth, 21" 2,800.00
251, toddler, 25" 2,600.00
251, 1099 character baby, o/c mouth, eyes, hair lashes, 16" . .1,300.00
251, 1099 character baby, o/c mouth, eyes, hair lashes, 18" . .1,700.00
252, pouty, c/m, inset eyes, papier-mache body, 18" 4,800.00
252, pouty, c/m, inset eyes, papier-mache body, 22" 7,200.00
257, 1900 toddler, o/c mouth, inset eyes, 16" 2,000.00
266, character, bsk head, closed dome, o/c mouth, 20" 2,400.00
301, bsk SkHd on compo, o/m, inset eyes, 16" 625.00

301, bsk SkHd on compo, o/m, inset eyes, 22" 875.00
301, bsk SkHd on compo, o/m, inset eyes, 30" 1,500.00
60, French WWI nurse, 5-pc body, SFBJ/13/0, 8½" 300.00
60, kiss-blower, cryer-walker, 22" 1,600.00
60, SkHd, compo w/str legs, o/m, curved arms, 15" 650.00
60, SkHd, papier-mache/compo, plunger cryer, o/m, 1-pc, 11" .400.00

Shirley Temple

Bsk, Japan, 7½" 245.00
Compo, 11", cowboy outfit, orig pin, EX 650.00
Compo, 11", in trunk, EX 750.00
Compo, 13", tagged bl/wht dress w/pin, 1930s, all orig 575.00
Compo, 15", OC, Ideal 550.00
Compo, 16", red dotted dress, velvet coat/hat, all orig 575.00
Compo, 18", OC, EX 585.00
Compo, 20", Ideal 600.00
Compo, 20", OC, NM 600.00
Compo, 20", tagged clothes, all orig, orig box 600.00
Compo, 22", teeth, orig bl dress w/daisies, Ideal, 1934, NM 650.00
Compo, 25", sailor suit, EX 750.00
Compo, 27", flirty eyes, orig, EX .900.00
Vinyl, 12", complete w/4 outfits, Ideal, 1957, MIB 250.00
Vinyl, 12", gr/wht dress, slip, complete, Ideal, 1957, MIB 150.00
Vinyl, 15", RpC, Ideal 245.00
Vinyl, 16", Rebecca, Ideal, 1972 .245.00
Vinyl, 16", Stand Up & Cheer dress, 1973, MIB 245.00
Vinyl, 17", OC, 1950s, M 300.00
Vinyl, 19", flirty eyes, all orig, 1957 . . . . .350.00
Vinyl, 36", OC, EX 1,500.00
Vinyl, 8", Stowaway, Ideal, 1982 . . . . .45.00

Simon and Halbig

Simon and Halbig was a large German doll firm that operated from ca 1870 until the 1930s. They were a popular supplier of bisque heads to French dollmakers of the 1870s and '80s. This company made dolls for such famous companies as Gimbel Bros., Jumeau, Kammer and Reinhardt, as well as many others. Halbig became the sole owner of the company in 1895 but did not register 'S&H' as his trademark until ten years later.

AW, SkHd, o/m, SH/13, 21" 600.00
Baby Blanche, SkHd, o/m baby, S&H, 16" 550.00
Baby Blanche, SkHd, o/m baby, S&H, 21" 750.00
CM Bergmann, SkHd, o/m, Simon & Halbig, 3 1/2, 18" 500.00
CM Bergmann, SkHd, o/m, 1895, Halbig/S&H5, 30" 1,100.00
CM Bergmann, SkHd, o/m, 1897, S&H6, 12" 350.00
Elenore, SkHd, o/m, CMB/Simon & Halbig, 18" 500.00
G68, SkHd, flirty eyes, 1908, S&H/K*R, 16" 550.00
Handwerck, SkHd, o/m, G/Halbig, 4, 26" 850.00
Handwerck, SkHd, o/m, 1893, 16" 450.00
Handwerck, SkHd, o/m, 1895, G/S&H/1, 16" 450.00
S&H3, all bsk, c/m, inset eyes, molded-on shoes, 6" 185.00
SkHd, 2 teeth, tongue, K*R/Simon & Halbig, 116a-38, 17" .2,200.00
10, SkHd, o/m, G/Halbig/S&H, 16" 450.00
10, SkHd, o/m, G/Halbig/S&H, 19" 550.00
10, SkHd, o/m, G/Halbig/S&H, 22" 650.00
10½, SkHd, o/m, flirty o/c eyes, S&H, 18" 550.00
100, SkHd, o/m, Simon & Halbig/S&C/G, 15" 425.00
100, SkHd, o/m, Simon & Halbig/S&C/G, 22" 650.00
101, SkHd, c/m, Simon & Halbig/K*R, 16" 4,200.00
1039, SkHd, o/m w/teeth, p/e, jtd arms/wrists, hh, 22" 650.00
1059, SkHd, swivel on ShPl, wood w/kid fashion, o/m, 19" . .2,600.00
109, SkHd, o/m, 1895, Handwerck/G/Halbig, 23" 675.00

114, SkHd, c/m, glass eyes, Simon & Halbig K*R/L, 14" 4,200.00
114, SkHd, c/m, glass eyes, Simon Halbig K*R/L, 20" 6,200.00
114, SkHd, c/m, Simon & Halbig K*R/L, 9" 1,200.00
115, SkHd, c/m, 1912, K*R/Simon & Halbig, 16" 2,500.00
115a, SkHd, c/m pouty, K*R/Simon & Halbig, 15" 2,400.00
1159, SkHd, adult, 1905, G/Simon & Halbig/S&H7, 14" ...1,000.00
1159, SkHd, adult, 1905, G/Simon & Halbig/S&H7, 18" ...1,500.00
1159, SkHd, adult, 1905, G/Simon & Halbig/S&H7, 24" ...2,400.00
116a, SkHd, c/m, K*R/Simon Halbig, 17" 2,300.00
117, SkHd, c/m, 1919, Simon & Halbig/K*R, 16" 3,200.00
117, SkHd, c/m, 1919, Simon & Halbig/K*R, 20" 4,400.00
117a, SkHd, c/m, K*R/Simon & Halbig, 16" 3,200.00
117a, SkHd, c/m, K*R/Simon & Halbig, 20" 4,400.00
117n, SkHd, o/m, Simon & Halbig/K*R, 20" 2,000.00
119, SkHd, o/m, 13/Handwerck 5/Halbig, 16" 550.00
121, SkHd, o/c mouth/teeth, flirty o/c eyes, 1920, K*R, 16" .1,200.00
121, SkHd, o/c toddler, 16" 1,200.00
121, SkHd, o/m, 1920, K*R/Simon & Halbig, 14" 950.00
121, SkHd, o/m, 1920, K*R/Simon & Halbig, 19" 1,500.00
122, SkHd, 1920, K*R/Simon & Halbig, 14" 850.00
126, SkHd, o/c mouth, SH, 23" 825.00
126, SkHd, o/m, Simon & Halbig/K*R, 14" 475.00
126, SkHd, o/m, Simon & Halbig/K*R, 19" 650.00
127, SkHd, o/m, K*R/Simon & Halbig, 18" 600.00
128, SkHd, o/m, K*R/Simon & Halbig, 14" 600.00
128, SkHd, o/m, K*R/Simon & Halbig, 19" 850.00
1296, SkHd, 1911, FS&Co/Simon & Halbig, 14" 425.00
1329, SkHd, o/m, olive, G/Simon & Halbig/SH, 14" 1,800.00
151, SkHd, o/c mouth, pnt eyes, S&H/1, 16" 5,500.00
156, SkHd, 1925, S&H, 18" 500.00
156, SkHd, 1925, S&H, 22" 650.00
159, SkHd, o/m, Simon & Halbig, 16" 475.00
179, SkHd, o/m, Simon & Halbig S11H DEP, 20" 600.00
1848, SkHd, o/m, Jutta Simon & Halbig, 16" 475.00
191, SkHd, o/m, Bergmann/CB, 18" 500.00
1923, SkHd, o/m, SH Sp 53/4/G, 14" 400.00
1923, SkHd, o/m, SH Sp 53/4/G, 21" 550.00
1923, SkHd, o/m, SH Sp 53/4/G, 26" 850.00
246, SkHd, o/m, 1900, K*R/Simon & Halbig, 18" 550.00
282, SkHd, o/m, SH, 14" 375.00
282, SkHd, o/m, SH, 18" 500.00
282, SkHd, o/m, SH, 22" 650.00
383, SkHd, flapper body, S H, 14" 900.00
402, SkHd, o/m, K*R SH, 16" 550.00
403, SkHd, o/c mouth, K*R, Simon & Halbig, 20" 2,800.00
403, SkHd, o/m, walker, K*R SH, 21" 1,400.00
409, SkHd, o/m, S&H, 24" 600.00
409, SkHd, o/m, S&H, 26" 750.00
409, SkHd, o/m, S&H, 30" 1,400.00
48m SkHd, o/m, 1905, Simon & Halbig/K*R, 27" 950.00
50, SkHd, c/m, Simon & Halbig, 16" 1,600.00
50, SkHd, o/m, 1900, K*R/Simon & Halbig, 14" 400.00
53, SkHd, c/m, brown bsk, Simon & Halbig/K*R, 16" 1,600.00
530, SkHd, o/m, G/Simon & Halbig, 21" 600.00
540, SkHd, o/m, G/Halbig/S&H, 16" 750.00
540, SkHd, swivel on bsk ShPl, o/m, S&H, G, 16" 750.00
550, SkHd, o/m, Simon & Halbig/S&H, 16" 450.00
570, SkHd, o/m, Halbig S&H/G, 18" 500.00
570, SkHd, o/m, walking, head turns, G/Halbig S&H, 18" 750.00
576, SkHd, o/m, Simon & Halbig, 16" 450.00
612, SkHd, o/m, MIG/S&H/CM Bergmann, 16" 475.00
670, SkHd, o/m, Simon & Halbig, 16" 475.00
70, SkHd, o/m, 1896, Halbig/K*R, 26" 850.00
719, SkHd, c/m, S&H DEP, 16" 1,800.00

719, SkHd, swivel, ShPl, c/m, S&H, DEP, 20" 2,300.00
739, SkHd, c/m, brn, S 5 H DEP, 14" 1,400.00
739, SkHd, c/m, brn, S 5 H DEP, 18" 2,200.00
759, SkHd, o/m, brn, S 10 H DEP, 20" 650.00
769, SkHd, c/m, S&H DEP, 17" 1,800.00
905, SkHd, swivel on ShPl, c/m, SH, 21" 3,000.00
908, SkHd, swivel on ShPl, c/m, SH, 16" 2,300.00
929, SkHd, c/m, S&H, DEP, 20" 2,300.00
939, SkHd, c/m, S 11H DEP, 17" 2,500.00
939, SkHd, o/c eyes, o/m, S16H, 30" 3,600.00
940, SkHd, closed dome, o/c mouth, S 2 H, 26" 3,200.00
945, SkHd, c/m, S 2 H DEP, 16" 2,000.00
99, SkHd, o/m, 1899, 11 1/2 Handwerck/Halbig, 16" 450.00

Steiner

Jules Nicholas Steiner established one of the earliest French doll manufactories in 1855. Having been a clockmaker, he began with mechanical dolls and his patents grew to include walking and talking dolls. In 1880 he registered a patent for a doll with moving eyes. This doll could be put to sleep by turning a rod that operated a wire attached to its eyes. Though these new innovations brought much acclaim to the Steiner company, it closed around 1910 because it could not compete with the less-expensive German dolls that were flooding the market at that time.

A Series, bsk, bl eyes, red wool antique dress, 25" 5,000.00
A Series, jtd body, wire-eyed, c/m, p/e, 13" 2,400.00
A Series, jtd compo body, c/m, pwt eyes, 16" 3,800.00
A Series, jtd w/str wrists, c/m, p/e, 14" 2,600.00
Bourgoin, compo, c/m, pwt eyes, 1870s, RpC, 16" 3,800.00
Bourgoin, compo, wire-eyed, RpC, 20" 4,500.00
C Series, bl eyes, orig wig/OC, 21½" 4,800.00
Mechanical, key wind, kicks/cries, teeth, RpC, 18" 1,800.00
Motschmann style, bsk, RpC, 18", EX 4,400.00

Steiner, open mouth with two rows of teeth, pull string, dolls says 'Mamma,' EX, 16", $2,400.00.

Vogue

Baby Dear, vinyl/cloth, pnt eyes, rooted hair, 1961, 12" 45.00
Brickette, vinyl, flirty o/c eyes, jtd waist, 1959, OC, 22" 80.00
Crib Crowd, hp, bent legs, OC, EX 550.00
Ginny, Bo Peep, hp, o/c eyes, pnt lashes, 1952, OC, 8", M ..250.00
Ginny, Merry Lee, hp, o/c eyes, pnt lashes, OC, 8", NM 250.00
Ginny, Nan, hp, o/c eyes, pnt lashes, 1951, OC, 8", EX 250.00
Ginny, Roller Skater, walker, hp, #47, 1955, OC, 8", EX 250.00
Love Me Linda, vinyl, brn pnt eyes, molded teardrop, OC, 15" ..30.00
Miss 1920, hp, orig taffeta dress/hat/shoes, 1950, 8", EX 400.00
Star Bright, vinyl/cloth, pnt eyes, rooted hair, 1966, OC, 18" ...40.00
Toddles, Groom, blk suit/tie/hat, wht shirt, 1945, 8", EX 325.00
Toddles, Russian girl, felt headpc, 1942, OC, 8", NM 375.00

Wax, Poured Wax

Over compo, ShHd, o/c eyes, auburn hair, orig dress, 18" 300.00
Over compo, ShHd, set eyes, molded hair, cloth body, 15" 250.00
Over compo, slit head, blk eyes, cloth body, 14" 450.00
Over papier-mache, jtd wooden body, wire-eyed, all orig, 11" ..400.00
Poured, bl pwt eyes, England, OC, 24" 2,200.00
Poured, glass eyes, set-in hair, cloth body, 19" 1,400.00

Door Knockers

Door knockers, those charming precursors of the door bell, come in an intriguing array of shapes and styles. The very rare ones come from England. Cast iron examples made in this country were often produced in forms similar to the more familiar doorstop figures.

Bronze, female nude held by male, 7", $385.00.

Butterfly, pnt CI, oval bk 145.00
Cameo, pnt CI, Victorian lady's head, 4" 165.00
Eagle, brass, #1552, EX 55.00
Eagle, bronze, heavy, 7½" 35.00
Foo dog, bronze, lg 100.00
Gargoyle, brass, lg 30.00
Girl knocking at door, pnt CI, 3½" 145.00
Heart shape, wrought iron, EX 85.00
Lion's head, CI, 1850s, 7x7½" 110.00
Minerva head, brass-plated CI, eng 1833, Wilson's Pat, 8½" ...85.00
Rooster, pnt CI, ca 1940s, 4¾x3" 150.00
Woman's hand, brass 20.00
Woman's hand, CI w/worn gr rpt, 4½" 20.00

Doorstops

Although introduced in England in the mid-1800s, cast iron doorstops were not made to any great extent in this country until after the Civil War. Once called 'door porters,' their function was to keep doors open to provide better ventilation. They have been produced in many shapes and sizes, both dimensional and flat backed, and in the past few years have become a popular, yet affordable collectible. While cast iron examples are the most common, brass, wood, and chalk were also used. An average price is in the $40 to $50 range, though some are valued at more than $200. Doorstops retained their usefulness and appeal well into the thirties.

The prices below reflect market values in the east where doorstops are now at a premium. For other areas of the country, it may be necessary to adjust prices down about 25%. In the listings below, items are assumed flat backed unless noted full figured and cast iron unless noted otherwise.

Key: ff — full figured

Amish Man, wide-brimmed hat, hand in pocket, ff, 8½x3¾" ..150.00
Aunt Jemima, hands on hips, CI w/pnt traces, ff, 8¾" 75.00
Aunt Jemima, hands on hips, 1-pc mold, no pnt, ff, 10½x6½" .175.00
Basket of Kittens, worn pnt, M Rosenstein, c 1932, 10x7" 250.00
Basket of Spring Flowers, CI, wht/pastel pnt, 5¾" 60.00
Beagle Pup, sits, front ft wide, ff, 8x7½" 150.00
Bellhop, stands in bl uniform w/red trim, #1244, 8⅞x4⅝" 175.00
Blk Man on Cotton Bale, top hat, wht clothes, 6⅞x6⅞" 265.00
Bobby Blake, boy holds teddy bear, Hubley, 9½x5¼" 265.00
Boston Terrier, begging, ff, 8¾x5" 145.00
Boston Terrier, stands, faces left, ff, 10x10" 65.00
Boston Terrier, w/paw up, ff, NM orig pnt, 9½x7" 185.00
Butler, vest & bow tie, hands on hips, 12½x6" 200.00
Carpenter, sits w/red shirt & hat, #665, ff, 5½x2¾" 100.00
Castle, atop mountain, winding road, 8x5¼" 100.00
Cat, blk & wht w/red bow tie, Eastern Specialty #62, 7x4½" ...100.00
Cat, licking paw, Sculptured Metal Studios, 10¾x7½" 245.00
Cat, sleeping, faces left, Nat'l Foundry, 3⅜x9⅝" 150.00
Charleston Dancers, couple in dance pose, Hubley, 8⅞x5⅜" ..265.00
Child, reaching, nude bkside, Elba Road MA label, 17x7" 265.00
Colonial Lady w/Fan, ff, 4¾x2⅝" 55.00
Colonial Pilgrim, tricorn hat, 1 arm held out, 8¾x5⅜" 200.00
Cottage, flowers on house, Hubley or Nat'l Foundry, 5¾x7½" ...75.00
Cottage, gr shutters, AA Richardson, Quincy MA, 5⅛x8" 75.00
Cricket, CI, Tri State Foundry, 10½" L 105.00
Daisy Bowl, mc flowers in gr bowl, Hubley #232, 7x6" 60.00
Deco Dancers, stylized/facing, CI/mc, mk Hubley, 8½" 535.00
Deco Lady, short slinky dress, hands to head, 17x6½" 220.00
Delphinium, mc flower basket, Hubley #490, 8¾x7¼" 75.00
Dickens Character, man in wig & glasses, CI/mc pnt, 15" 230.00
Dickens Character, old man & young girl, CI/mc pnt, 15" 270.00
Doberman Pinscher, stands, faces right, Hubley, ff, 8x8½" 150.00
Donald Duck, stop sign in hands, Disney, 1971, 8⅜x5¼" 155.00
Duck by Bush, wht w/yel ft & bill, 7½x10½" 185.00
Dutch Boy, blousy pants, wooden shoes, ff, 11x3½" 200.00
Dutch Girl, long red apron, ff, 6x6¾" 125.00
El Capitan, marching soldier w/gun at shoulder, 7¾x5¼" 150.00
Elf, CI w/mc rpt, ff, 10" 170.00
Elf w/Shield & Club, CI/mc pnt, 12¾" 150.00
Elk, wide antlers, rocky base, bronze-like finish, 11x10" 125.00
English Bulldog, wht w/blk spots, EX orig pnt, 5¾x8¾" 175.00
Fisherman at Wheel, yel norwester, gr wheel, 6¼x6" 60.00
Fisherman in Boat, yel norwester, 6¾x4" 145.00
Footmen, 2 side by side, red coats, blk pants, Hubley, 9x6" ...265.00
French Bulldog, seated, CI w/blk & wht porc finish, ff, 7" 85.00

Frog, stands upright, man-like pose, 14x7" 265.00
Frog on Mushroom, gr & yel pnt, ff, 4½x3⅝" 120.00
Fruits & Birds, red birds on fruit bowl, c 1929, 6½x5½" 100.00
Gaucho, faces right, red pants & knee boots, ff, 18½x7" 225.00
Geese, group of 3, CI, wht w/mc pnt, 8" 225.00
Girl, lifts skirt, stands on sq base, B&H #7798, 13x6¾" 220.00
Girl w/Bonnet, bow in hair, wide sash, WS mk, 8x5¼" 220.00
Girls, read bk to bk, sit on wide base, 5x8⅝" 265.00
Gladiolus, mc flowers in vase, Hubley #489, 10x8" 80.00
Gnome w/Shovel, red hat, bl shirt, worn pnt, 9½x4½" 225.00

Golfer, 10", $565.00.

Grandpa Rabbit, red vest, gr bow tie, 8⅝x4⅞" 275.00
Greyhound, running, CI/dk patina, Lake City Malleable, 12" L . .70.00
Greyhound, slim body, CI, traces of bronze, ff, 6½" 70.00
Horse, CI w/worn realistic pnt, no base, ff, 10¾" 150.00
Horse, jumping fence, Eastern Specialty #79, 7⅞x11¾" 225.00
Horse, King's Genius, unpnt CI, c 1938/Rife Loth Corp, 12" . .150.00
Indian w/Bow, CI w/worn red pnt, 12½" 225.00
Jonquil, yel flowers w/orange centers, Hubley #453, 7x6" 110.00
Judy, sits facing left, cat at ft, English, 11½x8¾" 265.00
Lady, curtsying, head bowed, VG orig pnt, 9¼x6⅞" 125.00
Lady, holds shawl, 1 hand to face, ff, 8x3½" 100.00
Lady w/Flower, holds hat low, ff, EX mc pnt, 6⅜x4⅛" 100.00
Lady w/Flower Baskets, ruffled cap, #1270, 8x4¾" 100.00
Lady w/Hooped Dress, worn mc pnt, 7x5¼" 55.00
lady w/Ruffled Skirt, flowers in hat & on skirt, 6⅜x4⅞" 100.00
Lighthouse of Gloucester MA, Greenblatt Studios #8, 11½x9" . .95.00
Lil Red Riding Hood, red hat & cape, Hubley #95, 9½x5" 265.00
Lil Red Riding Hood & Wolf, wolf at side/looks bk, 7½x9½" . .265.00
Little Miss Muffet, sits on toadstool, #121, 7¾x5" 150.00
Lobster, lg claws held high, blk pnt, 12½x6½" 225.00
London Royal Mail Coach, GR N-17 Pat Pending, 7x12¼" 65.00
Man in Chair, holds mug on knee, English, 9½x5¾" 225.00
Man w/Top Hat, hands behind bk, dk pnt, ff, 9⅜x3⅝" 150.00
March Hare, ears down, red bow tie, gr coat, 8¼x3¾" 225.00
Mayflower, choppy sea forms base, Eastern Specialty, 8¼x9" 65.00
Messenger Boy, bl uniform, holds bouquet, Hubley, 10x5⅜" . . .225.00
Monkey, sits w/chin in hand, CI w/brn pnt, ff, 8½" 250.00
Monkey on Barrel, gr/yel pnt, Taylor Cook #3, '30, 8⅜x4⅞" . .150.00
Moonface, winking expression, no pnt, 6½x5" 100.00
Mrs Sloper, holds twin babies/cat at ft, English, 10¾x6⅜" 225.00
Napoleon on horsebk, VG orig pnt, 6x6½" 85.00
Nude, Deco style, arms wide, holds lg circle, 9¼x6¼" 150.00

Nude, sitting, bronze-like pnt, Hubley, 8x3¼" 100.00
Old Woman, flower basket & parasol, B&H #7796, 11x7" . . .220.00
Organ Grinder, monkey at ft, faces left, NM pnt, 9⅞x5¾" . . .220.00
Oriental Girl, hands tucked in wide sleeves, ff, 7½x3¾" 125.00
Ostrich, wings up, faces left, dk pnt, #120, 8½x9" 225.00
Owl, fine feather details, B&H #7797, 15½x5" 265.00
Peacock by Urn, draped tail, Hubley #208, 7½x4¼" 125.00
Percheron, stands, faces left, Hubley, ff, 9x7¾" 125.00
Persian Cat, sits, faces left, head up, Hubley, ff, 8½x6½" 85.00
Pheasant, CI w/mc pnt, mk Everett, lt rust, 8" 125.00
Pirate Girl, sword in hands, chest/bags at ft, 13⅞x7¼" 225.00
Pointer Spaniel, cast aluminum w/worn blk & wht pnt, 15" L . . .85.00
Pointer Spaniel, CI w/wht & brn pnt, ff, minor wear, 15" L . . .115.00
Puppies in Basket, Rosenstein, c 1932, 7x7⅜" 265.00
Puss 'N Boots, wht cat in red boot, 8¼x5¾" 165.00
Rabbit, sitting, ears up, CI w/brn-gray wash & pk ears, 11" . . .135.00
Rabbit from Alice in Wonderland, CI w/mc rpt, Albany, 10" . .150.00
Rampant Lions, CI w/worn rpt, mk Rowbothan, 13¾", pr 80.00
Rooster, wht w/red comb & waddle, Spencer, 13¼x11" 265.00
Rose Basket, mc flowers, pk-hdld basket, Hubley #121, 11x8" . .80.00
Rose Vase, 3 mc roses in dk vase, Nat'l Foundry, 10½x7" 125.00
Santa, pack on bk, pnt wht metal, domed base, 1925, EX 195.00
Santa, Xmas tree at shoulder, pnt wht metal, 1915, 5", EX . . .200.00
Satyr Head, cornucopia hat, CI/VG blk pnt, 11" 230.00
Sax Player, Blk man in red coat plays instrument, 6⅞x6" 225.00
Scottie, sits, faces left, ff, 8x8¼" 125.00
Sophia Smith House, 2-story, 1 chimney, shutters, 8¼x5½" . . .100.00
Southern Belle, hat w/flowers at side, Nat'l Foundry, 11x6" 75.00
Spanish Girl, frilly skirt, mantilla & fan, WS mk, 9½x5½" 150.00
Spanish Guitarist, man w/instrument, pat pend mk, 11x3⅜" . . .275.00
Sunbonnet Girl, billowing dress, faces left, 9x5½" 175.00
Three Kittens in Basket, CI w/EX orig pnt, old recast, 6½" . . .235.00
Totem Pole, top figure w/wings spread wide, 12x8½" 100.00
Tropical Woman, holds fruit basket on head, 12x6¼" 150.00
Tulip Pot, mc w/blk-rimmed pot, Nat'l Foundry, 8¼x7" 60.00
Tulips, red flowers in vase w/bl bow, 12¾x6⅞" 100.00
Vase of Red Poppies, CI/mc pnt, Hubley, 11" 55.00
Whippet, stands, faces right, worn pnt, 6¾x7½" 65.00
White Caddy, sad expression, hold huge golf bag, 8x6" 265.00
Wine Man, many bottles in hands, worn mc pnt, 9½x7" 265.00
Wolfhound, CI, orig wht/brn/blk pnt, ff, 12" L, EX 155.00
Wolfhound, slim Deco style, Spencer, Guilford CT, 6½x3½" . .100.00
Woodsman, w/dog/pipe/axe, CI w/blk pnt, ff, 14" 100.00

Dorflinger

C. Dorflinger was born in Alsace, France, and came to this country when he was ten years old. When still very young, he obtained a job in a glass factory in New Jersey. As a young man, he started his own glassworks in Brooklyn, New York, opening new factories as profits permitted. During that time he made cut glass articles for many famous people including President and Mrs. Lincoln, for whom he produced a complete service of tableware with the United States Coat of Arms. In 1863 he sold the New York factories because of ill health and moved to his farm near White Mills, Pennsylvania. His health returned, and he started a plant near his home. It was there that he did much of his best work, making use of only the very finest materials. Christian died in 1915, and the plant was closed in 1921 by consent of the family.

Dorflinger glass is rare and often hard to identify. Very few pieces were marked — many only carried a small paper label which was quickly discarded.

Bowl, Harvard, str sides, 3x9" 225.00

Champagne, Strawberry Diamond w/Shield 75.00
Compote, diamond point w/initial on side, 9x9" 400.00
Coupe, Kalana Lily, etched, on 7¾" underplate 100.00
Pitcher, champagne; yel cut to clear, 14" 1,700.00
Punch bowl, Anona, 2-pc, 13¾x12", NM 1,800.00
Tumbler, Old Colony, 3¾", EX 125.00
Vase, cameo, red/frosted, sgn, 14x3½" 500.00
Vase, Kalana Pansy, flared top & bottom, 12" 140.00
Vase, Kalana Wild Rose, amethyst-stained flowers, 10" 185.00

Doulton, Royal Doulton

The range of wares produced by the Doulton Company since its inception in 1815 has been vast and varied. Their earliest wares produced in the tiny pottery in Lambeth, England, were salt-glazed pitchers, plain and fancy figural bottles — all utility-type stoneware geared to the practical need of everyday living. The original partners, John Doulton and John Watts, saw the potential for success in the manufacture of drain and sewage pipes and during the 1840s concentrated on this highly lucrative type of commercial ware. Watts retired from the company in 1854, and Doulton began experimenting with a more decorative style of product. As time went by, many glazes and decorative effects were developed, among them Faience, Impasto, Silicon, Carrara, Marqueterie, Chine, and Rouge Flambe. Tiles and architectural terra cotta were an important part of their manufacture. Late in the nineteenth century at the original Lambeth location, fine artware was decorated by such notable artists as Hannah and Arthur Barlow, George Tinworth, and J.H. McLennan. Stoneware vases with incised animal drawings, gracefully-shaped urns with painted scenes, and cleverly-modeled figurines rivaled the best of any competitor.

In 1882 a second factory was built in Burslem which continues even yet to produce the famous figurines, character jugs, series ware, and table services so popular with collectors today. Their Kingsware line, made from 1899 to 1946, featured flasks and flagons with drinking scenes, usually on a brown-glazed ground, some of which were limited editions while others were commemorative and advertising items. The Gibson Girl series, twenty-four plates in all, was introduced in 1901. It was drawn by Charles Dana Gibson and is recognized by its blue and white borders and central illustrations, each scene depicting a humorous or poignant episode in the life of 'The Widow and Her Friends.' Dickensware, produced from 1911 through the early 1940s, featured illustrations by Charles Dickens, with many of his famous characters. The Robin Hood series was introduced in 1914; the Shakespeare series #1, portraying scenes from the Bard's plays, was made from 1914 until World War II. The Shakespeare series #2 ran from 1906 until 1974 and was decorated with featured characters. The Nursery Rhymes series was produced first in earthenware in 1903 and later in bone china. In 1933 a line of decorated children's ware, the Bunnykins series, was introduced and continues to be made to the present day. About 150 'bunny' scenes have been devised, the earliest and most desirable being those signed by the artist Barbara Vernon.

The value of a figurine is appreciated by age, because of a limited production run, or by exceptional color and detail. Those signed by the artist or marked 'Potted' (indicating pre-1939 origin) are also more valuable. After 1920 wares were marked with a lion — with or without a crown — over a circlular 'Royal Doulton.'

Animals and Birds

Cairn Pup, #2589, begging, 4" 39.50
Cat, Persian, #999, blk/wht, 5" 90.00
Cat, Siamese, #2655, sitting, 5½" 80.00
Dog, Airedale, K-5 . . . . .40.00
Dog, Alsatian, #1116, 6¼" 95.00
Dog, Bulldog, #1044, brindle, sm .175.00

Dog, Bulldog, #146 . . . . .295.00
Dog, Bulldog w/flag, #6407 . . . . .125.00
Dog, Cairn, K11 . . . . .40.00
Dog, Cocker Spaniel, #1002, 6½" 95.00
Dog, Cocker Spaniel, #1036, 5" 95.00
Dog, Cocker Spaniel, #1187, golden, 5" 95.00
Dog, Cocker Spaniel, K-9 . . . . .40.00
Dog, Cocker Spaniel w/pheasant, #1138, blk & wht, 5¼" 125.00

Cocker Spaniel with pheasant, #1028, 5½", $210.00.

Dog, Dachshund, #1128, 4" 55.00
Dog, Dalmation, #1113, 5¾" 95.00
Dog, English Setter w/pheasant, #2529, 8" 300.00
Dog, Irish Setter, #1056, sm 120.00
Dog, Pekingese, K-6 . . . . .40.00
Dog, Pointer, #2624, 5⅜" 250.00
Dog, Sealyham, #1031 . . . . .165.00
Dog, Setter, #1049 . . . . .280.00
Dog, Terrier, #1014, rough haired, 4" 45.00
Dog w/bone, #1159, 3¾" 39.50
Elephant, #2644, 5½" 95.00
Hare, #2594, 1¾" 35.00
Hare, #979, 7½" 175.00
Kitten, #2582, sitting, 2¾" 40.00
Koala Bear 40.00
Langur Monkey, 4⅜" 350.00
Mountain Sheep, #2661 . . . . .170.00
Nyala Antelope, #2264, 5⅝" 170.00
Penguins, #133, dbl, 6" 200.00
Pheasant, #2632 . . . . .225.00
White-Tailed Deer, #2658, 5⅝" 345.00

Character Jugs

Ann Boleyn, D6644, lg 100.00
Ann of Cleves, D6653, hdl: horse's head w/ears raised, lg 225.00
Apothecary, D6567, lg 95.00
Apothecary, D6574, sm 60.00
Aramis, D6441, lg 95.00
Ard of 'Earing, D6588, lg 1,100.00
Ard of 'Earing, D6594, miniature 1,200.00
Arriet, D6208, lg, A 200.00
Arriet, D6250, miniature 75.00
Arriet, D6256, tiny 200.00

Arry, D6235, sm, A 75.00
Arry, D6249, lg 200.00
Auld Mac, D5823, lg 85.00
Auld Mac, D5824, sm, A 50.00
Auld Mac, D6257, tiny 225.00
Beefeater, D6233, GR hdl, sm, A 75.00
Beefeater, D6251, GR hdl, miniature 65.00
Blacksmith, D6571, lg 95.00
Blacksmith, D6578, sm 60.00
Bootmaker, D6572, lg 95.00
Cap'n Cuttle, D5842, sm, A 95.00
Captain Ahab, D6500, lg 95.00
Captain Ahab, D6506, sm 60.00
Captain Ahab, D6522, miniature 45.00
Captain Hook, D6601, sm 350.00
Cardinal, D6129, miniature 65.00
Cardinal, D6258, tiny 225.00
Catherine Howard, D6645, lg 95.00
Cavalier, D6114, lg 160.00
Cavalier, D6173, sm, A 75.00
Clown, D5610, red hair, lg 3,400.00
Dick Turpin, D5618, gun hdl, sm 60.00
Dick Turpin, D6485, gun hdl, lg 160.00
Dick Turpin, D6542, horse hdl, miniature 45.00

Dick Whitting, #6375, 7", $425.00.

Drake, D6174, sm, A 70.00
Falconer, D6533, bone china, lg 95.00
Falstaff, D6287, lg 95.00
Fat Boy, D5840, sm 95.00
Fat Boy, D6142, tiny 95.00
Field Marshall Smuts, D6198, lg 2,100.00
Fireman, D6697, lg 95.00
Fortune Teller, D6497, lg 550.00
Fortune Teller, D6503, sm 375.00
Friar Tuck, D6321, lg 395.00
Gaoler, D6570, lg 95.00
Gaoler, D6584, miniature 45.00
Gardener, D6570, lg 150.00
Gardener, D6638, miniature 65.00
Gardener, D6643, sm 85.00
George Washington, D6669, lg 95.00
Gladiator, D6556, miniature 375.00
Gondolier, D6589, lg 575.00

Gondolier, D6595, miniature 350.00
Gone Away, D6531, lg 95.00
Gone Away, D6538, sm 60.00
Gone Away, D6545, miniature 45.00
Granny, D5521, lg 85.00
Granny, D6520, miniature 45.00
Grant & Lee, D6698, lg 225.00
Guardsman of Williamsburg, D6575, sm 95.00
Guardsman of Williamsburg, D6582, miniature 60.00
Gulliver, D6560, lg 575.00
Gunsmith, D6580, sm 75.00
Henry Morgan, D6467, lg 85.00
Henry Morgan, D6467, sm 55.00
Henry VIII, D6642, lg 95.00
Henry VIII, D6647, sm 50.00
Jarge, D6295, sm 295.00
Jester, D5556, sm 125.00
Jockey, lg 325.00
John Barleycorn, D5327, lg 150.00
John Barleycorn, D5735, sm 75.00
John Barleycorn, D6041, miniature 65.00
John Doulton, 1980, sm 60.00
John Peel, D5731, sm, A 65.00
John Peel, D6130, miniature, A 45.00
Lobster Man, D6652, miniature 40.00
Long John Silver, D6386, sm 50.00
Lord Nelson, D6336, lg 325.00
Lumberjack, bone china, D6610, lg 95.00
Mad Hatter, D6598, lg 115.00
Mark Twain, D6654, lg 95.00
Mephistopheles, D5757, lg 1,950.00
Mikado, D6501, lg 550.00
Mikado, D6507, sm 325.00
Mikado, D6525, miniature 330.00
Mine Host, D6513, miniature 45.00
Monty, D6202, lg, A 95.00
Mr Micawber, D5842, sm, A 75.00
Mr Pickwick, D5839, 4½" 85.00
Mr Pickwick, D6260, tiny 225.00
Neptune, D6548, lg 95.00
Night Watchman, D6576, sm 65.00
North American Indian, D6611, lg 95.00
Old Charley, D5420, lg 85.00
Old Charley, D5527, sm, A 60.00
Old Charley, D6046, miniature 45.00
Old Charley, D6144, tiny 95.00
Old King Cole, D6036, lg 250.00
Old King Cole, D6037, sm 100.00
Old Salt, D65531, lg 95.00
Paddy, D5768, sm 60.00
Paddy, D6042, miniature 50.00
Paddy, D6145, tiny 95.00
Parson Brown, D5486, lg 160.00
Parson Brown, D5529, sm 65.00
Pied Piper, D6403, lg 95.00
Pied Piper, D6514, miniature 45.00
Punch & Judy Man, D6590, lg 550.00
Regency Beau, D6562, sm 675.00
Rip Van Winkle, D6438, lg 95.00
Robin Hood, D6205, lg 160.00
Robin Hood, D6234, sm 75.00
Robin Hood, D6252, miniature 60.00
Robinson Crusoe, D6532, lg 85.00
Robinson Crusoe, D6539, sm 50.00

Ronald Reagan, lg	395.00
Sairey Gamp, D5451, lg, A	85.00
Sairey Gamp, D6045, miniature	40.00
Sairey Gamp, D6146, tiny	95.00
Samuel Johnson, D6296, sm	275.00
Samuel Weller, D6147, tiny	95.00
Sancho Panza, D6456, lg	95.00
Santa Claus, D6668, doll hdl, lg	100.00
Santa Claus, D6690, stocking hdl, lg	100.00
Scaramouche, D6558, lg	750.00
Sergeant Buz Fuz, D5838, sm	115.00
Simon the Cellarer, D5504, lg	160.00
Simon the Cellarer, D5616, sm	65.00
Simple Simon, D6374, lg	475.00
Sleuth, D6635, sm	55.00
Smuggler, D6616, lg	95.00
St George, D6618, lg	285.00
St George, D6621, sm	145.00
Tam O'Shanter, D6632, lg	95.00
Tam O'Shanter, D6640, miniature	45.00
Toby Philpots, D5737, sm	60.00
Toby Philpots, D6043, miniature	50.00
Tony Weller, D5530, sm	55.00
Tony Weller, D5531, lg	150.00
Town Crier, D6530, lg	200.00
Town Crier, D6537, sm	130.00
Town Crier, D6544, miniature	125.00

Trapper, #6609, large, $95.00.

Trapper, D6612, sm	45.00
Ugly Duchess, D6599, lg	485.00
Ugly Duchess, D6603, sm	295.00
Uncle Tom Cobbleigh, D6637, lg	375.00
Veteran Motorist, D6633, lg	95.00
Vicar of Bray, D5615, lg	200.00
Walrus & Carpenter, D6600, lg	125.00
Walrus & Carpenter, D6608, miniature	60.00
Yachtsman, D6622, lg	95.00

Figurines

A Courting, HN2004	450.00
A La Mode, HN2544, gr dress	185.00
Adrienne, HN2152, red dress	130.00
Affection, HN2236	55.00
Afternoon Tea, HN1748, gr dress	1,250.00
Alice, HN2158, gr dress	125.00
All Aboard, HN2940, bl skirt	175.00
Amy, HN2958, wht dress	95.00

And So To Bed, HN2966	90.00
Angelina, HN1204	725.00
Anthea, HN1527	650.00
Antoinette, HN2326	140.00
Apple Maid, HN2160	400.00
April Shower, HN3024, gold trim	75.00
At Ease, HN2473, yel dress	200.00
Autumn Breezes, HN1934, red dress	195.00
Baby Bunting, HN2108	250.00
Ballerina, HN2116	250.00
Balloon Girl, HN2818, yel blouse	125.00
Bather, HN773, pk robe	1,400.00
Beachcomber, HN2487, purple shirt	175.00
Beat You To It, HN2871	250.00
Beggar, HN2175, orange sash	600.00
Bell O' the Ball, HN1997	250.00
Belle, HN754	550.00
Bess, HN2002, red cloak	250.00
Beth, HN2870	110.00
Biddy, HN1513, red dress	165.00
Biddy Penny Farthing, HN1843	195.00
Blacksmith of Williamsburg, HN2240	165.00
Blithe Morning, HN2021, bl & pk dress	175.00
Blossom, HN1667, orange shawl	850.00
Bluebeard, HN2105	375.00
Boatman, HN2417	160.00
Bride, HN2166	225.00
Bride, HN2873	130.00
Bridesmaid, HN2196	115.00
Broken Lance, HN2041	525.00
Buttercup, HN2309, yel dress	150.00
Camellia, HN2222, pk dress	250.00
Captain Cook, HN2889	285.00
Captain MacHeath, HN464, red jacket	695.00
Carpet Seller, HN1464	225.00
Catherine, HN2395	150.00
Cavalier, HN2716	180.00
Centurion, HN2726	175.00
Charlotte, HN2421	125.00
Charmian, HN1568	575.00
Child of Williamsburg, HN2421	125.00
Chinese Dancer, limited	650.00
Chloe, M29, red gown	300.00
Christine, HN2792, bl dress	200.00
Christmas Parcels, HN2851	250.00
Christmas Time, HN2110	350.00
Cicely, HN1516	650.00
Cissie, HN1809, red dress	95.00
Clare, HN2793	175.00
Claribel, HN1951, red dress	350.00
Clarinda, HN2724	175.00
Clarissa, HN1525	150.00
Cleopatra, HN2868	1,400.00
Clockmaker, HN2279	250.00
Cloud, HN1831	4,500.00
Clown, HN2890	275.00
Cobbler, HN1706	275.00
Coppelia, HN2115, bl & red	575.00
Country Lass, HN1991A	125.00
Courtier, HN1338	875.00
Craftsman, HN2284	400.00
Cup of Tea, HN2322, blk dress	135.00
Curtsy, HN327, J01 dress	1,300.00
Daffy Down Dilly, HN1712	235.00

Dainty May, HN1639, red dress 350.00
Dancers of the World, Kurdish, HN2867 ....595.00
Dancers of the World, Polish, HN2836, floral skirt 595.00
Dancers of the World, West Indian, HN2384, mc costume 595.00
Darling, HN1985, wht 85.00
Daydreams, HN1731, pk 175.00
Debbie, HN2385 ....95.00
Deidre, HN2020 ....325.00
Delphine, HN2136, bl dress 275.00
Detective, HN2359 ....195.00
Diana, HN1986, red dress 120.00
Dinky Do, HN2120, red 85.00
Doctor, HN2858, blk coat 150.00
Dorcas, HN1491 ....550.00
Dreamweaver, HN2283 ....200.00
Drummer Boy, HN2679 ....370.00
Duke of Edinburgh, HN2386 ....295.00
Dulcie, HN2305 ....145.00
Easter Day, HN2039 ....295.00
Elegance, HN2264, gr dress 150.00
Elizabeth, HN2946 ....175.00
Emma, HN2834 ....110.00
Empress Dowager, ltd ed 950.00
Enchantment, HN2178 ....150.00
Ermine Coat, HN1981 ....245.00
Evelyn, HN1622 ....1,250.00
Eventide, HN2814, bl dress 135.00
Fagin, HN534 ....50.00
Fair Lady, HN2193 ....125.00
Fairy, HN1532, yel mushroom 450.00
Fairyspell, HN2979 ....65.00
Falstaff, HN2054, red jacket 150.00
Faraway, HN2133, bl trim 195.00
Farmer's Wife, HN2069 ....495.00
Fiona, HN2694, red & wht dress 165.00
First Waltz, HN2862 ....190.00
Fleur, HN2368, gr dress 125.00
Fleur, HN2369, orange & bl 125.00
Fortune Teller, HN2159 ....395.00
Forty Winks, HN1974, wht apron 175.00
Four O'clock, HN1760 ....850.00
Francine, HN2422 ....85.00
Friar Tuck, HN2143, brn robe 450.00
Frodo, HN2912 ....60.00
Gainsborough Hat, HN46 ....950.00
Galadriel, HN2915 ....75.00
Gay Morning, HN2135 ....325.00
Geisha, HN634, blk & wht kimono 1,500.00
Genevieve, HN1962, red dress 220.00
Georgiana, HN2093, bl skirt 1,200.00
Geraldine, HN2348, brn dress 145.00
Gillian, HN1670, pk dress 795.00
Gladys, HN1740 ....425.00
Good Catch, HN2558 ....150.00
Good King Wenceslas, HN2118 ....285.00
Goody Two Shoes, HN2037, red dress 95.00
Gossips, HN2025 ....275.00
Grace, HN2318 ....165.00
Grand Manner, HN2723 ....175.00
Grandma, HN2052, bl shawl 350.00
Greta, HN1485 ....245.00
Guy Fawkes, HN98 ....950.00
Gwynneth, HN1980, red dress 225.00
Harmony, HN2824 ....175.00

Harp, HN2482, brn dress 1,200.00
Hazel, HN1796 ....350.00
Heather, HN2956, wht dress 75.00
Helen of Troy, HN2387 ....850.00
Helmsman, HN2499 ....225.00

Henrietta Maria, 1609-1666, 110/47, 1947, 9½", $450.00.

Her Ladyship, HN1977 ....295.00
Highwayman, HN527 ....550.00
Hilary, HN2335 ....135.00
Home Again, HN2167, red/orange dress 125.00
Honey, HN1963 ....550.00
Hornpipe, HN2161 ....550.00
Hostess of Williamsburg, HN2209 ....175.00
Huntsman, HN2492, gr jacket 175.00
Hurdy Gurdy, HN2796, bl dress 600.00
In Grandma's Days, HN340 ....975.00
Innocence, HN2842 ....150.00
Invitation, HN2170, pk dress 125.00
Iona, HN1346 ....1,750.00
Irene, HN1621, yel dress 300.00
Jacqueline, HN2000 ....475.00
James, HN3013, gray pants 100.00
Janet, HN1537 ....145.00
Janet, HN1916, pk skirt 200.00
Janice, HN2165 ....455.00
Jean, HN2032 ....365.00
Jennifer, HN2392, bl & wht dress 150.00
Jersey Milk Maid, HN2057 ....225.00
Jester, HN308 ....1,350.00
Joan, HN1422, dtd 1941 ....300.00
Jolly Sailor, HN2172, bl & wht shirt 525.00
Jovial Monk, HN2144, brn robe 185.00
Judge, HN2443 ....200.00
Julia, HN2705, orange dress 125.00
June, HN1691, floral dress 450.00
Kate Hardcastle, HN2028 ....700.00
Kirsty, HN2381, orange dress 125.00
La Sylphide, HN2138, wht costume 395.00
Lady Charmian, HN1949 ....225.00
Lady Musicians, w/certificates, in box, set of 12 ....9,600.00
Lady Pamela, HN2718, pk dress 155.00
Lambing Time, HN1890 ....175.00

Laura, HN2960, floral gown 135.00
Laurianne, HN2719 ....175.00
Lavinia, HN1955, red dress 95.00
Leading Lady, HN2269, lav dress 175.00
Leda & the Swan, HN2826 ....2,000.00
Lily, HN1798 ....195.00
Linda, HN2106, red cloak 125.00
Lisa, HN2310 ....145.00
Little Boy Blue, HN2062, bl smock 125.00
Little Bridesmaid, HN1433 ....125.00
Little Bridesmaid, M30 ....250.00
Long John Silver, HN2204 ....450.00
Loretta, HN2337 ....125.00
Lorna, HN2311, gr dress 145.00
Louise, HN2869 ....95.00
Lucy, HN2863, bl & wht dress 95.00
Lunchtime, HN2485 ....180.00
Lydia, HN1908, red dress 85.00
Magpie Ring, HN2978 ....75.00
Mandy, HN2476 ....75.00
Marguerite, HN1928 ....295.00
Marie, HN1635 ....350.00
Marietta, HN1699 ....550.00
Marjorie, HN2788, bl & wht dress 150.00
Mary, Mary, HN2044 ....145.00
Mary Jane, HN1990 ....525.00
Mask Seller, HN2103, gr coat 145.00
Masque, HN2554 ....195.00
Masquerade, HN2251, bl/gr skirt 275.00
Matilda, HN2011, red cape 475.00
Maureen, HN1770, red dress, dtd 1941 ....275.00
Maytime, HN2113 ....250.00
Meditation, HN2330 ....295.00
Melanie, HN2271, bl dress 135.00
Memories, HN2030 ....400.00
Mephistopheles & Marguerite, HN755 ....1,300.00
Midinette, HN2090, bl dress 275.00
Miss Demure, HN1402 ....195.00
Miss Muffet, HN1936, red coat 160.00
Miss Muffet, HN1937, gr coat 250.00
Mother's Help, HN2151 ....175.00
Mr Micawber, HN557, brn jacket, 7" 300.00
Mr Pickwick, HN2099 ....295.00
Mr Pickwick, HN556 ....350.00
Musicale, HN2756, ivory 90.00
My Teddy, HN2177 ....495.00
Nell, HN3014, pk dress 95.00
New Bonnet, HN1728, red gown, gr bonnet, 1935, rstr 750.00
New Companions, HN2770, bl shawl 160.00
Newsboy, HN2244, plaid hat 450.00
Nicola, HN2839, lav dress 195.00
Nina, HN2347 ....150.00
Ninette, HN2379 ....140.00
Officer of the Line, HN2733 ....150.00
Old Balloon Seller, HN1315, red jacket 175.00
Old King, HN358 ....950.00
Old Meg, HN2494 ....255.00
Old Mother Hubbard, HN2314 ....250.00
Olga, HN2463, gr dress 215.00
Omar Khayyam, HN2247 ....165.00
Once Upon a Time, HN2047 ....350.00
One That Got Away, HN2153 ....275.00
Orange Lady, HN1953, yel dress, gr shawl 200.00
Paisley Shawl, HN1987 ....250.00

Paisley Shawl, HN1988, red hat 175.00
Pantalettes, M15 ....250.00
Pantalettes, M31, bl suit 275.00
Parisian, HN2445 ....150.00
Parson's Daughter, HN337 ....650.00
Past Glory, HN2484 ....175.00
Patricia, HN1431, pk & bl dress 450.00
Patricia, M8 ....300.00
Paula, HN2906 ....135.00
Pearly Girl, HN2036 ....175.00
Peggy, HN2038, red dress 95.00
Penelope, HN1901 ....295.00
Pensive Moments, HN2704 ....195.00
Pied Piper, HN2102, blk 250.00

Pirouette, #2216, 1958, 6", $195.00.

Poacher, HN2043, gray jacket 225.00
Polly Peachum, HN620 ....350.00
Potter, HN1493 ....285.00
Premiere, HN2343, wht dress 175.00
Prince of Wales, HN2883, blk suit 350.00
Princess, HN430 ....2,750.00
Priscilla, M14 ....275.00
Professor, HN2281 ....175.00
Proposal, HN1209, man in bl coat 750.00
Punch & Judy Man, HN2765 ....175.00
Puppetmaker, HN2253, brn pants 425.00
Queen of Sheba, HN2328 ....850.00
Rachel, HN2919 ....175.00
Rag Doll, HN2142 ....85.00
Regal Lady, HN2709 ....145.00
Repose, HN2272, pk dress 185.00
Rest Awhile, HN2728 ....175.00
Reverie, HN2306 ....195.00
Rhapsody, HN2267, gr dress 225.00
River Boy, HN2128, bl pants, wht shirt 145.00
Rocking Horse, HN2072 ....1,750.00
Romance, HN2430 ....150.00
Romany Sue, HN1757, gr dress 950.00
Rosalind, HN2393 ....195.00
Rose, HN2123 ....75.00
Rosebud, HN1983, red shawl 450.00
Rosemary, HN2091, red dress 450.00
Rowena, HN2077 ....550.00
Rumplestiltskin, HN3025 ....100.00

Sabbath Morn, HN1982, red dress 265.00
Sailor's Holiday, HN2442 . . . . .195.00
Sam Weller, HN531, 4" 50.00
Santa Claus, HN2725 . . . . .175.00
Schoolmarm, HN2223 . . . . .175.00
Sea Sprite, HN2191 . . . . .300.00
Seafarer, HN2455 . . . . .225.00
Secret Thoughts, HN2382, gr dress .122.00
Serena, HN1868 . . . . .675.00
Serenade, HN2753, ivory 85.00
Shore Leave, HN2254 . . . . .185.00
Silk & Ribbons, HN2017, gr dress 135.00
Silversmith of Williamsburg, HN2208 . . . . .175.00
Simone, HN2378 . . . . .135.00
Sir Edward, HN2370 . . . . .350.00
Sir Ralph, HN2371, gray armor 350.00
Sleepy Darling, HN2953 . . . . .225.00
Sleepyhead, HN2114 . . . . .950.00
Soiree, HN2312 . . . . .130.00
Solitude, HN2810 . . . . .165.00
Sophie, HN2833 . . . . .95.00
Southern Belle, HN2229, red dress .145.00
Southern Belle, HN2425, bl & pk dress 150.00
Spring, HN2085 . . . . .395.00
Spring Flowers, HN1807 . . . . .275.00
St George & Dragon, HN2051 . . . . .395.00
Stephanie, HN2807 . . . . .140.00
Stitch in Time, HN2352 . . . . .135.00
Stop Press, HN2683 . . . . .175.00
Suitor, HN2132 . . . . .350.00
Summer, HN2086, rose dress 400.00
Sunday Best, HN2206 . . . . .195.00
Susan, HN2056 . . . . .300.00
Susan, HN2592 . . . . .175.00
Sweet & Twenty, HN1298, pk & red dress 250.00
Sweet Anne, HN1318, bl jacket 180.00
Sweet April, HN2215, pk dress 325.00
Sweet Dreams, HN2380, mc clothes 125.00
Symphony, HN2287 . . . . .250.00
Taking Things Easy, HN2677 . . . . .150.00
Tall Story, HN2248 . . . . .250.00
Teenager, HN2203 . . . . .235.00
Thank You, HN2732 . . . . .175.00
Thanks Doc, HN2731 . . . . .185.00
This Little Pig, HN1793, red blanket 95.00
Toinette, HN1940 . . . . .1,350.00
Tom, HN2864, bl pants 100.00
Top O' the Hill, HN1834, red dress .175.00
Top O' the Hill, HN1849, pk dress .175.00
Toymaker, HN2250 . . . . .325.00
Tuppence a Bag, HN2320, gr dress .135.00
Twilight, HN2256 . . . . .175.00
Uncle Ned, HN2094 . . . . .475.00
Uriah Heep, HN554, blk jacket & trousers 265.00
Uriah Heep, M45, blk suit 50.00
Veneta, HN2722 . . . . .125.00
Veronica, HN1517 . . . . .350.00
Victoria, HN2471 . . . . .150.00
Victorian Lady, HN728, red skirt 225.00
Viking, HN2375 . . . . .245.00
Vivienne, HN2073 . . . . .265.00
Votes for Women, HN2816 . . . . .195.00
Wayfarer, HN2362, gr jacket 185.00
We Willie Winkie, HN2050 . . . . .350.00

Welsh Girl, HN660 . . . . .1,800.00
Wigmaker of Williamsburg, HN2239 . . . . .165.00
Willy-Won't He, HN2150 . . . . .450.00
Windflower, HN1920 . . . . .375.00
Winsome, HN2220, red dress 145.00
Winter, HN2088 . . . . .365.00
Wistful, HN2396 . . . . .210.00
Woman Holding Child, HN703 . . . . .6,000.00
Wood Nymph, HN2192 . . . . .250.00
Young Knight, HN94 . . . . .3,000.00
Young Master, HN2872, red jacket .220.00
Yum-Yum, HN1268 . . . . .550.00

Flambe

Buddha, standing, 5" 245.00
Cat, sitting, #9, 5" 125.00
Dog of Fo 150.00
Dragon, 14" 500.00
Drake, 6½" 150.00
Duck, sitting, mk, 3½" L 75.00
Duck, swimming, 1½x3" 75.00
Elephant, trunk raised, Sung, 5½" .175.00

Fox, 4½", $150.00.

Fox, flat, 5½" L 75.00
Fox, recumbent, #14, 4" 75.00
Fox, sitting, 2¾x4" 150.00
Hare, #1157, 2¾" 80.00
Hare, ear up, #330, 2½" 95.00
Hare, recumbent, 2½x4¼" 125.00
Penguin, 6" 150.00
Tiger, sgn Noke, 14" 650.00
Tiger, 6x13" 750.00
Vase, bottle form, Noke Art, 12" 165.00
Vase, deer, 7" 165.00
Vase, ploughing scene, globular, 1930s, 6½" 110.00
Vase, scenic, 6½" 65.00
Vase, Sung, fish decor, sgn FM, 8" .795.00
Vase, Sung, florals, mc on purple, sgn Noke, 8½" 545.00
Vase, Veined Sung, ovoid, 10" 225.00
Vase, Veined Sung, woodcut, #1603, 7" 165.00
Vase, woodcut, #1603, 7¼" 95.00
Vase, woodcut, #1619, 11" 285.00

Series Ware

Biscuit jar, Dutch People, SP top/rim/hdl, mk, 6¼x4⅞" 225.00
Bottle, sheep in sunset, hinged top, mk, 5¼x2¼" 85.00

Bowl, Coaching Days, coach departing, 8" 130.00
Box, Robin Hood, rectangular, 2x3½x4½" 100.00
Charger, Dickensware, Tony Weller, 13½" 185.00
Child's set, Nursery Rhymes, bowl/plate/mug, ca 1909 . . . . .115.00
Cup, Nursery Rhymes, Old King Cole, w/Mother Goose saucer .50.00
Cup & saucer, demitasse; Dickensware, mk, 2¼" 55.00
Cup & saucer, Robin Hood, 2¾x6" 65.00
Jardiniere, Welsh Ladies, going to church, mk, 7⅛x7¼" 325.00
Match holder, Dutch People, scuttle shape, early mk, 2¾" 88.00
Match holder, Monks, profile on front, 2½" 70.00
Match striker, Dutch People, couple/crying child, mk, 3x4½" . .145.00
Mug, Dutch People, boy & girl, early mk, 1⅞x1⅜" 50.00
Mug, Welsh Ladies, 3 ladies & child, mk, 1⅜x1⅜" 69.00
Pitcher, Dickensware, Alfred Jingle, sq, mk, 7⅜" 125.00
Pitcher, English Cottages, on gold shaded to tan, mk, 6⅝" 88.00
Pitcher, Izaak Walton, Perch or Pike..., 12½" 225.00
Pitcher, Moorish Gate, 2 Arabs by gate, mk, 4¾x4" 80.00
Pitcher, Sea Shanty, sailors/ship/verses, mk, 6¾x4⅞" 150.00
Pitcher, Shakespeare, Portia, mk, 6⅜x4⅝" dia 110.00
Plate, Gibson Girl, 1904, 10½" 100.00
Plate, Golfers, Every Dog Has His Day, 10½" 175.00
Plate, Old English Inns, King's Head, Chigwell, 10" 40.00
Plate, Robin Hood, Friend of the Poor, mk, 8½" 35.00
Plate, Shakespeare, As You Like It, 10" 90.00
Plate, Treasure Island, Long John Silver w/crew, 13" 90.00
Sugar bowl, Fox Hunting, John Peel, huntsmen lead horses 40.00
Sugar shaker, Jackdaw of Rheims, SP lid, mk, 6¾x2½" 175.00
Teapot, Fisherwomen, mk, 5½" 195.00
Teapot, Robin Hood, Little John & Friar Tuck, 5½" 195.00
Tray, Dickensware, Bill Sykes, rectangular, mk, 11x5⅝" 88.00
Tray, Dickensware, Bill Sykes, sgn Noke, sq, 8½" 110.00
Tray, Gaffers, man in wht smock, top hat & cane, mk, 8x6¼" . .55.00
Tray, Zunday Zmocks, rectangular, mk, 9x6½" 95.00
Vase, Babes in Woods, flow bl w/gold, 6⅜x4⅜" 245.00
Vase, Coaching Days, ball form, mk, 5⅞" 145.00
Vase, Comical Hunt, mk, 4⅜" 85.00
Vase, cows in pastoral scene, mk, 4⅝" 100.00
Vase, Dickensware, Barnaby Rudge, mk, 4¾" 70.00
Vase, Dickensware, Old Peggoty, mk, 5¼x4⅛" 80.00
Vase, Dickensware, Sam Weller, sq, 3¼x2" 65.00
Vase, Dunolly Castle, mk, 4½x2¾" 165.00
Vase, Robin Hood, flattened sq form, 5½x2x4" 95.00
Vase, Robin Hood Slays Guy of Gisborne, mk, 5½" 95.00
Vase, Shakespeare, Cardinal Wolsey, hdls, mk, 8½x3¾" 165.00
Vase, Shakespeare, Ophelia in pk, hdls, 6⅜x4" 135.00
Vase, Shakespeare, Romeo & Juliet, mk, 12" 425.00
Vase, Warwick Castle, flow bl, 8¾" .110.00
Vase, Welsh Ladies, ladies & children on path to house, 7" . . .165.00
Vase, Welsh Ladies, 1¾x2¼" 75.00
Vase, Welsh Ladies, 2¾x2¼" 85.00

Stoneware

Beaker, hunt scene, brass rim 60.00
Biscuit jar, floral, bl/brn on tan, cobalt borders, mk, 7" 175.00
Ewer, Cerrara, M Marshall, 7" 135.00
Humidor, cattle/chilren incised, H Barlow, dtd 1878, 5¾" 500.00
Humidor, figures in relief, brn to tan, mk, 5x4¼" 118.00
Jug, Here's to Thee..., simulated leather, SP trim, 6" 110.00
Jug, puzzle; writings/sayings, Lambeth, 9" 225.00
Mug, bicycling scenes, wht on tan, brn hdl, Lambeth, 6" 275.00
Mug, King George V 55.00
Ring dish, owl figural, brn/tan, 4x3¼" 295.00
Tray, Kaola figure at bk, leaves at rim, Lambeth, 10½x5¼" 275.00

Vase, floral, sgn Florence Roberts, Lambeth, 1885, 10½" 165.00
Vase, horses/sheep, fleur-de-lis band, Hanna Barlow, 16" 1,500.00
Vase, Nouveau birds, sq, FC Pope, 9" .80.00

Stoneware vases signed Hanna Barlow, Left, incised
cows, ca 1903, 8", $625.00; Right, incised goats,
dated 1822, 10", $650.00.

Toby Jugs

Best Is None Too Good, D6266, 4½" .275.00
Cap'n Cuttle, D6266, 4½" 185.00
Cliff Cornell, brn, 9" 395.00
Falstaff, 5¼" 65.00
Fat Boy, D6264, 4½" 225.00
Happy John, D6070, 5½" 55.00
Honest Measure, D6108, 4½" 65.00
Huntsman, D6320, 7½" 95.00
Mr Furrow, D6701, 4" 45.00
Mr Micawber, D6262, 4½" 185.00
Mr Pickwick, D6261, 4½" 185.00
Reverend Cassock, D6702 . . . . .45.00
Sam Weller, D6265, 4½" 185.00
Sherlock Holmes, D6661, 8¾" 80.00
Sir Francis Drake, D6660, 9" 95.00
Sir Winston Churchill, D6175, 4" 45.00

Miscellaneous

Ash tray, John Barleycorn, D5602 . . . . .110.00
Bottle, liquor; coat-of-arms for Chivas, brn/tan, 8½" 95.00
Bottle, whiskey; Highland 95.00
Bottle, whiskey; Scottsman in relief .275.00
Bust, Sairey Gamp, D6047 . . . . .85.00
Cake plate, single rose center, sterling rim, 12" 75.00
Cookie jar, floral, pk/mauve on cream, Slater's Patent 125.00
Match holder, Mr Squeers, 2" 90.00
Napkin ring, Mr Micawber, M58 . . . . .400.00
Pitcher, floral on cream, turq jewels, Burslem, #139596, 5" . . .225.00
Teapot, Old Charley 1,950.00
Vase, blk scenic: house/cattails by lake, #8224, 9" 225.00
Vase, pastel flowers, 3 gold legs, Burslem, 4½" 120.00
Vase, tapestry, artist sgn, Slater's Patent, Lambeth, 11" 125.00

Decanter, Scotsman, 1 of 144 made for Asprey of London, 9", $4,000.

Dragon Ware

An undulating moriage dragon with a fierce expression decorates shaded gray bisque backgrounds in this type of ware that was very popular as gift-shop items during the forties and fifties. It was produced in Japan and may sometimes be found with the Nippon mark. Items listed below are unmarked unless noted.

Vase, marked Nippon, 7", $200.00.

Cigarette box, +2 ash trays 25.00
Cup & saucer, nude lithophane 25.00
Demitasse set, lithophane, 16-pc 130.00
Plate, 7" 15.00
Plate, 8" 18.00

Tea set, pearlized cups, 11-pc, serves 4 . . . . .65.00
Tea set, star/Lima mks, #30, 3-pc 85.00
Teapot, gold hdl, 7" 35.00
Vase, gold trim, 6" 85.00
Vase, 7" 65.00

Dresden

The term Dresden is used today to indicate the porcelains that were produced in Meissen and Dresden, Germany, from the very early 18th century well into the next. John Bottger, a young alchemist, discovered the formula for the first true porcelain in 1708 while being held a virtual prisoner at the palace in Dresden because of the King's determination to produce a superior ware. Two years later a factory was erected in nearby Meissen with Bottger as director. There fine tableware, elaborate center-pieces, and exquisite figurines with applied details were produced. In 1731, to distinguish their product from the wares of such potters as Sevres, Worcester, Chelsea, and Derby, Meissen adopted their famous crossed swords trademark. During the next century, several potteries were producing porcelain in the 'Meissen style' in Dresden itself. Their wares were marked with their own logo and the Dresden indication. Those listed here are from that era. See the Meissen section for examples with the crossed swords marking.

Vase with dome lid, hand-painted garden scene with group of people, ca 1880, 14", $850.00.

Bowl, Clementine portrait, pearl lustre rim, ftd, 2¾x7½" 320.00
Bowl, fruit; HP floral w/appl flower, openwork rim, 4x9" 175.00
Candlestick, dbl, appl roses, Baroque base, mk, 5x7", pr 180.00
Charger, equestrian cavaliers/ladies after Wouvermann, 15" . . .600.00
Cup & saucer, chocolate; man/lady in gilt reserve on dk bl 45.00
Ewer, maids/cupids, very ornate hdl/base, Wissmann, 12" 795.00
Figurine, allegorical group, dolphins & cupids, 17" L 750.00
Figurine, ballerina on toe, Popplesdorf mk, 7", M 150.00
Figurine, ballerina w/arms out, pk dress/bl shoes, 6" 170.00
Figurine, boy/girl feed ducks, scroll base, 1900s, 5", pr 200.00
Figurine, Dame de Courde Francois I, 1875, 8" 350.00
Figurine, dancing pr, he in red coat; she w/appl roses, 6" 195.00
Figurine, hunter in red coat w/dog, 13½" 600.00
Figurine, lady & 2 children w/lamb, 9" 500.00
Figurine, lady in chair, vase on table, dog, lace, 8x8" 325.00
Figurine, man & woman w/cupids, 14" 850.00
Figurine, Marquise de Vereuil, high collar/fan, 1667, 8" 350.00
Figurine, mother reads to 2 children on sofa, lace, mk, 8" 650.00

Figurine, 1800s man/lady, floral attire/gilt, 13", pr 250.00
Inkwell, floral, pot on tray, w/lid & blotter, 1880s 90.00
Loving cup, nymphs in gold reserves on red, 3-hdld, mk, 6½" . .365.00
Plate, couple/dog in garden, emb gold flowers, 10" 250.00
Standish, romantic reserves on maroon, stand+2 pots, 9" L 185.00
Urn, panels of lovers on red w/floral, R Klemm, 1900, 12" 395.00
Vase, ladies/cupid/children on wine w/gold, hdl, 1890, 12" 795.00

Dresser Accessories

Dresser sets, ring trees, figural or satin pincushions, manicure sets — all those lovely items that graced milady's dressing table — were at the same time decorative as well as functional. Today they appeal to collectors for many reasons. The Victorian era is well represented by repousse silver-backed mirrors and brushes and pincushions that were used to display ornamental pins for the hair, hats, and scarves. The hair receiver — similar to a powder jar but with an opening in the lid — was used to hold the lovely strands of hair retrieved from the comb or brush. These were wound around the finger and tucked in the opening to be used later for hair jewelry and pictures, many of which survive to the present day. (See Hair Weaving.)

Celluloid dresser sets were popular during the late 1800s and early 1900s. Some included manicure tools, pill boxes, and buttonhooks as well as the basic items. Because celluloid tends to break rather easily, a whole set may be hard to find today. (See also Plastics.) With the current interest in anything Art Deco, sets from the thirties and forties are especially collectible. These may be made of crystal, Bakelite, or silver and the original boxes just as lavishly appointed as their contents.

Bottle, scent; scroll/floral relief, milk glass w/gold, 9½" 30.00
Bottle, Scrolled Leaf, milk glass 55.00
Box, hairpin; SP, hinged lid, 4 ball ft, repousse, Webster 24.00
Box, milk glass, emb fruit, triple scallop form, 5x7" 65.00
Box, patch; Delft-like windmill, bl on wht china, 1¾x2¼" 110.00
Box, patch; floral, mc on amber glass, 1x2" 145.00
Box, patch; roses, red w/wht motif on cobalt glass, 1x2⅛" 165.00
Box, rubena stippled, faceted finial, St Louis, Fr, 5x3½" 118.00
Box, water scene on satin, sgn TOG, 3" dia 75.00

Dresser set, sterling mounted, McChesney, 1925, 16 pieces, $600.00.

Hair crimper, SP, MOP button, repousse floral hdl 20.00
Hair curler heater, alcohol lamp, scrolled Tufts SP, 8x5" 145.00
Hair receiver, SP, overall repouse, Wilcox, 4½" dia 32.00
Jar, amethyst glass, emb roses w/diagonals, rose finial 22.00
Jar, powder; gr glass, Ginaud, NY 22.00
Mirror, hand; sterling, Deco style, M .250.00
Mirror & brush, SP Nouveau floral, Derby, dtd 1900, EX 48.00
Mustache curler, sterling, repousse flowers, folding, 6" 45.00
Nail file, MOP, ca 1920, EX 7.50
Set, floral on cobalt, German china, 8-pc on 20x6" tray 325.00
Set, Gorham, repousse florals, 12-pc, 35-oz 450.00
Set, lav trim w/gold, Bavaria china, 5-pc on tray 175.00

Set, SP Nouveau florals, Derby, dtd 1897, brush+mirror 68.00
Tray, mirrored brass fr, oval, ball ft, mk Apollo, 11x8" 25.00
Tray, porc, cherub center, pk border, 11½x7¼" 35.00

Dryden

James Dryden opened his pottery in Ellsworth, Kansas, in 1946. Within a year, he was producing 2,000 pieces per week, and the pottery continued to grow. During the 1950s some of the pottery was subcontracted to Van Briggle. In 1956 Dryden moved to Hot Springs, Arkansas.

Ellsworth clay was dark tan, while pieces made in Hot Springs were of white clay, This helps to date the ware, all of which is marked. Various marks were used, but all include either the words 'Dryden' or 'Ozark Frontier.'

Basket, brn shades w/gold, mk 50.00
Ewer, tan & gr mottle, mk, w/sticker, 7½" 15.00
Figurine, elephant, bl, souvenir, 3x4" 18.00
Pitcher, bl, #98, 5¾" 10.00
Pitcher, brn, bird hdl, #94, w/souvenir sticker, 6½" 25.00
Pitcher, fish decor on blk, incised Ft Randall Dam, label, 4" 10.00
Pitcher, floral band w/butterfly, mc, sgn May-Lis, 11" 60.00
Spittoon, brn w/bl, sgn ARS, gold sticker, 8x8½" 45.00
Teapot, bl, w/lid 28.00
Vase, bl, boot form, mk, 4¾" 15.00
Vase, bl w/gr decor, sgn LOL-77, 3½x3¼" 15.00
Vase, blk, #104, 2¾x2¼" 15.00

Duncan and Miller

The firm that became known as the Duncan and Miller Glass Company in 1900 was organized in 1874 in Pittsburgh, Pennsylvania, a partnership between George Duncan, his sons Harry and James, and his son-in-law Augustus Heisey. John Ernest Miller was hired as their designer. He is credited with creating the most famous of all Duncan's glassware lines, Three Face. (See Pattern Glass.) The George Duncan and Sons Glass Company, as it was titled, was only one of eighteen companies that merged in 1891 with U.S. Glass. Soon after the Pittsburgh factory burned in 1892, the association was dissolved, and Heisey left the firm to set up his own factory in Newark, Ohio. Duncan built his new plant in Washington, Pennsylvania, where he continued to make pressed glassware in such notable patterns as Bagware, Amberette, Duncan Flute, Button Arches, and Zippered Slash. The firm was eventually sold to U.S. Glass in Tiffin, Ohio, and officially closed in August, 1955.

In addition to the early pressed dinnerware patterns, today's Duncan and Miller collectors enjoy searching for opalescent vases in many patterns and colors, frosted 'Satin Tone' glassware, acid-etched designs, and lovely stemware such as the Rock Crystal cuttings. Milk glass was made in limited quantity and is considered a good investment. Ruby glass, Ebony (a lovely opaque black glass popular during the twenties and thirties), and, of course, the glass animal and bird figurines are all highly valued examples of the art of Duncan and Miller.

Expect to pay at least 25% more than values listed for 'color' for ruby and cobalt and as much as 50% more in the Georgian, Pall Mall and Sandwich lines. Pink, green, and amber Sandwich is worth approximately 30% more than the same items in crystal. Milk glass examples of American Way are valued up to 30% higher than color, 50% higher in Pall Mall. Add approximately 40% to listed prices for opalescent items. Etchings, cuttings and other decorations will increase values by about 50%. For further study, we recommend *The Encyclopedia of Duncan Glass*, by Gail Krause; she is listed in the Directory under Pennsylvania.

Amberette #48, carafe 50.00
Amberette #48, punch cup 7.50
American Way, crystal; bowl, oval, 12½" 40.00
American Way, crystal; candlestick, 2", pr 27.50
American Way, crystal; plate, flat edge, 14" 45.00
American Way, crystal; plate, star shaped, 14" 45.00
American Way, crystal; vase, flared, 9½" 45.00
American Way, satintone; centerpiece, crimped, 12" 60.00
American Way, satintone; hors d'oeuvre, 6-part, 15" 70.00
Astaire, crystal; cocktail, 3-oz 8.50
Astaire, crystal; ice cream, ftd, 5-oz 9.00
Astaire, crystal; plate, 8½" 9.00
Astaire, satintone; goblet 12.50
Astaire, satintone; parfait, 5-oz 12.00
Astaire, satintone; tumbler, 2-oz 9.00
Bristol Diamond, clear w/gold; bowl, flat, shell shape 30.00
Bristol Diamond, clear w/gold; toothpick holder 27.50
Bristol Diamond, clear w/gold; wine 20.00
Canterbury, color; bowl, salad; 10" 32.50
Canterbury, color; candlestick, 6", pr 37.00
Canterbury, color; cigarette jar 25.00
Canterbury, color; plate, 14" 38.00
Canterbury, color; sugar bowl, 7-oz 22.50
Canterbury, crystal; cup & saucer 17.50
Canterbury, crystal; finger bowl 9.00
Canterbury, crystal; goblet, 9-oz 12.50
Canterbury, crystal; nappy, hdld, 6" 10.50
Canterbury, crystal; pickle tray, 8" 12.50
Canterbury, crystal; sugar bowl, 3-oz 10.00
Canterbury, crystal; sugar bowl, 7-oz 12.50
Canterbury, opal; vase, 12" 55.00
Caribbean, color; bowl, console; flared, 12" 40.00
Caribbean, color; bowl, vegetable; hdld, 9¼" 30.00
Caribbean, color; bowl, 8½" 35.00
Caribbean, color; candlestick, 1-light, w/bl prisms, 7¼" 65.00
Caribbean, color; ice bucket, hdld, 6½" 75.00
Caribbean, color; pitcher, milk; 16-oz, 4¾" 75.00
Caribbean, color; pitcher, syrup; 9-oz, 4¼" 65.00
Caribbean, color; pitcher, water; w/ice lip, 72-oz, 9" 185.00
Caribbean, color; plate, salad; 7½" 14.00
Caribbean, color; punch cup 10.00
Caribbean, color; punch ladle 50.00
Caribbean, color; vase, ball form, flared, ftd, 7¼" 25.00
Caribbean, color; vase, str sides, ftd, 8" 35.00
Caribbean, crystal; cruet 47.50
Caribbean, crystal; flower bowl, rnd, 12" 25.00
Caribbean, crystal; relish, 5-part 28.00
Chanticleer, crystal; tumbler, 9-oz 13.00
Colonial, crystal; finger bowl & plate 10.50
Colonial, crystal; goblet, 9-oz 9.00
Colonial, crystal; ice cream, ftd, 5½-oz 8.00
Colonial, crystal; pitcher, ½-gal 20.00
Colonial, crystal; punch cup, 5-oz 7.00
Colonial, crystal; shakers, non-corrosive top, 1½-oz, pr 15.00
Colonial, crystal; sugar bowl, 16-oz 10.00
Colonial, crystal; vase, carnation; 9¾" 20.00
Diamond, color; bowl, flared, 11½" 30.00
Diamond, color; bowl, oval, 10" 25.00
Diamond, color; candy box, 6" 38.00
Diamond, color; centerpiece, oval, hdld, 11" 30.00
Diamond, color; flower arranger, 5" 20.00
Diamond, color; goblet, 9-oz 18.00
Diamond, color; saucer champagne, 6-oz 15.00
Diamond, color; wine, 3½-oz 17.00

Diamond, crystal; bonbon, 2-part, hdld, 6½" 14.00
Diamond, crystal; candlestick, 1-light, 4", pr 35.00
Diamond, crystal; sweetmeat, crimped, hdls, 7" 12.50
Early American Sandwich, crystal; bonbon, w/lid, ftd, 5" 37.50
Early American Sandwich, crystal; bowl, salad; shallow, 12" 35.00
Early American Sandwich, crystal; cake salver, ftd, 13" 65.00
Early American Sandwich, crystal; candy jar 40.00
Early American Sandwich, crystal; chop plate, 12" 45.00
Early American Sandwich, crystal; compote, low ftd, 6" 15.00
Early American Sandwich, crystal; flower bowl, crimped, 11½" . . .45.00
Early American Sandwich, crystal; ice cream, 5-oz 12.50
Early American Sandwich, crystal; lily bowl, 12" 37.50
Early American Sandwich, crystal; nappy, fruit; 6" 10.50
Early American Sandwich, crystal; plate, bread & butter; 6" 8.50
Early American Sandwich, crystal; relish, 3-part, 10" 37.50
Early American Sandwich, crystal; saucer champagne, 5-oz 14.00
Early American Sandwich, crystal; vase, crimped, ftd, 5" 20.00
Early American Sandwich, crystal; vase, fan shape, ftd, 5" 20.00
Early American Sandwich, crystal; wine, 3-oz 15.00
Eternally Yours, crystal; bowl, salad; 10½" 33.00
Eternally Yours, crystal; candy box, 6" 42.50
Eternally Yours, crystal; cheese & cracker set, 11" 42.50
Eternally Yours, crystal; cordial, 1-oz 17.50
Eternally Yours, crystal; flower bowl, flared, 12" 33.00
Eternally Yours, crystal; goblet, 10-oz 23.00
Eternally Yours, crystal; iced tea, ftd, 13-oz 25.00
Eternally Yours, crystal; relish, 3-part, 12" 32.00
Eternally Yours, crystal; wine, 3-oz 20.00

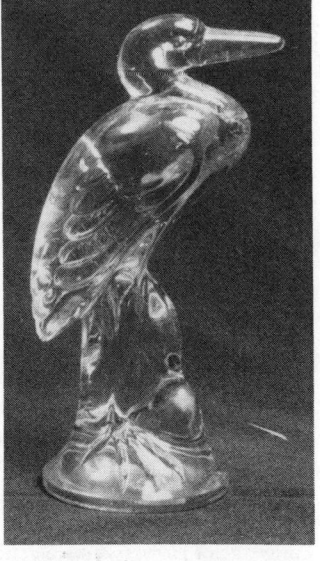

Figure of a heron, 7", $115.00.

First Love, color; bowl, oval, 14" 85.00
First Love, color; decanter, w/stopper, 16-oz 115.00
First Love, color; iced tea, ftd, 12-oz 27.50
First Love, color; plate, salad; rnd, 6" 23.50
First Love, color; vase, 8" 50.00
First Love, color; wine, 3-oz 35.00
First Love, crystal; bowl, salad; shallow, 11" 75.00
First Love, crystal; candelabrum, 3-light, w/prisms, 5" 105.00
First Love, crystal; candlestick, low, 4" 22.00
First Love, crystal; cocktail shaker, metal top, 18-oz 165.00
First Love, crystal; flower bowl, flared, 11" 80.00
First Love, crystal; ice bucket, chrome hdl/tongs, 6" 125.00
First Love, crystal; nappy, sq, 7" 27.00
First Love, crystal; saucer champagne, 5-oz 25.00

First Love, crystal; vase, ftd, 6" 50.00
Georgian, color; finger bowl & plate .35.00
Georgian, color; jug, ½-gal 35.00
Georgian, color; saucer champagne, ftd, 6-oz 17.50
Georgian, color; teacup & saucer .32.50
Georgian, color; wine 17.50
Georgian, crystal; chop plate, 14" .20.00
Georgian, crystal; ice cream, ftd, 5-oz 8.50
Georgian, crystal; parfait 8.50
Georgian, crystal; plate, 8½" 10.50
Georgian, crystal; vase, crimped, 8" 18.50
Grecian, color; cigarette holder, sq ftd, 3½" 80.00
Grecian, color; vase, sq ftd, 10" .70.00
Grecian, crystal; compote, sq ftd, 6" 27.50
Grecian, crystal; urn, sq ftd, hdld, 10" 70.00
Hobnail, color; bowl, crimped, hdld, 10" 42.50
Hobnail, color; bowl, fruit; sq, 10" 45.00
Hobnail, color; candy basket, hdld, 7" 35.00
Hobnail, color; candy jar, ftd, 1-lb 65.00
Hobnail, color; centerpiece, flared, 11½" 40.00
Hobnail, color; plate, bread & butter; 6" 28.50
Hobnail, color; plate, dessert; 7½" 35.00
Hobnail, color; plate, flat rim, 13" 50.00
Hobnail, color; teacup & saucer 16.50
Hobnail, crystal; bowl, oval, 12" .25.00
Hobnail, crystal; candy basket, hdld, 5" 22.50
Hobnail, crystal; compote, low, 6½" 17.00
Hobnail, crystal; decanter, w/stopper, 12-oz 35.00
Hobnail, crystal; nappy, dessert; hdls, 7" 15.00
Hobnail, crystal; relish, 3-part, hdls, 10" 27.00
Hobnail, crystal; vase, crimped, 4" 15.00
Hobnail, goblet, crystal, 9-oz 15.00
Hobnail, opal; ash tray, 3" 22.50
Hobnail, opal; saucer champagne, 5-oz 45.00
Hobnail, opal; wine, 3-oz 45.00
Laguna, color; ash tray, 5" 11.00
Laguna, color; cocktail, 3½-oz 8.50
Laguna, color; relish, 2-part, hdld, 14" 25.00
Laguna, crystal; candy box, 6½" 9.00
Laguna, crystal; creamer, 7-oz 8.00
Laguna, crystal; decanter, 32-oz .24.00
Laguna, crystal; vase, 12" 15.00
Language of Flowers, crystal; candlestick, 2-light, 7" 37.50
Language of Flowers, crystal; candy box, 3-part, 8" 65.00
Language of Flowers, crystal; cordial, 4½" 25.00
Language of Flowers, crystal; goblet, 7½" 24.00
Language of Flowers, crystal; ice cream, ftd, 5-oz 20.00
Language of Flowers, crystal; relish, 3-part, 3-hdld, 9" 45.00
Language of Flowers, crystal; sherbet, 6-oz, 4¾" 22.00
Language of Flowers, crystal; wine, 5¾" 25.00
Mardi Gras, crystal; shakers, pr .35.00
Mardi Gras, crystal; vase, 6½" 27.50
Murano, color; flower arranger, oval, 2½x3½x8" 30.00
Murano, color; plate, 14" 45.00
Murano, crystal; candle/flower arranger, 2½" 16.00
Murano, crystal; vase, flared, 7" .26.00
Pall Mall, crystal; bowl, oval, swan-hdld, 2¾x10x6¼" 45.00
Pall Mall, crystal; flower bowl, flared, 3½x12½" 24.00
Pall Mall, crystal; flower pan, crimped, 2¾x12" 22.50
Pall Mall, crystal; gardenia bowl, rnd, 2x11" 20.00
Pall Mall, crystal; plate, oval, 15x9½" 25.00
Passion Flower, crystal w/silver etch; bowl, oval, 11½" 55.00
Passion Flower, crystal w/silver etch; candy box, 6" 65.00
Passion Flower, crystal w/silver etch; plate, 14" 55.00

Passion Flower, crystal w/silver etch; urn, hdld, sq, 9½" 55.00
Passion Flower, crystal w/silver etch; vase, 10" 45.00
Plaza, color; bowl, flared, 16" 30.00
Plaza, color; candlestick, 2-light .65.00
Plaza, color; goblet 15.00
Plaza, color; ice cream 15.00
Plaza, color; saucer champagne .15.00
Plaza, color; shakers, non-corrosive tops, pr 35.00
Plaza, crystal; goblet 9.50
Plaza, crystal; iced tea, ftd 9.00
Plaza, crystal; plate, 6" 10.00
Plaza, crystal; plate, 7½" 10.50
Plaza, crystal; plate, 8½" 11.50
Plaza, crystal; teacup & saucer .11.50
Radiance, color; creamer, 6-oz 22.50
Radiance, color; ladle, punch 35.00
Radiance, color; plate, 8" 18.50
Radiance, color; punch set, 15-pc 225.00
Radiance, crystal; ash tray, 6" 11.00
Radiance, crystal; plate, 14" 42.50
Radiance, crystal; plate, 8" 13.00
Radiance, crystal; punch set, 15-pc 175.00
Radiance, opal; pitcher, ice-guard lip, ½-gal 225.00
Radiance, opal; rose bowl, 6" 50.00
Ripple, color; celery tray, 11" 20.00
Ripple, color; iced tea, #100, 12-oz 12.50
Ripple, color; plate, #100, 14" .45.00
Ripple, color; plate, 8" 12.50
Ripple, crystal; finger bowl 7.50
Ripple, crystal; pickle tray, #100, 8" 10.00
Ripple, crystal; plate, 14" 28.00
Sandwich, crystal; ash tray, 2¾x2¾" 8.00
Sandwich, crystal; bonbon, w/lid, ftd, 7½" 30.00
Sandwich, crystal; bowl, console; oblong, 12" 35.00
Sandwich, crystal; bowl, nappy; 2-part, 5" 12.00
Sandwich, crystal; bowl, nut; 3½" 8.00
Sandwich, crystal; bowl, salad; shallow, 12" 35.00
Sandwich, crystal; candlestick, 1-light, 4" 12.50
Sandwich, crystal; cigarette holder, ftd, 3" 25.00
Sandwich, crystal; compote, candy, flared, low ftd, 3¼" 16.00
Sandwich, crystal; compote, ftd, 4¼" 18.00
Sandwich, crystal; condiment set, 2 cruets/shakers/tray 75.00
Sandwich, crystal; goblet, 9-oz, 6" 16.50
Sandwich, crystal; iced tea, flat, 13-oz, 5¼" 18.00
Sandwich, crystal; iced tea, 12-oz, 5¼" 16.00
Sandwich, crystal; pickle tray, oval, 7" 15.00
Sandwich, crystal; pitcher, metal lid, 13-oz 40.00
Sandwich, crystal; plate, torte; 12" 40.00
Sandwich, crystal; plate, 9½" 25.00
Sandwich, crystal; sherbet 7.50
Sandwich, crystal; vase, epergne, threaded base, 7½" 30.00
Sandwich, crystal; vase, fan form, ftd, 5" 25.00
Sandwich, gr; plate, 8" 15.00
Sanibel, color; tray, mint; 7" 35.00
Sanibel, color; vase, oval, ftd, 5½x8x5" 67.50
Sanibel, crystal; bowl, fruit; 1¼x6" 15.00
Sanibel, crystal; bowl, salad; deep, 5½x11x10" 32.50
Sanibel, crystal; candy jar, 9" 45.00
Sanibel, crystal; celery tray, 2x9x6" 24.00
Sanibel, crystal; plate, salad; 8½" 20.00
Spiral Flutes, color; bowl, vegetable; oval, 10" 35.00
Spiral Flutes, color; creamer, oval 8.00
Spiral Flutes, color; cup, demitasse 20.00
Spiral Flutes, color; mug, 9-oz, 6½" 25.00

Spiral Flutes, color; pitcher, ½-gal 95.00
Spiral Flutes, color; plate, torte; 13⅝" 25.00
Spiral Flutes, color; sherbet 10.00
Spiral Flutes, color; sugar bowl, oval 8.00
Spiral Flutes, crystal; nappy .7.50
Spiral Flutes, crystal; plate, dinner 12.50
Spiral Flutes, crystal; plate, luncheon 10.00
Spiral Flutes, crystal; sherbet 8.50
Spiral Flutes, crystal; tumbler 10.00
Sylvan, crystal; candy box, 2-part, 7½" 28.50
Sylvan, crystal; celery tray, 3-part, hdld, 10" 32.00
Sylvan, crystal; swan, 12" .95.00
Sylvan, opal; bonbon, hdld, 5½" 27.50
Sylvan, opal; plate, salad; 7½" 35.00
Sylvan, opal; swan, 5½" 120.00
Sylvan, vaseline opal; swan, 12x13" 325.00
Tavern, crystal; finger bowl, 4" 6.00
Tavern, crystal; goblet, flared, 9-oz 10.00
Tavern, crystal; nappy, 4½" .6.00
Tavern, crystal; parfait, 5-oz .7.50
Tavern, crystal; sugar bowl, 16-oz 9.50
Tear Drop, crystal; bonbon, hdld, 6" 10.00
Tear Drop, crystal; bowl, salad; 9" 25.00
Tear Drop, crystal; candy box, 2-part, 7" 45.00
Tear Drop, crystal; candy dish, heart shape, 7½" 20.00
Tear Drop, crystal; celery tray, 3-part, 12" 20.00
Tear Drop, crystal; creamer, 6-oz 6.00
Tear Drop, crystal; ice cream, 5-oz 14.00
Tear Drop, crystal; marmalade, 4" 30.00
Tear Drop, crystal; orange juice, 8-oz 9.00
Tear Drop, crystal; plate, luncheon; 8½" 7.00
Tear Drop, crystal; plate, 4-hdld, 13" 25.00
Tear Drop, crystal; saucer champagne, 5-oz 14.00
Tear Drop, crystal; sherbet, 5-oz, 3½" 6.00
Tear Drop, crystal; vase, rnd, ftd, 9" 25.00
Terrace, color; bowl, salad; 9" 50.00
Terrace, color; cheese & cracker set, hdld, 11" 65.00
Terrace, crystal; bowl, fruit; flared, 10" 30.00
Terrace, crystal; plate, torte; rolled or flat rim, 18" 32.50
Three Feathers, crystal; candle holder, 4" 22.50
Three Feathers, crystal; candy box, 3-part, 7" 35.00
Venetian, crystal; bowl, oval, 12" 22.50
Venetian, crystal; vase, flower holder, 5" 22.50
Venetian, ruby; bowl, rnd, 8" 10.00
Victorian, crystal; cocktail or wine, 2½-oz 10.00
Victorian, crystal; creamer, 6-oz 8.00
Victorian, crystal; tumbler, ftd, 2-oz 8.00
Victorian, ruby; creamer, 6-oz 12.00
Victory, crystal; iced tea, ftd, 13-oz, 7½" 19.00

Durand

Durand Art Glass was a division of Vineland Glass Works in Vineland, New Jersey. Created in 1924, it was geared specifically toward the manufacture of fine handcrafted artware. Iridescent, opalescent, and cased glass was used to create such patterns as King Tut, reminiscent of Tiffany and Steuben. Production halted in 1931 after the death of Victor Durand. Very few examples are signed, and unmarked pieces are often mistaken for Steuben or Quezal. Unmarked items are often hard to sell, sometimes bringing only about half the price of a similar but signed piece.

Bowl, swirls, gr on gold, 7½" 475.00
Compote, gold, #5502, 6" .300.00

Compote, gr cased on gr irid base, 5¼" 325.00
Compote, ruby w/Spanish yel stem, 6" 500.00
Cordial, ruby w/Spanish yel stem, 5¾" 350.00
Finger bowl & underplate, ruby, scalloped 300.00
Ginger jar, King Tut, silver on gr, amber finial, 7" 1,300.00
Lamp, table; feathers, bl w/gold threads, 17" 850.00
Lamp, 8½" gold feathered shade; threaded base/filigree mt . . .1,200.00
Night light, 6½" gr texture dome shade, blk marble base 375.00
Plate, feathers, bl/opal/clear, unsgn, 8" 175.00
Rose bowl, King Tut, red/gold irid, ftd, unsgn, 5x5" 600.00
Tazza, lt amethyst, hdls, #744, 5¾x6½" 225.00

Vase, pulled feathers and threading, yellow cased, gold throat, signed/ numbered, 7¾", $750.00.

Vase, cluthra, wht w/blk base, urn shape, 12" 500.00
Vase, feathers, opal/bl-outlined on gold, threaded, 9" 800.00
Vase, feathers, opal/gr-outlined on gold, 13" 800.00
Vase, feathers, pk/wht on clear, ruby floral-cut top, 9" 900.00
Vase, feathers, turq/gold on opal, gold int, threaded, 9" 900.00
Vase, gold, ped ft, slim form, #2028-8, 8¾" 300.00
Vase, gold, sgn/#1772-6, 6", pr .550.00
Vase, hearts & vines, opal on bl, 11" 1,400.00
Vase, King Tut, bl-gr on gold, cylindrical, 9¾" 850.00
Vase, King Tut, silver on gr, gold int, drilled base, 8x10" 850.00
Vase, pk irid, lime gr int, 1968-6 . . . . .2,400.00
Vase, random threads on bl irid, 6x5" 695.00
Vase, swirls allover, bl on gold irid, 10" 625.00
Vase, wht w/bl int, 7" 300.00

Easter

Eggs, bunnies, chicks, and baskets have all become basic elements of our Easter celebrations; and the older, more interesting examples are being collected, often for nostalgic reasons, and displayed during the holidays to make the festivities brighter.

Candy container, bunny on wheels, compo 65.00
Candy container, egg, papier-mache, litho floral, 11x8" 65.00
Candy container, egg, Victorian girls tin litho, 3" 38.00
Card, chicks litho, unfolds into basket & eggs, 1925 . . . . .25.00
Egg, milk glass, Easter Greetings in relief, gilt floral 25.00
Egg, papier-mache, 8½" 35.00
Egg, sugar, Victorian decor, litho inside, lg 65.00
Plate, milk glass, Easter Greetings, chick/egg basket 35.00

Rabbit, celluloid, w/basket, 5" 32.00
Rabbit, straw stuffed, clothes, 20" 55.00

Elfinware

Made in Germany from about 1920 until the 1940s, these miniature vases, boxes, salt cellars, and miscellaneous novelty items are characterized by the tiny applied flowers that often cover their entire surface. Pieces with animals and birds are the most valuable, followed by the more interesting examples such as diminutive grand pianos, candle holders, etc. See also Salts, Open.

Basket, bl lustre, mk, miniature 25.00
Bottle, perfume; gr lustre 40.00
Figurine, pig, 1⅞x1¼" 70.00
Figurine, sheep pull cart, flowers, pk bows 35.00
Inkwell, 3x3¾" 35.00
Salt cellar, swan 55.00
Shoe, baby's high-top, appl flowers to top button, 3" 25.00
Stamp box 30.00
Teapot 30.00
Toothpick holder 23.00
Vase, allover florals, cylindrical, 2¾" .40.00

Left to right, vase, 2¾", $40.00; Swan, 2¼", $55.00.

English Stoneware Relief-Moulded Jugs

Early relief-moulded pitchers (ca 1830s-1840s) were made in two-piece molds into which sheets of clay were pressed. The relief decoration was deep and well defined, usually of animal or human subjects. Most of these pitchers were designed with a flaring lip and substantial footing. Gradually styles changed, and by the 1860s the rim had become flatter and the foot less pronounced. The relief decoration was not as deep, and foliage became a common design. By the turn of the century, many other types of pitchers had been introduced, and the market for these early styles began to wane.

Watch for recent reproductions; these have been made by the slip-casting method. Unlike relief-molded ware which is relatively smooth inside, slip-cast pitchers will have interior indentations that follow the irregularities of the relief decoration.

Adm Sidney Smith at siege of Acre, buff, Alcock, 1840s, 9" . . .300.00
Apostle, 8 figures, lt gray stoneware, Chas Meigh, 8" 155.00

Distin family/instruments, bl smear glaze/gilt, Alcock, 7" 290.00
Equestrian hunters, grapevines, lt gr, branch hdl, unmk, 6" 65.00
Ewer, bacchanalian scene in deep relief, Meigh, 1844, 10" 165.00
Good Samaritan, buff/tan, Jones & Walley, 1841, 8" 125.00
Gothic motif/scenes of Virgin, Minster Jug, Chas Meigh, 8" . . .165.00
Grapevines & cherubs, lav/wht, Alcock, ca 1850, 6" 165.00
Jousting knight, tan, mk W Ridgway & Son, 1840, 8¾" 115.00
Pitcher, Apostle, 8 figures, octagonal, 1842, 11" 175.00
Pitcher, Sir Walter Scott commemorative, gray-gr, Minton, 8" .200.00
Plants/classic scenes, gray/wht, snake hdl, att Spode/Masons . . .275.00
Scrolls/acanthus, Bacchus masks, satyr hdl, buff/tan, 7½" 90.00
Tavern/flying female/equestrian, bl stoneware, Ridgway, 6" 90.00
Teapot, stag hunt, serpent hdl/spout, buff, Turner, ca 1835 . . . .325.00
Toby-type figures w/foaming tankards set in foliage, tan, 8" 85.00

Epergnes

Popular during the Victorian era, epergnes were fancy centerpieces often consisting of several tiers of vases (called lilies), candle holders, dishes, or a combination of components. They were made in all types of art glass, and some were set in ornate plated frames.

Miniature, blue glass with enameled floral, 8", $125.00.

Bl, 3 lilies, wht int, 21" 700.00
Cobalt, 1 lg central lily, wht daisies, ftd bowl, 15x11" 325.00
Cobalt, 1 lily, gold florals, child's, miniature 145.00
Cranberry, 1 lily, appl leaves, 12" 225.00
Cranberry, 1 lily, crimped, etched decor, 12" 335.00
Cranberry, 4 lilies, clear rigaree, 10" bowl, 21" 575.00
Crystal frost, 1 sq lily, bl ruffled edge, sq base, 20" 395.00
Gr opal, 3 sq lilies, sq base, 20" 685.00

Gr opal, 4 lilies, appl rigaree, 21" 565.00
Jade gr translucent/wht, 1 scalloped lily in lily std, 11" 200.00
Orange to clear, threaded, 3 branches from base, Webb, 15" . . .695.00
Pk opal, 1 lily, ormolu mts & swan ormolu hdls, 23x17" 450.00
Rubena verde, 1 lily, 16" 285.00
Vaseline opal, 3 lilies, appl rigaree, 11" dia bowl, 24" 375.00
Vaseline opal, 4 lilies, threaded 395.00
Wht opal w/bl trim, 1 sq lily, sq base, 20" 425.00
Wht/gr ruffled dish, 3 jack-in-pulpit vases & baskets, 21" 440.00

Erphila

Rather difficult to find, these fine porcelain novelty items were made for only a short time in Czechoslovakia and Germany. They are stamped with 'Erphila' and the country of origin.

Box, powder; Colonial lady, hand out to side, 8" 115.00
Figurine, Setter, standing, 9¾" 45.00
Pitcher, rooster figural, stylized, 10" .55.00
Platter, iris & rose garlands rim, bouquet in center, 11" 25.00
Teapot, begging dog figural, 8¼" 55.00
Toby, Sam Weller, mk Dickens Jugs, Erphila, 4" 15.00
Tray, relish; roses/leaves on pearl, open hdls, 9x4" 32.00
Vase, pottery, Art Deco circles, high glaze, 5" 35.00
Wall pocket, pottery, Art Deco flowers, 7" 45.00

Eskimo Artifacts

While ivory carvings made from walrus tusks or whale teeth have been the most emphasized articles of Eskimo art, basketry and woodworking are other areas in which these Alaskan Indians excell. Their designs are effected through the application of simple yet dramatic lines and almost stark decorative devices. Though not pursued to the extent of American Indian art, the unique work of this northern tribe is beginning to attract the serious attention of today's collectors.

Pair of dolls, carved and incised stone heads , 12", $350.00.

Basket, coiled whale baleen, ivory finial on lid, 3¾" dia. 700.00
Basket, rye grass, openwork panels, embr USA, 4¼" H 990.00

Basket, woven rye grass, wool yarn lozenges, 5½" dia 2,000.00
Basket, X motif in bear grass, 9x8½", EX 185.00
Cane, musk ox & narwhal tusk, inset dots, 1959, 35" 375.00
Charm, Shaman's, cvd ivory doll, pre-historic, 4x1" 125.00
Container, wood, whale form, inset dots, 10¾" 550.00
Cribbage board, cvd ivory, eng walrus & fish, 1910, 2x14½" . . .220.00
Cribbage board, ivory, eng animals, mc pigment, 8⅝x14" 250.00
Cribbage board, ivory, many incised animals, 20¾" 1,200.00
Cribbage board, walrus tusk ivory, ornate cvg, 1958, 14" 275.00
Cvg, bull walrus, soapstone, ivory tusks, 1950s, 7½" 350.00
Cvg, duck, gr serpentine, sgn in syllabics, 11" 350.00
Cvg, hunter in kayak, ivory, crude details, 6⅜" L 700.00
Cvg, polar bear, soapstone, inset bone teeth, 1962, 7½" 275.00
Cvg, polar bear cubs wrestling, soapstone, 1950s, 3½" 240.00
Doll, cloth, traditional costume, ivory face, recent, 9¾" 135.00
Doll, fossil ivory, inlaid features, pre-historic, 1¾" 70.00
Harpoon, ivory w/steel tip, +wooden tip guard, 13" 50.00
Harpoon, wood & metal, 1950s, 68½", EX 100.00
Implement, ivory, curved form, pierced ends, eng decor, 15" . . .500.00
Knife, crooked; scrimshaw hdl: men cut up whale, 9½x4½" . . .200.00
Koryak, flying bird, ivory, ornate cvg, stained, 3⅞" 880.00
Lamp, stone, concave oval, groove for wick, ca 1000 AD, 7⅝" .800.00
Mask, burial; wood w/inset beads, convex oval, 1200 AD, 8" .2,000.00
Mask, cvd/pnt bird face, 1920, 10½x5½" 250.00
Mask, wood, teeth inlay in open mouth, ca 1500 AD, 14¾" .5,500.00
Mukluks, seal fur/red trade cloth/beads/wild mink, 16", NM . . .500.00
Mukluks, wolf fur, hard puckered sole, 1935, 12x10", pr 150.00
Napkin holder, walrus ivory, scrimshaw, 1920s, EX 45.00
Parka, otter fur w/fur lining, wild mink/wolverine trim, 46" . . .400.00
Pipe, bone bowl, split wood stem bound w/leather thong, 10" . . .80.00
Pipe, ivory, eng hunting friezes, geometrics, 7¾" 1,045.00
Pipe, ivory, 3-part, eng animal panels/bird friezes, 15½" 1,100.00
Pipe, soapstone/copper/wood/musk ox horn, ca 1963, 5¼" 50.00
Ring, ivory, 2 cvd walrus heads, ca 1950s, 1¼" 40.00
Sled bag, sealskin, sewn panels, 75" L 1,400.00
Sled runner, fossil ivory, w/2 holes, pre-historic, 7x2" 50.00
Teakettle, coiled basketry, blk/red wool yarn, high hdl, 7" 600.00
Tusk, eng hunting friezes/mammals, inscription, 22" 990.00
Whip, dog sled; braided thong w/bone hdl, ca 1960, EX 140.00

Fabris Porcelain

Similar in quality, workmanship, and design, fine Fabris porcelain sculptures might easily be confused with Meissen and Dresden pieces; only the red-iron anchor mark denotes the difference.

The French sculptor, Jean-Pierre Varion, formerly of the Vincennes factory, settled in Este, Italy, during the 1750s. He died soon after developing his own formula for porcelain. His wife, Fiorina, and a partner, Antonio Costa, formed a business and manufactured the first Fabris sculptures at Bassano del Grappa in 1875. Many of the figurines and groupings were after paintings by 18th-century artists such as Fragonard, the Rococo decorator; Longhi; and the playwright, Carlo Goldoni. Most of the figures and groups were of a limited production; strict attention was given to detail.

The Museum Collection, a 1980-1982 re-issue, utilized the very early molds. A gold anchor mark was used on this limited line only; after this period, they reverted back to the red-iron anchor.

Aunt, aunt on sofa chaperoning 2 lovers, 9x16" 2,000.00
Beauties, 2 ladies on flowered balcony, 8½x10" 650.00
Cecilia, girl w/wht skirt, 2 flower baskets, 4½x5¼" 300.00
Coppersmith, man sits/mends copper pot, tricorn hat, 5½x8" . .325.00
Flamenco Danco, girl in red bodice & lace dress, 13½" 950.00
Gertrude, flowered dress, knitting bag, 6x7" 425.00

Harlequin's Love, girl & clown in costume, seated, 11x15" ..2,700.00
Lady Beatrice, wht skirt, fashion magazine in lap, 7½x7½" 550.00
Lady Gardener, girl w/basket of flowers, 5x8" 350.00
Lovers, couple reclining on floral bed, 9x7" 750.00
Margarita, girl w/ft on bl pillow, wht skirt, 6x6" 350.00
Melon Vendor, brn pants, wht apron, & melons, 5½x10½" ...375.00
Musical, 2 figures: man at piano, woman singing, 6½x8½" 750.00
Rug Vendor, long bl coat, rugs over shoulder, 10" 550.00
Swing, girl on a swing in floral & leaf arbor, 10x11½" 1,500.00
2-Faced Woman, young girl on 1 side, old hag on other, 9" 450.00

Carriage, 2 horses and coachman, couple in cab, 22" long, $2,150.00.

Face Jugs, Contemporary

Grotesque, often humorous faces are the subject for handcrafted stoneware jugs made by various country potters, many of whom work in the southern states.

Devil face, brn w/unglazed horns, wht teeth, Brock, 9½" 160.00
Gray/wht diagonals, wht eyes/teeth/appl brows, mk CL, 13" ...275.00
Lg appl ears, wht eyes/teeth, sgn Joh Brock 8/50, 9" 95.00
Lizard on forehead, wht eyes/teeth, Chester Hewell, 9½" 125.00
Protruding eyes, wht teeth, incising at neck, BB Craig, 9" 130.00

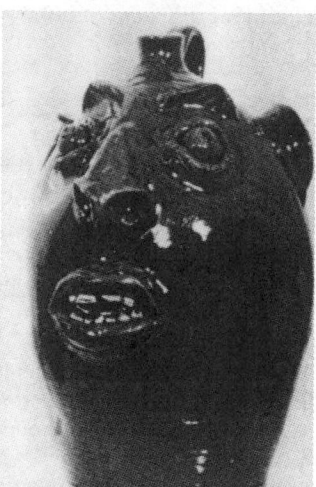

Red-brown glaze with drips of red-orange, white china teeth, signed Brown's Pottery, Arden, NC, R-88, 2-gal, $80.00.

Fairings

Fairings, small chinaware figural groups that portray amusing (if not risque) scenes of courting couples, marital woes, and family feuds, were popular purchases and prizes at 19th-century English fairs. From 1840 through the 1850s, their bases were embossed with marks that identified the manufacturer as well as the artist who applied the polychrome enameling. From 1860 until 1870, they were no longer marked and became smaller in size. During the 1870s, they retained their smaller size but once again were marked in relief, indicating manufacturer and artisan. Through the 1880s, all marks were omitted; but the bases were much more shallow than those from the 1860s. About 1890, the Staffordshire potters sold the molds to German manufacturers who marked their product with the name of their country until about 1900. Examples from this period are most commonly encountered. Fairings made in Germany in the early 20th century often have two holes in their bases.

Generally, the more complex groups and those that are marked bring the higher prices. Earlier examples from the sixties and seventies are of better quality. Similiar items such as small boxes and match holders with much the same type of theme and figural decoration are also listed here.

Baby & dog pull at doll, gold trim, 2¾x2½x5" 175.00
Box, boy on bed puts on pajamas 150.00
Box, cameo on front, musical instruments on lid, 3¾" 95.00
Box, child asleep in highchair, Staffordshire, 3⅜" 95.00
Box, child w/trumpet, doll in basket, Staffordshire, 3¾" 175.00
Box, piano figural, 2⅜" 75.00

Miniature inkwell, two sand thimbles and well inside, 5 ½", $2,000.00.

O Do Leave Me a Drop, 2 cats at bowl 225.00
Power of Love, lady w/tray, 3¼x3½" 185.00
Will We Sleep First or How?, 5½x4" 195.00
12 Months After Marriage, unmk, 3½x3½" 250.00
3 O'Clock in the Morning, lady in bed, 2¾x3¼" 200.00

Fans

The Japanese are said to have invented the fan. From there it went to China, and Portuguese traders took the idea to Europe. Though usually considered milady's accessory, even the gentlemen in 17th-century England carried fans! More fashionable than practical, some were of feathers and lovely hand-painted silks with carved ivory or tortoise sticks. Some French fans had peepholes. There are mourning fans, calendar fans, and those with advertising. All are collectible!

Our advisor for this category is Vicki Flanigan; she is listed in the Directory under Virginia.

Feathers w/bird in center, ivory hdls, lg, EX 85.00
Figures HP on paper, blk lacquered spine w/florals, China 150.00

Florals & birds HP on red silk, wood slats, 8x16", VG 75.00
Florals HP on blk silk, wood fr, 12x18", VG 75.00
Florals HP on satin, ivory sticks, sgn H Allen, 1890s, 24" 125.00
Lace, gold & silver cvd florals in MOP fr, ca 1900, Fr, 9½" 150.00
Leather, pierced, on cvd horn fr, 7x11", VG 100.00
Lotus blossoms embr on silk, Japan, 1930s, EX 30.00
Man at well helps woman water sheep, ivory rtcl sticks, 10" ...175.00
Needle lace, HP figural reserves sgn Mocholi, 1900, 12x22" ..100.00
NY street w/carriages & Nouveau lady, bk: Paris scene, VG 50.00
Ostrich plumes, pk & red, celluloid hdl, lg, NM 125.00
Ostrich plumes, wht, tortoise ribs, 15x24" 60.00
Peacock feather tips, HP scene, ivory sticks, ca 1800, EX 100.00
Scene HP on silk, lacquered sticks, Chinese, 1800s, 10x20" ...125.00
Shaker, ½-rnd, splint, mc bands, 9" across 60.00
Silk & feathers, metal sequins, pierced fr, tassel, 1860s 125.00

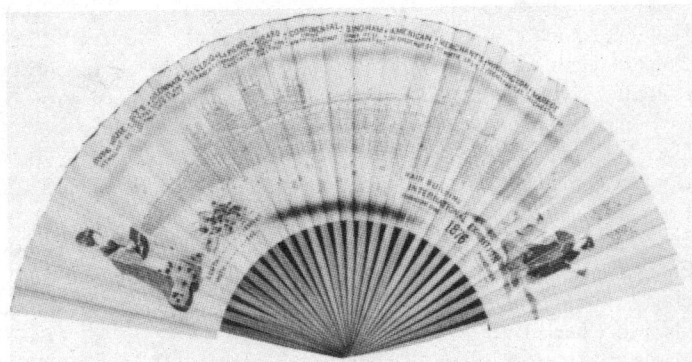

Souvenir of the 1876 Centennial Exhibition, Philadelphia; building and Oriental scene on paper, $130.00.

Farm Collectibles

Country living in the 19th century entailed plowing, planting, and harvesting; gathering eggs and milking; making soap from lard rendered on butchering day; and numerous other tasks performed with primitive tools of which we in the 20th century have had little first-hand knowledge. For more information on this subject, we recommend *Collecting Farm Antiques*, an identification and value guide by our advisor for this category Lar Hothem; his address is listed in the Directory under Ohio. See also Cast Iron; Woodenware; Wrought Iron.

Anvil, w/off-set, 200-lb 475.00
Bag, cotton-picking; Tuffy, 1950s, 54" 10.00
Book, Moline Universal, 1922 ....50.00
Bucket, pine, tin bands, old gr pnt, late 1800s, 9½" 85.00
Bull blinder, 2 leather pcs in lg harness, pat Apr 15, 1898 ......75.00
Corn dryer, twisted wire, 50 prongs, ca 1900, 37" L 36.00
Curry comb, CI, w/open-letter logo in hdl, 3½" 55.00
Engine, McCormick-Deering, gasoline, 1½-horsepower, EX ...350.00
Fence stretcher, gear type, EX 15.00
Hoof trimmer, bone hdls 15.00
Husking peg, leather strap, EX 12.50
Implement seat, CI, Buckeye, Akron, 1900s, 16x15x3½" 80.00
Implement seat, CI, Grand Detour IL, ca 1900, 16x15x4" 125.00
Implement seat, CI, heart form, openwork, ca 1900, 18x14" ...50.00
Implement seat, CI, Peerless, EX 190.00
Implement seat, CI, Peerless Reaper, EX 225.00
Implement seat, CI, Walter A Wood, EX 200.00
Lantern, barn; tin & copper, Buhl #575 ....85.00
Lantern, barn; wood w/tin font & kero burner, 11", VG 145.00
Oxbow, dbl yokes, EX 225.00

Pump, wood, CI spout/hdl pivot, pnt w/mfg stencil, 72" 65.00
Rake, wood w/curved wire braces, 82" 35.00
Rake, wrought iron, no hdl, 9½" W 20.00
Sausage grinder, wood w/stencil label: Coffman's/1845, 42" ...80.00
Sausage stuffer & lard press, Simmons Hdw, 4-qt, EX 45.00
Scoop, grain; wood, early 75.00
Sheath, scythe; chip cvg/animal-head end, sgn/1809, worn pnt 115.00
Shovel, grain; cherry, open D-hdl, handmade, ca 1810, EX 195.00
Shovel, grain; 1-pc cvd wood, open D-hdl, ca 1800, EX 240.00
Sign, HP canvas on wood, farm name/boys & cows, 40x60" ...500.00

Stirrups, wood and iron, from $25.00 to $45.00.

Thrashing flail, hickory & ash, 2-part, 1880s, EX 50.00
Yoke, ox training; single, 2 rings, old red pnt, EX 150.00
Yoke, shoulder; pine, old worn red pnt, 44" L 85.00

Fenton

Frank and John Fenton were brothers who founded the Fenton Art Glass Company in 1906 in Martin's Ferry, Ohio. The venture, at first only a decorating shop, began operations in July of 1905 using blanks purchased from other companies. This operation soon proved unsatisfactory, and by 1907 they had constructed their own glass factory in Williamstown, West Virginia. John left the company in 1909 and organized his own firm in Millersburg, Ohio.

The Fenton Company produced over 130 patterns of carnival glass. They also made custard, chocolate, opalescent, and stretch glass. This company has always been noted for its various colors of glass and has continually changed its production to stay attune with current tastes in decorating. In 1925 they produced a line of 'handmade' items that incorporated the techniques of threading and mosaic work. Because the process proved to be unprofitable, the line was discontinued by 1927. Even their glassware made in the past twenty-five years is already regarded as collectible. Various paper labels have been used since the 1920s; only since 1970 has the logo been stamped into the glass.

For information concerning Fenton Art Glass Collectors of America, Inc., see the Clubs, Newsletters, and Catalogs section of the Directory. See also Carnival Glass; Custard Glass; Stretch Glass.

Advertising sign, ice gr carnival or vaseline opal, ea 15.00
Advertising sign, jade gr, oval 65.00
Advertising sign, vaseline, 1980 ....25.00
Aqua Crest, basket, #1523, ca 1941-1942, 13" 180.00
Aqua Crest, bowl, fruit 40.00
Aqua Crest, bowl, 8½" 35.00
Aqua Crest, candlestick, #1523, 5", pr 55.00

Aqua Crest, cup & saucer, 1950s 35.00
Aqua Crest, plate, 8¼" 22.00
Aqua Crest, vase, #210, 4" 15.00
Aqua Crest, vase, dbl-crimp top, 8" 17.50
Aqua Crest, vase, tulip form, 5" 32.50
Aqua Crest, vase, 4½" 17.50
Beaded Melon, basket, gold overlay, 7" 75.00
Beaded Melon, creamer, gold overlay, #11 . . . . .35.00
Beaded Melon, rose bowl, dk gr overlay, 3½" 27.50
Beaded Melon, rose bowl, yel overlay, 4" 25.00
Beaded Melon, vase, gold overlay, 3½" 30.00
Beaded Melon, vase, rose overlay, #711, ca 1949, 8" 48.00
Big Cookies, basket, Mandarin red, wicker hdl, #1681, 5x10½".. 165.00
Big Cookies, basket, ruby, wicker hdl, #1681, ca 1933, 10½" . . .125.00
Big Cookies, macaroon jar, ebony, #1681, ca 1933, 7" 110.00
Bl Overlay, basket, #1924, 7" 45.00
Bl Overlay, vanity set, #192-A, 5½" bottle+jar 65.00
Bl Overlay, vanity set, 3-pc 85.00
Blk Rose, globe, for hurricane lamp, #7398, ca 1953 . . . . . . .45.00
Blk Rose, vase, hand form, #5155, ca 1953-1954, 10½" 100.00
Blk Rose, vase, tulip form, scalloped, #7250, 8½" 60.00
Block & Star, shaker, rose pastel, #5606, rare 20.00
Burmese, basket, 6¾x7¾" 45.00
Burmese, epergne, 4-lily, ltd ed 350.00
Burmese, vase, jack-in-the-pulpit; 11" 65.00

Cake basket, light turquoise opaque, 11" wide, $90.00.

Chinese Yel, basket, #1681 . . . . .165.00
Chinese Yel, candlestick, #315, ca 1925, 3½" 45.00
Coin Dot, basket, bl opal, 7" 65.00
Coin Dot, basket, cranberry opal, 7" 85.00
Coin Dot, bowl, cranberry opal, decor, 7" 50.00
Coin Dot, bowl, French opal, 6½" .20.00
Coin Dot, creamer, cranberry opal, 4" 40.00
Coin Dot, creamer & sugar bowl, bl opal 80.00
Coin Dot, decanter, cranberry opal, #894, 12" 90.00
Coin Dot, lamp, French opal w/HP roses, pr 125.00
Coin Dot, pitcher, cranberry opal, 6½" 80.00
Coin Dot, pitcher, lime opal, lg 125.00
Coin Dot, tumbler, bl opal 15.00
Coin Dot, tumbler, cranberry opal 25.00
Coin Dot, vase, French opal, 11" 50.00
Coin Dot, vase, French opal, 1925, 6¼" 40.00
Crystal Crest, plate, 10¼" 28.00
Crystal Crest, plate, 8½" 24.00
Crystal Crest, vase, tulip form, 4" .35.00
Daisy & Button, bonbon, milk glass, 5½" 11.00

Daisy & Button, bowl, milk glass, oval, #1929, 11" 25.00
Daisy & Button, candlestick, milk glass, ca 1953, pr 20.00
Daisy & Button, creamer, Colonial bl 16.00
Daisy & Button, plate, amber, 7½" .10.00
Daisy & Button, tray, amber, fan form, #957 . . . . .27.50
Daisy & Button, vase, milk glass, fan form, 8½" 24.00
Diamond Lace, candle holder, French opal, pr 22.50
Diamond Lace, epergne, French opal, #1948 . . . . .95.00
Diamond Optic, candy dish, gr, dolphin ft, 4" 55.00
Diamond Optic, goblet, ruby, water sz, 7" 25.00
Diamond Optic, sherbet, ruby 9.00
Diamond Optic, vase, bl opal, flared, 8½" 45.00
Dolphin, bonbon, royal bl, etched, ca 1936, #1621-E, 5½" 25.00
Dolphin, bowl, blk, oval, #1608, 10" 70.00
Dolphin, bowl, Chinese yel, ebony base, hdls, #1504-A, 5" H . . 110.00
Dolphin, bowl, jade gr, #1608, 10½" 70.00
Dolphin, candlestick, ruby 20.00
Dolphin, compote, ruby, #1533, 6" 45.00
Dolphin, plate, sandwich; pk, center hdl 40.00
Dolphin, vase, topaz stretch, fan form, 5" 60.00
Dot Optic, pitcher, bl opal, #1535, 9" 120.00
Dot Optic, pitcher, lime opal w/blk hdl, #1352, rare 150.00
Dot Optic, tumbler, cranberry opal, flat, #1353, 4" 22.00
Dot Optic, vase, cranberry opal, crimped top, 8" 95.00
Ebony, basket, cupped bowl, #1092, ca 1936 . . . . .40.00
Ebony, bowl, oval, 10½" 60.00
Ebony, candlesticks, #449, 8½", pr 85.00
Ebony, ice bucket 75.00
Ebony, vase, fan form, gold Mayflower etched, rare, 7¼" 125.00
Ebony, vase, fan form, 7¼" 45.00
Emerald Crest, bowl, soup; #680, 5½" 20.00
Emerald Crest, cake plate, 13" 75.00
Emerald Crest, epergne, lg 140.00
Emerald Crest, flowerpot w/saucer, 1-pc, #401 . . . . .75.00
Emerald Crest, tidbit tray, 2-tier, #7296, 1954-1955 . . . . . . .60.00
Figurine, cat, carnival, 11" 55.00
Figurine, rabbit, bl, 5x6" 55.00
Figurine, swan, bl 25.00
Georgian, claret, ruby, #1611, 4½-oz 18.00
Georgian, creamer & sugar bowl, ruby, #1611, pr 35.00
Georgian, cup & saucer, ruby, #1611 . . . . .18.00
Georgian, goblet, amber, #1611, 10-oz 12.00
Georgian, sherbet, ruby 10.00
Georgian, tumbler, jade gr, ca 1931-1938, 5" 20.00
Georgian, tumbler, moonstone, #1611, ca 1933 . . . . .18.00
Georgian, tumbler, ruby, 3¾" 5.00
Georgian, tumbler, ruby, 8-oz 10.00
Georgian, tumbler, ruby, 9-oz 7.50
Gold Crest, bonbon, sq, #36, 5½" .8.00
Gold Crest, bowl, crimped top, 8" 25.00
Gold Crest, top hat, crimped top, #1924, ca 1943-1944 . . . . . .40.00
Gold Crest, vase, dbl-crimped top, #201, 6" 20.00
Gold Crest, vase, sq, 3½" 12.50
Hobnail, ash tray, bl opal, fan form, #3872, 1950s, 5½" 18.00
Hobnail, ash tray, French opal, 5¼" 22.00
Hobnail, banana boat, milk glass .40.00
Hobnail, basket, cranberry opal, #3837, 7" 65.00
Hobnail, basket, French opal, #389, 6¼" 65.00
Hobnail, basket, French opal, 4" 30.00
Hobnail, basket, topaz opal, #3834, 4½" 45.00
Hobnail, bowl, bl opal, dbl-crimped top, #389, 9" 55.00
Hobnail, bowl, bl opal, 10" 65.00
Hobnail, bowl, cranberry opal, ruffled, 7" 50.00
Hobnail, bowl, French opal, #389, 11" 60.00

Hobnail, candlestick, French opal, #3870, pr 30.00
Hobnail, candy dish, bl opal, crimped top, folded sides, 5" 30.00
Hobnail, cat slipper, bl opal, #389 . . . . .28.00
Hobnail, condiment set, bl opal, #3809, 3-pc+hdld tray 80.00
Hobnail, creamer & sugar bowl, French opal, 3" 18.00
Hobnail, creamer & sugar bowl, rose pastel, #3906, ca 1950s . . .30.00
Hobnail, cruet, bl opal, w/stopper, sm 35.00
Hobnail, cruet, cranberry opal, sm 35.00
Hobnail, cruet, cranberry opal, w/stopper, 6" 60.00
Hobnail, cruet, cranberry opal, w/stopper, 6" 75.00
Hobnail, epergne, bl, mini 75.00
Hobnail, epergne, bl opal, 10" 120.00
Hobnail, epergne, bl opal, 4-pc 130.00
Hobnail, epergne, gr opal or yel opal, sm, ea 95.00
Hobnail, juice set, bl opal, 7-pc 155.00
Hobnail, lamp, Gone w/the Wind; cranberry opal 265.00
Hobnail, lamp, hurricane; peachblow, #3998 . . . . .90.00
Hobnail, pitcher, cranberry opal, 80-oz 200.00
Hobnail, pitcher, French opal, water sz 60.00
Hobnail, shakers, bl opal, #3806, pr 40.00
Hobnail, shakers, French opal, flat, pr .40.00
Hobnail, sherbet, French opal, #389 . . . . .7.00
Hobnail, tumbler, bl opal, #3945, 5-oz, 3½" 15.00
Hobnail, vase, bl opal, cornucopia, #397, mini 18.00
Hobnail, vase, bl opal, dbl-crimped top, ftd, #389, 6½" 38.00
Hobnail, vase, bl opal, fan form, #3959, 8" 32.00
Hobnail, vase, cranberry opal, cupped, flared, 5" 65.00
Hobnail, vase, cranberry opal, 4½" 32.00
Hobnail, vase, cranberry opal, 8" 90.00
Hobnail, vase, gr opal, tricorn, mini 20.00
Hobnail, vase, lime opal, tricorn, #389, 4" 30.00
Hobnail, wine, bl opal 15.00
Ivory Crest, basket, 8x6½" 45.00
Ivory Crest, candle holder, cornucopia form, 6¼" 30.00
Ivory Crest, vase, cornucopia form, #1523, pr 135.00
Ivory Crest, vase, 10" 80.00
Ivy, bowl, ruby overlay, ftd, #1021 . . . . .55.00
Jade Gr, candlesticks, 7", pr 40.00
Jade Gr, pitcher, w/lid 125.00
Jade Gr, rose bowl, cupped, ftd, 4" 35.00
Lilac, vase, fan form, #857, rare, 8" 125.00
Lilac Cased, shell bowl, #9020, 10" 95.00
Lincoln Inn, cup & saucer, ruby 18.00
Lincoln Inn, goblet, cobalt, water sz 25.00
Lincoln Inn, goblet, ruby, water sz 30.00
Lincoln Inn, sherbet, cobalt, 4¼" 24.00
Lincoln Inn, tumbler, cobalt, ftd, 6" 22.00
Lincoln Inn, tumbler, ruby, ca 1928-1938, 6" 35.00
Lincoln Inn, wine, jade gr, ca 1931, 4" 32.00
Mandarin Red, basket, #1093, ca 1933, 5½" 85.00
Mandarin Red, bowl, shallow, cupped, #2007, ca 1925, 9" dia . . .80.00
Mandarin Red, candlestick, 8", pr 120.00
Mandarin Red, vase, flared, #621, 6" .70.00
Melon Rib, bottle, scent; bl overlay, w/stopper, 4½" 25.00
Melon Rib, bottle, scent; bl overlay, w/stopper, 9" 35.00
Melon Rib, bottle, scent; pk overlay, w/stopper, 7" 25.00
Melon Rib, puff box, bl overlay, 4½" 25.00
Melon Rib, puff box, pk overlay, 4½" .27.50
Ming, basket, gr 95.00
Ming, bowl, pk, deep, 3-toe, 7" 30.00
Ming, jar, macaroon; gr, reeded hdl 125.00
Ming, pitcher, gr, ca 1934, 10" 90.00
Ming, tumbler, gr, flat, water sz 10.00
Mongolian Gr, basket, reeded hdl 95.00
Mongolian Gr, vase, fan form, 6" 45.00

Mongolian Gr, vase, 8½" 88.00
Peach Crest, basket, crystal hdl, #203, 7" 75.00
Peach Crest, basket, milk glass hdl, #203, 7" 80.00
Peach Crest, bowl, shell form, #9020, 10¼" 55.00
Peach Crest, candlestick, #1523, ca 1940-1950, 5", pr 55.00
Peach Crest, vase, tricorn, #187, 6" 20.00
Peach Crest, vase, tulip, #7250, 9" 50.00
Pekin Bl, bowl, #846, 8" 30.00
Pekin Bl, cake plate, ca 1924, 6¼" 32.00
Pekin Bl, candlestick, 3-toe, #848, pr .30.00
Pekin Bl, candy dish, #636, 10½" 45.00
Plymouth, champagne, ruby, 4" 10.00
Plymouth, goblet, ruby 15.00
Plymouth, highball, amber, #1620, 8-oz 18.00
Rib Optic, finger lamp, ruby overlay, appl amber hdl 85.00
Rib Optic, ivy ball, cranberry opal, w/o base, #705, 4" 50.00
Rib Optic, top hat, French opal, #1923, ca 1939, 6" 40.00
Rosalene, basket, threaded 55.00
Rosalene, bell 42.50
Rosalene, compote, 7x6¾" 55.00
Rose Crest, basket, #192, ca 1945-1947, 10" 95.00
Rose Crest, bonbon, sm 12.50
Ruby, candlestick, 5¾", pr 65.00
Ruby, tray, leaf form, #175, ca 1936, 8½" L 40.00
Ruby, vase, hat form, 8x9" 110.00
Ruby Overlay, bowl, flower; 9" 50.00
Ruby Overlay, epergne, 2-pc, #7202, ca 1955-1959 . . . . .50.00
San Toy, candlestick, etched, #249, ca 1936, 6" 30.00
San Toy, plate, etched, 3-ftd, #107, ca 1938, 8" 20.00
San Toy, vase, etched, #898, ca 1936, 11½" 60.00
September Morn, flower frog, blk opaque 175.00
September Morn, flower frog, crystal 90.00
September Morn, flower frog, lt gr, blk base 130.00
Sheffield, plate, ruby, #1800, ca 1936, 10" 37.50
Sheffield, tumbler, amethyst, #1800, ca 1936, 4¼" 25.00
Sheffield, tumbler, ruby, #1800, 4¼" 20.00
Sheffield, vase, ruby, cupped, 8" 25.00
Silver Crest, banana boat 20.00
Silver Crest, basket, #7237, 7" 32.00
Silver Crest, bell 32.50
Silver Crest, bottle, scent; w/stopper 22.00
Silver Crest, cake plate, high ftd, 13" .30.00
Silver Crest, cake plate, low ftd, 13" 25.00
Silver Crest, compote, crimped top, 8" 20.00
Silver Crest, epergne, 10½" 65.00
Silver Crest, nut dish, ftd 15.00
Silver Crest, plate, torte; 15¼" 55.00
Silver Crest, plate, 6¼" 7.00
Silver Crest, powder jar 22.00
Silver Crest, sandwich server, hdls 22.00
Silver Crest, tidbit tray, 2-tier 22.00
Silver Crest, tumbler, ftd 22.50
Silver Crest, vase, tricorn, 2¼" 22.00
Silver Crest, vase, violet decor, #186, 8" 27.00
Silver Turquoise, plate, 8½" 30.00
Silvertone, bowl, amber, flared, #1002, ca 1937, 9" 25.00
Silvertone, bowl, amethyst, flared, #1005, ca 1934, 6½" 27.50
Silvertone, candle holder, amber, 3-toe, flared, #1010, pr 40.00
Silvertone, pitcher, iced tea; etched, #1352, ca 1937 . . . . .65.00
Spiral/Bl Ridge, vase, #186, ca 1939, 8" 50.00
Spiral/Bl Ridge, vase, triangle, #894, 10½" 65.00
Thumbprint, compote, pk 15.00
Thumbprint, wine, Colonial bl 10.00
Vasa Murrhina, basket, gr/bl aventurine, 11¼" 95.00

Vasa Murrhina, vase, gr w/bl aventurine, 4" 35.00
Vasa Murrhina, vase, rose/gr aventurine, 11" 100.00

Fiesta

Fiesta is a line of dinnerware produced by the Homer Laughlin China Company of Newell, West Virginia, from 1936 until 1973. It was made in eleven different solid colors with over fifty pieces in the assortment. The pattern was developed by Frederic Rhead, an English Stoke-on-Trent potter who was an important contributor to the art-pottery movement in this country during the early part of the century. The design was carried out through the use of a simple band-of-rings device near the rim. Fiesta Red, a strong red-orange glaze color, was made with depleted uranium oxide. It was more expensive to produce than the other colors and sold at higher prices. Today's collectors still pay premium prices for Fiesta Red pieces. During the fifties the color assortment was gray, rose, chartreuse, and dark green. These colors are relatively harder to find and along with Fiesta Red and medium green (new in 1959) command the higher prices.

Fiesta Kitchen Kraft was introduced in 1939; it consisted of seventeen pieces of kitchenware such as pie plates, refrigerator sets, mixing bowls, and covered jars in four popular Fiesta colors.

As a final attempt to adapt production to modern-day techniques and methods, Fiesta was restyled in 1969. Of the original colors, only Fiesta Red remained. This line, called Fiesta Ironstone, was discontinued in 1973.

Two types of marks were used: an ink stamp on machine-jiggered pieces and an indented mark molded into the hollowware pieces.

In 1986 HLC reintroduced a line of Fiesta dinnerware in five colors: black, white, pink, apricot, and cobalt (darker and denser than the original shade). However, collectors feel the new ware will pose no threat to their investment. Yellow was added in 1989.

In the listings below, 'original colors' indicates only four of the original six — ivory, light green, turquoise, and yellow. Red and cobalt values are listed separately. For more information we recommend *The Collectors Encyclopedia of Fiesta, Harlequin, and Riviera* by Sharon and Bob Huxford, now in its sixth edition. Available at your local bookstore or from Collector Books.

Dinnerware and Accessories

Ash tray, '50s colors 38.00
Ash tray, orig colors 22.00
Ash tray, red or cobalt 28.00
Bowl, covered onion soup; cobalt 180.00
Bowl, covered onion soup; red 225.00
Bowl, covered onion soup; turq 550.00
Bowl, cream soup; '50s colors 28.00
Bowl, cream soup; med gr 65.00
Bowl, cream soup; orig colors 18.00
Bowl, cream soup; red or cobalt 24.00
Bowl, dessert; '50s colors, 6" 22.00
Bowl, dessert; med gr, 6" 50.00
Bowl, dessert; orig colors, 6" 14.00
Bowl, dessert; red or cobalt, 6" 20.00
Bowl, fruit; '50s colors, 4¾" 13.50
Bowl, fruit; '50s colors, 5½" 15.00
Bowl, fruit; med gr, 4¾" 40.00
Bowl, fruit; med gr, 5½" 20.00
Bowl, fruit; orig colors, 11¾" 80.00
Bowl, fruit; orig colors, 4¾" 9.00
Bowl, fruit; orig colors, 5½" 11.00
Bowl, fruit; red or cobalt, 11¾" 95.00
Bowl, fruit; red or cobalt, 4¾" 15.00
Bowl, fruit; red or cobalt, 5½" 14.00

Bowl, ftd salad; orig colors 110.00
Bowl, ftd salad; red or cobalt 140.00
Bowl, ind salad; med gr, 7½" 42.00
Bowl, ind salad; red, turq, & yel, 7½" 35.00
Bowl, nappy; '50s colors, 8½" 29.00
Bowl, nappy; med gr, 8½" 31.00
Bowl, nappy; orig colors, 8½" 12.00
Bowl, nappy; orig colors, 9½" 17.00
Bowl, nappy; red or cobalt, 8½" 25.00
Bowl, nappy; red or cobalt, 9½" 28.00
Bowl, Tom & Jerry, ivory w/gold letters 70.00
Bowl, unlisted; red or cobalt 100.00
Bowl, unlisted; yel 40.00
Candle holder, bulb; orig colors, pr .30.00
Candle holder, bulb; red or cobalt, pr 40.00
Candle holder, tripod; orig colors, pr 150.00
Candle holder, tripod; red or cobalt, pr 175.00
Carafe, orig colors 75.00
Carafe, red or cobalt 95.00
Casserole, '50s colors 100.00
Casserole, French; standard colors .210.00
Casserole, French; yel 125.00
Casserole, med gr 135.00
Casserole, orig colors 50.00
Casserole, red or cobalt 80.00
Coffeepot, '50s colors 95.00
Coffeepot, demi; orig colors 90.00
Coffeepot, demi; red or cobalt 105.00
Coffeepot, orig colors 68.00
Coffeepot, red or cobalt 80.00
Compote, orig colors, 12" 45.00
Compote, red or cobalt, 12" 70.00
Compote, sweets; orig colors 22.00
Compote, sweets; red or cobalt 30.00
Creamer, '50s colors 12.00
Creamer, ind; red 55.00
Creamer, ind; turq 120.00
Creamer, ind; yel 28.00
Creamer, med gr 21.00
Creamer, orig colors 9.00
Creamer, red or cobalt 12.00
Creamer, stick hdld, orig colors 12.00
Creamer, stick hdld, red or cobalt 15.00
Cup, demi; '50s colors 58.00
Cup, demi; orig colors 18.00
Cup, demi; red or cobalt 22.00
Egg cup, '50s colors 45.00
Egg cup, orig colors 23.00
Egg cup, red or cobalt 31.00
Gravy boat, '50s colors 30.00
Gravy boat, med gr 30.00
Gravy boat, orig colors 18.00
Gravy boat, red or cobalt 27.00
Lid, for mixing bowl #1-#3, any color 115.00
Lid, for mixing bowl #4, any color .125.00
Marmalade, orig colors 80.00
Marmalade, red or cobalt 115.00
Mixing bowl, #1, orig colors 35.00
Mixing bowl, #1, red or cobalt 52.00
Mixing bowl, #2, orig colors 25.00
Mixing bowl, #2, red or cobalt 34.00
Mixing bowl, #3, orig colors 27.00
Mixing bowl, #3, red or cobalt 42.00
Mixing bowl, #4, orig colors 32.00

Mixing bowl, #4, red or cobalt	46.00
Mixing bowl, #5, orig colors	42.00
Mixing bowl, #5, red or cobalt	52.00
Mixing bowl, #6, orig colors	60.00
Mixing bowl, #6, red or cobalt	82.00
Mixing bowl, #7, orig colors	95.00
Mixing bowl, #7, red or cobalt	120.00
Mug, Tom & Jerry; '50s colors	40.00
Mug, Tom & Jerry; ivory w/gold letters	31.00
Mug, Tom & Jerry; orig colors	22.00
Mug, Tom & Jerry; red or cobalt	30.00
Mustard, orig colors	72.00
Mustard, red or cobalt	100.00
Pitcher, disk juice; gray	140.00
Pitcher, disk juice; other standard colors	215.00
Pitcher, disk juice; red	130.00
Pitcher, disk juice; yel	18.00
Pitcher, disk water; '50s colors	85.00
Pitcher, disk water; med gr	90.00
Pitcher, disk water; orig colors	31.00
Pitcher, disk water; red or cobalt	45.00
Pitcher, ice; orig colors	42.00
Pitcher, ice; red or cobalt	60.00
Pitcher, jug, 2-pt; '50s colors	41.00
Pitcher, jug, 2-pt; orig colors	37.00
Pitcher, jug, 2-pt; red or cobalt	35.00
Plate, '50s colors, 10"	23.00
Plate, '50s colors, 6"	4.00
Plate, '50s colors, 7"	7.00
Plate, '50s colors, 9"	10.00
Plate, cake; orig colors	125.00
Plate, cake; red or cobalt	140.00
Plate, calendar; 1954 or 1955, 10"	27.00
Plate, calendar; 1955, 9"	32.00
Plate, chop; '50s colors, 13"	31.00
Plate, chop; '50s colors, 15"	34.00
Plate, chop; med gr, 13"	45.00
Plate, chop; orig colors, 13"	16.00
Plate, chop; orig colors, 15"	18.00
Plate, chop; red or cobalt, 13"	19.00
Plate, chop; red or cobalt, 15"	22.00
Plate, compartment; '50s colors, 10½"	20.00
Plate, compartment; orig colors, 10½"	11.00
Plate, compartment; orig colors, 12"	14.00
Plate, compartment; red or cobalt, 10½"	17.00
Plate, compartment; red or cobalt, 12"	20.00
Plate, deep; '50s colors	21.00
Plate, deep; med gr	31.00
Plate, deep; orig colors	14.00
Plate, deep; red or cobalt	21.00
Plate, med gr, 10"	27.00
Plate, med gr, 6"	5.00
Plate, med gr, 7"	8.00
Plate, med gr, 9"	12.00
Plate, orig colors, 10"	12.00
Plate, orig colors, 6"	3.00
Plate, orig colors, 7"	4.00
Plate, orig colors, 9"	5.00
Plate, red or cobalt, 10"	18.00
Plate, red or cobalt, 6"	4.00
Plate, red or cobalt, 7"	7.00
Plate, red or cobalt, 9"	10.00
Platter, '50s colors	22.00
Platter, med gr	32.00

Platter, orig colors	12.00
Platter, red or cobalt	19.00
Saucer, '50s colors	3.00
Saucer, demi; '50s colors	18.00
Saucer, demi; orig colors	6.00
Saucer, demi; red or cobalt	8.00
Saucer, med gr	4.00
Saucer, orig colors	1.50
Saucer, red or cobalt	2.00
Shakers, '50s colors, pr	17.00
Shakers, med gr, pr	18.00
Shakers, orig colors, pr	11.00
Shakers, red or cobalt, pr	13.00
Sugar bowl, ind; turq	125.00
Sugar bowl, ind; yel	45.00
Sugar bowl, w/lid, '50s colors, 3¼x3½"	22.00
Sugar bowl, w/lid, med gr, 3¼x3½"	27.00
Sugar bowl, w/lid, orig colors, 3¼x3½"	17.00
Sugar bowl, w/lid, red or cobalt, 3¼x3½"	22.00
Syrup, orig colors	95.00
Syrup, red or cobalt	110.00
Teacup, '50s colors	19.00
Teacup, med gr	19.00
Teacup, orig colors	13.00
Teacup, red or cobalt	19.00
Teapot, lg; orig colors	55.00
Teapot, lg; red or cobalt	70.00
Teapot, med; '50s colors	122.00
Teapot, med; med gr	175.00
Teapot, med; orig colors	50.00
Teapot, med; red or cobalt	65.00
Tray, figure-8; cobalt	32.00
Tray, figure-8; turq	95.00
Tray, figure-8; yel	100.00
Tray, relish; gold decor	95.00
Tray, relish; mixed colors, no red	75.00
Tray, utility; orig colors	15.00
Tray, utility; red or cobalt	20.00
Tumbler, juice; chartreuse, Harlequin yel or dk gr	70.00
Tumbler, juice; orig colors	14.00
Tumbler, juice; red or cobalt	20.00
Tumbler, juice; rose	20.00
Tumbler, water; orig colors	22.00
Tumbler, water; red or cobalt	30.00
Vase, bud; ivory	22.00

Vase, red, 12", $300.00 to $350.00.

Vase, bud; orig colors 27.00
Vase, bud; red or cobalt 37.00
Vase, orig colors, 10" 250.00
Vase, orig colors, 12" 260.00
Vase, orig colors, 8" 190.00
Vase, red or cobalt, 10" 315.00
Vase, red or cobalt, 12" 330.00
Vase, red or cobalt, 8" 250.00

Kitchen Kraft

Bowl, mixing; lt gr or yel, 10" 55.00
Bowl, mixing; lt gr or yel, 6" 45.00
Bowl, mixing; lt gr or yel, 8" 45.00
Bowl, mixing; red or cobalt, 10" 65.00
Bowl, mixing; red or cobalt, 6" 40.00
Bowl, mixing; red or cobalt, 8" 55.00
Cake plate, lt gr or yel 28.00
Cake plate, red or cobalt 35.00
Cake server, lt gr or yel 40.00
Cake server, red or cobalt 45.00
Casserole, ind; lt gr or yel 75.00
Casserole, ind; red or cobalt 85.00
Casserole, lt gr or yel, 7½" 55.00
Casserole, lt gr or yel, 8½" 60.00
Casserole, red or cobalt, 7½" 60.00
Casserole, red or cobalt, 8½" 70.00
Covered jar, lg; lt gr or yel 130.00
Covered jar, lg; red or cobalt 150.00
Covered jar, med; lt gr or yel 120.00
Covered jar, med; red or cobalt 140.00
Covered jar, sm; lt gr or yel 110.00
Covered jar, sm; red or cobalt 125.00
Covered jug, lt gr or yel 125.00
Covered jug, red or cobalt 150.00
Fork, lt gr or yel 30.00
Fork, red or cobalt 35.00
Metal frame for platter 15.00
Pie plate, lt gr or yel, 10" 30.00
Pie plate, lt gr or yel, 9" 25.00
Pie plate, red or cobalt, 9" 32.00
Refrigerator unit, lt gr or yel 20.00
Refrigerator unit, red or cobalt 25.00
Shakers, lt gr or yel, pr 55.00
Shakers, red or cobalt, pr 60.00
Spoon, lt gr or yel 40.00
Spoon, red or cobalt 45.00
Stacking refrigerator lid, lt gr or yel 35.00
Stacking refrigerator lid, red or cobalt 45.00

Finch, Kay

Kay Finch and her husband, Braden, operated a small pottery in Corona Del Mar, California, from 1939 to 1963. The company remained small, employing from twenty to forty local residents who Kay trained in all but the most requiring tasks, which she herself performed. The company produced animal and bird figurines, most notably dogs, Kay's favorites. Figures of 'Godey' type couples were also made, as were tableware (consisting of breakfast sets) and other artware. Most pieces were marked.

Our advisor for this category is Jack Chipman; he is listed in the Directory under California.

Ash tray, shell, pk lustre & wht 12.00

Bank, Panda figural, 9" 35.00
Cookie jar, Pup, dog, pk, HP details, 12¾" 150.00
Cookie jar, Puss, cat, wht, HP details, 11¾" 150.00
Figurine, Ambrosia, Persian cat, HP, 10¾" 225.00
Figurine, camel, HP, 5" 50.00
Figurine, Chinese court lady, HP details, 10½" 60.00
Figurine, girl w/bowed head, HP details, 7" 38.00
Figurine, Madonna w/bowed head, HP details, 7" 40.00
Figurine, Mitzi, Pomeranian, HP, 10" 200.00
Figurine, monkeys, HP details, 4x3½", pr 45.00
Figurine, penguin family, HP, set of 3 . . . . .85.00
Figurine, pig, standing, pk, HP details, 4" 25.00
Figurine, rabbit, HP details, ink mk, 2½x4" 30.00

Godey couple, 7½", $75.00 for the pair.

Planter, monkey form 25.00
Planter, turkey form, brn/gold, spread tail, 10x9x6" 70.00
Wall mask, Grecian man/lady, pk lustre w/gold, 10", pr 100.00

Findlay Onyx and Floradine

Findlay, Ohio, was the location of the Dalzell, Gilmore, and Leighton Glass Company, one of at least sixteen companies that flourished there between 1886 and 1901. Their most famous ware, Onyx, is very rare. It was produced for only a short time beginning in 1889 due to the heavy losses incurred in the manufacturing process.

Onyx is layered glass, usually found in creamy white with a dainty floral pattern accented with metallic lustre that has been trapped between the two layers. Other colors found on rare occasions include a light amber (with either no lustre or with gilt flowers), light amethyst (or lavender), and rose. Although old tradepaper articles indicate the company originally intended to produce the line in three distinct colors, long-time Onyx collectors report that aside from the white, production was very limited. Other colors of Onyx are very rare, and the few examples that are found tend to support the theory that production of colored Onyx ware remained for the most part in the experimental stage. Even three-layered items have been found (they are extremely rare) decorated with three-color flowers. As a rule of thumb, using white Onyx prices as a basis for evaluation, expect to pay two to three times more for colored examples.

Floradine is a separate line that was made with the Onyx molds. A single-layer rose satin glassware with white opal flowers, it is usually priced in the general range of colored Onyx.

Our advisors for this category are Betty and Clarence Maier; they are listed in the Directory under Pennsylvania.

Floradine

Box, dresser; sm crack in lid liner, 5½" dia 650.00
Creamer 945.00
Mustard 850.00
Spooner, 4¼" 925.00
Sugar bowl, w/lid, 3¾x4½" 95.00
Sugar shaker 1,250.00
Toothpick holder 1,100.00
Tumbler, 3¾", NM 550.00

Onyx

Bowl, wht w/silver decor, 2¾x7" 300.00
Butter dish, wht w/silver decor, 5½" dia 1,250.00
Celery vase, wht w/silver decor, 7" 450.00
Creamer, wht w/silver decor, 4½" 395.00
Jam jar, wht w/silver decor, w/lid 450.00
Mustard, raspberry pk w/dk rose decor, 3½" 1,075.00
Pitcher, wht w/silver decor, 4½" 600.00
Pitcher, wht w/silver decor, 8" 1,200.00

Shakers, Onyx, white with platinum flowers, $600.00 for the pair.

Shakers, wht w/silver decor, 3", pr 600.00
Spooner, wht w/silver decor, 4¼" 425.00
Sugar bowl, wht w/silver decor, w/lid, 5½" 500.00
Sugar shaker, wht w/silver decor, 5¼" 500.00
Syrup, wht w/silver decor, 7" 775.00
Toothpick holder, wht w/silver decor, 2½" 375.00
Tumbler, wht w/silver decor, 3¼" 325.00

Fire Fighting Collectibles

Fire fighting collectibles from the early 19th century reflect the feeling of pride the men had in their companies and in their role as volunteer fire fighters. Dress uniforms, fancy helmets, and trumpets filled with flowers recall the charisma of the 'Laddies' on parade. Leather buckets, bed keys, rattles, torches, lanterns, and riveted hose serve as reminders of their dedication to their calling.

In the 1860s municipal fire departments were formed in many urban areas. Alarm equipment began to evolve at about the same time. Horse-drawn apparatuses gave way to self-propelled machines soon after the turn of the century. Many cities were totally 'motorized' after WW, although sleighs and such were kept by many northern cities long after the horses were gone. Today many collectors find a fascination with these fire-fighting relics of the past.

Badge, Asst Chief, gold filled, CT 65.00
Badge, breast; Engineer, steamer, nickel 65.00
Badge, Captain, starburst/high eagle, goldtone, Dallas TX 75.00
Badge, Chief, goldtone center w/5 trumpets/eagle, LA 75.00
Badge, Ex-Chief, 5 trumpets/eagle, gold filled, NY 55.00
Badge, Honorary Captain, goldtone, C Braxmar, NY 50.00
Badge, Member E Syracuse FD, Maltese cross, nickel 30.00
Badge, 1 Bellmore, Advance HL&E Co, Cairnes, ca 1880, 2" ...35.00
Badge set, cap & breast; nickel, Utica FD 75.00
Bell, Apparatus, American/La France w/eagle, complete, 12" ..450.00
Bell, Gamewell, brass, center wind, 10" 225.00
Bell, Gamewell, chain wind, 10" 150.00
Bell, Gamewell, lady's leg tapper, wood case, 6" 600.00
Bell, Gamewell, oak case, 6", EX 650.00
Bell, gong, rotary, nickel/brass w/ft petal, 13" 300.00
Belt, parade; brass buckle, ca 1880s, EX 95.00
Book, Bucket Brigade to Flying Squadron, Jenness, 1909 ....85.00
Book, Rules & Regulations, 1901, EX 12.00
Bucket, leather, gr w/gold label: Wyeth & Stimson, 12", EX ...400.00
Bucket, leather, pnt scroll banner w/name & 1906, 13" 650.00
Bucket, leather, rpt w/yel label: Dovor VR, 10½" 150.00
Bucket, leather, yel pnt, ca 1830, EX 650.00
Bucket, leather w/gold, Washington Hook & Ladder, #2, EX ..850.00
Buckle, '#1,' brass/nickel scramble w/torch & hook 35.00

Painted leather fire bucket depicting a fireman and a flaming house, with name and '1822,' 12", EX, $8,500.00.

Extinguisher, Badger, soda/acid, brass, pony sz 50.00
Extinguisher, child's Apparatus-type, nickel over copper, EX ...85.00
Extinguisher, Pyrofite, amber glass cylinder w/cork, 11" 65.00
Extinguisher, Rough Rider Am La France, plain top, chrome ...75.00
Extinguisher, Texaco, brass 35.00
Extinguisher, Universal, soda/acid, copper/brass, 2½-gal 18.00
Grenade, Harden's, turq-bl, pat 1883, dia quilt, full, 6¾" 65.00

Gamewell House gong, $2,000.00.

Grenade, Harkness, sapphire w/blk streaks, half full, 6" 425.00
Grenade, Hayward's, cobalt, pat 1871, 6" 210.00
Grenade, Hayward's, lt aqua, prism panels, full, 6" 220.00
Grenade, Pyrene #C-105-P 35.00
Grenade, Pyrene #C-31 . . . . .10.00
Grenade, Red Comet, full, w/hanger in orig box 20.00
Grenade, Red Comet Firemaster, 6 in orig box 140.00
Grenade, Wilby 20.00
Helmet, leather, high eagle, Cairns, NY, 1895, EX 175.00
Helmet, leather, high eagle, CM Leonard Steamer, 48 Comb . .375.00
Helmet, leather, low front w/frontispiece, New Yorker 95.00
Helmet, tin, high eagle, Binghamton Exempt 275.00
Helmet, tin, Senator w/frontispiece, 'Rescue 1 AFD' 65.00
Lantern, Dewey Mill, hinged, lift cage .35.00
Lantern, Dietz Chief, brass, cold blast type 650.00
Lantern, Dietz King, Am la France, nickel/tin, bracket, NM . . .375.00
Lantern, Dietz King, brass, mk Dietz, EX 225.00
Lantern, Dietz King, nickeled tin, mk Dietz, G 135.00
Lantern, Dietz King, steel, EX 125.00
Lantern, Dietz Mill, steel, slide over cage w/water shield 95.00
Lantern, Dietz Queen, brass 650.00
Lantern, Ham's 1897 Pat, brass, mk Am Fire Engine Co 600.00
Nozzle, Callaghan, brass, 2½" w/1⅛" tip 110.00
Nozzle, Eastman deluge set, 3-way Siamese/stacked tips, 3½" . .400.00
Nozzle, parade hose; wood, orig red & silver pnt, EX 150.00
Nozzle, Rockwood, bayonet piercing 20.00
Nozzle, Rockwood, navy type, brass, 1½" & 2½", ea 45.00
Nozzle, standpipe, brass, no shut off, 1½" 8.00
Nozzle, 2½" Akron play pipe w/3 tips, EX 150.00
Reel, fire hose; eagle atop, Underwriters, 1902, 16x17x5" 185.00
Trumpet, SP, fireman's presentation, no names or dates, NM . .990.00
Trumpet, SP, fireman's presentation, w/names & dates, NM . .1,150.00

Fire Marks

During the early 18th century, insurance companies used fire marks —

signs of insurance — to indicate to the volunteer fire fighters which homes were covered by their company. Handsome rewards were promised to the brigade that successfully extinguished the blaze, so competition was fierce between rivals and sometimes resulted in an altercation at the scene to settle the matter of which brigade would be the one to fight the fire! Fire marks were originally made of cast iron or lead; later examples were sometimes tin or zinc. They were used abroad as well as in this country, and those from England tended to be much more elaborate. When municipal fire departments were organized in the mid- to late 1860s, volunteer departments and fire marks became obsolete.

Archibald Kenrick & Sons Ltd, emb tin, 3¼x7½", VG 25.00
FA w/hydrant & hose, CI, gr pnt, oval, EX 570.00
Fire Assoc of Philadelphia, emb hose/hydrant, CI, 1700s 150.00
Germantown 1843 Mutual Fire, CI, 8x11¼" 40.00
Guardian Assurance Co of London, copper 125.00
Masonic, CI, early 200.00
Protector, copper, fireman w/hose, burning building, 1825 . . . .190.00
United Firemen's Ins Co, 12-spoke wheels, CI, oval, 11x9⅜" . .240.00
4 clasped hands/No 906 on CI plaque, 10½x7" 300.00

Fireglow

A type of art glass attributed to Mt. Washington, fireglow is an opaque cafe au lait that glows with rich red 'fire' when held to a strong source of light.

Ewer, birds on tree branches, 7" 165.00
Rose bowl, mc florals, egg shape, 6-crimp top, appl ft 165.00
Vase, florals, 5½" 160.00
Vase, gold-traced mauve flowers & leaves, mk PK, 11" 250.00

Fireplace Implements

In the colonial days of our country, fireplaces provided heat in the winter and were used year round to cook food in the kitchen. The implements that were a necessary part of these functions were varied and have become treasured collectibles, many put to new use in modern homes as decorative accessories. Gypsy pots may hold magazines; copper and brass kettles, newly polished and gleaming, contain dried flowers or green plants. Firebacks, highly ornamental iron panels that once reflected heat and protected masonry walls, are now sometimes used as wall decorations.

By Victorian times, the cookstove had replaced the kitchen fireplace, and many of these early utensils were already obsolete. But as a source of heat and comfort, the fireplace continued to be used for several more decades. See also Wrought Iron.

Andirons, brass, dbl stds/2 ball finials, mk Hunneman, 12" 600.00
Andirons, brass, EX detail, 1820s, 20½" 475.00
Andirons, brass, Hession soldier figural, 1930s, 18" 145.00
Andirons, brass, ring top, Russell Clark & Co, 11x12" 350.00
Andirons, brass, sphinx form, Regency, 13" 1,200.00
Andirons, bronze, recumbent greyhound on draped base, 8" . . .600.00
Andirons, CI, G Washington on draped plinth, 1880s, 20" . . .1,000.00
Andirons, CI, G Washington w/legs apart, 1890s, 15x7x3" 350.00
Andirons, wrought iron, tooled, pyramid finials, 18" 95.00
Bellows, HP fruit on worn leather, EX 165.00
Bellows, mahog, shell cvg, trn hdls, prof rpl leather, 17" 200.00
Broiler, wrought iron, revolves, ftd, rattail hdl, 1840, EX 235.00
Broiler, wrought iron, thin rods on 4 slim ft, hdl, 20" 85.00
Broom, hearth oven; birch splint, ca 1860s, 10½" 80.00
Brush, hearth; horsehair, old gr pnt hdl w/gilt decor, 23" 40.00

Candle holder, wrought iron, twisted shaft, hanging, 18" 185.00
Crane, wrought iron, 1700s, 26½x35½" 150.00
Ember carrier, tin & iron w/long wood hdl, EX 395.00
Fender, brass, CI fr mk W Jackson's Sons NY, 1900s, 56" L 120.00
Fender, brass, pierced decor, lion-claw corners, 44x14" 155.00
Fender, brass, simple scrolls/florals, 1800s, 54" 225.00
Fender, brass, urn-form spindles, 1800s, 52" 280.00
Fender, CI, paw ft, shell/ribbon detail, 18x47" 175.00
Fender, wire/iron, brass rail/finials, serpentine, 15x45" 725.00
Fender, wrought iron fr/wire grill/brass rail, 1820s, 16x55" 850.00
Fireback, CI, anchors/fleur-de-lis emb, dtd 1788, 22x27" 970.00
Fireback, CI, man on horse, dtd 1746, 24" 1,600.00

**British fireback, cast iron, dated 1635, 22x26",
$700.00.**

Fireback, CI, man/horse, inscription above, foliage, 17x23" ...200.00
Fireback, CI, manger scene, angels in border, 1700s, 40" 1,400.00
Fireback, CI, scrolling leaves fr rectangle w/swags, 23x30" 700.00
Fireboard, 3-part, pnt as bird's eye maple w/line borders 900.00
Fork, toasting; rattail hdl, 28" 95.00
Grill, wrought iron, twisted rattail hdl, sm 85.00
Kettle shelf, CI, pierced 11x16½" top, 10" H 70.00
Kettle tilter, wrought iron, 1700s, EX 295.00
Mantel, orig yel grpt w/brn trim, 60x63" 170.00
Mantel, pine, cvd by Adam Deal, 1780s, 53x72" 1,250.00
Mantel w/upper panel, pine, reeded detail, 1780s, 92x61" 300.00
Peal, wrought iron, ram's horn hdl, 40½" 125.00
Pot, CI, 3-ftd, ca 1860, lg 50.00
Toaster, wire Maltese cross design, wood hdl 37.00

Fischer

Fine porcelain has been produced in the Herend area of Hungary since the late 18th century. In 1839 Moritz Fischer founded a pottery there where he produced copies of Meissen, Sevres, Leeds, and Far-Eastern tableware for replacement purposes. Figurines were introduced in 1850. At the Crystal Palace Exhibition in London, his work so pleased the Queen that she ordered tableware for Windsor Castle. Soon British aristocracy and U.S. presidents as well followed her lead, and the company continued to win honors and acclaim. It remained a family business until 1948 when it became property of the state. The factory was completely renovated and today is still recognized for its fine craftsmanship and attention to detail.

Basket, floral, mc w/gold, twig ft, reticulated, 9½x11¾" 650.00
Charger, floral, mc w/gold, 13" 325.00
Dish, butterfly figural, reticulated, 2 mks, 11½x10½" 255.00
Ewer, floral, bold mc w/heavy gold, 15¾" 350.00
Pitcher, reticulated lip, ball body, dolphin hdl, early, 11" 575.00
Pitcher, 5 scenic panels, fancy hdl, w/lid 235.00

**Pitcher, cobalt with
floral reserves, gold
trim, and reticulation,
$575.00.**

Fisher, Harrison

Harrison Fisher (1875-1934), noted illustrator and creator of the Fisher Girl, was the son of landscape artist, Hugh Antoine Fisher. His career began in his teens in San Francisco where he did artwork for the Hearst papers. Later in New York, his drawings of beautiful American women attracted much attention and graced the covers of the most popular magazines of the day — *Puck*, *Ladies' Home Journal*, *Saturday Evening Post*, and *Cosmopolitan*. He also illustrated novels, and his art books were treasured. His drawings appeared on thousands of post cards and on advertising items such as candy tins, pocket mirrors, calendars, and posters. His creation of the Fisher Girl, and his panel of six scenes of the *Greatest Moments in a Woman's Life* made him the most sought-after and well-paid illustrator of his day.

The Harrison Fisher Society, founded in 1977, maintains a communications network of collectors and dealers and also publishes a yearly exchange letter. The Society is listed under Clubs, Newsletters, and Catalogs.

Art book, A Dream of Fair Women, 1907, EX 150.00
Art book, A Girl's Life & Other Pictures, 1913, EX 395.00
Art book, American Beauties, 1909, EX 195.00
Art book, American Belles, 1911, EX 250.00
Art book, American Girls in Miniature, 1912, w/box, EX 250.00
Art book, Bachelor Belles, 1907, EX 150.00
Art book, Beauties, 1913, EX 285.00
Art book, Fair Americans, 1911, EX 185.00
Art book, Hiawatha, Special Edition, 1906, EX 95.00
Art book, Maidens Fair, 1912, EX 285.00
Art book, Pictures in Color, 1910, EX 395.00
Art book, The American Girl, 1909, w/box, EX 425.00
Art book, The Harrison Fisher Book, 1907, EX 195.00
Art book, The Little Gift Book, 1913, EX 185.00
Banner, Red Cross, nurse, w/Foringer's madonna, 41½x8½", EX .95.00
Bookplate, from American Beauties, fr 65.00

Candy tin, Dancing Girl, Tindeco, 2½x7" dia 40.00
Candy tin, Dancing Girl, Tindeco, 2¾x10" dia 70.00
Candy tin, His Pledge, heart shaped, Tindeco, 2x8½x8½" 70.00
Candy tin, Snowbird, Tindeco, 1¾x4" dia 40.00
Magazine cover, Cosmopolitan, ea 20.00
Magazine cover, Ladies' Home Journal, ea 22.00
Magazine cover, Saturday Evening Post, ea 18.00
Post card, average example, EX, ea 18.00
Post card, Greatest Moments, set of 6 in orig matting & fr 95.00
Post card, Six Senses, set of 6 in orig matting & fr 125.00
Poster, Have You Answered...Red Cross Christmas Roll Call ..125.00
Print, Evening Hour, orig fr, 8x11" 45.00
Print, King of Hearts, orig fr, 11x13" 65.00
Prints, orig, old & unmatted, 11x14", ea 35.00

Print, *Danger,* ca 1908, in old frame, $85.00.

Fishing Collectibles

Collecting old fishing tackle is becoming more popular every year. Though at first most interest was geared toward old lures and some reels, rods, advertising, and miscellaneous items are quickly gaining ground. Values are given for examples in excellent or better condition and should be used only as a guide. For more information contact our advisor Randy Hilst, an appraiser and collector whose address and phone number are listed in the Directory under Illinois.

Catalog, Creek Chub, 1943 ....40.00
Catalog, Heddon, 1941 ....45.00
Catalog, Pflueger, 1928 ....35.00
Catalog, Shakespeare, 1950 ....25.00
Lure, Al Foss Dixie Wiggler, metal 12.00
Lure, Al Foss Frog, metal 20.00
Lure, Al Foss Shimmy Spoon, metal 25.00
Lure, Creek Chub Baby Beetle, bead eyes, wood 75.00
Lure, Creek Chub Baby Wiggle Fish, glass eyes, wood 35.00

Lure, Creek Chub Beetle, bead eyes, wood 65.00
Lure, Creek Chub Midget Ding Bat, glass eyes, wood 15.00
Lure, Creek Chub River Rustler, glass eyes, wood 75.00
Lure, Creek Chub Striper Pikie, glass eyes, wood 30.00
Lure, Creek Chub Surfster, glass eyes, wood 25.00
Lure, Heddon #100 Underwater Minnow, glass eyes, wood 50.00
Lure, Heddon #210 Surface Lure, glass eyes, wood 20.00
Lure, Heddon Artistic Minnow, glass eyes, wood 100.00
Lure, Heddon Crazy Crawler, pnt eyes, wood 12.00
Lure, Heddon Gamefisher, no eyes, wood 20.00
Lure, Heddon Little Luny, pnt eyes, pyralin 75.00
Lure, Heddon Punkinseed, pnt eyes, wood, older model 35.00
Lure, Heddon Zig Wag, glass eyes, wood 16.00
Lure, Moonlight Pikaroon, glass eyes, wood 50.00
Lure, Moonlight Polly-Wog, glass eyes, wood 75.00
Lure, Paw Paw Bullhead, tack eyes, wood 80.00
Lure, Paw Paw Musky Hair Mouse, tack eyes, wood/deer hair ..150.00
Lure, Paw Paw Natural Hair Mouse, tack eyes, wood/deer hair ..30.00
Lure, Paw Paw Pike Caster, tack eyes, wood, 6½" 65.00
Lure, Paw Paw Shiner, pnt eyes, wood 10.00
Lure, Paw Paw Trout Caster, tack eyes, wood, 3¼" 70.00
Lure, Paw Paw Watta Frog, tack eyes, wood 25.00
Lure, Pflueger Electric Minnow, glass eyes, wood 300.00
Lure, Pflueger Globe, no eyes, wood 12.00
Lure, Pflueger Poprite, cvd eyes, wood 15.00
Lure, S Bend Dart Oreno, metal 7.00
Lure, S Bend Midget Surf Oreno, glass eyes, wood 25.00
Lure, S Bend Pike Oreno, tack eyes, wood 10.00
Lure, S Bend Surf Oreno, glass eyes, wood 25.00
Lure, S Bend Truck Oreno, tack eyes, wood 700.00
Lure, S Bend Underwater Minnow, glass eyes, 3-hook, wood ...35.00
Lure, S Bend Underwater Minnow, glass eyes, 5-hook, wood ...40.00
Lure, S Bend Whirl Oreno, no eyes, wood 75.00
Lure, Shakespeare Darting Shrimp, glass eyes, wood 200.00
Lure, Shakespeare Egyptian Wobbler, glass eyes, wood 30.00
Lure, Shakespeare Frog Skin Bait, tack eyes, wood 45.00
Lure, Shakespeare King Fish Wobbler, cvd eyes, wood 40.00
Lure, Shakespeare Special, cvd eyes, wood 10.00
Reel, Horton, Bluegrass #3 ....125.00
Reel, Pekin, Indiana style 30.00
Reel oiler, Shakespeare, bullet shape, approx 3" 20.00
Rod, Kingfisher, metal, 3-pc, 9 ft 15.00
Rod, Montague, bamboo, 3-pc w/extra tip, 9 ft 25.00

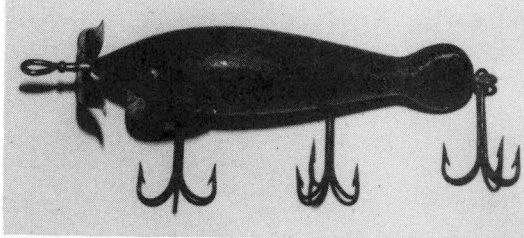

Heddon Spin Diver, wood with glass eyes, $250.00.

Flags

The brevity and imprecise language of the first Flag Act of 1777 allowed great artistic license for our early flag makers. As a result, vast and varied interpretations were produced until 1912 when stardards were established for the new 48-star flag. Early patterns range from 'scatter' arrangements to elaborate wreaths and 'Great Stars.' Most advanced flag collectors focus on early hand-sewn flags of 37 stars or less, particularly the very scarce pre-Civil War flags of 33 stars or less. Others prefer smaller flags of the hand-held variety which are less costly and easier to display.

Virtually all available 13-star flags are products of the nineteenth and twentieth centuries and are priced accordingly. Ordinary 48-star flags and later-day reproductions of earlier vintages usually generate little or no market interest. Late nineteenth century flags of 46, 45, and 44 stars have only limited appeal; however any flag of exceptional design, construction, or history is potentially marketable.

Historical flags must be accompanied by solid documentation such as sworn statements, letters, or supporting research; if the documentation is merely circumstantial, some measure of price concession is usually required.

Flags should be preserved as they are found; normal wear and tear is usually considered acceptable. Never try to trim, launder, or otherwise repair an antique flag. Because flag collectors are relatively few in number, pricing is somewhat subjective. Nevertheless, a familiarity with the special pricing factors listed below should serve well in producing a fair and equitable transaction.

American Flags of All-Sewn Construction — **See listing below.**
Larger Printed American Flags (average 2x3 ft.) — **60% of listing below.**
Smaller Printed Flags (11x14" range) — **30% of listing below.**
49 Star — **10.00-25.00**
48 Star — **5.00-15.00**
46-44 Star — **25.00-60.00**
43 Star (rare) — **Negotiable**
42-38 Star — **60.00-125.00**
37-34 Star — **125.00-250.00**
33 Stars or Less — **225.00 and up.**

Additional Pricing Factors and Marketing Features:

Decorative star patterns in the form of wreaths, 'Great Stars,' etc., range from top prices listed above to 75% additional.

Star patterns in rows of unusual numerical combinations are preferred to more commonly available patterns of the same period.

Updated flags modified through the application of additional stars should be classified according to their latter denomination but priced as premium items.

Unofficial flags of 42, 40, and 39 stars tend to command above-average prices for their respective periods.

Prices for 13-star flags generally correspond to the period in which they were made (as determined by physical analysis). Decorative star arrangements are common in 13-star patterns, and all but the most exceptional should be discounted as a pricing factor.

Hand-sewn flags of any denomination featuring 6- or 8-pointed stars can command top prices, up to 300% beyond the normal guide.

Any stripe pattern variation, as determined by either number of stripes or color sequence, is a desirable feature.

Any canton that is deeper or more shallow than the standard 7-stripe depth is a desirable feature.

Hand stitching, while preferable to machine stitching, is routinely found in flags of 38 stars or less and therefore discounted as an additional pricing factor in early vintage flags.

Homemade flags of unusual construction (embroidered, knitted, crocheted, etc.) command high-range prices as specified in the listing above; also primitive homemade flags of unique design.

Inscriptions, pictures, or printed messages on the face of a flag can generate modest to significant price increases.

Printed silk flags tend to attract slightly higher prices than printed muslin flags.

The commonly available miniature flags (5x7" and under) of sized muslin, which were printed in a variety of early vintage star patterns, are generally regarded as reproductions of negligable value.

American flags of proven historical significance are in continual demand. They may relate to any specific individual, institution, or event in American history and usually require supporting documentation. However, major items may fetch unprecedented prices. Flags of a military or political nature invariably rank above all other categories in terms of both prestige and price.

Our advisor for this category is Robert Banks; he is listed in the Director under Maryland.

Earl 'Scatter Pattern' of 19 stars (3 added later), hand stitched, mixed fabrics, 39x66", $660.00.

Florence Ceramics

Figurines marked 'Florence Ceramics' were produced in the forties and fifties in Pasadena, California. The quality of the ware and the attention given to detail are prompting a growing interest among today's collectors. The names of these lovely ladies, gents, and figural groups are nearly always incised into their bases. The company name is ink-stamped. Because this is a relatively new area of collecting and the rarity of many items has yet to be determined, examples are evaluated by size and the intricacy of design.

Our advisor for this category is Jack Chipman; he is listed in the Director under California.

Amelia, gold trim, 8½", $115.00.

Ann, 6" 75.00
Betty Mermaid 85.00

Camille, gr, 8½" 100.00
Chinese Girl, wht w/gr, orig label, planter, 7½" 30.00
Choir Boy, 6" 45.00
Clock, Sessions, cherub atop, 11" 125.00
Delia, 7½" 95.00
Edith, wht w/gold trim, 7½" 100.00
Gary, pk coat, 8½" 95.00
Irene, wht w/gold, 6" 65.00
Jim, gray suit, 6¼" 75.00
John Alden, 9¼" 125.00
Kay, pk, 5¾" 65.00
Louise, bl, 7½" 65.00
May, planter, 5½" 30.00
Peg, planter, 6" 30.00
Polly, planter, 6" 30.00
Priscilla, pk dress, 8" 95.00
Rhett, gray clothes, 9" 150.00
Roberta, pk, 9" 85.00
Sally, pk, 6¾" 95.00
Scarlett, royal red w/gold, 9" 150.00
Victor, wht w/blk, 9½" 100.00
Vivian, gr dress, w/umbrella, 8" 125.00

Florentine Cameo

Although its appearance may look much like English cameo, the decoration on this type of glass is not wheel cut or acid etched. Instead, a type of heavy paste — usually a frosty white — is applied to the surface to create a look very similar to true cameo. It was produced in France as well as England; it is sometimes marked 'Florentine.'

Vase, white birds and flowers on cranberry satin, 9", $215.00.

Vase, aqua, wht bird & foliage, mk, 8" 170.00
Vase, citron, wht leaves & bird, 5" 45.00
Vase, lav-pk, wht floral & butterflies, serpentine hdls, 12" 500.00
Vase, pk, wht morning-glories, 4-loop ribbon hdls, 12", pr 995.00

Flow Blue

Flow Blue ware was produced by many Staffordshire potters; among the most familiar were Meigh, Podmore and Walker, Samuel Alcock, Ridgway, John Wedge Wood (who often signed his work Wedgwood), and

Davenport. It was popular from about 1825 through 1860 and again from 1880 until the turn of the century. The name describes the blurred or flowing affect of the cobalt decoration, achieved through the introduction of a chemical vapor into the kiln. The body of the ware is ironstone, and Oriental motifs were favored. Later issues were on a lighter body and often decorated with gilt.

Our advisor, Mary Frank Gaston, has compiled a lovely book, *The Collector's Encyclopedia of Flow Blue China*, with full-color illustrations and current market values; you will find her address in the Directory under Texas.

Bonita pitcher, La Belle, Wheeling Potteries, 7", $225.00

Abbey, bowl, G Jones, ca 1900, 3x4½" 45.00
Abbey, bowl, G Jones, ca 1900, 5x9" 180.00
Abbey, chocolate pot, 6" 85.00
Abbey, creamer, G Jones 60.00
Abbey, dish, sq, 8½" 110.00
Abbey, plate, 10½" 28.00
Alaska, bowl, vegetable; open, Grindley, 9" 35.00
Alaska, egg cup, Grindley 35.00
Alaska, gravy boat, Grindley 50.00
Alaska, pickle dish, Grindley 20.00
Alaska, pitcher, Grindley, 5-cup, 6¾" 145.00
Alaska, platter, Grindley, 14" 110.00
Alaska, platter, Grindley, 16" 135.00
Albany, bowl, vegetable; w/lid, Johnson Bros 130.00
Albany, plate, Johnson Bros, 10½" 40.00
Alton, bowl, 10" 80.00
Amoy, bowl, serving; Davenport, 6x8" 195.00
Amoy, butter dish, Davenport 120.00
Amoy, pitcher, Davenport, ca 1844, 12" 435.00
Amoy, plate, Davenport, 8¼" 85.00
Amoy, plate, Davenport, 9" 110.00
Anemone, plate, Minton, 10" 50.00
Arabesque, cup & saucer, Mayer 85.00
Arabesque, plate, Mayer, 10½" 95.00
Arabesque, soup plate 95.00
Argyle, bowl, oval, Grindley, 10x7" 50.00
Argyle, bowl, vegetable; w/lid, Grindley, 9¼x6¾" 165.00
Argyle, butter pat, Grindley 30.00
Argyle, cup & saucer, Grindley 45.00
Argyle, gravy boat, w/underplate, Grindley 160.00

Argyle, plate, Grindley, 7" 25.00
Argyle, saucer 15.00
Argyle, tureen, vegetable; w/lid, Ford & Sons 225.00
Ashburton, gravy boat, w/undertray, Grindley 125.00
Ashburton, plate, Grindley, 6¾" 30.00
Astoria, plate, New Wharf Pottery, ca 1891, 9" 70.00
Baltic, bowl, vegetable; oval, w/lid, Grindley 145.00
Beauty Rose, bowl, dessert; 5½" 30.00
Beauty Rose, cup & saucer 50.00
Beauty Rose, plate, 6" 30.00
Beauty Rose, platter, 13¾" 90.00
Beauty Rose, soup plate 75.00
Belmont, butter pat 15.00
Belmont, platter, 10½" 65.00
Belmont, platter, 13" 95.00
Blue Danube, butter dish, Johnson Bros 195.00
Blue Danube, butter pat, Johnson Bros 25.00
Blue Danube, plate, Johnson Bros, 10" 45.00
Bouquet, bowl, vegetable; w/lid 145.00
Burleigh, bowl, vegetable; oval, w/lid, Burgess & Leigh, 9" 145.00
Burleigh, platter, Burgess & Leigh, 16x12" 200.00
Cambridge, bowl, New Wharf Pottery, 9" 38.00
Cambridge, dish, ice cream; New Wharf Pottery, 4¾" 35.00
Cambridge, platter, New Wharf Pottery, 14" 140.00
Cambridge, tureen, soup; New Wharf Pottery 275.00
Canton, plate, Edwards, 10½" 115.00
Canton, plate, Maddock, 7" 48.00
Canton, plate, 6" 20.00
Canton, sugar bowl, w/lid, Maddock 185.00
Carlton, cup & saucer, Alcock 85.00
Carlton, plate, Alcock, 8¼" 55.00
Cashmere, bowl, Ridgeway & Morley, 1¾x10¾" 135.00
Cashmere, cup & saucer, handleless 125.00
Cashmere, pitcher, Morley, 7⅝" 575.00
Cashmere, plate, 10½" 125.00
Cashmere, platter, 17½" 500.00
Cashmere, soup plate, Ridgeway & Morley, 12" 125.00
Cashmere, sugar bowl, w/lid 360.00
Chapoo, butter dish, Wedgwood 200.00
Chapoo, coffeepot 350.00
Chapoo, cup & saucer, Wedgwood 120.00
Chapoo, plate, 8" 95.00
Chapoo, platter, Wedgwood, 15¾" 350.00
Chapoo, platter, 14" 300.00
Chapoo, teapot 355.00
Chatsworth, pitcher, Grindley, 5½x6½" 180.00
Chatsworth, teapot, Hancock 200.00
Chen-Si, platter, octagonal, ca 1835, 16x12" 300.00
Chen-Si, platter, 17½x14" 350.00
Chiswick, plate, Ridgways, 9½" 55.00
Chiswick, platter, Ridgways, 14" 100.00
Chusan, butter dish, Podmore Walker 125.00
Chusan, cup, hot toddy; Morley 50.00
Chusan, pitcher, milk; Podmore Walker 250.00
Chusan, teapot, Clementson 300.00
Chusan, tureen, soup; Podmore Walker 275.00
Clarence, bone dish, Grindley 32.00
Clarence, bowl, vegetable; w/lid, Grindley, 8" 140.00
Clarence, pitcher, Grindley, 8" 145.00
Clarence, plate, Grindley, 10" 50.00
Clarence, platter, Grindley, 14" 100.00
Clayton, bowl, vegetable; Johnson Bros, 3¼x9¾x7¼" 58.00
Clayton, cup & saucer, demitasse; Johnson Bros 65.00
Clayton, soup plate, Johnson Bros, 9" 35.00
Clifton, cup & saucer, Grindley 45.00
Coburg, creamer, Edwards 175.00
Coburg, platter, Edwards, 17⅞" 400.00
Coburg, soup plate, Edwards, 10½" 85.00
Colonial, gravy boat, Meakin, 3½x8x3" 48.00
Colonial, relish, Meakin 75.00
Conway, bowl, vegetable; rnd, New Wharf Pottery, 9" 60.00
Conway, plate, New Wharf Pottery, 9" 50.00
Corean, tureen, w/lid, +8½" underplate 300.00
Dainty, butter pat, Maddock & Son 25.00
Dainty, platter, Maddock & Son, 10½" 70.00
Daisy, cup, demitasse; Burgess & Leigh 50.00
Daisy, plate, Burgess & Leigh, 10" 40.00
Davenport, gravy boat, Wood & Sons 80.00
Del Monte, soup plate, Johnson Bros 38.00
Derby, gravy boat, Furnival 65.00
Derby, gravy boat, Grindley 55.00
Derby, sugar bowl, w/lid, Grindley 65.00
Devon, bowl, oval, w/lid, Ford & Sons 110.00
Diana, bone dish, Grindley 35.00
Dorothy, bone dish, Wedgwood 30.00
Dorothy, plate, Johnson Bros, 9" 40.00
Dorothy, tureen, sauce; w/tray & ladle 165.00

Dresden tea pot, gold trim, 7½", $175.00.

Duchess, bowl, w/lid, Grindley, 5½x11" 125.00
Duchess, pitcher, Grindley, 9½", VG 210.00
Duchess, plate, Grindley, 9" 35.00
Duchess, platter, Grindley, 14x10" 95.00
Fairy Villas, bowl, Adams, 10" 90.00
Fairy Villas, bowl, vegetable; w/lid, Adams, 12½" L 195.00
Fairy Villas, cup & saucer, Adams 60.00
Fairy Villas, plate, Adams, 10" 80.00
Fairy Villas, plate, Adams, 7" 25.00
Fairy Villas, plate, Adams, 8" 45.00
Fairy Villas, sauce dish, Adams, 5½" 24.00
Festoon, chamber pot, Grindley 175.00
Floral, pitcher, 7" 150.00
Florida, bowl, Johnson Bros, 7½" 56.00
Florida, bowl, vegetable; oval, Grindley, 7" 55.00
Florida, bowl, vegetable; oval, Johnson Bros, 10" 75.00
Florida, gravy boat, Grindley 65.00
Florida, gravy boat, Johnson Bros 60.00

Florida, plate, Grindley, 6" 20.00
Florida, plate, Grindley, 9" 45.00
Florida, platter, Grindley, 14" 135.00
Florida, saucer, Johnson Bros, 6" .14.00
Formosa, bowl, vegetable; oval, Mayer, 13" 175.00
Formosa, soup plate, Mayer, 9½" .80.00
Gem, butter pat, Johnson Bros 13.00
Gem, gravy boat, w/undertray, Maddock & Son 48.00
Gem, soup plate, Johnson Bros 20.00
Geneva, bowl, vegetable; w/lid, New Wharf Pottery, 12x8" . .90.00
Geneva, pitcher, Royal Doulton, 4" 115.00
Georgia, bowl, Johnson Bros, 9" 48.00
Georgia, gravy boat, Johnson Bros .65.00
Georgia, plate, Johnson Bros, 10" .45.00
Georgia, sugar bowl, w/lid, Johnson Bros 120.00
Gironde, bowl, dessert, 5" 20.00
Gironde, butter pat, Grindley 16.00
Gironde, cup & saucer, Johnson Bros 45.00
Glenwood, bowl, vegetable; w/lid, Johnson Bros 175.00
Glenwood, cup & saucer, Johnson Bros 65.00
Glenwood, plate, Johnson Bros, 10" 55.00
Glenwood, plate, Johnson Bros, 9" 45.00
Gothic, bowl, vegetable; 1850s, 9⅝" 100.00
Gothic, gravy boat 145.00
Grace, gravy boat, Grindley 65.00
Grace, plate, Grindley, 6" 25.00
Grace, platter, Grindley, 13" 75.00
Grecian Scroll, wash bowl & pitcher, Mayer 600.00
Hamilton, bowl, Maddock & Son, 10" 50.00
Hamilton, soup plate, Maddock & Son 45.00
Holland, bowl, vegetable; oval, Johnson Bros, 9¾" 60.00
Holland, bowl, vegetable; w/lid, Johnson Bros 175.00
Holland, platter, Johnson Bros, 12x9" 110.00
Holland, platter, Johnson Bros, 18" 150.00
Hong Kong, plate, copper lustre highlights, ca 1850, 9" 100.00
Hong Kong, plate, Meigh, 10½" 98.00
Hong Kong, soup plate, Meigh, 10½" 110.00
Hudson, bowl, Meakin, 5" 30.00
Hudson, plate, Meakin, 9" 37.50
Idris, plate, Grindley, 9¾" 30.00
Indian Jar, creamer, Ford & Sons 165.00
Indian Jar, gravy boat, Furnival .100.00
Indian Jar, pitcher, Furnival, lg 175.00
Indian Jar, teapot, Furnival, EX .375.00
Iris, plate, Wilkinson, 5" 15.00
Ivanhoe, plate, Rebecca Repelling Templar, Wedgwood, 10" . . .75.00
Jenny Lind, plate, Wilkinson, 9" 75.00
Jewel, gravy boat, Johnson Bros 65.00
Keele, bowl, vegetable; oval, gold trim, w/lid, Grindley 110.00
Keele, plate, gold trim, Grindley, 6¾" 15.00
Keele, platter, Grindley, 16½" 135.00
Keele, soup plate, gold trim, Grindley, 8¾" 35.00
Kenworth, bowl, vegetable; oval, Johnson Bros, 9" 55.00
Kenworth, bowl, vegetable; oval, w/lid, Johnson Bros 125.00
Kenworth, relish tray, Johnson Bros, 8" 50.00
Kyber, bowl, vegetable; hdls, w/lid, Adams, 10½" 165.00
Kyber, charger, Adams, 12" dia .130.00
Kyber, cup, 2-hdld, Adams 85.00
Kyber, plate, Adams, 10" 100.00
Kyber, plate, Adams, 8" 65.00
Kyber, plate, Adams, 9" 75.00
Kyber, platter, Adams, 17" 300.00
Kyber, soup, flat, Adams, 10" 100.00
La Belle, bonbon, Wheeling, 7½" .50.00

La Belle, compote, loop hdls, Wheeling 160.00
La Belle, cracker jar, Wheeling 225.00
La Belle, pitcher, Wheeling, 2½-qt 250.00
La Belle, tray, Wheeling, 10½" 65.00
Lahore, plate, Corn, 10" 125.00
Lahore, plate, Phillips & Son, 7½" 50.00
Lahore, platter, Phillips & Son, 16½x12½" 265.00
Lakewood, butter pat, Wood 25.00
Lakewood, platter, Wood, 12½" 85.00
Lancaster, cup & saucer, New Wharf Pottery 60.00
Lancaster, gravy boat, New Wharf Pottery 65.00
Le Pavot, bowl, vegetable; w/lid, Grindley 135.00
Le Pavot, tureen, soup; Grindley, 12" 265.00
Leicester, gravy boat, E Bourne & Leigh 65.00
Leicester, plate, E Bourne & Leigh, 9" 50.00
Leicester, soup tureen, w/lid, Hancock 190.00
Linda, bowl, Maddock & Son, 9" .50.00
Linda, gravy boat, w/underplate, Maddock & Son 85.00
Linda, plate, Maddock & Son, 9" .40.00
Lobelia, plate, 8" 40.00
Lobelia, sugar bowl, w/lid 125.00
Lobelia, teapot, Phillips 200.00
Lobelia, wash set, pitcher & bowl 450.00
Lonsdale, gravy boat, Ridgways 80.00
Lorne, bone dish, Grindley 45.00
Lorne, bowl, cereal; Grindley 40.00
Lorne, creamer, Grindley 75.00
Lorne, plate, Grindley, 9⅞" 38.00
Lorne, platter, Grindley, 16" 100.00
Lorne, sauce dish, Grindley 25.00
Madras, bowl, vegetable; w/lid, Doulton 225.00
Madras, gravy boat, Doulton 75.00
Madras, platter, Doulton, 10" 85.00
Madras, soup plate, Doulton, 10" .80.00
Manhattan, bowl, vegetable; w/lid, Alcock 130.00
Manhattan, butter pat, Alcock, 3⅜" 22.50
Manhattan, plate, Alcock, 7½" 30.00
Manhattan, plate, Alcock, 9" 50.00
Manilla, creamer, Podmore Walker 275.00
Manilla, cup & saucer, handleless; Podmore Walker 125.00
Manilla, plate, Podmore Walker, 10" 100.00
Manilla, platter, Podmore Walker, 18" 400.00
Marechal Niel, bowl, vegetable; w/lid, Grindley 150.00
Marechal Niel, plate, Grindley, 6½" 20.00
Marechal Niel, platter, Grindley, 14½" 90.00
Marguerite, bone dish, Grindley 35.00
Marguerite, bowl, Grindley, 6" 30.00
Marguerite, bowl, vegetable; w/lid, Grindley 195.00
Marguerite, butter pat, Grindley 25.00
Marguerite, creamer & sugar bowl, w/lid, Grindley 250.00
Marguerite, cup & saucer, Grindley 65.00
Marguerite, gravy boat, w/underplate, Grindley 125.00
Marguerite, plate, Grindley, 10" 65.00
Marguerite, platter, Grindley, 11" .85.00
Marguerite, sauce dish, Grindley .15.00
Marguerite, soup plate, Grindley .35.00
Marie, platter, Grindley, 12" 60.00
Marie, sauce dish, Grindley 20.00
Marlborough, plate, Grindley 30.00
Marquis, plate, Grindley, 10" 35.00
Melbourne, bowl, vegetable; oval, w/lid, Grindley 135.00
Melbourne, butter pat, Grindley, 3¼" 27.50
Melbourne, creamer & sugar bowl, w/lid, Grindley 160.00
Melbourne, egg cup, Grindley 40.00

Melbourne, plate, Grindley, 9" 50.00
Melbourne, platter, Grindley, 11¼" 80.00
Melbourne, platter, Grindley, 16" 100.00
Melrose, tureen, sauce; w/lid, Doulton 150.00
Milan, pitcher, 8½" 135.00
Montana, gravy boat, w/underplate 135.00
Muriel, creamer, Hanley 80.00
Muriel, gravy boat, Hanley 40.00
Non Pareil, creamer, Burgess & Leigh 100.00
Non Pareil, plate, Burgess & Leigh, 10" 55.00
Non Pareil, plate, Burgess & Leigh, 7½" 42.00
Non Pareil, platter, Burgess & Leigh, 18" 275.00
Non Pareil, sauce dish, Burgess & Leigh 18.00
Normandy, bone dish, Johnson Bros 45.00
Normandy, gravy boat, attached underplate, 4¼x7½x5¾" 95.00
Normandy, plate, Johnson Bros, 10" 76.00
Oregon, cup & saucer, handleless; Mayer 85.00
Oregon, plate, Mayer, 7½" 45.00
Oregon, relish, Mayer, 9" 55.00
Oregon, tureen, sauce; rose finial, Mayer 320.00
Oriental, bowl, vegetable; oval, ftd, Ridgways, 11x8¾" 295.00
Oriental, bowl, vegetable; w/lid, Ridgways 245.00
Oriental, butter dish, Ridgways 225.00
Oriental, plate, Ridgways, 8" 48.00
Oriental, platter, Ridgways, 12¾" 175.00
Oriental, saucer, New Wharf Pottery, 6" 24.00
Osborne, bone dish, Ridgways, 6" 35.00
Osborne, bowl, vegetable; oval, w/lid, Ridgways, 9½" 165.00
Osborne, creamer 80.00
Osborne, platter, Ridgways, 14" 90.00
Osborne, tureen, gravy; w/attached underplate, Ridgways 95.00
Oxford, bowl, vegetable; rnd, w/lid, Johnson Bros 125.00
Oxford, plate, Johnson Bros, 6¾" 25.00
Oxford, platter, Ford & Sons, 15½x12" 90.00
Oxford, tureen, soup; w/ladle, Ford & Sons 295.00
Pansy, pitcher, bulbous, Warwick, 6" 125.00
Pansy, pitcher, 8" 185.00
Peach Royal, bone dish 38.00
Peach Royal, bowl, vegetable; oval, w/lid, Johnson Bros, 10" ..135.00
Peach Royal, butter pat 22.00
Peach Royal, creamer, Johnson Bros 65.00
Peach Royal, cup & saucer 45.00
Peach Royal, pitcher 85.00
Peach Royal, plate, Johnson Bros, 8" 25.00
Peach Royal, plate, Johnson Bros, 9" 35.00
Peach Royal, plate, 10" 50.00
Peach Royal, plate, 7" 30.00
Peach Royal, plate, 9" 35.00
Peach Royal, platter, Johnson Bros, 16" 125.00
Peach Royal, soup plate 50.00
Pekin, plate, Wilkinson, 9" 55.00
Pekin, platter, 14½x11" 325.00
Pelew, butter dish, Challinor 130.00
Pelew, cup & saucer, handleless; Challinor 95.00
Pelew, pitcher, Challinor, 11¾" 550.00
Pelew, plate, Challinor, 10¾" 110.00
Pelew, plate, Challinor, 9¾" 100.00
Persian Moss, bowl, 8½" 40.00
Persian Moss, cup & saucer 42.00
Persian Moss, soup plate, deep 42.00
Portman, bowl, ftd, Grindley 75.00
Portman, cup & saucer, Grindley 35.00
Princeton, bowl, vegetable; w/lid, Johnson Bros, 5¾x8" 110.00
Princeton, cup & saucer, Johnson Bros 40.00

Princeton, soup plate, flanged, Johnson Bros, 9" 32.00
Renown, bowl, vegetable; oval, w/lid, Staffordshire 125.00
Renown, bowl, vegetable; rnd, w/lid, Staffordshire 125.00
Renown, creamer & sugar bowl, w/lid, Staffordshire 100.00
Renown, cup & saucer, Staffordshire 35.00
Renown, plate, Staffordshire, 9" 25.00
Renown, platter, Staffordshire, lg 95.00
Renown, platter, Staffordshire, sm 50.00
Rhine, cup plate 55.00
Rhine, plate, Dimmock, 10" 70.00
Richmond, butter pat 25.00
Richmond, sauce dish 27.00
Rococo, butter pat, Maddock & Son 15.00
Rose, gravy boat, w/underplate, Grindley 65.00
Sabraon, creamer 200.00
Sabraon, gravy boat 165.00
Sabraon, platter, 9⅞" 120.00
Scinde, bowl, vegetable; oval, w/lid, Alcock 350.00
Scinde, cup & saucer, Alcock 130.00
Scinde, cup plate, Alcock 75.00
Scinde, pitcher, Alcock, 1840, 10" 450.00
Scinde, pitcher, Podmore Walker, 12½" 850.00
Scinde, plate, Alcock, 9" 85.00
Scinde, plate, 10" 100.00
Scinde, plate, 8" 75.00
Scinde, platter, Alcock, 13¾" 240.00
Scinde, platter, Walker, 15" 275.00
Scinde, platter, 16x12" 375.00
Scinde, sugar bowl, w/lid, Alcock 265.00
Scinde, tray, 16" 280.00
Shanghae, cup & saucer, Furnival 60.00
Shanghae, pitcher, Furnival, 7" 420.00
Shanghae, plate, Furnival, 9¼" 100.00
Shanghai, bowl, cereal; Grindley 45.00
Shanghai, cup & saucer, bouillon; Grindley 70.00
Shanghai, cup & saucer, Grindley 66.00
Shanghai, plate, Grindley, 10" 100.00
Shanghai, plate, W&E Corn, 10" 100.00
Shanghai, platter, Grindley, 14x10" 255.00
Shapoo, creamer, T&R Boote 245.00
Shapoo, cup & saucer, T&R Boote, ca 1842 ....100.00
Shapoo, soup plate, T&R Boote, ca 1842, 9½" 90.00
Shell, plate, Challinor, 9½" 65.00
Shell, sauce 45.00
Spinach, bowl, oyster; Libertas 88.00
Spinach, plate, Libertas, 7½" 42.50
Stanley, bowl, Johnson Bros, 2¼x8x7½" 56.00
Stanley, bowl, vegetable; Johnson Bros, w/lid, 6½x10x7½" 170.00
Stanley, gravy boat, Johnson bros, w/underplate 130.00
Stanley, platter, Johnson Bros, 12½x9½" 88.00
Temple, cup & saucer, handleless; Podmore Walker 125.00
Temple, pitcher, Podmore Walker, 6" 275.00
Temple, plate, Podmore Walker, 10" 100.00
Temple, plate, Podmore Walker, 8" 65.00
Temple, plate, Podmore Walker, 9" 85.00
Temple, sauce dish, Podmore Walker 40.00
Temple, saucer, Podmore Walker 28.00
Temple, tureen, sauce; Podmore Walker 165.00
Tivoli, platter, 10" 55.00
Togo, plate, Colonial Pottery, 8" 65.00
Togo, platter, Colonial Pottery, 12" 110.00
Tonquin, creamer, Adams 95.00
Tonquin, cup & saucer, handleless; Heath, ca 1850 ....130.00
Tonquin, plate, Adams, 9½" 100.00

Tonquin, platter, Heath, 15" 295.00
Tonquin, soup plate, Heath 110.00
Tonquin, wash bowl & pitcher, Adams, ca 1845 . . . . .950.00
Touraine, bowl, Stanley, 6¾" 32.00
Touraine, bowl, vegetable; Stanley, 10½" 90.00
Touraine, butter dish, Stanley 175.00
Touraine, creamer, Stanley 125.00
Touraine, cup & saucer, Stanley 65.00
Touraine, gravy boat, w/underplate .140.00
Touraine, plate, Stanley, 10" 80.00
Touraine, plate, Stanley, 9" 65.00
Touraine, platter, Stanley, 12½" 95.00
Touraine, sauce dish 18.00
Touraine, sugar bowl, open 80.00
Trent, plate, Ford & Sons, 10½" 55.00
Trent, soup plate, Ford & Sons, 9" 55.00
Troy, bowl, w/lid, Meigh, early, lg 350.00
Troy, plate, Meigh, 8" 48.00
Tulip, cup & saucer, Elsmore & Forster 50.00
Vermont, butter pat, Burgess & Leigh 22.50
Vermont, soup plate, Burgess & Leigh, 8⅞" 40.00
Verona, plate, Upper Hanley, 7½" 25.00
Verona, platter, Ford & Sons, nested set of 3 . . . . .235.00
Verona, sauce dish, Upper Hanley 15.00
Vienna, soap dish, w/lid, Johnson Bros 125.00
Virginia, platter, 16⅝" 145.00

Waldorf platter, New Wharf, ca 1892, 10½", $135.00.

Waldorf, bowl, vegetable; rnd, 9" 65.00
Waldorf, platter, New Wharf Pottery, 11" 140.00
Waldorf, sauce dish 24.00
Watteau, bowl, hdls, Doulton, 7" 40.00
Watteau, bowl, vegetable; Doulton, 1¾x10x8" 165.00
Watteau, bowl, vegetable; w/lid, Doulton 225.00
Watteau, compote, Doulton, 10¼" .150.00
Watteau, compote, reticulated, Doulton, 6½" 100.00
Watteau, mug, Doulton 110.00
Watteau, pitcher, Doulton, 6½" 100.00
Watteau, plate, Doulton, 10" 100.00
Watteau, plate, Doulton, 9" 80.00
Watteau, spittoon, Doulton, lg 285.00
Watteau, tray, tea service; Doulton, 16x14" 350.00
Watteau, tureen, sauce; w/underplate, Doulton 150.00
Watteau, wash set, Doulton, 5-pc 895.00

Waverly, bowl, vegetable; w/lid, Maddock & Son 140.00
Waverly, butter pat 25.00
Waverly, waste bowl, Grindley, 5¾" 58.00
Wentworth, bowl, vegetable; oval, hdls, w/lid, Meakin, 9" . . .95.00
Wentworth, butter pat, Meakin 10.00
Wentworth, gravy boat, Meakin, w/undertray 50.00
Whampoa, gravy boat, Mellor & Venables 150.00
Whampoa, plate, Mellor & Venables, 10½" 100.00
Whampoa, plate, Mellor & Venables, 7½" 55.00

Flue Covers

When spring house cleaning started and the heating stove was taken down for the warm weather season, the unsightly hole where the stovepipe joined the chimney was hidden with an attractive flue cover. They were made with a colorful litho print behind glass with a chain for hanging. Although scarce today, some scenes were actually reverse painted on the glass itself. The most popular motifs were florals, children, and lovely ladies. Square, rectangular, or diamond shapes are more valuable than oval or round covers, especially when Victorian ladies or children are pictured. Occasionally flue covers were made in sets of three — one served a functional purpose, while the other two were added to provide a more attractive wall arrangement. They range in size from 7"-8" to 13"-14", but 9" is the average.

Brass, cottage & flower garden, England, 10", pr 28.00
Brass, rural winter scene, EX 12.50
Little girl w/flowers, under glass 28.00
Tin, seasons, stamped, colorful 15.00
Victorian children, under glass, 9" 35.00

Victorian maid, gold glitter trim, 12" diameter, $75.00.

Vintage car, under glass 45.00

Folk Art

That the creative energies of the mind ever spark innovations in functional utilitarian channels as well as toward playful frivolity is well documented in the study of American folk art. While the average early settler rarely had free time to pursue art for its own sake, his creative energy exemplified itself in fashioning useful objects carved or otherwise ornamented beyond the scope of pure practicality. After the advent of the Industrial Revolution, the pace of everyday living became more leisurely, and country folk found they had extra time. Not accustomed to sitting idle, many turned to carving, painting, or weaving. Whirligigs, imaginative toys for the children, and whimsies of all types resulted. Though often rather crude, this type of early art represents a segment of our heritage and as such has become valued by collectors. See also Baskets; Decoys; Frakturs; Samplers; Trade Signs; Weathervanes; Wood Carvings.

Ash tray holder, lady bellhop, wood, EX pnt, 37x7" 85.00
Birdhouse, caboose form, wood, EX details/pnt, 10x20x6" 70.00
Birdhouse, hollowed birch bark log, bentwood roof, 1930s 90.00
Birdhouse, log cabin, gr shingled roof, old pnt, 8x10x12" 65.00
Birdhouse, wood, shake shingles, steps, pnt, 1940s, 12x9x7" 65.00
Calligraphy, Acts of Faith, Hope & Charity..., 3¾x3¾" 40.00
Calligraphy, eagle/shield, penmanship award, 20x26" 300.00
Church, 32 windows in door, orig pnt, shingles, 7x5x2½" 40.00
Cupboard, crate w/pine door, appl spool halves, pnt, 21x20" . . .150.00
Cvg, bat, cvd vertebra from lg mammal, ca 1900, 8x4½x3½" . . .80.00
Cvg, Indian Chief, sitting, sandstone, sgn CE, 1900s, 14" 200.00
Cvg, sheep, sandstone, free standing, EX detail, 9" 450.00
Drawing, charcoal, detailed landscape, in shadow box, 36x26" .110.00
Drawing, pencil, sailboats, sgn/dtd 1891, orig fr, 26x21" 350.00
Gourd, pnt as man w/cap & tie, wht suit, ca 1900, 7x5½" 135.00
Instrument, dulcimer-like, pine, 1-string, 1800s, 35" L 125.00
Noisemaker, wood, ratchet style, fancy pnt, 1900, 7x5x1" 45.00
Painting, calf at rail fence, blk border, ca 1900, 15x11½" 125.00
Painting, church at Christmas, oil on canvas, 1890s, 19x14" . . .265.00
Painting, fisherman at river, primitive, 1800s, 19x13½" 45.00
Painting, lady in lacy dress, oil, sgn/dtd 1930s, 25x21" 250.00
Painting, wagon train, oil on board, ca 1900, fr, 17½x28" 125.00
Paper cutting, family record/florals, dtd 1804, 34x28" 325.00
Paper cutting, floral medallions, sgn, 11x13" 250.00

Miniature Adirondack rocking chair, New York, early 20th century, 10", minor loss, $200.00.

Rocking horse, cvd, tack eyes, plank seat, 1900, 11x27x19" . . .185.00
Theorem on paper, fruit plate, appl border, fr, 10x12", VG 400.00
Theorem on paper, in pencil, urn of flowers, 1825, 13x10" 200.00
Theorem on velvet, bowl w/flowers, NY, 1825, 11x12" 4,000.00

Whirligig, Blk man, sorrowful, wood/mc pnt, 1900s, sm 85.00
Whirligig, Blk man on high-wheel bike, lg prop, 1900s, 25" .2,600.00
Whirligig, flying duck, paddle wings, tack eyes, 1900, 25" 95.00
Whirligig, Indian chief in canoe, paddle arms, 1930s, 11x18x5" .85.00
Whirligig, Mammy washing, wood, 1930s, 16x11x2" 95.00
Whirligig, man, 3-D, paddle arms, tack eyes, 1930s, 13x9x4" . .265.00
Whirligig, soldier, paddle arms, EX pnt, 1920s, 15x3x2" 185.00
Whirligig, windmill, wood/tin, EX pnt, 25x15x2½" 85.00
Whirligig, windmill/Dutch girl churns, wood/tin, 23x22x15" . .125.00

Fostoria

The Fostoria Glass Company was built in 1887 at Fostoria, Ohio, but by 1891 it had moved to Moundsville, West Virginia. During the next two decades, they produced many lines of pressed patterned tableware and lamps. Their most famous pattern, American, was introduced in 1915 and has been produced continuously since that time in well over two hundred different pieces. From 1920 to 1925, top artists designed tablewares in colored glass — canary (vaseline), amber, blue, orchid, green, and ebony — in pressed patterns as well as etched designs. By the late thirties, Fostoria was recognized as the largest producer of handmade glassware in the world. The company ceased operations in Moundsville in 1986.

Our advisor for this category is Michael Baker; he is listed in the Directory under West Virginia. We are assisted in our listings by the Fostoria Glass Society of America, Inc., whose mailing address may be found in the Directory under Clubs, Newsletters, and Catalogs.

Animals and Birds

Colts, sitting 35.00
Deer, sitting or standing 35.00
Duck w/3 ducklings, amber, set 50.00
Eagle, bookend 95.00
Elephant, bookends, blk, pr 75.00
Horse, bookends, blk, pr 75.00
Horse, bookends, pr 32.00
Owl, bookend, scarce 100.00
Pelican 50.00
Penguin 25.00
Polar bear 35.00
Pony, bl 20.00
Sea horse, bookend 75.00
Seal 85.00
Seal, frosted 60.00
Seal, wisteria 85.00
Squirrel 20.00
Squirrel, frosted 20.00
Whale 20.00

American, ash tray, oval, 5½" 12.00
American, ash tray, sq, 2⅞" 6.00
American, basket, 10" 25.00
American, bell 75.00
American, bottle, cologne; w/stopper, 6-oz, 5¾" 50.00
American, bottle, cordial; w/stopper, 9-oz, 7¼" 67.50
American, bowl, bonbon; 3-ftd, 6" 15.00
American, bowl, celery; oblong, 10" 14.00
American, bowl, centerpc; hat shape, 15" 125.00
American, bowl, centerpc; 11" 40.00
American, bowl, deep, 8" 42.50
American, bowl, float; oval, 10" 32.50

American, bowl, fruit; flared, 4¾" 15.00
American, bowl, fruit; shallow, 13" 50.00
American, bowl, hdl, tricorner, 5" 11.00
American, bowl, hdl, 4½" 8.00
American, bowl, lemon; w/lid, 5½" 30.00
American, bowl, lily pond; 12" 55.00
American, bowl, nappy, 4½" 10.00
American, bowl, oval, deep, 11¾" 37.50
American, bowl, pickle; oblong, 8" 13.00
American, bowl, relish/celery; 3-part, 11" 30.00
American, bowl, rolled edge, 11½" 37.50
American, box, cigarette; w/lid, 4¾" 30.00
American, box, glove; 9½x3½" 150.00
American, box, handkerchief; w/lid, 5⅝x4⅝" 125.00
American, box, 2" sq 175.00
American, bud vase, flared, 8½" 20.00

American, cake stand, $57.50.

American, candlestick, chamber type w/finger hold, 2" 20.00
American, candlestick, Eiffel Tower, 7¼" 100.00
American, candlestick, octagon ft, 6" 20.00
American, candlestick, rnd ft, 6½" 150.00
American, candy dish, w/lid, ped ft 15.00
American, comport, jelly; w/lid, 6¾" 30.00
American, comport, w/lid, 5" 22.50
American, creamer, individual, 4¾-oz 7.50
American, cup, ftd, 7-oz 9.00
American, cup, punch; flared rim 10.00
American, decanter, w/stopper, 24-oz, 9¼" 70.00
American, goblet, tea; #2056, low ft, 12-oz, 5¾" 13.00
American, goblet, water; #2056, hex ft, 10-oz, 6⅞" 12.50
American, goblet, wine; #2056, hex ft, 2½-oz, 4⅜" 10.50
American, hat, 4" 35.00
American, hurricane lamp, complete, 12" 120.00
American, ice bucket, w/tongs 50.00
American, jam pot, w/lid 40.00
American, marmalade, w/lid, chrome spoon 35.00
American, mayonnaise, w/liner, ladle 30.00
American, mug, beer; 12-oz, 4½" 32.50
American, pitcher, flat, 1-qt 20.00
American, plate, cake; hdls, 10" 16.00
American, plate, dinner; 9½" 15.00
American, plate, salad; crescent, 7½x4⅜" 37.50
American, plate, torte; 18" 75.00
American, platter, oval, 10½" 37.50
American, pretzel jar, w/lid, 8⅞" 250.00
American, ring holder 100.00
American, rose bowl, 3½" 14.00
American, sauce boat, w/liner 52.50

American, shaker, 3¼", ea 9.50
American, sherbet, hdld, 4½-oz, 3½" 40.00
American, straw holder, w/lid, 10" 225.00
American, sugar shaker 37.50
American, syrup, w/drip-proof top 25.00
American, toothpick 17.50
American, tray, ice cream; oval, 13½" 52.50
American, tray, oval, hdls, 6" 35.00
American, tray, pin; oval, 5½x4½" 40.00
American, tray, sandwich; center hdl, 12" 33.00
American, tray, service; hdls, 9½" 27.50
American, tumbler, juice; #2056, ftd, 5-oz, 4¾" 10.00
American, tumbler, water; #2056, ftd, 9-oz, 4⅞" 12.00
American, tumbler, whiskey; #2056, 2-oz, 2½" 11.00
American, vase, flared, 7" 67.50
American, vase, straight sided, 6" 25.00
American, vase, swung, 10" 125.00
Baroque, bl; ash tray 15.00
Baroque, bl; bowl, fruit; 5" 16.00
Baroque, bl; bowl, hdls, 10" 40.00
Baroque, bl; bowl, pickle; 8" 16.50
Baroque, bl; bowl, rolled edge, 11" 35.00
Baroque, bl; bowl, 3-ftd, 7" 25.00
Baroque, bl; candelabrum, 3-light, 24-lustre, 9½" 60.00
Baroque, bl; candlestick, 5½" 20.00
Baroque, bl; comport, 4¾" 22.50
Baroque, bl; cup 15.00
Baroque, bl; ice bucket 60.00
Baroque, bl; mustard, w/lid 45.00
Baroque, bl; plate, 8" 11.00
Baroque, bl; rose bowl, 3¾" 40.00
Baroque, bl; shakers, pr 110.00
Baroque, bl; sherbet, 5-oz, 3¾" 17.50
Baroque, bl; sugar bowl, ftd, 3½" 12.00
Baroque, bl; tumbler, old fashioned; 6½-oz, 3½" 30.00
Baroque, bl; tumbler, water; 9-oz, 4¼" 26.00
Baroque, bl; vase, 6½" 38.00
Baroque, crystal; bowl, celery; 11" 12.00
Baroque, crystal; bowl, cereal; 6" 15.00
Baroque, crystal; bowl, cream soup 12.50
Baroque, crystal; bowl, flared, 12" 21.50
Baroque, crystal; bowl, jelly; w/lid, 7½" 25.00
Baroque, crystal; bowl, vegetable; oval, 9½" 25.00
Baroque, crystal; candlestick, 3-light, 6" 15.00
Baroque, crystal; mayonnaise, w/liner, 5½" 15.00
Baroque, crystal; pitcher, 6½" 150.00
Baroque, crystal; plate, 9" 15.00
Baroque, crystal; platter, oval, 12" 22.00
Baroque, crystal; rose bowl, 3¾" 18.00
Baroque, crystal; tray, oval, 11" 10.00
Baroque, crystal; tumbler, juice; 5-oz, 3¾" 12.00
Baroque, crystal; vase, 7" 15.00
Baroque, yel; bowl, flared, 12" 27.50
Baroque, yel; bowl, hdls, 4 styles, 4", ea 13.50
Baroque, yel; bowl, sq, 6" 12.00
Baroque, yel; candelabrum, 2-light, 16-lustre, 8¼" 40.00
Baroque, yel; candlestick, 4" 12.50
Baroque, yel; creamer, individual, 3¼" 10.00
Baroque, yel; oil, w/stopper, 5½" 235.00
Baroque, yel; pitcher, ice lip, 7" 375.00
Baroque, yel; plate, 7" 7.00
Baroque, yel; platter, oval, 12" 35.00
Baroque, yel; shakers, individual, pr 85.00
Baroque, yel; sherbet, 5-oz, 3¾" 15.50

Baroque, yel; sugar bowl, ftd, 3½" 11.00
Baroque, yel; tumbler, cocktail; ftd, 3½-oz, 3" 16.00
Baroque, yel; vase, 7" 37.50

**Coin Glass, candy urn, ruby, 13",
$110.00.**

Colony, crystal; ash tray, rnd, 6" 15.00
Colony, crystal; bowl, bonbon; 5" 9.00
Colony, crystal; bowl, cream soup 35.00
Colony, crystal; bowl, flared, 11" .32.50
Colony, crystal; bowl, fruit; 10" .27.50
Colony, crystal; bowl, salad; 7¾" 20.00
Colony, crystal; bowl, salad; 9¾" 30.00
Colony, crystal; candlestick, 7" .15.00
Colony, crystal; comport, w/lid, 6½" 30.00
Colony, crystal; ice bucket 45.00
Colony, crystal; oil, w/stopper, 4½-oz 35.00
Colony, crystal; pitcher, milk; 16-oz 37.50
Colony, crystal; plate, bread & butter; 6" 4.00
Colony, crystal; plate, dinner; 9" 17.50
Colony, crystal; punch bowl, ftd, 13¼" 275.00
Colony, crystal; rose bowl, 6" .25.00
Colony, crystal; shakers, 3⅝", pr 12.50
Colony, crystal; sugar bowl, individual, 2¾" 5.00
Colony, crystal; tumbler, ftd, 12-oz, 5¾" 17.50
Colony, crystal; tumbler, juice; 5-oz, 3⅝" 14.00
Colony, crystal; vase, cornucopia form, 9" 50.00
Colony, crystal; vase, cupped, 7" 35.00
Fairfax, amber; bouillon, ftd 7.00
Fairfax, amber; bowl, centerpc; 15" 20.00
Fairfax, amber; bowl, cereal; 6" 9.00
Fairfax, amber; bowl, lemon; hdls, 9" 6.00
Fairfax, amber; creamer, flat 10.00
Fairfax, amber; cup, flat 4.00
Fairfax, amber; pail, whipped cream 25.00
Fairfax, amber; plate, canape 3.00
Fairfax, amber; plate, torte; 14" 14.00
Fairfax, amber; shakers, ftd, pr 30.00
Fairfax, amber; stem, water, 10-oz, 8¼" 17.50
Fairfax, amber; tray, center hdl, 11" 12.00
Fairfax, bl; bonbon 12.50
Fairfax, bl; bowl, baker, oval, 9" 25.00
Fairfax, bl; bowl, soup; 7" 20.00
Fairfax, bl; comport, 7" 15.00
Fairfax, bl; creamer, ftd 11.00

Fairfax, bl; ice bucket 40.00
Fairfax, bl; oil, ftd 105.00
Fairfax, bl; pitcher 160.00
Fairfax, bl; plate, grill; 10¼" 12.00
Fairfax, bl; plate, salad; 7" 5.00
Fairfax, bl; plate, torte; 14" .17.50
Fairfax, bl; platter, oval, 12" 32.00
Fairfax, bl; sauce boat 30.00
Fairfax, bl; sherbet, high, 6-oz, 6" 13.00
Fairfax, bl; stem, wine, 3-oz, 5½" 25.00
Fairfax, bl; sugar bowl, ftd, open 10.00
Fairfax, bl; sugar bowl lid 30.00
Fairfax, bl; tumbler, ftd, 5-oz, 4½" 12.00
Fairfax, gr; bowl, centerpc; oval, 13" 22.50
Fairfax, gr; bowl, nappy, rnd, 8" 14.00
Fairfax, gr; candlestick, flattened top 10.00
Fairfax, gr; creamer, tea 9.00
Fairfax, gr; flower holder, oval 20.00
Fairfax, gr; oil, ftd 90.00
Fairfax, gr; plate, cake; 10" .15.00
Fairfax, gr; plate, dinner; 10¼" 15.00
Fairfax, gr; platter, oval, 15" 32.00
Fairfax, gr; sauce boat liner .10.00
Fairfax, gr; stem, claret, 4-oz, 6" 18.00
Fairfax, gr; sugar bowl, flat .12.00
Fairfax, gr; tumbler, ftd, 9-oz, 5¼" 12.50
Fairfax, orchid; ash tray 20.00
Fairfax, orchid; bottle, salad dressing 95.00
Fairfax, orchid; bowl, dessert; hdls, lg 17.00
Fairfax, orchid; bowl, fruit; 5" 8.50
Fairfax, orchid; bowl, nappy, rnd, 8" 22.00
Fairfax, orchid; cup, ftd 8.00
Fairfax, orchid; mayonnaise .12.00
Fairfax, orchid; pail, whipped cream 40.00
Fairfax, orchid; plate, dinner; 10¼" 21.00
Fairfax, orchid; plate, luncheon; 9½" 12.00
Fairfax, orchid; platter, oval, 10½" 27.00
Fairfax, orchid; stem, cocktail, 3-oz, 5¼" 20.00
Fairfax, orchid; sweetmeat 11.00
Fairfax, orchid; tray, celery; 11½" 16.00
Fairfax, orchid; tray, relish; 11½" 15.00
Fairfax, orchid; tumbler, ftd, 12-oz, 6" 15.00
Fairfax, rose; bowl, whipped cream 8.00
Fairfax, rose; bowl, 12" 15.00
Fairfax, rose; mayonnaise 9.00
Fairfax, rose; plate, bread & butter; 6" 2.00
Fairfax, rose; plate, salad; 8" 4.50
Fairfax, rose; set, cheese & cracker 20.00
Fairfax, rose; stem, cordial, ¾-oz, 4" 25.00
Fairfax, rose; sugar pail 25.00
Fairfax, rose; tray, relish; 8½" 7.00
Fairfax, topaz; ash tray 17.50
Fairfax, topaz; bowl, centerpc; 12" 20.00
Fairfax, topaz; bowl, soup; 7" 14.00
Fairfax, topaz; butter dish, w/lid 90.00
Fairfax, topaz; cream soup liner, 7" 3.50
Fairfax, topaz; cup, after dinner 12.50
Fairfax, topaz; mayonnaise ladle 10.00
Fairfax, topaz; plate, bread; 12" 12.00
Fairfax, topaz; plate, luncheon; 9½" 7.00
Fairfax, topaz; platter, oval, 10½" 19.00
Fairfax, topaz; saucer, after dinner 5.00
Fairfax, topaz; stem, low sherbet, 6-oz, 4¼" 11.00
Fairfax, topaz; stem, wine, 3-oz, 5½" 22.50

Fairfax, topaz; sweetmeat 9.00
Fairfax, topaz; tumbler, ftd, 12-oz, 6" 14.00
June, bl; bowl, baker, oval, 9" 65.00
June, bl; bowl, bonbon 25.00
June, bl; bowl, centerpc; 11" 50.00
June, bl; bowl, Grecian, 10" 60.00
June, bl; bowl, lemon 25.00
June, bl; bowl, soup; 7" .37.50
June, bl; candlestick, 5" 30.00
June, bl; candy dish, w/lid, 3-part 155.00
June, bl; comport, 6" 55.00
June, bl; creamer, ftd 20.00
June, bl; creamer, tea 35.00
June, bl; cup, ftd 27.50
June, bl; goblet, cocktail; 3-oz, 5¼" 40.00
June, bl; ice bucket 90.00
June, bl; mayonnaise, w/liner 45.00
June, bl; pail, whipped cream 145.00
June, bl; plate, bread & butter; 6" 6.00
June, bl; plate, cake; hdls, 10" 45.00
June, bl; plate, canape 18.00
June, bl; plate, dinner; 10¼" 50.00
June, bl; plate, luncheon; 8¾" 12.00
June, bl; sauce boat 110.00
June, bl; saucer 7.50
June, bl; sherbet, high, 6-oz, 6" 29.00
June, bl; sugar pail 150.00
June, bl; tray, celery; 11½" 40.00
June, bl; tray, center hdl, 11" 45.00
June, bl; tray, relish; 8½" 22.00
June, bl; tumbler, ftd, 12-oz, 6" 30.00
June, bl; tumbler, ftd, 5-oz, 4½" 27.50
June, bl; vase, fan form, ftd, 8½" 135.00
June, crystal; ash tray 23.00
June, crystal; bowl, bonbon 12.50
June, crystal; bowl, mint 10.00
June, crystal; bowl, nappy, ftd, 6" 10.00
June, crystal; bowl, whipped cream 10.00
June, crystal; bowl, 10" .20.00
June, crystal; candlestick, 3" 12.00
June, crystal; comport, 7" 22.00
June, crystal; creamer, ftd 12.00
June, crystal; decanter .150.00
June, crystal; goblet, claret; 4-oz, 6" 30.00
June, crystal; goblet, cordial; ¾-oz, 4" 40.00
June, crystal; grapefruit .25.00
June, crystal; ice dish 21.00
June, crystal; oil, ftd 165.00
June, crystal; pitcher 195.00
June, crystal; plate, chop; 13" 20.00
June, crystal; plate, grill; 10" 16.00
June, crystal; plate, salad; 7½" 5.00
June, crystal; platter, 15" 30.00
June, crystal; saucer, after dinner 6.00
June, crystal; shakers, ftd, pr 60.00
June, crystal; sugar bowl, ftd 12.00
June, crystal; tumbler, ftd, 9-oz, 5¼" 15.00
June, crystal; vase, 8" 60.00
June, rose; bowl, bouillon; ftd 20.00
June, rose; bowl, centerpc; 12" 42.50
June, rose; bowl, cereal; 6" 23.50
June, rose; bowl, fruit; 5" 18.00
June, rose; candlestick, 2" 15.00
June, rose; cup, ftd 22.00

June, rose; decanter 350.00
June, rose; goblet, wine; 3-oz, 5½" 45.00
June, rose; grapefruit 50.00
June, rose; grapefruit liner 40.00
June, rose; parfait, 5¼" .47.50
June, rose; plate, cake; hdls, 10" 35.00
June, rose; platter, 12" .40.00
June, rose; sauce boat liner 25.00
June, rose; set, cheese & cracker 40.00
June, rose; sugar bowl, tea 30.00
June, rose; tumbler, ftd, 12-oz, 6" 27.50
June, topaz; ash tray 32.00
June, topaz; bowl, centerpc; w/flower frog, oval, 13" 47.50
June, topaz; bowl, dessert; hdls, lg 35.00
June, topaz; bowl, finger; w/liner 45.00
June, topaz; bowl, whipped cream 14.00
June, topaz; candlestick, Grecian, 3" 25.00
June, topaz; candy dish, w/lid, 3-part 90.00
June, topaz; comport, 5" 27.50
June, topaz; cream soup, ftd 30.00
June, topaz; cup, after dinner 35.00
June, topaz; finger bowl liner, 6" 5.00
June, topaz; oyster cocktail, 5½-oz 23.00
June, topaz; plate, chop; 13" 35.00
June, topaz; plate, dinner; sm, 9½" 15.00
June, topaz; plate, luncheon; 8¾" 10.00
June, topaz; platter, 12" 40.00
June, topaz; saucer, after dinner 8.00
June, topaz; sherbet, high, 6-oz, 6" 25.00
June, topaz; vase, 8" 135.00
Kashmir, gr; bowl, cream soup 22.00
Kashmir, gr; bowl, finger 15.00
Kashmir, gr; bowl, fruit; 5" 13.00
Kashmir, gr; bowl, 10" .40.00
Kashmir, gr; candlestick, 2" 15.00
Kashmir, gr; candlestick, 9½" 40.00
Kashmir, gr; creamer, ftd 17.50
Kashmir, gr; cup 15.00
Kashmir, gr; grapefruit .37.50
Kashmir, gr; grapefruit liner 27.50
Kashmir, gr; pitcher, ftd 350.00
Kashmir, gr; plate, dinner; 10" 35.00
Kashmir, gr; plate, salad; rnd, 7" 6.00
Kashmir, gr; saucer, rnd 5.00
Kashmir, gr; set, cheese & cracker 65.00
Kashmir, gr; shakers, pr 90.00
Kashmir, gr; sherbet, high, 6-oz 17.50
Kashmir, gr; stem, cocktail, 3-oz 22.00
Kashmir, gr; stem, cordial, ¾-oz 85.00
Kashmir, gr; stem, ftd, 2½-oz 25.00
Kashmir, gr; stem, wine, 2½-oz 32.00
Kashmir, gr; sugar bowl, ftd 15.00
Kashmir, yel; ash tray 25.00
Kashmir, yel; bowl, baker; 9" 37.50
Kashmir, yel; bowl, cereal; 6" 22.00
Kashmir, yel; bowl, soup; 7" 25.00
Kashmir, yel; candlestick, 5" 22.50
Kashmir, yel; candy dish, w/lid 65.00
Kashmir, yel; comport, 6" 35.00
Kashmir, yel; cup, after dinner; ftd 25.00
Kashmir, yel; ice bucket 65.00
Kashmir, yel; oil, ftd 250.00
Kashmir, yel; plate, bread & butter; 6" 5.00
Kashmir, yel; plate, grill; 10" 22.00

Kashmir, yel; plate, luncheon; 9" 9.00
Kashmir, yel; plate, salad; 8" 8.00
Kashmir, yel; sauce boat, w/liner 75.00
Kashmir, yel; stem, claret, 4-oz 28.00
Kashmir, yel; stem, cocktail, ftd, 3½-oz 22.00
Kashmir, yel; stem, whiskey, ftd, 2-oz 25.00
Kashmir, yel; vase, 8" 85.00
Trojan, rose; ash tray, lg 27.50
Trojan, rose; bowl, bonbon 13.00
Trojan, rose; bowl, centerpc; 12" 33.50
Trojan, rose; bowl, cereal; 6" 22.00
Trojan, rose; bowl, cream soup; ftd 18.00
Trojan, rose; bowl, finger; w/6¼" liner 22.00
Trojan, rose; bowl, lemon 16.00
Trojan, rose; bowl, whipped cream 11.00
Trojan, rose; candlestick, 3" 15.00
Trojan, rose; comport, 6" 25.00
Trojan, rose; creamer, ftd 17.50
Trojan, rose; cup, ftd 16.00
Trojan, rose; goblet, cocktail; 3-oz, 5¼" 25.00
Trojan, rose; goblet, wine; 3-oz, 5½" 40.00
Trojan, rose; ice bucket 65.00
Trojan, rose; mayonnaise, w/liner 30.00
Trojan, rose; parfait 37.00
Trojan, rose; pitcher 265.00
Trojan, rose; plate, chop; 13" 37.50
Trojan, rose; plate, dinner; 10¼" 32.50
Trojan, rose; plate, luncheon; 8¾" 10.00
Trojan, rose; plate, salad; 7½" 7.50
Trojan, rose; platter, 15" 65.00
Trojan, rose; sauce plate 20.00
Trojan, rose; saucer, after dinner 7.50
Trojan, rose; set, cheese & cracker 45.00
Trojan, rose; sherbet, low, 4¼" 16.00
Trojan, rose; sugar bowl, ftd 17.50
Trojan, rose; sweetmeat 13.50
Trojan, rose; tray, celery; 11½" 22.50
Trojan, rose; tray, center hdl, 11" 32.50
Trojan, rose; tumbler, ftd, 2½-oz 30.00
Trojan, rose; tumbler, ftd, 9-oz, 5¼" 15.50
Trojan, topaz; ash tray, sm 22.50
Trojan, topaz; bowl, baker, 9" 45.00
Trojan, topaz; bowl, bouillon; ftd 16.00
Trojan, topaz; bowl, fruit; 5" 15.00
Trojan, topaz; bowl, mint; 3-ftd 17.00
Trojan, topaz; bowl, soup; 7" 23.00
Trojan, topaz; bowl, 10" 30.00
Trojan, topaz; candlestick, 2" 15.00
Trojan, topaz; candlestick, 5" 19.50
Trojan, topaz; candy dish, w/lid, ½-lb 100.00
Trojan, topaz; creamer, tea 35.00
Trojan, topaz; cup, after dinner 27.50
Trojan, topaz; goblet, claret; 4-oz, 6" 40.00
Trojan, topaz; goblet, cordial; ¾-oz, 4" 65.00
Trojan, topaz; goblet, water; 10-oz, 8¼" 27.50
Trojan, topaz; grapefruit 40.00
Trojan, topaz; grapefruit liner 35.00
Trojan, topaz; ice dish 30.00
Trojan, topaz; oil, ftd 235.00
Trojan, topaz; pail, whipped cream 100.00
Trojan, topaz; plate, bread & butter; 6" 5.00
Trojan, topaz; plate, cake; hdls, 10" 25.00
Trojan, topaz; plate, canape 15.00
Trojan, topaz; plate, dinner; sm, 9½" 16.00

Trojan, topaz; plate, grill; rare, 10¼" 35.00
Trojan, topaz; platter, 12" 42.00
Trojan, topaz; sauce boat 60.00
Trojan, topaz; saucer 4.50
Trojan, topaz; shakers, ftd, pr 70.00
Trojan, topaz; sherbet, high, 6" 20.00
Trojan, topaz; sugar pail 95.00
Trojan, topaz; tray, relish; 8½" 15.00
Trojan, topaz; tray, service 27.50
Trojan, topaz; tumbler, ftd, 5-oz, 4½" 22.50
Trojan, topaz; vase, 2 styles, 8", ea 120.00
Versailles, bl; ash tray 30.00
Versailles, bl; bowl, baker, 9" 55.00
Versailles, bl; bowl, centerpc; 11" 45.00
Versailles, bl; bowl, cream soup; ftd 25.00
Versailles, bl; bowl, dessert; hdls, lg 50.00
Versailles, bl; bowl, finger; w/liner 32.00
Versailles, bl; bowl, lemon 20.00
Versailles, bl; bowl, soup; 7" 37.00
Versailles, bl; candlestick, 5" 30.00
Versailles, bl; candy dish, w/lid, ½-lb 110.00
Versailles, bl; candy dish, w/lid, 3-part 120.00
Versailles, bl; comport, 6" 35.00
Versailles, bl; comport, 8" 75.00
Versailles, bl; cream soup liner, 7½" 8.00
Versailles, bl; creamer, tea 30.00
Versailles, bl; cup, after dinner 40.00
Versailles, bl; decanter 350.00
Versailles, bl; goblet, claret; 4-oz, 6" 65.00
Versailles, bl; goblet, water; 10-oz, 8¼" 32.50
Versailles, bl; grapefruit 60.00
Versailles, bl; grapefruit liner 40.00
Versailles, bl; ice dish 40.00
Versailles, bl; pail, whipped cream 115.00
Versailles, bl; parfait 35.00
Versailles, bl; pitcher 350.00
Versailles, bl; plate, bread & butter; 6" 5.00
Versailles, bl; plate, cake; hdls, 10" 35.00
Versailles, bl; plate, canape; 6" 65.00
Versailles, bl; plate, dinner; 10¼" 45.00
Versailles, bl; plate, luncheon; 8¾" 10.00
Versailles, bl; platter, 12" 40.00
Versailles, bl; sauce plate 25.00
Versailles, bl; saucer, after dinner 6.00
Versailles, bl; set, cheese & cracker 65.00
Versailles, bl; shakers, ftd, pr 110.00
Versailles, bl; sherbet, high, 6" 25.00
Versailles, bl; sugar bowl lid 125.00
Versailles, bl; sugar pail 155.00
Versailles, bl; sweetmeat 17.50
Versailles, bl; tray, center hdl, 11" 35.00
Versailles, bl; tray, relish; 8½" 40.00
Versailles, bl; tumbler, ftd, 2½-oz 40.00
Versailles, bl; tumbler, ftd, 9-oz, 5¼" 25.00
Versailles, bl; vase, fan form, ftd, 8½" 140.00
Versailles, bl; vase, 8" 150.00
Versailles, gr; bowl, baker, 9" 35.00
Versailles, gr; bowl, bonbon 13.00
Versailles, gr; bowl, centerpc; oval, 13" 35.00
Versailles, gr; bowl, centerpc; 11" 30.00
Versailles, gr; bowl, cereal; 6" 20.00
Versailles, gr; bowl, cream soup; ftd 16.00
Versailles, gr; bowl, fruit; 5" 15.00
Versailles, gr; candlestick, 5" 20.00

Versailles, gr; candy dish, w/lid, 3-part 75.00
Versailles, gr; comport, 6" 25.00
Versailles, gr; creamer, ftd 15.00
Versailles, gr; cup, ftd 17.50
Versailles, gr; decanter 250.00
Versailles, gr; goblet, claret; 4-oz, 6" 40.00
Versailles, gr; goblet, water; 10-oz, 8¼" 27.50
Versailles, gr; grapefruit 40.00
Versailles, gr; grapefruit liner 30.00
Versailles, gr; ice dish 30.00
Versailles, gr; oil, ftd 250.00
Versailles, gr; parfait 27.50
Versailles, gr; plate, bread & butter; 6" 4.00
Versailles, gr; plate, canape; 6" 40.00
Versailles, gr; plate, dinner; 10¼" 35.00
Versailles, gr; plate, luncheon; 8¾" 8.00
Versailles, gr; platter, 15" 60.00
Versailles, gr; sauce boat 60.00
Versailles, gr; saucer, after dinner 4.00
Versailles, gr; set, cheese & cracker 50.00
Versailles, gr; shakers, ftd, pr 80.00
Versailles, gr; sherbet, low, 4¼" 20.00
Versailles, gr; sugar bowl lid 85.00
Versailles, gr; sweetmeat 12.00
Versailles, gr; tray, center hdl, 11" 25.00
Versailles, gr; tray, service 30.00
Versailles, gr; tumbler, ftd, 2½-oz 30.00
Versailles, gr; tumbler, ftd, 9-oz, 5¼" 20.00
Versailles, gr; vase, fan form, ftd, 8½" 85.00
Versailles, pk; ash tray 24.00
Versailles, pk; bottle, salad dressing; sterling top 275.00
Versailles, pk; bowl, bouillon; ftd 16.00
Versailles, pk; bowl, centerpc; 12" 25.00
Versailles, pk; bowl, lemon 13.00
Versailles, pk; bowl, mint; 3-ftd 16.00
Versailles, pk; bowl, soup; 7" 25.00
Versailles, pk; bowl, 10" 30.00
Versailles, pk; candlestick, 2" 15.00
Versailles, pk; candy dish, w/lid, ½-lb 65.00
Versailles, pk; comport, 7" 27.00
Versailles, pk; creamer, tea 27.50
Versailles, pk; cup, after dinner 25.00
Versailles, pk; goblet, cocktail; 3-oz, 5¼" 25.00
Versailles, pk; goblet, cordial; ¾-oz, 4" 75.00
Versailles, pk; ice bucket 62.50
Versailles, pk; mayonnaise, w/liner 35.00
Versailles, pk; oyster cocktail 20.00
Versailles, pk; pail, whipped cream 85.00
Versailles, pk; pitcher 250.00
Versailles, pk; plate, chop; 13" 30.00
Versailles, pk; plate, dinner; sm, 9½" 14.00
Versailles, pk; plate, grill; 10" 20.00
Versailles, pk; plate, salad; 7½" 6.00
Versailles, pk; plate, sauce 20.00
Versailles, pk; platter, 12" 30.00
Versailles, pk; saucer 4.00
Versailles, pk; sherbet, high, 6" 20.00
Versailles, pk; sugar, tea 27.50
Versailles, pk; sugar pail 95.00
Versailles, pk; tray, celery; 11½" 30.00
Versailles, pk; tray, relish; 8½" 30.00
Versailles, pk; tray, service/lemon 32.50
Versailles, pk; tumbler, flat tea 80.00
Versailles, pk; tumbler, ftd, 12-oz, 6" 22.50

Versailles, pk; tumbler, ftd, 5-oz, 4½" 20.00
Versailles, pk; vase, 8" 100.00
Versailles, yel; ash tray 25.00
Versailles, yel; bowl, bonbon 15.00
Versailles, yel; bowl, bouillon; ftd 17.50
Versailles, yel; bowl, centerpc; oval, 13" 40.00
Versailles, yel; bowl, cereal; 6" 22.00
Versailles, yel; bowl, cream soup; ftd 20.00
Versailles, yel; bowl, fruit; 5" 16.00
Versailles, yel; bowl, whipped cream 13.00
Versailles, yel; candlestick, 3" 17.50
Versailles, yel; comport, 7" 30.00
Versailles, yel; creamer, ftd 15.00
Versailles, yel; cup, ftd 19.00
Versailles, yel; decanter 250.00
Versailles, yel; goblet, cocktail; 3-oz, 5¼" 28.00
Versailles, yel; goblet, water; 10-oz, 8¼" 30.00
Versailles, yel; goblet, wine; 3-oz, 5½" 42.00
Versailles, yel; grapefruit 40.00
Versailles, yel; ice bucket 75.00
Versailles, yel; mayonnaise, w/liner 40.00
Versailles, yel; parfait 30.00
Versailles, yel; plate, canape; 6" 55.00
Versailles, yel; plate, chop; 13" 35.00
Versailles, yel; plate, grill; 10" 25.00
Versailles, yel; plate, salad; 7½" 7.00
Versailles, yel; platter, 15" 60.00
Versailles, yel; sauce boat 60.00
Versailles, yel; saucer 5.00
Versailles, yel; sherbet, low, 4¼" 22.00
Versailles, yel; sugar bowl, ftd 15.00
Versailles, yel; sweetmeat 14.00
Versailles, yel; tray, celery; 11½" 50.00
Versailles, yel; tray, service 35.00
Versailles, yel; tumbler, ftd, 12-oz, 6" 25.00
Versailles, yel; tumbler, ftd, 2½-oz 37.50
Versailles, yel; tumbler, ftd, 5-oz, 4½" 22.00
Versailles, yel; vase, fan form, ftd, 8½" 85.00
Vesper, amber; ash tray 30.00
Vesper, amber; bowl, console; 11" 27.50
Vesper, amber; bowl, fruit; 5½" 10.00
Vesper, amber; bowl, soup; deep, 8" 21.00
Vesper, amber; bowl, soup; shallow, 7¾" 20.00
Vesper, amber; bowl, 9" 32.00
Vesper, amber; candlestick, 3" 15.00
Vesper, amber; candlestick, 9" 35.00
Vesper, amber; candy jar, w/lid 80.00
Vesper, amber; cheese dish, ftd 20.00
Vesper, amber; comport, 8" 40.00
Vesper, amber; creamer, fat, ftd 20.00
Vesper, amber; cup 14.00
Vesper, amber; cup, after dinner 20.00
Vesper, amber; finger bowl liner, 6" 5.50
Vesper, amber; grapefruit liner 30.00
Vesper, amber; ice bucket 60.00
Vesper, amber; pitcher, ftd 295.00
Vesper, amber; plate, bread & butter; 6" 5.00
Vesper, amber; plate, center hdl, 11" 25.00
Vesper, amber; plate, dinner; 10½" 29.00
Vesper, amber; plate, luncheon; 8½" 8.50
Vesper, amber; plate, server; 15" 45.00
Vesper, amber; platter, 10½" 25.00
Vesper, amber; saucer, after dinner 9.00
Vesper, amber; sherbet, low 15.00

Vesper, amber; stem, cordial; ¾-oz 70.00
Vesper, amber; stem, sherbet 16.00
Vesper, amber; stem, wine; 2¾-oz 30.00
Vesper, amber; sugar bowl, fat, ftd 20.00
Vesper, amber; tumbler, ftd, 12-oz 20.00
Vesper, amber; tumbler, ftd, 5-oz 15.00
Vesper, amber; tumbler, ftd, 9-oz 16.00
Vesper, amber; urn, sm 65.00
Vesper, amber; vase, 8" 75.00
Vesper, bl; bowl, cereal; 6½" 22.00
Vesper, bl; bowl, fruit; 5½" 16.00
Vesper, bl; bowl, soup; shallow, 7¾" .30.00
Vesper, bl; candlestick, 3" 30.00
Vesper, bl; candlestick, 9" 50.00
Vesper, bl; comport, 6" 35.00
Vesper, bl; comport, 7" 40.00
Vesper, bl; comport, 8" 50.00
Vesper, bl; creamer, fat, ftd 25.00
Vesper, bl; cup, after dinner 35.00
Vesper, bl; saucer, after dinner 15.00
Vesper, bl; sugar bowl, fat, ftd 25.00
Vesper, bl; urn, lg 120.00
Vesper, bl; vase, 8" 110.00
Vesper, gr; ash tray 25.00
Vesper, gr; bowl, bouillon; ftd 12.00
Vesper, gr; bowl, cereal; 6½" 15.00
Vesper, gr; bowl, console; 13" 27.50
Vesper, gr; bowl, cream soup 12.50
Vesper, gr; bowl, finger 15.00
Vesper, gr; candlestick, 9" 30.00
Vesper, gr; candy jar, w/lid, ftd 100.00
Vesper, gr; comport, 7" 25.00
Vesper, gr; creamer, ftd 14.00
Vesper, gr; cup 12.00
Vesper, gr; grapefruit 35.00
Vesper, gr; ice bucket 55.00
Vesper, gr; oyster cocktail 16.00
Vesper, gr; plate, chop; 13" 32.00
Vesper, gr; plate, dinner; sm, 9½" 11.00
Vesper, gr; plate, salad; 7½" 6.00
Vesper, gr; plate, w/indent for cheese 18.00
Vesper, gr; platter, 12" 35.00
Vesper, gr; sauce boat, w/liner 75.00
Vesper, gr; saucer 4.00
Vesper, gr; stem, cocktail, 3-oz 22.50
Vesper, gr; stem, parfait 25.00
Vesper, gr; stem, water 22.50
Vesper, gr; stem, 2½-oz 20.00
Vesper, gr; sugar bowl, ftd 14.00
Vesper, gr; sugar bowl lid 125.00
Vesper, gr; tray, celery 15.00
Vesper, gr; tumbler, ftd, 9-oz 15.00
Vesper, gr; urn, lg 70.00
Vesper, gr; urn, sm 60.00
Vesper, gr; vase, 8" 70.00

Fraktur

Fraktur is a German style of black letter text type. To collectors the fraktur is a type of hand-lettered document used by the people of German descent who settled in the areas of Pennsylvania, New Jersey, Maryland, Virginia, North and South Carolina, Ohio, Kentucky, and Ontario. These documents recorded births and baptisms and were used as bookplates and as certificates of honor. They were elaborately decorated with colorful folk-art borders of hearts, birds, angels, and flowers. Examples by recognized artists and those with an unusual decorative motif bring prices well into the thousands of dollars. Frakturs made in the late 1700s after the invention of the printing press provided the writer with a prepared text that he needed only to fill in at his own discretion. The next step in the evolution of machine-printed frakturs combined woodblock-printed decorations along with the text which the 'artist' sometimes enhanced with color. By the mid-1800s, even the coloring was done by machine. The vorschrift was a handwritten example prepared by a fraktur teacher to demonstrate his skill in lettering and decorating. These are often considered to be the finest of frakturs. Those dated before 1820 are most valuable.

The practice of fraktur art began to diminish after 1830 but hung on even to the early years of this century among the Pennsylvania Germans ingrained with such customs.

Key:
brd — board	p/i — pen and ink
lp — laid paper	wc — watercolored
pr — printed	wp — wove paper

Birth Record

P/i/wc, girls/columns/urns, anchor artist, 1843, 32x15" 1,850.00
P/i/wc/lp, birds/angels, flying angel artist, 12x16", VG 3,000.00
P/i/wc/lp, flying angel artist, 1796, veneer fr, 8x13", VG 1,400.00
P/i/wc/lp, tulips/data, M Brechall, EX color, 16x16" 3,600.00
P/i/wc/wp, EX floral, 4-color, 1768, mtd on brd, 8x13" 3,200.00
P/i/wc/wp, floral/lg letter, 5-color, sgn/no date, 8x8" 450.00
P/i/wc/wp, flowers/hearts, att Brechall, 1830, 8x13", VG 1,100.00
P/i/wc/wp, lg heart/parrots/angels/etc, 1821, 12x16", VG 2,750.00
Pr/p/i/wc/wp, florals, Brechall/1912, 9x13", VG 750.00
Pr/wc, angels/tulips, Dructer/1821, 15x19", VG 350.00
Pr/wc, Birth & Baptism, DP Lange/1813/1822, 15x18", VG . . .150.00
Pr/wc, Birth & Baptism, Kastner/Columbus OH/1840, 16x19" .550.00
Pr/wc, stylized foliage/3 hearts, F Krebs/1797, 13x15" 650.00
Pr/wc/lp, angels w/trumpets, birds/etc, 1807, 15½x18", EX 400.00

Watercolor and ink, German birth record, ca 1802, restored, 13x16", $1,200.00.

Miscellaneous

Bookplate, p/i/wc, florals, Spangenborg, dbl, fr, 8½x10½" . . .3,500.00

Bookplate, p/i/wc/wp, florals/name, att Spangenborg, 8x9" . .**1,800.00**
Certificate, baptism; p/i/wc/lp, tulips/birds, 1815, 10x15" **700.00**
Certificate, p/colored i/wp, names/1883, 8x10", EX **250.00**
Certificate, p/i/wc/wp, interlaced foil/ribbon, 8x12", VG **260.00**
Drawing, p/i/wc, angels/birds/eagle, PA, sgn/1863, 12x14" **165.00**
Drawing, p/i/wc, bird on flowering branch, fr, 3¾x5½" **525.00**
Drawing, p/i/wc, birds/hearts/flowers, sgn/1817, fr, 6x8" **1,000.00**
Drawing, p/i/wc/wp, urns/tulips/lg birds, sgn/1824, 12x14" . .**3,900.00**
House blessing, pr/pencil/wc, birds/flowers, 1860, 15x18" **350.00**
House blessing, pr/wc, hearts/zigzag border, stains, 16x19" **325.00**
P/i/wc; peacocks/tulips/star/parrots, sgn/1807, 16x19", EX . .**12,000.00**
Valentine, p/i/wc inscription, heart cutout, 7x7", EX **850.00**
Verse, p/i/wc, oval wreath/geometrics, 4-color, fr, 3x4" **395.00**
Vorchrift, p/i/wc/lp, lg letters, 179(?), 8x13", EX **400.00**
Wc on wp, text, 2-way road to heaven/hell, Brenholtz/1828 .**4,900.00**

Frames

Styles in picture frames have changed with the fashion of the day, but those that especially interest today's collectors are the deep shadow boxes made of fine woods such as walnut or cherry, those with Art Nouveau influence, and the oak frames decorated with molded gesso and gilt from the Victorian era.

Bird's-eye veneer, ogee, flat liner, 3⅝" W, 28x25" **105.00**
Brass, florals/leaves, oval, French, 1860, 6x4½", EX **50.00**
Brass & copper, rope design edge, rnd, easel bk, 6¼" **42.00**
Bronze, eagle & US army emblem, 9½x7½" **125.00**
Bronze, florals emb, 8¾x5¾" **190.00**
CI, swivels in ftd fr, ornate, wht pnt, 18" **25.00**
Curly maple, rfn, 2" W, 16¾x20½" **85.00**
Garnets, prong set, 1¾" dia **125.00**
Mission oak, brass buttons at cross-points, 21x18½" **25.00**
Pewter, scrolls, cherub's head at top, 1920, 7x6" **55.00**
Pine, brn sponging w/fingerprint border, 2" W, 17x13" **175.00**
Poplar, chip-cvd relief designs, oval window, 5½x3½" **150.00**
Poplar, combed yel/dk brn pnt, 1¾" W, 17x13" **150.00**
Silver, branch/bird, eng/repousse, shaped top, English, 9" **800.00**
Silver, maid picks apples, eng/repousse, WI Broadway, 13¾" .**2,400.00**

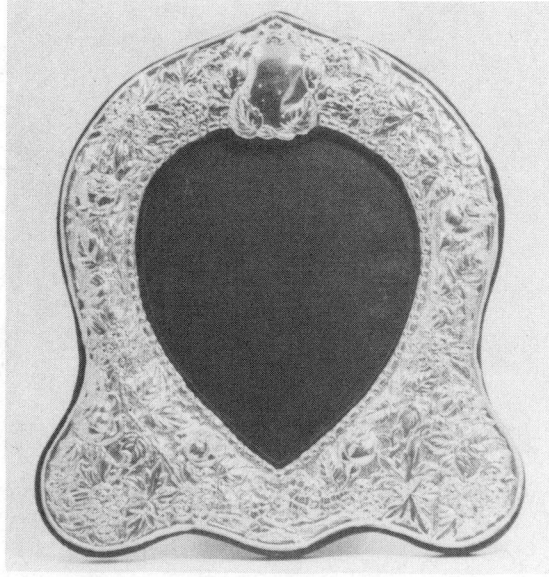

Sterling with repousse florals and vines, velvet back, no mark, 12", $350.00.

Walnut, scalloped, arched, hand cvd, ca 1850, 11½x9x¾" **100.00**
Walnut, 6-sided, made from 1 pc, cvd foliage/gadrooning, 11" . .**65.00**

Frances Ware

Frances Ware, produced in the 1880s by Hobbs, Brockunier and Company of Wheeling, West Virginia, is a clear or frosted tableware with amber-stained rim bands. The most often found pattern is Hobnail, but Swirl was also made.

Hobnail, clear; bowl, 7½" **55.00**
Hobnail, clear; butter dish **85.00**
Hobnail, clear; creamer **50.00**
Hobnail, clear; finger bowl, 4" **35.00**
Hobnail, clear; pitcher, 8½" **95.00**
Hobnail, clear; spooner **40.00**
Hobnail, clear; water set, 5-pc **215.00**
Hobnail, frosted; bowl, 2½x5½" **40.00**
Hobnail, frosted; butter dish **120.00**
Hobnail, frosted; creamer **75.00**
Hobnail, frosted; shakers, pr **75.00**
Hobnail, frosted; spooner **65.00**

Frosted Hobnail pitcher, 8½", $165.00.

Hobnail, frosted; sugar bowl, w/lid **75.00**
Hobnail, frosted; syrup **150.00**
Hobnail, frosted; toothpick holder **75.00**
Hobnail, frosted; tray, cloverleaf, 12" **125.00**
Hobnail, frosted; tray, oblong, 14" **150.00**
Hobnail, frosted; tumbler **45.00**
Swirl, clear; shakers, pr **55.00**
Swirl, clear; syrup **90.00**
Swirl, frosted; cruet, orig stopper, miniature **260.00**
Swirl, frosted; mustard jar **140.00**
Swirl, frosted; sugar shaker, orig lid **125.00**
Swirl, frosted; syrup, pat dtd **145.00**
Swirl, frosted; tumbler **35.00**

Franciscan

Franciscan is a trade name used by Gladding McBean and Co.,

founded in northern California in 1875. In 1923 they purchased the Tropico plant in Glendale where they produced sewer pipe, gardenware, and tile. By 1934 the first of their dinnerware lines, El Patio, was produced. It was a plain design but made in bright, attractive colors. El Patio Nouveau followed in 1935, glazed in two colors — one tone on the inside, a contrasting hue on the outside. Coronado, a favorite of today's collectors, was introduced in 1936. It was styled with a wide, swirled border and was made in pastels in both a satin and glossy finish. Before 1940 fifteen patterns had been produced. The first hand-decorated lines were introduced in 1937, the ever-popular Apple pattern in 1940, Desert Rose in 1941, and Ivy in 1948. Many other hand-decorated and decaled patterns were produced there from 1934 to 1984.

Dinnerware marks before 1940 include 'GMcB' in an oval, 'F' within a square, or 'Franciscan' with 'Pottery' underneath (which was later changed to 'Ware.') A circular arrangement of 'Franciscan' with 'Made in California USA' in the center was used from 1940 until 1949. At least forty marks were used before 1975; several more were introduced after that. At one time, a paper label was used.

The company merged with Lock Joint Pipe Company in 1963, becoming part of the Interpace Corporation. In July of 1979, Franciscan was purchased by Wedgwood Limited of England, and the Glendale plant closed in October, 1984.

Our advisor, authority Delleen Enge, has compiled an informative book, *Franciscan Ware*, with current values. You will find her address in the Directory under California. See also Gladding McBean.

Coronado

Bowl, cereal	10.50
Bowl, cream soup	13.00
Bowl, vegetable; serving, oval	25.00
Bowl, vegetable; serving, rnd	13.00
Candlestick, pr	25.00
Candy dish, rnd, w/lid	45.00
Casserole, w/lid	25.00
Cigarette box	35.00
Coffeepot, demitasse	45.00
Creamer & sugar bowl, w/lid	28.00
Cup & saucer	10.00
Cup & saucer, demitasse	20.00
Gravy boat, w/attached plate	25.00
Nut cup, ftd	14.00
Plate, chop; 12"	20.00
Plate, chop; 14"	30.00
Plate, 10½"	15.00
Plate, 6½"	7.00
Plate, 7½"	8.50
Plate, 8½"	9.50
Platter, 11½"	20.00
Platter, 15½"	30.00
Saucer, cream soup	5.50
Shakers, pr	13.00
Sherbet	9.00
Teapot	35.00

El Patio

Bowl, cereal	10.00
Bowl, fruit	9.00
Bowl, salad; 3-qt	22.00
Bowl, vegetable; oval	28.00
Butter dish	28.00
Creamer	8.00
Cup	8.00

Cup, jumbo	16.00
Gravy boat, w/attached underplate	24.00
Plate, bread & butter	6.00
Plate, 10½"	12.00
Plate, 8½"	10.00
Saucer	3.00
Saucer, jumbo	6.00
Sherbet	9.00
Sugar bowl, w/lid	15.00
Teapot, w/lid, 6-cup	35.00

Franciscan Fine China

The main line of fine china was called Masterpiece. There were at least four marks used during its production from 1941 to 1977. Almost every piece is clearly marked. This china is true porcelain, the body having been fired at a very high temperature. Many years of research and experimentation went into this china before it was marketed. Production was temporarily suspended during the war years. More than 170 patterns and many varying shapes were produced. All are valued about the same with the exception of the Renaissance group, which is 25% higher.

Bowl, vegetable; serving, oval	45.00
Cup	15.00
Plate, bread & butter	15.00
Plate, dinner	25.00
Plate, salad	18.00
Saucer	10.00

Hand-Painted Embossed Earthenware

Values listed here apply to these patterns: Apple, Desert Rose, Ivy, Meadow Rose, Forget-Me-Not, October, Strawberry, Fresh Fruit, and others.

Ash tray, ind	10.00
Bowl, batter	35.00
Bowl, lug hdl, sm	14.00
Bowl, soup; flat	14.00
Bowl, vegetable; sm	12.00
Bowl, vegetable; w/lid	35.00
Bowl, 7½"	25.00
Bowl, 8¼"	35.00
Casserole, stick hdls, 12-oz	20.00
Coaster, 3¾"	15.00
Coffeepot	45.00
Compote, lg	25.00
Creamer, lg	14.00
Creamer & sugar bowl, sm	48.00
Cup & saucer, demitasse, ea	20.00
Cup & saucer, jumbo	25.00
Egg cup	14.00
Goblet	22.00
Mug	18.00
Pickle dish, 10¼"	28.00
Pitcher, water	40.00
Pitcher, 1-pt	16.00
Plate, chop; 14"	50.00
Plate, grill; 10¾"	25.00
Plate, 10½"	20.00
Plate, 6½"	10.00
Plate, 8½"	14.00
Plate, 9½"	18.00
Platter, 12½"	30.00
Platter, 19½"	95.00

Relish, 3-part, 11" 20.00
Shakers, Rosebud, pr 18.00
Shakers, tall, pr 25.00
Sugar bowl, open, sm 25.00
Sugar bowl, w/lid, lg 26.00
Tray, 3-tier 35.00
Tumbler, 5⅛" 15.00

Apple tureen, 8½", $95.00.

Frankart

During the 1920s, Frankart, Inc., of New York City, produced a line of accessories that included figural nude lamps, bookends, ash trays, etc. These white metal composition items were offered in several finishes including verde green, jap black, and gun-metal gray. The company also produced a line of caricatured animals, but the stylized nude figurals have proven to be the most collectible today. With few exceptions, all pieces were marked 'Frankart, Inc.' with a patent number or 'pat. appl. for.' All pieces listed are in very good original condition unless otherwise indicated.

Our advisor for this category is Walter Glenn; he is listed in the Directory under Georgia.

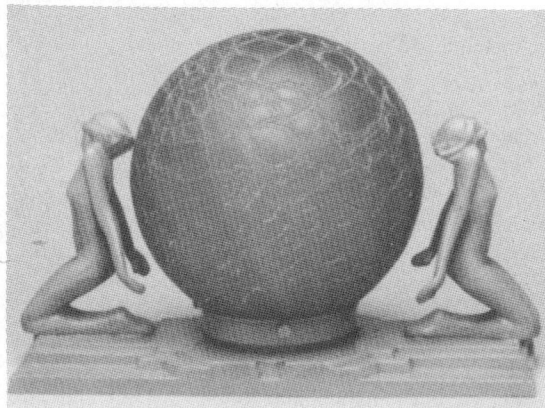

Lamp, two nudes kneel back to back as if to support amber crackle glass shade, 9½", NM, $800.00.

Ash tray, gaucho on horse, pottery sombrero ash tray, 8" 285.00
Ash tray, nude on tiptoe bends backwards, holds tray, 10½" ...390.00
Ash tray, seated honey bear holds honeypot ash tray, 5½" 185.00
Ash tray, stretched out dachshund over sq ash tray, 5" 125.00
Bookends, futuristic long-necked female heads, 7", pr 210.00

Bookends, nudes in headstand support books, 10", pr 285.00
Bookends, stylized circus ponies, 5", pr 140.00
Candlestick, standing nudes hold candle cup aloft, 13", pr 425.00
Cigar lighter, Shriner's head/symbols, Atlantic City NJ, 1927 ..195.00
Lamp, dancing nude silhouettes against glass panel, 11" 635.00
Lamp, nude extends arms bk, glass as butterfly wings, 10¼" ..1,250.00
Lamp, stylized prancing horse, parchment shade, 7" 210.00
Lamp, 2 nudes stand at sides of cvd rectangular glass, 10½" 950.00
Match holder, burro w/pack on back, holds matches, 8" 140.00

Frankoma

The Frank Pottery, founded in Oklahoma in 1933 by John Frank, became known as Frankoma in 1934. The company produced decorative figurals, vases, and such, marking their ware from 1936-38 with a pacing leopard 'Frankoma' mark. These pieces are highly sought. The entire operation was destroyed by fire in 1938, and new molds were cast — some from surviving pieces — and a similar line of production was pursued. The body of the ware was changed in 1954 from a honey tan to a red brick clay, and this, along with the color of the glazes (over forty have been used), helps determine the period of production. A Southwestern theme has always been favored in design as well as in color selection.

In 1965 they began to produce a limited-edition series of Christmas plates, followed by a bottle vase series in 1969. Considered very collectible are their political mugs, bicentennial plates, Teenagers of the Bible plates, and the Wildfire series. Their ceramic Christmas cards are also very popular items with today's collectors.

Frankoma celebrated their 50th Anniversary in 1983. On September 26 of that same year, Frankoma was again destroyed by fire. Because of a fireproof wall, master molds of all 1983 production items were saved, allowing plans for rebuilding to begin immediately. 'Grand Opening' was celebrated in July, 1984.

For a more thorough study of the subject, we reommend that you refer to *Frankoma Treasures* by Phyllis and Tom Bess, our advisors; you will find their address in the Directory under Oklahoma.

Ash tray, cigar; #455, 1934-1957, 5" 18.00
Ash tray, cocker spaniel, Ada clay, #460, 1948-1949 ....35.00
Ash tray, elephant, #459, 1951-1952, 6½" 56.00
Ash tray, fish, #T-8, 1962-1976, 7" 20.00
Ash tray set, #459, 1942, 6-pc 35.00
Baker, Lazybones; #4-V, 1953-1960, 6" 45.00
Ban-O-Bug, 1965-1967 ....15.00
Bookend, female figure, seated, w/Taylor name, #425, 5½" ...300.00
Bookend, Leopard, Ada clay, #421, 1934-1942, 4½x8½" 100.00
Bookend, Mountain Girl, Ada clay, #425, 5¾" 85.00
Bookend, Ocelot, Ada clay, #422, 1934-1938, 7¼" 100.00
Bookend, Walking Ocelot, w/Taylor name, #424 ....300.00
Bowl, ball form, ped ft, #42, 6½" 20.00
Bowl, Carved Cactus, #207, 1949-1950, 10" 35.00
Bowl, ped ft, #101-P, 6" 14.00
Bowl, rectangular, flat, #206, 7" 10.00
Button, non-production item, rare 15.00
Cacti-Pin, 1945, 1½" 50.00
Candelabrum, #306, 11¾" 48.00
Candle holder, Ada clay, #304, pr 25.00
Candle holder, sq, #307, 1942, pr 30.00
Canteen, Thunderbird, #59, 6½" 6.00
Casserole, #946, 1948-1954, ind 25.00
Christmas card, 1947-1948 ....75.00
Christmas card, 1950-1951 ....70.00
Christmas card, 1952, Donna Frank 45.00
Christmas card, 1953-1954 ....65.00

Christmas card, 1955-1956 . . . . .70.00
Christmas card, 1958 . . . . .50.00
Christmas card, 1960 . . . . .50.00
Christmas card, 1967-1968 . . . . .35.00
Christmas card, 1972 . . . . .15.00
Christmas card, 1973-1974 . . . . .20.00
Christmas card, 1975, bird in hand, Grace Lee, rare 80.00
Christmas plate, 1966 . . . . .95.00
Christmas plate, 1968 . . . . .35.00
Christmas plate, 1971-1973 . . . . .22.50
Christmas plate, 1977-1980 . . . . .18.00
Compote, shell form, #214, 1942-1950, 6" 8.00
Cornucopia, #57, 1942-1949, 9½" 20.00
Cornucopia, Ada clay, #56, 1942-1949, 7" 25.00
Creamer, mk Frank Potteries, 5" 150.00
Creamer & sugar bowl, #87-A & #87-B, 1942-1953 . . . . .15.00
Decanter, Fingerprint, #84, 1942-1949, 1-qt, 7" 30.00
Donkey mug, 1975, Autumn Yel 15.00
Donkey mug, 1976, Centennial Red 20.00
Donkey mug, 1978, Woodland Moss 20.00
Donkey mug, 1980, Terra Cotta 20.00
Elephant mug, 1968, Wht Sand 75.00
Elephant mug, 1969, Nixon/Agnew, Flame 60.00
Elephant mug, 1970, bl 55.00
Elephant mug, 1972, Prairie Gr 38.00
Flower bowl, #88, 1960-1978, 15" L 16.00
Flower bowl, mk Frank Potteries, 2" 185.00
Flower holder, Boot, stars on sides, Ada clay, #507, 3½" 10.00
Flower holder, Boots on Thong, Ada clay, #507-S, mini, 3½" . . .15.00
Flower holder, Duck, #184, 3¾" 90.00
Grease jar, w/lid, #46, 1938, 3¾" 18.00
Honey jar, Bee Hive, #803, 12-oz 5.00
Honey jar, Bee Hive, Ada clay, #803, 12-oz 20.00
Honey jug, Swirl, w/orig waxed cork, #833 . . . . .35.00
Jar, cvd decor, #70, 1934-1949, 4¾" 25.00
Jug, w/stopper, pacing leopard mk, #86, ½-gal, 7" 45.00
Jug, w/stopper, 1934-1935, 3-cup, 5" 45.00
Lamp base, from #28 vase 45.00
Lamp base, from Wagon Wheel sugar bowl 45.00
Marionette head, rare 50.00
Medallion, NY World's Fair, dtd 1964-1965, 1½" dia 25.00
Mug, War God, #T-3, 1962-1963, 12-oz 12.00
Pitcher, Autumn Yel, 2-qt 10.00
Pitcher, Eagle, #555, 1942-1964, 2⅜" 8.00
Pitcher, Guernsey, gr, mini 7.00
Pitcher, jug form, #554, 1942, 2¾" 15.00
Pitcher, Mayan, Ada clay, #82 . . . . .25.00
Planter, Log, #9-L, 11" 10.00
Planter, Madonna of Grace, #231-B, 6" 35.00
Planter, Oblong Cactus, #206, 1949-1952, 10½" 6.00
Plaque, Will Rogers, borderless, 1934-1935, 4x4¾" 38.00
Pow Wow Pot, #829, complete w/12 skewers, 1957-1961 . . . .40.00
Ring, Pansy, 1950-1957, 12" .15.00
Rose jar, w/lid, #32, 1934-1938, 5¼" 95.00
Sculpture, Amazon Woman, mk Frank Potteries, #101, 6¼x8" . .300.00
Sculpture, Blk Man w/His Donkey, Gun-Metal Gray, 8" 200.00
Sculpture, Bucking Bronco, no stepped base, #423, 5" 65.00
Sculpture, Circus Horse, Cherokee Red, #138, 4½" 65.00
Sculpture, Cocker Spaniel, #144, 1949, 8½" 50.00
Sculpture, Collie Head, #22, 7" 45.00
Sculpture, Donna Ruth, pacing leopard mk, #113, 7¾" 150.00
Sculpture, English Setter, #163, 2⅞" 45.00
Sculpture, Fan Dancer, Ada clay, #113 . . . . .180.00
Sculpture, Fawns, #100/#101, 8", pr 30.00

Sculpture, Flower Girl, #700, 1942-1952, 5½" 70.00
Sculpture, Gardener Boy, belted pants, #702, 1942-1949, 7" . . .100.00
Sculpture, Gardener Boy, Prairie Gr, bibbed pants, #702, 7" . . .100.00
Sculpture, Greyhound, 6 petals on bk base, 1983 repro, 14" 15.00
Sculpture, Head of Blk Woman, pacing leopard mk, #128, 9" . .175.00
Sculpture, Indian Bowl Maker, discontinued glaze, #123, 6" 35.00
Sculpture, Indian Chief, #131, 5" 35.00
Sculpture, Indian Chief, Ada clay, 1938-1953, #142, 8" 75.00
Sculpture, Indian Head, Ada clay, #135, 3¾" 15.00
Sculpture, Indian Maiden, Wht Sand, #101, 13" 20.00
Sculpture, Madonna of Grace, 1941-1942, 5¾" 65.00
Sculpture, Pacing Leopard, #104-L, 15" 185.00
Sculpture, Peter Pan, SAI on bk, #100, 6" 40.00

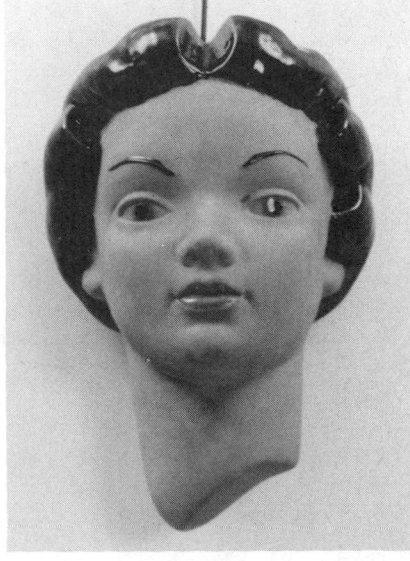

Phoebe, terra cotta with black hair and hand-painted features, 7½", $125.00.

Sculpture, Prancing Colt, #117, 8" 185.00
Sculpture, Prancing Percheron, mk Frank Potteries, 4¾" 250.00
Sculpture, Puma, Redbud, #165, 1942-1957, 3" 50.00
Sculpture, Seated Puma, Ada clay, #114, 1934-1963, 7½" 70.00
Sculpture, Squirrel, #105, 6" 5.00
Sculpture, Terrier, unmk, 1942, 5¼x6½" 60.00
Sculpture, Torch Singer, #126, ca 1934, 13½" 400.00
Sculpture, Trojan Horse, #162, 2½" 35.00
Sculpture, Walking Elephant, #169, 1¾" 60.00
Sculpture, Wedding Bell, rare 50.00
Serva-Tray magazine rack, #34-M, 1955-1970, 20" 60.00
Shakers, Ada clay, #94-H, pr 10.00
Shakers, Bull, #166, 2", pr 50.00
Shakers, Dutch Shoe, turq or Terra Cotta Rose, #915-H, 4", pr . .25.00
Shakers, Modern, #45-H, 1936-1942, 2", pr 10.00
Shakers, Teepee, #47, 1942-1960, 2⅞", pr 10.00
Sign, Frankoma Pottery, late 1940s-1960 . . . . .65.00
Swan, #228, open tail, 7½" 25.00
Swan, #229, 1950-1963, 9" 25.00
Trade token, 1" dia 35.00
Tray, oval, #36, 1955-1964, 12" .25.00
Tray, Palm Leaf, #T-11, 1962-1967, 17" 20.00
Trivet, American Eagle, #AETR, 1976-1978 . . . . .5.00
Trivet, Liberty Bell, #LBTR, 1973-1978 . . . . .5.00
Trivet, Rooster, #94-TR 5.00
Trivet, Wagon Wheel, #94-TR 35.00
Trivet, Zodiac, #ZTR, 1971-1976 . . . . .10.00
Tumbler, Bamboo, #T-2, 1962-1976, 14-oz 10.00
Tumbler, juice; #90-C, 1938-1965, 3-oz, 2½" 3.00
Vase, #505, 1950-1951, 2¾" 15.00

Vase, bird hdls, pacing leopard mk, #85 . . . . .50.00
Vase, bottle form, Chinese Red, #14, 9½" 125.00
Vase, bottle form, color other than Chinese Red, #14, 9½" 25.00
Vase, bud; blk onyx, high gloss 20.00
Vase, bud; ivory, scalloped 20.00
Vase, bulbous, ivory, 1934-1936, 2¾" .30.00
Vase, Cactus, Ada clay, #4, 1949-1964, 7" 25.00
Vase, Cockatoo, pacing leopard mk, 5x8" 100.00
Vase, collector; V-1, Prairie Gr, 1969, 15" 45.00
Vase, collector; V-10, Morning-Glory Bl, wht int, 11½" 40.00
Vase, collector; V-11, Morning-Glory Bl, 1979, 11½" 40.00
Vase, collector; V-13, blk & Terra Cotta, 1981, 13" 35.00
Vase, collector; V-2, turq, 1970, 12" 35.00
Vase, collector; V-3, red & blk, 1971, 12" 60.00
Vase, collector; V-5, Flame Red, 1973, 13" 65.00
Vase, collector; V-8, Freedom Red & wht, 1976 . . . . .55.00
Vase, Cross, #804, 1955-1961, 6½" 20.00
Vase, Flying Goose, #60-B, 6" 15.00
Vase, Grecian, #50, 1942-1952, 9½" .25.00
Vase, leaf hdls, early glaze, #71, 1942, 10" 45.00
Vase, Lotus, #66, 1949, 17" 65.00
Vase, mk Frank Potteries, #501 . . . . .150.00
Vase, pacing leopard mk, #502, 6" 60.00
Vase, pacing leopard mk, pre-1938, 3⅝" 50.00
Vase, Pinnacle, gold, mk Frank Potteries, 6¾" 175.00
Vase, Ram's Head, pacing leopard mk, #38, 1934-1949, 6" 45.00
Vase, Ring, low, #13, 1936-1938, 3" 45.00
Vase, Ring, turq, #500, 1951-1952 . . . . .15.00
Vase, scalloped top, #79, 1934-1938, 7" 85.00
Vase, scalloped top, #79, 1940-1949, 7½" 38.00
Vase, Snail, #31, 6" 10.00
Vase, Swan, #168, 3" 55.00
Vase, Terra Cotta Rose, #505, mini 18.00
Vase, Thunderbird, #506, 3½" 20.00
Vase, Wagon Wheel, #94, 1942-1961, 7" 15.00
Wall pocket, Acorn, Ada clay, #190, 6" 20.00
Wall pocket, Negro, late 1930s, 2½" .85.00
Wall pocket, Wagon Wheel, #94-Y, 1949-1953, 7" 20.00

Fraternal Organizations

Fraternal memorabilia is a vast and varied field. Emblems representing the various organizations have been used to decorate cups, shaving mugs, plates, and glassware. Medals, swords, documents, and other ceremonial paraphernalia from the 1800s and early 1900s are especially prized.

Elks

Butter pot, ceramic, elk head 12.00
Charm, watch; gold enamelling 25.00
Cuff links, enamelled, pr 3.00
Flask, ceramic, emb symbols, wht w/brn, dtd 1912, 4½x2½" . . .120.00
Plaque, cvd wood, stag w/clock & scroll, rpr, 21x24" 100.00
Print, Little Elk Wearing His 1st Pin, fr, 10x13", EX 32.00

Masons

Anvil, wood, colorful symbols, 5x12x3½" 150.00
Ash tray, brass, 1934 . . . . .25.00
Book, True Masonic Guide, leather bound, c 1870, EX 50.00
Champagne, Pittsburgh/Louisville, 1909 . . . . .45.00
Cruet, blown, appl hdl, ca 1800, EX .16.00
Cup & saucer, handleless; soft paste, floral 10.00

Frame and document of admission to membership dated 1892, 35x21", $280.00.

Goblet, St Paul, 1908 . . . . .65.00
Lodge bench, upholstery, rstr 250.00
Loving cup, china, 3-hdl, Philadelphia, 1903-1910, 7½" 85.00
Napkin ring, SP, 1911 . . . . .35.00
Paperweight, glass, symbols, mushroom cap, Pittsburgh Glass . . .95.00
Paperweight, glass, 3 eng symbols on base, 2½" dia 95.00
Pendant, 14k shield, silver compass/eagle/lion, 1880, 1½" 700.00
Pie server, sterling, ornate 10.00
Pin, lady's, gold & pearl, 1880 . . . . .30.00
Pitcher, ceramic, emblem, bl on wht, Mayer China, 10" 55.00
Plate, ceramic, Jerusalem Chapter, lady in hat w/fan, 1907 . . . .35.00
Plate, ceramic, Los Angeles, 1906, 6" .45.00
Register certificate, 1895, 22x28" 50.00
Seal, Chicago, dtd 1920 . . . . .12.50
Shelf, walnut w/cut-out symbols, rpr, 19½x11", pr 70.00
Snuff box, silver/MOP, armorials/emblems, Birmingham, 3" . .1,400.00
Spoon, SP, building eng in bowl, Chicago/Indian on hdl 32.00
Sword, dress; ivory hdl, w/sheath, early 160.00
Tie bar, 10k gold 65.00
Tie tack, 14k gold 16.00
Watch fob, St George's Lodge #16 . . . . .20.00

Odd Fellows

Book, History & Laws, 1886 . . . . .10.00
Robe, ceremonial, bl/blk w/gold braid, 1900 . . . . .80.00
Septre, ceremonial, wood, crown on hdl, 18" 70.00
Shaving mug, ceramic, name & emblem, EX 65.00
Sign, rvpt, hand/seeing eye/heart, fr, 30x22" 265.00
Torch, ceremonial, tin/wood, ca 1890, 22" 65.00
Trivet, CI, horse shoe w/eagle, symbols, 6½" 75.00
Watch fob 17.50

Shrine

Bowl, ceramic, emblems, oblong, Warwick, 9½" 10.00
Bracelet, man's, 18k gold, 1920s, 2½-oz 1,200.00
Champagne, alligators, New Orleans, 1910, M 85.00
Champagne, 3 scimitars, desert scene, dtd 1911 . . . . .70.00
Cup & saucer, glass, tulip form, orange/clear, 1906 . . . . .75.00
Fez, parade marshall's, jeweled, early, EX 50.00
Goblet, ruby, St Paul MN, 1908 . . . . .30.00
Mug, ceramic, Saratoga Indian, 1903 .68.00
Plate, glass, man in fez, bandaged head, lg smile, 10" 65.00
Tumbler, Pittsburgh, 1900 . . . . .55.00

Fraunfelter

Charles Fraunfelter organized his company in Zanesville, Ohio, in 1915. It was known as the Ohio Pottery Company until 1923. During this period their main product was a line of utilitarian articles for chemical laboratories made of hard paste porcelain. In 1918 they used the same body to produce a brown and white line called 'Petrascan.' By 1920 a line of hotel ware was added. The company organized in 1923 and became known as Fraunfelter China Company; but after the death of Fraunfelter in 1925, the business fell into hard times and eventually closed altogether in 1939.

Casserole, floral, yel w/blk leaves, metal stand & lid 25.00
Coffeepot, floral, yel on bl 15.00
Teapot, floral, chrome top 25.00
Teapot, ribbed, tan 9.00
Vase, pine cones/needles, dk brn on orange, Lessell, 8¾" 125.00

French Enameled Ware

Box, cigar; mini ivory portrait in lid, brass base, 8" L 350.00
Plaque, portrait of 18th-century lady, gold leaf fr, 5" dia 750.00
Settee & 2 chairs, courting scenes, mini 350.00

Fruit Jars

As early as 1829, canning jars were being manufactured for use in the home preservation of foodstuffs. For the past twenty-five years, they have been sought as popular collectibles. At the last estimate, over four thousand fruit jars and variations were known to exist. Some are very rare, perhaps one-of-a-kind examples known to have survived to the present day. Among the most valuable are the black glass jars, the amber Van Vliet, and the cobalt Millville. These often bring prices in excess of $3,000.00 when they can be found. Aside from condition, values are based on age, rarity, color, and special features.

Our advisor for this category is John Hathaway; he is listed in the Directory under Maine.

A Kline Pat Oct 27 1863 (on glass stopper), aqua, pt, rare 50.00
Acme (on shield w/stars & stripes), clear, qt 2.00
Agnew & Co Pittsburgh, Pat Apl 1887, clear, qt, rare 80.00
Almy, aqua, qt, rare 125.00
American (Eagle & Flags), lt gr, gal, rare 125.00
American (Nagco), aqua, ½-gal, rare 25.00
Atlas, E-Z Seal, amber, qt, rare 35.00
Atlas, E-Z Seal, aqua, 48-oz, rare 17.00
Atlas, E-Z Seal, aqua, 58-oz, rare 45.00
Atlas (Clover) Good Luck, clear, qt 4.00
Atlas E-Z Seal, aqua, ½-gal 7.00
Atlas E-Z Seal, clear, ½-pt 2.00
Atlas Good Luck, Lightening dimple neck seal, clear, ½-pt 12.00
Atlas Mason, clear, qt 2.00
Atlas Mason, clear, ½-pt 5.00
Ball Ideal, bk: Bicentennial Medallion, bl, qt 4.00
Ball Ideal, bk: Pat July 14 1908, bl, ½-pt 15.00
Ball Ideal, bl, ½-gal 5.00
Ball Perfect Mason's, amber, ½-gal, rare 35.00
Baltimore Glass Works, no Willoughby stopper, aqua, qt 275.00
Banner (circled), Pat Feb 9 1864, aqua, ½-gal 90.00
Best Amber, qt 350.00
Bostwick Perfection Jar, clear, pt, rare 45.00
Buckeye 1, correct clear lid, aqua, ½-gal, rare 200.00

C Ihmsen & Son Pittsburgh Pa (on base), sky bl, qt, rare 100.00
Canton Domestic Fruit Jar, clear, pt, rare 150.00
Canton Manufacturing Co Boston (on base), amber, ½-pt 6.00
Clyde, The; (script), unembossed lid, clear, pt 10.00
Cohansey (arched), aqua, pt, rare 45.00
Cohansey (arched), aqua, ½-pt 125.00
Common Sense Jar, bk: Gregory's Pat Aug 17 1869, aqua, qt ..900.00
Conserve Jar, clear, ½-pt 30.00
Crown (Crown emblem), ground lip, aqua, midget 15.00
Crystal Jar CG, clear, qt, rare 25.00
Cunningham & Co Pittsburgh (on base), dk aqua, pontil, qt ..210.00
Cunningham & Co Pittsburgh PA (base), aqua, qt, rare 35.00
Darling ADM (monogram), aqua, qt 40.00
Darling Imperial (ADM monogram), aqua, midget 215.00
Dexter (circled by fruits & vegetables), aqua, ½-gal 70.00
Dexter Improved (circle of fruit), aqua, ½-gal, rare 60.00
Doolittle Pat Dec 3 1910 (on lid), clear, pt, rare 65.00
Double Safety, clear, ½-pt 8.00
Drey Perfect Mason (2 lines), clear, ½-pt 15.00
DSG Co, aqua, ½-gal, rare 35.00
Durham (in circle), aqua, qt, rare 25.00
Eagle, orig clamp, aqua, qt, rare 90.00
EGCO Imperial (monogram), aqua, midget 40.00
Electric (world globe) Fruit Jar, aqua, qt, rare 80.00
Electric Trademk (script in circle), aqua, pt 8.00
Empire, The; aqua, qt, rare 75.00
Eureka Pat Dec 27 1864, aqua, qt, rare 70.00
Franklin Dexter Fruit Jar, aqua, ½-gal, rare 35.00
Gem, The; aqua, ½-gal 10.00
Genuine Mason (in flag), aqua, pt 10.00
Globe, amber, qt, rare 50.00
Griffin's Pat Oct 7 1862 (on lid), aqua, qt, rare 150.00
H&C (in circle), aqua, pt, rare 20.00
Hansee's Place Home Jar, clear, pt, rare 75.00
Hero (over cross), aqua, qt, rare 55.00
Hilton Pat Mar 10 1868, repro clamp, aqua, qt, rare 550.00
Improved Jam, bk: LG Co, aqua, pt, rare 100.00
Independent Jar, clear, midget 75.00
J Marden & Co (vertical), clear, ½-pt 15.00
J&B (in octagon) Fruit Jar, Pat June 14 1889, aqua, ½-gal 40.00
JFNCo (monogram on milk glass lid), amber, qt, rare 30.00
Joshua Wright Philada, lt yel-gr, ½-gal 400.00
Kerr Mason, self sealing, amber, qt 20.00
King (on banner below crown), clear, qt 10.00
King (on banner w/flags), clear, ½-pt 35.00
Klines Pat Oct 27 (on blown stopper), aqua, qt, rare 125.00
Knowlton Vacuum (star) Fruit Jar, aqua, qt 25.00
L&W (on side), orig tin lid & wire, aqua, qt, rare 85.00
Lafayette (script), aqua, pt, rare 150.00
Leader, The; amber, qt, rare 130.00
Lyon & Bossard's Jar Stroudsburg PA, all orig, aqua, qt 450.00
Marion Jar Mason's, Pat Nov 30 1858, reg lid, aqua, pt, rare 30.00
Mason Fruit Jar (3 lines), aqua, pt 10.00
Mason Jar of 1858 Trademk (in circle & sq), aqua, ½-gal 90.00
Mason Jar of 1872, aqua, qt, rare 35.00
Mason's (cross), Pat Nov 30 1858, amber, qt, rare 125.00
Mason's (cross), Pat Nov 30 1858, unlined lid, aqua, gal 575.00
Mason's (shield) Union, no lid, aqua, ½-gal, rare 125.00
Mason's #2 Pat Nov 30 1858, aqua, midget 30.00
Mason's CFJCo Improved, amber, rare, ½-gal 150.00
Mason's CFJCo Improved, bk: Clyde NY, midget 65.00
Mason's Crystal Jar, clear, ½-gal, rare 40.00
Mason's Improved, bk: hourglass, aqua, midget 75.00
Mason's Improved (cross), aqua, midget 15.00

Mason's Improved Trade Mark, bk: CFJCo, aqua, midget 35.00
Mason's Pat Nov 30 1858, amber, qt, rare 125.00
Mason's Pat Nov 30 1858, base: WCD, aqua, midget 75.00

Mason's Patent Nov 30th 1895, zinc lid, ground lip, Crowleytown, aqua pint, $575.00 at auction.

My Choice, unembossed lid, aqua, ½-gal, rare 200.00
NE Plus Ultra Airtight, Bodine & Bros, aqua, no lid, qt 1,200.00
Pansey (panelled), clear, qt, rare 200.00
Pat Mar 26 1867 BB Wilcox, aqua, ½-gal, rare 75.00
Pat Oct 29 1868 (on lid), aqua, qt, rare 45.00
Porcelain Lined, aqua, midget 150.00
Porcelain Lined, aqua, qt, rare 15.00
Potter/Bodine Airtight...Apr 13 1858, aqua, wax seal, 2-qt 750.00
Potter/Bodine Philphilida (script), aqua, qt, rare 125.00
Presto Glass Top, bk: Mfg by IL Glass Co, clear, ½-pt 7.00
Princess (in shield & frame), clear, pt, rare 25.00
Protector (arched), aqua, qt, rare 50.00
Puritan, The; bk: LS Co, aqua, qt, rare 175.00
Putnam Glass Works Zanesville O (on base), aqua, qt, rare 35.00
Queen, bk: CFJCo, aqua, ½-gal, rare 30.00
Quick Seal (in circle), Pat July 14 1908, bl, qt 3.00
Royal of 1876, orig insert, zinc band, aqua, qt, rare 150.00
S McKee & Co (on base), wax sealer, aqua, qt, rare 25.00
Simplex (in diamond on side), clear, ½-pt 10.00
Sko Queen Trademk, clear, ½-pt 10.00
Smalley Full Measure (AGS monogram) Qt, zinc lid, amber, qt .50.00
Smalley's Nu-Seal (in diamond), clear, ½-pt 45.00
Standard (arched), bk: W McC Co, lt sky bl, rare, ½-gal 100.00
Star (bellow stippled star), clear, qt, rare 50.00
Star (bellow stippled star), clear, ½-gal, rare 50.00
Star (over star emblem), aqua, qt, rare 159.00
Sun (in circle w/radiating rays), aqua, qt, rare 60.00
To Open Pry Rubber at Notch (on lid), clear, ½-pt 5.00
Trade Mark Lightening, base: HWP, amber, ½-gal, rare 175.00
Trade Mark the Dandy, amber, ½-gal 150.00
Trademark Mason's CFJCo Improved, aqua, midget, rare 25.00
Victory (in shield on lid), twin wire clamps, clear, ½-pt 15.00
Western Pride Pat June 22 1875 (all erased), aqua, qt, rare 15.00
Winslow Jar, aqua, ½-gal, rare 60.00
Woodbury Improved WGW, aqua, qt, rare 30.00

Fry

Henry Fry established his glassworks in 1901 in Rochester, Pennsylvania. There, until 1933 when it was sold to the Libbey Company, he produced glassware of the finest quality. In the early years, they produced beautiful cut glass; and when it began to wane in popularity, Fry turned to the manufacture of occasional pieces and oven glassware. He is perhaps most famous for the opalescent pearl glass called 'Foval.' It was made in combination with crystal or colored trim; because it was in production for only a short time in 1926 and 1927, it is hard to find.

Collectors of depression-era glassware look for the opalescent reamers and opaque green kitchenware made during the early thirties. See also Kitchen Collectibles, Glassware.

Bottle, hobstars/leaf spray cuttings, 8-panel, 8½" 195.00
Candlestick, Foval, opal w/appl bl collars/threads, 10½", pr ...200.00
Creamer, yel, pinched top forms 3 bl-gr loops, 4", 6" H hdl 70.00
Cruet, hobstars & fans, notched hdl, orig stopper, sgn 165.00
Cup & saucer, Foval, opal w/gr hdl 75.00
Measuring cup, gr opaque 30.00
Pitcher, Foval, opal w/bl hdl, 8" 120.00
Plate, Foval, bl rim, 9½" 65.00
Plate, Foval, gr rim, 7" 35.00
Sugar bowl, Foval, bl ft & finial, ogee sides 225.00
Sugar bowl, Optic, opal stripes w/appl bl hdls 50.00
Tea set, Foval, silver overlay bands, bl/wht, 7-pc 1,075.00
Teapot, Foval, gr w/silver trim 175.00
Vase, bud; Foval, 10" 95.00
Vase, Foval, gold/blk rim decor, widely flared, 7" 350.00
Vase, Foval, widely flared, 4¾x7¾" 150.00

Fulper

The Fulper Pottery was founded in 1899, after nearly a century of producing utilitarian stoneware under various titles and managements. Not until 1909 did Fulper venture into the art pottery field. Vasekraft, their first art line, utilized the same heavy clay body used for their utility ware. Although shapes were unadorned and simple, the glazes they developed were used with such flair and imagination (alone and in unexpected combined harmony) that each piece was truly a work of art. Graceful Oriental shapes were produced to compliment the important 'famille rose' glaze developed by W.H. Fulper, Jr. Other shapes and glazes were developed in line with the Arts and Crafts movement of the same period.

During WWI, doll's heads and Kewpies were made to meet the demand for hard-to-find imports. Figural perfume lamps and powder boxes were made both in bisque and glazed ware. Examples prized most highly by collectors today are those made before a devastating fire destroyed the plant in 1929, resulting in an operations takeover by Martin Stangl later that same year.

Several marks were used: a vertical 'Fulper' in a line reserve, a horizontal mark, a Vasekraft paper label, 'Rafco,' 'Prang,' and 'Flemington.'

Fulper values are to a major degree determined by the desirability of the glazes combined with the factors of size and form. Lamps with colored glass inserts are rare and highly prized.

Bowl, brn/cream flambe w/bl touches, bl int, angle hdls, 9½" ..120.00
Bowl, copper oxide on gr crystalline drip, oval, hdls, 12x7" 125.00
Bowl, dk bl drip on med bl, oblong, low, 16" 160.00
Bowl, effigy; yel/purple flambe, buff/brn base, 7x10½" 650.00
Bowl, gold/rust/gr flambe, 5 fish/waves w/in, 11" 700.00
Bowl, gr crystalline, shoulder hdls, oval, vertical mk, 12x7" 78.00
Bowl, gr crystalline/pk flambe, hdls, 8" 75.00
Bowl, gray/gr flambe, 5x10" 45.00
Bowl, hammered, strapped, #503 ....100.00
Bowl, lily; brn mirror, Prang, 7" 80.00
Bowl, lily; gr & Chinese bl, 7" 80.00
Bowl, vines on gr, 4-ftd, 10" 155.00

Bowl vase, artichoke mold, ivory/mahog/gr metallic, 6x8" 650.00
Box, powder; blk-haired figural lady in floral dress 225.00
Candlestick, brn/bl, hdl, 2½x5" 45.00
Candlestick, pk/gray, hdl, 5" 50.00
Candlestick, turq w/crystalline, 3 low hdls, flat, 1½x6" 135.00

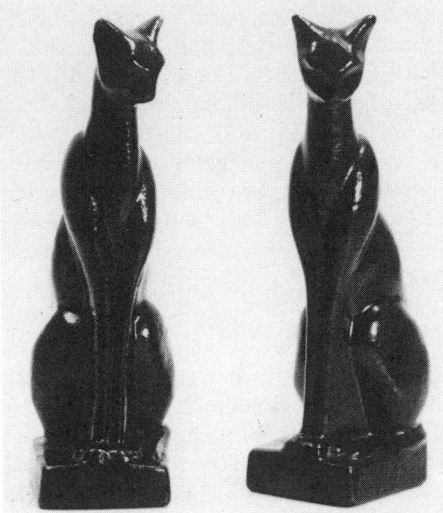

Cats, black metallic glaze, 10", $375.00 for the pair.

Figurine, cat, gun metal/buttermilk flambe, rstr, 10" L 400.00
Jug, musical, brn mirror 95.00
Lamp, blk/silver-gr flambe w/24 pcs set-in glass, rstr, 17" 6,000.00
Lamp, gr/blk/butterscotch flambe w/24 pcs set-in glass, 14" .12,000.00
Mug, gr w/brn streaks, 5x4" 60.00
Pilgrim flask, gr to silvery blk to bl flambe, 10x8" 725.00
Vase, aqua drip on gr, 3 hdls, 8" 135.00
Vase, bl crystalline on rust flambe, 4 loop hdls, 13x10½" 950.00
Vase, bl crystalline over gr/brn, relief at neck, 7" 150.00
Vase, bl crystalline w/cream drip, spherical w/ped ft, 7" 110.00
Vase, bl crystalline w/pk, hdls, Deco style, 5" 80.00
Vase, bl w/lt silver crystals, looped hdls, flared ft, 13" 375.00
Vase, bl/brn metallic flambe, akimbo/diagonal-bar hdls, 6x9" ..650.00
Vase, bl/gr crystalline, gourd shape, Prang, 4x6" 95.00
Vase, blk over tan, 6" 125.00
Vase, brn drip over taupe, 3 rim-to-shoulder hdls, 6½" 85.00
Vase, copper dust crystalline, flared base/rim, 13x8" 700.00
Vase, famille rose (some clay showing), urn form w/hdls, 9" ...175.00
Vase, gr crystalline w/bl streaks, appl disks, flared rim, 7" 100.00
Vase, gr w/brn spots, raised decor, octagonal, 8" 375.00
Vase, gr/brn crystalline, shoulder hdls, vertical stamp, 7½" 65.00
Vase, gun metal/gr crystalline over mirrored bl, 7½x6" 225.00
Vase, hammered med on lt gr, 3 scroll hdls, ped base, 11" ...1,600.00
Vase, ivory matt, 12" 175.00
Vase, lt bl crystalline w/brn flambe, trumpet form, 14" 750.00
Vase, lt bl-gr w/pea gr crystalline, bulbous, hdls, 6¼" 300.00
Vase, med bl w/gr & brn drip, emb mushrooms at base, 9", EX .500.00
Vase, mirror blk mottle to cream, rolled rim, 16x5½" 2,100.00
Vase, mirror blk to silvery gr flambe, buttressed, 8" 225.00
Vase, mirrored bl flambe, squat/bulbous, tiny rim, 6x10" 350.00
Vase, mirrored bl texture, slim classic form, 11½x4" 275.00
Vase, mirrored blk flambe over yel-gr, incurvate, 8x5" 750.00
Vase, mirrored blk w/lt silver crystals, ftd/hdls, 12x8" 400.00
Vase, mirrored brn drips on cream flambe to tan, 8x10½" 950.00
Vase, mirrored brn flambe to gr gloss, incurvate, 5½x7" 150.00
Vase, mirrored olive gr to gun metal flambe, 12x10" 950.00
Vase, mustard to mocha gloss, emb mushrooms at base, 10x4" .700.00
Vase, olive to bl flambe, flat rim-to-low width hdls, 9½x8" 275.00
Vase, pea gr w/lt gr flambe, bulbous w/collar & hdls, 9x8" 450.00

Vase, purple semi-matt w/bl specks, akimbo hdls, 9" 300.00
Vase, rose w/gr flambe drip, collared bulbous form, 10x8" 400.00
Vase, silver lustre w/HP buff leaves, flared top/ft, 13x7" 800.00
Vase, streaky violet semi-matt, oval w/4 cut-out hdls, 8x9" 800.00
Vase, wht, hdls, 3½" 40.00
Vase, wht on wht, rose in relief, 7½" 60.00
Vase, yel flambe to seafoam, sm pointed side hdls, 11x8½" 425.00

Furniture

From the cabinetmaker's shop of the early 1800s with apprentices and journeymen who learned every phase of the craft at the side of the master carpenter, the trade had evolved by the mid-century to one with steam-powered saws and turning lathes and workers who specialized in only one operation. By 1870 the Industrial Revolution was in progress, and large factories in the East and Midwest turned out increasingly elaborate styles, ornately machine carved and heavily inlaid. Rococo, Egyptian, and Renaissance Revival furniture adapted well to factory production. Eastlake offered a welcome respite from Victorian frumpery and a return to quality handcrafting. All of these styles remained popular until the turn of the century.

As early as 1880, factories began using oak; early mail-order catalogs offered oak furniture, simply styled and lighter in weight, since long-distance shipping was often a factor. Mission, or Craftsman, a style introduced around 1890, was simple to the extreme. Stickley and Hubbard were two of its leading designers. Other popular Victorian styles were Colonial Revival, Cottage, Bentwood, and Windsor. Prices are as variable as the styles.

Key:
Am — American   G — good
brd — board   Geo — Georgian
Chpndl — Chippendale   grpt — grainpainted
Co — Country   hdbd — headboard
cvd — carved   hdw — hardware
cvg — carving   Hplwht — Hepplewhite
c&b — claw and ball   NE — New England
do — door   QA — Queen Anne
drw — drawer   trn — turning
Emp — Empire   Vict — Victorian
Fed — Federal   W/M — William and Mary
Fr — French   : — over (example: 1 do:2 drw ——
ftbd — footboard   1 door over 2 drawers)

Bed

Curly maple, trn/chamfered/rope-cvd tall posts, 86" H 1,600.00
Day bed, cherry/curly maple, trn posts, rope rails, 74" L 800.00
Day bed, curly maple, trn posts/rails, 77" H, EX 1,600.00
Day bed, Mission Oak, end angled up, loose leather cushions ..650.00
Day bed, walnut, rope rails, trn posts/top rails, 66" L 175.00
Gilt metal-mtd burlwood Louis XVI style, 60x57" 475.00
Grpt, trn posts w/urn finials, shaped hdbd, 1830s, 41" H 800.00
Hdbd, Nouveau walnut w/marquetry scene w/Pan, 66x56" 700.00
Mahog Chpndl tall post, Marlborough ft, w/canopy fr, 1770s .7,000.00
Marjorelle, walnut, shaped hdbd w/openwork, cvd, 55" 6,000.00
Rope, curly maple posts w/acorn finials, scroll hdbd, full 585.00
Rope, curly maple trn cannonball posts, shaped hdbd, 56" H .1,200.00
Rope, curly maple trn posts w/bell & goblet detail, 52" H 900.00
Rope, curly maple trn posts/ft rail, poplar hd/ftbrd, 44" 250.00
Rope, maple/poplar trn posts, 1-brd hdbd, 62" H 325.00
Rope, poplar, EX trn cannonball posts, detailed hdbd, full 450.00
Sleigh, mahog, sq/shaped side posts extend to block legs 425.00

Stickley, G; day bed, 6 slats on high end, unmk, 1901 . . . . .750.00
Tall post, blk/red grpt w/stencil leaves, w/canopy, 85" 1,450.00
Tiger maple Sheraton, pine hdbd, w/tester, rfn, 66" 2,500.00
Trundle, poplar/maple, hand-wrought casters, PA, 1820s 200.00

Carved rosewood tall-back Victorian bed, att to Mitchell and Rammelsburg, Cincinnati, ca 1860, $4,000.00.

Bench

Bucket, pine w/worn rpt over bl, cut-out ends, drw, 31x58" . .4,700.00
Bucket, poplar, sq nails, worn gray pnt, 25x28" 190.00
Kneeling, pine, cut-out ft, re-uphl 225.00
Limbert, settle #559¾, even arm/wide slats, branded, 90" 1,300.00
Mammy's, Windsor, grpt/stencil, 50" 475.00
Settle, Mission Oak, 9-slat bk/2 ea end, rpl cushion, 67" 1,100.00
Settle, Windsor, bamboo trn, 1825, rstr/rpr, 80" 650.00
Stenciled, EX orig, scroll arms/3 vase splats, 74" 1,000.00
Stickley, G; settle #205, even arm/wide slats, rfn, 56" 2,700.00
Stickley, G; settle #206, even arms:3 slanted slats, decal . .20,000.00
Stickley, L&JG; crib settle #728, 13-slat bk/5 ea end, 76" . . .6,250.00
Stickley, L&JG; settle #263, drop-arm/7-slat, branded, 78" . .4,750.00
Water, pine/gray pnt, 2-shelf, bootjack ft, 33", VG 300.00
Windsor, grpt, 3-part bk, butterfly crests, bamboo trn, 76" . . .3,300.00

Blanket Chest

Cherry, dvtl, base molding, trn ft, 1-brd top, 23x38" 425.00
Decorated, yel w/ochre swirls, NY, ca 1820, 23x42x18", M . .2,000.00
Pine Co Chpndl, lift top, drw, orig hdw, 1775, 38" W 600.00
Pine w/brn vinegar grpt, wht pnt name/1891, wear/rpr, 52" W .700.00
Pine w/European decor, grpt/wht floral reserves, dtd 1815 . . . . .400.00
Pine w/EX orig dk red, 2-drw, NE, 1780s, 39" W 2,900.00
Pine w/PA decor, vinegar pnt/rpt trim, dvtl, trn ft, 51" W 475.00
Pine/poplar w/brn grpt on orange, sq posts/trn ft, 27x35" 925.00
Poplar, dvtl, trn ft, till missing, rpl/rfn, 43" W 250.00
Poplar, rfn/red stripes, dvtl case & bracket ft, 44" W 245.00
Poplar w/orig yel pnt & smoke grpt, trn legs, 43" W 1,000.00
Poplar w/PA rpt decor, dvtl, 2-drw, rpl ft, 51" W 600.00

Poplar w/traces of PA decor & '1763,' dvtl, 85" W, VG 900.00
Walnut, 2 dvtl drw/case, orig lock/hinge, rpl ft, 46" W 1,000.00

Bookcase

Limbert, #358, 2 8-pane do, 57x48" .2,000.00
Limbert, #359, 3-do, flared legs, label, 57x67" 2,600.00
Limbert, 3-do, shelves adjust, branded, rare, 57x67" 4,500.00
Mahog Chpndl, 2 do:slant lid:4 drw, MA, 1789, 76" 14,000.00
Mahog Fed, 2-part, projecting cornice:2 glaze do, 83" 2,500.00
Mahog Geo III, 2-part, 2 glaze do:slant front, 90x41" 4,000.00
Pnt/stencil Emp, arch/inset panel:2 glaze do/paw ft, 65x55" .11,000.00
Stickley, G; #542, 2 8-pane do, decal, rfn, 56x36" 4,000.00
Stickley, L&JG; #614, 1 16-pane do, 4 keyed-thru tenons . . .3,000.00
Stickley, L&JG; #642, open, thru-tenon top/base, rfn, 55" . . .1,200.00

Cabinet

Apothecary, cherry Co Chpndl, 27-drw, bracket ft, 47x40" . .7,250.00
Cincinnati, corner, gallery top, spools/2 cvd do, 57", EX 750.00
Marjorelle, mahog/fruitwood, open shelf:2 inlaid do, 42" 5,000.00
Side, porc/ormolu-mtd ebonized wood Napoleon III, 45x58" .1,600.00
Stickley, G; china #815, 8-pane dbl do, label, varnish, 64" . .5,750.00
Stickley, G; china #820, 1 12-pane do, rfn, 60x36" 2,300.00

Candlestand

Birch, ovolo-cornered 15" top:trn std:tripod, rfn 550.00
Cherry, 1-brd 13x14" top w/molded edge, trn column:tripod . . .900.00
Cherry Co, 1-brd 13x15" top w/gallery edge, rpr/rpl 725.00
Cherry Hplwht, 13x18" tilt top, ring/urn std, spider legs 4,200.00
Cherry Hplwht, 16½" sq 2-brd tilt top w/canted corners 525.00
Cherry w/inlay Co Hplwht, sliding drw, slim snake ft 2,600.00
Cherry w/16½" dish-trn walnut top, snake ft w/cvd toes 375.00
Curly maple Co Hplwht w/simple inlay, 17x20" tilt top 700.00
Mahog Chpndl, 18" tilt top w/bird cage, tripod 2,400.00
Mahog Chpndl, 18" top:spiral/urn std:tripod w/ribbed pad ft .9,000.00
Mahog Co Hplwht, rpl 16x22" tilt top:trn/foliage-cvd std 525.00
Maple w/traces of red Shaker-type, 1800s, age split in top 250.00
Maple/tiger maple QA, dish top, 1760s, old rstr 700.00

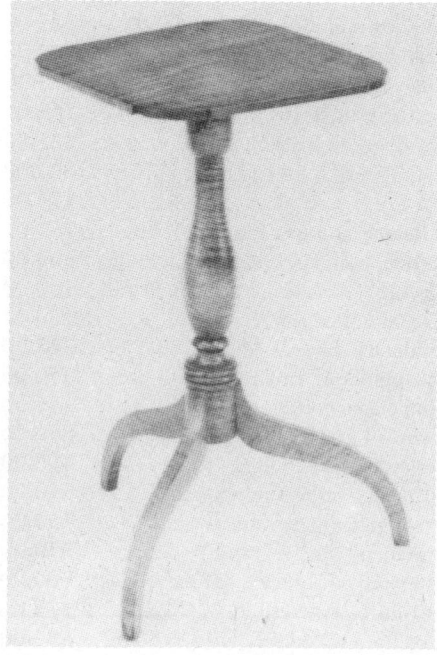

Tiger maple Federal candlestand, England, ca 1810, $1,900.00.

Chair

Adirondac rocker, worn pnt, minor damage 325.00
Arm, cherry Co QA, EX/unusual cvgs, serpentine front 4,200.00
Arm, fruitwood Fr Provincial, 3-slat bk, rush seat 200.00
Arm, fruitwood QA Transitional, Spanish ft, EX 2,000.00
Arm, mahog Chpndl, cvd/pierced crest, scroll hand rests 1,000.00
Arm, mahog Chpndl, pierced splat, slip seat, rfn/rpr 350.00
Arm, mahog/rosewood Vict, cvd crest, tufted uphl 400.00
Armchair, walnut Vict, leafy crest/floral-cvd legs, pr 550.00
Banister-bk side, fruitwood/oak, NE, 1720s, old rfn 300.00
Banister-bk side, heart/crown crest, 18" H seat, 1725 . . . . . .1,200.00
Banister-bk side, trn legs/posts, bulbous stretcher, rpt 875.00
Belter, att; arm, laminated rosewood w/grapevine cvg 9,250.00
Belter, att; side, laminated rosewood w/openwork bk fr 1,100.00
Belter, side, rosewood, floral/scrollwork cvg, curved legs 1,200.00
Belter, side, rosewood, openwork crest & down sides, unsgn .1,200.00
Corner, walnut QA, scrolled slip seat, vase splats, rstr 1,400.00
Dunlap, att; side, maple QA, yoke bk, dbl-bulb stretcher . . .2,250.00
Godwin, Edward; ebonized, open arm, fretwork bk, 1877 . . . .2,400.00
Hofstater, recliner, mahog, foliate cvd arms/stiles, bk pad 300.00
J&J Meeks, arm, rosewood Rococo, pierced/cvd, 1860 . . . . . .4,200.00
Ladderbk arm, 3 shaped slats+1, trn legs/posts, bulbous ft 450.00
Ladderbk arm rocker, 4-slat, sausage trn, rpr/rpl 400.00
Ladderbk arm rocker, 4-slat w/nipple finials, rpt, EX 160.00
Ladderbk side, apple wood w/bl pnt, 5 arched slats, 1700s . . .2,700.00
Ladderbk side, hickory, 2 arched slats, trn ft & finials 175.00
Ladderbk side, maple, 4-slat, trn posts, bulbous ft, rfn 250.00
Ladderbk side, 2-slat, EX trn, blk pnt, rpl splint seat 125.00
Ladderbk side, 4 arched slats, flame grpt w/red beneath 295.00
Lifetime, att; flat-arm Morris, 4-slat sides, rfn 850.00
Limbert, Morris #520, spade cutouts front & sides, label 2,350.00
Lock, Henry; Windsor, bow-bk side, 9-spindle, saddle seat . . .1,550.00
Lolling, mahog-fr Sheraton, inlay panels on reeded legs 16,000.00
Lolling, walnut-fr QA, trn legs/posts, scrolled X-stretcher . . .1,000.00
Nutting, Wallace; Windsor, fan-bk side, w/comb 500.00
Piano, mahog w/marquetry, spiral spindles/finials, swivels 450.00
Rocker, arrow-bk Boston, pnt/stencil, ca 1840 . . . . .450.00
Rocker, lady's sewing; maple w/bird's eye, caned seat/bk 150.00
Rocker, mahog Vict, tufted leather continuous bk/seat 650.00
Rohlfs, Chas; rocker, oak, 3 canvas straps form bk rest 8,500.00
Side, birch Chpndl ribbon-bk, sq legs 650.00
Side, cherry Co Chpndl, pierced vase splat, rpl rush seat 250.00
Side, cherry Hplwht, pierced urn splat, curved crest, pr 1,150.00
Side, cherry QA, block/vase trn legs, vasiform splat, 1750 . . . .800.00
Side, cherry w/orig finish Chpndl, ribbon-bk, pierced slats 500.00
Side, Co QA, bobbin trn, duck ft, simple crest, vase splat 750.00
Side, curly maple, sabre leg, rpl cane seat, rfn 200.00
Side, curly maple Co Sheraton, trn legs, rush seats, pr 500.00
Side, Empire, extensive re-decor, minor wear, pr 250.00
Side, mahog Chpndl, Gothic bk, EX cvd/pierced splat, Phila 2,250.00
Side, mahog Chpndl, rpl bk splat, 1775 . . . . .1,500.00
Side, maple Co Chpndl, pierced splat/shaped crest/rush seat . . .450.00
Side, QA, Spanish ft/vase splat/shaped crest, re-decor/rpr . . .1,450.00
Side, quarter-sawn oak, relief cvd foliage/Indian head bk 375.00
Side, Sheraton, EX trns, smoked yel pnt/worn blk stripes 100.00
Side, tiger maple Emp, cane seat, 1840s, rfn 110.00
Side, walnut/cherry Co Chpndl ribbon-bk, rpl seat, 1800s 550.00
Side, ½-spindle bk, orig red/blk grpt, gr/yel stripes 125.00
Sproson, Windsor, continuous arm brace-bk/saddle seat 1,325.00
Stickley, G; arm rocker #2625, 6 vertical slats in bk, unmk . . .325.00
Stickley, G; arm rocker #323, 5-slat sides/4-slat bk, unmk 900.00
Stickley, G; armchair, metal/wood inlaid in 3-slat bk, rpr . . .3,400.00
Stickley, G; armchair #310½, 3-slat bk, decal, EX 425.00

Stickley, G; armchair #324, fixed bk, 5-slat sides, decal 1,000.00
Stickley, G; armchair #350A, new cushion, decal, 38½" 450.00
Stickley, G; armchair #386, spindle sides/bk, unmk, 49" 9,000.00
Stickley, G; child's rocker #341, 3-slat bk, 25x18", EX 550.00
Stickley, G; rocker #317, 5 vertical bk slats, 38", VG 225.00
Stickley, G; rocker #365, 3-slat bk, brand, rpl seat, rfn 650.00
Stickley, G; side #350, 3 vertical slats, branded, rpl/rfn 275.00
Stickley, L&JG; armchair #497, fixed bk, 5-slat sides, label . .2,700.00
Stickley, L&JG; armchair #750, V top:5-slat, unmk Onondaga .300.00
Stickley, L&JG; armchair #816, open-arm/6-slat bk, branded .275.00
Stickley, L&JG; Morris, heavy bow arms/4-slat sides, decal . .9,800.00
Stickley, L&JG; Morris #471, 6-slat sides, new cushion/rfn . .1,600.00
Stickley, L&JG; Morris #830, open-arm/4-slat bk, red mk, EX .750.00
Stickley, L&JG; Morris rocker #831, new cushions, decal, EX .750.00
Stickley, L&JG; rocker #453, corbels under arms, 37", EX 750.00
Stickley, L&JG; side, 8-spindle bk, decal, torn seat 625.00
Stickley, L&JG; side #754, 4 sm+1 lg slat in bk, rpl seat 350.00
Stickley, L&JG: Morris, arched arm supports, Handicraft . . .1,700.00
Stickley Bros, Morris #343, 3 slats under arms, metal tag 1,900.00
Suters, Windsor, fan-bk side repro, branded, VA, pr 260.00
Tuck, Samuel; Windsor, bow-bk side, 9-spindle, 1795, NM . .1,200.00
Windsor, bow-bk arm, EX detail, knuckle arms, VG 775.00
Windsor, bow-bk arm, 9-spindle, 1800, split in seat, EX 350.00
Windsor, bow-bk side, 7-spindle, shaped seat, rpl/rfn 275.00
Windsor, bow-bk side, 8-spindle, bamboo trn, all orig, rpt 600.00
Windsor, bow-bk side, 9-spindle, saddle seat, trn legs 450.00
Windsor, bow-bk w/knuckle arms, EX detail, rpt over bl 6,700.00
Windsor, brace-bk, bulbous trn, old pnt, rpl/rpr 500.00
Windsor, brace-bk, fine trn/splay legs, RI, 1780s, rfn, EX . . .1,100.00
Windsor, Co arm, bamboo trn/spindles/rabbit ears, rpt 250.00
Windsor, comb-bk arm, scrolled crest ears, EX trn, rpt 3,200.00
Windsor, continuous arm, bulbous trn legs/arm supports, EX .1,350.00
Windsor, continuous arm, splay base/bulbous trn, rfn 1,000.00
Windsor, fan-bk side, 9-spindle, shaped crest, VG 350.00
Wing, Am QA, typical form, 1750s 2,200.00

Chair Set

Captain's, brn w/blk & yel striped rpt over salmon, 6 for 1,500.00
Side, arrow-bk Windsor, 1830s, rstr/re-decor, 4 for 450.00
Side, balloon bk, mc floral decor, 5 for 350.00
Side, balloon bk, PA decor, sgn Shuyer, 6 for 2,700.00
Side, blk rpt w/gold stenciling, plank seats, 5 for 200.00
Side, Co Sheraton Hitchcock type, rpt/rpl seats, 6 for 270.00
Side, curly/bird's eye maple Co Sheraton, EX detail, 6 for . . .3,300.00
Side, mahog Geo III style, pierced vase splats, 6 for 750.00
Side, maple w/curl/bird's eye Co Sheraton, 2-slat bk, 4 for . . .600.00
Side, pnt w/traces of decor & striping, 5 for 475.00
Side, pnt/floral stencil, trn legs, shaped plank seat, 4 . . . . . . .1,000.00
Side, walnut Nouveau, tall pierced foliate bk, Fr, 4 for 440.00
Side, Windsor, bamboo cvg, shaped central spindle, 6 for . . .1,200.00
Side, Windsor, bamboo trn, red pnt over blk, 4 for 1,680.00
Side, 3 arrow spindles in bk, rush seat, 1800s, 6 for 425.00
Windsor, bow-bk side, 7-spindle, bamboo trn, VG, 6 for 1,950.00
Windsor, thumb-bk side, 1830s, EX rfn, 5 for 475.00

Chest

Allison, Richard; mahog/flame grain veneer/inlay, 44x44" . . .2,500.00
Applewood Hplwht, 4-drw, orig brasses, VT, 1750s, 35x39" .2,750.00
Birch Fed, 4 grad drw, rpl hdw, 42x37" 2,600.00
Camphor wood, brass bound, rfn, 19x21x41" 600.00
Cherry Chpndl, ogee ft, beaded fr/edge top, rfn/rpl, 35x38" .2,400.00
Cherry Co Sheraton, sq posts, 2 sm/short drw:4, 53x44" 700.00

Cherry Co Sheraton, 4-drw, trn ft, rpr/rfn, 42x40" 600.00
Cherry Hplwht w/simple inlay, Fr feet, rfn/rpl, 40x43" 1,300.00
Curly maple, bird's eye veneer top drw, scroll ft, 45x45" 400.00
Curly maple Co Emp, trn posts, 4 dvtl drw, trn ft, 47x45" 850.00
Curly maple Sheraton, bird's eye facings, 41" W, EX 1,800.00
Curly maple veneer/walnut X-band Co Sheraton, bow front .1,950.00
Curly walnut PA Hplwht, fluted ¼-columns, 68x40" 6,500.00
Dower, poplar w/EX PA decor, name/1790, 50" W, VG 12,000.00
Japanned Regency, chinoiserie decor, 3 drw:high base, 51" .1,800.00
Mahog Emp bow front, 2 drws atop, twist columns, 39x46" .1,100.00
Mahog Fed bow front, EX cvd posts, shaped crest, 37x45" . . .400.00
Mahog Geo III, serpentine, 4-drw, ogee bracket ft, 44" W . . .2,500.00
Mahog late Emp marble top w/mirror, ca 1840 . . . . .650.00
Mahog veneer w/inlay Hplwht bow front, 4-drw, 34x38" . . .15,000.00
Mahog veneer/curly maple/bird's eye Emp, 3-drw step-bk, 35" .550.00
Maple w/some curl Chpndl, 6-drw, orig brasses, 42x36" 2,700.00
Maple/birch Co Emp, trn/rope-cvd posts, 2 sm step-bk drw:4 . .400.00
Mule, pine Co Chpndl, 4-drw, 1-brd ends, cut-out ft, 41x38" . .625.00
Mule, pine w/red pnt Co Chpndl, scroll ft, lift lid, 42x39" . . .1,800.00
Mule, poplar, scrolled base, dvtl drw, appl lid molding, 38" 275.00
Pine w/worn grpt over orig red Co Chpndl, 4-drw, VG 1,700.00
Poplar w/orig 2-tone brn grpt Co Empire, appl post trn, 48" . .650.00
Satinwood Geo III style, pnt cameos/swags, 2 sm drw:5, 49" .2,000.00
Stickley, G; #625, 2 short:2 long drw, mirror, decal, EX 3,900.00
Stickley, G; #906, 2 drw:4, iron pulls, decal, rfn, 45x40" 7,500.00
Stickley, G; #913, 9-drw, Ellis design, label/decal, 51" 13,500.00

Gustav Stickley 9-drawer tall chest #913, unsigned, refinished, pulls replaced, 50", $4,000.00.

Stickley, G; 2 drw:4 long, bk splash, unmk, 48x40" 1,600.00
Stickley, L&JG; chiffonier #111, 2 do conceal 6 drw, rstr . .2,900.00
Sugar, cherry, dvtl, lift lid, 2-part int/2-drw, KY, 37" W 1,000.00
Tiger maple, 3 short drws:2, +5 long grad drw, 1775, 63" . . .5,500.00
Walnut Co Hplwht, high cut-out ft, scrolled apron, 36x42" .1,400.00
Walnut Fed bow front, inlaid top, shaped skirt, 40x40" 2,700.00
Walnut Hplwht, 10 dvtl cock-beaded drw, Fr ft, 72x42" 3,500.00

Commode

Elm/burl walnut Louis XV/XVI style, serpentine, 28" W 935.00
Gilt metal-mtd parquetry fruitwood bombe form, 53" W 700.00
Mahog bow front, 1-drw, splay bracket ft, 1800s, 24" W 480.00
Mahog/marquetry Louis XV style, 18" dia top w/florals 400.00
Pine w/NM orig red flame grpt, lift lid, do/drw, 30x31" 325.00
Pine w/orig bird's eye maple grpt, marbleized top, 40" W 450.00
Walnut/marquetry Louis XV/XVI style, marble-top, 38" 1,650.00
Walnut/parcel gilt Rococo style, serpentine marble top, 26" .2,090.00

Cupboard

Cherry/poplar Co, 2 3-pane do/2 dvtl drw, sgn, rfn, 84x48" . .1,050.00
Corner, cherry, molded cornice:12-pane do:2 do, 86x42" 3,500.00
Corner, cherry, molded cornice:2 8-pane do:2, 91x53", EX . .1,600.00
Corner, cherry, wide cornice:2 3-pane do:2, 1-pc, 82x41" . . .3,300.00
Corner, curly maple, 2 glazed do, 3 drw:2 do, 83x55" 2,800.00
Corner, curly maple, 2 8-pane do:2, rpl/rfn, 83x43" 5,800.00
Corner, mixed wood, VG gr-gray pnt, panel do/simple, 81" . .1,050.00
Corner, pine Ontario, 2 glazed do:2 panel do, 1850, 81x55" .1,700.00
Corner, poplar w/grpt, scalloped bracket ft, 80x47" 2,700.00
Corner, walnut Biedermeier, 1825, 40x35" 225.00
Corner, walnut w/band & fan inlay, 2 panel do:2, PA, 83" . .3,050.00
Hanging, cherry, reeded trim/detail, 1-brd do, 18x14" 300.00
Hanging, walnut/cherry, dvtl/panel do, provenance, 36" 325.00
Jelly, pine w/old bl-gr pnt, orig hdw/panel do, 60x53" 800.00
Jelly, poplar w/brn-red flame grpt, 2 drw:panel do, 49x44" . . .2,100.00
Pewter, pine w/orig finish, open faced, NE, 1800s, 66x40" . . .2,800.00
Pewter, poplar, cornice & appl pilasters w/edge cvg, 69x40" . . .900.00
Pewter, primitive pine, open w/brd-&-batten base do, 74x35" .800.00
Pine w/orig red grpt, 1-pane do, cvd top spandrels, 27x18" 250.00
Poplar Co, stripped, panel ends/bk/do, CI latch, 27x30" 250.00
Poplar Co, 3 layers pnt, brd-&-batten base do, 80x43" 800.00
Poplar w/bl rpt, panel do/2 dvtl drw, 2-pc, 84x50" 1,300.00
Poplar w/re-grpt, dvtl, trn ft/panel do, 3 base drw, 89" 2,050.00
Poplar/pine, 2 6-pane do:pie shelf:3 drw:2 do, 85x56", VG . .2,600.00

Desk

Cherry Chpndl, slant top, fluted ¼-columns, 1760s, 38" W . .7,000.00
Cherry QA, 9 pigeonholes+13 drw, rpl hdw, 36" W, EX 1,600.00
Curly maple, top w/tambour do, fold-down shelf, 48" W 800.00
Guindani, oak Renaissance-style drop front, 1920s, 41x43" . . .600.00
Lap type, mahog Geo style w/brass mts, mirrored int, 17" 325.00
Lap type, mahog Regency, brass bound, 2 secret drw, 19" 400.00
Lap type, stained mahog w/wht-metal mts, strapwork, 13x11" . .165.00
Limbert, 1-drw, bookshelves on sides, wicker insert, brand 550.00
Mahog Art Deco, bateau leather/gilt top:dbl ped sides, 80" 825.00
Mahog Chpndl, fan cvg, well-fitted int, drop front, 42x41" . .3,250.00
Mahog Chpndl, oxbow, simple int, splay bracket base, 42" . .2,000.00
Mahog Chpndl kneehole, plain base/apron, 1790, 30x33" . . .1,500.00
Mahog Chpndl kneehole, shaped base/apron, 1780, 32x35" 13,000.00
Mahog Geo III, 3 short drw ea ped, shaped bracket ft, 32" . . .2,000.00
Maple Chpndl, oxbow slant front, 1790s, 43x37" 7,000.00
Maple Co Fed, slant front, 4-drw, bracket ft, 39x36" 1,400.00
Marjorelle, cvd oak, 3-drw top on 2 ped supports, 59" 1,100.00
Office, cherry Vict, slant lid/2-drw, EX rfn, 48" W 350.00
Pine Co, slant lid, int w/3 drws+shelf, 1800s, 30x41" 1,300.00
Pine Co, slant lid w/pull-out supports, open int, 37x29" 600.00
Pine/maple Co QA on fr, slant lid:fitted int:drw, 36x30" 1,100.00
Plantation, cherry, 2 3-pane do:lift lid:1-drw, 73x39" 1,000.00
Roll top, oak, 4 drw ea ped, 1890, 60" W 1,500.00
Rous, Alexander; rosewood Am Rococo Revival, 3-shelf bk .6,900.00

Stickley, G; #708, organizer at bk of 40" top:2 drw, decal 1,100.00
Stickley, G; #729, fall front, 2 short drw:3 long, 43x36" 2,200.00
Stickley, G; dbl ped, 9-drw, orig leather top/tacks, 48", EX . .2,100.00
Stickley, L&JG; partner's, oak, faceted wood pulls, 72" W . .38,000.00
Walnut Chpndl, slant front, ogee bracket ft, 1780s, 39x39" . .3,500.00

Walnut slant-front Queen Anne desk-on-stand, 28" wide, $6,000.00.

Wooten, postmaster's, walnut, ornate gallery w/finials 7,500.00
Wooten, postmaster's, walnut w/maple drws & boxes, 1874 . .5,000.00

Dry Sink

Curly maple w/poplar do panels, rpl/rfn, 55" W 2,200.00
Pine, brd/batten do, open well thin top shelf, rpr/rpl 635.00
Pine, cut-out ft, top well w/crest, rebuilt, 29x43" 250.00
Poplar, copper sink:sm drw+2 recessed, panel do, 33x43x21" . .375.00
Poplar, cut-out sides w/top shelf, drw to side, 48" W, EX 1,075.00

Highboy

Cherry QA, flat top, pinwheel/fan cvg, 1750s, 79x37" 17,000.00
Cherry QA, flat top, 2-part, fan cvg in apron, 1775, 73" . . .11,500.00
Cherry w/orig finish CT QA bonnet top, sunburst cvg, 83" .27,500.00
Curly maple Co QA, 10-drw flat top, scrolled apron, 70" 5,000.00
Curly maple QA, 2-part, fan-cvd drw/apron, 73x40" 16,000.00
Maple w/some curl Co QA, cabriole legs/duck ft, 64", VG . . .2,500.00
Pnt QA, flat top, 2-part, New England, 1700s, 69x40" 12,500.00
Tiger maple QA style, bonnet top w/spiral finials, 42x20" . . .8,000.00

Lowboy

Maple QA style, scalloped apron w/trn drops, 25" W 900.00

Tiger maple Chpndl, cut-out apron, PA 1780, 35" W 20,000.00
Tiger maple QA style, shaped/beaded apron, 32" W 1,300.00
Walnut QA, acorn drops, MA, 1750, 35" W 15,000.00

Pie Safe

Butternut, 12 punched tins w/whirligigs/stars, old pnt, 58" 650.00
Poplar, 3 punched tin panels, high cut-out base, rpr/rfn 650.00
Poplar w/red pnt, 12 tin panels w/flowers in pots, 45x40" 725.00
Walnut, tin panels w/basket of fruits, mortised/pinned, 56" 900.00

Secretary

Cherry Chpndl, bonnet top:bookcase:c&b ft, CT, 84" 62,500.00
Curly maple, top: glass do/3 sm drw; base: 4-drw, 77x38" 1,500.00
Mahog, 2 panel do:slant lid:4 drw:bracket ft, 84", VG 1,550.00
Mahog Chpndl w/custom inlay, arched do, fitted int, 94" . . .2,000.00
Mahog Eastlake, cvd, drop front, 56" 500.00
Mahog Fed, 2-part, 2 cathedral panel do:slant front, 80x48" .3,750.00
Mahog w/EX figure Chpndl, fitted int, slant lid, 89" 5,000.00
Oak Continental, bombe style, cvg on 3 drw/lid, 1880s, 92" .2,000.00

Settee

Kohn, J&J; bentwood elm/cane, bk: 3 heart-form lobes, 55" . . .330.00
Mahog, shaped/cvd bk w/uphl cushion & seat, English, 1900 . .225.00
Mahog Emp, winged paw ft/acanthus-cvd crest, 64" 2,100.00
Mahog Geo, triple-bk, dolphin ft. floral pendants, 72" 7,000.00
Satinwood w/line inlay Regency, scroll crest ends/arms, 69" .2,200.00
Walnut Vict w/Rococo-cvd fr, serpentine bk, +armchair 400.00
Walnut-fr Geo II style, English, 2nd period, 47" 1,300.00
Windsor, shaped crest:41 trn spindles, plank seat, pnt, 81" . .4,000.00

Shelf

Burl walnut/ormolu Louis Philippe, cartouch form, 38x26" 750.00
Mahog Vict, well-cvd Geo & Gothic motifs, 24" 400.00
Pewter, oak English, 2-tier, cut-out crest, 35x65", VG 475.00
Pewter, pine, shoe ft, natural finish, 1780s, 45x33" 450.00
Pine, 3-tier, scalloped crest/urn final, trn posts, 32x28" 750.00
Walnut, scrolled bk & sides, crest w/finial, 20x12¾" 125.00

Sideboard

Cherry w/EX inlay PA Hplwht, EX serpentine front, 68" L . .7,500.00
Mahog Hplwht, 1 drw:3, 1790s, 44" L 1,700.00
Mahog veneer Sheraton, mahog facings, 1800, 75", VG 600.00
Mahog w/geometric inlay Hplwht, flame veneer facade, 78" . . .950.00
Mahog w/inlay Fed, serpentine, NY, ca 1800, 72" 8,500.00
Mahog w/line inlay late Geo III, shaped/curved facade, 72" . .3,300.00
Mahog w/string & bellflower inlay Fed, serpentine, 64" 17,000.00
Mahog/inlay Geo III, serpentine X-banded top:drw, 69" W .12,500.00
Mahog/veneer, band/line inlay Eng Sheraton, serpentine, 72" .350.00
Pine Co Emp, step-bk top w/2 drw+EX cut-out crest, 70x63" . .225.00
Stickley, G; #814, slat plate rail:3 drw+2 do, label, 66" 3,000.00
Stickley, G; #816, slat plate rail:long drw:3+2 do, 48" 1,700.00

Sofa

Art Deco overstuffed/tufted kidney shape, 3-part bk, 32x84" . .300.00
Haines, Ephriam, att; mahog Fed, acanthus/rosettes cvg, 77" .4,500.00
Kittinger, att; Chpndl camel-bk, mahog base, 82" 750.00
Mahog Emp, rectangular crest:uphl bk, scroll arms, 89" 1,000.00

Mahog Emp, shaped bk/leaf-cvd scroll arm rests/paw ft, 74" . . .500.00
Mahog Fed, str floral-cvd crest, cvd/trn legs, 1820, 77" 5,000.00
Mahog Rococo, medallion bk w/minor cvg, ca 1850s 550.00
Mahog Vict, inset tufted velvet bk & curved arms, 49x69" . .1,100.00
Mahog Vict, tufted velvet arms/bk, line/flower cvg, 49x69" . .1,100.00
Rosewood Rococo Revival, vintage/floral cvg, re-uphl, 77" . .1,300.00
Vict, 3-part bk w/fruit-cvd crests, serpentine apron, 66" 2,500.00

Stand

Bookstand, Mission Oak, V-shelf, cut-out/shaped sides, sm 130.00
Cherry, trn legs/1-brd 20" sq top, 1-drw, rfn 175.00
Cherry w/curly veneer fronts, 2-brd top, trn legs 325.00
Cherry w/gr rpt Co Hplwht, dvtl drw, rpl 16x19" top 500.00
Cherry w/inlay Hplwht, dvtl drw, 1-brd 20" sq top, rfn 3,100.00
Cherry w/mahog veneer, drop leaf/trn legs/1-drw, 20x25" top . .200.00
Cherry w/red stain Co Hplwht, drw, 2-brd 18x20" top 300.00
Cherry/mahog veneer, 2 dvtl drw, 16x22" top+9½" leaves 345.00
Co Hplwht w/EX re-grpt, dvtl drw, 17x18" top, 28½" 500.00
Crock, 3 curved tiers, trn bk ft, gr rpt, 25x48" 225.00
Curly maple, rpl 20" bird's eye top, 11½" drop leaves 600.00
Curly maple, trn legs/2 dvtl drw, drop leaf, rpl 20" sq top 600.00
Curly maple, trn/panel legs, 19" center-hinged top 350.00
Curly maple Co Sheraton, trn legs w/high ft, 20" sq top 875.00
Limbert, magazine #304, 4-shelf, branded, 42x16" 950.00
Pine Co Hplwht, sq tapered legs, 1-brd 16" top 350.00
Pine w/red pnt Co Hplwht, 2-brd 24" top removes, VG 500.00
Poplar, trn legs, 1-brd 17x20" top, 28" 180.00
Sewing, mahog veneer Fed, paw/ball ft, trn acorn drops 275.00
Stickley, G; plant stand #41, 4 splay legs, 14" sq top, rfn . . .1,100.00
Stickley, G; plant stand #660, 18" sq top, no mk 1,100.00
Stickley Bros, magazine, spindle sided, Quaint, 39x26" 650.00
Walnut, trn legs, 1 dvtl drw, 1-brd 18x24" top, rfn 175.00
Walnut w/curly maple drw, 20" 1-brd top, 2 drws, rfn 300.00

Stool

Footstool, Co Windsor, worn pnt, rag carpet top, 7x13½" 70.00
Footstool, Mission Oak, rpl seat/studs, 2-slat sides, 24" W 500.00
Footstool, Moravian, chip-cvd top, 3 whittled legs, rpt 55.00
Footstool, pine, well-shaped cut-out ft, rpt, 7½x10x13" 70.00
Footstool, walnut, scalloped legs/apron, rfn, 8x8x16" 85.00
Piano, mahog, dolphin supports, 1800s 250.00
Piano, mahog Vict, 16x23" cushion seat, curlicue legs 170.00
Stickley, G; footstool #300, orig leather/finish, branded 4,000.00
Stickley, G; gout stool #302, EX orig leather, 4 legs 500.00
Stickley, L&JG; footstool #391, new leather, rfn, 18x19x14" . .475.00

Table

Banquet, mahog/cherry Co Sheraton, 3-part, extends to 99" . .2,600.00
Breakfast, mahog WM IV, cvd cylinder support, melon ft, 48" .700.00
Card, cherry Hplwht, sq top opens to 36x38", drw, rfn 1,700.00
Card, cherry w/inlay Hplwht, curly maple veneers, rpr/rfn . . .3,250.00
Card, mahog Fed, D-end apron w/flame veneer & medallion .1,100.00
Card, mahog Sheraton, reeded legs, NE, 1820s, outstanding . .450.00
Card, mahog w/inlay Sheraton, North Shore MA, 1800s, . . .1,700.00
Card, mahog w/inlay Sheraton, reeded legs, demilune, EX . . .1,000.00
Card, mahog w/string inlay Hplwht, flute-cvd edge, 36" W . .7,250.00
Card, solid curly maple Hplwht, shaped top, rfn 11,250.00
Coffee, Noguchi, blonde mahog/glass, kidney shape, unsgn 700.00
Console, mahog/ormolu Louis Philippe, S-legs, drw, 40" W .2,500.00
Console, rosewood Rococo, lg fan cvg in base, marble top . . .1,500.00
Cricket, pine Co English, 3-leg, 3-brd 32" dia top, VG 375.00

Dressing, pine w/orig decor, high bk splash, 1820s, EX 850.00
Drop leaf, birch Co Sheraton, EX trn, 18x42" top 260.00
Drop leaf, cherry, trn legs/stretchers, 12x38" top 1,150.00
Drop leaf, curly maple Co Hplwht, 20x41" top 800.00
Drop leaf, curly maple/cherry Co Sheraton, 18x36" top 525.00
Drop leaf, mahog QA, scrolled end aprons, 12x41" top 6,000.00
Drop leaf, mahog w/orig finish QA, 37" dia top, VG 9,000.00
Drop leaf, maple Co QA, cabriole legs, 13x42" top 1,450.00
Drop leaf, maple w/curl Hplwht, 1-brd 17x46" top+18" leaves .600.00
Drop leaf, walnut Emp, trn/acanthus-cvd legs, 20x38" top 250.00
Drop leaf, walnut QA, 16x46" top+18" leaves, swing legs . . .3,750.00
Harvest, Co Hplwht, mortised/pinned, 2-brd 31x138" top, VG 600.00
Hutch, birch, trn posts/stretchers, 2-brd 28x42" top, VG 775.00
Hutch, hardwood/pine Co Hplwht, 48" 2-brd top, red traces .1,950.00
Hutch, shoe ft, scrolled 1-brd ends, 41x43" top, PA 1,600.00
Hutch, 2nd coat red over orig, NE, 1750s, 50" dia 4,500.00
Lifetime, 36" dia top/shelf, X-stretcher support, rfn 800.00
Limbert, #146, geometric cutouts ea end/arched apron, 45" .2,100.00
Limbert, #153, 4 sq cutouts ea side, keyed-thru corbel, 48" .3,000.00
Limbert, #158, 54" oval top/oval shelf, cutouts, brand 10,000.00
Limbert, #172, corbel legs, keyed-tenon shelf, brand, rfn . . .1,900.00
Limbert, dining #1493, 48" dia top, ped base, brand, EX 950.00
Limbert, drop-leaf gate-leg, 48x38" top, brand 2,000.00
Limbert, library #10, 10 corbels support 36x36" top, M 2,700.00

Limbert octagonal top table #120, 45" wide, $1,000.00.

Limbert, tabourette #240, 20" top/cut-out sides/shelf, rfn 3,250.00
Limbert, 48" 8-side top, 4 wide legs w/cutouts, brand, rfn 6,000.00
Marble top, walnut Vict, cvd apron/curved legs, 37" W 500.00
Marble top, walnut Vict, trn std w/4 scroll legs, 21" top 625.00
Marble top, walnut Vict, 4-leg center-urn base, 29x27" top 400.00
Michigan Chair Co, 32x21" top:chamfered slab sides, rfn 400.00
Pembroke, cherry Co Hplwht, drw, cut-corner 20x36" top . . .1,300.00
Pembroke, mahog Co Hplwht, 1-drw, sq tapered legs, 19x32" . .575.00
Pembroke, mahog Hplwht, 1-drw, 1780s, EX rfn, 18x37" top 1,400.00
Pembroke, mahog w/EX inlay Hplwht, Baltimore, 18x30" . .12,250.00
Pembroke, mahog/inlay/burl medallions Hplwht, 9" leaves . .8,000.00
Pembroke, mahog w/inlay Hplwht, 17x34" top, rpl drw 450.00
Sawbuck, chestnut/pine/orig red pnt, RH, 1775, 23x38" top .2,100.00
Sewing, mahog Geo III, HP floral band, 1-drw, 16" W, 28" H . .850.00
Stickley, G; #667, 30" dia top, arched X-stretchers, decal . . .2,900.00
Stickley, G; game, orig leather top has tear, 48" dia 5,000.00
Stickley, G; lamp, stacked stretchers/tenoned-through legs . .2,000.00
Stickley, G; library #614, leather top/tacks, decal, 42" W 4,000.00

Stickley, G; library #614, 2-drw, iron pulls, brand/labels 1,100.00
Stickley, G; library #652, 1-drw, hammered pull, decal, 36" . . 1,200.00
Stickley, G; library #655, mahog/13 spindles ea end, decal . . 5,250.00
Stickley, G; taboret #601, 14" dia top, partial label, EX 700.00
Stickley, G; trestle, shoe ft/stretcher, decal, rfn, 30" 800.00
Stickley, G; 2-drw/medial shelf, orig hdw, label, 54" 1,300.00
Stickley, L&JG; #540, 2-tier, 24" dia top, rnd shelf, EX 1,000.00
Stickley, L&JG; #573, 18" top, sm shelf, rfn 600.00
Stickley, L&JG; #574, cut-corner 18" sq top, branded, rfn 700.00
Stickley, L&JG; #587, hidden drw, 28x10" top, paper label . . . 450.00
Stickley, L&JG; drop-leaf #509, shoe ft, label, 24" open 2,900.00
Stickley, L&JG; half-table, 22" triangular top, 3-leg, unmk 450.00
Stickley, L&JG; library, 2 drw/4 slats ea side, rfn 54" top 800.00
Stickley, L&JG; taboret #515, 8-sided, 4-leg/shoe ft, decal . . . 1,700.00
Stickley Bros, library, 3-slat sides, 1-drw, 48" 475.00
Stickley Bros, 18" sq top, wider lower shelf, 32" 750.00
Stickley Bros, 3-spindle sides, 17" sq top, metal tag, 34" 1,100.00
Tavern, gray Windsor base, 2-brd unpnt pine breadbrd top 975.00
Tavern, hardwood/pine Co QA, 1-brd 25x42" top, rpt, VG . . 1,400.00
Tavern, maple QA, duck ft, gr-pnt 35x28" top, 1750s, EX . . . 3,500.00
Tavern, pine w/2-color grpt, stenciled foliage, 30" oval 1,000.00
Tavern, pine/birch Co QA, 1-brd 24" sq top, trn legs, drw . . 1,375.00
Tavern, poplar w/red & blk grpt, trn legs, 1 drw, 36" top 750.00
Tea, mahog English Chpndl, 1-brd 29" dia pie-crust top 1,500.00
Tea, mahog PA Chpndl, 28" top:birdcage:tripod w/snake ft . . 5,500.00
Tea, walnut Chpndl, 34" tilt top:birdcage:EX tripod, Phila . . 6,500.00
Tilt top, ebony-banded Biedermeier, paw ft, 40" dia 1,500.00
Tilt top, mahog Chpndl, cabriole legs/shod club ft, 33" dia . . 1,800.00
Tilt top, mahog w/inlay Hplwht, urn post:spider legs, 15x23" . . 600.00
Tilt top, mahog w/natural finish Chpndl, rfn, 25" dia 725.00
Work, birch/pine w/orig red Hplwht, galleried shelf, 20x18" . 2,500.00
Work, butternut Co Hplwht, 2 dvtl drw, top removes, 34x36" . 625.00
Work, curly maple/mahog X-band/cvgs Co Emp, step-bk . . . 1,300.00
Work, pine Co Hplwht, 2-brd 27x48" top, pnt base, VG 300.00

Wardrobe

Mahog Vict, do ea side mirror+3 drw, minor cvg 1,400.00
Poplar w/brn grpt, cut-out ft, 2 do, 2 base drw, 48x44" 700.00
Stickley, G; 2-do w/diamond-Xd slats, label/brand, 64x41" . . 4,500.00
Walnut Vict, lg mirror do:drw, ornate high crest, 100x44" . . . 1,400.00

Washstand

Cherry w/bird's eye veneer Co Sheraton, 6-drw, 42" W 650.00
Corner, mahog Fed, bow front, base drw, trn legs, 28" W 525.00
Corner, mahog Sheraton, sm shelf in pyramid gallery, 1880 . . 950.00
Corner, pnt Fed, medial shelf, shaped splashbrd, 24" W 1,900.00
Mahog Sheraton, gallery, burl base drw, cut-out 18x16" top . 2,950.00
Pine Co Sheraton w/pnt & stenciling, trn legs/base drw, sm . . 250.00
Pine w/red rpt, dvtl gallery/base drw, slim trn ft/legs 200.00

Miscellaneous

Armoire, gilt pnt Venetian, foliate-cvd shaped crest, 88" 2,500.00
Armoire, Mallard, att; 2 arch do w/cvg, 1850s 2,000.00
Armoire, walnut Louis XV, 2 cvd panel do, 1750s, 95x70" . . 2,300.00
Bin, pine w/rpt, 3-part int, lift lid, 38x37" 275.00
Bureau plat, gilt bronze-mtd Louis XV style, leather top 1,000.00
Bureau plat, marquetry Louis XV style, ormolu mts, 48" W . . 2,100.00
Bureau plat, tulip/kingwood, Louis XV style, serpentine, 45" . 2,000.00
Canterbury, Circassian walnut Vict, pierced panels, 20x15" . . 650.00
Canterbury, mahog Fed, incurvate partitions, trn spindles . . 4,250.00
Cellarette, mahog Am Regency style, rope twists/paw ft, 27" . 1,100.00

Chaise lounge, cvd walnut fr, 1850s, 70" 1,350.00
Etagere, mahog Fed, acorn finials, base drw, 57x20" 2,100.00
Etagere, rosewood, cvd w/scrolls, marble-top base, 1850s . . . 4,000.00
Etagere, walnut Am Rococo Revival, pierced crest, 102" 1,200.00
Fire screen, walnut/Aubusson panel Louis XV style, 36x30" . . 375.00
Hall tree, walnut German, cvd acanthus, branch hangers, 70" . 200.00
Kas, fruitwood, appl fluting/decorative molding, 1700s, 79" . 5,500.00
Kas, pine, 2 drws:2 panel do, NJ, 1700s, 58x46" 1,700.00
Parlor set, Meeks, att; Stanton Hall pattern, 6-pc 13,500.00
Pedestal, mahog Vict w/appl mask cvgs, orig, 39" 475.00
Pedestal, mahog/ebonized Eastlake, 1880, 40" 375.00
Pole screen, mahog Chpndl, tapestry on EX trn pole:tripod . . 1,200.00
Pole screen, mahog Hplwht w/theorem on velvet, 55" 1,050.00
Rack, magazine; Quaint, #4602, 2-slat sides, rfn, 37" 750.00
Rack, plate; Shop o/t Crafters, #330, marquetry, 32x40" 1,200.00
Stand, hall; walnut Victorian, Gothic cutouts, mirror, 89" 600.00
Stickley, G; smoking cabinet #78, drw:do, copper straps, mk . 8,000.00
Vitrine, gilt metal mtd Vernis Martin decor Louis XV, 41x29" . 800.00

Galle

Emile Galle was one of the most important producers of cameo glass in France. His firm, founded in Nancy in 1874, produced beautiful cameo in the Art Nouveau style during the 1890s, using a variety of techniques. He also produced glassware with enameled decoration, as well as some fine pottery — animal figurines, table services, vases, and other objects d' art. In the mid-1880s, he became interested in the various colors and textures of natural woods and as a result began to create furniture which he used as yet another medium for expression of his artistic talent. Marquetry was the primary method Galle used in decorating his furniture, preferring landscapes, Nouveau floral and fruit arrangements, butterflies, squirrels, and other forms from nature. It is for his furniture and his cameo glass that he is best known today. In the listings that follow, values are for signed examples unless noted. 'X mark' refers to Croix de Lorraine.

Our advisor for this category is Don Williams; he is listed in the Directory under Iowa.

Cameo

Bowl, floral, brn/salmon on wht frost, short ftd base, 5x8" . . . 2,700.00
Bowl, floral, red/tan on clear, polished, boat form, 2½" H . . . 6,000.00
Bowl, simple floral, lav/frost, polished, 4-lobed, 2½" H 1,750.00
Box, pods/leaves, burgundy on gold frost, 4½" sq 2,000.00
Chandelier, floral, red/wine on yel, bowl form, 13½" 7,000.00
Egg, berries/leaves, gold on gr frost, w/lid, 7¾" 1,600.00
Lamp, desk; 2-arm std/shield base, floral lily shades, 22" 8,800.00
Lamp, floral, gr/bl on amber, conical w/trumpet base, 25" . . 16,000.00
Lamp, floral, red/translucent, dome on slim baluster, 13" . . . 7,700.00
Lamp, hibiscus, red/pk on wht, dome w/slim baluster, 17" . . 17,000.00
Sconce, daisies/leaves, purple/bl on yel,½-bowl form, 7" . . . 3,300.00
Sconce, floral, olive on gray w/gr,½-bowl form, 22" W 4,000.00
Sconce, poppies, amber/wht, iron mts, triangular, 10", pr . . . 8,000.00
Vase, berries, brn on gr, stick neck, 8" 750.00
Vase, berries, shiny brn on gold frost, slim w/ped ft, 8" 850.00
Vase, berries/leaves, shiny gold on pk/gr frost, 13" 1,300.00
Vase, bittersweet/vines, amber/gr on frost, 6-sided, 9" 1,850.00
Vase, bittersweet/vines, gr/lime on pk, flared neck, 20" 4,900.00
Vase, branches/leaves, dk/lime gr on pk, cylindrical, 25" 4,000.00
Vase, branches/leaves, pk & gr on wht, slim w/disk ft, 27" . . . 4,900.00
Vase, bridge/figure/trees, gr/brn on wht to pk, slim, 10½" . . . 3,000.00
Vase, butterflies/grass, brn/amber on wht, slim, ftd, 15" 2,400.00
Vase, chrysanthemums, salmon on pk, baluster form, 12" . . . 4,000.00

Vase, clematis, lav on gold frost, sgn w/star, 5" 800.00
Vase, clematis, violet on amber, ovoid, 12½" 4,900.00
Vase, daffodils, gold on frost, 14" 2,000.00
Vase, daffodils, shiny yel w/gr-gold leaves, frosted top, 10" . . .1,900.00

Vase, day lilies in Chinese red over black with midnight blue highlights, cast bronze foot, signed, total height 8", $10,000.00.

Vase, dragonflies, gr/tan on wht w/bl, bronze base, 28" 22,000.00
Vase, ferns, brn/gr on wht, swollen cylinder, 17½" 5,200.00
Vase, ferns, burgundy on gold frost, burgundy base, 12" 1,300.00
Vase, floral, bl on frost, cone shaped, 5½" 625.00
Vase, floral, burgundy on orange frost, tapered, 4" 450.00
Vase, floral, gr on wht, 6x3½" 825.00
Vase, floral, gr/violet on pk, trumpet form, 18½" 3,500.00
Vase, floral, lav on lav mottle, petal top, polished, 9" 2,100.00
Vase, floral, lav/gr on frost, hdld flask form, 5" 1,500.00
Vase, floral, pk w/gr leaves & base on lt bl/wht, 7¾" 1,250.00
Vase, floral, red/brn on amber to wht, slim, 22" 4,100.00
Vase, floral, red/wht, flattened form w/scalloped rim, 5" 1,500.00
Vase, floral, wine on gold, deeply cut, tapered, 7" 750.00
Vase, floral, wine on salmon, stick neck, 7", pr 1,900.00
Vase, floral (lg)/leaves, purple/tan, sq oviform, 8½" 5,500.00
Vase, floral/lg leaves, shiny maroon on coral frost, 5" 950.00
Vase, grape clusters, wine on lime, baluster, 7½" 2,200.00
Vase, grapevines, burgundy on 3-color mottle, 15" 4,000.00
Vase, grapevines, gold on wine & pk frost, stick neck, 8" 1,500.00
Vase, lake/trees, brn on yel mottle, eng/polished, 12" 1,800.00
Vase, lake/trees, gr/brn on clear w/pk, cylinder, 11" 2,000.00
Vase, lake/trees, pk/gr-brn on frost, slim form, 7" 1,700.00
Vase, lake/trees/mtns, bl/mauve on gr to wht, 14" 5,500.00
Vase, lake/trees/mtns, violet on frost, slim form, 6½" 1,450.00
Vase, leaves, gr on pk frost 4x2½" 65.00
Vase, lily pads/dragonfly, bl/tan on frost, bottle form, 7" 1,850.00
Vase, mold-blown cherries, lav on wht, 11½" 9,000.00
Vase, mold-blown fuchsia, red/purple on amber, 12" 8,200.00
Vase, morning-glories, bl on pk frost, slim form, 7½" 1,750.00
Vase, pansies/leaves, brn/yel on yel/wht, triangular, 3¾" 625.00
Vase, pond/flora, gr on pk, flared oviform, 5½" 1,350.00
Vase, poppies, apricot on amber, eng details, 9¾" 1,000.00
Vase, seaweed/crab, wine on lime, trumpet form, 9" 2,400.00

Vase, sweet peas, lav on pk frost, 3¾" 700.00
Vase, sweet peas, yel-gr on pk frost, pear form, mk, 7½" 850.00
Vase, water lilies, lav on lt bl/frost, 5½" 1,450.00

Enameled Glass

Bottle, scent; gr w/etched & HP florals, gilt, sgn, 5¼" 1,850.00
Bottle, scent; lake scene w/man & boat, sq form, 4¾" 1,980.00
Mug, amber w/mc flowers & leaves, 5½" 1,500.00
Pitcher, amber w/grasshopper on flower stem, 10" 2,200.00
Pitcher, red/brn mottle w/appl gr serpent hdl, floral, 3" 1,650.00
Vase, amber w/bl trefoil cross & flowers, gilt, 13" 2,000.00

Marquetry, Wood

Cabinet, butterflies/vines above, bridge scene below, 64x30" .8,000.00
Table, medieval king/queen, 24" shield-form top, 3-leg 1,500.00
Table, nest of 3; 2 w/seascapes & boats; 3rd: landscape 2,100.00
Table, occasional; sailboats in bay, lyre-shaped legs, 26" 1,500.00
Table, 2-tier; hydrangeas/butterflies, shaped 32" top 2,200.00
Tray, church ruins in forest, griffin hdls, octagonal, 20" 1,650.00

Fruit wood marquetry octagonal tray with mountains and castle ruin, signed in marquetry, 24" wide, $1,760.00.

Pottery

Centerpc, basket form w/mc blossoms & leaves, 7½", NM 500.00
Ewer, poppies on dk brn, short stem ft, 7" 500.00
Figurine, male pug/female cat, stripes/flowers, 12", EX, pr . . .4,000.00
Figurine, owl, brn/wht/blk/earth tones, on rnd base, 13" 4,000.00
Pitcher, emb leaves HP in earth tones, upright spout, 6" 350.00
Pitcher, flowers/butterflies on gold w/bl & brn, slim, 15" 950.00
Vase, dragonfly/florals, cut-away scalloped areas, 6" 400.00
Vase, sailboats/fishermen/shells, hdls+top loop, ftd, 9" 1,600.00
Wall pocket, bonnet form w/flowers, hangs from ribbon, 12" . .220.00

Gambling Memorabilia

Book, Blue Book, Mason & KC Cards, devices/etc, 1930, EX . . .60.00
Book, Foster's Practical Poker, Bretano's, 1905, 253-pg, EX 50.00
Book, Handbook of Swindling, D Jerrold, 1857, 242-pg, EX 35.00
Book, Sucker's Progress, hard bk, Asbury, 1938, 490-pg, EX 35.00
Booklet, playing cards; Stanley Cohen, 1916, 31-pg 60.00
Box, dealing; gaffed skeleton, Will/Finch, rare 2,000.00

Box, poker chip; oak w/lift-out tray, 200 clay chips 225.00
Card press, Faro; holds approx 10 decks, key missing 250.00
Card trimmer & marker, brass w/ivory hdl, rare, 3x5½" 600.00
Chips, bl eng tiger on wht, 6 for 20.00
Chips, lion eng on ivory, 39mm, EX 40.00
Chips, poker; slate, complete set, MIB 125.00
Chips, Stop Monkeying, GH Harris, 1896, complete set of 100 .50.00
Chuck-a-Luck dice game, bar top, 12" 150.00
Coppers, Faro; octagonal, 4 red & 8 blk 120.00
Dice, poker; celluloid, set of 5 . . . . .25.00
Dice cup, leather, w/cover, mk El Paso Saddlery 75.00
Dice drop, wood, eye-cup type 165.00
Dice drop, wood, octagonal w/bezels, early, EX 225.00
Dice machine, King Six Jr, wood/glass, marquee, 12x17" dia . . .425.00
Keno goose, oak, w/balls, EX 450.00

Walnut Keno Goose, revolving dice holder, 1880s, 20", $425.00.

Photograph, 2 men playing cards on a barrel 20.00
Print, A Raise in the South, Truth, 1895 . . . . .125.00
Rack, poker chip; rnd trn wooden hdl, 150 clay chips 75.00
Register, for euchre & bezique, Card Fabrique, 1870s, EX 35.00
Table, orig cash drawer, BC Wills & Co, EX 6,500.00
Wheel, bicycle wheel w/wooden border, HP #'s, 1900, 32" 225.00
Wheel, hazzard; wood w/CI spokes in base & top 300.00
Wheel, wood, 8 HP wedge sections, 19½", on 20" wood base . .180.00
Whist marker, rules on bk, DeLaRue, ca 1890, pr 5.00

Gameboards

Gameboards handmade in the 18th and 19th centuries have come to be regarded as highly-prized collectibles by devotees of Americana and folk art. Some are elaborately laid out and their bright primary colors as well chosen as a deliberate work of art — these often bring prices reaching upwards of a thousand dollars. Even those less imaginative are usually valued from a few to several hundred dollars.

Checkers/parcheesi, pnt wood, octagonal, 1900, 19x19" 150.00
Checkers, blk/wht sqs in raised border, 16x14" 175.00
Checkers, EX pnt, handmade, ca 1890s, 16x15" 150.00
Checkers, gray-lined yel/blk sqs, red/orange/blk edge 2,200.00
Checkers, maroon/blk, gilt striping, 4-color border 375.00
Checkers, pine w/3-color pnt, NY, 1850s, 13½x15" 900.00

Folding Parcheesi gameboard from the mid-19th century, painted in red, yellow, green, blue, white, and maroon, 18", $750.00.

Games and Puzzles

Games from the 19th century, chess boards and pieces, and dominoes have always been popular collectibles. Recently board games of the 19th and 20th century have gained in popularity — especially those produced prior to 1850. The early products of W.B. Ives were the first board games to be made in the U.S.A. Some were made in Europe at an even earlier date, and they too are very collectible. The lithography of the early games is not as spectacular as it is on examples from 1870 to the start of WWI. Those most prized by today's collectors were produced in great numbers during the latter third of the 19th century when manufacturers hired the finest artists and lithographers available to produce work that equaled the finest prints of that era. It is this artwork and printing that attracts most collectors, rather than the intrigue of the game.

For those interested in learning more, there are two magazines which often print game-related articles. They are *Antique Toy World* and *Collectors Showcase*. There is also a national club, the American Game Collectors Association, P.O. Box 1179, Great Neck, NY, 10023.

Puzzles were invented in 1760 by an English map-maker whose intention it was to facilitate the teaching of geography. By the mid-1850s, both America and Europe were producing children's puzzles. The earliest examples were made of wood and were hand-cut. Die-cut cardboard puzzles were first manufactured in the 1890s, and 'adult' puzzles came into vogue. Although wood continued to be used, plywood replaced solid wood during the twenties and thirties, and interlocking pieces made them easier to construct. Hand-colored, hand-cut, or special-interest 19th-century puzzles are favorites of today's collectors; character-related and quality wooden puzzles are also very desirable. See also Personalities.

Games

Across the Continent, dice game, Parker Bros, VG 45.00
Aerospace, race game, Wolverine, VG 35.00
Air Mail, stamps/money/goggles, ca 1920, NM 75.00
Alice in Wonderland, McLoughlin Bros, 1905, EX 110.00
American Heritage, Civil War game, Milton Bradley 35.00
Around the World w/Nellie Bly, McLoughlin Bros, 1890, EX . .275.00
Art Linkletter's People Are Funny, 1954, complete 15.00
Astro Launch, space game, tin, Ohio Art 25.00
Beat the Clock, 1954, EX 22.00

Bingo, lithoed box, 1939, NM 15.00
Bobbsey Twins on the Farm, 1957, NM 25.00
Bomb the Navy, battleship on lid, Pressman, NM 22.00
Boys in Blue, lithoed cards, McLoughlin Bros, 1891 . . . . .175.00
Camelot, Parker Bros, 1955 . . . . .25.00
Carpet Bowl, 8 bowls & jack, Australia, 1950s, MIB 40.00
Charles Dickens Game, Cruikshank-Phiz illus, Parker Bros, '11 .85.00
Civil War, Parker Bros, 1963 . . . . .12.00
Combat, Vic Marrow, 1963 . . . . .25.00
Crossword Lexicon, Parker Bros, 1937 . . . . .18.00
Dating Game, 2nd edition, complete, EX 17.50
Derby Horse Racing, Delmar, 1949, EX 25.00
Dick Tracy, Selchow & Righter, 1961 .25.00
Dodging Donkey, target game, Parker Bros, 1924, EX 35.00
Donkey Party, lithograph on muslin, Saalfield, 1928 . . . . .15.00
Donkey Party, Saalfield, 1940s 18.00
Dr Kildaire, Richard Chamberlain, 1962 . . . . .25.00
Duke's Bowling Cards, 1932, EX 25.00
Errand Boy, McLoughlin Bros, EX in box 225.00
Evening at Home, Victorian folding board games, EX 20.00
Finance & Fortune, Parker Bros, 1937, NM 30.00
Fish Pond, McLoughlin Bros, 1890s, VG 75.00
Football, board game, metal football, EX in box 35.00
Fortune Teller, 1905, EX 20.00
Frontierland, board game, Walt Disney's orig, EX 15.00
Frontline Jeep Patrol, board game, plastic cars, EX in box 15.00
Geography Up To Date, graphic cover, Parker Bros 15.00
Gone w/the Wind, Scarlett O'Hara..., 1940, MIB 150.00
Halma, board game, EI Horsman, 1885, complete 50.00
Hardy Boys Treasure, complete, NMIB 20.00
Harry's Grand Slam, 1962, MIB 15.00
Hats Off Clowns, 1920s, MIB 30.00

Land of Lost, NM in box 18.00
Lil Abner, game board, 1946 . . . . .15.00
Limited Mail & Express Game, Parker Bros, 1894, lg, EX 550.00
Little Lulu Adventure, Milton Bradley, 1945, EX 75.00
Lone Ranger, Parker Bros, 1938 . . . . .95.00
Madam Morrow's Fortune Telling, card game, McLoughlin Bros 65.00
Mah-Johng, Regensteiner, 1923, EX 25.00
Make-a-Million, 1938, EX 38.00
Mansion of Happiness, Sallis, EX 300.00
Mary Poppins, Parker Bros, 1964, NM 20.00
Monopoly, 1930s, complete, EX 20.00
Mr Bug Goes to Town, board game, 1955, EX 8.00
Pirate & Traveller, Milton Bradley, 1936 . . . . .60.00
Pirate & Traveller, 1911 . . . . .18.00
Poosh-M-Up, pinball type, wood fr, complete, EX 32.00
Premium Game Logomachy, McLoughlin Bros, 1883, EX 225.00
Ringling Bros & BB Official Circus, 35 pcs, 1940s, EX 30.00
Royal Game of India, Parker Bros, 1940, EX 25.00
Sleeping Beauty, Parker Bros, 1958, NM 25.00
Sliced Nations, Selchow & Righter, 1881 . . . . .195.00
Sunken Teasure, 1948, complete, EX .15.00
Super Phaser II, target game, Mego, 1976, MIB 60.00
Tattler Quiz, owl on lid, Parker Bros, 1947, EX 12.00
Test Driver, Chrysler Corp, Milton Bradley, 1956 . . . . .27.50
Tom Hamilton's Football, players pictured, 1935, NM 85.00
Touring, Parker Bros, 1926 . . . . .30.00
Toy Town School, Milton Bradley, 1913, MIB 48.00
Winnie the Pooh, Parker Bros, 1959 . . . . .35.00

Puzzles

Yankee Doodle Cube Puzzles, consisting of six Thomas Nast cartoon images of Uncle Sam, McLoughlin, 12x10", EX, $375.00.

Battle of Manila, McLoughlin Bros, EX 225.00
Blocks, Little Folks picture, McLoughlin Bros, EX 400.00
Blocks, Little Gem & ABC picture, McLoughlin Bros, EX 300.00
Blocks, Sawyer Sunday Bible, wood box, dtd 1889, EX 100.00
Child on rocking horse, McLoughlin Bros, 1897, MIB 160.00
Dissected Map of US, McLoughlin Bros, 1887, w/box 55.00
Fuzzy Wuzzy series, animal in garden, Selchow & Righter, EX . . .10.00
Home Scroll, boy on rocking horse, McLoughlin Bros, EX 175.00
Knight on horsebk, Parker Bros, 1901 .25.00
Little Black Sambo, sgn Fern Bisel Peat 65.00
Little Daisy's picture strips, McLoughlin Bros, Victorian 200.00
Our Gang, in soda fountain scene, dtd 1932, EX 58.00
Peep at the Circus, McLoughlin Bros, set of 4 in wood box 250.00
Steamer & Hose, Milton Bradley, ca 1900, 40", orig box 215.00
Storyland Scroll, Little Bo Peep on cover, McLoughlin Bros . . .250.00

Hi-Way Henry, paper litho on cardboard, rare, EX, $425.00.

Higgly Piggly, farm animals, 1953 . . . . .25.00
Historical Perspectives, ca 1830, EX 350.00
Home Baseball, McLoughlin Bros, EX 700.00
Jolly Clown, colorful, 1932 . . . . .30.00
Jr Combination Board, 1905, EX 20.00
KY Derby, 1930s, EX in orig box 40.00

Superman the Movie, 1978 . . . . .25.00
US map, wood, Parker Bros, EX 12.00
Victorian girl w/rake, litho puzzle, McLoughlin Bros 100.00
Victrola Talking Machines, record shape, 1909, NM 85.00
3 Stooges, 2 puzzles, MIB 12.50
4-Footed Friends, picture cubes, McLoughlin Bros, wood box . .350.00

G. A. R. Memorabilia

The 'The Grand Army of the Republic' was first conceived by Chaplain W.J. Rutledge and Major B.J. Stephenson early in 1864 when they were tent-mates during our own Civil War. These men, deciding that if they were spared, vowed to each other to establish an organization that would preserve friendships and memories formed during this time. Shortly after the war ended, Rutledge and Stephenson made their desires a reality. The first National Convention of the Grand Army of the Republic was held in Indianapolis, IN, on November 20, 1866. Since that time this organization has continued to help disabled soldiers, making provisions for families of deceased veterans and working for the aid of all servicemen in need of assistance.

Many items are surfacing from the early encampments, held at both the state and national level, which is due to the wide variety of souvenir items that were made.

Membership badge, cannon bronze, eagle over flag and star, 2nd issue, $40.00.

Badge, Encampment, State & National, various dates/places . . .30.00
Badge, membership; cannon bronze, eagle/flag/star, 3rd issue . . .25.00
Badge, membership; nickel, eagle/flag/star, 2nd issue 40.00
Badge, membership; 3rd Battalion, 1st issue 50.00
Belt & buckle, EX 18.00
Button, uniform; brass, various mfgrs, coat/vest sz, ea 1.50
Cane, Washington, Grant's bust at top, 1892, EX 50.00
Canteen, 1892 . . . . .80.00
Cup, tin, souvenir, emb 25.00
Cup, tin, souvenir, printed in red & bl 20.00
Flag, w/ribbon & eagle pin, 1861-1866, EX 30.00

Flag stand, dtd 1888, EX 35.00
Goblet, pressed glass, souvenir 35.00
Grave marker, bronze, varied designs 20.00
Grave marker, CI, varied designs 25.00
Grave urn 22.00
Hat, CI, souvenir, blk & gold 20.00
Hat, wreath w/GAR 10.00
Lamp globe, GAR symbol etched on frost, 4½x7" 75.00
Match safe, CI, lg wall type, w/logo & all corps insignia 200.00
Paperweight, 28th Nat'l Encmpt 1894, eagle/flag, 3" dia, EX . . .100.00
Pocket flask, mc label on glass disk, 33rd Encmpt 1899, 5" 650.00
Ribbon, memorial to Gen Grant, 1800s 35.00
Spoon, cannon bronze, souvenir 25.00
Spoon, SP, varied dates & designs 20.00
Sword, ceremonial, w/scabbard, clean 150.00
Tumbler, 1889 . . . . .35.00

Gas Globes and Panels

Gas globes and panels, once a common sight, have vanished from the countryside but are being sought by collectors as a unique form of advertising memorabilia. Early globes from the 1920s, now referred to as 'one-piece globes,' were made of molded milk glass and were globular in shape. The gas company name was etched or painted on the glass. Few of these were ever produced, and this type is valued very highly by collectors today.

A new type of pump was introduced in the early 1930s; the old 'visible' pumps were replaced by 'electric' models. Globes were changing at the same time. By the mid-thirties, a five-piece globe consisting of a pair of inserts, two retaining rings, and a metal body were being produced in both 15" and 16½" sizes. Collectors prefer to call globes that are not one-piece or plastic 'three-piece' glass' (Type 2) or 'metal body, glass inserts' (Type 3). Though metal body globes (Type 3) were popular in the 1930s, they were common in the 1920s, and some were actually made as early as 1915. Though rare in numbers, their use spans many years. In the 1930s, Type 2 and Type 3 globes became the replacements of the one-piece globe. The most recently manufactured gas globes, used since the late 1940s, are made with a plastic body that contains two 13½" glass lenses.

Note: Standard Crowns with raised letters are one-piece globes that were made in the 1920s; those made in the 1950s (no raised letters), though one-piece, are not regarded as such by today's collectors. Both variations are listed below.

Our advisor for this category is Scott Benjamin; he is listed in the Directory under California.

Texaco Ethyl, embossed glass globe, 1-piece body, 15" diameter, EX condition, $450.00.

Type 1, Plastic Body, Glass Inserts —— 1931-1950s

Ashland Diesel 110.00
Champlin 100.00
Dixie, plastic band 125.00
DX Ethyl 85.00
DX Lubricating Gasoline, tan body 135.00
Falcon 300.00
Frontier Gas, Rarin' To Go, w/horse 225.00
Marathon, no runner 70.00
Never Nox Ethyl 150.00
Shamrock, oval body 125.00
Spur 75.00
Texaco Sky Chief 80.00
Viking, pictures Viking ship 175.00
Wood River 110.00
66 Flite Fuel, Phillips 120.00
66 Flite Fuel, Phillips, shield shape 125.00

Type 2, Glass Frame, Glass Inserts —— 1926-1940s

American 185.00
Atlantic Hi-Arc, glass gill body 175.00
Coltex Service Gasoline, unused 250.00
Derby 165.00
Esso, 13", pr 150.00
Frontier Gas, no horse 175.00
Indian Gas, Red Dot 175.00
Koolmotor, clover shape 350.00
Pure 175.00
Shell, milk glass, clam shape 250.00
Sinclair H-C, narrow glass body, Red Dot 185.00
Sinclair Pennant 250.00
Skelly Anomarx w/Ethyl 250.00
Skelly Powermax 175.00
Spartan 210.00
Standard Blue Crown 300.00
Texaco Diesel Chief 200.00
Texaco Star, blk outline on 'T' 200.00
Trophy, Our Premium Gasoline 185.00
White Flash, gill body 185.00
WNAX 200.00

Type 3, Metal Frame, Glass Inserts —— 1915-1930s

Atlantic Ethyl, 16½" 350.00
Atlantic White Flash, 16½" 350.00
Essolene, 16" 250.00
Happy Gas, metal band, 16½" 250.00
Mobil Gas, winged horse, metal fr, NM 275.00
Mobilfuel Diesel, lg horse, high profile, metal band ..275.00
Multipower (Marathon), 15" 750.00
Pure, porc body, 15" 400.00
Purol Gasoline, w/arrow, porc body 750.00
Purol Pep, porc body 450.00
Red Crown Ethyl 425.00
Rocor, w/eagle, metal fr 600.00
Sunland Ethyl, 15" 275.00
Sunoco, 15", pr 250.00
Tidex, 16" 250.00
Tydol, cast faces, 15" 450.00
Tydol, 16½" 300.00

Type 4, One-Piece Glass Globes, No Inserts, Co. Name Etched, Raised or Enameled —— 1914-1931

Champlin Gasoline 750.00
Dixie, etched 900.00
Gasoline, etched 350.00
Good Gulf 500.00
Mobil Oil Gargoyle 500.00
Musgo 1,800.00
Pierce Pennant, etched 1,350.00
Red Crown, rnd, etched 1,800.00
Republic, English Globe 275.00
Shell, rnd, etched 400.00
Sinclair, etched, milk glass 650.00
Sinclair Aircraft, etched 2,000.00
Sinclair Aircraft, pnt 1,500.00
Sinclair H-C, pnt 600.00
Skelly 600.00
Standard Crown, different colors 275.00
Standard Red Crown Ethyl, emb letters 450.00
Super Shell, clam shape 500.00
Super Shell, rnd, etched 1,200.00
Texaco, milk glass, emb letters, brass collar 450.00
That Good Gulf Gasoline, emb letters, orig pnt 650.00
White Eagle, eagle shape, blunt nose 750.00
White Rose, pnt 1,600.00

Gaudy Dutch

Inspired by Oriental Imari wares, Gaudy Dutch was made in England from 1800 to 1820. It was hand decorated on a soft-paste body with rich underglaze blues accented in orange, red, pink, green, and yellow. It differs from Gaudy Welsh in that there is no lustre (except on Water Lily). There are seventeen patterns, some of which are: War Bonnet, Grape, Dahlia, Oyster, Urn, Butterfly, Carnation, Single Rose, Double Rose, and Water Lily.

Butterfly, creamer 850.00
Butterfly, cup plate 675.00
Butterfly, pitcher, milk; 4", M 800.00
Butterfly, plate, 6½", M 650.00
Butterfly, plate, 9¾", M 800.00
Butterfly, sugar bowl, M 900.00
Butterfly, tea bowl & saucer, EX 650.00
Butterfly, teapot, squat baluster form, 5", M 1,400.00
Butterfly, waste bowl 900.00
Carnation, bowl, 8¼", NM 600.00
Carnation, plate, 8", EX 450.00
Carnation, plate, 9¾", EX 550.00
Carnation, tea bowl & saucer, M 450.00
Carnation, tea bowl & saucer, rstr 265.00
Dahlia, sugar bowl 850.00
Dahlia, tea bowl & saucer 650.00
Double Rose, creamer, M 500.00
Double Rose, plate, 10" 525.00
Double Rose, plate, 7", M 425.00
Double Rose, soup plate, 9", M 450.00
Double Rose, tea bowl & saucer, M 425.00
Double Rose, teapot, NM 1,200.00
Double Rose, waste bowl, 3x5½", EX 400.00
Dove, plate, 10", M 575.00
Dove, sugar bowl, w/lid 500.00

Dove, tea bowl & saucer, M 500.00
Dove, waste bowl, M 570.00
Grape, creamer 500.00
Grape, plate, pnt flaking, 9¾" 250.00
Grape, plate, toddy, 5", NM 375.00
Grape, plate, wear/sm rpr, 8" 300.00
Grape, plate, 7", M 425.00
Grape, tea bowl & saucer, EX 250.00
Grape, teapot, hairlines/lt stains, 6½" 500.00
Grape, teapot, imperfections 600.00
Oyster, plate, 9½", NM 400.00
Oyster, soup plate, 8½", EX 450.00
Oyster, tea bowl & saucer, M 425.00
Single Rose, coffeepot, dbl gourd form, 10¾", M ...1,200.00
Single Rose, plate, 7", M 410.00
Single Rose, plate, 8", M 450.00
Single Rose, sugar bowl, w/lid, M 575.00
Single Rose, tea bowl & saucer, M 425.00
Strawflower, creamer 650.00
Strawflower, plate, 8", M 550.00
Strawflower, tea bowl & saucer, M 550.00
Sunflower, plate, 6½" 600.00
Sunflower, tea bowl & saucer, M 550.00
Urn, creamer 600.00
Urn, plate, sectional border, 7" 500.00
Urn, plate, 5", M 450.00
Urn, waste bowl, M 400.00
War Bonnet, creamer, M 600.00
War Bonnet, plate, minor flaking, 8" 325.00
War Bonnet, plate, toddy; M 475.00
War Bonnet, plate, 7", M 650.00
War Bonnet, tea bowl & saucer, NM 475.00
War Bonnet, teapot 1,250.00
Water Lily, tea bowl & saucer, EX 725.00
Zinnia, plate, 8½", NM 550.00

Gaudy Ironstone

Gaudy Ironstone was produced in the mid-1800s in Staffordshire, England. Some of the ware was decorated in much the same colors and designs as Gaudy Welsh, while other pieces were painted in pink, orange, and red with black and light blue accents. Lustre was used on some designs, omitted on others. The heavy ironstone body is its most distinguishing feature.

Key:
pc — polychrome   ug bl —— underglaze blue

Bowl, waste; Strawberry, pc/ug bl/purple lustre, 5⅜", EX 150.00
Bowl & pitcher, floral, bl/wht, 14" dia; 12", EX 425.00
Creamer, Morning-Glory, paneled, foliage hdl, 6½", EX 145.00
Creamer, Strawberry, pc/ug bl/purple lustre, 6", NM 350.00
Cup & saucer, floral, pc/purple lustre, no hdl, EX 50.00
Cup & saucer, floral, pc/purple lustre, no hdl, Walley, EX 115.00
Cup & saucer, floral w/urn, pc/purple lustre, no hdl, 6 for 510.00
Cup & saucer, Strawberry, pc/ug bl/purple lustre, no hdl 100.00
Cup & saucer, vintage, pc/purple lustre, no hdl, stains 65.00
Dish, Strawberry, copper/pk lustre, w/lid, 8-sided, 9½", EX 300.00
Pitcher, harlequin emb, pc floral/purple lustre, 9", EX 150.00
Pitcher, Morning-Glory, paneled, ug bl, 8" 210.00
Pitcher, roses/florals emb, pc/ug bl, 8", EX 225.00
Plate, floral, pc/ug bl/purple lustre, Walley, 8½" 95.00

Plate, Morning-Glory, ug bl/purple lustre, stains, 8½" 50.00
Plate, Morning-Glory, 8", M 85.00
Plate, rose, 4-color, 9½" 85.00
Plate, Strawberry, copper/pk lustre, 10", NM 110.00
Plate, Strawberry, w/morning-glories, 8", VG 70.00
Platter, Strawberry, copper/pk lustre, 14" L, NM 275.00
Relish dish, Strawberry, copper/pk lustre, 8", NM 85.00
Soup plate, Strawberry, pc/ug bl/purple lustre, 9¾", NM 200.00
Sugar bowl, Morning-Glory, ug bl, paneled, leaf hdls, 8" 145.00
Sugar bowl, Strawberry, paneled, re-attached finial, 8½" 200.00
Sugar bowl, Strawberry, pc/ug bl/lustre, paneled, hdls, NM 475.00
Teapot, Strawberry, paneled, chips/hairlines, 10" 210.00
Teapot, Strawberry, pc/ug bl/lustre, paneled, 10", NM 775.00
Tureen, sauce; Imari design, mk Patent, +tray, 7¾" L 275.00

Strawberry butter dish, EX, $350.00; Set of 10" plates, 3 marked Elsmore Forster and Co., EX, $650.00.

Gaudy Welsh

Gaudy Welsh was an inexpensive hand-decorated ware made in both England and Wales from 1820 until 1860. It is characterized by its colors — principally underglaze blue, orange-rust, and copper lustre — and by its uninhibited patterns. Accent colors may be yellow and green. (Pink lustre may be present, since lustre applied to the white areas appears pink. A copper tone develops from painting lustre onto the dark colors.) The body of the ware may be heavy ironstone, creamware, earthenware, or porcelain; even style and shapes vary considerably. Patterns, while usually floral, are also sometimes geometric and may have trees and birds.

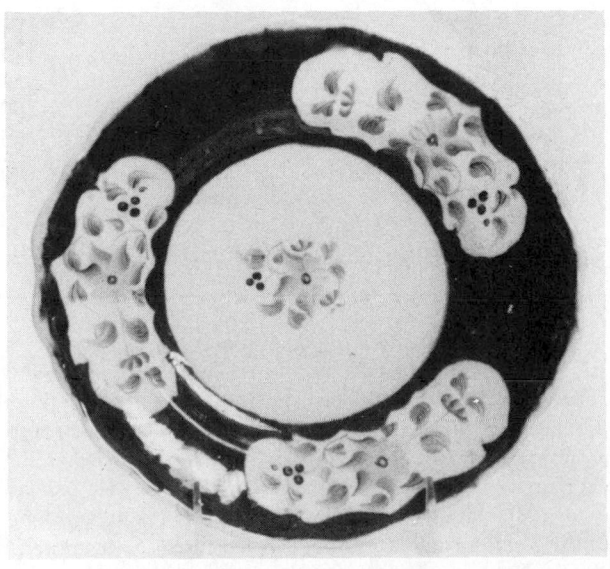

Plate, Columbine, 8½", $60.00.

Daisy & Chain, creamer 70.00
Daisy & Chain, cup & saucer 65.00
Daisy & Chain, sugar bowl, w/lid 120.00
Flower Basket, bowl, 10½" 165.00
Flower Basket, plate, 12-sided, purple lustre trim, 8⅞" 75.00
Flower Basket, plate, 8½" 45.00
Flower Basket, sugar bowl, w/lustre, lion's-head hdls, lid 140.00
Flower Basket, tea bowl & saucer 70.00
Grape, cup & saucer 70.00
Grape, mug, cobalt leaves/rust-colored vine, 2¼x2¼" 60.00
Grape, wash bowl & pitcher, vulture hdl, mk Stone China, M .700.00
Grape II, mug, cobalt floral, orange petals, 2⅜x2⅛" 75.00
Morning-Glory, bowl, red/gr berries, octagonal, 8⅝", NM 85.00
Morning-Glory, bowl, shell form, 7½" L, EX 60.00
Morning-Glory, creamer, 5", EX .75.00
Morning-Glory, cup & saucer, 5", EX 60.00
Morning-Glory, pitcher, underglaze bl w/purple lustre, 8" 135.00
Morning-Glory, plate, toddy; 4⅜" 30.00
Morning-Glory, plate, 8", NM 60.00
Morning-Glory, platter, copper lustre, 14½", EX 135.00
Morning-Glory, tea set, leaf hdls, pot: 6¼", 3-pc, EX 400.00
Oyster, bowl, ftd, 6x10½" 80.00
Oyster, bowl, 6" 65.00
Oyster, creamer, 1820s, 3¾", M .80.00
Oyster, cup & saucer 65.00
Oyster, jug, hot water 100.00
Oyster, pitcher, 4½x4½" 85.00
Oyster, plate, dessert; 5½" 40.00
Poppy, cup & saucer 65.00
Shanghai, creamer 90.00
Shanghai, plate, 5½" 60.00
Strawberry, creamer 85.00
Strawberry, mug, 4" 135.00
Strawberry, plate, 7¾" 50.00
Strawberry, plate, 8½" 65.00
Strawberry, tea bowl & saucer 90.00
Tulip, creamer 65.00
Tulip, cup & saucer 65.00
Tulip, mug, miniature, 1⅞" 25.00
Tulip, plate, 6" 25.00
Tulip, plate, 9" 65.00
Tulip, teapot, ca 1840 . . . . .135.00
Tulip, waste bowl, 6½" 85.00
Wagon Wheel, mug, 2½" 65.00
Wagon Wheel, pitcher, 8½" 175.00
Wagon Wheel, plate, 5½" 32.00
Wagon Wheel, plate, 7½" 50.00
Wagon Wheel, plate, 8" 65.00
Wagon Wheel, tea cup & saucer, rare 65.00
Wagon Wheel, tea set, flow bl, child's, complete 525.00

Geisha Girl

Upon the discovery of tea in China some four thousand years ago, civilization was beset with a small problem — what to use in serving this special beverage. One solution came in the form of 'Geisha Girl' porcelain. At the end of the 19th century, this lovely type of Japanese tea service found its way to the west. Produced in more than sixty-five patterns, this fine porcelain features geishas going about the everyday activities of Japanese life. Mt. Fuji is very often included in the background along with a wide variety of flora and fauna. Though some items were entirely hand painted and others were hand decorated over decals, most were made by the raised stencil method. Tea sets, snack sets, children's items, salt and pepper

shakers, and even such items as mustache cups may be found. Pieces were bordered in one of many bright colors — red, yellow, blue, green, or brown. As interest continues to climb, so will the values. For further information, we recommend *The Collector's Encyclopedia of Geisha Girl Porcelain* by Elyce Litts, available at your local bookstore or Collector Books.

Biscuit jar, Leaving the Teahouse, fluted, red/gold 45.00
Bowl, Footbridge B, red, 8" 26.00
Bowl, Inside the Teahouse, lt gr, 8¾" 75.00
Bowl, master berry; Garden Bench I, red w/gold buds 35.00
Bowl, master berry; Gardening, red 35.00
Bowl, master nut; Lady in Rickshaw B, cobalt bl/gold 20.00
Bowl, soup; Geisha in Sampan A, brn/gold 28.00
Candy dish, Picnic A, bamboo hdl, gold, 5½x6½" 25.00

River pattern chocolate pot, $100.00; Tea pot, $65.00; Set of 6 cups and saucers, $90.00; Creamer and sugar bowl, $25.00.

Cocoa set, Garden Bench D, red, 11-pc 100.00
Cocoa set, Mother & Daughter, scalloped, red, 11-pc 135.00
Cookie jar, Fan A, cobalt bl 115.00
Creamer, Garden Bench B, ribbed, cobalt bl, 4" 10.00
Creamer, Mother & Son B, melon ribbed, red w/gold lacing 20.00
Cup & saucer, Battledore, dk apple gr 15.00
Cup & saucer, Fan B, red w/gold buds 15.00
Dish, relish; Courtesan Processional, 8x5" 28.00
Dish, sauce; Flower Gathering A, cobalt bl w/gold lacing, 4½" . .12.00
Egg cup, Cloud A, red 20.00
Gravy boat, Temple B, red w/gold 20.00
Jar, mustard; Parasol C, red/yel .12.00
Nappy, Lantern Gateway, cobalt bl/gold 25.00
Pitcher, Waterboy, cobalt w/gold, 4" 15.00
Plate, Basket A, fluted swirl, dk apple gr, 8½" 30.00
Plate, Children in Boat, fluted swirl, bl w/gold lacing, 8½" 30.00
Plate, Chrysanthemum Garden, fluted swirl, red, 6" 5.00
Plate, Duck Watching A, gold, 6" .10.00
Plate, Feeding the Carp B, red w/gold trim, 7" 15.00
Plate, Gardening, red, 10½" 35.00
Plate, Writing A, scalloped, cobalt w/gold, 7⅜" 15.00
Platter, cake; Lesson/Parasol A in center, red/gold, 10½" 38.00
Pot, demitasse; Picnic B, red/gold 30.00
Powder jar, Boat Dance, ribbed, gr w/gold trim 25.00
Powder jar, Flower Gathering A, pine gr 15.00
Shakers, Child Reaching for Butterfly, red 10.00
Shakers, Dressing, red 10.00
Spooner, Processional Parasol, red 10.00
Vase, Cloud A, cobalt bl, 5½" 30.00

Georgia Art Pottery

The first Georgia Art Pottery was fired in Cartersville in August 1935.

A variety of wares was produced; during the fifties, a Niloak-like swirl ware was made. In 1983 the pottery was awarded the Georgia Governer's Award, and examples of their ware were displayed in the Smithsonian. Earlier pieces were marked Georgia Art Pottery (GAP); these usually demand the highest prices due to the fine glazes used in their manufacture. Later items were stamped 'W.J. Gordy, Hand Made,' after the company's founder.

Chamberstick, glossy bl, twin hdl, mk GAP 75.00
Ewer, speckled brn, stamped WJG, 7" 30.00
Mug, mottled matt gr, mk GAP, 4½" .55.00
Vase, dull bronze, hand-incised, mk 1st piece, 7" 500.00
Vase, dull swirl, imp WJ Gordy, 7" 75.00
Vase, flower arranger; cobalt, imp mk, 5" 20.00

Vase, dull bronze, hand incised mk: 8-12-35, Cartersville GA, 1st piece, W.J.G. in circle, 7", $500.00.

German Porcelain

Unless otherwise noted, the porcelain listed in this section is marked simply 'Germany.' Products of other German manufactures are listed in specific categories. See also Pink Pigs; Elfinware.

Figural group, shepherd holding birdcage, ca 1890s, 9", $650.00.

Bottle, scent; flower finial, appl flowers, 11" 250.00
Bowl, lilies, pk/wht/lav on pk, gold trim, unmk, 2¾x10½" 48.00
Bowl, 2 maids in Grecian garden, reticulated, 9" 80.00
Box, lady in fancy gown figural, 7x4" 88.00

Candelabrum, 3-arm, appl florals, central urn, paw ft, 13" 175.00
Chocolate pot, lovers in garden, much gilt, Kauffman, 10" 150.00
Figurine, Colonial lady, bk open to hold flowers, 8½" 75.00
Figurine, dancing girl, blk/gold attire, mk MIG, 10" 80.00
Figurine, Edwardian couple, man w/cape; lady w/fan, 11", pr . . .295.00
Figurine, girl in pk hat & floral pants holds goose, mk, 5" 65.00
Figurine, news vendor, bl coat/brn hat, Scheibe-Kister, 6" 80.00
Plate, Dachsund pups drink milk, scrolled/beaded rim, mk, 7" . . .20.00
Tea set, roses, pk on wht, US Zone, 15-pc 150.00

Centerpiece, 2 figures on base, applied flowers, numbered, 12½", $450.00.

Gladding McBean and Company

This company was established in 1875 in Lincoln, California. They first produced only clay drainage pipes, but in 1883 architectural terra cotta was introduced, which has been used extensively in the United States as well as abroad. Sometime later a line of garden pottery was added. They soon became the leading producers of tile in the country. In 1923 they purchased the Tropico Pottery in Glendale, California, where in addition to tile they also produced huge garden vases. Their line was expanded in 1934 to included artware and dinnerware.

At least fifteen lines of art pottery were developed between 1934 and 1942. For a short time they stamped their wares with the Tropico Pottery mark; but the majority was signed 'GMcB' in an oval. Later the mark was changed to 'Franciscan' with several variations. After 1937 'Catalina Pottery' was used. (All items marked 'Catalina Pottery' were made in Glendale.)

Bowl, Coronado Art Ware, low, satin ivory, 13" 28.00
Candle holder, Tropico Art Ware, wht .15.00
Candle holders, Capistrano Art Ware, sq, celadon/ivory, pr 25.00
Coffeepot, demitasse; Ruby Art Ware 65.00
Compote, Catalina Art Ware, ivory 18.00
Cup & saucer, Ruby Art Ware 25.00
Flower bowl, Tropico Art Ware 17.50
Goose on ped base, Capistrano Art Ware, oatmeal gloss 20.00
Plate, Coronado Art Ware, flat, satin ivory, 13" 18.00
Vase, Catalina Art Ware, ribbed, coral satin, 7¾" 24.00
Vase, Coronado Art Ware, bulbous base, satin ivory, 8½" 25.00

Vase, Encanto Art Ware, flat, flambe 22.00
Vase, Nautical Art Ware, cornucopia form 20.00
Vase, Ox Blood Art Ware, bl int, 11" 80.00

Vase, lady's head, cupped hands form opening, 7", $22.50.

Goebel

F.W. Goebel founded the Hummelwork Porcelain Manufactory in 1871, located in Rodental, West Germany. They produced porcelain figurines, plates, and novelties, the most famous of which are the Hummel figurines (these are listed in a separate section). There were many other series produced by Goebel — Disney characters, birds, animals, Art Deco figurines, and the Friar Tuck Monks that are especially popular.

Ash tray, poodle, full bee 25.00
Bank, Friar Tuck Monks 30.00
Barometer, Cardinal, 3-line mk 100.00
Bird, Red-Breasted Nuthatch, 6" 40.00
Calendar, Friar Tuck Monks 35.00
Condiment set, Friar Tuck Monks, full bee, 3-pc 65.00
Creamer & sugar bowl, Friar Tuck Monks, w/lid, on tray 70.00
Dealer sign, Wildlife Collection, w/bird figural, official mk 95.00
Decanter, rabbit, crown mk, +6 wines 125.00

Figurine, 3 dancing girls in slacks, leaning forward, ca 1930, 8", $300.00.

Figurine, flapper showgirl plays guitar, mk/#d, 10" 175.00
Figurine, George Washington, V mk, 5½" 25.00
Figurine, girl plays cello, 8½" 135.00

Figurine, rabbit, brn w/ladybug on tail, 1959 mk 35.00
Figurine, rabbit w/baby, stylized bee/W Germany, 6" L 45.00
Figurine, sea gull, flies over waves, 3-line mk, 4x8½" 50.00
Font, Holy Water, crown mk 35.00
Mug, Friar Tuck Monks, lg 35.00
Mustard jar, Friar Tuck Monks, stylized bee 25.00
Sugar bowl, Friar Tuck Monks, stylized bee, 4½" 25.00
Wall pocket, umbrella, crown mk, full bee 45.00

Goldscheider

The Goldscheider family operated a pottery in Vienna for many generations before seeking refuge in the United States following Hitler's invasion of their country. They settled in Trenton, New Jersey, in the early 1940s where they established a new corporation, producing objects of art and tableware items. In 1946 Marcel Goldscheider established a pottery in Staffordshire where he manufactured bone china figures, earthenware, etc., marked with a stamp of his signature.

Colonial gentleman, 7", $90.00.

Ash tray, German Shepherd, 5½x7½" 45.00
Bust, Bali head, pk turban, Barbara Baldwin, 12¾" 220.00
Bust, Madonna, USA 150.00
Figurine, Chinese girl w/fan, 12" 150.00
Figurine, Deco dancer, 15" 250.00
Figurine, girl & boy arm in arm, she w/bouquet, 8½" 220.00
Figurine, lady w/basket of flowers, pk dress, 7½" 75.00
Figurine, Prince of Wales, Peggy Poacher, 6¾" 75.00
Figurine, Southern Belle, 10½" 85.00
Figurine, stork, neck bent downward, 6¾" 125.00
Figurine, Venice, 12" 150.00
Figurine, woman in gray/blk, urn on shoulder, Polter, 15" ...1,250.00
Music box, Colonial girl, 7" 95.00
Plaque, Nouveau lady, A Zehle, 8" 125.00
Wall mask, brn-haired girl, red lips, aqua scarf, 11¼" 175.00

Gonder

Lawton Gonder grew up a ceramist. By the time he opened his own pottery in December, 1941, he had a solid background in both production and management. Gonder Ceramic Arts, Inc., purchased the old Peters and Reed — Zane Pottery in South Zanesville, Ohio. There they turned out quality commercial ware with graceful shapes in both Oriental and contemporary designs. Their greatest achievements were the development of their superior glazes: flambe; 24k gold crackle; and Chinese crackle glazes in celadon, ming yellow, and blue. Most of the ware is marked with 'Gonder' impressed in script and a mold number.

Bowl, bulbous, E-12	8.50
Ewer, gray, fluted, 6"	8.00
Figurine, coolie, gray, 9"	15.00
Figurine, horse's head, bl/gr onyx glaze, 13" L	40.00
Figurine, Oriental water carrier, gray, 14½"	25.00
Planter, swan, yel/pk mottling	20.00
Teapot, Rings, bl, #662	12.00
Vase, gr/pk, 7"	12.00
Vase, gray/pk, fan form, E-5, pr	20.00

Vase, fantasy creatures in relief on yellow gloss, initialled, $85.00.

Goofus Glass

Goofus was an inexpensive type of lustre-painted pressed glassware made by many companies during the first two decades of the 20th century. Bowls and trays are most common, and red and gold combinations are found more often than blues and greens. Authority Carolyn McKinley has compiled a lovely book, *Goofus Glass, An Illustrated Value Guide*, available at your favorite bookstore.

Bowl, dahlia, scalloped, gold, ornate, 10x4"	45.00
Bowl, dogwood, orig pnt, 3x9½", EX	45.00
Bowl, field flowers, crimped/ruffled rim, orig pnt, 3½x8"	40.00
Bowl, pears/cherries/plums, crimped, EX orig pnt, 4x7"	35.00
Bowl, pine cones & leaves, ruffled rim, M orig pnt, 10"	50.00
Bowl, reindeer in center, EX	18.00
Bowl, teardrops/hearts, red/gold center, fluted rim, 8¾"	32.00
Cake plate, acorn & leaf, amethyst, 12"	20.00
Lamp, oil; cabbage rose, milk glass, miniature, 9"	50.00
Lamp, Roses in the Snow, rare orig chimney, rpt, 15"	100.00
Pin tray, basketweave, gold w/red rose, orig pnt, 4½" L	25.00
Plate, cake; carnation border, elk center, 13"	50.00
Plate, grapes in center, fancy gold rim, orig pnt, 8½"	40.00
Plate, roses in center, 8½"	20.00
Shakers, poppy, EX orig pnt, 3", pr	35.00
Tray, basketweave & rose, orig red/gold pnt, 7x10"	30.00
Tray, dresser; roses w/in heart form, minor rstr, 6" W	55.00
Tumbler, grapes, gold on crackle, orig pnt, 4"	40.00

Vase, bird in a berry patch, red/gold rpt, 10"	25.00
Vase, daisies, group of 4, molded hdls, orig pnt, 12"	40.00
Vase, dogwood blossoms & hearts, 6-sided, EX pnt, 15"	38.00
Vase, grape clusters, 3 w/latticework between, orig pnt, 10"	20.00
Vase, iris on bl glass, rare, minor rstr, 6½"	28.00
Vase, mixed fruit, rpt gold on clear, 10"	35.00
Vase, peacock in a tree, red/gr/gold, M orig pnt, 15"	100.00

Vase, large roses in relief, 9", $65.00.

Vase, single rose, EX orig pnt, 9½"	30.00
Vase, Statue of Liberty, rare	95.00

Goss

William Henry Goss received his early education at the Government School of Design and as a result of his merit was introduced to Alderman William Copeland, who owned a large pottery firm. Under the influence of Copeland, Goss quickly learned the trade and soon became their chief designer. Little is known about this brief association, and in 1858 Goss left to begin his own business. After a short-lived partnership with a Mr. Peake, Goss opened a pottery on John Street, Stoke-on-Trent, but by 1870 he had moved to his business to a location near London Road. This pottery became the famous Falcon Works.

Many of the early pieces made by Goss were left unmarked and are difficult to discern from products made by the Copeland factory; but after he had been in business for about fifteen years, all of his wares were marked. Today, unmarked items do not command the prices of the later marked wares.

Adulphus William Henry Goss joined his father's firm in the 1880s. He introduced cheaper lines, though the more expensive lines continued in production. Shortly after his father's death in 1906, Adulphus retired and left the business to his two younger brothers. The business suffered from problems created by a war economy, and in 1936 Goss assets were held by Cauldron Potteries Ltd. These were eventually taken over by the Coalport Group, who retained the right to use the Goss trademark. Messrs. Ridgeway Potteries bought all the assets in 1954, as well as the right to use the Goss trademark and name. Now it remains to be seen if Goss ware will ever be produced again.

Abbots cup, Fountains Abbey	25.00
Ancient Irish bronze pot, Ulster	20.00

Bowl, beer; dragon 25.00
Bowl, Scarlett, #38660 ....35.00

Burn's Cottage, 5½" long, $85.00.

Candle snuffer, Aseroovy crest on wht, 2¼" 50.00
Candlestick, owls, 6" 75.00
Eddystone Lighthouse, Herne Bay 45.00
Ewer, Arundal, 4½" 20.00
Ewer, Shrewsbury, 4" 20.00
Huer's House 200.00
Irish Mather, Hastings 20.00
Jersey fish basket, 4" L 25.00
Look Out House 140.00
Manx Cottage 105.00
Monument to Death of King William II, Christ Church 40.00
Night light, R Burns, 6" 150.00
Old Salt pot, Seven Oaks 20.00
Plate, Armorial, 10" 25.00
Rufus Stone 40.00
Shakespeare's House 100.00
St Nicholas Chapel 200.00
Vase, amphora, 1911 Coronation, 4" 40.00
Vase, Southwold, 6" 40.00
Yorick's Skull 150.00
1st & Last House 135.00

Gouda

Since the 18th century the main center of the pottery industry in Holland was in Gouda. One of its earliest industries, the manufacture of clay pipes, continues to the present day. The artware so easily recognized by collectors today was first produced about 1885. It was decorated in the Art Nouveau manner. Stylized florals, birds, and geometrics were favored motifs; only rarely is the design naturalistic. The Nouveau influence was strong until about 1915. Art Deco was attempted but with less success. Though most of the ware is finished in a matt glaze, glossy pieces in both pastels and dark colors are found on occasion and command higher prices. Decoration on the glossy ware is usually very well executed. Most of the workshops failed during the depression, though earthenware is still being made in Gouda and carries the Gouda mark. Until very recently, Regina was still making a limited amount of the old Gouda-style pottery in a matt finish. Watch for the Gouda name, which is usually a part of the backstamp of the various manufacturers.

Bowl, Art Nouveau floral, bl/gr/red w/turq, 5¾" 90.00
Bowl, mc on blk, 3-section, Regina & crown mk, 4x8" 85.00
Candlestick, floral, yel/gr on blk, house mk, Spino, 7", pr 150.00
Candlestick, mc on wht, flared base, ring hdl, house mk, 7¼" ...75.00

Candlestick, mc top w/blk spiral center, flared base, 7¼" 85.00
Candlestick, 6 autumn colors, flared, house mk, 7x3¾" 85.00
Compote, Daisy, hdls, 5x7¼" 95.00
Lantern, Art Nouveau decor, house mk, 6" 115.00
Lantern, Art Nouveau designs, 6" 95.00
Shoe, floral decor, 5½" 30.00
Shoe, turq w/mc decor, house mk, 2¼x2½x5½" 65.00
Tumbler, floral, mc on blk, house mk, 4⅜x3⅝" 55.00
Urn, band of stylized blossoms, mk DAM III, w/lid, 17", NM ..400.00
Vase, Art Nouveau floral, mc, 6½" 60.00
Vase, floral, bulbous, house mk, Areo Royal Gouda, 5¾" 85.00
Vase, floral, stylized, mc on dk gr, ped ft, mk Ivora, 9" 75.00
Wall pocket, floral, rust/cream on blk, 1926, 9" 100.00

Vase, stylized florals, ca 1900, 7", $80.00.

Graniteware

Graniteware, made of a variety of metals with enamel coatings, derives its name from its appearance. The speckled, swirled, or mottled effect of the vari-colored enamels may look like granite — but there the resemblance stops. It wasn't especially durable! Expect at least minor chipping if you plan to collect.

Graniteware was featured in 1876 at Phily's Expo. It was mass-produced in quantity, and enough of it has survived to make at least the common items easily affordable. Color is an important consideration in evaluating an item; cobalt, brown, green swirl, or old red and white items are unusual, thus more expensive. Pieces of heavier weight, seam constructed, and those with wooden handles and tin lids are usually older.

In recent months, magazine articles featuring decorating ideas with an emphasis on the 'country look' have caused the price of graniteware to escalate — a trend which is likely to continue.

Our advisor for this category is Helen Greguire; she is listed in the Directory under New York. Watch for her new graniteware book which is tentatively due out this summer. It will be published by Collector Books. For the address of the National Graniteware Society, see the section on Clubs, Newsletters, and Catalogs.

Batter jug, gray, w/lid & tin cap on spout, rare, lg 275.00
Bowl, mixing; robin's egg bl mottle, med sz, NM 40.00

Bowl, red, wht int, nested set of 3 . . . . .85.00
Bowl, soup; gray 20.00
Bread box, wht, rectangular 35.00
Bread riser, bl swirl, tin lid, NM 395.00
Bread riser, cream & gr, NM 185.00
Bread riser, gray mottle, w/lid, sm, NM 170.00
Bucket, berry; bl & wht marbleized, 8" 75.00
Bucket, berry; bl & wht swirl 75.00
Bucket, berry; gray, wire hdl, 5½" 35.00
Bucket, berry; sky bl, tin lid, bail hdl, M 45.00
Butter dish, wht, rnd, w/lid 125.00
Can, cream; red, w/lid & bail, 1-qt 55.00
Can, milk; wht, Dutch girl in bl 75.00
Candlestick, bl & wht mottle, rare, NM 385.00
Candlestick, dk gr 95.00
Candlestick, wht, NM 65.00
Canister set, lt gr, aluminum lids, 6", set of 3 . . . . .135.00
Canister set, sky bl w/wht letters, set of 4, NM 195.00
Casserole, bl & wht swirl, w/lid, EX .75.00
Casserole, gray, w/lid 45.00
Chamber pot, bl swirl, w/lid 95.00
Chamber pot, gray, child's sz 30.00
Chamber pot, lav w/HP girl feeding geese, child's sz 25.00
Chamber pot, turq swirl, w/bail & lid, tall, EX 95.00
Chamberstick, yel or gr, ea 40.00
Coffee boiler, bl & wht speckled, 12" 85.00
Coffee boiler, cobalt & wht swirl, matching granite lid, M 250.00
Coffee boiler, crysolite swirl, matching granite lid, M 375.00
Coffee boiler, turq & wht swirl, matching granite lid, M 225.00
Coffee urn, gray mottle & brass spout, w/lid, 5-gal, NM 245.00
Coffeepot, bl & wht swirl, w/lid, 8-cup, M 225.00
Coffeepot, brn & wht marbleized, gooseneck spout, w/lid, NM .395.00
Coffeepot, gray, CI hdl, lg 95.00
Coffeepot, gray, pewter lid, 13x11", M 255.00
Coffeepot, gray, pewter lid & trim, 9½" 250.00
Coffeepot, gray, 2-cup, M 95.00
Coffeepot, gray, 4-cup, lg, M 70.00
Coffeepot, gray mottle, w/screw-on lid, NM 195.00
Coffeepot, lt bl speckled, NM 295.00
Colander, bl & wht swirl, wht int, collar base, hdls 275.00
Colander, gray, dbl-ped ft, lg, NM 55.00
Colander, gray, teardrop form, ring on bk, rare, VG 215.00
Colander, gray mottle, star piercing .65.00
Colander, robin's egg bl swirl, EX 235.00
Colander, sky bl, wht int, hdls, NM .145.00

Comb case, gray, 7½" long, VG+, $595.00.

Cream can, green and white, 1-pint, $35.00.

Cream can, bl & wht swirl, 1-qt, NM 175.00
Creamer, gray & wht mottle, rare, 5½", NM 210.00
Creamer, wht w/red trim, 6", NM 55.00
Dbl boiler, blk & wht lg swirl, 3-pc, rare 295.00
Dbl boiler, cream & gr, hdls, w/lid, rare, 8x9" dia 65.00
Dbl boiler, crysolite swirl, M 325.00
Dipper, gray mottle 23.00
Dipper, wht w/red trim 21.00
Dust pan, red, VG 195.00
Egg poacher, bl, wht int, EX 125.00
Egg poacher, gray, w/lid, hdls, 6 indents, complete, NM 185.00
Fish poacher, gray mottle, w/lid & hdld insert, NM 215.00
Flask, cobalt, porc stopper, M 165.00
Funnel, cobalt, EX 28.00
Funnel, fruit jar filler; cobalt & wht swirl, rare 175.00
Funnel, gray, bulbous 22.00
Funnel, sky bl, wht int, side hdl, sm, NM 30.00
Grater, sky bl, curved, oblong, open loop hdl, M 125.00
Grater, wht, Perfect, w/wood pusher, clamp-on style 65.00
Kettle, gr speckled, hdls, w/lid, 6-qt .22.00
Kettle, gray, wooden bail, lg 32.00
Kettle, robin's egg bl speckled, 6-qt, EX 40.00
Ladle, cream & gr, M 23.00
Ladle, wht, pierced, EX 65.00
Measure, gray mottle, 1-cup 85.00
Mold, corn, gray w/corn imprint, M .190.00
Mold, octagonal, cobalt, M 85.00
Mold, tube cake; bl & wht lg swirl, VG 235.00
Mug, childs; brn 35.00
Mug, cobalt & wht lg swirl, NM 60.00
Mug, mush; bl & wht mottle, 7½x6", VG 115.00
Pail, water; bl & wht swirl, M 165.00
Pail, water; cobalt & wht swirl, lg, EX 175.00
Pail, water; cobalt & wht swirl, sm .190.00
Pan, angel food cake; gray mottle, rnd, EX 40.00
Pan, baking; cobalt & wht swirl, rectangular, M 135.00
Pan, cake; crysolite swirl, NM 85.00
Pan, milk; gr & wht swirl, NM 85.00
Pan, milk; gray mottle, 2½x11" 25.00
Pan, muffin; cobalt & wht swirl, 8-cup, NM 235.00
Pan, pie; bl & wht swirl, VG 35.00
Pan, pudding; gr & wht marbleized, 7", EX 75.00
Pan, pudding; gray mottle, 9", EX 20.00

Pan, sauce; teal bl speckled, w/lid, mini 50.00
Pan, tube; gray, 11½", NM 45.00
Pitcher, bl & wht swirl, 12", NM 170.00
Pitcher, gray & wht mottle, water sz 85.00
Pitcher, sky bl, wht int, sm, G 70.00
Pitcher, turq & wht swirl, milk sz, 9½", NM 175.00
Pitcher & bowl set, turq & wht swirl, 2-pc, NM 245.00
Plate, cobalt, dinner sz 22.00
Plate, cobalt & wht swirl, M, 9" 80.00
Plate, gray, luncheon sz, M 25.00
Plate, lt gr w/dk gr trim, dinner sz, M 30.00
Rack, lid; bl 125.00
Rack, onion; gray speckled, M 120.00
Rack, utensil; gray, w/3 utensils, M 265.00
Rack, utensil; wht 125.00
Roaster, bl, Savory, 9x18x12", M 45.00
Roaster, bl & wht lg swirl, VG 195.00
Roaster, brn & wht swirl, w/lid, hdls, lg, 3-pc, NM ...265.00
Roaster, gr & wht mottle, VG 225.00
Salt box, azure bl, M 110.00
Skillet, cobalt & wht marbleized, 8", M 165.00
Skillet, egg frying; wht, mini 75.00
Skillet, gray, 8½" 65.00
Skimmer, sky bl, triangular holes, flat/oblong, w/hdl, NM 140.00
Soap dish, gray swirl, EX 30.00
Spatula, wht, M 35.00
Spoon, wht w/red hdl, 16", NM 15.00
Sugar shaker, wht trimmed in gr, rare, M 195.00
Syrup, med bl, M 145.00
Tea strainer, sky bl, perforated bottom, NM 125.00
Teakettle, bl & wht marbleized, EX 275.00
Teakettle, bl & wht mottle, gooseneck spout, lg 235.00
Teakettle, cobalt & wht swirl, NM 285.00
Teakettle, cobalt swirl over CI, re-dipped, NM 135.00
Teapot, bl & wht w/eagle 38.00
Teapot, cream & gr, 4-cup, M 65.00
Teapot, gray mottle, gooseneck, sm, 4-cup, NM 50.00
Teapot, red & wht marbleized, blk-trimmed hdl, old, 8", NM ..950.00
Teapot, solid brn, blk trim, 3-cup 45.00
Teapot, turq & wht swirl, gooseneck spout, sm, VG 175.00
Tumbler, azure bl, w/label, VG 135.00
Wash pan, gray, hdls, 15" dia 30.00
Washboard, cobalt, Imperial 70.00

Green and Ivory

Green and ivory are the colors of a type of country pottery decorated with in-mold designs very similar to those of the more familiar blue and white wares. It is unmarked and was produced from about 1910 to 1935 by many manufacturers as part of their staple line of kitchenwares.

Bowl, Daisy & Waffle, 10" 45.00
Bowl, Reverse Pyramid & Picket Fence, set of 4 ....175.00
Bowl, Wedding Ring, 10" 40.00
Butter crock, Daisy & Waffle, w/lid 95.00
Mug, Grape 40.00
Pitcher, Basketweave & Morning-Glory, rope hdl, 9" 150.00
Pitcher, Cow, EX color & detail, 7½" 125.00
Pitcher, Cow, graduated set of 3, NM 325.00
Pitcher, Flying Birds, top & bottom gr 150.00
Pitcher, Indian Head in War bonnet, waffle body, 8½", NM ...150.00
Pitcher, Pine Cone, 9" 135.00
Pitcher, Rose on Trellis, lg 95.00

Pitcher, Apricot, 8", $125.00.

Spittoon, Cosmos, 6" 75.00
Spittoon, Waffle & Grape, salesman's sample, 2" 75.00
Toothpick holder, Swan 25.00
Umbrella stand, Irises, 20" 250.00

Green Opaque

Introduced in 1887 by the New England Glass Company, this ware is very scarce due to the fact that it was produced for less than one year. It is characterized by its soft green color and a wavy band of gold reserving a mottled blue metallic stain. It is usually found in satin; examples with a shiny finish are extremely rare.

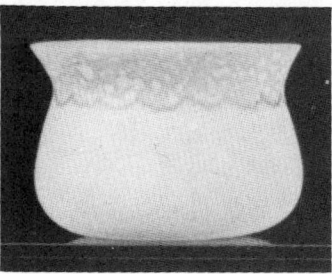

Bowl, 4", $275.00.

Bowl, deep, 4" dia 275.00
Cruet, tricorn, 5½" 1,000.00
Shakers, squat form, EX mottling, 2¾", pr 475.00
Spooner, fine mottling & gold, 4½" 650.00
Tumbler, fine mottling & gold 450.00
Tumbler, Optic Ribs, fine mottling, gold border 575.00
Vase, gold border, 3¾x4⅛" 650.00

Greenaway, Kate

Kate Greenaway was an English artist who lived from 1846 to 1901. She gained world-wide fame as an illustrator of children's books, drawing children clothed in the styles worn by proper English and American boys and girls of the very early 1800s. Her book, *Under the Willow Tree*, published in 1878, was the first of many. Her sketches appeared in leading magazines, and her greeting cards were in great demand. Manufacturers of china, pottery, and metal products copied her characters to decorate children's dishes, tiles, and salt and pepper shakers as well as many other items. See also Almanacs; Napkin Rings; Sewing.

Book, Birthday Book for Children, EX 75.00
Book, Kate Greenaway Biography, 1905, EX 225.00
Book, Mother Goose, Greenaway illus, Rutledge, NY, 48-pg 80.00
Butter pat, children playing 35.00
Cup & saucer, pk lustre 125.00
Engraving, Harper's Bazaar, Jan 1879, full-pg 25.00
Figurine, boy w/basket, porc, 1893 mk, 8½x4" 525.00

Jewel box, brass filigree, 6" diameter, $375.00.

Plate, ABC, girl in lg hat, Staffordshire, 7" 85.00
Toothpick holder, girl sits on stump, basket on bk, bsk 40.00
Toothpick holder, 2 girls sit beside basket, glass 85.00

Greentown Glass

Greentown glass is a term refering to the product of the the Indiana Tumbler and Goblet Company of Greentown, Indiana, ca 1894 to 1903. Their earlier pressed glass patterns were #1, a pseudo-cut glass design; #137, Pleat Band; and #200, Austrian. Another line, Dewey, was designed in 1898. Many lovely colors were produced in addition to crystal. Jacob Rosenthal, who was later affiliated with Fenton, developed his famous chocolate glass in 1900. The rich shaded opaque brown glass was an overnight success. Two new patterns, Leaf Bracket and Cactus, were designed to display the glass to its best advantage, but previously existing molds were also used. In only three years, Rosenthal developed yet another important color formula, golden agate. The Holly Amber pattern was designed especially for its production. The Dolphin covered dish with a fish finial is perhaps the most common and easily-recognized piece ever produced. Other animal dishes were also made; all are highly collectible. There have been many repros — not all are marked! See the Pattern Glass section for clear pressed glass, only colored items are listed here. See also Chocolate Glass; Animal Dishes with Covers.

Austrian, bowl, rectangular, canary, 8" L 130.00
Austrian, compote, canary 125.00
Austrian, cordial, canary 130.00
Austrian, sugar bowl, w/lid, chocolate, 2½" 145.00
Brazen Shield, goblet, bl 100.00
Brazen Shield, sauce dish, bl, 4⅜" 35.00
Brazen Shield, spooner, bl 78.00
Brazen Shield, water set, bl, 7-pc 450.00

Cactus, butter dish, chocolate 190.00
Cactus, butter dish, ped ft, chocolate 540.00
Cactus, compote, chocolate, 9¼" 225.00
Cactus, cracker jar, chocolate 230.00
Cactus, cruet, chocolate, w/stopper 175.00
Cactus, nappy, chocolate, hdls 135.00
Cactus, plate, chocolate, 7½" 95.00
Cactus, sauce, ftd, chocolate 40.00
Cactus, spooner 98.00
Cactus, syrup, w/metal lid, chocolate 175.00
Cactus, toothpick holder, chocolate .65.00
Cactus, tumbler, chocolate 50.00
Cord Drapery, bowl, fluted, emerald gr, 6" 135.00
Cord Drapery, butter dish, emerald gr, 4¾" 175.00
Cord Drapery, cake plate, ftd, amber 150.00
Cord Drapery, pitcher, water; emerald gr 225.00
Cord Drapery, spooner, cobalt 100.00
Cord Drapery, syrup, chocolate 190.00
Cord Drapery, tumbler, cobalt 125.00
Cupid, butter dish, wht opaque 90.00
Cupid, creamer, chocolate 300.00
Cupid, spooner, Nile gr 280.00
Cupid, sugar bowl, w/lid, wht opaque 100.00
Daisy, butter dish, wht opaque 60.00
Daisy, mustard, w/lid, emerald gr frost 75.00
Daisy, sugar bowl, open, chocolate 100.00
Dewey, butter dish, canary, lg 90.00
Dewey, butter dish, emerald gr, 4" .70.00
Dewey, creamer, emerald gr, 5" 70.00
Dewey, cruet, amber 135.00
Dewey, cruet, emerald gr 145.00
Dewey, pitcher, amber 110.00
Dewey, pitcher, water; canary 135.00
Dewey, spooner, chocolate 195.00
Dewey, sugar bowl, chocolate 100.00

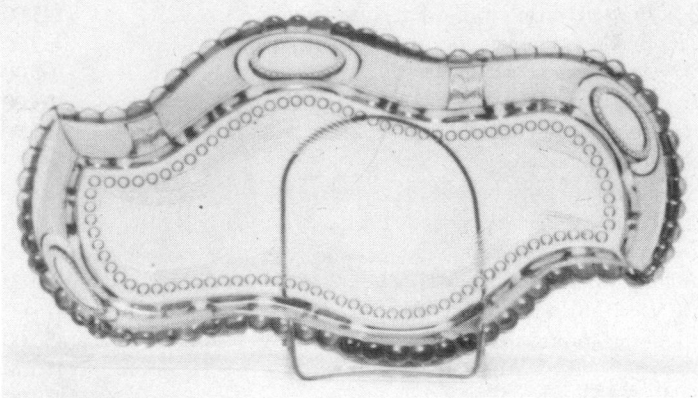

Dewey serpentine tray in amber, large, $75.00.

Dewey, tray, serpentine, emerald gr, sm 50.00
Dewey, tumbler, amber 50.00
Dish, covered; cat on hamper, cobalt, 4½" 295.00
Dish, covered; dolphin, beaded edge, chocolate 195.00
Dish, covered; dolphin, smooth edge, chocolate 300.00
Dish, covered; hen on nest, canary .225.00
Dish, covered; hen on nest, chocolate 400.00
Dish, covered; rabbit, amber 135.00
Early Diamond, pitcher, emerald gr 150.00
Early Diamond, tumbler, chocolate 145.00
Fleur-de-lis, butter dish, chocolate .500.00
Fleur-de-lis, creamer, chocolate 145.00

Fleur-de-lis, spooner, chocolate 160.00
Fleur-de-lis, tumbler, chocolate 100.00
Herringbone Buttress, bowl, emerald gr, 6" 140.00
Herringbone Buttress, cruet, emerald gr 265.00
Herringbone Buttress, sauce dish, emerald gr 70.00
Herringbone Buttress, wine, emerald gr 160.00
Holly Amber, bowl, rectangular, 4x10" 900.00
Holly Amber, bowl, 8½" 600.00
Holly Amber, butter dish 1,400.00
Holly Amber, cake stand 2,400.00
Holly Amber, compote, open, 4½" dia 850.00
Holly Amber, compote, w/lid, 12x8½" 1,800.00
Holly Amber, compote, w/lid, 4½" dia 950.00
Holly Amber, creamer 595.00
Holly Amber, cruet, 6½" 1,850.00
Holly Amber, mug, rare size, 4½" 535.00
Holly Amber, nappy, hdld 465.00
Holly Amber, plate, 7¼" 650.00
Holly Amber, relish, hdls 300.00
Holly Amber, sauce, 3½" 220.00
Holly Amber, sauce, 4¼" 250.00
Holly Amber, shakers, orig caps, 3¼", pr 550.00
Holly Amber, sugar bowl, w/lid 750.00
Holly Amber, syrup, SP hinged lid, 5¾" 900.00
Holly Amber, toothpick holder, sm 375.00
Holly Amber, tumbler, beaded rim 525.00
Holly Amber, tumbler, plain rim 350.00
Holly Amber, vase, 6" 550.00
Leaf Bracket, bowl, chocolate, 8" 80.00
Leaf Bracket, butter dish, chocolate 145.00
Leaf Bracket, celery tray, chocolate, 11" 100.00
Leaf Bracket, creamer, chocolate 85.00
Leaf Bracket, cruet, chocolate 185.00
Leaf Bracket, pitcher, chocolate 385.00
Leaf Bracket, relish, oval, chocolate, 7¼" 85.00
Leaf Bracket, salt shaker, chocolate 90.00
Leaf Bracket, sugar bowl, w/lid, chocolate 145.00
Leaf Bracket, tumbler, chocolate 55.00
Novelty, Dewey Bust, amber 160.00
Novelty, Indian Head, clear 165.00
Novelty, Mitted Hand, Nile gr 385.00
Novelty, skillet, Nile gr 380.00
Novelty, trunk, wht opaque 135.00
Novelty, wheelbarrow, amber 120.00
Pitcher, Heron, chocolate 450.00
Pitcher, Ruffled Eye, amber 130.00
Pitcher, Ruffled Eye, chocolate 475.00
Pitcher, Running Deer, chocolate 450.00
Pitcher, Squirrel, chocolate 450.00
Scalloped Flange, vase, chocolate 70.00
Scalloped Flange, vase, Nile gr 225.00
Shuttle, butter dish, chocolate 800.00
Shuttle, creamer, chocolate 400.00
Shuttle, nappy, chocolate 150.00
Shuttle, punch cup, chocolate 95.00
Shuttle, sugar bowl, w/lid, chocolate 485.00
Shuttle, tumbler, chocolate 80.00
Stein, deer & oak tree, chocolate 400.00
Stein, indoor drinking scene, chocolate, 5" 160.00
Stein, indoor drinking scene, Nile gr, 5¾" 90.00
Stein, outdoor drinking scene, chocolate 135.00
Stein, outdoor drinking scene, Nile gr 120.00
Teardrop & Tassel, butter dish, wht opaque 125.00
Teardrop & Tassel, goblet, emerald gr 200.00

Teardrop & Tassel, pickle dish, chocolate 250.00

Teardrop and Tassel pitcher in cobalt, 8½", $165.00.

Teardrop & Tassel, sauce dish, chocolate, 4½" 165.00
Teardrop & Tassel, spooner, cobalt 80.00
Teardrop & Tassel, spooner, Nile gr 150.00
Teardrop & Tassel, tumbler, cobalt 55.00
Toothpick holder, dog's head, Nile gr 150.00
Toothpick holder, picture fr, teal bl 275.00
Toothpick holder, sheaf of wheat, amber 160.00
Toothpick holder, witch's head, Nile gr 110.00
Tumbler, Uneeda Milk Biscuit, chocolate 120.00

Grueby

William Henry Grueby joined the firm of the Low Art Tile Works at the age of fifteen; and in 1894, after several years of experience in the production of architectural tiles, founded his own plant, the Grueby Faience Company, in Boston, Massachusetts. Grueby began experimenting with the idea of producing art pottery and had soon perfected a fine glaze — soft and without gloss — in shades of blue, gray, yellow, brown, and his most successful, cucumber green. In 1900 his exhibit at the Paris Exposition Universelle won him three gold medals.

Grueby pottery was hand thrown and hand decorated in the Arts and Crafts style. Vertically-thrust stylized leaves and flowers in relief were the most common decorative devices. Tiles continued to be an important product — unique (due to the matt glaze decoration) as well as durable. Grueby tiles were often a full inch thick. Obviously incompatible with the Art Nouveau style, the artware was discontinued soon after 1910. The ware is marked in one of several ways: 'Grueby Pottery, Boston, USA'; 'Grueby, Boston, Mass.'; or 'Grueby Faience.' The artware is often artist signed.

Bowl, swirl, gr gloss, 1¼x8" 285.00
Paperweight, scarab form, bl/yel mottle 225.00
Tile, galleon, brn/yel w/wht sails on 2-tone bl, sgn EH, 8" 850.00
Tile, horses, wht on gr grass, bl sky, sgn KC, 6x6" 450.00
Tile, lily pads, lt/dk gr on red clay, 2-part, 6x12" 475.00
Vase, butterscotch, leaves & buds, sgn WP, bulbous, 7x9" ...6,500.00
Vase, cream, buds/stems/leaves in yel, crimped, AB, 4½" 1,900.00
Vase, dk gr, leaves/buds, gourd form, sgn IP, 7½" 1,100.00
Vase, dk gr w/feathering, leaves at bulbous bottom, 10½" 2,500.00
Vase, gr, Arts & Crafts design, minor prof rpr, 9½" 600.00
Vase, gr, daffodils/leaves in yel/lav/bl, sgn LEH, rpr, 11" 3,700.00

Vase, gr, leaves, upright in high relief, 5½" 800.00
Vase, gr, leaves at base+7 yel trefoils at top, sgn RE, 13" 2,200.00
Vase, gr, leaves on bottom, artist sgn/dtd, 6½" 700.00
Vase, gr, leaves w/buds extending upward, W Post, 8" 900.00
Vase, gr, leaves/buds, trilobe top, Faience/WP, 8x4" 1,250.00
Vase, gr, leaves/buds in yel, sgn EF, 10x7½" 2,500.00
Vase, gr, lotus leaves around swollen base, sgn MS, 4¾x6" 600.00
Vase, gr, row of 7 tooled leaves, collared, 1902, 9x7" 1,750.00
Vase, gr, tooled melon ribbing, collared, 5½x4" 500.00
Vase, gr, 3 rows of tooled/appl petals+5 buds, MS, 14x8½" . .2,300.00
Vase, gr, 4 encircling tooled leaves, collared, 3x4" 700.00
Vase, gr, 7 red buds alternate w/wide leaves, Faience, 7x8" . .5,000.00
Vase, gr, 7 yel trefoils+7 rnded leaves, bulb base, 12x10" 3,000.00
Vase, gr w/feathering, 9 lt melon ribs, Faience, 16x10" 3,000.00

Vase, green with upright leaves in a lighter tone, signed DS, dated 1901, 9", $1,750.00.

Vase, mauve, leaves, closed neck, Faience/156, 5½x6½" 1,900.00
Vase, yel, 3 groups of slim gr leaves, sgn ER/dtd, 9" 2,000.00

Gutta Percha

Gutta Percha is the plastic substance from the latex of several types of Malaysian trees. It resembles rubber but contains more resin. A patent for the use of this material in manufacturing an early type of plastic was issued in the 1850s, and it was used extensively for daguerreotype cases and picture frames. Numbers in the following listings refer to *American Miniature Case Art* by Rinhart, an excellent reference that is now out of print. When found, copies of this book usually sell for $100.00 to $150.00.

Our advisor for this category is Roberta Etter; she is listed in the Directory under England.

Case, children, lady & pets, 4¾x3", EX 125.00
Case, half-plate, Agriculture/Industry, women/trumpets, NM . .200.00
Case, half-plate, Holy Family, EX 100.00
Case, 16th plate, Am Indian head, tintype w/in 75.00
Case, 4th plate, Country Dance, NM .225.00
Case, 4th plate, Gypsy Fortune Teller, Rinhart #46 . . . . .80.00
Case, 4th plate, hanging floral urn, tintype w/in 70.00
Case, 4th plate, Tryst 80.00
Case, 4th-plate, shield w/eagle/cannons/flags, M 95.00
Case, 6th plate, Calmady Children, Rinhart #42, EX 70.00
Case, 6th plate, geometrics, Rinhart #180 . . . . .50.00

Case, 6th plate, Masonic symbols, VG 40.00
Case, 6th plate, Monitor & Fort, M 125.00
Case, 6th plate, Proud Elk, Rinhart #82, EX 75.00
Case, 6th plate, scallop shell, Rinhart #171, VG 50.00
Case, 6th-plate, floral, lava cameo in center, M 125.00
Case, 6th-plate, lady in Daguerreian Gallery, w/dag 90.00
Case, 9th plate, Chess Players, EX 50.00
Case, 9th plate, jewel motif, VG 20.00
Case, 9th-plate, CW Union, shield/flags w/13 stars, Scovill 60.00
Necklace, lg links, 20" +2½" rose pendant 55.00
Token, Jefferson bust, Union Coffee, NY, 1½" 22.00

Case, Indian Chief, sixth-plate, $100.00.

Hair Weaving

A rather unusual craft became popular during the mid-1800s. Human hair was used to make jewelry (rings, bracelets, lockets, etc.) by braiding and interlacing fine strands of hair into hollow forms with pearls and beads added for effect. Hair wreaths were also made, often using hair from deceased family members as well as the living. They were displayed in deep satin-lined frames along with mementoes of the weaver or her departed kin. The fad was abandoned before the turn of the century. See also Mourning Collectibles.

Necklace with pendant cross, $100.00.

Box, patch; ivory & gold, braid under glass, rose gold mts 295.00
Bracelet, 14k fittings, eng Ophelia, orig box 115.00
Braid, ¾" braid w/15k fittings, amethyst in clasp 250.00

Brooch, glass over braid, 32 seed pearls in gold fr, 1⅛" 60.00
Brooch, hair flowers under crystal, 18k w/2 rows of pearls 475.00
Brooch, oval w/2 drop hair acorns, gold twist cartwheel 60.00
Brooch/earrings, hairwork disks w/14k wirework overlay 475.00
Charm, hair anchor w/gold wire spiral around shaft, 1½" 75.00
Fob, lyre of openwork tubing w/gold-filled fittings, ⅞" 55.00
Necklace, w/sm compass, So Turns My Heart to Thee, MIB ...125.00
Ring, 14k, blk enamel around monogram, intricate engraving .225.00
Scarf pin, horseshoe hair tube w/gold-on-brass mts, 1880s 65.00
Wreath, blonde hair in walnut shadow box, pk satin lined, EX .250.00
Wreath, flowers/bird, shadow box fr, shirred lining, 24x26" ...200.00
Wreath, varied hair forms basket in center, in shadow box fr ...185.00

Hall

The Hall China Company of East Liverpool, Ohio, was established in 1903. Their earliest product was whiteware toilet seats, mugs, jugs, etc. By 1920 their restaurant-type dinnerware and cookingware had become so successful that Hall was assured of a solid future. They continue today to be one of the country's largest manufacturers of this type of product.

Hall introduced the first of their famous teapots in 1920; new shapes and colors were added each year until about 1948, making them the largest teapot manufacturer in the world. These and the dinnerware lines of the thirties through the fifties have become popular collectibles. For more thorough study of the subject, we recommend *Hall China* by Margaret and Kenn Whitmyer; their address may be found in the Directory under Ohio.

Acacia, bean pot, New England, #4 ....65.00
Acacia, casserole, Radiance 28.00
Acacia, jug, w/lid, Radiance, #3 ....55.00

Basketball teapot, ultramarine, $295.00.

Batter bowl, Five Band, red 38.00
Batter jug, Sundial, red 55.00
Blue Blossom, batter jug, Sundial 125.00
Blue Blossom, bean pot, New England, #4 ....125.00
Blue Blossom, bowl, thick rim, 8½" 30.00
Blue Blossom, butter dish, Zephyr style 175.00
Blue Blossom, casserole, Sundial, #1 ....35.00
Blue Blossom, cookie jar, Five Band 125.00
Blue Blossom, jug, #2, ball 50.00

Blue Blossom, teapot, Streamline 150.00
Blue Blossom, teapot, Sundial 150.00
Blue Bouquet, bowl, #3, Radiance, 6" 8.00
Blue Bouquet, bowl, flared, 7¾" 20.00
Blue Bouquet, bowl, soup; flat, 8½" 11.00
Blue Bouquet, bowl, thick rim, 7½" 15.00
Blue Bouquet, bowl, vegetable; 9¼" 18.00
Blue Bouquet, casserole, Radiance 28.00
Blue Bouquet, coffeepot, Five Band 46.00
Blue Bouquet, creamer, modern 7.00
Blue Bouquet, drip jar, thick rim 17.00
Blue Bouquet, gravy boat 22.00
Blue Bouquet, jug, #3, ball 28.00
Blue Bouquet, plate, 8¼" 6.00
Blue Bouquet, platter, oval, 13¼" 17.00
Blue Bouquet, sugar bowl w/lid, modern 12.00
Blue Garden, casserole, Sundial, #4 ....24.00
Blue Garden, sugar bowl, w/lid, morning 26.00
Blue Garden, teapot, New York 95.00
Blue Willow, teapot, Boston 45.00
Bowl, Five Band, cobalt, 8¾" 11.00
Bowl, Radiance, ivory, 10" 8.00
Bowl, Radiance, red, 3½" 4.00
Cactus, batter bowl, Five Band 35.00
Cactus, coffeepot, Five Band 24.00
Cactus, coffeepot, Viking 26.00
Cactus, jug, Five Band, 2-qt 48.00
Cactus, stack set, Radiance 50.00
Cameo Rose, bowl, cereal; tab hdl, 6¼" 8.00
Cameo Rose, bowl, soup; flat, 8" 8.00
Cameo Rose, bowl, vegetable; rnd, 9" 14.00
Cameo Rose, casserole 30.00
Cameo Rose, gravy boat, w/tray 18.00
Cameo Rose, plate, 8" 4.50
Cameo Rose, platter, 13¼" 15.00
Cameo Rose, sugar bowl, w/lid 13.00
Cameo Rose, teapot, 6-cup 35.00
Canister, Radiance, ivory, 2-qt 20.00
Carafe, Five Band, cobalt 75.00
Clover, casserole, Radiance 28.00
Clover, shakers, w/hdl, ea 14.00
Clover, teapot, Windshield 75.00
Coffee server, Sundial, cobalt 115.00
Coffeepot, Five Band, cobalt 38.00
Cookie jar, red, Banded 45.00
Cookie jar, Sundial, red 100.00
Crocus, bowl, fruit; 5½" 3.00
Crocus, bowl, Radiance, #4, 7½" 12.00
Crocus, bowl, soup; flat, 8½" 11.00
Crocus, bowl, vegetable; rnd, 9" 15.00
Crocus, cake plate 16.00
Crocus, coffeepot, Medallion 38.00
Crocus, creamer, Medallion 10.00
Crocus, drip jar, open, #1188 ....28.00
Crocus, gravy boat 20.00
Crocus, pie plate 18.00
Crocus, plate, 8¼" 4.00
Crocus, platter, oval, 13¼" 15.00
Crocus, sugar bowl, w/lid, Medallion 12.00
Crocus, teapot, Medallion 24.00
Crocus, water bottle, Zephyr style 100.00
Fantasy, batter jug, Sundial 100.00
Fantasy, casserole, Sundial 32.00
Heather Rose, bowl, salad 10.00

Heather Rose, bowl, sauce; 5¼" 3.00
Heather Rose, bowl, vegetable; w/lid 14.00
Heather Rose, coffeepot, Terrace 25.00
Heather Rose, milk jug 12.00
Heather Rose, plate, 10" 4.00
Heather Rose, platter, 15½" 12.00
Heather Rose, sugar bowl, w/lid 8.00
Meadow Flower, casserole, Radiance 30.00
Meadow Flower, cookie jar, Five Band 75.00
Morning Glory, bowl, 6" 8.00
Morning Glory, drip coffee 65.00
Mt Vernon, bowl, cereal; tab hdl 5.00
Mt Vernon, bowl, sauce; 5¼" 3.00
Mt Vernon, bowl, soup; flat 5.00
Mt Vernon, bowl, vegetable; w/lid 12.00
Mt Vernon, plate, 10" 4.00
Mt Vernon, tureen, w/lid 18.00
Mums, bowl, soup; flat, 8½" 10.00
Mums, casserole, Medallion 32.00
Mums, custard, Radiance, #1 ....6.00
Mums, platter, oval, 11¼" 16.00
Mums, stack set, Radiance 55.00
Orange Poppy, bowl, fruit; 5½" 4.00
Orange Poppy, bowl, Radiance, #6, 10" 25.00
Orange Poppy, bowl, salad; 9" 12.00
Orange Poppy, cake plate 12.00
Orange Poppy, canister set, 4-pc, metal 38.00
Orange Poppy, casserole, oval, 11¼" 70.00
Orange Poppy, casserole, w/lid, rnd, #76 ....28.00
Orange Poppy, coffeepot, S-lid 38.00
Orange Poppy, cookie jar, pretzel hdl 65.00
Orange Poppy, jug, Radiance, #4 ....25.00
Orange Poppy, plate, 7" 4.50
Orange Poppy, platter, oval, 13¼" 17.00
Orange Poppy, shakers, hdls, ea 8.00
Orange Poppy, soap dispenser, metal 33.00
Orange Poppy, teapot, Bellvue 90.00
Orange Poppy, teapot, Doughnut 90.00
Orange Poppy, teapot, Streamline 65.00
Pastel Morning Glory, bowl, fruit; 5½" 4.00
Pastel Morning Glory, bowl, soup; flat, 8½" 28.00
Pastel Morning Glory, bowl, vegetable; oval 15.00
Pastel Morning Glory, bowl, vegetable; rnd, 9" 15.00
Pastel Morning Glory, casserole, Radiance 25.00
Pastel Morning Glory, jug, #3, ball 25.00
Pastel Morning Glory, jug, w/lid, Radiance, 5" 55.00
Pastel Morning Glory, plate, 8¼" 4.50
Reamer, Medallion, lettuce gr 300.00
Red Poppy, bowl, cereal; 6" 7.00
Red Poppy, bowl, Radiance, #3, 6" 10.00
Red Poppy, bowl, Radiance, #5, 9" 16.00
Red Poppy, bowl, salad; 9" 12.00
Red Poppy, bowl, soup; flat, 8½" 10.00
Red Poppy, bowl, vegetable; oval, 10¼" 18.00
Red Poppy, bowl covers, plastic, set of 8 ....35.00
Red Poppy, cake safe, metal 24.00
Red Poppy, canister set, rnd, 4-pc 32.00
Red Poppy, coffeepot, Daniel 22.00
Red Poppy, custard, Radiance 4.00
Red Poppy, drip jar, open, #1188 ....22.00
Red Poppy, gravy boat 18.00
Red Poppy, jug, #3, ball 26.00
Red Poppy, plate, 9¼" 6.00
Red Poppy, platter, oval, 11¼" 14.00

Red Poppy, shakers, hdld, ea 8.00
Red Poppy, sugar bowl, w/lid, Daniel 8.00
Red Poppy, tablecloth, cotton 65.00
Red Poppy, teapot, New York 40.00
Red Poppy, tray, metal, rectangular 17.00
Red Poppy, tumbler, frosted glass 10.00
Red Poppy, waste can, rnd, cone shape, metal 24.00
Red Poppy, waste can, step-on, metal 30.00
Richmond, bowl, soup; flat 5.00
Richmond, bowl, vegetable; oval 7.00
Richmond, jug, Radiance 10.00
Rose Parade, bowl, salad; 9" 16.00
Rose Parade, casserole, tab hdl 20.00
Rose Parade, drip jar, tab hdl 16.00
Rose Parade, jug, Pert, 5" 16.00
Rose Parade, teapot, Pert, 4-cup 24.00
Rose White, bean pot, tab hdl 36.00
Rose White, bowl, #5, 9" 12.00
Rose White, custard 7.00
Rose White, jug, Pert, 6½" 16.00
Royal Rose, bowl, thick rim, 7½" 14.00
Royal Rose, casserole, thick rim 20.00
Royal Rose, drip jar, thick rim 16.00
Royal Rose, jug, #3, ball 28.00
Serenade, bowl, fruit; 5½" 3.00
Serenade, bowl, Radiance, #3, 6" 7.00
Serenade, bowl, Radiance, #5, 9" 12.00
Serenade, bowl, salad; 9" 10.00
Serenade, bowl, soup; flat, 8½" 9.00
Serenade, coffeepot, Terrace 28.00
Serenade, gravy boat 18.00
Serenade, platter, 13¼" 14.00
Serenade, pretzel jar 50.00
Serenade, saucer 1.00
Shaggy Tulip, stack set, Radiance 65.00
Shaggy Tulip, teapot, Radiance 90.00
Silhouette, bowl, flared, 7¾" 18.00
Silhouette, bowl, fruit; 5½" 4.50
Silhouette, bowl, Medallion, #3, 6" 12.00
Silhouette, bowl, Medallion, #5, 8½" 18.00
Silhouette, bowl, Radiance, #5, 9" 28.00
Silhouette, bowl, soup; flat, 8½" 12.00
Silhouette, bowl, vegetable; rnd, 9" 15.00
Silhouette, bread box, metal 70.00
Silhouette, canister set, metal, 4-pc 40.00
Silhouette, casserole, Medallion 28.00
Silhouette, coffeepot, Medallion 32.00
Silhouette, drip jar, Medallion 16.00
Silhouette, jug, Simplicity 65.00
Silhouette, plate, 8¼" 6.00
Silhouette, platter, oval, 11¼" 14.00
Silhouette, pretzel jar 65.00
Silhouette, shakers, Five Band, ea 8.00
Silhouette, sugar bowl, w/lid, Medallion 12.00
Silhouette, teapot, New York 65.00
Silhouette, tray, oval, metal 28.00
Silhouette, whisk, wooden hdl 25.00
Springtime, bowl, cereal; 6" 6.00
Springtime, bowl, rnd, 9" 15.00
Springtime, gravy boat 16.00
Springtime, jug, Radiance, #6 ....26.00
Springtime, pie plate 14.00
Springtime, platter, oval, 11¼" 14.00
Teapot, Adele, maroon 65.00

Teapot, Aladdin, Chinese red, oval infuser 65.00
Teapot, Aladdin, pk, swag, gold label 38.00
Teapot, Automobile, cobalt 350.00
Teapot, Baltimore, gold decor 35.00
Teapot, Boston, gr w/gold, 2-cup 28.00
Teapot, Cleveland, warm yel w/gold 32.00
Teapot, Doughnut, Indian red 250.00
Teapot, Globe, cobalt w/gold 75.00
Teapot, Hollywood, emerald w/gold, 6-cup 32.00
Teapot, Hollywood, marine bl w/gold 38.00
Teapot, Illinois, maroon w/gold 125.00
Teapot, Kansas, emerald gr w/gold 175.00
Teapot, Melody, warm yel 85.00
Teapot, Nautilus, maroon w/gold 85.00
Teapot, New York, wheat/poppy pattern, 6-cup 45.00
Teapot, Philadelphia, cobalt w/gold, 4-cup 35.00
Teapot, Rhythm, Chinese red 95.00
Teapot, Star, cobalt w/gold 85.00
Teapot, Sundial, red, 6-cup 60.00
Teapot, Surfside, gr w/gold 55.00
Tulip, bowl, Radiance, #4, 7½" 10.00
Tulip, bowl, rnd, 9" 16.00
Tulip, bowl, soup; flat, 8½" 10.00
Tulip, bowl, thick rim, 7½" 15.00
Tulip, coffeepot, Perk 35.00
Tulip, gravy boat 18.00
Tulip, plate, 10" 9.00
Tulip, plate, 6" 4.00
Tulip, platter, oval, 13¼" 17.00
Tulip, shakers, hdld, ea 10.00
Wild Poppy, baker, oval 24.00
Wild Poppy, bean pot, New England, #3 . . . . .65.00
Wild Poppy, canister, Radiance 65.00
Wild Poppy, creamer, Hollywood 15.00
Wild Poppy, sugar bowl, w/lid, New York 16.00
Wild Poppy, teapot, Radiance 95.00
Wild Poppy, teapot, 4-cup, New York 65.00
Wildfire, bowl, oval 13.00
Wildfire, bowl, rnd, 9" 15.00
Wildfire, bowl, soup; flat, 8½" 10.00
Wildfire, bowl, thick rim, 8½" 16.00
Wildfire, coffee dispenser, metal 18.00
Wildfire, cup & saucer 7.50
Wildfire, drip jar, thick rim 15.00
Wildfire, gravy boat 16.00
Wildfire, jug, Radiance, #5 . . . . .24.00
Wildfire, plate, 10" 8.00
Wildfire, platter, 13¼" 15.00
Yellow Rose, bowl, cereal; 6" 5.00
Yellow Rose, bowl, soup; flat, 8½" 9.00
Yellow Rose, casserole, Radiance 18.00
Yellow Rose, coffeepot, Norse 38.00
Yellow Rose, creamer, Norse 6.00
Yellow Rose, plate, 6" 3.00
Yellow Rose, plate, 9" 6.00
Yellow Rose, platter, oval, 13¼" 8.00
Yellow Rose, sugar bowl, w/lid, Norse 11.00

Hallmark

In 1973 Hallmark introduced a line of decorated molded-plastic ornaments that have recently become popular with collectors. Also of interest are their ball-type ornaments (especially those issued as part of a series) as well as their small plastic party-type favors now known as Merry Miniatures. A magazine edited by Rosie Wells, our advisor for this category, is available if you want more information; Rosie also publishes a yearly official Secondary Price Guide. Her address is listed in the Directory under Clubs, Newsletters, and Catalogs, and again under Illinois. Items listed below are assumed to be in mint condition and in the original box.

1973, Betsy Clark Musicians, MIB 50.00
1973, Boy Caroler, yarn ornament, M in package 20.00
1973, Elves, glass ball ornament, MIB 40.00
1974, Angel, wht, glass ball ornament, MIB 50.00
1974, Charmers, glass ball ornament, dtd, MIB 30.00
1974, Snowgoose, glass ball ornament, MIB 60.00
1975, Betsy Clark, satin ball ornament, dtd set of 2, MIB 35.00
1975, Currier & Ives, wht satin ornament, dtd, MIB 35.00
1975, Mrs Santa, yarn ornament 17.00
1975, Nostalgia, Rocking Horse, ornament, MIB 155.00
1976, Yesteryears, Locomotive, dtd, MIB 118.00
1977, Peanuts Dog House, glass ball ornament, M in package . . .50.00
1978, Mother, dtd, glass ball ornament, MIB 17.50
1979, Calico Kitty, sewn ornament 5.00
1979, Rocking Horse, cloth trimmer 7.50
1979, Tiffany, Angel, tree topper, MIB 32.50
1980, Frosty Friends, A Cool Yule, 1st ed 455.00
1980, Heavenly Minstrel, special ed .375.00
1981, Rocking Horse, 1st ed 275.00
1981, Snowman chimes, NM 23.00
1982, Cycling Santa, special edition, MIB 90.00
1982, Tree chimes, brass, MIB 29.00
1985, Sugarplum Cottage, lighted ornament 20.00
1985, Village Church, lighted ornament 30.00
1986, Reindeer Champs Dasher, 1st ed 75.00

Halloween

The origin of Halloween can be traced back to the ancient practices of the Druids of Great Britain who began their New Year on the 1st of November. The Druids were pagans and their New Year's celebrations involved pagan rites and superstitions. They believed that as the old year came to an end the Devil would gather up all the demons and evil in the world and take them back to Hell with him. Witches were women who had sold their souls to the Devil and, with their black cat in attendance, flew up through their chimneys on brooms. When the Roman Catholic Church came into power in 700 A.D., they changed the holiday into a religious event called 'All Saints Day,' or 'Allhallows.' The evening before, October 31, became 'Allhallow's Eve' or 'Halloween.' Today Halloween is strictly a fun time, and Halloween items are fun to collect. Pumpkin-head candy containers of papier mache or pressed cardboard, noisemakers, post cards with black cats and witches, costumes, and decorations are only a sampling of the variety available. See also Candy Containers.

Candy container, cat, compo, blk/gray w/yel & red, 4½" 65.00
Candy container, cat, mohair covered, Germany, 1920s, EX . . .235.00
Candy container, goblin, compo, mc, Germany, 2½", EX 95.00
Candy container, goblin on candy box, compo, Germany, 3" . . .95.00
Candy container, pumpkin man, compo, orange/gr, 6" 125.00
Clapper, wood, witch on broom, city skyline, 8¼x4½" 85.00
Costume, jester, orange/blk w/brass bells, 1930s, EX 65.00
Costume, Uncle Sam, cloth, Collegeville Costumes, orig box . . .55.00
Decoration, blk cat, papier-mache, 4" .85.00
Decoration, blk cat musician, diecut, HE Luhrs 15.00
Decoration, blk cat w/arched bk, diecut, Germany, lg 45.00
Decoration, blk cat's head, pressed cb, mk USA, 12x12" 45.00

Decoration, cat w/cymbals, dressed, diecut, Germany, 7½" 45.00
Decoration, Dracula, pressed cb, Japan, 1950s 45.00
Decoration, moon w/cat on nose, diecut cb, Luhrs, USA, 14" ...45.00
Decoration, owl, papier-mache, orange, 3½" 45.00
Decoration, owl, papier-mache, orange/blk, glass eyes, 10" ...110.00
Decoration, owl perched on twig, diecut, Germany, 8½" 45.00
Decoration, owl sits w/in man-in-moon, diecut, 5" dia 45.00
Decoration, owl w/wings wide, diecut, Germany, 15" W 45.00
Decoration, witch, diecut, 16" 50.00
Decoration, witch on pumpkin, papier-mache, 6" 55.00

Pressed paperboard decorations, marked Germany, Pumpkin-head witch and black cat, 16", $65.00; Witch and Man in the Moon, 10", $45.00.

Fan, cat face, paper w/crepe paper trim, 12½" 65.00
Figurine, pumpkin man/witch, papier-mache, Germany, 4", pr ..70.00
Horn, conical, Minnie/Mickey motif, W Disney/Marx Bros, 7" ..45.00
Jack-O'-Lantern, molded cb/paper inserts, Germany, 1900, 5" ..70.00
Jack-O'-Lantern, papier-mache, faces both sides, 10½" 70.00
Jack-O'-Lantern, papier-mache, printed tissue features, 4" 65.00
Jack-O'-Lantern, papier-mache, tissue screen, battery, 7" 65.00
Jack-O'-Lantern, tin litho, owl/moon/bats, 1930s, 5x6" 45.00
Lantern, candle; tin, in cb cat's head, USA, 1920s, 11" 65.00
Lantern, candle; witch/cat/devil tin litho, folding, 9" 65.00
Lantern, skull, milk glass, metal fr, 1920s 45.00
Mask, man's head, molded wire mesh, pnt face, ca 1920, 8" 70.00
Nodder, pumpkin head on log, compo, orange/blk, 6" 485.00
Noisemaker, bentwood w/printed paper heads, MIG, 6¾" 40.00
Noisemaker, orange/blk tin litho, Chein, 5½" dia, 11" L 40.00
Noisemaker, pumpkin, paper, German ratchet style, 8x5x2½" .155.00
Noisemaker, witch/elves/cats, tin litho, Germany 35.00
Punch board, Japan, 3½x2½", NM 45.00
Rattle, face on wood & tissue drum shape, 8" L, EX 55.00
Rattle, witches/cats on tin litho, Gotham, 6x4" dia 35.00
Tambourine, cats/witches on tin, T Cohn USA, 1½x7¼" 45.00
Tambourine, people dance about pumpkin face, tin, 6½" dia ...45.00

Hamada, Shoji

Soji Hamada is the most famous of all Japanese potters. He was a former chemist who worked with Bernard Leach in the 1920s to rediscover the art of Oriental 'rural' pottery. All of Hamada's ceramics were fired in a wood-fired kiln. He used only local clays, oxides, and ash glazes ground by hand. Hamada used a seal mark during the early 1920s when he was at St. Ives, England. After returning to Japan in 1923, his work was never signed. Instead he signed the wooden boxes he used for shipping.

Bottle vase, buff w/rust temmoku, wax-resist leaf, sq, 10" 3,750.00
Bottle vase, dk iron, sq, 7½" 3,000.00
Bottle vase, rust mottle, gr brush strokes, rectangular, 8" 2,000.00
Brush pot, iron pnt leaf, hexagonal, 4" 3,600.00
Pitcher, iron brn, 9½" 4,400.00
Pitcher, oatmeal w/brn brush strokes on red stoneware, 9" ...1,000.00
Plate, wht slip & iron red leaves on gray stoneware, 10" 880.00
Tea bowl, buff, brn flared ft, 5½" 4,400.00
Tea bowl, greenish ash, iron brushwork on stoneware, 4" 1,325.00
Vase, celadon & iron, oval, 7½" 5,600.00
Vase, olive brn, tooled bands, stoneware, 10" 775.00

Hampshire

The Hampshire Pottery Company was established in 1871 in Keene, New Hampshire, by James Scollay Taft. Their earliest products were redware and stoneware utility items such as jugs, churns, crocks, and flowerpots. In 1878 they produced majolica ware which met with such success thay they began to experiment with the idea of manufacturing art pottery. By 1883 they had developed a Royal Worcester type of finish which they applied to vases, tea sets, powder boxes, and cookie jars. It was also utilized for souvenir items that were decorated with transfer designs prepared from photographic plates.

Cadmon Robertson, brother-in-law of Taft, joined the company in 1904 and was responsible for developing their famous matt glazes. Colors included shades of green, brown, red, and blue. Early examples were of earthenware, but eventually the body changed to semi-porcelain. Some of his designs were marked with an M in a circle as a tribute to his wife, Emoretta. Robertson died in 1914, leaving a void impossible to fill. Taft sold the business in 1916 to George Morton, who continued to use the matt glazes that Robertson had developed. After a temporary halt in production during WWI, Morton returned to Keene and re-equipped the factory with the machinery needed to manufacture hotel china and floor tile. Because of the expense involved in transporting coal to fire the kilns, Morton found he could not compete with potteries of Ohio and New Jersey who were able to utilize locally available natural gas. He was forced to close the plant in 1923.

Pitcher, slate blue with pink highlights, leaves and vines form spout and handle, 8", $150.00.

Bowl, Oak Leaf, gr & wht, 3x6" 65.00
Bowl, swastikas emb on gr, 2½x6¾" 40.00
Bowl vase, lily pads at shoulder, gr matt, 6" dia 100.00
Inkwell, cylinder w/front pierced to hold 3 pens, gray-gr 250.00
Pitcher, molded leaves form spout, vine hdls, bl w/pk, 8" 150.00
Plate, Central Square, 8" 25.00
Shaving mug, leafy branches, bl w/gold, scuttle type, 4x4½" . . .65.00
Teapot, butterfly finial, brn, squat ovoid w/D-hdl, 5" 425.00
Vase, bl w/wht touches, #38, 8" 145.00
Vase, feathered drip, gr on dk bl, #95, M in circle, 7½" 150.00
Vase, gr, ball form w/melon-rib panels, #119, 5" 150.00
Vase, gray matt, 8" 125.00
Vase, leaves, gr matt, hdls, ped ft, mk, 8x6" 225.00
Vase, leaves/buds, dk bl, #33, M in circle, 7" 180.00
Vase, leaves/vines wind to ft, gr mottle, trumpet form, 15" 325.00
Vase, oval panels, dk bl matt, #132, 3x5¾" 130.00
Vase, overlapping leaves, bl-gr mottled matt, 8x8" 425.00
Vase, 6 lg leaves alternate w/buds, gr matt, label, 16x9" 600.00

Handel

Chipped and sanded 15" shade #5465, bronzed metal standard, $1,800.00

Philip Handel was best known for the art glass lamps he produced at the turn of the century. His work is similar to the Tiffany lamps of the same era. Handel made gas and electric lamps with both leaded glass and reverse-painted shades. Chipped ice shades with a texture similar to overshot glass were also produced. China and glassware decorated by Handel are rare and command high prices on today's market. Teroma is a term used to describe glassware decorated on the obverse (outside) with paint that has a sandy finish. Many of the chinaware blanks were supplied by Limoges.

Lamps

Boudoir, rvpt daisies on sanded/chipped-ice shade, 13" 1,500.00
Chandelier, 4 Prairie School ldgl lantern drops, 22x22" 2,400.00
Desk, gr chipped-ice shade; base sgn Mosserine #6010, M 800.00
Desk, ldgl 6½" dome brickwork shade; swivel-arm base 1,750.00
Desk, oblong shade w/landscape; patinated metal base, 17" . .1,300.00
Desk, rvpt sailing ship 7" cylinder shade, orig pull, 12" 600.00
Floor, rvpt 10" sanded chipped-ice dbl-parrot sgn FL shade . .8,250.00
Lantern, hex dome over 6 ldgl panels w/tulips, unsgn, 18" . . .5,500.00
Night light, pnt parrots/flowers on acorn shade, 8", VG 350.00
Shade only, wild roses HP on ogee form w/top opening, 12" . . .400.00
Student, 2-arm, cream/red lily-form shades, sgn, 24" 1,400.00
Table, chipped/sanded 15" Dutch windmill shade; metal std .1,800.00
Table, ldgl 18" apple blossom shade; sgn bronze base, 22" . . .6,500.00
Table, pnt/rvpt 14" sanded chipped-ice forest shade; 20" 950.00
Table, pnt/rvpt 18" sanded sunset shade; tree/roots base 2,500.00
Table, rvpt 16" autumn chipped-ice shade; Japan-style base . .2,750.00
Table, rvpt 18" chipped-ice autumn scene shade; sgn std 2,400.00
Table, rvpt 18" chipped-ice Egyptian village sgn shade, 24" . .4,100.00
Table, rvpt 18" landscape scene; patinated std w/dome base . .1,500.00
Table, rvpt 18" sanded floral/bluebird-band shade; 24" 2,750.00
Table, rvpt 18" sanded Treasure Island shade; simple std . . .13,750.00
Table, rvpt 18" sunset scene #6957 shade; acorn pulls, 23" . . .2,700.00
Torchere, rvpt daisies on sanded/chipped-ice cylinder, 16" 700.00

Miscellaneous

Candlestick, windmills, HP by Gubsich, #4213, 8½", pr 1,100.00
Humidor, Dutch scene, gr tones on sanded/chipped ice, 5" . .1,000.00
Humidor, Teroma, tropical seascape w/ship, sgn Bedigie, 9" .3,000.00
Vase, Opal Ware, lilies, mc on aqua-bl, 11" 550.00
Vase, Teroma, mtns/trees, #4210, 8" 1,500.00

Harker

The Harker Pottery was established in East Liverpool, Ohio, in 1840. Their earliest product was yellowware and Rockingham produced from local clay. After 1900 whiteware was made from imported materials. The plant eventually grew to be a large manufacturer of dinnerware and kitchenware, employing as many as three hundred people. It closed in 1972 after it was purchased by the Jeanette Glass Company. Perhaps their best-known lines were their Cameo wares, decorated with white silhouettes in a cameo effect on contrasting solid colors. Floral silhouettes are standard, but other designs were also used. Blue and pink are the most often found background hues; a few pieces are found in yellow.

Bean pot, Amy, ind 4.00
Bowl, Cameo, bl, 8" 8.00
Bowl, Deco Dahlia, 5½" 2.50
Bowl, utility; Amy, 9" 10.00
Cake lifter, Amy 10.00
Casserole, Deco Dahlia, w/lid 15.00
Cup, Deco Dahlia 3.00
Cup & saucer, Cameo, bl, shell form 6.00
Cup & saucer, Chesterson, gray 5.00
Cup & saucer, Petit Point II 6.50
Fork & spoon, Amy 32.00
Gravy boat, Deco Dahlia, w/underplate 15.00
Jug, batter; Amy, w/lid 25.00
Mug, soup; Petit Point II 7.00
Plate, Apple & Pear, 11" 10.00
Plate, Cameo, bl, 6" 3.50
Plate, Chesterton, bread & butter sz 3.00
Plate, Chesterton, gray, dinner sz 5.00
Plate, Deco Dahlia, 10" 6.50
Plate, Mallow & Pansy, 12" 10.00
Plate, Petit Point II, dinner sz 5.00
Platter, Deco Dahlia, 13½" 10.00
Platter, Deco Dahlia, 15½" 12.50
Platter, Petit Point II, 12" 8.00
Rolling pin, Amy 65.00
Rolling pin, Cameo, bl 32.00
Rolling pin, Fruits 45.00
Rolling pin, Petit Point 65.00
Rolling pin, Silhouette 75.00

Sugar bowl, Cameo, pk, w/lid 7.50
Sugar scoop, Amy 32.00

Harlequin

Harlequin dinnerware, produced by the Homer Laughlin China Company of Newell, West Virginia, was introduced in 1938. It was a lightweight ware made in maroon, mauve blue, and spruce green, as well as all the Fiesta colors except ivory (see Fiesta). It was marketed exclusively by the Woolworth stores, who considered it to be their all-time best seller. For this reason, they contracted with Homer Laughlin to reissue Harlequin to commemorate their 100th anniversary in 1979. Although three of the original glazes were used in the reissue, the few serving pieces that were made were restyled, and collectors found the new line to be no threat to their investments.

The Harlequin animals, including a fish, lamb, cat, penguin, duck, and donkey, were made during the early 1940s, also for the dime-store trade. Today these are very desirable to collectors of Homer Laughlin China.

In the listings that follow, the values designated 'high' are for these colors: maroon, gray, medium green, spruce green, chartreuse, dark green, rose, red, and light green, with the latter five perhaps 20% under listed prices. 'Low' listings are for examples in mauve blue, turquoise, and yellow. *The Story of Fiesta* by Sharon and Bob Huxford is available in its sixth edition and contains a more thorough study of this subject. Available from Collector Books or your local bookstore.

Animals, non-standard colors 85.00
Animals, standard colors 45.00
Ash tray, basketweave, high 27.00
Ash tray, basketweave, low 23.00
Ash tray, regular, high 24.00
Ash tray, regular, low 21.00
Bowl, '36s oatmeal; high 10.00
Bowl, '36s oatmeal; low 7.00
Bowl, '36s; high 18.00
Bowl, '36s; low 12.00
Bowl, cream soup; high 13.00
Bowl, cream soup; low 10.00
Bowl, fruit; high, 5½" 7.00
Bowl, fruit; low, 5½" 5.00
Bowl, ind salad; high 18.00
Bowl, ind salad; low 12.00
Bowl, mixing; Kitchen Kraft, mauve bl, 8" 75.00
Bowl, mixing; Kitchen Kraft, red or spruce gr, 6" ...55.00
Bowl, mixing; Kitchen Kraft, yel, 10" 85.00
Bowl, nappy; high, 9" 18.00
Bowl, nappy; low, 9" 12.00
Bowl, oval baker, high 18.00
Bowl, oval baker, low 12.00
Butter dish, high, ½-lb 53.00
Butter dish, low, ½-lb 47.00
Candle holder, high, pr 65.00
Candle holder, low, pr 55.00
Casserole, w/lid, high 55.00
Casserole, w/lid, low 40.00
Creamer, high lip, any color 31.00
Creamer, ind; high 12.00
Creamer, ind; low 10.00
Creamer, novelty, high 15.00
Creamer, novelty, low 11.00
Creamer, regular, high 9.00
Creamer, regular, low 6.00

Cup, demitasse; high 32.00
Cup, demitasse; low 20.00
Cup, lg, any color 53.00
Egg cup, dbl, high 16.00
Egg cup, dbl, low 10.00
Egg cup, single, high 18.00
Egg cup, single, low 12.00
Gravy boat, high 16.00
Gravy boat, low 10.00
Marmalade, any color 65.00
Perfume bottle, any color 33.00
Pitcher, service water; high 40.00
Pitcher, service water; low 27.00

Service water jug and tumblers, see listings for values.

Pitcher, 22-oz jug, high 27.00
Pitcher, 22-oz jug, low 16.00
Plate, deep; high 16.00
Plate, deep; low 9.00
Plate, high, 10" 13.00
Plate, high, 6" 4.00
Plate, high, 7" 6.00
Plate, high, 9" 11.00
Plate, low, 10" 9.00
Plate, low, 6" 3.00
Plate, low, 7" 4.00
Plate, low, 9" 6.00
Platter, high, 11" 11.00
Platter, high, 13" 17.00
Platter, low, 11" 7.00
Platter, low, 13" 11.00
Saucer/ash tray, high 28.00
Saucer/ash tray, ivory 45.00
Saucer/ash tray, low 23.00
Shakers, high, pr 11.00
Shakers, low, pr 8.00
Sugar bowl, w/lid, high 13.00
Sugar bowl, w/lid, low 9.00
Syrup, any color 120.00
Teacup, high 8.00
Teacup, low 5.00
Teapot, high 50.00
Teapot, low 35.00
Tray, relish; mixed colors 120.00
Tumbler, high 28.00
Tumbler, low 23.00

Hatpin Holders

Most hatpin holders were made from 1860 to 1920 to coincide with the period during which hatpins were popularly in vogue. The taller types were required to house the long hatpins necessary to secure the large hats that were in style from 1890 to 1914. They were usually porcelain, either decorated by hand or by transfer with florals or scenics, although some were clever figurals. Glass examples are rare, and those of slag or carnival glass are especially valuable.

If you are interested in collecting or dealing in hatpins or hatpin holders, you will find that authority Lillian Baker has several fine books available on the subject, including her most recent publication *Hatpins and Hatpin Holders*, complete with beautiful color illustrations and current market values. She is listed in the Directory under California. For information concerning the International Club for Collectors of Hatpins and Hatpin Holders, see the Clubs, Newsletters, and Catalogs section of the Directory. Our advisor for this category is Robert Larsen; he is listed in the Directory under Nebraska.

Austria, HP florals, saucer type 65.00
Bavaria, mc roses, artist sgn 65.00
Carnival glass, Grape & Cable, marigold, Northwood, 7" 200.00
Daisy & Button, clear, silver top w/pinholes, rare, 8" 300.00
Flow Blue, sgn Shung, Wood & Sons, #d, 5" 145.00
MZ Austria, floral, +stickpin holder & ring tree on tray 325.00
Nippon, scenic w/gold trim, open top, gr wreath mk 65.00
Rosenthall, gr china w/silver overlay 225.00
Royal Bayreuth, musicians, sgn Dixon .295.00
Royal Bayreuth, red poppy figural, bl mk 350.00
Royal Bayreuth, roses, yel on gr, w/tray, mk 175.00

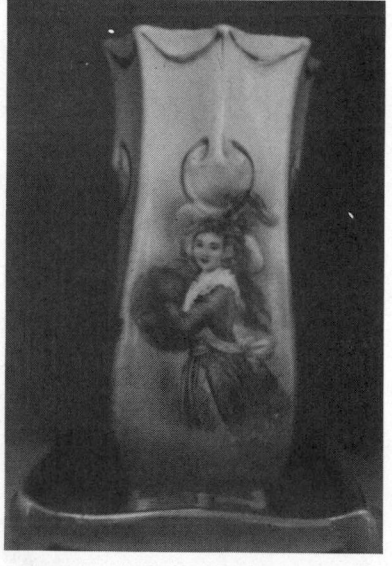

Royal Bayreuth, girl with muff, 3½", $395.00. Photo courtesy of Vern Gaston.

RS Germany, tulips, pk on gr, +hair receiver/powder jar, mk . .125.00
RS Prussia, HP pk roses, drape mold, attached tray, w/lid 200.00
Schafer & Vater, cameo on urn form, 5¼" 185.00
Suhl Prussia, florals, gold border, 5" 80.00
Unmk china, dbl-faced figural, lady 1 side, man on other 250.00
Unmk china, red roses, 2 hdls 65.00

Hatpins

A hatpin was used to securely fasten a hat to the hair and head of the wearer. Hatpins, measuring from 4" to 12" in length, were worn from approximately 1850 to 1920. During the Art Deco period, hatpins became ornaments rather than the decorative functional jewels that they had been. The hatpin period reached its zenith in 1913 just prior to World War I, which brought about a radical change in women's headdress and fashion. About that time, women began to scorn the bonnet and adopt 'the hat' as a symbol of their equality. The hatpin was made of every natural and manufactured element in a myriad of designs that challenge the imagination. They were contrived to serve every fashion need and complement the milliner's art. Collectors often concentrate on a specific type: hand-painted porcelains, sterling silver, commemoratives, sporting activities, carnival glass, Art Nouveau and/or Art Deco designs, Victorian Gothics with mounted stones, exquisite rhinestones, engraved and brass-mounted escutcheon heads, gold and gems, or simply primitive types made in the Victorian parlor. Some collectors prefer the long pin-shanks while others select only those on tramblants or nodder-type pin-shanks.

If you are interested in collecting or dealing in hatpins, see the information in the Hatpin Holders introduction concerning reference books and a national collectors' club. Our advisor for this category is Robert Larson; he is listed in the Directory under Nebraska.

Key: cab —— cabochon

Amethyst glass 18.00
Blk jet stone on 1¼" domed top, twist-wire caging 40.00
Brass/amethyst, 1¼" tilt top w/hook to hang on seat bk 195.00
Gold, 14k, sm top w/designs 85.00
Ivory, figural bear dancing on solid ball 150.00
Mosaic, intricate colors, designs, or flowers, 1½", ea 125.00
Porc ball, HP lady's head, 1½" dia 175.00
Rhinestone w/amethyst stones, lacy design, 1½" 55.00
Rhinestones, prong set, on domed 1¼" brass filigree top 55.00
Sterling, Deco eng ½x¼" triangle top, hollow, mk 45.00
Sterling, figural bear by tree 125.00
Sterling, Nouveau lady 85.00
Sterling, 4-leaf clover form, mk, 1" W 40.00

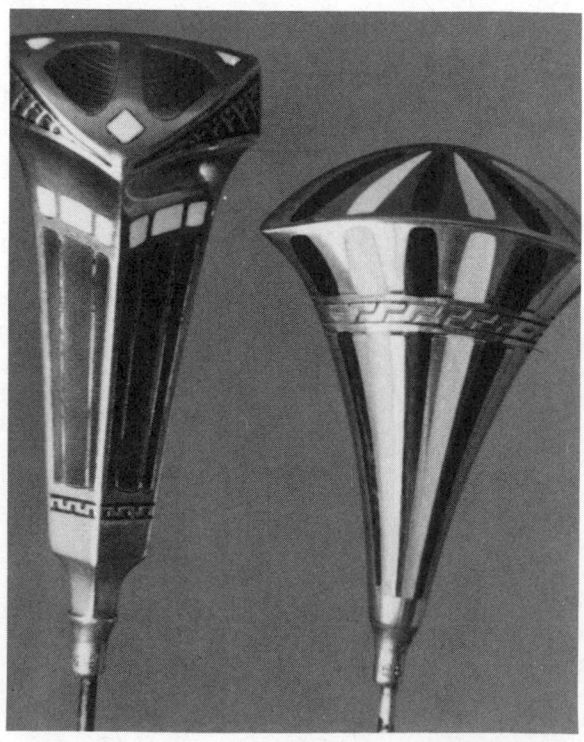

Cloisonne on sterling, 10" pins with 2¼" chased and engraved heads, marked sterling, dated 1844 and 1858 respectively, $125.00 each. Photo courtesy of Vern Gaston.

Haviland

The Haviland China Company was organized in 1840 by David Haviland, a New York china importer. His search for a pure white, non-porous porcelain led him to Limoges, France, where natural deposits of suitable clay had already attracted numerous china manufacturers. The fine china he produced there was translucent and meticulously decorated, with each piece fired in an individual sagger.

It has been estimated that as many as 60,000 chinaware patterns were designed, each piece marked with one of several company backstamps. 'H. & Co.' was used until 1890 when a law was enacted making it necessary to include the country of origin. Various marks have been used since that time including 'Haviland, France'; 'Haviland & Co. Limoges'; and 'Decorated by Haviland & Co.' Various associations with family members over the years have resulted in changes in management as well as company name. In 1892 Theodore Haviland left the firm to start his own business. Some of his ware was marked 'Mont Mery.' Later logos included a horseshoe, a shield, and various uses of his initials and name. In 1941 this branch moved to the United States. Wares produced here are marked 'Theodore Haviland, N.Y.' or 'Made In America.'

Though it is their dinnerware lines for which they are most famous, during the 1880s and 1890s they also made exquisite art pottery using a technique of underglaze slip decoration called Barbotine, which had been invented by Ernest Chaplet. In 1885 Haviland bought the formula and hired Chaplet to oversee its production. The technique involved mixing heavy white clay slip with pigments to produce a compound of the same consistency as oil paints. The finished product actually resembled oil paintings of the period, the texture achieved through the application of the heavy medium to the clay body in much the same manner as an artist would apply paint to his canvas. Primarily the body used with this method was a low-fired faience, though they also produced stoneware.

Authority Mary Frank Gaston has compiled a lovely book, *Haviland Collectibles and Objects of Art*, with full-color illustrations and current values; you will find her address in the Directory under Texas. Numbers in the listings below refer to pattern books by Arlene Schleiger.

Pitcher, embossed and hand-painted floral, applied mark with impressed name, 1850s, 10", $140.00.

Basket, floral/clover, gold trim/hdl, 1893-1930, 4x5¼" 130.00
Basket, HP violets, ca 1876-1930 . . . . .98.00
Cake plate, Her Majesty, Satsuma form, 8½x12" 165.00
Cake stand, Marseille form, ca 1876-1930, 2x9" 90.00
Chamberstick, rosebuds/flowers, Marseille form, 3x5½" 135.00
Chocolate pot, floral/gold decor, star form, 1893-1931, 8" 160.00

Chocolate pot, pk/gr roses w/gold decor, ca 1888-1896, 10" . . .170.00
Chocolate pot, roses, melon-rib body, brn hdl, 9" 275.00
Chocolate pot, Star form, ca 1893-1930, 8" 160.00
Chocolate set, Baltimore Rose, Ranson, 1893-1930, 12-pc . .2,800.00
Coffeepot, pk/wht apple blossoms/gold decor, 1903-1925, 9¼" .165.00
Coffeepot, rose finial, ca 1876-1889, 10" 165.00
Coffeepot, undecorated, ca 1850s-1865, rare, 10½" 425.00
Compote, Lace form, ca 1876-1889, 9x7½" 130.00
Cracker jar, Rouen, HP violets, ca 1895-1903, 7¼" 150.00
Creamer, wht w/gold trim, scalloped top, 1850s-1865, 5" 45.00
Creamer & sugar bowl, wht w/gold band, 1850s-1865 . . . . .155.00
Cup & saucer, demitasse; birds/flowers, gold-beaded border 50.00
Cup & saucer, demitasse; gold decor, Ranson form 50.00
Cup & saucer, floral w/turq border, ca 1876-1880 . . . . .45.00
Cup & saucer, pk floral in center, Ranson form 80.00
Dessert set, Old Blackberry, Napkin Fold form, 4-pc 475.00
Dish, fruit w/gold trim, leaf form, 5½x5¾", pr 120.00

Stoneware ewer, relief pine cones, sgraffito butterflies, signed with Chaplet's Rosary mark, 8", $1,000.00.

Humidor, wht w/gold decor, elephant form, 1850s-1865, 8" **11,000.00**
Jardiniere, Terra Cotta, sculpted flowers, unsgn, 1873-1882 . .1,600.00
Jardiniere, wht w/gold decor, Marseille form, 4x9¾" 175.00
Mayonnaise dish/underplate, leaf shape, wht w/gold trim 80.00
Pitcher, Moss Rose, gold trim, ca 1850-1865 . . . . .80.00
Pitcher, Portia form, ca 1893-1930 . . . . .155.00
Pitcher, Sandoz, duck form, ca 1904-1920s, artist sgn 550.00
Pitcher, water; HP, emb flowers, gold trim, 1850s-1865, 10" . . .135.00
Plate, Baltimore Rose, Ranson form, 1893-1930, 8½" 60.00
Plate, floral w/gold trim, HP, ca 1893-1930 . . . . .60.00
Plate, Hotel China, gold decor on cobalt, 9½" 110.00
Plate, oyster; cobalt w/gold trim, 1888-1896, 8½" 90.00
Plate, oyster; floral, ca 1887, 10" 85.00
Platter, floral, pk on wht, gold & wht bows, Limoges, 16x11" . . .45.00
Platter, Railroad China, violets/daisies, 9¼x6¼" 110.00
Powder box, floral w/gr & gold trim, star form, 1893-1930 . . . .140.00
Ring tree, yel flowers w/gold trim, ca 1893-1930, 3x4¼" 80.00
Sardine box, HP, fish form hdl, ca 1888-1896, 1¼x4½" 90.00
Soup plate, Oriental scenic, ca 1893-1930, 10" 70.00
Sugar bowl, rose finial, ca 1876-1889, 7" 70.00
Teapot, floral/gold decor, Henry II form, 1876-1889, 8" 150.00
Teapot, pk floral/gr ivy, ca 1893-1930, 5" 70.00
Teapot, Sandoz, penguin form, ca 1904-1920s, 5¾" 500.00
Teapot, wht w/gold band, ca 1850s-1865, 7½" 65.00
Tobacco jar, Sandoz, monkey form, artist sgn, 1904-1920s 450.00
Tray, Drop Rose, wht, ca 1876-1930, 15¾x10¾" 475.00

Tureen, Napkin Fold form, shell finial/hdls, 8¼x12½" 175.00
Tureen, wht w/gold decor, Marseille form, 1888-1896, 9x12" . .250.00
Vase, cobalt w/gold decor & hdls, Marseille form, 13¼" 900.00
Vase, cream bsk finish, Marseille form, 1876-1889, 8½" 250.00
Vase, gourd; Terra Cotta, floral, 1873-1882, 7¼" 950.00
Vase, HP mc roses, gold hdls, 1893-1930, 12" 200.00
Vase, HP pk/bl marbled effect, ca 1893-1930, 7" 85.00
Vase, scenic, appl gold w/emb floral on cobalt, 16½" 1,500.00
Vase, Terra Cotta, mc floral decor, 3-ftd, 5" 450.00
Vase, Terra Cotta, sculpted flowers, 12", pr 1,000.00
Vase, Terra Cotta, sculpted mc flowers, jug form, 14" 1,650.00
Wash set, red bands w/gold trim, 7-pc 850.00

Hawkes

Thomas Hawkes established his factory in Corning, New York, in 1880. He developed many beautiful patterns of cut glass, two of which were awarded the Grand Prize at the Paris Exposition in 1889. By the end of the century, his company was renowned for the finest in cut glass production. The company logo was a trefoil form enclosing a hawk in each of the two bottom lobes with a fleur-de-lis in the center.

Our advisors for this catgory are Jeanette and Marvin Stofft; they are listed in the Directory under Indiana.

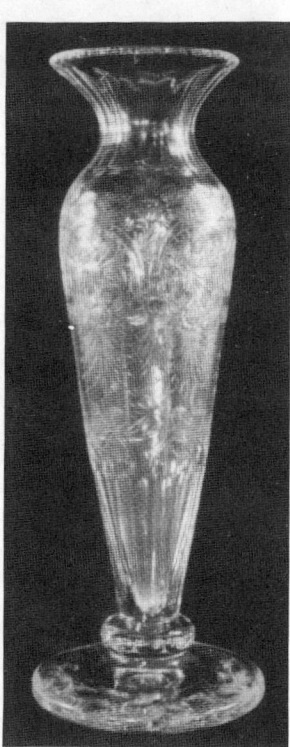

Vase, floral etching, stamped mark, 18", $600.00.

Basket, eng decor, shallow; SP rim & bail, mk, mini 70.00
Basket, stars/lineation/notching; SP ped base, 12½" 325.00
Bottle, whiskey; silver overlay thistles & leaves, 12" 245.00
Bowl, flowers/leaves cutting, shallow, 7" 75.00
Bowl, Russian, 10" 425.00
Bowl, vines/berries, bulbous/flared on ftd base, 14" 325.00
Candlestick, florals, copper wheel eng, mk, 11¾", pr 500.00
Celery dish, intaglio fruit baskets, cornucopias & florals 125.00
Celery dish, intaglio strawberries, central hobstar 175.00
Cordial, Adam, set of 6 . . . . .450.00
Creamer & sugar bowl, nailhead/hobstar/fan cutting 150.00
Cruet, verre de soie, eng ribbons/scrolls, eng stopper, 7" 270.00
Lamp, prism-cut stem, 30 4" prisms, mk, 13x6" 575.00
Pitcher, Harvard, cut or clear buttons, fancy hdl, mk, 9" 185.00

Pitcher, Harvard & hobnails in diamond field w/fans, 5x5½" . .190.00
Punch bowl, hobstars, vesicas, 2-pc, 8½x10½" 750.00
Rose bowl, Venetian, 5x6" 350.00
Tray, Sheraton, sgn, 10x7" 195.00
Tumbler, triple-mitre cane, monogram, trefoil mk, 10 for 575.00
Vase, Gracia, bands/lines/medallions, Ferrar #364, 9x4½" 220.00
Vase, moss gr, cut Phoenix bird & flowers, sgn, 10" 275.00

Heisey

A.H. Heisey began his long career at the King Glass Company of Pittsburgh. He later joined the Ripley Glass Company which soon became Geo. Duncan and Sons. After Duncan's death, Heisey became half-owner along with his brother-in-law, James Duncan. In 1895 he built his own factory in Newark, Ohio, starting production in 1896 and continuing until Christmas of 1957. At that time, Imperial Glass Corporation purchased some of the moulds. In 1968 they removed the old 'Diamond H' from any moulds they put into use.

During their highly successful period of production, Heisey made fine hand-crafted tableware with simple, yet graceful designs. Early pieces were not marked. After November 1901, the glassware was marked either with the 'Diamond H' or a paper label. Blown ware is often marked on the stem, never on the bowl or foot. For information concerning Heisey Collectors of America, see the Clubs, Newsletters, and Catalogs section of the Directory.

Animals and Birds

Airdale 450.00
Asiatic Pheasant 375.00
Bull, sgn 1,400.00
Chick, head down 60.00
Chick, head up 60.00
Clydesdale 450.00
Clydesdale, Harvey amber 1,500.00
Colt, kicking 190.00
Colt, kicking, amber 550.00
Colt, kicking, cobalt 950.00
Colt, rearing 175.00
Colt, rearing, amber 575.00
Colt, rearing, cobalt 950.00
Colt, standing 85.00
Colt, standing, amber 550.00
Colt, standing, cobalt 900.00
Cygnet 175.00
Dolphin, candlestick, #110, pr 350.00
Dolphin, candlestick, moongleam, #110, pr 1,000.00
Donkey 250.00
Duck, ash tray 125.00
Duck, ash tray, flamingo 195.00
Duck, ash tray, marigold 350.00
Duck, flower block 130.00
Duck, flower block, hawthorne 275.00
Elephant, amber, lg 2,000.00
Elephant, amber, med 2,000.00
Elephant, amber, sm 1,750.00
Elephant, lg 350.00
Elephant, med 250.00
Elephant, sm 195.00
Fish, bookend 100.00
Fish, candlestick 125.00
Fish, match holder 150.00
Fish, Tropical 1,200.00

Flying Mare 2,000.00
Flying Mare, dk amber 3,500.00
Frog, cheese plate, #1210, flamingo 125.00
Frog, cheese plate, marigold 350.00
Frog, cheese plate, moongleam 200.00
Gazelle 1,200.00
Giraffe, head bk 175.00
Giraffe, head to side 175.00
Goose, wings down 350.00
Goose, wings half 95.00
Goose, wings up 115.00
Hen 425.00
Hen, amber 1,000.00
Horse head, bookend 125.00
Horse head, bookend, amber 2,000.00
Horse head, cigarette box, #1489, 4½x4" 75.00
Irish Setter, ash tray 30.00
Irish Setter, ash tray, flamingo 45.00
Irish Setter, ash tray, moongleam 55.00
Kingfisher, flower block, flamingo 225.00
Kingfisher, flower block, hawthorne 300.00
Kingfisher, flower block, moongleam 250.00
Mallard, wings down 250.00
Mallard, wings half 95.00
Mallard, wings up 150.00
Piglet, sitting 75.00
Piglet, standing 75.00
Plug Horse 95.00
Plug Horse, amber 600.00
Plug Horse (Oscar), cobalt 1,000.00
Pouter Pigeon 700.00
Rabbit, paperweight 175.00
Ringneck Pheasant 150.00
Rooster, amber, 5⅜" 2,500.00
Rooster, Fighting, 8" 150.00
Rooster, stem cocktail 55.00
Rooster, vase, 6½" 95.00
Rooster, 5⅜" 425.00
Rooster head, cocktail 50.00
Rooster head, cocktail shaker, 1-qt 95.00
Scotty 120.00
Show Horse 500.00
Sow 500.00
Sparrow 75.00

Swan, ind nut, #1503 ....18.00
Swan, master nut, #1503 ....45.00
Wood Duck 500.00

Dinnerware

Adam, crystal; tumbler, ftd, #3376, 10-oz 18.00
Adam, crystal; wine, #3376, 3-oz 25.00
Adam, flamingo; claret, #3376, 4-oz 25.00
Adam, flamingo; cocktail, oyster; #3376, 4-oz 25.00
Admiralty, crystal; cocktail, oyster; #3424, 4½-oz 25.00
Admiralty, crystal; goblet, #3424, 9-oz 45.00
African, flamingo; goblet, #3370, 8-oz 40.00
African, moongleam; saucer champagne, #3370, 6-oz 40.00
Albemarle, crystal; parfait, #3368, 4½-oz 20.00
Albemarle, flamingo; finger bowl, #3309 ....15.00
Albemarle, marigold; claret, #3368, 4-oz 30.00
Albemarle, sahara; comport, high ftd, #3368, 7" ...85.00
Barbara Fritchie, crystal; claret, #3416, 3¾-oz ...25.00
Barbara Fritchie, crystal; finger bowl, #3335 .....12.00
Barbara Fritchie, crystal; saucer champagne, #3416, 6-oz ...30.00
Barbara Fritchie, sahara; cordial, tall, #3416, 1-oz 350.00
Biltmore, crystal; cocktail, #3316, 3-oz 12.00
Biltmore, crystal; goblet, #3316, 10-oz 15.00
Biltmore, crystal; tumbler, ftd, #3316, 10-oz 12.00
Carcassonne, cobalt; cocktail, oyster; #3390, 3-oz 60.00
Carcassonne, flamingo; flagon, #3390, 12-oz 95.00
Carcassonne, moongleam; jug, ftd, #3390, 3-pt 195.00
Carcassonne, moongleam; saucer champagne, #3390, 6-oz 25.00
Carcassonne, sahara; finger bowl, ftd, #3390 ......25.00
Charter Oak, crystal; tumbler, #3362, 10-oz 10.00
Charter Oak, hawthorne; comport, high ftd, #3362, 7" 140.00
Charter Oak, marigold; parfait, #3362, 4½-oz 50.00
Charter Oak, moongleam; goblet, luncheon; #3362, 8-oz 32.00

Crystolite footed cake stand, 11" diameter, $325.00.

Circle Pair, moongleam; goblet, #2516 ....50.00
Coarse Rib, crystal; bowl, nappy, #407, 4½" 8.00
Coarse Rib, crystal; ice bucket, #407 ....55.00
Coarse Rib, crystal; jug, #407, ½-gal 65.00
Coarse Rib, crystal; mustard, w/lid, #407 ....23.00
Coarse Rib, crystal; oil, #407, 6-oz 40.00
Coarse Rib, crystal; saucer champagne, #407, 5½-oz 14.00
Coarse Rib, crystal; tumbler, iced tea; #406, 12-oz 15.00
Coarse Rib, marigold; plate, #407, 8" 45.00
Coarse Rib, moongleam; bowl, nappy, #406, 4½" 15.00

Swan candlestick, 6½", $135.00.

Coarse Rib, moongleam; tray, pickle; #407, 6" 25.00
Coarse Rib, moongleam; tumbler, #406, 8-oz 40.00
Coleport, crystal; bowl, nappy, #1486, 8" 25.00
Coleport, crystal; goblet, #1486, 8-oz 35.00
Coleport, crystal; sherbet, #1486, 5½-oz 15.00
Coleport, crystal; tumbler, #1486, 10-oz 12.00
Comet Leaf, crystal; sherbet, #1306, 5-oz 25.00
Coronation, crystal; cocktail shaker, #4054, 28-oz 75.00
Coronation, crystal; soda, #4054, 8-oz 12.00
Coventry, crystal; cordial, #4090, 1-oz 125.00
Coventry, crystal; goblet, low ftd, #4090, 10-oz 35.00
Coventry, zircon; claret, #4090, 4½-oz 95.00
Coventry, zircon; goblet, low ftd, #4090, 10-oz 140.00
Creole, alexandrite; cocktail, #3381, 4-oz 150.00
Creole, alexandrite; finger bowl, ftd, #3381 . . . . .85.00
Creole, alexandrite; goblet, short, #3381, 11-oz 150.00
Creole, alexandrite; parfait, #3381, 5-oz 135.00
Delaware, flamingo; goblet, luncheon; #3324, 9-oz 38.00
Delaware, flamingo; parfait, #3324, 4½-oz 38.00
Delaware, flamingo; saucer champagne, #3324, 6½-oz 28.00
Delaware, hawthorne; sherbet, #3324, 6½-oz 38.00
Diamond Rose, crystal; saucer champagne, #3386, 6½-oz 25.00
Diamond Rose, flamingo; goblet, #3386, 11-oz 60.00
Diamond Rose, sahara; pilzner, #3386, 10-oz 95.00
Duquesne, crystal; goblet, #3389, 9-oz 20.00
Duquesne, sahara; parfait, #3389, 5-oz 25.00
Duquesne, sahara; wine, #3389, 2½-oz 40.00
Duquesne, tangerine; finger bowl, #4071 . . . . .70.00
Empress, crystal; bowl, salad; #1401, 10" 30.00
Empress, crystal; plate, #1401, 12" 25.00
Empress, crystal; plate, sq, #1401, 10½" 65.00
Empress, flamingo; candlestick, #1401, 6", pr 225.00
Empress, flamingo; tray, celery; #1401, 13" 25.00
Empress, moongleam; comport, ftd, #1401, 6" 60.00
Empress, moongleam; dessert, oval, #1401, 10" 55.00
Empress, moongleam; platter, oval, #1401, 14" 55.00
Empress, moongleam; tumbler, ftd, #1401, 8-oz 125.00
Empress, sahara; bowl, floral; rolled edge, #1401, 9" 40.00
Empress, sahara; creamer, ftd, #1401 . . . . .35.00
Fairacre, crystal; goblet, #3555, 10-oz 18.00
Fairacre, flamingo; claret, #3555, 4½-oz 25.00
Fairacre, moongleam; goblet, luncheon; #3555, 10-oz 30.00
Fairacre, moongleam; parfait, #3555, 5-oz 35.00
Fern, crystal; plate, w/hdl, #1495, 15" 33.00
Gascony, sahara; creamer, #3397 .90.00
Gascony, sahara; saucer champagne, #3397, 6-oz 75.00
Gayoso, flamingo; parfait, #3312, 5-oz 18.00
Gayoso, marigold; cordial, #3312, 1-oz 200.00
Gayoso, marigold; sherbet, #3312, 5½-oz 30.00
Ipswich, crystal; candy jar, w/lid, #1405, ½-lb 70.00
Ipswich, flamingo; sherbet, #1405, 4-oz 35.00
Ipswich, moongleam; creamer, #1405 . . . . .60.00
Ipswich, sahara; plate, sq, #1405, 7" 18.00
Jamestown, crystal; saucer champagne, #3408, 6-oz 18.00
Jamestown, sahara; vase, #3408, 9" 200.00
Jamestown, sahara; wine, #3408, 2-oz 175.00
Kenilworth, crystal; champagne, #4092, 5½-oz 30.00
Kenilworth, crystal; cordial, tall stem, #4092, 1-oz 95.00
Kimberly, crystal; sherbet, #4091, 5½-oz 20.00
Kimberly, zircon; wine, #4091, 2-oz 150.00
King Arthur, flamingo; cocktail, #3357, 3½-oz 25.00
King Arthur, flamingo; tumbler, iced tea; ftd, #3357, 12-oz 25.00
King Arthur, moongleam; goblet, luncheon; #3357, 10-oz 40.00
Kohinoor, crystal; ash tray, #1488 .18.00

Kohinoor, crystal; cocktail, #4085, 3-oz 28.00
Kohinoor, zircon; bowl, fruit; #1488, 15½" 125.00
Kohinoor, zircon; cigarette holder, #1488 . . . . .145.00
Kohinoor, zircon; finger bowl, #4085 . . . . .75.00
Kohinoor, zircon; goblet, low ftd, #4085, 9-oz 125.00
Kohinoor, zircon; wine, #4085, 2½-oz 150.00
Mariette, crystal; cocktail, #3414, 3½-oz 20.00
Mariette, crystal; cordial, #3414, 1-oz 75.00
Mariette, crystal; saucer champagne, #3414, 6-oz 20.00
Monte Cristo, crystal; cordial, #3411, 1-oz 75.00
Monte Cristo, sahara; wine, #3411, 2½-oz 150.00
Narrow Flute w/Rim, flamingo; tray, pickle; #473, 6" 20.00
New Era, cobalt; cordial, #4044, 1-oz 250.00
New Era, cobalt; tumbler, ftd, #4044, 10-oz 80.00
New Era, crystal; cup & saucer, #4044 . . . . .40.00
New Era, crystal; saucer champagne, #4044, 6-oz 15.00
Octagon, crystal; basket, #500, 5" .75.00
Octagon, flamingo; bowl, ftd, #1229, 8" 28.00
Octagon, flamingo; tray, oblong, #500, 6" 20.00
Octagon, marigold; plate, sandwich; #1229, 10" 55.00
Octagon, moongleam; ice bucket, #500 . . . . .75.00
Octagon, moongleam; jelly, #1229, 5½" 20.00
Octagon, sahara; creamer, #500 . . . . .28.00
Old Dominion, alexandrite; goblet, short, #3380, 10-oz 150.00
Old Dominion, crystal; cocktail, #3380, 3-oz 15.00
Old Dominion, flamingo; parfait, #3380, 5-oz 25.00
Old Dominion, moongleam; cordial, #3380, 1-oz 150.00
Old Dominion, sahara; goblet, tall, #3380, 10-oz 40.00
Old Glory, crystal; comport, high ftd, #3333, 6" 55.00
Old Glory, crystal; wine, #3333, 2-oz 25.00
Old Glory, hawthorne; cordial, #3333, 1-oz 180.00
Old Glory, hawthorne; goblet, #3333, 9-oz 125.00
Old Glory, hawthorne; parfait, #3333, 4½-oz 85.00
Old Sandwich, crystal; cigarette holder, #1404 . . . . .90.00
Old Sandwich, crystal; jug, #1404, ½-gal 85.00
Old Sandwich, crystal; plate, sq, #1404, 8" 15.00
Old Sandwich, flamingo; shakers, #1404, pr 100.00
Old Sandwich, moongleam; goblet, low ftd, #1404, 10-oz 65.00
Old Sandwich, moongleam; toddy, #1404, 6½-oz 20.00
Old Sandwich, sahara; claret, #1404, 4-oz 25.00
Park Lane, crystal; claret, #4055, 4-oz 20.00
Park Lane, crystal; cocktail, #4055, 3-oz 15.00
Penn Charter, crystal; claret, #3360, 4½-oz 20.00
Penn Charter, flamingo; goblet, #3360, 8½-oz 50.00
Penn Charter, flamingo; saucer champagne, #3360, 6-oz 35.00
Penn Charter, hawthorne; cocktail, oyster; #3360, 4-oz 45.00
Plateau, crystal; finger bowl, #3359 . . . . .15.00
Plateau, flamingo; jug, #3359, ½-gal 135.00
Plateau, marigold; saucer champagne, #3359, 6½-oz 45.00
Pleat & Panel, crystal; oil, #1170, 3-oz 40.00
Pleat & Panel, flamingo; bowl, nappy, #1170, 8" 30.00
Pleat & Panel, flamingo; dish, vegetable; #1170, 9" 30.00
Pleat & Panel, flamingo; goblet, luncheon; #1170, 7½-oz 25.00
Pleat & Panel, moongleam; comport, w/lid, low ftd, #1170, 6" ..70.00
Pleat & Panel, moongleam; marmalade, #1170, 4¾" 35.00
Pleat & Panel, moongleam; sherbet, #1170, 5-oz 20.00
Pleat & Panel, moongleam; tumbler, iced tea; #1170, 12-oz 30.00
Plymouth, sahara; cocktail, #3409, 3½-oz 70.00
Plymouth, sahara; parfait, #3409, 5-oz 80.00
Plymouth, sahara; soda, ftd, #3409, 5-oz 20.00
Portsmouth, crystal; sherbet, #3440, 7-oz 15.00
Portsmouth, moongleam; goblet, #3440, 9-oz 40.00
Pyramid, flamingo; soda, ftd, #3379, 5-oz 60.00
Pyramid, moongleam; goblet, #3379, 10-oz 75.00

Quator, crystal; bonbon, ftd, #355 . . . . .15.00
Quator, marigold; creamer, ftd, #355 . . . . .65.00
Quator, moongleam; creamer, ftd, #355 . . . . .35.00
Rampul, flamingo; sherbet, #3325, 6-oz 25.00
Rampul, hawthorne; goblet, #3325, 9-oz .125.00
Ramshorn, crystal; goblet, #3365, 9-oz 40.00
Ramshorn, flamingo; saucer champagne, #3365, 6-oz 30.00
Ramshorn, flamingo; sherbet, #3365, 6-oz .25.00
Ramshorn, moongleam; bowl, fruit salad; #3365, 5" 20.00
Ribbed Octagon, flamingo; cup & saucer, #1231 . . . . .25.00
Ribbed Octagon, moongleam; candlestick, #1231, pr 50.00
Ribbed Octagon, moongleam; tray, celery; #1231, 12" 30.00
Ridgeleigh, crystal; bowl, fruit; #1469, 12" 45.00
Ridgeleigh, crystal; bowl, nappy, sq, #1469, 5" 15.00
Ridgeleigh, crystal; centerpiece, #1469, 8" 35.00
Ridgeleigh, crystal; claret, #1469 . . . . .25.00
Ridgeleigh, crystal; cordial, #4069, 1-oz .125.00
Ridgeleigh, crystal; cup & saucer, #1469 . . . . .30.00
Ridgeleigh, crystal; goblet, #4069, 8-oz 50.00
Ridgeleigh, crystal; marmalade, w/lid, #1469 . . . . .40.00
Ridgeleigh, crystal; plate, rnd, #1469, 8" 12.00
Ridgeleigh, crystal; plate, sq, #1469, 8" 25.00
Ridgeleigh, crystal; plate, torte; #1469, 13" 35.00
Ridgeleigh, crystal; punch bowl, #1469, 11" 115.00
Ridgeleigh, crystal; saucer champagne, #1469 . . . . .30.00
Ridgeleigh, crystal; tray, oblong, #1469, 10½" 28.00
Ridgeleigh, crystal; vase, #1469, 10" 45.00
Ridgeleigh, sahara; ash tray, sq, #1469 . . . . .35.00
Rococo, crystal; bonbon, #1447 . . . . .22.00
Rococo, crystal; comport, #1447, 6" 55.00
Rococo, sahara; bowl, nappy, hdld, #1447, 8" 50.00
Rococo, sahara; shakers, #1447, pr 85.00
Saturn, crystal; creamer, 1485 . . . . .18.00
Saturn, crystal; parfait, 1485, 5-oz 18.00
Saturn, crystal; plate, torte; 1485, 15" 35.00
Saturn, zircon, bowl, nappy; #1485, 5" 40.00
Saturn, zircon; bowl, flower; #1485, 13" .125.00
Saturn, zircon; bowl, salad; #1485, 11" 75.00
Saturn, zircon; bowl, salad; hdld, #1495, 11" 95.00
Saturn, zircon; bowl, sauce; #1495 . . . . .45.00
Saturn, zircon; comport; #1485, 7" 125.00
Saturn, zircon; creamer; #1495 . . . . .95.00
Saturn, zircon; goblet, #1485, 10-oz 75.00
Saturn, zircon; plate, #1485, 8" 40.00
Saturn, zircon; plate, sandwich; #1495, 13" 95.00
Saturn, zircon; plate, torte; #1485, 15" 45.00
Saturn, zircon; tray, tid-bit; #1485 . . . . .95.00
Savoy Plaza, crystal; cordial, #3418, 1-oz 125.00
Savoy Plaza, crystal; goblet, #3418, 10-oz 45.00
Savoy Plaza, crystal; wine, #3418, 3-oz 55.00
Saxony, sahara; goblet, short stem, #3394, 12-oz 50.00
Saxony, sahara; soda, ftd, #3394, 12-oz 35.00
Spanish, cobalt; claret, #3404, 4-oz 150.00
Spanish, cobalt; comport, #3404, 6" 275.00
Spanish, crystal; cordial, #3404, 1-oz 70.00
Stanhope, crystal; bowl, salad; #1483, 11" 35.00
Stanhope, crystal; candy box, w/lid, #1483, 6" 65.00
Stanhope, crystal; claret, #4083, 4-oz 30.00
Stanhope, crystal; ice bucket, hdld, #1483 . . . . .50.00
Stanhope, crystal; plate, torte; hdld, #1483, 12" 30.00
Stanhope, crystal; sugar bowl, hdld, #1483 . . . . .18.00
Stanhope, crystal; wine, #1483, 2½-oz 30.00
Sussex, flamingo; finger bowl, #419 . . . . .25.00
Sussex, flamingo; goblet, #419, 8-oz 55.00

Sussex, moongleam; cocktail, #419, 2½-oz 45.00
Sussex, moongleam; saucer champagne, #419, 5½-oz 45.00
Sweet Ad-o-line, crystal; goblet, #1423, 14-oz 300.00
Trojan, crystal; claret, #3366, 4-oz 25.00
Trojan, crystal; comport, ftd, #3366, 7" 45.00
Trojan, hawthorne; parfait, #3366, 4½-oz 75.00
Trojan, moongleam; tumbler, ftd, #3366, 10-oz 25.00
Tudor, crystal; banana split, ftd, #412, 8" .25.00
Tudor, crystal; bottle, water; #411 . . . . .60.00
Tudor, crystal; bowl, fruit; #411, 10" 40.00
Tudor, crystal; goblet, #411, 8-oz 18.00
Tudor, crystal; jug, #411,½-gal 75.00
Tudor, crystal; parfait, #412, 4½-oz 25.00
Tudor, crystal; saucer champagne, #413, 6-oz 15.00
Tudor, crystal; shakers, #411, pr 35.00
Tudor, crystal; sherbet, low ftd, #413, 5½-oz 15.00
Tudor, crystal; tray, celery; #411, 12" 28.00
Tudor, hawthorne; cigarette box, w/lid, #413 . . . . .125.00
Tudor, hawthorne; compote, jelly; hdls, #411, 5" 40.00
Tudor, moongleam; bonbon, hdls, #411 .30.00
Tudor, moongleam; goblet, #411, 8-oz 40.00
Tudor, moongleam; goblet, luncheon; #411, 7-oz 30.00
Twentieth Century, crystal; sherbet, ftd, #1415, 4-oz 15.00
Twentieth Century, flamingo; tumbler, ftd, #1415, 9-oz 40.00
Twentieth Century, sahara; pitcher, milk; #1415, 1-pt 95.00
Twist, crystal; creamer, #1252 . . . . .20.00
Twist, crystal; tumbler, #1252, 8-oz 12.00
Twist, flamingo; saucer champagne, #1252, 5-oz 25.00
Twist, marigold; bowl, nappy, #1252, 8" .45.00
Twist, marigold; ice bucket, #1252 . . . . .140.00
Twist, marigold; mayonnaise, #1252 . . . . .60.00
Twist, moongleam; creamer, ftd, #1252 . . . . .35.00
Twist, moongleam; iced tea, ftd, #1252, 12-oz 40.00
Twist, moongleam; platter, oval, #1252, 12" 45.00
Twist, moongleam; sugar bowl, ftd, #1252 . . . . .35.00
Universal, crystal; claret, #3304, 4½-oz 12.00
Universal, crystal; cocktail, #3304, 3½-oz 10.00
Universal, crystal; cordial, #3304, 1-oz 20.00
Universal, crystal; wine, #3304, 2½-oz 10.00
Velvedere, crystal; bowl, salad; #3311, 5" .12.00
Velvedere, crystal; cocktail, #3311, 3½-oz 12.00
Velvedere, crystal; cordial, #3311, 1-oz 30.00
Velvedere, crystal; sherbet, ftd, #3311, 5½-oz 12.00
Velvedere, moongleam; bowl, salad; #3311, 5" 25.00
Victorian, cobalt; bowl, nappy, #1425, 8" 350.00
Victorian, cobalt; goblet, #1425, 9-oz 250.00
Victorian, cobalt; vase, #1425, 4" 150.00
Victorian, crystal; punch bowl, #1425 . . . . .195.00
Victorian, crystal; rose bowl, #1425 . . . . .45.00
Victorian, crystal; vase, ftd, #1425, 9" 45.00
Victorian, sahara; plate, sandwich; #1425, 13" 100.00
Victorian, sahara; saucer champagne, #1425, 5-oz 55.00
Victorian, sahara; shakers, #1425, pr 125.00
Victorian, sahara; tumbler, ftd, #1425, 10-oz 65.00
Wabash, crystal; jug, ftd, #3350, 3-pt 90.00
Wabash, flamingo; tumbler, ftd, #3350, 10-oz 25.00
Wabash, hawthorne; goblet, #3350, 10-oz 75.00
Wabash, marigold; claret, #3350, 4-oz 65.00
Wabash, moongleam; parfait, #3350, 5-oz 45.00
Waldorf, crystal; bowl, fruit; low ftd, #3318, 5-oz 10.00
Waldorf, crystal; claret, #3318, 4-oz 22.00
Waldorf, crystal; cordial, #3318, 1-oz 45.00
Waldorf, crystal; goblet, #3318, 11-oz 22.00
Yeoman, crystal; candy box, w/lid, #1184, 6" 30.00

Yeoman, crystal; cup & saucer, #1184 . . . .**24.00**
Yeoman, crystal; salver, low ftd, #1184, 10" **25.00**
Yeoman, crystal; tray, oblong, #1184, 12" **22.00**
Yeoman, flamingo; ash tray, hdld, #1184, 4" **35.00**
Yeoman, flamingo; bowl, nappy, deep, #1184, 8" **25.00**
Yeoman, flamingo; bowl, vegetable; #1184, 6" **15.00**
Yeoman, flamingo; finger bowl & plate, #1184 . . . . **25.00**
Yeoman, marigold; platter, oval, #1184, 12" **45.00**
Yeoman, moongleam; platter, oval, #1184, 15" **35.00**
Yeoman, moongleam; relish, 3-part, #1184, 13" **30.00**
Yeoman, sahara; comport, deep, low ftd, #1184, 6" **35.00**
Yeoman, sahara; finger bowl, #1184 . . . .**25.00**
Yeoman, sahara; goblet, #1184, 8-oz **30.00**

Vase, #444, Colonial pattern,
1913, 12", $395.00.

Heubach

Gebruder Heubach is a German porcelain company that has been in operation since the 1800s producing quality figurines and novelty items. They are perhaps most famous for their doll heads and piano babies, most of which are marked with the circular rising sun device containing an 'H' superimposed over a 'C.'

Our advisor for this category is Don Williams; he is listed in the Directory under Iowa.

Baby, crawling, frilly gown, mk, 5" **250.00**
Baby, crawling, long blonde hair, ruffled gown, 7" L **225.00**
Baby, crawling, wht gown, kicking legs, 5½x8" **415.00**
Baby, sitting, 6½" **350.00**
Baby on tummy, ft Xd, wht gown/pk trim, unsgn, 4" **175.00**
Baby sits w/ice skates, night light, 3½" **450.00**
Baby w/grapes, reclining, intaglio eyes, mk, 8" **300.00**
Bear, dressed, w/flowers, waits at door, sgn **225.00**
Box, bell w/ribbon finial, cherubs at base, mk **245.00**
Box, shell w/baby peeking out, sm baby on lid, 4½x4½" **600.00**
Boy rugby player, EX detail/color, mk, 6" **300.00**
Dutch children, sitting, mk, 8¾x5x6½" **600.00**
Dutch children sit w/baskets on bks, mk, 5½x3x5", pr **450.00**
Dutch children stand bk to bk, mk, 7¼x4¾" **300.00**
Fat Boy, bl coat, yel trim, blk top hat, 2 mks, 7" **500.00**
Girl in pk pleated skirt, gr sash, mk, 5¾" **110.00**
Girl stands by vase, mk, 6½" **150.00**

Hound dog, lt gray, sad blk eyes, dk gray nose, mk, 4½" **75.00**

Just Like Mama and Papa, 8", $550.00 for the pair.

Man w/ax; lady w/baby & jug, 12½", pr **725.00**
Mother & baby rat w/old shoe, mk **165.00**
Pin dish, Indian in full dress, wht on gr jasper, mk **65.00**
Pitcher, Beethoven figural, rare **100.00**
Planter, shepherdess w/3 sheep & ram at front, 7½x11x6½" . . .**550.00**
Sheep dog, begging, wht w/yel eyes & coral collar, sgn **200.00**

Hickman, Royal Arden

Born in Willamette, Oregon, Royal A. Hickman was a genius in all aspects of design interpretation. Mr. Hickman's expertise can be seen in the designs of the lovely Heisey figurines; Kosta crystal; Bruce Fox aluminum; Three Crowns aluminum; Vernon Kilns; and Royal Haeger Pottery as well as hand-crafted silver, furniture, and paintings.

Because Mr. Hickman moved around during much of his lifetime, his influence has been felt in all forms of the media. Designs from his independent companies include 'Royal Hickman Pottery and Lamps' (sold through Ceramic Arts, Inc., of Chattanooga, Tennessee), 'Royal Hickman's Paris Ware,' 'Royal Hickman — Florida,' and 'California, Designed by Royal Hickman.' The following listings will give examples of pieces bearing the various trademarks.

Our advisor for this category is Lee Garmon; she is listed in the directory under Illinois. See also Royal Haegar; Vernon Kilns, Melinda pattern.

Bruce Fox Aluminum

Banana leaf, mk Royal Hickman-RH 6, 22½" L **15.00**
Dish, lobster, lg **40.00**
Dish, 3-point leaf, sgn Royal Hickman, 15½" L **15.00**
Platter, fish, EX detail, sgn Royal Hickman-RH 3, 13x9" **50.00**

California, Designed by Royal Hickman

Bowl, red w/blk highlights, #607, 9½" **15.00**
Figurine, deer, apple gr w/wht spots, appl eyes, 15" **25.00**
Figurine, giraffe & young, pk w/blk spots & base, 11x7" **35.00**
Swan, red w/blk highlights, #643, 17" **40.00**

Miscellaneous Signatures

Bowl/planter, oblong, foam trim, incised Royal Hickman/132, 9". 10.00
Bowl/planter, oval, foam trim, incised Royal Hickman/106, 8" . . 10.00
Vase, fish figurine, stoneware, crystal glaze, label, 9" 25.00

Royal Hickman — Florida

Vase, fish on waves, gr w/wht marble, 9½" 25.00
Vase, horse's head, gray w/wht mane, 13¾" 75.00
Vase, modernistic free-form, #578, 14" 30.00

Historical Glass

Glassware commemorating particularly significant historical events became popular in the late 1800s. Bread trays were the most common form; but plates, mugs, pitchers, and other items were also pressed in clear as well as colored glass. It was sold in vast amounts at the 1876 Philadelphia Centennial Exposition by various manufacturers who exhibited their wares on the grounds. It remained popular well into the 20th century.

In the listings that follow, numbers refer to a book by Lindsey, a standard guide used by many collectors. See also Bread Plates; Pattern Glass.

Bone dish, Dewey, man-in-moon form, milk glass, L-384, 7" . . . 220.00
Bowl, US Grant, Patriot & Soldier, octagonal 65.00
Bust, Columbus, frosted, after Lotto portrait, L-6, 5", NM 190.00
Bust, Dewey, frosted, mk Manila 1898, unrecorded, 5" 60.00
Bust, Lt Richard Hobson, frosted, L-382, 5" 265.00
Bust, Pres McKinley, frosted, L-354, 5¼" 310.00
Bust, Washington, wht satin, L-259, 6", EX 500.00
Butter dish, Rear Admiral Wm T Sampson (1840-1902) 40.00
Calabash, Roosevelt-TVA, aqua, qt 60.00
Covered dish, battleship, L-468 . . . . 25.00
Covered dish, battleship, Remember...Maine, emerald, L-465 . . 200.00
Covered dish, battleship Oregon, L-469, 6½" L, EX 75.00
Covered dish, kitchen stove, flatiron hdl, L-149, 7" 300.00
Covered dish, locomotive, L-138, VG 150.00
Flask, Paul Jones, L-48 . . . . 20.00
Goblet, Capitol at Washington 38.00
Goblet, Centennial Commemorative, flag/shield, 1776/1876 . . . 40.00
Goblet, Knight's of Labor, oversized, EX 40.00
Goblet, Philadelphia Centennial 30.00
Goblet, Texas Centennial Commemorative 30.00
Goblet, 3 Presidents, rare 325.00
Jar, Remember the Maine, milk glass insert, orig metal cap 165.00
Jar, Statue of Liberty, w/eagle, clear w/gilt, L-530, 12" 60.00
Lamp chimney, Admiral Dewey, Hero of. . ., etched, L-385 . . . 160.00
Lamp chimney, Columbus, etched on frosted band, L-9, 8" . . . 250.00
Match holder, flag shield/Am/1492-1892, bl opaque, 4" 175.00
Mug, Bumper to Flag, Dia Quilt, flint, pt 70.00
Mug, Cleveland/Thurman Campaign of 1888, L-327 . . . . 165.00
Mug, Columbus/Washington Commemorative, L-2, child's 80.00
Mug, Knights of Labor, L-513, pt 35.00
Mug, Martyrs, L-272 . . . . 55.00
Mug, Peabody 70.00
Paperweight, Assassinated Presidents w/verse 65.00
Paperweight, Columbus w/globe, gold outlines, 3½x4½" 210.00
Paperweight, Gen JJ Pershing, gold rvpt, L-404, 4" dia 160.00
Paperweight, Remember...Maine, wht/mc, att Union, 2½" 150.00
Pitcher, Dewey, L-401, 9" 100.00
Pitcher, Texas Centennial, Alamo, 9" 80.00
Plaque, Lincoln Logs, amber, L-278, 8½" 100.00

Plate, U.S. Grant, Let Us Have Peace, 10¼" diameter, $450.00.

Plaque, Lincoln Logs, milk glass/brn flashing, L-287, 6¾" 225.00
Plate, Garfield, 101 border, L-300, 9" 50.00
Plate, McKinley, bust, lattice border, milk glass, L-341, 9" 110.00
Plate, McKinley, Protection & Plenty, L-333, 7¼" 60.00
Plate, Pope Leo, L-240 . . . . 25.00
Plate, Washington, 13-star border, milk glass, old 45.00
Relish, Centennial, dtd hdls 30.00
Relish, Flaming Sword 35.00
Salt, Benjamin Franklin 95.00
Shaker, Eagle 30.00
Shaving mug, Garfield, milk glass, L-307, 5" 125.00
Statuette, Abraham Lincoln, sgn Gillinder, 6" 325.00
Toothpick holder, hand & torch, amber, L-529 . . . . 75.00
Toothpick holder, US flags/Xd cannon, Preparedness, L-483 . . 225.00
Tray, water; factory/Tiffin Glass Co-1888, 11" dia 285.00
Tray, water; Old State House, L-32, 12⅜" dia 95.00
Trough, bl, L-151 . . . . 20.00
Tumbler, America, L-458 . . . . 18.00
Tumbler, Bay State, flint, EX 75.00
Tumbler, CA state seal, Eureka, intaglio in base 85.00
Tumbler, Civil War, flint, L-148 . . . . 150.00
Tumbler, Dewey/Schley, flags & eagle 48.00
Tumbler, Dewey/Schley in laurel wreath, Am & Cuban flags . . . 75.00
Tumbler, Grant, Let Us Have Peace, L-285 . . . . 65.00
Tumbler, Hobson, in laurel wreath, frosted 60.00
Tumbler, Lincoln Tribute, L-282 . . . . 22.00
Tumbler, McKinley, Our Next President 48.00
Tumbler, Motto, L-224 . . . . 7.00
Tumbler, Nelson of America, L-397 . . . . 28.00
Tumbler, Remember the Maine 25.00
Tumbler, soldier, Don't Touch My Flag, Spanish Amer War 60.00
Water set, Dewey, pitcher: L-400; +6 tumblers: L-398 . . . . 300.00
Whiskey, Bumper to Flag/Union Forever, flint 100.00

Hobbs, Brockunier, and Co.

Hobbs and Brockunier's South Wheeling Glass Works was in operation during the last quarter of the 19th century. They are most famous for their peachblow, amberina, Daisy and Button, and Hobnail pattern glass. The mainstay of the operation, however, was druggist items and plain glassware — bowls, mugs, and simple footed pitchers with shell handles. See also Frances Ware.

Carafe, Block, frosted w/amber flash, lg 145.00
Creamer, Hobnail, bl, sq rim, 4", EX 165.00
Cruet, Hobnail, cranberry opal, orig stopper 295.00
Goblet, Block, amber frost, rare 110.00
Pitcher, Hobnail, amberina rosy-fuchsia to amber, 7¾" 465.00
Pitcher, Hobnail, bl frost, 4" 105.00
Pitcher, Hobnail, vaseline opal, sq mouth, water sz 250.00
Syrup, Hobnail, cranberry, sgn, pat pewter top 290.00
Table set, Hobnail, vaseline opal, 4-pc 375.00
Toothpick holder, Hobnail, amber 30.00
Vase, Hobnail, frosted, str crimped top, 6" 35.00

Homer Laughlin

The Homer Laughlin China Company of Newell, West Virginia, was founded in 1871. The superior dinnerware they displayed at the Centennial Exposition in Philadelphia in 1876 won the highest award of excellence. From that time to the present, they have continued to produce quality dinnerware and kitchenware, many lines of which are becoming very popular collectibles. Most of the dinnerware is marked with the name of the pattern and occasionally with the shape name as well. The 'HLC' trademark is usually followed by a number series, the first two digits of which indicate year of manufacture. See also Fiesta; Harlequin; Riviera.

Amberstone, ash tray 17.00
Amberstone, bowl, vegetable 7.00
Amberstone, casserole 28.00
Amberstone, creamer 5.00
Amberstone, dessert dish 3.00
Amberstone, jam jar, w/lid 30.00
Amberstone, pie plate 23.00
Amberstone, sauce boat stand 16.00
Americana, creamer 5.00
Americana, sauce boat, w/liner 20.00
Americana, sugar bowl, w/lid 9.00
Casualstone, bowl, salad; jumbo, 10" 10.00
Casualstone, bowl, vegetable; rnd 7.00
Casualstone, coffee server 16.00
Casualstone, cup & saucer 6.00
Casualstone, mug, jumbo 6.00
Casualstone, platter, oval, 13" 7.00
Casualstone, sauce boat 8.00
Casualstone, sugar bowl, w/lid 5.00

Conchita, bowl, fruit; 5" 5.50
Conchita, plate, deep; 8" 9.00
Conchita, platter, 11½" 11.00
Epicure, bowl, soup 4.00
Epicure, coffeepot 25.00
Epicure, creamer 5.00
Epicure, plate, 6½" 3.00
Epicure, shakers, pr 7.50
Epicure, teacup & saucer 6.50
Hacienda, bell 28.00
Hacienda, bowl, vegetable; 8" 14.00
Hacienda, casserole, Nautilus 55.00
Hacienda, plate, 6" 3.00
Hacienda, platter, w/oval well, 13½" 14.00
Hacienda, sauce boat 12.00
Hacienda, teapot 35.00
Jubilee, bowl, fruit 2.00
Jubilee, bowl, mixing; Kitchen Kraft, 10" 85.00
Jubilee, casserole 14.00
Jubilee, cup & saucer 4.50
Jubilee, platter, 11" 3.00
Jubilee, sauce boat 6.00
Laughlin Art China, bowl, American Beauty, 10" 90.00
Laughlin Art China, jardiniere, flow blue, 10x14½" 300.00
Laughlin Art China, pot, demitasse; Currant 135.00
Laughlin Art China, vase, Currant, 16" 125.00
Mexicana, bowl, vegetable; 8½" 12.00
Mexicana, cup & saucer 9.00
Mexicana, egg cup, rolled edge 18.00
Mexicana, plate, deep; 8" 9.00
Mexicana, plate, 7" 4.00
Mexicana, platter, 10" 9.00
Mexicana, sauce boat 11.00
Priscilla, bowl, fruit; 9½" 12.00
Priscilla, creamer 5.00
Priscilla, plate, 8" 3.50
Priscilla, sauce boat, 8½" 7.00
Rhythm, bowl, fruit; 5½" 3.00
Rhythm, bowl, mixing; Kitchen Kraft, 6" 55.00
Rhythm, bowl, soup 6.00
Rhythm, cup & saucer 7.00
Rhythm, plate, 6" 2.00
Rhythm, plate, 9" 4.00
Rhythm, platter, 11½" 7.00
Rhythm, sauce boat, cobalt 10.00
Rhythm, spoon rest, gr 145.00
Rhythm, sugar bowl, w/lid 6.00
Rhythm Rose, bowl, nested, med 11.00
Rhythm Rose, casserole, Kitchen Kraft, 8½" 14.00
Rhythm Rose, creamer 4.50
Rhythm Rose, plate, 9" 4.00
Rhythm Rose, platter, 13" 7.00
Rhythm Rose, sugar bowl, w/lid 6.00
Serenade, bowl, nappy, 9" 7.00
Serenade, pickle dish 8.00
Serenade, plate, 10" 7.00
Serenade, shakers, pr 9.00
Serenade, sugar bowl, w/lid 9.00
Serenade, teapot 38.00
Tango, bowl, nappy, 8¾" 6.00
Tango, creamer 4.00
Tango, plate, deep 5.00
Tango, plate, 10" 7.00
Tango, sugar bowl, w/lid 6.50

Conchita, see listings for specific values.

Virginia Rose, bowl, nested, sm .9.00
Virginia Rose, bowl, vegetable; w/lid 30.00
Virginia Rose, bowl, vegetable; 7½" 4.00
Virginia Rose, butter dish,½-lb .45.00
Virginia Rose, cake plate 14.00
Virginia Rose, pitcher, milk; 5" .9.00
Virginia Rose, plate, 10½" 5.50
Virginia Rose, sauce boat 11.00
Wells Art Glaze, bowl, nappy, 8" 6.00
Wells Art Glaze, casserole 20.00
Wells Art Glaze, pickle dish, w/hdls 5.00
Wells Art Glaze, platter, oval, 15½" 11.00
Wells Art Glaze, sauce boat 6.00
Wells Art Glaze, syrup, w/decals 11.00
Wells Art Glaze, teapot 20.00

Hull

The A.E. Hull Pottery was formed in 1905 in Zanesville, Ohio, and in the early years produced stoneware specialities. They expanded in 1907, adding a second plant and employing over two hundred workers. By 1920 they were manufacturing a full line of stoneware, art pottery with both air-brushed and blended glazes, florist pots, and gardenware. They also produced toilet ware and kitchen items with a white semi-porcelain body. Although these continued to be staple products, after the stock market crash of 1929, emphasis was shifted to tile production. By the mid-thirties interest in art pottery production was growing; over the next fifteen years, several lines of matt pastel floral-decorated patterns were designed, consisting of vases, planters, baskets, ewers, and bowls in various sizes.

The Red Riding Hood cookie jar, patented in 1943, proved so successful that a whole line of figural kitchenware and novelty items were added. They continued to be produced well into the fifties. Through the forties their floral artware lines flooded the market, due to the restriction of foreign imports. Although best known for their pastel matt-glazed ware, some of the lines were high gloss. Rosella, glossy coral on a pink clay body, was produced for a short time only; and Magnolia, although offered in a matt glaze, was produced in gloss as well.

The plant was destroyed in 1950 by a flood which resulted in a devastating fire when the floodwater caused the kilns to explode. The company rebuilt and equipped their new factory with the most modern machinery. It was soon apparent that the matt glaze could not be duplicated through the more modern processes, however, and soon attention was concentrated on high-gloss artware lines such as Parchment and Pine and Ebb Tide. Figural planters and novelties, piggy banks, and dinnerware were produced in abundance in the late fifties and sixties. By the mid-seventies dinnerware and florist ware were the mainstay of their business. The firm discontinued operations in 1986.

Our advisor, Brenda Roberts, has compiled a lovely book, *The Collectors Encyclopedia of Hull Pottery*, with full-color photos and current values, which has been recently reprinted. You will find her address in the Directory under Missouri. Mark Supnick (see Directory under Florida) has written a new book, *Collecting Hull Pottery's Red Riding Hood*, published in the summer of 1989.

Advertising plaque, 1938, 5x11" 600.00
Athena, cornucopia, #608, 8½" 15.00
Basket, #79, emb Brn-Eyed Susans, bl hdl 18.00
Blossom, bowl, mixing; #20, 9½" 30.00
Blossom, pitcher, #29, 16-oz 25.00
Blossom, teapot, #26, 42-oz 65.00
Blossomflite, basket, T-2, C in circle, 6" 25.00
Blossomflite, candle holder, T-11, hdls, pr 22.00
Blossomflite, console bowl, T-10, 16½" 50.00

Blossomflite, cornucopia, T-6, metallic interior, 10½" 22.00
Blossomflite, teapot, T-14, 8¼" 40.00
Bouquet, pitcher, #22, 64-oz 65.00
Bouquet, pitcher, #29, 32-oz 30.00
Bouquet, shakers, #25, 3½", pr 25.00
Bow Knot, basket, B-12, 10½" 250.00
Bow Knot, basket, B-25, 6½" 75.00
Bow Knot, bowl, console; B-16, gr & bl, 5¾x4¾x14" 90.00
Bow Knot, cornucopia, dbl, B-13, 13" 75.00
Bow Knot, jardiniere, B-18, 5¾" 50.00
Bow Knot, plaque, B-28, 10" 350.00
Bow Knot, teapot, B-20, 6" 135.00
Bow Knot, vase, B-10, 10½" 110.00
Bow Knot, vase, B-2, 5" 35.00
Bow Knot, vase, B-4, 6½" 50.00
Bow Knot, wall pocket, B-27, whisk broom form, 8" 50.00
Bowl, #25, H in circle, 7" 12.00
Bowl, #34, gr on cream, leaf shape, scalloped, 2½x10½x9" 12.00
Butterfly, bowl, B-7, rectangular, 6x9" 20.00
Butterfly, ewer, B-15, 13½" 75.00
Butterfly, lavabo set & hanger, B-24, B-25 . . . . .75.00
Butterfly, pitcher, B-11, 8¾" 40.00
Butterfly, vase, B-14, triangular, 3-ftd, 10" 20.00
Calla Lily, bowl, #500/32, 10" 70.00
Calla Lily, cornucopia, #570-33-8 . . . . .39.00
Calla Lily, vase, #502/33, 6½" 35.00
Calla Lily, vase, #505, hdls, 6" 40.00
Camellia, basket, hanging; #132, 7" 80.00
Camellia, cornucopia, #101, 8½" 50.00
Camellia, creamer, #111, bl & pk, 5" 20.00
Camellia, ewer, #115, 8½" .80.00
Camellia, vase, #102, 8½" .60.00
Camellia, vase, #103, 8½" .42.50
Camellia, vase, #118, swan form, 6½" 35.00
Camellia, vase, #126, hand form, 8½" 75.00
Camellia, vase, #135, 6¼" .30.00
Camellia, vase, #139, lamp form, 10½" 110.00
Camellia, vase, #143, scalloped top, fan form, 8½" 45.00
Candy dish, gray froth on dk gray, gold trim, w/lid, 9" 22.00
Cinderella, creamer, #28, HP flowers, cream gloss, 4½" dia 15.00
Coronet, swan, #213, wht w/gr trim 20.00
Dancing Girl, #955, 7" 24.00
Debonair, cookie jar, 8¾" 30.00
Dogwood, cornucopia, #522, 4" 25.00
Dogwood, ewer, #505, 6½" 75.00
Dogwood, vase, #509, 6½" 30.00
Dogwood, window box, #508, 10½" 65.00
Early Art, vase, #80-6, H in circle, 8" 25.00
Early Utility, mug, #265, emb Happy Days, H in circle, 4½" . . .20.00
Early Utility, stein, #498, Am Legion, H in circle, 6½" 30.00
Ebb Tide, ewer, E-10, 14½" 80.00
Floral, bowl, mixing; #40, 9" 20.00
Floral, grease jar, #45, 5¾" 20.00
Flowerpot, #150, fluted, bl stippled, wht int 7.50
Flowerpot, #150, med bl gloss, fluted 8.00
House & Garden, pitcher, brn, 9½" 12.00
Imperial, bowl, #117, dk gr, basketweave, 9" 5.00
Imperial, planter, A-10, leaf panels, olive/brn, 3½x7x7" 6.00
Iris, ewer, #401, 13½" 170.00
Iris, vase, #402, 7" 45.00
Magnolia, glossy; basket, H-14, 10½" 95.00
Magnolia, glossy; candle holder, H-24, 4", pr 40.00
Magnolia, glossy; centerpiece, H-23, ftd, 13" 35.00
Magnolia, glossy; creamer, H-21 . . . . .9.00

Magnolia, glossy; ewer, H-11, bl floral, 8½" 35.00
Magnolia, glossy; teapot, H-20, 6½" 55.00
Magnolia, glossy; vase, H-2, pk, hdls, 5½" 16.00
Magnolia, glossy; vase, H-6, bl floral, 6½" 20.00
Magnolia, glossy; vase, H-8, gold trim, 8½" 40.00
Magnolia, matt; console bowl, #26, 12½" 60.00
Magnolia, matt; cornucopia, #19, 8½" 50.00
Magnolia, matt; creamer, #24, 3¾" 20.00
Magnolia, matt; pitcher vase, #14, ftd, 4¾" 25.00
Magnolia, matt; sugar bowl, #25, 3¾" 20.00
Magnolia, matt; vase, #12, 6¼" 25.00
Magnolia, matt; vase, #17, 12¼" 100.00
Magnolia, matt; vase, #2, 8½" 40.00
Magnolia, matt; vase, #3, side hdls, 8½" 34.00
Magnolia, matt; vase, #9, 10½" 65.00
Mardi Gras, vase, #49, Deco, pk & bl, ftd, matt, 9" 30.00
Mirror Brown, coffee server, w/lid 12.00

Ebb Tide pitcher,
14", $70.00.

Nuline Bak-Serve, bean pot, w/lid, B-19, 5½" 30.00
Nuline Bak-Serve, custard, B-14, 2¾" 5.00
Nuline Bak-Serve, pitcher, C-29, 7" 25.00
Old Spice, mug, ship Grand Turk decor 12.00
Orchid, bud vase, #306, 6¾" 40.00
Orchid, lamp base, 10" 170.00
Orchid, vase, #302, 4¾" 25.00
Orchid, vase, #304, hdls, 10¾" 150.00
Parchment & Pine, basket, S-3, 8" 42.00
Parchment & Pine, cornucopia, S-2, 7¾" 25.00
Parchment & Pine, cornucopia, S-6, 11¾" 40.00
Parchment & Pine, vase, S-1, 6½" 18.00
Pitcher, beer; stoneware, w/6 steins 200.00
Planter, #104, duck, purple & gr 30.00
Planter, #154, lt gr, melon rib, oval, 8½" 6.00
Planter, #204, lady's head, rose beige gloss, 5½" 23.00
Planter, #38, poodle, bl/pk hat & bow, ivory face, yel hair 32.00
Planter, #43, roses, pk & cream gloss, ftd, 6¼" 22.00
Planter, #61, kitten, ivory, 7¾x7" 20.00
Planter, #61, pheasant, mc, 8" 22.00
Planter, #71, scrolled, gr int, pk ext, 12¾" 20.00
Planter, #80, swan, bow tie, gr & pk, 7¼x6" 20.00
Planter, #94, twin geese, 10" 30.00
Planter, #954, Colonial lady, cream & bl gloss, 8" 20.00
Planter, F-11, gr, scrolled rim, vertical rib, 6½x4¾x2¼" 5.00
Planter, F-8, leaf relief, dk gr, 6¼x3" 5.00

Planter, goose, flying 15.00
Poppy, ewer, #610, 13½" 300.00
Poppy, planter, #602, 6½" 60.00
Poppy, vase, #607, 6½" 40.00
Red Riding Hood, bank, standing 175.00
Red Riding Hood, bank, wall hanging 300.00
Red Riding Hood, butter dish 150.00
Red Riding Hood, canister, cereal 300.00
Red Riding Hood, canister, salt 325.00
Red Riding Hood, canister, tea, coffee, sugar, or flour; ea 225.00

Red Riding Hood cookie jar,
$95.00.

Red Riding Hood, creamer, side pour 40.00
Red Riding Hood, creamer, tab hdl 55.00
Red Riding Hood, jar, dresser; w/bow, 9" 175.00
Red Riding Hood, jar, wolf (any) 300.00
Red Riding Hood, lamp 500.00
Red Riding Hood, matchbox, wall hanging 300.00
Red Riding Hood, mustard jar, w/lid & spoon 175.00
Red Riding Hood, pitcher, batter 120.00
Red Riding Hood, pitcher, side pour, 7" 95.00
Red Riding Hood, pitcher, standing milk 95.00
Red Riding Hood, shakers, lg pr 35.00
Red Riding Hood, shakers, sm, pr 25.00
Red Riding Hood, spice jar (all types) 200.00
Red Riding Hood, string holder 315.00
Red Riding Hood, sugar bowl, open 35.00
Red Riding Hood, sugar bowl, w/lid 125.00
Red Riding Hood, syrup pitcher 85.00
Red Riding Hood, teapot or hot chocolate pot, ea 95.00
Red Riding Hood, wall pocket/planter 195.00
Rosella, basket, R-12, 7" 80.00
Rosella, creamer, R-3, 5½" 15.00
Rosella, sugar bowl, open, R-4, 5½" 20.00
Rosella, vase, R-1, glossy, 5⅜" 20.00
Rosella, vase, R-2, 5" 20.00
Royal, basket, W-9, 8¾" 25.00
Royal, jardiniere, #75, 7" 24.00
Serenade, ash tray, S-23, 13x10½" 35.00
Serenade, basket, S-14, 12x11½" 125.00
Serenade, candy dish, S-3, 8¼" 40.00
Serenade, casserole, w/lid, 9" 40.00
Serenade, ewer, S-2, 6½" 30.00
Serenade, pitcher, S-21, 10½" 55.00
Serenade, vase, S-4, hat form, 5¼" 26.00
Sueno Tulip, bud vase, #104-33, 6" 35.00

Sueno Tulip, jardiniere, #115-33, 7" 90.00
Sueno Tulip, jardiniere, #117-30, bl, 4x5" 35.00
Sueno Tulip, vase, #103-33, 6" 75.00
Sueno Tulip, vase, #107-33, 6" 35.00
Sun Glow, bowl, #50, 9½" 20.00
Sun Glow, flowerpot, #98, 7½" 20.00
Sun Glow, pitcher, #52, 24-oz 20.00
Sun Glow, vase, #89, 5½" 15.00
Sun Glow, vase, #95, 8½" 25.00
Sun Glow, wall pocket, #82, whisk broom, 8¼" 20.00
Thistle, vase, #53, 6½" 25.00
Tokay, basket, #11, half-moon form, 10½" 50.00
Tokay, cornucopia, #10, 10¾" 22.00
Tokay, urn, #5, 5½" 22.00
Tuscany, dish, #19, leaf form, 13" 20.00
Urn, #419, wht matt, horizontal rib, 6" 7.00
Vase, #108, maroon w/gr on tan gloss, suspended, hdl, 8x6" . .22.00
Vase, #73, Bird of Paradise, yel & gr 16.00
Vase, #99, Unicorn, gr & gold, 11½" 35.00
Vase, dbl bud; peach & gr, 9¼" 22.00
Wall pocket, #84, mandolin, wht gloss 24.00
Water Lily, candle holder, L-22, 4½", pr 50.00
Water Lily, cornucopia, L-27, 12" .65.00
Water Lily, creamer, L-19, 5" 25.00
Water Lily, ewer, L-17, 13½" 155.00
Water Lily, jardiniere, L-23, 5½" .42.00
Water Lily, sugar bowl, L-20, w/lid, 5" 25.00
Water Lily, vase, L-1, apricot & walnut, 5½" 25.00
Water Lily, vase, L-13, 10½" 70.00
Water Lily, vase, L-5, 6½" 25.00
Water Lily, vase, L-9, 8½" 60.00
Wildflower, basket, W-16, 10½" .110.00
Wildflower, cornucopia, #58, 6¼" 35.00
Wildflower, cornucopia, W-7, 7½" 45.00
Wildflower, ewer, W-11, 8½" 70.00
Wildflower, ewer, W-19, 13½" 150.00
Wildflower, sugar bowl, open, #74, 4¾" 35.00
Wildflower, vase, #71, 12" 135.00
Wildflower, vase, W-15, 10½" 60.00
Wildflower, vase, W-3, 5½" 25.00
Wildflower, vase, W-5, 6½" 40.00
Wildflower, vase, W-6, 7½" 40.00
Window box, #74, gr w/wht foam 8.00
Woodland, glossy; candle holder, W-30, pr 35.00
Woodland, glossy; cornucopia, W-10, 11" 30.00
Woodland, glossy; cornucopia, W-2, 5½" 20.00
Woodland, glossy; jardiniere, W-7, 5½" 28.00
Woodland, glossy; lamp base, incised M Wilson, 1952, 14¾" . .240.00
Woodland, glossy; teapot, w/lid 45.00
Woodland, glossy; wall pocket 30.00
Woodland, matt; basket, hanging; W-31, 5½" 75.00
Woodland, matt; cornucopia, dbl, W-23, 14" 200.00
Woodland, matt; cornucopia, W-10, 11" 35.00
Woodland, matt; vase, W-1, 5½" .30.00
Woodland, matt; vase, W-16, 8½" 50.00
Woodland, matt; wall pocket, W-13, 7½" 55.00

Hummel

Hummel figurines were created through the artistry of Berta Hummel, a Franciscan nun called Sister M. Innocentia. The first figures were made about 1935 by Franz Goebel of Goebel Art Inc., Rodental, West Germany. Plates, plaques, and candy dishes are also produced; and the older, discon-tinued editions are highly-sought collectibles. Generally speaking, an issue can be dated by the trademark. The first Hummels, from 1934-1950, were either incised or stamped with the 'Crown WG' mark. The 'full bee in V' mark was employed with minor variations until 1959. At that time the bee was stylized and represented by a solid disk with angled symmetrical wings completely contained within the confines of the 'V.' The three-line mark, 1964-1972, utilized the stylized bee and included a three-line arrangement, 'c by W. Goebel, W. Germany.' Another change in 1970 saw the 'stylized bee in V' suspended between the vertical bars of the 'b' and 'l' of a printed 'Goebel, West Germany.' Collectors refer to this mark as the 'last bee' or 'Goebel bee.' The current mark in use since 1979 omits the 'bee in V.' For a more thorough study of the subject we recommend *Hummel Figurines and Plates, A Collectors Identification and Value Guide*, by Carl Luckey, available at your local book dealer. Idiosyncrasies in the numerical order of the following listings are due to computer sorting.

Key:
ce — closed edition   GB — Goebel bee
CM — crown mark   SB — stylized bee
FB — full bee

Knitting Lesson, #256, 3-line mark, 7½", $350.00.

#III/110, Let's Sing, candy box, 3-line mk, 6" 165.00
#III/53, Joyful, candy box, FB, 6¼" 325.00
#III/57, Chick Girl, candy box, FB, 5¼" 325.00
#III/58, Playmates, candy box, FB, 5¼" 335.00
#III/69, Happy Pastime, candy box, FB, 6" 335.00
#10/I, Flower Madonna, wht, SB, 9½" 90.00
#10/III, Flower Madonna, color, SB, 13" 375.00
#109/II, Happy Traveller, SB, 8" 255.00
#109/0, Happy Traveller, SB, 5" 70.00
#11/0, Merry Wanderer, 3-line mk, 4¾" 90.00
#110/I, Let's Sing, FB, 3⅞" 180.00
#112/I, Just Resting, FB, 5" 230.00
#113, Heavenly Song, candle holder, SB, 3½x4¾" 5,000.00
#114, Let's Sing, ash tray, 3-line mk, 3½x6¾" 80.00
#115/116/117, Advent Group, candle holder, SB, 3½", set 125.00
#118, Little Thrifty, 3-line mk, 5" 85.00
#119, Postman, SB, 5¼" 110.00
#12/I, Chimney Sweep, 3-line mk, 5½" 110.00
#12/2/0, Chimney Sweep, 3-line mk, 4" 90.00
#123, Max & Moritz, 3-line mk, 5¼" 115.00

#124/I, Hello, 3-line mk, 7" 140.00
#124/0, Hello, FB, 6¼" 190.00
#125, Vacation Time, plaque, 3-line mk, 4x4¾" 160.00
#126, Retreat to Safety, plaque, FB, 4¾x5" 250.00
#127, Doctor, FB, 4¾" 140.00
#128, Baker, SB, 4¾" 80.00
#129, Band Leader, SB, 5¼" 115.00
#13/V, Meditation, 3-line mk, 13¾" 1,200.00
#13/0, Meditation, FB, 6" 180.00
#130, Duet, FB, 5¼" 265.00
#131, Street Singer, 3-line mk, 5" 85.00
#132, Star Gazer, FB, 4¾" 220.00
#133, Mother's Helper, SB, 5" 115.00
#134, Quartet, plaque, SB, 6x6" 225.00
#135, Soloist, 3-line mk, 4¾" 70.00
#136/V, Friends, SB, 10¾" 680.00
#137/B, Child-in-Bed, plaque, SB, 2¾x2¾" dia 45.00
#139, Flitting Butterfly, plaque, 3-line mk, 2½x2½" 40.00
#14/A & B, Bookworms, bookends, SB, 5½" 300.00
#140, Mail Coach, plaque, FB, 4½x6¼" 300.00
#141/3/0, Apple Tree Girl, SB, 4" 75.00
#142/3/0, Apple Tree Boy, 3-line mk, 4" 90.00
#144, Angelic Song, 3-line mk, 4¼" 100.00
#145, Little Guardian, SB, 3¾" 70.00
#147, Devotion or Angel Shrine, font, FB, 3x5" 60.00
#15/II, Hear Ye Hear Ye, 3-line mk, 7½" 230.00
#150/2/0, Happy Days, FB, 4¼" 150.00
#152/A/II, Umbrella Boy, 3-line mk, 8" 935.00
#152/A/0, Umbrella Boy, SB, 5" 400.00
#152/B/0, Umbrella Girl, FB, 4¾" 600.00
#153/0, Auf Wiedersehen, SB, 7" 160.00
#154/I, Waiter, CM, 7" 650.00
#16/I, Little Hiker, 3-line mk, 5½" 100.00
#163, Whitsuntide, 3-line mk, 7¼" 195.00
#164, Worship, FB, 2¾x4¾" 60.00
#166, Boy w/Bird, ash tray, 3-line mk, 3¼x6¼" 100.00
#167, Seated Angel w/Bird, font, FB, 3¼x4¼" 60.00
#168, Standing Boy, plaque, FB, 4⅛x5½" 675.00
#170/III, School Boys, FB, 10" 2,200.00
#171, Little Sweeper, 3-line mk, 4½" 85.00
#172/II, Festival Harmony, SB, 10¾" 275.00
#174, She Loves Me She Loves Me Not, 3-line mk, 4¼" ...100.00
#175, Mother's Darling, SB, 5½" 185.00
#176/0, Happy Birthday, FB, 5½" 200.00
#177/III, School Girls, CM, 9½" 2,250.00
#179, Coquettes, SB, 5¼" 165.00
#18, Christ Child, FB, 2x6" 125.00
#180, Tuneful Goodnight, plaque, SB, 4x4¾" 245.00
#182, Good Friends, FB, 4" 200.00
#183, Forest Shrine, SB, 7x9" 495.00
#186, Sweet Music, 3-line mk, 5¼" 105.00
#188, Celestial Musician, 3-line mk, 7" 180.00
#194, Watchful Angel, FB, 6½" 300.00
#195/2/0, Barnyard Hero, 3-line mk, 4" 100.00
#197/2/0, Be Patient, SB, 4¼" 120.00
#199/0, Feeding Time, FB, 4¼" 200.00
#20, Prayer Before Battle, 3-line mk, 4¼" 90.00
#200/0, Little Goat Herder, 3-line mk, 4¾" 135.00
#203/2/0, Signs of Spring, FB, 4" 180.00
#204, Weary Wanderer, SB, 6" 165.00
#207, Heavenly Angel, font, SB, 2x4¾" 30.00
#21/0, Heavenly Angel, CM, 4¼" 250.00
#21/0/2, Heavenly Angel, 3-line mk, 6" 90.00
#217, Boy w/Toothache, 3-line mk, 5½" 120.00

#218/0, Birthday Serenade, FB, 5¼" 645.00
#22/0, Angel w/Birds, font, 3-line mk, 2¾x3½" 25.00
#220/2/0, We Congratulate, 3-line mk, 4" 110.00
#226, Mail Coach, SB, 4¼x6¼" 395.00
#227, She Loves Me She Loves Me Not, table lamp, SB, 7½" ..210.00
#229, Apple Tree Girl, table lamp, 3-line mk, 7½" 250.00
#23/III, Adoration, SB, 9" 275.00
#230, Apple Tree Boy, table lamp, FB, 7½" 695.00
#24/I, Lullaby, candle holder, 3-line mk, 3¼x5" 100.00
#24/III, Lullaby, candle holder, FB, 6x8" 700.00
#243, Madonna & Child, font, SB, 3¼x4" 35.00
#246, Holy Family, font, 3-line mk, 3x4" 30.00
#25, Angelic Sleep, candle holder, 3-line mk, 3½x5" 105.00
#256, Knitting Lesson, SB, 7½" 425.00
#258, Which Hand?, 3-line mk, 5¼" 80.00
#26/0, Child Jesus, font, SB, 5x1½" 30.00
#262, Heavenly Lullaby, SB, 3½x5" 235.00
#27/III, Joyous News, SB, 4¼x4¾" 750.00
#28/II, Wayside Devotion, 3-line mk, 7½" 200.00
#28/III, Wayside Devotion, SB, 8½" 285.00
#307, Good Hunting, SB, 5¼" 125.00
#311, Kiss Me, no socks, 3-line mk, 6" 120.00
#315, Mountaineer, SB, 5¼" 695.00
#317, Not For You, 3-line mk, 6" 120.00
#32/0, Little Gabriel, 3-line mk, 5" 75.00
#322, Pharmacist, SB, 6" 800.00
#33, Joyful, ash tray, FB, 3½x6" 160.00
#332, Soldier Boy, 3-line mk, 6" 110.00
#336, Close Harmony, 3-line mk, 5½" 200.00
#337, Cinderella, eyes closed, 3-line mk, 5½" 180.00
#34, Singing Lesson, ash tray, 3-line mk, 3½x6¼" 100.00
#340, Letter to Santa Claus, SB, 7" 2,500.00
#35/I, The Good Shepherd, font, SB, 2¾x5¾" 100.00
#357, Guiding Angel, 3-line mk, 2¾" 50.00
#36/I, Child w/Flowers, font, SB, 3½x4½" 100.00
#367, Busy Student, SB, 4¼" 495.00

Follow the Leader, #369, 3-line mark, 7", $750.00.

#37, Herald Angels, candle holder, 3-line mk, 2¼x4" 105.00
#378, Easter Greetings, 3-line mk, 5½" 340.00
#392, Little Band, 3-line mk, 4¾x3" 160.00

#42/0, Good Shepherd, SB, 6¼" 90.00
#42/1, Good Shepherd, FB, 7½" 2,500.00
#43, March Winds, 3-line mk, 5" 80.00
#44/A, Culprits, table lamp, 3-line mk, 9½" 250.00
#44/B, Out of Danger, table lamp, SB, 9½" 300.00
#45/0, Madonna w/Halo, 3-line mk, 10½" 50.00
#46/0, Madonna w/o Halo, FB, 10¼" 100.00
#47/II, Goose Girl, 3-line mk, 7½" 300.00
#47/3/0, Goose Girl, FB, 4" 165.00
#48/V, Madonna, plaque, CM, 8¼x10½" 2,250.00
#48/0, Madonna, plaque, SB, 3x4" 70.00
#49/I, To Market, 3-line mk, 6¼" 300.00
#49/3/0, To Market, SB, 4" 135.00
#50/0, Volunteers, FB, 5½" 245.00
#51/I, Village Boy, SB, 7¼" 150.00
#51/0, Village Boy, FB, 6" 220.00
#52/I, Going to Grandma's, SB, 6" 300.00
#54, Silent Night, candle holder, 3-line mk, 4¾x5½" 150.00
#55, St George, 3-line mk, 6¾" 225.00
#56/A, Culprits, FB, 6¼" 250.00
#56/B, Out of Danger, 3-line mk, 6¼" 130.00
#57/I, Chick Girl, SB, 4¼" 165.00
#57/0, Chick Girl, 3-line mk, 3½" 100.00
#58/I, Playmates, 3-line mk, 4½" 160.00
#58/0, Playmates, FB, 4" 165.00
#59, Skier, SB, 5¼" 140.00
#61/A & B, Playmates & Chick Girl, bookends, FB, 6" 500.00
#62, Happy Pastime, ash tray, 3-line mk, 3½x6¼" 125.00
#63, Singing Lesson, SB, 2¾" 75.00
#65, Farewell, CM, 4¾" 650.00
#66, Farm Boy, 3-line mk, 5¼" 135.00
#67, Doll Mother, 3-line mk, 4¾" 150.00
#68/0, Lost Sheep, SB, 5½" 95.00
#68/2/0, Lost Sheep, 3-line mk, 4½" .90.00
#69, Happy Pastime, 3-line mk, 3¼" 100.00
#70, The Holy Child, 3-line mk, 6¾" .80.00
#71, Stormy Weather, SB, 6¼" 300.00
#72, Spring Cheer, 3-line mk, 5" 70.00
#73, Little Helper, FB, 4¼" 140.00
#74, Little Gardener, 3-line mk, 4¼" .85.00
#75, White Angel, font, 3-line mk, 1¾x3½" 25.00
#78/III, Infant of Krumbad, FB, 5¼" .60.00
#78/VI, Infant of Krumbad, SB, 10" .150.00
#78/VIII, Infant of Krumbad, SB, 13½" 250.00
#78/0, Infant of Krumbad, 3-line mk, 1¾" 100.00
#79, Globe Trotter, SB, 5" 110.00
#80, Little Scholar, SB, 5½" 110.00
#81/0, School Girl, 3-line mk, 5¼" 90.00
#81/2/0, School Girl, 3-line mk, 4¼" .85.00
#82/II, School Boy, FB 7½" 500.00
#82/2/0, School Boy, 3-line mk, 4" 90.00
#83, Angel Serenade w/Lamb, SB, 5" 200.00
#84/V, 84/5, Worship, SB, 13" 800.00
#85/0, Serenade, FB, 4¾" 140.00
#86, Happiness, SB, 4¾" 85.00
#87, For Father, FB, 5½" 200.00
#88/I, Heavenly Protection, 3-line mk, 6¾" 250.00
#89/I, Little Cellist, SB, 6" 120.00
#89/II, Little Cellist, 3-line mk, 8" 300.00
#91/A & B, Angel at Prayer, font, SB, 2x4¾", pr 50.00
#92, Merry Wanderer, 3-line mk, 4¾x5⅛" 100.00
#93, Little Fiddler, plaque, SB, 4¾x5⅛" 100.00
#94/3/0, Surprise, 3-line mk, 4¼" 110.00
#95, Brother, 3-line mk, 5½" 100.00

#96, Little Shopper, 3-line mk, 4¾" .100.00
#98/0, Sister, 3-line mk, 5¾" 100.00
#98/2/0, Sister, SB, 4¾" 75.00
#99, Eventide, CM, 4¾" 700.00

Hutschenreuther

Sources do not agree as to when the Carl Hutschenreuther factory was initially established in the Bavarian district of Germany. Most indicate a year near the middle of the 19th century. Carl's sons, Christian and Lorenz, later formed their own companies and operated independently until 1969. At that time Carl and Lorenz merged; and that firm is still in business today producing limited edition plates, figurines, dinnerware, and other fine china.

Our advisor for this category is Jack Gunsaulus; he is listed in the Directory under Michigan.

Dresser set, geometric floral, 5-pc, on 12" gold tray 150.00
Figurine, dancer, leaping/arms raised, sgn K Tutter, 11" 220.00
Figurine, jungle cat, 9½" 250.00
Figurine, nude, wht on gold ball, 1930 . . . . .225.00
Figurine, tigers, Art Deco, 1920s, 9½" 750.00
Plaque, portrait of lady, sgn Wagner, #107, 6x4" 750.00
Plate, Clementine portrait, sgn, gr/pk paneled rim, 9½" 700.00
Plate, Indian brave decal w/HP details, gilt border, 12" 45.00
Plate, mc floral w/18k gold, sgn F Prissy, mk, 8" 30.00
Plate, pheasant, artist sgn, 8" 25.00
Plate, pk/gilt bands, 1900s, 10½", set of 12 . . . . .650.00

Cabinet plates painted by Vorberger, ca 1900, 9½" diameter, $700.00 each.

Imari

Imari is a generic term which covers a broad family of wares. It was made in more than a dozen Japanese villages, but the name is that of the port from whence it was shipped to Europe. There are several types of Imari. The most common features a design with panels of birds, florals, or people surrounding a central basket of flowers. The colors used in this type are underglaze blue with overglaze red, gold, and green enamels. The Chinese also made Imari wares which differ from the Japanese type in several ways — the absence of spur marks, a thinner-type body, and a more consistent control of the blue. Imari-type wares were copied on the continent by Meissen and by English potters, among them Worcester, Derby, and Bow.

Bowl, bird/gardens, fluted, 1850, 10" 150.00
Bowl, brocade panels/shippo-tsunagi bands, bell form, 8" 90.00
Bowl, dragon pursuing pearl, ext w/leaves & peaches, 2x6" . . .130.00
Bowl, floral medallion & rim panels, deep, 1830s, 11" 550.00
Bowl, garden w/flower vases, floral rim, 1880s, 11" 195.00

Bowl, mythological horse in floral/fretwork surround, 9" 275.00
Bowl, phoenix bird in flowering landscape, octagonal, 9" 400.00
Bowl, sailing vessel w/3 men on deck, 1830s, 11" 1,000.00
Bowl, vase of flowers, 2 floral borders, 1700s, 11" 500.00
Bowl, 3 Friends, hexagonals/floral rim, 1700s, w/lid, 5" 90.00
Charger, flowering urn, vignette border w/tree, 18" 350.00
Charger, potted plant center, brocade bands, 1880s, 12" 150.00
Charger, rnd reserve w/rose-sprouting tree, 1880s, 16" 325.00
Charger, sm phoenix bird & pinwheels, 1880s, 16" 250.00
Charger, warriors at abyss, brocade rim, Meiji, 13" 425.00
Charger, 3 dragons/clouds/pearls in border, 1800s, 18", pr ...1,200.00
Dish, floral twigs in sm floral medallion, shell form, 8" 700.00
Dish, flying phoenix/paulownia tree, peach form, Meiji, 9" 500.00
Figurine, geisha in traditional costume, 1880s, 15" 400.00
Platter, floral reserves on bird/floral ground, lobed, 18" 750.00
Platter, peonies/rocks, center: single flower, 1700s, 11" 250.00
Tray, basket w/floral twigs, floral reserves, 8-sided, 14" 825.00
Vase, bijin in fan-shaped reserves, brocade ground, 23" 1,200.00
Vase, children in garden reserve on millefiori, 1800s, 16" 350.00
Vase, floral/fans, teakwood stand, 1800s, 20" 800.00

Vases, orange on white reserves within a millefiori
field, 19th century, 16", $600.00 for the pair.

Imperial Glass

Although the Imperial Glass Company was organized in 1901, it was not until three years later that they began to manufacture glassware. Their early products were jelly glasses, hotel tumblers, etc.; but by 1910 they were making a name for themselves by pressing quantities of Carnival Glass, the iridescent colored glassware that was popular during that time. From 1916 to 1920, they used the lustre process to make a line they called Imperial Jewels, now referred to as stretch glass. Opalescent glassware was introduced in the thirties and was made in Sea Foam, Harding Blue, Moss Green, and Burnt Almond. In contrast to their colored lines, Candlewick was a simple pattern in crystal glass, yet one for which the company is best known. (All of these types are listed by specific category in this book.) Free-Hand Ware, art glass made entirely by hand using no molds, was made for a short time only from about 1923 to 1928. Nu-Cut was made to imitate cut glass; it was produced in crystal as well as color and was introduced in 1914.

The company closed in 1931 but soon reorganized and reopened as the Imperial Glass Corporation. In 1940 they bought the molds and assets of the Central Glass Works of Wheeling, West Virginia, and in 1958 they purchased molds from Cambridge and Heisey. Although Imperial later used these molds to reproduce the older pieces, since 1951 they have indicated their issues with the 'I' superimposed over a 'G' trademark. The company sold out to Lenox in 1973 but continues today to make hand-pressed giftware items. See also Animal Dishes with Covers; Candlewick; Carnival Glass; Opalescent Glass; Stretch Glass.

Animals and Birds

Dog, Airdale, cobalt 35.00
Dog, Champ Terrier, caramel slag 200.00
Donkey, caramel slag, mk Heisey 50.00
Duck, caramel slag 18.00
Elephant, gr carnival, mk Heisey, ltd ed, med 50.00
Pony, standing/rearing/or kicking, ultra bl, mk Heisey, ea ...20.00
Rabbit, paperweight, milk glass, mk Heisey 10.00
Swan, caramel slag, mk, 9¼" 95.00
Swan, purple slag, 4" 38.00
Wood duck, caramel slag 27.50

Bookends, Cathay, concubine, satin, pr 285.00
Bottle, bar; Cape Cod, #244, w/stopper 60.00
Bowl, apple baker; Cape Cod, 6" 8.00
Bowl, Cape Cod, bl, 5" 20.00
Bowl, Cape Cod, 6" 5.00
Bowl, fruit; Cape Cod, 4½" 3.00
Butter dish, Cape Cod 25.00
Cake plate, Cape Cod, 72-candle, rare 125.00
Cake stand, Cape Cod, 11" 42.00
Candlestick, Cathay, dragon 115.00
Champagne, Cape Cod, #1602 ....6.00
Claret, Cape Cod 7.50
Coaster, Cape Cod, amber, 4¼" 14.00
Cocktail, Cape Cod, 3½-oz 8.00
Compote, Cape Cod, ftd, w/lid, 6" 45.00
Cordial, Cape Cod 10.00
Creamer & sugar bowl, Cape Cod 15.00
Cruet, Cape Cod, #160/119, 4-oz, w/stopper 20.00
Decanter, Cape Cod, 24-oz 50.00
Epergne, 2-pc, rare 165.00
Goblet, Cape Cod, red, 11-oz 20.00
Goblet, Cape Cod, 11-oz 10.00
Goblet, Cape Cod, 7-oz 7.00
Gravy boat, Cape Cod, 18-oz 55.00
Horseradish, Cape Cod 65.00
Marmalade, Cape Cod 15.00
Martini mixer, Big Shot Series, red 85.00
Multiserver, Cape Cod, #160/93, 12" 45.00
Mustard, Cape Cod, 3-pc 27.50
Old Fashioned, Cape Cod, #160 ....7.00
Parfait, Cape Cod 12.50
Pitcher, Cape Cod, milk sz, 16-oz 35.00
Pitcher, Cape Cod, 60-oz 65.00
Plate, Cape Cod, cupped, 14" 20.00
Plate, Cape Cod, 10" 30.00
Plate, Cape Cod, 4½" 4.50
Plate, Cape Cod, 8" 9.00
Punch set, Cape Cod, 15-pc 200.00
Relish, Cape Cod, 3-part, 9½" 18.00
Relish, Cape Cod, 4-part, 9" 30.00
Relish, Cape Cod, 6-part, 11¼" 30.00
Salt & pepper mill, Cape Cod 40.00
Shakers, Cape Cod, ftd, pr 8.00

Shakers, Cape Cod, pr+tray 22.00
Sherbet, Cape Cod, high 6.00
Sherbet, Cape Cod, low 4.00
Sunday, Cape Cod, #1602 . . . . .5.50
Tumbler, Big Shot Series, ruby, 12-oz 15.00
Tumbler, Big Shot Series, ruby, 16-oz 20.00
Tumbler, Cape Cod, ftd, 6-oz 8.00
Tumbler, iced tea; Cape Cod, flat 8.00
Vase, freehand, bl/gold textured irid, flared, 5" 110.00
Vase, freehand, hearts on cobalt, paper label, 10" 250.00
Vase, freehand, leaves/veins, bl on wht, gilt int, 6" 325.00
Vase, freehand, open hearts & vines, emerald gr, 9" 175.00
Vase, freehand, trailing vines on bl, baluster, label, 11¾" 325.00
Whiskey, Cape Cod 10.00
Wine, Cape Cod, #1602, 3½" 7.00

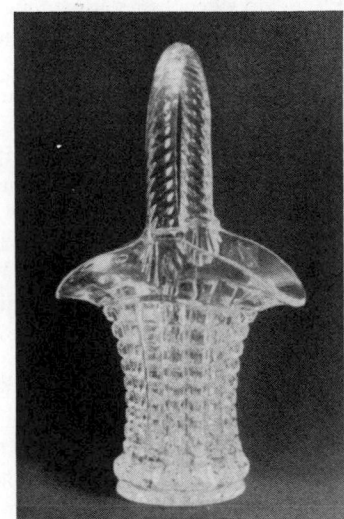

Basket, 9½", $35.00.

Imperial Porcelain

The Blue Ridge Mountain Boys were created by cartoonist Paul Webb and translated into three-dimension by the Imperial Porcelain Corporation of Zanesville, Ohio, in 1947. These figurines decorated ash trays, vases, mugs, bowls, pitchers, planters, and other items. The Mountain Boys series were numbered 92 through 108, each with a different and amusing portrayal of mountain life. Imperial also produced American Folklore miniatures, twenty-three tiny animals one inch or less in size, and the Al Capp Dogpatch series. Because of financial difficulties, the company closed in 1960.

American Folklore Miniatures

Cat, 1½" 40.00
Cow, 1¾" 35.00
Hound dogs 35.00
Plaque, store ad, Am Folklore Porcelain Miniatures, 4½" 300.00
Sow 30.00

Blue Ridge Mountain Boys by Paul Webb

Ash tray, #101, man w/jug & snake .75.00
Ash tray, #103, hillbilly & skunk 75.00
Ash tray, #105, baby, hound dog, & frog 110.00
Ash tray, #106, Barrel of Wishes, w/hound 75.00
Ash tray, #92, 2 men by tree stump, for pipes 125.00

Box, cigarette; #98, dog atop, baby at door, sq 115.00
Decanter, #100, outhouse, man, & bird 75.00
Decanter, #104, Ma leaning over stump, w/baby & skunk 95.00
Decanter, man, jug, snake, & tree stump, Hispch Inc, 1946 . . . .75.00
Figurine, #101, man leans against tree trunk, 5" 75.00
Figurine, man on hands & knees, 3" .80.00
Figurine, man sitting, 3½" 85.00
Figurine, man sitting w/chicken on knee, 3" 95.00
Jug, #101, Willie & snake 75.00

Mug, Bearing Down, #94, $85.00.

Mug, #94, dbl baby hdl, 4¼" 95.00
Mug, #94, ma hdl, 4¼" 75.00
Mug, #94, man w/bl pants hdl, 4¼" .75.00
Mug, #94, man w/yel beard & red pants hdl, 4¼" 75.00
Mug, #99, Target Practice, boy on goat, farmer, 5¾" 85.00
Pitcher, lemonade 200.00
Plack, store ad, Handcrafted Paul Webb Mtn Boys, rare, 9" . . .500.00
Planter, #100, outhouse, man, & bird 75.00
Planter, #104, Ma leaning over stump, w/baby & skunk 95.00
Planter, #105, man w/chicken on knee, washtub 110.00
Planter, #110, man, w/jug & snake, 4½" 65.00
Planter, #81, man drinking from jug, sitting by washtub 75.00
Shakers, Ma & Old Doc, pr 95.00

Miscellaneous

Items in this section that are designated 'IP' are miscellaneous novelties made by Imperial Porcelain; the remainder are of interest to Paul Webb collectors, though made by an unknown manufacturer. Prints on calendars and playing cards are signed 'Paul Webb.'

Calendar, 1954, 12 sgn scenes, Brown & Bigelow, complete 35.00
Figurine, cat in high-heeled shoe, 5½" L 40.00
Hot pad, Dutch boy w/tulips, rnd, IP 30.00
Ink blotters, sgn scenes, ea 8.00
Mug, #29, man hdl, sgn Paul Webb, 4¾" 25.00
Planter, #106, dog sitting by tub, IP .75.00
Planter, #26, man & tree stump, sgn Paul Webb, bl 25.00
Planter, #27, man, jug, & barrel, sgn Paul Webb 25.00
Planter, #81, Uncle Rafe, dog by washtub, IP, 4" L 75.00
Playing cards, ad: Rafe Oiling Gun, Brown & Bigelow, MIB 45.00
Shakers, pigs, 5", pr 95.00

Shakers, standing pigs, IP, 8", pr 95.00

Indian Tree

Indian Tree was a popular dinnerware pattern produced by various potteries since the early 1800s to recent times. Although backgrounds and borders vary, the Oriental theme is carried out with the gnarled, brown branch of a pink-blossomed tree. Among the manufacturers' marks, you may find represented such notable firms as Coalport, S. Hancock and Sons, Soho Pottery, and John Maddock and Sons.

Bowl, Johnson Bros, 5½" 4.00
Bowl, Johnson Bros, 7" 6.50
Bowl, vegetable; Johnson Bros, w/lid 35.00
Cheese dish, Copeland, 9" 55.00
Creamer, Johnson Bros 5.00
Cup & saucer, Johnson Bros 7.00
Plate, Johnson Bros, 10" 6.00
Plate, Johnson Bros, 6" 2.50

Platter, marked Hancock & Sons, 11½", $30.00.

Inkwells and Inkstands

Receptacles for various writing fluids have been used since ancient times. Through the years they have been made from countless materials — glass, metal, porcelain, pottery, wood, and even papier-mache. During the 18th century, gold or silver inkstands were presented to royalty; the well-known silver inkstand by Philip Syng, Jr., was used for the signing of the Declaration of Independence, and impressive brass inkstands with wells and a pounce pot (sander) were proud possessions of men of letters. When literacy vastly increased in the 19th century, the dip pen replaced the quill pen; and inkwells and inkstands were widely used and produced in a broad range of sizes in functional and decorative forms — from ornate Victorian to flowing Art Nouveau and stylized Art Deco designs. However, the acceptance of the ballpoint pen literally put inkstands and inkwells 'out of business.' But their historical significance and intriguing diversity of form and styling fascinate today's collectors.

Basalt, trn sides, 3 quill holes, mk, 1700s, 1¾x2¼" 90.00
Blown, GII-18, b3m, dk olive-amber, disk mouth/pontil, 2" ...300.00

Blown, pitkin, yel-olive, right swirl, disk mouth/pontil 350.00
Brass, Egyptian head, glass insert, EX 125.00
Brass, fox head in center, crystal insert, England, 1870s 150.00
Bronze, bird & chick, cold pnt, Austria, 1900, 3" 250.00
Bronze, Dartmoor pixie/stump/toadstools, English, 1900, 4" ...225.00
Bronze, dog's head, 1880s, 5" 500.00
Bronze, girl w/tray, ½-figure, Fr, 1880, 4" 200.00
Bronze, walrus head, 1880, 4½" 600.00
Cast metal, camel, saddled, 6" 75.00
Cast metal, laughing man, evil look, glass insert 65.00
Cut glass, amber, sq, w/amber hinged lid, 2¾x2½" 355.00
Cut glass, bl, sq, w/hinged bl lid, 2¾x2½" 225.00
Cut glass, gr, dbl, stag's head in center of SP fr, 4x7" 235.00
Cut glass, hexagon, w/sterling hinged lid, 2½x2" 250.00
Glass, blockhouse, pat 1898, mk Pittsburgh PA 100.00
Glass, clear swirl w/repousse sterling hinged lid, 4x3" 395.00
Glass, dbl snail, metal stand, ground mouths, 7½" L 150.00
Glass, emb yel swirl, hinged top 125.00
Glass, Mt Washington, rnd, wht w/enameling, 2½x2½" 295.00
Glass, opal w/mc florals, worn gilt, 2⅜", EX 225.00
Glass, pressed, sq, w/hinged sterling lid, 3¼x2¼" 225.00
Glass, rnd, controlled bubble, loose sterling lid, 5" dia 450.00
Glass, snail, in CI stand, revolves, 3x5x2" 160.00
Glass, teakettle, cobalt, paneled, smooth base, 2", NM 350.00
Glass, teakettle, lt bl opaque, pear form, att Sandwich, 2¾" ...700.00
Glass, teakettle, yel-amber, sheared/ground lip, 2⅛" 725.00
Glass in CI fr w/pen rack, Pat Mar 12, 1878, Clipper, 4½" 85.00
Pewter, rnd, w/quill holes, unmk, 3½x5" 150.00
Porc, built-in pen holder, sand well, & insert, Sevres 145.00
Porc, figural, Uncle Tom & Eva w/sander & well, 3½" 350.00
Porc, floral, attached tray, Dresden 125.00
Pottery, boat shape, 2 quill holes, Rockingham glaze, 3" L 100.00
Redware, ribbed sides, rope edges, Rockingham glaze, 2x5x3" ..350.00
Rock crystal insert in ftd ormolu base, 7x3½" 300.00
SP, Art Nouveau angels, resilvered 550.00
Stoneware, curling gray stone shape, beaded edge, 2½" dia 65.00
Stoneware, 1⅞x3⅜" dia, EX 65.00
Wood, orig brn grpt/stencil, label: S Silliman, 3½" dia 175.00
Wood, trn, brn flame grpt, blk trim, Silliman & Co, 3" dia 85.00

Double Snail in cast iron stand, dated 1878, 8½" long, $185.00.

Insulators

The telegraph was invented in 1844. The devices developed to hold the electrical transmission wires to the poles were called insulators. The telephone, invented in 1876, intensified their usefullness; and, by the turn of the century, thousands of varieties were being produced in glass of various colors, pottery, and wood. Of the more than 3,000 types known to exist, today's collectors evaluate their worth by age and rarity of color. Aqua and green are the most common colors in glass, dark brown the most common in ceramic. Threadless insulators, made between 1850 and 1870, bring prices well into the hundreds.

In the listings that follow, the CD numbers are from an identification system developed in the late 1960s by N.R. Woodward. CD refers to 'Consolidated Design.' SB denotes smooth base, RDP denotes round drip points, and SDP denotes sharp drip points. Many insulators are embossed with patent dates.

Those seeking additional information about insulators are encouraged to contact the National Insulator Association, whose address may be found in the Directory under Clubs, Newsletters, and Catalogs.

CD 102, BGM Co, SB, purple 18.00
CD 102, California, SB, bl 15.00
CD 102.2, Westinghouse, SB, bl 130.00
CD 106, Star, SB, olive gr 8.00
CD 112, New England Telegraph & Telephone, SB, gr 80.00
CD 121, Diamond, SB, purple, foreign 15.00
CD 122, McLaughlin, RDP, apple gr 6.00
CD 130.7, AGM, SB, aqua, foreign 10.00
CD 138, Kerr, SB, clear 4.00
CD 141, no name (Hot Cross Bun,) SB, emerald gr 9.00
CD 143, CNR, SB, aqua 10.00
CD 150.2, Telefonos Ericson, SB, lt gr, foreign 30.00
CD 155, Armstrong's DPL, SB, clear 1.00

White Tatum #1, CD 154, amethyst, 4" wide, $11.00.

CD 162, SS&Co, SB, lime gr 75.00
CD 168, Hemingray, SB, carnival 25.00
CD 190/191, Am Telegraph & Telephone, SB, jade gr, 2-pc 35.00
CD 263, Hemingray, SB, bl 80.00
CD 270, no name, SB, gr 150.00
CD 292.5, Boston, SB, dk gr 95.00
CD 317, Chambers, SB, lime gr 150.00
CD 320, Pyrex, SB, clear 9.00
CD 724, Chester, SB, dk cobalt, threadless 600.00
CD 728, Boston Bottle Works, SB, lt aqua, threadless 60.00
CD 731, McKee, SB, aqua, threadless 130.00
CD 733, Brookfield, SB, aqua, threadless 200.00
CD 743, no name, SB, deep amber, threadless 300.00

Irons

Irons come in all shapes and sizes; there are sadirons, fluting irons, and tailor's irons, to name but the most common. Hooded sadirons, patented about 1870, supposedly shielded the ironer's hand from the heat. Box irons from the late 1800s had hinged rear doors to accomodate heated slugs. Charcoal irons worked on the same principal, but removing the ashes was a nuisance! Even the gas irons of the early twentieth century had drawbacks. Pressure on the tank controlled the flame. Too little meant no heat, too much could result in an accident! Denatured alcohol and boiling water were also used as heat sources. Electric irons, though invented around the turn of the century, were not used to any great extent until electricity became a commonplace commodity several decades later.

Our advisor for this category is Rosella Tinsley; she is listed in the Directory under Kansas.

Asbestos, detachable hdl, pat May 22, 1900, 5" 30.00
Asbestos, sleeve style, dtd May 20, 1900 ....38.00
Bless & Drake, Newark NJ, wood hdl 45.00
Bonnie Dover, child's, early electric 25.00
Brass, wood hdl, lift-up gate, iron slug, 1850, 6" 125.00
C&P Prod, child's, electric 25.00
Charcoal, pat Oct 3, 1916, EX 35.00
Charcoal, rooster finial, lg 50.00
Charcoal, unusual dbl-dolphin hdl, EX 85.00
Denmark, brass, early 1800s 68.00
Dover, child's, hooded, #902 ....40.00
Dover #912, sadiron, wood/wire straight hdl 68.00
Durabilit-Winstead, wood grip, electric, EX 36.00
Fluter, Geneva, pat 1866 ....85.00
Fluter, Penn-American Machine, Philadelphia, EX 98.00
Fluter, Streeter, 2-pc w/hinged bottom, pat 1860 ....55.00
Fluter, The Best, 2-pc 38.00
Goffering, CI w/brass fluted center, wood hdl, 9x9x6" 85.00
Goffering, slug & base #13, 1700s, 7x15" 220.00
Improved Plaiter & Fluter, wood & dk tin, orig label, 1876 .....95.00
Montgomery Wards, gas, wood hdl, early 30.00
Sadiron, hand forged, open twist hdl, 1-pc, 1700s, EX 95.00
Sensible No 6, NRSA Co, child's, wood hdl 38.00
Sunny Suzy, child's, electric, stainless, Bakelite hdl, '40s 20.00
Whieldon China, gr, child's, ca 1800, 2¾" 195.00
Wolverine, child's, 1950s, EX 12.50

Tailor's sadiron, smithy made, forged-on handle, ca 1800s, $35.00.

Ironstone

During the last quarter of the 18th century, English potters began experimenting with a new type of body that contained calcinated flint and a higher china clay content, intent on producing a fine durable whiteware

— heavy, yet with a texture that would resemble porcelain. To remove the last trace of yellow, a minute amount of cobalt was added, often resulting in a bluish-white tone. Wm. and John Turner of Caughley and Josiah Spode II were the first to manufacture the ware successfully. Others, such as Davenport, Hicks and Meigh, and Ralph and Josiah Wedgwood, followed with their own versions. The latter coined the name 'Pearl' to refer to his product and incorporated the term into his trademark. In 1813 a 14-year patent was issued to Charles James Mason, who called his ware Patented Ironstone. Francis Morley, G.L. Asworth, T.J. Mayer, and other Staffordshire potters continued to produce ironstone until the end of the century. While some of these patterns are simple to the extreme, many are decorated with in-mold designs of fruit, grain, and foliage on ribbed or scalloped shapes. In the 1830s transfer-printed designs in blue, mulberry, pink, green, and black became popular; and polychrome versions of Oriental wares were manufactured to compete with the Chinese trade. See also Mason's Ironstone.

Our advise for this category comes from Hospice House Antiques, whose address is listed in the Directory under Illinois.

Baker, Hebe, oval, open, Alcock, 9⅜x7⅛" 60.00
Baker, Wheat, oval, JF, sm 55.00
Baker, Wheat, oval, Turner & Goddard, lg 60.00
Bowl, sauce; Baltic, w/lid & ladle, T Hulmes 135.00
Bowl, sauce; Ceres, w/lid, Elsmore & Forster 120.00
Bowl, sauce; Columbia, w/lid & underplate, Goodwin, 1850s . .125.00
Bowl, sauce; Fish Hook, w/lid, Meakin 95.00
Bowl, sauce; Leaf Fan, w/lid, Alcock, 7⅞" 95.00
Bowl, vegetable; Ivy Wreath, w/lid, Meir & Son 70.00
Bowl, vegetable; Sydenham, tulip lid, T&R Boote, sm 175.00
Casserole, Plain Square, rectangular, w/lid, Wedgwood 35.00
Casserole, Wheat & Clover, w/lid, Turner & Goddard, lg 75.00
Compote, Gothic, tall ped, Edwards, 1850s 75.00
Creamer, Grenade, T&R Boote, 1860s, 5½" 65.00
Cup, handleless coffee; Wheat in Meadow 22.00
Cup, hot toddy; Columbia 25.00
Cup, hot toddy; 1851 Octagon, T&R Boote 30.00
Cup & saucer, handleless; Ceres, Elsmore & Forster, sm 60.00
Cup & saucer, handleless; Chinese Shape, Shaw 40.00
Cup & saucer, handleless; Wheat, J&G Meakin, 1860s 30.00
Cup & saucer, Paris, Alcock 30.00
Gravy boat, Ceres, Elsmore & Forster, 1859 . . . . .55.00
Gravy boat, Fuchsia, bulbous, 1860s, 5¼" 35.00
Ladle, plain w/fleur-de-lis on hdl 40.00
Nappy, Mocho, T&R Boote 12.00
Nappy, Vintage, Challinor 12.00
Pitcher, milk; Ceres, Elsmore & Forster, 8½" 125.00
Pitcher, milk; Sydenham, T&R Boote, 7⅞" 185.00
Pitcher, syrup; Panelled Columbia, 1850s 135.00
Plate, Bell Flower, Edwards, dinner sz 18.00
Plate, cake; Fuchsia, J&G Meakin, 1860s 35.00
Plate, cake; Grape Octagon, C Meigh 50.00
Plate, Fluted Pearl, Wedgwood, 1847, 9½" 18.00
Plate, Forget-Me-Not, Alcock, child's sz 16.00
Plate, soup; Paris, Alcock 30.00
Platter, Sydenham, oval, T&R Boote, 16x11¾" 50.00
Punch bowl, Berry Cluster, w/hdls, Furnival 145.00
Punch bowl, Scrolled Bubble, Pankhurst 175.00
Relish, Fish Hook, Meakin 20.00
Relish, Fluted Pearl, Wedgwood, dtd 1847 . . . . .40.00
Relish, Wheat, J&G Meakin 30.00
Shaving mug, plain, ring hdl 20.00
Sugar bowl, Ceres, w/lid, Elsmore & Forster, lg 75.00
Sugar bowl, Fish Hook, Meakin, sm .55.00
Teapot, Ceres, Elsmore & Forster, 9¾" 225.00

Teapot, Ceres, Turner & Goddard, 1860s, 10" 225.00
Teapot, Chinese Shape, Shaw 195.00
Teapot, Pearl Sydenham, J&G Meakin, 1850s 145.00
Teapot, Trent, Alcock 125.00
Toothbrush holder, Bell Flower, w/lid, Burgess, 1860s 55.00
Waste bowl, Shaw's 1856 Fan, lg 65.00

Ivory

Technically, true ivory is the substance composing the tusk of the elephant; the finest type comes from those of Africa. However, tusks and teeth of other animals — the walrus, the hippopotamus, and the sperm whale, for instance — are similar in composition and appearance and have also been used for carving. The Chinese have used this substance for centuries, preferring it over bone because of the natural oil contained in its pores, which not only renders it easier to carve but also imparts a soft sheen to the finished product. Aged ivory usually takes on a soft caramel patina, but unscrupulous dealers sometimes treat new ivory to a tea bath to 'antique' it! A bill passed in 1978 reinforced a ban on the importation of whale and walrus ivory. All examples listed here are Oriental in origin unless noted otherwise.

Apple, int scene: pine tree/pagoda/equestrian, 4½" 150.00
Apple w/leaf & stem, village scene, 3¼" 150.00
Beauty w/peonies & bud in left hand, long robe, 1880s, 10" . . .250.00

Birth of Venus, European, early 20th century, 16", $1,100.00.

Busk, chip-cvd hex signs/pinwheels/etc, dtd 1767, 12" 220.00
Bust of Stephanus, plumed hat/cape, ebony fr, European, 4½" . .135.00
Crocodile, open mouth w/cvd teeth, 17" 175.00
Cupid as child, aims bow upward, on column, French, 7" 360.00
Dr's Lady, reclines on bed, wood base, 7" 175.00
Emperor/empress on throne, beaded necklace, 8", pr 200.00
Fisherman, pole/fish/basket, terrain base, sgn, 6" 150.00
Fisherwoman in lg hat, fishing pole/basket, 1870s, 6" 225.00

Foo dog, seated, lift-off head, coral/jewels, 5", pr 180.00
Girl w/instrument, seated, 4", set of 4 . . . . .350.00
Girl w/pipes in flowing robes, rolled hairdo, 5" 150.00
Glove stretcher, finely cvd 40.00
Immortal w/high forehead holds fan, attendant on ladder, 4" . .250.00
Kogo, phoenix bird on lid, Greek Key border lid/base, 2" dia 75.00
Lady, rooster at ft, birds on shoulder, French, 1800s, 8" 465.00
Lion of Lucerne, prone/stake through bk, Continental, 5" L . . .500.00
Lohan, holds staff/pomegranate, sgn, on cvd stand, 12" 200.00
Man, barefoot/2 sm boys on bk, Masanobu/seal, 1900, 5" 900.00
Necklace, graduaded beads, ivory clasp, American, 24" 85.00
Okimono, warrior/eagle w/MOP eyes in death struggle, 6½" . . .475.00
Phoenix bird in flower garden, wings raised, coral eyes, 5" 295.00
Sangen player w/box of drws slung to side, Masayuki, 7" 600.00
Snuff bottle, horse & tigers cvgs, 2½x1½", +top/spoon 155.00
Tiger & lion confronting, MOP eyes, Tamakuni, 1900, 7" 650.00
Toggle button, man holds mask & cutting tool, 2¼" 140.00
Traveller, right ft on dog, holds staff/parasol, sgn, 6" 250.00
Traveller w/2 children, 1 on his bk, 2nd at ft, sgn, 7" 200.00
Tusk cvg, 8 doves on branch, wood stand, 1900, 22½" 750.00
Warrior in chain mail w/sword & shield, 8" 160.00
Whistle, age cracks, 2⅝" 85.00
3 fishermen pull net, boy w/dragonfly below, Gyokushu, 12" . . .900.00

Jack-in-the-Pulpit Vases

Popular novelties at the turn of the century, jack-in-the-pulpit vases were made in every type of art glass produced. Some were simple, others elaborately appliqued and enameled. They were shaped to resemble the lily for which they were named.

Amberina, swirled w/HP decor, 3-legged base w/trim, 12" 445.00
Bl/opal satin, orange/wht HP flowers, 6" 150.00
Brn to bl to lt gr, appl leaf/flower, ruffled, 8¼" 90.00
Cream opal w/brn leaf overlay, gold decor, 12½" 160.00
Gold overlay w/mica, clear rim on ruffled top, 5x3¼" 110.00
Gr opal, vaseline 5-petal ft, coil stem, 8½x5¼" 88.00
Gr opal stripes, appl gr leaf/pk flower, 9" 125.00
Gr opaque, maroon ruffled/hobnailed edge, 7½x7⅛" 110.00
Gr overlay, clear appl ft, 6¼x5¾" 95.00
Lt gray, pk int, ruffled, 6½x3⅝" 69.00

Spangle glass, green with maroon and white, silver mica, 8", $110.00.

Vaseline to bl opal, fluted, flared, 7x5" 85.00
Yel/pk/bl pastel stripes, crystal base, 10" 215.00

Japanese Lustreware

During the 1920s, inexpensive tea sets, lamps, and novelty items were imported from Japan that were decorated primarily in lustre colors of white (called mother-of-pearl), blue, and tan. Often they were given away as premiums to those who would solicit magazine subscriptions from among a few of their friends. Today Japanese Lustre Ware is one of the newest items of collector interest on the market.

Condiment set, 2 cruets/shakers/mustard jar, bl & tan 28.00
Lamp, bird/leaves/lily base, rose decor on paper shade, 10" 25.00
Shakers, ball-form faces, pr 10.00
Shakers, bulbous, on tray w/center hdl, 4" L 8.00
Shakers, yel chick in shell, hdl, 1929, pr 10.00

Sugar castor and creamer, blue lustre, hand-painted flowers, $12.00.

Tea set, bluebird decor, child's sz, 13-pc, serves 4 . . . . .45.00
Tea set, 6 plates/cups/saucers, teapot/sugar bowl/creamer 30.00
Toothpick holder, grotesque bird w/wings wide, open mouth, 5" .10.00

Jervis

W.P. Jervis began his career as a potter in 1898. By 1908 he had his own pottery in Oyster Bay, New York. His shapes were graceful; often he decorated his wares with sgraffito designs over which he applied a matt glaze. Many pieces were incised 'Jervis' in a vertical arrangement. The pottery closed around 1912.

Bowl, geometric band cvd at rim, bl/wht, die stamp, 3x6" 550.00
Bowl, lime w/dk gr specks, hand thrown, 4x9" 80.00
Bowl vase, gr, 6 lg leaf-cvd rim-to-base hdls, 8x12", NM 2,000.00
Mug, motto: Joys that are to come..., floral reserve, mk OB 300.00
Vase, gr matt w/tan drip on neck, gr body, gourd form, 6" 950.00
Vase, sgraffito narcissus on royal bl, cylindrical, 5¾" 600.00
Vase, trees/clouds/geometrics incised, brn/bl/wht, 5x3" 800.00

Jewelry

Jewelry as objects of adornment has always been regarded with special affection. Whether it be a trinket or a costly ornament of gold, silver, or enameled work, jewelry has personal significance to the wearer. The art of the jeweler is valued as is any art object, and the names of Lalique or Faberge on collectible pieces bring prices demanded by the signed works of Picasso. Once the province of kings and noblemen, jewelry now is a legacy of all strata of society. The creativity reflected in the jeweler's art has resulted in a myriad of decorative adornments for men and women, and the modern usage of 'lesser' gems and base metals has elevated the value and increased the demand for artistic merit so that now it is considered by collectors to be on a par with intrinsic value. Luxuriously appointed pieces of Victorian splendor and Edwardian grandeur now compete with the unique, imaginative renditions of jewelry produced in the exciting Art Nouveau period as well as the adventurous translation of jewelry executed in man-made materials versus natural elements. Today prices for gems and gemstones crafted into antique and collectible jewelry are based on artistic merit, personal appeal, pure sentimentality, and intrinsic value.

Our advisor for this category is Rebecca Dodds; her address may be found in the Directory under Florida. If you are interested in collecting or dealing in jewelry, you will find that authority Lillian Baker has several fine books available on the subject — *100 Years of Collectible Jewelry: 1850-1950*; *Art Nouveau and Art Deco Jewelry*; and *Fifty Years of Collectible Fashion Jewelry: 1925-1975*. These books are complete with beautiful full-color illustrations and current market values. Mrs. Baker is listed in the Directory under California. See also Plastics.

Key:
A/C — Arts and Crafts	grad — graduated
AD — Art Deco	gp — gold plated
AN — Art Nouveau	gw — gold washed
cab — cabochon	k—karat
comp — complementary	plat — platinum
ct — carat	tw — total weight
dia — diamond	wg — white gold
dwt — penny weight	yg — yellow gold
gf — gold filled	

Amulet, gr jadeite, openwork w/dragon & calligraphy cvg 250.00
Bar pin, plat, 21 European dmn tw 2+cts, EX 1,100.00
Bar pin, 14k w/yg filigree, 10 old dmn tw 2ct+9 sapphires . . .1,700.00
Bar pin, 14k wg, blk onyx w/strip ea side set w/dmn tw .82 . . . .450.00
Bar pin, 15k, peridots, 3+4 hung from 5 gold hoops+4 rubies . .500.00
Bracelet, bangle; Coro, gf, eng decor, ¼" W 16.00
Bracelet, bangle; 14k yg, 16 sapphires+16 cultured pearls 750.00
Bracelet, bangle; 9k rose gold, openwork, English, 40dwt 750.00
Bracelet, Bela Vorus, cvd ivory w/2 abstract heads, 2" W 2,400.00
Bracelet, cvd jade, old 45.00
Bracelet, Danecraft, sterling, 5 oval links w/florals, AD 18.00
Bracelet, Gucci, 18k, 3-row pave of 104 dmn tw 1.75ct 3,100.00
Bracelet, pk coral, mermaid form, 1800s, EX 175.00
Bracelet, silver scrollwork, malacite center stone, Mexican 42.00
Bracelet, sterling w/vermeil, basketweave links, AD, wide 65.00
Bracelet, 10k, 7 oval segments ea w/cvd lava cameo of lady 400.00
Bracelet, 14k, aquamarine .60ct in ea of 8 leaf-form links 325.00
Bracelet, 14k, curb links, 97 grams 1,600.00
Bracelet, 14k, dk bl sapphires tw 8.25+40 dmn tw 2.80ct 1,600.00
Bracelet, 14k, 106 sq rubies tw 10.60cts, flexible mt 1,100.00
Bracelet, 14k, 54 dmn tw 3.15ct, flexible mt 1,500.00
Bracelet, 14k y/wg, 9 amethysts tw 10.35+40 dmn tw .40ct 700.00
Bracelet, 14k yg, chain link, 81dwt 1,300.00

Bracelet, 14k gold with moonstones and rubies, Art Deco, ca 1940, $750.00.

Bracelet, 18k y/wg, 24 dk bl sapphires tw 13.50+48 sm dmn .1,000.00
Bracelet, 18k yg mt w/13 faceted & cab semi-precious stones . .600.00
Bracelet, 18k yg S-link, 66.5dwt .1,700.00
Bracelet, 7 cameos+5 yg button links ea w/.22 dmn, 1880s 300.00
Bracelet, 9k gold filigree links w/5 tourmalines+MOP cabs 450.00
Bracelet, 900 silver, English coins, old 25.00
Bracelet watch, 14k mesh, 10 sm dmn+10 sm sapphires 1,150.00
Brooch, brass, enamel flower w/dangling chains, HP pk beads . . .20.00
Brooch, gp, flowers in vase, geometric shapes, '40s, 4½" 8.00
Brooch, Jomaz, gf, leaf form w/rhinestones & faux pearl 45.00
Brooch, King Tut, SP, rnd, hammered bk, 2" 10.00
Brooch, plat, blk opal oval+dmn sunburst fr tw 2.35ct 5,750.00
Brooch, plat filigree AD marquis mt w/13 dmn tw .70ct 750.00
Brooch, shell cameo, Bacchante profile, 14k fr/twist wire 550.00
Brooch, unmk wg openwork floriform mt, 71 dmn tw 3.75ct .1,400.00
Brooch, 10k/plat, citrine 21ct+25 dmn tw 2.24ct 2,000.00
Brooch, 14k dolphin, eye set w/.03ct ruby, 9dwt 550.00
Brooch, 14k fish, .15ct dmn eye, mouth: 5mm cultured pearl . .350.00
Brooch, 14k marquis openwork w/5 dmn tw .20+23 turq cabs . .350.00
Brooch, 14k openwork mt w/4 relief portraits+17 dmn tw .34 . .400.00
Brooch, 14k shrimp, eye set w/.03ct dmn 300.00
Brooch, 14k yg, 3 sm rubies center flower form, 7.2dwt 125.00
Brooch, 18k starfish w/3 dmn tw .12 at tip of 1 arm 260.00
Charm, 14k, ballet slippers, solid 35.00
Charm, 14k, birthday cake, candles pop up, 1940s 40.00
Charm, 14k, cuckoo clock, bird pops out, thick, old 95.00
Charm, 14k, ladder to success, colored stones, 1940s 40.00
Cuff links, horses' heads under glass, pr 7.50
Earrings, Bulgaria, 18k, 2.50ct cab ruby+1.65 cab amethyst 900.00
Earrings, Coro, mc stones/rhinestones in flower basket 12.00
Earrings, HAR, rhinestones & turquoise stones in cluster 12.50
Earrings, plat star-form mt w/6 dmn tw 1.15ct 1,200.00
Earrings, sterling, filigree butterfly, screw bk 10.00
Earrings, 14k wg, 42 dmn tw .60ct+23 rubies tw 1ct 800.00
Earrings, 14k y/wg, pierced mt w/pave of 50 dmn tw 2ct ea . .2,500.00
Earrings, 14k 6-prong Tiffany mt w/.45ct dmn, tw .90ct 725.00
Earrings, 14k/silver, ea w/European dmn .40+10 tw 1.40 . . . .1,700.00
Earrings, 18k, amethyst 2.50ct cab+23 dmn tw .28ct, Italian .1,300.00
Earrings, 18k, hoops, 28dwt 600.00
Fur clip, Eisenberg, rhinestones, rnd, lg 185.00
Fur clip, Eisenberg, rhinestones, teardrop form, 1940s 165.00
Fur clip, Nettie Rosenstein, sterling, bell w/clapper 65.00
Handkerchief holder, 14k, fans w/chain & ring, 2dwt, rare 175.00
Locket, 14k, heart form w/glass inside, 4dwt 125.00
Locket, 18k wg filigree mt, bl enameled w/.08 dmn, on chain . .850.00
Necklace, Baroque pearls, 2-strand of 97 . . . . .300.00

Necklace, blk pearls, 3-strand of 127, clasp: tw .75ct dmn ...2,400.00
Necklace, Cartier, 37 pearls w/37 blk onyx beads, 34" 1,500.00
Necklace, choker; 28 cultured pearls, ea 9mm 900.00
Necklace, cultured pearls, 1-strand of 94, 7mm-7.5mm 700.00
Necklace, cultured pearls, 2-strand of 154, 4mm-8.5mm 700.00
Necklace, cultured pearls, 4-strand, clasp: 23ct amethyst 1,700.00
Necklace, cultured pearls, 67 grad to 9mm, 14k clasp w/pearl ..450.00
Necklace, cvd gr glass flower groups, 15" 12.50
Necklace, dmn-shape Austrian crystal & rnd drops, Czech, 16" ..32.00
Necklace, Egyptian long bib, gilt metal w/7 pendant drops 15.00
Necklace, faux pearl, plastic beads, 8mm, 58" 6.00
Necklace, gold on copper, filigree & red glass beads, 56" 20.00
Necklace, Miriam Haskel, pk glass & rhinestones, bird clasp 88.00
Necklace, opal beads 3-12mm+rock crystal spacers, dmn clasp .900.00
Necklace, Peking glass, lt gr rondells & gr tube beads, 39" 30.00
Necklace, silver & gp pendant & tassels on silver chain, 48" 85.00
Necklace, silvery borealis, cut & faceted, 3-strand, 16" 36.00
Necklace, topaz borealis, 3-strand, rhinestone clasp, 20" 40.00
Necklace, yg, aqua/garnet/peridot/amethyst in drop, 31dwt 275.00
Necklace, yg, beads, Vict, 25dwt 450.00
Necklace, yg, 3 coral cabs, enameling, 35dwt 425.00
Necklace, 14k yg herringbone, 18", 12.5dwt 300.00
Necklace, 14k yg herringbone, 24", 8.38dwt 325.00
Necklace, 2¾" HP owl on branch on gold color snake chain 25.00
Necklace+bracelet, G Jensen, grapes/leaves as links, 12dwt ...600.00
Pendant, Arta, Munich Germany, teardrop faceted rose quartz .475.00
Pendant, cultured pearl on gf heart, fine gf chain 16.00

Pendant, diamond, pearl, and plique-a-jour Art Nouveau, on 14k gold chain, $1,500.00.

Pendant, gf, floral spray w/rhinestones & aqua stones, '40s 20.00
Pendant, L Guatrait, winged maid, plique-a-jour, pearl drop .2,000.00
Pendant, lg amethyst heart drop on yg jeweled crown mt 500.00
Pendant, pk crystal, gw fr w/eng flowers & filigree, 1½" 16.00
Pendant, plat chain w/.53 dmn+2 at .51ct ea on drop links ..2,600.00
Pendant, plique-a-jour, Egyptian leaf motif w/drop pearl 350.00
Pendant, sterling, cloisonne rose under glass 20.00
Pendant, sterling, Jewish cut-out star in 1¼" dia fr 16.00
Pendant, 14k, 27 bl sapphires tw .54ct+23 pearls, +chain 350.00
Pendant, 14k AN maid's head w/wings, .07 dmn/sm pearl ...1,800.00
Pendant, 14k oval w/real spinel +8 dmn tw .25ct, heavy chain .900.00
Pendant, 14k wg, dmn drop 2.55ct, mt: 3 sm dmn tw .06ct ..5,600.00
Pin, cameo, wht glass on blk pin, brass filigree fr, 1½" 36.00
Pin, Coro, pk stones on stem held by bow 17.50
Pin, enamel, geometric sq, oval tigereye stone, 1½" 7.50
Pin, filigree silver, circle w/bow, Victorian, 1¾" 6.00
Pin, Georg Jensen, sterling, 2 birds/shaft of wheat, #250 ......225.00
Pin, gf, flower w/pk gold look, gr stones, 2½" W 12.50
Pin, gf, tulip & leaf, AD, 4½" 18.00

Pin, HAR, starfish, coral & wht enamel 15.00
Pin, Liberty, silver w/enamel, orange cherries on bl, 2" 275.00
Pin, Liberty, silver w/enamel, winged scarab, hallmk, 1¾" 250.00
Pin, plat, 28 dmns tw 2.8ct, open circlet, handmade 1,400.00
Pin, R Lalique, gold snarling creature on opal, 1¼" dia 8,000.00
Pin, sterling, lily, Mexican, 2" 12.50
Pin, sterling, Reja, leaf form w/gr stones & rhinestones 40.00
Pin, wht porc, girl silhouette, brass bk, 1¾" 15.00
Pin, 14k yg, mixed semi-precious stones, open circlet, EX 375.00
Pin, 14k yg, tourmaline & peridots, crescent form 325.00
Ring, cameo, 14/22k shank dtd 1856 ....380.00
Ring, Gerard Sandoz, silver band w/airplanes, turq cab 8,000.00
Ring, gf, blk glass w/intaglio cameo 20.00
Ring, Gucci, 18k yg nugget mt w/pave of 13 dmn tw 1ct 900.00
Ring, man's, plat, 3 sq sapphires tw 2.55+4 dmn tw .28ct 700.00
Ring, man's, 18k, European dmn 2.27ct in modern mt 4,400.00
Ring, man's, 18k, 12x19mm lapis slab 400.00
Ring, man's, 18k wg, 2.24ct dmn w/in sq bezel 2,600.00
Ring, plat, dmn .72ct, +4 marquis/8 sm dmn tw .15ct 2,250.00
Ring, plat, dmn solitaire 2.80ct+2 sm marquis tw .24ct 4,000.00
Ring, plat, dmn 3.20ct in Tiffany-type V-box mt 4,500.00
Ring, plat, emerald-cut 1.18 dmn+6 baguettes tw .20ct 1,800.00
Ring, plat, openwork, 3 emerald-cut dmn tw .90+10 tw .25ct ..800.00
Ring, plat, 2 pearls, 10mm & 9.7mm 225.00
Ring, plat filigree, European dmn .66ct+2 .46 ea+10 sm 1,600.00
Ring, plat filigree, European 1.22ct dmn+32 sm dmn 2,000.00
Ring, sterling, aquamarine w/16 marcasites, 1920s, lg 65.00
Ring, sterling, oval obsidian w/bead decor, lg 45.00
Ring, sterling, 2 lapis/1 tigereye striped inserts, heavy 55.00
Ring, 10k, faux citrine, wg eng pc ea side w/4 dmn chips 65.00
Ring, 14/18k yg, 12x13x4mm opal cab+24 dmn tw .60ct ...750.00
Ring, 14k, blk opal cab 4.69ct+4 dmn tw .12ct 2,600.00
Ring, 14k, dmn solitare .72ct 1,300.00
Ring, 14k, emerald-cut 2ct sapphire in 40-dmn fr tw 1.55ct ...750.00
Ring, 14k, sapphire 2.53ct+20 rnd dmn tw .62ct 1,100.00
Ring, 14k, wht opal 2.30ct cab+12 3.5mm cultured pearls 150.00
Ring, 14k, 5 baguette-cut rubies tw 1.10+16 dmn tw .65ct 700.00
Ring, 14k fluted mt w/oval 1.10 sapphire+12 dmn tw .20ct 550.00
Ring, 14k wg, V-box mt w/.65 European dmn+2 tw .04ct 250.00
Ring, 14k wg mt w/3 dmn tw .67ct+10 single cut tw .25ct 600.00
Ring, 14k y/wg, amethyst oval 5.50ct+16 dmn tw .50ct 400.00
Ring, 14k yg, blk onyx in wg filigree, Eastern Star emblem 95.00
Ring, 18k, dmn emerald-cut .71+2 baguettes tw .15ct 900.00
Ring, 18k, emerald-cut emerald 9.5ct+18 dmn tw 1.02ct 2,000.00
Ring, 18k openwork dome mt w/41 dmn tw 5.75ct 1,900.00
Ring, 18k stylized flowerhead w/48 dmn tw 1.55ct 600.00
Ring, 18k wg filigree, 16 dmn tw .20ct+1 European cut .35ct ..450.00
Ring, 18k yg, dome set w/36 sapphires, heavy 1,700.00
Set, gp mt w/garnets, bracelet, star brooch, ring, earrings 600.00
Stickpin, 14k, lg opal, unmk, old 35.00
Watch chain, 18k, unmk yg button-form fob, 15", 61dwt 900.00

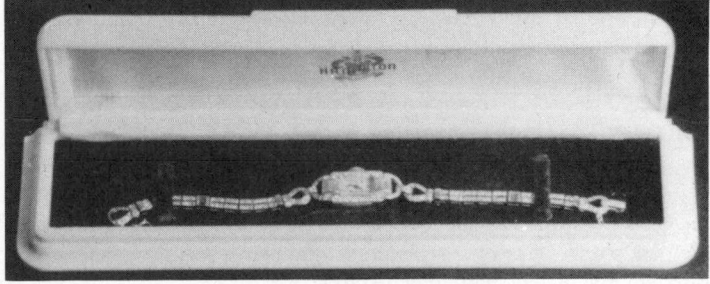

Hamilton watch, total weight of diamonds: 4 carats, in original case, $3,600.00.

Judaic

The items listed below are representative of objects used in both the secular and religious life of the Jewish people. They are evident of a culture where silversmiths, painters, engravers, writers, and metal workers were highly gifted and skilled in their art. Most of the treasures shown in recently-displayed exhibits of Judaica were confiscated by the Germans during the late 1930s up to 1945; by then eight Jewish synagogues and fifty warehouses had been filled with Hitler's plunder.

Amulet case, Italian silver, cartouch form, ca 1800, 5¼" **3,000.00**
Beaker, German silver, scale motif, ca 1800, 2¾" **800.00**
Burial Society knife, Turkish wood/brass/steel, 1800, 3¾" ...**2,200.00**
Charity box, German sheet copper, cylindrical, 1800s, 5" **225.00**
Circumcision knife, Continental brass hdl, 1700s, 6¾" **700.00**
Esther scroll, Palestine, cvd case, stonework decor, 1930s **500.00**
Halitza shoe, E Europe, leather, typical design, 1800, EX **800.00**
Hanukah lamp, Bezalel brass, priest w/lamp, 1915, 10½" **25.00**
Hanukah lamp, Dutch silver, hearts/flowers, 1880, 3¼" **2,500.00**
Hanukah lamp, English silver, scrolls/foliage, 1920, 14½" ...**1,650.00**
Havdalah compendium, German silver, rooster form, 1900, 7" .**900.00**
Kiddush cup, Polish silver, tulip form, eng, ca 1800, 5½" **950.00**
Mezuza, Sezalel silver cased, inscriptions, scroll w/in, 3½" **600.00**
Passover plate, Continental pewter, ca 1800, 14" dia **200.00**
Purim bowl, Russian silver, gilt int, Moscow, 1845, 6" dia ...**2,300.00**
Ram's horn, German, chased bands of X-hatching, 1600s, 16" .**600.00**
Sabbath lamp, Dutch brass, hanging, ca 1700, 17" **1,850.00**
Shekel, silver, war against Rome, 1 AD **1,600.00**
Spice container, Dutch silver, rooster form, 1891, 11" **825.00**
Spice container, silver filigree, duck form, 1800s, 6½" **3,200.00**
Spice tower, German pewter mtd wood, lion top, 1700s, 8" ..**1,300.00**
Spice tower, Polish silver, bells & pennants, 1800s, 9¾" **1,500.00**
Torah binder, German, embr silk on linen, 1809, 142x7" **650.00**
Torah crown, Italian silver, foliage, 3 mks, 1750s, 9½" **3,300.00**
Torah finial, N African silver/gold filigree, 1700, 10" pr **2,200.00**
Torah pointer, Near Eastern primitive wood, 1800s, 14" **385.00**
Torah shield, German silver, sq w/arched top, 1890s, 9" **28.00**
Urn, Bezalel silver inlay/brass, thistle form, 1910, 6½" **1,300.00**

Jugtown

The Jugtown Pottery was started about 1920 by Juliana and Jacques Busbee, in Moore County, North Carolina. Ben Owen, a young descendant of a Staffordshire potter, was hired in 1923. He was the master potter, while the Busbees experimented with perfecting glazes and supervising design and modeling. Preferred shapes were those reminiscent of traditional country wares and classic Oriental forms. Glazes were various: natural clay oranges, buffs, 'tobacco-spit' brown, mirror black, white, 'frogskin' green, a lovely turquoise called Chinese blue, and the traditional cobalt-decorated salt glaze. The pottery gained national recognition; and, as a result of their success, several other local potteries were established. Jugtown is still in operation, however they no longer use their original glaze colors which are now so collectible.

Bean pot, orange lustre, 5" **40.00**
Bowl, redware, 7½" **15.00**
Cup, frogskin gr, sm **45.00**
Jar, redware w/orange glaze, 6¾", EX **45.00**
Pie pan, orange, blk concentric-circled int, 9½" **35.00**
Pitcher, gr w/bl, bulbous w/pinched spout, 5½" **55.00**
Vase, Chinese bl, EX form, 6" **250.00**
Vase, Chinese bl over red, bulbous, 4½" **180.00**

Vase, Chinese bl w/much red, 2 sm hdls at top, 6" **275.00**
Vase, Chinese bl w/red, red clay body, 4" **150.00**
Vase, Chinese gr w/dk red, pinched on sides, 8" **500.00**
Vase, gr/red thick gloss on red clay, imp mk, 4½" **115.00**
Vase, lt to dk brn gloss, ogee sides, hand thrown, 10½" **95.00**

Vase, metallic glaze, four applied handles, 8½", $75.00.

K. P. M. Porcelain

Under the tutelage of Frederick the Great, King of Prussia, porcelain manufacture was instituted in Berlin in 1751 by William K. Wegeley. In jealous competition with Meissen, hard-paste porcelain was produced — dinnerware, figurines, vases, etc. — some of which were undecorated while other pieces were hand painted in Watteau scenes, landscapes, or florals. It soon became evident that the factory was unable to offer serious competition. The King withdrew his support, and the factory failed in 1757. In 1761 Johann Ernst Gotzkowsky bought the rights and attempted a similar operation which soon failed due to financial difficulties. Still determined to gain the same recognition enjoyed by Meissen, the King bought the plant in 1763 and ruled the operation with an iron hand, often assuring his success by taking advantage of his position. The King died in 1786, but production has continued and quality tableware and decorative porcelains are still being made on a commercial basis. Earliest marks were simply 'G' or 'W,' followed by the sceptre mark. After 1830 'K.P.M.' with an orb or eagle was adopted.

Our advisor for this category is Don Williams; he is listed in the Directory under Iowa.

Box, Celadon, dk gr insect finial, 3" **50.00**
Ewer, appl swan on front, bl w/gold ped, 12", NM **350.00**
Figurine, carriage & 4 horses w/driver & lady, mk, 6x13" **750.00**
Figurine, couple at table, Baroque plinth, mk, 7x11" **750.00**
Night light, bsk, 3 owl faces, holds candle, mk, 4⅛x3¾" **225.00**
Plaque, Diana/maid, nude/bathing, after Boucher, 9½x7½" ..**3,950.00**
Plaque, Guardian Angel, sgn Wagner, after Raupp, 10x8" ...**4,000.00**
Plaque, gypsy girl, oval, in elaborate cvd fr, 9" **2,900.00**
Plaque, lady's portrait, gold leaf fr, oval, 10x7½" **3,500.00**
Plaque, Madonna & Child, sgn Wagner, 1900, 12x9" **4,200.00**
Plaque, peasant girl w/urn, gilt fr, 13" **3,400.00**
Plaque, Queen Louisa of Prussia, sgn Wagner, oval, 9" **2,500.00**
Plaque, Reflection (portrait), sgn Wagner, gilt fr, 8½" **3,200.00**
Plaque, Romeo & Juliet, sgn Baerschneider, 10" **3,000.00**
Plaque, Terpsichore, dancing, w/8 Muses, 1900, 9x11" **3,400.00**

Plaque, The Bath of Psyche, after Frederick, gilt fr, 12" 3,200.00

Painting on porcelain, signed L Spinzel, plaque: 7x10", $6,500.00.

Kayserzinn Pewter

J.P. Kayser Sohn produced pewter decorated with relief-molded Art Nouveau motifs in Germany during the late 1800s and into the twentieth century. Examples are marked with 'Kayserzinn' and the mold number within an elongated oval reserve.

Bonbon, shell form w/Art Nouveau nude, sgn/#4136, 8x6¾" ..175.00
Bowl, stylized floral, raised/shaped border, #4368, 17½" 250.00
Cake basket, arched vine hdl, 6 sm ft, chased, 17" L 3,500.00
Chalice, 3 branch hdls emanate from base, #4300, 14", pr ...1,400.00
Chamberstick, Nouveau flower holder on leaf, #4235, 10" 65.00
Inkwell, sphinx's head finial, #4333, 11¾" L 440.00
Napkin rings, florals, mk 48.00
Pitcher, fish/cattails/water lilies, #4022, ca 1900, 8" 150.00
Platter, foliage, #4162, 20½x13" 195.00
Punch bowl, claw & ball ft, cherub finial, heart reserve 550.00
Sugar bowl, Dragon Ship form, open, 8" L 150.00

Pitcher, Mephistopheles, #4061, 12", $350.00.

Keen Kutter

Keen Kutter was a brand name of E.C. Simmons Hardware, used from about 1870 until the mid-1930s. In 1923 Winchester merged with Simmons but continued to produce Keen Kutter-marked knives and tools. The merger dissolved, and in 1940 the Simmons Company was purchased by Shapleigh Hardware. Older items are very collectible. For further study, we recommend *Keen Kutter*, an illustrated price guide by Jerry and Elaine Heuring, available at your favorite bookstore or public library.

Our advisor for this category is Jim Calison; his is listed in the Directory under New York.

Adz, w/hdl 25.00
Apple peeler, EX 85.00
Auger, ship's 10.00
Axe, dbl-bit; w/hdl 25.00
Axe, single-bit; w/hdl 20.00
Bit extender 22.00
Box, tool; oak wall mt, brass emblem, decal, M 250.00
Butcher's block, maple 250.00
Calipers 22.00
Can opener, CI, dtd 1895, EX 30.00
Chisel, 11" 20.00

Electric clock, 15x15", $125.00.

Food chopper, KK #11 ....12.50
Food grinder, KK #13, w/cutters 15.00
Food grinder, KK #21 ....25.00
Gasoline can, 5-gal 48.00
Hammer, claw, 7-oz 20.00
Hammer, mason's 50.00
Hammer, tack; claw, KK #5 ....16.00
Hatchet, hewing; w/hdl 25.00
Hatchet, roofer's 8.00
Innertube, 32x4" sz 190.00
Jar, beater; bl banded w/KK advertising 65.00
Knife, butcher; EX 15.00
Knife, office; yel hdl, 2-blade, EX 27.50
Knife, pocket; Spirit of St Louis, ltd ed, MIB 165.00
Knives & forks, 12 in box 50.00
Level, KK #13, 12" 25.00
Lock, trunk; EX 125.00
Manicure set 22.00

Matchbook	8.00
Nail puller	35.00
Nippers, screwdriver on end, lg	30.00
Padlock	85.00
Pencil, carpenter's, M	10.00
Plane, coffin; 8"	30.00
Plane, KK #15	25.00
Plane, KK #6	30.00
Pliers, slip joint	20.00
Post card	10.00
Razor hone, KK #15	15.00
Router, KK #71	45.00
Sausage grinder, KK #112	20.00
Saw, hand; KK #83, sm	20.00
Saw, hand; KK #88, 22"	30.00
Saw, keyhole	20.00
Scissors, buttonhole; pat July 1, 1884	30.00
Scissors, 8"	10.00
Screwdriver, 10"	12.50
Shears, grass	20.00
Shears, mule	18.00
Shears, poultry; EX	85.00
Steel, butcher's	12.50
Steel, sharpening	20.00
Thermometer, wood	65.00
Waffle iron	95.00
Wrench, alligator; KK #60	40.00
Wrench, pipe; KK #14	15.00
Wrench, pipe; 10"	20.00

Kelva

Kelva was a trademark of the C.F. Monroe Company of Meriden, Connecticut, used on an opaque mold-blown glassware that was hand decorated with pastel florals and often set in ormolu holders. It was very similar to the company's other lines, Nakara and Wave Crest; only those pieces bearing the Kelva mark are listed here. All three types were in production from about 1900 until WWI. Hand-painted pieces bring much higher prices than those with decals. For more information we recommend *Wave Crest, The Glass of C.F. Monroe* by Wilfred R. Cohen, available at your local bookstore or from Collector Books.

Box, green with florals, hexagonal, 6" wide, $500.00.

Biscuit jar, floral, wht on peach, SP lid & hdl, rare	800.00
Box, beaded florals, watch in lid	500.00

Box, floral, pk on bl-gray, mirror in lid, 4½" dia	510.00
Box, petunias, pk on gr, 3¾x8" dia	650.00
Box, pk apple blossoms, ormolu rim & hdls, 6" dia	300.00
Box, poppies/vines/seed pods on gr, mk, 2¾x4½"	235.00
Box, wild roses/beaded ribbons on gr, 6" dia	400.00
Cigarette urn/match holder, wild roses, fitted brass tray	500.00
Ferner, floral, bl/wht on dk pk, ftd, 6¼x7¾"	550.00
Napkin ring, floral on pk, SP rim, 2" W	200.00
Pin tray, 8-sided, ormolu base, 5½" L	200.00
Shakers, floral, pk on gr, 3", pr	300.00
Tray, floral, pk on bl, oval mirror: 3x2¼", 6¼x4"	500.00
Vase, lilies, pk on lt yel & gr, ormolu hdls/ft, 13"	1,250.00
Whisk broom holder, floral, pk on bl	650.00

Kentucky Derby Glasses

Since the 1940s, souvenir glasses have commemorated the famous Kentucky Derby; recently these have become popular collectibles, especially among race fans. Among the most valuable is the plastic Beetleware tumbler from the forties, the shorter version made in 1945, and the 1950 tumbler which is now valued at around $100.00. On the Gold Cup glass from 1952, current winners are shown along with those from the previous year. There were two from 1958 — one was the Gold Bar tumbler and the other, called the Iron Liege, both were simply leftover '57 glasses with the 1958 winners added at the top.

1940s, aluminum	125.00
1940s, plastic Beetleware	250.00
1945, short	350.00
1945, tall	125.00
1948	45.00
1949, He Has Seen Them All	45.00
1950	100.00
1950	150.00
1952, Gold Cup	40.00
1953	35.00
1954	30.00
1955	27.00
1956	26.00
1957	25.00
1958, Gold Bar	24.00
1958, Iron Liege	37.50
1959-1960, ea	20.00

1960, $20.00.

1961	18.00

1962-1963, ea	16.00
1964-1965, ea	15.00
1966	14.00
1967-1968, ea	13.00
1969	12.00
1970	10.00
1971	9.00
1972	8.00
1973	7.00
1974	6.00
1975	5.00
1976	4.50
1977-1978, ea	4.00
1979-1980, ea	3.50
1981-1982, ea	3.00
1983	2.50
1984-1986, ea	2.00
1987-1988, ea	1.50

Kew Blas

Kew Blas was a trade name used by the Union Glass Company of Somerville, Massachusetts, for their iridescent art glass produced from 1890 until about 1920. The glass was made in imitation of Tiffany and achieved notable success.

Candlesticks, swirled and iridescent, ground pontil, signed, 8", $475.00 for the pair.

Compote, gold ribbed bowl, sgn, 4x5½"	250.00
Creamer, feathers, gr/gold on opal, gold hdl/int, 4½"	900.00
Tumbler, gold, 4 indents at base, 4"	235.00
Vase, bl-gold border on marigold, ribbed trumpet form, 12"	800.00
Vase, leaves, gr/gold-traced on opal, gold int, ped ft, 5"	2,500.00
Vase, pulled feathers, gold/gr on wht, gold int, 5½x2¾"	750.00
Vase, pulled leaves in gr/opal, gr/gold swirl base, 6½"	900.00
Vase, zippered pattern, gr/gold, rose bowl form, sgn, 4½"	575.00

King's Rose

King's Rose is a soft-paste ware that was made in Staffordshire, England, from about 1820 to 1830. It is closely related to Gaudy Dutch in body type as well as the colors used in its decoration. The pattern consists of a full-blown, orange-red rose with green, pink, and yellow leaves and accents.

Our advisor for this category is Richard Marden; he is listed in the Directory under New Hampshire.

Bowl, deep, ca 1810, 7"	150.00
Creamer, EX	150.00
Creamer, vine border	185.00
Cup & saucer, handleless; line border, minor wear	95.00
Cup & saucer, handleless; scalloped, M	145.00
Cup & saucer, scalloped rim, Queen's, EX	75.00
Plate, pk lustre border, Queen's, 4⅝", EX	30.00
Plate, vine border, 6½", EX	100.00
Platter, 12½"	250.00
Sauce boat	150.00
Soup, sectional border, 9¾", NM	135.00
Soup plate, sectional border, 9"	150.00
Sugar bowl, scalloped, Queen's	200.00
Toddy, vine border, 5¾"	70.00

Kitchen Collectibles

During the last half of the 1850s, mass-produced kitchen gadgets were patented at an astonishing rate. Most were ingeniously efficient. Apple peelers, egg beaters, cherry pitters, food choppers, and such were only the most common of hundreds of kitchen tools well designed to perform only specific tasks. Today all are very collectible.

Our advisor for this category is Rosella Tinsley; she is listed in the Directory under Kansas. See also Appliances, Electric; Molds; Primitives; Tinware; Wooden Ware.

Cast Iron Bakers and Kettles

Ash tray, Griswold #0, rnd	58.00
Bread pan, Griswold #22	35.00
Brownie pan, Griswold #9	80.00
Cake mold, lamb, Griswold	95.00
Cake mold, rabbit, Griswold	225.00
Corn stick pan, Griswold #262, miniature, old	95.00
Corn stick pan, Griswold #273, Crispy	35.00
Corn stick pan, Wagner, Krusty Korn Kobs, July 6, 1920	95.00
Dutch oven, Griswold #9, later version, w/lid	40.00
Dutch oven, Kentucky Store Co on lid, early, 10½"	195.00
Griddle, Griswold #10, oval	50.00
Griddle, Griswold #11	60.00
Griddle, Griswold #6	48.00
Griddle, Griswold #9, rnd hdl, 10½" dia	48.00
Griddle, Martin #10, rectangular	40.00
Griddle, Wagner #6	66.00
Griddle, Wapak #9, rectangular	30.00
Meat loaf pan, Griswold, lg emblem	65.00
Muffin pan, Griswold #17	45.00
Muffin pan, 8 fruit forms, mk Cast in USA, 7½x15"	40.00
Patty mold, Griswold #1, shallow, MIB	75.00
Popover pan, Griswold #10	35.00
Pot, Wagner, heart shape, w/lid, 2½-qt	40.00
Rack, Dutch oven; Griswold	150.00
Sauce pan, Kenrick & Co Improved ½-Pt, wrought hdl, 4"	55.00
Skillet, breakfast; Griswold #666	30.00
Skillet, egg; Griswold #53	22.00
Skillet, fish; Wagner	27.00
Skillet, Griswold #10, lg emblem, no smoke ring, EX	26.00
Skillet, Griswold #11, Erie, w/smoke ring, EX	150.00
Skillet, Griswold #11, lg emblem, w/smoke ring	100.00
Skillet, Griswold #12, lg emblem, w/smoke ring	85.00

Skillet, Griswold #2, Erie 95.00
Skillet, Griswold #3, Erie 50.00
Skillet, Griswold #3, lg emblem, no smoke ring 25.00
Skillet, Griswold #3, lg emblem, w/smoke ring 30.00
Skillet, Griswold #4, lg emblem 40.00
Skillet, Griswold #5, sm emblem, no smoke ring 22.00
Skillet, Griswold #6, Erie, EX 45.00
Skillet, Griswold #6, lg emblem, no smoke ring 40.00
Skillet, Griswold #7, Erie 40.00
Skillet, Griswold #7, lg emblem, w/smoke ring 48.00
Skillet, Griswold #7, Victor 40.00
Skillet, Griswold #8, Erie, w/lid, EX 40.00
Skillet, Griswold #8, Victor 40.00
Skillet, Griswold #9, lg emblem, no smoke ring 22.00
Skillet, Martin #3 ....15.00
Skillet, Martin #8 ....16.00
Skillet, Oderless 95.00
Skillet, Wagner, 4½" 28.00
Skillet, Wagner #1102, 12" 45.00
Skillet, Wagner #5 ....18.00
Skillet, Wapak #9 ....28.00
Skillet rack, Griswold 100.00
Skillet/griddle, #108 ....55.00
Teakettle, Griswold, 6-qt 45.00
Teakettle, Wagner, 1-gal 60.00
Teakettle, Wagner, 5-qt 25.00
Teakettle, wrought iron hdl, 7" 40.00
Trivet, Griswold, 5-leg, for coffeepot 75.00
Trivet, hexagonal, Griswold, sm 15.00
Waffle iron, Griswold #8, American, early version 120.00
Waffle iron, Griswold #8, American, later version, +stand 120.00
Waffle iron, Wagner, wood hdl, pat Feb 22, 1910, EX 125.00

Glassware

Batter jug, jadite, w/lid 135.00
Batter jug, pk, Cambridge 65.00
Batter set, crystal, w/blk lids, 3-pc, Paden City 95.00
Bowl, cobalt, in metal holder, Hazel Atlas, 8½" 20.00
Bowl, cobalt, Restwell, 5¾" 11.00
Bowl, gr, w/spout, 9½" 24.00
Bowl, mixing; Chalaine bl, 9" 45.00
Bowl, mixing; delphite, ribbed, Jeannette, 7½" 34.00
Bowl, mixing; gr, panelled, Hocking, 11½" 16.00
Bowl, mixing; gr, Rest-Well, 7½" 26.00
Bowl, mixing; gr clambroth, 8¾" 18.00
Bowl, mixing; jadite, ribbed, 9¾" 28.00
Bowl, mixing; jadite, tab hdl, 9½" 9.00
Bowl, mixing; pk, Rest-Well, 8½" 11.00
Bowl, mixing; pk, ruffled edge, Hex Optic, 8¼" 19.00
Bowl, wht, Crisscross, Hazel Atlas, 6¾" 4.00
Butter dish, crystal, emb 'Butter' 19.00
Butter dish, custard w/gr stripe, McKee 38.00
Butter dish, delphite, Jeannette 90.00
Butter dish, delphite, McKee 110.00
Butter dish, gr, Block Optic, Hocking 28.00
Butter dish, gr, Hex Optic, Jeannette, 1-lb 58.00
Butter dish, gr, Jeannette, 2-lb 95.00
Butter dish, lt amber, ¼-lb 24.00
Butter dish, pk, emb B, Jeannette, 2-lb 100.00
Butter dish, Skokie gr, McKee 33.00
Butter dish, wht, w/decor, Hazel Atlas 60.00
Butter knife, crystal, w/gr hdl 19.00
Cake plate, pk, emb snowflake 18.00

Canister, coffee; delphite, Jeannette, 40-oz 90.00
Canister, fired-on red, ribbed, w/glass lid, 47-oz 19.00
Canister, fired-on yel, ribbed ball form, w/lid 14.00
Canister, gr, glass lid, Hazel Atlas 34.00
Canister, Seville yel, press-on lid, McKee, 48-oz 50.00
Canister, Skokie gr, w/metal screw-on lid, McKee, 28-oz 34.00
Canister, sugar; wht clambroth, w/label 24.00
Canister, tea; custard, McKee, 48-oz 28.00
Canister, wht clambroth, w/metal lid, lg 24.00
Casserole, lt amber, w/lid & underliner, Cambridge 20.00
Cookie jar, blk, LE Smith Co 38.00
Cookie jar, gr, barrel form 45.00
Cookie jar, gr, Party Line, Paden City 55.00
Crock, gr, Hocking, 5" 17.00
Decanter, gr, ribbed, Hocking 38.00
Decanter, peacock bl, Imperial 23.00
Egg cup, lt amber, Paden City 8.50
Egg cup, yel, Hazel Atlas 4.00
Funnel, crystal, 5" 11.00
Funnel, gr, ribbed, 4½" 38.00
Gravy boat, gr, w/underliner, Cambridge 48.00
Gravy boat, lt amber, 2-spout, Cambridge 24.00
Gravy boat, pk, 2-spout, Cambridge 24.00
Ice bucket, blk, w/lid 45.00
Ice bucket, gr, Hex Optic 16.00
Ice bucket, gr, Party Line, Paden City 21.00
Ice bucket, gr clambroth, w/lid, Fenton 80.00
Knife, crystal, pnt flowers, BK Co, 9¼" 17.00
Knife, crystal, pnt flowers, Westmoreland 24.00
Knife, crystal, 3-Star, 9¼" 9.00
Ladle, amber, Cambridge 13.00
Ladle, lt bl, Radiance 24.00
Match holder, delphite, w/lettering, Jeannette 28.00
Measuring cup, custard, McKee, 4-cup, rare 23.00
Measuring cup, gr clambroth, Hocking, 2-cup 90.00
Measuring cup, pk, US Glass, 2-cup 95.00
Measuring pitcher, Chalaine bl, 4-cup 85.00
Measuring pitcher, delphite, McKee, 4-cup 120.00
Measuring pitcher, gr w/wht dots, Hazel Atlas, 2-cup 45.00
Measuring pitcher, Skokie gr, McKee, 4-cup 23.00
Mug, cobalt, Cambridge 45.00
Mug, gr, ftd, Jeannette 24.00
Mug, gr, ribbed, Hocking 23.00
Mug, pk, Adam's Rib 14.00
Mug, yel, Hazel Atlas 30.00
Napkin holder, frosted crystal 33.00
Napkin holder, pk, Paramount, US Glass 95.00
Pitcher, batter; gr, ribbed, Hocking 24.00
Pitcher, batter; red, w/tray 95.00
Pitcher, milk; cobalt 45.00
Pitcher, milk; fired-on bl, ribbed, 16-oz 6.00
Pitcher, syrup; pk, Cambridge 50.00
Pitcher, syrup; yel, Heisey 70.00
Pitcher, syrup; yel, w/liner, Fostoria 60.00
Pitcher, utility; pk, US Glass 33.00
Pitcher/reamer, gr, US Glass, 3-pc 150.00
Pretzel jar, gr, ribbed, Hocking 55.00
Range set, Red Circle w/Flowers, Hocking Vitrock, 5-pc 26.00
Range set, Red Tulip, Hocking Vitrock, 5-pc 24.00
Refrigerator container, delphite, Jeannette, 4x4" 14.00
Refrigerator container, fired-on yel, ribbed, 9x5¼" 5.00
Refrigerator container, gr, Tufglas, 3x6" 24.00
Refrigerator container, jadite, 5x5" 17.00
Refrigerator container, lt amber, 4x4" 7.00

Refrigerator container, pk, rnd, tab hdl 23.00
Refrigerator tray, Seville yel, McKee, 8¼x12½" 29.00
Rolling pin, wht clambroth, wooden hdls 130.00
Salt box, crystal, w/lid 13.00
Salt box, wht, w/wood lid, US Glass 75.00
Shakers, gr clambroth, Hocking, 8-oz, ea 13.00
Shakers, jadite, cone shape, pr 12.00
Shakers, pk, emb 'Salt/Pepper,' Hazel Atlas, pr 30.00
Shakers, Skokie gr, w/blk lettering, McKee, ea 9.00
Soap dish, bl, Home Soap Co 24.00
Stack set, pk, MacBeth Evans 45.00
Sugar shaker, gr, w/gold screw-on top, 1950s 50.00
Sugar shaker, wht clambroth, 1 lg hole in top 36.00
Teapot, wht, w/glass lid, McKee 24.00
Towel bar, Chalaine bl, 17" 28.00
Tray, custard, rnd, McKee, 11" 17.00
Tumbler, cobalt, mk HA 12.00
Tumbler, wht, Hazel Atlas, 8-oz 5.00
Vase, bud; delphite, Jeannette 19.00
Vase, delphite 22.00
Water bottle, fired-on red, ribbed 9.00
Water bottle, gr, w/metal screw-on top, Hocking 19.00
Water bottle, gr transparent, Hocking .48.00
Water bottle, red transparent, ribbed, Hocking 45.00
Water bottle, Skokie gr, McKee 95.00
Water dispenser, Skokie gr, McKee 80.00

Apple corer/segmenter, dk tin, rnd, side strap hdls 37.00
Apple peeler, Little Star, CI, curved arm, EX 85.00
Apple peeler, Rival, commercial 295.00
Apple peeler, Sargeant & Foster, pat 1856 . . . . .95.00
Apple peeler, Whittemore, CI, mechanical, 1887 . . . . .75.00
Apple peeler, Wht Mountain #13, Goodell, 1890s 45.00
Apple peeler, wood, crank hdl, 4 prongs hold apple, on board . .185.00
Apple peeler, wood, pewter fittings, mtd on board, ca 1800 . . .350.00
Apple peeler, wood, sawtooth gears, 3-prong, mtd on board . . .195.00
Bread slicer, oblong wood box, iron slicer w/hdl at end 110.00
Cherry seeder, Champion, chrome, multiple action 35.00
Cherry seeder, Enterprise #18, pat 1903 . . . . .32.00
Cherry seeder, Goodell, EX 35.00
Cherry seeder, Logan & Strobridge, New Brighton PA 32.00
Cherry seeder, New Standard Mt Joy, CI, ca 1900, EX 36.00
Cherry seeder, Rollman #3, CI, EX 45.00

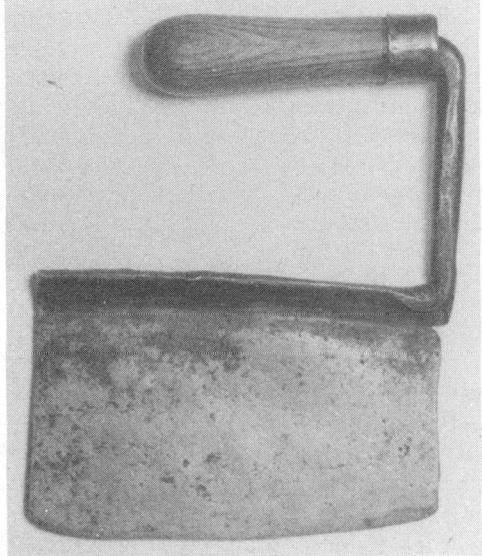

Chopper, wrought blade, 1700s, $95.00.

Chopper, Cox, wrought semi-circle, brass ferrule, 12" W 110.00
Chopper, Dandy, knife assembly, pat pending, 7½" 10.00
Chopper, Enterprise #12 . . . . .45.00
Chopper, NRS, 2-blade, iron/metal, NY, 1899, EX 30.00
Chopper, pumpkin; hand crank, pat 1869, EX 350.00
Chopper, Rollman #11, CI, clamps on, 6½x3½x2½" 35.00
Chopper, scrolled Queen Anne blade, scroll-end hdl 1,100.00
Churn, wooden dasher & lid, tin bands, rare, 1-qt, 9" 195.00
Clothes sprinkler, Chinaman, Sprinkle Plenty, ceramic 15.00
Clothes sprinkler, Dutch girl, ceramic .20.00
Clothes sprinkler, elephant, gray & pk, ceramic 28.00
Clothes sprinkler, fireman, ceramic, EX 18.00
Clothes sprinkler, Myrtle, ceramic, Pfalzgraff 65.00
Colander, brass, wrought iron rim/hdls, EX piercing, 10" 155.00
Cookie mold, heart in hand, bow & arrow, rings, CI, 4½x6" . . .110.00
Cream whip, tin, Fries 50.00
Cream whip, tin, 4 looped legs, crank hdl 85.00
Cutter, french fry; Ekco, 10" 12.50
Cutter, kraut; cherry, heart cutout in rnd crest, 7x19" 165.00
Cutter, kraut; curly maple, arched crest, EX figure, 21x7" 200.00
Dipper, brass w/wrought iron hdl, 11½" 95.00
Dipper, wrought iron & brass, shaped hdl, 16¾" 135.00
Dough scraper, iron w/tooled brass hdl, blade mk BLS/1868 . . .325.00
Dough scraper, iron w/tooled brass hdl, blade mk PD/1850 . . .350.00
Egg beater, A&J, tin w/wood hdl, pat 1923, w/bowl, EX 22.00
Egg beater, Dover #14, CI/tin, 1890s, 17", EX 36.00
Egg beater, Eagle Precision, chrome/red plastic, 12½" 14.00
Egg beater, Taplin's Dover Patent Improved, pat 1903 . . . . . . .30.00
Egg beater, Tarrytown NY 22.00
Egg beater, Turbine-Cassidy, Fairbanks, slotted disk, 10" 33.00
Funnel, brass, oval collar, 1860s, 5x6x7" 50.00
Garlic press, wood, 2-part, hinged, trn hdls, knob ends 95.00
Grater, Gilmore, 1897 . . . . .10.00
Grater, half-rnd pierced tin w/cvd wood bk & hdl, 12½" 85.00
Grater, nutmeg; Mapleton table model, EX 28.00

Nutmeg grater, The Edgar, ca 1880, 5½", $65.00.

Grater, nutmeg; tin/wood, hand crank, 6¼" 85.00
Grater, nutmeg; trn wood, 3-pc, 7½x3½" 195.00
Grater, nutmeg; wood, bottle shape, rasp on hdl, 2½" 260.00
Grater, pierced tin, on hewn board, early nails, 13" L 88.00
Grinder, Griswold #11, Erie 50.00
Grinder, Griswold #2, Erie 40.00
Herb masher, maple, mushroom shape, 5" dia 45.00
Hot plate, Griswold, 2-burner, floor-length base, EX 85.00

Hot plate, Griswold, 3-burner, EX 65.00
Ice cream freezer, Wht Mtn, pat June 12, 1923, 6-qt 45.00
Ice shaver, Griswold, Classic, CI 60.00
Knife, butter; BUTTER cvd in hdl, brass blade w/etched leaf . . .75.00
Knives & forks, bone hdls, ca 1800, set of 6 ea 150.00
Lemon squeezer, CI, fluted bowl, 8" 25.00
Lemon squeezer, maple, hinged, 2-part, 2½x10½" 40.00
Lemon squeezer, Pearl, CI, EX 35.00
Lemon squeezer, wood, on legs, wood base, lg 195.00
Lifter, Handee Helper, slotted tin 6.00
Lifter, pie; Triumph 38.00
Meat tenderizer, CI, wood hdl, ca 1850, 2x2½x3" 38.00
Meat tenderizer, stoneware w/Albany slip, pat Dec 25, 1877 . . . .65.00
Mortar & pestle, Griswold, CI 200.00
Noodle maker, CI/tin, Cleveland OH, pat 1908-20, EX 95.00
Orange squeezer, wood, like lemon squeezer but larger, 20" 95.00
Pie crimper, all brass, heavy, 6¼" 55.00
Pie crimper, bone, crimped wheel, curved serrated end, 7" 165.00
Pie crimper, brass, w/3-color segmented horn hdl, 6¾" 65.00
Pie crimper, brass w/wooden hdl, ca 1840 . . . . .40.00
Pie crimper, ivory, simple tooled hdl w/cutout, 6⅜" 95.00
Pie crimper, ivory w/wooden hdl, 6" 75.00
Potato masher, A&J, gr hdl 4.00
Raisin seeder, Enterprise 1895 . . . . .30.00
Raisin seeder, Everett, wire grid, wood hdl, ca 1893, 2x3¼" 55.00
Raisin seeder, EZY, iron, table clamp, pat May 21, 1895 . . . . . .125.00
Raisin seeder, Lightning, CI, mechanical, 1895 . . . . .55.00
Rolling pin, blown, olive-gr, pontil, att Mt Vernon, 14" 125.00
Rolling pin, cobalt, blown, poem/'Crimea' in worn pnt, 19" 95.00
Rolling pin, dbl bar, w/split banister ends, trn, 1810 . . . . .325.00
Rolling pin, Kelvinator, milk glass 68.00
Rolling pin, nailsea, gr w/wht loops, 16" 130.00
Rolling pin, opal w/HP decor, pontil, 14" 55.00
Sifter, arched legs, iron blades & crank, 10x6x8½" 260.00
Sifter, Duplex, tin, red wood hdl, dbl style 18.00
Spatula, brass w/wrought iron hdl, well-shaped blade, 17" 125.00
Sugar nippers, steel, early 1800s, EX 175.00
Tea ball, screen wire & dk tin, egg shape, 2½x1½" 25.00

Knives

Knife collecting as a hobby began in earnest during the 1960s when government regulations required for the first time that knife companies mark their product with the country of origin. The few collectors and dealers cognizant of this change at once began stockpiling the older knives made before this law was enacted. Another impetus to the growing interest in this area came with the Gun Control Act of 1968, which severely restricted gun trading. Frustrated gun dealers transferred their attention to knives. Today there are collectors clubs in many of the states. The ones to look for are American knives made before 1970, though of course there are exceptions. Most collectors prefer the average to large-size knives and/or unusual patterns in mint or near-mint condition. Case knives continue to be the most popular. However, the knives of other US makers are eagerly sought after as well. Knives produced in other countries still have a very limited following.

Our advisor for this category is Charles D. Stapp; he is listed in the Directory under Indiana.

Key: bd —— blades

Pocket Knives

Belknap, 5386, bone hdl, sheepfoot 3-bd, 3½", M 40.00

Case, B1097, Christmas tree hdl, 1-bd, tested XX, 1920-40, M .395.00
Case, B151-L, faux onyx hdl, 1-bd, tested XX, 1920-40, M 605.00
Case, C61050-SAB, bone hdl, 1-bd, USA, 1965-69, 5⅛", M .205.00
Case, M100, gr bone hdl, 1-bd, tested XX, 1920-40, 3¼", M . .175.00
Case, M110, metal spay hdl, 1-bd, tested XX, 1920s, 3", M . . .140.00
Case, M344, all metal hdl, 3-bd, 3¼", M 145.00
Case, R1051, candy-stripe hdl, 1-bd, tested XX, M 320.00
Case, 11013-SH, walnut hdl, 1-bd, tested XX, 1920-40, 4", M .140.00
Case, 1116-SP, bud walnut hdl, 1-bd, USA, 1965-69, 3½", M . .45.00
Case, 2109-B, slick blk hdl, 1-bd, tested XX, 1920-40, 3¼", M .165.00
Case, 2136-B, slick blk hdl, 1-bd, tested XX, 1920-40, 4⅛", M .125.00
Case, 2138-SS, slick blk hdl, 1-bd, 10-dot, 1970, 5⅝", M 30.00
Case, 2172, slick blk hdl, 1-bd, tested XX, 1920-40, 5½", M .1,000.00
Case, 2207, slick blk hdl, 2-bd, tested XX, 1920-40, 3½", M . . .315.00
Case, 31048-SP, yel compo hdl, 1-bd, XX, 1940-64, 4⅛", M . . .50.00
Case, 5231, stag hdl, 2-bd, tested XX, 3¾", M 330.00
Case, 5355, stag hdl, 3 wharncliffe bd, tested XX, 3¾", M 705.00
Case, 61011, gr bone hdl, 1-bd, tested XX, 1920-40, 4", M . . .305.00
Case, 61011, gr bone hdl, 1-bd, XX, 1940-55, 4", M 95.00
Case, 61011, laminated wood hdl, 1-bd, USA, 1965-69, M 30.00
Case, 61048, gr bone hdl, 1-bd, tested XX, 1920-40, 4⅛", M . .155.00
Case, 61048-SP, Rogers bone hdl, 1-bd, XX, 1940-64, 4⅛", M . .95.00
Case, 61050, gr bone hdl, 1-bd, tested XX, 1920-40, 5⅛", M . .470.00
Case, 61100, bone hdl, 1-bd, tested XX, 1920-40, M 550.00
Case, 6143, brn bone hdl, 1-bd, tested XX, 1920-40, 5", M . . .155.00
Case, 6165-SAB, red bone hdl, 1 flat bd, XX, 1940-64, M 215.00
Case, 6165-SAB, stag hdl, 1-bd, tested XX, M 340.00
Case, 6185, bone hdl, 1-bd, XX, 1940-64, 3⅝", M 80.00
Case, 6200, gr bone hdl, 2-bd, tested XX, 1920-40, 3⅞", M . . .570.00
Case, 62009, bone stag hdl, 2-bd, 10-dot, 1970, 3¼, M 40.00
Case, 62009½, gr bone hdl, 2-bd, XX, 1940-55, 3¼", M 125.00
Case, 62048-SP, delrin hdl, 2-bd, USA, 1965-69, 4", M 30.00
Case, 6205-RAZ, rough blk hdl, 2-bd, XX, 1940-50, 3¾", M . .255.00
Case, 62055, gr bone hdl, 2-bd, tested XX, 1920-40, 3½", M . . .140.00
Case, 6214½, Rogers bone hdl, 2-bd, tested XX, 1920-40, 3⅜" .170.00
Case, 6225½, bone hdl, 2-bd, USA, 1965-69, 3", M 30.00
Case, 6265-SABDR, wood hdl, 2-bd, 10-dot, 1970, 5¼", M . . .140.00
Case, 63109, gr bone hdl, 3-bd, tested XX, 3½", M 405.00
Case, 81051, pearl hdl, 1-bd, tested XX, M 395.00
Case, 8308, pearl hdl, 2-bd, tested XX, 1920-40, 3¼", M 405.00
Case, 9201, cracked ice hdl, 2-bd, XX, 1940-64, 2⅝", M 25.00
Case, 92100, faux pearl hdl, 2-bd, tested XX, 1930s, 4⅝", M . . .605.00
Case, 9220, faux pearl hdl, 2-bd, tested XX, 1930s, 2¾", M 195.00
Case, 9265-SAB, faux pearl hdl, 2-bd, tested XX, '20s, 5", M . .405.00
Primble, 5037, long pull hdl, 2-bd, 4¼", M 95.00
Primble, 732, faux pearl hdl, 4-bd, 3¼", M 30.00
Primble, 902, faux bone hdl, 2-bd, 2⅞", M 25.00
Primble, 910, faux peachseed hdl, 2-bd, 3¼", M 30.00
Primble, 921, peachseed bone hdl, stainless 3-bd, 2¾", M 25.00
Queen, 33, winterbottom bone hdl, 4-bd, 3½", M 40.00
Queen, 57, pearl hdl, 3-bd, 3⅜", M 35.00
Queen, 6105, stag hdl, 2-bd, 3½" 40.00
Queen, 8415, stag hdl, 2-bd, 3⅝", M 30.00
Remington, RC090, blk bone hdl, 3⅜", M 80.00
Remington, R015, pyremite hdl, M 105.00
Remington, R1065, wht pyremite hdl, 3⅜", M 85.00
Remington, R1128, cocobolo hdl, M .1,000.00
Remington, R1243, bone hdl, M 345.00
Remington, R1293, bone hdl, M 195.00
Remington, R1324, pearl hdl, M 220.00
Remington, R1630, buffalo horn hdl, M 300.00
Remington, R193, bone hdl, M 175.00
Remington, R2603, bone hdl, M 70.00
Remington, R265, pyremite hdl, 4", M 185.00

Remington, R3064, pearl hdl, 4", M 395.00
Remington, R3263, bone hdl, M 305.00
Remington, R3455, pyremite hdl, M 175.00
Remington, R3554, pearl hdl, M 355.00
Remington, R358, cocobolo hdl, 3¾", M 165.00
Remington, R3595, stag hdl, M 345.00

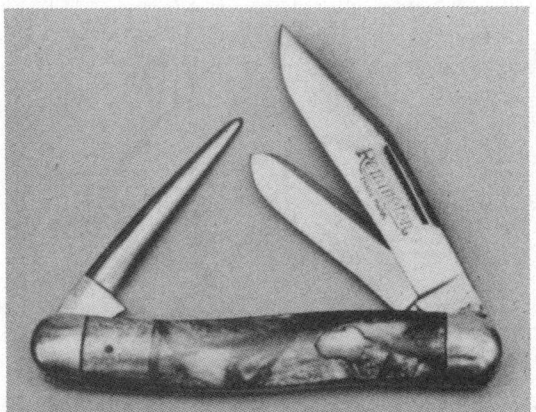

Remington Stockman, R-3565, brown swirl pyremite handle, acorn shield, 4", M, $250.00.

Remington, R3858, cocobolo hdl, M 205.00
Remington, R4548, cocobolo hdl, M 145.00
Remington, R590, buffalo horn hdl, 3¼", M 245.00
Remington, R6249, metal hdl, M 80.00
Remington, R6781, redwood hdl, M 95.00
Remington, R682, blk hdl, 3", M 180.00
Remington, R7493, bone hdl, M 305.00
Remington, R965, pyremite hdl, 4¼", M 155.00
Schrade Cut Co, L1153, bone hdl, 1-bd, 3⅜", M 50.00
Schrade Cut Co, SB2151, cocobolo hdl, 2-bd, 3⅜", M 55.00
Schrade Cut Co, S2152¾, ebony hdl, 3⅜", M 50.00
Schrade Cut Co, 11034⅝, ivory celluloid hdl, 3⅝", M 45.00
Schrade Cut Co, 1131, cocobolo hdl, 3½", M 55.00
Schrade Cut Co, 1157¾, clip blade hdl, M 70.00
Schrade Cut Co, 1404¾-W, faux ivory celluloid hdl, 3⅜", M . . . 95.00
Schrade Cut Co, 1514M, marine pearl pyralin hdl, 4", M 145.00
Schrade Cut Co, 2014-G, gr pearl pyralin hdl, 3⅝", M 95.00
Schrade Cut Co, 2061, cocobolo hdl, 3⅝", M 55.00
Schrade Cut Co, 2132, ebony hdl, 3¼", M 55.00
Schrade Cut Co, 2214-S, tortoise celluloid hdl, 3½", M 90.00
Schrade Cut Co, 2394½-B, blk celluloid hdl, 3¾", M 55.00
Schrade Cut Co, 2424-S, tortoise celluloid hdl, 3⅛", M 55.00
Schrade Cut Co, 7116-T, mother-of-pearl hdl, 3⅜", M 55.00
Schrade Cut Co, 7444-S, tortoise celluloid hdl, 2⅞", M 130.00
Schrade Cut Co, 7609-SS, sterling silver hdl, 2¼", M 45.00
Schrade Cut Co, 7704-PT, smoked pearl celluloid hdl, 2⅞", M . 30.00
Schrade Cut Co, 778-RB, stainless steel hdl, 2-bd, 2⅞", M . . . 30.00
Schrade Cut Co, 7786, mother-of-pearl hdl, 3¼", M 55.00
Schrade Cut Co, 7812, ebony hdl, 4", M 145.00
Schrade Cut Co, 7936-T, mother-of-pearl hdl, 2½", M 35.00
Schrade Cut Co, 8118-T, buffalo horn hdl, 3⅜", M 95.00
Schrade Cut Co, 8182, ebony hdl, 3⅝", M 95.00
Schrade Cut Co, 9703-B, bone hdl, 2⅞", M 65.00
Winchester, 1608, cocobolo hdl, 3⅜", M 75.00
Winchester, 2051, wht celluloid hdl, 2⅝", M 145.00
Winchester, 2314, pearl hdl, 3", M 95.00
Winchester, 2320, pearl hdl, 2⅞", M 85.00
Winchester, 2603, cocobolo hdl, 3⅜", M 155.00

Winchester, 2649, ebony hdl, 3¾", M 165.00
Winchester, 2862, stag hdl, 3⅜", M 95.00
Winchester, 2871, stag hdl, 3¾", M 230.00
Winchester, 2934, stag hdl, 3⅜", M 95.00
Winchester, 2980, stag hdl, 3⅝", M 175.00
Winchester, 2996, stag hdl, 3¾", M 175.00
Winchester, 3020, celluloid hdl, 3½", M 305.00
Winchester, 3035, gold celluloid hdl, 3⅜", M 175.00
Winchester, 3349, pearl hdl, 3", M 195.00
Winchester, 3925, stag hdl, 3⅝", M 325.00
Winchester, 3950, stag hdl, 3⅝", M 280.00
Winchester, 3953, stag hdl, 3¼", M 180.00
Winchester, 3977, stag hdl, 3⅜", M 245.00
Winchester, 4930, stag hdl, 3¼", M 295.00

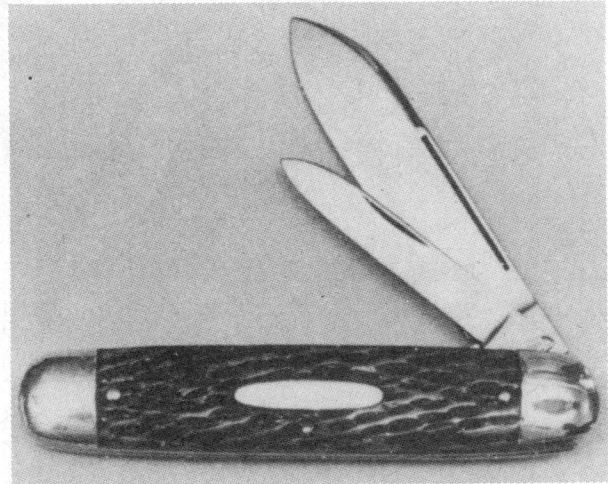

Schrade Walden, #297, peachseed bone handle, 4½", M, $150.00.

Miscellaneous

Bowie, bone hdl, silvered nickel hilt, Joseph Allen, 10" 75.00
Bowie, 6" Sheffield blade, fancy ivory grip, 1850s, +scabbard . . 130.00
Bowie, 6½" Sheffield blade, 2-pc stag horn grip, 1880s 115.00
Bowie, 7" Sheffield, stag horn grip, 1850s, EX 110.00
Bowie, 8" Singleton-Priestman-Sheffield blade, 1861, lg, EX . . 110.00
Camp, J Russell Gr River Works on 11" blade, 1870s, 17" 75.00
Hunting, 12½" eng blade, Fr, 1800-1850, EX, +sheath 80.00
Hunting, 6½" etched Herder/Solingen blade, 1900s, +sheath . . 50.00
S Am cowboy, mk 7½" blade, brass hilt w/silver, 1860s 75.00
Safari, heavy 8½" blade, ebony grip, 1880s, +sheath 60.00
Trapper's skinning, 5" upturned blade, wood grip, 1870s, EX . . . 55.00
Utility, Russell Gr River mks, 3½" blade, 1880s, VG 35.00

Knowles, Taylor, Knowles

Isaac Knowles and Isaac Harvey operated a pottery in East Liverpool, Ohio, in 1853, where they produced both yellowware and Rockingham. In 1870 Knowles bought Harvey's interests and took as partners John Taylor and Homer Knowles. Their principal product was Ironstone china, but Knowles was confident that American potters could produce as fine a ware as the Europeans. To prove his point, he hired Joshua Poole, an artist from the Belleek Works in Ireland. Poole quickly perfected a Belleek-type china, but fire destroyed this portion of the company. Before it could function again, their hotel china business had grown to the point that it required their full attention in order to meet market demands. By 1891 they were able to try again. They developed a bone china, as fine and thin as before, which they called Lotus. Henry Schmidt from the Meissen factory in Germany decorated the ware, often with lacy filigree applications or hand-formed leaves and flowers to which he added further decoration with liquid slip applied by means of a squeeze bag. Due to high production costs resulting from so much of the fragile ware being damaged in firing and because of changes in tastes and styles of decoration, the Lotus Ware line was dropped in 1896. Some of the early ware was marked 'KT &K China'; later marks have a star and a crescent with 'Lotus Ware' added.

For further study we recommend *American Belleek* by our advisor, Mary Frank Gaston; her address is listed in the Directory under Texas.

Lotus Ware

Bonbon, appl twigs, 4 twig ft, scalloped, 7½" L, NM 150.00
Bowl, appl flowers, beaded rim, openwork hdls, 4x6¾" L 600.00
Bowl, rtcl ribbing/beading, gold on wht, +VG liner, 4½" 550.00
Bowl, webbing/prunus flowers, gold on wht, mk, 4¼x4½" 325.00
Creamer, twig base, gold traced, turq beads, 3½" 225.00
Creamer, wht, no decor, 2½" 105.00
Ewer, floral sprays/garlands, 10", NM .700.00
Rose bowl, leaves/berries in heavy gold, ftd, mk, 4" H 700.00

Kosta

Kosta glassware has been made in Sweden since the mid-1700s. Their designer-type art glass from the 20th century is becoming very collectible.

Bowl, wht clam shells at base, sgn, 2½" .25.00
Candlestick, 5½" 15.00
Paperweight, frosted, air-trap Saturn/bl & orange moons 110.00
Rose bowl, clear, 3 top ridges, sgn Linch, 1½" 55.00
Sculpture, gr-to-amethyst crystal, rhomboidal, 9" 350.00
Vase, crystal, flattened form w/teardrop base, #1721, 6" 100.00
Vase, gray w/cut clear oval front & bk, bl-gr int, 8" 200.00
Vase, int bl layer w/air-trap animals, sgn Gordon, 7" 495.00
Vase, obelisk form, mk, 8" 275.00
Vase, paperweight; bl swirls in clear, sgn Warff, 5¼" 150.00
Wine, 6 cut panels, gr w/clear stem, 5", 6 for 125.00

Vase, thick-walled with internal streaks of green and clusters of air bubbles, exterior engraved with tropical fish, signed Vicke Lindstrand, 9", $400.00.

Kutani

Kutani, named for the Japanese village where it originated, was first produced in the 17th century. The early ware, Ko Kutani, was produced for

only about thirty years. Several types were produced before 1800, but these are rarely encountered. In the 19th century, kilns located in several different villages began to copy the old Kutani wares. This later, more familiar type has large areas of red with gold designs on a white ground decorated with warriors, birds, and flowers in controlled colors of red, gold, and black.

Bowl, Hundred Arhats on gilt/red brocade, Kinrande, 12" 250.00
Charger, water/rocks/dwellings, ext: 3 peonies, 1800s, 13" 495.00
Chocolate pot, birds/peonies/people, red/gold, ca 1870s, 8½" . .125.00

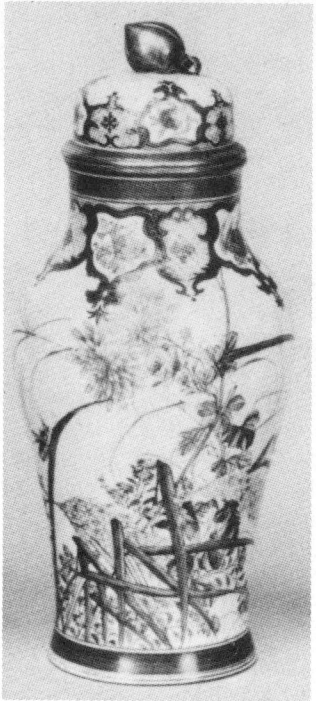

Jar, birds and grasshoppers amid foliage, 1800s, 15", $250.00.

Labels

Before the advent of the cardboard box, wooden crates were used for transporting products. Paper labels were attached to the crates to identify the contents and the packer. These labels often had colorful lithographed illustrations covering a broad range of subjects. Eventually the cardboard box replaced the crate, and the artwork was imprinted directly onto the carton. Today these paper labels are becoming collectible — primarily for the art, but also for their advertising appeal.

Apple, America's Delight, mtn orchards stone litho, 1920, CA . . .4.00
Apple, Buffalo, buffalo w/horns, 1930, CA 10.00
Apple, Don't Worry, rosy-cheeked boy w/apple, 1940, CA 3.00
Apple, KY Cardinal, red bird on twig, CA 12.00
Apple, Sawmill Peak, mtn view, dammed river, 1940, CA 2.00
Apple, Yakima Chief, Indian chief, 1930, CA 10.00
Asparagus, Coin, stacks of gold/silver coins, 1940, CA 6.50
Asparagus, Pride of River, Mississippi river boat, 1930, CA 7.50
Cigar, Continental, G Washington in uniform, EX 25.00
Cigar, Cuban Specials, lady offers man box of cigars, M 17.50
Cigar, Deep Water, train track leads to ocean, VG 48.00
Cigar, El Coloso, geisha girl, M 30.00
Cigar, Flor Fina, man on horsebk blows horn, M 22.00
Cigar, High Toned, dog watches 1880s boy smoke cigar, M 30.00
Cigar, La Normandy, man slays dragon, nude women, M 20.00
Cigar, Navigator, Columbus in center globe, M 60.00
Cigar, Old King Cole, Parrish 75.00

Cigar, Priscilla, pilgrims, ship on horizon, M 25.00
Cigar, Strawberry 12.50
Cigar, Three Sisters, 3 women look to sea, M 14.00
Cigar, Willie Walker, man in red coat w/tails, M 65.00

Atta Boy, Citrus Ass'n, $5.00.

Citrus, Blue & Gray, generals clasp hands, 1930, FL 17.50
Citrus, Kiss Me, 2 children, 1940, FL 7.50
Citrus, Prince of Wales, man in purple clothes, 1940, FL 3.00
Citrus, Tru-Type, Indian smokes pipe, FL 12.50
Lemon, Basketball, women playing, 1920, CA 37.50
Lemon, Cutter, boat in ocean, 1940, CA 4.00
Lemon, Evening Star, San Fernando Mission, 1930, CA 4.00
Lemon, First American, Indian brave & teepee, 1916, CA 55.00
Lemon, Gateway, riders in forest, 1930, CA 3.00
Lemon, Montecito Valley, grove stone litho, 1920, CA 25.00
Lemon, Umpire, early American football game, 1920, CA 40.00
Orange, Carro Amano, Italian couple by pushcart, 1920, CA 5.00
Orange, Collegiate, school building, 1930, CA 7.50
Orange, De Luxe, Blk butler serves couple, CA 235.00
Orange, Gold Buckle, orange grove in belt fr, 1930, CA 5.00
Orange, Good Cheer Inn, carriage Xmas scene, 1947, CA 5.00
Orange, Indian Belle, Indian couple/grove/mtns, 1915, CA 45.00
Orange, Laurel, 3 oranges w/gr leaves, 1930, CA 3.00
Orange, Merry Christmas, oranges & blossoms, 1916, CA 37.50
Orange, Orchard King, crowned orange, 1930, CA 4.00
Orange, Poinsettia, wrapped orange & lg flower, 1930, CA 8.00
Orange, Princess, crowned lady & oranges, 1930, CA 4.00
Orange, Redskin, Indian by campfire, 1920, CA 24.00
Orange, Sunflower, lg yel sunflower, 1920, CA 4.00
Pear, Bellboy, bellhop in red serves pear, 1930, CA 5.00
Pear, Covered Wagon, scout points to oxen/wagon, 1930, CA . . .4.00
Pear, Polly, colorful bird on perch, CA 12.00
Pear, Tulip, 3 colorful tulips, 1920, CA 7.50
Tobacco, Little African, A Dainty Morsel, boy & alligator 45.00
Vegetable, Cheerio, man in top hat, 1930 . . . . .4.00
Vegetable, Mustang, bucking wht horse, 1950 . . . . .2.00
Yam, Champ, football player w/sweet potato, LA 5.00
Yam, Treasure, treasure chest, tropical scene, LA 3.50

Labino

Dominick Labino was a glass blower who until mid-1985 worked in his studio in Ohio, blowing and sculpting various items which he signed and dated. A ceramic engineer by trade, he was instrumental in developing the heat-resistant tiles used in space flights. His glassmaking shows his versatility in the art. While some of his designs are free-form and futuristic, others are reminiscent of the products of older glasshouses. Because of problems with his health, Mr. Labino became unable to blow glass himself; he died in late 1986. Work coming from his studio after mid-1985 will be signed 'Labino Studios, Baker,' indicating ware made by his prodigy, E. Baker O'Brien. In addition to her own compositions, she continues to use many of the colors developed by Labino.

Bowl, amber w/gold & red swirls, sgn/1974, 6½" 350.00
Bowl, bl/purple/gr/yel/red swirls in clear, sgn/1965, 4x6" 500.00
Bowl, blurina irid, wide rim, sgn/1968, 7½" 900.00
Goblet, clear w/yel, long twist stem, 1967, 9" 750.00
Pitcher, bl opal, freeform, sgn/1971, 8½" 225.00
Plate, gr, sgn/1974, 10" 200.00
Sculpture, Suspension, bl, sgn/1974, 10" 4,500.00
Vase, amber, owl form, sgn/1982, 4" 500.00
Vase, bl irid, ribbed, sgn/1971, 9" .400.00
Vase, bud; bl-gr, paperweight base, sgn/1967, 6" 300.00
Vase, frosted irid w/appl thick bl strings, sgn/1963, 6½" 750.00
Vase, gr to red, ribbed, sgn/1981, 3½" 250.00
Vase, lav w/yel & bl swirls, sgn/1978, 4¾" 300.00
Vase, pk/gr, molded swirled prunts, sgn/1971, 7" 350.00
Vase, purple w/gr & gold, 2 pointed rim extensions, 5" 500.00
Vase, sculptured immersion, 2 layers pk veil+bubble, 6½" . . .1,900.00
Vase, thick bl intersecting ropes on clear frost, 1963, 6½" 750.00
Vase, twist stem in clear/yel, goblet form, sgn/1967, 9" 750.00

Vase, thick applied stringing on rose red, 1967, 5", $200.00.

Lace, Linens, and Needlework

It has been recorded that lace was found in the tombs of ancient Egypt. Lace has always been a symbol of wealth and fashion. Italian laces are regarded as the finest ever produced, but the differences between them and the laces of France are nearly indistinguishable. Needlework was revived during the 18th century and became the favorite of feminine pastimes. Examples of many forms are readily available today — tatting, embroidery, needlepoint, and crochet — and, though fragile in appearance, have withstood the ravages of time with remarkable durability.

Key:
embr — embroidered   ms — machine sewn
hs — hand sewn

Back splash, linen, ecru, pullwork, embr owls, fringed, 36x19" . .28.00
Back splash, linen, ecru, silk-embr girls, fringed, 34x18" 30.00
Back splash, linen, embr, pullwork, 23x17" 25.00
Bed tick, homespun linen, plaid, buttons, 1800s, 63x46½", M . .185.00
Bedspread, crochet, Popcorn, wht, 72x88"+fringe, NM 285.00
Bedspread, machine fillet & net, ecru, full sz, EX 75.00
Bolster cover, Irish linen, crochet border, 21x60" 60.00
Bolster cover, Irish linen, floral embr, scalloped, 32x86" 65.00
Bolster cover, linen, embr birds, 34x70" 55.00
Bun warmer, Fr style w/linen pockets, Battenburg, 14" dia 110.00
Bun warmer, linen w/Battenburg border, ecru, standard sz 15.00

Centerpiece, Battenburg scalloped border, 12" dia 45.00
Centerpiece, 5" sq plain center, Battenburg corners, 12" sq 45.00
Chair cover, crochet, linked stars, 20x16" 25.00
Chair cover, lace fillet, ecru, serpentine bottom, 17x15" 25.00
Chair set, crochet, wht, American eagle on bk pc, 3-pc 45.00
Crochet panel, Sunbonnet Girl, 11x16" 40.00
Doily, Battenburg star pattern, ecru, 12" dia 70.00
Doily, crochet, dbl star, ecru, 16" dia .35.00
Doily, crochet, pinwheels, ecru, 7" dia .35.00
Doily, crochet, stars w/scalloped border, ecru, 13" dia 35.00
Doily, crochet, wheel spokes, scalloped, 10" dia, pr 75.00
Doily, drawn linen center w/Nandutti lace border, 11" dia 75.00
Doily, octagonal, 5½" Battenburg lace border, 17½" 85.00
Doily, Pointe de Venice, wht, 12" dia .65.00
Doily, X-stitch, bl on wht linen, bl scallop border, 10x11" 25.00
Handkerchief, linen w/Royal Battenburg lace, 15x15" 65.00
Mat, bread tray; linen w/scalloped eyelet border, 5x9" 22.50
Mat, crochet, 'Baby' fillet, 5x8" 10.00
Needlework on silk, fruit/butterfly, 10x11", EX 325.00

Silkwork picture, Abraham Meeting the Daughters of Jethro, 1825, 29x28", EX, $550.00.

Place mat, linen, embr florals, insertion, 16x11" 45.00
Runner, Battenburg, 14x30", NM 65.00
Runner, Battenburg fleur-de-lis, 19x74" 95.00
Runner, crochet, sailing ship in center, beige, 13½x21" 65.00
Runner, dbl drawn, 22x70" 25.00
Runner, oval w/5" Battenburg border, 16½x34" 85.00
Runner, Tambour lace, ecru, 42x15" 35.00
Runner, 3 linen squares inserted in Battenburg, 18x52" 88.00
Sack, bl/wht checked cotton, ms, drawstrings, 16x25" 65.00
Scarf, Battenburg border, 13x20" 25.00
Scarf, Battenburg border, 18x70" 35.00
Sham, embr florals & Good Night in center, 23½x28" 32.00
Sham, embr wreath/birds in corners/hem, 28x31", pr 65.00
Sham, Irish linen, lace insert, pr 48.00
Sham, Irish linen, ruffles, pr 65.00
Sham, Irish linen, triple punchwork, pr 72.00
Sham, linen, bl, wht scallop trim 15.00
Sham, pieced/appl, plaids/solids, 27x27", EX, pr 335.00
Sham, single ruffle, 4 appliques, embr cows, pr 30.00
Sheet, homespun linen, hs hem/central seam, 74x76" 45.00
Sheet, homespun wool, hs hem/central seam, wear, 67x78" 45.00
Show towel, flowers/etc/name in red & bl X-stitch, 56x17" 150.00
Table piece, Battenburg, 8" plain center, sq, 17" 50.00
Table piece, 5½" Battenburg lace border, octagonal, 17½" 85.00
Tablecloth, Battenburg, tri-drawn center, rose embr, 78x92" . .550.00
Tablecloth, Battenburg, 90x68" 275.00
Tablecloth, Battenburg & cotton, 54x54" 65.00

Tablecloth, Battenburg border, 24" plain center, 52" dia 40.00
Tablecloth, Battenburg butterfly lace, linen center, 68" 245.00
Tablecloth, Battenburg grapeleaf pattern w/inserts, 68" dia 250.00
Tablecloth, Battenburg mixed pattern, 52x52" 165.00
Tablecloth, crochet, Medallions, 78" sq 85.00
Tablecloth, dbl-woven wht-on-wht cotton, embr roses, 82x86" . .70.00
Tablecloth, Irish crochet inserts, embr grapes, 76x92" 475.00
Tablecloth, linen, cut & embr, 72x84" 70.00
Tablecloth, linen, griffins/gargoyles, ecru, hs, 120x72" 750.00
Tablecloth, linen, ornate Venetian needle lace, 98x92" 500.00
Tablecloth, linen, quad-drawn, 50x50" 45.00
Tablecloth, linen, red/wht, 51x56", +6 napkins 175.00
Tablecloth, linen, red/wht floral pattern, 57x57" 145.00
Tablecloth, linen, scroll embr, ecru, 64x82" 60.00
Tablecloth, linen, wht, 72x104", +12 napkins 185.00
Tablecloth, linen, wide tatted border, 42" dia 35.00
Tablecloth, machine lace, daisy floral, 108x60" 65.00
Tablecloth, machine lace, ecru & wht, 68x82" 35.00
Tablecloth, machine lace, floral, scalloped, 82x68" 35.00
Tablecloth, overshot, brn/wht, 40x60" 400.00
Tablecloth, Quaker lace, ecru, scalloped border, 68x88" 55.00
Tablecloth, Victorian paisley, 3-color, Victorian, 132x62" 175.00
Tea cosy, Battenburg, EX 50.00
Wall hanging, stumpwork, couple/cottage, 1700s, 12" dia 300.00

Lachenal

Bowl, modeled as flower, olive/gray/ivory crackle, sgn, 11" 225.00
Bowl, 6-point star, bl/olive on gr wash, 6½" 200.00
Pitcher, naturalistic branch hdl, lt bl/brn drip, 16" 400.00

Lacy Glassware

Lacy glass became popular in the late 1820s after the development of the pressing machine. It was decorated with allover patterns — hearts, lyres, sheaves of wheat, etc. — and backgrounds were completely stippled. The designs were intricate and delicate, hence the term 'lacy.' Although Sandwich produced this type of glassware in abundance, it was also made by other eastern glassworks as well as in the midwest. By 1840 its popularity on the wane and a depressed economy forcing manufacturers to seek less expensive modes of production, lacy glass began to be phased out in favor of pressed pattern glassware. When no condition is indicated, the items listed below are assumed to be without obvious damage; minor roughness is normal. See also Sandwich Glass.

Dish, eagle in center, attributed to Sandwich, 7" wide, NM, $600.00 at auction.

Bowl, Heart, att Sandwich Glass, 11¾" 1,600.00

Plate, toddy, Thistle, Sandwich Glass, rim chip, 5¼" 30.00
Salt cellar, amethyst, Neal SC-15, French, EX 200.00
Sugar bowl, Acanthus Leaf & Shield, Sandwich Glass, EX 300.00
Tie back, floral, opal, pewter post, 2½", pr 165.00
Whiskey, L-150-5 or 7, fired-on decor very worn 175.00
Whiskey taster, canary, 9-panel, att Sandwich Glass 120.00
Whiskey taster, cobalt, 9-panel, NM .120.00

Lalique

Beginning his lengthy career as a designer and maker of fine jewelry, Rene Lalique at first only dabbled in glass, making small panels of pate-de-vere (paste-on-paste) and cire perdue (wax casting) to use in his jewelry. He also made small flacons of gold and silver with his glass inlays, which attracted the attention of M.F. Coty, who commissioned Lalique to design bottles for his perfume company. The success of this venture resulted in the opening of his own glassworks at Combs-la-Ville in 1909. In 1921 a larger factory was established at Wingen-sur-Moder in Alsace-Lorraine. By the thirties Lalique was world renown as the most important designer of his time.

Lalique glass is lead based, either mold blown or pressed. Favored motifs during the Art Nouveau period were dancing nymphs, fish, dragonflies, and foliage. Characteristically the glass is crystal in combination with acid-etched relief. Later, some items were made in as many as ten colors — red, amber, and green among them — and were occasionally accented with enameling. These colored pieces, especially those in black, are rare and highly prized by advanced collectors.

During the twenties and thirties, Lalique designed several vases and bowls reminiscent of American Indian art. He also developed a line in the Art Deco style decorated with stylized birds, florals, and geometrics. In addition to vases, clocks, automobile mascots, stemware, and bottles, many other useful objects were produced. Items made before his death in 1945 were marked 'R. Lalique'; later the 'R' was deleted even though some of the original molds were still used. Numbers found on the bases of some pieces are catalog numbers.

Our advisor for this category is John Danis; he is listed in the Directory under Illinois.

Key:
cl/fr — clear and frosted   RL — signed R. Lalique
L — signed Lalique   RLF — signed R. Lalique, France

Ash tray, fish w/bubbles intaglio, cl/fr, RLF, 6" dia 195.00
Bottle, scent; Camille, ribbed frieze, bl fr, RLF/RLF, 2½" . . .4,600.00
Bottle, scent; dk bl w/orig mirrored Worth display, mk, 4" 450.00
Bottle, scent; Farouche, heart shaped, for Ricci, sgn, 4" 295.00
Bottle, scent; Je Reviens, smoke w/turq stopper, sgn, 4½" 125.00
Bottle, scent; Le Jade, gr fr, imp Roger et Gallet/RL, 3" 4,400.00
Bottle, scent; nude kneels amid flowers, cl/fr, L, 4¾" 4,100.00
Bottle, scent; 12 Figurines avec Bouchon, fr, RL, 11½" 4,950.00
Bowl, Gui, mistletoe, cl to opal, RLF, 9⅜" 600.00
Bowl, Jardiniere St Hubert, RL, #3461 . . . . .3,750.00
Bowl, Marguerite, overlapping florals, cl, RLF, 13½" 990.00
Bowl, Persian ibexes & frosted grasses at base, mk L, 5x6" 275.00
Box, powder; 3 dancing nudes & garlands, RL, 1½x3⅝" 245.00
Box, Quatre Scarabees, scarabs, blk, RL, 2¼" 5,900.00
Box, symmetrical scallops, removable lid, bl fr, RL, 2¾" 3,000.00
Candlestick, flower form, low ft, fr, RLF, 1930s, 9⅛" 1,750.00
Car mascot, Hirondelle, sparrow, cl/fr, RLF, 5¾" 3,000.00
Car mascot, Levrier, greyhound, cl w/lav tint, RLF, 7¾" 1,300.00
Card holder, fruit basket, fr, RLF, 1½", set of 6 . . . . .3,500.00
Centerpiece, Ange, praying angels frieze, opal, RLF, 14½" . . .3,850.00
Centerpiece, Flora Bella, petal bands, bl, RLF, 15⅜" 8,800.00

Chandelier, Gaillon, acanthus, bowl form, fr, RLF, 17¾" 6,000.00
Chandelier, Oranges, bowl form, cl/fr amber, RLF, 15" 2,800.00
Clock, blossoms & stems, rnd form, cl/fr, L, 4½" 1,300.00
Clock, Inseparables, RL 3,150.00
Figurine, Coq Nain, rooster w/fine plumage, cl/fr, RLF, 8" . . .2,600.00
Figurine, draped lady w/goblet in hand, fr, RL, 5⅝" 1,850.00
Figurine, eagle head, RLF, 4½" 300.00
Figurine, Guinea hen, cl/fr, RLF, ca 1930, 6¾" 715.00
Figurine, Mogenne Violee, draped female, fr, RLF, 11" 4,100.00
Figurine, Sirene, mermaid in curled position, opal, RL, 4" . . .2,200.00
Figurine, turkey, sgn L, France, 3½" 50.00
Goblet, silver & cire perdue rose blossoms, fr, L, 7¼" 4,400.00
Incense burner, Sirens, fr/gray stain, RL 2,450.00
Luminaire, Gros Poisson Vagues, cl, bronze base, RL, 15" . . .7,700.00
Mirror, Rond Grand Eglantines, floral, RLF, 17" dia 16,500.00
Paperweight, mermaid intaglio, cl/fr, RLF, 2¼x3¼" 295.00
Pendant, Cherries, red/amber, triangle shape 975.00
Pendant, 2 nudes on floral ground, gr wash, RL, 1932, 2⅛" 990.00
Tester, scent; brambles/D'Orsay, 5-bottles, fr, RLF, 9" L 3,800.00
Tumbler, Jaffa, serrated ribs, cl/fr amber, 5¾" 215.00
Vase, Acanthes, oviform, yel cased, L, 11" 6,000.00
Vase, Actina, serrated curves, opal, RLF, 8½" 1,650.00
Vase, allover leaves, canister w/flange, cl/fr, RLF, 9" 1,200.00
Vase, Archers, bows drawn for birds, fr opal, RL, 10¾" 3,300.00
Vase, Armorique, artichoke form, opal, ca 1932, RLF, 9" 1,850.00
Vase, bud; fern leaves in panels, cl/fr, RLF, 4¾" 225.00
Vase, Danaides, Danaus' daughters, opal, RLF, 7¼" 4,950.00
Vase, Davos, geometric nodule clusters, mauve, RLF, 11¼" . . .3,500.00
Vase, Druides, berry branches, fr w/brn wash, RLF, 7" 880.00
Vase, Epines, thorny branches, yel opal w/gr wash, RLF, 9" . .1,200.00
Vase, Farandole, dancing cherub base, opal, flared, RLF, 7" . . .800.00
Vase, Formose, fish swimming, red cased, RL, 7" 12,000.00
Vase, Gobelet 6 Figurines, mythical maidens, cl/fr, RL, 7" . . .1,750.00
Vase, grasshoppers, raspberry-red, RL, ca 1937, 10¾" 4,400.00
Vase, Grenade, geometrics, blk, spherical, RLF, 4½" 4,400.00
Vase, Gros Scarabees, cl, brn patina in recesses, L, 11½" 3,500.00

Vase, Lievres, turquoise-blue with band of rabbits, molded in intaglio: R. Lalique, 6", $3,800.00.

Vase, Margaret, berries/birds on lg sq lug hdls, RLF, 9" **4,600.00**
Vase, Moissac, stylized leaves, opal, V-form, RLF, 5" **1,700.00**
Vase, Monnaie Du Pape, berries, gr, ovoid, RLF, 9" **7,000.00**
Vase, Montmorency, cherries, cl/fr, RLF, U-form, 8" **1,300.00**
Vase, Morgan, rings w/Xing lines, blk HP dots, RLF, 6½" ...**1,750.00**
Vase, Mures, berries, opal w/gold & bl tinge, RLF, 7½" **1,870.00**
Vase, Nefliers, blooming tree, cl w/gray wash, RL, 5¼" **300.00**
Vase, Nimroud, cl w/blk triangular leaves, RL, 7¾" **7,700.00**
Vase, Oranges, fr w/blk-brn foliage, RL, RLF #964, 11⅜" **2,300.00**
Vase, Oursin, molded nodules, spherical, bl fr, RL, 7½" **1,700.00**
Vase, overlapped/graduated fans, ovoid, amber, RLF, 7" **1,400.00**
Vase, Perles, pearl bands, gray-cased opal, RL, 4¾" **4,400.00**
Vase, Perruches, parakeets, bulbous, fr, RL, 10" **2,400.00**
Vase, Pierrefonds, curled thorny strap hdls, cl/fr, RL, 6" ...**3,300.00**
Vase, Plumes, spherical, fr w/gray wash, RL, 8½" **770.00**
Vase, Poissons, stylized fish, yel cased, RL, 9½" **8,800.00**
Vase, Rampillon, lt smoke, #991 ....**1,850.00**
Vase, Rouces, brambles, ovoid, bl, RLF, 9" **1,800.00**
Vase, Rouces, brambles, ovoid, cased w/gr wash, RLF, 9" **1,200.00**
Vase, Rouces, brambles, ovoid, fr, RL/L, 9" **700.00**
Vase, Rouces, brambles, ovoid, gr, RL, 9" **1,600.00**
Vase, Soucis, Marguerites, flared rim, cl/bl fr, RLF, 6¾" **7,000.00**
Vase, Thistles, ovoid, gr, RLF/#979, 8½" **3,500.00**
Vase, Thistles, ovoid, gray w/orange stain, RLF, 9½" **880.00**
Wine, dancing nudes on stem, cl/fr, sgn, 6" **110.00**

Lamps

The earliest lamps were simple dish containers with a wick that hung over the edge or was supported by a channel or tube. Grease and oil from animal or vegetable sources were the first fuels used. Ancient pottery lamps, crusie, and Betty lamps are examples of these early types. In 1784 Swiss inventor Ami Argand introduced the first major improvement in lamps. His lamp featured a tubular wick and a glass chimney. During the first half of the 19th century, whale oil, burning fluid (a highly explosive mixture of turpentine and alcohol), and lard were the most common fuels used in North America. Many lamps were patented for specific use with these fuels.

Kerosene was the first major breakthrough in lighting fuels. It was demonstrated by Canadian geologist Dr. Abraham Gesner in 1846. The discovery and drilling of petroleum in the late 1850s provided an abundant and inexpensive supply of kerosene. It became the main source of light for homes during the balance of the 19th century and for remote locations until the 1950s.

Although Thomas A. Edison invented the electric lamp in 1879, it was not until two or three decades later that electric lamps replaced kerosene household lamps. Millions of kerosene lamps were made for every purpose and pocketbook. They ranged in size from tiny night or miniature lamps to tall stand or piano lamps. Hanging varieties for homes commonly had one or two fonts (oil containers), but chandeliers for churches and public buildings often had six or more. Wall or bracket lamps usually had silvered reflectors. Student lamps, parlor lamps (now called Gone-with-the-Wind lamps), and patterned glass lamps were designed to complement the popular furnishing trends of the day. From about 1910, Aladdin lamps with a mantle became the mainstay of rural America, providing light that compared favorably with the electric light bulb. Gaslight, introduced in the early 19th century, was used mainly in homes of the wealthy and public places until the early 20th century. Most fixtures were wall or ceiling mounted although some table models were also used.

Few of the ordinary early electric lamps have survived. Many lamp manufacturers made the same or similar styles for either kerosene or electricity, sometimes for gas. Top-of-the-line lamps were made by Pairpoint, Phoenix, Tiffany, Bradley and Hubbard, and Handel. See also these specific sections.

For those seeking additional information concerning oil lamps, we recommend *Oil Lamps — The Kerosene Era in North America*, and *Oil Lamps II — Glass Kerosene Lamps*, by Catherine M.V. Thuro. J.W. Courter is an authority on Aladdin lamps who has written several fine books and collectors' manuals as well as annual value guides. These are available at your bookstore or from Collector Books.

One of our advisors for this category is Ruth Osborne; she is listed in the Directory under Ohio.

Aladdin Lamps

Alacite, G-211, candelabrum, electric, M **130.00**
Alacite, G-230, regency lamp, electric, EX **22.00**
Alacite, G-234, golden pheasant, table lamp, electric, EX **125.00**
Alacite, G-25, boudoir lamp, electric, NM **15.00**
Alacite, G-257, oak leaf decor, electric **32.00**
Beehive, B-81, gr crystal, complete, EX **75.00**
Beehive, B-83, ruby crystal, EX **280.00**
Cathedral, #107, clear, NM **80.00**
Cathedral, B-112, rose moonstone, NM **170.00**
Colonial, #106, amber, complete, EX orig **125.00**
Colonial, B-104, clear, EX orig **88.00**
Corinthian, B-100, clear, complete, EX **60.00**
Corinthian, B-103, clear, EX orig **60.00**
Corinthian, B-104, clear, blk base **55.00**
Corinthian, B-106, clear font, amber ft, NM **85.00**
Corinthian, B-116, rose moonstone, EX orig **85.00**
Corinthian, B-126, wht moonstone font, rose moonstone ft, EX .**95.00**
Crystal, G-130, figurine lamp, electric, EX **525.00**
Hanging lamp, #12, w/plain shade, EX **220.00**
Hanging lamp, #3, w/shade #203, EX **500.00**
Hanging lamp, #4, w/shade #203, NM **325.00**
Hanging lamp, #7, all orig, unused, M **1,100.00**
Hanging lamp, #8, w/orig shade, EX **400.00**
Hanging lamp, Model B, w/parchment shade, EX **170.00**
Lincoln Drape, B-60, alacite, short **300.00**
Lincoln Drape, B-62, ruby crystal, old, short, EX **400.00**
Lincoln Drape, B-74, clear, tall, EX **1,250.00**
Lincoln Drape, B-75, alacite, scalloped ft, tall **225.00**
Lincoln Drape, B-77, ruby, old, tall, NM **450.00**
Majestic, B-121, rose moonstone, EX **165.00**
Majestic, B-121, rose moonstone, VG **70.00**
Oriental, B-131, gr, EX orig **100.00**
Oriental, B-131, gr, VG **50.00**
Oriental, B-133, silver, EX **110.00**
Practicus, hanging, w/shade, NM **525.00**
Queen, B-95, wht moonstone, VG **65.00**
Queen, B-97, gr moonstone, EX **145.00**
Quilt, B-86, gr moonstone, complete, NM **110.00**
Quilt, B-91, wht moonstone font, rose moonstone ft, EX **135.00**
Simplicity, B-27, alacite, gold lustre, EX **225.00**
Simplicity, B-29, gr, VG **60.00**
Solitare, B-70, wht moonstone, EX **1,000.00**
Treasure, B-136, chromium, NM **185.00**
Treasure, B-137, bronze, EX **75.00**
Venetian, #102, peach, EX **80.00**
Venetian, #103, rose, M **115.00**
Venetian, #99, clear, EX **225.00**
Vertique, B-88, yel moonstone, complete, EX **375.00**
Vertique, B-93, wht moonstone, EX orig **385.00**
Victoria, B-25, china, EX **275.00**
Washington Drape, B-40, gr crystal, rnd base, VG **60.00**
Washington Drape, B-48, gr, bell stem, NM **135.00**
Washington Drape, B-49, amber, bell stem, complete, EX **210.00**

Chandeliers

Washington Drape, B-52, amber, filigree stem, EX 75.00
Washington Drape, B-53, clear, no oil fill, plain stem, EX 85.00
Washington Drape, B-55, amber, plain stem, NM 70.00

Chandeliers

Brass, bl to wht 14" bowl shade w/HP raspberries, brass mt . .1,200.00
Brass, 3-arm, burmese shades, 32" filigree shaft, pr 1,550.00
Brass, 3-arm, frost/clear scalloped shades, electric, EX 375.00
Brass, 3-arm, lg central shade, French, 1890s 500.00
Brass, 4-arm, portraits on 15" milk glass shades, EX 650.00
CI, 2-arm, floral/X-hatch clear/frosted shades, 34", EX 225.00
CI, 4-arm, clear fonts, #2 burners, pearl-top chimneys, EX 425.00
Copper, hammered, 4-arm, slag glass shades, ca 1910 . . . . .300.00
Crystal, 6 glass branches, Georgian style, prisms, 35" 550.00
Gilt brass & ironstone, 5-arm, Victorian style, 25", EX 750.00

Decorated Kerosene Lamps

Bl stain cut to clear font, clear/frost shade, 8 prisms, 21" 600.00
Cobalt cut to clear font, blk amethyst ft, 9½", EX 150.00
Cobalt cut to wht to clear, dbl-cut std, Sandwich, 12" 1,800.00
Cranberry cut to clear, milk glass stem, gold trim, 10" 250.00
Cranberry cut to clear font/shade, marble base, 17¼", EX 300.00
Gr cut to clear font, cut/frosted shade, marble base, 26" 1,850.00
Gr cut to clear font, wht ft, gilt base, 9½", EX 300.00
Gr stain cut to clear, brass stem, marble base, 13" 400.00
Ruby stain cut to clear, brass stem, marble base, 14½" 250.00
Ruby stain cut to clear, brass stem, marble base, 18" 725.00
Wht cut to clear, milk glass stem/ft, gold trim, 22½" 325.00
Wht cut to clear font, stepped base, Victor burner, 17" 1,100.00
Wht cut to cranberry font, brass stem, marble base, 12½" . . .1,300.00

Fairy Lamps

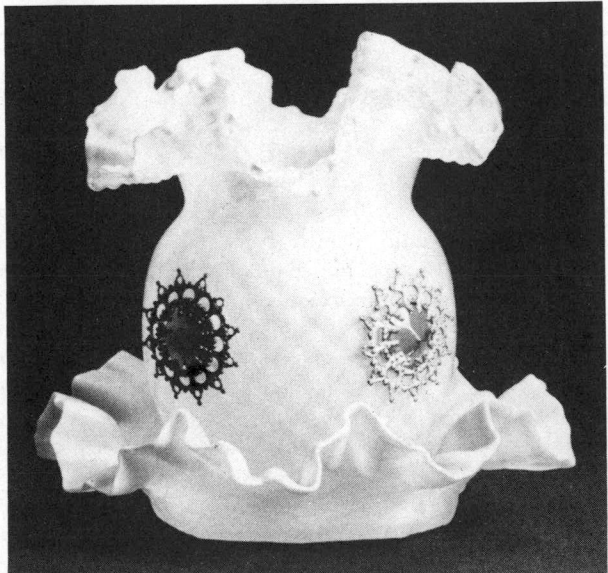

**Diamond Quilted pink opaline with jewels, French, 7",
$550.00.**

Bl Dia Quilt MOP, clear Clarke base, 4⅝x4" 165.00
Bl opaque, stippled w/emb beads, Clarke base, 5⅛x2⅞" 85.00
Bl verre moire, wht loopings, Clarke cup, 3⅝x5¾" 395.00
Bsk 3 face (cat/owl/dog), glass eyes, ftd, #d, scarce 250.00
Burmese, HP decor, burmese insert, Webb, 6" 1,550.00
Burmese, HP florals, clear base mk Will of Wisp, 4" 250.00

Burmese, unmk, clear mk Clarke flower-bowl base, 5½x6" 295.00
Cleveland, bl/wht satin stripes, 3-part, 6¼" 650.00
Cranberry overshot, crown figural for 1887 Jubilee, 4½" 195.00
Cranberry verre moire, 2 on dbl-branch Cricklite base, 16¾" . .495.00
Cranberry verre moire w/wht loopings, Clarke base, 4¼" 175.00
Gr overlay, wht lined, dome shade, mk Clarke base, 4¼x4" . . .110.00
Gr verre moire, wht loops, Clarke base, 3¾x2¾" 165.00
Mc spatter, 2 on dbl-branch cut Cricklite base, 17¾" 450.00
Pk Dia Quilt MOP, clear mk Clarke base, 5½" 190.00
Puffy rvpt vintage shade, tall std, no candle holder, 8" 250.00
Rainbow satin Swirl, crimped top, clear Clarke base, 5½" 450.00
Rose Dia Quilt MOP, clear mk Clarke base, 3½x3" 145.00
Rose Tapestry w/burmese shade, Doulton, 7¼x7" 660.00
Silver inclusions on gr 135.00
Wht opal overshot, crown figural, Clarke base, 4½x3" 175.00
Yel Swirl MOP satin, wht int, ruffled base, 5x5¾" dia 455.00

Gone-with-the-Wind and Banquet

Arabian on milk glass, 10" Tam-O'-Shanter shade, 21", EX . . .350.00
Brass Corinthian column std, eng glass globe, 1880s, 28" 200.00
Bull's Eye, red satin, altered shade ring, 10" shade, 25" 200.00
Cherub's face blown out on red satin 9½" shade, 24½" 800.00
Desert scenes, blown-out lions' heads on milk glass, 23", EX . . .350.00
Floral HP on milk glass, brass ring, #2 burner, 12½", EX 165.00
Floral HP on milk glass, 10" Tam-O'-Shanter shade, 26", EX . .275.00
Floral HP on milk glass w/emb decor, 10½" shade, 25½" 575.00
Floral HP on milk glass w/emb decor, 9½" shade, 20", EX 550.00
Floral HP on opaque gr-pnt top/base, electrified, 26", EX 300.00
Floral HP on satin glass, 10½" shade, 25½", EX 575.00
Grape & Leaf, red satin, 29" 650.00
Illinois, scalloped open globe, ball font, Solar burner, 22" 450.00
Leaves emb on 9¾" red satin shade, 23", EX 475.00
Lions' heads blown out on 10" red satin glass shade, 23", EX . . .800.00
Mermaids/waves HP on milk glass, Tam-O'-Shanter shade, 25" . .500.00
Mtns transfer on milk glass, 20¾", EX 250.00
Mums HP on milk glass, 10" shade, 19½", EX 350.00
Plumes emb on milk glass, gr scrolls, #2 burner, 13", EX 215.00
Puffy Drape, red satin, reticulated brass base, 27" 650.00
Quilted Diamond Drape, red satin, brass ftd, 27" 600.00
Roses emb on satin, electrified, 24" .640.00
Sailboats/windmills on milk glass, 8½" shade, 21¼", EX 350.00
Shepherd scene HP on milk glass, ball shade, ewer hdls, 30" . . .700.00
Swirl emb on red satin 9" shade, 20½", EX 550.00
Victoria, red satin, 10¼" shade, 27", EX 500.00

Hanging Lamps

Florals HP on milk glass, clear font, brass fr, prisms, EX 350.00
Hall, Bull's Eye, amber, brass fr, electrified, 27", EX 200.00
Hall, Bull's Eye, cranberry, smoke bell, brass fr, 39", EX 450.00
Hall, clear/frosted acid-etched crown-top shade, brass fr 165.00
Hall, floral, bl on milk glass, bl hobnail font, brass fr 350.00
Hall, frosted cut to clear hex globe, brass fittings, 31" 450.00
Hall, Optic Rib cranberry shade, brass fr, orig smoke bell 350.00
Hall, Ribbed Panel, cranberry, smoke bell, brass fr, 22" 250.00
Hall, Swirled Rib, cranberry shade/clear font, brass fr, 30" 375.00
Hobnail, amberina, brass fittings, 10x9" 345.00
Hobnail cranberry shade/font holder, gr font/fr, 14", EX 1,400.00
Jeweled red brass shade, clear font, red brass fr, prisms, EX 525.00
Morning-Glories on burmese color, clear/frost font, prisms 350.00
Pansies HP on milk glass, clear font, brass fr, EX 300.00
Rubena w/optic opal stripes, 10" shade 375.00

Tea roses HP on milk glass, clear font, brass cottage fr 225.00
Wht Bristol shade, brass-washed metal fr, 6", EX 325.00

Pink roses on opaque glass globe, brass fittings, 14" diameter, $350.00.

Lanterns

Brass, eng star/T Barrett Serge of Police on blown globe 350.00
Candle, tin, 3-corner shape w/turret top, 18½", VG 210.00
Candle, 3-sided glass, pierced tin top, Parker, 1855, 15½" 120.00
Coach, tin/brass, bull's eye, reflectors, hinged door, 13" 125.00
Dietz #1 Climax, tin, 2 glass sides, bl japanning, 16", VG 75.00
Isinglass & iron, conical hood/cylinder body, 15" 140.00
Paul Revere, punched tin, rpr/rpt, 13½", VG 145.00
Skater's, brass, pat Mar 1864, 1866, 1888, 7½", VG 165.00
Skater's, brass w/gr globe, 6¾", EX .295.00
Steam Gauge & Lantern Co, tin, 3 glass sides, 20", VG 60.00
Tin, blown globe, whale oil burner, ring hdl, 10" 365.00
Tin, diamond & star cutouts, glass globe, dbl burner, 10" 75.00
7 glass panels, hexagonal w/mercury reflector, tin font, 16" . . .250.00

Lard Oil/Grease

Betty, wrought iron, wire pick/hanger, 5" 175.00
Brass on tin, dbl spout, saucer base, rpr, 7½" 90.00
Brass on tin, spout guard, chain hanger/pick/tweezer, 11x4" 90.00

Rush light, acorn pan, scrolled support, tripod, 1700s, 14" . . .1,100.00
Rush light, wrought, socket counterbalance, twisted std, 9" 195.00
Smith pat Aug 8, 1854, tin/iron, saucer base, 6", EX 550.00

Miniature Lamps, Kerosene

Amethyst, 6½x2½", mtd on sq hdld tray, EX 130.00
Angels/florals fired on pk cased, rpl burner, 8", EX 350.00
Artichoke, gr/lav on milk glass, nutmeg burner, 7½", EX 600.00
Beaded Drape, Gone-w/the-Wind, nutmeg burner, 9", M 335.00
Beaded Hearts, clear 155.00
Beaded Swirl, brn/gold end-of-day, hornet burner, 8" 150.00
Block, milk glass, complete, 6½" 110.00
Cameo, florals, wht/raspberry, rpl burner, att Webb, 11" 3,600.00
Ceramic, cat on pillow form, HP, rpl burner, 5⅝", EX 200.00
Cloisonne decor on porc, ball shade, brass ft/shoulder, 9" 200.00
Cone, pk-cased satin, nutmeg burner, 8", EX 300.00
Cranberry threads on clear, pewter fr & burner, 6" 395.00

Crocodile Tears, milk glass, 9", $500.00.

Daisy & Cube, amber, nutmeg burner, 7½", EX 350.00
Daisy & Leaf emb on milk glass, rpl burner, 8¼", EX 275.00
Delft-style cherubs on porc, rpl burner, 6", EX 300.00
Dia Quilt, peach MOP satin, SP metal base, 11x4" 750.00
Dia Quilt, pk MOP satin, appl frosted ft/hdls, 12", EX 3,000.00
Dia Quilt, yel cut velvet, nutmeg burner, 6⅝", EX 2,500.00
Drape, cranberry w/amber scallops on ped base, 6¼" 300.00
Florals, gold on red cased, nutmeg burner, 8½", EX 550.00
Florals, orange & gold on bl cased, nutmeg burner, 8", EX 700.00
Girl w/cart on bsk, lined wicker shade, acorn burner, 9" 850.00
Heron decor, burner mk BB, pat June 1, 1869, att Sandwich . . .295.00
Invt T'print, gr, finger lamp, complete, 6¼" 75.00
Little Buttercup emb on hdl, amethyst, acorn burner, 2¾" 115.00
Log Cabin, bl clambroth figural, #1 burner, 3x4¾", EX 750.00
Log Cabin, clear figural, complete, 3½", NM 355.00
Octavia, gr, orig burner & chimney, EX 125.00
Optic Honeycomb, cranberry, Am collar, rpl burner, 6½" 220.00
Optic panels, cranberry, hornet burner, 8¼", EX 225.00
Owl's face, milk glass, nutmeg burner, 7¾", EX 1,700.00
Panelled Cosmos, mc on milk glass, nutmeg burner, 8", EX . . .350.00
Pansies HP on bl satin, petal-shaped shade, ribbed base, 8" . . .660.00
Pk to wht cased, emb decor, rpl burner, 10", EX 650.00
Queen's Necklace, Findlay, rare 225.00
Rainbow lustre on milk glass, nutmeg burner, 7¼", VG 500.00

Raindrop, bl MOP satin, frosted ft, nutmeg burner, 8", EX ...2,500.00
Raindrop, wht MOP satin, frosted ft, nutmeg burner, 8", EX .1,400.00
Ribbed, bl satin, ped base, orig ball shade, M 400.00
Ribbed, cranberry, finger lamp, complete, 6" 145.00
Royal Ivy, cranberry/clear, rnd base w/ball shade, 6½" 375.00
Shells appl/frosted on rainbow MOP satin, rpl burner, 12" ...2,500.00
Shoe form, bl opaque, #0 burner, Atterbury, 3", EX 950.00
Shoe form, clear, emb Patd June 30 1868, Atterbury, 3" 400.00
Silver overlay leaves/berries on gr satin, rpl burner, 14" 900.00
Snowflake, cranberry opal, all orig 850.00
Spider Web, emb scrolls/flowers, red satin, acorn burner, 7" 400.00
Stars & 'Twinkle' emb on base, amethyst, acorn burner, 6¾" ..250.00
Swan, milk glass, brass collar, chimney & burner, 4" 275.00
Sweetheart, crystal, Findlay 140.00
Windmills/boats emb on bl opaque panels, hornet burner, 7½" .375.00
Zipper Loop, ruby stain, 10½" 140.00

Pattern Glass Lamps

Acanthus Leaf, jade gr/wht, oil burner, Sandwich, 11", VG ...400.00
Apollo, bl, w/burner, 12" 275.00
Aquarius, amber, ftd, finger lamp 165.00
Beaded Hearts, clear w/frost, flat, finger lamp 135.00
Beaded Hearts, massive, 8 toes, 8¾" 145.00
Bellflower, scalloped ft, w/collar, 7", NM 200.00
Bull's Eye, gr, #2 burner, 10", EX 175.00
Bull's Eye, gr, ftd, finger lamp 130.00
Bull's Eye & Ellipse, flint, camphene burner, 11", NM 150.00
Bull's Eye w/Fleur-de-Lis, whalc oil burner, flint, 10", EX 225.00
Cathedral, clear font, bl stem/ft, bl Hobnail shade, 20" 275.00
Coin Spot, aqua opal, finger lamp 250.00
Columbian Coin, fluid burner, 12", NM 275.00
Coolidge Drape, cobalt, appl hdl, finger lamp, 3½", EX 200.00
Daisy, milk glass, 9¼" 195.00
Daisy, 10¾" 145.00
Daisy & Bow Knot, cobalt, #2 burner, 9⅝", EX 125.00
Daisy & Button, bl, finger lamp 155.00
Diamond & Fan, amber, 8" 135.00
Diamond Sunburst, bl, flat, finger lamp 125.00
Dogtooth & Panel, bl, appl hdl, finger lamp, 5", EX 180.00
Emblem, fluid burner, 6¾", EX 100.00
Emblem, hand lamp, Lindsey-63, 10" 100.00
Feather Duster, amber, 8" 140.00
Feather Duster, canary, 8¼" 150.00
Giant Sawtooth, whale oil burner, flint, 11", NM 150.00
Heart, gr, finger lamp 275.00
Invt T'print, cranberry opal spatter, finger lamp 350.00
Jenny Lind, milk glass stem/base, clear font, pat dtd 275.00
Lomax, dtd 1870, kerosene burner, hand lamp 50.00
Loop, waisted w/monumental bases, att NE, 11½", NM, pr 375.00
Lowell Loop, bl opaque, #2 burner, finger lamp, 6¼", EX 250.00
Moon & Stars, Deco style, 1930s, 4½" 100.00
Optic, cranberry, clear appl hdl, finger lamp, 5½" 175.00
Panelled Diamond Point, orig oil burner, 10½", M 120.00
Peacock Feather, bl, ftd, finger lamp, 6", EX 190.00
Periwinkle, fluted brass std w/marble base, 9", EX 100.00
Periwinkle, scalloped ft, brass collar, 6¾", NM 75.00
Petal & Bulging Loops, ftd, finger lamp, Eagle burner 45.00
Pillow Encircled, cobalt, #2 burner, 10", EX 125.00
Prince Edward, gr opaque, 8¼" 135.00
Princess Feather, #2 burner 87.50
Princess Feather, milk glass, #2 burner, 9½", EX 150.00
Ribbed Panel, custard, Rayo base, oil burner, 18½" 245.00
Riverside Empress, gr, finger lamp 175.00

Riverside Panel, gr font, clear stem 145.00
Rosa, gr, 8½" 100.00
Rosa, red flowers/gr foliage on clear, 8" 75.00
Sheldon Swirl, bl opal font, clear stem, 7⅝", EX 450.00
Snowflake, bl opal, stand lamp 295.00
Snowflake, clear opal, finger lamp, Hobbs, 8¼", EX 300.00
Snowflake, clear opal, stand lamp 225.00
Snowflake, cranberry opal, Hobbs, stand lamp 500.00
Three Face, 9" 250.00
Torpedo, flat, finger lamp 80.00
Tulip, jade gr opaque/wht, late, 11" 275.00
Venice, 8½" 110.00
Waffle, whale oil burner, 11½", NM 175.00
Wheat in Shield, 10¼" 155.00

Peg Lamps

Amethyst stain cut to clear, Kosmos-Brenner burner, 11", EX .250.00
Bl Swirl MOP ruffled shade, matching font, ornate, 16½" 760.00
Pk overlay mushroom shade, brass candlestick, 17½" 625.00
Pk satin half shade, fancy SP brass candlestick, 18", EX 450.00
Pk shaded, wht int, brass holder w/bearded head, 16" 825.00
Yel overlay mushroom shade, brass candlestick, 15x6½" 525.00
8-sided, pewter collar, brass/pewter burner, complete, VG 165.00

Reverse Painted Lamps

Cottage scene on 15" sgn/#d shade; urn std w/glass ball 600.00
Florals on umbrella shade; cherubs on pot metal base, 20" 250.00
Peacock on stone wall 17" dimpled shade; mk Jefferson base .1,200.00
Water/houses/pine trees on 16" shade, bronze unsgn base 700.00

Student Lamps, Kerosene

Dbl, amber cased shades, electrified, early, 24¼" 1,000.00
Dbl, gr cased umbrella shades, brass fr, electric, 25" 1,000.00
German, milk glass shade, pat 1863/1873, 21" 325.00
Gr cased rnd shade w/emb & gilt decor, electrified, 23" 850.00
Gr cased shade, NP brass fr, 20½", EX 550.00
Manhattan, gr cased shade, NP brass, electrified, 20½", EX 450.00
Manhattan, milk glass shade, brass, dtd Dec 25, '77, 20½" 400.00
Milk glass shade, brass cylinder font, 23" 250.00
Milk glass shade, mk/1863 on burner, brass fr, 19½", EX 325.00
W Lincoln pat 1879, burnished brass fr, 17½", EX 425.00
Walton's Pat Nov 6, 1866, Scovil 1864 on burner, 13", EX 300.00

Whale Oil/Burning Fluid

Admiral Dewey, copper/brass shell-form font w/ship, 8½" L ...500.00
Blown globe font w/5-step cloverleaf base, no burner, 6" 125.00
Blown teardrop font, stepped cloverleaf base, 11", pr 450.00
Bull's Eye w/Bars, flint, att Sandwich, 9", NM, pr 150.00
Canary yel waisted loop font, monumental base, 11" 850.00
Clear font, pewter collar, twin-tube burner, Sandwich, 9" 120.00
Clear tapered cylindrical font, twin-tube burner, 5", EX 110.00
Cup plate base, dbl-drop burner, att Sandwich, 6½", NM 700.00
Cut/pressed, cone font/faceted blown knop std, NE Glass, 11" .275.00
Flint, hex base, loop font w/brass collar, 8", EX 125.00
Globular pressed font w/prisms, stepped marble base, 13" 325.00
Harp (Lyre), flint, Sandwich, 8", NM 150.00
Heart, T'print, & Waffle, rpl burner, 9", EX 200.00
Jade opaque, fluted, on brass std/marble base, Sandwich, 7" ...375.00
Lion's Head, Flower Basket base, globe font, NE, 7", EX, pr .1,100.00
Loop, appl hdl, brass collar, camphene burner, 6" 110.00

Loop pattern, sapphire blue, with original whale oil burners, 10", $1,200.00 for the pair.

Loop, sapphire bl, orig oil burner, 9", NM 400.00
Milk glass, blown, slant-sided font, lg finger hold, 3" 85.00
Sheet brass, snuffer cap, 9" 375.00
Sparking, free blown, appl hdl, 2", M 250.00
Star, orig oil burner, Sandwich, 10½", pr 400.00
Tin, blk pnt, single burner, appl hdl, 6" saucer, 6½" 75.00
Vine, orig oil burner, Sandwich, 10", NM 175.00
2-Printie Block, dk purple-bl, hex base, att NE Glass, 6" 1,200.00

Miscellaneous

Argand, cast brass, ring-shaped font, NE Glass Co, 12¾" 750.00
Argand, cast metal w/brass decor, cut/etched shade, EX 550.00
Argand, dbl, cast brass, milk glass shades, 18¼", pr 550.00
Argand, dbl, cast brass/bronze, orig burners/holders, 16", EX ...400.00
Bracket, blk iron, clear font, mercury glass reflector, 14" 95.00
Brass, kero burner, mk Perkins & House..., pat 1857-71, 9" 200.00
Candle, 15 bezel-set jewels, scrolled arm, 7" burner, 24" 175.00
De Keravenan-Jones, mechanical, wheel-cut ball shade, 12½" .600.00
Desk, Emeralite, dome-shaped gr cased shade, adjusts, 13" 250.00
Float, 1 clear bowl, gilt-metal stand, blk iron base, 11" 75.00
Float, 1 clear bowl, gilt-metal stand, slate base, 11½" 75.00
Float, 2 clear bowls, gilt-metal stand, slate base, 10¾" 110.00
Float, 3 cobalt bowls, fluted brass stem, 14¾", EX 100.00
Hitchcock, mechanical, NP brass, 12⅜", EX 395.00
Miner's, Sticking Tommy, iron, fancy shaft & hook 250.00
Miner's spout, brass collar/lid, C George, pat 1908, 4" 40.00
Miner's spout, tin, Geo Anton, Monongehela WA, 2½", EX ...45.00
Ripley wedding, bl fonts/wht center, milk glass base, 12" 1,000.00
Sconce, prisms/clear beads on gilt fr, electric, 14", pr 350.00
Turq porc base, clear/frost ball shade, English, 24½x7" 550.00

Le Verre Francais

Le Verre Francais was produced during the 1920s by Schneider at Epinay-sur-Seine in France. It was a commercial art glass in the cameo style composed of layered glass with the designs engraved by acid. Favored motifs were stylized leaves and flowers or geometric patterns. It was marked with the name in script or with an inlaid filigrane.

Our advisor for this category is Don Williams; he is listed in the Directory under Iowa.

Cameo

Lamp, fiddle-head leaves on dome shade/baluster std, 20" ...2,500.00
Lamp, stylized floral panels, red to wine on orange, 13½" 1,950.00
Lamp, 13" shade w/scarab beetles; wrought base w/berries ...2,500.00
Lamp, 9½" shade & base w/cats & brickwork frieze, 15½" ...7,000.00
Vase, baskets of fruit, brn on orange mottle, gray ft, 9" 600.00
Vase, butterflies, bl-flecked red on aqua to yel, ftd, 7" 935.00
Vase, carnations, lav/orange on yel/bl, ftd ovoid, 8½" 550.00
Vase, Deco floral branches, brn on wht to apricot, 20" 900.00
Vase, floral vines at shoulder, brn on orange to yel, 23" 1,550.00
Vase, leafy vines, red on lav/pk flecked, cylindrical, 18" 1,100.00
Vase, mums, brn w/bl on orange mottle, gray ft, hdls, 12" 800.00
Vase, oranges, tangerine to gr on flecked yel, ftd, 8½" 440.00
Vase, roses, red to wine on yel mottle, trumpet form, 12" 700.00
Vase, 12 geese fly over rushes, brn w/bl splotches, 5x7¼" 700.00

Vase, sunflowers, violet on rose mottle, marked Ovington, 13", $850.00.

Leeds, Leeds-Type

The Leeds Pottery was established in 1758 in Yorkshire and under varied management produced fine creamware, often highly reticulated and transfer printed, shiny black-glazed Jackfield wares, polychromed pearlware, and figurines similar to those made in the Staffordshire area. Little of the early wares were marked; after 1775 the impressed 'Leeds Pottery' mark was used. From 1781 to 1820, the name 'Hartley Greens & Co.' was added. The pottery closed in 1898.

Today the term 'Leeds' has become generic and is used to encompass all polychromed pearlware and creamware — wherever its origin. Thus similar wares of other potters — Wood, for instance — is often incorrectly called 'Leeds.' Unless a piece is marked or can be definitely attributed to Leeds by confirming the pattern to be authentic, 'Leeds-Type' would be a more accurate nomenclature.

Key:
rtcl — reticulated   sp — soft paste

Bowl, openweave/rtcl, w/matching dome lid, mk, 8x7" 750.00
Bowl, simple florals, panels, swan finial, 1830s, w/lid 160.00
Bowl+flower arranger top, creamware, emb swags/hdls, mk, 7" .265.00
Charger, bl feather edge, bl chinoiserie motif, 15", NM 900.00
Creamer, sp, 3-color pineapple, bl rim, rpr, 4", VG 70.00
Creamer, sp, 4-color floral band/brn stripes, flakes, 3¾" 55.00
Plate, bl feather edge, 4-color eagle, 9½", EX 350.00
Plate, creamware, rtcl, emb, no mk, 8½", NM 90.00
Plate, gr feather edge, 4-color eagle, 7", NM 400.00
Plate, rtcl rim, mk, 1800s, 5¾", NM 80.00
Plate, sp, bl feather edge, chinoiserie motif, 6½", EX 150.00
Platter, emb putti, feather edge, 1780s, 18" L 3,000.00
Sugar bowl, sp, gaudy floral/bl bands, rpr/flakes, 6" 250.00
Tray, creamware, rtcl, emb swags, rope hdls, no mk, 9", EX 68.00
Waste bowl, sp, 4-color floral/emb ribs, 3x6", EX 150.00

Legras

Legras and Cie was founded in St. Denis, France, in 1864. Production continued until about 1914. In addition to their enameled wares, they made cameo art glass decorated with outdoor scenes and florals executed by acid cuttings through two to six layers of glass. Their work is signed 'Legras' in relief.

Cameo

Bowl, ships/mtns/lakes on orange 4¼x3¼" 275.00
Bowl, winter scene, 3½x12" 750.00

Vase, vines, red on pink, signed in cameo, 15", $525.00.

Vase, arboreal landscape, HP details, cylindrical, 6" 330.00

Vase, forest scene, pnt details, 10½", pr 900.00
Vase, maple leaves, magenta on frost, sgn, 9" 535.00
Vase, mums w/draped festoons, purple on textured frost, 14" ...425.00
Vase, river scene w/lg trees, gr/yel/olive on gray, 9½" 800.00
Vase, sea grasses/flowers, brn on burmese, 14" 650.00
Vase, shells/murex/seaweed, maroon/gr/brn on ivory, 23" 1,550.00
Vase, sweetpeas, lav w/gold leaves on frost, 18" 900.00
Vase, thistles, brn shaded, sgn, 8" 575.00
Vase, trees/2 dogs, orange on lt bl chipped ice, 9½" 1,200.00

Enameled Glass

Bowl, water lilies, gold/bl on tan, amber int, 9½" 275.00
Tray, vintage, 17½" dia 170.00
Vase, berries, gr & wht, sgn, 4" 95.00
Vase, leaves, maroon on acid-cut clear ground, 11¾" 500.00
Vase, shepherd/flock/church, HP on yel, cylincrical, 11" 150.00
Vase, winter scene, 15¾" 350.00
Vase, woodland scene, mc on clear, 10" 325.00

Lenox

Walter Scott Lenox, former art director at Ott and Brewer, and Jonathan Coxon founded The Ceramic Art Company of Trenton, New Jersey, in 1889. By 1906 Cox had left the company and to reflect the change in ownership, the name was changed to Lenox, Inc. Until 1930 when the production of American-made Belleek came to an end, they continued to produce the same type of high-quality ornamental wares that Lenox and Coxon had learned to master while in the employ of Ott and Brewer. Their superior dinnerware made the company famous, and since 1917 Lenox has been chosen the official White House China.

Our advisor for this category is Mary Frank Gaston; she is listed in the Directory under Texas. See also Ceramic Art Company.

Atomizer, Scottie dog begging, yel 250.00
Bookends, Blk lady's torso, Deco, gr mk, pr 225.00
Bouillon set, Empress 45.00
Bowl, fruit; Montclair 18.00
Bowl, Lotus Leaf, wht, shape #37 ....95.00
Bowl, Temple Blossom, vegetable, oval 55.00
Bowl, wht ware, dragon-shaped hdls, wreath mk, 13" 120.00
Bust, Deco girl, wht on wht, #2138, gr wreath mk 140.00
Cake stand, Ming, low ped 65.00
Candlestick, Column, gold mk, 5½", pr 35.00
Chocolate pot, roses & gold paste, sgn, palette mk, 7" 275.00
Creamer, Ming 60.00
Creamer & sugar bowl, Lenox Rose 100.00
Creamer & sugar bowl, Washington's 200th Birthday, w/lid 95.00
Cup, Ming, blk mk 40.00
Cup & saucer, Caribee 30.00
Cup & saucer, Empress 40.00
Cup & saucer, Montclair, old style 30.00
Cup & saucer, Sachet 28.00
Figurine, First Waltz, ltd ed, 1984 ....125.00
Figurine, flapper's head, 4" 87.00
Figurine, Floradora, no decor 265.00
Figurine, lady reading book, much lace, M 250.00
Figurine, seal on ledge, ivory, 6x4" 150.00
Lamp, boudoir; Deco lady w/hoop skirt & fan forms shade, 9" ..265.00
Lamp, nude figural, 1929, 12½" 675.00
Mug, bl florals w/gold, lily pads at rim/base, gold hdl 55.00
Pitcher, lemons/blossoms on gr shaded, palette mk, 10¾" 195.00
Pitcher, Patriots, wht w/bl garlands & emb figures, 9" 150.00

Pitcher, pk textured w/wht hdl, girl's mask spout, 7½" 95.00
Pitcher, silver overlay w/floral cameo, palette mk, 8" 500.00
Plate, Caribee, dinner sz 25.00
Plate, Empress, dinner sz 35.00
Plate, fuchsia border w/heavy silver overlay border, 10" 135.00
Plate, Ming, salad sz 18.00
Plate, Montclair, salad sz 12.00
Plate, soup; Caribee 35.00
Plate, Westfield, dinner sz 25.00
Platter, Empress, lg 150.00
Salt cellar, swan figural, gr mk .25.00
Shakers, Orchard, pr 22.00
Shakers, Rhodora, pr 70.00
Shell, gold rim, bl mk, 9" 40.00
Sugar bowl, Ming, open 45.00
Swan, bl mk, 8½" 75.00
Swan, gold mk, 2" 15.00
Swan, gold mk, 5" 50.00

Teapot, brown with silver overlay, $150.00.

Tea set, Virginian, gold hdls, 11" pot, 3-pc 350.00
Teapot, silver overlay, blk mk .150.00
Toby jug, Theodore Roosevelt, Penfield design, 8" 225.00
Vase, bud; multiflorals on porc, 6" 35.00
Vase, Empire, swan hdls, 1930 gr mk, 10½" 65.00

Letter Openers

Brass, dueling pistol, fancy, 5¼" 10.00
Brass, Pittsburgh Coal, Indian on hdl 18.00
Brass, rifle figural 12.00
Brass, Vestal Chemical Labs, 1957 . . . . .20.00
Brass & bronze, Honeywell Heating 30.00
Bronze, Pittson Coal, Chicago 10.00

Bronze, three owls on branch on handle, 8", $40.00.

Cast metal, alligator head, EX 20.00

Chromed steel, Irwin Auger Bit, Wilmington, auger hdl 25.00
Hammered sterling silver w/flat jade blade, 1910, 8½" 275.00
Sterling, Jacobi & Jenkins, floral relief, 7" 125.00

Libbey

The New England Glass Company was established in 1818 in Boston, Massachusetts. In 1892 it became known as the Libbey Glass Company. At Chicago's Columbian Expo in 1893, Libbey set up a ten-pot furnace and made glass souvenirs. The display brought them world-wide fame. Between 1878 and 1918, Libbey made exquisite cut and faceted glass, considered today to be the best from the brilliant period. The company is credited for several innovations — the Owens bottle machine that made mass-production possible and the Westlake machine which turned out both electric light bulbs and tumblers automatically. They developed a machine to polish the rims of their tumblers in such a way that chipping was unlikely to occur. Their glassware carried the patented Safedge guarantee.

Libbey also made glassware in numerous colors — cobalt, ruby, pink, green, and amber. In 1935 it was bought by Owens-Illinois and remains a division of that company. See also Amberina and other specific types.

Atomizer, cut glass, enamel-on-brass top, signed with a sword, 5½", $195.00.

Bowl, cut, Anita, scalloped sawtooth edge, 8" 225.00
Compote, amberina, Baby T'print, paper label, #3022, 4x6" . . .650.00
Compote, amberina, ribbed, #3021, 6x7¼" 1,000.00
Compote, amberina, ribbed, 3x8" 550.00
Compote, Morning-Glory, opal ribs/dk rose int, clear ft, 7" 975.00
Cruet, straw dmn/fan & stars, hobstar base, petticoat form 100.00
Maize, bowl, gr husks, 8¾" 165.00
Maize, butter dish, gr/brn husks 650.00
Maize, celery vase, gr husks 165.00
Maize, cruet, bl husks, 7" 950.00
Maize, pickle castor, gr husks, SP fr 500.00
Maize, pitcher, amber w/bl husk, clear hdl, barrel form, 9" 585.00
Maize, pitcher, gr husks, strap hdl, barrel form, 9" 335.00
Maize, shakers, bl husks, pr 185.00
Maize, sugar shaker, gr husks, 5½" 235.00
Maize, sugar shaker, yel husks, 5½" 200.00
Maize, syrup, gr husks, 6" 300.00
Maize, toothpick holder, gold-traced gr husks 450.00
Maize, tumbler, 4½" 200.00
Maize, vase, gr husks, 6½" 65.00
Maize, vase, 6½" 75.00
Pitcher, tankard; pinwheel/nailhead/hobstars, step-cut spout . .250.00

Tray, Kimberly, 6-point star, hobstars/fan, 18x10" 950.00
Vase, amberina, flared/flat rim on slim ovoid, disk ft, 8" 685.00
Wine, appl cobalt lily pads, sgn, 4" 200.00

Lightning Rod Balls

Amethyst, sun colored 7.50
Bl opaque, Moon & Star 17.50
Bl opaque, 10-sided, D&S 30.00
Cobalt, Nat'l 18.00
Mercury glass, gold 25.00
Mercury glass, silver 20.00
Milk glass, Hawkeye 12.50
Milk glass, Nat'l 15.00
Wht swirl 12.00

Limoges

From the mid-18th century, Limoges was the center of the porcelain industry of France, where at one time more than forty companies utilized the local kaolin to make a superior quality china, much of which was exported to the United States. Various marks were used; some included the name of the American export company (rather than the manufacturer) and 'Limoges.' After 1891 'France' was added. Pieces signed by factory artists are more valuable than those decorated outside the factory by amateurs.

For a more thorough study of the subject, we recommend you refer to *The Collector's Encyclopedia of Limoges Porcelain* by our advisor Mary Frank Gaston, who is listed in the Directory under Texas. Her book has beautiful color illustrations and current market values.

Bowl, draped lady in floral swing, gold/jewels, mk, 3x10" 200.00
Bowl, punch; grapes, 3-color on pk, gold trim, T&V, 5x10" . . .250.00
Bowl, punch; grapes w/in & w/o on bl mottle, 16", +stand 400.00
Bowl, yel wild roses, gold hdl, 3-compartment, 9¾" 50.00
Box, cigarette; bird/flowers, gold on wht, +matchbox holder . . .115.00
Box, floral, artist sgn, oval, 7½x5½" .90.00
Box, sardine; fish/seaweed, T&V, 5½x4½", +10x9" tray 225.00
Chocolate pot, floral, mc on burgundy, melon ribs, mk, 9½" . . .175.00
Chocolate pot, mc borders w/gilt on wht, 11", +4 c/s 375.00
Chocolate pot, red poppies in panels on gr-leaf motif, 10" 250.00
Compote, oranges/leaves w/gilt, 3½x4¾" 55.00
Cup & saucer, bouillon; pk & bl flowers w/gilt 25.00
Dish, floral, gilt on dk bl, 3-lobed, 3-part hdl, 12" 165.00
Dish, floral on pk shaded, 3-lobed, 3-branch hdl, 13" 135.00
Hair receiver, florals HP on yel, T&V .45.00
Night light, florals, front opens for candle, sgn/1920, 6½" 235.00
Pitcher, lemonade; grapes, 3-color, Baroque hdl, T&V, 12" . . .165.00
Pitcher, tankard; grapes on shaded ground, JPL, 12" 185.00
Pitcher, tankard; monk w/glasses & bottle, gilt, T&V, 14½" . . .400.00
Plaque, fish, artist sgn, 15" 145.00
Plaque, lady w/long hair holds roses, sgn, mk, 13¾" 235.00
Plate, bearded man composing, sgn Fehl, cobalt rim, 9⅝" 175.00
Plate, Birds of N Africa, sgn, Rococo border, 13", pr 475.00
Plate, Boars in Snow, Coronet 125.00
Plate, buildings/landscape, sgn, gilt scalloped rim, 13", pr 375.00
Plate, fisherman, Rococo border, 12½", facing pr 495.00
Plate, floral, sgn Stafford, 9" 35.00
Plate, game bird, gilt rim, L Straus, 9", 6 for 550.00
Plate, Grecian lady w/swan, gilt rim, mk, 12½" 145.00
Plate, hummingbird scenic, artist sgn, gilt rim, mk, 10" 150.00
Plate, lady w/2 dancing children, gilt border, 13" 150.00
Plate, lady's portrait, sgn, Rococo border, 10½" 175.00

Plate, leopard or tiger, sgn Del, Rococo, 13", pr 495.00
Plate, lg yel roses, Rococo border, no mk, 13" 225.00
Plate, Nouveau maid w/oak leaves on gold & brn, 11" 125.00
Plate, roses, mc on gr, gilt Rococo border, unmk, 13" 225.00
Plate, shepherdess w/lamb & nobleman, sgn Mongars, mk, 10" .135.00
Platter, mums, mc on wht w/gold, 15x13" 145.00

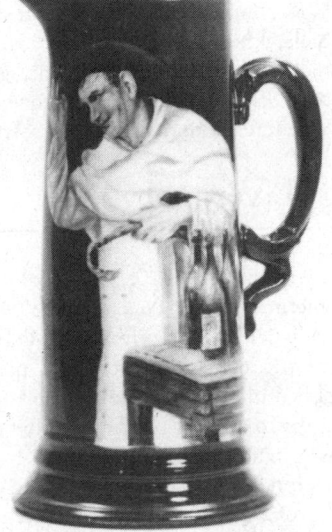

Tankard, man by table tips hat to monk, marked JP, #559, 12", $395.00.

Teapot, bellflowers w/gilt, sgn CF, lg, +creamer/sugar bowl 110.00
Tile, mother/child portrait, artist sgn, T&V, 6x13" 695.00
Vase, acorns, brn shades w/gilt, artist sgn, 7½" 110.00
Vase, couple run in forest, sgn DeRilhac, hdls, Coronet, 15" . . .695.00
Vase, maiden reserve, jewels, pillow form, red mk, 9⅜x6" 235.00
Vase, violets, flower form w/gilt hdl, mk, 2¾x3" 45.00
Vase, 2 deer at forest's edge, ovoid, JPL, 10¼" 175.00

Lithophanes

Lithophanes are porcelain panels with relief designs of varying degrees of thickness and density. Transmitted light brings out the pattern in graduated shadings — lighter where the procelain is thin and darker in the heavy areas. They were cast from wax models prepared by artists and depict views of life from the 1800s, religious themes, or scenes of historical significance. First made in Berlin about 1803, they were used as lamp shade panels, window plaques, or candle shields. Later, steins, mugs, and cups were made with lithophanes in their bases. Japanese wares were sometimes made with dragons or geisha lithophanes. See also Dragon Ware; Steins.

Table screen, lady and child, KPM, 21", $500.00.

Lamp, 10" H 4-panel cylinder w/genre scenes, wht/gold base . 1,025.00
Mug, allover color w/wht pnt decor, HP monk reserve, 6½" 95.00
Panel, Christ holds orb w/cross, Inri/Die incised, 6½x8" 185.00
Panel, Niagara Falls, trapezoid, 5x3¼x5¼" 150.00
Panel, Nurnberg Gegen Osten, city, train & boat, PPM #398 .120.00
Panel, St Ann, PPM-337, 5¼x4⅜"; in stained glass fr 195.00
Panel, 2 women in garden, #224/61, 9x7" 275.00
Plaque, buildings & 3 children, boats on river, #d, 3½x5" 90.00
Shade, 4 hunt scenes, lg 285.00
Shade, 6 scenic trapezoid panels, sgn/#d, 6¼x12" 675.00
Stein, drinking scene, man w/cane, gun in base, .3L 200.00
Table screen, mother/child int scene, KPM, #184142, 20" 500.00

Liverpool

In the late 1700s, Liverpool potters produced a creamy ivory ware, sometimes called Queen's Ware, which they decorated by means of the newly-perfected transfer print. Made specifically for the American market, patriotic inscriptions, political portraits, or other States themes were applied in black with colors sometimes added by hand. (Obviously their loyalty to the crown did not inhibit the progress of business!) Before it lost favor in about 1825, other English potters made a similar product; today Liverpool is a generic term used to refer to all ware of this type.

Our advisor for this category is Richard Marden; he is listed in the Directory under New Hampshire.

Jug, color transfer of American brig 'Three Sisters,' Masonic square and compass, 9½", EX, $750.00.

Jug, Farmer's Arms, rural scenes, silver-resist bands, 12" 2,500.00
Jug, Free Mason's Arms, text/1822 at spout, mc, 7", EX 300.00
Jug, Liberty w/in 1 of 3 sm reserves, red/gr, 7", EX 550.00
Jug, ship, Independence on banner, verse, 6½", NM 1,350.00
Jug, Washington Apotheosis, gold decor, 11", EX 1,100.00
Jug, Washington in Glory, Am ship, mc, 9½" 900.00
Jug, Washington/Apotheosis, ship scene, 8", EX 900.00
Jug, Washington's grave, plan of city of WA, 10" 2,600.00
Jug, Washington's tomb, figure of Justice, 13" 1,300.00
Mug, British ship, 4", EX 120.00
Mug, God Speed Plough/Peace & Plenty, blk w/mc, 5½", EX . .175.00
Mug, Jemmy's farewell, sailor/girl/ship, 1785, 6" 220.00
Mug, map of N Am/England, detailed, 3½", VG 850.00
Plaque, Geo Washington bust, blk transfer, 8x9" 650.00
Plate, Admiral Nelson medallion, blk tranfer, 10" 275.00
Tile, animals/birds, blk transfer on wht, 5" 100.00

Lladro

Lladro porcelains are currently being produced in Labernes Blanques, Spain. Their retired and limited edition figurines are popular collectibles.

Anniversary Waltz 300.00
Aroma of the Islands 300.00
At the Ball 350.00
Ballet Trio 725.00
Bedtime 300.00
Biking in the Country 360.00
Children Praying 285.00
Courting Time 425.00
Feeding Time 265.00
Flapper 225.00
Folk Dancing 250.00
Girl Selling Balloons, 10" 180.00
Goose Trying To Eat 200.00
Here Comes the Bride 675.00
Hindu Lady, 12½" 195.00
Little Gardener 425.00
Lover's Serenade 325.00
Lovers in the Park 750.00
Matrimony 350.00
Midwife 175.00
Music Time 500.00
My Flowers 375.00
My Hungry Brood 330.00
Oriental Girl 350.00
Peace Offering, w/base 365.00
Poetry of Love 500.00
School Marm 265.00
Schoolgirl 345.00
Tenderness 265.00
Valencia Lady 450.00
Waiting Backstage 265.00
Wedding Day 245.00
Will You Marry Me? 625.00

Lobmeyer

J. and L. Lobmeyer, contemporaries of Moser, worked in Vienna, Austria, during the last quadrant of the 1800s. Most of the work attributed to them is decorated with distinctive enameling; favored motifs are people in 18th-century garb.

Vase, blue and white enamel vines and diapering with gilt lines, large, $6,000.00.

Bonbon, HP gold/wht decor on bl, ped ft, 3½" 185.00
Candy compote, flowers/scrolls, 2¼x5" 160.00
Champagne, 18th-century man/flowers/scrolls 250.00
Goblet, allover floral, fishscale decor 185.00
Goblet, 18th-century lady, sgn 200.00
Punch cup, pk HP coral, 4-leaf clover shape, hdl, sgn 185.00
Salt cellar, girl in bottom, gold trim, shallow, 2¼" 165.00
Tumbler, maid w/parasol w/in mc florals, 12-panel, sgn 350.00

Locke Art

Cup, ice cream; Kalana Poppy, ftd, sgn 115.00
Finger bowl, Wild Rose & Fern, sgn, 4½" 55.00
Goblet, Ivy, sgn 95.00
Pitcher, Rose, sgn, 8" 265.00
Pitcher, Vintage, 24-ray star base, sgn, 8" 450.00
Salt cellar, Vintage, ped ft, 2¼x1¼" 68.00
Sherbet, Vintage, saucer base, sgn 175.00
Tumbler, cherries, ribbed, sgn, 5¼" 140.00
Tumbler, Grape & Vine, sgn 80.00
Vase, Buds & Poppies, flared, sgn, 5" 425.00
Vase, Peonies, ruffled, sgn, 5" 525.00
Whiskey, wheat sheaves, sgn, 2⅝" 135.00

Locks

The earliest type of lock in recorded history was the wooden cross bar used by ancient Egyptians and their contemporaries. The early Romans are credited with making the first key-operated mechanical lock. The ward lock was invented during the Middle Ages by the Etruscans of Northern Italy; the lever tumbler and combination locks followed at various stages of history with varying degrees of effectiveness. In the 18th century, the first precision lock was constructed. It was a device that utilized a lever-tumbler mechanism. Two of the best-known of the early 19th-century American lock manufacturers are Yale and Sargent, and today's collectors value Winchester and Keen Kutter locks very highly. Factors to consider are rarity, condition, and construction. Brass and bronze locks are generally priced higher than those of steel or iron.

Key:
bbl — barrel   st — stamped

Brass Lever Tumbler

Good Luck, standard large size, 2⅞", $90.00; Good Luck, miniature, 1½", $150.00; Good Luck, miniature, 1", $200.00.

Ames Sword Co, Perfection stamped on shackle, 2¾" 40.00
Bingham's Best Brand, BBB emb on front, 3¼" 125.00
Cleveland 4 Way, Cleveland 4 Way emb on front, 3⅝" 70.00
Eagle Lock Co, word Eagle emb on front, scrolled, 3" 50.00
Jackson's stamped Jackson's on front, 2½" 25.00
Keen Kutter, shape of KK emblem, KK emb on front, 4¾" 95.00
Romer & Co, Romer & Co stamped on dust cover, 3" 40.00
Ruby, Ruby emb in scroll on front, 2¾" 25.00
Safe, Safe emb in scroll on front, 2⅜" 20.00
Siberian, Siberian emb on shackle, 2½" 60.00
Sphinx, sphinx & pharaoh head emb on front, 2¾" 35.00
W Bohannan & Co, SW emb in scroll on front, 2⅜" 30.00
Winchester, Winchester emb on front, 3" 100.00

Combinations

Chicago Combination Lock Co, stamped on front, brass, 2¾" ...80.00
Corbin Sesamee 4-Dial Brass Lock, stamped Sesamee, 2¾" 12.00
Edwards Mfg Co No-Key, stamped on lock, brass, 2¾" 50.00
Junkunc Bros Mfrs, all stamped on bk, brass, 1⅞" 25.00
Number or letter disk type (4 disks), brass, 2¾" 90.00
Sq lock case of steel, stamped Pat Germany, 4-wheel, 3½" 95.00

Eight-Lever Type

Armory, brass, Armory 8-Lever stamped on front 20.00
Goliath, steel, Goliath 8-Lever stamped on front 20.00
Miller, steel, Miller 8-Lever stamped on front 15.00
Samson, brass, Samson 8-Lever stamped on front 18.00

Iron Lever Tumbler

Bull, word Bull emb on front, 2⅝" 15.00
Bulldog, word Bulldog & face of dog emb on front, 2¾" 15.00
Dan Patch, Dan Patch emb on front, horseshoe on bk, 2¾" ...110.00
Dragon, word Dragon & dragon emb on front, 2⅞" 25.00
Indian Head, Indian head emb on front, 3" 60.00
Jupiter, word Jupiter/star & moon emb on front, 3¼" 18.00
Karo, word Karo emb on front, CI, 3⅛" 25.00
Nineteen O Three, 1903 emb on front, iron, 3⅞" 90.00
Unique, word Unique emb on front, 3¼" 60.00
Yale & Towne, lion face emb on front, shackle mk Y&T, 3" 70.00

Lever Push Key

Champion, emb Champion 6-Lever, brass push-key type, 2¼" ..25.00
Climax, emb Climax 6-Lever, iron push-key type, 2¼" 30.00
Columbia, emb Columbia 6-Lever, brass push-key type, 2¼" ...35.00
Dash, emb Dash 6-Lever, iron push-key type, 2¼" 25.00
Excelsior, emb Excelsior 6-Lever, brass push-key type, 2¼" 25.00
Harvard, emb Harvard 4-lever, brass push-key type, 2" 50.00
Keystone, emb Keystone 6-Lever, brass push-key type, 2¼" 30.00
Smith & Egge Mfg Co, Smith & Egge stamped on front, 3" 65.00
Ten Star, emb Ten Star 6-Lever, 2¼" 40.00

Logo — Special Made

Brass pancake push key emb US Internal Revenue, 2¼" 150.00
Heart-shape brass lever type emb Shults Co, bbl key, 2¾" 35.00
Heart-shape brass lever type st Board Education, bbl key, 3½" ..40.00
Sq brass pin-tumbler case st Regd US Mail, int counter, 2¾" ..110.00
Sq Yale-type brass pin tumbler, emb w/Texaco & star, 3" 25.00
Sq Yale-type brass pin tumbler, st Shell Oil Co on body, 3⅛" ..15.00
Sq Yale-type brass pin tumbler, st US/A/tree/Forest Svc, 2⅞" ..90.00

Pin-Tumbler Type

Corbin, brass, Corbin in oval stamped on body, 3⅝" 25.00
Eagle, brass, Eagle stamped on body, 2⅞" 15.00
Hope, brass, Hope emb on body, 2½" 10.00
Pearl, brass, Pearl emb on body, 2⅛" 12.00
Sargent, brass, Sargent emb on body, 3" 10.00
Segal, iron, Segal emb on shackle, 3¾" 35.00
Yale, brass, Yale emb on body, Made in England on shackle, 3" .45.00
Yale, brass, Yale emb on body, Yale & Towne on shackle, 2⅝" . .25.00

Scandinavian (Jail House) Type

JHW Climax Co, iron, 2⅞" 40.00
Star, emb line on bottom, iron, 3¾" 65.00
Star, iron, 2½" 50.00
99 Miller, emb 99, brass, 1¾" 65.00
999 Miller, emb 999, brass, 2½" 65.00

Six-Lever Type

Eagle, brass, Eagle Six Lever stamped on body 12.00
Edwards, iron, Edwards stamped on body 15.00
Safe, brass, Safe stamped on body 15.00
Yale, brass, Yale emb on front 10.00

Story and Commemorative

AYPEX Seattle (Alaska Yukon Pacific Expo) emb tin/iron, 3" .100.00
CI, emb ornate scroll motif throughout body of lock, 3½" 150.00
CI, emb skull/X-bones w/florals, NH Co on bk, 3¼" 250.00
CQD/sinking ship Titanic & SOS waves emb on brass, 2¾" 90.00
Eagle/stars/shield & stars, emb CI, Eagle Liberty, 2½" 200.00
1901 Pan Am Expo, brass, emb w/buffalo, 2⅝" 125.00

Warded Type

Army, iron pancake ward key, emb letters, 2½" 25.00
Globe, iron sq lock case, emb US on bk, 2⅜" 15.00
Hex, iron, sq lock case, emb US on bk, 2⅛" 80.00
Navy, iron pancake ward key, bk: scrolled emb letters, 2½" 20.00
Red Cross, brass sq case, emb letters, 2" 8.00
Rex, steel case, emb letters, 2⅝" 15.00
Safe, brass sq case, emb letters, 1⅞" 8.00
Safety First, brass pancake type, emb letters, 2¾" 15.00
Secure, iron pancake type, emb letters, 2⅝" 20.00
Sprocket, brass oval shape, emb letters, 2⅛" 45.00
Try Me, iron pancake type, emb letters, 2½" 20.00
Winchester, brass sq case, stamped letters, 2¾" 65.00

Wrought Iron Lever Type (Smokehouse Type)

DM&Co, barrel key, 4¼" 15.00
MW&Co, barrel key, 2⅝" 10.00
MW&Co, flat key, 3½" 20.00
S&Co, barrel key, 3" 8.00

Loetz

The Loetz Glassworks was established in Klostermule, Austria, in 1840. After Loetz's death the firm was purchased by his grandson, Johann Loetz Witwe. Until WWII the operation continued to produce fine artware, some of which made in the early 1900s bears a striking resemblance to Tiffany's, with whom Loetz was associated at one time. In addition to the iridescent Tiffany-style glass, he also produced threaded glass and some cameo. Signed pieces bring premium prices.

Our advisor for this category is Don Williams; he is listed in the Directory under Iowa.

Biscuit jar, gr splotches on cream, SP mts, unsgn, 6" 195.00
Biscuit jar, red-brn threads on gr, brass mts, 8" 145.00
Bowl, bl w/gr irid mottle, trefoil rim, sgn, 4½" H 825.00
Bowl, floral cameo, lav on off-wht, clear cased, sgn, 6½" 300.00
Bowl, purple irid, threaded/crimped, 6", +bronze serpent fr 485.00
Inkwell, bl/purple irid, brass lid, unsgn 240.00
Inkwell, narrow melon ribbing, hinged Loetz lid, 4½" 425.00
Jar, vine cameo/lattice, blk on wht, clear cased, sgn, 7" 4,250.00
Rose bowl, gr irid, purple threading, ground pontil, att, 5" 125.00
Shade, gr threads on yel irid, oil spots, sphere, sgn, 11" 3,000.00
Tumbler, cameo leaves/tendrils, cobalt on opal, Bolek, 4" . . .2,000.00

Vase, silvery gray stripes and dots on green oil-spotted ground, signed, 6", $2,500.00.

Vase, amber irid, swirled silver, ruffled cylinder, att, 13" 300.00
Vase, bl oil spots on lt gr, long trumpet neck, unsgn, 18" 1,000.00
Vase, brn-gold, red scallop shells on base, sgn, 6" 990.00
Vase, clear/amber/irid mottle, 8-aperature fan form, sgn, 8" 800.00
Vase, cobalt w/irid mottling, 2 upright hdls, att, 4" 600.00
Vase, cobalt w/silvery bl feathers, brass fr, unsgn, 12" 375.00
Vase, cranberry, wht frosted rigaree, att, 8½x3½" 220.00
Vase, floral cameo, lt/dk brn on wht, clear cased, sgn, 12" 800.00
Vase, gold, trumpet form w/4 swirling arms, sgn, 11", EX, pr .2,500.00
Vase, gold irid w/amber pulls & purple trails, unsgn, 12" 150.00
Vase, gold w/HP iris, 3 ormolu ft, 10½" 200.00
Vase, gr, appl rigaree, sgn, 5½x6" 500.00
Vase, gr, 3-sided scalloped top, sgn, 11x5½" 295.00
Vase, gr & brn oil spots, goose neck, sgn, 13" 1,500.00
Vase, gr irid, red feathering, att, 5" 110.00
Vase, gr irid, spotted indents, flared top, att, 7½x5½" 165.00
Vase, gr irid mottled, 4 indented sides, sq, 7x6½" 200.00
Vase, gr w/bl irid threading on dimpled sides, att, 6½" 650.00
Vase, gr w/drape mold, ruffled, in ornate bronze fr, 15" 1,250.00
Vase, gr w/irid, thick threading at neck, sgn, 15" 800.00
Vase, jack-in-pulpit; bl irid w/threads/oil spots, 6¾" 1,500.00

Vase, jack-in-pulpit; silver overlay teardrops, gold, sgn, 9" . . .**4,000.00**
Vase, lt gr w/bl-gr irid, conch shell on wave-like ft, 7½" **1,200.00**
Vase, opal w/brn pulled design, stick neck, 5" **130.00**
Vase, opal w/oil spots, appl amber butterflies, unsgn, 10" **1,200.00**
Vase, red, threaded, 4" **130.00**
Vase, rose to gold irid, crimp-top fan form, bun base, 9" **550.00**
Vase, silver overlay floral, tan irid w/wht waves, sgn, 4" **1,450.00**
Vase, silver overlay florals on gray irid, unsgn, 5½" **800.00**
Vase, silver overlay iris w/gr waves & shapes, sgn, 7" **2,750.00**
Vase, silver w/gridwork & allover waves, ball form, sgn, 6" . .**1,800.00**
Vase, swirled colors in metal mt w/cherub, trumpet form, 14" . .**350.00**
Vase, wht spider web ground w/appl gr grapes, bun ft, 15" **295.00**
Vase, yel irid w/allover gold oil spots, att, 12" **330.00**

Lomonosov Porcelain

Founded in 1744, the Lomonosov porcelain factory made exquisite porcelain miniatures for the Czar and other Russian nobility. One of the first factories of its kind, Lomonosov primarily produced vases and delicate sculptures. In the 1800s Lomonosov became closely involved with the Russian Academy of Fine Arts, a connection which has continued to this day, as the company continues to supply the world with these fine artistic treasures.

Figurine, baby giraffe, #2350 . . . .**45.00**
Figurine, bear, squatting, #6447 . . . .**9.50**
Figurine, buck, #6545 . . . .**90.00**
Figurine, chipmunk, sitting, #8520, miniature **5.00**
Figurine, chow-chow, #1841 . . . .**11.00**
Figurine, dachshund, #7474, miniature **3.00**
Figurine, doe, #6546 . . . .**90.00**
Figurine, donkey, lying, #1842 . . . .**15.00**
Figurine, foal, brn, #6523, lg **55.00**
Figurine, foal, wht, #6414 . . . .**16.50**
Figurine, foal, wht, #6512, lg **35.00**
Figurine, giraffe, head raised, #6515 . . . .**80.00**
Figurine, hippopotamus, #7403, miniature **3.00**
Figurine, lamb, #6576 . . . .**10.00**
Figurine, leopard, #6552, lg **100.00**
Figurine, lion cub, #6439, lg **15.00**
Figurine, lion cub, #6440, sm **10.00**
Figurine, moose, #6438 . . . .**97.50**
Figurine, polar bear, #6444, sm **16.50**
Figurine, polar bear, #6449, lg **100.00**
Figurine, polar bear, walking, #6553 . . . .**127.50**
Figurine, poodle, #6560 . . . .**15.00**
Figurine, rabbit, #9427, miniature **9.50**
Figurine, raccoon, sitting, #6503 . . . .**12.50**
Figurine, robin, #2350, lg **15.00**
Figurine, sea gull, #6579 . . . .**23.00**
Figurine, terrier, standing, #6527 . . . .**22.50**
Figurine, tiger cub, #9424, miniature **12.50**
Figurine, Yakut woman w/dog, #6244 . . . .**65.00**
Figurine, Yakut woman w/fish, #6195 . . . .**58.00**
Figurine, zebra, standing, #6540 . . . .**20.00**

Longwy

The Longwy workshops were founded in 1798 and continue today to produce pottery in the north of France near the Luxembourg-Belgian border. The ware for which they are best known was produced during the Art Deco period, decorated in bold colors and designs. Earlier wares made during the first quarter of the nineteenth century reflected the popularity of Oriental art, cloisonne enamels in particular. The designs were executed by impressing the pattern into the moist clay and filling in the depressions with enamels. Examples are marked 'Longwy,' either impressed or painted under glaze.

Bowl, mc on aqua, cobalt int, ftd, blk mk, 10" **300.00**
Candelabrum, 3 scrolling brass arms, 11x7½" **110.00**
Candlestick, on brass std, 8 cut crystal prisms, 10", pr **185.00**
Charger, ltd ed, sgn Chavallier, #d, 14½" **375.00**
Charger, 2 elephants/female/jungle, Chas Catteau, 15" **2,450.00**
Ewer, Islamic motif, ca 1900, 7½" **150.00**
Plate, bird/flowers, mk, 8" **125.00**
Table lamp, red cylinder w/mc floral on 5½" blk base **135.00**
Trivet, Primavera, woman w/exotic foliage, after Mattise, 8" . .**850.00**
Vase, aqua/coral/red/yel/bl design, mk, 5" **100.00**
Vase, Art Deco florals on bl, Primavera, 6" **125.00**
Vase, bird & palm tree on turq, cylindrical, 7" **295.00**

Vase, Mattise nudes, exotic foliage, marked Primavera, 15", $1,500.00.

Lonhuda

William Long was a druggist by trade who combined his knowledge of chemistry with his artistic ability in an attempt to produce a type of brown-glazed slip-decorated artware similar to that made by the Rookwood Pottery. He achieved his goal in 1889 after years of long and dedicated study. Three years later he founded his firm, the Lonhuda Pottery Company. The name was coined from the first few letters of the last name of each of his partners, W.H. Hunter and Alfred Day. Laura Fry, formerly of the Rookwood company, joined the firm in 1892, bringing with her a license for Long to use her patented airbrush-blending process. Other artists of note, Sarah McLaughlin, Helen Harper, and Jessie Spaulding, joined the firm and decorated the ware with nature studies, animals, and portraits, often signing their work with their initials. Three types of marks were used on the Steubenville Lonhuda ware. The first was a linear composite of the letters 'LPCO' with the name 'Lonhuda' impressed above it. The second, adopted in 1893, was a die-stamp representing the solid profile of an Indian, used on ware patterned after pottery made by the American Indians. This mark was later replaced with an impressed outline of the Indian head with 'Lonhuda' arching above it. Although the ware was successful, the business floundered due to poor management. In 1895 Long became a partner of Sam Weller and moved to Zanesville where the manufacture of the Lonhuda line continued. Less than a year later, Long left the Weller company. He was associated with J.B. Owens until 1899, at which time he moved to Denver, Colorado, where he established the Denver China and Pottery Company in 1901. His efforts to produce Lonhuda utilizing local clay were highly successful. Examples of the Denver Lonhuda are sometimes marked with the LF (Lonhuda Faience) cipher contained within a canted diamond form.

Jug, bull portrait, EX art, #806, 5" 500.00
Vase, floral, bulbous on raised ft, sm short neck, sgn, 5½" 125.00
Vase, floral, cylinder neck, sgn Wm Long, 11" 425.00
Vase, floral, hdls, artist sgn, #330, 3½" 90.00
Vase, ftd, herd of cows, pillow form, 11½" 4,000.00
Vase, gr leaves, bulbous w/long neck, sgn STR, 8¾" 170.00
Vase, lg fish/waves, integral hdls, 5x8½" 525.00

Lu Ray Pastels

Lu Ray Pastels dinnerware was introduced in the early 1940s by Taylor, Smith, and Taylor of East Liverpool, Ohio. It was offered in assorted colors — Persian Cream, Sharon Pink, Surf Green, Windsor Blue, and Gray — in complete place settings as well as many service pieces. It was a successful line in its day and is once again finding favor with collectors of American dinnerware.

Bowl, cream soup 17.50
Bowl, fruit; 5½" 4.50
Bowl, mixing; lg 45.00
Bowl, salad; lg 30.00
Bowl, soup; 9" 8.50
Bowl, tab hdl, 6" 10.00
Bowl, vegetable; oval 10.00
Bowl, vegetable; 9" 8.50
Butter dish, w/lid, ¼-lb 22.50
Casserole, w/lid 55.00
Coffeepot, demitasse; ovoid, w/lid 50.00
Coffeepot, demitasse; str sides, w/lid 85.00
Creamer 5.00
Creamer, demitasse; ovoid 20.00
Creamer, demitasse; str sides 40.00
Cup & saucer 7.50
Cup & saucer, demitasse 12.50
Egg cup 12.00
Egg cup, Chatham Gray, rare color 15.00
Epergne 50.00
Muffin cover, w/8" underplate 50.00
Pitcher, bulbous w/flat bottom 35.00
Pitcher, ftd 40.00
Pitcher, juice; ovoid 55.00
Pitcher, syrup 40.00
Plate, cake 15.00
Plate, Chatham Gray, rare color, 7" 6.00
Plate, chop; 14" 16.00
Plate, grill 11.00
Plate, serving; tab hdl 15.00
Plate, very rare, 8" 15.00
Plate, 10" 10.00
Plate, 6" 2.00
Plate, 7" 3.00
Plate, 9" 5.00
Platter, oval, 11½" 8.00
Platter, oval, 13" 10.00
Sauce boat, fast-stand 15.00
Sauce pitcher 15.00
Saucer, cream soup 12.50

Shakers, pr 8.50
Sugar bowl, w/lid 9.00
Sugar bowl, w/lid, demitasse; ovoid 20.00
Sugar bowl, w/lid, demitasse; str sides .40.00
Teapot, w/lid, curved spout 35.00
Teapot, w/lid, flat-top spout 45.00

Teapot, with flat spout, $45.00, with curved spout, $35.00.

Tidbit, 2-tier 18.00
Tray, pickle 12.00
Tumbler, juice 18.00
Tumbler, water 30.00

Lunch Boxes

Early 20th-century tobacco companies such as Union Leader, Tiger, and Dixie issued a series of square containers with flat metal carrying handles designed to be used for lunch boxes after the contents had been otherwise enjoyed. (See Advertising, specific companies.) By 1930 oval lunch pails with colorful lithographed decorations on tin were being manufactured to appeal directly to children. These were made by Ohio Art, who in 1950 changed from the oval to the standard rectangular shape more often seen today. In 1950 the Aladdin Company issued the first of their character lunch boxes, decorated with pictures of Hopalong Cassidy, Roy Rogers, Bozo, etc., fully fitted with matching thermos bottles. Early boxes sometimes were die-pressed so that the shape of the character stood out in relief. Character decals were applied to the corresponding embossed design. The thermos bottles, however, were lithographed and by the mid-fifties, so were the boxes.

Other companies — ADCO Liberty; Landers, Frary & Clark; and American Thermos — also produced character pails. Today's collectors often tend to specialize in those dealing with a particular subject. Western, space, TV series, Disney movies, or cartoon characters are among the most popular.

Our advisor for this category is Allan Smith; he is listed in the Directory under Texas.

Annie, w/thermos, 1981 . . . . .12.00
Beatles, bl tin, 1966 . . . . .175.00
Bobby Sherman, 1972 . . . . .30.00
Buck Rogers, w/thermos, 1979 . . . . .30.00
Charlie's Angels 13.00
Daniel Boone, Aladdin 50.00
Dark Crystal, w/thermos, 1982 . . . . .12.00
Empire Strikes Back, 1980 . . . . .12.00
ET, w/thermos 15.00
Gunsmoke, 1959 . . . . .50.00
Hopalong Cassidy, w/thermos, VG 35.00
Hopalong Cassidy, 1950, NM 60.00
Indiana Jones, w/thermos 13.00

Lawman, 1961, VG 50.00
Little House on the Prairie 13.00
Lone Ranger, w/thermos, 1980 ....15.00
Magic Kingdom, Aladdin, WD, 1979, w/thermos 20.00
Mickey's Wonderful World, w/thermos, 1980 ....18.00
Munsters, w/thermos, M 100.00
Munsters, 1965, EX 75.00
Peanuts, Snoopy at piano 12.00
Planet of the Apes, 1974 ....15.00
Return of the Jedi, w/thermos 15.00
Roy Rogers & Dale Evans, 1953 ....50.00
Roy Rogers Chow Wagon 65.00
Roy Rogers Ranch, w/thermos, EX 50.00
School Bus, Aladdin, WDE 20.00
Secret Agent, w/thermos, 1964 ....30.00
Snoopy, dome top, 1968, EX 15.00
Space 1999, NM 15.00
Superman, 1967 ....80.00
Tom Corbett, w/thermos, bl, 1952 ....110.00

VW Bus, Omni-Graphics, ca 1960, 11" long, $90.00.

Wild Bill Hickock & Jingles, 1955, EX 40.00
Wild Wild West, 1969, EX 60.00
Yel Submarine, 1968, VG 95.00

Lutz

From 1869 to 1888, Nicholas Lutz worked for the Boston and Sandwich Glass Company where he produced the threaded and striped art glass that was popular during that era. His works were not marked; and, since many other glassmakers of the day made similar wares, the term Lutz has come to refer not only to his original works but to any of this type.

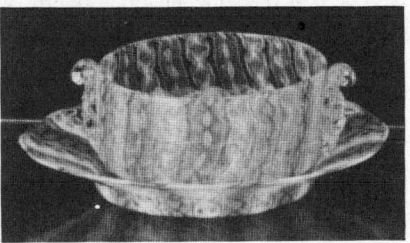

Finger bowl, pink and gold stripes separated by white latticinio, baby-face handles, $150.00.

Compote, lav/pk/opal swirl, entwined snake stem, 7" 250.00
Decanter, chartreuse, gold/wht stripes, appl decor, 12½" 300.00
Ewer, pk/wht/gold lattice, gold-flecked clear hdl, 12" 140.00
Finger bowl, pk/gold stripes, wht latticinio, baby-face hdl 150.00

Lemonade, clear w/bl threading, eng top half, att 250.00
Nut dish, pk/wht, fluted, 3¾" 80.00
Tumbler, opal stripes, bl threaded bottom half, att, 3" 225.00
Wine glass, bl/opaque wht/clear swirl, att 120.00

Maastricht

Maastricht, Holland, was the site of the De Sphinx Pottery, founded in 1836 by Petrus Regout. They made earthenware decorated with transfer prints as well as dinnerware with gaudy hand-painted designs. Potteries are still working in this area today.

Bowl, Oriental scene, 8" 40.00
Bowl, stick spatter, gaudy floral, 9", EX 25.00
Bowl, waste; mc marbleized decor, 3½x5" 35.00
Pitcher, milk; Canton, mc Oriental motif 40.00
Plate, Abbey, 8" 20.00
Plate, stick spatter, gaudy floral, Petrus Regout, 11" 20.00
Plate, stick spatter, gaudy floral, 11", NM 42.50
Plate, stick spatter, mc floral, mk 9" 40.00
Plate, stick spatter, mc floral, 7½" 20.00

Magazines

Magazines are collected for their cover prints and for the information pertaining to defunct companies and their products that can be gleaned from the old advertisements. In the listings that follow, items are assumed to be in very good condition unless noted otherwise. See also Fisher, Harrison; Movie Memorabilia; and Parrish, Maxfield.

Key:
M — mint condition, in original wrapper
EX — excellent condition, spine intact, edges of pages clean and straight
VG — very good condition, the average as-found condition

Century, 1884, Apr, Wht House articles 7.50
Collier's, 1902, Oct 25, Leyendecker cover, M 8.00
Collier's, 1906, Apr 7, Japanese artist cover, M 7.00
Cosmopolitan, 1894, Jan 10.00
Craftsman, 1914, Mar, EX 27.50
Delineator, 1898, July, EX 12.00
Gentleman's, 1758, Feb, VG 12.00
Harper's Monthly, 1857, June to Nov, bound 20.00
Harper's Weekly, 1866, May 12, levee at Cincinnati 9.00
Harper's Weekly, 1898, Jan to June, Remington illus 50.00
Harper's Weekly, 1905, June 10, Japan's victory, EX 10.00
Ladies' Home Journal, 1909, fashion issue 14.00
Life, 1936, Feb 8, Winter on the Range cover, M 21.00
Life, 1936, Nov 23, Volume 3, #1, EX 40.00
Life, 1936, Nov 30, West Point cadet cover, EX 27.50
Life, 1937, Apr 19, Queen Mary cover, EX 15.00
Life, 1937, June 14, US Senator cover, EX 15.00
Life, 1937, May 3, Harlow in Hollywood cover, M 16.00
Life, 1937, Nov 1, Jupiter & Mercury on Broadway cover, EX ...10.00
Life, 1937, Nov 29, US Capitol cover, EX 10.00
Life, 1937, Sept 6, Harpo Marx cover, EX 10.00
Life, 1938, Apr 18, Paulette Goddard cover, EX 18.00
Life, 1938, Feb 14, Queen of Egypt cover, EX 18.00
Life, 1938, May 30, Commander of the Czech Army cover, EX ..18.00
Life, 1938, Sept 26, county fair cover, EX 10.00

Life, 1939, July 24, Ann Sheridan cover, EX 9.00
Life, 1942, Dec 28, Raphael's Madonna cover, EX 6.00
Life, 1943, Dec 27, Soldier's Madonna cover, EX 7.00
Life, 1946, Nov 25, 10th Anniversary issue, EX 10.00
Life, 1956, Oct 8, Masonic Grand Masters cover, M 6.00
Life, 1963, Dec 13, President Johnson cover, M 9.00
Life, 1968, Dec 20, Mark Twain cover, M 7.00
Look, 1939, Apr 11, Lindbergh cover & story 12.50
Look, 1965, June 1, Princess Grace & Princess Stephanie, G 4.00
Look, 1966, Aug 23, Bobby Kennedy cover, EX 7.00
Look, 1966, June 14, JFK's Legacy cover, M 5.00
Look, 1966, May 3, KKK cover, G 4.00
Look, 1967, Jan 24, Vol II, Death of a President cover, EX 11.00
Look, 1970, Oct 20, Indian fashions cover, EX 5.00
Look, 1971, Aug 10, Ed Kennedy cover, EX 5.00
Look, 1971, June 15, Nixon & Patricia cover, EX 6.00
Mother Earth News, 1976, Mar, Organic Gardening cover, M ...6.00
National Geographic, 1887-1889, ea 30.00
National Geographic, 1900-1905, ea 18.00
National Geographic, 1905-1908, ea 15.00
National Geographic, 1909-1910, ea 12.00
National Geographic, 1911-1915, ea 6.00
National Geographic, 1916-1920, ea 4.00
Playboy, 1954, Apr 200.00
Playboy, 1968, Dec, Christmas issue, EX 10.00
Playboy, 1969, June, Gore Vidal interview, EX 9.00
Playboy, 1970, Apr, Girls of Israel cover, EX 10.00
Saturday Evening Post, 1906, Mar 31, M 11.00
Saturday Evening Post, 1935, Jan 1, Leyendecker cover, VG 15.00
Saturday Evening Post, 1963, Dec 14, JFK memorial cover, EX ..9.00
Saturday Evening Post, 1965, July 17, James Bond Cult cover, G .5.00
Texas Monthly, 1976, Oct, Barbara Jordan cover, M 6.00
Texas Monthly, 1980, May, Small Texas Towns cover, M 5.00
Woman's World, 1911, July, EX 12.00

Majolica

Majolica is a type of heavy earthenware, design-molded and decorated in vivid colors with either a lead or tin type of glaze. It reached its height of popularity in the Victorian era; examples from this period are found in only the lead glazes. Nearly every potter of note, both here and abroad, produced large majolica jardinieres, umbrella stands, pitchers with animal themes, leaf shapes, vegetable forms, and nearly any other nature theme that came to mind. Few, however, marked their ware. Among those who did were Minton, Wedgwood, and George Jones in England; Griffin, Smith and Hill (Etruscan) in Phoenixville, Pennsylvania; and Chesapeake Pottery (Avalon and Clifton) in Baltimore.

Basket, florals w/3 birds, 3 branch hdls, 18" 395.00
Basket, Morning-Glory, oval, twig hdl, Holdcroft, 6½x8½" 550.00
Bouquet holder, fish form, arched tail, att Geo Morley, 9¾" ...175.00
Bouquet holder, fish form, tail arched to head, Morley, 11" 225.00
Bowl, Bird & Fan, Shorter & Boulton, 5" 125.00
Bowl, Cabbage Leaf & Floral, luggage strap, 12" 325.00
Bowl, Chrysanthemum, oval, scalloped rim, Wedgwood, 13" L ..275.00
Bowl, florals, red & wht on wht, serrated rim, 9½" 75.00
Bowl, grapevine frieze, mc on brn, 3 ball ft, 3¾x10¾" 150.00
Bowl, leaves, gr on gr, Wedgwood, 2x6" 60.00
Bowl, primroses, yel on turq, Geo Jones, 5½" 135.00
Bowl, shell form, ped ft, Holdcroft, 8" 275.00
Box, sardine; boat form, stripes, 'Sardinia,' 8" L 450.00
Box, sardine; fish in relief on lid, sq, 6" 500.00
Box, sardine; fish on leaves, basket-form base, Geo Jones, 8" ...900.00

Box, sardine; Pineapple, fish finial, w/underplate, 4½x8½" 450.00
Butter dish, Bamboo, Etruscan 325.00
Butter pat, Green Leaf, Wedgwood, 3" 38.00
Cake plate, berries, gr-traced on cream, Haynes, 1880s, 10½" ..115.00
Cake plate, Shell & Seaweed, Etruscan, 9", M 575.00
Cake stand, Cauliflower, Etruscan, Griffin-Smith-Hill, 9" 250.00
Cake stand, Maple, Etruscan, Griffin-Smith-Hill, 5½x9½" 195.00
Cake stand, Pineapple, gr/yel/brn, ped ft, mk, 5½x9¾" 250.00
Cake stand, pk w/gr leaves, tree base, Etruscan, 9½" 195.00
Cake stand, strawberries/blossoms on lt bl, Zell 85.00
Centerpc, man on stump at center, Phillips & Pearce, 8x18" ..300.00
Centerpc, shell held by putti on stump, bl/brn/gr/cream, 14" ...650.00
Cheese keeper, Daisy & Fence, Geo Jones, 11" 2,500.00
Cheese keeper, Dogwood, wht on bl, twig hdl, G Jones, 10" .1,500.00
Compote, crane & heron, water lily mold, American, 7x10" ...395.00
Compote, Daisy, Etruscan, ped ft, lg 295.00
Compote, Daisy, pebbled body w/ribbon band, Fielding, 5x9" ..300.00
Compote, Maple Leaf, Griffin-Smith-Hill, 1879 mk 250.00
Compote, reticulated, waterbaby forms base, Minton, 7x9" ...600.00
Compote, shell w/3 dolphin supports, Wedgwood, 4x9" 295.00
Creamer, Melon, Holdcroft, sm 80.00
Creamer, Wild Rose, Etruscan, 4½" 85.00
Creamer & sugar bowl, Water Lily 155.00
Cup & saucer, Shell & Seaweed, Etruscan 250.00
Dessert set, Pond Lily, Etruscan, Griffin-Smith-Hill, 8-pc 450.00
Figurine, bird on leafy perch, 4-color, Continental, 12" 225.00
Figurine, Indian steps into canoe, mc, #d, 19½" L 400.00
Game dish, hare & duck, basketweave base, Minton, 12" ...2,000.00
Game dish, quail & rabbit, Geo Jones, 12" 2,750.00
Holy water font, cherubs supporting crown fr HP virgin, 12" ..350.00
Humidor, Blk boy w/watermelon slice on trunk, Austria, 6" L ..265.00
Humidor, cat w/ball, French 150.00
Humidor, pipe finial, Germany 95.00
Humidor, Shell & Seaweed, Etruscan, Griffin-Smith-Hill, 6" ..900.00
Inkwell, twin birds, heads lift to show well, 9" L 450.00
Jardiniere, baby satyr & lion-head masks, Minton, 10½" 1,000.00
Jardiniere, conch shell w/Chinese creatures, Portuguese, 6½" ..195.00
Jardiniere, hyacinths/insects/butterfly, mc on brn, 6½" 375.00
Jardiniere, Lily, leaves & flower, 7½x6¼" +pedestal 200.00
Jardiniere, ram's head ea side, paw ft, sgn H, 9¾x9½" 400.00
Jug, Tower, figures & ivy, jester's-head finial, Minton 900.00
Lamp base, 3 cranes & bullrushes on triangular base, 22½" 650.00
Match holder, drummer figural, Holdcroft, 3" 285.00
Oyster server, 3 tiers, fish & eel form hdl, Minton, 10x12" ..3,200.00
Paperweight, owl, brn on mc flower base, mk Mayer, 3x4" 110.00
Pin tray, leaf form, Etruscan 60.00
Pitcher, antelope under tree, 7¾" 175.00
Pitcher, Basketweave & Blossom, turq/brn/cream w/pk, 7½" 95.00
Pitcher, Begonia Leaf on Bark, 7½" 95.00
Pitcher, Cauliflower, Wedgwood, milk sz 150.00
Pitcher, conch ea side, mc on gr & brn, Wedgwood, 10" 1,500.00
Pitcher, Corn, Etruscan, Griffin-Smith-Hill, rare, 6" 295.00
Pitcher, Edward & Alexandra Commemorative, 5½" 235.00
Pitcher, Fan & Scroll, Fielding, 6" 145.00
Pitcher, floral, butterfly lip, 7" 160.00
Pitcher, Flying Stork 275.00
Pitcher, Grant portraits, Am flag & eagle, English, 8½" 295.00
Pitcher, hunt scene, dog figural hdl, Wedgwood, mc 295.00
Pitcher, jumping fish ea side, mc on cobalt, unmk, 8" 300.00
Pitcher, owl figural, EX color, unmk Morley, 8" 225.00
Pitcher, palm trees on bark ground, 6¾" 125.00
Pitcher, parrot figural, bamboo hdl, att Geo Morley, 9¼" 250.00
Pitcher, Shell & Seaweed, Etruscan, sm 195.00
Pitcher, shell figural, Fielding, 8" 325.00

Pitcher, pug dog figural, no mark, 9", $395.00.

Pitcher, Stork in Marsh, eel figural hdl, 9½" 295.00
Planter, Fern & Bamboo, w/underplate, Wardle, 6½x8" 195.00
Planter, Shell & Seaweed, England, 6" 195.00
Plate, Blackberry w/Basketweave, Etruscan, 8½" 115.00
Plate, castle scene, blk on wht, Geo Jones & Sons, rare 165.00
Plate, Cauliflower, Etruscan, 9" 130.00
Plate, Cosmos, Etruscan, Griffin-Smith-Hill, 11¼" 160.00
Plate, crane ea side of lily pads, Geo Jones, 10¾" 200.00
Plate, Grape Leaf, fruit & flower, Wedgwood, 8½" 125.00
Plate, Leaf & Fern, gr on turq w/ochre rim, Geo Jones, 8" 155.00
Plate, Lily Blossom, Holdcroft, 8" 80.00
Plate, napkin on basketweave, mc, Morley, 8¾" 200.00
Plate, oyster; Morning-Glory, mc on turq, Holdcroft, 9½" 225.00
Plate, oyster; Shell & Seaweed, 6 shells, Geo Jones, 8½" 350.00
Plate, oyster; Shell & Seaweed, 7 shells, Minton, 9" 225.00
Plate, oyster; wave divided by seaweed, mc on wht, 9¼" 150.00
Plate, strawberries/blossoms/butterfly on lt bl, Zell, 11" 48.00
Plate, Strawberry, ribbed ground, Clifton Avalon, 11" 110.00
Plate, 2 gnomes & bird in flight, recessed center, 11" 150.00
Platter, Begonia Leaf, leaf border, 14" .160.00
Platter, Cattail & Fish, bl ground, Holdcroft, 25" 750.00
Platter, cherries & butterflies on turq, Germany, 11" 75.00
Platter, Dog & Doghouse, mc on cream, 11" 125.00
Platter, Oak Leaf w/Acorns & Twigs on turq, unmk, 10" 325.00
Platter, Shell & Seaweed, mc on cream, Choisy Le-Roy, 11" . .200.00
Platter, Strawberry, raised rim, English mk, 15" 400.00
Punch bowl, Sunflower & Classical Urn, S Lear, 13" 1,100.00
Salmon dish, salmon relief lid, basket base, Geo Jones, 24" . .2,800.00
Server, Strawberry, attached center cup, Geo Jones, 10" 600.00

Server, Strawberry, G Jones, 13", +creamer/sugar bowl/spoon . .900.00
Server, Strawberry, G Jones, 15", +creamer/sugar ea end 900.00
Spoon warmer, conch w/seaweed form, Geo Jones, 5½x7" 550.00
Spoon warmer, sea urchin supports shell, 6½" 300.00
Syrup, Coral, Etruscan, pewter lid, rare 395.00
Syrup, floral frieze, ftd, pewter lid, Wedgwood, 7½" 550.00
Syrup, Sunflower, cobalt, Etruscan 295.00
Teapot, berries/insects/frog, Geo Jones, 6", +cr/sug 1,700.00
Teapot, Chinaman form, open mouth spout, Minton, 5½" . .1,800.00
Teapot, Fan & Bird, mc on cream, England, 6", +cr/sug 400.00
Teapot, Fan & Bird, Wedgwood, 6", +4" creamer/5" sugar 950.00
Teapot, Fern & Bamboo, Wardle of Hanley, 6", +5 pcs 500.00
Teapot, Water Lily, lily finial, 4½", +cr/sug 375.00
Tray, bread; Corn, gr/yel/brn on basketweave, 13" 425.00
Tray, bread; Oak, Etruscan, Griffin-Smith-Hill, 12" 175.00
Tray, bread; Pineapple, yel/br w/cobalt center, Wardle, 13" . . .250.00
Tray, bread; Spare Not, Waste Not, Want Not, 6¾" 110.00
Tray, bread; Wheat & Basketweave, inscription, 13½" 225.00
Tray, condiment; birds & strawberries, Geo Jones, 15x8½" . .1,200.00
Tumbler, wishbone decor rim, circles at base, Etruscan, 4" 250.00
Tureen, dead rabbit & bird on lid, Minton, ca 1863, 14½" L .1,800.00
Umbrella stand, bird on stump, artist sgn, Holdcroft, 36" 2,000.00
Vase, bird on branch form, 7" 250.00
Vase, Crane & Prunus, appl flower on bk, rare, 6" 200.00
Vase, flower, red on gr shaded, brn dbl hdls, 5¼", M 60.00
Vase, iris form, molded base, dbl openwork hdls, unmk, 5½" 60.00
Vase, lady w/fan by tree trunk figural, Continental, 12" 275.00
Vase, masks in relief, HP hunt scene, Italy, 1800s, 16" 225.00
Vase, Shrewbury, poppies/fleur-de-lis, 4 hdls, Minton, 11" 800.00
Vase, vines/scrolls, dbl-column hdls, ovoid, Copeland, 11½" . .200.00
Wine caddy, Bacchus/grapes, receptacles ea side, Jones, 13" . .2,400.00
Wine cooler, bacchanalian scene on wht, Wedgwood, 10" 700.00

Malachite

Malachite is a type of art glass that exhibits strata-like layerings in shades of green — similar to the mineral in its natural form.

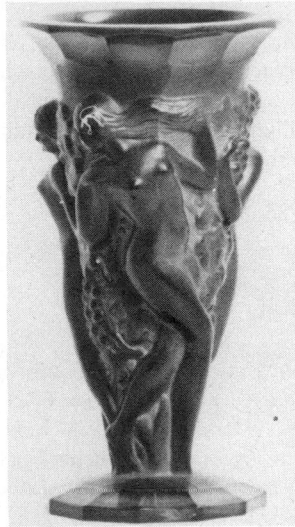

Vase, nudes in high relief, 9", $295.00.

Strawberry server, George Jones, 11" wide, $1,200.00.

Ash tray, 4 Zodiac panels, mk Moser, 5½" dia 85.00
Basket, nude/4 cherubs, wide hdl, 6" .150.00
Box, powder; flower & fruit relief, rnd .30.00
Figurine, Buddha, seated on lotus base, 7½" 80.00
Tray, card; reclining Nouveau nude relief, 8x3" 165.00
Vase, nude/grapevines, faceted base, flared rim, 9½" 295.00

Vase, standing nudes, trees, 5" 185.00

Mantel Lustres

Bristol, crown-form top, HP/gilt, 2 rows prisms, 16", pr 300.00
Bristol, pk overlay, heavy gold/florals, prisms, 16", pr 450.00
Dog figures on base, prisms, 11½", pr .180.00

**Green satin glass with enameled florals and ribbon swags, 12",
$250.00 for the pair.**

Overlay, amber cut to clear, 10 ball/arrow prisms, 10", pr 300.00
Overlay, cranberry cut to clear, portraits/florals, 12", pr 900.00
Overlay, wht cut to gr, petal cutting, gilt, prisms, 11", pr 400.00
Ruby glass, plain w/knop stem, prisms, 10½", pr, EX 240.00
Spiral-cut cup/bobeche/base, beaded drops, 1820, 10", pr 750.00

Maps and Atlases

Maps are highly collectible, not only for historical value but also for
their sometimes elaborate artwork, legendary information, or data that has
been proven erroneous. There are many types of maps including geographi-
cal, military, celestial, road, and railroad. The most valuable are those made
before the mid-1800s.

Key:
hc — hand colored   p — publisher

Atlases

Ancient Geography, Butler/Carey-Lea-Blanchard, Phila, 1834 . .42.00
Asher & Adams, US states & 60 counties, 1871, VG 150.00
Bradley's World, lg folio, WM Bradley & Bro, Phila, 1889 . . . . .90.00
Classical Geography, Blanchard & Lea, Phila, 1858, VG 45.00
Cram's Heart of Our Country, 1909, 580-pg 35.00
Cram's Universal, 1897, 636-pg, EX 50.00
Dr Brook's... Geography, Darton & Clark, London, 1838 . . . . . .12.00
EH Burritt's, lg folio, Huntington, Hartford, 1835, VG 250.00
General, hc sheets, Gotha, Justus Perthes, 1835, VG 75.00
Geographie Historique..., Fr text, Gaugondy, Paris, 1755 . . . . . .75.00
Greece, 31 copper eng plates, M Mills, Dublin, 1795, VG 85.00
History of USA, leather bound, Shaffner, London/NY, VG 40.00
Johnson's New Illus..., hc, AJ Johnson, NY, 1863, 100-sheet . .400.00

Mitchell's Ancient, sm folio, Butler, Phila, 1844, G 20.00
Mitchell's New General, 76 hc maps, Phila, 1860, EX 450.00
Mitchell's School, Cowperthwait, Phila, 1838, VG 90.00
Olney's School, hc, Robinson, CT, 1844, VG 75.00

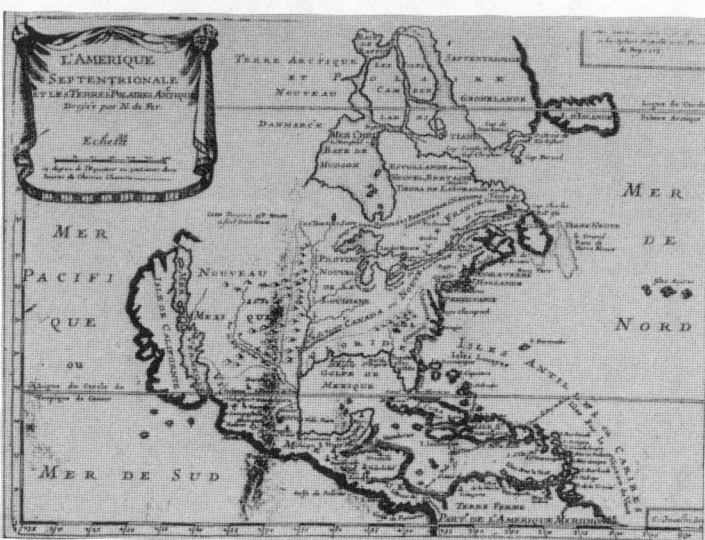

**Atlas, Petit et Nouveau, Paris, 1705, 19 maps, showing California as an
island, leather bound, 10x14", VG, $450.00.**

Smiley's, hc, Grigg & Elliot, 1839, VG .12.00
System of Universal ..., Malte-Brun, Boston, 1844, VG 175.00
Tunison's Peerless Universal...World, Tunison, IL, 1887, VG . . .75.00
United States of America, J Mclish, 1818, EX 525.00

Maps

America, CA peninsula, Homann, Nuremberg, 1720, 19x22" . .600.00
America, hc/fancy cartouch, Seutter, Augsburg, 1744, 10x8" . .250.00
Barbary Coast, eng/hc/cartouch, Jansson, 1650, 19x22" 100.00
British Isles, eng/hc, Ortelius, Antwerp, 1570s, 14x20" 350.00
City of Washington, blk/wht on linen, Russell, London, 1800 .475.00
Florida, hc counties, Cowperthwait, 1850, EX 50.00
Floride-Louisiane, eng/margins, Bellin, Paris, 1757, 9x13" 90.00
Grece Moderne, hc/margins, de Fer, Paris, 1726, 9x14" 50.00
Guinea, hc/cartouch, Jansson, Amsterdam, 1645, 16x20" 50.00
Indiana, Indian settlements, hc, p Finley, 1831, 9x11" 85.00
Inferior Germania, full wash coloring, Bertius, Paris, 1618 . . . . .50.00
Japan, hc/margins/dbl folio, Vaugondy, Paris, 1757, 19x22" . . .115.00
Mexico, eng/hc, eagle cartouch, Conder, 1780, 12x15" 80.00
Mexico, hc, matted, p Matthew Carey, 1814, 15x17" 280.00
New Spain, Mexico City inset, Kitchen, London, 1795, 11x15" .70.00
North America, hc/margins, Vaugondy, Paris, 1766, 8x12" 75.00
Noweau Mexique, CA as island, Duval, Paris, 1670, 4x5" 110.00
Scotland, hc/margins, DeWit, Amsterdam, 1680, 16x20" 110.00
Sperm & Wht Whale, Maury & Wyman, Endicott/NY, 1853 . .350.00
Suffolk County, hc/cartouch, Ogilby, London, 1675, 13x17" . .200.00
Tartaria, copper eng/hc/margins, Duval, Paris, 1689, 6x8" 35.00
Tartaria, hc/cartouches, Hondius, Amsterdam, 1630s, 14x20" .350.00
Udrone, copper eng/hc, Bertius, Flanders, Paris, 1617 . . . . .40.00
USA, full hc/wide margins, Goodrich, Elliot, NY, 1858, EX 30.00
World, eng/hc, G Blaeu, Amsterdam, 1635, 16x21½", VG . .2,000.00

Marblehead

What began as therapy for patients in a sanitarium in Marblehead,
Massachusetts, has become recognized as an important part of the Arts and

Crafts movement in America. Results of the early experiments under the guidance of Arthur E. Baggs in 1904 met with such success that by 1908 the pottery had been converted to a solely commercial venture. Simple vase shapes were often incised with stylized animal and floral motifs or sailing ships. Some were decorated in low relief; many were plain. Simple matt glazes in soft yellow, gray, wisteria, rose, tobacco brown, and their most popular, Marblehead blue, were used alone or in combination. The Marblehead logo is distinctive — a boat with full sail and the letters 'M' and 'P.' The pottery closed in 1936.

Chamberstick, gr, 4" 65.00
Creamer, trees, brn on gr w/brn flecks, artist sgn, 3¼" 400.00
Pitcher, medallion & galleon, 6-color, 4¾" 600.00
Pitcher, tree band, brn on sage, bl int, angle hdl, AB, 6" 850.00
Plaque, basket of flowers, 4-color, 6" 425.00
Tile, galleon, brn/cream on bl/gr water, fr, 6" 450.00
Tile, galleon, wht on bl, in fr, 6½" 350.00
Tile, ship w/smoking stack, lt & dk bl/wht clouds, 4½" 225.00
Vase, bl, hand thrown, 4½" 135.00
Vase, bl over gray, ribbed/ringed, flared, AE Baggs, 5½" 550.00
Vase, geometric cvg, tobacco brn, wide body, unmk, 5" 425.00
Vase, gr, 4 conforming buttresses w/dk geometrics, 9½x12" ..6,600.00
Vase, grapes/florals, khaki/med & dk bl, cylindrical, 6x5" 900.00
Vase, gray, cylindrical, 3½x2¼" 90.00
Vase, gray matt w/bl specks, 4" 85.00
Vase, pomegranates/vertical branches, 3-color, H Tutt, 7" ...2,700.00
Vase, rabbits, bl on gray w/brn flecks, brn body, 3¼" 650.00
Vase, roses, blk-lined/yel on dk bl, ovoid, 3½" 450.00
Vase, roses, long-stemmed; brn/gr/yel on ochre, 3x4" 575.00
Vase, stylized stem/leaf/rose band, ochre/brn/yel/gr, 3x4" 575.00
Vase, stylized tree w/long trunk, 2-color, 6" 600.00
Vase, wide band w/floral branches, lt/dk bl on gray, 6" 1,200.00
Vase, wisteria, dk on med bl, tapered cylinder, 7x6", NM ...1,250.00
Vase, 4 dragonflies, gr on gray, 3¼x4¼", NM 375.00
Vase, 4 stylized trees form rim border, olive on pea gr, 5¾" ..1,800.00

Vase, 6 panels of stylized green leaves and blue berries outlined in brown on oatmeal-yellow, marked MP, artist signed, 6", $1,300.00.

Marbles

Marbles have been popular with children since the mid-1800s. They've been made in many types from a variety of materials. Among some of the first glass items to be produced, the earliest marbles were made from a solid glass rod broken into sections of the proper length which were placed in a tray of sand and charcoal and returned to the fire. As they were reheated, the trays were constantly agitated until the marbles were completely round. Other marbles were made of china, pottery, steel, and natural stones.

Below is a listing of the various types, along with a brief description of each. When size is not otherwise indicated, prices are listed for mint condition marbles of average size, ½" to 1".

Agates: stone marbles of many different colors — bands of color alternating with white usually encircle the marble; most are translucent.

Ballot Box: handmade (with pontils), opaque white or black, used in lodge elections.

Bloodstone: green chalcedony with red spots, a type of quartz.

China: with or without glaze, in a variety of hand-painted designs — parallel bands or bull's-eye designs most common.

Clambroth: opaque glass with outer evenly spaced swirls of one or alternating colors.

Clay: one of the most common older types; some are painted while others are not.

Comic Strip: a series of twelve machine-made marbles with faces of comic strip characters, Peltier Glass Factory, Illinois.

Crockery: sometimes referred to as Benningtons; most are either blue or brown, although some are speckled. The clay is shaped into a sphere, then coated with glaze and fired.

End of the Day: single-pontil glass marbles — the colored part often appears as a multicolored blob or mushroom cloud.

Goldstone: clear glass completely filled with copper flakes that have turned gold-colored from the heat of the manufacturing process.

Indian Swirls: usually black glass with a colored swirl appearing on the outside next to the surface, often irregular.

Latticinio Core Swirls: double-pontil marble with an inner area with net-like effects of swirls coming up around the center.

Lutz Type: glass with colored or clear bands alternating with bands which contain copper flecks.

Micas: clear or colored glass with mica flecks which reflect as silver dots when marble is turned. Red is rare.

Onionskin: spiral type which are solidly colored instead of having individual ribbons or threads, multicolored.

Peppermint Swirls: made of white opaque glass with alternating blue and red outer swirls.

Ribbon Core Swirls: double-pontil marble — center shaped like a ribbon with swirls that come up around the middle.

Rose Quartz: stone marble, usually pink in color, often with fractures inside and on outer surface.

Solid Core Swirls: double-pontil marble — middle is solid with swirls coming up around the core.

Steelies: hollow steel spheres marked with a cross where the steel was bent together to form the ball.

Sulfides: generally made of clear glass with figures inside. Rarer types have colored figures or colored glass.

Tiger Eye: stone marble of golden quartz with inclusions of asbestos, dark brown with gold highlights.

Vaseline: machine-made of yellowish-green glass with small bubbles.

For a more thorough study of the subject, we recommend *Antique and Collectible Marbles, Revised Second Edition*, an identification and value guide by Everett Grist; you will find his address in the Directory under Illinois.

Agate, contemporary, carnelian, 1¾" 50.00
Agate, gr & wht, ¾" 70.00
Banded Opaque, gr & wht, 2" 375.00
Banded Opaque, red & wht, 1¾" 250.00
Banded Opaque, red & wht, ¾" 50.00

Banded Transparent Swirl, bl, ¾" 5.00
Banded Transparent Swirl, lt gr, 1¾" 150.00
Bennington, bl, 1¾" 15.00
Bennington, bl, ¾" 1.00
Bennington, brn, 1¾" 10.00
Bennington, fancy, 1¾" 20.00
Bennington, fancy, ¾" 2.00
China, decorated, glazed, apple, 1¾" 300.00
China, decorated, glazed, rose, 1¾" 300.00
China, decorated, glazed, wht w/geometrics, 1¾" 45.00
China, decorated, unglazed, geometrics & flowers, ¾" ...200.00
Clambroth, opaque, bl & wht, 1¾" 500.00
Clambroth, opaque, bl & wht, ¾" 75.00
Clear Swirl Lutz-type, clear w/wht & gold swirls, ¾" 65.00
Cloud, w/mica, red & wht, 1¼" 150.00
Cloud, yel, rare, 1¾" 150.00
Comic, Cotes Bakery, advertising 250.00
Comic, Kayo, rare 55.00
Comic, Little Orphan Annie 40.00
Comic, Moon Mullins 55.00
Comic, set of 12 ....550.00
Comic, Skeezix 45.00
Cork Screw, machine-made 1.00
End of Day, bl & wht, 1¾" 200.00
Goldstone, ¾" 35.00
Indian Swirl, 1¾" 600.00
Indian Swirl, ¾" 150.00
Indian Swirl Lutz-type, gold flakes, ¾" 200.00

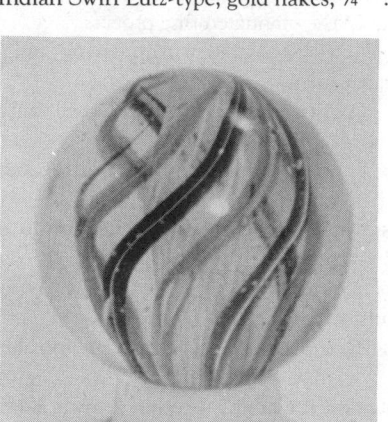

Latticinio Swirl, 1⅞", $100.00.

Line Crockery, clay, wht w/zigzag gr & bl lines, ¾" 5.00
Mica, bl, ¾" 15.00
Mica, gr, 1¾" 250.00
Onionskin, w/mica, 1¾" 350.00
Onionskin, w/mica, ¾" 60.00
Onionskin, 1¼" 85.00
Onionskin, 16-lobe, unusual, 2" 500.00
Onionskin, 2" 275.00
Onionskin, ¾" 50.00
Onionskin, 4-lobe, 1¼" 175.00
Onionskin Lutz-type, gold flakes, 1¾" 800.00
Opaque Glass Swirl Lutz-type, bl, yel, gr, or vaseline, ¾" ...100.00
Opaque Swirl, gr, ¾" 35.00
Peppermint Swirl, opaque, red, wht, & bl, ¾" 75.00
Pottery, tan w/purple lines, 1¾" 15.00
Ribbon Core Lutz-type, clear or transparent colors, 1¾" ...700.00
Slag, machine-made, sm 1.00
Slag, machine-made, 1¼" 40.00

Solid Opaque, bl, ¾" 30.00
Solid Opaque, gr, 1¾" 200.00
Sulfide, alligator, 1¾" 160.00
Sulfide, baboon, 2⅛", NM 230.00
Sulfide, bear, sitting, 1⅝", EX 80.00
Sulfide, bear, standing, 1¾", M 140.00
Sulfide, bear, standing, 1⅜", M 180.00
Sulfide, bear, walking, 1", M 110.00
Sulfide, bird w/long feathers, 1½", M 150.00
Sulfide, boy on stump, 1⅝", NM 350.00
Sulfide, camel, 2" 175.00
Sulfide, cat, 1¼" 75.00
Sulfide, chicken, 1⅛" 65.00
Sulfide, child in dress, 2" 275.00
Sulfide, child w/ball & mallet, 1¾" 600.00
Sulfide, coin w/number 7, 2" 375.00
Sulfide, cow, grazing, 2⅛", NM 225.00
Sulfide, cow, 1⅛" 100.00
Sulfide, dbl eagle, very rare, 1¾" 675.00
Sulfide, dog, begging, 2", NM 160.00
Sulfide, dog, long haired, 1¼", NM 135.00
Sulfide, dog, running, 1¾", M 170.00
Sulfide, dog, sitting, 1½", M 140.00
Sulfide, dog, sleeping, 2", EX 180.00
Sulfide, dog, whippet, 1½", M 120.00
Sulfide, donkey, 1⅝", NM 125.00
Sulfide, dove, 1⅝", M 160.00
Sulfide, dove on post, 1⅛" 278.00
Sulfide, eagle, 1⅝" 185.00
Sulfide, eagle on post, 2", EX 285.00
Sulfide, elephant, 1⅝", M 160.00
Sulfide, fish, 1½", NM 120.00
Sulfide, fish, 2⅛", M 200.00
Sulfide, fox, 1½", EX 130.00
Sulfide, goat, 1¾", M 190.00
Sulfide, goat, 2", NM 225.00
Sulfide, goat, 2, M 300.00
Sulfide, hen on nest, 1½", M 120.00
Sulfide, horse, grazing, 1⅜", NM 150.00
Sulfide, horse, grazing, 1⅝", EX 180.00
Sulfide, horse, running, 1½", M 180.00
Sulfide, lamb, 1¼", EX 100.00
Sulfide, lamb, 1¾", M 140.00
Sulfide, lion, lt purple glass, 1⅝", EX 275.00
Sulfide, lion, 1½", EX 160.00
Sulfide, lion, 1⅝", NM 150.00
Sulfide, lion, 2", NM 200.00
Sulfide, llama, 1⅝", M 140.00
Sulfide, monkey, 1⅛" 95.00
Sulfide, owl, spread-winged, 1¼" 300.00
Sulfide, papoose, 2" 400.00
Sulfide, pelican, 1¼" 275.00
Sulfide, pig, 1¼" 90.00
Sulfide, pig, 2", M 180.00
Sulfide, prairie chicken, 1¼", M 325.00
Sulfide, rabbit, running, 1¾", M 120.00
Sulfide, rabbit, running, 2" 140.00
Sulfide, rabbit, 1⅛" 65.00
Sulfide, raccoon, 2" 200.00
Sulfide, ram, 2" 175.00
Sulfide, rooster, lt yel, 1¾" 175.00
Sulfide, rooster, 1½", M 140.00
Sulfide, rooster, 2", M 180.00
Sulfide, Santa Claus, 2" 400.00

Sulfide, squirrel w/nut, 1½", M 125.00
Sulfide, squirrel w/nut, 2", EX 300.00
Sulfide, steer, 1⅝", M 125.00
Sulfide, wild boar, 1½", NM 90.00
Sulfide, wild boar, 2¼", NM 225.00

Marine Collectibles

See also Steamship Collectibles and Scrimshaw.

Binnacle, brass, w/compass & compensating balls, 48" 500.00
Blubber spade, rusted, 67" 225.00
Cabinet, teak, 4 drws+doors, hdw dtd 1897, 30x46x25" 1,250.00
Carving, right whale, pine, branded C Voorhees, 18" 300.00
Diver's helmet, copper/brass, mk Galeazzi, EX 600.00
Harpoon, for Greener gun, arctic whaling type, 23" 225.00
Lantern, ship's; brass, copper rivets, hdl, 16", M 450.00
Octant, ebony/brass w/ivory scale, J Whyte-Glasgow, w/case . .350.00
Octant, Spencer/Browning/Rust, in case, EX 650.00
Octant, walnut w/incised holly wood scale, early 1,200.00

Ships' plaques, brass with anvil in logo, 12" long, $100.00; Gotaverken Co, dated 1949, machinery press form, 15" long, $250.00.

Pulley, bone w/copper eyelet, worn canvas/ropework, 4¾" 350.00
Rudder head, brass, in the form of 2 anchors, 19" 550.00
Sea chest, bl-gr pnt w/name, fitted compartment, 1850s, 51" . .700.00
Sea chest, bl-pnt pine, canvas top, HP ship in lid, 38", VG 125.00
Sea chest, eagle/banner/name cvd on lid, 14", +1902 diary 375.00
Sextant, Dobbie Son Hutton-London, brass, 3 eyepcs, w/case . .350.00
Sextant, Heath London, dtd 1903, orig mahog case, EX 600.00
Sextant, Negretti & Zamba, Sidney, Australia, 1880s, EX 675.00
Ship model, bark, whale bone, pnt bkground, 1875, 11x15" . .1,400.00
Ship model, fully rigged, pnt, 27x36" 225.00
Stamp, figure of a baleen whale, cvd wood, 1850s, sm 650.00
Tarpoon, toggle; early, 33½" 225.00
Trade card, A1...Clipper Barque...Thorndike, 1874, 6x4½" 400.00

Martin Bros.

The Martin Bros. were studio potters who worked from 1873 until 1914, first at Fulham and later at London and Southall. There were four brothers, each of whom excelled in their particular area. Robert, known as Wallace, was an experienced stonecarver. He modeled a series of grotesque bird and animal figural caricatures. Walter was the potter, responsible for throwing the larger vases on the wheel, firing the kiln, and mixing the clay. Edwin, an artist of stature, preferred more naturalistic forms of decoration. His work was often incised or had relief designs of seaweed, florals, fish, and birds. The fourth brother, Charles, was their business manager. Their work was incised with their names, place of production, and letters and numbers indicating month and year.

Bird, fixed wood base, sgn/1911, 8", EX 3,500.00

Figure, imp musician, seated X-legged, cream/lt brn, 5", EX . . .360.00
Figure, Norwich Bellman, cream glaze, fixed wood base, 6" . .1,000.00
Jug, smiling face, bk: sinister, beige/wht/brn, 5-1910, 6" 750.00
Pitcher, snake hdl, 5" 125.00
Vase, allover cvd foliage, dk bl/brn bands, 1876, 5½", pr 350.00
Vase, blk-brn metallic bark texture, sq cylinder, 3½" 350.00

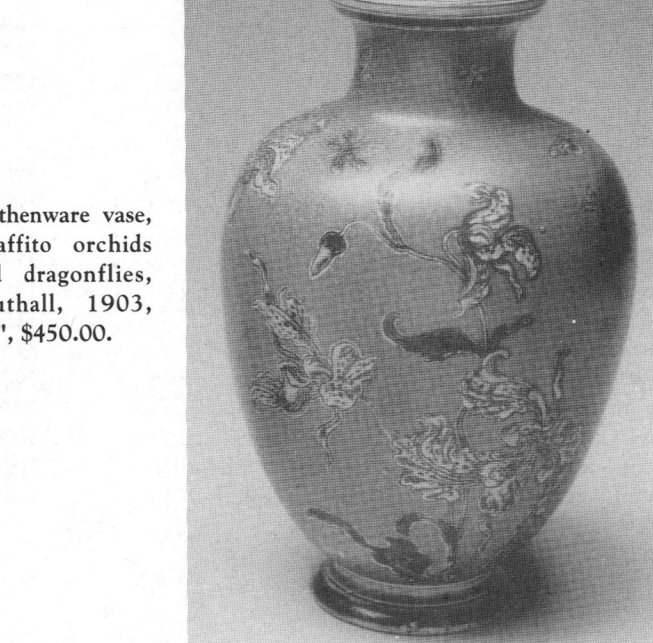

Earthenware vase, sgraffito orchids and dragonflies, Southall, 1903, 9½", $450.00.

Vase, fish/eels/seaweed cvg, sgn/1888, 9x8½" 1,200.00
Vase, grotesque, 4-necked, claw feet, 13" 650.00
Vase, leaves/dragons cvg, bl/brn, rnd w/slim neck, mk, 8" 900.00
Vase, studded surface, bl/mauve, sq oviform, B-37-XL, 9½" 145.00

Mary Gregory

Mary Gregory glass, for reasons that remain obscure, is the namesake of a Boston and Sandwich Glass Company employee who worked for the company for only two years in the mid-1800s. Although no evidence actually exists to indicate that glass of this type was even produced there, the fine colored or crystal ware decorated with figures of children in white enamel is commonly referred to as Mary Gregory. The glass, in fact, originated in Europe and was imported into this country where it was copied by several eastern glasshouses. It was popular from the mid-1800s until the turn of the century. It is generally accepted that examples with all-white figures were made in the U.S.A., while gold-trimmed items and those with children having tinted faces or a small amount of color on their clothing are European. Though amethyst is rare, examples in cranberry command the higher prices. Blue ranks next; and green, amber, and clear items are worth the least.

Bottle, barber; cobalt, tennis players, pontil scar, 8", pr 425.00
Bottle, scent; amber, girl skipping, SP top, 4" 250.00
Bottle, wine; cranberry, boy, orig stopper, 7⅛" 195.00
Bottle, wine; lav stain, girl, 9¼x3¼" 145.00
Box, cranberry, running boy, metal trim & ft, 3½x2½" 275.00
Box, jewel; amber, 2 children at play, 6" dia 300.00
Box, jewel; amethyst, boy picks flowers, ring hdls, 4" dia 400.00
Box, jewel; bl, girl w/basket, 5" dia .325.00
Box, jewel; cobalt, boy & girl, ball form, brass mts, 5" dia 425.00

Box, jewel; cranberry, boy & girl, ormolu mts, 4½x6" 700.00
Box, jewel; sapphire bl, boy & girl, brass mts, 4½x5½" 600.00
Box, patch; cobalt, girl w/hat, 1¼x1⅞" 175.00
Box, patch; lime gr, girl, 1¾x2⅜" 165.00
Cruet, bl, boy in short pants by trees 300.00
Cruet, cranberry, drummer boy, clear hdl/hollow stopper 425.00
Cruet, gr, boy in garden, clear stopper 275.00
Decanter, amber, boy in riding clothes, 13½x4¼" 325.00
Fairy lamp, gr, girl, clear Clarke base, 6" 495.00
Goblet, cobalt, boy feeds birds, clear ft, 5¾" 150.00
Jug, cranberry, boy, gold hdl/rim, mini, 1¾" 225.00
Mug, amber, boy, lt ribbing, appl hdl, 4¼" 125.00
Mug, amber, girl, 4x2¼" 150.00
Mug, lt gr, boy, 3⅜x2¾" 125.00
Night light, amethyst, boy w/flag, ormolu rim/ft, 9x3" 395.00
Pitcher, clear, girl chasing butterfly, crimped rim, 9½" 100.00
Pitcher, cranberry, boy in riding clothes, 7" 225.00
Pitcher, cranberry, 2 facing boys, clear hdl, 9" 415.00
Pitcher, delphinium bl, Invt T'print, boy w/ball, 7" 165.00
Pitcher, lime gr, boy, 6⅝x4¼" 125.00
Pitcher, lt sapphire bl, girl in gold dress, 10¾x4½" 275.00
Rose bowl, cranberry, girl, gold trim on collared base, 2" ...200.00
Stein, aqua, boy, pewter lid, rare, 13" 295.00
Stein, cranberry, boy, pewter lid w/pk glass insert, 5½" 300.00
Stein, sapphire bl, Invt T'print, boy, pewter lid/insert, 7" 300.00
Toothpick holder, bl, girl holds branch, gold trim 200.00

Tray, children in meadow on apricot (rare color), 8x11", $650.00.

Trinket dish, cranberry, girl, brass ftd base, 2x3" dia 145.00
Trinket dish, gr, girl in garden, Atlantic City 1898, 3⅝" 175.00
Vase, amber, girl reaches for butterfly, 10" 245.00
Vase, bl, boy in garden, 4" 85.00
Vase, bl, girl w/hat, scalloped, 12⅜", pr 550.00
Vase, blk amethyst, boy & girl, 10¾x4⅞", pr 450.00
Vase, cobalt, cherubs/florals, gold/wht, ormolu, 9½", pr 325.00
Vase, cobalt, girl in wht, ped ft, 7½x3⅜", pr 225.00
Vase, cobalt, lady by fence, flower-form top, facing pr, 13" ...575.00
Vase, cranberry, boy & girl, cylinder w/bulbous base, 6", pr ...325.00
Vase, cranberry, girl, 4¼x1⅝" 105.00
Vase, cranberry, girl w/rope of flowers, 9½" 250.00
Vase, gr, girl sits on shore, reeded snail hdl, ft, 11⅝" 265.00
Vase, honey amber, boy & girl, gold-trimmed hdls, 10", pr ...450.00
Vase, lime gr, boy w/oars over shoulder, 6⅝x3½" 125.00
Vase, med gr, girl w/pitcher at pump w/boy beside, 14" 265.00
Vase, orange, boy, 4⅛" 85.00
Vase, orange, girl in apron, 6x2" 118.00

Vase, pigeon blood, Victorian lady, ormolu base, 14", pr 1,250.00
Vase, pk overlay, girl in long dress, 9½", pr 295.00
Vase, pk satin overlay, girl on rock/butterflies, 8½x5" 365.00
Vinaigrette, sapphire bl, girl, oval, orig top, 2½x1¼" 195.00

Mason's Ironstone

In 1813 Charles J. Mason was granted a patent for a process said to 'improve the quality of English porcelain.' The new type of ware was in fact ironstone which Mason decorated with colorful florals and scenics, some of which reflected the Oriental taste. Although his business failed for a short time in the late 1840s, Mason re-established himself and continued to produce dinnerware, tea services, and ornamental pieces until about 1852 at which time the pottery was sold to Francis Morley. Ten years later, Geo. L. and Taylor Ashworth became owners. Both Morley and the Ashworths not only used Mason's molds and patterns but often his mark as well. Because the quality and the workmanship of the later wares do not compare with Mason's earlier product, collectors should take care to distinguish one from the other. Consult a good book on marks to be sure.

Cup & saucer, handleless; rose, 4-color, mk 25.00
Jug, Bandana, orange/gold/blk, mk, 5¼", M 195.00
Jug, Chrysanthemum, bl, mk, 1860, 3", M 130.00
Jug, Chrysanthemum, bl/orange, mk, 1860, 5¼", M 235.00
Jug, fence & bird, mk, 1825, 6", M 135.00
Jug, Mazareen/mc cartouch, mk, 1860, 6", M 250.00
Jug, pagoda & bridge, mc, 1840, 7½", M 125.00
Jug, Willow-type, mc, mk, 1880, 2", M 165.00
Jug & basin, Willow type, mc, 1880, M 350.00
Platter, chinoiserie, mc, 1820-30, 17", M 150.00

Platter, gaudy floral, ca 1820, 12", $225.00.

Massier

Clement Massier was a French artist-potter who in 1881 established a workshop at Golfe Juan, France, where he experimented with metallic lustre glazes. (One of his pupils was Jacques Sicardo, who brought the knowledge he had gained through his association with Massier to the Weller Pottery Company in Zanesville, Ohio.) The lustre lines developed by Massier incorporated nature themes with allover decorations of foliage or flowers on shapes modeled in the Art Nouveau style. The ware was usually incised with the Massier name, his initials, or the location of the pottery. Massier died in 1917.

Bowl, 3 butterflies inside, irid, paper label/#11160, 4½" 150.00
Bowl vase, allover pansies, blk/magenta irid, sgn/dtd, 15" . . .3,600.00
Vase, cloverleaves, irid colors, sgn/1900, 5¾" 275.00
Vase, cloverleaves, toothpick holder shape 150.00
Vase, cloverleaves/spots, irid, horn-like rim points, 5¾" 275.00
Vase, iris, olive/gray/maroon irid, cylinder w/sq neck, 9" 500.00
Vase, thistles/grasses, irid brn/burgundy, att, 9" 175.00

Match Holders

Before the invention of the safety match in 1855, matches were kept in matchboxes and carried in pocket-size match safes because they ignited so easily. John Walker, an English chemist, invented the match more than one hundred years ago — quite by accident. Walker was working with a mixture of potash and antimony, hoping to make a combustible that could be used to fire guns. The mixture adhered to the end of the wooden stick he had used for stirring. As he tried to remove it by scraping the stick on the stone floor, it burst into flames. The invention of the match was only a step away! From that time to the present, match holders have been made in amusing figural forms as well as simple utilitarian styles and in a wide range of materials. Most were wall-hanging; a few were table-top models — all designed to keep matches conveniently at hand. See also Advertising; Majolica.

Acorns on 2 lg oak leaves, CI, hanging, 5½x8" 110.00
American Shield, clear glass, shield form, 1492/1892, 4" 140.00
Bacchus head, CI, open pocket w/grapes & leaves, hanging 85.00
Dog, bsk, dressed, smoking pipe 77.00
Dog (full bodied) on lid, CI, ribbed urn on ped base, 3x4" 65.00
Frog, CI, open mouth, old pnt, ca 1900, 2x4x3½" 65.00
High-button shoe, CI figural, rectangular base, 4x5" 45.00
Horse's hoof, brass, 3-D turtle on hinged lid, 4¾x4¾x6" 88.00
Hunting pouch/game cvg, walnut, minor damage, 12" 100.00
Janus-type dbl classical heads, Wedgwood, dtd 1849, 4x5" 165.00
Miss Liberty's head, clear glass, 4½", EX 80.00
Pig, brass, open top, short legs, 1800s, 2x4½" 130.00
Rifles & game, bag forms safes, CI, 10x6" 65.00

Stoneware, salt glaze with cobalt bands and letters, 5½x7", $150.00.

Tin, bl japanning/yel stencil scrolls, scalloped bk, 3x4" 65.00
Tin, Compliments JN Jordan, Ely IO, EX 55.00
Tin, worn old gr pnt, ca 1900, 6x3x3" .15.00

Match Safes

Match safes, aptly-named cases used to carry matches in the days before cigarette lighters, were used during the last half of the 19th century until about 1920. Some incorporated added features — hidden compartments, cigar cutters, etc. — some were figural, and others were used by retail companies as advertising give-aways. They were made from every type of material, but silverplated styles abound. See also Advertising; Majolica.

Advertising, Coleman's Mustard, football scene, sterling 375.00
Advertising, Hunter Baltimore Rye, celluloid, M 65.00
Advertising, Lord York Cigars 45.00
Alligator, Monon Route 275.00
Butterfly/flowers/ferns bright cut on SP, mk 55.00
Cigars in bundle, SP figural 85.00
Doctor's bag, sterling figural 275.00
Dog w/whistle, SP figural 185.00
Fish, brass figural 145.00
Frog, bronze w/encircling brass bucket, 1870s, 2x2½" 150.00
Gladstone's face, brass filigree, hinged lid, button release 75.00
Golfer, sterling figural 275.00
Horse, SP & enamel figural 90.00
King of Hearts, SP, w/scorer 85.00
Man's head, brass, 1½x2" 110.00

Nouveau lady smoking, sterling, 2½", $85.00.

Pig, SP figural, head opens, base striker, 1½x¾x2½" 85.00
Punch, SP figural, base w/striker opens, 2⅜x1¼" 135.00
Repousse florals on SP, mk 45.00
Repousse scrolls/flowers/inscription on SP, mk 48.00
Repousse tulips & monogram on sterling 75.00
Walnut, SP figural, top opens, striker on bk, 1¼x1¾" 75.00

McCoy

The third generation McCoy potter in the Roseville, Ohio, area was Nelson, who with the aid of his father, J.W., established the Nelson McCoy Sanitary Stoneware Company in 1910. They manufactured churns, jars, jugs, poultry fountains, and foot warmers. By 1925 they had expanded their wares to include majolica jardinieres and pedestals, umbrella stands and cuspidors, and an embossed line of vases and small jardinieres in a blended brown and green matt glaze. From the late twenties through the mid-forties, a utilitarian stoneware was produced, some of which was glazed in the soft blue and white so popular with collectors today. They also used a dark brown mahogany color and a medium to dark green — both in a high gloss. In 1933 the firm became known as the Nelson McCoy Pottery Company. They expanded their facilities in 1940 and began to make the novelty artware, cookie jars, and dinnerware that today are synonomous with 'McCoy.' To date more than two hundred cookie jars of every theme and description have been produced. Some are very common. Mammy, the Clown, and the Bear (although very old) are easy to find; while the Dalmations, Christmas Tree, and Kangaroo, for instance, (though not so old) are harder to locate. The Indian and the Teepee, both made in the fifties, are two of the most popular and some of the most expensive!

More than a dozen different marks have been used by the company; nearly all incorporate the name 'McCoy,' although some of the older items were marked 'NM USA.' For further information, consult *The Collectors' Encyclopedia of McCoy Pottery* by Sharon and Bob Huxford, available at your local bookstore or public library.

Our McCoy cookie jar advisor is Judy Posner; she is listed in the Directory under Pennsylvania.

Cookie Jars

Animal Crackers 35.00

Apollo Age, $200.00.

Apple, 1950-64 ....25.00
Apple on Basketweave 30.00
Bananas 50.00
Barnum's Animals 125.00
Bear, cookie in vest 40.00
Bear, upside down, blk/wht 25.00
Betsy Baker 75.00
Black Kettle, w/immovable bail, HP flowers 20.00
Bobby Baker 30.00
Caboose 95.00
Chef 50.00
Chiffoniere, Early American Chest 50.00
Chinese Lantern 45.00
Chipmunk 75.00
Christmas Tree 275.00
Circus Horse 125.00
Clown Bust 35.00
Clown in Barrel 45.00
Clyde Dog 25.00
Coalby Cat 95.00
Coffee Grinder 25.00

Coffee Mug 20.00
Colonial Fireplace 65.00
Cookie Barrel 20.00
Cookie Boy 95.00
Cookie Cabin 50.00
Cookie Jug, dbl loop, brn 20.00
Cookie Jug, single loop, 2-tone gr rope 18.00
Cookie Jug, w/cork stopper, brn & wht 15.00
Cookie Log 30.00
Cookie Safe 35.00
Cookstove 25.00
Corn 85.00
Covered Wagon 40.00
Cylinder, w/red flowers 20.00
Dalmations in Rocking Chair 200.00
Dog on Basketweave 45.00
Drum 50.00
Duck on Basketweave 35.00
Dutch Boy 30.00
Dutch Girl, boy on reverse 45.00
Dutch Treat Barn 50.00
Elephant 95.00
Elephant w/Split Trunk, rare 150.00
Engine 85.00
Forbidden Fruit 35.00
Friendship 75.00
Frontier Family 40.00
Fruit in Bushel Basket 45.00
Gingerbread Boy 25.00
Globe 150.00
Grandfather Clock 45.00
Granny 45.00
Hamm's Bear 95.00
Happy Face 25.00
Hen on Nest 75.00
Hillbilly Bear, rare 300.00
Hobby Horse 95.00
Honey Bear 45.00
Indian 175.00
Jack-O'-Lantern 200.00
Kangaroo, bl 195.00
Kettle, jumbo sz 25.00
Kissing Penguins 40.00
Kitten on Basketweave 45.00
Kittens on Ball of Yarn 65.00
Kookie Kettle, blk 20.00
Lamb on Basketweave 35.00
Leprechaun 300.00
Liberty Bell 30.00
Little Clown 35.00
Lollipop 40.00
Mac Dog 55.00
Mammy 150.00
Mammy w/Cauliflower 300.00
Modern 20.00
Monk 30.00
Mother Goose 95.00
Mr & Mrs Owl 75.00
Oaken Bucket 20.00
Old Churn 20.00
Pears on Basketweave 30.00
Pelican 85.00
Pepper, yel 22.00
Picnic Basket 45.00

Pineapple	40.00
Pineapple, Modern	25.00
Pirates Chest	45.00
Pot Belly Stove, blk	25.00
Puppy, w/sign	55.00
Quaker Oats	150.00
Red Barn, cow in door, rare	135.00
Rooster, 1955-1957	65.00
Rooster, 1970-1974	35.00
Round w/HP Leaves	25.00
Sad Clown	35.00
Snoopy on Doghouse	125.00
Snow Bear	40.00
Strawberry, 1955-57	25.00
Strawberry, 1971-75	20.00
Teapot	25.00
Tepee	175.00
Tilt Pitcher, blk w/roses	26.00
Tomato	25.00
Touring Car	45.00
Tudor Cookie House	75.00
Tulip on Flowerpot	35.00
Turkey	125.00
Upside Down Bear, panda	25.00
WC Fields	95.00
Wedding Jar	55.00
Windmill	55.00
Wishing Well	25.00
Woodsy Owl	95.00
Wren House	75.00
Yosemite Sam	85.00

Miscellaneous

Bank, St Bernard	15.00
Bank, Woodsy Owl	25.00
Beverage jug, Sunburst Gold, w/lid	30.00
Bookend/planter, violin, pr	18.00
Bookends, swallows, pr	30.00
Bowl, shoulder; bl, ringed, rectangular base, 9"	22.00
Bowl, shoulder; pk/bl stripes, 1930s	18.00
Coffee server & warmer, El Rancho Bar-B-Que	40.00
Coffeepot, Grecian, gr & gold, w/creamer & sugar bowl	40.00
Decanter, Apollo Len, Sims Distillery	40.00
Decanter, Jupiter 60, train set, 4-pc	200.00
Decanter, 1932 Pierce Arrow Sport Phantom	40.00
Dresser caddy, lion	18.00
Elephant, Victory Depends on You, WWII era	12.00
Grease jar, cabbage form	25.00
Ice tub, El Rancho Bar-B-Que	25.00
Jardiniere, holly/berries emb on turq matt, modeled hdls	18.00
Lamp, cowboy boots form, orig shade, lg	50.00
Mug, Nixon caricature, rare	65.00
Pitcher, buccaneer emb on dk gr, shield mk	30.00
Pitcher, staves/bands emb on gr barrel form, shield mk	25.00
Pitcher, water lily emb on gr, fish hdl, 1935	20.00
Pitcher, WC Fields	35.00
Planter, banana boat	30.00
Planter, cradle	7.00
Planter, duck w/umbrella	45.00
Planter, Liberty Bell	50.00
Planter, North Pole	9.00
Planter, pheasant	12.00
Planter, rolling pin w/Boy Blue	15.00

Planter, Village Smithy	14.00
Sombrero serv-all, El Rancho Bar-B-Que	75.00
Spoon rest, butterfly form	35.00
Spoon rest, penguin form	35.00
Tea set, Pine Cone, 3-pc	40.00
Vase, Onyx, 7"	12.00
Wall pocket, clock	22.00
Wall pocket, mailbox	15.00
Wall pocket, Sunburst Gold	15.00
Window box, Butterfly	8.00

McCoy, J. W.

The J.W. McCoy Pottery Company was incorporated in 1899. It operated under that name in Roseville, Ohio, until 1911 when McCoy entered into a partnership with George Brush, forming the Brush-McCoy Company. During the early years, McCoy produced kitchenware, majolica jardinieres and pedestals, umbrella stands, and cuspidors. By 1903 they had begun to experiment in the field of art pottery and, though never involved to the extent of some of their contemporaries, nevertheless produced several art lines of merit. Their first line was Mt. Pelee, examples of which are very rare today. Two types of glazes were used, matt green and an iridescent charcoal gray. Though the line was primarily mold formed, some pieces evidence the fact that while the clay remained wet and pliable it was pulled and pinched with the fingers to form crests and peaks in a style not unlike George Ohr.

The company rebuilt in 1904 after being destroyed by fire, and other artware was designed. Loy-Nel Art and Renaissance were standard brown lines, hand decorated under the glaze with colored slip. Shapes and artwork were usually simple but effective. Olympia and Rosewood were relief-molded brown-glaze lines decorated in natural colors with wreaths of leaves and berries or simple floral sprays. Although much of this ware was not marked, you will find examples with the die-stamped 'Loy-Nel Art, McCoy' or an incised line identification.

Corn, tankard	125.00
Loy-Nel Art, bowl, pansies, hdls, 9" W	50.00
Loy-Nel Art, jardiniere, pansies, 3 ball ft, 6"	85.00
Loy-Nel Art, lamp base, irises, minor scratches, 8½"	65.00
Loy-Nel Art, spittoon, wild roses, flared rim	85.00
Mt Pelee, ewer, gr, volcanic surface	275.00
Olympia, mug, band of grapes/leaves	100.00
Olympia, vase, ears of corn, cylindrical, 11"	185.00

Vase, Olympia, 12",
$150.00.

Rosewood, pitcher, berries/leaves, cylinder neck, 10" 185.00
Rosewood, vase, floral, squat w/rim hdl, sm 100.00
Rosewood (Pre-1903 Line), vase, orange streaks, waisted, 9" 50.00
Umbrella stand, matt gr, 21" 90.00

McKee

McKee Glass was founded in 1853 in Pittsburgh, Pennsylvania. Among their early products were tableware of both the flint and non-flint variety. In 1888 the company relocated to avail themselves of a source of natural gas, thereby founding the town of Jeanette, Pennsylvania. One of their most famous colored dinnerware lines, Rock Crystal, was manufactured in the 1920s. During the thirties and forties, colored opaque dinnerware, Sunkist reamers, and 'bottoms up' cocktail tumblers were popular as well as a line of black glass vases, bowls, and novelty items. All are popular items with today's collectors. The company was purchased in 1916 by Jeanette Glass, under which name it continues to operate. See also Animal Dishes with Covers; Depression Glass; Kitchen Collectibles; Reamers.

Bottoms Up, butterscotch 50.00
Bottoms Up, frosted, w/coaster 75.00
Bottoms Up, jadite, no coaster 40.00
Bottoms Up, jadite, w/coaster 75.00
Box, vaseline, sparrow finial, rnd, sgn 125.00
Candlestick, tulip socket, wafer stem, 1800s, EX 135.00
Clock, Tambour, amber 375.00
Jardiniere, Red Ships, #25, jadite 30.00
Lamp, nude, gr 150.00
Vase, draped nude, Chalaine bl, 8½" 165.00

Medical Collectibles

The field of medical-related items encompasses a wide area from the primitive bleeding bowl to the X-ray machines of the early 1900s. Other closely related collectibles include apothecary and dental items. Many tools that were originally intended for the pharmacist found their way to the doctor's office, and dentists often used surgical tools when no suitable dental instrument was available. A trend in the late 1700s toward self-medication brought a whole new wave of home-care manuals and 'patent' medical machines for home use. Commonly referred to as 'quack' medical gimmicks, these machines were usually ineffective and occasionally dangerous.

Book, Homeopathic Domestic Physician, 1854, EX 18.00
Book, Science of Surgery, engravings, 1884, 1100-pg, VG 22.00
Caustic stick, mk Sterling Silver Seamless Tube, ca 1840 . . . . .185.00
Chest, dental; mahog, Sandwich glass pulls, NM 6,500.00
Ear trumpet, banjo type, collapsible, T Hawksley, 2-pc 365.00
Ear trumpet, parabaloid, blk-pnt brass, tip missing, ca 1860 . . . .110.00
Enema set, w/instructions, ca 1825, Green 400.00
Hammer, reflex; blk rubber, metal hdl, Bell/Croyden, ca 1920 . .65.00
Inhaler, nasal; for asthma, Rogers 75.00
Instruments, gynecological, Tiemann & Co, NY, 6-pc+case . . .995.00
Kit, eye surgeon's, Ernst-Maw-Coxeter-Rauschke, ca 1860 . . . .400.00
Kit, travelling surgeon's, leather, 16 instruments, EX 250.00
Knife, amputation; Liston type, blk hdl, Wood, ca 1870, 14" . .185.00
Knife, scarifier; trigger type, ca 1830, M 210.00
Machine, druggist pill-making; wood/brass, 18 slots, EX 175.00
Mask, anesthesia; brass, folding, ca 1870 . . . . .75.00
Mold, false teeth; brass 50.00
Phleme, bone cased, 3 blades, Boyals a Toulouse, 1840, EX 160.00
Phleme, spring operated, steel blade, brass case, 2¾" L 65.00

Quack machine, Challenge, ultra-violet machine, EX 35.00
Quack machine, Electreat Shocking Pain Reliever, 1920, MIB . .35.00
Quack machine, Electro, walnut case, nickeled metal 65.00
Quack machine, Master Violet Rays 65.00
Quack machine, Mesco #44-DD, incomplete 20.00
Quack machine, Radiolux Ultraviolet kit, complete, orig case . . .35.00
Quack machine, Tucker's Violet Ray .20.00
Saw, bone cutter, ebony grips, orig brass & mahog box 995.00
Spoon, castor oil; Gibson type, pewter, ca 1837, unmk 265.00
Spoon, medicine; mk Gibson, Inventor, ca 1837, EX 325.00
Spoon, medicine; pewter, Dixon & Son 300.00
Spoon, sterling/gold wash, openwork hdl, Blackinton, +case 95.00
Stethoscope, lacquered fruitwood, ca 1860 . . . . .335.00
Stethoscope, monaural, blk lacquered, 1-pc, ca 1890 . . . . .165.00
Syringe, bone ivory, ca 1680 . . . . .275.00
Thermometer, abalone case, gold-filled trim 75.00
Thermometer, gold, Immisch 450.00
Tongue depressor, brass, mk British Make, ca 1890 . . . . .75.00
Tongue depressor, silver, mk Sterling, JCB in script, 1890 . . . .175.00
Tongue depressor, SP, hinged, BG in script, ca 1860 . . . . .180.00
Tongue scraper, clear tortoise & ivory, ca 1840 . . . . .140.00
Tooth extractor, wooden hdl, EX 80.00
Tooth key, ebony hdl, ca 1860, EX .365.00
Vaccinator, ivory, folding blade, George III, ca 1790 . . . . .375.00

John Bull eye cups, clear, 2½", $25.00; in green, dated 1917, $150.00.

Meissen

The Royal Saxon Porcelain Works was established in 1710 in Meissen, Saxony. Under the direction of Johann Freidrick Bottger, who in 1708 had developed the formula for the first true porcelain body, fine ceramic figurines with exquisite detail and tableware of the highest quality were produced. Although every effort was made to insure the secrecy of Bottger's discovery, others soon began to copy his ware; and in 1731 Meissen adopted the famous crossed sword trademark to identify their own work. The term 'Dresden ware' is often used to refer to Meissen porcelain, since Bottger's discovery and first potting efforts were in nearby Dresden. See also Onion Pattern.

Bowl, floral on wht, yel border w/3 cartouches, 1929, 12" 125.00
Bowl, floral/butterfly medallions, 8-sided, X-swords, 10x13" . . .135.00
Bowl, grapevines on cobalt w/gold, openwork, mk, 8x12" 185.00

Bowl, medallion on cobalt, gold rim, shallow, X-swords, 10" ...275.00
Bowl, 4 scenes w/flowers on aqua, X-swords, 9" 125.00
Box, floral/couple on lid, shaped sides, X-swords, 3½" L 425.00
Candle holder, leaf form w/buds, gold on wht, mk, 5½" 85.00
Coffeepot, daises/roses on wht, rose finial, recent, 10" 135.00
Compote, floral on wht, openweave/floral-reserve border, 9" .375.00
Cup, demitasse; courting scene/floral panels w/gold, AR mk ...125.00
Cup & saucer, angel medallion on yel, X-swords, miniature 65.00
Cup & saucer, demitasse; leaf molded, gold trim, X-swords 65.00
Cup & saucer, Deutsche Blumen florals/gold, 1774-1814 .....250.00
Cup & saucer, single pk rose, gold trim, serpentine hdl 65.00
Cup & saucer, X-swords in pattern, scalloped, mk 60.00
Dish, floral, leaf form, appl hdl, X-sword, 7½x6½" 70.00
Dish, hdl formed of 2 pk & gray flamingos, 1910, 7½" H ...1,600.00
Ewer, allegorical: Fire, 4 appl figures, dragon hdl, 27" 1,300.00
Figurine, boy & girl w/string instrument, X-swords, 1870s, 7" ..580.00
Figurine, child & cherub at play, X-swords, 1830, 5" 495.00
Figurine, Columbia, goddess of continents, 4½", EX 325.00
Figurine, couple w/grapes, 1700s attire, mk, 1880s, 17", pr 880.00
Figurine, couple w/sheep, 1700s attire, 1880s, 6¾" 525.00
Figurine, Courting of the Princess, amorous couple, 9x8" 525.00
Figurine, Entrapped Cupid, rnd socle base, 1900, 8" 600.00
Figurine, Fire of Eros, 2 adults & cupids, ca 1880, 10" 875.00
Figurine, girl holds floral-filled bonnet, 1880s, 5" 320.00
Figurine, harlequin, dancing/holds flagon & hat, 10½" 300.00
Figurine, horse head, wht, on ebonized base, 7", pr 300.00
Figurine, Je Les Punis, 1900, 5¾" 225.00
Figurine, lady w/flower basket, Rococo, X-swords, 1890s, 7" ...775.00
Figurine, Leda & Swan, w/cupids & angels, 1900, 7½" 875.00
Figurine, Leda & Swan, w/kneeling cupid, 1870, 7" 850.00
Figurine, lovers/sheep/3 lg trees, #485/52, 1880s, 9½" 450.00
Figurine, man w/basket of fish & net, N-146/#121, 21½" 900.00

Figurine, putto holds 2 fish, kneels by baskets, 1880s, 4" 300.00
Figurine, putto sits on table by hearth w/kettle, 1900, 5" 300.00
Figurine, putto stands, flower basket in left arm, 1900, 5" 225.00
Figurine, rooster perched on melon, sgn, 1910, 15½" 1,300.00
Figurine, Spring, maid w/flower garland, 8" 300.00
Figurine, St George & Dragon, mk, 5½", pr 425.00
Figurine, Wine & Song, 2 putti, 1 w/ewer, 2nd w/drum, 5" ...350.00
Inkpot w/lid & stand, chinoiserie reserves on wht, 7" dia 660.00
Jar, HP bouquet/floral sprays on wht, flower finial, 15" 300.00
Jardiniere, scenic panels/florals w/gold, w/lid, AR mk, 18" ...975.00
Lamp, 3 putti support basketweave font, pk satin shade, 13" .1,100.00
Plate, birds & insects, cobalt/gold rim, X-swords, 9½" 110.00
Plate, floral medallions, gold scallop, X-swords, 12" 265.00
Plate, floral spray, openwork/floral-reserve border, 9½" 90.00
Plate, floral sprays, gold scalloped rim, X-swords, lg 95.00
Plate, floral w/butterflies, scalloped, struck swords, 9½" 55.00
Plate, floral w/gold, X-swords, 6¾" 25.00
Plate, grapes & vines in relief w/gold, X-swords, 11½" 125.00
Plate, grapes & vines in relief w/gold, X-swords, 8½" 55.00
Plate, leaves relief, wht on cobalt, X-swords, 12" 200.00
Plate, rose/butterflies/bugs, cobalt on wht, X-swords, 9½" 110.00
Platter, X-swords in pattern, X-swords mk, 21x15" 295.00
Platter, 3 floral sprays in cavetto, scalloped, 12" dia 150.00
Salt cellar, boy sits amid 2 baskets, X-swords, ca 1750 ....550.00
Sweetmeat, ea modeled as 18th-century lady or man, 7", pr ...900.00
Vase, floral w/gold borders, urn form, X-swords, 10" 150.00
Vase, 2 scenic panels, AR mk, 12" 485.00

Mercury Glass

Mercury glass was popular during the 1850s and enjoyed a short revival at the turn of the century. It was made with two thin layers, either blown with a double wall or joined in sections, with the space between the walls of the vessel filled with a mixture of tin, lead, bismuth, and mercury. The opening was sealed to prevent air from dulling the bright color. Though most examples are silver, blue and gold can be found on occasion.

Bottle, vintage eng, amber-flashed cut neck, bulbous, 7½" 175.00
Bowl, ruffled rim, 3" 20.00
Candlesticks, bl, 14", pr 100.00
Candlesticks, teardrop stem, domed base, 6", pr 80.00
Compote, gold, knop stem, 8¼" 100.00
Match holder 37.50

Mythological group, man and lady with torch, angel and seated Fortuna, late 1800s, 15", $800.00.

Child's mug with leaves, $55.00.

Figurine, Night, ca 1860, 22", EX 1,600.00
Figurine, nude stands by tree stump, Scheurich, 1920, 14" ...1,200.00
Figurine, putto holds grapevine in both hands, 1915, 5" 200.00

Pitcher, eng floral, clear hdl, early, water sz 225.00
Salt, master; silver, gold int, initials on plug, 2½" 85.00
Salt, silver w/gold lining, HP foliage, 2⅞" 25.00
Spooner, HP floral 40.00
Toothpick holder 32.00

Vase, floral sprays in panel, mc on silver, 10", pr 200.00
Vase, ftd tumbler form, 6" 45.00
Vase, HP deer & foliage, bulbous, 7" 35.00
Witch ball, 18", +stand 150.00

Merrimac

Founded in 1897 in Newburyport, Massachusetts, the Merrimac Pottery Company primarily produced tile and gardenware. In 1901, however, they introduced a line of artware that is now attracting the interest of collectors. Marked examples carry an impressed die-stamp or a paper label, each with the firm name and the outline of a sturgeon, the Indian word for which was Merrimac.

Vase, gr drip over olive, swollen cylinder, 11", EX 400.00
Vase, gr matt w/feathering, sm flaring neck, 5" 150.00
Vase, gr matt w/feathering, 4¼" 130.00
Vase, gr-wash top/dripping yel band over rust, rpr, 10x10" 850.00
Vase, leaves, appl, squat/bulbous, sgn EG, dtd 1903, 2½x4" ... 700.00
Vase, orange-red clay w/clear overglaze, imp mk, 4½x8", NM .. 110.00
Vase, 3 open crocus on slim stems, gr mottle, 4½", NM 400.00

Vase, mottled green with relief crocus, signed EG (?), 4½", near-mint condition, $400.00.

Metlox

The Metlox Manufacturing Company was founded in 1927 in Manhattan Beach, California, but it was not until the forties that they began producing the dinnerware for which they have become famous.

Well-known sculptor Carl Romanelli designed artware in the late 1930s and early 1940s (and again briefly in the 1950s). His work is especially sought after today.

Our advisor for this category is Jack Chipman; he is listed in the Directory under California.

Antique Grape, creamer & sugar bowl, w/lid 12.50
Antique Grape, cup & saucer 7.00
Antique Grape, plate, 10½" 6.00
California Ivy, bowl, fruit; 5¼" 6.00
California Ivy, chop plate, 13" 20.00
California Ivy, cup & saucer 7.50
California Ivy, plate, 10" 7.50
California Ivy, plate, 6" 3.50
California Ivy, platter, oval, 13" 20.00
California Ivy, soup, 7" 8.50
California Ivy, sugar bowl 10.00
California Provincial, bowl, divided vegetable 30.00
California Provincial, bread tray 35.00

California Provincial, chop plate, rnd 25.00
California Provincial, pitcher, milk; 1-qt 35.00
California Provincial, plate, salad 4.00
Cookie jar, clown 45.00
Cookie jar, dog's head, Cockapoo 30.00
Cookie jar, Raggedy Andy 35.00
Cookie jar, rose 35.00
Cookie jar, squirrel on stump 28.00

Figure of an Indian, Romanelli, 9", $65.00.

Fruits, canister set, wood lids, 4-pc 75.00
Homestead Provincial, bowl, divided vegetable; hdld 27.50
Homestead Provincial, bowl, vegetable; open, 10" 17.50
Homestead Provincial, bread server 20.00
Homestead Provincial, candlestick 12.00
Homestead Provincial, coffeepot 40.00
Homestead Provincial, creamer & sugar bowl, w/lid 20.00
Homestead Provincial, cup & saucer 10.00
Homestead Provincial, gravy bowl 15.00
Homestead Provincial, match holder, wall hanging 25.00
Homestead Provincial, mug, lg 12.50
Homestead Provincial, mustard, part of cruet set 17.50
Homestead Provincial, plate, dinner sz 7.50
Homestead Provincial, plate, 6" 4.00
Homestead Provincial, platter, oval, 13½" 17.50
Homestead Provincial, shakers, milk-can style, pr 12.50
Red Rooster Provincial, ash tray, 8" 10.00
Red Rooster Provincial, bowl, salad; 11½" 20.00
Red Rooster Provincial, chop plate, 13½" 15.00
Red Rooster Provincial, egg cup 15.00
Red Rooster Provincial, plate, dinner; 10" 9.00
Red Rooster Provincial, plate, salad; 7" 5.00
Red Rooster Provincial, platter, oval, 11" 10.00
Red Rooster Provincial, tureen, soup; w/ladle, rare 100.00
Romanelli artware, figure of cowgirl, 9½" 75.00
Romanelli artware, sea horse vase, 9¼" 45.00
Romanelli artware, swordfish vase, 9" 45.00
Romanelli artware, waterbearer bud vase, 9¼" 60.00
Sculptured Grape, bowl, fruit, 6¼" 5.00
Sculptured Grape, bowl, vegetable; oval, 9½" 12.50
Sculptured Grape, creamer & sugar bowl, w/lid 17.50
Sculptured Grape, cup & saucer, coffee 7.50
Sculptured Grape, plate, dinner, 10½" 6.00
Sculptured Grape, soup, flat, 8" 7.00

Mettlach

In 1836 Nicholas Villeroy and Eugene Francis Boch, both of whom were already involved in the potting industry, formed a partnership and established a stoneware factory in an old restored abbey in Mettlach, Germany. Decorative stoneware with in-mold relief was their specialty, steins in particular. Through constant experimentation, they developed innovative methods of decoration. One process, called chromolith, involved inlaying colorful mosaic designs into the body of the ware. Later, underglaze printing from copper plates was used. Their stoneware was of high quality, and their steins won many medals at the St. Louis Expo and early world's fairs. Most examples are marked with an incised castle and the name 'Mettlach.' The numbering system indicates size, date, stock number, and decorator. Production was halted by a fire in 1921 — the factory was not rebuilt.

Our advisor for this category is Ron Fox; he is listed in the Directory under New York.

Key:
L — liter   PUG — print under glaze

Armorial charger, crest of 14 German states, #2013, 27" diameter, $15,000.00.

#1044/1014, plaque, PUG, Munich Child/walking steins, 17" . . 700.00
#1044/1143, plaque, PUG, drinking cavaliers, 17", M 600.00
#1044/1144, plaque, PUG, drinking cavaliers, Schlitt, 17", M . 600.00
#1044/1205, plaque, PUG, drinking cavaliers, 17½", M 600.00
#1044/411, plaque, PUG, barmaid, 15", M 250.00
#1048, plaque, etched, king on throne w/attendants, 16" 650.00
#1108, plaque, etched, Rhine castle, gold rim, 1895, 17" 900.00
#1132, stein, etched, violinist, ½-L 500.00
#1180, stein, relief, branchwork & verse, ½-L, M 150.00
#1191, stein, mosaic, ½-L, M 350.00
#1395, stein, etched, cards, ½-L, M 500.00
#1431½, stein, PUG, pipe & verse, ½-L, M 200.00
#1526, stein, PUG, cavalier & verse on gray, 1-L, M 300.00
#1526, stein, PUG, Munich Child, ¼-L, M 200.00
#1526/1145, stein, PUG, cavalier, ½-L 200.00
#1526/1502, stein, PUG, soldiers, base chip, ½-L, M 200.00
#1526/592, stein, PUG, couple & verse, ½-L, M 200.00
#1526/663, stein, PUG, beekeeper occupational on gray, ½-L . 300.00
#1526/7201, stein, PUG, man eating w/Munich Child, ½-L . . . 250.00
#1566, stein, etched, highwheeler, ½-L, M 800.00
#1642, stein, etched, man drinking, Warth, ½-L, M 300.00

#1645, stein, etched, mandolin player, base flake, 1-L 300.00
#1698, stein, etched, storefront, ½-L, M 300.00
#1725, stein, etched, lovers, sgn Warth, ¼-L, M 350.00
#1759, stein, relief, innkeeper, mc, 1-L, M 400.00
#1786, stein, etched, St Florian, no head, 1-L, M 700.00
#1830, stein, etched, cavalier, 2-L, M 1,200.00
#1909, stein, PUG, Bartholomay's Rochester, .3-L, M 100.00
#1909/1009, stein, PUG, dwarfs at wine press, ½-L, M 265.00
#1909/702, stein, PUG, Gambrinus on parade, flake, ½-L 300.00
#1934, stein, etched, soldiers, ½-L, M 800.00
#1997, stein, etched & PUG, portrait in shield, ½-L 300.00
#2001-A, book stein, lawyer, ½-L 500.00
#2001-B, book stein, doctor, ½-L, M 500.00
#2001-F, book stein, architect, glaze flake, ½-L 500.00
#2002, stein, etched, Munich Child & city, ½-L 385.00
#2024, stein, etched, Berlin, ½-L, M 600.00
#2065, stein, etched, cavalier & barmaid, Schlitt, 2-L 850.00
#2089, stein, etched, angel feeds man, Schlitt, ½-L, M 600.00
#2092, stein, etched, dwarf & clock, pewter lid, ½-L, EX 450.00
#2093, stein, etched, cards, ½-L 575.00
#2100, stein, etched, German & Roman soldier, sgn, .3-L, M . . 450.00
#2112, plaque, etched, dwarf in nest, Schlitt, 16", M 1,500.00
#2127, vase, etched, children dance in panel, hdls, 12½" 250.00
#2140/760, stein, PUG, 52 Infantry Regt, ½-L, M 600.00
#2146, plaque, etched, infantry men, Stocke, 15½", M 1,200.00
#2180/955, stein, PUG, cavaliers, Schlitt, 3-L, M 800.00
#2184/966, stein, PUG, dwarfs, ½-L 350.00
#2195, plaque, Rheinstein plaque, 17½", M 800.00
#2204, stein, relief, eagle w/Bl Max medal, mc, ½-L, M 500.00
#2206, stein, etched, tavern scene, 3-L 1,000.00
#2210, stein, relief, bowling scenes, 2-L, M 400.00
#2226, punch bowl, PUG, cavaliers, 2-L 400.00
#2271/1055, stein, PUG, drunken cavaliers, ½-L, M 300.00
#2277, stein, etched, Nurnberg, ½-L, M 500.00
#2281, stein, etched, 23rd Nat'l Guard Armory NY, ½-L 1,500.00
#2361-A, plaque, etched, Wartburg Castle, 17", M 1,000.00
#2362, plaque, etched, Heidelburg castle, tiny flake, 17" 800.00
#2373, stein, etched, St Augustine, alligator hdl, ½-L 700.00
#2391, stein, etched, Lohengrin, 1-L, M 2,000.00
#2391, stein, etched, Lohengrin, ½-L, M 800.00
#2394, stein, etched, Siegfried's youth, ½-L, M 800.00
#24, stein, relief, cavaliers, ½-L, M 250.00
#2402, stein, etched, Siegfried courting, ½-L 800.00
#2419/1044, stein, PUG, drunken judges, 5-L 1,200.00
#2448, pitcher, cameo, dancers, 2-L, M 250.00
#2479, stein, cameo, 3 knight scenes, flake, ¼-L 400.00
#2580, stein, etched, Die Kannenburg, 1-L, M 1,000.00
#2585, stein, etched, Munich Child, Munich in relief, 1-L 800.00
#2690, stein, etched, cavaliers & lions, 1½-L 1,400.00
#2715, stein, cameo, zither player & dancers, .3-L, M 450.00
#2740, plaque, etched, mother & baby centaur, 18½", M 1,600.00
#2765, stein, etched, knight on wht horse, Schlitt, 1-L 3,500.00
#280/678, stein, PUG, parade, ½-L, M 300.00
#2828, stein, relief, Wartburg on body & lid, ½-L 1,800.00
#2833-E, stein, etched, soldiers, ½-L, M 500.00
#2888, stein, etched, 3 men walking, 1-L, M 600.00
#2894, stein, etched, Heidelberg student, ½-L, M 2,000.00
#3085, stein, etched, postman, ½-L, M 350.00
#3182, plaque, etched, town of Hohkonigsburg, 17", M 1,100.00
#5165, plaque, Delft, Stolzenfels castle, 17½", M 400.00
#6, stein, relief, Germania, Moses & Noah, 1½-L 300.00
#6, stein, relief, Germania, Moses & Noah, 2-L, M 350.00
#7074, plaque, relief, cupid/lady, wht on gr, 1907, sq, 8" 395.00
#762, stein, relief, couple dancing, flakes, 1-L 250.00

#783, stein, relief, children playing, ½-L, M 250.00

Stein, carnival players and drinkers, signed Hienrich Schlitt, #2778, ½-L, $750.00.

Midwestern Glass

As early as 1814, blown glass was made in Ohio. By 1835 glasshouses in Michigan were producing similar pattern-molded types that have long been highly regarded by collectors. During the latter part of the 19th century, all six of the states of the Northwest Territory were mass-producing the pressed glass tableware patterns that were then in vogue. Various types of art glass were produced in the area until after the turn of the century. Items listed here are attributed to the Midwest by certain physical characteristics known to be indigenous to that part of the country. See also Findlay Onyx; Greentown Glass; Libbey; Zanesville Glass.

Bottle, aqua, 13 swirled ribs, EX impression, club form, 8¾" . . .225.00
Bottle, calabash; aqua, 24 right-swirl ribs, pontil, 10" 160.00
Bottle, club; aqua, 16 left-swirl ribs, collar mouth, 8" 130.00
Bottle, gold-amber, left swirl, rolled mouth, globular, 8" 400.00
Bottle, gold-amber, 24 right-swirl ribs, globular, 8" 350.00
Bottle, nursing; lt gr, 19-rib broken swirl, bulbous lip, NM 65.00
Creamer, dk gr-aqua, tooled rim, pontil, 1830-1850, 4" 475.00
Dish, yel-amber, inward-rolled rim, pontil, 1½x6" dia 550.00
Flask, aqua, 16 right-swirl ribs, pontil, lt stain, 6½" 170.00
Flask, chestnut; aqua, 18 swirl ribs, 5¼" 100.00
Flask, chestnut; bright gr, 24 vertical ribs, pontil, 5½" 1,100.00
Flask, chestnut; gold-amber, left swirl, sheared mouth, 4¾" 190.00
Flask, chestnut; gold-amber, 10-diamond, 4¾" 700.00
Flask, chestnut; gold-amber, 24 vertical ribs, pontil, 5½" 450.00
Flask, chestnut; lt gr, 18 vertical ribs swirl in neck, 6¾" 100.00
Flask, dk aqua, sheared mouth, ribs/swirls, ca 1830, 7¾" 150.00
Flip, bl-gr, plain rim, pontil, 6" 55.00
Plate, aqua, ribbed, folded rim, 8" 300.00

Militaria

Because of the wide and varied scope of items available to collectors of militaria, most tend to concentrate mainly on the area or areas that interest them most or that they can afford to buy. Some items represent a major investment and because of their value have been reproduced. Extreme caution should be used when purchasing Nazi items. Every badge, medal, cap, uniform, dagger, and sword that Nazi Germany issued is being reproduced today. Some repros are crude and easily identified as fakes, while others are very well done and difficult to recognize as reproductions. Purchases from WWII veterans are usually your safest buys. Reputable dealers or collectors will normally offer a money-back guarantee on Nazi items purchased from them. There are a number of excellent Third Reich reference books available in bookstores at very reasonable prices. Study them to avoid losing a much larger sum spent on a reproduction.

Our advisor for this category is Ron Willis; he is listed in the Directory under Oklahoma.

Imperial German

Badge, cap; Karpathenkorps, silver metal, 2-prong bk, M 40.00
Collartabs, red w/doubletress, gilt w/blk border, EX 12.00
Gorget, WWI, silver eagle w/silvered nickel chain, crown mk .235.00
Grenade, WWI, wire hdl, steel head, EX 130.00
Helmet, Curassier, all brass, 1-pc construction, EX 275.00
Helmet, Thuringen Infantry officer, leather, spike/crest, NM . .450.00
Identity disk, WWI, zinc oval w/raised letters, 10" 17.50
Jumper, drill; Kriegsmarine, wht herringbone, draw waist, NM .35.00
Leggings, WWI, mountain troop, padded, w/buckles, 1911, EX . .30.00
Medal, Berlin Shooting Society, silvered metal w/ribbon 22.00
Medal, War Service, Oldenburg miniature, EX 10.00
Medallion, WWI, gray metal, soldier silhouette, 1¾" dia 18.00
Patch, WWI, medic's specialty, yel embr on navy cloth, EX 12.00
Poster, WWI, memorial for fallen soldier, 15x20", EX 75.00
Service bar, Landwehr 2nd Class, crossed swords, 1842-1913 . . .14.00
Shoulderboards, Stellvertreter; WWI, red/gold on field gray 20.00
Sword, court; officer's, str etched blade, mk FH, +scabbard 125.00
Tunic, M-16, field gray, hidden buttons, slash pockets, EX 80.00
Tunic, WWI, blk ripcord, pk piping, EX 45.00
Watch fob, Iron Cross commemorative, wht metal, 1914-15 . . . .22.00

Third Reich

Award, Infantry shooting, Musterlager school, 1939, 11x16" 45.00

German Army arm band, with ink stamp, $25.00.

Axe, fireman's dress, wht metal w/blk hdl, mk E&H Horster . . .225.00
Backpack, fur-covered flap, gray canvas/brn leather, 1938 . . . . . .25.00
Badge, Anti-partisan, bronze, hollow, stamped, vertical, EX 180.00
Badge, Kriegsmarine Blockade Runner, narrow/vertical, mk 85.00
Badge, Kriegsmarine Destroyer, narrow vertical style, VG 55.00
Badge, Luftwaffe pilot, riveted 2-pc, hallmk, EX details 175.00

Badge, wound; Blk Condor Legion, stamped metal, blk pnt, EX .35.00
Bayonet, Army dress, 9½" blade, +frog/NCO trodell/scabbard ..50.00
Bayonet, fireman's dress, 9½" sawtooth blade, +frog/sheath ...195.00
Bayonet, K-98, Bakelite hdl, Waffenampt stamp, +webbed frog .35.00
Bayonet frog, K-98, blk leather, mk, dtd 1943, EX 15.00
Book, payment; contributors to SS, blk w/silver SS, EX 70.00
Boots, blk leather, w/strap/7-buckle top, toe cleats, VG 100.00
Buckle, belt; Luftschutz, 1-pc aluminum, EX 12.00
Buckle, belt; Red Cross officer's, 2-pc aluminum 95.00
Bust, Adolf Hitler, bronzed metal, 7½", VG 90.00
Cap, Afrikakorps overseas, embr Army eagle & cocard, EX 60.00
Cap, Army Panzer officer's overseas, field gray, embr eagle ...120.00
Cap, Luftwaffe, M-43, summer, embr trapezoid, 1944, EX 50.00
Cap, Luftwaffe Panzer officer's, M-43, blk wool w/bullion 650.00
Carrying case, Red Cross Medics, brn leather w/strap, 11x8x2" .35.00
Collartabs, SS Brigadefuhrer, aluminum wire on blk velvet 200.00
Dagger, Kriegsmarine officer's, etched blade, Eikhorn 250.00
Dagger, Red Cross officer's, yel hdl, unmk, EX, +scabbard 300.00
Desk, Luftwaffe bomber's, portable, leather top, 12x15", EX ...145.00
Drum, snare; Hitler Youth, brass body, mk Sonoi, EX 125.00
Emblem, National Sports, golden bevo embr on blk, EX 10.00
Flag, table; Vice Admiral, Iron Cross/blk dots on wht, sm 90.00
Gas mask, w/all straps, gray canister, spare lenses, EX 50.00
Gloves, Waffen & Army motorcycle, gray leather & cloth, EX ..30.00
Hanger, for SS dagger, blk leather, vertical style, mk 75.00
Helmet, Luftwaffe M-40, single decal, combat style, EX 80.00
Helmet, M-40, panzer gray pnt on steel, complete, EX 80.00
Helmet, Special RFSS, M-16 pattern, early 1930s, EX 1,250.00
Helmet cover, WWII, Waffen SS, spring loaded, reversible ...125.00
Hewer, Red Cross, sawtooth blade, +scabbard & leather frog .185.00
Hood, for Luftwaffe overcoat, bl-gray w/drawstring, NM 12.00
Jacket, Army or Luftwaffe, rain camo reverses to wht, EX 200.00
Jacket, Waffen SS, reversible spring/snow camo, EX 1,100.00
Knife, boot; Bakelite grips, 5¾" blade, +fiber case 80.00
Life preserver, WWII Luftwaffe, mk Schwimweste, VG 150.00
Magazine, Obersaltzberg, Hitler/Braun, 106-pg 15.00
Medal, Cossacks Cavalry Red Cross, stamped aluminum, EX ..95.00
Medal, Schlesien Eagle, gray-pnt medal, vertical, 3-pc 36.00
Mess kit, olive-drab pnt, dtd 1944, EX 20.00
Mug, beer; mk RFS in bl, ½-liter, EX 55.00
Necktie, Afrikakorps, gr, mk, EX 10.00
Pennant, Hitler Youth, diamond/running youth, 16x27", VG ...70.00
Pin, WWII, Flemish SS, wht metal w/blk enamel, EX 45.00
Plate, presentation; SS Allach Julfest, floral, 1942, NM 200.00
Post card, Hitler in Vienna photograph, 1938, EX 15.00
Rucksack, Afrikakorps, all canvas w/straps, D-rings, VG 60.00
Shield, Demjansk w/Luftwaffe cloth bk, heavy zinc, EX 70.00
Shirt, Afrikakorps, pullover w/4 buttons, no pockets, EX 85.00
Sleeve eagle, Waffen SS, tropical, tan embr on blk, EX 32.00
Smock, Luftwaffe sniper's, rain camo, non-reversible, VG 325.00
Sword, Army officer's, Eikhorn, EX 125.00
Tunic, Afrikakorps Infantry, w/breast eagle/collartabs, EX 165.00
Tunic, Army, summerweight gr herringbone w/embr eagle, EX .175.00
Tunic, Luftwaffe Flakfelfer, bl-gray, eagle/patches, lady's 200.00
Utensil set, aluminum, folding fork & spoon, EX 12.00

Japanese

Armband, Civil Defense commander's, EX 17.50
Award certificate, patriotic ladies' assoc, 1932, EX 10.00
Award document, for 1915 Enthronement medal, EX 35.00
Badge, Reserve, gilt star, anchor/Xd swords, lg, EX 17.50
Bayonet, Ariska, str crossguard, wood hdl, +scabbard 17.50
Bowl, Army, star on inside rim, 2x7", EX 15.00

Bowl, rice; Army, star on outside rim, 3x4¾", EX 20.00
Canteen, Army, complete w/stopper & straps 20.00
Cape, Army officer's, waterproof, w/hood & collartabs, EX 50.00
Dagger, officer's, gilt wash, sharkskin hdl, +scabbard, EX 100.00
Figure, Admiral Togo, bronze, 19½", EX 600.00
Foot locker, Army officer's, wood w/leather straps, EX 88.00
Gas mask, WWII, civilian's, complete w/straps & filter, EX 12.50
Gloves, olive drab wool, fur lined, EX 20.00
Grenade, glazed ceramic, body only, EX 40.00
Helmet, Army, model 1920, star on front, w/canvas liner, EX ...60.00
Helmet, Marine landing forces, mum emblem, camo net, EX ..150.00
Helmet, Tanker, complete w/liner & chinstrap, mk, EX 225.00
Jacket, Army Tanker cadet's, olive drab wool, 1944, EX 40.00
Medal, China Incident, complete w/ribbon & case, M 25.00
Medal, Order of Rising Sun, w/ribbon, +blk lacquered case 35.00
Medal, Order of Sacred Treasure, silver & enamel, w/ribbon 45.00
Medal, WWI Victory, complete w/ribbon, EX 80.00
Medal, 1894-95 War, bronze, complete in blk-lacquered case ..48.00
Medal, 1904-1905 War w/Russia, w/ribbon, NM 22.00
Medallion, Admiral Togo bust/warship on bk, 2", +case 155.00
Medallion, China War, gilt bronze, battle scene, +case 65.00
Meter, map; Army, roller discus calculater, 4 scales, EX 25.00
Passbook, Army, pre-WWII, EX 20.00
Raincoat, Army officer's, tan waterproof material, EX 35.00
Ribbon, Imperial Navy, from Donald Duck hat, EX 20.00
Saddlebag, brn leather, EX 20.00
Saki cup, Army Star, lacquered, 90mm, EX 12.50
Telescope, artillery spotting; 25x2 power, Nikko, +case 250.00
Tunic, Army, tropical, 1942, EX 35.00
Tunic & pants, Army officer's, w/collartabs, EX 150.00
Wings, Navy Pilot Defense Force, gilt/silver, pin-bk, NM 12.50
Wings, WWII, Army Air Corps, aluminum wire/gilt on bl 25.00
Wings, WWII, pilot's, yel/silver embr on bl, VG 30.00

United States

Badge, Air Force Fire Chief, wht metal/gilt, 2-pc, 2½" 15.00
Badge, Nat'l Guard recruiter, bronze, triple clutch-bk, 2" 7.50
Badge, Navy Co Commander, metal w/enamel, eagle/anchor ...32.00
Badge, Navy officer, Command at Sea, gilt metal, star/anchor ..10.00
Badge, WWII, Navy Sub Medical officer, Gensco, pin-bk 22.00
Bayonet, rifle; WWII, Marine, M1-Grand, EX, +scabbard 40.00
Book, WWII, Thirty Seconds Over Tokyo, 1st ed, EX 15.00
Boots, WWII, USN pilot, leather, EX 70.00
Canister, WWII, held chemicals for purifying sea water, EX 8.00
Canteen, WWII, aluminum w/canvas cover, EX 7.00
Cap, visor; Army officer's, olive drab w/braid, EX 20.00
Cap, visor; 1941 pattern olive-drab herringbone twill, M 20.00
Cap, WWII, engineer's, olive drab, red/wht piping, EX 20.00
Cape, WWII, Navy nurse's, navy bl wool w/red lining, EX 50.00
Cigarette lighter, Korean War, Navy, ship eng, Zippo 12.50
Collar brass, WWI, Infantry, Xd rifles, bronze, EX 8.00
Compass, WWII, Air Force pilot's, wrist type, Waltham, EX ...22.50
Field pack, WWII, Marine combat, olive-drab canvas, EX 25.00
Fishing kit, survival; Vietnam War, Air Force, complete 17.50
Flare bag, WWII AAF, A-6 type, w/compartments, VG 12.00
Flight bag, USAF, B-4 type, VG 20.00
Flight helmet, WWII AAF, B-6, leather w/fleece lining 45.00
Flight pants, WWII AAF, A-11 type, alpaca lined, VG 40.00
Flight suit, Vietnam, Nomex, EX 45.00
Flight suit, WWII, Army/Air Force, summer A-4, gabardine ...100.00
Gloves, WWII, Army/Air Force flier's, summer type B-3A, EX ..48.00
Goggles, WWII, gr plastic lenses, blk-pnt metal, early, EX 85.00
Goggles, WWII, Mark I, Wilson style, blk-pnt brass fr, EX 80.00

Handbook, pilot's, AT-6C & SNJ-4, dtd 1942, wing/prop cover .45.00
Helmet, Army, M-35, red pnt on steel w/Civil Defense emblem .17.50
Helmet, flying; WWII, Army/Air Force, A-9, cotton, EX 30.00
Helmet, Vietnam War, steel w/paratrooper-type liner, EX 75.00
Helmet, WWI, Marine Corps, emblem on front, gr pnt, EX ...125.00
Helmet, WWII, Army/Air Force flier's, sheepskin lined, EX 90.00
Insert, shoe; WWII, Army/Air Force, electric, Q-1, M 15.00
Insignia, collar; Army Infantry, brass, screw-bk, 1897-1901 ......8.00
Jacket, WWII, Marine Corps, Ike style, gr dress, EX 27.50
Jacket, WWII, Marine Corps, PFC chevrons/collar brass, lady's .36.00
Leggings, WWI, Army officer's, pigskin, eyelet lace-up, EX 15.00
Leggings, WWII, Marine Corps, tan canvas, NM 8.00
Life vest, WWII, aviator's Mae West type, B-4, EX 55.00
Light, survival; WWII, Army/Air Force, waterproof Bakelite ...12.50
Map, escape; WWII, Japan/Korea/E China Sea, unused, NM ...22.50
Medal, Army, Cuban Occupation, w/wrapped brooch, EX 85.00
Medal, Asiatic Pacific Campaign, early WWII type brooch, NM .12.00
Medal, Coast Guard, Expert Rifleman, w/ribbon 25.00
Medal, Marine Corps, China Service, complete w/ribbon, EX ...27.50
Medal, Navy Expeditionary, knob type w/ribbon, NM 12.00
Medal, WWII, Bronze Star, w/ribbon & WWII brooch, M 22.00
Medal, WWII, Navy, Good Conduct, type II, w/bar & ribbon ..25.00
Medal, WWII, Navy, Occupation, w/Asia bar, EX 12.50
Newspaper, Stars & Stripes, WWI, 1918 issue, 8-pg, EX 8.00
Packboard, WWII, Army, plywood & canvas, dtd, EX 27.50
Pouch, WWII, aviator's, for 45 revolver, waterproof, EX 17.50
Rations, survival; Air Force, 3 dehydrated bars in foil, EX 7.00
Rifle, training; Pettibone Bros, Civil War era, EX 160.00
Rucksack, WWII, mtn troop, tubular steel fr, complete, EX ...45.00
Scarf, WWII, Army officer's, tan wool knit, fringe, 10x46" 7.50
Shirt, WWII, Army, olive-drab wool, PFC stripes, EX 8.00
Shirt, WWII, Army officer's, common pattern, EX 7.50
Shoes, WWII, Army/Air Force flier's, sheepskin lined, EX 60.00
Shoulder bag, WWII, Marine, olive-drab canvas, 4x12x12" 17.50
Shoulderboards, WWII, Navy officer's, blk on gray, NM 15.00
Shovel, WWII, folding type, Ames, w/canvas case, VG 20.00
Sling, for Springfield rifle, VG 12.50
Trousers, WWII, Navy aviator's, sheepskin lined, +suspenders .100.00
Tunic, Army, bl dress, ca 1902, EX 65.00
Tunic, WWII, Marine Corps, gr dress, insignias/patches, EX 35.00
Tunic & pants, WWII, Army sergeant's, insignias/patches, EX ..27.50
Uniform, Korean-Viet Nam War, lady's dress, gr, 3-pc, EX 25.00
Vest, survival; WWII, Army/Air Force, C-1, 15 pouches, EX ...50.00
Wings, WWII, Navy flight surgeon, gold/silver, Vanguard, 2¾" .48.00
Wings, WWII, paratroop jumper's, sterling, EX 20.00
Wings, WWII, pilot's, pin-bk, sterling, 3" 35.00
Wristwatch, WWII AAF, pilot's, A-17 type, EX 95.00

Other Types

Australia, battle jacket, WWII, olive-drab wool, EX 30.00
Austria, medal, 1898 Golden Jubilee, w/triangular ribbon, M ...18.00
Austria, pants, post-WWII, Army, camo, non-reversible, EX ...32.00
Belgium, neck badge, Order of Crown 1897, commander's, EX .130.00
British, half wing, WWII, RAF bombadier, King's Crown 12.50
British, medal, Air Crew Europe Star, w/ribbon, NM 90.00
British, medal, Atlantic Star, WWII, complete w/ribbon, NM, ..25.00
British, medal, Burma Star, w/ribbon, NM 15.00
British, medal, WWI Victory, w/ribbon, NM 10.00
Czechoslovakia, medal, 25-yr Labor Service, bronze, EX 12.50
E Germany, collartabs, Army general's, bullion embr on gr 25.00
France, breast badge, Metropolitan paratrooper's, Drago, NM ...18.00
France, kepi, Army NCO's, powder bl w/maroon top, EX 22.00
France, medal, Legion of Honor, commander's, M in case 225.00

French Foreign Legion, tunic, pre-WWII, officer's, gr w/red ...135.00
Greece, medal, Balkan War 1912-1913, 5 bars & ribbon, EX ...80.00
Imperial Russia, medal, Blameless Service, silver w/ribbon 135.00
Imperial Russia, medal, Order of St George, silver cross 80.00
Italy, cap badge, WWII, Army overseas, eagle on olive drab 8.00
Italy, helmet, WWII, Army, no liner or strap, EX 12.00
Italy, medal, 1914-1918 War, w/WWI 2nd Armata ribbon, EX ..12.50
Korea, jacket, Vietnam War, Marines, camo, 2-pocket 32.00
Korea, shoulder insignia, Vietnam War, Army, tiger's head 12.50
Netherlands, Commemorative Cross, WWII, bar ribbon mt, NM 22.00
Netherlands, tunic, WWII, Infantry officer's, field gr, EX 30.00
New Zealand, gloves, Air Force pilot's, brn leather, NM 88.00
Poland, badge, WWII, Air Force signaler's, bronze w/silver 40.00
Poland, medal, Conquest of Berlin, w/service ribbon, EX 40.00
Rhodesia, field cap, Army, visored cotton camo w/neck flap 70.00
Russia, badge, WWII, Red Cross Proficiency, red/wht enamel ...17.50
Turkey, Star, Order of Jedjidjie, silver/enamel, X-lg 165.00
West Germany, wings, paratrooper officer's, aluminum/gilt 12.00

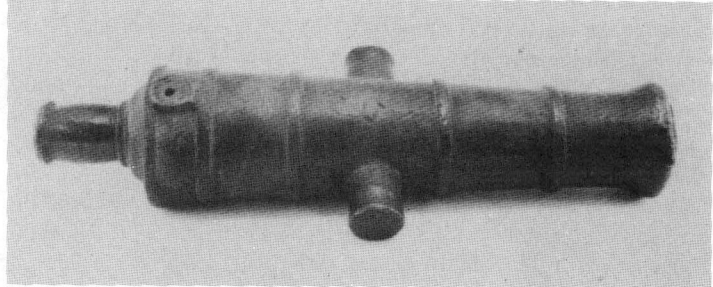

Cast bronze cannon barrel, early 1880s, 21" long, $325.00.

Milk Glass

    Milk glass is the current collector's name for milk-white opaque glass. The early glassmaker's term was Opal Ware. Originally attempted in England in the 18th century with the intention of imitating china, milk glass was not commercially successful until the mid-1800s. Pieces produced in the U.S.A., England, and France during the 1870-1900 period are highly prized for their intricate detail and fiery, opalescent edges. Opaque glass produced in colors is often referred to as 'blue milk glass,' etc. See also Animal Dishes with Covers; Bread Plates; Historical Glass; Vallerysthal; Westmoreland.

Bowl, Drunken Sailor, lattice rim, Atterbury, 3x9x7½" 50.00
Bowl, raised florals, reticulated rim, ca 1880, 4½x8½" 250.00
Box, clam form, red/gold decor, mk McKee 45.00
Compote, Apple Blossom, lattice edge 25.00
Compote, Scroll Hexagon, scalloped rim, Challinor, 8x8" 135.00
Covered dish, battleship, Dewey bust at top, 6½" L 95.00
Covered dish, battleship, L-466, EX orig gilt, 8" L 75.00
Covered dish, covered wagon, L-128, 6" L 125.00
Covered dish, drum, cannon finial, L-147, 4" dia, EX 60.00
Covered dish, Emblem/Eagle, L-55, 6½", EX 50.00
Covered dish, log cabin, orig held mustard, orig pnt/label 95.00
Covered dish, Uncle Sam on battleship base 45.00
Jar, canning; battleship Maine commemorative, no top, 5" 70.00
Jar, canning; owl, eagle on lid, minor rim chips, 6⅜" 115.00
Jar, Flaccus, elk head, orig insert, no band 200.00
Jar, milk; 3 bears dressed as humans, w/lid, 4", EX 110.00
Match holder, Indian, gold decor, 3" 130.00
Mug, Gooseberry, 1⅞" 30.00
Novelty, hatchet, 6" 12.00

Plate, anchor/cannon, porthole border, 7" 30.00
Plate, Ancient Castle 30.00
Plate, angel head, 9" 20.00
Plate, Apple Blossom, lattice edge, 10½" 25.00
Plate, California Golden Bear, slight underfill, 9" 110.00
Plate, chain/anchor border, sloop relief in center, 7½" 50.00
Plate, Columbus bust, 1492-1892, spades/clubs on rim, 9½" 35.00
Plate, Contrary Mule 30.00
Plate, Cupid & Psyche 38.00
Plate, Diamond & Shell 8.00
Plate, eagle/fleur-de-lis/flag openwork border, gilt, 7" 50.00
Plate, Easter Chicks, scroll/leaf border, 7" 35.00
Plate, Easter Ducks, 6" 25.00
Plate, Fleur-de-lis, dtd 35.00
Plate, Gothic, 9¼" 8.00
Plate, Indian Chief, swag/scallop border, 7" 42.50
Plate, Leaf & Scroll, sq 35.00
Plate, Niagara Falls, openwork leaf border, 7½" 40.00
Plate, Serenade 40.00
Plate, Sunken Rabbit 35.00
Plate, US Battleship, EX orig decor, 7" 50.00
Plate, WM Jennings Bryan, flag/star border, 7⅜" 120.00
Plate, Wm McKinley, bust in center, lattice border, 9" 110.00
Plate, Woof-Woof, 5½" 50.00
Plate, 3 Bears, 7¼" 38.00
Plate, 3 kittens, lattice border, opal ears 22.00
Plate, 3 owls, gold trim, dtd July 2, 1901 . . . . .30.00
Plate, 4 cherubs, lace border, 9" 17.00
Platter, fish, pat 1872, 10" 28.00
Platter, Retriever, dog after bird, 13" 120.00
Shaker, Johnny Bull, w/orig lid 95.00
Sugar bowl, Roman Cross 10.00
Vase, Mephistopheles, 2" horns, pointed ears, 8½" 55.00

Tray, Actress, blue washed and gilded, 11", $75.00.

Millefiori

Millefiori was a type of art glass produced during the late 1800s. Literally, the term means 'thousand flowers,' an accurate description of its appearance. Canes, fused bundles of multicolored glass threads such as are often used in paperweights, were cut into small cross sections, arranged in the desired pattern, refired, and shaped into articles such as cruets, lamps,

and novelty items. It is still being produced, and many examples found on the market today are of fairly recent manufacture. See also Paperweights.

Cup and saucer, $100.00.

Dish, swan form, gold flecks, appl eyes, 6x5" 65.00
Lamp, hanging; 6" shade, wrought iron fittings, 26" 195.00
Lamp, table; mushroom shade, dbl-gourd base, 18" 325.00
Paperweight, teapot form, solid, 3x5" 135.00
Shoe, ruffled, frosted, sm 95.00
Tumbler, bl ground, 4" 125.00
Vase, mc canes w/clear opal windows, 5" 150.00
Vase, stick neck, 8" 75.00

Miniatures

There is some confusion as to what should be included in a listing of miniature collectibles. Some feel the only true miniature is the salesman's sample; other collectors consider certain small-scale children's toys to be appropriately referred to as miniatures, while yet others believe a miniature to be any small-scale item that gives evidence to the craftsmanship of its creator. For salesman's samples, see specific category; other types are listed below. See also Dollhouses and Furnishings; Children's Things.

Ranking at the top of today's leading collectibles, scaled 1:12" miniatures represent the work of hundreds of artisans who supply local shops with highly prized one-of-a-kind articles and specialties, all scaled one inch to the foot. Many leading producers and distributors of collectibles have entered the field as well. Clubs for miniature enthusiasts have sprung up throughout the United States, Canada, and abroad. Authority Lillian Baker has compiled a lovely book, *Creative and Collectible Miniatures*, with many full-color photos; you will find her address in the Directory under California.

Armchair, 2 arched splats, splint seat, red rpt, 15½", EX 225.00
Bandbox, wht/gray fruit on navy & yel wallpaper, 1800s, 4½" . .325.00
Blanket chest, pine w/brn grpt over gr, dvtl, till, 12" L 300.00
Blanket chest, pine w/orig gr pnt, trn ft, dvtl, 12½" L 400.00
Book, snap-lock scrolls front & bk, 3 leaves, dtd 1896, 1x⅞" 28.00
Box, pine w/gr pnt & 3-color floral, dome top, 3¼", EX 65.00
Bureau, walnut, 3-drw, porc knobs/ornaments, 1850s, 15" 300.00
Candlelabrum, 3-light, crystal 20.00
Chamberstick, opal glass, ornate hdl, Sandwich, 2" 110.00

Chest of drw, curly maple Fed 4-drw/bracket ft, 1820s, 12" ..1,300.00
Chest of drw, mahog Chpndl bow front, 3-drw, 1800, 12x11" ..200.00
Dresser, orig bl-gr pnt, wood pulls, 3-drw, 1880, 11x12" 1,500.00
Dresser, walnut/pine, attached mirror, 3-drw, 1850s, 21" 200.00

Grain-painted Empire bureau, old repair, 10", $325.00.

Pot, tole, worn red pnt, loose hinge, 2⅜" 150.00
Printing press, CI, 6½" 65.00
Tea table, tilt top, vase/ring post on tripod, 1800s, 13" 275.00
Wash set, florals w/gold on lt pk, 7-pc 195.00

Minton

Thomas Minton established his firm in 1793 at Stoke on Trent and within a few years began producing earthenware with blue-printed patterns similar to the ware he had learned to decorate while employed by the Caughley Porcelain Factory. The Willow pattern was one of his most popular. Neither this nor the porcelain made from 1798 to 1805 was marked (except for an occasional number series), making identification often impossible.

After 1805 until about 1816, fine tea services, beehive-shaped honey pots, trays, etc. were hand decorated with florals, landscapes, Imari-type designs, and Neoclassic devices. These were often marked with crossed 'L's. From 1816 until 1823, no porcelain was made. Through the twenties and thirties, the ornamental wares with colorful decoration of applied fruits and florals and figurines in both bisque and enamel were usually left unmarked. As a result, they have been erroneously attributed to other potters. Some of the ware that was marked bears a deliberate imitation of Meissen's crossed swords. From the late twenties through the forties, Minton made a molded stoneware line — mugs, jugs, teapots, etc. — with florals or figures in high relief. These were marked with an embossed scroll with an 'M' in the bottom curve. Fine parian ware was made in the late 1840s, and in the fifties Minton perfected and produced a line of quality majolica for which they gained widespread recognition. During the Victorian era, M.L. Solon decorated pieces in the pate-sur-pate style, often signing his work; these examples are considered to be the finest of their type. After 1862 all wares were marked 'Minton' or 'Mintons,' with an impressed year cipher. See also Majolica; Pate-Sur-Pate.

Bowl, floral reserves on cobalt w/gold, #499, 1810, 12½" 1,400.00
Bowl, vegetable; Gold Rose, w/lid 65.00
Chess piece, girl warrior, ca 1800 ....25.00
Cup & saucer, demitasse; Cockatrice 18.00
Figurine, Sea Breezes, ivory & bronze on porc, 9" 195.00
Jug, mk Society of Arts Prize Jug 1846 No 300, 5" 150.00
Plaque, man in robe looks down valley, mc, 24x12" 380.00
Plate, pate-sur-pate, 3 bl reserves, sgn Birks, 10" 150.00
Plate, salad; Cockatrice, turq 12.00

Plate, scene on wht, gilt swag, pk border, 1800s, 9", 12 for 400.00
Tile, King Henry, 6" 65.00
Tile, Taming of the Shrew, 6" 65.00
Urn, romantic reserve on bl, gilt rings/chains, 19", pr 2,475.00
Vase, rose garlands/vignettes, scroll hdls, sq ped ft, 8" 190.00
Vase, rustic landscape reserve on royal bl, hdls, 1835, 10" 325.00

Mirrors

The first mirrors were made in England in the 13th century of very thin glass backed with lead. Reverse-painted glass mirrors were made in this country as early as the late 1700s and remained popular throughout the next century. The simple hand-painted panel was separated from the mirrored section by a narrow slat, and the frame was either the dark-finished Federal style or the more elegant, often-gilded Sheraton.

Mirrors changed with the style of other furnishings; but whatever type you purchase, as long as the glass sections remain solid, even broken or flaking mirrors are more valued than replaced glass. Careful resilvering is acceptable if excessive deterioration has taken place.

Key:
Emp —— Empire   Hplwht —— Hepplwhite
Fed —— Federal   QA —— Queen Anne

Chip-cvd chestnut, rnds/half-rnds/dmns, 1800s, 8½x9" 353.00
Chpndl mahog/pine scroll, cvd/gilt shell in crest, 41x22" 1,200.00
Chpndl mahog/pine scroll, flame grain, rpl, 34" 1,100.00
Chpndl mahog/pine scroll, gilt gesso/phoenix finial, 51" 4,500.00
Chpndl mahog/pine scroll, label: S Cariss, 36x20" 1,100.00

Walnut veneer Chippendale, mid-1700s, 44", $3,000.00.

Courting, Fed, pnt/cvd columns/hearts/etc, cornice, 12" 4,750.00
Emp convex, foliage/acorns cvg, eagle atop, gesso/gilt, 32" ...2,500.00
Emp tiger maple fr, rpl glass, 30x20" 550.00
Fed architectural, acanthus/rope cvd ½-columns, 37" 275.00
Fed architectural, mahog, acorn drops, rvpt, reed sides, 32" ...300.00
Fed architectural, 3-panel rvpt w/seashells & compote, 40" 180.00
Fed mahog, molded cornice over inlaid panel, 36x16½" 275.00

Geo II walnut/parcel gilt, eagle finial, mfg label, 60" 1,000.00
Hired man's, rectangular, ring at top of fr, 1800, 5½x8" 65.00
Hplwht, gilt filigree crest w/urn & flowers, EX orig, 19½" . . 13,500.00
Italian Baroque-style giltwood, acanthus/shell cvg, 34" 475.00
Mahog scroll, molded fr, 4 ears rpl/rpr crest, 19x12" 225.00
Mahog scroll w/line inlay, gilt liner, rpl/rfn, 29x16" 450.00
Mahog scroll w/line inlay, old finish & glass, 1800s, 32x17" . . . 400.00
Pine, gilded, 48x24½" 60.00
Plateau, bronze, ornate hdl, fancy ft, 14" 195.00
Plateau, SP scrolls, cut-out sides, miniature, 8" 70.00
QA, walnut veneer on pine, scrolled/cut-out crests, 31x13" . . 1,750.00
QA pine, molded fr & scrolled crest, worn, 24x13½" 800.00
QA pine, worn red pnt, floral decor, rpr, 18x11" 2,800.00
QA walnut, gilt shell in crest, rpr/re-gilt, 28" 1,400.00
QA walnut scroll, EX open-cvd/gilt crests & sides, 52x26" . . 3,250.00
QA-style mahog, 3 gilt petals in ornate crest, 1875, 32" 200.00
QA-style tiger maple, scroll/arch pediment, 46½" 250.00
Shaving, Geo III mahog, shield-form glass, serpentine case 300.00
Shaving, Hplwht mahog w/inlay, lacy pulls, rfn, 24x19" 300.00
Shaving, Hplwht mahog w/inlay edge, 3-drw/oval mirror, 20" . 275.00
Shaving, Hplwht mahog w/line inlay, dvtl drw, rfn/rpr, 14" . . . 225.00
SP, Nouveau cherubs, heart shape, Dominick & Haff, 17½" . 1,650.00
Victorian hall, plaque shape w/sm mirror, horn coat hooks 100.00

Mocha

Mocha Ware is a utilitarian pottery made principally in England (and to a lesser extent in France) between 1780 and 1840 on the then prevalent creamware and pearlware bodies. Initially, only those pieces decorated in the seaweed pattern were called 'Mocha,' while geometrically-decorated pieces were referred to as 'Banded Creamware.' Other types of decorations were called 'Dipped Ware.' During the last thirty to forty years the term 'Mocha' has been applied to the entire realm of 'Industrialized Slipware' — pottery decorated by the turner on his lathe using coggle wheels and slip cups.

Mocha was made in numerous patterns — Tree, Seaweed or Dandelion, Rope (also called Worm or Loop), Cat's-eye, Tobacco Leaf, Lollypop or Balloon, Marbled, Marbled and Combed, Twig, Geometric or Checkered, Banded, and slip decorations of rings, dots, flags, tulips, wavy lines, etc. It came into its own as a collectible in the latter half of the 1940s and has become increasingly popular as more and more people are exposed to the rich colorings and artistic appeal of its varied forms of abstract decoration.

The collector should take care not to confuse the early pearlware and creamware Mocha with the later kitchen yellowware, graniteware, and ironstone sporting mocha-type decoration that was produced in America by such potters as J. Vodrey, George S. Harker, Edwin Bennett, and John Bell. This type was also produced in Scotland and Wales and was marketed well into the 20th century.

Bowl, earthworm on orange band, emb gr rim, EX 450.00
Bowl, seaweed, brn on buff band, minor staining, 3x6½" 325.00
Cup & saucer, seaweed on rust, oversize, cup: 2½x4¼" 1,300.00
Ewer, earthworm/coggled/whiplash bands, rpr chip, 8", NM . . . 600.00
Mug, allover brn/tan combings in rings, leaf hdls, 6", EX 600.00
Mug, earthworm/stripes on tan band, emb leaf hdl, 5", VG 300.00
Mug, marbleized brn, emb floral swags, rpr, 4½", VG 250.00
Mug, quasi-geometric, long/short brn lines, 5¾", EX 625.00
Mug, 4" wide quasi-geometric band, leaf-end hdl, 3", EX 600.00
Pepper castor, cat's eyes, bl/tan bands, ftd, 4½", EX 350.00
Pitcher, blk wavy lines/bl bands, late, 8", M 160.00
Pitcher, earthworm, wht on 2 bl bands, 6" 550.00
Pitcher, earthworm on wide gr-brn band, prof rpr, 6", pr 950.00

Pitcher, earthworm/emb bands, 4-color, stains/chips, 6⅜" 425.00
Pitcher, seaweed, blk on wide red band, prof rstr, 8" 775.00
Pitcher, seaweed on orange, brn bands, emb leaf hdl, 5", EX . . . 500.00
Pitcher, tulips/emb bands, 5-color, cracks/stains/rpr, 7" 825.00
Pitcher, 3-color 'leaf'/brn & emb gr bands, 6", EX 675.00
Punch bowl, tan band w/cat's eyes+earthworm band, rpr, 10" . . 900.00
Shaker, earthworm, brn/blk on bl/wht stripe band, chips, 4½" . 225.00
Shaker, earthworm, 3-color on gray band, minor chips, 4½" . . . 525.00
Shaker, seaweed, dk brn on tan band, chipped/rpr, 3⅞" 110.00
Shaker, seaweed, 4-color bands, lip/dome chips, 4½" 375.00
Waste bowl, squiggles, yel/dk brn on wht, 4x7", EX 375.00

Mug, earthworm on rust band, hairlines, 6", $795.00.

Molds

Food molds have become a popular collectible — not only for their value as antiques, but because they also revive childhood memories of elaborate ice cream Santas with candy trim, or barley sugar figurals adorning a Christmas tree. Ice cream molds were made of pewter and came in a wide variety of shapes and styles. Chocolate molds were made in fewer shapes but were more detailed. They were usually made of tin, copper, and occasionally of pewter. Hard candy molds were usually metal, although the primitive maple sugar molds (usually simple hearts, rabbits, and other animals) were carved from wood. Cake molds were made of cast iron or cast aluminum and were most common in the shape of a lamb, a rabbit, or Santa Claus.

Our advisors for this category are Dale and Ruth Van Kuren; they are listed in the Directory under New York.

Chocolate Molds

Baby, sitting 65.00
Basket, nearly str sides, 3x6½" 45.00
Boys wearing jumpsuits/caps, ea: 1x2", on 11x11" tray 40.00
Bugs Bunny, tin, 2x5¼" 14.00
Bunny, fat, 2-part, hinged, 7x8½" 40.00
Cherub on rocking horse, tin, hinged, mk Ringers, 3½" 65.00
Chocolate-covered cherries, ea: ¼" dia, on 11x11" tray 20.00
Christmas wreath, tin, 1½x1½" 7.00
Circus elephant, wearing a cap, 1½x3¾" 35.00
Clown, full figure, tin, 4x1½" 30.00
Cradle, 3-part, K-344 . . . . 40.00

Davy Crockett 75.00
Duck, 5x5" 48.00
Duck w/cap & bow tie, 2-part, tin, hinged, 7x5" 65.00
Duckling w/hat, 2-part, tin, 3¾x2¼" 35.00
Dutch boy, full figure, hinged, Holland mk, 6½x4½" 70.00
Easter egg, sits on 3 ft, CI, 2-part, early 1800s 95.00
Egg, cherub decor, sm 40.00
Egg, rabbit decor, med 45.00
Egg, webbing ea side, sm 35.00
Fireplace w/Noel, ea: 3x5¼" on 11x11" tray 70.00
Frogs, ea: 1½x2½" on 9¾x22" tray 50.00
George Washington, tin, 2½x1½" .15.00
Heart & flower, sheet style, mk Fabriek, 21½x9½" 65.00
Heart w/roses, tin, 2x2¼" 8.00
Hen, nesting, 2-part, 3x3½" 85.00
Hen, sitting, med 65.00
Horse, running, 4x3" 38.00
Hound dog, sitting, no mk, 2-part, 4½x5½" 60.00
Indian head, tin, 1½x1¾" 10.00
Jack-O'-lantern, tin, 2¾x2¾" 25.00
Kris Kringle, riding a horse 145.00
Lamb, standing, 2-part, hinged, 11x5" 50.00
Owl, 4½x3" 38.00
Rabbit, basket on bk, tin, Germany, 19x9½x4½" 110.00
Rabbit, clamped, 5-sided, no hinges, USA 40.00
Rabbit, clothes & umbrella, mk Anton Reich #26012, 4½x2½" .65.00
Rabbit, E-8000, 9½x18" 175.00
Rabbit, sits/flower at base, 2-part, hinged/heavy, 5½x9½" 75.00
Rabbit, sitting, sm 50.00
Rabbits in cars, 2-part, hinged, 6½x12" 50.00
Rabbits play saxaphones, ea: 3x5½", on 10x14" tray 68.00
Rabbits pull carts, hinged, 6x11½" 70.00
Rooster, E-8080, 7x8" 110.00
Santa, full figure, tin, 2½x2" 25.00
Santa, full figure, 2-part, tin, 7¼x3" 85.00
Santa & reindeer, 2-part, tin, 4x3¼" 50.00
Santa face, smiling, tin, 1¼x2" 15.00
Santa w/candy cane, 2-part, 3½x2" 15.00

Santa on donkey, 6½"; St. Nick on horseback, 7"; both marked Holland, $200.00 each.

Scotty dog, lg 95.00
Strip, birds, babies w/hats, ea: 2¼x3½", 16" L 135.00
Swan, lg 195.00
Teddy bear, med 170.00
Toddler, standing 85.00
Turkey, mk Eppelsheimer, 5x4" 65.00

Turtle, tin, 1½x2¼" 9.00

Hard Candy Molds

Boy in rowboat, TM-245, groove for stick, 1½x2" 48.00
Bust of Napoleon, TM-103, groove for stick, 1½x2" 68.00
Castle w/flag, #43, groove for stick, 1¾x1½" 72.00
Cat, sitting up, TM-222, groove for stick, 1¾x2" 58.00
Dog, howling, TM-249, groove for stick, 2¼x2¼" 52.00
Goat, jumping, TM-157, groove for stick, 1¾x2" 52.00
Horse, walking, tin, groove for stick, 1¾x3" 15.00
Lamb, TM-128, groove for stick, 1¼x2" 55.00
Lion, 3-part, TM-0040, groove for stick, 4x5" 110.00
Lion w/cubs, groove for stick, TM-248, 2x2" 65.00
Rooster, TM-243, groove for stick, 2x2¼" 50.00
Squirrel eating nut, TM-155, groove for stick, 2x2½" 62.00
Witch on broom, tin, groove for stick, 3¼x1½" 18.00

Ice Cream Molds

Alligator, highly detailed, S-394 . . . . .70.00
Apple, #238, med 20.00
Apples, K-102 . . . . .30.00
Apricot, CC-0018 . . . . .28.00
Arctic explorer, S-510, rare 110.00
Asparagus spear, E-223, 8¼" 42.00
Banana, #157 . . . . .35.00
Banjo, S-545 . . . . .50.00
Basket, #471 . . . . .45.00
Basket, fancy scrolls, #203 . . . . .25.00
Basket, oval, fluted, #204 . . . . .25.00
Basket, wicker, 3-part, K-598 . . . . .30.00
Bassinet, S&Co #203 . . . . .35.00
Billy goat, grazing 30.00
Bird's nest, E-945 . . . . .47.50
Bird's nest w/4 eggs, #552, 3" 25.00
Book, open, #957, 5" 30.00
Bride w/long flowing veil, E-1148 .58.00
Buddha, #476 . . . . .40.00
Camel, E-681 . . . . .78.00
Cat, sitting, S-170 . . . . .70.00
Cherries, #108, 4" 25.00
Chick, CC-0024, mk Brevete SGDC 34.00
Child of Spring, E-682 . . . . .68.00
Chrysanthemum, K-589 . . . . .35.00
Clover, 4-leaf, #335, 4" 25.00
Colonial lady's skirt, E-1185 . . . . .26.00
Corn in husk, S-270 . . . . .50.00
Cradle, 3-part, K-344 . . . . .40.00
Cucumber, E-226 . . . . .27.00
Cupid on wedding bell, E-1019 . . . . .34.00
Cupids, cracking eggs, E-1082 . . . . .66.00
Dahlia, #366, 3" 25.00
Duck, nesting, #622, 4" 30.00
Duck egg, K-188 . . . . .14.00
Easter egg, E-906 . . . . .25.00
Easter egg, E-907 . . . . .12.00
Egg, raised yolk, CC, 3" 25.00
Elephant, E-656 . . . . .50.00
Elk's head, 3-part, rare, K-493 . . . . .66.00
Fisherman sitting, #951, 5" 70.00
Football, 3-part, K-381 . . . . .35.00
Football player, K-491 . . . . .70.00
Goat, rearing, S-346 . . . . .78.00

Goose egg, K-298 . . . . .12.50
Grape cluster, #278, 5" 35.00
Halloween cat, raised bk, E-644 . . . . .55.00
Harp, aluminum, K-361, 1940s 30.00
Horn of plenty, E-1007 . . . . .45.00
Horse, rearing, E-639 .56.00
Indian, K-458, dtd 1896 . . . . .75.00
Lemon wedge, CC, 3" .20.00
Lettuce leaf, #1143, 4" 20.00
Liberty Bell, 4th of July, 1776, S-473 . . . . .35.00
Lilac flowerette 50.00
Lion's head, turned, CC, 3" 30.00
Lobster, E&Co, 5½" L 100.00
Lobster, K-330, sm 55.00
Locomotive, tender & 2 Pullman cars, EX 500.00
Masonic square & compass, K-323 . . . . .35.00
Medallion, British National Coat of Arm, K-564 . . . . .45.00
Medallion, orange relief, K-410 . . . . .22.00
Medallion, scalloped, fancy high-relief design, K-452 . . . . .30.00
Morning-glory, E-297 .34.00
Mother Hubbard, E-981, dtd 1890 . . . . .75.00
Napoleon, S-426 . . . . .60.00
Pear, E-248 . . . . .35.00
Piece of pie, E-1097 . . . . .40.00
Pineapple, K-156 . . . . .47.00
Ping-Pong balls, 4-part, K-592 . . . . .35.00
Ping-Pong racquet, K-591 . . . . .40.00
Plymouth Rock, E-995 . . . . .42.00
Potato, #154 . . . . .34.00
Potato, CC-0008, mk CC & Brevete 30.00
Pug dog, S-390 . . . . .65.00
Pup tent, S-515 . . . . .40.00
Ring, wedding; K-608 .35.00

Rose, #582, attributed to Krauss, $50.00.

Santa w/pack, 7" H 50.00
Shamrock, E-1039 . . . . .35.00
Slipper, 3-part, #570 . . . . .35.00
Slippers, S-284 . . . . .42.00
Sneakers, 3-part, S-382 . . . . .80.00
Thimble, K-372 . . . . .75.00
Tomato, CC-0022 . . . . .25.00
Truck, 1¼x2¾" 25.00

Valentine in envelope, E-1046, dtd 1896 . . . . . .60.00
Valentine in envelope, stamp/heart on front, K-506 . . . . .48.00
Wishbone, K-322 . . . . .50.00
Yellow Kid, K-476, rare 86.00

Maple Sugar Molds

Beaver, full-bodied, 1-pc cvg, 5x9" 150.00
Heart, wood, cvd design, ca 1890, 8x3¼" 135.00
Heart, wood, deeply-cvd tail, 2x11x4" 125.00
Heart w/ferns, wood, 1-pc cvg, rectangular, ca 1800, 4x7" 260.00
Hearts, wood, ornate cvg, 1800s, 1¾", 2½", & 3¼", EX 185.00
Openwork on rnd fluted cups, CI, 1840s, 12 in 11x16" fr 95.00
Strawberry, deeply-cvd pine, rectangle, 1830s, 1¾x5½x9" 150.00
Tin, 6 rnd crimped cups on rectangular tin plate, 6x9" 55.00
3 hearts, wood, deep cvg, rectangular, ca 1800, 22½x7" 440.00

Miscellaneous

CI, fish, 3-ftd, PA, ca 1890, 13x5½" 100.00
CI, pineapple w/geometrics, Albany Foundry, 1800s, 4½x6" . . .110.00
Copper, geometric w/cylinder center, 5" dia 85.00
Copper, Gothic arch, rnd ring w/hdl, early, 2½x5½" 40.00
Copper, jumping fish, 10" 115.00
Copper, Turk's head, dvtl, EX emb detail, 10½" dia 135.00
Copper/tin, abstract swirls, dvtl, oval, 4x7x4½" 150.00
Copper/tin, fruit design, scalloped sides, 11½x13½" 165.00
Copper/tin, lion, recumbent, oval, 5x6½x4½" 150.00
Copper/tin, pear, oval, 5" L 55.00
Copper/tin, pineapple, 6x4½" .65.00
Copper/tin, rose, oval, lt rust, 7" L 85.00
Copper/tin, roses & 3 leaves, oval, 7" 85.00
Copper/tin, sheaf of wheat, oval, lt rust, 6" 35.00
Copper/tin, starflower, 3¾" 40.00
Copper/tin, thistle, oval, 5x6½x4⅞" 110.00
Copper/tin, turtle, minor dents, 10½" L 165.00
Pewter, 8 designs, wood bk, springerle 225.00
Tin, fish, oval, lt rust, 9" L 55.00
Tin, fish, 11½" 95.00
Tin, melon shape, 2-pc 20.00
Tin, squirrel, ca 1900, 3x12x10" 36.00

Monmouth

The Monmouth Pottery Company was established in 1892 in Monmouth, Illinois. Their primary products were salt-glazed stoneware crocks, churns, and jugs, Bristol, spongeware, and brown glaze. In 1906 they were absorbed by a conglomerate called the Western Stoneware Company. Monmouth became their #1 plant and until 1930 continued to produce stoneware marked with their maple leaf logo. Items marked 'Monmouth Pottery Co.' were made before 1906; after the merger, 'Co.' was dropped, and 'Ill.' was substituted.

Ash tray, gray, advertising, 3 sets of ftprints, 9" 10.00
Basket, emb bow, 7½" 18.50
Birdbath ornament, frog on stump form, buff, 1930s, 8x6" 90.00
Bowl, mixing; rust-orange, sponging, 12-panel, 3x7¼" 50.00
Cookie Jug 25.00
Jardinere, Aztec, 7" 65.00
Mug, short, squat, band around center, mk 5.00
Pitcher, brn, 6" 10.00
Pitcher, cobalt, water sz 16.00
Vase, Lotus, gray & bl, 8" 20.00

Vase, brown glaze, rope-trimmed handles, 12", $65.00.

Monot and Stumpf

The firm of Monot and Stumpf was organized in 1868, the merger of the E.S. Monot and F. Stumpf glassworks; it was located in Pantin, France. They produced fine art glass of various types until circa 1892, when the company reorganized and became known as the Cristallerie de Pantin.

Bowl, pk opaline, twist brass fr w/claw ft, 6" 395.00
Salt cellar, brn opal w/tan edge, gold int, 1½x1⅞" 65.00
Vase, cranberry, irid int, swirled, 4½" 185.00

Mont Joye

Mont Joye was a type of acid-cut French cameo glass produced by Cristallerie de Pantin in Paris around the turn of the century. It is accented by enamels.

Our advisor for this category is Don Williams; he is listed in the Directory under Iowa.

Planter, gold decor on gr frost, 7½" 250.00
Rose bowl, HP violets on frost/clear, 4½x4" 400.00

Vase, acid-cut and gilded chrysanthemums on green, 10", $425.00.

Vase, acorns, gold on gr frost, 13½" 425.00
Vase, cluster flowers, gold w/gr leaves on raisin, 12" 400.00
Vase, floral, gold on gr, mk, 6" 375.00
Vase, floral, lav/gold on textured frost, cylinder, 12" 450.00
Vase, leaves/berries, bl & gold on gr texture, 20" 600.00
Vase, poppies, enamel/gilt on frost, flat flanged rim, 20" 1,000.00

Moorcroft

William Moorcroft was an English potter who worked for MacIntyre Potteries from 1897 to 1913, signing his pieces with his last name or 'W. M.' In 1913 he established a workshop in Burslem, England, where he produced tablewares and a line of fine Art Nouveau vases, bowls, etc., which until 1919 were marked with the printed or impressed block lettered 'Moorcroft, Burslem.' After that, the patented 'W. Moorcroft' signature mark was used, and after 1921 'Made in England' was added. Note: Except for pieces with the salmon-pink ground, all of William's work was signed. Those he refused to sign because he personally did not like them.

William Moorcroft died in 1945, and his son Walter continued in the business. Walter soon created his own designs, but he signed only the larger examples. Today W. Moorcroft Ltd. continues to use many of the same methods of hand-applied, slip-trailed decoration that William developed. Walter recently retired, and his brother William John is presently in charge of the company. He is developing his own designs that are introducing a new look to the Moorcroft line.

Bowl, fish/seaweed, red/bl mottle, ftd, imp mk/sgn WM, 6½" ..750.00
Bowl, Florian, poppies, yel/gr on bl, ca 1898, 8½" 700.00
Bowl, mushrooms, red/yel/bl on dk ground, script mk, 8½" 850.00
Bowl, orchids on wht, sgn Walter/MIE, w/lid, 3x6" 175.00
Bowl, pomegranates on dk bl, sgn WM/MIE, 5x6½" 300.00
Box, berries, purple/pk/yel/gr on bl, sgn WM/MIE, 5" dia 225.00
Box, cigarette; iris, burgundy on wht, Walter/imp mk, 2x4¾" ...40.00
Box, pomegranate/berries on dk bl, script mk, 7¾" L 250.00
Dish, orchids on wht, sgn Walter/MIE, w/lid, 3x6" 50.00
Jar, poppies, mc on bl, dome lid, 1940, 8", NM 300.00
Jardiniere, 3 heart/vine reserves, lav/bl on gr, 1914, 10" 700.00
Lamp base, anemones on bl to gr, sgn Walter, ca 1949, 9¾x8" .125.00
Lamp base, orchids, mc on dk bl, script mk/MIE/label, 9½" 125.00
Match holder, thistle blooms/coat of arms, 1897-1913 mk, 3" ..350.00
Pitcher, floral, purple/pk on gr, script mk/MIE, 5¾" 225.00
Sugar bowl, crocus, pk/yel on gr, Walter/imp mk, 2½" 30.00
Teapot, berries/lg leaves, mc on dk bl, sgn WM, 6" 250.00
Vase, berries/leaves on gr & dk bl, script mk/imp mk, 6½" 200.00
Vase, floral, pk/purple on dk bl, sgn WM/imp mk/MIE, 5" 150.00
Vase, Florian, bl/gr poppies, bottle neck, MacIntyre, 10" 440.00
Vase, Florian, bl/yel on bl, cylindrical, 1914, 10" 350.00
Vase, Florian, red daisies, MacIntyre, ca 1902, 5½" 400.00
Vase, Florian, wht floral on lt/dk bl, script mk, 3½" 275.00
Vase, Florian, wild roses, lt/dk bl, slender neck, 10" 700.00
Vase, fruit, red/bl/orange on dk bl, script mk/MIE, 8" 375.00
Vase, Gesso Faience, stylized leaves, 1898, 6" 450.00
Vase, Hazeldene, hills/trees, moonlit bl, 1925, 8" 600.00
Vase, Hazeldene, silver rim, squat ovoid, 1925, 2½" 300.00
Vase, Honesty, allover stippling, dk/lt bl, Florian mk, 6" 775.00
Vase, lg floral, red/purple on dk bl & gr, Walter/imp mk, 7½" ..100.00
Vase, orchids, pk on dk bl, paper label, sgn Walter, 3¾" 50.00
Vase, orchids, pk/yel/bl/gr on dk bl, Walter/imp mk, 3¾" 50.00
Vase, pansies, reddish-purple on dk bl, ca 1913-16, 5¾" 300.00
Vase, pansies on dk bl, script mk/imp mk/MIE, M-18, 8½" 400.00
Vase, pomegranates, mc on dk bl, silver collar/rim, 10" 500.00
Vase, pomegranates, mc on dk bl, WM/MIE, 6x6½" 300.00
Vase, pomegranates, pk/bl on dk bl, sgn WM/MIE, 5¾x3" 200.00

Vase, pomegranates, 1918-1929 mk, 7x3½" 285.00
Vase, pomegranates/berries, bulbous/slim neck, ca 1914, 13" . . .770.00
Vase, poppies, lav on lt bl, baluster form, ca 1935, 9" 285.00
Vase, poppies, red/purple on dk bl, sgn Walter/MIE, 5½" 100.00
Vase, prunus blossoms on red, script mk/#59, 9" 770.00
Vase, trees/lake/hills, tan on bl, imp mk/sgn WM in bl, 12" . .1,200.00

Vase, 4-color mushrooms on green, impressed Moorcroft, Made in England, paper label, 14", $2,450.00.

Morgan, Matt

From 1883 to 1885, the Matt Morgan Art Pottery of Cincinnati, Ohio, produced fine artware, some of which resembled the pottery of the Moors with intense colors and gold accents. Some of the later wares were very similar to those of Rookwood, due to the fact that several Rookwood artists were also associated with the Morgan pottery. Some examples were marked with a paper label, others with either a two- or three-line impression: 'Matt Morgan Art Pottery Co.,' with 'Cin. O.' sometimes added.

Charger, dragon relief, bronze/gold, 16" 500.00
Honey jug, leaves/butterfly cvg, Limoges style, Daly, 6½" 275.00
Jug, whiskey; cornstalks relief, bl w/gold, mk, 1883, 7" 425.00
Vase, clouds & birds, gold trim, sgn Hirschfeld, mk, 8x6" 545.00
Vase, reeds/dragonflies, Limoges style, NJ Hirschfeld, 4½" 200.00

Moriage

The term 'moriage' refers to certain Japanese wares decorated with applied slipwork designs. There are several methods used to achieve the characteristic relief effect. The decorative devices may be designed sepa-

rately and applied to the vessel, piped on in narrow ribbons of clay (slip-trailed), or built up by brushing on successive layers of liquified slip. See also Nippon.

Box, scenic lid, overall HP decor, club shape, mk, 2x2¾" 35.00
Chocolate pot, floral medallions, wht lacy moriage on gr, 9" . . .225.00
Cracker jar, roses, pk & lav on wht, hdls, 7½" 125.00
Ewer, floral on gr w/beige & wht lacy slipwork, 8½" 195.00
Ewer, panels of roses, beading/floral moriage, 6x5½" 195.00
Pitcher, floral, pk on wht, gr slip netting, 6" 85.00
Pitcher, rose panels, heavy beadwork, squat, 6x6½" 150.00
Sugar shaker, roses on lt gr, barrel form 80.00
Tea set, roses on mauve, pot/creamer/sugar bowl+5 c/s 650.00
Urn, florals/bird/leaves/buds, gold slipwork, Japan, 10" 185.00
Vase, birds in flight, florals on gr, 6½" 235.00
Vase, floral medallions, wht on lav, 8" 175.00

Vase, florals and netting, ogee handles, 10", $180.00.

Mortar and Pestle

Mortars are bowl-shaped vessels used for centuries for the purpose of grinding drugs to a powder or grain into meal. The masher or grinding device is called a pestle.

Brass, miniature, 1" +pestle 18.00
Bronze, English, 1700s, 7½", +pestle 200.00
Burl, 6½", +trn beech pestle 350.00
Ceramic, drugstore display, 12", +pestle 95.00
Ironstone, +wood hdl pestle w/ironstone terminal, 6x9½" 85.00
Maple, trn/hewn w/old red pnt, 8", w/ceramic & wood pestle . . .85.00
Poplar, trn, minor age cracks, 7", +trn pestle 75.00
Wood, trn, 7", +copper-banded pestle stamped Revere 250.00

Mortens Studio

Oscar Mortens was already established as a fine sculptural artist when he left his native Sweden to take up residency in Arizona. During the 1940s he developed a line of detailed animal figures which were distributed through the Mortens Studios, a firm he co-founded with Gunnar Thelin. Thelin hired and trained artists to produce Mortens' line, which he called Royal Designs. More than two hundred dogs were modeled and over one hundred horses. Cats and wild animals such as elephants, panthers, deer, and elk were made, but on a much smaller scale. Bookends with sculptured dog heads were shown in their catalogs, and collectors report finding wall plaques on rare occasions. The material they used was a plaster-type composition with wires embedded to support the weight. Examples were marked 'Copyright by the Mortens Studio' either in ink or decal. Watch for flaking, cracks, and separations — crazing seems to be present in some degree in many examples. When no condition is indicated, the items listed below are assumed to be in near-mint condition, allowing for minor crazing.

Afghan, tan & charcoal, standing, 7", M 85.00
Beagle, ivory/tan/blk, standing, 6" 65.00
Cocker Spaniel pup, golden tan, sitting, 3x3½", M 35.00
Collie, standing, tan & ivory, 6x7" 70.00
Dalmation, ivory & blk, standing, 5½x7½", M 75.00
Dalmation, 3" 35.00
Doberman, blk w/tan, recumbent, 4x8", M 85.00
German Shepherd, tan & charcoal, recumbent, 7x4", NM 65.00
Great Dane, tan w/blk, recumbent, 5¼x8½", NM 60.00
Irish Setter, rust, standing, 6x7", M 70.00

Pomeranian, paper label, 4" tall, $50.00.

Samoyed, ivory w/blk eyes & nose, sitting, 4x4¼", M 65.00
Sealyham Terrier, standing, 4x5¾", EX 65.00
Springer Spaniel, ivory & blk, 5x5½", M 65.00

Morton Pottery

Six potteries operated in Morton, Illinois, at various times from 1877 to 1976. Each traced its origin to six brothers who immigrated to America to avoid military service in Germany. The Rapp brothers established their first pottery near clay deposits on the south side of town where they made field tile and bricks. Within a few years, they branched out to include utility wares such as jugs, bowls, jars, pitchers, etc. During the ninety-nine years of pottery operations in Morton, the original factory was expanded by some of the sons and nephews of the Rapps. Other family members started their own potteries where artware, gift-store items, and special-order goods were produced. The Cliftwood Art Pottery and the Morton Pottery Company had showrooms in Chicago and New York City during the 1930s. All of Morton's potteries were relatively short-lived operations with the Morton Pottery Company being the last to shut down on September 8, 1976. For a more thorough study of the subject, we recommend *Morton's Potteries: 99 Years* by Doris and Burdell Hall; their address can be found in the Directory

under Illinois.

In the listings that follow VP refers to Vincent Price National Treasures items which were made for Sears and Roebuck from 1967 to 1968.

Morton Pottery Works — Morton Earthenware Co. (1877-1917)

Bank, Acorn Stoves advertising, dk gr, acorn shape 50.00
Bowl, wht-banded yellowware, 4½" to 7¾", nested set of 5 ....140.00
Chamber pot, yellowware, hdld, 9" dia 50.00
Pie baker, brn Rockingham, 10" dia 45.00
Pie baker, yellowware, 10" dia 85.00
Pitcher, cobalt, rare, 1-pt 55.00
Stein, German motto top & bottom, brn Rockingham 60.00
Stein, German motto top & bottom, dk gr 75.00
Teapot, Rebecca at the Well, brn Rockingham, 2-pt 45.00

Cliftwood Art Potteries, Inc. (1920-1940)

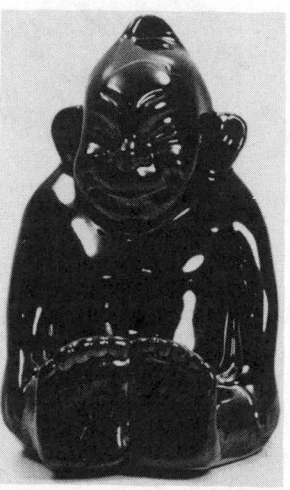

Cliftwood Art Potteries, Inc., billiken figure, Rockingham glaze, 8½", $55.00.

Bookends, logs w/appl woodpeckers, brn drip glaze, pr 85.00
Compote, appl dolphin base, bl mulberry, 6" 75.00
Console set, low-ftd compote & 2 candlesticks, cobalt bl 80.00
Figurine, bald eagle, natural colors, 8½' 75.00
Flower frog, Loralee seated on rocks, chocolate drip 50.00
Lamp, desk; lion & lioness on knolls, blk pillars, pr 125.00
Lamp, table; invt pear shape, molded hdls, chocolate drip, 21" ..55.00
Matchbox holder, pk w/gr drip on wht, wall mt, 5" 35.00
Vase, snake, fish figural hdls, cobalt, #132, 18¼" 80.00

Midwest Potteries, Inc. (1940-1944)

Figurine, bl heron, natural colors w/gold, 11" 35.00
Figurine, fighting cock, brn/gr spray, 6¼" 12.00
Figurine, lady w/Russian wolfhound, wht, 11" 40.00
Figurine, nude, September Morn, wht, 12" 45.00
Figurine, parrot on stump, bl/yel spray, 4½" 12.00
Figurine, rabbits kissing, wht w/gold, 2½" 20.00
Pitcher, duck figural, cattail hdl, yel/bl spray, 9¾" 22.00
Shakers, scottie dogs, wht matt, 3", pr 10.00
Vase, bud; hand, wht, 4½" 12.00
Vase, gr/brn spray, hdls, miniature, 3¾" 8.00

Morton Pottery Company (1922-1976)

Bank, pig form, bl, wall hanger, 5" 15.00

Bookends, Atlas on books/world on shoulders, wht w/gold, pr ...20.00
Bowl, mixing; gr/yel/brn spatter, nested set of 3, 7" to 9" 120.00
Cookie jar, hen, chick finial, wht w/brushed blk trim 50.00
Cookie jar, turkey, chick finial, brn w/red wattle 65.00
Cookie jar, turkey, chick finial, wht 95.00
Creamer & sugar bowl, hen & rooster, wht w/blk trim, 4" 18.00
Food mold, heart shape, brn Rockingham, VP, 10x7½" 35.00
Lamp, TV; buffalo on rocky cliff, 11" 50.00
Lollypop tree, gr, perforations for sucker sticks, 9¾" 30.00
Mug, Santa, natural colors, 3" 12.00
Nappy, bl spongeware on off-wht, VP, 8½" dia 35.00
Pie baker, gr/brn/yel spatter, 9" dia 100.00
Pitcher, advertising blank on side, gr/brn/yel spatter, 4½" 80.00
Pitcher, water; bl spongeware, VP, 9" 55.00
Pitcher, water; gr/brn/yel spatter, ice lip, VP, 7" 90.00
Pitcher & bowl set, brn Rockingham, VP 135.00
Planter, Santa on chimney, natural colors, 7" 15.00
Planter, snowman, wht w/blk hat & gr scarf, 9¾" 18.00
Plate, Santa face, natural colors, 8" dia 20.00
Salt box, wht, w/lid, VP 30.00
Tray, dresser; lady's collar, HP brooch 12.00
Tray, dresser; man's collar, blk bow tie 14.00
Wall pocket, long basket w/emb flower, pastel, VP, 7½" 16.00
Wall pocket, parrot & grapes, bl/gr/yel/pk, VP, 8½" 20.00

American Art Potteries (1947-1961)

Bowl, bulb; water lily shape, mauve & pk spray, 5" dia 15.00
Cup & saucer, demitasse; stylized flower, orchid & pk spray 12.00
Doll parts: head/arms/legs, hand decor, blk hair, 3" dia 50.00
Figurine, Hampshire hog, blk w/wht band, gr base, 5½" 30.00
Figurine, quail, brn spray, 6½" 18.00
Flower frog, frog, gr & yel spray, 5x3" 8.00
Flower frog, turtle, gr & yel spray, 5½x3¾" 10.00
Pitcher vase, ewer type, bl mottle, 14" 16.00
Planter, baby shoes on heart base, pk decor 20.00
Planter, basket, simulates woven wood, chartreuse/wht, 3¾" 6.00
Planter, pheasant, open bk, natural colors, 18" L 25.00
Planter, teddy bear sits on HP building blocks 10.00

Mosaic Tile Co.

The Mosaic Tile Company was organized in 1894, in Zanesville, Ohio, by Herman Mueller and Karl Langenbeck, both of whom had years of previous experience in the industry. They developed a faster, less-costly method of potting decorative tile, utilizing paper patterns rather than copper molds. By 1901 the company had grown and expanded with offices in many major cities. Faience tile was introduced in 1918, greatly increasing their volume of sales. They also made novelty ash trays, figural boxes, bookends, etc., though not to any large extent. Until they closed during the 1960s, Mosaic used various marks that included the company name or their initials — 'MT' superimposed over 'Co.' in a circle.

Ash tray, wht/blk dog stands in center, 6x7" 155.00
Cookie jar, Mammy 200.00
Figurine, buffalo, wht gloss, 8x12" 210.00
Figurine, dog, recumbent w/head up, ivory, 8" L 120.00
Soap dish, turtle form, bl, shallow, 4" 35.00
Tankard, grapevines relief on brn glaze, 13" 100.00
Tile, Fortune & the Boy, 6" 75.00
Tile, Lincoln's profile, wht on bl, 3½" 30.00
Tile, Longfellow's Dome, 6" 25.00
Tile, Mary & Lamb 25.00

Tile, profile of man, white on blue, 7½", $115.00.

Moser

Ludwig Moser began his career as a struggling glass artist, catering to the rich who visited the famous Austrian health spas. His talent and popularity grew and in 1857 the first of his three studios opened in Karlsbad, Czechoslovakia. The styles developed there were entirely his own; no copies of other artists have ever been found. Some of his original designs include grapes with trailing vines, acorns and oak leaves, and richly enameled, deeply cut or carved floral pieces. Sometimes jewels were applied to the glass as well. Moser's animal scenes reflect his careful attention to detail. Famed for his birds in flight, he also designed stalking tigers — even elephants — all created in fine enameling.

Moser died in 1916, but the business was contined by his two sons who had been personally and carefully trained by their father. They merged with Meyer's Nephews Glassworks in 1921, and continued to produce quality glass until the Nazi invasion in 1938 when these fine Jewish artists were all placed in concentration camps.

When identifying Moser, look for great clarity in the glass; deeply carved, continuous engravings; perfect coloration; finely applied enameling (often covered with thin gold leaf); and well-polished pontils.

Our advisor for this category is Don Williams; he is listed in the Directory under Iowa. Items listed below are enameled unless noted otherwise.

Biscuit jar, clear to cranberry, florals, 7½" 135.00
Bottle, scent; cobalt, mc leaves/gold foliage, 5½x2" 135.00
Bowl, bl, HP flowers & leaves, 8" 150.00
Box, amber, gold/wht fernery, HP bees, sgn, 2½x3½x4" 265.00
Box, amethyst, HP florals, amber salamanders on lid, 4½" 600.00
Box, bl, gold floral, metal rim/catch, sgn, 3½x6½" 235.00
Box, cranberry, birds/florals, brass mts/hdls, oblong, 5" H 1,400.00
Box, cranberry, heavy gold, mc leaves/berries, 5½" H 700.00
Box, cranberry, scenic lid, ormolu mts, att, 6½" dia 350.00
Box, gr, mc floral/butterfly, brass ft/hdl, 4¾" H 750.00
Card holder, gr to clear, floral etched, sgn 125.00
Champagne, clear to cranberry, mk, 6½x4" 250.00
Champagne, clear w/mc florals, 8½" 130.00
Compote, clear to amber, dog/deer in woods intaglio, 6x8½" .235.00
Compote, clear to cranberry, gold intaglio grapes, 6x8½" 235.00
Compote, clear to gr, wht overlay, floral panels, 7x6" 175.00
Compote, wht to cranberry, cut ovals, HP grapes, mk, 7x8½" ..225.00

Cruet, cobalt, HP/appl grapes & leaves, ftd, 17" 1,100.00
Cruet, cranberry, gold/mc decor, gold hdl/stopper, 8" 900.00
Cruet, gr to clear, gold leaves/hdl/stopper, flat sided, 8½" 775.00
Cup & saucer, demi; cranberry w/birds & flowers 300.00
Goblet, heavy gold-encrusted decor, set of 6 . . . . .400.00
Lamp, ruby, mc enamel, sgn, rpl shade, 17" 1,500.00
Pitcher, bl, gold florals, mini, 3" 325.00
Pitcher, bl, HP wht florals, mk, 9½", +4 4" tumblers 225.00
Pitcher, clear to amethyst, HP florals, clear hdl, mk, 8x6" 235.00
Pitcher, cranberry, Invt T'print, florals, clear hdl, 10" 200.00
Pitcher, cranberry, Invt T'print, mc florals w/gold, sgn, 9" . . .1,200.00
Rose bowl, lady pours drink, gilt, 6-crimp, ribs, unmk, 4¾" 125.00
Tea caddy, cranberry, HP florals & gold, 4 paw ft, 7½" L 375.00
Tumbler, cranberry, gold leaves/flowers/foliage, unmk, 4¼" 75.00
Tumbler, HP decor w/raised cabochon jewels, panels, 5¼" 345.00
Tumbler, Rhine, chartreuse bows w/gold grapes, 7½" 70.00
Vase, amber, appl bl drips, HP floral, trumpet form, 12" 585.00
Vase, amber crackle, 3 appl fish, HP flowers, att, 6", pr 550.00
Vase, amethyst to clear, jewels/florals, ewer form, unmk, 6" . . .225.00
Vase, bl, mc florals, clear ball stem w/airtraps, 8" 175.00
Vase, bl, wht florals, 4-ftd metal base, mk, 12" 165.00
Vase, cameo, strawflower, burgundy on amber, bulbous, 8" . .1,050.00
Vase, canary yel, appl acorns/mc gold-lined leaves, ftd, 4½" . . .375.00
Vase, clear to cranberry, HP geometrics w/gold, mk, 12½" 200.00
Vase, clear to gr, floral intaglio, gilt decor, #d, 8" 290.00
Vase, cobalt, florals w/gold, 7½x3", pr 125.00
Vase, cranberry, gold & wht florals, mk, 12x5¼" 230.00
Vase, cranberry, mc oak leaves/gold foliage, unmk, 4¾" 225.00
Vase, cranberry, mc oak leaves/gold foliage/HP wasp, 4¼" 450.00
Vase, cranberry, raised gold, bulbous, mk, 14½x8" 355.00
Vase, cranberry, 3 floral/3 gold panels, ped ft, mk, 15" 330.00
Vase, cranberry, 6 appl floral medallions w/gold, mk, 9½x5" . . .200.00
Vase, dragons/butterflies, cylinder, gilt-metal ft, 14½" 600.00
Vase, gr, gold florals, mk, 8x5½" 125.00
Vase, gr, mc figures/garden, 1895/Gutenbergbund-Wein, 15" .1,450.00
Vase, gr opal to clear, red/yel poppies w/gold, ribbed, 11" 325.00
Vase, gr to clear, cut florals, 8½" 325.00
Vase, gr to clear, intaglio cut, paneled, 9" 900.00
Vase, jack-in-pulpit; clear to gr, gold trim, scalloped, 8" 180.00

Wine decanter, cobalt with applied acorns and bugs, heavy gold trim, 16", +2 matching 6" goblets, $2,900.00 for the 3 pieces.

Wine, marquetry, purple, iris intaglio, clear stem 1,500.00
Wine, Rhine, chartreuse bows w/gold grapes, 6" 55.00
Wine, Rhine, rubena verde, grapes/leaves/insect, sgn, 4" 325.00
Wine taster, bl to clear w/heavy enamel & gold, paneled, 2½" .200.00

Moss Rose

Moss Rose was a favorite dinnerware pattern of many Staffordshire and American potters from the mid-1800s. In America the Wheeling Pottery of West Virginia produced the ware in large quantities, and it became one of their best sellers, remaining popular well into the nineties.

Bowl, vegetable; w/lid, Meakin, 11½x7" 60.00
Butter pat, sq, Meakin, EX 15.00
Coffeepot, EC & Co, 9" 80.00
Coffeepot, Haviland, lg 65.00
Cup & saucer, unmk 15.00
Egg cup, set of 6, MIB 28.00
Gravy boat, w/underplate, Green & Co, England 37.50
Plate, dinner; unmk, 10" 15.00
Plate, Meakin, 7" 12.50
Plate, Powell & Bishop, 10" 20.00
Plate, soup; Meakin, 9" 16.00
Platter, rectangular, Meakin, 14x10" .30.00
Platter, unmk, 13" 20.00
Shaving mug, unmk 22.00
Soap dish, Delaware 45.00
Tea set, Japan, 16-pc+lids 60.00
Toothbrush holder, unmk, 5¼" 32.00
Tray, tiered, unmk 15.00
Tureen, gold trim, w/lid, unmk 75.00
Wash set, unmk, 11" pitcher+13½" bowl 265.00

Mother-of-Pearl Glass

Mother-of-Pearl glass was a type of mold-blown satin art glass popular during the last half of the 19th century. A patent for its manufacture was issued in 1886 to Frederick S. Shirley, and one of the companies who produced it was the Mt. Washington Glass Company of New Bedford, Massachusetts. Another was the English firm of Stevens and Williams. Its delicate patterns were developed by blowing the gather into a mold with inside projections that left an intaglio design on the surface of the glass, then sealing the first layer with a second, trapping air in the recesses. Most common are the Diamond Quilted, Raindrop, and Herringbone patterns. It was made in several soft colors, the most rare and valuable is rainbow — a blend of rose, light blue, yellow, and white. Occasionally it may be decorated with coralene, enameling, or gilt.

Our advisors for this category are Betty and Clarence Maier; they are listed in the Directory under Pennsylvania.

Basket, Dia Quilt, bl, crimped, pointed camphor hdl, 3" 120.00
Basket, Herringbone, pk, ruffled, twisted thorn hdl, 9" 250.00
Basket, Raindrop, bl, frosted looped thorn hdl, 10" 250.00
Bottle, scent; Acorn, chartreuse, gold prunus, Webb, 5" 700.00
Bowl, Coin Spot, bl, 3 frosted ft, berry pontil, 6½" 200.00
Bowl, Coin Spot, rainbow, gilt florals, tricorn, Webb, 3x4½" . .350.00
Bowl, Dia Quilt, bl, 3 frosted trunk vases form ft, 5x6" 450.00
Bowl, Dia Quilt, pk, gold prunus/mc bird, crimped, 8" 375.00
Bowl, Dia Quilt, rainbow, yel ft, berry pontil, mk Pat, 9½" 575.00
Bowl, Dia Quilt, rainbow, 3 vaseline ft, mk Pat, 5x10" 1,150.00
Bowl, Dia Quilt, wht, ruffled, 9" 100.00
Bowl, Herringbone, wht/lime int, ferns/butterfly, Webb, 11" . .450.00

Bowl, Rivulet, chartreuse shaded, appl ruffled base, 3x4" 245.00
Cruet, Dia Quilt, bl shaded, reed hdl, matching stopper, 7" 650.00
Cruet, Dia Quilt, pk, frosted hdl/stopper, 5½" 300.00
Cruet, Dia Quilt, pk, thorn hdl/stopper, mini, 5" 575.00
Decanter, Dia Quilt, bl, frosted hdl/stopper, 8½" 200.00
Ewer, Dia Quilt, pk, frosted hdl, slim w/tricorn top, 8" 175.00
Ewer, Dia Quilt, pk, frosted thorn hdl, 12" 300.00
Finger bowl, Dia Quilt, bl, fluted, 4½" 130.00
Finger bowl, Herringbone, pk, hexagonal 60.00
Finger bowl, Herringbone, red to pk, 3x3⅝" 175.00
Ginger jar, Dia Quilt, apricot, frosted berry finial, 7½" 350.00
Jar, Dia Quilt, pk to wht, gilt floral/butterfly, Webb, 4" 250.00
Lamp shade, Dia Quilt, yel shaded, melon ribs, 6¼x9" 165.00
Pitcher, Dia Quilt, bl, reeded frosted hdl, sq mouth, 6½" 325.00
Pitcher, Dia Quilt, pk, amber reeded hdl/ruffled top, 9" 400.00
Pitcher, Herringbone, pk, ribbed, frosted hdl, 8" 275.00
Pitcher, Raindrop, bl, bl reeded hdl, 4½x3" 225.00
Pitcher, Ribbed Ribbon, brn to tan, pk liner, twist hdl, 7" ...2,150.00
Rose bowl, Herringbone, apricot shaded, 8-crimp, 3½x3½" 195.00
Rose bowl, Herringbone, red to pk, 8-crimp, 3½x3½" 195.00
Rose bowl, Rivulet, chartreuse shaded, 8-crimp, 3¼x3⅞" 275.00

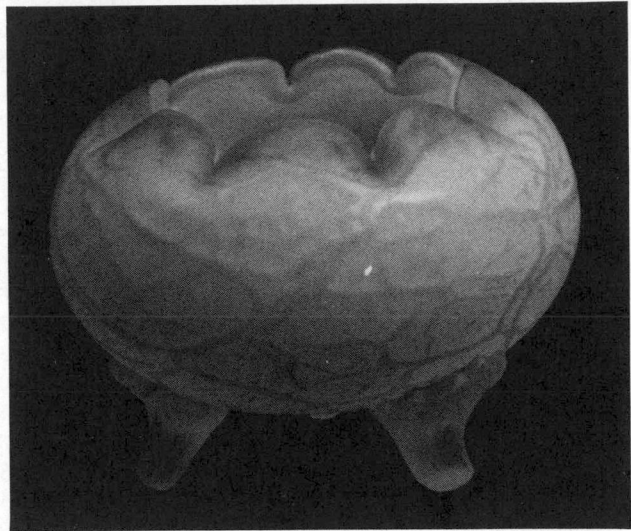

Rose bowl, Rivulet, white with rainbow edge, 6" diameter, $1,500.00.

Shaker, Raindrop, bl shaded 235.00
Sweetmeat, Dia Quilt, rainbow, silver twist hdl/mts, 3½" 425.00
Tumbler, Dia Quilt, butterscotch 60.00
Tumbler, Dia Quilt, yel, HP daisies/foliage 245.00
Tumbler, Moire, pk 175.00
Vase, Acorn, gold, pinched tricorn top, 5½" 350.00
Vase, Acorn, lt bl, pinched tricorn top, 5½" 275.00
Vase, Coin Spot, bl, fluted top, 7⅜x4⅛" 195.00
Vase, Coin Spot, bl, gold prunus, stick form, 7¼" 300.00
Vase, Coin Spot, peach shaded w/HP floral twig, ruffled, 9" ...550.00
Vase, Dia Quilt, amber, HP birds/florals, bulbous, 9½", pr 700.00
Vase, Dia Quilt, bl, ruffled, 4⅛" 125.00
Vase, Dia Quilt, bl, silver overlay florals/vines, 10" 1,050.00
Vase, Dia Quilt, bl shaded, frosted/ruffled top, 5½" 195.00
Vase, Dia Quilt, lav-pk w/vaseline on neck, ribbed, 10" 495.00
Vase, Dia Quilt, peach shaded, melon ribbed, 6⅞x3⅞" 155.00
Vase, Dia Quilt, peachblow color, pinched sides, 7", pr 225.00
Vase, Dia Quilt, pk, gold flowers/3 insects, Webb, 9½" 350.00
Vase, Dia Quilt, rainbow, lobed rim/ringed trumpet neck, 6" ..895.00
Vase, Dia Quilt, rainbow, scissor-cut ruffle, 3¾x5½" 750.00
Vase, Dia Quilt, yel, bulbous, stick neck w/cup top, 8½" 125.00

Vase, Dia Quilt, yel, trumpet neck w/ruffle, 6" 165.00
Vase, Drapery, apricot w/gold, bulbous bottom, att S&W, 7½" .300.00
Vase, Drapery, rose to pk, ruffled fan form, 6¼x3½" 225.00
Vase, Federzeichnung, brn, mk Pat, 10x5" 1,750.00
Vase, Herringbone, peach shaded, frosted neck, 6¼" 195.00
Vase, Herringbone, pk shaded, fold-down top, 6" 230.00
Vase, Honeycomb, bl to wht, fold-down ruffled top, 9½" 175.00
Vase, Moire, pk to wht, ruffled, 12½" 225.00
Vase, Moire, rose, floral/coralene, dbl-ring neck, Webb, 9" 550.00
Vase, Raindrop, bl, ruffled w/pinched sides, 8½", pr 300.00
Vase, Raindrop, lt gr to wht, HP morning-glories, Webb, 10" ..475.00
Vase, Ribbon, rose red, bulbous w/dimpled sides, 5½" 495.00
Vase, Snowflake, peach shaded, bulbous, 5" 395.00
Vase, Spiral, pk, deeply scalloped/ruffled, att Webb, 6½" 160.00
Vase, Swirl, lav to rose shaded, gourd neck, S&W, 6" 350.00

Mourning Collectibles

During the 18th and early 19th centuries, ladies made needlework pictures, samplers, paintings on ivory plaques, watercolor drawings, etc. to commemorate the death of a loved one. Elements contained in nearly all examples are the tomb, mourners, a weeping willow tree, and data relating to the deceased. Often plaits of hair were included. Today these are recognized and valued as a valid form of folk art.

Embr on silk, tomb/urn/willow, data/1802, mk fr, 10x12", EX ..475.00

Picture, embroidered silk, inked inscription, and hand-painted details, Balch School, Providence, Rhode Island, ca 1827, EX, 24x27", $16,000.00 at auction.

Pin, marquise-shaped ivory w/HP scene dtd 1794, 2" 2,640.00
Sampler, tomb-shape reserve, data/1842, needlepoint, 23x21" .150.00
Sampler, urn w/'JP,' weeping willows, data/1805, 15x11" 250.00
Watercolor, dedication/1833 on monument, bldgs, 11x15" ..1,650.00
Watercolor, pen/ink, gilt paper applique, dtd 1818, 21x21" ..2,600.00

Movie Memorabilia

Movie memorabilia covers a broad range of collectibles, from books and magazines dealing with the industry in general to the various promotional materials which were distributed to arouse interest in a particular film. Many collectors specialize in a specific area — posters, pressbooks, stills, lobby cards, or souvenir programs (also referred to as premier booklets). In the listings below, a one-sheet poster measures approximately 27" x 41", three-sheet: 41" x 81", and six-sheet: 81" x 81". See also Autographs; Cartoon Art; Personalities.

Gone with the Wind, First Edition, May 1936 imprint, New York, $150.00.

Book, If I Had Million, R Andrews, Paramount, 1931, 280-pg . . 18.00
Book, Squaw Man, J Faversham, MGM, 1906, 294-pg, EX 50.00
Display card, Big Land, Alan Ladd/V Mayo, 1957, 22x28" 12.00
Display card, Casanova Brown, Gary Cooper, 1944, 22x28" 28.00
Display card, Egg & I, Claudette Colbert, 1947, 22x28" 24.00
Display card, Great Gildersleeve, H Peary, 1942, 22x28" 18.00
Display card, Jack & Beanstalk, Abbott/Costello, 1952, 22x28" . 35.00
Display card, Lumberjack, William Boyd, 1944, 22x28" 48.00
Display card, Miracle in Harlem, S Guyse, 1948, 22x28" 18.00
Display card, Mouse That Roared, P Sellers, 1959, 22x28" 20.00
Display card, Till We Meet Again, R Milland, 1944, 22x28" . . . 25.00
Display card, Young Philadelphians, Newman, 1959, 22x28" . . . 15.00
Insert card, Alias Nick Beal, R Milland, 1949, 14x36" 28.00
Insert card, Blue Hawaii, Elvis Presley, 1961, 14x36" 65.00
Insert card, Christmas Eve, Raft, 1947, 14x36" 25.00
Insert card, East of Eden, J Dean, 1955, 14x36" 250.00
Insert card, Fighting O'Flynn, D Fairbanks Jr, 1949, 14x36" 22.00
Insert card, From This Day Forward, Fontaine, 1946, 14x36" . . . 14.00
Insert card, Psycho (Hitchcock), J Leigh, 1960, 14x36" 125.00
Insert card, Sabrina, Bogart, 1954, 14x36" 30.00
Insert card, San Quentin, Bogart, 14x36" 50.00
Insert card, Silk Stockings, Astaire, 1957, 14x36" 30.00
Insert card, Some Like It Hot, M Monroe, 1958, 14x36" 150.00
Insert card, Southern Yankee, Red Skelton, 1948, 14x36" 30.00
Lobby card, Adventures of Marco Polo, Cooper, 1937, 11x14" . . 12.00
Lobby card, Another Man's Poison, B Davis, 1951, 11x14" 38.00
Lobby card, Battle Circus, Bogart, 1953, 11x14" 22.00
Lobby card, Body & Soul, J Garfield, 1947, 11x14" 28.00
Lobby card, Buck Privates Come Home, Abbott/Costello, 1947 . 45.00
Lobby card, Calcutta, Ladd, 1946, 11x14" 20.00
Lobby card, Chimp at Oxford, Laurel & Hardy, 1946, 11x14" . 100.00

Lobby card, Command Decision, Gable, 1948, 11x14" 15.00
Lobby card, Double Dealing, Hoot Gibson, 11x14", EX 20.00
Lobby card, Fight Never Ends, Joe Louis, 11x14" 50.00
Lobby card, Flame of Barbary Coast, Wayne, 1947, 11x14" 35.00
Lobby card, Gone w/the Wind, fr, 1939, 11x14", NM 350.00
Lobby card, Happy Land, Don Ameche, 1943, 11x14" 7.50
Lobby card, Her Greatest Love, Theda Bara, 1917, 11x14" 86.00
Lobby card, Hills of the Home, Lassie, 1948, 11x14" 15.00
Lobby card, Key to the City, Gable, 1950, 11x14" 15.00
Lobby card, Merrily We Live, Bennett, 1938, 11x14" 48.00
Lobby card, Our Relations, Laurel & Hardy, 1936, fr, EX 165.00
Lobby card, Prison Bait, all Blk cast, 11x14" 25.00
Lobby card, Remarkable Andrew, W Holden, 1942, 11x14" 12.00
Lobby card, Revenge of the Zombie, J Carradine, 1943, 11x14" . 28.00
Lobby card, Ride 'Em Cowboy, Abbott/Costello, 1942, 11x14" . . 40.00
Lobby card, Sunset in Wyoming, G Autry, 1942, 11x14" 14.00
Lobby card, Swan, Grace Kelly, 1956, 11x14" 12.00
Lobby card, Wabash Avenue, Betty Grable, 1950, 11x14" 32.00
Magazine, Cinema Arts, Garbo cover, Vol 1 #1, June 1937 . . . . . 70.00
Magazine, Hollywood, Jane Russell cover, June 1941, VG 25.00
Magazine, Look, Liz Taylor cover, Oct 4, 1966 . . . . 11.00
Magazine, Modern Screen, Betty Davis cover, Aug 1938 . . . . . . 25.00
Magazine, Modern Screen, Dionne Quintuplets cover, July '36 . . 30.00
Magazine, Modern Screen, Garbo/Stokowski cover, June 1938 . . 35.00
Magazine, Modern Screen, Gregory Peck cover, Aug 1946 . . . . . 10.00
Magazine, Modern Screen, Joan Blondell cover, Nov 1939 . . . . . 25.00
Magazine, Modern Screen, Louise Rainer cover, June 1937 . . . . 30.00
Magazine, Motion Picture, M Dietrich cover, July 1937 . . . . 35.00
Magazine, Movie Mirror, Alice Faye cover, Dec 1938 . . . . 20.00
Magazine, Movie Mirror, Ginger Rogers cover, Sept 1937 . . . . . 25.00
Magazine, Photoplay, Betty Compson cover, Aug 1924 . . . . 20.00
Magazine, Photoplay, Esther Williams cover, July 1948 . . . . 10.00
Magazine, Photoplay, Jean Crain cover, May 1946 . . . . 12.00
Magazine, Silver Screen, Susan Haywood cover, Sept 1944 . . . . . 13.00
Poster, Angel on My Shoulder, Paul Muni, 1946, 41x81" 80.00
Poster, Big Store, Marx Brothers, 1941, 14x18", EX 95.00
Poster, Broadway, Raft & O'Brien, 1942, 27x41" 30.00
Poster, Bye Bye Birdie, A Margaret, 1963, 27x41" 15.00
Poster, Come Fill the Cup, J Cagney, 1951, 41x81" 45.00
Poster, Diamonds Are Forever, James Bond, 1971, 1-sheet 48.00
Poster, For a Few Dollars More, Eastwood, 1967, 40x60" 80.00
Poster, Foxes of Harrow, Rex Harrison, 1941, 22x28" 38.00
Poster, Her Cardboard Lover, N Shearer, 1942, 81x81" 200.00
Poster, Hoodlum Saint, Powell, 1946, 27x41" 30.00
Poster, It's Only Money, J Lewis, 1962, 3-sheet 15.00
Poster, Kennel Murder Case, W Powell, 1933, 27x41" 250.00
Poster, Little Giant, Abbott/Costello, 1946, 27x41" 40.00
Poster, Man Betrayed, John Wayne, 1941, 81x81" 175.00
Poster, Mantan Moreland w/all-star Blk cast, 1-sheet 20.00
Poster, Misfits, M Monroe, 1961, 1-sheet 100.00
Poster, Passage to Marseilles, Bogart, 1944, 1-sheet 350.00
Poster, Picnic, Holden & Novak, 1956, 22x28" 25.00
Poster, Pillow Talk, Doris Day, 1959, 27x41" 30.00
Poster, Queen Bee, Crawford, 1955, 27x41" 55.00
Poster, Raider Emden, Louis Ralph, 1928, 27x41" 180.00
Poster, Road to Happiness, John Boles, 1938, 1-sheet 48.00
Poster, Solid Gold Cadillac, Holliday, 1956, 27x41" 20.00
Poster, Stallion Road, Ronald Reagan, 1947, 27x41" 125.00
Poster, Stronger Will, Percy Marmont, 1928, 27x41" 150.00
Poster, Tales of Terror, Aldo Ray, 1962, 3-sheet 20.00
Poster, Target Zero, C Bronson, 1956, 27x41" 25.00
Poster, Thunderball, James Bond, 1965, 30x40" 80.00
Poster, To Kill a Mockingbird, G Peck, 1963, 3-sheet 28.00
Poster, Twilight in Sierras, R Rogers, sgn, '50, 27x41" 65.00

Poster, We Were Strangers, J Garfield, 1949, 27x41" 60.00
Poster, What Price Glory, Cagney, 1952, 27x41" 40.00
Poster, When Strangers Marry, Mitchum, 1944, 27x41" 30.00
Poster, Young Widow, Russell, 1946, 27x41" 40.00
Poster, 30 Foot Bride of Candy Rock, Costello, 1959, 27x41" ...18.00
Pressbook, Bronze Venus, Lena Horne, EX 25.00
Pressbook, College Swing, Burns/Allen, 1938, 34-pg 50.00
Pressbook, FBI Story, James Stewart, 1959, 16-pg 18.00
Pressbook, It's a Big Country, G Cooper, 1951, 12-pg 20.00
Pressbook, Jailhouse Rock, Elvis Presley, MGM, 1957 ....25.00
Pressbook, Longest Day, John Wayne, 1964, 8-pg 15.00
Pressbook, Magnificent Seven, Yul Brynner, 1960, 4-pg 12.00
Pressbook, Mogambo, Clark Gable, MGM 25.00
Pressbook, One, Two, Three; J Cagney, 1961, 12-pg 20.00
Pressbook, River of No Return, M Monroe, 1954, 16-pg 28.00
Pressbook, Rocket Ship, B Crabbe, 1940, 8-pg 75.00
Program, Gone with the Wind, MGM, illus, 18-pg, EX 75.00
Program, King of Kings, DeMille 25.00
Program, Red River, John Wayne 35.00
Still, Annie Oakley, Barbara Stanwyck, 1935, 8x10" 5.00
Still, Citizen Kane, Orson Welles/Joseph Cotton, 1941 ....12.00
Still, Forward Pass, Sally O'Neal, 1929 ....9.50
Still, I'm No Angel, Mae West, 1933 ....15.00
Still, It Started w/a Kiss, G Ford, 1959, 8x10" 4.00
Still, Little Giant, Edward G Robinson, 1933 ....12.00
Still, Racket Busters, H Bogart, 1937, 8x10" 15.00
Still, Royal Wedding, Fred Astaire/Jane Powell, 1951 ....7.00
Still, Three Smart Girls, Deanna Durbin, 1936 ....8.00
Title card, Big Parade, John Gilbert, ca 1930 ....150.00
Title card, Call of the Wild, C Gable, 1935 ....200.00
Title card, Last of the Mohicans, R Scott, 1936 ....175.00
Title card, Night Is Young, Ramon Novarro, 1935 ....75.00
Title card, We're Not Married, M Monroe, 1952 ....45.00
Trailer, Becket, Richard Burton, 1964, 35mm 8.00
Trailer, How To Murder Your Wife, J Lemmon, 1963, 35mm 7.00
Trailer, Magnificent Matador, A Quinn, 1955, 35mm 6.00
Trailer, Revenge of Gladiators, R Brown, 1965 35mm 5.00
Trailer, Tiko & the Shark, Al Kauwe, 1962, 35mm 4.00
Window card, Abie's Irish Rose, A Nichols, 1928, 14x22" 40.00
Window card, Blue Bird, Shirley Temple, 1940, 14x22" 150.00
Window card, East Side of Heaven, B Crosby, 1939, 14x22" 50.00
Window card, Legend of Lost, Wayne, 1957, 14x22" 25.00
Window card, Night of the Hunter, R Mitchum, 1855, 14x22" .30.00
Window card, Only Angels Have Wings, Grant, 1939, 14x22" .150.00
Window card, Strange Door, B Karloff, 1951, 14x22" 30.00
Window card, Stranger Wore a Gun, Scott, 3-D, 1953, 14x22" .30.00
Window card, Tall Men, Gable & Russell, 1955, 14x22" 40.00
Window card, The Blob, McQueen, 1958, 14x22" 25.00
Window card, Tingler, Vincent Price, 1959, 14x22" 30.00
Window card, Village Barn Dance, Doris Day, 1940, 14x22" ...38.00
Window card, Viva Las Vegas, Elvis, 1964, 14x22" 25.00

Mt. Washington

The Mt. Washington Glass Works was founded in 1837 in South Boston, Massachusetts, but moved to New Bedford in 1869 after purchasing the facilities of the New Bedford Glass Company. Frederick S. Shirley became associated with the firm in 1874. Two years later the company reorganized and became known as the Mt. Washington Glass Company. In 1894 it merged with the Pairpoint Manufacturing Company, a small Brittania works nearby, but continued to conduct business under its own title until after the turn of the century. The combined plants were equipped with the most modern and varied machinery available and boasted a working force with experience and expertise rival to none in the art of blowing and cutting glass. In addition to their fine cut glass, they are recognized as the first American company to make cameo glass, an effect they achieved through acid-cutting methods. In 1885 Shirley was issued a patent to make Burmese, pale yellow glassware tinged with a delicate pink blush. Another patent issued in 1886 allowed them the rights to produce Rose Amber, or amberina, a transparent ware shading from ruby to amber. Pearl Satin Ware and Peachblow, so named for its resemblance to a rosy peach skin, were patented the same year. One of their most famous lines, Crown Milano, was introduced in 1893. It was an opal glass either free-blown or pattern-molded, tinted a delicate color and decorated with enameling and gilt. Royal Flemish was patented in 1894 and is considered the rarest of the Mt. Washington art glass lines. It was decorated with raised, gold-enameled lines dividing the surface of the ware in much the same way as lead lines divide a stained glass window. The sections were filled in with one or several transparent colors and further decorated in gold enamel with florals, foliage, beading, and medallions.

Our advisors for this category are Betty and Clarence Maier; they are listed in the Directory under Pennsylvania. See also Salt Shakers; Burmese; Crown Milano; Royal Flemish; etc.

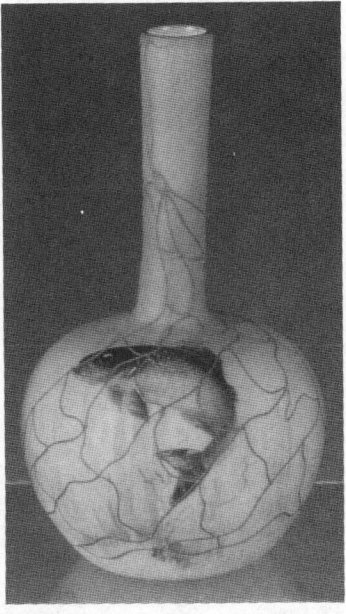

Vase, opaque white with a fish caught in a net, Burmese-colored ground, 10", $1,000.00.

Biscuit jar, blown-out oak leaf, pk/brn mums, 9½" 550.00
Biscuit jar, florals, melon ribbed, SP mts, 7" dia 450.00
Biscuit jar, 3-color crescents on wht, beaded bl waves 325.00
Bowl, mums/gold-traced leaves, bl int, ruffled, 10½" 185.00
Celery vase, Hobnail, amberina; Aurora SP fr, 9" 500.00
Celery vase, Venetian Diamond, amberina, sq top, 6¼x4" 335.00
Compote, Napoli, yel mums/gr leaves, gold tracing, 10x7" 585.00
Condiment, ribbed w/floral, shakers/mustard in mk holder 350.00
Creamer, crackled w/fish & water plants, 4½" 125.00
Creamer & sugar, floral twig, pk bl on wht, SP fittings 325.00
Cruet, tiny bl flowers/autumn leaves on ribbed wht, gilt 1,250.00
Jar, Albertine, emb Hobnail Star, HP zinnias, brass lid, 4" 200.00
Jar, Camellia, pk satin w/HP scrolls & florals, SP lid, 5" 100.00
Jar, Dia Quilt, wht w/HP ivy, SP lid w/turtle finial, 4¼" 325.00
Pitcher, crysanthemums, yel on clear, 10x6¼" 585.00
Plate, Santa Maria, World's Fair 1893, wht satin, 6" 300.00
Shakers, Columbian Expo 1893 emb, egg form, orig tops, pr ...150.00
Shakers, florals, swirled acorn form, orig tops, pr 130.00
Shakers, florals, yel on bl, egg form, orig top 85.00
Shakers, florals on burmese color, egg form, orig top, pr 110.00
Sugar shaker, berries/leaves, melon ribbed, 3¾" dia 275.00

Sugar shaker, floral on lt pk frost, fig form 375.00
Sugar shaker, pansies on yel, egg form 250.00
Sugar shaker, 3 Palmer Cox Brownies on wht opaque, 4" 185.00
Syrup, shiny burmese color w/HP florals, ribbed, SP mts, 8" . . .450.00
Vase, bird/branch, rust/gold/gr on beige, trumpet neck, 12" 795.00
Vase, daisies, bulbous, SP top & hdls, 6x4½" 350.00
Vase, jack-in-pulpit; wht satin w/HP floral, ruffled, 14" 325.00
Vase, Lava, bulbous body, ring hdls, ca 1878, 4" 1,675.00
Vase, Lava, bulbous w/tall slim neck, 10" 1,750.00
Vase, wht satin, ribbed, ruffled, lily form, 7" 125.00

Mulberry China

Mulberry china was made by many of the Staffordshire area potters from about 1830 until the 1850s. It is a transfer-printed earthenware or ironstone named for the color of its decorations, a purplish-brown resembling the juice of the mulberry. Shades vary; some pieces look almost gray with only a hint of purple. Some of the patterns — Corean, Jeddo, Pelew, and Formosa, for instance — were also produced in Flow Blue ware. Others seem to have been used exclusively with the mulberry color.

Our advisor for this category is Mary Frank Gaston; she is listed in the Directory under Texas.

Allegheny, cup plate 45.00

Athens plate, marked W. Adams & Son, 9", $35.00.

Beauties of China, bowl, sauce; w/lid, Mellor & Venables 150.00
Beauties of China, plate, 9" 50.00
Blossom, sauce tureen, w/ladle, Ashworth 185.00
Bochara, plate, 10" 50.00
Bochara, wash bowl, 14" 100.00
Castle Scenery, plate, Furnival, 7¼" 25.00
Chusan, plate, Podmore Walker, 8¼" .25.00
Cologne, bowl, vegetable; w/lid, Alcock, lg 175.00
Corea, plate, 12-sided, Clementson, 9½" 60.00
Corea, platter, 8-sided, Clementson, 15¾x12⅛" 160.00
Corean, bowl, 9" 85.00
Corean, plate, Podmore Walker, 10" 75.00
Corean, plate, Podmore Walker, 8½" .50.00
Corean, plate, Podmore Walker, 9" 55.00
Corean, sugar bowl, lion hdls 125.00
Corean, teapot, Podmore Walker, 8" .225.00
Cyprus, bowl, vegetable; w/lid 175.00

Cyprus, plate, Davenport, 9" 66.00
Cyprus, platter, 8-sided, Davenport, 13¾x10⅜" 150.00
Foliage, soup, E Walley, ca 1850 . . . . .35.00
Genoa, coffeepot, Davenport, 9⅞" 175.00
Hyson, cup & saucer, handleless 55.00
Jeddo, compote, tall ped, Adams 350.00
Jeddo, creamer, Adams 110.00
Jeddo, pitcher, milk; 1-pt 90.00
Jeddo, plate, 10" 35.00
Jeddo, platter, ca 1845, 15½x12" 160.00
Jeddo, teapot 250.00
Jeddo, tureen, sauce; w/ladle 115.00
Madras, plate, 10" 124.00
Marble, cup & saucer, handleless; A Shaw 50.00
Marble, toothbrush holder, w/lid 40.00
Medina, pitcher, Jacob Furnival, 5" .127.50
Moss Rose, pitcher, 11½" 350.00
Neva, plate, Challinor, 8" 58.00
Ning Po, cup plate 35.00
Percy, plate, 9½" 45.00
Peru, gravy boat, Holdcroft 65.00
Peru, soup, Holdcroft, 11" 30.00
Peruvian, nappy, Wedgwood, 5⅛" 18.00
Peruvian, sugar bowl, w/lid 90.00
Peruvian, teapot 160.00
Rhone Scenery, creamer, hexagonal, TJ&J Mayer, 5¼" 110.00
Rhone Scenery, plate, luncheon; TJ&J Mayer, 8⅝" 30.00
Rhone Scenery, plate, TJ&J Mayer, 9⅝" 45.00
Rhone Scenery, platter, TJ&J Mayer, 13½x10½" 90.00
Rhone Scenery, relish dish, TJ&J Mayer 20.00
Rhone Scenery, teapot, TJ&J Mayer, ca 1850, 8½" 175.00
Rhone Scenery, tureen, 8-sided/ftd, w/lid, TJ&J Mayer, 10x8" .140.00
Rose, plate, T Walker, 6½" 25.00
Rose, platter, T Walker, 15½" 125.00
Seaweed, plate, w/shells, Ridgway, 10¾" 65.00
Shapoo, creamer, Hughes, 5⅞" 75.00
Strawberries, plate, 8½" 50.00
Temple, cup & saucer, handleless; Podmore Walker, 4" 100.00
Temple, plate, Podmore Walker, ca 1850, 8¾" 40.00
Temple, plate, 10" 55.00
Temple, plate, 9½" 50.00
Tivoli, bowl, vegetable; 10¼" 100.00
Vincennes, bowl, vegetable; 6-sided, w/lid, Alcock 195.00
Vincennes, platter, Alcock, 17½x13½" 175.00
Vincennes, sugar bowl, w/lid, Alcock 135.00
Washington Vase, cup & saucer, handleless; Podmore Walker . .60.00
Washington Vase, pitcher, milk; Podmore Walker 185.00
Washington Vase, pitcher, water; Podmore Walker, 8½" 250.00
Washington Vase, plate, Podmore Walker, 7¾" 25.00
Washington Vase, plate, Podmore Walker, 9¾" 40.00
Washington Vase, platter, 16x12" 160.00
Washington Vase, sugar bowl, w/lid, Podmore Walker, 9½" . . .255.00

Muller Freres

Henri Muller established a factory in 1900 at Croismare, France. He produced fine cameo art glass decorated with florals, birds, and insects in the Art Nouveau style. The work was accomplished by acid engraving and hand finishing. Usual marks were 'Muller,' 'Muller Croismare,' or 'Croismare, Nancy.' In 1910 Henri and his brother Deseri formed a glassworks at Luneville. The cameo art glass made there was nearly all produced by acid cuttings of up to four layers with motifs similar to those favored at Croismare. A good range of colors was used, and some pieces were gold flecked. Handles and decorative devices were sometimes applied by hand. In addition to the cameo glass, they also produced an acid-finished glass of bold mottled colors in the Deco style. Examples were signed 'Muller Freres' or 'Luneville.'

Our advisor for this category is Don Williams; he is listed in the Directory under Iowa.

Cameo

Bowl vase, lady's slipper, rose/bl on yel to bl, 14" dia **1,925.00**
Lamp, landscape, red/brn, 14" dome shade, ball base, 15" . .**13,200.00**
Vase, cottages/boats, blk/orange, 3 cuts, Luneville, 2¼" **650.00**
Vase, lake viewed through trees, brn on melon, cylinder, 8" .**1,000.00**
Vase, lake viewed through trees, 2¾" **475.00**
Vase, lake/bird in tree, amber/brn on yel, flat sided, 8" **1,500.00**
Vase, landscape w/mtn, trees in foreground, baluster, 9" . . .**2,475.00**
Vase, lg wisteria pendants, dk bl/gr on gray to yel, 15½" **3,575.00**
Vase, river, 2 children on banks, gr on gray mottle, 7" **2,000.00**
Vase, seaport/people, orange/turq on gray, baluster, 18" **9,900.00**
Vase, shepherd/flock, gr/red/coral, 3 cuts, mk, 4½x4⅜" **1,200.00**

Cameo vase, snowball branches and birds cut from 4 layers, signed, 12", $6,500.00.

Vase, tulips, yel on aqua, wheel cvd, sgn w/butterfly, 11" **3,750.00**
Vase, village/sailboats, purple/peach, 3 cuts, 6x2¾" **750.00**
Vase, windmill & cottages by shore, 3 cuts, Luneville, 13" . . .**1,500.00**

Miscellaneous

Box, clear w/gray/orange/purple/gr mottle, dome lid, 7" dia **600.00**
Chandelier, mottle purple frost center dome, 3 lily lights **1,650.00**
Vase, mc mottle on wht frost, 5½" **245.00**
Vase, silver foil int decor, Deco period, sgn, 5¾" **575.00**
Veilleuse, scarab form, wrought iron legs, sgn, 8" L **2,350.00**

Muncie

Muncie Pottery, established in Muncie, Indiana, by Charles O.

Grafton, was produced from 1922 until about 1935. It is made of a heavier clay than most of its contemporaries; the styles are sturdy and simple. Early glazes were bright and colorful. In fact, Muncie was advertised as the 'rainbow pottery.' Later, most of the ware was finished in a matt glaze. The more collectible examples are those modeled after Phoenix Glass vases — sculptured with lovebirds, grasshoppers, and goldfish. Their line of Art Deco-style vases bear a remarkable resemblance to the Consolidated Glass Company's Ruba Rombic line. Vases, candlesticks, bookends, ash trays, bowls, lamp bases, and luncheon sets were made. A line of garden pottery was manufactured for a short time. Items were frequently impressed with MUNCIE in block letters. Letters such as A, K, E, or D and the numbers 1, 2, 3, 4, or 5 often found scratched into the base are finishers' marks.

Bookends, mauve/cream gloss, owls in relief **75.00**
Candle holder, lt gr matt, mold pressed, 3 hdls, 2½", pr **35.00**
Chamberstick, gr/rose matt, 4x5¼" W **35.00**
Strawberry jar, hanging, gr matt, 5" **110.00**
Vase, blk & yel flambe, 8" **45.00**
Vase, gr matt, grasshoppers in relief, 6½" **90.00**
Vase, gr/rust matt, folded rim, 5x8" W **50.00**
Vase, gun metal semi-matt, hand turned, 2 hdls, 8" **55.00**
Vase, lav/gr matt, Deco, star form, 4" **45.00**
Vase, orange peel, Deco, star form, 4" **65.00**
Vase, tan matt, 4 hdls, 3x3x7" H **55.00**
Vase, turq matt, hand turned, ruffled top, 2 hdls, 6" **35.00**

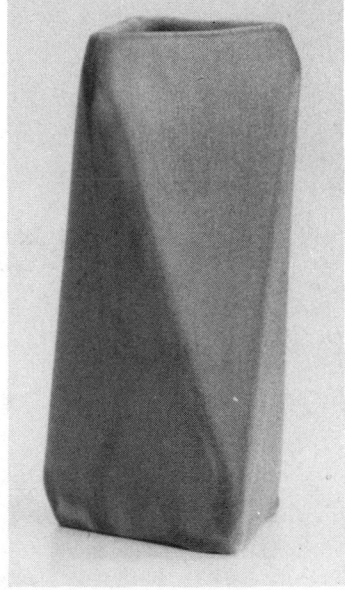

Vase, Ruba Rombic type, turquoise-blue, triangular panels, marked 'A,' 7", $55.00.

Musical Instruments

The field of automatic musical instruments covers many different categories ranging from tiny dolls and trinkets concealing musical movements to huge organs and orchestrions which weigh many tons. Music boxes, first made in the late 18th century by Swiss watchmakers, were produced in both disk and cylinder models. The latter type employs a cylinder studded with tiny projections. As the cylinder turns, these projections lift the tuned teeth in the 'music comb,' and the melody results. The value of the instrument depends upon the length of the cylinder and the quality of workmanship, though other factors must also be considered. Those in ornate cabinets or with extra features such as bells, mechanical birds, etc., often sell for much more. Units built into matching tables sell for about twice the amount they would bring otherwise. While small and medium-size units are still being made today, most of the larger ones date from the 19th century. Disk-type music boxes utilize interchangeable steel disks with projecting studs, which by means of an intervening 'star wheel' cause a music comb to play. There are many different variations and mechanisms. Most were made in Germany, but some were produced in the United States. Among the most popular makes are Polyphon, Symphonion, and Regina. The latter was made in Rahway, New Jersey, from about 1894 through 1917.

Player pianos were made in a wide variety of styles. Early varieties consisted of a mechanism which pushed up to a piano and played on the keyboard by means of felt-tipped fingers. These use sixty-five note rolls. Later models have the playing mechanisms built in. At first these also used sixty-five note rolls, but those produced from about 1908 until 1940 use eighty-eight note rolls.

Coin-operated electric pianos are deluxe versions of player pianos. These incorporate expression mechanisms so that by using special-made rolls they can play the hand-recorded rolls of famous pianists. Popular makes include Ampico, Duo-Art, and Welte. Roll-operated organs were made in many forms, ranging from table-top models to large foot-pumped versions. Of the latter, the Aeolian Orchestrelle is considered to be one of the best.

Unless noted, prices given are for instruments in fine condition, playing properly, with cabinets or cases in well-preserved or refinished condition. In all instances, unrestored instruments sell for much less, as do pieces with broken parts, damaged cases, and the like. On the other hand, particularly superb examples in especially ornate case designs and pieces which have been particularly well restored often will command more.

Our advisor for mechanical instruments is Fran Mayer; she is listed in the Directory under Connecticut.

Key:
c — cylinder   d — disk

Mechanical

Regina music box, carved walnut case, plays 15½" disks, 12x18x21", $3,100.00.

Box, Capital Cuffbox A, EX orig	3,000.00
Box, Criterion, 12" d, cherry case, EX orig	1,350.00
Box, Criterion, 15½" d, oak case, 84", M rstr	4,000.00
Box, Criterion, 20½" d, cvd oak floor model, 78", EX	8,000.00
Box, cylinder, 6 bells w/honeybee beaters, 28x13x11", rstr	3,800.00
Box, Kalliope, 20½" d, upright, 12 bells, EX orig	3,850.00
Box, Mandoline Expression, walnut veneer/inlay, +stand	4,000.00
Box, Mermod Sublime Harmonie, 11" interchangeable d,	2,200.00
Box, Polyphon, 14½" d, dbl comb, inlaid walnut, 12-bell	4,700.00
Box, Polyphon, 19⅝" d, upright, EX orig	4,250.00
Box, Polyphon, 19⅝" d, upright, rstr	4,600.00
Box, Polyphon, 24" d, walnut case, 76", EX orig	8,400.00
Box, Polyphon Serpentine, 11" d, table model	1,600.00
Box, Regina, 12" d, oak case, EX orig	1,495.00
Box, Regina, 15½" d, dbl comb, cvd case, M rstr	5,000.00
Box, Regina, 15½" d, dbl comb, EX orig	3,700.00
Box, Regina, 15½" d, oak case, coin-op, +24 disks	3,500.00
Box, Regina, 20½" d, w/base cabinet, NM	5,500.00
Box, Regina, 27" d, mahog/art glass, +24 disks	17,000.00
Box, Regina, 27" d, quarter-sawn oak, 1900s, 84", EX	9,995.00
Box, Regina, 8¼" d, mahog, EX	975.00
Box, Regina #38, 20¾" d, oak case, rstr	13,500.00
Box, Regina #40, 15½" d changer, rosewood, art case, NM	6,500.00
Box, Regina #8-A, 27" d, automatic, coin op, M	15,000.00
Box, Regina Hexaphone #102, EX orig	3,600.00
Box, Sublime Harmonie Interchangeable, walnut, 6-drw	40,000.00
Box, Symphonion, 11⅞" d, dbl comb, vertical table model	3,600.00
Box, Symphonion, 17⅝" d, cvd case, floor model, EX orig	6,000.00
Box, Symphonion, 25" d, upright, rstr, 90"	8,500.00
Box, Symphonion, 9" d, built-in bells, German, M	1,400.00
Calliope, Nat'l, full rstr	11,500.00
Calliope, Tangley CA-43, EX orig	7,000.00
Nickelodeon, Capitol, violin pipes, M rstr	18,000.00
Nickelodeon, Coinola, EX orig	3,700.00
Nickelodeon, Coinola Keyboard, VG unrstr	3,700.00
Nickelodeon, Nat'l, 8-roll changer, +150 rolls, unrstr	2,650.00
Nickelodeon, Seeburg A, w/lamps, early, EX	7,000.00
Nickelodeon, Seeburg B, art glass, rstr oak case, NM	4,950.00
Nickelodeon, Violano, Mills, single, M, +6 orig rolls	9,500.00
Nickelodeon, Western Electric C, rstr	7,000.00
Nickelodeon, Western Electric Selectra X, oak, 1920s, NM	7,500.00
Nickelodeon, Wurlitzer Race Horse, NM	9,500.00
Orchestrion, Coinola F, cabinet syle, w/flute pipes	9,500.00
Orchestrion, Coinola Midget, rstr	16,000.00
Orchestrion, Coinola X, cabinet style, EX	13,800.00
Orchestrion, Khul & Klat, EX orig	2,750.00
Orchestrion, Losche, EX orig	3,500.00
Orchestrion, Phillips Violine, European, EX rstr	2,900.00
Orchestrion, Western Electric Special, all orig	14,800.00
Orchestrion, Wurlitzer Bijou, M	17,000.00
Orchestrion, Wurlitzer C, keyboard, art glass, EX orig	18,500.00
Organ, band; N Tonawanda #188, for 150 Wurlitzer roll	17,500.00
Organ, band; Wurlitzer #146	15,000.00
Organ, band; Wurlitzer #150	22,500.00
Organ, dance; Auburo, w/accordion & sax	15,000.00
Organ, dance; De Cap Elite, 94-key, EX orig	35,000.00
Organ, dance; Mortier, 350 pipes, 180" W	35,000.00
Organ, dance; Mortier, 87-key, NM	40,000.00
Organ, Dutch street; book operated, 165 pipes, on cart	15,000.00
Organ, fair; Limonaire, 49-key, fancy facade	21,500.00
Organ, Kimball Electramatic, EX orig	1,000.00
Organ, Seeburg HO, horseshoe console, self-contained, EX	4,500.00
Organette, Auerophone	425.00
Organette, Orguinette #3, dbl reeds, floor model, EX orig	2,000.00

Organette, Rolmonica, Chromatic, rare 600.00
Organette, Rolmonica, hand-wind harmonica, paper rolls, EX .150.00
Organette, Symphonia, rstr 850.00
Organette, Victoria, cb strip, EX 450.00
Piano, grand; Chickering Ampico, 1923, 78", VG rstr 17,000.00
Piano, baby grand; Hamilton, Welte-Mignon action, old rstr 4,250.00
Piano, cabinet style; Red Welte, oak, EX orig 3,900.00
Piano, Fox Pianotainer, EX orig 5,000.00
Piano, grand; Aeolian Duo-Art, EX orig 4,500.00
Piano, grand; Chickering Ampico A, restrung/rfn, 77" 6,900.00
Piano, grand; Fisher Ampico, art case, harpsichord, 9 legs . . .5,200.00
Piano, grand; Knabe Ampico, 61", old rstr 5,500.00
Piano, grand; Marshall Wendel Ampico A, rstr, +50 rolls . . .3,500.00
Piano, grand; Mason & Hamlin Ampico, burl walnut, 68" .13,500.00
Piano, grand; Mason & Hamlin Ampico, 68", M rstr 15,000.00
Piano, grand; Stroud Duo-Art, tubed sides, recent, NM 3,000.00
Piano, grand; Weber Duo-Art, 1920, 71", EX orig 4,000.00
Piano, grand; Weber Duo-Art, 1930, 68", M orig 4,500.00
Piano, grand; Weber Duo-Art, 69", rstr 9,500.00
Piano, mini; Koehler & Campbell, Cantonese red, 88-key . . .5,500.00
Piano, upright; Behr Brothers, mahog case, unrstr 600.00
Piano, upright; Fischer Marque Ampico, EX orig 950.00
Piano, upright; Flexotone Electrelle, figured walnut, EX 1,200.00
Piano, upright; Griggs, oak case, EX orig, +850 rolls 3,500.00
Piano, upright; Jesse French, 88-note player, M rstr 5,800.00
Piano, upright; Knabe Ampico, EX orig 1,600.00
Piano, upright; Steinway Duo-Art, M rstr 12,000.00
Piano, upright; Story & Clark, 88-note, rstr 2,000.00
Piano, upright; Stroud Duo-Art, EX orig 800.00
Piano, upright; Weber Duo-Art, EX orig 1,150.00
Piano, upright; Welte reproducer, w/roll changer, EX orig . .11,500.00
Piano, Weber Duo-Art, Wm/Mary art case w/inlay VG 5,500.00
Piano, Weber Grandezza, NM 16,000.00
Piano, Wurlitzer IX, EX 800.00
Push-up, Wilcox & Wht, 58-note, w/organ 400.00

Non-Mechanical

Accordion, Hohner, by Besh Ge Toors, +VG case, EX 125.00
Accordion, Ludwig Parsifal Melodion, steel, 11x10x5½" 25.00
Autoharp, Zimmerman, spruce top, pat May 1882, 18x9½", G . .50.00
Banjo, Supertone label, 5-string, 36", EX 95.00
Clarinet, McClellan Universal, #34N-81-4260L, +case 150.00
Concertina, Campells Improved Melodion, fancy, 1880s, lg 95.00
Concertina, Lachenal, 20-button, London, VG in case 110.00
Drum, Excelsior, wood, gut snares, rope tension, 16x10", G . . .50.00
Drum, Gretsch, snare style, 14x12", VG 40.00
Drum, snare, bird's eye maple, EX 75.00
Fife, Geo Cloos, Improved, silver-banded ends, 6 holes, 17" 50.00
Fife, rosewood w/brass ends, Cival War era, EX 40.00
Harmonica, Horner, brass, M 65.00
Organ, lap; rosewood body, orig bellows, dtd 1844, 10x19x10" .125.00
Organ, reed; Estey, 2 manual keyboards, oak, 1910, EX 3,000.00
Piano, grand; Knabe, rosewood, ca 1885, EX rstr 15,000.00
Piano, grand; Matushek, rfn rosewood, ca 1875, 36x66", EX .3,000.00
Piano, grand; Steinway, sq, 1871, EX 2,500.00
Saxaphone, True-Tone #213133, low pitch, nickel, pat 1914 . .245.00
Tamborine, 10 nickel jingles, ivory/pearl inlays, 8½", G 25.00
Trumpet, Barclay, Czech, brass, +case, EX 195.00
Trumpet, Ludwig, nickel, wood case, EX 195.00
Violin, Amati Amati, 2 bows, deluxe case, NM 550.00
Xylophone, JC Deagan, Chicago, dtd July 21, 1914, EX 800.00
Zither, Anton Heimeyer, rosewood front, MOP tuners, 22x12" .75.00
Zither, Franz Schwarzer, MO, rosewood, bone turners, 22x11" . .75.00

Zither, J Schilt Solothurn, rosewood, early, 10x12½", VG 50.00
Zither, rosewood top, marquetry, teardrop shape, 10x11", EX . .220.00
Zither, Viohol's Emp State, rosewood, herringbone inlay, G 75.00

Mustache Cups

Mustache cups were popular items during the late Victorian period, designed specifically for the man with the mustache! They were made in silverplate as well as china and ironstone. Decorations ranged from simple transfers to elaborately applied and gilded florals. To properly position the 'mustache bar,' special cups were designed for the 'lefties' — these are the rare ones!

Blue Onion, 1800s 85.00
Lady w/flowers transfer, lg 35.00
Pk lustre w/gold floral band, Germany, 4½" 35.00
Roses, red on gr, Germany 55.00
Rust & gr pattern, Paragon China, ca 1904 . . . . .68.00
SP, cut/beaded decor, Eureka Silver, 1901, +saucer 110.00

Stylized multicolored flowers with gilt on white, numbered, 3¾", $65.00.

Nailsea

Nailsea is a term referring to clear or colored glass decorated in contrasting spatters, swirls, or loops. These are usually white but may also be pink or blue. It was first produced in Nailsea, England, during the late 1700s but was made in other parts of Britain and Scotland as well. Originally used for decorative novelties only, by 1845 pitchers, tumblers, and other practical items were being made from Nailsea-type glass. See also Lamps.

Bottle, gemel; clear w/bl spirals, appl rigaree, 9" 90.00
Bottle, scent; yel w/wht loops, ball base, silver cap/trim, 7" 425.00
Bowl, sapphire bl w/wht loops, crystal ft/hdls, 6¼x7⅝" 175.00
Candlestick, clear w/opal loops, folded lip, 10" 135.00
Decanter, wht opaque, cranberry loops, bubble stopper, 12" . . .250.00
Flask, clear, wht loops, pontil, sheared mouth, 6" 70.00
Flask, red w/tight wht loops, pontil, 6" 150.00
Flask, red-amber w/wht spirals, sheared mouth, pontil, 4½" 200.00
Flask, scent; pk w/wht swirls, blown, 1800s, 5¼" 200.00
Flask, wht w/horizontal rose & cobalt loops, pontil, 7½" 140.00
Flask, wht w/lg red loops, pontil, 7⅝" 170.00
Pitcher, cranberry w/wht loops, 7½" .185.00

Powder horn, clear w/wht loops, appl rings/mouth, 10" 95.00
Rolling pin, red w/wht loops, 15½" L 210.00
Sweetmeat jar, yel satin w/red loops, SP rim/hdl/lid, 4x4" 265.00
Vase, yel w/wht loops, 9" 145.00

Fluid lamp, teal blue with white loopings, Pairpoint, 12", $750.00; Witch ball, clear with blue, white, and faint cranberry loopings, 5½", $190.00; Powder horn whimsey on stand, clear with red loopings, 12", $190.00.

Nakara

Nakara was an opaque glassware made soon after the turn of the century by the C.F. Monroe Company. Though shapes were plainer and colors deeper, it was very similar to their famous Wave Crest line. Boxes of all sizes, pin trays, and dresser items of every sort were decorated with delicate hand-painted florals and 'squeeze-bag' lace reserves transfer printed with portraits of classical figures, birds, or Victorian ladies. Ormolu handles, bases, and collars, and scented satin box linings added opulence to the already elegant ware. The company closed in 1916. For more information, we recommend *Wave Crest: The Glass of C. F. Monroe* by Wilfred R. Cohen, available from Collector Books or your local bookstore.

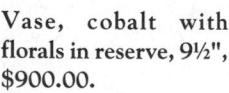

Vase, cobalt with florals in reserve, 9½", $900.00.

Ash tray, florals/swags, bl/wht on rose, mk, 4½" dia 275.00
Bonbon, floral on bl, open 260.00
Bowl, floral, SP rim w/upright bk fr, sq, 4½" 275.00
Box, cherubs, pk & gr, 4" 325.00
Box, floral on bl, mk, 2½x4" dia 275.00

Box, Greenaway figures on bl, 6" $800.00
Card holder, floral on gr 400.00
Hair receiver, florals/swags on bl 400.00
Humidor, geometrics, 5" 500.00
Pin tray, florals on gr, unmk 85.00
Plate, Queen Louise in reserve on bl, ormolu fr 1,200.00
Vase, florals in fr of wht dots on bl to pk, ormolu ft, 14" 785.00
Vase, roses, pk on dusty pk to gray-bl, ornate ft/hdls, 8" 600.00

Napkin Rings

Napkin rings became popular during the late 1800s. They were made from various materials. Among the most popular and collectible today are the various silverplated figural types made by American manufacturers.

When no condition is indicated, the items listed below are assumed to be all original and in very good to excellent condition. A timely warning: inexperienced buyers should be aware of excellent reproductions on the market, especially the wheeled pieces. These do not have the fine detail and patina of the originals and tend to have a more consistent, soft pewter-like finish. Over the past year, the larger figurals in excellent condition have appreciated considerably. Only those with a blackened finish, corrosion, or broken and/or missing parts have maintained their earlier price levels.

Key:
gw — gold washed   SH&M — Simpson, Hall, & Miller
R&B — Reed & Barton

Baby, crawling, ring on bk 150.00
Bear on stool, paws on ring, scalloped base, Middletown #68 . .250.00
Bird, fledgling atop nest, mouth open for feeding 65.00
Bird, wings/tail out, on leaf base, Toronto #1142 . . . . .135.00
Bird on leafy branch atop ring, ftd base, Toronto #028 . . . . . . .135.00
Bird stands on ped by ring, wings spread, Meriden #222 . . . . . . .80.00
Boy, kneeling, body forms ring, Meriden #224 . . . . .175.00
Boy removes sock aside ring, Derby #341 . . . . .250.00
Boy rolls ring, lady watches, oblong base, Tufts #1597 . . . . .375.00
Branches form chair, ring on seat 125.00
Bud vase w/spout on ring, circular base, R&B #1337 . . . . .150.00
Bulldog sits chained to doghouse, sq base, SH&M #207 . . . . . .295.00
Cat, glass eyes, body forms ring 250.00
Cat, lg, contemplative, Meriden #232 .200.00
Cat atop ring on rnd base arches bk at dog, Rogers #296 . . . . . .225.00
Cat pushing ring w/paws, no base 75.00
Cherub, winged/bashful, on tiered base w/ring, Tufts #1546 . . .225.00
Cherub atop ring holds rein on robin .200.00
Cherub crawls to arrow/wishbone, heart base, Meriden #4350 . .150.00
Cherub plays flute, book forms ring, ftd base, Derby #320 . . . . .300.00
Cherub sits on ring, holds dog on leash, Tufts #1543 . . . . .250.00
Cherub w/spear rides fish, tail supports ring, Meriden 295.00
Cherub wears cap, sits against ring, Pairpoint #52 . . . . .125.00
Cherubs, kneel w/ring between, rectangular base, R&B #1320 . .295.00
Chick on end of wishbone, Rococo base, ring elevated 65.00
Chick stands behind ring, oval ball-ftd base, Meriden #222 . . . . .75.00
Cockatoos perch on emb dome-shape ftd base, Meriden 225.00
Cow, flower-covered base, by tipped-over pail, Meriden #268 . .195.00
Crocodile carries ring on bk, Meriden #0202 . . . . .125.00
Deer (doe) on circular base w/ring aside, Toronto #1106 . . . . . .195.00
Deer sits on platform under fretwork ring, ball ft 275.00
Dog, lg, holds ring on bk, rope in mouth, no base 175.00
Dog chases bird up ring, oval base, R&B #1110 . . . . .150.00
Dog rests forepaws on lattice ring, sq ftd base 100.00
Dog sits by keg, ring on circular base, Tufts #1531 . . . . .150.00
Dolphins, 2 hold ring between tails 295.00

Fans, Oriental, 2 form ring, flowers/hummingbirds 95.00
Fox pulls cart, wheels turn 295.00
Frogs lean against ring, lily-leaf base, Meriden 250.00
Girl, gun on shoulder, stands on sq base, SH&M 375.00
Girl on stomach w/ring on bk, oval base, Wilcox #01548 . . . . .250.00
Girl pats dog in front of ring, R&B #1642 . . . . .300.00
Girl pets kitten, stands behind ring, Babcock #207 . . . . .225.00
Girl sits on base, Xd legs, ring in bk, R&B #1829 . . . . .175.00
Girl sits on bench beside ring, rectangular base, Derby 250.00
Girl w/pigtails pushes ring, Rogers #280 . . . . .185.00
Girl wearing bonnet holds ring, octagonal base, SH&M 150.00
Greenaway boy sits sleeping before ring, Pairpoint 195.00
Greenaway boy w/bat & ball 235.00
Greenaway boy w/cookie, dog begs, rectangular base, Rogers . .295.00
Greenaway girl w/bonnet & hood sits by ring, Derby 195.00
Greenaway girl w/hands on ring, Barbour Bros 175.00
Horse behind fence that juts from beaded ring, Meriden 195.00
Horse prances, pulls flowered ring on wheels, Rogers #213 . . . .295.00
Horse prances atop ring, pyramid base, Meriden #130 . . . . .150.00
Horse w/ring on bk, sq ball-ftd base 150.00
Horseshoe on ring, w/horse's head & Good Luck emb, SH&M . .85.00
Jack & Jill climb up hill-shaped ring, Tufts #1667 . . . . .375.00
Knight in armor w/upraised torch stands beside ring 145.00
Lady stands behind ring, 6-leafed ftd base, Tufts #3405 . . . . . .200.00
Lady w/purse in hand, rectangular base, Aurora #45 . . . . .225.00
Leaf base w/pepper, salt atop ring, basket hdl, Meriden #22 . . .135.00
Lion stands beside ring, rectangular base 150.00
Little Red Riding Hood w/basket touches ring, R&B 260.00
Nude male runner w/torch, sq base, resilvered 195.00
Owl sits on ring, log base, Rogers #248 . . . . .95.00
Parrot, glass eyes, on loop hdl by ring, #4338 . . . . .175.00
Parrot, glass eyes, sitting on perch, ring on bk 100.00
Parrot, swivel perch, +s&p, 4-ball ped ft, Meriden #168 . . . . . .230.00
Peacock sits on ring, rnd base, Meriden #234 . . . . .150.00
Pear/leaves hang from ring, leaf base, Middletown #140 . . . . . .95.00
Pheasant leans on limb that holds ring, Meriden #246 . . . . . . .150.00
Pig stands beside ring, rnd base 125.00
Rabbit crouches on log-type base, holds ring w/ears 150.00
Rabbit sits under log tree, ring atop, R&B #1520 . . . . .200.00
Rat on haunches by patterned ring, oblong base, Tufts #1619 . .150.00
Rifles, 2 Xd sets, filigree ring between, Meriden #335 . . . . .150.00
Rooster crows from atop shovel that holds ring, Meriden 120.00
Rose w/leaves at front of ring, tiered oval base, Rogers 65.00

Sphinx holds up ring w/bud vase atop, Aurora #45 . . . . .150.00
Squirrel climbs tree, ring atop, rnd base, R&B #1150 . . . . .125.00
Squirrel stands on rock base, body forms ring 150.00
Sunflower base, octagonal, Meriden #37 . . . . .65.00
Turtle crawls w/ring on bk, Meriden #193 . . . . .150.00
Wheelbarrow holds ring, flat shield-type base, Tufts #1537 . . . .125.00

Nash

A. Douglas Nash founded the Corona Art Glass Company in Long Island, New York. He produced tableware, vases, flasks, etc. using delicate artistic shapes and forms. After 1933 he worked for the Libbey Glass Company.

Bonbon, Chintz, bl, ped ft, 2⅞x5" 225.00
Bowl, Beryl, bl appl hdls, ftd, 3½" 130.00
Bowl, gold irid, ribbed, #502, 13½" 660.00
Candlestick, Chintz, dk red w/gray, ball stem, 4", pr 4,150.00
Champagne, Bl Grotto, 7¼" 110.00
Compote, Chintz, gr w/wide red & opal striped rim, sgn, 4" . . .300.00
Finger bowl, Chintz, gr/amethyst/clear 70.00
Finger bowl, Chintz, pk/gr stripes 65.00
Goblet, Chintz, lt aqua, orange stripes, stemmed, 8" 75.00
Goblet, pk, threaded, clear twist stem, mk Libbey, 7" 145.00
Plate, Chintz, lt aqua, orange stripes, 6¼" 23.00
Tumbler, Chintz, dk bl/gr, clear ped & ball stem, 6¼" 110.00
Vase, amber w/brn spirals, ball base/long gourd neck, 11" 600.00
Vase, gold irid, flared, mk, 12x5" 765.00

Natzler, Gertrude and Otto

The Natzler's came to the United States from Vienna in the late 1930s. They settled in Los Angeles where they continued their work in ceramics, for which they were already internationally recognized. Gertrude created the forms; Otto formulated a variety of interesting glazes — among them volcanic, crystalline, and lustre.

Bowl, curdled running scarlet over black matt, 6", NM, $550.00; Vase, medium to dark blue streaks with scattering of gray crystalline, 4", $715.00.

Sailor boy with anchor, Reed & Barton #1346, 3½", $275.00.

Bowl, frothy cream semi-gloss/red clay ft, N380, 3¼x4¼" 275.00
Bowl, volcanic gray-brn w/yel highlights on blk, 1950, 6½" . . .500.00
Vase, brn/lt gr streaky matt, flattened/'slit' top, 13x13" 850.00
Vase, gold-yel surface waves on terra cotta, sm rim, 5" dia 450.00
Vase, gr/brn on 'canvas,' bulbous bottom, K139, 8½x4" 700.00
Vase, gray crystalline on med/dk bl streaks, sm rim, 4x4" 700.00
Vase, yel gloss, cylinder w/stepped-in base, 5x3¾" 375.00

Netsukes

Netsukes are miniature Japanese carvings made with holes called Himitoshi, either channeled or within the carved design, that allow it to be threaded onto a waist cord and worn with the kimono. Because the kimono had no pockets, the Japanese man hung his tools, his pipe, tobacco pouch, and other daily necessities from his sash. The netsuke was the toggle that secured them all. Although most are of ivory, others were made of bone, wood, metal, porcelain, or semi-precious stones. Some were inlaid or lacquered. They are found in many forms, but figurals are the most common and desirable. They range in size from 1" up to 3", which was the maximum size allowed by law. Most netsukes represented the religion, mythology, and the habits of the average person; there was no written word, hence carvers depicted the daily life of the people.

Careful study is required to recognize the quality of the netsuke. Many have been made in Hong Kong in recent years; and even though some are very well carved, these are considered copies and avoided by the serious collector. There are many books that will help you learn to recognize quality netsukes, and most reputable dealers are glad to assist you. Use your magnifying glass to check for repairs. In the listings that follow, netsukes are ivory unless noted otherwise.

Acrobat balances w/hands on drum, unsgn, 1800s, 1⅞" 600.00
Badger priest & Karako, Shomin w/kakihan, late 1800s, 1⅝" . .165.00
Badger w/sake pot & leaf hat, inlaid eyes, unsgn, 1800s, 2" 770.00
Bamboo shoot, wood, EX details, Yoshishige, 1800s, 2¼" 500.00
Boy & old man w/turtle on leash, Nansai, 1800s, 1⅝" 600.00
Boy beside recumbent ox, minor wear, unsgn, 2" 385.00
Clam dream, wood, pavilion amid trees, Bokuju, 1800, 2¼" . . .440.00
Courtesan w/pup at ft, wood, lacquered robes, Zeshin, 2½" . .1,045.00
Daikoku peeks out of mallet/karako peeks in, Teichi, 1¾" 500.00

Daruma, wood with inlaid bronze face, signed Ippo, 1½", $900.00.

Dragon coiled in clouds, wood, spherical, Ikko, 1800s, 1¾" 880.00
Ferret atop lobed gourd, mouse beside, wood, Shoju, 1⅜" . . .1,155.00
Frog, wood, inlaid eyes, EX details, Masanao, 1800s, 1¾" 440.00
Frog on gourd, snake coiled inside, unsgn, 1800s, 1" 660.00
Gama Sennin lies w/toad on bk, unsgn, late 1700s, 2" 715.00
Goat, recumbent, wood w/inlaid eyes, Kyoto school, 1¾" . . .1,000.00
Hare, cockerel, & chick, inlaid eyes, Hosho, 1800s, 1⅝" 770.00
Hoeei sits w/sack, 3 boys about him, Norishige, 1800s, 1½" . . .880.00
Houseboat, upper deck w/sliding doors, Ryukosai, 1800s, 1⅜" . .600.00

Kwanyu pulls beard, inlaid eyes, Mitsuhiro, 1700s, 2¼" 880.00
Lobster & crab on pile of fish, Ryumin, late 1800s, 2¼" 660.00
Man w/basket of beans sits on stump, sgn, 1800s, 1⅝" 440.00
Monkey sits on tortoise, wood, Masanao, 1800s, 1½" 880.00
Monkey w/young, wood, inlaid eyes, Masanao, 1800s, 1¾" 600.00
Okame stands in elegant robe, Somin, late 1800s, 2¼" 495.00
Oni kneels w/club on shoulder, wood, Shoju, 1800s, 1½" 500.00
Oni w/drum on lap, inlaid clothes/drum, unsgn, 1800s, 1⅜" . . .600.00
Ox, recumbent, inlaid eyes, jaw rstr, Tomotada, 1700s, 2¼" .2,000.00
Rat, finely cvd hairwork, inlaid eyes, Tomokazu, 1800s, 2" 495.00
Rat gnaws candle, eyes/wick inlaid, Okatomo, 1800s, 1⅞" . . .2,300.00
Rats in group, inlaid eyes, Ikko Shoryo, late 1800s, 1¾" 770.00
Sake drinker dances on 1 ft, Hogyuku, late 1800s, 2½" 600.00
Samurai & youth w/sword between, Nansai, late 1800s, 1¾" . . .330.00
Sennin & tiger, wood, inlaid eyes, Sadakata, 1800s, 1¾" 660.00
Sennin w/branch of peaches/basket on bk, unsgn, 1700s, 2¾" .550.00
Shishi mask, wood, movable jaw, unsgn, 1700s, 1¾" 550.00
Shishi w/ball, inlaid eyes, Mitsuharu, late 1800s, 1¾" 660.00
Shishi w/ball, wood, inlaid eyes, Yoshiyama, 1800s, 1½" 275.00
Shoki crouches over Oni w/sword, Kimitomo, 1800s, 1⅜" 385.00
Shoki on Oni w/drawn sword, wood, inlaid eyes, Shoku, 1¾" . .440.00
Skeleton leans on base of skull, wood, unsgn, 1800s, 1¾" 450.00
Snails on mushroom, wood, fine details, Sari, 1700s, 1½" . . .1,500.00
Snake coiled about frog, inlaid eyes, Masatsugu, 1800s, 1¼" .1,300.00
Takarabune w/7 Gods of Good Fortune, Ryukyo, 1800s, 1¼" . .825.00
Tennin w/drum, flowing robe, unsgn, late 1800s, 2¾" 330.00
Tiger chases tail, wood, unsgn, late 1700s, 1¼" 770.00
Tiger sits w/monkey on bk, wood/inlaid eyes, Masayuki, 1½" . .550.00
Warrior tackles boar, inlaid eyes, Shuzan, 1800s, 2⅛" 550.00
Witch grimacing, swirling robe, unsgn, 1800s, 2⅛" 935.00
Wolf crouches over branch of loquats, unsgn, 1800s, 1½" 495.00
2 boars on jutting rock, ivory/wood, Kokei w/kakihan, 1⅜" 880.00
2 karako w/fishbowl between, Shumin, late 1800s, 1⅝" 550.00
2 monkeys gather loquats in branches, wood, Ikko, 1700s, 2" . .660.00
7 Gods of Good Fortune in open boat, Ryumin w/kakihan, 2" .715.00

New Geneva

In the early years of the 19th century, several potteries flourished in the Greensboro, Pennsylvania, area. They produced utilitarian stoneware items as well as tile and novelties for many decades; all failed well before the turn of the century.

Pitchers, brown floral on reddish clay, 7¾", EX, $350.00; 8½", $550.00.

Doll's head, cobalt features, 4#/8", EX 2,300.00
Flowerpot, attatched base, in brn: 2 names/floral, 8", EX 500.00
Jar, brn floral/foliage on red clay, appl hdls, 10", NM 775.00
Jug, stencil: ST Suit MD Little Brn Pig, 1880, 6¼", NM 375.00
Pitcher, floral, brn on red-buff, tooled shoulder band, 8¾" 900.00
Pitcher, foliage, rust on red bsk, minor wear, 12" 550.00
Vase, floral, brn brushed on gray, 9½", EX 850.00

New Hall

The New Hall Company was established in the early 1780s in the Shelton district of England. In the early years, they produced hardpaste dinnerware typically decorated with simple floral sprays, often assigning a number rather than a name to their patterns. By 1812, a bone china body was favored and styles revised to suit the fashion. Decorations became more elaborate. Much of the ware was unmarked and is often attributed to Worcester. Occasionally a piece was marked 'New Hall' within a double circle. Production ceased by 1835.

Bowl, floral, mc, 2½x5", EX 35.00
Creamer, floral, mc, 4⅜", NM 65.00
Cup & saucer, pk/bl/gr floral+brn King's roses, pk border 110.00
Sugar basin, bl/gold borders, molded ring hdls, 1800, 5" 260.00

New Martinsville

The New Martinsville Glass Company took its name from the town in West Virginia where it began operations in 1901. In the beginning years, pressed tablewares were made in crystal as well as colored and opalescent glass. Considered an innovator, the company was known for their imaginative applications of the medium in creating lamps made entirely of glass, vanity sets, figural decanters, and models of animals and birds. In 1944 the company was purchased by Viking Glass, who continued to use many of the old molds — the animals molds included. They marked their wares 'Viking' or 'Rainbow Art.' Viking recently ceased operations and has been purchased by the Dalzell company; and they, too, are making the animal birds and animal models. Although at first they were not marked, future productions are to be marked with an acid stamp. Dalzell/Viking animals are in the $50.00 to $60.00 range. See also Depression Glass.

Bookend, gazelle, ea 65.00
Bookend, nautilus shell, ea 30.00
Bookend, porpoise, orig, ea .1,000.00
Bookend, porpoise, 3 on wave, Viking, ea 75.00
Bookend, sailing ship, ea 40.00
Bookend, starfish, ea 65.00
Bookends, German shepherd, ea 45.00
Bookends, wolfhound, ea 75.00
Bottle, cat form, crystal 10.00
Box, Martha Washington, pk satin 95.00
Cake plate, Prelude, ped ft 45.00
Candlestick, Florentine, dbl 10.00
Candlestick, seal, sm 40.00
Champagne, Prelude 15.00
Cocktail, Carlton 12.50
Cocktail, Prelude 12.50
Cordial, Prelude 13.00
Cruet, Janice, lt bl, w/stopper 65.00
Cruet, Prelude, w/stopper, 4-oz 35.00
Cup, Prelude 10.00
Figurine, baby chick 25.00
Figurine, bear, mother 180.00

Figurine, bear, young 45.00
Figurine, elephant 80.00
Figurine, fish, teal, tall 35.00
Figurine, hen 65.00
Figurine, horse, head up 95.00
Figurine, pony, amber & aqua bl, Viking, 12" 75.00
Figurine, rooster, lg 75.00
Figurine, seal w/ball, 7" 65.00
Figurine, squirrel, no base 35.00
Figurine, squirrel, on sq/flat base 40.00
Figurine, tiger 175.00
Goblet, Carlton 12.50
Goblet, Prelude, water sz 18.00
Old Fashion, Prelude, heavy base 16.00

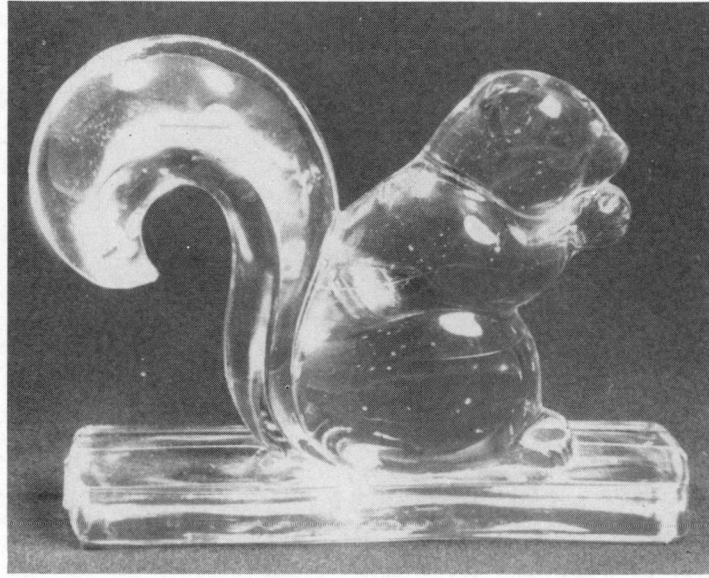

Squirrel, 5" long, $40.00.

Vase, Dove, crystal 60.00

Newcomb

The Newcomb College of New Orleans, Louisiana, established a pottery in 1895 to provide the students with first-hand experience in the fields of art and ceramics. Using locally dug clays — red and buff in the early years, white-burning by the turn of the century — potters were employed to throw the ware which the ladies of the college decorated. Until about 1910, a glossy glaze was used on ware decorated by slip painting or incising. After that a matt glaze was favored. Soft blues and greens were used almost exclusively, and the decorative themes were chosen to reflect the beauty of the South. 1930 marked the end of the matt-glaze period and the art-pottery era.

Various marks used by the pottery include an 'N' within a 'C,' sometimes with 'HB' added to indicate a 'hand-built' piece. The potter often incised his initials into the ware, and the artists were encouraged to sign their work. Among the most well-known artists were Sadie Irvine, Henrietta Bailey, and Fannie Simpson.

Newcomb pottery is evaluated to a large extent by two factors: design and condition. In the following listings, items are assumed matt unless noted otherwise.

Bowl, floral, bl/wht on bl, S Irvine, 2¼x7" 450.00
Bowl, floral at shoulders, 4-color, H Bailey, 5½" 650.00
Candlestick, ribbed, cream on bl, S Irvine, 3½" 700.00
Jar, lemons/foliage, pnt/cvd, sgn UE, 6" dia 3,500.00

Jar, pk floral band on base, dome lid, bulbous, 5½" **1,800.00**
Mug, sunflowers on intertwined stems, glossy, Lonnegan, 4" . **1,600.00**
Paperweight, daisies/bl band at edge, sgn AM/JM, 3¾" **300.00**
Pitcher, yel/gr buds on lt/dk bl bands, glossy, Bailey, 8" **2,400.00**
Plaque, oak trees/moss, AF Simpson, oak fr/label, 9½x12" . . . **3,000.00**
Plaque, pine trees/moon, bl/gr/yel, EX detail, label, 9x6" **3,600.00**
Plate, incised fish at rim, bl tones, MF Baker, 9½" **900.00**
Vase, bayou scene, sgn CN/KS/#18, 6" **700.00**
Vase, bl/red matt, hand thrown, J Meyer, 2½" **110.00**
Vase, daffodils, 4-color, sgn AM, 4½" **725.00**
Vase, floral (lg), bl/yel on med bl, S Irvine, #209, 7" **850.00**
Vase, floral at shoulder, M Morel/J Meyer, cylindrical, 4½" **350.00**

Vase, floral bouquets, green leaves over dark blue ground blend at base into solid green, incised blue top band, marked JM, B in circle, AF Simpson, #EY74, 9", $2,400.00.

Vase, floral neck band, gourd form w/hdls, C Littlejohn, 6" . . . **700.00**
Vase, floral neck band, wht/bl on dk bl, AF Simpson, 3" **375.00**
Vase, floral neck band, wht/red/gr on bl, S Irvine, #90, 6" **500.00**
Vase, floral pendants, bl/rose/purple, S Irvine, 5" **650.00**
Vase, grape clusters, S Irvine, 8½x4½" **750.00**
Vase, grapes cvd at neck, lt gr/med & dk bl, A Munson, 5½" . . **850.00**
Vase, ribbed, gr/bl/pk on bl, S Irvine, bulbous, #2, 2¼" **650.00**
Vase, rice stalks, cvd/pnt, 4-color, sgn MSL, 5" **1,900.00**
Vase, roses at neck, wht on bl/gr, HB Meyer/K, 5½" **900.00**
Vase, trees/moss/moon, bl/gr w/yel, S Irvine, #35, 6" **675.00**
Vase, trees/moss/moon, sharply defined, AF Simpson, 6½" . . . **900.00**
Vase, trees/moss/moon, sharply defined, AF Simpson, 7½" . . **1,250.00**
Vase, 3 incised irises, wht/turq/lt bl, M LeBlanc, 6½x4" **3,800.00**
Vase, 3 irises/thin leaves, bl/gr, S Irvine, 12½x5" **2,900.00**
Vase, 4 flowers, 1 in ea top corner, pk/bl, S Irvine, 3½" **425.00**

Vase, 8 flowers, yel w/turq stems on yel/cream, H Joor, 6" . . . **3,000.00**

Newspapers

In addition to historic content, there are other factors that can add or take away the value of an old newspaper. These factors are: whether or not the account is a 'first report' (the first time that the news appeared — a 'later-report' is a subsequent reporting); location of articles on the event (those with front-page articles are more highly valued); displayability (size of headlines, presence of photos or graphics to illustrate the event, etc.); whether the paper is from a small or large town; a daily or weekly; and charisma of the paper or event. Prices listed here are for a typical mid-sized town paper with front-page coverage and medium-size headlines.

Papers that do not cover a specific event are called 'atmosphere' newspapers. While these are not as valuable, they offer interesting insight into a particular era through ads for runaway slaves, ships' schedules, jobs wanted, etc. Many have interesting articles on topics such as mermaids, hangings, sea voyages, and a host of other topics.

For a more complete price guide and information on how to determine values as well as how to grade historic newspapers, detect reprints, where to buy and sell originals, and much more, the Newspaper Collectors Society of America offers a *Free Mini-Course About Historic Newspapers*. To obtain your copy of the 32-page primer and extensive price guide, send $1.00 to NCSA, Box 19134-S, Lansing, MI 48901. From it you will learn, for instance, how to recognize the original April 15, 1865, *New York Herald* version of the report of Lincoln's assassination from among the thousands of reprints which abound today. This booklet could save collectors from making bad investments and prevent dealers from loosing their honest reputation.

Key:
lr — letter   pub — publisher

1784-1799, Atmosphere paper **17.00**
1800-1859, Atmosphere paper **5.00**
1861, Civil War opens, first reports **85.00**
1861, Civil War opens, later reports **45.00**
1861-1865, Atmosphere papers, Confederate **25.00**
1861-1865, Atmosphere papers, Union **4.00**
1861-1865, Major battles of Civil War, Confederate titles **115.00**
1861-1865, Major battles of Civil War, first reports **40.00**
1861-1865, Major battles of Civil War, later reports **20.00**
1862, Emancipation Proclamation **60.00**
1863, Battle of Gettysburg, first reports **80.00**
1863, Battle of Gettysburg, later reports **40.00**
1863, Gettysburg address **110.00**
1865, Capture & death of J Wilkes Booth **45.00**
1865, End of Civil War, first reports **160.00**
1865, End of Civil War, later reports **60.00**
1865, Fall of Richmond **55.00**
1865, Harper's Weekly, Apr 29 edition **90.00**
1865, Leslie's Illustrated Newspaper, Apr 29 edition **125.00**
1865, Lincoln assassination, NY Herald, Apr 15, 10 AM **1,200.00**
1865, Lincoln assassination, NY Herald, Apr 15, 2 AM **500.00**
1865, Lincoln assassination, NY Herald, Apr 15, 3 AM **350.00**
1865, Lincoln assassination, other titles, first reports **125.00**
1865, Lincoln assassination, other titles, later reports **50.00**
1866-1900, Atmosphere papers **3.00**
1871, Chicago fire, Chicago paper, 1st reports **400.00**
1871, Chicago fire, later reports **40.00**
1871, Chicago fire, other first reports **75.00**
1872, Grant elected 2nd term **12.00**
1876, Custer's Last Stand, first reports **125.00**

The Philadelphia Inquirer.

PRICE TWO CENTS.   PHILADELPHIA, TUESDAY, APRIL 25, 1865.   PRICE TWO CENTS.

PRESIDENT LINCOLN'S REMAINS IN INDEPENDENCE HALL.

OUR DEAD PRESIDENT

AN INTERIOR VIEW OF THE RAILROAD CAR CONVEYING THE REMAINS OF PRESIDENT LINCOLN.

Highly displayable with exeptional large front page engraving covering the many funerals of Abe Lincoln; good condition: $125.00; excellent: $250.00 or more. Photo courtesy R.J. Brown Archives.

1876, Custer's Last Stand, later reports 55.00
1876, Tilden defeats Hayes, lg graphics 80.00
1876, Tilden defeats Hayes, no graphics .35.00
1877, Hayes declared president 17.00
1880, Garfield elected 18.00
1881, Billy the Kid killed 110.00
1881, Garfield assassinated 30.00
1881, Gunfight at OK Corral 130.00
1882, Jesse James killed, first reports .130.00
1882, Jesse James killed, later reports .60.00
1884, Grover Cleveland elected 12.00
1885, Ulysses S Grant dies 40.00
1889, Johnstown flood 30.00
1892, Grover Cleveland reelected 2nd term 17.00
1892, Lizzie Borden crime & trial 15.00
1898, Sinking of Maine, NY Journal or World 250.00
1898, Sinking of Maine, other titles 50.00
1898, Spanish American War begins 35.00
1898, Spanish American War ends 35.00
1900, James Jeffries defeats Jack Corbett to retain title 12.00
1900, McKinley elected 2nd term 17.00
1900-1945, Atmosphere paper 1.00

1901, McKinley assassinated 28.00
1903, Wright Brother's flight 300.00
1904, Teddy Roosevelt elected 17.00
1906, San Francisco earthquake, in San Francisco paper 185.00
1906, San Francisco earthquake, other titles 50.00
1908, Taft elected 10.00
1912, Sinking of Titanic, first reports 185.00
1912, Sinking of Titanic, later reports 85.00
1912, Wilson elected 15.00
1914, WWI begins 30.00
1915, Lusitania sunk, first reports 85.00
1916, Woodrow Wilson elected 12.00
1917, US declares war 27.00
1918, November 11 Armistice 25.00
1920, Harding elected 12.00
1920, Prohibition takes effect 22.00
1920, Women's Suffrage, 19th amendment 22.00
1924, Coolidge elected 12.00
1925, Scopes 'Monkey' trial verdict 22.00
1926, Tunney defeats Jack Dempsey 25.00
1927, Babe Ruth hits 60th home run .175.00
1927, Lindbergh in Paris, first reports 65.00
1927, Lindbergh in Paris, later reports 25.00
1928, Hoover elected 12.00
1929, Byrd flies to South Pole 15.00
1929, St Valentine's Day Massacre 45.00
1929, Stock Market crash 40.00
1931, Al Capone found guilty 35.00
1932, FDR elected 1st term 12.00
1932, Lindbergh baby found dead 20.00
1933, Prohibition repealed 18.00
1934, Bonnie & Clyde killed 35.00
1934, Dillinger killed, Chicago title 185.00
1934, Dillinger killed, other titles 55.00
1936, FDR elected 2nd term 10.00
1936, King Edward renounces crown 13.00
1937, Amelia Earhart vanishes 15.00
1937, Hindenbergh explodes, first reports 40.00
1937, Hindenbergh explodes, later reports 25.00
1939, Gone w/Wind, Atlanta Constitution/Journal, Dec 15-16 .75.00
1939, Gone w/the Wind, either Atlanta title, Dec 17-19 . . . . . .17.00
1939-1945, Major battles in the war 18.00
1940, FDR elected 3rd term 12.00
1941, Pearl Harber attacked, Honolulu Star-Bulletin 1,000.00
1941, Pearl Harbor attacked, Dec 8 issues, first reports 25.00
1941, Pearl Harbor attacked, other titles w/lg headlines 40.00
1944, D-Day 20.00
1944, FDR elected 4th term 12.00
1945, FDR dies 12.00
1945, First atomic bomb dropped 25.00
1945, Japan surrenders 25.00
1945, VE-Day or VJ-Day 30.00
1948, Babe Ruth's death 100.00
1948, Dewey Defeats Truman, Chicago Daily Tribune 700.00
1950, US enters Korean War 12.00
1953, Truce signed to end Korean War .17.00
1956, Eisenhower elected 2nd term 8.00
1957, Soviets launch Sputnik 15.00
1958, Alaska joins Union, Alaska title 35.00
1959, Hawaii joins Union, Honolulu title 35.00
1960, JFK elected 8.00
1961, Alan Shepard, 1st American in space 12.00
1961, Roger Maris hits 61st home run, breaks Ruth's record 85.00
1962, Death of Marilyn Monroe 20.00

1962, John Glenn orbits the earth **12.00**
1963, JFK assassination, Nov 22, Dallas title **45.00**
1963, JFK assassination, Nov 22, other titles **12.00**
1963, JFK assassination, papers dtd Nov 23 to Nov 26 . . . . **5.00**
1964, LBJ elected **7.00**
1967, Superbowl I **12.00**
1968, Bobby Kennedy assassination **12.00**
1968, Martin Luther King assassination **15.00**
1968, Nixon elected 1st term **5.00**
1969, Moon landing **17.00**
1973, Vietnam peace pacts signed **7.00**
1974, Nixon resigns **12.00**
1976, Carter elected **3.00**
1977, Death of Elvis, Memphis paper **40.00**
1977, Death of Elvis, other titles **8.00**
1980, Chicago Sun-Times error: It's Reagan & Ford **3.00**
1980, Death of John Lennon, NY title **12.00**
1986, Challenger explodes **7.00**

Niloak

Benton, Arkansas, was an area rich with natural clay, high in quality and easily accessible. During the last half of the 1800s, a dozen potteries flourished there; but by 1898 the only one remaining was owned by Charles Dean Hyten. In 1909 he began to experiment, trying to preserve in his finished ware the many colors of the native clay. By 1912 he had perfected a method that produced the desired effect. He obtained a U.S. patent for his handcrafted Niloak Mission pottery, characterized by swirling layers of browns, blues, red, and buff clays. Only a few early pieces were glazed both inside and out; these are extremely rare. After the process was perfected, only the interior was glazed. The ware was marked 'Niloak,' the backward spelling of Kaolin, a type of fine porcelain clay. No sooner had production began than the pottery burned, but Hyten rebuilt and added a stoneware line called Eagle Pottery. Hywood, an inexpensive novelty ware, was introduced in 1929 in an attempt to boost sales during the onset of the depression years. Until 1934 when the management changed hands, the line was marked 'Hywood-Niloak.' After that, 'Hywood' no longer appeared on the ware. Hyten left the pottery in 1941; in 1946 the operation closed.

Ash tray, Mission Ware, w/metal contoured cap **75.00**
Bowl, Mission Ware, w/frog, 3½x9" **75.00**
Bowl, Mission Ware, 5x3½" **55.00**
Candle holder, Mission Ware, w/finger grip, 2¼x5½" **125.00**
Candlestick, Mission Ware, 7" **95.00**
Creamer, stylized florals in relief, lt bl, 3½" **12.00**
Ewer, high gloss, 12" **19.00**
Fern dish, Mission Ware, 3¾x8" **110.00**
Figurine, 'razor-back' w/Arkansas emb, maroon **35.00**
Figurine, deer, pk, 5¾" **12.00**
Figurine, parrot on pleated basket, 6" **22.50**
Humidor, Mission Ware, w/lid, 5½" **210.00**
Inkwell, Mission Ware, hinged metal lid, 2¾" **150.00**
Jar, Mission Ware, pierced lid, 4" **175.00**
Juice set, florals in relief, pk, pitcher+4 3½" mugs **45.00**
Lamp, Mission Ware, metal fittings, 12" **210.00**
Lamp base, Mission Ware, 9½" **175.00**
Match holder, Mission Ware, 3½" **45.00**
Mug, Mission Ware, 4½" **45.00**
Mug, pk gloss, 3½" **8.00**
Pitcher, lemonade; Mission Ware, 8" **165.00**
Pitcher, tankard; Mission Ware, 12" **225.00**
Planter, camel, wht matt, 5x5½" **25.00**

Planter, canoe, maroon matt, 11" L **35.00**

Deer planter, dusty rose, 8x7½", $30.00.

Planter, wooden shoe style, pk gloss, 3¼x5" **12.50**
Vase, Grecian style, maroon matt, 7" **17.50**
Vase, Mission Ware, cylindrical, 9" **85.00**
Vase, Mission Ware, flared neck, bulbous bottom, 10" **85.00**
Vase, Mission Ware, flared neck, 3½" **30.00**
Vase, Mission Ware, hourglass shape, 6½" **52.00**
Vase, Mission Ware, orig label, 12x8" **125.00**
Vase, Mission Ware, red/brn/gr hi-glaze, Pat pending, 9½" . . . **130.00**
Vase, Mission Ware, rose bowl, 5x7" **55.00**
Vase, Mission Ware, rose bowl shape w/ped ft, 4½x6" **55.00**
Vase, Mission Ware, teardrop form, 12" **110.00**
Vase, Mission Ware, teardrop form w/tab hdls, 8" **85.00**

Vase, Mission Ware, 4½", $50.00.

Wall pocket, geometric design, yel matt, 4x5½" **35.00**
Wall pocket, Mission Ware, 3½x5½" **75.00**

Nippon

Nippon generally refers to Japanese wares made during the period from 1891 to 1921, although the Nippon mark was also used to a limited extent on later wares (accompanied by 'Japan'). Nippon, meaning Japan, identified the country of origin to comply with American importation restrictions. After 1921 'Japan' was the acceptable alternative. The term does not imply a specific type of product and may be found on items other than porcelains. In the listings that follow, the numbers refer to these specific marks:

#1 — China E-OH	#5 — Rising Sun
#2 — M in Wreath	#6 — Royal Kinran
#3 — Cherry Blossom	#7 — Maple Leaf
#4 — Double T Diamond	#8 — Royal Nippon, Nishiki
in Circle	#9 — Royal Moriye Nippon

Authority Joan Van Patten has recently released the third volume of her lovely series *The Collector's Encyclopedia of Nippon Porcelain*, with many full-color photos and current prices; you will find her address in the Directory under New York. In the following listings, items are assumed hand painted unless noted otherwise.

Ash tray, blk cat center, brn brick rim, gr #2, 5" 120.00
Ash tray, dachshund figural, moriage, w/matchbox holder 475.00
Ash tray, elk in winter reserve, sq, gr #2, 5¼" 110.00
Ash tray, moose center, nuts at rim, hexagonal, #2, 6" 110.00
Ash tray, owl on branch on bl shaded, tricorn, gr #2, 5½" 150.00
Ash tray, tiger, blown out 700.00
Ash tray, tree by river, band decor, triangular, #2, 4¾" 85.00
Ash tray, Wedgwood type, ped base 350.00
Basket, florals down sides, gold ribbons & trim, 7" 75.00
Basket, moriage, rnd form, integral hdl, #9, 5¼" 350.00
Bonbon, river scene on lid, Imperial mk, 5" dia 140.00
Bottle, scent; gold floral overlay, bl #7, 6" 160.00
Bowl, berry; florals & swags, pierced, #7, 5¼", +saucer 65.00
Bowl, bird on branch, oval w/curled hdls, #2, 7½" 120.00
Bowl, butterflies, mc & gold on bl shaded, gold rim, #2, 8" 80.00
Bowl, Egyptian lady reserve, canted corners, hdls, #2, 6" 185.00
Bowl, elk at river, earth tones, gr #2, 7¼" 100.00
Bowl, moriage, pine cones & needles, hdls, unmk, 7½" 80.00
Bowl, nut; iris, pk on wht, gold rim, #5, 6", +4 3" bowls 120.00
Bowl, nuts & leaves, earth tones, gr #2, 7¼" 80.00
Bowl, pastoral scene w/lake beyond, gr #2, 8½" 225.00
Bowl, peacock & florals on blk, Nippon mk, 8½" 85.00
Bowl, swans on lake w/lily pads, gold rim, #7, 8½" 120.00
Box, fruit & flowers, gold trim, w/lid, gr #2, 7" dia 225.00
Box, powder; roses, pk on gr shaded, gold rim/ft, #7, 5½" 65.00
Box, trinket; floral, piano form, #2, 2½x5" 265.00
Cake plate, roses, gold beads/rim #7, 10½", +6 6" plates 500.00
Cake set, roses, wht/yel on shaded tan, gold hdls, 7-pc 50.00
Calendar, desk; sampan scenic, gr #2, 3x4½" 175.00
Calling card tray, deer scene, earth tones, gr #2, 5½" 170.00
Candle lamp, pastoral scene/pk roses, gr #2, 12¼" 1,250.00
Candlestick, peacock/florals on wht w/gold, RC mk, 6", pr 240.00
Candlestick, people walking dog, pyramid form, gr #2, 8" 150.00
Celery dish, 3 rose reserves, fancy gold/cobalt, #7, 13" 265.00
Chamberstick, sampan scene in saucer base, gr #2 . . . . .100.00
Charger, birds & flowers, mc on blk, octagonal, mk, 18" 235.00
Cheese dish, roses, gold overlay/hdl, slant top, spoke mk, 7" . . .165.00
Chocolate set, grapes, mc on yel, bl #7, 11" pot+4 c/s 500.00
Chocolate set, open floral w/gold, gr #2, 9" pot+6 c/s 400.00
Chocolate set, rose reserve, gold beads, #7, 10" pot+4 c/s 800.00
Chocolate set, roses, pk on wht w/gold, #7, 10" pot+4 c/s 500.00
Chocolate set, tiny roses w/gold, gr RC mk, 9" pot+4 c/s 275.00
Coffeepot, roses, pk/wht on cream, gold overlay, bl #7, 8" 185.00
Compote, Wedgwood, cream on lav, #2, 5¼" H 465.00
Cookie jar, florals on aqua, gold net & beads, unmk, 7½" 275.00
Cookie jar, peonies, pk on wht, gold overlay rim/hdl, #7, 9" . . .275.00
Cookie jar, roses, mc on yel, gold beads, squat, #2, 8½" 350.00

Cracker jar, roses, pk/yel on wht, angle hdls, gr #2, 9" W 120.00
Creamer & sugar bowl, iris reserve, daisies at rim, #2 . . . . .130.00
Creamer & sugar bowl, mc roses, gold hdls, gr #2 . . . . .60.00
Creamer & sugar bowl, moriage, Nile scene w/floral, ftd 130.00
Creamer & sugar bowl, moriage, red roses, bl #2 . . . . .130.00
Cup & saucer, apples, gold beaded border, bl #7 . . . . .40.00
Demitasse set, butterflies, blk on wht w/gold, #2, serves 6 . . . . .225.00
Demitasse set, floral, pk & bl w/gold, mk, 10" pot+6 c/s 450.00
Demitasse set, gold decor on wht, #7, 9" pot+4 c/s 350.00
Demitasse set, gold dragons on wht, gr #2, 9" pot+6 c/s 450.00
Demitasse set, river scene, earth tones, #1, 8½" pot+6 c/s 250.00
Dish, sardine; scenic, gold fish finial, gr #2, +underplate 135.00
Dish, Wedgwood, 3-sectioned, raised center, #2, 7" 265.00
Dresser set, berries, red on gr w/gold, 4-pc 215.00
Ewer, floral reserves w/gold, bl #7, 13" 400.00
Ewer, roses, mc on tan shaded, gold trim, bl #7, 10" 200.00
Ewer, roses at top, heavy gold overlay, bl #7, 7½" 285.00
Ewer, scenic reserves, heavy gold, bl #7, 12" 425.00
Ewer, tapestry, man/lady scenic, gold rim/hdl/base, #7, 11" 885.00
Ferner, floral band, relief molded hdls, gr #2, 3¾x8½" 275.00
Ferner, lion, earth tones, ftd, gr #2, 5¾" 275.00
Ferner, lion relief, gold on brn, gr #2, 8½x5½" 600.00
Ferner, moriage, florals, open hdls, ftd, #9, 7" 295.00
Ferner, scenic, jewels, octagonal, 3-ftd, gr #2 . . . . .85.00
Ferner, scenic w/roses, gold collar, 6-panel, #7, 4½x10" 265.00
Ferner, silhouettes, 6-sided, gr #2, 6¾" 165.00
Ferner, silhouettes of warriors on brn, gr #2, 3¼x6" 150.00
Ferner, squirrel in tree reserve, #2, 5¾" 225.00
Ferner, tree & river scene between columns, gr #2, 5" 250.00
Fish set, fish figurals, HP mk, 17½" platter+5 9" plates 900.00
Hair receiver, river scene, cobalt-rimmed lid/base, #5, 3" 45.00
Hair receiver, roses, cobalt/gold overlay rim, gr #7, 4½" 75.00
Humidor, collie relief, gr #2, 6" 750.00
Humidor, daffodils, earth tones w/gold, gr #2, 6" 365.00
Humidor, Egyptian motif, bright colors, gr #2, 4¾" 350.00
Humidor, house & woods, unmk, 4" 90.00
Humidor, Indian in canoe, earth tones, hexagonal, #2, 10" 525.00
Humidor, Indian in canoe, hexagonal, #12, 5½x6½" 325.00
Humidor, Indian w/feathers, symbols in narrow bands, #2, 6" . .500.00
Humidor, lg dog, earth tones, rim decor, gr #2, 7" 500.00
Humidor, playing cards, gr #2, 4½" 325.00
Humidor, river scene, earth tones, knob finial, gr #2, 6¾" 350.00

Humidor, stag and dogs relief, 7", $900.00.

Humidor, windmill scenic, hexagonal, 5½" 225.00

Humidor, 3 horses in profile in wide band, gr #2, 6¾" 450.00
Inkwell, boats & palm trees, unmk, 4" 85.00
Inkwell, florals & ribbons, earth tones, #2, 3" 120.00
Jug, whiskey; windmill & house, florals, jewels, 7½" 400.00
Jug, wine; scenic medallion, gold overlay, jewels, #7, 9½" 575.00
Lamp, floral, pk on gr shaded, gold base/hdls, #7, 17" 265.00
Lamp, river scene, fancy gold base/hdls, gr #2, 13½" 275.00
Lamp, roses, mc on wht w/cobalt & gold, unknown mk, 14½" .265.00
Lazy susan, cranes, wht on bl, gold trim, papier-mache box 95.00
Letter holder, florals & scenic w/gold, gr #4 . . . . .145.00
Mustard pot, roses reserve, cobalt & gold beads, bl #7, 3¼" 125.00
Pancake server, gold overlay on cream, HP mk, 8¾" 120.00
Pitcher, floral, gold overlay & beads, squat, #7, 6½" 150.00
Pitcher, lemonade; orange poppies w/gold trim, +6 mugs 235.00
Pitcher, tankard; berries, red on tan, Imperial mk, 12" 325.00
Pitcher, tankard; florals/ribbons entwined, gold trim, #7, 13" . .400.00
Planter, boat scene, decor at 4 holes for hanging, gr #2, 5x4" . .400.00
Planter, desert scene, 3 hdls for hanging, gr #2, 5" 300.00
Plaque, bulldog on brn, gr #2, 12½" 700.00
Plaque, camel scene, gr #2, 10" 225.00
Plaque, deer at stream, fancy gold & enamel rim, #2, 10" 250.00
Plaque, house by river, gold rim, #2, 10¾" 225.00
Plaque, Indian portrait reserve, fancy border, bl #7, 10" 800.00
Plaque, lobster on table, gr #2, 12" .285.00
Plaque, rose medallion w/trees, 9", pr 165.00
Plaque, shepherd w/sheep & dog, mk, 10" 225.00
Plaque, wht roses, fancy wide gold border, bl #2, 10" 250.00
Plate, berries, red on tan, Imperial mk, 10" 100.00
Plate, deer scene, fancy gold on cobalt, #2, 10" 300.00
Plate, horses watering, gold overlay trim, gr #2, 10½" 200.00
Plate, house by river, earth tones, gr #2, 7¾" 100.00
Plate, mountain scene, fancy gold-on-cobalt rim, #7, 10" 300.00
Plate, mums, gold scalloped rim, bl #7, 9" 225.00
Plate, red house in snow scene, HP mk, 6½" 60.00
Plate, rose medallions, gold overlay & beads, #7, 10" 160.00
Plate, sampan scene, earth tones, gold rim, #3, 7½" 100.00
Plate, windmill scene, gold overlay on cobalt rim, #2, 6½" 165.00
Platter, fruit basket/cabbage/fish, blk & gold rim, #2, 16" 450.00
Platter, pheasants, gold overlay, oval, bl #7, 17½" 650.00
Platter, pheasants, gold overlay rim, gr #2, 16¾" 550.00
Punch bowl, florals w/grapes, gold-banded rim, ftd, #2, 11" . . .250.00
Punch bowl & stand, scenic/roses, cobalt band, gold hdls 375.00
Reamer, gold overlay on cream, gr #2, 4½" 180.00
Rose bowl, Wedgwood trim, orchids on wht, #2, 5¾" 525.00
Shakers, butterflies, gr w/gold trim, pr 30.00
Shaving mug, Indian reserve, stylized band, gr #2, 3¾" 150.00
Smoke set, camel scene, symbols in band, gr #2, 6-pc 850.00
Stein, cartoon character, HP trim, 7" 450.00
Stein, moose profile, earth tones w/gold, bl #7, 7¼" 400.00
Stickpin holder, floral w/blk contrast, gold beads, 1¾" 150.00
Sugar shaker, floral/gold overlay on wht, gr #2, 5" 125.00
Tea caddy, roses reserve, mc beads on yel, Nippon mk, 4½" . . .175.00
Tea set, cranes, pagoda mk, 6½" pot, +cr/sug+6 c/s 350.00
Tea set, cranes on cream, gold trim, gr #2, 6" pot, +14 pcs 350.00
Tea set, mc floral w/gold, #5, pot,+14 pcs 200.00
Tea set, rose medallions, gold overlay, gr #7, 4¾", 3-pc 350.00
Tea set, roses, yel on peach, gold beads, #7, 15-pc 450.00
Tea set, scenic reserve on red w/gold overlay, #2, serves 6 . . . .450.00
Tea strainer, roses, pk on wht, gold overlay, bl #7 . . . . .120.00
Tea strainer, roses on cream, gold overlay, gr #2, 4½" 80.00
Teapot, geese flying in aqua sky, gold jewels/trim, sm 130.00
Tile, Egyptian lady, stylized mc band, octagonal, #2, 6¼" 120.00
Toothpick holder, floral reserve, gold overlay, gr #2, 2½" 50.00
Toothpick holder, river scene, earth tones w/gold, #2, 2" 75.00

Urn, chrysanthemum reserve, fancy gold overlay, bl #7, 13" . . .650.00
Urn, floral, pk on lt gr, gold beads & trim, #6, 9½" 400.00
Urn, horses watering, gold overlay, 2-pc bolted, #2, 15¼" 950.00
Urn, lilies on cream, gold overlay, 2-pc bolted, #2, 8½" 275.00
Urn, portrait reserve, lacy gold/beads, #7, 12" 725.00
Urn, river scene, gold beads, rnd hdls, w/lid, bl #7, 9" 400.00
Urn, river scene reserve, pk florals, gold trim, #7, 21" 1,100.00
Urn, river scenic band, gold trim, 2-pc bolted, #2, 24½" 1,400.00
Urn, roses, gold beads & trim, hdls, w/lid, #6, 11" 400.00
Urn, roses, wht on cream w/gold, 2-pc bolted, #2, 18" 575.00
Urn, roses reserves on bl, gold beads, w/lid, bl #7, 14" 975.00
Urn, sailing ships, earth tones w/gold, bolted, #2, 16½" 650.00
Urn, scenic, cobalt w/fancy gold, 2-pc bolted, #7, 19" 1,850.00
Urn, scenic medallion, fancy gold overlay, bolted, #2, 19" . . .1,800.00
Vase, camel scene, angle hdls, ftd, gr #2, 5½" 145.00
Vase, desert scene, gold hdls, ftd ball form, #7, 8½" 265.00
Vase, fisherman reserve, gold overlay on wht, #2, 12" 300.00
Vase, floral, gold on brn, slim w/wide base, #7, 10" 200.00
Vase, floral, peach on wht, gold trim, ring hdls, #2, 10" 325.00
Vase, floral, pk w/gold, sq base, ruffled/folded rim, #7, 9" 225.00
Vase, floral (vining), wht on gr, gold hdls, gr #2, 6" 100.00
Vase, floral medallion on gr, gold trim, gr #2, 8" 185.00
Vase, floral reserves, Greek Key trim, sq hdls, #2, 13½" 300.00
Vase, floral reserves w/gold, angle hdls, gr #2, 10½" 150.00
Vase, grapes, lav on gold, urn form, gr #7, 10¾" 275.00
Vase, grapes, purple shaded on wht, gold overlay, #2, 13" 250.00
Vase, horse & rider, sq sides, hdls, Imperial mk, 7" 245.00
Vase, horses drinking, gold overlay, hdls, gr #2, 10¼" 500.00
Vase, house by stream, brn/gr w/gold, squat, hdls, #2, 8½" 220.00
Vase, house/river reserve, gold beads, hdls, spoke mk, 5½" 85.00
Vase, hunting reserve, heavy gold, ring hdls, gr #2, 15" 525.00
Vase, iris, long-stemmed, earth tones, ftd, gr #2, 5½" 90.00
Vase, iris on turq-beaded ground, gold trim/hdls, #2, 7" 175.00
Vase, leaves, gold on brn, Greek Key border, hdls, #2, 6½" 200.00
Vase, leaves & ribbons on wht, sea horse hdls, #7, 8½" 225.00
Vase, man in cart scene, gold rim/hdls, gr #2, 13" 550.00
Vase, mc roses, ring hdls, ruffled neck w/gold, bl #7, 10" 325.00
Vase, moriage, gr on wht, cylindrical w/flared base, #7, 7" 165.00
Vase, mtn scenic w/rose panels & gold, hdls, 15" 425.00
Vase, mums in oval reserve, gold overlay/cobalt, #7, 9½" 225.00
Vase, orchids, pk on wht w/gold, urn form, bl #7, 10½" 225.00
Vase, orchids, pk on wht w/gold, urn form, gr #7, 13" 350.00
Vase, orchids in wide band, gold beads, rnd hdls, #7, 9¾" 185.00
Vase, orchids w/long stems & leaves, gold rim/hdls, #2, 13" . . .350.00
Vase, pagodas/bridges/mtns, gold overlay on wht, #7, 11¼" . . .275.00
Vase, paneled scene, florals w/gold, gr #2, 24½" 550.00
Vase, pastoral scene on band, cylindrical, hdls, #2, 7" 100.00
Vase, peonies, mc w/gold, slim w/ruffled rim, HP mk, 11½" . . .250.00
Vase, peonies, red on lt bl, angle hdls, #7, 7½" 120.00
Vase, peonies on gr, gold hdls, flared cylinder, #2, 8½" 250.00
Vase, people in wide band, beading, angled hdls, gr #2, 8" 300.00
Vase, river reserve, ring hdls, urn form, gr #2, 9½" 275.00
Vase, river reserve on turq, gold angle hdls, gr #2, 10½" 250.00
Vase, river scene, basket form, gr #2, 11" 225.00
Vase, river scene, fancy neck/base decor, urn form, #2, 12" . . .350.00
Vase, river scene, sq hdls, urn form, Imperial mk, 7" 150.00
Vase, river scene on band, 4 angle hdls, Imperial mk, 6" 120.00
Vase, river scene reserve, gold beads, hdls, gr #2, 13" 365.00
Vase, roses, gold ft/ring hdls/ruffled neck, #7, 12" 325.00
Vase, roses, gold integral hdls, sm neck, 3½x8½" 160.00
Vase, roses, mc on cream, gold overlay, sm hdls, HP mk, 12" . .300.00
Vase, roses, mc on cream, gold ruffled rim, bl #7, 5½" 100.00
Vase, roses, mc on wht, gold bands, integral hdls, #7, 5½" 150.00
Vase, roses, mc on wht, gold hdls, jug form, #7, 11" 300.00

Vase, roses, mc w/gold beads on peach, urn form, #7, 14" 185.00
Vase, roses, moriage trim, squat urn form, bl #7, 8" 225.00
Vase, roses on stem, pk on yel w/gold, hdls, gr #2, 12" 200.00

**Vase, roses relief, 10½",
$450.00.**

Vase, sailboat reserve, heavy gold, ftd, hdls, #2, 14" 350.00
Vase, sampan/palm scene, gold trim, gr #2, 7¾" 165.00
Vase, scenic band, stemmed florals on blk, gold rim, #8, 12" ...200.00
Vase, storks w/young, bulbous w/sm neck, gold hdls, #7, 8" 225.00
Vase, tall tree scene, cylindrical, gr #7, 12" 450.00
Vase, tall tree scene, hdls, gr #2, 4½" 150.00
Vase, trees & dog reserve, Deco motif, ring hdls, 15" 585.00
Vase, trees/mtns/river, angle hdls, bl Imperial mk, 11½" 165.00
Vase, windmill scene, sq hdls, ftd, cylindrical, #2, 11" 300.00
Vase, winter scene in banded reserve, gold hdls, bl #7, 10" 300.00

Nodders

So called because of the nodding action of their heads and hands, nodders originated in China where they were used in temple rituals to represent deity. Early in the 18th century, the idea was adapted by Meissen and by French manufacturers who produced not only china nodders but bisque as well. Most nodders are individual—couples are unusual. The idea remained popular until the end of the 19th century and was used during the Victorian era by toy manufacturers.

Andy Gump, bsk, Germany, 4" 150.00
Baby, bsk, pk & wht gown, pulling off bl sock, 4½" 175.00
Black schoolboy sits in chair, holds slate, 5½x2x3" 125.00
Bulldog, pnt papier-mache, Germany, 1900, 8½" 85.00
Chinaman, bsk, Germany, 2½" 60.00
Chubby Chaney, bsk, Germany 95.00
Donkey, celluloid, Occupied Japan, 6x7½" 30.00
Flapper in cloche hat seated w/fan, mc bsk, 3½" 95.00
Granny wears glasses, Staffordshire 225.00
Happy Hooligan, compo, circular base, 1910, 10¾", NM 675.00
Oriental man holds pipe, bald w/queue & mustache, bsk, 3" 65.00
Orientals sit w/legs Xd, mc, bsk, 3⅛", pr 125.00
Rachel, bsk, Germany, 3½" 100.00
Sultan w/turban & mustache, peach/wht w/gold, 3½" 70.00

Turtle, compo fibre, HP, 5" L 65.00
Victorian couple, porc, bl w/gold on wht, 7", pr 190.00
Victorian lady w/cat, mc, bsk, 7" 125.00

Seated Oriental man, no mark, 6", $300.00.

Noritake

The Noritake Company was first registered in 1904 as Nippon Gomei Kaisha. In 1917 the name became Nippon Toki Kabushiki Toki. The 'M' in wreath mark is that of the Morimura Brothers, distributors with offices in New York. It was used until 1941. The tree crest mark is the crest of the Morimura family.

The Noritake Company has produced fine porcelain dinnerware sets and occasional pieces decorated in the delicate manner for which the Japanese are noted. Their Azalea pattern was produced exclusively for the Larkin Company, who gave the lovely ware away as premiums to club members and their home agents. From 1916 through the thirties, Larkin distributed the fine china which was decorated in pink Azaleas on white with gold tracing along edges and handles. Early in the thirties, six pieces of crystal hand painted with the same design were offered: candle holders, a compote, a tray with handles, a scalloped fruit bowl, a cheese and cracker set, and a cake plate. All in all, seventy different pieces of Azalea were produced. Some, such as the fifteen-piece child's set, bulbous vase, china ash tray, and the pancake jug, are quite rare. Marks varied over the years; the earliest was the blue rising sun Nippon mark, followed by the Noritake M in wreath with variations. Later the ware was marked 'Noritake, Azalea, hand painted, Japan.'

Authority Joan Van Patten has compiled a lovely book, *The Collector's Encyclopedia of Noritake*, with many full-color photos and current prices; you will find her address in the Directory under New York. In the following listings, examples are hand painted unless noted otherwise. Numbers refer to these specific marks:

#1 — Tree Crest   #2 — M in Wreath
#3 — N in Wreath

Azalea

Basket, mint; Dolly Varden, #193 ....145.00
Bonbon, #184, 6¼" 45.00
Bowl, deep, #310 ....50.00

Bowl, fruit; shell form, #188, 7¾"	325.00
Bowl, oatmeal; #55, 5½"	18.00
Bowl, vegetable; divided, #439, 9½"	235.00
Bowl, vegetable; oval, #101, 10½"	40.00
Butter chip, #312, 3¼"	40.00
Butter dish, #314	90.00
Butter tub, w/insert, #54	44.00
Cake plate, #10, 9¾"	50.00
Candy jar, #313	525.00
Casserole, gold finial, w/lid, #371	420.00
Casserole, w/lid, #16	75.00
Celery tray, closed hdls, #444, 10"	240.00
Celery/roll tray, #99, 12"	50.00
Child's set, #253, 15-pc	1,500.00
Coffeepot, AD; #182	500.00
Compote, #170	70.00
Condiment set, #14, 5-pc	60.00
Creamer & sugar bowl, #122	115.00
Creamer & sugar bowl, #449, ind	130.00
Creamer & sugar bowl, #7	50.00
Creamer & sugar bowl, AD; open, #123	100.00
Cruet, #190	175.00
Cup & saucer, #2	17.50
Cup & saucer, AD; #183	25.00
Cup & saucer, bouillon; #124, 3½"	20.00
Egg cup, #120	40.00
Gravy boat, #40	50.00
Jam jar set, #125, 3-pc	125.00
Mayonnaise set, scalloped, #453, 3-pc	440.00
Mustard jar, #191	47.50
Pitcher, milk jug; #100, 1-qt	175.00
Plate, #4, 7½"	10.00
Plate, bread & butter; #8, 6½"	10.00
Plate, cream soup; #363	65.00
Plate, dinner; #13, 9¾"	20.00
Plate, grill; 3-compartment, #338, 10¼"	95.00
Plate, soup; #19, 7⅛"	18.00
Plate, sq, #315, 7⅝"	45.00
Platter, #17, 14"	55.00
Platter, #186, 16"	325.00
Platter, #311, 10¼"	180.00
Platter, #56, 12"	38.00
Refreshment set, #39, 2-pc	42.00
Relish, #194, 7⅛"	70.00
Relish, loop hdl, 2-part, #450	300.00
Relish, oval, #18, 8½"	17.50
Relish, 4-part, #119, 10"	110.00
Saucer, fruit; #9, 5¼"	10.00
Shakers, #126, ind, pr	32.00
Shakers, bell form, #11, pr	27.50
Shakers, bulbous, #89, pr	25.00
Spoon holder, #189, 8"	75.00
Syrup, #97, w/underplate	95.00
Tea tile, #169, 6"	45.00
Teapot, #15	80.00
Teapot, gold finial, #400	420.00
Toothpick holder, #192	90.00
Vase, bulbous, #452	925.00
Vase, fan form, ftd, #187	125.00
Whipped cream set, #3, 3-pc	35.00
Ash tray, lady figural, red skirt forms bowl, #2, 5¼"	245.00
Ash tray, lady holds skirt wide, yel lustre rim, #2, 4¼"	70.00

Bottle, scent; flower basket on cream, red #2, 6"	100.00
Bowl, florals on bl, bird at rim, gr #2, 7½"	110.00
Bowl, fountain reserve, gold lustre rim/hdls, red #2, 9½"	55.00
Bowl, gold-lined florals, gold lustre rim/hdls, #2, 9½"	40.00
Bowl, iris, mc on tan, bl lustre w/gold rim/hdls, #2, 10½"	40.00
Bowl, parrot on branch, blk border w/gold trim, #2, 10"	40.00
Bowl, peacocks, bl & gold Oriental-style border, #2, 7¼"	40.00
Bowl, roses on cream, orange scalloped rim, red #2, 5"	35.00
Box, clown figural, head finial, gr #2, 5½"	250.00
Box, elephant figural, ornate howdah, red #2, 6½"	225.00
Box, powder puff; clown, gr #2, 4"	125.00
Box, powder puff; lady in flowered dress & bonnet, #2, 4"	125.00
Box, powder puff; orange lustre lid w/bird finial, #2, 4"	125.00
Cake plate, pheasants in lg medallion, pk/gold rim, #2, 8"	40.00
Cake plate, river scene, geometric border, hdls, red #2, 11"	45.00
Cake plate, sampan scene, gold/bl lustre, hdls, #2, 9¾"	40.00
Cake plate, Tree in Meadow, pierced hdls, 9¾"	20.00
Candlestick, bird on branch on bl, decor base, #2, 8", pr	130.00
Candlestick, butterfly, bl on orange lustre, #2, 5½", pr	120.00
Candlestick, peacock/floral reserve, gold lustre, #2, 9", pr	135.00
Candlestick, red bird on wht, bl base & top, gr #2, 8", pr	125.00
Candy dish, Deco lady on blk & red, red #2, 6½" dia	185.00
Candy set, swan figural, red #2, 7½" swan+2 ea 5"	135.00
Celery dish, cream w/red trim, leaf form, gr #2, 12½"	40.00
Celery dish, 4 flower medallions in bl rim, oval, #2, 12"	38.00
Chamberstick, bl flower on orange lustre, ring hdls, #2, 2¼"	85.00
Chamberstick, Egyptian bands on orange lustre, #2, 6½", pr	145.00
Chamberstick, orange lustre, blk trim, ring hdls, #2, 4¾"	70.00
Chocolate pot, gold overlay on wht, gr #2, 9"	65.00
Chocolate set, floral on wht w/gold, hexagonal, #2, 5-pc	225.00
Cigarette urn, lovebirds, bell shape, bird finial, #2, 5"	120.00
Compote, florals at 1 side of bl lustre rim, hdls, #2, 8½"	60.00
Compote, ladies form stem to hold bowl, red #2, 7" H	245.00
Condiment set, parrots on red, gold trim, gr #2, 4-pc	80.00
Creamer, lg mixed florals on cream w/orange lustre, #2, 5¾"	32.00
Demitasse set, river scene, gold trim, red #2, 15-pc	285.00
Dish, trinket; camel scene, earth tones, center hdl, mk, 2¼"	25.00
Flower holder, bird figural, bl w/orange lustre, #2, 4½"	175.00
Humidor, floral panels on bl, wht band, gr #2, 6"	200.00
Humidor, stylized owls reserve on red & blk w/gold, #2, 5¾"	300.00
Humidor, Tree in Meadow	345.00
Inkwell, clown figural, red #2, 4"	245.00
Jar, potpourri; bl & wht lustre, rose finial, red #2, 6"	80.00
Jar, potpourri; floral, mc on bl, rose finial, #2, 6½"	90.00
Lamp, river scene w/house, earth tones, gr #2, 10"	145.00
Lemon dish, lemons center, gold lustre rim, red #2, 5¾"	25.00
Match holder, Deco lady smoking, #2, 1¾"	70.00
Mug, river scene, earth tones, gr #2, 3¼"	65.00
Napkin ring set, Deco style, red #2, 2¼" W, MIB	95.00
Night light, lady figural, orange lustre dress, #2, 9¾"	800.00
Plaque, Deco lady on orange lustre, gr #2, 8¾"	130.00
Plaque, river scene, earth tones, #2, 6½"	100.00
Plaque, steamship in water, RC mk, 10"	165.00
Plate, game; ring-necked drake, fruit & swag rim, #2, 8½"	85.00
Plate, Tree in Meadow, 7½"	11.50
Platter, game; elk, floral medallion rim, #2, 16", +8 plates	565.00
Punch bowl, Oriental scene on red w/gold, ped base, #2, 16"	425.00
Punch bowl, peacock medallion w/gold, #2, 16", +8 cups	550.00
Punch bowl, river scene, striped band, ped base, #2, 13½"	425.00
Relish, Tree in Meadow, 2-compartment	28.00
Sauce dish, fruits on cream, flower form, red #2, 4"	40.00
Sauce dish, peacock & florals, gold lustre rim, #2, 4½"	40.00
Serving dish, etched gold floral, red #2, 7" L	70.00
Shakers, river scene, lt earth tones, gr #2, 2½", pr	25.00

Smoke set, butterflies on bl, gr rim, #2, 7½" tray+3 pcs 275.00
Smoke set, florals, blk on red w/gr band, #2, 8" tray+3 pcs 250.00
Smoke set, florals on red w/blk trim, red #2, 7" tray+2 pcs 175.00
Sugar shaker, floral band on wht, lustre top, #2, 6½" 32.00
Sweetmeat set, Deco fruit, gr #2, 2-pc 100.00
Syrup, scenic, gold trim, gr #2, 4½", +undertray 60.00
Tea set, orange & wht lustre, bud finials, gr #2, 15-pc 135.00
Toothpick holder, Tree in Meadow 50.00
Tray, Deco fruit forms border, gold hdls, red #2, 11" L 65.00
Urn, river reserve on red w/gold, red #2, 12" 200.00
Urn, sm florals at top w/gold overlay on wht, #2, 10¼" 200.00
Vase, bird & tree trunk figural, gr #2, 5¼" 195.00
Vase, Deco lady on red lustre, red #2, 8½" 135.00
Vase, floral, mc on cream shaded, gold hdls, gr #2, 11¼" 135.00
Vase, floral, mc on cream shaded, ribbed, ftd, #2, 5½" 85.00
Vase, flower basket gold overlay on blk, basket form, #3, 9" ...185.00
Vase, parrots on yel w/gold trim & hdl, basket form, #2, 6" 95.00

Double vase with parrot, 7", $195.00.

Vase, red w/gold hdl & int, ruffled basket form, #2, 5½" 95.00
Vase, river/bridge in band on gr, urn form, mk, 9¼" 125.00
Vase, roses, long-stemmed on wht w/gold, gr #2, 8½" 115.00
Vase, sampan scene, gold overlay at neck/hdls, #1, 10" 215.00
Vase, tulip figural, lav w/gr leaves, red #2, 5½" 195.00
Vase, Wedgwood, med bl & wht, hdls, bl #3, 9½" 325.00
Wall pocket, butterflies on orange lustre, red #2, 9" 85.00

Norse

The Norse Pottery was established in 1903 in Edgerton, Wisconsin, by Thorwald Sampson and Louis Ipson. A year later it was purchased by A.W. Wheelock and moved to Rockford, Illinois. The ware they produced was inspired by ancient bronze vessels of the Norsemen. Designs were often incised into the red clay body, dragon handles and feet were favored decorative devices, and they achieved a semblance of patina through the application of metallic glazes. The ware was marked with a stylized 'N' containing a vertical arrangement of the remaining letters of the name. Production ceased after 1913.

Bowl, incised rising sun, 2 dragon's-head hdls, imp, #50 ......125.00
Candlestick, blk w/gold snaked looped at base, #54, 12", pr ...150.00

Jar, incised scrollwork at shoulder, lid w/finial, 6½" 140.00
Mug, incised decor, blk w/bronze wash, #51, 5" 135.00

Bowl vase, #11, $120.00.

Vase, geometrics at top, gold remains, #45, 4½" 50.00
Vase, serpent hdls, faces on 3 ft, metallic, #70, 3¾x7" 140.00

North Dakota School of Mines

The School of Mines of the University of North Dakota was established in 1890, but due to a lack of funding, it was not until 1898 that Earle J. Babcock was appointed as Director, and efforts were made to produce ware from the native clay he had discovered several years earlier. The first pieces were made by firms in the east from the clay Babcock sent them. Some of the ware was decorated by the manufacturer; some was shipped back to North Dakota to be decorated by native artists. By 1909 students at the University of North Dakota were producing utilitarian items — tile, brick, shingles, etc. — in conjunction with a ceramic course offered through the Chemistry Department. By 1910 a ceramic department had been established, supervised by Margaret Kelly Cable. Under her leadership, fine artware was produced. Native flowers, grains, buffalo, cowboys, and other subjects indigenous to the state were incorporated into the decorations. Some pieces have an Art Nouveau — Art Deco style easily attributed to her association with Frederick H. Rhead, with whom she studied in 1911. During the twenties the pottery was marketed on a limited scale through gift and jewelry stores in the state. From 1927 until 1949 when Miss Cable announced her retirement, a more widespread distribution was maintained with sales branching out into other states. The ware was marked in cobalt with the official seal — 'Made at School of Mines, N.D. Clay, University of North Dakota, Grand Forks, N.D.' in a circle. Very early ware was sometimes marked 'U.N.D.' in cobalt by hand.

Bowl, brn, beehive form, sgn Huck/#2754, 4" 175.00
Bowl, wheat band/lines, #130, 3½x4" 190.00
Bowl vase, cvd oxen & covered wagons, gr/brn, mk JH, 4x6½" .400.00
Candle holder, tan, w/hdl, artist sgn 35.00
Cup, tooled line design, gr gloss, brn body, 3x4" 160.00
Lamp, brn, bulbous, instructor sgn, 1930s, 7½x7" 225.00
Rose bowl, bl, sgn Bechteel, #22746 ....145.00
Vase, bl marbleized, sgn Huck, 7¼" 235.00
Vase, cream, bulbous, sgn Summers, 4½" 100.00
Vase, cream to brn, bulbous, 5" 65.00
Vase, dk gr w/lt gr top w/hint of brn, 3¼" 110.00
Vase, floral, lt bl w/gun metal center on dk bl, Huck, 4¾" 375.00

Vase, floral cvg, bl w/dk bl flecks, Cable, 3½x5½" 225.00
Vase, floral on dk bl w/lt bl lines top & base, Huck, 4¾" 375.00
Vase, geese in band, blk on dk brn, #1039, sgn, 3", NM 300.00
Vase, gr to purple, 1930, 5½" 75.00
Vase, gr w/gray touches top/inside, sgn Devins/Huck, 7½" 110.00
Vase, horse/rider emb, lt bl vellum, mk J/38, 4¾" 300.00
Vase, Prairie Rose, sgn Ude Grad Huckfield, #573, 8" 450.00
Vase, rose, flared rim, sgn E Eiland, 5½" 135.00
Vase, turkey cvd at neck, gr semi-matt/brn clay, sgn, 3¼" 200.00
Warming base, gr, openwork side w/cowboy, sgn Winge, 6½" . .300.00

Trivet, Conestoga wagon with oxen, green and gray, signed Huckfield, 4¾", $150.00.

Northwood

The Northwood Company was founded in 1896 in Indiana, Pennsylvania, by Harry Northwood, whose father, John, was the art director for Stevens and Williams, an English glassworks. Northwood joined the National Glass Company in 1899 but in 1901 again became an independent contractor and formed the Harry Northwood Glass Company of Wheeling, West Virginia. He marketed his first carnival glass in 1908, and it became his most popular product. His company was also famous for its custard, goofus, and pressed glass. Northwood died in 1923, and the company closed. See also Carnival; Custard; Goofus; Opalescent; Pattern Glass.

Bottle, scent; pull-up loops, 3-color, SP lid, 1¾x1⅛" 385.00
Bowl, berry; Geneva, gr, sm 15.00
Bowl, Leaf Medallion, clear w/gold, 9" 30.00
Bowl, Southern Gardens, ftd, gr w/gold, 11" 65.00
Butter dish, Leaf Umbrella, cranberry, rare 600.00
Butter dish, Royal Ivy, rubena 225.00
Butter dish, Royal Oak, rubena, acorn finial 210.00
Butter dish, Teardrop Flower, bl w/gold 150.00
Carafe, water; rubena, threaded 135.00
Celery vase, Cable & Cherries, clear frost, HP decor 75.00
Compote, Grape Frieze, sm 35.00
Compote, Intaglio, gr w/gold 45.00
Compote, Star of David & Bows, gr w/gold, sm 35.00
Cracker jar, Cable & Cherries, clear frost 75.00
Creamer, Cherry & Plum, clear frost .35.00
Creamer, Grape & Gothic Arches, gr w/gold 20.00
Creamer, Intaglio, gr w/gold 65.00
Creamer, Invt Fan & Feather, gr w/gold 85.00

Creamer, Jeweled Heart, clear frost, HP decor 35.00
Creamer, Leaf Medallion, cobalt w/gold 95.00
Creamer, Louis XV, gr w/gold 38.00
Creamer, Posies & Pods, gr w/gold .65.00
Creamer, Royal Ivy, rubena frost 165.00
Creamer, Strawberry & Cable, clear w/red & gold 70.00
Cruet, Royal Oak, EX gold, orig milk glass stopper 145.00
Jar, dresser; Royal Oak, rubena frost, SP lid, scarce 100.00
Jar, marmalade; Royal Ivy, rubena frost, SP lid 100.00
Pickle castor, Royal Oak, rubena frost, Meriden fr 210.00
Pitcher, Cable & Cherries, clear frost, HP decor, water sz 85.00
Pitcher, Cherry & Lattice, clear frost, HP decor, water sz 70.00
Pitcher, mc pull-ups on crystal, fancy appl hdl, 6x5" 295.00
Pitcher, Panelled Cherry, EX gold trim, water sz 115.00
Pitcher, Poinsettia, dk bl w/cobalt hdl, water sz 345.00
Pitcher, Royal Ivy, rainbow frosted craquelle, water sz 285.00
Pitcher, Royal Ivy, rubena frost, water sz 285.00
Punch cup, Cable & Cherries, clear frost 30.00
Rose bowl, emb Rippled Herringbone+pk pull-ups, 4¾" H 550.00
Rose bowl, pull-up, pk w/lav feather swirls, bl int, 4x4½" 1,100.00
Rose bowl, swirls in wht/yel/puce, bl int, 4½" dia 250.00
Spooner, Cherry & Plum, clear frost .35.00
Spooner, Grape & Gothic Arches, gr w/gold 40.00
Spooner, Peach, gr 65.00
Spooner, Posies & Pods, gr w/gold .50.00
Spooner, Royal Oak, clear frost 75.00
Sugar bowl, Cherry & Plum, w/lid, clear frost 35.00
Sugar bowl, Peach, w/lid, gr 95.00
Sugar bowl, Posies & Pods, w/lid, gr w/gold 95.00
Sugar bowl, Strawberry & Cable, w/lid 100.00
Sugar bowl, Strawberry & Cable, w/lid, clear w/red & gold . . .110.00
Sugar bowl, Teardrop Flower, w/lid, bl w/gold 25.00
Syrup, Royal Ivy, rubena frost, orig spring lid, scarce 495.00
Toothpick holder, Royal Oak, clear frost 45.00
Tumbler, Leaf Medallion, gr w/gold .35.00
Tumbler, Leaf Mold, cranberry spatter w/mica 65.00
Tumbler, Memphis, gr w/gold 30.00
Tumbler, Oriental Poppy, bl 25.00
Tumbler, Oriental Poppy, gr w/gold .28.00
Tumbler, Peach, gr w/gold 30.00
Tumbler, Royal Ivy, rubena craquelle 75.00
Vase, cased, appl amber leaves/dates/ft, pk ruffle, 10", pr 250.00
Vase, cranberry threads on wht, fan form, crimped rim, ftd . . .1,000.00
Vase, feathers, brn on peach, robin's egg bl int, 5½x3" 750.00
Vase, pull-up, rose on yel, gourd form w/stick neck, 10" 995.00

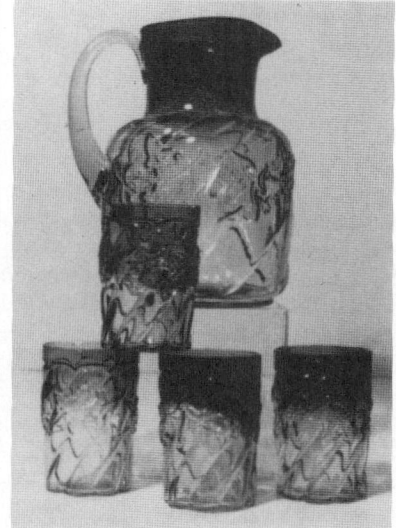

Water set, Royal Ivy, rubena, $400.00 for 5-piece set.

Nutcrackers

The nutcracker, though a strictly functional tool, is a good example of one to which man has applied ingenuity, imagination, and engineering skills. Though all were designed to accomplish the same end, hundreds of types exist in almost every material sturdy enough to withstand sufficient pressure to crack the nut. Figurals are popular collectibles, as are those with unusual design and construction. Patented examples are also desirable.

Alligator, brass, 7½" 35.00
Alligator, CI, orig pnt, 1890s, 13" 85.00
Clamp-on style, CI, mechanical, pat 1914 . . . . .26.00
Dog, mk LA Athoff, Laporte IN 48.00
Dog, St Bernard, bronze 50.00
Dog, St Bernard, CI, old 60.00
Elephant, CI, old red pnt, twine tail, 5x9¾" 68.00
Reed's Rocket, CI, rocket shape on wood base, adjusts, MIB 20.00
Sailor w/lady in short skirt kiss when squeezed, brass, 6¼" 65.00
Santa's head, wood, old, EX 30.00
Squirrel, CI, dtd 1913 . . . . .25.00
Squirrel, CI, mtd on walnut block, ca 1850s, EX 95.00

Bearded elf, 10", $285.00.

Occupied Japan

Items marked 'Occupied Japan' have become popular collectibles in the last few years. They were produced during the period from the end of World War II until April 18, 1952, when the occupation ended. By no means was all of the ware exported during that time marked 'Occupied Japan' — some was marked 'Japan' or 'Made In Japan.' It is thought that because of the natural resentment felt by the Japanese toward the occupation, only a fraction of these wares carried the 'Occupied' mark. Even though you may find identical 'Japan'-marked items, because of its limited use, only those with the 'Occupied Japan' mark are being collected to any great extent. Values vary considerably based on the quality of workmanship. Generally, bisque figures command much higher prices than porcelain, since on the whole they are of a finer quality.

Our advisor for this category is Florence Archambault; she is listed in the Directory under Rhode Island. She represents the Occupied Japan Club, whose mailing address may be found in the Directory under Clubs, Newsletters, and Catalogs. All items in the listings that follow are assumed ceramic unless noted otherwise.

Ash tray, gr & wht w/flowers, 3⅝" 3.50
Ash tray, horse pulling wagon, wht, 3¼" 7.00
Ash tray, Indianapolis IN in center, 4¾" 5.00
Ash tray, metal, Statue of Liberty in center, 5¼" 10.00
Ash tray, palm trees in center, 4¾" 5.00
Atomizer, bl glass 30.00
Bowl, wht w/pk floral int, gold trim, 5¾" 9.00
Candlestick, metal, 5", pr 24.00
Cigarette box, pk floral w/4 ash trays, 3¾x2¾" 21.00
Cup & saucer, bl floral, mk Gold China 14.00
Cup & saucer, blk w/floral int, gold trim, mk Chugai China . . .14.00
Cup & saucer, children's, Bl Willow, 2¾x3½" 10.00
Cup & saucer, children's, elephant w/flag, 1¾" 9.00
Cup & saucer, demitasse; HP red/bl roses, gold trim 10.00
Cup & saucer, demitasse; red w/tulips 12.00
Cup & saucer, demitasse; relief scrolls, HP flowers 9.50
Cup & saucer, floral medallions on yel, gold hdl 12.00
Cup & saucer, flow blue, mk Trimont China 12.00
Cup & saucer, gold overlay on cream .12.00
Cup & saucer, mc floral, gold trim, mk Merit 11.00
Cup & saucer, red/wht beaded panels, mk Saja Fancy China 12.00
Cup & saucer, wht w/gold trim & hdl .12.00
Doll, celluloid, kewpie, 2¾" 14.00
Doll, celluloid, pk baby, 5½" 20.00
Doll, celluloid, pk crocheted dress, 6" .35.00
Doll, china, red dress, 3¼" 23.00
Figurine, accordion player, 4" 7.00
Figurine, angel w/horn, bsk, 5" 25.00
Figurine, ballerina w/bl net dress & orange hat, 4½" 24.00
Figurine, boy sits w/broken sprinkler, 4½" 20.00
Figurine, boy sits w/duck, 3¾" 25.00
Figurine, boy sits/plays violin, blk shirt/brn pants, 3¾" 10.00
Figurine, boy stands w/parrot on arm, 5" 12.00
Figurine, boy w/begging dog, 5" 20.00
Figurine, bride & groom, bsk, 5" 25.00
Figurine, cat w/fiddle, 2" 7.00
Figurine, Colonial man & woman w/flowers, 7", pr 70.00
Figurine, Colonial man holds flowers, brn coat, 10" 40.00
Figurine, Colonial man leans on fence, bsk, 7½" 40.00
Figurine, Colonial man stands, lady sits, 5¼" 19.00
Figurine, courting couple w/lambs, bsk, 8¼x9¼" 250.00
Figurine, cow, blk/wht, 2¾x4" 9.00
Figurine, cupid on sled, bsk, 5" 25.00
Figurine, cupid w/donkey, bsk, 4" 23.00
Figurine, cupid w/flower snail, bsk, 4½x6" 30.00
Figurine, cupid w/moon, 3½" 9.00
Figurine, dog begging, 2½" 5.00
Figurine, dogs, terriers, brn/wht, 3½" .14.00
Figurine, dogs in brn basket, 3¼" 10.00
Figurine, Dutch girl w/milk can, 6" 22.00
Figurine, flower gatherers, bsk, 10¼" .175.00
Figurine, girl, basket at bare ft, 5¼" 15.00
Figurine, girl stands w/dog, 4¼" 10.00
Figurine, Indian in canoe w/plastic flowers 19.00
Figurine, Indian squaw, 4½" 11.00
Figurine, lady w/dog, pk hat/yel dress, bsk, 6" 25.00
Figurine, little girl holds open book, red/bl dress, 3¾" 14.00
Figurine, man & woman leans on fence, bsk, 9", pr 150.00
Figurine, man w/flower, bsk, 10¼" 50.00
Figurine, monkeys, wht, set of 3, 1¾", ea 4.50
Figurine, musketeer, 5" 9.00
Figurine, Oriental lady stands/holds fan, 5" 15.00
Figurine, Oriental man & woman pray, 7⅝", pr 65.00
Figurine, Oriental man plays banjo, 10" 50.00

**Lady with basket; man with musical instrument, 10",
$110.00 for the pair.**

Figurine, Oriental man sits w/rabbits, 4" .35.00
Figurine, Oriental man sits/plays flute, gr jacket, 4⅜" 10.00
Figurine, pastoral lady holds mandolin, 6" 15.00
Figurine, poodle, 3" 12.00
Figurine, puppies in basket, 2½" 9.00
Figurine, Spanish guitar player, 4¼" 9.00
Figurine, squirrels, 4½x5" 19.00
Lamp, Colonial couple arm in arm, metal base, 10½" 30.00
Lighter, cigarette; ceramic, wht w/mc flowers, gold trim, 2⅞" . . .15.00
Lighter, cigarette; metal, Indian 9.00
Mug, barrel form, bearded man figural hdl, 4¾" 30.00
Mug, barrel form, man in red shirt figural hdl, 4¾" 30.00
Pitcher, red tulips, blk/gold trim, 3" 7.50
Planter, angel w/yel hair, pk wing tips, 3½" 12.00
Planter, bird on tree branch, 3" 10.00
Planter, cupid w/gold rings & lady w/lyre, bsk, 8¼x9¼" 200.00
Planter, Donald Duck, 3" 13.00
Planter, Dutch girl pushes cart, 2¾" 7.50
Planter, frog, 2¼" 9.00
Planter, monkey clown plays accordion, 3¾" 9.00
Planter, Oriental girl pushes cart, 4" .10.00
Planter, Oriental girl w/fan, 6" 13.00
Planter, Oriental man plays mandolin, 4" 7.00
Planter, window box w/bl scallops, flowers, 6½x3½x2½" 12.00
Plaque, Colonial couple holds hands, bsk, 6½x5¾" 35.00
Plaque, Colonial lady holds umbrella, bsk, 7x4¾" 28.00
Shakers, bride & groom, pr 20.00
Shakers, corn cobs, pr 12.00
Shakers, Geisha girls, pr 21.00
Shakers, Humpty Dumpty, pr 30.00
Shakers, Indians in canoe, pr 20.00
Shakers, metal, 2¼", pr 20.00
Shakers, strawberry, 3¾", pr 18.00
Shelf sitter, boy holds pnt can & brush, 4¼" 15.00
Shelf sitter, boy plays accordion, 4" 13.00
Shelf sitter, couple fishes from bench, bsk, 4" 15.00
Shelf sitter, girl sits w/bucket, 3" 11.00
Teapot, tomato form, 5½" 45.00
Teapot, windmill form, 5" 38.00
Toby jug, lady's head, 2¼" 8.00
Toby jug, man w/gray hair, bl hat/vest, full figure, 2" 10.00

Toby jug, man's head, dark mustache/blk hat, 4" 22.00
Toby mug, bearded man, blk hat/hdl, 2¾" 12.00
Toby mug, blk-bearded man, winking, squirrel hdl, 5" 30.00
Toby mug, Colonial man, blk hat/coat, 2¾" 12.00
Toby mug, man in long coat, full figure, 2½" 15.00
Toby mug, man's head, blk hat/red bow tie, 4¾" 32.00
Toby mug, man's head, wht hair, winking, brn hdl, 4" 24.00
Toothpick holder, clown saluting, 2½" .8.50
Toothpick holder, man sit/holds top hat, red trim 8.00
Toothpick holder, nude girl sits beside floral vase, 3" 12.00
Tray, metal, Niagara Falls/Rainbow Bridge 7.00
Vase, bud; dancing girl on front, 4" 12.00
Vase, flower relief, wht w/yel trim, 3" .5.00
Vase, fruit relief, cobalt on blk w/gold, 3¾" 12.00
Vase, HP floral medallions, gr band/gold trim, 3¾" 10.00
Vase, mc flowers on wht, gold hdls, 4½" 14.00
Vase, wht, floral relief, side hdls, 3½" .6.00
Vase, wht w/flower basket on front, cat faces emb on sides, 5" . . .21.00
Wall plaque, Colonial man/woman swing, oval, 7x4½", pr 55.00

Ohr, George

George Ohr established his pottery around 1893 in Biloxi, Mississippi.
The unusual style of the ware he produced and his flamboyant personality
earned him the dubious title of 'the mad potter of Biloxi.' Though
acclaimed by some of the critics of his day to be perhaps the most
accomplished thrower in the history of the industry, others overlooked the
eggshell-thin walls of his vessels, each a different shape and contortion, and
saw only that their 'tortured' appearance contradicted their own sedate
preferences.

Ohr worked by himself with only minimal help from his son. His work
was typically pinched and pulled, pleated, crumpled, dented, and folded.
Lizards and worms were often applied to the ware, each with detailed,
expressive features. He was well recognized, however, for his glazes,
especially those with a metallic patina. The ware was marked with his
name, alone or with 'Biloxi' added. Ohr died in 1918.

Our advisors for this category are Fer-Duc, Inc.; they are listed in the
Directory under New York.

Bird feeder, sgn 650.00
Bowl, dk brn & gr gloss w/brn specks, 1x3½" 145.00
Bowl, 4 colors alternate, ruffled, 11 indents, ftd, 3x5" 600.00
Conch shell, orange/brn/gr-sponged gloss, 5½x9½", EX 2,500.00
Cup, rust w/dk brn flecks, incised inscription, 2¾" 475.00
Inkwell, raspberry gloss, pinched/ruffled, no lid, 1½x4¾" 500.00
Jar, celadon/olive-gr gloss, 2 pleated bands, w/lid, 4x4½" 800.00
Mug, gun metal/gr, 3 ear-shape hdls, bulging rim, rpr, 4½" 700.00
Pitcher, gr/brn gloss w/gray spots, dbl hdl, 3¾" 500.00
Pitcher, gr/tan, emb soldiers/battle, dimpled base, 9½" 950.00
Pitcher, rose, gr drip rim/base, ruffled, shaped hdl, 3" 1,400.00
Pot, tan/gr splotches, amorphous w/heart-shaped rim, 2x3" 425.00
Vase, army-gr gloss, deep in-body twist at bottom, 4½" 850.00
Vase, brn bsk, twisted/ruffled top, 6½", NM 180.00
Vase, brn flambe/rust, deeply twisted/ruffled rim, 4½x4" 800.00
Vase, brn lustre, rim rolls in on 2 sides/out on 2, 3½x4" 1,100.00
Vase, brn w/gun metal, tight central twist, pinched, 5" 750.00
Vase, brn/gr gloss, ripped rim, indented 'features,' 4x3" 475.00
Vase, bsk finish, corseted, rim on bottom, 5" 425.00
Vase, cinnamon, bowl form, 4½" dia .200.00
Vase, dk bl/gr/pk/yel lustre, ripped/pinched rim, 4x5" 1,100.00
Vase, dk bl/rose/gr glossy drips, wide pleated rim, 4½x4" 1,900.00
Vase, feathered pk/gr/bl/yel, brn specks, bulging top, 4x4" 1,200.00
Vase, gold-brn w/gr spots, flared, waisted, 7½x3" 600.00

Vase, gr tones w/sponged dk teal, lg dimple ea side, 4¾x4½" . . .**425.00**
Vase, gun metal/dk gr gloss, waisted w/1 side pinched, 4" **1,400.00**
Vase, metallic/gr, bk: brn gloss, crimped collar/cvd boat, 6" **700.00**
Vase, speckled brn mirror glaze, slightly pinched rim, 6" **400.00**
Vase, splotchy mustard/gr, 'heart'-form rim, 2x3½" **425.00**

Vase, mottled brown-green gloss, signed in block letters, 4", $750.00.

Old Ivory

Old Ivory dinnerware was produced during the late 1800s in Selesia. The patterns are referred to by the numbers stamped on the bottom of each piece. The mark sometimes includes a crown and the name 'Selesia.' Patterns #16 and #84 are the easiest to find and come in a wide variety of table items. Values are about the same for both patterns. Other floral designs include pink, yellow, and orange roses; holly; and lavender flowers — all on the same soft ivory background.

Berry set, #16 or #84, 6½" master+6 ind **250.00**
Berry set, #69, 9½" master+4 5½" ind **165.00**
Berry set, #82, 7-pc **275.00**
Bowl, #16 or #84, 10" **85.00**
Bowl, #22, 10" **150.00**
Bowl, cereal; #15, 6½" **20.00**
Cake plate, #16 or #84, pierced hdls **75.00**
Cake plate, #200 . . . .**100.00**
Cake plate, #22 . . . .**140.00**
Cake set, #16 or #84, 7-pc **225.00**
Cake set, Clarion XI, 12" chop plate+ 6 7½" plates **250.00**
Celery dish, #16 or #84 . . . .**70.00**
Chocolate pot, #15 . . . .**295.00**
Chocolate pot, #15, +4 c/s **550.00**
Chocolate pot, #73, +6 c/s **695.00**
Chocolate pot, Thistle, gold finial & trim, 9½" **195.00**
Chocolate set, #16 or #84, pot+5 c/s **625.00**
Coffee cup & saucer, #16 or #84 . . . .**58.00**
Cracker jar or biscuit jar, #16 or #84 . . . .**325.00**
Creamer, #16 or #84 . . . .**45.00**
Creamer & sugar bowl, #11, w/lid **120.00**
Cup, chocolate; #28 . . . .**40.00**

Chocolate pot, #118, 9", $485.00.

Dresser set, #16 or #84, powder jar & hair receiver, EX **160.00**
Gravy boat, #16 or #84, attached underplate **400.00**
Mustard jar, #16 or #84 . . . .**200.00**
Nappy, #16 or #84, hdls **60.00**
Plate, #11, Clarion, 7¾" **28.00**
Plate, #121, 7" **28.00**
Plate, #16 or #84, 8½" **45.00**
Plate, #16 or #84, 9½" **125.00**
Plate, #200, 6" **20.00**
Plate, #75, 7¾" **32.00**
Plate, Thistle, crown mk, 6¼" **15.00**
Plate, Thistle, scalloped, 8¼" **45.00**
Relish, #15 . . . .**36.00**
Relish, #16 or #84 . . . .**40.00**
Relish, #33, 8x4¾" **50.00**
Saucer, #82 . . . .**15.00**
Shakers, #16 or #84, pr **125.00**
Sugar bowl, w/lid, #16 or #84 . . . .**45.00**
Sugar shaker, #84 . . . .**285.00**
Teapot, #16 or #84 . . . .**275.00**
Toothpick holder, #10 . . . .**165.00**

Old Paris

Old Paris porcelains were made from the late 18th century until about 1900. Seldom marked, the term refers to the area of manufacture rather than a specific company. In general, the ware was of high quality and characterized by classic shapes, colorful decoration, and gold application.

Bowl, floral on wht, emb buds/vines, vine hdls, 17" L **400.00**
Bowl, gilt detail on emb wht, 1850, 9" **120.00**
Cache pot+undertray, gilt arches, lion head hdls, 5¾", pr **250.00**
Coffee can & saucer, maid/attendants on lt bl w/gilt, 2½" **240.00**
Creamer & sugar bowl, Anneau D'Or, 1830s **120.00**
Mantel garniture, bust portraits, 13" urn+2 vases **600.00**
Plate, floral sprays, bl borders, Honore, 1850, set of 12 . . . .**300.00**
Platter, floral, gilt/claret rims, Honore, grad set of 4 . . . .**2,450.00**
Tureen+underplate, floral sprays, bl borders, Honore, 1850 . . .**300.00**
Vase, courting couple w/instruments, ribbed baluster, 22" **850.00**
Vase, cupid & flowers, pastels, sgn/dtd 1823, 13¼" **260.00**
Vase, floral, leaf-cast scroll hdls, scroll base, 13" **175.00**
Vase, floriform, HP couple, 2 3-D children on base, 18", pr **425.00**
Vase, gilt calla lilies/leaves w/mc floral panels, 9", pr **375.00**

Vase, mother/children in garden reserve, 1800s, 22", pr 1,800.00
Vase, Neo-Persian, scrolls/floral reserves on pk, 1865, 16" 300.00
Vase, portrait, heavy gilt, florals, sq base, 13", pr 425.00
Vase, portrait of lady on red w/gold, fan form, 14x7" 325.00
Vase, scrolling vine HP on silver, molded rim/base, 9", pr 350.00
Veilleuse, plain wht, ca 1860 ....60.00

Bowl, 17" long, $400.00; Vases, ladies in reserves, 14", $400.00 for the pair.

Old Sleepy Eye

Old Sleepy Eye was a Sioux Indian chief who was born in Minnesota in 1780. His name was used for the name of a town as well as a flour mill. The Sleepy Eye Milling Company of Sleepy Eye, Minnesota, contracted the Weir Pottery Company of Monmouth, Illinois, to make steins, vases, salt crocks, and butter tubs which the company gave away to their customers in each bag of their flour. A bust profile of the old Indian and his name decorated each piece of the blue and gray stoneware. In addition to these four items, the Minnesota Stoneware Company of Red Wing made a mug with a verse which is very scarce today.

In 1906 Weir Pottery merged with six others to form the Western Stoneware Company in Monmouth. They produced a line of blue and white ware using a lighter body, but these pieces were never given as flour premiums. This line consisted of pitchers (five sizes), steins, mugs, sugar bowls, vases, trivets, and mustache cups. These pieces turn up only rarely in other colors and are highly sought by advanced collectors.

Advertising items such as trade cards, pillow tops, thermometers, paperweights, letter openers, post cards, cookbooks, and thimbles are considered very valuable.

The original ware was made sporadically until 1937. Brown steins and mugs were produced in 1952.

Barrel, grapevine-effect banding 1,200.00
Butter crock, Flemish 500.00
Calendar, 1904 ....350.00
Cookbook, Indian on cover, Sleepy Eye Milling Co, 4¾x4" 55.00
Cookbook, loaf of bread shape, NM 250.00
Coupon, for ordering cookbook 60.00

Dough scraper, tin/wood, To Be Sure, EX 350.00
Fan, Indian chief, die-cut cb, 1900 ....175.00
Flour sack, cloth, mc Indian, red letters 275.00
Ink blotter 100.00
Label, barrel end; mc Indian portrait, 16", NM 125.00
Label, egg crate; Indian chief in color, 1930s, 9x11" 25.00
Letter opener, bronze 850.00
Match holder, pnt 1,500.00
Match holder, wht 850.00
Milk carton 18.00
Mirror, advertising, 1935 ....35.00
Mug, bl & wht, 4¼" 175.00
Mug, verse, Redwing, EX 1,300.00
Paperweight, bronzed company trademk 500.00
Pillow cover, Sleepy Eye & tribe meet Pres Monroe 600.00
Pillow cover, trademk center w/various scenes, 22", NM 600.00
Pitcher, #1 ....150.00
Pitcher, #2 ....185.00
Pitcher, #3, rare 250.00
Pitcher, #4 ....275.00
Pitcher, #5 ....300.00
Pitcher, gold & brn, 1981 ....125.00
Pitcher, standing Indian, good color, #5 size 1,250.00
Post card 90.00
Ruler, wooden 400.00
Salt crock, Flemish 450.00
Sign, self-fr tin, Old Sleepy Eye Flour, 20x24" 2,000.00
Sign, tin, Sleepy Eye Flour & Cereal Products 3,500.00
Spoon, demitasse; emb roses in bowl, Unity SP 75.00
Spoon, Indian-head hdl 100.00
Stein, bl & wht, 7¾" 500.00

Stein, brown, 1952, 5½", $350.00.

Stein, brn & wht 900.00
Stein, brn & yel, Western Stoneware 900.00
Stein, cobalt 750.00
Stein, Flemish 475.00
Stein, ltd edition, 1979-1984, ea 100.00
Sugar bowl, bl & wht, 3" 600.00
Tumbler, etched, 1979 commemorative 25.00
Vase, bl & wht, good color, 9" 425.00
Vase, brn on yel, rare color 800.00
Vase, Indian & cattails, Flemish, 8½" 375.00
Watch fob, Sleepy Eye Mills, Indian, M 30.00

O'Neill, Rose

Rose O'Neill's Kewpies were introduced in 1909 when they were used to conclude a story in the December issue of *Ladies' Home Journal*. They were an immediate success, and soon Kewpie dolls were being produced world-wide. German manufacturers were among the earliest and also used the Kewpie motif to decorate chinaware as well as other items. The Kewpie is still popular today and can be found on products ranging from Christmas cards and cake ornaments to fabrics and wallpaper.

In the following listings, 'sgn' indicates that the item is signed Rose O'Neill. Unsigned items are of little interest to collectors. Items marked 'Germany' are sometimes reproductions.

Ad, They Wanted Jell-O, 1919 ....12.00
Bank, compo, Kewpie, nude, sits w/arms around knees, 12" 48.00
Book, Brownie Primer, O'Neill illus, 1905 ....25.00
Book, Jell-O & the Kewpies, O'Neill illus, 1915, 20-pg 35.00
Book, Kewpies & the Runaway Baby, O'Neill illus, 1928, EX ...25.00
Book, Kewpies' Health Book, 1929, EX 75.00
Book, Little Kewpie Book, O'Neill illus 10.00
Book, 2nd Brownie Book, O'Neill illus 20.00
Candy container, glass, Kewpie figural, Germany, 3" 45.00
Candy container, Kewpies, Borgfeldt, NM 160.00
Charm, Kewpie figural, sterling 20.00
Cup & saucer, sgn, Germany 55.00
Door knocker, brass, Kewpie figural 60.00
Dresser set, Kewpies, 4 pcs on 10x7" tray, Royal Rudolstadt ...950.00
Feeding dish, 7 Kewpies, sgn Rose O'Neill, Royal Rudolstadt ..235.00
Flannel, seashore, 1914 ....20.00

Kewpies, each signed Rose O'Neill, 5¼", $125.00 each.

Kewpie, bsk, in basket, sgn, Germany, 3" 350.00
Kewpie, bsk, jtd arms, heart label, sgn, 5" 185.00
Kewpie, bsk, jtd arms, sgn on ft, 7" 185.00
Kewpie, bsk, label on chest, sgn ft, 1920, 6" 185.00
Kewpie, bsk, sits, holds blk cat, 3¼" 400.00
Kewpie, bsk, stands w/arms up, sgn, 2" 150.00
Kewpie, bsk, w/teddy bear, sgn, Germany, 4" 150.00
Kewpie, celluloid, Blk, sgn Rose O'Neill, dtd 1913, 2⅜" 85.00
Kewpie, celluloid, Germany, 1913 label, 8" 135.00
Kewpie, celluloid, jtd arms, bl wings, O'Neill pat #, 2½" 150.00
Kewpie, chalkware, carnival figure 50.00
Kewpie Bride & Groom, bsk, Germany, 4½" 250.00
Kewpie Bride & Groom, bsk, sgn on ft, Japan, pr 125.00
Kewpie Clown, plush, O'Neill tag, EX 75.00
Kewpie Dottie Darling, c Rose O'Neill, sm 100.00

Kewpie Farmer, bsk, sgn Rose O'Neill, 4" 385.00
Kewpie Gal, mk on head & body, Christmas dress, 14" 185.00
Kewpie Gal, sgn Rose O'Neill 39.00
Kewpie Governor, bsk, sits in wicker chair, Germany 385.00
Kewpie Graduate, celluloid, sgn Rose O'Neill, 4" 115.00
Kewpie Guitar Player, bsk, sgn, Germany, 3½" 275.00
Kewpie Hot 'N Tot, sgn on ft, Cameo, MIB 90.00
Kewpie Huggers, bsk, sgn O'Neill, 3¾" 225.00
Kewpie Kuddles, yel plush, Krueger, 10" 125.00
Kewpie Oriental, bsk, sgn, rare 300.00
Kewpie Santa, Royal Society, sgn Rose O'Neill, 1913 ....55.00
Kewpie Sweeper, bsk, w/trash can & broom, sgn, 5" 400.00
Kewpie Thinker, bsk, sgn, Germany, 4" 265.00
Kewpie Traveller, bsk, Germany, 3½" 150.00
Kewpie Traveller, bsk, sgn ft, 3½" 275.00
Lamp, Kewpie decor, metal, Ronson, 1920s 150.00
Letter opener, planter, Kewpies, faint mk 65.00
Magazine page, Harper's Bazaar, O'Neill illus, 1909 ....10.00
Mug, 5 action Kewpies, sgn, Royal Rudolstadt, 3½" 150.00
Pincushion, bsk Kewpie half-doll, sgn, 2¾" 325.00
Pincushion, SP, Kewpie ea side 200.00
Pitcher, 7 Kewpies on bl, sgn, Germany, 2½" 200.00
Place-card holder, Kewpie lying on bk, bsk, Germany 110.00
Plaque, 3 Kewpies on bench, bl jasper, triangular, 4½" 265.00
Plaque, 3 Kewpies w/butterflies, bl jasper, crescent, sgn 265.00
Plate, Kewpie band, 1973, 8" 25.00
Plate, Kewpies, sgn Rose O'Neill, Royal Rudolstadt, 8" 200.00
Plate, sgn, Royal Rudolstadt, 6", +bowl/cup/saucer 275.00
Post card, Kewpies at play, EX 40.00
Poster, Kewpies, sgn Rose O'Neill, lg 25.00
Powder box, Kewpies, Germany 125.00
Shakers, Kewpies on tummies, old Japan, pr 40.00
Sign, Kewpie Santa diecut, easel bk, sgn Rose O'Neill, 1913 ....50.00
Talcum container, Kewpies, orig clothes, sticker, 1913 ....185.00
Tea set, Kewpies, Rose O'Neill, Germany, 23-pc 650.00
Teapot, lustre, sgn O'Neill, tray mk Germany 135.00
Thimble, metal, Kewpies, mk 35.00
Toothpick holder, glass, standing Kewpie, mk 45.00
Tray, pin; Kewpies, Royal Rudolstadt 40.00
Tray, 8 Kewpies, sgn Rose O'Neill, Rudolstadt, 10" 295.00
Vase, Kewpies, wht on bl jasper, sgn, 4x3½x1½" 350.00
Whistle, brass, Kewpie figural 20.00

Onion Pattern

The familiar pattern known to collectors as Onion acquired its name through a case of mistaken identity. Designed in the early 1700s by Johann Haroldt of the Meissen factory in Germany, the pattern was a mixture from earlier Oriental designs. One of its components was a stylized peach, which was mistaken for an onion; as a result, the pattern became known by that name. Usually found in blue, an occasional piece may also be found in pink. The pattern is commonly associated with Meissen, but it has been reproduced by many others including Villeroy and Boch and Royal Copenhagen.

Basket, reticulated, rustic hdls form ft, oval, 10" L 325.00
Basket, reticulated, shallow, Meissen, 1890s, 7", pr 250.00
Bone dish, X-swords 85.00
Bowl, divided, hdls, X-swords, 9½x11" L 225.00
Bowl, notched corners, X-swords, sq, 9" 275.00
Bowl, reticulated gold band, Royal, ca 1880s, 8" 190.00
Bowl, scalloped, X-swords, 3¼x4¾" dia 120.00
Cache pot, gilt borders, Meissen, 1890s, 5½" 225.00

Canister, Pepper, barrel form, 3½" 35.00
Cheese board, unmk 75.00
Coffeepot, 1800s, 9½" 375.00
Compote, reticulated, X-swords, 8½x9" 325.00
Compote, slightly shaped, Meissen, 1890s, 15" dia 425.00
Compote, twisted knopped stem, Meissen, 8¾x9" 375.00
Creamer, X-swords, late 75.00
Cup & saucer, demitasse; mk Meissen in oval, Germany 30.00
Dish, shell shape, Meissen, 1900, 7¾", pr 220.00
Eye cup, no mk 18.00
Invalid feeder, Caduseus mk 150.00
Letter opener, brass blade, Germany 35.00
Pie crimper 60.00
Pitcher, water; Rococo shape, X-swords, 1860s, 7" 225.00
Plate, dinner; 1900s, 10½" 70.00
Plate, fruit grouping, ca 1850, 9½" 150.00
Plate, scalloped, reticulated, X-swords, 8" 110.00
Plate, sq, Meakin, 7" 30.00
Plate, X-swords, 9¼" 50.00
Platter, shaped, Meissen, 1890s, 15½", pr 475.00
Platter, X-swords, 1850s, 21" 425.00
Rolling pin 200.00
Sauce boat, w/attached undertray, X-swords, 3½x4⅞x8" 160.00

Sauce boat, Meissen, one-piece, 10½" long, $175.00.

Shaving mug, w/matching brush 50.00
Strainer, wooden hdl 75.00
Tea set, doll's sz, 10-pc 165.00
Teapot, X-swords, late, 10" 325.00
Tray, scroll/leaf rim, gilt, quatrefoil, Meissen, 20½" L 550.00
Trivet, unmk 35.00
Tureen, soup; putto finial, Meissen, 1900s, 10½" 900.00
Tureen, soup; shell hdls, dome lid, 1900, 10½" H 650.00
Tureen, w/lid, Meissen, 1940s, 5½x12x10" 495.00
Utensil holder, hanging, 15-slot, lg 150.00
Vase, ftd, X-swords, 5" 85.00

Opalescent Glass

First made in England in 1870, opalescent glass became popular in America around the turn of the century. Its name comes from the milky-white opalescent trim that defines the lines of the pattern. It was produced in table sets, novelties, toothpick holders, vases, and lamps.

Alaska, banana boat, bl 250.00
Alaska, berry set, bl, 7-pc 275.00
Alaska, bowl, bl, sq, 8" 95.00

Alaska, butter dish, bl or vaseline 260.00
Alaska, butter dish, bl w/HP floral 295.00
Alaska, celery tray, bl 135.00
Alaska, celery tray, vaseline 125.00
Alaska, creamer, bl 70.00
Alaska, creamer, vaseline 60.00
Alaska, creamer, vaseline, HP floral 70.00
Alaska, cruet, bl, w/stopper 265.00
Alaska, cruet, vaseline 225.00
Alaska, cruet, vaseline, HP floral 265.00
Alaska, pitcher, water; bl 325.00
Alaska, pitcher, water; bl w/HP floral 450.00
Alaska, pitcher, water; clear 225.00
Alaska, pitcher, water; vaseline 350.00
Alaska, sauce, bl 25.00
Alaska, sauce, gr w/HP floral 30.00
Alaska, shakers, bl or vaseline, pr 65.00
Alaska, spooner, bl 65.00
Alaska, spooner, vaseline 45.00
Alaska, sugar bowl, bl, w/lid 150.00
Alaska, sugar bowl, vaseline, w/lid 130.00
Alaska, tumbler, vaseline 60.00
Arabian Nights, pitcher, water; cranberry 500.00
Arabian Nights, tumbler, bl 60.00
Arabian Nights, tumbler, cranberry 85.00
Argonaut Shell, berry set, clear, 7-pc 275.00
Argonaut Shell, butter dish, bl 275.00
Argonaut Shell, compote, jelly; vaseline 75.00
Argonaut Shell, creamer, bl 75.00
Argonaut Shell, cruet, bl 275.00
Argonaut Shell, pitcher, water; bl 350.00
Argonaut Shell, spooner, bl 150.00
Argonaut Shell, sugar bowl, bl, w/lid 200.00
Argonaut Shell, tumbler, vaseline 100.00
Astro, bride's bowl, bl, ruffled, 8" 35.00
Beaded Ovals in Sand, butter dish, gr 250.00
Beaded Ovals in Sand, creamer, bl 70.00
Beatty Rib, creamer, ind; clear 20.00
Beatty Rib, sugar bowl, bl, w/lid 125.00
Beatty Rib, table set, bl, 4-pc 265.00
Beatty Rib, toothpick holder, clear 24.00
Beatty Swirl, butter dish, bl 150.00
Beatty Swirl, celery vase, bl 75.00
Beatty Swirl, pitcher, water; bl 130.00
Beatty Swirl, syrup, bl, rare 200.00
Beatty Swirl, tray, water; vaseline 75.00
Bubble Lattice, pitcher, water; cranberry 325.00
Bubble Lattice, sugar bowl, bl, w/lid 160.00
Buttons & Braids, pitcher, water; bl 135.00
Buttons & Braids, pitcher, water; cranberry 295.00
Buttons & Braids, tumbler, bl 35.00
Buttons & Braids, tumbler, cranberry 85.00
Chrysanthemum Base Reverse Swirl, mustard, bl 135.00
Chrysanthemum Base Swirl, butter dish, cranberry 300.00
Chrysanthemum Base Swirl, spooner, bl 75.00
Chrysanthemum Base Swirl, syrup, bl 175.00
Chrysanthemum Base Swirl, toothpick holder, cranberry 90.00
Chrysanthemum Base Swirl, tumbler, cranberry 85.00
Circled Scroll, butter dish, bl 295.00
Circled Scroll, compote, gr 125.00
Circled Scroll, cruet, bl 350.00
Circled Scroll, shakers, bl, pr 175.00
Circled Scroll, sugar bowl, bl, w/lid 225.00
Circled Scroll, tumbler, gr 80.00

Coin Spot, celery vase, cranberry 150.00
Coin Spot, compote, peach 35.00
Coin Spot, creamer, bl 50.00
Coin Spot, pitcher, water; bl, 9" 120.00
Coin Spot, pitcher, water; clear 85.00
Coin Spot, pitcher, water; cranberry 250.00
Coin Spot, sugar shaker, bl, bulbous base 85.00
Coin Spot, sugar shaker, cranberry, ring neck 120.00
Coin Spot, tumble-up, cranberry 250.00
Coin Spot, tumbler, cranberry 45.00
Daisy & Fern, cruet, Netted Blossom mold, bl 110.00
Daisy & Fern, pitcher, water; bl 165.00
Daisy & Fern, pitcher, water; clear 95.00
Daisy & Fern, pitcher, water; cranberry, solid hdl 225.00
Daisy & Fern, syrup, bl 120.00
Daisy & Fern, tumbler, cranberry 45.00
Daisy in Criss Cross, pitcher, water; bl 275.00
Daisy in Criss Cross, syrup, bl 245.00
Daisy in Criss Cross, syrup, cranberry 345.00
Diamond Spearhead, butter dish, gr 275.00
Diamond Spearhead, butter dish, vaseline 195.00
Diamond Spearhead, celery vase, bl 110.00
Diamond Spearhead, compote, bl 95.00
Diamond Spearhead, creamer, cobalt 125.00
Diamond Spearhead, cup, cobalt 75.00
Diamond Spearhead, goblet, bl 95.00
Diamond Spearhead, mug, bl 45.00
Diamond Spearhead, pitcher, water; cobalt 450.00
Diamond Spearhead, pitcher, water; gr 325.00
Diamond Spearhead, sugar bowl, cobalt, w/lid 175.00
Diamond Spearhead, sugar bowl, gr, w/lid 135.00
Diamond Spearhead, syrup, cobalt .400.00
Diamond Spearhead, tumbler, vaseline 45.00
Dolly Madison, butter dish, bl 290.00
Dolly Madison, creamer, bl 75.00
Dolly Madison, pitcher, water; gr 350.00
Dolly Madison, spooner, gr 75.00
Dolly Madison, sugar bowl, gr, w/lid 125.00
Dolly Madison, tumbler, bl 75.00

Double Greek Key butter dish, light blue, $285.00.

Double Greek Key, celery vase, bl 115.00
Double Greek Key, creamer, bl 65.00
Double Greek Key, shakers, bl, pr 180.00
Double Greek Key, spooner, bl 70.00
Double Greek Key, sugar bowl, bl, w/lid 150.00

Double Greek Key, toothpick holder, bl 175.00
Double Greek Key, tumbler, bl 65.00
Drapery, pitcher, water; bl 165.00
Drapery, rose bowl, aqua 95.00
Drapery, rose bowl, bl 75.00
Drapery, water set, bl, 7-pc 375.00
Drapery, water set, clear, 7-pc 250.00
Everglades, butter dish, bl w/gold .225.00
Everglades, butter dish, vaseline 275.00
Everglades, compote, jelly; bl w/gold 85.00
Everglades, compote, jelly; vaseline 110.00
Everglades, creamer, bl 80.00
Everglades, cruet, vaseline 395.00
Everglades, pitcher, water; vaseline 360.00
Everglades, spooner, vaseline 85.00
Everglades, sugar bowl, bl w/gold .150.00
Everglades, sugar bowl, vaseline, w/lid 150.00
Everglades, tumbler, bl 65.00
Everglades, tumbler, bl w/gold 75.00
Fern, shaker, cranberry 50.00
Fern, spooner, cranberry 120.00
Flora, bowl, master berry; vaseline 95.00
Flora, butter dish, bl 245.00
Flora, butter dish, vaseline 175.00
Flora, butter dish, vaseline w/gold .210.00
Flora, celery vase, bl 110.00
Flora, compote, jelly; bl, rare 135.00
Flora, creamer, vaseline 80.00
Flora, cruet, vaseline 375.00
Flora, pitcher, water; vaseline 450.00
Flora, shakers, bl, pr 350.00
Flora, shakers, vaseline, pr 300.00
Flora, spooner, vaseline 70.00
Flora, sugar bowl, vaseline, w/lid 110.00
Flora, toothpick holder, bl 400.00
Flora, toothpick holder, vaseline 300.00
Flora, tumbler, vaseline 75.00
Fluted Scrolls, bowl, master berry; bl 65.00
Fluted Scrolls, butter dish, bl, HP decor 215.00
Fluted Scrolls, butter dish, vaseline 165.00
Fluted Scrolls, creamer, bl 55.00
Fluted Scrolls, creamer, vaseline 60.00
Fluted Scrolls, cruet, vaseline, orig stopper 175.00
Fluted Scrolls, dresser jar, vaseline, w/lid 55.00
Fluted Scrolls, pitcher, water; bl 225.00
Fluted Scrolls, pitcher, water; vaseline 195.00
Fluted Scrolls, puff box, bl 55.00
Fluted Scrolls, puff box, vaseline 50.00
Fluted Scrolls, spooner, bl 50.00
Fluted Scrolls, sugar bowl, vaseline, w/lid 88.00
Fluted Scrolls, water set, clear, 5-pc 225.00
Frosted-Leaf & Basketweave, butter dish, bl 250.00
Frosted-Leaf & Basketweave, creamer, bl 135.00
Frosted-Leaf & Basketweave, sugar bowl, bl, w/lid 165.00
Frosted-Leaf & Basketweave, sugar bowl, vaseline, w/lid 145.00
Hobnail, pitcher, bl, clear threaded hdl, 5½" 50.00
Hobnail, pitcher, cranberry, sq mouth, lg 185.00
Hobnail, pitcher, milk; vaseline, clear reeded hdl 115.00
Hobnail, pitcher, rubena, clear hdl, +6 tumblers 750.00
Hobnail, pitcher, yel, 7" 225.00
Honeycomb & Clover, butter dish, bl 300.00
Honeycomb & Clover, pitcher, water; bl 350.00
Honeycomb & Clover, sugar bowl, bl, w/lid 200.00
Honeycomb & Clover, tumbler, bl 85.00

Idyll, butter dish, bl 325.00
Idyll, creamer, clear 36.00
Idyll, creamer, gr 85.00
Idyll, spooner, gr, 4½x3½" 70.00
Idyll, sugar bowl, bl, w/lid 175.00
Idyll, toothpick holder, bl 210.00
Idyll, tumbler, bl 90.00
Intaglio, bowl, master berry; bl 100.00
Intaglio, butter dish, bl 350.00
Intaglio, compote, jelly; bl 30.00
Intaglio, compote, jelly; vaseline 39.00
Intaglio, creamer, bl, HP decor 55.00
Intaglio, creamer, clear 20.00
Intaglio, creamer, vaseline 45.00
Intaglio, cruet, bl, w/bl stopper 165.00
Intaglio, pitcher, water; bl 200.00
Intaglio, sugar bowl, vaseline, w/lid 90.00
Intaglio, tumbler, bl 100.00
Inverted Fan & Feather, creamer, bl .135.00
Inverted Fan & Feather, pitcher, water; bl 495.00
Inverted Fan & Feather, sugar bowl, bl, w/lid 200.00
Inverted Fan & Feather, tumbler, bl 75.00
Iris w/Meander, berry set, vaseline, 6-pc 220.00
Iris w/Meander, bowl, master berry; bl, 10" 90.00
Iris w/Meander, butter dish, bl 265.00
Iris w/Meander, compote, jelly; bl 45.00
Iris w/Meander, creamer, vaseline 75.00
Iris w/Meander, cruet, vaseline 350.00
Iris w/Meander, pitcher, water; bl 375.00
Iris w/Meander, pitcher, water; vaseline 300.00
Iris w/Meander, shakers, bl, pr 200.00
Iris w/Meander, spooner, bl 75.00
Iris w/Meander, sugar bowl, bl, w/lid 150.00
Iris w/Meander, sugar bowl, gr, w/lid 125.00
Iris w/Meander, toothpick holder, clear 45.00
Iris w/Meander, toothpick holder, vaseline 75.00
Iris w/Meander, tumbler, bl 75.00
Jackson, butter dish, bl 250.00
Jackson, butter dish, vaseline 225.00
Jackson, cruet, vaseline 165.00
Jackson, pitcher, water; vaseline 450.00
Jackson, powder box, bl 55.00
Jackson, shakers, vaseline, pr 175.00
Jackson, spooner, vaseline 60.00
Jackson, sugar bowl, bl, w/lid 110.00
Jackson, tumbler, vaseline 80.00
Jewel & Flower, butter dish, clear 95.00
Jewel & Flower, butter dish, vaseline 225.00
Jewel & Flower, creamer, vaseline 85.00
Jewel & Flower, cruet, bl 300.00
Jewel & Flower, pitcher, water; bl 450.00
Jewel & Flower, shakers, vaseline, pr 130.00
Jewel & Flower, sugar bowl, vaseline, w/lid 145.00
Jewel & Flower, tumbler, bl 80.00
Jeweled Heart, compote, bl 125.00
Jeweled Heart, cruet, bl 395.00
Jeweled Heart, nappy, clear, ruffled, 6" 22.00
Jeweled Heart, spooner, bl 110.00
Jeweled Heart, sugar bowl, bl, w/lid .175.00
Jeweled Heart, toothpick holder, bl .225.00
Leaf Chalice, rose bowl, gr, ped ft 45.00
Leaf Chalice, sugar bowl, gr, ped ft, w/lid 55.00
Lustre Flute, butter dish, bl 280.00
Lustre Flute, creamer, bl 85.00

Lustre Flute, pitcher, water; bl 325.00
Lustre Flute, spooner, bl 85.00
Lustre Flute, sugar bowl, bl, w/lid 175.00
Lustre Flute, tumbler, bl 65.00
Palm Beach, butter dish, bl 275.00
Palm Beach, compote, vaseline 175.00
Palm Beach, creamer & sugar bowl, bl, w/lid 195.00
Palm Beach, pitcher, water; bl 385.00
Palm Beach, pitcher, water; vaseline .350.00
Palm Beach, sauce, bl 25.00
Palm Beach, spooner, bl 85.00
Palm Beach, tumbler, bl 85.00
Paneled Holly, berry set, bl opal, 6-pc 350.00
Paneled Holly, butter dish, bl 300.00
Paneled Holly, creamer, bl 75.00
Paneled Holly, pitcher, water; bl 500.00
Paneled Holly, spooner, bl 65.00
Paneled Holly, sugar bowl, bl, w/lid .225.00
Paneled Holly, tumbler, bl 75.00
Poinsettia, bowl, clear, ruffled, 3-ftd .40.00
Poinsettia, pitcher, water; bl, tankard form 275.00
Poinsettia, sugar shaker, bl 150.00
Poinsettia, syrup, bl 300.00
Poinsettia, tumbler, bl 50.00
Regal, butter dish, clear 125.00
Regal, butter dish, gr w/gold 235.00
Regal, celery vase, bl 125.00
Regal, cruet, bl 400.00
Regal, pitcher, water; bl 290.00
Regal, spooner, gr 55.00
Regal, sugar bowl, bl, w/lid 145.00
Reverse Swirl, creamer, bl 150.00
Reverse Swirl, spooner, bl 95.00
Reverse Swirl, spooner, cranberry 110.00
Reverse Swirl, sugar bowl, bl, w/lid .175.00

Ribbed Herringbone pitcher, blue, 8½", $350.00; in cranberry, $450.00.

Ribbed Spiral, butter dish, bl 350.00
Ribbed Spiral, compote, bl 47.00
Ribbed Spiral, creamer, bl 50.00
Ribbed Spiral, plate, vaseline 23.00
Ribbed Spiral, shakers, vaseline, pr 185.00

Ribbed Spiral, sugar bowl, bl, w/lid 175.00
Ribbed Spiral, tumbler, bl 75.00
Scottish Moor, pitcher, water; cranberry 375.00
Scroll w/Acanthus, butter dish, bl .350.00
Scroll w/Acanthus, creamer, bl 60.00
Scroll w/Acanthus, cruet, bl, w/clear stopper 195.00
Scroll w/Acanthus, cruet, vaseline 350.00
Scroll w/Acanthus, pitcher, water; vaseline 350.00
Scroll w/Acanthus, spooner, bl 65.00
Scroll w/Acanthus, sugar bowl, vaseline, w/lid 125.00
Scroll w/Acanthus, tumbler, bl 75.00
Shell, butter dish, bl 450.00
Shell, compote, bl 110.00
Shell, cruet, bl 350.00
Shell, pitcher, water; bl 500.00
Shell, sauce, clear, 6 for 150.00
Shell, spooner, bl 95.00
Shell, toothpick holder, bl 400.00
Shell, tumbler, bl 75.00
Spanish Lace, pitcher, water; clear 95.00
Spanish Lace, rose bowl, clear 35.00
Spanish Lace, shakers, cranberry, pr 175.00
Spanish Lace, sugar shaker, bl 135.00
Spanish Lace, tumbler, cranberry 75.00
Sunburst on Shield, creamer, bl 125.00
Sunburst on Shield, cruet, vaseline .650.00
Sunburst on Shield, pitcher, water; bl 500.00
Sunburst on Shield, spooner, vaseline 85.00
Sunburst on Shield, sugar bowl, clear, w/lid 30.00
Sunburst on Shield, sugar bowl, vaseline, w/lid 175.00
Sunburst on Shield, tumbler, bl 100.00
Swag w/Brackets, berry set, gr, 7-pc 200.00
Swag w/Brackets, compote, gr 30.00
Swag w/Brackets, pitcher, water; vaseline 250.00
Swag w/Brackets, sauce, vaseline 25.00
Swag w/Brackets, shakers, bl, pr 175.00
Swag w/Brackets, spooner, gr 45.00
Swag w/Brackets, sugar bowl, gr, w/lid 75.00
Swag w/Brackets, toothpick holder, bl 300.00
Swag w/Brackets, tumbler, bl 60.00
Swag w/Brackets, tumbler, clear 30.00
Swirl, hat, clear, lg 75.00
Swirl, pitcher, water; bl 125.00
Swirl, pitcher, water; clear 60.00
Swirl, sugar shaker, cranberry 150.00
Swirl, toothpick holder, cranberry, scarce tumbler shape 65.00
Tokyo, compote, gr 33.00
Tokyo, creamer, bl 65.00
Tokyo, cruet, bl, w/clear stopper 175.00
Tokyo, pitcher, water; bl 300.00
Tokyo, shakers, bl, pr 180.00
Tokyo, sugar bowl, clear, w/lid 50.00
War of Roses, boat dish, vaseline, 3x7½x2½" 50.00
Water Lily & Cattails, bowl, master berry; clear, ruffled 35.00
Water Lily & Cattails, butter dish, bl 375.00
Water Lily & Cattails, creamer, bl 45.00
Water Lily & Cattails, pitcher, water; bl 395.00
Water Lily & Cattails, sugar bowl, bl, w/lid 175.00
Water Lily & Cattails, tumbler, bl 50.00
Wild Bouquet, berry set, clear, 6-pc .145.00
Wild Bouquet, butter dish, bl 400.00
Wild Bouquet, compote, jelly; bl 125.00
Wild Bouquet, compote, jelly; clear 45.00
Wild Bouquet, cruet, bl 295.00

Wild Bouquet, pitcher, water; bl 250.00
Wild Bouquet, sugar bowl, bl, w/lid 200.00
Wild Bouquet, toothpick holder, bl .275.00
Wild Bouquet, tumbler, bl 100.00
Wild Bouquet, tumbler, gr 60.00
Wreath & Shell, bowl, master berry; bl 85.00
Wreath & Shell, butter dish, bl 225.00
Wreath & Shell, celery vase, bl 165.00
Wreath & Shell, cracker jar, bl 550.00
Wreath & Shell, creamer, bl 110.00
Wreath & Shell, pitcher, water; bl 350.00
Wreath & Shell, rose bowl, bl 75.00
Wreath & Shell, salt dip, bl 110.00
Wreath & Shell, sauce, vaseline 18.00
Wreath & Shell, spittoon, lady's, vaseline 90.00
Wreath & Shell, spooner, bl 75.00
Wreath & Shell, spooner, vaseline 65.00
Wreath & Shell, sugar bowl, vaseline, w/lid 130.00
Wreath & Shell, toothpick holder, bl 225.00
Wreath & Shell, toothpick holder, vaseline w/decor 250.00
Wreath & Shell, tumbler, bl 70.00

Opaline

A type of semi-opaque opal glass, opaline was made in white as well as pastel shades and is often enameled. It is similar in appearance to English bristol glass, though its enamel or gilt decorative devices tend to exhibit a French influence.

Bottle, scent; bl, pk spiral trim, bl teardrop stopper, 7" 100.00
Box, jewel; blk, floral/birds/insects, metal mts, Fr, 6" L 300.00
Box, jewel; Roman viaduct scene on lid, ormolu mts/hdls, 5" . .225.00
Box, wht w/cobalt/gold/lav/bl decor, ormolu ft, 4¼x4¼" 155.00
Chamberstick, gr & MOP shell, ormolu mts, 3¼x4" 150.00
Jar, wht, medallion transfer/HP florals, brass bail/lid 150.00
Rose bowl, appl acanthus leaves, rigaree, S&W, 6" 175.00
Syrup, pk apple blossoms, Belleware, hinged lid 110.00
Vase, scenic, mk Richardson, ca 1850s, 8½" 145.00

Openers

Around the turn of the century, manufacturers began to seal bottles with a metal cap that required a new type of bottle opener. Now the screw cap and the flip top have made bottle openers nearly obsolete. There are many variations, some in combination with other tools. Many openers were used as means of advertising a product. Various materials were used, including silver and brass.

A figural bottle opener is defined as a figure designed for the sole purpose of lifting a bottle cap. The actual opener must be an integral part of the figure itself. The major producers of iron figurals were Wilton Products, John Wright Inc., Gadzik Sales, and L & L Favors. Openers may be free-standing and three-dimensional, wall hung, or flat. They can be made of cast iron (often painted), brass, bronze, or aluminum.

Those seeking additional information concerning figural bottle openers are encouraged to contact the Figural Bottle Opener Collectors, whose address can be found in the Directory under Clubs, Newsletters, and Catalogs.

Auto jack, chrome, 1920s 25.00
Bird dog, paw uplifted, opener on chest, CI 45.00
Blk face w/wide grin, pnt aluminum, red bow tie 160.00
Blk Man, CI, wall hanging 95.00

Bull's head, extended tail hdl, 6" 28.00
Clown face, brass 35.00
Clown head w/bow tie, CI, 4-color pnt, 4½" 45.00
Cowboy & cactus, pot metal, EX pnt 100.00
Crab, CI, EX pnt 15.00
Deco nude w/hands behind head, brass 50.00
Donkey, CI, orig pnt, 3" 10.00
Donkey, Democrat, CI, 1940, M 12.50
Donkey, sitting, mouth is opener, CI, VG pnt, 3⅝" 25.00
Drunk at palm tree, bald head, CI w/EX orig pnt 40.00
Drunk at sign post, St Petersburg FL, CI 15.00

Drunk in top hat with bottle, wall mount, 5", $45.00.

Duck w/head up, CI w/worn pnt, 3", EX 45.00
Elephant, Pink; CI, orig pnt 38.00
Elephant, sitting, trunk looped overhead, CI, EX pnt, 3⅛" 45.00
Elephant, walking/trunk looped overhead, CI, worn pnt, 2½" ...25.00
English Setter, CI 40.00
Fish, stainless steel & wood, 9½" 10.00
Goat, opener below beard, CI, worn pnt, 4¼" 80.00
Goat, sitting, horns curve bk, CI w/worn pnt 40.00
Head, blk hair/mustache, 4-eyed, CI, orig pnt, wall mt, EX 25.00
Indian, Iroquois Beer, copper & steel 40.00
Juan Ponce de Leon bust in relief, Puerto Rico crest 20.00
Lamb w/ewe, recumbent, CI w/gold & silver rpt, 4" 30.00
Lobster, CI, EX orig pnt 20.00
Mallard duck, CI, EX pnt 50.00
Monkey by tree stump, CI, NM pnt, 2¾x2¾" 150.00
Palm tree, CI, worn mc pnt, 4½" 105.00
Parrot, corkscrew in bk, aluminum, 5" 15.00
Parrot, sitting, mouth is opener, CI, VG pnt, 3¼" 40.00
Parrot, w/can punch, CI w/orig mc pnt, minor wear, 5" 45.00
Parrot on perch, CI, dtd 1952, 5¾" 25.00
Pelican, CI, wht body, orange bill, gr base, 3½", EX 30.00
Shark, aluminum, EX 15.00
Squirrel, CI 30.00
Turtle, corkscrew tail, pot metal, EX 25.00
4-Eyed lady, Wilton, pnt CI, EX 35.00
4-Eyed man, Wilton, pnt CI, G 35.00

Optical Items

Collectors of Americana are beginning to appreciate the charm of antique optical items, and those involved in the related trade find them particularly fascinating. Anyone, however, can appreciate the evolution of technology apparent when viewing a collection of old eye wear and at the same time admire the primitive ingenuity involved in their construction.

Binoculars, Fernglas 1908, orig label, German instructions 30.00
Binoculars, ivory w/brass fittings, 3½", VG 130.00
Lorgnette, sterling w/filigree hdl, EX 55.00
Microscope, Bausch & Lomb, brass, turret style, EX 150.00
Microscope, Bausch & Lomb, 1915, lg, in wood case, NM 325.00
Microscope, German, brass, 1920s, sm, +case, EX 75.00
Microscope, Microcraft, Porter Chemical Co, 1954, +manual ..25.00
Microscope, Orange Judd, NY, pat 1878, M in box 215.00
Opera glasses, MOP & brass, LeMaire, France 65.00
Opera glasses, MOP & brass, mk Verdi Paris, EX in case 65.00
Spectacles, folding, silver fr w/sliding ear pcs, hall mk 100.00
Spectacles, gold Pince Nez, w/chain/hairpin, +case, EX 20.00
Spectacles, nickel silver, octagonal glass, ca 1850 ......22.00
Spectacles, slightly wing shaped w/rhinestones, France, 1940s ..35.00
Spyglass, monocular; ivory/brass, age cracks, ca 1840 ....125.00
Verometer (eyeglass tester), Bausch & Lomb, electric, M 175.00

Orientalia

The art of the Orient is an area of collecting currently enjoying strong collector interest, not only in those examples that are truly 'antique' but in the 20th-century items as well. Because of the many aspects involved in a study of Orientalia, we can only try through brief comments to acquaint the reader with some of the more readily-available examples and suggest specialized reference sources for detailed information.

Celadon, introduced during the Ching Dynasty, is a green-glazed ware developed in an attempt to imitate the color of jade. Designs are often incised or painted on over glaze in heavy enamel applications. Chinese export ware was designed to appeal to Western tastes and was often made to order. During the 18th century, vast amounts were shipped to Europe and on westward. Many of these dinnerwares were given specific pattern names — Rose Mandarin, Fitzhugh, Armorial, Rose Medallion, and Canton are but a few of the more familiar. Cinnabar is carved lacquer work, often involving hundreds of layers built one at a time on a metal or wooden base. Later pieces are red; older examples tend to darken.

The Chinese were introduced to snuff in the 17th century, and their carved and painted snuff bottles typify their exquisite taste and workmanship. These small bottles, seldom measuring over 2½", were made of amber, jade, ivory, and cinnabar; tiny spoons were often attached to their stoppers. By the 18th century, some were being made of porcelain, others were of glass with delicate designs tediously reverse painted with minuscule brushes sometimes containing a single hair. Copper and brass were used but to no large extent. See also Canton; Champleve; Cloisonne; Coralene, Oriental; Dragon Ware; Geisha Girl; Imari; Ivory; Kutani; Moriage; Netsuke; Nippon; Noritake; Peking Glass; Rose Medallion; Satsuma; Soapstone.

Key:
Ch — Chinese	FV — Famille Verte
ctp — contemporary	E — export
cvg — carving	hdwd — hardwood
do — door	Jp — Japan
drw — drawer	Ko — Korean
Dy — Dynasty	lcq — lacquer
FJ — Famille Juane	rswd — rosewood
FN — Famille Noire	tkwd — teakwood
FR — Famille Rose	

Banko

Creamer & sugar bowl, tapestry, gr/wht/gray, lg 110.00
Humidor, 7 gods of good luck in relief, ca 1900 ....425.00

Moon flask, money/fruit trees/cranes relief, mc/gold, 1885 ....485.00
Teapot, duck figural, mc on gray 310.00
Vase, gray w/wasps, 7¼" 375.00
Vase, Mezzo-Relievo scene of tea house & waterfall, 12¼" 225.00

Blanc de Chine

Deity, seated, serene face, flowing gown, 1700s, 5½" 200.00
Doe, potted flowers in saddle, on rockwork plinth, 12" 200.00
Guanyin on lotus ped, red lotus/mums/symbols, 14" 450.00
Hotei, stands, chest/belly exposed, holds scrolls/box, 10" 1,300.00
Kwan Yien, seated, flowing gown, ruyi sceptre, 5" 500.00
Lady reclining beside mythological animal, 1700s, 6½" 1,600.00

Blanc de Chine winepot, 17th/18th century; dragons form spout, handle, and finial, 6½", $5,250.00.

Blue and White Porcelain

Bowl, dragon/flaming pearl/etc, ext w/scrolls, Arita, 7x15" 950.00
Bowl, dragon/foliage, int: floral medallion, Ming Dy, 12" 750.00
Bowl, floral, geometric panel border, Arita, 1800s, 14" 425.00
Bowl, flowering bush, shaped scroll reserve to side, 12" 700.00
Bowl, panels of dignitaries/birds/lotus, late Quing Dy, 18" 400.00
Bowl, panels w/court women or autumn foliage, 8" 165.00
Bowl, pine tree border, phoenix medallion, Jp, 1890s, 12" 160.00
Bowl, precious objects/cranes, Arita, 3x4" dia, pr 150.00
Bowl, yinyang, flying horse/dragon, Qianlong, 11" 365.00
Bowl, 2 carps, Lohans on sides, 7½x11" 325.00
Brush box, dragons/flaming pearls, Wanli style, 1800s, 11" ...300.00
Charger, conch shell center, prunus/leaves, 1700s, 13" 500.00
Charger, diaper/cloud scroll band, pavilion, Nanking, 14" 250.00
Charger, mtn landscape w/pavilion, Jp, 1890s, 18" 150.00
Charger, sm floral int, scroll motif ext, Arita, 1800s, 17" 400.00
Coffeepot, E, scholar on bridge/pavilions, 1850s, 10" 275.00
Cup, foliage/flowers, int w/flower, Arita, 1700s, 3x3", pr 150.00
Dish, lg dragon in center, 2 dragons on ext, Qianlong, 14" 800.00
Jar, bamboo/mums/etc, 4 fu dog hdls, Provincial, 14" 425.00
Jar, ginger; cracked ice/prunus, wood lid, 1800s, 8½" 220.00
Jar, scalloped reserves of 100 Antiques on cracked ice, 11" 200.00
Jar, spice; stylized floral/foliage, dome lid, 1880s 935.00
Jar, waterway scene, ruyi/lappet band, fu dog finial, 31" 1,650.00

Jar, waterway/boats, ruyi/lappet bands, dome lid, 27" 1,100.00
Jar, 2 boys support lg jar, allover prunus, 1800s, 16" 400.00
Jar, 2 meiren play majung, court women watch, Kangxi, 15" ...385.00
Jardiniere, cranes in lily pond, bulbous, 12x14", pr 500.00
Jardiniere, water/pines/pavilions/precious emblems, 15", pr ..1,200.00
Pilgrim flask, dragon in reserve, openwork floral hdls, 12" 220.00
Pilgrim flask, fines/flowerheads, hdls, Ch'ing Dy, 11" 900.00
Pilgrim flask, group of venders on lotus ground, hdls, 12" 330.00
Planter w/underplate, dragon/phoenix, contemporary, 13", pr ..385.00
Plate, scholars/immortals scene, brn rim, Ming Dy style, 13" ...250.00
Plate, 100 Antiques, Kangxi, 9½" 495.00
Platter, E, pavilion/pines/waterway, octagonal, 1700s, 16" 275.00
Teapot, stylized Chinese characters lid & base, Arita, 7½" 200.00
Tray, dragon/cloud scrolls/flaming pearls, 1880s, 8", pr 165.00
Umbrella stand, floral cutouts, scholars/etc in garden, 12" 250.00
Vase, abstract peonies/tendrils, key-fret band, 1800s, 17" 165.00
Vase, fisherman/river, bk: calligraphy, mk, 1800s, 14" 650.00

Vase, figures and pavilions, Kangxi, 16", EX, $1,500.00.

Bronze

Bodhisattva on dbl lotus throne, Ming Dy, 9½x5½" 300.00
Bowl, bulb; relief band w/dragon, scroll legs, 1800s, 10" 300.00
Bull, walking w/head lowered, 1800s, 13½x27" 1,200.00
Censer, animal-head hdls, appl/openwork bamboo, 28" 1,200.00
Censer, 2-part duck form, abstract feathers, 1700s, 7x6" 275.00
Gong, 2 stippled rows, 18" ovoid form, in lacquered stand 650.00
Incense burner, dragon hdls, fu dog finial, Jp, 19x15x7" 450.00
Incense burner, tripod/lotus ft, rnd hdls, Ming Dy, 4½x5" 120.00
Koro, floral emb, loose ring hdls, animal atop, 1900, 18" 250.00
Lioness & 2 cubs on rocky outcropping, Ch, 1890s, 8½" 225.00
Monk, seated/yawning, ivory extremities, mk Hidemitsu, 9" .1,500.00
Planter, flanged band, S-curve/key-fret motif, Jp, 7" 300.00
Scholar in flowing gown, on ftd base, Jp, 5½" 100.00
Urn, band w/tao-tieh mask, calligraphy, ring hdls, 1900, 13" ...175.00
Urn, bird/foliate relief, on 3-leg base w/turtles, Jp, 27" 450.00
Urn, fu lion finial, kylin mask hdls, openwork top, 23" 500.00
Vase, appl dragon twines about long neck, Jp, 1800s, 18" 600.00

Head of Buddha, Chinese, 16", $500.00.

Coromandel floor screen, 1800s, brown lacquer ground, 126" long, $2,900.00.

Vitrine, Ch, gold/red pnt chinoiserie, roof canopy, 65x25" 600.00

Hardstones

Amber, dk red, buddha, EX detail, minor chip, 11½" 400.00
Amethyst, beauty in flowing robe w/fan, 6½" 165.00
Amethyst, phoenix bird in peony bush w/bird, 7½" 360.00
Amethyst, urn, peach branches cvg, 6" 220.00
Amethyst, vase, deeply cvd peonies, flower lid, 11x9" 650.00
Aventurine quartz, Buddhist rosary, 108 jade beads 425.00
Coral, Ho Xiangu w/flywhisks over shoulders, 6¾" 550.00
Coral, pk, girl in flowing kimono w/flower basket, 2x1½" 80.00
Coral, red, beauty, left hand to ear, 2½" 160.00
Goldstone, sprites/flower baskets/torch, silver inlay, 7" 325.00

Vase, bulbous on dome base, pinched/flared rim, Jp, 13" 50.00
Vase, dragon figural, squat w/octagonal neck, now lamp, 22" ..525.00
Vase, eng/inlaid: gilt/silver/mc leaves on brn, 1900, 6" 275.00
Vase, textured w/appl crabs, gr-brn patina, Jp, 12" 225.00

Celadon

Bottle, pear form, cup-like mouth, Yi Dy, 1600s, 9" 1,000.00
Bowl, cvd floral spring, ribbed cavetto, Ming Dy, 10" 400.00
Bowl, florals/foliage underglaze, 1700-1800, 17" 1,000.00
Bowl, palmettes/vines underglaze, on wood stand, 10½" 650.00
Candle holder, canister base w/saucer bobeche, Yi Dy, 4½" 200.00
Dish, palmette/leaf emb, Sung Dy, 8" 275.00
Jar, ginger; floral tree/animals in bl, branch on lid, 8" 100.00
Jar, mc raised floral w/much gold, w/lid, 6x4½" 85.00
Jar, multifloral relief, mc/gilt, inner lid, 6x4½" 95.00
Planter, cvd peonies/tendrils by rim, wht int, 5", pr 145.00
Vase, bl disks/emblems HP, wht accents, fu dog hdls, 23" 250.00
Vase, fruiting branches in high relief, stick neck, 23" 440.00
Vase, scholar HP, mock lion hdls, 1880s, 18" 275.00
Vase, scholars/mums HP, appl dragons/fu dog hdls, 25" 250.00
Vase, 3 children in high relief, standing children hdls, 14" 220.00

Furniture

Altar table, Ch hdwd, openwork apron: scrolls/brackets, 75" ...550.00
Armchair, Ch, cvd/pierced crest w/dragons, serpent arms, 52" .650.00
Armchair, Ch, EX cvg w/birds & flowers, worn/rpr 600.00
Bench, Ch, birds/flowers cvg, openwork crest/apron, 50" L ..1,400.00
Cabinet, Ch, EX cvg, abalone/ivory-inlaid gilt panels, 87" ..1,400.00
Cabinet, Ch gilt/lacquer, 2 pr doors w/court scenes, 42x44" ...275.00
Cabinet, corner; arched doors w/gilt scenes, 36" 660.00
Chair, side; Ch, bird/floral cvg on bk & apron, curved legs 450.00
Chest, Ko softwood, iron strapwork hinges, 23x55" 330.00
Coffee table, lacquer, gold/gr lotus & Greek Key, 39" dia 250.00
Desk, Ch, EX cvd crest/apron/curved legs, fitted top, 56" 1,600.00
Stand, Ch tkwd, cvd, 3-D bats on legs, soapstone top, 14" 215.00
Table, bird/florals cvg, cvd apron/curved legs, 23½" dia 400.00
Table, Ch, bird/floral-cvd apron, curved legs, 2-drw, EX 550.00
Table, Ch E, allover floral cvg, 14" dia top w/marble, 18" 225.00
Table, Ch tkwd, cvd openwork fr w/blossoms, 20x21x36" L ...545.00

Bright green jade horse, deeply carved, 20" long, $16,000.00.

Jade, bl-gr, lady w/flowers in right/fan in left hand, 8" 295.00
Jade, celadon, mtns/Shoulao+2 deer, inscriptions, 1800s, 8" ...400.00
Jade, gr mottle, perched bird, cvd stand, 7", pr 350.00
Jade, lt gr, beauty holds fan & spray of flowers, 6½x3½" 225.00
Jade, lt gr, bi, rosettes/vines cvg, cvd wood stand, 6½" 350.00
Jade, lt gr, censer, animal hdls/mask ft/lion finial, 4" 300.00
Jade, lt gr, lady in flowing robes holds bamboo rod, 8½" 350.00
Jade, lt gr, ruyi sceptre, flowers/butterflies cvg, 16½" 350.00
Jade, lt gr, vase w/dragon, dragon/ring hdls, 8½x4½" 250.00
Jade, med gr, phoenix/sm birds on flowering branch, 8½x5" ...280.00
Jade, med gr, phoenix/sm birds under pine tree, 8½x7" 325.00

Jade, med gr, 2 birds in peony tree, 6½x4" 250.00
Jade, med gr w/wht, 2 facing birds on floral branch, 6x5½" 225.00
Jade, onion, bowl, deer/vines relief, rectangular, 6½" 400.00
Jade, ruyi scepter, dragons/panels of chimera, 14½" 240.00
Jade, spinach, dbl dragon finial/hdls, loose rings, 7½x12" 750.00
Jade, spinach, plaque, mtns/bridge/calligraphy cvg, 12x9" 700.00
Jade, spinach, plaque, sages/terrace/bridge/etc, 11x9" 1,100.00
Jade, spinach, urn, dragon finial, ring hdls, 12x8" 600.00
Jade, yel, wedding vase, relief salamanders/bats, 5" 850.00
Jade, yel-gr, ewer, allover cvg/beast finial/ring hdls, 12" 770.00
Jadeite, gr-wht w/gr striations, boy astride ox, 5½" 800.00
Jadeite, lt celadon, bowl, lily pad w/bud at corner, 5½" 275.00
Jasper, gr w/oil spots, bowl, short ring ft, 4½" dia 440.00
Lapis lazuli, Manjusri on bk of lion, 7", ...175.00
Malachite, rabbit, ears bk, scratches w/ft, 2x3" 185.00
Nephrite, vase, cabbage leaf cluster form w/EX cvg, mk, 4" 495.00
Serpentine, bowl w/dome lid & undertray, 6", pr 550.00
Tigereye, court lady w/flowing scarves & peony, 5½"   250.00
Tigereye, fu lion, running, supports book on tail, 4½x5" 275.00
Tigereye, tang horse, neighing, 1 ft up, w/saddle, 4x5" 325.00
Turquoise, kylin, reclining, 3x4" 350.00

Inro

Brn lcq, water container/ladle decor, 4-case, 3½" 475.00
Gold lcq, lucky symbols/treasures, ojime+manju, 5-case 800.00
Gold/silver lcq, 4-case, 4" 600.00
Ivory, ladies, cvd/HP, 3-case, ca 1920, 2" 275.00
MOP birds inlay, brn lcq, wood netsuke, 3-case 230.00

Lacquer

Bodhisattva, celestial robe/ornate crown/dog, Ming Dy, 10" .1,000.00
Bowl, peach grove/trees on hill, gilt hdls, 1900, 7", EX 350.00
Box, berries/leaves/butterflies, cinnabar, 8x11" 60.00
Box, bird/tree/wind chime, gold dust finish, 5x13x15" 1,000.00
Box, EX dragon motif, cinnabar, bl pnt int, 5" L, NM 300.00
Box, floral branch/river on nashiji, Meiji period, 2¾" 300.00
Box, flower/leaves/butterfly, gilt on blk, 13" L 125.00
Box, jewel; gilt/red hiramakie florals, rnd corners, 9" L 200.00
Box, jewel; hiramakie scene on lid, 1880s, 10" W 150.00
Box, travellers in river landscape, gilt on red, 15" L 200.00
Box, wisteria, takamaki-e on aventurine, 1700s, 10½" 1,200.00
Box, 2 fan reserves w/scenes, gilt on brn, 1900, 6" 200.00
Buddha, seated in dhyanasana, gilt, 1600s, 11x9" 1,000.00
Container, lobed gourd w/cvd blossoms, cinnabar, 4¾" 250.00
Food container, hexagonals, mc w/gilt, dome lid, 12" dia 700.00
Jar, storage; cvd figured scene, cinnabar, 1880s, 12", EX 225.00
Scholar divinity on qilong, holds scroll, gilded, 20" 800.00
Screen, 3-panel, red/gold hiramakie fish & flora, 44" 225.00
Shrine, travelling; Bodhisattva/lotus throne, mc, 15" 1,000.00
Tray, cranes/flowering branch, gilt on brn, 21" 150.00
Tray, figures/garden, gilt on blk, Canton, 1880s, 25", EX 400.00
Tray, flowers/vines, gilt on brn, 17" 100.00
Tray, gold hiramakie mums on nashiji on blk, 1900s, 19x16" . .700.00
Tray, pagodas/bldgs/bridge/florals, cinnabar, 12x14" 95.00
Tray, samurai battle, gilt/red/brn/blk, cvd ivory face, 18" 1,900.00
Trunk, bail hdls/shou medallions/bats, gilt/red, 12x19", pr 330.00
Vase, landscapes w/figures & flowers, cinnabar, 12", pr 270.00

Porcelain

Bough pot, florals on turq, 1800s, 5x6" L, +cvd stand, pr 200.00
Bowl, E, coat of arms, bk: same, gilt rim, 1700s, 9½" 300.00

Bowl, E, flora/birds/butterflies, bl/red/gilt, 11", EX 1,100.00
Bowl, E/FR, mtns/pagodas/boats, int: landscape, 1825, 9" 300.00
Bowl, FV, 100 Antiques/soldiers, scalloped/ftd, Kangxi, 10" . . .770.00
Candle holder, horse form, ornate saddle/blanket, 11", pr 275.00
Charger, FV, peacock/flowers, butterfly border, 14½" 350.00
Charger, Orange Fitzhugh, initialed banner/eagle, 16" 850.00
Cider jug, E, floral sprays in brn/gilt, bbl form, 1795, 8" 600.00
Creamer, E, sm floral, helmet form, 5" 180.00
Figurine, boy holds vase, collar/bib, mock Ming mk, 10", pr . . .300.00
Fishbowl, FJ, mums/lotus/serpent, bird/floral bands, 14x16" . . .600.00
Fishbowl, FV, scholars/ages/meiren/armed courtiers, 20x21" .1,400.00
Garden seat, FJ, birds/garden, emb bosses, pierced top, 18" 700.00
Jar, allover autumn flowers, dome lid, 1880s, 17" 275.00
Jar, ginger; FV, battle scenes, now lamp, 1800s, 12", pr 650.00
Jar, storage; FN, lotus/mum network, 1880s, 12", pr 1,400.00
Jardiniere, continuing immortal scene, ruyi-head bands, 23" .1,400.00
Jardiniere, mums/birds on powder bl, Kangxi style, 14", EX . . .165.00
Joss stick holder, FR, elephant form w/HP florals, 5", pr 2,800.00
Joss stick holder, FV, standing boy holds jar, Ming Dy, 11" 500.00
Mug, E, orange fishscale decor w/floral panels, 1800s, 6" 325.00
Pilgrim flask, E, courtyard scene, bk: armorial, 1800s, 16" . . .1,700.00
Pillow, reclining cat on celadon base, brn accents, 13" L 135.00
Pillow, reclining lady form, abstract florals, Cizhou, 16" 220.00
Plaque, RF, lady riding deer w/male escort, cvd fr, 30x17" 250.00
Plate, court women/children, ruyi/palmette bands, 18" 220.00
Plate, cup & saucer; armorial, motto/4 scenes, worn, 1750 . . .1,800.00
Plate, E, floral, bl/wht, octagonal rim, 9", EX 80.00
Plate, E, Tobacco Leaf, 1760, 9" 600.00
Plate, E/FV, precious symbols on rim, floral center, Kangxi 220.00
Plate, Rose Canton, 8½", set of 12 . . . . .225.00
Platter, E, Brn Fitzhugh, on mahog stand, 1900, 17" 1,800.00
Platter, E/FR, armorial, floral/fruit sprays & fans, 15" 550.00
Platter, E/FR, mtn/river/pagodas/boats, 1770-80, 20" 800.00
Puzzle pot, FV, fu dog surmount on rtcl bowl top, 8" 220.00
Scholar, standing, draped bl garment, 7" 70.00
Scholar, standing w/scrolls, mc, mk Ch, 11" 125.00
Stand, teapot; E/FR, European lovers, leaf form, 1800 . . . . .300.00

Storage jar, Famille Noire, chrysanthemums on black, 1880s, 12", $1,400.00.

Sugar bowl, E, floral, twist hdls, fruit finial, att Samson 150.00
Teapot, Rose Canton, unmk, 7¾x5⅛", +cr/sug 325.00
Tray, E, shield w/initials, gilt egg/dart rim, 1780, 10" 1,100.00
Tureen, E/FR, int genre scene on lid/base, gilt, 1760, 9" . . .800.00
Umbrella stand, FJ, immortals/birds in fan reserves, 11" 300.00

Urns, famille verte, Kangxi, fu puppy finials, 18", $1,500.00 for the pair.

Vase, beauties engaged in scholarly pursuits, 16", pr 700.00
Vase, dragons/cloud, leaf motif, dragon hdls, Canton, 18" 175.00
Vase, FN, bird/flowering branches, mtd as lamp, 13½" 440.00
Vase, FR, 5-color urns/flowers on wht, dome lid, 1800s, 17" . . .300.00
Vase, FV, genre reserves on foliate network, ram hdls, 25" 900.00
Vase, FV, 4 scholars in reserves on scrollwork, 1800s, 23" . . .1,100.00
Vase, iris on shaded bl, Jp, 12" 300.00
Vase, lg/sm battle reserves on floral, fu dog hdls, 15", EX 425.00
Vase, lg/sm genre reserves, appl snakes, fu dog hdls, 36" 900.00
Vase, lizards relief, maiden/phoenix birds, Canton, 14" 120.00
Vase, Rose Canton, mask/ring hdls, 1880s, 10" 300.00
Vase, stag/court woman on terrace, w/poem, 1880s, 18", pr 440.00
Vase, 5 figural children on floral baluster form, 1880s, 8" 250.00

Pottery

Bottle, transparent wht glaze, Song Dy, 11" 480.00
Bowl, figures/textile borders in mc, mk Ryozan, 1900, 5½" 850.00
Bowl, lt transparent gray, Song-Yuan Dy, 6" 130.00
Bowl, rooster/chickens in floral landscape, 15½" 1,000.00
Bowl, tea dust glaze, brass-mtd rim, Ming Dy, 7" 200.00
Censer, sang de boeuf, 3 mask/paw ft, 6¾", EX 275.00
Court lady, flowing gown/elaborate headdress, Tang Dy, 17" . .600.00
Dogs, snarling, gr, imp seal mk, 9¾" L, pr 800.00
Ewer, henan glaze, bird-head spout, dome lid, Song Dy, 7" 500.00
Jar, beauties/attendants reserves, mc/gilt/dk bl, 1900, 7" 150.00
Jar, sang de boeuf, flat lid w/knob, 1800s, 7" 220.00
Jardiniere, thick wht glaze, 15", pr .440.00
Planter, sang de boeuf, globular, flattened rim, 5" 200.00
Sage, seated/hands clasped, turq, 9½" 200.00
Tile, roof; man on serpent, 1800s 300.00
Tile, roof; priest standing, 1800s 300.00
Tile, roof; warrior on deer, 1800s 300.00

Vase, bl flambe, mottled brn at rim, Quandong Province, 9½" .400.00
Vase, deer in landscape, Kinkozan, Meiji period, 18" 450.00
Vase, emb peach medallion, mock lion hdls, 1800s, 11" 600.00
Vase, flambe, hexagonal baluster, later Quing Dy, 17" 350.00
Vase, liver glaze, flared rim, 13" 250.00
Vase, mirror blk, baluster form, Kangxi mk, drilled, 18" 800.00
Vase, mirror blk, baluster on splayed ft, 1800s, 5½" 150.00
Vase, mythical steeds/stylized waves, w/lid & cvd base, 12" 350.00
Vase, powder bl, bulbous w/flared rim, 7" 350.00
Vase, samurai reserves, mock ring hdls, Kyoto, 1900, 23" 220.00
Vase, sang de boeuf, modified zun-form, 1800s, 12" 550.00
Vase, sang de boeuf, quatrelobed, fu dog hdls, 1800s, 15" 300.00

Caparisoned horse, gray pottery, Northern Wei, 6th century, 12", $13,000.00.

Snuff Bottles

Agate, tiger cub w/butterfly relief on front, ivory stand 1,100.00
Carnelian, cvd in high openwork relief, wood stand 80.00
Celadon jade, lt gray, 1820s 300.00
Cloisonne, bl panels w/mc flowers & butterfly on blk, 3" 80.00
Copper, famille rose enamel, bl Qianlong 4-character mk 800.00
Coral, cvd as a monkey holding a ribbon, 1800 . . . . .275.00
Feicui jade, apple/emerald gr, cvd in low relief, disk form 1,700.00
Glass, rvpt, blk overlay 50.00
Hair crystal, dense blk inclusions, turq/pk bead stopper 475.00
Horn, jeweled silver metal mtd, Mongolian, 1800s 150.00
Ivory, allover cvg, elephant-head/ring hdls, 3⅛" 475.00
Ivory, horse/floral tree cvg, bk: 2 tigers, 2½", +spoon 165.00
Ivory, panels front/bk: 2 people under pine tree, 3" 75.00
Jade, cvd as ear of corn, 4 brn husks w/gr stalk stopper 750.00
Jade, rust/brn/gray striated w/gr inclusions, uncvd, +stand 325.00
Lapis lazuli, cojoined gourd forms, gold flecked, 1880s, sm 90.00
MOP w/relief cvg on front, dbl neck, 2⅜" 275.00
Porc, figure scene, bl/wht/iron glazed, bell form, 1800s 75.00
Porc, FR, emb red leaves on crackleware, coral stopper, 4" 200.00
Porc, FR, figure scenes, cylindrical 40.00
Rose quartz, flowering branch cvg, flattened/tapered, Ch 100.00
Rose quartz, low-relief cvg ea side, ivory stand 75.00
Rvpt, bird/florals, bk: dragonfly, gr jade stopper, 3x2½" 185.00
Smoky crystal, cvd as cicada, dk tone .80.00

Suzhou agate, gray w/dk brn patches, rust swirl, uncvd 275.00
Turq, traveller in flowering landscape cvg, flattened ovoid 175.00
Yel agate, cvd as a finger citrus fruit, 1800s, wood stand 75.00

Sumida

Bowl, boy on rim, 5" 100.00
Brush pot, 2 appl monkeys, seal signature, 4" 130.00
Humidor, men in relief, man finial, seal sgn, 6⅜x4¼" 275.00
Mug, appl figure makes offering to bird, 5" 90.00
Mug, figure on red, mks, 4⅝x3" 95.00
Pitcher, tankard; appl figures, seal signature, 12½" 550.00
Teapot, lady/flowers, Art Deco shape 265.00
Vase, appl man w/basket of rocks on side, red base, 6¾x3" 125.00
Vase, geisha relief, bl on red, 4¾x4½" 75.00
Vase, 4 children on red, 9½x4⅜" 175.00

Textiles

Coat, bl satin, emb florals/insects, satin cuffs, 1800s 275.00
Coat, fireman's, calligraphy on coarse blk/red/wht cloth 60.00
Coat, flowers & insects embr on blk satin, ca 1900, EX 150.00
Coat, flowers embr on bl silk, embr sleeve bands, ca 1900 ......65.00
Coat, flowers/bats/insects, gold satin cuffs, quartz buttons 250.00
Coat, gold bamboo embr on bl silk, Jp, 1900s 125.00
Coat, insects w/gilt embr on blk satin, bl borders, 1900 ......110.00
Handbag, silk emb bird, jade ring hdls, ca 1900, 10", EX 145.00
Hanging, tapestry, flowers/symbols on salmon, 1900, 23x75" ..200.00
Jacket, braids/cutwork on blk silk, Satsuma buttons, 1880s 180.00
Kimono, floral sprays/roses embr on silk, ca 1910 ....90.00
Panel, birds/flowers embr on satin, ca 1880, 72" L, set of 3 ....300.00
Panel, floral vines embr on red w/sequins, 1800s, 46x46" 150.00

Priest cloak, embroidered and appliqued with Buddhas and Bodhisattvas, gold embroidery, silk lined, 49", $2,500.00.

Robe, silk ch'i-fu embr w/5-claw dragons & mtns, 1800s 225.00
Robe, tapestry-woven dragon on bl ch'i-fu, 1800s 450.00
Skirt, damask, figures in landscapes embr in panels, 1800s 200.00
Throne cover, tapestry, 5-claw dragon on silk, 1880s, 32x40" ..325.00
Trousers, silk damask w/blk satin cuffs, lady's, 1900 ....80.00
Valance, crane/mtns/waves w/floral borders, fringed, 25x59" ...150.00
Wedding shirt, animals & birds embr on pleated red silk, 2-pc .135.00

Woodblock Prints, Japanese

Farm scene, from Famous Views...Old Provinces, 1850s, 9x18" .220.00

Hiroshige, Sagamigawa, from Fuji Sanjurokkei, Oban Tat-e ..220.00
Hokusai, Carrying the Bride, 1820s, lg Oban 550.00
Kunisada, Battle of Takadachi, Oban diptych 250.00
Kunisada, 4 Actors in Character, sgn, Oban triptych 150.00
Kuniyoshi, Maruko To Yui, sgn, Oban Toko-e 800.00
Kuniyoshi, woman in garden, 14x9½" 600.00
Paul Jacoulet, Flocons de Deige, Pengyong Coree, 16x12" ...1,000.00
Paul Jacoulet, La Mariee, owl seal, 15½x12", EX 300.00
Paul Jacoulet, La Statuette Thang, peony seal, 15½x12" 650.00
Sekino Junichiro, Bunraku Puppet, 1956, Oban 80.00
Shunei, Actor Ichikawa Danjuro, in character, Hosoban 260.00
Shunsen, Passing Ferries, Oban Yoko-e 150.00
Yoshitora, Battle Scene, Oban triptych 300.00
Yoshitoshi, man chased by wolves, 13x8¾" 100.00
Yoshitoshi, Watanabe Minamoto Sadatsuna, Oban Tate-e 250.00
Yoshitoshi, 3 Men in Landscape, Oban triptych 150.00

Miscellaneous

Box, silver, chased w/clouds & dragons, 1½x5½" L 225.00
Cvg, bearded man court dress/kannuri headdress, wood, 21" ...275.00
Cvg, Bodhisattva stands on lotus base, wood, mc traces, 10" ...110.00
Cvg, bookseller, wood/ivory w/lacquer, Ryuun, 1900, 11½" ..2,500.00
Cvg, Guanyin on lotus base holds lotus flower, wood, 44" 500.00
Figure, deity on rock, patinated metal, wood base, Jp, 17" 400.00
Figure, farm couple w/rake/broom, silvered brass, Jp, 11", pr ...300.00
Puppets, noble couple, elaborate: silk/fur/embr, 17", pr 425.00
Rvpt, mtn/dignitary/warrior, 10½x26" 225.00
Scroll, hanging; Buddha, watercolor on paper, 1700s, 57x32" ..300.00
Scroll, hanging; lady, 1800s, fr, 26x12½" 250.00
Suit of armor, lacquered steel w/gilt, Jp, Edo-Meiji period ...2,300.00
Teapot, enamel, clouds on rust, panels of ducks/florals, 4" 60.00
Tsuba, bronze, cast gilt/silver flowers, 1800s 100.00
Vase, rvpt glass, 3 travellers/mtns/hut, cylinder neck, 14" 250.00
Watercolor on silk, Equestrian Entourage, 1800s, fr, 25x53" ...275.00

Orrefors

Orrefors Glassworks was founded in the early 1900s in the Swedish province of Smaaland. Utilizing the expertise of designers such as Lindquist and Gate, it produced art glass of the highest quality. Various techniques were used in achieving the decoration; some were wheel engraved, others were blown through a unique process that formed controlled bubbles or air pockets resulting in unusual patterns and shapes.

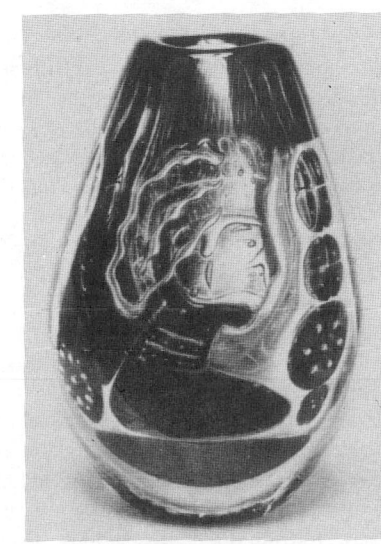

Ariel glass vase designed by Edvin Ohrstrom, air-trap design of a young woman's profile and a dove, stylized geometric borders, 8", $1,650.00.

Bottle scent; simple 4-sided panel cuts, bubble stopper, 7½" 95.00
Bowl, canoe; bl netting w/air bubble in ea sq, S Palmquist 150.00
Bowl, half circles in vertical panels, label/sgn, 10" 175.00
Decanter, elegant/simple, label/sgn, 9½" 200.00
Decanter, eng underwater fisherman, mk C-2784, 12" 225.00
Decanter, 3 tiers of blowouts, sgn, 9" 165.00
Toothpick holder, brn stripes/air stripes in clear, Ohrstrom 225.00
Vase, Ariel, musician/lady in gondola, Ohrstrom, 1962, 7" ..2,200.00
Vase, Ariel, rows of bubble-center blk cells, Ohrstrom, 4" ...1,200.00
Vase, eng girls/flowers, paper label, mk, 1950, 4" 95.00
Vase, Graal, blk fish/seaweed, thick glass, Hald, 7½" 575.00
Vase, Graal, fish/seaweed, spherical, sgn, 5¼" 475.00
Vase, lady w/baby intaglio, bulbous, 4-sided, sgn, 5½" 85.00
Vase & underplate, eng frieze of nudes, Simon Gate, 5" 2,750.00

Ott and Brewer

The partnership of Ott and Brewer began in 1865 in Trenton, New Jersey. By 1876 they were making decorated graniteware, parian, and 'ivory porcelain' — similar to Irish belleek though not as fine and of different composition. In 1883, however, experiments toward that end had reached a successful conclusion, and a true belleek body was introduced. It came to be regarded as the finest china ever produced by an American firm. The ware was decorated by various means — hand painting, transfer printing, gilding, and lustre glazing. The company closed in 1893, one of many that failed during that depression. In the listings below, the ware is belleek unless noted otherwise.

Our advisor for this category is Mary Frank Gaston; she is listed in the Directory under Texas.

Bouillon, Cactus, gold thistles & hdls, w/underplate, mk 400.00
Bowl, pk lustre int, gold rim, 3½" 110.00
Cake plate, Tridacna, gold decor, rare, 9½" 225.00
Cup & saucer, gold paste flowers, thin 145.00
Cup & saucer, soup; gold paste flowers & butterfly, thin 125.00
Cup & saucer, Tridacna, gold florals/etc, 2 hdls, 6" dia 195.00
Pitcher, pk/gold water lilies, gold leaves, mk, 8¼x6½" 1,400.00
Plate, flowers, pk & gold paste, ruffled, 9" 190.00
Sweetmeat, fluted gold decor, 5" 175.00
Teapot, Tridacna, yel w/gold, wht loop hdl, mk, 4" 300.00
Tray, pin; bl/wht florals, gr/brn leaves, ruffled, 4¼" 145.00

Overbeck

The Overbeck Studio was established in 1911 in Cambridge City, Indiana, by four Overbeck sisters. It survived until the last sister died in 1955. Early wares were often decorated with carved designs of stylized animals, birds, or florals with the designs colored to contrast with the background. Others had tooled designs filled in with various colors for a mosaic effect. After 1937, Mary Frances, the last remaining sister, favored handmade figurines with somewhat bizarre features in fanciful combinations of color. Overbeck ware is signed 'OBK.' Large vases from 8" to 12" usually command prices from $1,000 to $3,000 on today's market.

Figurine, cat, long haired, brn/gray, 3", NM 250.00
Figurine, dog, turq w/blk dots, lav ears, big paws, 2x3¼" 225.00
Figurine, duck, quacking, lg ft, 2½x4½" 225.00
Figurine, girl in pk bonnet, w/lg duck, grassy mound, 4" 375.00
Figurine, Southern Belle, 4 ruffled layers on skirt, 7x5½" 250.00
Trivet, 2 stylized ponies, 6-color, sgn EG, 6½" dia 425.00
Vase, allover geometric floral, pk/turq/lav/blk, sgn, 10" 1,600.00
Vase, birds in flight, wht on bl, sgn EH, 5½" 1,400.00

Vase, cvd wht rams w/yel horns, thorns, 5-color, sgn, 5½" ...3,800.00
Vase, fish/sea plants, olive on brn, mk OBK/EH, 5½x5" 1,400.00
Vase, geese w/in 9 rnd sections, mc on mauve, sgn EH, 6" ...1,500.00
Vase, geometric floral, V-form on high ft, sgn EF, 10x5" 1,600.00
Vase, girls/cats/spirals, ochre on lt bl, sgn OBK/EF, 11x8" ...1,700.00
Vase, stylized rabbits/flowers, khaki on brn, sgn EF, 8x5" 2,300.00
Vase, 3 cvd panels w/stylized trees, pk on lt brn, EF, 5½" 800.00

Covered box, allover birds and blossoms, original paper label, 8" high, $850.00.

Overshot

Overshot glass is characterized by the beaded or craggy appearance of its surface. Earlier ware was irregularly textured, while 20th-century examples tend to be more uniform.

Basket, amethyst to clear, clear hdl, ruffled, 5½x5" 115.00
Basket, orange to vaseline, octagonal, appl hdl, 7x6" 195.00
Bowl, cranberry to clear, emb hobnails, metal ft, 7⅝x11" 225.00
Pitcher, cranberry, clear reeded hdl, 6¼" 125.00
Pitcher, cranberry to clear, clear reeded hdl, 7½" 170.00
Pitcher, lt bl w/red-amber hdl, 7" 90.00
Pitcher, peachblow color, clear hdl, att Mt WA, 8", NM 200.00
Pitcher, pk, w/ice cubicle, clear rope hdl around neck, 10" 190.00
Pitcher, tankard; cranberry, clear reed hdl, 9" 165.00

Owens Pottery

J.B. Owens founded his company in Zanesville, Ohio, in 1891, and until 1907, when the company decided to exert most of its energies in the area of tile production, made several quality lines of art pottery. His first line, Utopian, was a standard brown ware with underglaze slip decoration of nature studies, animals, and portraits. A similar line, Lotus, utilized lighter background colors. Henri Deux, introduced in 1900, featured incised Art Nouveau forms inlaid with color. (Be aware that the Brush McCoy Pottery acquired many of Owens' molds and reproduced a line similar to Henri Deux, which they called Navarre.) Other important lines were Opalesce, Rustic, Feroza, Cyrano, and Mission, examples of which are rare today.

The factory burned in 1928, and the company closed shortly thereafter. Values vary according to the quality of the artwork and subject matter.

Examples signed by the artist bring higher prices than those that are not signed.

Bookends, puppy on rectangular base, 4-color, 4½" 220.00
Bowl, Utopian, floral, sgn DH, 3½x6" 95.00
Bowl vase, Feroza, metallic w/pk & gr, hdls, 3½x10" 60.00
Ewer, Utopian, pansies, Steele, 6" 170.00
Ewer, Utopian, silver overlay on side/rim/hdl, berries, 6½" . .1,500.00
Jardiniere, Lotus, butterflies, 10½x7½" 400.00
Jardiniere, Utopian, chrysanthemums, yel, 9½x12x10" 95.00
Jardiniere & ped, Matt Utopian, tulips, ruffled, 24" 450.00
Jug, Opalesce, pansies, gr coralene on gold, 5x6" 350.00
Jug, Utopian, corn, 7½" 130.00
Lamp, Utopian, floral, artist sgn, 11" 150.00
Mug, Utopian, cherries, sgn TS, 5" 75.00
Mug, Utopian, skull on book, cross, candle, sgn EB, 5", EX . . .500.00
Pitcher, Aborigine, Indian motif, red/beige/blk, 7½" 110.00
Pitcher, Lotus, stork & lotus flower, 6¼" 175.00
Pitcher, Lotus, stork & lotus flower, 7¾" 235.00
Pitcher, tankard; Utopian, cherries, 12" 175.00
Pitcher, tankard; Utopian, woodbine in autumn colors, 12" . . .175.00
Plaque, stucco cottage/road, 5-color, 'cloisonne,' 11x17" 1,500.00
Vase, Aborigine, decorative bands on red clay, early mk, 6" . . .150.00
Vase, Aqua Verde, pierced neck, bulbous base, 6¾x5¼" 150.00
Vase, Aqua Verde, pine cones/needles emb, bulbous, 6½" 120.00
Vase, bud; Utopian, cherries, artist sgn, 10", NM 125.00
Vase, Feroza, cattails, gun-metal irid, 10" 325.00
Vase, Feroza, Nouveau emb, conical, 5¾" 150.00
Vase, glossy scenic: tree silhouettes, lt gray/gr, #227, 8" 450.00
Vase, Henri Deux, incised lady's head, hdls, mk, 6½x9½" 450.00
Vase, Lightweight, floral on brn, sgn, 3" 95.00
Vase, Lotus, dbl hdls, X-235, 5x8" .175.00
Vase, Lotus, emb orange/gr leaves at neck, 7" 95.00
Vase, Matt Utopian, daffodils, #1010, 10½" 275.00
Vase, Opalesce, floral, slim neck, 8" 250.00
Vase, Sudanese, flowers/leaves in red & gold on blk, 10" 195.00
Vase, Utopian, autumn leaves on brn, sgn E Bell, 3½x5½" 95.00
Vase, Utopian, berries, sgn, 6" 95.00
Vase, Utopian, cat portrait, #309, 14¾" 750.00
Vase, Utopian, clover, sgn VA, stick neck, 7" 90.00
Vase, Utopian, floral, sgn, 12" 200.00
Vase, Utopian, floral, sgn, 5" 100.00
Vase, Utopian, pansies, sgn CB, ftd jardiniere form, 3x4¼" 50.00
Vase, Utopian, wild rose, ovoid, 10½x4x3⅝" 200.00

Utopian vase, portrait of Indian, 12", $1,000.00.

Paden City

The Paden City Glass Company began operations in 1916 in Paden City, West Virginia. The company's early lines consisted largely of the usual pressed tablewares, but by the 1920s production had expanded to include colored wares in translucent as well as opaque glass in a variety of patterns and styles. The company maintained its high standards of hand-made perfection until 1949, when under new management much of the work formerly done by hand was replaced by automation. The Paden City Glass Company closed in 1951; and its earlier wares, the colored patterns in particular, are becoming very collectible.

Bowl, centerpc; Crow's Foot, floral etched, +2 candlesticks 65.00
Bowl, Far East, 5½" 2.50
Bowl, Far East, 7½" 6.00
Bowl, fruit; World's Fair 1939 logo, mk, 10" 50.00
Candlestick, Bridal Bouquet, crystal, 2-light, pr 35.00
Candlestick, red, 2½" 15.00
Candy dish, Crow's Foot, red, sq 40.00
Candy dish, Springtime, pk, w/lid 55.00
Compote, Crow's Foot, red, 5¼" H .25.00
Creamer & sugar bowl, Crow's Foot, red, ftd 48.00
Creamer & sugar bowl, Crow's Foot, silver florals 55.00
Creamer & sugar bowl, Gazebo, crystal 30.00
Cup, demitasse; Ivy 5.00
Cup & saucer, Crow's Foot, red 12.50
Cup & saucer, Ivy 17.50
Decanter, Utopia, crystal, etched, rare, 1-qt 80.00
Figurine, Chinese pheasant, bl, 5¾x13¾" 80.00
Figurine, fighting cock, 9" 150.00
Figurine, pony, standing, 5" 50.00
Figurine, pouter pigeon 69.00
Figurine, squirrel on log, 5¼" 45.00
Goblet, water; Lotus etch 10.00
Gravy boat, pk w/gold decor, +undertray 50.00
Mayonnaise, Springtime, heavy silver overlay 150.00
Plate, Crow's Foot, red, 6" 15.00
Plate, Far East, 10½" 5.00
Plate, Far East, 8¼" 4.00
Platter, Crow's Foot, red, 11" 20.00
Samovar w/bird, bl, etched 295.00
Server, Blk Forest, gr 40.00
Shakers, Party Line, ruby, pr 45.00
Sherbet, Lotus etch, low 10.00
Sugar bowl, Nora Bird, pk, rnd hdls .25.00
Vase, Lela Bird, pk, 10" 70.00

Paintings on Ivory

Miniature works of art executed on ivory from the 1800s are assessed by the finesse of the artist, as is any fine painting. Signed examples and portraits with an identifiable subject are usually preferred.

Abraham Lincoln, sgn, Springfield 1861, paper mt, in case . .1,000.00
Blonde child, wht dress/red coral necklace, lacquer fr, 5" 300.00
Child, red dress, obelisk in bkground, w/hair braid, 2½x3" 400.00
Cleo De Merode, flowers in hair, sgn, filigree fr, 3½x2½" 160.00
Gent, primitive, faded colors, losses, 2¾x2¼" 150.00
Lad, EX detail, hair braid, eng initials, 1¾x2" 550.00
Lad in bl frock coat, silver case w/eng name/1849, 2½x3" 175.00
Lad on gold-flecked bl ground, lacquer case, 3½x4½" 125.00
Lady, balloon-sleeve dress, jewelry, drapery in bk, 5x5½" 350.00

Lady, landscape bkground, drapery, Am School, 1800s, 3x2½" . **200.00**
Lady, sgn, piano tile fr, 3¼" **195.00**
Lady w/long hair, gold brooch case w/eng initials, 1⅝" **150.00**
Lady w/spaniel, sgn, 5¾x4⅝" **145.00**
Moses Cleveland, sgn FM Wassallo/1856, on celluloid, 7x7" . . .**175.00**
Naval officer, sgn A Dickinson/1826, mtd on pastebrd, 3x2¾" .**350.00**
Romantic couple, brass fr, 3¼" **120.00**

Either 3x2" portrait in pierced brass frame with cartouch crest, $200.00.

Pairpoint

The Pairpoint Manufacturing Company was built in 1880 in New Bedford, Massachusetts. It was primarily a metalworks whose chief product was coffin fittings. Next door, the Mt. Washington Glassworks made quality glasswares of many varieties. (See Mt. Washington for more information concerning their artware lines.) By 1894 it became apparent to both companies that a merger would be to their best interest.

From the late 1890s until the 1930s, lamps and lamp accessories were an important part of Pairpoint's production. There were three main types of shades, all of which were blown: puffy — blown-out reverse-painted shades (usually floral designs); ribbed — also reverse painted; and scenic — reverse painted with scenes of land or seascapes (usually executed on smooth surfaces, although ribbed scenics may be found occasionally). Cut glass lamps and those with metal overlay panels were also made. Scenic shades were sometimes artist signed; and, although many are unmarked, some are stamped 'Pairpoint Corp.' Blown-out shades may be marked 'Pat July 9, 1907.' Bases were made from bronze, copper, brass, silver, or wood and are always signed.

Because they produced only fancy, handmade artware, the company's sales lagged seriously during the depression; and, as time and tastes changed, their style of product was less in demand. As a result, they never fully recovered; consequently part of the buildings and equipment were sold in 1938. The company reorganized in 1939 under the direction of Robert Gunderson and again specialized in quality hand-blown glassware. Isaac Babbit regained possession of the silver departments, and together they established Gunderson Glassworks, Inc. After WWII, because of a sharp decline in sales, it again became necessary to reorganize. The Gunderson-Pairpoint Glassworks was formed, and the old line of cut, engraved artware was reintroduced. The company moved to East Wareham, Massachusetts, in 1957. But business continued to suffer, and the firm closed only one year later. In 1970, however, new facilities were constructed in Sagamore under the direction of Robert Bryden, sales manager for the company since the 1950s.

In 1974 the company began to produce lead glass cup plates which were made on commission as fund raisers for various churches and organi-

zations. These are signed with a 'P' in diamond and are becoming quite collectible. See also Napkin Rings.

Key:
pwt — paperweight

Glassware

Biscuit jar, florals/leaves/berries on pk, melon ribs, 9" **365.00**
Bottle, scent; bl opaque w/floral, pwt stopper, 7½" **225.00**
Bottle, scent; gr w/clear ft, pwt stopper, 7" **200.00**
Bottle, scent; pwt top w/11 roses on gr, bubble bottom, 6" **130.00**
Bowl, Ambero, gr w/rvpt pk water lilies & gr leaves, 8½" **700.00**
Bowl, centerpc, cut decor, 16", +2 pr 14" candlesticks **450.00**
Bowl, Delft, 9½" **300.00**
Bowl, ruby, eng border w/flowers & vines, 14½" **200.00**
Box, glove; iris/leaves in gold on wht w/pk emb, 9½" L **700.00**
Candlestick, cobalt, clear knob w/bubbles, 4", set of 4 . . . .**225.00**
Chalice, cranberry, eng grapevines, bubble-ball base, 12" **200.00**
Cocktail, rouge flambe, stemmed **70.00**
Compote, Colics, butterfly in web, 6x6½" **58.00**
Compote, Diamond Quilt, Rosaria, clear stem **125.00**
Cup, opaque, water lily w/attached leaf saucer, 3½" dia **100.00**
Pitcher, presentation; cobalt to lt bl w/gold, 16½" **400.00**
Tumbler, intaglio butterflies & daisies, heavy, 3¼" **30.00**
Vase, Ambero, lime, etched, rvpt yel/red/orange leaves, 12" .**1,200.00**
Vase, crackled w/fish & water plants, att, 5" **175.00**

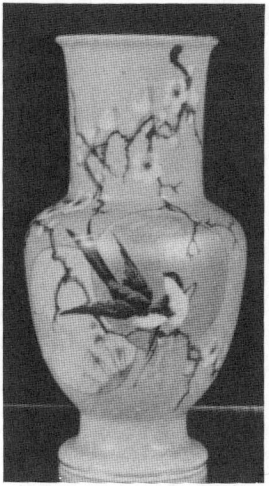

Vase, opaque white with fruit and snowbirds, 12", $500.00.

Lamps

Base, bronzed metal w/marble ft, sgn, 23¼" **200.00**
Base, wht opaque w/lg florals on bl/gr/wht mottle, 12" **275.00**
Candle, puffy rvpt pansy shade; trn wood stand, no mk, 10" . . .**525.00**
Candle, yel texture 8" bell shade w/grapes; trn ft, 24", pr **2,200.00**
Cut/frosted 8¾" shade+prisms (1 gone); dolphin/marble base . .**500.00**
Puffy 4" floral shade; urn-form copper patina base, 11" **800.00**
Puffy 5" red/yel floral mk shade; hdld urn base #3079, 11" . . .**1,500.00**
Rvpt 12" band-of-roses bell-form sgn shade; sgn wood base . .**1,700.00**
Rvpt 15" shade w/houses/fields/etc, sgn Fisher; vase std **1,750.00**
Rvpt 15" 3-butterfly w/daisy band shade; 3-prong gold std . . .**1,750.00**
Rvpt 16" church/farm wagon/pumpkin field shade; sgn base .**1,900.00**
Rvpt 16" winter scene w/house, EX; slim sgn std, 22" **1,500.00**
Rvpt 17" birds/apple blossom shade; gr patina #3050 base . . .**3,600.00**
Rvpt 17" man w/dog & cabin shade; sgn 3-part base, 22" **1,400.00**
Rvpt 17½" trees/butterflies shade; sgn base, 21" **2,000.00**
Rvpt 18" beehive shade w/tropical birds; #3054 urn std, 23" .**3,500.00**
Rvpt 19½" New Bedford harbor shade; sgn vasiform base **3,500.00**

Rvpt 8½" galleon/sunset sky shade; SP dolphin base, 13¾" . . **1,600.00**

Table lamp, reverse painted 16" shaded with rural autumn landscape, signed, 19½", $1,900.00.

Silverplate

Basket, eng swan in bottom, ftd, fancy hdl **125.00**
Bottle, scent; air bubble ball holder & stopper **150.00**
Bowl, nut; lg leaves form bowl, cabbage ft, figural squirrel **150.00**
Box, dresser; w/HP floral opaque glass lid inset, 4" dia **125.00**
Box, jewel; ftd, eng lid, orig lining **185.00**
Box, pin; A Woman's Friend **35.00**
Candelabrum, 5-branch, Victorian, 15x15", NM **220.00**
Candlestick, fluted & ribbed design, 10", pr **125.00**
Card case, w/chain, sgn **75.00**
Coaster, wine; pierced, Sheffield **85.00**
Cup, folding, eng florals, mk **35.00**
Curling iron burner, w/ftd decorated dresser box **150.00**
Mug, shaving; floral repousse, fancy hdl, gold wash, lg **110.00**
Napkin ring, satchel w/hdl **65.00**
Paperweight, cherub figural **90.00**
Thermometer, sitting rabbit figural, 6¼" **175.00**
Tray, eng florals/leaves, ornate borders, hdls, 13x19½" **195.00**

Pairpoint Limoges

Limoges china china blanks were imported from France in strict accordance with Pairpoint specifications. They were decorated by Pairpoint in designs that ranged from simple to elaborate florals and scenics. These are easily identified — look for the Pairpoint name over a crown with the Limoges name below. You may also find similar ware marked 'Pairpoint Minton.'

Bowl, mums, gold on eggshell, fish finial, hdls/lid, 8" **485.00**
Ewer, mums on rose, gold hdl & highlights, 16" **250.00**
Tureen, mums foliage, fish finial, 8x6½x6" **465.00**
Vase, cherub w/tray of flowers, bk: poppies, hdls, 15" **1,350.00**

Vase, gladiolus, cherub w/peonies, w/gilt, cobalt hdls, 15" . . .**1,200.00**

Paper Dolls

No one knows quite how or when paper dolls originated. One belief is that they began in Europe as 'pantins' (jumping jacks) and were frequently worn as part of the costume. By the late 1790s, they were being mass-produced. During the nineteenth century, most paper dolls portrayed famous dancers and opera stars such as Fanny Elssler and Jenny Lind. In the late 1800s, the Raphael Tuck Publishers of England produced many series of beautiful paper dolls; retail companies used them as advertisements to further the sale of their products. Around the turn of the century, many popular women's magazines began featuring a page of paper dolls.

Most familiar to today's collectors are the books with dolls on cardboard covers and clothes on the inside pages. These made their appearance in the late 1920s and early thirties. The most collectible (and the most valuable) are those representing celebrities, movie stars, and comic-strip characters of the thirties and forties.

Authority Mary Young has compiled an informative book, *Collector's Guide to Paper Dolls*, with current prices; you will find her address in the Directory under Ohio. When no condition is indicated, the dolls listed below are assumed to be in mint, uncut, original condition. Cut sets will be worth about half price, if all dolls and outfits are included and pieces are in very good condition. If dolls were produced in die-cut form, these prices reflect such a set in mint condition with all costumes and accessories.

A Friend Paper Doll, Boucher, w/clothes/scissors, 1967 . . . .**5.00**
Ann & Joe, MA Donohue, #80C **20.00**
Babyland-Bobby, Samuel Gabriel, #D121, 1921 . . . .**25.00**
Barney Bear, advertising, w/baseball uniform **25.00**
Betsy Ballerina, DeJournette Mfg **25.00**
Betsy McCall, Biggest Paper Doll; Samuel Gabriel, #D90, 1955 .**18.00**
Betsy McCall Dress 'N Play, McCall Publishing, #801, 1963 . . . .**12.00**
Betty & Dick Tour USA, Avalon Industries, #D100, 1940 . . . . .**17.50**
Betty & Peggy, Platt & Munk, #230B, 1937 . . . .**8.00**
Betty Ann & Audrey, Platt & Munk, #210A **30.00**
Betty Ann & Her Friends, Platt & Munk, #210, 6 dolls/clothes .**30.00**
Bible Think & Do, CR Gibson, #4936, Book 1 . . . .**3.00**
Bob & Nan, MA Donohue, #80A **20.00**
Bobby, Doll To Dress; MS Publishing, #900 . . . .**20.00**
Bride Doll, Frann Paper Dolls, 1955 . . . .**18.00**
Bright Eyes, DeJournette Mfg, #85 . . . .**5.00**
Brownie Paper Doll, DeJournette Mfg, #11-947 . . . .**10.00**
Carol & Her Dresses, Samuel Gabriel, #D117 . . . .**18.00**
Claire, DeJournette Mfg, #72 . . . .**10.00**
Corinne, American Colortype Co, #703, w/outfit, 13" **30.00**
Costume Party, Samuel Gabriel, #D137 . . . .**40.00**
Cousin Kate, Samuel Gabriel, #D90, w/2 outfits **25.00**
Cutie Paper Dolls, Milton Bradley, #4053, w/clothes **15.00**
Daisy Dolly, Goldsmith Publishing, #516, 1922 . . . .**17.00**
Debby Dolls, Jaymar Specialty, #980 . . . .**12.00**
Dennison Dolls & Dresses, Dennison Mfg, #37 . . . .**30.00**
Design-A-Doll, Dennison Mfg, #11, 1950 . . . .**8.00**
Dinah Shore & George Montgomery, 1959 . . . .**40.00**
Dollie Dimple, complete in orig envelope, ca 1894 . . . .**125.00**
Dollies a la Mode, Samuel Gabriel, #896 . . . .**30.00**
Dolls from the Land of Mother Goose, Platt & Munk, #221 . . . .**22.50**
Dolly's Kut-Out Clothes, #3081, doll & paper patterns **10.00**
Dotty & Danny on Parade, Burton Playthings, #875, 1935 . . . . .**22.50**
Early American Dolls, Platt & Munk, #224A, 1963 . . . .**6.00**
Ever-New Doll, Samuel Gabriel, #D115, w/4 heads **18.00**
Fancy Dress Dolls, Samuel Gabriel, #896 . . . .**30.00**
Fashion Art Dolls, Art Award, #6000 . . . .**4.00**

Five Flying Americans, Grinnell Lithographic, #C1010, 1940 . .25.00
Gay Dolls, Platt & Munk, #225A, 1942 . . . . .6.00
Gina, DeJournette Mfg, #R80 . . . . .5.00
Glendora, DeJournette Mfg, #1000 . . . . .10.00
Glenn, Janex Corporation, #2002, 1971 . . . . .5.00
Gone w/Wind, Merrill, 18 dolls w/108 costumes, 1940, EX 175.00
Heidi, DeJournette Mfg, #200, w/clothes 8.00
Ivy, Janex Corporation, #2000, 1971 . . . . .5.00
Jane Russell, 1955 . . . . .25.00
Johnny Jones, Goldsmith Publishing, #516, 1922 . . . . .17.00
Let's Build Our Camp, Samuel Gabriel, #D144, 1930 . . . . .20.00
Let's Play Paper Dolls, McLoughlin, #551, 1938 . . . . .20.00
Little Alice Busy Bee, American Colortype, #626 . . . . .25.00
Little Dreamer, cut, 6 outfits, 34" 75.00

Little Fanny, S. & J. Fuller, London, 1810, seven outfits in original envelope, 10x12", $700.00.

Little Nurse, Reuben H Lilja, #909 . . . . .12.00
Littlest Darling, DeJournette Mfg, #222 . . . . .8.00
Look Who I Am, Hart Publishing, 18" doll, book, 1952 . . . . . . .10.00
Lovey & Dovey Magic Dolls, Parker Bros, 1951 . . . . .15.00
Mammy & Kinky-Top, Dennison Mfg, Blk mother/child 25.00
Marie & Patsy Ann, American Colortype, #25, 1927 . . . . .17.50
Marilyn Monroe, 1979, uncut, 31 costumes, M 20.00
Mark Antony, Blaise Publishing, #1001, 1963 . . . . .15.00
Mary Miles Minter, Percy Reeves, 1920 . . . . .45.00
Mimi, The French Model; DeJournette Mfg, #2200 . . . . .20.00
Miss Airlanes, Children's World Publishing, #101 . . . . .15.00
Miss America Magic Doll, Parker Bros, ca 1953 . . . . .18.00
Miss Holly Day, DeJournette Mfg, #2201 . . . . .18.00
Miss Nurse Dress-Up Kit, Colorforms, #408 . . . . .3.00
My Doll Jill, Samuel Gabriel, #D79, w/clothes/hats 15.00
My Fair Lady, Avalon, #401 . . . . .18.00
Nursery Favorite, MA Donohue, #672, 1913 . . . . .30.00
Nursery Lullabies, Children's Press, #R1002, 1950 . . . . .3.50
Our Happy Family, Samuel Gabriel, #D141, 1929 . . . . .20.00
Pansy Prattle, Goldsmith Publishing, #516, 1922 . . . . .17.00
Party of the Paper Dolls, McLoughlin, #552, 1938 . . . . .20.00
Patsy, Children's Press, #3002, 1946 . . . . .15.00
Petticoat Junction, Avalon, #301 . . . . .18.00
Playmate, DeJournette Mfg, #800 . . . . .15.00
Playtime Fashions, Stephens Publishing, #135, 1946 . . . . .6.00
Playtime Pals, Current, #5607, 1982 . . . . .4.00
Poky-Hontas, DeJournette Mfg 10.00

Pony Tail, Samuel Gabriel, #116 . . . . .12.00
Princess Elizabeth Magic Doll, Parker Bros 25.00
Rag Doll Sue, Harter Publishing, #H100, 1931 . . . . .30.00
Real Sleeping Doll, McLoughlin, #556, w/bottle/clothes, 1939 . .22.50
School Mates, Samuel Gabriel, #D100 . . . . .18.00
Shirley Temple, Samuel Gabriel, #301, 1961 . . . . .20.00
Sister Helen, Kaufmann & Strauss, #12, 1915 . . . . .40.00
Sisters, Samuel Gabriel, #D135 . . . . .25.00
Six Playtime Dolls, Grinnell Lithographic, #C1004, 1940 . . . . . .25.00
Sleeping Beauty & Prince Charming, DeJournette Mfg, #2002 . .20.00
Smile Dress-Up Set, Colorforms, #581, 1971 . . . . .3.00
Snuggly Dolls, Charles E Graham, #0225 . . . . .25.00
Susie, Judy, Laura, & Annie; Aldon Industries 7.00
Sweet Alice, Tuck, complete w/orig envelope, dtd 1894 . . . . . .125.00
Ted & Bob, MA Donohue, #81C, no clothes 20.00
Teena the Teenager, Avalon, #701-2 .4.00
Teeny Weeny Pretty Dollies, Charles E Graham, #02 . . . . .15.00
Ten Round About Dolls, McLoughlin, #555, 1936 . . . . .25.00
Tina the Talking Paper Doll, Colorforms, #5550, w/clothes 10.00
Tiny Twinkle, Charles E Graham, #0221 . . . . .18.00
Toddler Twins, Samuel Gabriel, #D134 . . . . .25.00
Twinnies, Samuel Gabriel, #D107, ca 1933 . . . . .30.00
United We Stand, children in uniform, uncut, 1940s, EX 60.00
Vicki Velcro, Samuel Gabriel, #130 .10.00
Wedding Bells, Dot & Peg Productions, 1945 . . . . .15.00
Wendy Walks, Merry Mfg, #6504, 1965 . . . . .10.00
When I Grow Up, Current, #3216, 1980 . . . . .5.00
Winkle Family, Samuel Gabriel, #D127 . . . . .40.00
Winky Winnie, Jaymar Specialty, #994 . . . . .12.00
Your Own Quintuplets, Burton Playthings, #275, 1935 . . . . . . .25.00

Paperweights

The term 'paperweight' technically refers to any small, heavy object used to hold down loose papers. They have been made from a broad range of materials; many have been sold as souvenirs or given away by retail companies as advertising premiums. But today those attracting the most interest are the antique and contemporary artists' glass weights.

During the mid-1800s, the French factories of St. Louis, Baccarat, and Clichy incorporated millefiori and lampwork into glass domes which were called paperweights. This was done commercially and was probably the result of earlier efforts by Pierre Bigaglia of Venice. These 'baubles' were eagerly snapped up. Weights from the French factories that originally sold for a mere $2.00 to $3.00 are today commanding prices of $500.00 and up, depending on condition and craftsmanship. Many have been damaged but are restored or restorable. Interest waned in the late 1860s, and production nearly came to a halt. Clichy closed in the late 1800s. Baccarat is known to have made weights until about 1910 and again in the 1920s and 1930s. In the early 1950s, a revival of interest in paperweights resulted in renewed production at both Baccarat and St. Louis.

In the United States, production started in the 1850s, a little later than in France; and paperweights continued to be in vogue a little longer. The New England and Sandwich factories along with Millville, New Jersey, are the best-known manufacturers of weights made in the 1920s and 1930s. Today several well-known glass artists such as Kaziun, Whittemore, Ysart, and Stankard are making weights with a floral motif as well as other designs.

Paperweight collecting began with the 19th-century weights, but much knowledge and interest was lost during the period when production drastically declined. During the 1920s, collector-interest began to pick up and by 1950 had intensified to the point that books and articles on the subject began to be published. The Paperweight Collectors' Association was formed in 1953. It has bi-annual conventions, and there are several state and regional associations. Interest in weight collecting shows continuous growth.

   Note: Prices do not reflect the usual 10% buyer's fee charged by most auction houses. Furthermore,there are many factors which determine value, particularly of antique weights. Auction-realized prices of contemporary weights are usually other than issue price; 'list price' may be for weights issued earlier and reduced for clearance or influenced by market demand and other factors. The dimension given at the end of the description is diameter.

   Key:
   A — antique   latt — latticinio
   cl — clear   mill — millefiori
   con — concentric   o/l — overlay
   fct — faceted   pm — pastry mold
   gar — garland   pwt — paperweight
   grd — ground   sil — silhouette
   jsp — jasper

Ayotte, Rick

Bl Jay, pk/wht rhododendron on cl, 3½" 335.00
Brn Thrasher on Cherokee rose, 2⅛" 225.00
English Sparrow pr on gr-leaf branch on opaque tan, ltd ed 500.00
Lg wht swan on translucent cobalt, ltd ed 500.00
Lovebirds on brn branch w/blossoms, 1985, 3¼" 385.00
Mother robin & young on gr branch, cl encased, lt ed 550.00
Robin feeds worm to 3 young, 2 layers, lt bl grd 600.00
Yel-Throated Warbler, lt purple/yel irises 600.00

Baccarat, Antique

Bl/wht buttercup+wht bud+5 leaves w/in mill ring, star base .3,200.00
Close pack, flower/chicken/dog/horse sil, dtd 1847, 2½" 1,450.00
Close pack mill w/Gridel sil, sgn/dtd 1847 canes, magnum . . .6,500.00
Close pack mill w/Gridel sil, sgn/dtd 1848 canes 1,650.00
Gr flash o/l, con mill rings w/gr shamrocks & wht stardust . . .3,200.00
Pansy in gar, serrated petals/cane center, star base, 3" 3,600.00
Purple/yel pansy w/5 gr leaves star base, mini 600.00
Salmon camomile+2 pk buds+6 leaves, bl/wht cane border . .3,200.00
Scattered mill on lace grd w/many sil+1849 dtd cane 1,600.00
Scattered mill/upset muslin, 3 sil+whirl & cog canes, 2" 400.00
Scrambled, lace/mc canes, mini 600.00
Wht anemone w/bl border, star base, 3¼" 1,400.00
5 red tulip buds in cl, star base, 2⅝" 1,600.00

Antique Baccarat, seven circles of multicolored millefiori canes, 3", $350.00 at auction.

Baccarat, Modern

Carpet grd Zodiac, complex canes w/sil of signs & date, 3" 325.00

Complex mill canes scattered on fine latt, 1974, 3" 160.00
Gridel goat on butterscotch w/red & wht canes+17 sil, mini . . .300.00
Opaque lav w/gold bees spaced around lg gold dot, 2½" 40.00
Pattern mill, rows of horizontal peppermint cane sections 85.00
Sulfide, Caesar profile on ruby, mk, 4" 75.00
Sulphide, Abraham Lincoln, 6/1 fct, o/l waffle base, 1962 . . . . .160.00
Sulphide, Adlai Stevenson, purple o/l, star base/sides+4 fct 150.00
Sulphide, Gen Bonaparte, 6/1 fct on dk ruby, 1974, 2⅝" 65.00
Sulphide, JF Kennedy on dk red, 6/1 fct, 2¾" 80.00
Wht-edged bl dahlia on opal, 4 leaves, 1972, 2⅞" 275.00

Banford, Bob

Bee over 10-petal red flower+2 buds, honeycomb fct 600.00
Pk clematis w/floral cane center, irid foliage, opal, fct 350.00
Red/wht o/l, spear side cuttings, 16-petal bl flower+2 buds 850.00
Spray of 5 lt bl flowers+3 buds, star base 500.00
Wheatflower+bud on cranberry grd .450.00
2 bl flowers/buds on wht trellis over lt bl, 7/1 fct, 2⅛" 235.00
3 flowers in vase on lt bl jsp grd 400.00
4 bl 6-petal flowers+bud & gr leaves on cl honeycomb, 2⅞" . . .300.00

Banford, Ray

Floral w/gr leaves & stalks, 2¾" 400.00
Morning-glories on trellis, diamond-cut base 600.00
Rose, 3-color, multifaceted, 2¾" 325.00
Rose+3 buds, star base 400.00
2 pk roses+3 buds, pk/gr, 3¼" 350.00
2 purple iris+bud, yel/wht o/l, flutes/dots fct, sgn, 2¾" 425.00
3 purple/yel pansies+gr leaves+wht bellflowers, grid base 1,000.00

Caithness

Flat bouquet w/6 flowers on bl, tube cane gar, pontil, 3" 325.00
Lobster 125.00
Mill scattered at random on wht latt over bl, 2⅞" 75.00
Pk shaded/striped clematis & leaves on dk bl, 2⅝" 70.00
Sagittarius 125.00
Snake, red aventurine+yel/red spots,on gr/tan pebbles, 3" 220.00

Clichy, Antique

Barber-pole checker, turq/wht, 1 pk & gr/1 wht & gr rose . . .2,950.00
Checker, con mill on lace w/central pk & gr rose 1,500.00
Checker, pk/wht rose, fct, 3¼" 1,450.00
Pattern mill, bl/wht pm w/in ring of 6 more+star+rose, 1¾" . . .210.00
Pk rose+6 pm canes, mini 600.00
Red pm cane atop cobalt/wht swirl 1,250.00
Space mill w/6 canes including wht/gr rose, mini 450.00
Trefoil, turq grd w/7 lg pm canes .2,650.00
Turq/wht swirl w/lg red pm cane center 1,500.00
3 con mill stars w/pk & gr rose center, fct 2,600.00
3 con rings of cogs/roses around 4-color cog on dk bl, 2½" . . .1,100.00
7-row close con mill in wht muslin & gr/wht tube basket, 3" .1,400.00

Gentile

Aqua/blk butterfly by bl/wht flower, bubbles in base, unsgn 25.00
Eagle+13 stars in gold over royal bl, bubbles, unsgn 25.00
Geo & Martha WA, pastel on wht w/mc mushroom, sgn 1959 . .80.00
LB Johnson+sepia picture on wht plaque, 3-color mushroom . . .80.00
Loyal Order of Moose PAP, emblem in gold over royal bl 12.50

Remember Pearl Harbor, bombing scene, sgn 25.00
5-petal gr flower, mercury bubbles, mc scalloped base, sgn 18.00

Kaziun, Charles

Bottle, yel lily in base/stopper, gold-dusted lt bl, 3½" 1,200.00
Long-stem Sandwich rose+bud+7 leaves/gold bee on bl, 2½" . .900.00
Pattern mill, 7/1 fct, red/gold grd, bl/wht torsade, 2" 500.00
Red flower+gr leaves on gold-shot gr grd, ped ft, 1¼" 350.00
Sunbonnet Sue sil on turq w/pk & gr torsade+6 sm sil canes .1,700.00
Wht-tipped purple crocus, ped base, 2⅞" 1,900.00
Yel flower w/gr leaves on gold-shot lav grd, ped ft, 1¼" 275.00
Yel rose, ped base, 3" 1,750.00
Yel-tipped lav tulip, ped base, rare color, 3¼" 2,800.00

Lundberg Studios

Bl forget-me-not w/butterflies over cl 250.00
Cvd basket w/mc hydrangeas, mini 220.00
European wildflower w/leaves over cl grd 220.00
Pk fish/bl man-o'-war on bl irid, fct, mini 230.00
Pk tiger lily w/gr leaves, cl encased, ped base, mini 160.00

New England Glass

Apple, clear rnd base, 3" dia 900.00
Bl poinsettia+bud+leaves w/dewdrops on wht latt swirl, 2½" . .325.00
Crown, 2⅛" 700.00
Henry Clay bust on flat hexagon form, 1851, att, 3½" W 375.00
Upright bouquet, red/wht/bl/mc on wht latt basket, 2⅝" 2,250.00
Yel/red apple on cl cookie base 1,400.00
5 pears+4 cherries+8 leaves on wht latt basket, 2½", NM 600.00
5 ripe yel fruits+leaves+4 red cherries on latt basket, 3" 350.00

Perthshire

Bouquet on blk grd, sgn cane in center, 1978, 2⅞" 275.00
Carpet grd, 7 sil canes on cream & gr cane grd, 1977, 3⅛" 180.00
Christmas flower in cl, 1 top fct, star base, 1975, 2⅝" 100.00
Damson plums on waffle-cut grd, 1977, 2½" 195.00
Gar w/5 sil: balloon/steamship/bicycle/car/steam engine, 3" . . .170.00
Mini bl flower on wht latt basket, cane sgn, 1985, 2⅛" 145.00
Pattern mill w/cane & torsade, 1977 . . . . .65.00
3 bluebells on stem in cl, star base, fct, 1978, 2¼" 170.00

Rosenfeld, Ken

Cabbage rose bouquet w/bl bellflowers & gr tendrils 400.00
Pk dahlia+pk/wht bl-edge flower+dk brn blossom on cl, 2⅝" . .110.00
Upright pk rose+bud w/gr leaves on brn stems on cl, 2¾" 120.00
Upright spray: 3 pk+2 bl flowers+bl bud, semicircular, 2½" 220.00
3 pk+purple rose bouquet w/gr foliage on cl, 1985 . . . . .160.00

Sandwich Glass

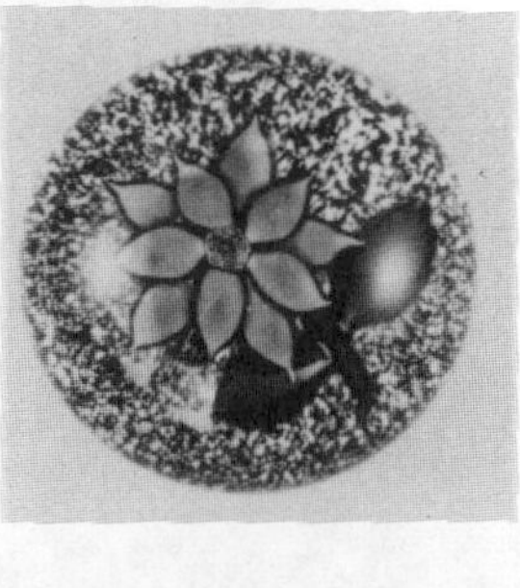

Sandwich Glass Co., ten-petal red poinsettia with central millefiori cane, green stem and leaves, on textured blue and white jasper ground, 2¾", $350.00.

Broken canes in abstract positions, 2½" 450.00
Poinsettia, Lutz rose center in lt bl, dewdrop bubbles, 3" 850.00
Red rose/swirl center+lg bud/wide greenery on coarse latt 550.00
Scrambled latt, loose array of ribbon twists & latt, 2⅜" 55.00
12-petal dk bl poinsettia w/wht honeycomb center, 2⅞", EX . .350.00
12-petal wht-w/bl-spots wheatflower w/red tube center, 3½" . . .500.00

St Louis, Antique

Close pack con mill, duck sil center+4 dog sil in 3rd row 3,750.00
Con mill, 8 rings, dtd 1848, 2⅝" .2,500.00
Crown, red/gr twist ribbons+lacy latt twists 2,800.00
Fct mushroom, pk/bl/red/wht, bl torsade, star base, 3¼" 3,250.00
Lg dahlia, purple w/5 sm gr leaves, cl star base 3,850.00
Mixed fruit w/gr leaves over wht latt grd 1,600.00
Mushroom, red/wht/bl w/bright bl stem, allover fct, 2⅛" . . .1,850.00
Patterned mill on latt grd, red/gr periphery canes 750.00
Pk camomile bloom+pk bud+4 gr leaves over wht latt grd . . .2,750.00
Wafer dish, mill base, bl/wht torsade rim 1,200.00
2 red cherries on branch w/gr leaves, many sm fcts 2,800.00
7-flower upright bouquet w/lg central orange blossom 2,450.00

St. Louis, Modern

Basket of latt/spiral twists w/mill flowers, 1981, 4" L 700.00
Gold inclusion of Gen WA on horsebk+13 stars, 1976, 3" 225.00
Lampwork dahlia w/date & sgn cane, pistachio on cl, fct, 3" . . .300.00
Mongolfiere hot air balloon, bl w/gilt, 1983, 3⅝" 650.00
Red/wht bouquet on lt bl latt swirl, cane sgn/date, 3⅛" 275.00
Sulphide, Armour, Cupid enclosed by bl flowers on red, fct . . .385.00
Sulphide, Gen de Gaulle on bl, red/wht o/l, 5/1 fct, 1977 . . . .135.00
Sulphide, King St Louis, cog cane gar, 5/1 fct, 1967, 2⅝" 95.00
Sulphide, Queen Elizabeth II Coronation, dtd 1953, 3" 135.00
3 mini cherries on wht latt swirl, 3-row+lg top fct, 1985 . . . . .195.00
5-layer shaded bl dahlia, fct, 1970, 3¼" 300.00
7 upright clematis on latt mushroom, red/wht/cl o/l, 4¼" 2,100.00

Stankard, Paul

Braided bouquet of mc wildflowers, #d, 1892, 3¼" 1,250.00
Dk bl flowers w/leaves, stem, roots, 1980, 3⅜" 800.00
Fct, yel/wht/bl wildflowers on emerald, B364, 1981, 3¼" 550.00
Lt yel flower w/leaves+opening seed pod, sgn, 3" 800.00
Mountain Hawthorn w/root system, 1984 . . . . .700.00
Pk flower w/2 blooms, leaves/seed pod, #d, 1981, 3" 900.00
Sippiswisset Bouquet, blackberries/flowers, 1890, 3¼" 1,500.00
Water lily w/buds & roots on gr, 1984 . . . . .800.00
Yel Cactus Flowers on red, 4+3 buds, root system, 1984, 3" . .1,000.00

Tarsitano, Debbie

Gar of 6 pk & bl flowers w/upright wht center flower 525.00
Opening Night Bouquet, 3 lg red flowers+3 wht sprigs, 2¾" . . .350.00
Pansy+bud on star base 575.00
Red/yel poppies+wild grasses+2 wht bellflowers, compound . .1,800.00
Striped pk pompom w/yel stamen, star base, 6/1 fct, sgn 400.00
Wht/yel flowers+buds, leaves/stems, bl base w/cutting, 2⅞" . . .700.00
3 bl bellflowers w/wht int & leaves on cl, sgn, 2⅝" 425.00
4 5-petal striped pk flowers w/yel stamens & wht buds, 3" 600.00

Tarsitano, Delmo

Bee on nest over sandy grd by strawberry w/3 blossoms 900.00
Gr-stripe lizard+yel flower on sandy grd, 3¼" 850.00

Spider on bl pond, 2 yel flowers/foliage, 8/1 fct, 3" 650.00
Spider on bl web & rocky grd w/gr plants 700.00
Spider on flower's leaves in water & sandy soil, sgn, 3¼" 375.00
2 peaches w/9 leaves, star base 400.00
3 strawberries w/3 blossoms 600.00

Trabucco, Victor

Blk-spotted wht lizard by sm pk flower on sandy jsp grd, 3¼" . .450.00
Butterfly w/daisies & bud, 1981 .350.00
Crab apple w/open flower+2 buds, 1983 . . . . .400.00
Ice block, butterfly w/2 daisies, 1981 . . . . .450.00
Red rose w/bud & knotweed, 1984, magnum 750.00
Yel bellflower w/foliage, 1982 . . . . .275.00
Yel/blk butterfly+pk upright peony & bud, fct, 1984 . . . . . . .450.00
3 bl dolphins, fct 250.00

Whitefriars

Con mill w/rings of red/wht/lt gr/cobalt 350.00
Con rings of lt gr/red/pk/bl, 1848 dtd cane 475.00
Con rows of cogs & tubes w/central lg pm cane, 3½" 90.00
Prince Charles, 1969 . . . . .50.00

Whittemore, Francis D.

Nosegay, lt bl grd, ped base, 1984 . . . . .400.00
Pk rose on gr leaves, ped ft, 2½x1⅞" 150.00
Pk rose/gr leaves on cl ped, cane sgn, 2½x1⅞" 235.00
Red/lt pk rose w/4 lg leaves, tilted/ped base, 3⅛" 275.00
2 yel lady slippers w/foliage on emerald gr, 2¼" 250.00
5-petal bl flower w/yel center+1 bud+5 leaves on pk, 2½" 150.00

Ysart, Paul

Brn salamander on rocky grd 450.00
Con mill on opaque cobalt, mc/PY canes in center, 3" 275.00
Pattern mill on lt purple, 5 groups complex mill+5 cogs, 3" . . .325.00
Patterned mill over tomato red, 5 lg+5 sm, unsgn, 2¾" 300.00
Pk/wht 5-petal flower w/gr stem on purple, sgn w/H cane, 2¾" .120.00
Pk/wht-stripe dahlia over opal, derby hat form, sgn H, 1¾" . . .275.00
Spotted fish over rocky grd w/seashell 500.00

Miscellaneous

American, life-size moving fly w/in, 2", EX 150.00
Blenko, yel swirl around 1 lg central bubble, unsgn 15.00
Bohemian, A, spaced mill on lace tuft, 6/1 fct, red/wht o/l . .2,100.00
Bohemian, close-pack scrambled mill tubes/latt+eagle, 2½" 80.00
Bohemian, mill w/monkey+heart+6 canes, upset muslin, 2⅝" . .850.00
Bridgeton Studios, Ziegler & Phelps; tropical fish, 3" 75.00
Buzzini, Chris; 2 upright bl bellflowers+wht blossoms on cl . . .285.00
Chinese, dbl red yel-center clematis on yel latt swirl, 2½" 90.00
Chinese, rowed mill, sm 20.00
D'Albret, Cristal; sulphide, FDR on purple, ⅝x2¾" 75.00
D'Albret, Cristal; sulphide, Pres & Mrs Kennedy on gr, 3" 60.00
Deacon, John; bl/wht lobed cane gar on latt w/6 flowers, 3" . . .275.00
Degenhart, purple crocus/leaves, tilted/ped base, 4½" 160.00
Grubb, Randy; periwinkle-bl flower+bud+2 sm orange flowers .230.00
Hamon, Robert; dk pk flower grows from gr pot, tall oval 20.00
Hamon, Robert; Dunbar Golden Jubilee on pillow, unsgn 12.50
Hansen, Ronald; bluebird on twig, 5/1 fct, 2" 80.00

Hansen, Ronald; lt bl 6-petal flower on claret, ftd, 1⅜x1⅞" 75.00
Hansen, Ronald; snake on dk red w/wht underside, 2" 95.00
J Glass, mill butterfly/gar on mill, purple grd, fcts 325.00
J Glass, 3 pk flowers on pk & gr latt swirl 175.00
Kain, Lewis; wht/orange clematis over lt bl, unsgn, 2⅛" 135.00
Larsen, Emil; Millville rose, pk-tipped red petals, 4¼" 2,350.00
Lewis, Pete; 2-purple/3-yel petal pansy w/star center, 2⅛" 425.00
Manson, William; butterfly at sunset, 1981 . . . . .425.00
Millville, umbrella, red/wht/bl/gr mottle, 3¾x3¼" 100.00
Mt WA, pk poinsettia/gr leaves on mc swirled mound, 3½" . . .200.00
Orient & Flume, frog on lily pad over bl, sgn Sellers, 2¾" 75.00
Parabelle, bl/purple mill gar on wht latt w/7 'Clichy' roses 140.00
Rosenfeld, Ken; 2 lg lav cabbage roses+strawberry+clematis . . .300.00
Smith, Gordon; dbl red clematis, 3⅛" 250.00
Stand, lady's slipper w/roots, sgn, 1983, cube style, 2⅜" 750.00
Stand, mc bouquet tied w/gr stems & leaves on cl grd 1,500.00
Val St Lambert, 7 3-color roses in 3-color surround, 3½" 175.00

Papier-Mache

The art of papier-mache was mainly European. It originated in Paris around the middle of the 18th century and became popular in America during Victorian times. Small items such as boxes, trays, inkwells, frames, etc., as well as extensive ceiling moldings and larger articles of furniture were made. The process involved building layer upon layer of paper soaked in glue then coaxed into shape over a wood or wire form. When dry it was painted or decorated with gilt or inlays. Inexpensive 20th-century 'notions' were machine processed and mold pressed. See also Christmas; Candy Containers.

Basket, MOP bands, scalloped, gold-stenciled edge, 7" dia 50.00
Box, HP St Petersburg scene, sgn, Russian, 1800s, 4" L 100.00
Handscreen, cartouch form w/MOP scene, 1800s, 15½", pr 165.00
Mask, man w/blk horsehair beard/mustache/hair, 1900, 15" 70.00
Milliner's head, mc pnt features, 15", EX 250.00
Noisemaker, carrot form, wood mouthpc, German, 1900, 8½" . .55.00
Roly-poly clown, bright pnt, 4" 60.00
Toy, hen, wire/spring legs, wood base w/wheels, 1900, 10x7x4". 175.00
Tray, floral branches, mc on blk w/gilt, lacquered, mk, 26" . .1,300.00
Tray, HP florals, lg/sm birds, gilt decor, 1850s, 30" L 5,000.00

Tray, bay scene with figure in foreground, signed, ca 1825, 31" long, $1,800.00.

Parian Ware

Parian is hard-paste unglazed porcelain made to resemble marble. First made in the mid-1800s by Staffordshire potters, it was soon after produced in the United States by the U.S. Pottery at Bennington, Vermont. Busts and statuary were favored, but plaques, vases, mugs, and pitchers were also made.

Arab mare & foal, after Mene, English, 9", EX 400.00
Bust, Apollo, Germany, 7" 75.00
Bust, Rev CH Spurgeon, Robinson-Ledbetter, 1878, 13" 140.00

Bust of Charles Sumner, 10½", $95.00.

Bust, Shakespeare, circular base, unmk, 7½" 60.00
Figurine, barefoot farm boy w/hat & jug at fountain, 8¾" 55.00
Figurine, boy reading newspaper, oversz clothes, imp mk, 10" . .125.00
Figurine, Omphale on throne chair, club in hand, 16" 225.00
Figurine, 3 Graces, after Canova, att Copeland, 21" 400.00
Jug, lav/wht, figures, lion & unicorn mk, 9¾x5⅜" 155.00
Jug, ribs, yel/gold Greek Key rim, ca 1852, Minton, 6½" 90.00
Plaque, Greek man/rabbit/bird/dog, lady/child, Eneret, 11" 60.00
Vase, fox w/dead rabbit, bark-textured fan vase at bk, 6x5½" . . .55.00

Parrish, Maxfield

Maxfield Parrish was a painter and illustrator who began his career in the last decade of the 19th century. His work remained prominent until the early 1940s. His most famous painting, *Daybreak*, was published in print form and sold nearly two thousand copies between 1910 and 1930. All prices are for framed prints except for those from the 1960s.

Advertising, Djer Kiss, girl in swing, LHJ, 1921, 14x10" 75.00
Advertising, Goodrich Tires, Sat Eve Post, 1923, 13½x10" 40.00
Advertising, Swift's Premium Ham, ca 1921, 14x11" 125.00
Book, Arabian Knights, 1941 . . . . .95.00
Book, Golden Age, EX 165.00
Book, Poems of Childhood, orig 95.00
Book, Tanglewood Tales, 10 illus, 1st edition, EX 85.00
Bookplate, Golden Age & Dream Days, 7¾x6" 15.00
Bookplate, Lady Violetta, Knave of Hearts, 1925, 12½x10½" . . .80.00

Bookplate, Manager, Knave of Hearts, 1925, 12½x10½" 70.00
Bookplate, Prince, Knave of Hearts, 1925, 12½x10½" 85.00
Calendar, Calender of Friendship, photo cover, 1926, 53-pg 25.00
Calendar, Enchantment, Edison/Mazda, 1926, 19x8½" 145.00
Calendar, Lantern Bearers, Dodge Publishing, 1920, 53-pg 45.00
Calendar, Old Glen Mill, Brown/Bigelow, 1954, 17x11½" 165.00
Calendar, Peaceful Valley, Brown/Bigelow, 1955, 18x13" 150.00
Calendar, Perfect Day, Brown/Bigelow, 1943, 23x11" 145.00
Calendar, Venetian Lamplighter, Edison/Mazda, 1924, 18x9" . .150.00
Calendar, Village Brook, Brown/Bigelow, 1941, 17x12¾" 125.00
Card, Christmas; Christmas Morn/Winter Sunrise, ca 1949, M . .15.00
Card, Christmas; Silent Night/Winter Night, 1942, 7⅝x5¼" . . .15.00
Card, Christmas; When Christmas Comes, 1950s, 7½x5¼", M . .15.00
Card, greeting; Mill Pond, 1940s 10.00
Card, greeting; Twilight Hour, ca 1950s, 7¼x6", M 15.00
Figure, Drum Major, jtd, compo/wood, Parrish design, 18", EX .150.00
Figure, Radiotrons, jtd, compo/wood, Parrish design, 16" 275.00
Frontispiece, Sinbad Plots Against the Giant, Collier's 55.00
Label, cigar box; Old King Cole, 10x6" .45.00
Label, crane & mountains, Crane's Chocolate, 1915, 5½x8" 85.00
Magazine cover, Collier's, Thanksgiving, 1906, 14½x10½" 70.00
Magazine cover, Life, self-portrait, Jan 31, 1924 . . . . .60.00
Magazine cover, Scribner's, Nativity scene, Dec 1900 . . . . .50.00
Matchbook, Old King Cole matches, opens at top, rare, unused .25.00
Playing cards, Broadmoor Hotel, scarce, 1925 . . . . .165.00
Playing cards, Contentment, Edison Mazda, unopened 175.00
Playing cards, In the Mountains, Brown/Bigelow, complete, M .135.00
Post card, Christmas Morn, uncirculated, M 8.00
Post card, When Christmas Comes 8.00
Poster, Scribner's Fiction Number: Aug, sgn/1897, 20x14" . .1,000.00
Print, Air Castles, ca 1904, fr, 15x11" .135.00
Print, Atlas, nude giant holds up sky, fr, 1909, 13½x11" 130.00
Print, Canyon, orig fr, 12x15" 125.00
Print, Christmas Eve, sgn, 11x11½", EX 65.00
Print, Cleopatra, EX matt & fr, sm 225.00
Print, Cleopatra, fancy fr, med sz 500.00
Print, Cleopatra, lg, fancy Deco fr, M 800.00
Print, Cleopatra, sm 140.00
Print, Contentment, ca 1959, 11x7" 90.00
Print, Daybreak, ca 1924, 15x12" 125.00
Print, Dinkey Bird, nude on swing, fr, 1905, 17½x12½" 130.00
Print, Dream Castles, nude youth/castle, 1912, 10x7½" 90.00
Print, Dreaming, ca 1960s, 14x12", M 50.00
Print, Early Autumn, lg 125.00
Print, Ecstasy, 11x15¼" 200.00
Print, Enchantment 175.00
Print, Garden of Allah, full margins, med sz 175.00
Print, Garden of Allah, Reinthall/Newman, NY, orig fr, lg 225.00
Print, Garden of Allah, sm 60.00
Print, Golden Hours, lg 350.00
Print, Golden Hours, sm 110.00
Print, Hilltop, ca 1926, fr, 20x12" 285.00
Print, Interlude, 3 maidens w/lutes, orig fr, 1924, 18x14" 175.00
Print, King of the Blk Isles 75.00
Print, Lute Players, ca 1924, fr, 30x18" 400.00
Print, magazine; With Trumpet & Drum, LHJ, blk/wht, 1903 . . .20.00
Print, New Hampshire, fr, 19x24" 95.00
Print, Old Glen Mill, fr, 16¾x13" 150.00
Print, Path to Home, Brown/Bigelow, 1950, orig fr, 13x11" . . .100.00
Print, Peace of Evening, Brown/Bigelow, 16x12", M 95.00
Print, Peaceful Valley, fr, 17x13½" 125.00
Print, Pied Piper, plays flute, 1909, orig fr, 24x10" 425.00
Print, Pool of the Villa Este, fr, 15x13" .65.00
Print, Prelude, orig fr, 13x16" 100.00

Print, Prince, House of Arts, ca 1925, fr, 12x10" 115.00
Print, Quiet Solitude, Brown/Bigelow, 1961, 19x16" 75.00
Print, Reveries, lg 350.00
Print, Sandman, gnome w/sack, orig fr, 1905, 8½x6½" 40.00
Print, Sea Nymphs, ca 1908, 16½x12" 135.00
Print, Sheltering Oaks, 16x19", M 45.00
Print, Stars, ca 1959, 11x7" 90.00
Print, Twilight, Brown/Bigelow, ca 1961, orig, 19x16" 90.00
Print, Twilight, ca 1935, orig fr, 30x12½" 195.00
Print, Twilight, fr, 18x22" 125.00
Print, Under Summer Skies, Brown/Bigelow, 1959, 19x16" 85.00
Print, Wild Geese, ca 1924, fr, 15x12" 135.00
Print, Winkin, Blinken, & Nod; orig fr, lg 95.00

Morning, 17½x14", $135.00.

Puzzle, Prince, 1925, complete in orig 12x9½" box 85.00
Puzzle, Queen's Page, 1925, complete in orig 12x9½" box 85.00
Tape measure, 2 knaves, Edison/Mazda, scarce, NM 65.00

Pate-De-Verre

Simply translated, pate-de-verre means paste of glass. In the manufac-turing process, lead glass is first ground, then mixed with sodium silicate solution to form a paste which can be molded and refired. Some of the most prominent artisans to use this procedure were Almaric Walter, Daum, Argy-Rousseau, and Decorchemont.

Bust of a satyr, amethyst, mk Despret/#1099, 6½" 880.00
Dish, clear/red streaked, cvd w/flowers, 8-side lip, 8" L 1,980.00
Sculpture, woman's head, yel, sgn Despret, 4" L 440.00
Vase, rim decor, gr/rust/purple mottle, Decorchemont, 4" . . .1,325.00
Vase, water beetles at rim, streaky bl/gr, Decorchemont, 2" . .4,000.00

Pate-Sur-Pate

Pate-sur-pate, literally paste-on-paste, is a technique whereby relief decorations are built up on a ceramic body by layering several applications of slip, one on the other, until the desired result is achieved. Usually only two colors are used, and the value of a piece is greatly enhanced as more color is added. See also Rousseau, Argy; Walter, A.

Box, lady w/flute sits on branch, mk JG&Cie/Limoges, 5½" . . .200.00
Box, 2 putti on dolphins on lid, bombe form, Limoges, 8" 200.00
Plaque, dancer, wht/dk bl, sgn A Barriere, Limoges, 6x5" 150.00

Plate, maiden at her bath, white and gold on salmon pink, KPM mark, 10" square, in giltwood frame, $800.00.

Vase, floral, wht on bl, integral gilt hdls/base, 10" 295.00
Vase, pilgrim; lilies, wht on gr w/gold, hdls, 7¾" 425.00
Vase, putti, wht on gr, disk form w/gold neck & ft, sgn, 7" 550.00

Pattern Glass

Pattern Glass was the first mass-produced fancy tableware in America and was much prized by our ancestors. From the 1840s to the Civil War, it contained a high lead content and is known as 'Flint Glass.' It is exception-ally clear and resonant. Later glass was made with soda lime and is known as non-flint. By the 1890s pattern glass was produced in great volume in thousands of patterns, and colored glass came into vogue. Today the highest prices are often paid for these later patterns flashed with rose, amber, canary, and vaseline; stained ruby; or made in colors of cobalt, green, yellow, amethyst, etc. Demand for pattern glass declined by 1915, and glass fanciers were collecting it by 1930. No other field of antiques offers more diversity in patterns, prices, or pieces than this unique and historical glass that represents the Victorian era in America. For a more thorough study on the subject, we recommend *The Collector's Encyclopedia of Pattern Glass*, by Mollie Helen McCain, available from Collector Books. See also Bread Plates; Cruets; Historical Glass; Salt and Pepper Shakers; Salts, Open; Sugar Shakers; Syrups; specific manufacturers such as North-wood.

Actress, bowl, 9½" 68.00
Actress, celery vase, frosted 130.00
Actress, cheese dish 245.00
Actress, compote, open, 7¼x7¼" 45.00
Actress, creamer 75.00
Actress, goblet 80.00
Actress, marmalade jar 125.00
Actress, relish dish, Love's Request Is Pickles 45.00
Actress, shakers, orig tops, pr 90.00
Admiral Dewey, see Greentown, Dewey
Almond Thumbprint, champagne, non-flint 40.00
Almond Thumbprint, salt cellar, master; 8-sided stem, flint 27.50
Amazon, butter dish 55.00

Amazon, creamer 40.00
Amazon, goblet, 4½" 32.00

Amazon

Amazon, goblet, 6" 34.00
Amberette, see Klondike
Anthemion, pitcher, water; 8¼" 45.00
Apollo, celery vase, etched 35.00
Apollo, sugar bowl, w/lid, etched 40.00
Aquarium, pitcher, water; gr 300.00
Arabesque, goblet 25.00
Arched Grape, champagne 50.00
Arched Grape, goblet 25.00
Argus, creamer 75.00
Argus, egg cup 25.00
Argus, goblet 35.00
Argus, sauce dish, flat, flint, 4¼" 9.00
Argus, tumbler, ftd, 5" 60.00
Art, compote, w/lid, 9½x6" 50.00
Ashburton, celery vase, scalloped, flint 95.00
Ashburton, compote, open, low std, flint, 7½" 64.00
Ashburton, creamer, appl hdl, flint 195.00
Ashburton, egg cup, dbl, flint 100.00
Ashburton, goblet, flint 30.00
Ashburton, mug, flint, 4¾" 70.00
Ashburton, sugar bowl, w/lid 140.00
Ashburton, tumbler, bar; flint 57.00
Ashburton, wine, str stem, flint 36.00
Atlas, cordial 38.00
Atlas, pitcher, milk tankard; ruby stained 125.00
Atlas, salt cellar, ind 15.00
Atlas, toothpick holder 15.00
Aurora, decanter, ruby stained, orig stopper 150.00
Aurora, pitcher, water; ruby stained 95.00
Aurora, wine, ruby stained 40.00
Austrian, cordial 45.00
Austrian, creamer, clear w/gold 35.00
Austrian, nappy, w/lid 55.00
Austrian, see also Greentown, Austrian
Austrian, tumbler 22.00
Austrian, vase, 8¼" 45.00
Baby Thumbprint, see Dakota
Balder, see Pennsylvania
Ball & Swirl, goblet 15.00
Baltimore Pear, cake stand, high std 50.00
Baltimore Pear, pitcher, water; lg 95.00
Baltimore Pear, sauce dish, ftd, 4" 24.00
Banded Portland, creamer, ind; clear w/gold 15.00
Banded Portland, toothpick holder 25.00
Banded Portland, vase, 9" 40.00
Banded Portland, wine 30.00
Banner, butter dish 95.00
Bar & Diamond, cup & saucer 30.00

Bar & Diamond, shakers, pr 25.00
Bar & Diamond, wine 27.50
Bar & Diamond (Kokomo), pitcher, tankard form, 10½" ...50.00
Bar & Diamond (Kokomo), water set, ruby stained 265.00

Banded Portland

Barberry, compote, open, w/lid, 6" 45.00
Barberry, pitcher, water; bulbous 90.00
Barberry, sauce dish, ftd 10.00
Barberry, tumbler, ftd 22.00
Barley, celery vase 25.00
Barley, pitcher, water 48.00
Barley, relish, wheelbarrow, ca 1882, rare 100.00
Barley, spooner 22.00
Barred Forget-Me-Not, creamer 30.00
Barred Forget-Me-Not, goblet 37.50
Barred Forget-Me-Not, pitcher, water 45.00
Barred Forget-Me-Not, sugar bowl, w/lid 40.00
Barred Oval, creamer 20.00
Barrel Huber, see Huber
Basket Weave, goblet 23.50
Basket Weave, pitcher, milk; gr 70.00
Basket Weave, plate, hdls, bl, 8¾" 19.50
Basket Weave, sugar bowl, w/lid, bl 37.50
Beaded Band, goblet 25.00
Beaded Band, spooner 25.00
Beaded Dewdrop, see Wisconsin
Beaded Grape, bowl, flat, sq, gr, 5¼" 20.00
Beaded Grape, creamer, gr 40.00
Beaded Grape, tumbler, water; clear w/gold 22.00
Beaded Grape Medalon, goblet 30.00
Beaded Grape Medallion, pitcher, water 120.00
Beaded Loop, relish dish, 7½x3¾" 10.00
Beaded Loop, see Oregon
Beaded Medallion, bottle, castor; orig stopper 26.00
Beaded Medallion, egg cup 17.50
Beaded Medallion, pitcher, water 100.00
Beaded Medallion, sugar bowl, open 20.00
Beaded Mirror, see Beaded Medallion
Beaded Rosette, goblet 40.00
Beaded Swirl, see Swirled Column
Beaded Tulip, plate, 6" 22.00
Bearded Head, see Viking
Bellflower, bottle, cologne; orig label/stopper, 7" ..375.00
Bellflower, bottle, cologne; yel-gr opaque, rpl stopper, 9" ..525.00

Bellflower, butter dish, beaded-edge bowl, rare, 6½" dia 250.00
Bellflower, cake dish, low std, sauce-dish base, 3", NM 1,300.00
Bellflower, castor set, 5-bottle, pewter stand, rpl stoppers 325.00
Bellflower, celery vase 145.00
Bellflower, compote, dome lid, low std, 8½x8", NM 225.00
Bellflower, compote, open, low std, scalloped rim, 4¾x8" 140.00
Bellflower, creamer, dbl vine, appl hdl 150.00
Bellflower, decanter, dbl vine, w/orig stopper, pt 235.00
Bellflower, decanter, dbl vine, 12" 375.00
Bellflower, decanter, mirror-cut shoulder, rpl stopper, pt 300.00
Bellflower, dish, oval, 9", NM 300.00
Bellflower, egg cup, single vine 40.00
Bellflower, goblet, cut 350.00
Bellflower, goblet, 12 panels under bowl, knop stem 350.00
Bellflower, honey dish, 3" 25.00

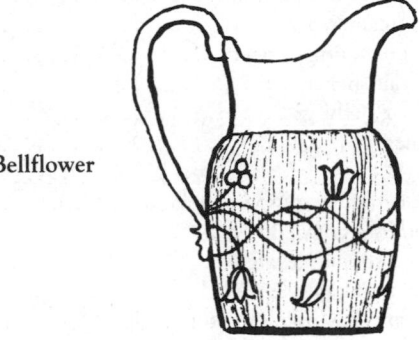

Bellflower

Bellflower, lamp, fluid; int pattern, milk glass base, 10" 400.00
Bellflower, lamp, fluid; 7", NM, pr 350.00
Bellflower, pitcher, dbl vine, 9", NM 225.00
Bellflower, pitcher, milk; 7¾" 325.00
Bellflower, salt cellar, master; scalloped rim 50.00
Bellflower, sauce, lt apple gr, NM 175.00
Bellflower, sugar bowl, dbl vine, open 50.00
Bellflower, syrup, appl hdl, David Baker pat lid 500.00
Bellflower, syrup, 10-panel, lt gr tint, orig tin top, 9" 700.00
Bellflower, tumbler, ¼" plain rim band 95.00
Bellflower, whiskey, appl hdl 375.00
Bellflower, wine, bbl, knop stem, flint 100.00
Bent Buckle, see New Hampshire
Bethlehem Star, pitcher, water 60.00
Bethlehem Star, tumbler 30.00
Bevelled Diamond & Star, bowl, flat, 7" 15.00
Bevelled Diamond & Star, pitcher, milk; 7" 30.00
Bevelled Diamond & Star, shakers, pr 15.00
Bigler, creamer 80.00
Bigler, goblet 42.50
Bigler, tumbler, short stem 57.00
Bird & Fern, see Hummingbird
Bird & Strawberry, cake stand, 9" dia 60.00
Bird & Strawberry, compote, open, low std, scalloped, 7½" 75.00
Bird & Strawberry, sauce dish, ftd, 4" 17.50
Bird & Strawberry, sugar bowl, w/lid 75.00
Birds in Swamp, goblet 70.00
Blackberry, celery vase, scalloped rim, rnd stem & ft 65.00
Blackberry, egg cup, dbl 35.00
Blaze, creamer, molded hdl 48.00
Bleeding Heart, butter dish 60.00
Bleeding Heart, cake stand, 9¼" 70.00
Bleeding Heart, pitcher, water; appl hdl 140.00
Block, wine, ruby stained 35.00
Block & Double Bar, pitcher, tankard; ruby stained 135.00
Block & Fan, goblet, ruby stained 98.00

Block & Fan, ice tub 45.00
Block & Fan, spooner 30.00
Block & Star Spearpoint, goblet 17.50
Block w/Thumbprint, goblet 18.00
Blue Jay, see Cardinal Bird
Bow Tie, compote, open, 10½x5½" 65.00
Bow Tie, creamer 42.00
Bow Tie, goblet 65.00
Bow Tie, pitcher, 5½" or 6½", ea 45.00
Bow Tie, pitcher, 8" or 9", ea 85.00
Bow Tie, sauce dish, flat 15.00
Bow Tie, tumbler 55.00
Bradford Blackberry, goblet, flint 67.50
Broken Column, celery vase, cobalt 48.00
Broken Column, decanter, 10½" 85.00
Broken Column, pitcher, water; ruby stained 225.00
Broken Column, spooner, ruby stained 120.00
Broken Column, tumbler, water 40.00
Buckle, butter dish, acorn finial, flint 60.00
Buckle, goblet 25.00
Buckle, goblet, flint 42.00
Buckle, lamp, brass/iron base 175.00
Buckle, sauce dish, flat 7.50
Buckle, spooner 30.00
Buckle, sugar bowl, w/lid, flint 60.00
Buckle w/Star, creamer 35.00
Buckle w/Star, sugar bowl, w/lid 45.00
Buckle w/Star, tumbler, bar 50.00
Bull's Eye, goblet 55.00
Bull's Eye, spooner, flint 42.00
Bull's Eye, whiskey, flint 155.00
Bull's Eye & Daisy, tumbler, water; clear w/gold 12.00
Bull's Eye & Daisy, wine, pk eyes 17.50
Bull's Eye & Fan, creamer, 3¼" 15.00

Bull's Eye & Fan

Bull's Eye & Fan, sauce dish, flat, 5¼" 11.00
Bull's Eye & Fan, tumbler, water; bl w/gold 30.00
Bull's Eye & Spearhead, compote, Findlay, 7½" 55.00
Bull's Eye Band, see Reverse Torpedo
Bull's Eye in Heart, see Heart w/Thumbprint
Bull's Eye w/Diamond Point, bottle, bar; qt 85.00
Bull's Eye w/Diamond Point, honey dish, 3½" 20.00
Bull's Eye w/Diamond Point, sauce 18.00
Bull's Eye w/Fleur-de-lis, decanter, bar lip, flint, pr 350.00
Bull's Eye w/Fleur-de-lis, goblet 80.00
Button Arches, goblet, clambroth 35.00
Button Arches, pitcher, milk 37.50
Button Arches, pitcher, water tankard, 11" 125.00
Button Arches, toothpick holder, ruby stained, frosted band 35.00
Button Arches, tumbler, ruby stained, frosted band 30.00
Button Arches, wine, ruby stained, vintage etched 35.00
Cabbage Rose, cake stand, 9½" 65.00
Cabbage Rose, compote, open, low std, 7½" 100.00
Cabbage Rose, goblet 40.00

Cabbage Rose, pitcher, 3-pt 150.00
Cabbage Rose, wine 45.00
Cable, bottle, bar; qt 125.00
Cable, goblet 70.00
Cable, honey dish 15.00
California, see Beaded Grape
Canadian, butter dish 85.00
Canadian, pitcher, water 95.00
Canadian, wine 46.00
Cane, goblet, bl 37.50
Cane, sugar bowl, w/lid 45.00

Cane

Cane, waste bowl, amber 32.50
Cane & Rosette, compote, open, 6¾x6" 20.00
Cardinal Bird, goblet 33.00
Cardinal Bird, pitcher, water 115.00
Cathedral, butter dish, amethyst 125.00
Cathedral, cake stand, amber, 10" 50.00
Cathedral, relish tray, fish shape, ruby stained 55.00
Cathedral, wine, bl 52.00
Centennial, see Liberty Bell
Chain, wine or goblet, ea 18.00
Chain w/Diamonds, see Washington Centennial
Champion, pitcher, water 65.00
Chandelier, cake stand, 7x10" 65.00
Chandelier, creamer 32.00
Chandelier, goblet 55.00
Chandelier, goblet, etched 60.00
Chandelier, tumbler 35.00
Checkerboard, sugar bowl, w/lid 30.00
Checkerboard, tumbler, 4½" 15.00
Cherry & Cable, pitcher, water 82.00
Church Windows, sugar bowl, w/lid 25.00
Classic, creamer 110.00
Classic, pitcher, water; log ft 275.00
Classic, sauce dish, ftd 25.00
Clear Diagonal Band, pitcher, water 45.00
Clear Diagonal Band, spooner 22.00
Coin, see US Coin
Colonial, salt cellar, master; flint 17.50

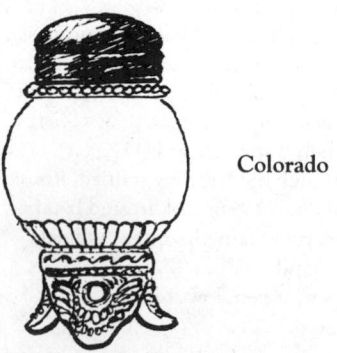

Colorado

Colorado, celery vase 45.00
Colorado, dish, tricorner 7.50
Colorado, sugar bowl, ind; open, gr w/gold 30.00
Colorado, toothpick holder 30.00
Columbian Coin, butter dish, frosted coins 165.00
Columbian Coin, creamer, frosted coins 150.00
Columbian Coin, goblet, gold coins 75.00
Columbian Coin, pitcher, milk; gold coins 170.00
Columbian Coin, spooner, frosted coins 42.50
Comet, goblet, flint 100.00
Compact, see Snail
Coral Gables, goblet 20.00
Coral Gables, wine 20.00
Cord & Tassel, cake stand, 10" 50.00
Cord & Tassel, wine 40.00
Cord Drapery, butter dish, ftd, w/flange 70.00
Cord Drapery, creamer, 5" 40.00
Cord Drapery, cruet, orig stopper 90.00
Cord Drapery, salt shaker 45.00
Cottage, compote, jelly; gr 47.00
Cottage, creamer 25.00
Cottage, plate, 9" 35.00
Croesus, bowl, berry; flat, purple w/gold, 8" 165.00
Croesus, butter dish, gr w/gold 175.00
Croesus, butter dish, purple w/gold 220.00
Croesus, creamer, ind; purple w/gold 120.00
Croesus, cruet, gr w/EX gold, orig stopper, lg 190.00
Croesus, pitcher, water; gr w/gold 225.00
Croesus, plate, purple, 7" 300.00
Croesus, relish tray, boot shape, purple w/gold 85.00
Croesus, shakers, purple w/gold, pr 145.00
Croesus, sugar bowl, ftd, w/lid, purple w/gold 175.00
Croesus, sugar bowl, purple w/gold, w/lid, M 160.00
Croesus, toothpick holder, purple w/gold 110.00
Crossed Disks, sauce dish, ftd, hdld 7.50
Crow's Foot, see Yale
Crown Jewels, see Chandelier
Cryptic, see Zippered Block
Crystal Ball, see Atlas
Crystal Wedding, banana stand 95.00
Crystal Wedding, creamer 45.00

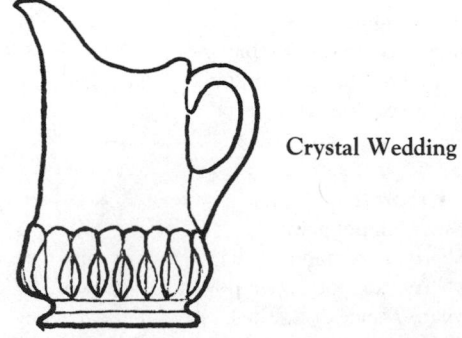

Crystal Wedding

Crystal Wedding, creamer, etched 56.00
Crystal Wedding, pitcher, water; sq 175.00
Crystal Wedding, sugar bowl, w/lid 50.00
Cube & Diamond, see Log & Star
Cube w/Fan, see Pineapple & Fan
Cupid & Venus, champagne 95.00
Cupid & Venus, compote, w/lid, high std 95.00
Cupid & Venus, pitcher, milk 65.00
Cupid & Venus, pitcher, water; amber 200.00
Cupid & Venus, plate, amber, 8" 70.00

Cupid & Venus, wine 90.00
Currant, goblet 37.50
Currant, platter, 9x6" 35.00
Currant, spooner 35.00
Currant, wine 37.50
Currier & Ives, pitcher, water 72.00
Currier & Ives, spooner 25.00
Currier & Ives, wine 20.00
Curtain, creamer 28.00
Curtain Tie-Back, goblet, flat 22.50
Curtain Tie-Back, spooner 30.00
Cut Log, celery vase 35.00
Cut Log, compote, open, high std, 8¼x6½" 50.00
Cut Log, compote, w/lid, 5¼x6½" 40.00
Cut Log, relish, rectangular, 8x5" 20.00
Cut Log, sugar bowl, ind; open 35.00
Cut Log, wine 25.00
Dahlia, bread tray, oval, hdls 40.00
Dahlia, butter dish, amber 85.00
Dahlia, champagne, amber 95.00
Dahlia, egg cup, dbl 58.00
Dahlia, goblet 37.50
Dahlia, goblet, amber 62.00
Dahlia, mug, vaseline, 3⅛" 50.00
Dahlia, pitcher, water 80.00
Dahlia, pitcher, water; bl 125.00
Dahlia, spooner, vaseline 45.00
Dahlia, sugar bowl, gr, w/lid 50.00
Daisy & Button, bottle, cologne; orig stopper 25.00
Daisy & Button, bowl, oval, sm 7.50
Daisy & Button, butter dish, rnd, amber 65.00
Daisy & Button, canoe, scalloped edge, amethyst, 12" ...60.00
Daisy & Button, dish, fan shape, 7x10½" 12.00
Daisy & Button, plate, amber, 6" 12.00
Daisy & Button, platter, amber, 13½x9" 35.00
Daisy & Button, powder jar, amber 28.00
Daisy & Button, shoe, dtd, gold finish, 7" 58.00
Daisy & Button, tray, tricorner, gr, 12½" 60.00
Daisy & Button, tumbler, water 17.50
Daisy & Button w/Crossbar, butter dish 50.00
Daisy & Button w/Crossbar, celery vase, vaseline 52.00

**Daisy & Button
w/Crossbar**

Daisy & Button w/Crossbar, mug, yel, 2⅞" 25.00
Daisy & Button w/Crossbar, pitcher, water; amber, 8" ...80.00
Daisy & Button w/Crossbar, water set, amber, 9-pc 188.00
Daisy & Button w/Thumbprint, cake basket, yel, 11x7x5½" ...130.00
Daisy & Button w/Thumbprint, pitcher, water; bl stripe ...95.00
Daisy & Button w/Thumbprint, sauce dish, sq, amber stripe ...17.50
Daisy & Button w/V Ornament, creamer, amber 28.00
Daisy & Button w/V Ornament, pitcher, water; amber 95.00

Daisy & Button w/V Ornament, sauce dish, flat, amber 16.50
Daisy & Button w/V Ornament, waste bowl, amber 30.00
Dakota, butter dish, etched 70.00
Dakota, celery vase, ped ft 27.50
Dakota, compote, jelly; etched, w/lid, 6" 60.00
Dakota, goblet 28.00
Dakota, mug, ruby stained 36.00
Dakota, spooner, ped ft, etched 37.50
Dakota, sugar bowl, open 30.00
Dakota, sugar bowl, w/lid, etched 60.00
Dakota, tray, water; flat, ruffled edge 75.00
Dakota, wine 25.00
Deer & Dog, goblet, etched, U shape 65.00
Deer & Dog, spooner 60.00
Deer & Oak Tree, pitcher, water 155.00
Deer & Pine Tree, creamer, apple gr 90.00
Deer & Pine Tree, mug, amber 37.50
Deer & Pine Tree, mug, olive gr w/gold, 2½" 45.00
Delaware, banana boat, rose w/gold, 11½x7" 65.00
Delaware, bowl, flat, octagonal, clear w/gold, 9" 25.00
Delaware, butter dish, rose w/gold 145.00
Delaware, creamer, rose w/gold 70.00
Delaware, pitcher, tankard; gr w/gold, 9½" 100.00
Delaware, punch cup, gr w/gold 40.00
Delaware, sauce dish, rnd, gr w/gold, 4" 27.50
Delaware, spooner 47.50
Delaware, sugar bowl, w/lid, rose w/gold 110.00
Delaware, vase, gr w/gold, 6" 50.00
Dew & Raindrop, goblet 40.00
Dew & Raindrop, punch cup 7.50
Dew & Raindrop, wine 17.00
Dewdrop Band, goblet 12.50
Dewdrop w/Star, creamer, appl hdl 34.00
Dewey, bowl, ftd, 8" 45.00
Dewey, mug 32.00
Dewey, tumbler 48.00
Diagonal Band, goblet 25.00
Diagonal Band, jam jar, w/lid 25.00
Diagonal Band w/Fan, champagne 30.00
Diagonal Band w/Fan, plate, 8" 12.50
Diagonal Band w/Fan, shakers, pr 50.00
Diagonal Band w/Fan, wine 25.00
Diamond & Sunburst, goblet 22.00
Diamond & Sunburst, spooner 20.00
Diamond Cut w/Leaf, creamer 23.00
Diamond Horseshoe, see Aurora
Diamond Medallion, see Grand
Diamond Point, celery vase, flint 70.00
Diamond Point, creamer, flint 120.00
Diamond Point, decanter, flint, w/orig stopper, qt 95.00
Diamond Point, goblet, non-flint 40.00
Diamond Point, sauce dish, flint, 5¼" 15.00
Diamond Point, spill, flint 40.00
Diamond Point, sugar bowl, w/lid, flint 65.00
Diamond Point w/Ribs, goblet, flint 52.50
Diamond Quilted, compote, open, low std, amber, 5½" ...15.00
Diamond Quilted, compote, open, low std, amber, 9⅜" ...22.50
Diamond Quilted, sauce, flat, bl, 5⅛" 15.00
Diamond Quilted, wine 18.00
Diamond Thumbprint, cake stand, 3x8⅜" 175.00
Diamond Thumbprint, sugar bowl, w/lid 145.00
Dinner Bell, see Cottage
Doric, see Feather
Double Leaf & Dart, see Leaf & Dart

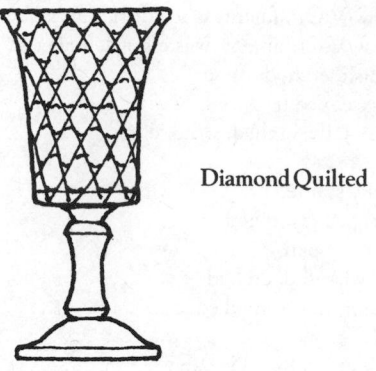

Diamond Quilted

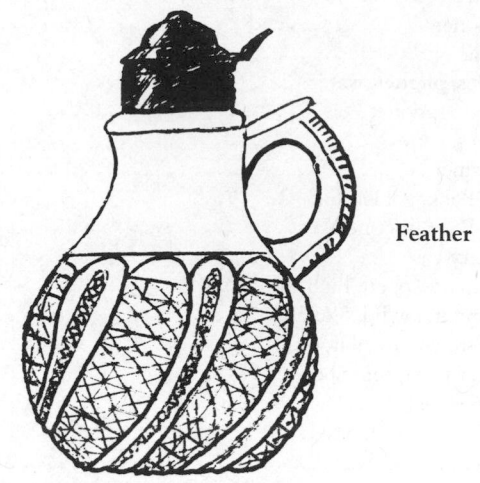

Feather

Double Wedding Ring, see Wedding Ring
Drapery, butter dish 45.00
Drapery, goblet 32.00
Drapery, spooner 35.00
Drum, butter dish 95.00
Drum, creamer 50.00
Egg in Sand, goblet 32.00
Egg in Sand, sugar bowl, w/lid 34.00
Egg in Sand, tray, 12½x8" 35.00
Egg in Sand, wine 30.00
Egyptian, creamer 45.00
Egyptian, goblet 40.00
Egyptian, pitcher, water 165.00
Elephant, see Jumbo
Emerald Green Herringbone, see Florida
Empress, butter dish, gr w/gold 100.00
Empress, creamer & sugar bowl, gr w/gold 150.00
Empress, pitcher, water 70.00
Empress, tumbler, gr w/gold 50.00
English Hobnail Cross, see Klondike
Esther, berry set, gr w/gold, 7-pc 135.00
Esther, compote, open, amber stained, 8" 85.00
Esther, compote, w/lid, high std, gr w/gold, 7½" 110.00
Esther, cruet, orig stopper, gr w/gold 200.00
Esther, ice cream tray, gr w/gold 145.00
Esther, jam jar, gr w/gold 32.00
Esther, relish dish, gr w/gold, 9x5" 24.00
Esther, sauce bowl, ftd, gr w/gold 15.00
Esther, shakers, gr w/gold, pr 95.00
Esther, spooner, gr w/gold 55.00
Esther, sugar bowl, w/lid, gr w/gold 75.00
Esther, table set, gr, 4-pc 325.00
Esther, tray, ice cream; gr w/gold 145.00
Esther, tumbler 35.00
Esther, tumbler, gr w/gold 47.50
Etched Band, wine 15.00
Etched Dahlia, goblet 17.50
Etched Dakota, see Dakota
Eureka, compote, jelly 50.00
Excelsior, bottle, bar; flint, pt 45.00
Excelsior, butter dish, flint 90.00
Excelsior, sugar bowl, w/lid, flint 85.00
Eyewinker, butter dish 70.00
Eyewinker, cake stand, 9" 85.00
Eyewinker, creamer 55.00
Eyewinker, sauce dish, flat, sq, 3¾" 15.00
Fairfax Strawberry, see Strawberry
Fan w/Crossbars, see Champion
Fan w/Diamond, butter dish 40.00
Fan w/Diamond, pitcher, water 55.00
Fan w/Diamond, spooner 20.00

Feather, cake stand, 8" 35.00
Feather, cruet, orig stopper 45.00

Feather, sauce dish, flat, 4" 10.00
Feather, tumbler, water 50.00
Festoon, pitcher, water 55.00
Festoon, relish dish, 9x5½" 36.00
Festoon, waste bowl 48.00
Fine Cut, goblet, amber 42.00
Fine Cut, hat, bl, 2¼" 28.00
Fine Cut, plate, amber, 10" 17.50
Fine Cut, tumbler, water 17.50
Fine Cut & Block, butter dish, ftd 78.00
Fine Cut & Block, compote, open, bl, 7¾" 68.00
Fine Cut & Block, goblet, buttermilk 28.00
Fine Cut & Block, sauce dish, flat, bl blocks, 5¼x5" ..16.50
Fine Cut & Diamond, see Grand
Fine Cut & Feather, see Feather
Fine Cut & Panel, plate, bl, 7" 30.00
Fine Cut & Panel, tray, water; amber 60.00
Fine Cut & Panel, wine, amber 35.00
Fine Cut Medallion, see Greentown, Austrian
Fine Rib, butter dish, flint 75.00
Fine Rib, celery vase, ftd, flint 45.00
Fine Rib, goblet, flint, 6¼" 70.00
Fine Rib, spooner, flint 65.00
Fine Rib, wine, flint 44.00
Fine Rib w/Cut Ovals, goblet, flint 235.00
Fingerprint, see Almond Thumbprint
Fishscale, butter dish 48.00
Fishscale, cake stand, 9" 30.00
Fishscale, relish tray, teardrop shape 20.00
Flamingo Habitat, bowl, 10" 42.50
Flamingo Habitat, sauce dish, ftd, 3¾x4¼" 12.50
Flamingo Habitat, sugar bowl, w/lid 45.00
Flat Diamond & Panel, bottle, castor; for mustard, flint ..17.50
Flat Diamond & Panel, egg cup 40.00
Flat Diamond & Panel, sauce dish, flat, 3½" 10.00
Flat Diamond & Panel, tumbler, bar; flint 75.00
Florida, butter dish, gr 52.00
Florida, celery vase, flat 27.50
Florida, goblet 25.00
Florida, plate, 7½" 12.00
Florida, tumbler, water 18.00
Florida, tumbler, water; gr 28.00
Frosted Circle, compote, open, 9x6" 35.00
Frosted Circle, goblet 28.00

Frosted Circle, tumbler 25.00
Frosted Flower Band, creamer 47.50
Frosted Flower Band, sauce dish, ftd, 3⅜" 15.00
Frosted Leaf, butter dish, flint 150.00
Frosted Leaf, egg cup 125.00
Frosted Leaf, spooner, flint 90.00
Frosted Leaf, wine, flint 175.00
Frosted Lion, see Lion
Frosted Roman Key, egg cup, flint 47.50
Frosted Roman Key, goblet, flint 45.00
Frosted Stork, butter dish 85.00
Frosted Stork, spooner 45.00
Galloway, butter dish 60.00
Galloway, compote, jelly 35.00
Galloway, mug 40.00
Galloway, pitcher, ruby stained, water sz 175.00

Galloway

Galloway, pitcher, water 70.00
Galloway, toothpick holder 30.00
Galloway, tumbler, ruby stained 55.00
Galloway, wine 47.00
Garden Fruits, pitcher, water; appl hdl, 10" 45.00
Garden Fruits, sugar bowl, w/lid 27.50
Garden of Eden, bowl, oval 10.00
Garden of Eden, platter 20.00
Garden of Eden, sauce dish, ftd, 4⅛" 8.00
Garfield Drape, goblet 45.00
Garfield Drape, pitcher, milk .70.00
Garfield Drape, pitcher, water 100.00
Garfield Drape, spooner 28.00
Gem, see Nailhead
Good Luck, see Horseshoe
Grand, celery vase, ftd 25.00
Grand, goblet 27.50
Grand, spooner 20.00
Grand, wine 32.00
Grape & Festoon, plate, stippled leaf, 6" 18.00
Grape & Festoon, relish dish, 7x4¼" 17.50
Grape & Festoon, spooner, stippled leaf 23.00
Grape & Festoon w/Shield, creamer 35.00
Grape & Festoon w/Shield, mug, 3" 20.00
Grape & Festoon w/Shield, spooner 25.00
Grape Band, butter dish, flint 75.00
Grape Band, salt cellar, master; non-flint 25.00
Grape Band, tumbler, flint 37.50
Grasshopper, celery vase, amber 80.00
Grasshopper, sauce dish, ftd, etched 15.00
Grasshopper, spooner 55.00

Guardian Angel, see Cupid & Venus
Hairpin, celery vase 35.00
Hairpin, champagne, knop stem 55.00

Hairpin

Hairpin, spooner, rayed base .38.00
Hairpin, tumbler, whiskey; appl hdl, flint 47.50
Haley's Comet, butter dish 75.00
Haley's Comet, cake stand 75.00
Haley's Comet, pitcher, water .87.50
Haley's Comet, wine 28.00
Hamilton, cake stand 150.00
Hamilton, compote, open, 8x8" 70.00
Hamilton w/Leaf, butter dish, clear leaf 60.00
Hamilton w/Leaf, creamer, molded hdl 50.00
Hamilton w/Leaf, goblet, clear leaf 45.00
Hamilton w/Leaf, plate, hdls, 10½" 60.00
Hand, compote, w/lid, 6" 58.00
Hand, cordial 87.50
Hand, tumbler 135.00
Hand, wine 50.00
Hartley, pitcher, water; bl 85.00
Hartley, sauce dish, ftd, amber, 4" 15.00
Hawaiian Lei, cake stand, 9¾" 30.00
Hawaiian Lei, cup & saucer 35.00
Hawaiian Lei, shakers, pr 48.00
Hawaiian Lei, wine 30.00
Heart w/Thumbprint, goblet .50.00
Heart w/Thumbprint, punch cup 20.00
Heart w/Thumbprint, relish, heart shape, hdls 25.00
Heart w/Thumbprint, tumbler, water 35.00
Heart w/Thumbprint, vase, gr w/gold, 6" 70.00
Heart w/Thumbprint, wine 50.00
Hearts & Spades, see Medallion
Heavy Panelled Finecut, salt cellar, ind 10.00
Heavy Panelled Finecut, salt cellar, ind; yel 16.00
Heavy Panelled Finecut, tumbler, bar 18.00
Heavy Panelled Finecut, tumbler, water 12.50
Herringbone Band, see Ripple
Herringbone Buttress, see Greentown, Herringbone Buttress
Hexagon Block, sauce dish, flat, etched, amber stained, 4¼" 12.50
Hexagon Block, tumbler, water; etched, amber stained 35.00
Hickman, compote, open, 5½x8" 20.00
Hickman, pitcher, water 50.00
Hickman, punch cup, gr 13.00
Hickman, relish dish, sq, 4" 15.00
Hidalgo, celery vase, flat base, amber stained 33.00
Hidalgo, goblet, etched top, rnd stem 20.00
Hinoto, goblet, flint 65.00
Hinoto, tumbler, ftd 40.00
Holbrook, see Pineapple & Fan
Holly, cake stand, lg 125.00
Holly, sauce dish, flat 20.00
Holly, spooner 55.00
Holly Amber, see Greentown, Holly Amber
Honeycomb w/Flower Rim, bowl, berry; gr 46.00

Hops & Barley, see Wheat & Barley

Horn of Plenty, compote, open, flint, 6x8" 110.00

Horn of Plenty, compote, open, flint, 9½x10¼" 185.00

Horn of Plenty, decanter, faceted stopper, flint, qt 100.00

Horn of Plenty, goblet, flint 77.50

Horn of Plenty, plate, flint, 6" 68.00

Horn of Plenty, sugar bowl, pagoda lid, flint 115.00

Horn of Plenty, tumbler, whiskey; hdl, flint 245.00

Horseshoe, celery vase 60.00

Horseshoe, creamer, hotel type, 6½" .97.00

Horseshoe

Horseshoe, relish bowl, 9x5" 16.00

Horseshoe, sauce dish, ftd, 4" 16.00

Huber, champagne 25.00

Huber, claret, 10-panel 27.50

Huber, goblet 25.00

Huber, salt cellar, master 20.00

Huber, wine, 8-panel 20.00

Hummingbird, butter dish 50.00

Hummingbird, goblet, bl 70.00

Hummingbird, pitcher, water; bl 126.00

Hummingbird, tray, amber, 13x9¾" .160.00

Hummingbird, tumbler, amber 55.00

Icicle w/Star, pitcher, water 25.00

Idaho, see Snail

Illinois, pitcher, tankard form, SP rim 100.00

Illinois, plate, sq, 7" 20.00

Illinois, sugar bowl, w/lid 50.00

Illinois, toothpick holder 30.00

Illinois, tumbler 25.00

Indian Tree, see Barley

Indiana, see Greentown, Cord Drapery

Indiana Swirl, see Feather

Inverted Fan & Feather, see Custard, Opalescent, Slag Glass

Inverted Fern, honey dish, 3½" 15.00

Inverted Fern, plate, 6" 95.00

Inverted Fern, salt cellar, master 30.00

Inverted Fern, tumbler 90.00

Iris Column, see Broken Column

Iris w/Meander, creamer, clear w/gold 45.00

Iris w/Meander, pitcher, water; bl w/gold 165.00

Iris w/Meander, see Opalescent Glass

Iris w/Meander, sugar bowl, w/lid, clear w/gold 55.00

Ivy in Snow, butter dish 55.00

Ivy in Snow, compote, jelly 30.00

Ivy in Snow, syrup 72.50

Ivy in Snow, wine 30.00

Jacob's Ladder, cake plate, 10" 50.00

Jacob's Ladder, creamer 35.00

Jacob's Ladder, goblet 67.50

Jacob's Ladder, goblet, water; amber .40.00

Jacob's Ladder, pitcher, water; bulbous 165.00

Jacob's Ladder, plate, 6" 24.00

Jacob's Ladder, salt cellar, master 30.00

Jacob's Ladder, sauce dish, ftd, 4½" 15.00

Jersey Swirl, plate, 10" 30.00

Jersey Swirl, wine 18.00

Jewel w/Dewdrop, compote, jelly; 6" .45.00

Jewel w/Moondrop, pitcher, water 60.00

Jewelled Moon & Star, cake stand, 8½" 30.00

Jewelled Moon & Star, compote, open, 8x9" 40.00

Jewelled Moon & Star, goblet, clear w/gold 30.00

Jewelled Moon & Star, tumbler, water; clear w/gold 25.00

Job's Tears, see Art

Jumbo, compote, w/lid, 11½" 475.00

Jumbo, powder jar, w/lid, frosted 155.00

Jumbo, salt cellar 80.00

Kansas, see Jewel w/Moondrop

Kentucky, cruet, orig stopper 35.00

Kentucky, plate, sq, 7" 17.50

Kentucky

Kentucky, punch cup, gr 15.00

Kentucky, sauce dish, ftd, 3¼" 6.00

Kentucky, wine, gr 30.00

King's Crown, bowl, berry; boat shape, ruby stained 135.00

King's Crown, compote, jelly 47.50

King's Crown, goblet 25.00

King's Crown, pitcher, water tankard, 13" 125.00

King's Crown, shakers, pr 32.00

King's Crown, toothpick holder, etched, ruby stained 40.00

King's Crown, wine 30.00

Klondike, butter dish, frosted w/amber stain 385.00

Klondike, celery vase, frosted w/amber stain, 5½x3¾" 200.00

Klondike, creamer, frosted w/amber stain 225.00

Klondike, cruet, frosted w/amber stain, 6½" 525.00

Klondike, relish, frosted w/amber stain, boat shape, 9x4" 125.00

Klondike, sauce dish, frosted w/amber stain; SP holder, 5¾" . . .100.00

Klondike, sugar bowl, w/lid, frosted w/amber stain 250.00

Klondike, syrup, frosted w/amber stain, pewter lid, 7½" 600.00

Kokomo, see Bar & Diamond

La Clede, see Hickman

Lace, see Drapery

Ladder w/Diamonds, creamer, ind; clear w/gold 15.00

Ladder w/Diamonds, shakers, pr 22.00

Ladder w/Diamonds, tumbler, water; clear w/gold 13.00

Ladder w/Diamonds, tumbler, water; ruby stained w/gold 25.00

Lady Hamilton, butter dish 35.00

Lady Hamilton, goblet 20.00

Lady Hamilton, platter, frosted, 13x9" 30.00

Lady Hamilton, sauce dish, flat, 4" 6.00

Lady Hamilton, tumbler, bar 36.00

Late Block, see Red Block

Late Buckle, see Buckle w/Star

Lattice & Oval Panels, see Flat Diamond & Panel

Lawrence, see Bull's Eye

Leaf, see Maple Leaf

Leaf & Dart, butter dish 80.00
Leaf & Dart, goblet 26.00

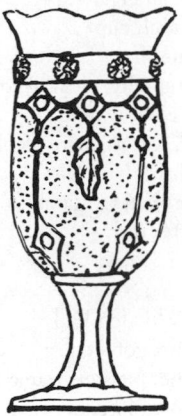

Leaf & Dart

Leaf & Dart, spooner 30.00
Leaf & Dart, wine 34.00
Leaf Bracket, see Greentown, Leaf Bracket
Leaf Medallion, see Northwood, Leaf Medallion
Liberty, butter dish 45.00
Liberty, creamer 30.00
Liberty, tumbler 30.00
Liberty, wine 18.50
Liberty Bell, butter dish 135.00
Liberty Bell, butter dish, miniature 150.00
Liberty Bell, compote, open, low std, 8" dia 95.00
Liberty Bell, creamer, reeded appl hdl 95.00
Liberty Bell, goblet 45.00
Liberty Bell, plate, 6¼" 70.00
Liberty Bell, sauce dish, ftd, 4½" 30.00
Liberty Bell, spoon holder 65.00
Liberty Bell, sugar bowl, w/lid .95.00
Lily of the Valley, butter dish, ftd 67.50
Lily of the Valley, creamer, 3-ftd 75.00
Lily of the Valley, goblet 50.00
Lily of the Valley, pitcher, water sz 125.00
Lily of the Valley, sauce dish, flat, 4" 12.00
Lincoln Drape, pitcher, water .325.00
Lincoln Drape, spill 45.00
Lincoln Drape w/Tassel, goblet, water; flint 125.00
Lion, butter dish 100.00
Lion, celery vase, 8¾" 80.00
Lion, compote, open, low std, flint, 5x7¾" dia 65.00
Lion, compote, w/lid, high std, 11½x7¾" 160.00
Lion, goblet 70.00
Lion, marmalade jar 95.00
Lion, pitcher, water; clear hdl, 9" 250.00
Lion, relish tray, lion hdls 44.00
Lion, spooner 65.00
Lion, sugar bowl, 8½" 155.00
Log & Star, goblet 20.00
Log Cabin, creamer 125.00
Log Cabin, jam jar, w/lid 300.00
Log Cabin, pitcher, water 325.00
Log Cabin, sugar bowl, w/lid .275.00
Long Spear, see Grasshopper
Loop, cordial, flint 34.00
Loop, goblet 16.00
Loop, goblet, flint 27.00
Loop, salt cellar, master; flint 22.50
Loop, wine 12.50
Loop & Dart, egg cup 25.00

Loop & Dart, egg cup, flint 32.00
Loop & Dart, pitcher, water 75.00
Loop & Dart, relish 20.00
Loop & Dart, spooner, flint 35.00
Loop & Moose Eye, compote, open, flint, 3½x7" 35.00
Loop & Moose Eye, egg cup, flint 30.00
Loop w/Stippled Panels, see Texas
Lotus, see Garden of Eden
Magnet & Grape, goblet, frosted leaf, flint 70.00
Magnet & Grape, goblet, frosted leaf & shield, flint 275.00
Magnet & Grape, sauce dish, frosted leaf, flat, flint 22.50
Magnet & Grape, whiskey, frosted leaf, flint 135.00
Maine, butter dish 45.00
Maine, creamer 27.50
Maine, wine, gr 60.00
Maple Leaf, butter dish 80.00
Maple Leaf, compote, jelly; gr .42.50

Maple Leaf

Maple Leaf, finger bowl, yel, flint 48.00
Maple Leaf, goblet, vaseline 100.00
Maple Leaf, tumbler, water; frosted 32.00
Maryland, cake stand, 8" 45.00
Maryland, compote, jelly 22.00
Maryland, goblet 30.00
Maryland, sauce dish, flat, 3¾" 10.00
Mascotte, bowl, shallow, etched, 2¾x9" 35.00
Mascotte, cake stand, 10" 50.00
Mascotte, compote, open, 7x5" 30.00
Mascotte, pitcher, water 60.00
Mascotte, pitcher, water; etched 70.00
Mascotte, spooner, etched 35.00
Mascotte, sugar bowl, w/lid 45.00
Massachusetts, cordial 60.00
Massachusetts, goblet 47.00
Massachusetts, plate, 8" 30.00
Massachusetts, tumbler, juice; clear w/gold 20.00
Massachusetts, tumbler, whiskey 15.00
Medallion, cake stand, 9¼" 23.00
Medallion, spooner, bl 42.50
Medallion, sugar bowl, w/lid, amber 40.00
Medallion, wine 20.00
Melrose, goblet 20.00
Melrose, pitcher, water; tankard form, 10" 40.00
Melrose, sugar bowl, w/lid 32.50
Melrose, wine, etched 22.50
Michigan, celery vase 32.00
Michigan, goblet, clear w/gold .40.00
Michigan, pickle dish 14.00
Michigan, pitcher, water; maiden's blush w/gold, 12" . . .175.00

Milton, see Log & Star
Minerva, cake stand, 10½" 95.00
Minerva, cake stand, 12" 145.00
Minerva, creamer 40.00
Minerva, goblet 88.00
Minerva, pitcher, water 175.00
Minerva, plate, warrior in center, 10½" 58.00
Minerva, spooner 38.00
Minnesota, creamer, ind 20.00
Minnesota, creamer, 3¼" 28.00

Minnesota

Minnesota, goblet 25.00
Minnesota, tumbler, water 17.50
Minnesota, wine 30.00
Minor Block, see Mascotte
Mirror, see Galloway
Missouri, goblet 42.00
Missouri, sauce dish, gr, 4½" 14.00
Missouri, spooner 24.00
Missouri, wine, gr 45.00
Mitered Diamond Point, see Zig Zag
Monkey, butter dish 185.00
Monkey, mug 85.00
Monkey, spooner 50.00
Moon & Star, butter dish 65.00
Moon & Star, cake stand, 10" 60.00
Moon & Star, compote, w/lid, high std, 8" 70.00
Moon & Star, creamer 50.00
Moon & Star, goblet 35.00
Moon & Star, sauce dish, ftd, 4" 12.00
Moon & Star, tumbler, bar; flint 67.50
Nail, bowl, flat, ruby stained, etched, 6" 47.50
Nail, cake stand, 10" dia 45.00
Nail, goblet 45.00
Nail, goblet, ruby stained, etched 60.00
Nail, sauce dish, ftd, 3½" 12.00
Nail, wine 50.00
Nail, wine, etched 55.00
Nailhead, plate, sq, 7" 18.00
Nailhead, plate, 9" 18.00
Nailhead, sugar bowl, open 15.00
Nailhead, wine 22.00
Netted Swan, sugar bowl, w/lid 75.00
New England Pineapple, creamer 70.00
New England Pineapple, egg cup, flint 40.00
New England Pineapple, spooner 35.00
New England Pineapple, wine, flint 140.00

New Hampshire, bowl, 8" 16.00
New Hampshire, butter dish 65.00
New Hampshire, creamer 30.00
New Hampshire, punch cup 8.50
New Hampshire, tumbler 20.00
New Jersey, compote, jelly; clear w/gold 20.00
New Jersey, goblet, clear w/gold 38.00
New Jersey, pitcher, water; clear w/gold 47.50
New Jersey, sauce dish, flat, clear w/gold, 4¼" 10.00
Notched Rib, see Broken Column
Oak Leaf Band, butter dish 47.50
Oak Leaf Band, mug 40.00
Oak Leaf Band, pitcher, 6" 35.00
Oaken Bucket, see Wooden Pail
One Hundred & One, goblet 35.00
One Hundred & One, pitcher, water; bulbous 115.00
One Hundred & One, plate, 6" 15.00
One Hundred & One, sugar bowl, w/lid 45.00
One-O-One, see One Hundred & One
Open Rose, butter dish 50.00
Open Rose, egg cup 22.00

Open Rose

Open Rose, spooner 40.00
Open Rose, sugar bowl, w/lid 42.00
Open Rose, tumbler 48.00
Oregon, carafe, whiskey 25.00
Oregon, creamer 32.00
Oregon, relish tray, 7½x3¾" 12.00
Oregon, spooner, ftd 25.00
Oriental, sugar bowl, w/lid 65.00
Oriental, tumbler, water 32.00
Orion, see Cathedral
Ostrich Looking at Moon, goblet .125.00
Palmette, celery vase 40.00
Palmette, goblet 36.00
Palmette, pitcher, water 127.50
Panelled Cherry, see Cherry & Cable
Panelled Daisy, celery vase 30.00
Panelled Daisy, creamer 45.00
Panelled Daisy, plate, sq, 9" 28.00
Panelled Dewdrop, butter dish 65.00
Panelled Dewdrop, celery vase 40.00
Panelled Dewdrop, wine 22.50
Panelled Diamond Cut & Fan, see Hartley
Panelled Forget-Me-Not, compote, open, 7x7" 35.00
Panelled Forget-Me-Not, creamer, amber 47.00
Panelled Forget-Me-Not, sugar bowl, w/lid 42.00
Panelled Herringbone, see Florida
Panelled Nightshade, goblet, bl 67.50
Panelled Nightshade, wine 20.00
Panelled Star & Button, butter dish 42.00

Panelled Star & Button, mug, 3" 15.00
Panelled Star & Button, wine 20.00
Panelled Thistle, cake stand, 8½" or 8¾", ea 40.00
Panelled Thistle, celery vase 28.00
Panelled Thistle, pitcher, milk 58.00
Panelled Thistle, sugar bowl, w/lid .30.00
Panelled Thistle, wine 24.00
Pavonia, cup plate 30.00
Pavonia, goblet 25.00
Pavonia, salt cellar, master 20.00
Pavonia, spooner 40.00
Pavonia, tumbler, ruby stained 37.50
Peerless, see Lady Hamilton
Pennsylvania, butter dish, clear w/gold 50.00
Pennsylvania, decanter, orig stopper 95.00
Pennsylvania, plate, 8" 30.00

Pennsylvania

Pennsylvania, sauce dish, flat, 5¼" .10.00
Pennsylvania, spooner, clear w/gold 25.00
Pennsylvania, tumbler, ruby stained 50.00
Pennsylvania, wine 17.50
Pillar, claret, flint 58.00
Pillar, creamer 70.00
Pillar, goblet 50.00
Pillow Encircled, creamer 30.00
Pillow Encircled, pitcher, water 45.00
Pillow Encircled, tumbler, water; etched 15.00
Pineapple & Fan, creamer 30.00
Pineapple & Fan, goblet 17.50
Pineapple & Fan, pitcher, water; amber 68.00
Pineapple & Fan, spooner 25.00
Pineapple & Fan, tumbler, water; amber 30.00
Pineapple Stem, see Pavonia
Pioneer, see Westward Ho
Pioneer's Victoria, bowl, shallow, ruby stained 40.00
Pioneer's Victoria, tumbler, water; ruby stained 25.00
Pioneer's Victoria, wine tray 16.00
Pittsburgh Daisy, cake stand, 8½" .20.00
Pittsburgh Daisy, wine 20.00
Pleat & Panel, pitcher, water 60.00
Pleat & Panel, plate, sq, 6" 25.00
Pleat & Panel, sauce dish, ftd 15.00
Pleat & Panel, sugar bowl, open 25.00
Pleat & Panel, waste bowl 25.00
Plume, cake stand, 8¼" or 10", ea .50.00
Plume, goblet 25.00
Plume, spooner 25.00
Plume, sugar bowl, open 20.00
Pointed Jewel, goblet 25.00
Pointed Jewel, sugar bowl, w/lid 30.00

Pointed Panelled Daisy & Button, see Queen
Pointed Thumbprint, see Almond Thumbprint
Polar Bear, goblet 110.00
Polar Bear, goblet, frosted 125.00
Polar Bear, ice bowl 80.00
Polar Bear, pitcher, water; frosted .265.00
Popcorn, goblet, w/ear 50.00
Popcorn, sugar bowl, w/lid, w/ears 42.00
Portland, butter dish 47.50
Portland, creamer, 4" 20.00
Portland, cruet 50.00
Portland, spooner 37.50
Portland, sugar bowl, w/lid 42.00
Portland, wine 26.00
Powder & Shot, egg cup, flint 47.50
Powder & Shot, salt cellar, master; flint 40.00
Prayer Rug, see Horseshoe
Pressed Leaf, compote, w/lid, 8¼x10" 67.50
Pressed Leaf, goblet 22.50
Pressed Leaf, sauce dish, flat, flint, 4" 10.00
Pressed Leaf, sugar bowl, w/lid 40.00
Primrose, plate, amber, 4½" 12.00
Primrose, platter, amber, 12x8" 25.00
Primrose, relish tray, 8x5¼" 14.00
Primrose, wine 20.00
Prince Albert, goblet 30.00
Prince Albert, tumbler, water 16.00
Princess Feather, celery vase 40.00
Princess Feather, creamer 45.00
Princess Feather, egg cup 27.50
Princess Feather, goblet 35.00
Priscilla, egg cup 20.00
Priscilla, goblet 45.00
Priscilla, tumbler 26.00
Prism w/Diamond Points, butter dish 62.00
Prism w/Diamond Points, egg cup .32.50

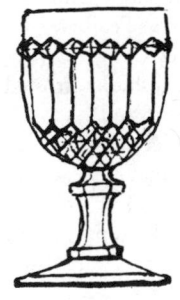

Prism w/Diamond
Points

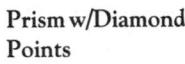

Prism w/Diamond Points, goblet 45.00
Prism w/Diamond Points, sugar bowl, w/lid 45.00
Prism w/Diamond Points, tumbler .40.00
Pygmy, see Torpedo
Queen, creamer, amber 22.00
Queen, goblet, bl 40.00
Queen, pitcher, water; amber 65.00
Queen, wine 25.00
Raindrop, cake plate 30.00
Raindrop, cake plate, bl 45.00
Raindrop, egg cup, dbl, amber 36.00
Raindrop, syrup 32.50
Raindrop, wine 12.50
Recessed Ovals, goblet 15.00
Recessed Ovals, wine 18.00
Recessed Pillared Red Top, see Nail
Red Block, creamer 60.00

Red Block, rose bowl, 4" 65.00
Red Block, spooner 40.00
Red Block, tumbler 35.00
Red Block, tumbler, water 35.00
Red Top, see Button Arches
Regal Block, goblet 16.00
Regal Block, wine 18.00
Reverse Torpedo, bowl, shallow, ruffled, 10½" 80.00
Reverse Torpedo, goblet 60.00
Reverse Torpedo, pitcher, water; 10" 155.00
Reverse Torpedo, spooner 30.00
Ribbed Ivy, butter dish .95.00
Ribbed Ivy, compote, open, low std, 8" 75.00
Ribbed Ivy, sauce dish, flat, 4" 12.50
Ribbed Ivy, spooner 40.00
Ribbed Palm, champagne, flint 120.00
Ribbed Palm, egg cup 30.00
Ribbed Palm, salt cellar, master 38.00
Ribbed Palm, spooner 40.00
Ribbed Palm, sugar bowl, w/lid 65.00
Ribbon, compote, open, dolphin stem, 8x8" 200.00
Ribbon, compote, w/lid, high std, 8" 80.00
Ribbon, spooner 35.00
Ribbon, sugar bowl, w/lid 60.00
Ribbon Candy, compote, w/lid, low std, 5" 32.00
Ribbon Candy, creamer .25.00
Ribbon Candy, pitcher, milk 37.50
Ribbon Candy, plate, 8" .22.00
Ribbon Candy, spooner .25.00
Ribbon Candy, tumbler .30.00
Ribbon Candy, wine 42.00
Ripple, goblet 20.00
Ripple, spooner 20.00
Ripple, wine 32.50
Ripple Band, see Ripple
Rising Sun, goblet, gold trim 20.00
Rising Sun, goblet, purple trim 25.00
Rochelle, see Princess Feather
Roman Key, egg cup 45.00
Roman Key, sauce dish, flat, frosted, 4¼" 12.00
Roman Key, wine, frosted 65.00
Roman Rosette, celery vase 32.00
Roman Rosette, goblet 36.00
Roman Rosette, mug, 3½" 16.00
Roman Rosette, shakers, pr 30.00
Rope Bands, creamer 24.00
Rope Bands, tumbler 17.50
Rose in Snow, butter dish, sq 47.50

Rose in Snow

Rose in Snow, cake stand, 8½" 75.00
Rose in Snow, compote, w/lid, low std, 7" 70.00
Rose in Snow, creamer, sq 35.00
Rose in Snow, goblet 32.50
Rose in Snow, pitcher, water 85.00
Rose in Snow, pitcher, water; bl 225.00
Rose in Snow, sauce dish, flat, 4" 8.00
Rose Leaves, goblet 25.00
Rose Sprig, boat, relish; bl 36.00
Rose Sprig, cake stand, bl 70.00
Rose Sprig, goblet 25.00
Rose Sprig, pitcher, water 47.50
Rosette, celery vase, ftd .20.00
Rosette, compote, jelly; 4½x4½" 22.00
Rosette, pitcher, milk 45.00
Rosette, plate, hdl, 9" 15.00
Rosette & Palms, plate, 10" 16.50
Rosette & Palms, sugar bowl, w/lid 40.00
Royal Crystal, see Tarantum's Atlanta
Royal Ivy, see Northwood, Royal Ivy
Royal Oak, see Northwood, Royal Oak
Ruby Thumbprint, see King's Crown
Sandwich Star, decanter, w/bar lip, 1-qt 65.00
Sandwich Star, spill, clambroth 435.00
Sawtooth, celery vase, knop stem, flint 57.50
Sawtooth, creamer, appl hdl, non-flint 35.00
Sawtooth, egg cup, flint .47.50
Sawtooth, salt cellar, master; w/lid, non-flint 30.00
Sawtooth, spooner, non-flint 20.00
Sawtooth, wine, non-flint 25.00
Sawtooth Band, see Amazon
Scalloped Daisy Red Top, see Button Arches
Scalloped Loop, see Yoked Loop
Scroll, celery vase 30.00
Scroll, pitcher, water 70.00
Scroll, spooner 25.00
Scroll w/Flowers, mustard jar 45.00
Scroll w/Flowers, pitcher, water 47.50
Scroll w/Flowers, spooner 25.00
Sedan, see Panelled Star & Button
Seneca Loop, see Loop
Sequoia, see Heavy Panelled Finecut
Shell & Jewel, bowl, 8" .22.00
Shell & Jewel, creamer .35.00
Shell & Jewel, tumbler, water 20.00
Shell & Tassel, bowl, azure bl, 5x10" 85.00
Shell & Tassel, compote, open, 8x8" 45.00
Shell & Tassel, plate, oyster 230.00
Shell & Tassel, spooner .35.00
Shell & Tassel, tray, ice cream 55.00
Sheraton, creamer 22.00
Sheraton, goblet, bl 45.00
Sheraton, pitcher, water; amber 57.50
Sheraton, relish, hdld, bl 30.00
Sheraton, spooner 20.00
Shoshone, cake stand, gr 60.00
Shoshone, creamer, amber stained 47.50
Shoshone, creamer, gr 35.00
Shoshone, sauce dish, flat, sq, clear w/gold, 5" 15.00
Shovel, compote, jelly 17.50
Shovel, goblet 20.00
Shovel, tumbler 15.00
Shrine, bowl, 8" 32.00
Shrine, celery 42.00

Shrine, pitcher, cider; ½-gal 135.00
Shrine, sugar bowl, w/lid 50.00
Shuttle, butter dish 40.00
Shuttle, cordial 30.00
Shuttle, mug 25.00
Shuttle, see also Greentown, Shuttle
Shuttle, wine 20.00
Skilton, bowl, flat, 2½x4¾" 13.00
Skilton, creamer 30.00
Skilton, pitcher, water 45.00
Skilton, wine 35.00
Smocking, goblet 60.00
Smocking, spill, flint 40.00
Smocking, sugar bowl, w/lid 125.00
Snail, bowl, flat, 2¾x9" 37.50
Snail, creamer 50.00
Snail, pitcher, tankard 95.00
Snail, shakers, pr 65.00
Snail, spooner 35.00
Snail, syrup 80.00
Snakeskin & Dot, celery vase 32.00
Snakeskin & Dot, creamer 35.00
Snakeskin & Dot, sugar bowl 45.00
Spades, see Medallion
Spirea Band, cake stand, amber, 11" 50.00
Spirea Band, goblet, amber 30.00
Spirea Band, platter, bl, 10¾x8½" 38.00
Spirea Band, shakers, amber, pr 30.00
Spirea Band, wine 18.00
Sprig, bowl, scalloped, 9¾" 45.00
Sprig, goblet 35.00
Sprig, sugar bowl, w/lid 50.00
Squirrel, sugar bowl, open 55.00
Star Rosetted, bowl, oval, 7¼x5" 7.00
Star Rosetted, butter dish 45.00
Star Rosetted, relish dish, 3-hdld, 9¾x5" 12.00
Star Rosetted, sugar bowl, w/lid 42.00
Stars & Stripes, cordial 12.50
Stars & Stripes, creamer 15.00

Stars & Stripes

Stars & Stripes, pitcher, water 37.50
Stars & Stripes, wine 12.00
States, compote, open, 9" 60.00
States, creamer 30.00
States, syrup 75.00
States, tumbler 22.00
Stedman, champagne 35.00
Stedman, egg cup, flint 20.00
Stedman, goblet 30.00
Stedman, sauce dish, flat, 4" 15.00
Stedman, wine 45.00
Stepped Flute, champagne, flint 37.50
Stippled Chain, butter dish 50.00
Stippled Chain, goblet 25.00
Stippled Chain, pitcher, water 65.00

Stippled Chain, spooner 25.00
Stippled Forget-Me-Not, creamer 25.00
Stippled Forget-Me-Not, pitcher, water 50.00
Stippled Forget-Me-Not, sugar bowl, w/lid 36.00
Stippled Grape & Festoon, butter dish 55.00
Stippled Grape & Festoon, goblet 32.00
Stippled Grape & Festoon, relish 28.00
Stippled Grape & Festoon, wine 40.00
Stippled Ivy, egg cup 28.00
Stippled Ivy, goblet 30.00
Stippled Ivy, sauce, flat 9.50
Stippled Ivy, spooner 28.00
Stippled Roman Key, goblet 32.00
Stippled Panelled Flower, See Maine
Stippled Scroll, see Scroll
Stork, celery vase, frosted 65.00
Straight Banded Worchester, tumbler, ftd 40.00
Strawberry, goblet 32.00
Strawberry, pitcher, water; bulbous 115.00
Strawberry, spooner 35.00
Sunburst, creamer, appl hdl 30.00
Sunburst, goblet 25.00
Sunburst, plate, 7" 9.00
Sunk Honeycomb, mug, ruby stained, 3" 15.00
Sunk Honeycomb, salt cellar 7.50
Sunk Honeycomb, shakers, ruby stained, pr 40.00
Sunken Primrose, see Florida
Swan, butter dish 85.00
Swan, creamer 45.00
Swan, mug 30.00
Swan, pitcher, water 150.00
Swan, spooner 40.00
Swirl, see Jersey Swirl
Tape Measure, goblet 20.00
Tape Measure, sauce dish, 4" 7.50
Tarantum's Atlanta, powder jar, w/lid 25.00
Tarantum's Atlanta, tumbler, water; ruby stained 47.50
Teardrop, goblet 20.00
Teardrop, tumbler, water; etched 22.50
Teardrop & Diamond Block, see Art
Teardrop & Tassel, bowl, 7" 40.00
Teardrop & Tassel, butter dish 50.00
Teardrop & Tassel, celery vase 40.00

Teardrop & Tassel

Teardrop & Tassel, creamer 42.00
Teardrop & Tassel, sauce dish, 4" 12.50
Teardrop & Tassel, see also Greentown, Teardrop & Tassel
Texas, goblet 42.00
Texas, toothpick holder 25.00
Theatrical, see Actress
Thousand Eye, cake stand, 3-knob stem, gr 60.00
Thousand Eye, mug, amber, 2½" 18.00
Thousand Eye, mug, amber, 3⅜" 20.00
Thousand Eye, plate, sq, apple gr, 5¾" 12.50

Thousand Eye, sugar bowl, w/lid, vaseline 50.00
Thousand Eye, wine 25.00
Three Face, butter dish 120.00
Three Face, cake stand, 9⅜" dia 150.00
Three Face, celery vase 85.00
Three Face, champagne, saucer type 150.00
Three Face, claret 150.00
Three Face, compote, w/lid, 10" 235.00
Three Face, compote, w/lid, 6x4½" 75.00
Three Face, compote, w/lid, 8½x6" 145.00
Three Face, goblet 85.00
Three Face, pitcher 275.00
Three Face, spooner 85.00
Thumbprint, see Argus
Thumbprint Band, see Dakota
Thunderbird, see Hummingbird
Torpedo, bowl, flat, 8½x2¾" 18.00
Torpedo, celery vase .40.00
Torpedo, creamer 40.00
Torpedo, goblet 50.00
Torpedo, pitcher, ruby stained, 8½" 88.00
Torpedo, pitcher, water; etched, 11" 100.00
Torpedo, pitcher, water; 11" 75.00
Torpedo, sugar bowl w/lid, ...65.00
Torpedo, tumbler, water 32.00
Torpedo, tumbler, water; ruby stained 45.00
Torpedo, wine 75.00
Tree of Life, bowl, flat, 5" 12.50
Tree of Life, compote, w/lid, 6x8" 75.00

Tree of Life

Tree of Life, creamer, Portland, appl hdl, sgn Davis 66.00
Tree of Life, sauce dish, Portland, leaf shape, 5⅞x4¼" 15.00
Tree of Life, syrup, milk glass 75.00
Triangular Prism, goblet 18.00
Triple Triangle, celery tray, ruby stained 40.00
Triple Triangle, goblet, ruby stained 40.00
Triple Triangle, mug, ruby stained 30.00
Truncated Cube, creamer, ind; ruby stained 35.00
Truncated Cube, goblet .28.00
Truncated Cube, pitcher, tankard 50.00
Truncated Cube, salt cellar, ruby stained 20.00
Truncated Cube, wine 27.50
Tulip, tumbler, ale; flint 56.00
Tulip w/Ribs, tumbler, whiskey; hdld, flint 45.00
Tulip w/Sawtooth, celery vase, flint 75.00
Tulip w/Sawtooth, goblet 28.00
Tulip w/Sawtooth, mug, flint 75.00
Tulip w/Sawtooth, sugar shaker 47.50
Tulip w/Sawtooth, wine, flint 60.00
Two Panel, butter dish, amber 50.00
Two Panel, creamer, bl .40.00

Two Panel, goblet 25.00
Two Panel, sauce dish, ftd, oval, amber 15.00
Two Panel, wine, bl 38.00
US Coin, butter dish, frosted 525.00
US Coin, compote, open, low std, frosted, 7" 400.00
US Coin, compote, w/lid, high std, frosted, 8" 535.00
US Coin, epergne, frosted, rare 1,100.00
US Coin, relish dish, frosted, 7½" 250.00
US Coin, sauce, ftd, frosted 135.00
US Coin, sugar bowl, w/lid, frosted 365.00
US Coin, syrup, frosted 500.00
US Coin, toothpick holder, clear, silver dollars 180.00
US Coin, toothpick holder, frosted 265.00
US Coin, tumbler, clear 120.00
Valencia Waffle, compote, w/lid, bl, 8¼x7" 75.00
Valencia Waffle, pitcher, water; amber 66.00
Valencia Waffle, sauce dish, ftd, sq, 4" 15.00
Vermont, creamer, gr w/gold, 4" 50.00
Vermont, goblet, gr w/gold 60.00
Vermont, pitcher, water; gr w/gold 85.00
Vermont, see also Custard Glass
Vermont, vase 17.50
Viking, apothecary jar .52.00
Viking, celery vase 50.00
Viking, salt cellar, master 45.00
Viking, sugar bowl, w/lid 65.00
Virginia, see Banded Portland
Waffle, compote, 5¼x7" .35.00
Waffle, creamer, flint .137.50
Waffle, salt cellar, master 30.00
Waffle, waste bowl, ruffled top, flint 77.50
Waffle & Thumbprint, compote, open, high std, 8" 85.00
Waffle & Thumbprint, goblet 60.00
Waffle & Thumbprint, sugar bowl, w/lid 165.00
Waffle & Thumbprint, wine 55.00
Washington, decanter, orig stopper, qt 200.00
Washington, pitcher, water 235.00
Washington, salt cellar, master; rnd 30.00
Washington Centennial, cake stand, 8¼" 48.00

Washington Centennial

Washington Centennial, celery vase, ftd 40.00
Washington Centennial, goblet 44.00
Washington Centennial, pitcher, milk 90.00
Washington Centennial, sauce dish, flat 10.00
Wedding Bells, creamer .50.00
Wedding Bells, spooner .32.00
Wedding Bells, sugar bowl, w/lid 50.00
Wedding Ring, pitcher, water 160.00
Wedding Ring, sauce dish, 4" 20.00
Wedding Ring, syrup 97.50

Westward Ho, butter dish	185.00
Westward Ho, compote, open, high std, 6"	125.00
Westward Ho, compote, w/lid, oblong, 8x10"	275.00
Westward Ho, creamer	130.00
Westward Ho, mug, rare, 2"	225.00
Westward Ho, pitcher, water	200.00
Westward Ho, sauce dish, ftd	30.00
Westward Ho, sugar bowl, w/lid, 4½"	170.00
Wheat & Barley, butter dish, bl	75.00
Wheat & Barley, compote, jelly; open	20.00
Wheat & Barley, goblet	27.50
Wheat & Barley, plate, hdls, amber, 11"	25.00
Wheat & Barley, salt cellar, bl	37.50
Wildflower, cake stand, amber	50.00
Wildflower, compote, open, low std, apple gr, 7"	25.00
Wildflower, creamer	28.00
Wildflower, pitcher, water	50.00
Wildflower, relish bowl, amber, 9¼x4"	20.00
Wildflower, salt cellar, turtle form, apple gr	32.00
Wildflower, tray, oval, apple gr, 11x13"	57.50
Wildflower, tray, oval, 13x11"	40.00
Willow Oak, bowl, w/lid, 7"	40.00
Willow Oak, cake stand, amber, 8¾"	45.00
Willow Oak, celery vase	40.00
Willow Oak, creamer	30.00
Willow Oak, goblet	35.00
Willow Oak, mug, amber, 3¾"	40.00
Willow Oak, sugar bowl, w/lid	40.00
Windflower, compote, w/lid, low std	60.00
Windflower, goblet	37.50
Windflower, sugar bowl, w/lid	50.00
Wisconsin, celery vase	45.00
Wisconsin, cup & saucer	45.00
Wisconsin, shakers, pr	45.00
Wooden Pail, butter dish, amber	75.00
Wooden Pail, creamer, amethyst	85.00
Wooden Pail, goblet, amethyst	75.00
Wooden Pail, spooner, amber	42.00
X-Ray, creamer	30.00
X-Ray, spooner	25.00
X-Ray, water set, pitcher+6 tumblers, gr	235.00
Yale, butter dish	40.00
Yale, spooner	25.00
Yoked Loop, sugar bowl, open	20.00
Yoked Loop, tumbler, whiskey; hdld	28.00
Zig-Zag, wine	20.00
Zipper Slash, champagne	30.00
Zippered Block, creamer, ruby stained	80.00

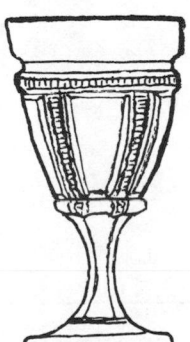

Zippered Block

Zippered Block, goblet	38.00
Zippered Block, sugar bowl, w/lid, ruby stained	100.00

Paul Revere Pottery

The Saturday Evening Girls were a social group of young Boston ladies who met to pursue various activities, among them pottery making. Their first kiln was bought in 1906, and within a few years it became necessary to move to a larger location. Because their new quarters were near the historical Old North Church, they chose the name Paul Revere Pottery. With very little training, the girls produced only simple ware. Until 1915 the pottery operated at a deficit; then a new building with four kilns was constructed on Nottingham Road. Vases, miniature jugs, children's tea sets, tiles, dinnerware, and lamps were produced, usually in soft matt glazes often decorated with incised, hand-painted designs from nature. Occasional examples in a dark high gloss may also be found.

Several marks were used: 'P.R.P.'; 'S.E.G.'; or the circular device, 'Boston, Paul Revere Pottery' with the horse and rider.

The pottery continued to operate; and, even though their product sold well, the high production costs of the handmade ware caused the pottery to fail in 1946.

Bowl, bl semi-gloss, SEG, 2¾x6½"	60.00
Bowl, bl-gr allover drip on yel clay, PRP, 2½x4½"	70.00
Bowl, floral band on yel, SEG/F-16, 2¼x9"	325.00
Bowl, floral band on yel gloss, SEG/1-15, 2x5"	350.00
Bowl, geese in band on bl & gr, SEG/AM/7-15, 11½"	600.00
Bowl, gun metal, turq int, SEG/6-22, 6x12"	90.00
Bowl, iris band on bl & tan, SEG/AM/4-14, 10"	1,300.00
Bowl, trees & hills in band on med gr, SEG/AN/6-10, 8½"	550.00
Calendar holder, trees/lake/house, SEG/SN, paper label, 3"	195.00
Cup, bands, gray/blk on mustard, PRP, 2x3"	35.00
Cup, dk bl-gray high-gloss, bl/wht drip int, PRP, 3½"	50.00
Flower frog, robin's egg bl, SEG	25.00
Pitcher, orange/gr drip on rust clay, PRP, 1¾"	40.00
Pitcher, tortoise & hare in band on bl, SEG/FR, 4½"	850.00
Pitcher, trees & hills in band on dk bl gloss, label, 7x8"	500.00
Pitcher, Viking ships in band on bl, SEG/IG/11-11, 10", EX	950.00
Planter, iris in band on bl, rectangular, SEG/AM, 9" L	1,000.00
Plate, 8 pigs in band, HOS monogram, SEG/LS, 8½"	1,300.00

Plate, running rabbits in band, inscription, 7½", $325.00; Bowl, signed F.L., 5½", $295.00; Cake plate with geese and initials, signed F.L., 9", $450.00.

Salt cellar, bl high-gloss, ftd, paper label, ¾x3"	25.00
Tile, dog/scene/'That Was All...,' SEG, 4x6"	525.00

Tile, form/design of PRP trademark, 6-color, 4⅜" dia 200.00
Tile, trees/landscape, PRP, 4" dia .200.00
Toothpick holder, chick on med bl gloss, SEG, 1½" 75.00
Trivet, geometric bands, overlapping sqs, SEG/AM, 5" dia 150.00
Trivet, simple geometric, 3-color, 4-ftd, SEG/RB, 5¼" 275.00
Vase, bl high gloss, apothecary jar form, SEG/3-22, 6" 110.00
Vase, turq drip over mustard, cylinder, paper label, 4½" 80.00

Pauline Pottery

Pauline Pottery was made from 1883 to 1888 in Chicago, Ill., from clay imported from the Ohio area. Its founder was Mrs. Pauline Jacobus, who had learned the trade at the Rookwood Pottery. Mrs. Jacobus moved to Edgerton, Wisconsin, to be near a source of suitable clay, thus eliminating shipping expenses. Until 1905 she produced high-quality wares, able to imitate with ease designs and styles of such masters as Wedgwood and Meissen. Her products were sold through leading department stores, and the names of some of these firms may appear on the ware. Not all were marked; and, unless signed by a noted local artist, positive identification is often impossible. Marked examples carry a variety of stamps and signatures: 'Trade Mark' with a crown, 'Pauline Pottery,' and 'Edgerton Art Pottery' are but a few.

Bowl, yel roses on yel semi-gloss, 3½x9½" 250.00
Ewer, floral/butterfly, Limoges style, mk, 9½" 400.00
Vase, gold-traced bl flowers w/gr leaves, sgn Edwards, 12" 500.00
Vase, sm flowers on dk brn, sgn/1880, 8" 500.00

Peachblow

Peachblow, made to imitate the colors of the Chinese Peachbloom porcelain, was made by several glasshouses in the late 1800s. Among them were New England Glass; Mt. Washington; Webb; and Hobbs, Brockunier, and Company. Its pink shading was achieved through action of the heat on the gold content of the glass. While New England's peachblow shades from pink to cool white, Mt. Washington's tends to shade from peach to ivory. Although usually glossy, a satin (or acid) finish was also produced, and many pieces were enameled and gilded. In the 1950s, Gunderson-Pairpoint Glassworks initiated the reproduction of Mt. Washington peachblow using an exact duplication of the original formula. Though of recent manufacture, this glass is very collectible. In the listings that follow, the finish is glossy unless noted acid.

Our advisors for this category are Betty and Clarence Maier; they are listed in the Directory under Pennsylvania.

Bottle, scent; floral sprays, faceted stopper, Mt WA, 5" 950.00
Bowl, prunus/branch/bird in gold, amber ft, Webb, 7½" 795.00
Bowl, ruffled flared rim, NE Glass, 5½" 375.00
Card tray, HP daisies, ruffled shell form, Mt WA, 5" dia 2,250.00
Compote, Gunderson, 5x6" 220.00
Condiment, floral on 3" bbl shakers+mustard, Mt WA 3,500.00
Creamer, Gunderson, 3½" 210.00
Creamer, Wheeling, 4" 600.00
Cruet, Gunderson, 10" 300.00
Cup, wht opaque reed hdl, NE Glass 225.00
Darner, inscribed World's Fair-1893 . . . . .160.00
Mustard, acid, pewter rim/hdl, Wheeling, 3" 325.00
Mustard, SP hdl/lid, Wheeling, 2¾" 400.00
Pear, NE Glass, 5" L, M 200.00
Pitcher, bl/wht floral, appl wht hdl, tricorn top, Webb, 5" 350.00
Pitcher, sq top, Wheeling, 7½x6" 985.00
Punch cup, acid, Wheeling 375.00

Rose bowl, fluted rim, NE Glass, 4" dia 450.00
Rose bowl, inscribed World's Fair-1893, NE Glass 250.00
Rose bowl, Matsu-No-Ke, berry pontil, S&W, 3½" 925.00
Rose bowl, 8-crimp top, Webb, 3x3¼" 225.00
Shakers, ball form, orig flat tops, Wheeling, 2¾", pr 600.00
Sugar bowl, open, Gunderson, 3½" .170.00
Sweetmeat, gold bamboo, gold rim/lid/hdl, S&W, 3x5" 865.00
Sweetmeat, gold bamboo & hdl, gold-color mts, Webb, 5" 600.00
Toothpick holder, crimped top, NE Glass 550.00
Toothpick holder, pinched tricorn top, NE Glass, 2¼" 400.00
Tumbler, acid, EX color, Wheeling, 3⅝" 300.00
Tumbler, NE Glass, 3⅝" 350.00
Tumbler, Wheeling, 3¾" 325.00
Vase, acid, HP bird on branch, att Webb, 6" 175.00
Vase, acid, stick neck, NE Glass, 8" 350.00
Vase, acid, tapered form, Wheeling, 11", pr 2,100.00
Vase, emb swirls, fancy crystal applique & ft, Webb, 5¾" 550.00
Vase, gold floral/lg butterfly, flat-side/stick neck, 9" 400.00
Vase, gold flowers/leaves/buds on lav branches, PFK mk, 10" . .650.00
Vase, gold flowers/leaves/lg butterfly, hdls, Webb, 8x5½" 695.00
Vase, gold prunus/butterfly, SP top/rim/hdl, Webb, 6" 895.00
Vase, gold wheat heads/bands/etc, Webb, 8" 850.00
Vase, hdls, sq base, Gunderson, 8½" 150.00
Vase, lily; NE Glass, 12" 800.00
Vase, Morgan, orig glass griffin stand, Wheeling, 10" 3,100.00
Vase, petit point flowers/butterfly, 5¾" 400.00
Vase, ribbed, 'World's Fair-1893,' tricorn folded top, 3¾" 250.00
Vase, stick neck, Wheeling, 11" 1,100.00
Vase, stick neck, 8" 600.00
Vase, wht opaque fluted appl hdls, sq top, NE Glass, 4" 700.00

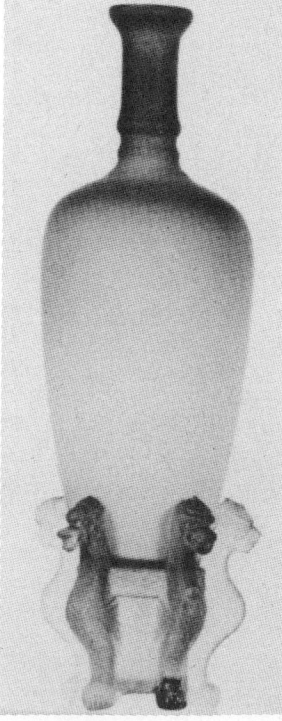

Wheeling Morgan vase, satin, frosted amber dragon base, 10", $3,100.00.

Peking Glass

The first glasshouse was established in Peking in 1680. It produced glassware made in imitation of porcelain, a more desirable medium to the Chinese. By 1725 multi-layered carving that resulted in a cameo effect lead to the manufacture of a wider range of shapes and colors. The factory was closed from 1736 to 1795, but glass made in Po-shan and shipped to Peking for finishing continued to be called Peking glass. 20th-century ware is usually decorated in soft frosted colors on relief-molded designs. See also Orientalia; Snuff Bottles.

Bottle, scent; floral, gr on wht, red stopper, 4" 135.00
Bottle, snuff; floral, red on wht, w/lid 175.00
Bowl, floral/leaves/butterfly, bl on wht, teakwood stand, 7" 250.00
Bowl, prunus/lilies, bl on wht, 1880s, 4", pr 220.00
Bowl, purple, steep sides/ring ft, 4½", pr 220.00
Vase, cranes/peonies, gr on wht, Ching Dynasty, 14", pr 850.00
Vase, dragons, red on wht, 12⅜" 595.00
Vase, ducks/lotus, red on wht, dbl-ring neck, 9x6", pr 550.00
Vase, peonies/plum blossoms, yel, stick neck, 1900, 12", pr 700.00
Vase, prunus/florals, red on wht, 9x4", pr 365.00

Peloton

Peloton glass was first made by Wilhelm Kralik in Bohemia in 1880. This unusual art glass was produced by rolling colored threads onto the transparent or opaque glass gather as it was removed from the furnace. Usually more than one color of threading was used, and some items were further decorated with enameling. It was made with both shiny and acid finishes.

Cruet, amber w/strings, 6" 350.00

Pitcher, enameled floral, green stringing on clear, gilt trim, 5", $225.00.

Rose bowl, pk overshot w/mc strings, 7½x3½" 225.00
Rose bowl, wht w/mc strings, clear ft, 3-crimp top, 4x3½" 195.00
Rose bowl, wht w/pastel strings, 6-crimp top, 2¼x2½" 245.00
Sweetmeat jar, dk rose w/mc strings, SP lid/hdl, 5½" 560.00
Tumbler, mc strings 210.00
Vase, lav-pk w/mc strings, emb ribs, clear wafer ft, 6x3⅝" 250.00
Vase, wht w/mc strings, clear twisted rigaree, ftd, 3¾" 265.00
Vase, wht w/mc strings, pinched neck, trifold rim, 4¾x4" 295.00

Pennsbury

New in the collectibles market, Pennsbury Pottery is drawing quite a

following! Established in the 1950s in Morrisville, Pennsylvania, by Henry Below, the company produced dinnerware and novelty items, much of which was sold in gift shops along the Pennsylvania Turnpike. Henry and his wife, Lee, worked for years at the Stangl Pottery before striking out on their own. Lee and her daughter were the artists responsible for many of the early pieces, the birds among them. Pennsbury pottery was hand painted, some in blue on white, some in multicolors on caramel. Pennsylvania Dutch motifs, Amish couples, and barber shop singers were among their most popular decorative themes. Sgraffito, or hand incising, was used extensively. The company marked their wares 'Pennsbury Pottery' or 'Pennsbury Pottery, Morrisville, PA.'

In October of 1969 the company closed; contents of the pottery were sold in December of the following year, and in April of 1971 the buildings burned to the ground. Items marked Pennsbury Glenview or Stumar pottery (or these marks in combination) were made by Glenview after 1969. Pieces manufactured after 1976 were made by the Pennington Pottery. Several of the old molds still exist, and the original Pennsbury Caramel process is still being used on novelty items, some of which are produced by Lewis Brothers, N.J. Pennsbury dinnerware was not continued after the closing. For those wishing to learn more, we recommend *Pennsbury Pottery Video Book 1* and accompanying 1987-88 price guide offered by Shirley Graff and BA Wellman. You will find Mr. Wellman's address in the Directory under Massachusetts.

Ash tray, Hex, scalloped, 8" 20.00
Ash tray, It's Making Down, 5" 15.00
Ash tray, tulip in heart, octagonal, 3¼x5" 18.00
Ash tray, Western & Atlantic RR, oval 45.00
Bowl, Amish, 9" 35.00
Bowl, cereal; rooster, red, 5½" 14.00
Bowl, pretzel; eagle 35.00
Bowl, pretzel; quartet, 2x12x8" 36.00
Butter dish, rooster 30.00
Cake stand, Harvest, 11½x4½" 39.00
Candy dish, rooster, blk, heart-shape 20.00
Canister, coffee; Folkart, wooden lid, 4½x6½" 60.00
Casserole; rooster, red, w/lid, 9" 42.00
Cigarette box, eagle, 2½x4½" 18.00
Coaster, quartet, 4" 15.00
Compote, rooster, blk, ftd, 5" 30.00
Cruet, Amish man, orig stopper 45.00
Dutch oven, rooster 165.00
Egg cup, rooster, red 18.00
Figurine, chickadee 68.00
Mug, beer; Amish couple, 4½" 24.00
Mug, beer; Here's Looking at You 25.00
Mug, beverage; Davy Crockett, 4½" 65.00
Pitcher, Amish, 4" 18.00
Pitcher, eagle w/banner, 6" 25.00
Pitcher, tulip, 3-qt 65.00
Plaque, Amish, 7x5" 23.50
Plaque, birds in heart, 7x5" 23.00
Plaque, God Bless Our Mortgaged Home, 7x5" 23.00
Plaque, Reading RR, Iron Horse Ramble, 1960, 6x8" 45.00
Plate, angel, Christmas, 1970, 8" 30.00
Plate, E Pluribus Unum, eagle, 8" 18.00
Plate, Harvest, 11" 30.00
Platter, blk rooster, oval, 13½x11" 38.00
Platter, Hex, oval, 8x11" 30.00
Shakers, Amish, figural head, pr 23.50
Shakers, red rooster, pr 18.00
Teapot, rooster, red, 4-cup 32.00
Tray, Give Us This Day, sheaves of wheat, 6½x9½" 32.00
Wall pocket, bl flowers w/gr border 35.00

Barn Swallow, 6", $100.00.

Pens and Pencils

The first metallic writing pen was patented in 1809, and soon machine-produced pens with steel nibs gradually began replacing the quill. The first fountain pen was invented in 1830; but, due to the fact that a suitable metal for the tips had not yet been developed, they were not manufactured commercially until the 1880s. The first successful commercial producers were Waterman in 1884 and Parker with the Lucky Curve in 1888.

The self-filling pen of 1890 featured the soft, interior sack which filled with ink as the metal bar on the outside of the pen was raised and lowered. Variations of the pumping mechanism were tried until 1932 when Parker introduced the Vacumatic, a sackless pen with an internal pump.

Our advisors for this category are Judy and Cliff Lawrence; they are listed in the Directory under Florida. For those seeking additional information, a magazine is published monthly by the Pen Fancier's Club, whose address can be found in the Directory under Clubs, Newsletters, and Catalogs. In the listings that follow, all pens are lever-filled unless otherwise noted.

Key:
AF — aeromatic filler
BF — button filler
CF — cartridge filler
CPT — chrome-plated trim
ED — eyedropper filler
GFM — gold-filled metal
GPT — gold-plated trim
HR — hard rubber
LF — lever filler
NPT — nickel-plated trim
TD — touchdown filler
VF — vacumatic filler

Ballpoint Pens

Eberhard Faber, 1946, brn/GF cap, EX 65.00
Eversharp, CA, 1946, bl/GF cap, M 95.00
Eversharp, CA, 1947, GFM, EX 125.00
Eversharp, Skyline, CA, 1944, maroon w/striped cap, EX 50.00
Eversharp, Skyline, CA, 1948, brn/gold striped cap, M 50.00
Reynolds, International, 1945, aluminum,.GF clip, EX 150.00
Reynolds, Rocket, 1946, aluminum/chrome clip, EX 85.00
Sheaffer, Stratowriter, 1946, GFM, M 95.00

Fountain Pens

Conklin, Endura, 1929, blk & gold marble, med sz, EX 80.00

Conklin, Good Service, 1929, gr marble w/blk ends, EX 185.00
Eversharp, Leowy, 1950, maroon w/CPT cap, EX 50.00
Eversharp, Skyline Presentation, 1945, bl, VG 60.00
Moore, 1940, bronze w/silver stripes, M 90.00
Parker, Duofold Jr, 1926, red, BF, EX 85.00
Parker, Duofold Jr, 1928, red, BF, EX 85.00
Parker, Duofold Sr, 1926, Big Red, BF, EX 265.00
Parker, Duofold Sr, 1926, desk style, blk/wht/gold onyx base ...350.00
Parker, Duofold Sr, 1928, Big Red, BF, EX 265.00
Parker, Duofold Sr Prototype, '28, yel w/blk band, rare, M 895.00
Parker, Ladies Jack-Knife Safety, 1915, blk-chased HR, BF 250.00
Parker, Ladies True Blue, Modern bl & wht, BF, G 50.00
Parker, Lady Duofold, 1925, red HR, EX 80.00
Parker, Lucky Curve #2½, 1917, blk-chased HR, NPT, NM ...125.00
Parker, Lucky Curve #20, 1900, jointless, blk HR, ED, EX 350.00
Parker, Lucky Curve #23, 1904, red/blk marbled, HR, ED, EX .265.00
Parker, Lucky Curve #33, 1906, blk HR, gold filigree, ED, EX ..725.00
Sheaffer, Demonstrator, 1925, gr jade marble, cutouts, M 250.00
Sheaffer, Demonstrator, 1932, gr transparent plastic, M 170.00
Sheaffer, Feathertouch 500, 1939, red w/pearl stripes, EX 50.00
Sheaffer, Lifetime, 1925, blk, man's model, EX 225.00
Sheaffer, Lifetime, 1932, blk, man's model, EX 250.00
Sheaffer, Lifetime Crest Triumph, 1946, blk, GF cap, EX 135.00
Sheaffer, Lifetime Triumph, 1946, gr w/pearl stripes, EX 75.00
Sheaffer, Wht Dot Sentinel Triumph, 1951, blk, TD, EX 45.00
Sheaffer, 5-30, 1926, gr jade marble w/blk ends, EX 65.00
Wahl-Eversharp, Gold Seal Equipoise, '31, marbled, med, EX ..185.00
Wahl-Eversharp, Gold Seal Giant Doric, 1932, Kashmir, EX ..595.00
Wahl-Eversharp, Gold Seal Personal Point, '28, marbled, EX ..650.00
Wahl-Eversharp, Skyline, 1946, brn, M 45.00
Waterman, Hundred Year, 1943, blk w/GF cap, EX 165.00
Waterman, Ideal #0542½-S Safety, 1913, GFM, EX 700.00
Waterman, Ideal #13, 1900, blk HR, ED, rare, EX 150.00
Waterman, Ideal #52½, 1928, red-mottled HR, EX 45.00

Mechanical Pencils

Conklin, Endura, 1929, lady's, sapphire, EX 39.00
Cross, 1950, GFM, EX 35.00
Eversharp, Skyline Presentation Repeater, 1945, GF top, VG ...24.00
Eversharp, Skyline Repeater, 1946, bl/silver striped cap, EX 24.00
Eversharp, 5th Ave Presentation Repeater, 1943, GF top, EX ...30.00
Parker, Deluxe Challenger, 1937, emerald/blk marble, EX 22.00
Parker, Duofold, 1928, yel w/blk vintage bands, EX 85.00
Parker, Duofold, 1930, gr jade marble, EX 75.00
Parker, Duofold Deluxe Sr, 1928, Moderne blk & pearl, EX ...125.00
Parker, Duofold Deluxe Sr, 1930, Moderne blk & pearl, EX ...125.00
Parker, Duofold Sr, 1926, Big Red, EX 165.00
Parker, True Blue, lady's, 1931, NM 42.00
Parker, 51, 1944, brn w/GF top, EX 35.00
Sheaffer, Miniature, 1932, blk, EX 18.00
Sheaffer, Tuckaway 500, 1947, blk, EX 18.00
Sheaffer, 400, 1938, gold w/pearl stripes, EX 15.00
Waterman, Lady Patricia, 1935, red marble, NPT, M 40.00
Waterman, 1935, silver/red marble, NPT, EX 35.00

Sets

Conklin, Endura, 1930, gr pearl marble, EX 395.00
Eversharp, Skyline Presentation, 1945, maroon, GF caps, EX ...90.00
Moore, Maniflex Desk, 1930, pearl & blk, LF, EX 75.00
Parker, Blue Diamond, 51, 1946, gray/GF caps, M 195.00
Parker, Maxima Vacumatic, 1938, gold pearl stripe, VF, NM ..450.00

Sheaffer, Admiral, 1959, gr, TD, M 35.00
Sheaffer, Wht Dot Sentinel Triumph Tuckaway, 1950, TD, EX .60.00
Sheaffer, 3-25, 1932, lady's, pearl & blk marble, EX 55.00
Wahl-Eversharp, Gold Seal Sig, 1929, gr/bronze marble, EX . . .750.00
Wahl-Eversharp, Skyline, 1943, gr, GFM cap & derby, VG 90.00
Waterman, Citation Taperite, 1947, blk, EX 80.00
Waterman, Ideal, 1945, gold marble, M 50.00

Personalities, Fact and Fiction

One of the largest and most popular areas of collecting today, if trade-paper ads and articles be any indication, is character-related memorabilia. Everyone has favorites, whether they be comic-strip personalities or true-life heroes. The earliest comic strip dealt with the adventures of the Yellow Kid, the smiling, bald-headed Oriental boy always in a nightshirt. He was introduced in 1895, a product of the imagination of Richard Fenton Outcault. Today, though very hard to come by, items relating to the Yellow Kid bring premium prices.

In 1902 Buster Brown and Tige, his dog and constant companion (more of Outcault's progenies), made it big in the comics as well as in the world of advertising. Shoe stores appealed to the younger set through merchandising displays that featured them both. Today the items from their earlier years are very collectible.

Though her 1923 introduction was unobtrusively made through only one newspaper, New York's *Daily News*, Little Orphan Annie, the vacant-eyed redhead in the inevitable red dress, was quickly adopted by hordes of readers nationwide; and before the demise of her creator, Harold Gray, in 1968, she starred in her own radio show. She made two feature films, and in 1977 'Annie' was launched on Broadway.

Other early comic figures were Moon Mullins, created in 1923 by Frank Willard; Buck Rogers by Philip Nowlan in 1928; and Betty Boop, the round-faced, innocent-eyed, chubby-cheeked Boop-Boop-a-Doop girl of the early 1930s. Bimbo was her dog and KoKo her clown friend.

Popeye made his debut in 1929 as the spinach-eating sailor with the spindly-limbed girlfriend, Olive Oyl, in the comic strip *Thimble Theatre*, created by Elzie Segar. He became a film star in 1933 and had his own radio show that during 1936 played three times a week on CBS. He obligingly modeled for scores of toys, dolls, and figurines, and especially those from the thirties are very collectible.

Tarzan, created around 1930 by Edgar Rice Burroughs, and Captain Midnight, by Robert Burtt and Willfred G. Moore, are popular heroes with today's collectors. During the days of radio, Sky King of the Flying Crown Ranch (also created by Burtt and Moore) thrilled boys and girls of the mid-1940s. Hopalong Cassidy, Red Rider, Tom Mix, and the Lone Ranger were only a few of the other 'good guys' always on the side of law and order.

But of all the fictional heroes and comic characters collected today, probably the best loved and most well known is Mickey Mouse. Created in the late 1920s by Walt Disney, Micky (as his name was first spelled) became an instant success with his film debut, Steamboat Willie. His popularity was parlayed through windup toys, watches, figurines, cookie jars, puppets, clothing, and numerous other products. Items from the 1930s are usually copyrighted 'Walt Disney Enterprises'; thereafter, 'Walt Disney Productions' was used.

Authority David Longest has recently released the second volume of his fine series, *Character Toys and Collectibles*, with full-color photos and current market values; you will find his address in the Directory under Indiana. Both books are recommended to those wanting more information.

Our advisors for this category are Cathy and Norm Vigue; they are listed in the Directory under Massachusetts. See also Autographs; Banks; Big Little Books; Cartoon Books; Children's Books; Comic Books; Cookie Jars; Dolls; Lunch Boxes; Movie Memorabilia; Paper Dolls; Pin-Back Buttons; Posters; Toys.

Addams Family, card game, Milton Bradley, 1965, EX 22.00
Addams Family, thermos, gr plastic, Hanna Barbera, 1974, EX . .13.00
Alice in Wonderland, gloves, Wells Lamont, orig tag, M 18.00
Alice in Wonderland, sheet music, In a World of My Own, EX .17.00
Amos & Andy, cb standups, Pepsodent premium, 1930, 8½", pr .25.00
Amos & Andy, radio script, Amos' Wedding, 1935 . . . . .25.00
Amos & Andy, sheet music, 3 Little Words, 1930 . . . . .15.00
Andy Gump, bsk nodder, 1920s 60.00
Andy Panda, bank, tin suitcase form, EX 35.00
Andy Panda, book, Story Hour series, 1949, 7x4", NM 10.00
Archie, drinking glass, red/yel graphics, 1970 . . . . .8.00
Babe Ruth, doll, orig striped uniform, 32" 450.00
Babe Ruth, pen knife/key chain, 1927, EX 45.00
Babe Ruth, wrist watch, orig in plastic baseball 350.00
Batman, alarm clock, 1960s, MIB 175.00
Batman, belt, Morris Belt Co, 1966, M on orig card 50.00
Batman, book, paperback, Batman Vs the Penguin, NM 12.00
Batman, cape & mask, Ben Cooper, 1966, M in pkg 35.00
Batman, coins on illustrated card, 20 asst, plastic, 1966, M 20.00
Batman, lamp, plastic, kneeling figure, 1976, 11½" 30.00
Batman, license plate, tin, 1966, unused, 6x12" 15.00
Batman, motor-plane, electric, Remco, 1966, M in orig box 75.00
Batman, wrist watch, Babbs, 1977, EX 48.00
Batman, Yo-Yo, 1978, M 10.00
Batman & Robin, game, Hasbro, 1965, EX 38.00
Batman & Robin, thermos, 1966, EX .20.00
Beatles, calendar, 1965, 2½x5", EX 68.00
Beatles, color book, 1964, M 40.00
Beatles, disk-go-case, purple, NM 50.00
Beatles, game, Flip Your Wig, complete 80.00
Beatles, pin, Yel Submarine, HP brass, 1", set of 8 . . . . .18.00
Beatles, tray, red tin, Great Britain 65.00
Beetle Bailey, color book, 1964, M 15.00
Betty Boop, doll, porc, jtd, MIB 35.00
Betty Boop, nodder, Hong Kong, KES, 1970s 50.00
Betty Boop, perfume bottle, glass figural, 1930s, 3½", EX 20.00
Betty Boop, wall vase, Betty twisting Bimbo's ear 135.00
Beverly Hillbillies, card game, EX 18.00
Big Bird, alarm clock, 2-bell, windup, 1975, M 12.50
Blondie, bookmark, 1951, 2x8", NM .15.00
Blondie, game, Blondie Goes to Leisureland, 1940, NM 24.00
Blondie & Dagwood, book, paperback, Foothill Folly, 1947, M . . .8.00

Buck Rogers All-Fair card game, each card with color illustrations, $375.00. Photo courtesy of Hake's Americana, York, PA.

Buck Rogers, Atomic pistol, MIB 425.00
Buck Rogers, board game, 3 in 1, 3 boards, 1934, M 395.00
Buck Rogers, colorforms, 1979, M 6.00
Buck Rogers, game, Milton Bradley, 1979, sealed 7.50
Buck Rogers, holster/belt, leather, 1930s, EX 170.00
Buck Rogers, print set, rubber stamps, 1930s, 23 w/no box 125.00
Buck Rogers, Repeller Ray Ring, rare 500.00
Buck Rogers, Sonic Ray gun, plastic, 1950s, MIB 85.00
Buck Rogers, Space Ranger kit, Sylvania, 1952, +envelope, M .145.00
Buck Rogers, Storybook, orig, Kelloggs premium 85.00
Buffalo Bill, puzzle, in orig envelope, 1933, 65-pc, NM 23.00
Bugs Bunny, sticker/color book, Whitman, 1930, M 21.00
Bugs Bunny, wrist watch, 1970s, M 20.00
Buster Brown, comic book, #43, EX 5.00
Buster Brown, letter & coupons for stockings, 1905 ....50.00
Buster Brown, playing cards, leather case 55.00
Buster Brown, Yo-Yo, ca 1960s 15.00
Campbell Kids, kaleidoscope, vegetable soup can look-alike 15.00
Captain Kangaroo, Let's Build a House game, 1954, EX 10.00
Captain Kangaroo, mug, purple w/flickering eyes 12.00
Captain Marvel, buzz bomb, Fawcett, 1945 ....15.00
Captain Marvel, iron-on transfer, 1940s, 7", EX 4.00
Captain Marvel, Jr Ski Jump, Fawcett, 1944, M in envelope 20.00
Captain Marvel, Magic Flute, Fawcett, c 1946, on orig card 40.00
Captain Marvel, paper doll book, 1945, unused 65.00
Captain Midnight, Medal of Membership, Skelly, 1940 ....12.00
Captain Midnight, Mirror Magic Decoder, 1948 ....40.00
Captain Midnight, mug, Ovaltine 15th Anniversary, 1957 ....20.00
Captain Midnight, mug, shake-up; 1940s, M 50.00
Captain Midnight, Mystery Dial Codegraph, 1940 premium 27.00
Captain Midnight, Secret Squadron Decoder, 1955-56 ....85.00
Captain Midnight, stamp album w/16 stamps, Skelly Oil, 1940 ..35.00
Casper the Ghost, game, 1950s, MIB 20.00
Casper the Ghost, Golden Record, 1962 ....5.00
Charles Lindbergh, medallion, Deco woman, bronze, 3" 75.00
Charles Lindbergh, medallion, 1st Flight, bronze, 3" 45.00
Charles Lindbergh, pin-bk button, face/airplanes/flags 35.00
Charlie Chaplin, ash tray, figural, c LEGO 20.00
Charlie Chaplin, booklet, 10 movie stamps, 1915, 2¼x3¼" 25.00
Charlie Chaplin, doll, tin ball-&-socket body, 7½" 450.00
Charlie Chaplin, music box, plastic, Hong Kong, 1981 ......30.00
Charlie Chaplin, music box, revolving figure, Bubbles, 1973 ....20.00
Charlie Chaplin, Mystery Movie drawing book, 3-pg, 2x3¼", M .40.00
Charlie Chaplin, pencil box, full figure, 8x2" 50.00
Charlie Chaplin, photocard, Essannay, 1915 ....10.00
Charlie McCarthy, book, A Day w/..., 1938 ....30.00
Charlie McCarthy, comic book, In the Haunted House, 1948 ...15.00
Charlie McCarthy, comic book, Rocket Ship, #6, 1950, EX 20.00
Charlie McCarthy, figure, pnt rubber, 9", EX 35.00
Charlie McCarthy, Flying Hats game, EX 30.00
Charlie McCarthy, paper money, 20-pc, unopened, M 27.50
Charlie McCarthy, puppet, Maxwell premium, 22", M 60.00
Charlie McCarthy, radio party game, 21 die-cut figures, M 45.00
Cinderella, bank, compo, c 1950, M 28.00
Cinderella, Halloween costume, Disney, 1950, MIB 30.00
Cinderella, picture locket, M in pkg 22.00
Cinderella, record, 1963, sealed 15.00
Cinderella, wrist watch, Bradley, MIB 45.00
Dagwood, marionette, wood/plastic, Hazelle, 1950s, 14", MIB ..25.00
Dale Evans, statue, Hartland, MIB 90.00
Dale Evans, wrist watch, US Time, early, 1940s, EX w/box 145.00
Davy Crockett, belt, blk leather, emb buckle, 1950s, M 6.50
Davy Crockett, card game, boxed, 1950s, M 8.50
Davy Crockett, cereal bowl, milk glass, 1950s 8.00

Davy Crockett, charm bracelet, 7-pc, 1950s, M on card 50.00
Davy Crockett, figural lamp base, bronzed metal 55.00
Davy Crockett, inflatable horse, 1950s, lt wear 48.00
Davy Crockett, Injun Shooting Gallery, Disney, MIB 75.00
Davy Crockett, jeans, khaki w/brn fringe, Disney, M 38.00
Davy Crockett, money belt, vinyl, 1950s, M 6.50
Davy Crockett, play money, 1950s 4.00
Dennis the Menace, bowl, yel/red 14.00
Dennis the Menace, puppet, vinyl head/cloth body, EX 50.00
Dick Tracy, camera, blk plastic, 1950s, orig box, 5", EX 28.00
Dick Tracy, Jr handcuffs, tin, 1950s, M on orig litho card 22.00
Dick Tracy, paint pook, ca 1935, lg, EX 65.00
Dick Tracy, post card, issued by Coca-Cola, 1942 ....15.00
Dick Tracy, poster, Dick Tracy Vs Cueball, 1946, 41x27", EX ..85.00
Dick Tracy, puppet set, 1961, pr 25.00
Dick Tracy, puzzle, Jaymar, 1950s, 20x15", NM 20.00
Dick Tracy, Super Detective Mystery card game, 1941, NM 35.00
Dick Tracy, suspenders, on orig display card, 1950s, EX 22.50
Dionne Quintuplets, book, We're 2 Years Old, ca 1936, M 25.00
Dionne Quintuplets, calendar, color, 1946 ....22.00
Dionne Quintuplets, calender, This Year They Are 5, 1939 ....22.50
Dionne Quintuplets, cereal bowl, metal, NM 45.00
Dionne Quintuplets, doll set, jtd bsk, in orig cradle, '30s 375.00
Dionne Quintuplets, hand fan, funeral home advertising 18.00
Dionne Quintuplets, paper dolls, Colgate Palmolive mailer 55.00
Dionne Quintuplets, sheet music, Quintuplets Lullaby, EX 25.00
Dionne Quintuplets, spoon set, SP, 5 for 140.00
Donald Duck, Army paint book, Whitman #668, '42, unused ...45.00
Donald Duck, bank, ceramic, ca 1950 ....40.00
Donald Duck, bank, ceramic, WD, London, NM 40.00
Donald Duck, bean bag party game, Parker Bros, 1939, EX 75.00
Donald Duck, camera, mk WDP, Herbert-George, Chicago 35.00
Donald Duck, card game, Whitman, 1949, EX 16.00
Donald Duck, figure, bsk, w/bugle, Japan, 3" 85.00
Donald Duck, figure, celluloid, 1930, 6" 160.00
Donald Duck, figure, glazed china, 6", EX 125.00
Donald Duck, figure, rubber, Dell, 1968 ....40.00
Donald Duck, pitcher, milk; Leeds, 1940s 48.00
Donald Duck, plate, Patriot China, 1936, 8", EX 65.00
Donald Duck, pull toy, paper litho over wood, Fisher Price, NM .85.00
Donald Duck, ring, sterling, Donald in relief 48.00
Donald Duck, shakers, ceramic, Leeds, pr 32.00
Donald Duck, toy sweeper, tin litho, Chein, 1940, EX 90.00
Donald Duck, Tricky Joe Football game, 1950, NM in box 15.00
Dopey, Blk hand puppet, WDE, 1930s, rare 135.00
Dopey, costume, cloth mask, Disney, 1940s, EX 35.00
Dopey, linen book, 1938, EX 25.00
Dopey, music box, WD, EX 115.00
Dopey, night light, tin w/cardboard Dopey, battery-op 145.00
Dr Doolittle, Game-Pac card set, Whitman, 1967, MIB 15.00
Dr Jekyll & Mr Hyde, puzzle, 1975, sealed, 36", M 10.00
Dumbo, charm, sterling, ¾" 48.00
Dumbo, creamer, trunk is spout, 1940s 30.00
Dumbo, pin-bk D-X pin, 1940s, NM but no label on bk 28.00
Dumbo, song book, ca 1940, EX 20.00
Elsie the Cow, cook book, World's Fair 22.00
Elsie the Cow, ring, celluloid 10.00
Elvis Presley, dog tag, picture & service #, dtd 1956 .....10.00
Elvis Presley, drink mixer, miniature guitar 8.00
Elvis Presley, hat, blk cloth w/orig photo card, 1956, M ...65.00
Elvis Presley, King of Rock game, M 5.00
Elvis Presley, playing cards 5.00
Elvis Presley, pocket watch, windup, Bradley, 1984 ....45.00
Elvis Presley, teddy bear cologne, dtd 1957, MIB 100.00

Felix the Cat, jtd wood doll, leather ears, Sullivan, 1924, 8" ...250.00
Felix the Cat, target set, Lido, 1950s, MIB 40.00
Ferdinand the Bull, figure, bsk, Disney, 1930s, M 35.00
Flash Gordon, belt buckle, 1930s, on orig card 50.00
Flash Gordon, Christmas card, Flash & Dale, 1950s, NM 20.00
Flash Gordon, Christmas card, Mac Raboy Art, 1950s, EX 20.00
Flash Gordon, color book, MC Williams Art, 1952 ....20.00
Flash Gordon, Commando set, 1952, M on orig store display ...60.00
Flash Gordon, paint book, ca 1935, lg, EX 85.00
Flash Gordon, picture record, City of Sea Caves 30.00
Flash Gordon, space wrist compass 30.00
Flintstones, ash tray, pottery 38.00
Flintstones, bank, Fred figural, vinyl, 1971, 13", EX 20.00
Flintstones, Barney doll, vinyl, Dakin, 1970, 6", M 18.50
Flintstones, color book, 192-pg, EX 20.00
Flintstones, comic book, World's Fair souvenir, 1964, M 7.00
Flintstones, Fred puppet, vinyl/cloth, Knickerbocker, 1962 ......8.00
Flintstones, game, 1961, NM 23.00
Flintstones, Pebbles doll, fully clothed, Ideal, 16", EX 26.00
Gabby Hayes, fishing set, 2 poles & reels in tin container 150.00
Garfield, wrist watch, MIB 28.00
Gene Autry, book, GA Goes to the Circus, 1950, EX 15.00
Gene Autry, boot box label 12.00
Gene Autry, cap pistol, pearl grips, Kenton, MIB 95.00
Gene Autry, color book, 1949, NM 45.00
Gene Autry, color book, 1953, EX 32.00
Gene Autry, guitar, 'round-up,' wood, EX 195.00
Gene Autry, guitar, Emenee, MIB 200.00
Gene Autry, guitar, Melody Ranch, EX 195.00
Gene Autry, horseshoe nail ring, on orig card 28.00
Gene Autry, paper dolls, Whitman, 53-pc, uncut 75.00
Gene Autry, pin-bk button, w/Champion 10.00
Gene Autry, wrist watch, gun moves, 1948, EX 200.00
Gene Autry, wrist watch, Wilane, EX portrait 110.00
GI Joe, walkie talkie, gr plastic, Hasbro, 1964, 8", M 28.00
Gideon, figure, bsk, 3", EX 48.00
Goofy, figure, bsk, 3" 50.00
Green Hornet, secret compartment ring, rare 375.00
Grumpy, soap, Lightfoot Schultz, 1934, MIB 40.00
Herman Munster, puppet, EX 35.00
Hopalong Cassidy, autograph book, simulated wood, EX 21.00
Hopalong Cassidy, badge, Eaco, M on orig card 25.00
Hopalong Cassidy, badge, metal, 1950s, EX 10.00
Hopalong Cassidy, badge, Sheriff, brass, M 15.00
Hopalong Cassidy, bedspread, chenille, 75x102", EX 150.00
Hopalong Cassidy, bicycle horn, NM in orig box 90.00
Hopalong Cassidy, binoculars, metal, Galter, good decal 30.00
Hopalong Cassidy, birthday card, Cardoza, M 24.00
Hopalong Cassidy, blk denim pants, Blue Bell, all labels 65.00
Hopalong Cassidy, cap pistols, Wyandotte, +holster, MIB ...250.00
Hopalong Cassidy, Chinese checkers, Wm Boyd, 1950 ....45.00
Hopalong Cassidy, Chuck Wagon set, plate/cup/bowl, MIB ...65.00
Hopalong Cassidy, color book, 1950, 10x14", NM 30.00
Hopalong Cassidy, cowboy clothes, 1949, MIB 225.00
Hopalong Cassidy, cowgirl outfit, Iskin, EX in box 135.00
Hopalong Cassidy, cowgirl outfit, Iskin, 3-pc, MIB 160.00
Hopalong Cassidy, dart board, tin litho, 2-sided 65.00
Hopalong Cassidy, dart board, metal, gun & darts, 1950, MIB .100.00
Hopalong Cassidy, dominoes, Milton Bradley, M 85.00
Hopalong Cassidy, lamp, revolving waterfall, EX 195.00
Hopalong Cassidy, milk carton, EX 7.50
Hopalong Cassidy, mug, bl logo & scene on milk glass 8.50
Hopalong Cassidy, mug, w/mc decal 20.00
Hopalong Cassidy, neckerchief, dtd 1950, NM 12.50

Hopalong Cassidy, night light, Spun Honey, plugs in, EX 7.50
Hopalong Cassidy, pencil box, gun & holster decor, M 50.00
Hopalong Cassidy, pencil sharpener, Hasbro 18.00
Hopalong Cassidy, Picturegun Theatre, EX in orig box 200.00
Hopalong Cassidy, pin-bk button, 1950, 3" dia 15.00
Hopalong Cassidy, poster, matted, 1950s, 22½x28", EX 45.00
Hopalong Cassidy, radio, red, Arvin, EX 165.00
Hopalong Cassidy, roller skates 45.00
Hopalong Cassidy, shooting gallery, windup, EX in box 150.00
Hopalong Cassidy, Thank-You card, 8½x6½", EX 10.00
Hopalong Cassidy, thermos, yel, VG 15.00
Hopalong Cassidy, wrist cuffs, leather, EX 75.00
Hopalong Cassidy, wrist watch, 1950s, MIB 150.00
Hopalong Cassidy, Zoomerang gun, MIB 200.00
Hopalong Cassidy, 5¢ candy bar box, die-cut cover, 1950s 175.00
Howdy Doody, Adventure game, Milton Bradley, EX 45.00
Howdy Doody, bath sponge, face/name emb on front, EX 25.00
Howdy Doody, beach chair, aluminum, child's sz, EX 120.00
Howdy Doody, cowboy hat, red, med, EX 25.00
Howdy Doody, dominoes set, early, EX 35.00
Howdy Doody, drinking glass 10.00
Howdy Doody, Flip-a-Ring game, 1950, M in pkg 10.00
Howdy Doody, follow-the-dots book, Whitman #1410, '55, M ..20.00
Howdy Doody, iced teaspoon, ca 1950s 15.00
Howdy Doody, marionette, compo, all orig, 14" 165.00
Howdy Doody, marionette, wood/rubber, 7", EX 30.00
Howdy Doody, night lamp, Howdy sitting, 1950s, NM 125.00
Howdy Doody, place mat, paper, 1950s, 14x10" 15.00
Howdy Doody, record, It's Howdy Doody Time, M 15.00
Howdy Doody, wrist watch, 40th Anniversary, It's HD Time ...50.00
Huckleberry Hound, bank, red plastic figural, 1960s, 9½" ...15.00
Huckleberry Hound, bracelet w/6 charms, 1959, M on orig card .30.00
Huckleberry Hound, pencil sharpener, plastic figural, 1960s 6.50
Huckleberry Hound, tie clip & cuff links, metal, 1959, M 20.00
Huckleberry Hound, plaque, Hanna Barbera, 1978, 12", NM ...10.00
Incredible Hulk, speedboat, plastic, 1979, 8", MIB 10.00
Jack Armstrong, Big 10 Football game, Wheaties, 1933, M 45.00
Jayne Mansfield, figure, rubber, blk bikini, 1957, 22" 115.00
Jetsons, record, Hanna Barbera, 1961, NM 15.00
Joe Louis, chalkware bust, sgn in script, EX pnt, 8½" 220.00
Joe Palooka, book, Ham Fisher, 1958, 14-pg 10.00
John Lennon, radio w/figure on top, EX 40.00
Katzenjammer Kids, jigsaw puzzle, 1942, EX 30.00
Kermit the Frog, wrist watch, MIB 36.00
Krazy Cat, nursing bottle, Comfy 35.00
Lil Abner, color book, 1947, EX 25.00
Little Joe, doll, Bonanza, w/accessories, 1960s, 8", EX 30.00

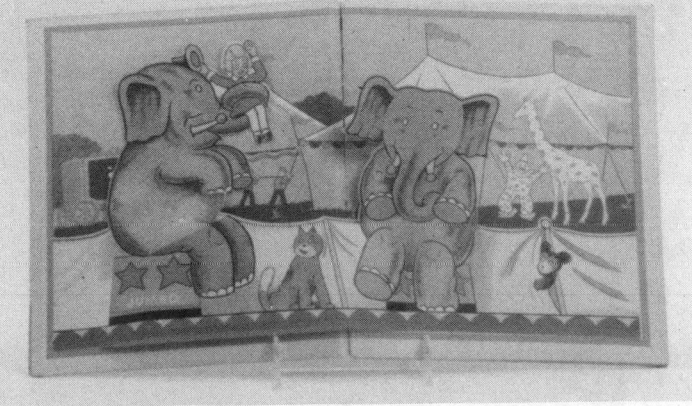

Little Orphan Annie, pop-up book, 9x8", $75.00.

Little Orphan Annie, Aztec Sun Dial wrist watch 85.00
Little Orphan Annie, board game, Treasure Isle, EX 60.00
Little Orphan Annie, book, Bucking the World, #4, EX 28.00
Little Orphan Annie, book, Never Say Die, #5 . . . . .28.00
Little Orphan Annie, card game, 1927, EX in box 35.00
Little Orphan Annie, color book, 1930s, EX/uncolored 35.00
Little Orphan Annie, decoder, 1936 . . . . .25.00
Little Orphan Annie, manual/decoder/order form, '36, M in pkg..95.00
Little Orphan Annie, penny book, 1934, 6 in orig holder, NM . .95.00
Little Orphan Annie, place setting, lustreware, 3-pc 75.00
Little Orphan Annie, stove, gr w/decals, +3 pots, EX 65.00
Little Orphan Annie, wrist watch, EX 90.00
Little Orphan Annie & Sandy, shakers, figurals, '40s, NM, pr . . .30.00
Little Orphan Annie & Sandy, toothbrush holder, EX 135.00
Lone Ranger, Atom Bomb ring, EX .75.00
Lone Ranger, badge, Deputy, star form, EX 22.00
Lone Ranger, board game, Parker Bros, 1938, EX 45.00
Lone Ranger, brush, 1939 . . . . .18.00
Lone Ranger, certificate, Pledge to Parents, 1938, EX 25.00
Lone Ranger, cowboy outfit, 5-pc, Yank Boy, 1947, EX in box .160.00
Lone Ranger, cowgirl outfit, Esquire, 1947, MIB 130.00
Lone Ranger, dart/target game, tin litho, Marx, '38, 16x28" 95.00
Lone Ranger, first aid kit, tin, 1938, EX 40.00
Lone Ranger, flasher belt buckle, 1976, M 12.00
Lone Ranger, guitar, Jefferson, EX 95.00
Lone Ranger, gun & holster set, 1950s, EX 85.00
Lone Ranger, holster, 1940s, EX 40.00
Lone Ranger, Merita Bread premium photo, +mailer 30.00
Lone Ranger, official souvenir program, 1950s, NM 35.00
Lone Ranger, paint book, Whitman, 1950s, EX 15.00
Lone Ranger, paint box, tin litho, 1950s, M 22.00
Lone Ranger, pencil case, 1959, EX .20.00
Lone Ranger, pocket knife, ca 1940, NM 35.00
Lone Ranger, ring toss set, 1950s, EX in orig box 65.00
Lone Ranger, rocking horse, 1938, NM 175.00
Lone Ranger, rodeo play set, Marx, 1950s, EX 100.00
Lone Ranger, scrapbook, Whitman, 1950s, unused 20.00
Lone Ranger, Signal Siren flashlight, w/Silver Bullet Code, M . .65.00
Lone Ranger, Silver Bullet knife, NM 35.00
Lone Ranger, Silver Bullet w/compass inside 20.00
Lone Ranger, snow globe, LR roping calf, EX 30.00
Lone Ranger, toothbrush holder, compo, 1938, NM 38.00
Lone Ranger, Weber Bread wrapper, 1940s, scarce 40.00

Maggie & Jiggs, puzzle, ca 1930, 8x10", EX, 4 in orig box 45.00
Man from UNCLE, card game, Milton Bradley, complete, EX . .18.00
Marilyn Monroe, book, Norma Jean, Guiles, 1969, EX 8.00
Marilyn Monroe, post card, 1953, NM 5.00
Mary Poppins, crayon/pnt set, Hasbro, 1965, 15x12", M 20.00
Mary Poppins, doll, vinyl, 12", MIB 48.00
Mickey & Minnie Mouse, cup & saucer, silver hdl, Disney 95.00
Mickey & Minnie Mouse, napkin holder, 3-D mice, celluloid . .280.00
Mickey & Minnie Mouse, sand sifter, Ohio Art 80.00
Mickey & Minnie Mouse, shakers, Brechner, pr 45.00
Mickey Mouse, beach chair & stool, pie-eyed, folding, early . . .300.00
Mickey Mouse, bell harness, WDE, 1930s 85.00
Mickey Mouse, book, Adventure of MM, McKay, 1931, M 155.00
Mickey Mouse, book, MM's Summer Vacation, 1948, 7x4", VG .10.00
Mickey Mouse, book, Whitman #711, 1936, lt wear 58.00
Mickey Mouse, Book for Coloring, diecut, Saalfield #2121, NM .75.00
Mickey Mouse, books, Library of Games, 6-volume set, NM 95.00
Mickey Mouse, bubble gum card, #51, early 1930s, M 20.00
Mickey Mouse, candy box, tin hexagon, hinged lid, sm 180.00
Mickey Mouse, card game, Post Toasties premium, 1935, EX . . .45.00
Mickey Mouse, cereal bowl, Beetleware, WDE, 1938, M, 4 for . .65.00
Mickey Mouse, cereal bowl, china, WD, 1930s, NM 75.00
Mickey Mouse, charm, celluloid figural, EX 10.00
Mickey Mouse, Coming Home game, Marx Bros, 1934, rare 60.00
Mickey Mouse, doctor kit, plastic, 1960, MIB 35.00
Mickey Mouse, doll, wood, jtd, w/ears &tail, 3½", NM 95.00
Mickey Mouse, dominoes, WDE, 1938, boxed set, NM 55.00
Mickey Mouse, figure, bsk, playing horn, 1930s, 4½" 100.00
Mickey Mouse, figure, compo, from '30s Lionel circus train, M .180.00
Mickey Mouse, figure, plastic, windup, 1960s, 7", NM 60.00

Mickey Mouse, velvet with felt hands, wooden nose, glass button eyes, rubber tail, English, early, 11", $750.00.

Lum & Abner's Adventures in Hollywood & 1938 Family Almanac, blk/wht illus, 32-pg, $21.00. (Photo courtesy of Hake's Americana, York, PA.)

Mickey Mouse, figure, wood, jtd arms, 1927, 8" 250.00
Mickey Mouse, film, Milkmaid, VG orig box 18.00
Mickey Mouse, fire truck, Sun Rubber Co, 1940s, 6½", EX 35.00
Mickey Mouse, greeting card, Hall Bros, 1930s 35.00
Mickey Mouse, hairbrush, sterling w/pnt MM, baby's 38.00
Mickey Mouse, handkerchief, MM football player, 1950s, NM . .12.50
Mickey Mouse, handkerchief, Walt Disney, ca 1936, 8½" 25.00
Mickey Mouse, kaleidoscope, WDE, 1940s, EX 75.00
Mickey Mouse, lawn ornament, die-cut wood, 1930s 75.00
Mickey Mouse, mask & vest, Cooper, 1960, M in pkg 10.00
Mickey Mouse, movie projector, WDE, 1935, VG, +4 films . . .175.00
Mickey Mouse, night light, glass w/figural insert, WDE, NM . . .95.00
Mickey Mouse, night light, hard plastic, Japan 18.00
Mickey Mouse, nodder, WDP 95.00

Mickey Mouse, official store pin, 1937 ....25.00
Mickey Mouse, Old Maid card game, WDE, 1937, MIB 50.00
Mickey Mouse, pencil box, Dixon, #2909, 1930s, EX 65.00
Mickey Mouse, pencil sharpener, Hasbro, 1960s, 5", M 13.50
Mickey Mouse, Pin the Tail game, Marx Bros, M in envelope ...65.00
Mickey Mouse, pitcher, milk; figural, Japan, 7x6½" 125.00
Mickey Mouse, planter, ceramic, Brechner, 1950s, 6x5½", M ..45.00
Mickey Mouse, pocket mirror, WDE 20.00
Mickey Mouse, pocket watch w/fob, 1933, EX orig 600.00
Mickey Mouse, pop-up book, Circus, 1933, NM 300.00
Mickey Mouse, pop-up book, Ye Olden Days, 1934 ....150.00
Mickey Mouse, pop-up book, 3 pop-ups, 1933, EX 200.00
Mickey Mouse, post card, Walt Disney, ca 1940s, EX 30.00
Mickey Mouse, pull toy, pnt wood, Jaymar 48.00
Mickey Mouse, puzzle, framed tray, Whitman, 1950s 12.00
Mickey Mouse, radio, wht plastic, General Electric, 1960s, M ...60.00
Mickey Mouse, recipe scrapbook, w/48 color cards, +mailer ...350.00
Mickey Mouse, ring, gold-tone metal 68.00
Mickey Mouse, ring, sterling, 1930s 50.00
Mickey Mouse, Scatter Ball game, Marx Bros, 1934, lt wear ...150.00
Mickey Mouse, Schoolmaster blackboard, standing, '39, EX ...155.00
Mickey Mouse, sheet music, Who's Afraid of Big Bad Wolf 18.00
Mickey Mouse, Slugaroo-Baseball game, 1950, NM in box 35.00
Mickey Mouse, spoon, Branford Silverplate, 1930s 20.00
Mickey Mouse, tambourine, WDE 40.00
Mickey Mouse, tea set, china, WDE, 21-pc 280.00
Mickey Mouse, tea set, tan lustreware, ca 1933, 17-pc, EX 130.00
Mickey Mouse, tie clasp, brass, 1960s, MIB 5.00
Mickey Mouse, tool chest, metal, early Disney art, WDE, VG ...65.00
Mickey Mouse, toothbrush holder, bsk, 5", EX 225.00
Mickey Mouse, toy chest, 1930s, EX 150.00
Mickey Mouse, travel alarm, Phinney Walker 35.00
Mickey Mouse, valentine, mechanical tipping hat, 1939, EX ...22.50
Mickey Mouse, wall clock, watch form, blk strap, Welby, NM ..22.50
Mickey Mouse, washing machine, WDE, 1934, MIB 650.00
Mickey Mouse, watering can, tin, Ohio Art, 7", M 95.00
Mickey Mouse, wrist watch, Elgin, WDP, lg 27.00
Mickey Mouse, wrist watch, English Timex, 1940, EX 150.00
Mickey Mouse, wrist watch, leather band, Ingersoll, '39, MIB ..250.00
Mickey Mouse, wrist watch, metal band, Ingersoll, 1933, MIB .375.00
Mickey Mouse, wrist watch, red band, Ingersoll, 1947, MIB ...175.00
Mickey Mouse, wrist watch, Timex, 1968, EX, no box 35.00
Mickey Mouse, wrist watch, US Time, 1947, M 95.00
Mickey Mouse, wrist watch, 50-Yr/ltd ed, Bradley, 1983, MIB ..50.00
Mickey Mouse Club, birthday cups, 6-oz, unused 8.00
Mickey Mouse Club, Duncan Yo-Yo, 1956, M 15.00
Mickey Mouse Club, newsreel-type projector, EX 30.00
Mickey Mouse Club, thermos, early 1960s, M ···············22.00
Mickey Mouse Club, tiddly winks, logo on cover, EX 10.00
Mighty Mouse, Rescue game, 1956, MIB 25.00
Mighty Mouse, wrist watch, Bradley, 1969, M 46.00
Minnie Mouse, figure, bsk, playing mandolin, 3½", EX 90.00
Minnie Mouse, pop-up book, 1933, NM 200.00
Minnie Mouse, wrist watch, animated hands, 1958, EX orig 38.00
Miss Piggy, wrist watch, 1980, MIB 25.00
Mister Magoo, book, 1958, 8x6", EX 6.00
Monkees, bracelet, M on card 25.00
Monkees, puppet, cloth body w/4 heads, Mattel, 1966, NM ...68.00
Monkees, stage pass, unused 6.00
Munsters, thermos, tin litho, 1965, 6½", EX 20.00
Mutt & Jeff, croquet game, holes under glass, 1928 ....30.00
Peter Gun, board game, complete, EX 27.50
Peter Pan, book & record, Magic Mirror, 1962 ....15.00
Peter Pan, pencil case, Disney, 1950s 20.00

Peter Pan, puzzle, Walt Disney, 1950s, MIB 13.50
Peter Potamus & So So, card game, Whitman, 1965 ....28.00
Peter Rabbit, puzzle, Milton Bradley, '14, 9x12", 3 in box, M ...50.00
Pinocchio, bank, ceramic, WD, London, NM 25.00
Pinocchio, bank, vinyl figural, 1960s, 8", EX 5.00
Pinocchio, barrette, bow-shaped plastic w/decal 15.00
Pinocchio, figure, bsk, 3" 50.00
Pinocchio, figure, movable arms & legs, ca 1960s 42.00
Pinocchio, post card, set of 12, in folder, EX 25.00
Pinocchio, souvenir song album, 1939, NM 35.00
Pinocchio, story book, Cocoa-Malt ad on bk, 1939, EX 35.00
Pluto, book, Pluto the Pup, linen, 1937, WDE 18.00
Pluto, nursing bottle, Comfy 35.00
Pluto, planter, Pluto w/wheelbarrow, 1940s 48.00
Popeye, ash tray, glass in plaster base, lt wear 98.00
Popeye, backpack, 1979, M 10.00
Popeye, bank, tin, dime register, 1929, EX 65.00
Popeye, Bingo game, 1930, EX in box 35.00
Popeye, bowl & plate, Melmac, 1950s 22.00
Popeye, boxing gloves, Everlast, 1950s, MIB 65.00
Popeye, brush, mc on blk, King Features, 1929, EX 45.00
Popeye, card game, dtd 1934, in leather case 40.00
Popeye, card game, Ed-U-Cards, 1961, MIB 15.00
Popeye, chalk/crayon set, 1956, MIB 12.50
Popeye, charm bracelet, SP, metal base w/3-D detail, 1930s 75.00
Popeye, Christmas tree topper, HP ceramic, 1960s, 9½", NM ...15.00
Popeye, doll, cloth, 1960s, 14", M 21.50
Popeye, embroidery set, Hasbro, 1960s, 16x12" 15.00
Popeye, figure, Dakin, mc, 7½", EX 6.50
Popeye, Getar, crank plays Popeye the Sailor Man, 1960s, MIB .40.00
Popeye, iron-on transfer, 1940s, 7", EX 4.00
Popeye, lantern, tin figural, Linemar, MIB 165.00
Popeye, napkin holder, early, plastic w/Popeye decal 48.00
Popeye, night light, vinyl figural, 1959, 7", NM 40.00
Popeye, paint book, Whitman #2081, 1937, unused 80.00
Popeye, pencil sharpener, die-cut plastic w/decal 32.00
Popeye, Pirate pistol, tin litho, Marx, 1935, MIB 250.00
Popeye, pocket watch, rare, MIB 475.00
Popeye, pop-up book, Hag of the 7 Seas, 1935, EX 100.00
Popeye, puzzle, mc, 1932, 9¾x7½", NM 20.00
Popeye, Roly-Poly target, orig packaging, 1958, NM 70.00
Popeye, spinach can, Mattel, 1957 ....25.00
Popeye, valentine card, early 1930s, rare 28.00
Popeye, wrist watch, 1930s, EX 350.00
Porky Pig, wrist watch, 1970s, MIB 50.00
Red Ryder, BB gun, Daisy, picture/writing in wood stock, EX ..125.00
Red Ryder, paint book, 1941, EX 25.00
Red Ryder, Pony contest pin-bk button 7.50
Red Ryder, target game, cb, Whitman, 1939, EX in box 75.00
Reddy Kilowatt, enameled pin, 1955, M on orig card 12.50
Rifleman, board game, 1959, EX 25.00
Roy Rogers, bank, boot shape, brass, EX 38.00
Roy Rogers, belt, leather, 18 studs, EX 45.00
Roy Rogers, binoculars, EX 45.00
Roy Rogers, book, Bullet Leads the Way, Whitman, 1953 .....12.00
Roy Rogers, camera, H George, EX 25.00
Roy Rogers, camera, w/flash, M 85.00
Roy Rogers, Chuck Wagon Stage, windup, Marx, MIB 175.00
Roy Rogers, color book, 1951, unused 25.00
Roy Rogers, cut-out dolls, Whitman, 1954, EX 45.00
Roy Rogers, figure, Hartland 95.00
Roy Rogers, guitar, Jefferson 45.00
Roy Rogers, harmonica, M on orig card 25.00
Roy Rogers, horseshoe set, ca 1950s, MIB 75.00

Roy Rogers, lamp, Happy Trails, Plaster Mfg, Chicago, 12" 145.00
Roy Rogers, lamp, plastic/plaster, VG shade 125.00
Roy Rogers, paint book, 1st edition, 1944, EX 35.00
Roy Rogers, photo, Comic Book premium, 1940s, +envelope . . .60.00
Roy Rogers, plate, Rodeo by Universal 25.00
Roy Rogers, puzzle, Whitman, 1952, 11½x9", VG 5.00
Roy Rogers, record player, RCA 175.00
Roy Rogers, saddle, tooled leather, child's, EX 250.00
Roy Rogers, shirt, NM 45.00
Roy Rogers, song folio #1, EX 25.00
Roy Rogers, spurs, metal w/blk leather straps, EX 28.00
Roy Rogers, Tuck-A-Way gun, M on store card 35.00
Roy Rogers, wrist watch, 1940s, EX .50.00
Roy Rogers, Yo-Yo, plastic, 1950s 16.00
Roy Rogers & Trigger, bank, metal, EX 68.00
Roy Rogers & Trigger, bedspread, red/wht, 1940s, EX 45.00
Roy Rogers & Trigger, scarf 25.00
Roy Rogers & Trigger, wallet, brn leather, 1950s, M 25.00
Shirley Temple, book, ...Wee Willie Winkie, Saalfield, '37 . . . . .60.00
Shirley Temple, book, from movie Stowaway, 1937, 32-pg, NM .30.00
Shirley Temple, book, Little Colonel, Saalfield, EX 35.00
Shirley Temple, book, Through the Day, 1936, EX 12.00
Shirley Temple, breakfast set, 3-pc 75.00
Shirley Temple, bridge deck, Littlest Colonel, 1935, NM 37.50
Shirley Temple, child's dress, tagged, 1930, M 40.00
Shirley Temple, creamer, cobalt glass .38.00
Shirley Temple, magnetic TV Theatre 75.00
Shirley Temple, mug, cobalt glass 48.00
Shirley Temple, Passtime Box, Saalfield, #1732 . . . . .48.00
Shirley Temple, photo, hand tinted, orig fr, 1936, 13x10½" 35.00

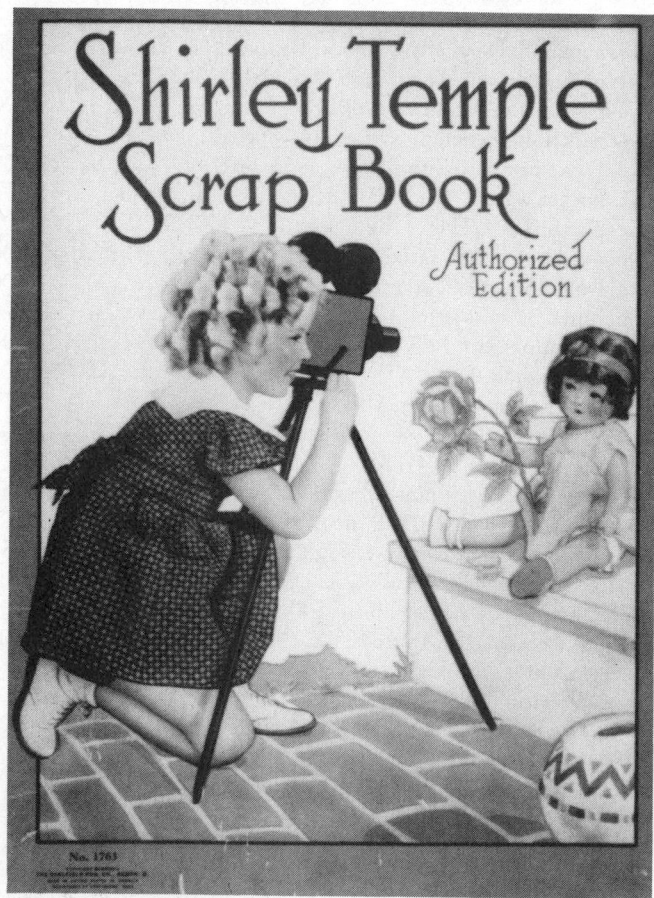

Shirley Temple scrapbook, Saalfield, ca 1937, 15x11", EX, $18.00. (Photo courtesy of Hake's Americana, York, PA.)

Shirley Temple, sewing cards, Saalfield, 1936, EX in box 30.00
Shirley Temple, sheet music, On the Good Ship Lollipop 12.50
Shirley Temple, sheet music, Stowaway 7.50
Sleeping Beauty, crib mobile, plastic figures, Kenner, M 32.00
Sleeping Beauty, figure, Dell Rubber, 1950s, 5", NM 38.00
Smokey the Bear, key chain 12.00
Snoopy, alarm clock, 1958 . . . . .40.00
Snoopy, wrist watch, floating tennis ball, 1958 . . . . .55.00
Snoopy, wrist watch, pk face, dtd 1958, NM 55.00
Snoopy, wrist watch, red, 1968, lg 32.00
Snow White, board game, Milton Bradley, 1937, NM 120.00
Snow White, cake & pastry flour bag .15.00
Snow White, picture puzzle set, WDE, 2 in orig box 100.00
Snow White, sheet music, Heigh-Ho, 1938, EX 12.00
Snow White, Showplace magazine, souvenir ed, Feb 1938, EX . .25.00
Snow White, Tinkertoy sand set, WDE, 1938, rare, MIB 375.00
Snow White, valentine, mechanical, 1938, NM 20.00
Snow White, wrist watch, US Time, 1950s, EX orig 55.00
Snow White & 7 Dwarfs, charm, pnt metal, 3-D, set of 8 . . . . .45.00
Snow White & 7 Dwarfs, folding ladder, 1930s, 9½", MIB 255.00
Snow White & 7 Dwarfs, souvenir album, WDE, 1938, EX 35.00
Snow White & 7 Dwarfs, story book, 96-pg 75.00
Sonja Henie, ice skates, 1938, MIB 40.00
Soupy Sales, cards, early 1960s 15.00
Steve Canyon, color book, EX 15.00
Steve Canyon, helmet, 1959, MIB 45.00
Superman, color book, Whitman #1181, 1965, 128-pg 15.00
Superman, color book, Whitman #1189, ca 1960s 12.00
Superman, glasses, EX 4.00
Superman, Krypto ray gun, Daisy 85.00
Superman, Krypton rocket, 1956, EX 165.00
Superman, pin-bk button, mc, ca 1939, rare, 1⅜", M 90.00
Superman, record player, 1978 . . . . .40.00
Superman, sign, Eat Superman Bread, paper, 1¼x11", EX 85.00
Superman, spoon, Imperial, EX 7.50
Tarzan, flicker ring, gold plastic, 2 scenes 8.00
Thumper, book, hard cover, Grosset/Dunlap, 1942, EX 24.00
Tom Corbett, binoculars, metal, EX 38.00
Tom Corbett, flashlight gun, plastic, Marx 60.00
Tom Mix, Big Big Book, Scourge of Paradise Valley, EX 25.00
Tom Mix, booklet, The Life of..., 1933, EX 40.00
Tom Mix, catalog of Straight Shooter premiums, 1935 . . . . . . .20.00
Tom Mix, color book, M 45.00
Tom Mix, compass-magnifier, brass, 1940s 50.00
Tom Mix, gun, wood, take-a-part, 1939, EX 75.00
Tom Mix, jigsaw puzzle, Rexall Drugs, 1930s, M in mailer 35.00
Tom Mix, Look-Around ring, 1946 . . . . .60.00
Tom Mix, movie, My Girl, 16mm, orig box 35.00
Tom Mix, neckerchief, Ralston Straight Shooters Club 35.00
Tom Mix, poster, radio show promotion, 1947, 22x17" 10.00
Tom Mix, Secret Belt buckle, no belt .65.00
Tom Sawyer, paint set, EX litho, Paramount Pictures, 1931 . . . .70.00
Tom Thumb Jr, typewriter, EX in orig box 20.00
Tonto, Indian outfit, Esquire Novelty Co, ca 1950s, MIB 55.00
Tonto, Merita Bread premium photo, +letter & mailer 45.00
Uncle Wiggily, book, hard bound, 1940 . . . . .10.00
Walt & Skeezex, toothbrush holder 30.00
WC Fields, pitcher, Turtle Bay Whiskey, KY, rare, 8" 85.00
Wild Bill Hickock, dbl gun & holster set, MIB 95.00
Winnie the Pooh, game, 1964 . . . . .20.00
Winnie the Pooh, necklace, brass figural, 1964, MIB 10.00
Winnie the Pooh, wrist watch 44.00
Wonder Woman, wrist watch, 1977 . . . . .42.00
Woody Woodpecker, figure, rubber bend/flex, mc, 1970, EX . . .4.50

Woody Woodpecker, paper dolls/costumes, 1968 . . . . .20.00
Wyatt Earp, board game, 1958 . . . . .30.00
Wyatt Earp, cap gun, Bunt Line Special, Hubley, EX 40.00
Wyatt Earp, crayon & stencil set, MIB 60.00
Wyatt Earp, cut-out color book, 80-pg, 1958 . . . . .18.00
Wyatt Earp, dbl gun & holster set, Esquire, MIB 250.00
Yellow Kid, ad poster for cartoon strip, yel/bl, 27x18" 600.00
Yellow Kid, figure, cast metal, early, 6½", EX 550.00
Yellow Kid, figure, compo head/body, jtd, w/orig button, 7" . . .395.00
Yogi Bear, Ball Toss game, 1960, MIB 45.00
Yogi Bear, record, TV theme song, Hanna Barbera, 1961, NM . .11.50
Yogi Bear, sticker book, Hanna Barbera, 1974, M 10.00
Yogi Bear, wrist watch, early 1960s 45.00
Zorro, doll, w/4 outfits, plastic, WD, 1950s, M 30.00
Zorro, pencil/pnt set, Hasbro, 1960s, 21x12" 32.00
Zorro, pump rifle, worn 22.00
Zorro, puzzle, #8609, WDE, M 12.50
Zorro, Secret Sight mask, M on card 45.00
Zorro, wrist watch, WDP, 1950s, MIB 98.00
007, Action Vapor pen, 1966, M on orig card 125.00
007, Goldfinger game, complete, EX/NM 32.00
007, James Bond Secret Agent game, complete, NM 35.00
007, Playboy Magazine, Nov 1965 . . . . .28.00
007, puzzle, helicopter scene, MIB 12.00
007, Thunderball game, complete, EX 30.00
3 Bears, puzzle, M Bradley, 1905, 12½x17½", 3 in box 150.00
3 Little Pigs, ash tray, china, Disney, 1930s, NM 48.00
3 Little Pigs, Treasure Chest bank, 1930s, EX 85.00
3 Little Pigs, valentine, Hall Bros, ca 1934, EX 25.00
3 Stooges, fan club kit, letter/cards/photos/etc, 1959 . . . . .90.00
3 Stooges, record, Wreck the Halls w/Boughs of Holly, M 21.00
7 Dwarfs, figures, rubber, Seiberling, 1930s 375.00

Peters and Reed

John Peters and Adam Reed founded their pottery in Zanesville, Ohio, just before the turn of the century, using the local red clay to produce a variety of wares. Moss Aztec, introduced about 1912, has an unglazed exterior with designs molded in high relief and the recesses highlighted with a green wash. Only the interior is glazed to hold water. Pereco (named for Peters, Reed and Company) is glazed in semi-matt blue, maroon, or cream. Orange was also used very early, but such examples are rare. Shapes are simple with in-mold decoration sometimes borrowed from the Moss Aztec line. Wilse Blue is a line of high-gloss medium blue with dark specks on simple shapes. Landsun, characterized by its soft matt multicolor or blue and gray combinations, is decorated either by dripping or by hand brushing in an effect sometimes called Flame or Herringbone. Chromal, in much the same colors as Landsun, may be decorated with a realistic scenic, or the swirling application of colors may merely suggest one. (Brush-McCoy made a very similar line called Chromart. Neither will be marked; and, due to the lack of documented background material available, it may be impossible make a positive identification. Collectors nearly always attribute this type of decoration to Peters and Reed.) Shadow Ware is a glossy, multicolor drip over a harmonious base color. When the base is black, the effect is often iridescent.

Perhaps the most familiar line is the brown high-glaze artware with the 'sprigged'-type designs. Although research has uncovered no positive proof, it is generally accepted as having been made by Peters and Reed. It is interesting to note that many of the artistic shapes in this line are recognizable as those made by Weller, Roseville, and other Zanesville area companies. Other lines include Mirror Black, Persian, and an unidentified line which collectors call Mottled Colors. In this high-gloss line, the red clay body often shows through the splashed-on multicolors.

In 1922 the company became known as the Zane Pottery. Peters and Reed retired, and Harry McClelland became president. Charles Chilcote designed new lines, and production of many of the old lines continued. The body of the ware after 1922 was light in color. Marks include the impressed logo or ink stamp 'Zaneware' in a rectangle.

Bookends, Pereco, Arts & Crafts upright sq on sq base, 5" 75.00
Bowl, Moss Aztec, pine cones, sgn Ferrell, 3x6½" 50.00
Bowl, Pereco, nail head decor, recessed band, 2x4¾" 30.00
Candlesticks, Mirror Blk, 10", pr 50.00
Jardiniere, Chromal, landscape, 6x7" 175.00
Jardiniere, Moss Aztec, grapes & leaves, sgn Ferrell, 7½" 80.00
Jug, Brn Ware, sprigged garlands, 5½" 55.00
Jug, wine; Brn Ware, grapes & leaves, unmk, 6¼x5" 68.00
Loving cup, Brn Ware, lion's head & florals, 3-hdld 165.00
Planter, Brn Ware, wreath, hdl across top, 5½x8" 55.00

Vase, blue and green streaks over red ground, 9½", $75.00.

Vase, Brn Ware, lions' heads & floral garlands, 12" 155.00
Vase, Shadow Ware, blk w/gr drip, 9" 75.00
Vase, 4 HP brn/bl trees on yel matt, 7½" 75.00
Wall pocket, Egyptian Ware, gr w/profile 95.00
Wall pocket, Moss Aztec, 9" 75.00

Pewabic

The Pewabic Pottery was formally established in Detroit, Michigan, in 1907 by Mary Chase Perry Stratton and Horace James Caulkins. The two had worked together since 1903, firing their ware in a small kiln Caulkins had designed especially for use by the dental trade. Always a small operation which relied upon basic equipment and the skill of the workers, they took pride in being commissioned for several important architectural tile installations.

Some of the early artware was glazed a simple matt green; occasionally other colors were added, sometimes in combination, one over the other in a drip effect. Later Stratton developed a lustrous crystalline glaze. The body of the ware was highly fired and extremely hard. Shapes were basic, and decorative modeling, if used at all, was in low relief. Mary Stratton kept the pottery open until her death in 1961. In 1968 it was purchased and reopened by Michigan State University.

Several marks were used over the years: a triangle with 'Revelation Pottery' (for a short time only); 'Pewabic' with five maple leaves; and the impressed circle mark.

Box, bl/pk/purple/yel/gr irid, cat on lid, 3x4" L 250.00
Paperweight, pk/brn irid, 4" W 90.00
Vase, bl irid, purple/pk/brn highlights, bulbous, 5½" 400.00
Vase, bl metallic w/pk & yel highlights, 2¼" 85.00
Vase, bl/gold irid, 3½x2½" 275.00
Vase, bl/gold mirror irid w/pk touches, mk, 5¼" 550.00

Vase, blue and soft green streaky matt, early maple leaf mark, 5½", $500.00.

Vase, bud; bl irid drip on oatmeal, paper label, 6½" 600.00
Vase, dk gr w/dk bl flecks, pk/yel highlights, imp mk, 4" 475.00
Vase, dk/lt bl metallic w/pk highlights, hand thrown, 6½" 250.00
Vase, dk/lt bl/copper, bulbous/flared ft, label, 9x6", EX 600.00
Vase, gr matt w/brn specks, minor glaze bubbles, 6" 180.00
Vase, gr w/dk pk irid, 2½" 150.00
Vase, gray irid to brn, bulbous w/collar neck, 10x6" 350.00
Vase, metallic/volcanic lt gold-gr w/pk & purple irid, 4x5" 425.00

Pewter

Pewter is a metal alloy of tin, copper, very small parts of bismuth and/or antimony, and sometimes lead. Very little American pewter contained lead, however, because much of the ware was designed to be used as tableware, and makers were aware that the use of lead could result in poisoning. (Pieces that do contain lead are usually darker in color and heavier than those that have no lead.) Most of the fine examples of American pewter date from 1700 to the 1840s. Many pieces were melted down and recast into bullets during the American Revolution in 1775; this accounts to some extent why examples from this period are quite difficult to find. The pieces that did survive may include buttons, buckles, and writing equipment as well as the tableware we generally think of.

After the Revolution, makers began using antimony as the major alloy with the tin in an effort to regain the popularity of pewter, which glassware and china was beginning to replace in the home. The resulting product, known as britannia, had a lustrous silver-like appearance and was far more durable. While closely related, britannia is a collectible in its own right and should not be confused with pewter.

Key: tm — touch mark

Basin, angel tm/Fein Block Zinn, eng initials on rim, 3x13" . . .150.00
Basin, eagle tm/S Kilbourn, 2⅝x10" .900.00
Basin, Francis Piggott, eng bottom w/'FK,' minor wear, 9" 150.00
Basin, Gershom Jones, 1775, minor denting, 6" 550.00
Basin, Richard Austin, incised rim line, imp mk/#8, 8" 200.00
Basin, Samuel Danforth, 1800s, faint tm, 6⅝" 400.00

Basin, Samuel Ellis, 8" 250.00
Basin, Spencer Stafford, 1820s, minor signs of use, 7¾" 300.00
Basin, Thos D Boardman, 1820s, 8", EX 300.00
Basin, unmk, 6¼" 150.00
Beaker, unmk Am, 3" 55.00
Bowl, hdls, raised base, dome lid w/finial, rpr, 10x9½" 275.00
Box, soap; unmk Am, rnd, hinged lid, 4⅜" 125.00
Candlestick, att J&H Graves or Ostrander & Norris, 9¾", pr . .350.00
Candlestick, pushup, battering/soldered rpr, 7", EX, pr 400.00
Candlestick, pushup, 9", pr 490.00
Candlestick, R Gleason, 8" 300.00
Candlestick, unmk Am, w/insets, 9½", pr 325.00
Chalice, communion; worn SP, 8", pr 200.00
Chalice, communion; 6⅛", pr 350.00
Chalice, unmk Am, att TD Boardman, 7½", NM 225.00
Chalice, unmk Am, 5¼", pr 300.00
Chamberstick, att Meriden Britannia, gadroon molding, 4" . . .225.00
Chamberstick, scalloped/beaded edge, 5¼" dia 95.00
Chamberstick, whale oil burner, 2⅛", EX 175.00
Charger, Continental tm, 1775, normal wear, 14¾" 250.00
Charger, indistinct European tm, 16½", EX 215.00
Charger, partial tm '...& Compton, London,' 12" dia, EX 185.00
Charger, S Stafford tm (by Timothy Brigden), 13½", NM 750.00
Charger, Thos Leapidge, 1700s, minor pitting, 15" 200.00
Charger, unmk, 20" 250.00
Coffeepot, lighthouse; F Porter/Westbrook #1 tm, 11", EX 350.00
Coffeepot, lighthouse; James Putnam, 11", M 550.00
Coffeepot, Roswell Gleason, pear shape, 12" 450.00
Coffeepot, Rufus Dunham, str line tm, 12", EX 400.00
Coffeepot, Sage & Beebe, blk hdl & finial, sm 400.00

Pigeon-breasted coffeepot, unmarked American, 11", $425.00; Lighthouse flagon, Eben Smith, Bevery MA, small repair/minor dents, 10", $350.00.

Compote, unmk, 12x10½" 80.00
Dish, AG tm, hinged lid, minor wear/pitting, 1¾x4⅜" 220.00
Dish, deep; Continental, 11¾" 150.00
Dish, deep; Wm Calder, 1830s, 10⅜", EX 450.00
Dish, Samuel Hamlin, 1775, well preserved, 13½" 600.00
Dish, unmk English, oval, pitted, 11x15" L 175.00
Flagon, communion; Roswell Gleason, ca 1840, cleaned, NM .500.00
Flagon, communion; 14" 700.00
Flagon, TB&S Stafford, old resoldering, 10" 6,000.00
Flagon, unmk Continental, battered/rpr, 9½" 185.00
Funnel, unmk English, 3½" dia, 4½" L 175.00
Ladle, John Yates, minor pitting, 13½" 80.00
Ladle, unmk turned wood hdl, 1820s, EX 95.00
Lamp, camphene; Morey & Smith, bell form, 4¼" 200.00
Lamp, camphene; unmk Am, NE, 1840s, 7½", EX 250.00
Lamp, chamber; R Gleason, saucer base/hdl, lemon font, 4½" . .300.00

Lamp, chamber; Taunton Britannia, whale oil, 3¾", pr 650.00
Lamp, gimbal; att Capen & Molineaux, brass burner, 5¾" 300.00
Lamp, gimbal; unmk Am, camphene burners/ring hdl, 8", EX . .300.00
Lamp, sparking; unmk, single drop spout, rare, 4½" 125.00
Lamp, spout; Continental, w/orig pickwick & lid, 11" 170.00
Lamp, whale oil; Eben Smith, acorn font, ftd, 6" 300.00
Lamp, whale oil; Israel Trask, ca 1840, 6¼" 400.00
Lamp, whale oil; Roswell Gleason, 9", EX 500.00
Lamp, whale oil; Smith & Co, cylindrical, ftd, 6½" 250.00
Mold, food; English registry mk, fruit top, 6" 65.00
Mug, unmk Am, cast ear hdl, soldered rpr, 4" 85.00
Mug, unmk Am, slight pitting/minor dings, 1840s, pt, 4⅝" 250.00
Mug, unmk English, pouring spout, monogram, 5½", EX 100.00
Pitcher, cider; Rufus Dunham, 2-qt, 6½" 350.00
Pitcher, unmk Am, ca 1840, w/lid, 12", NM 475.00
Plate, Ashbil Griswold, eagle tm, wear/scratches, 8" 310.00
Plate, David Melville, 1850s, normal use, 8" 350.00
Plate, Francis Piggot, 9⅜" 65.00
Plate, George Lightner, 8", NM 275.00
Plate, Gershom Jones, 1775, normal wear, 8½" 200.00
Plate, Gershom Jones, 1775, well preserved, 8½" 300.00
Plate, H Little London, minor wear, 9⅜" 185.00
Plate, Jacob Whitmore, 1770s, minor pitting, 8" 250.00
Plate, John Danforth, minor wear/pitting, rare, 9" 575.00
Plate, John Jupe, smooth brim, 9¼", set of 4 . . . . .300.00
Plate, London tm, 8¾" 60.00
Plate, Love tm, pitted, 7¾" 275.00
Plate, NW tm, wear/sm split, 12" 150.00
Plate, Samuel Pierce Sr/early eagle tm, 8", NM 250.00
Plate, Smith & Feltman Albany, minor wear/sm dents, 10" 200.00
Plate, Thos Boardman & Hart NY, 9⅜" 350.00
Plate, Thos D Boardman, lion tm, 9⅜" 325.00
Plate, Thos D Boardman, 2 eagle tm, minor wear, 8" 300.00
Plate, Thos D Boardman & Co, minor wear/bk pitted, 9⅜" 300.00
Plate, Thos Swanson/Samuel Ellis, 2 tm, 1770s, 7⅞", pr 150.00
Plate, unmk Am, minor wear, 7¾", pr 180.00
Plate, unmk Am, script initials on bk, 5", EX 175.00
Plate, Wm Will, MS/1784 scratched on bk of rim, 9½", EX . .1,175.00
Platter, English tm, minor wear, 14x18" L 300.00
Porringer, att Danforth or Boardman, English-style hdl, 3¼" . . .175.00
Porringer, att David Melville, flowered hdl, 5", EX 150.00
Porringer, att Richard Lee, basin form, 1800s, 2¼" 150.00
Porringer, CE tm, cast Old English hdl, 4⅝" 250.00
Porringer, FB tm (Fred Bassett), Old English hdl, 4", EX 500.00
Porringer, IC, crown hdl, 4⅛", EX 125.00
Porringer, IG tm, cast crown hdl, 4" .275.00
Porringer, New England, crown hdl, ca 1800, 4¼" 300.00
Porringer, partial tm, minor denting, 3¼" 75.00
Porringer, Samuel Hamlin Jr, flower hdl, 1820s, 5⅜" 700.00
Porringer, SG (att Samuel Green), cast crown hdl, 5½" 335.00
Porringer, Thos D & Sherman Boardman, crown hdl, 5" 325.00
Porringer, unmk, flower hdl, minor pitting, 3¼" 175.00
Porringer, unmk, heart/crescent hdl, 3½" 275.00
Porringer, unmk Am, crown hdl, NE, 1880s, 5" 200.00
Salt box, unmk Continental, floral eng/'Mah 1646,' 9" 500.00
Soup plate, Boardman & Hart, 11" 300.00
Soup plate, Love tm, 1½x11" 300.00
Sugar bowl, unmk Am, strap hdl, w/lid, 6¾", EX 100.00
Tall pot, G Richardson, Cranston RI, #3, 10½" 425.00
Tall pot, Sellew & Co, 10½", EX 225.00
Tall pot, T Sage, wooden wafer finial, resoldered spout 750.00
Tankard, unmk Continental, lid dtd 1764, battered/rpr, 9½" . . .135.00
Teapot, A Porter str-line tm, 7" 200.00
Teapot, Eben Smith, globular, MA, 1830s, minor pitting, 7" . .300.00

Teapot, HB Ward & Co, str line tm, bulbous, 1845, 8½" 350.00
Teapot, James Dixon & Sons, wood hdl w/blk pnt, 11" 85.00
Teapot, Josiah Danforth, mk '#14,' 1830s, 7¾" 275.00
Teapot, R Gleason, flaring shaped body, 8½" 200.00
Teapot, unmk, pear form, minor battering, 6½" 200.00

Phoenix Bird

Blue and white Phoenix Bird china has been produced by various Japanese potteries from the early 1900s. With slight variations, the design features the Japanese bird of paradise and scroll-like vines of Kara-Kusa, or Chinese grass. Although some of their earlier ware is unmarked, the majority is marked in some fashion. More than forty different stamps have been reported, with 'Made in Japan' the one most often found. Newer items, if marked at all, carry a paper label. Compared to the older ware, the coloring of the new is whiter and the blue more harsh; the design is sparse with more ground area showing. Although collectors buy even 'new' pieces, the older is of course more highly prized and valued. For further information we recommend *The Collectors Encyclopedia of Nippon, Third Series*, by Joan Van Patten, whose address is in the Directory under New York.

Bowl, berry; 8¾" 28.00
Bowl, serving; scalloped, 9" 40.00
Bowl, 5" 8.00
Butter pat 10.00
Coaster, 3" 18.00
Creamer, 2¾" 18.00
Cup, custard; mk 15.00
Cup & saucer, AD 14.00
Cup & saucer, Japan 18.00
Egg cup, single, 2¼" 15.00
Ginger jar, 6" 20.00
Gravy boat, w/separate 9" underplate .48.00
Pitcher, milk; 4⅝" 30.00
Plate, dinner; 10" 45.00
Platter, oval, 15" 75.00
Platter, 12½" 35.00
Shakers, 3¼", pr 32.00
Sugar bowl, 4½" 35.00
Teapot, mk #19, 5" 55.00
Teapot, 2¾x7" 60.00
Tray, relish; hdls, 10" 30.00

Phoenix Glass

Founded in 1880 in Monaca, Pennsylvania, the Phoenix Glass Company became one of the country's foremost manufacturers of lighting glass by the early 1900s. Today, however, collectors are primarily interested in the 'Sculptured Artware' produced in the 1930s and 1940s. These beautiful mold-blown pieces are most often found in white milk glass or crystal with various fired-on color treatments or a satin finish.

Phoenix did not mark their 'Sculptured Artware' line; instead, a silver and black or gold and black foil label in the shape of the mythical phoenix bird was used.

Quite often glassware made by the Consolidated Lamp and Glass Company of nearby Coraopolis, Pennsylvania, is mistaken for Phoenix wares. Although the style of the glass is very similar, one distinguishing characteristic is that perhaps 80% of the time Phoenix applied color to the background, leaving the raised design plain in contrast, while Consolidated generally applied color to the raised design and left the background plain. The glassware of both firms is of equal quality and comparable value. For more information, see the section on Consolidated Glass.

Sculptured Artware

Aster, vase, bright yel on wht, 7" 55.00
Bachelor Button, vase, dk bl on crystal, 6" 60.00
Box, floral, gr on crystal, 3-part, w/lid, 8" 60.00
Candy dish, violets, aqua on crystal, open, 7½" 35.00
Dancing Girl, vase, slate bl on wht, 12" 265.00
Dancing Nymphs, plate, wht on crystal, Reuben Line, 18" ...325.00
Diving Girl, bowl, amber on crystal, 14" 150.00
Fern, lamp, slate bl w/MOP fronds 85.00
Figured, vase, gr on wht, 6" 55.00
Freesia, vase, pk florals/gr leaves on bl ground, flared, 8" 85.00
Philodendron, lamp, tan on wht, MOP leaves 135.00
Philodendron, vase, dk gr, 11" 65.00
Pine Cone, vase, (no cones), brn on wht, 6½" 75.00
Strawberry, console bowl & candle holders, rose on wht, 10½" .150.00
Thistle, vase, milk glass, 1976 ....95.00
Thistle, vase, pk on crystal, 18" 325.00
Water Lily, bowl, milk glass, 14" 115.00
Wild Geese, vase, MOP over milk glass, 1976, mk PGCo 50.00
Wild Geese, vase, pk geese on wht satin ground, 9¼" 140.00
Wild Rose, vase, amber, 10½" 65.00
Wild rose, vase, cedar rose on crystal, 10½" 120.00
Zodiac, vase, red on wht, MOP figures, 10" 450.00

Miscellaneous

Lace Dewdrop, bowl, milk glass, w/lid, lg, 8½" 30.00
Lace Dewdrop, comport, red bkground on wht, w/lid, 9" 35.00
Lace Dewdrop, spoon holder, slate bl on wht 25.00
Light shade, Ball Twist #5204, straw opal, 6" dia 55.00
Light shade, Flame #5069, crystal satin, 7¾" L, 3" fitter 35.00
Light shade, Grape Cluster, ruby, 7" L, 3" fitter 45.00
Light shade, Wart, flint opal, ruffled, 4" L, 2" fitter 32.00

Vase, Starflower, blue on white, 7", $80.00.

Phonographs

The phonograph, invented by Thomas Edison in 1877, was the first practical instrument for recording and reproducing sound. Sound wave vibrations were recorded on a tinfoil-covered cylinder and played back with a needle that ran along the grooves made from the recording, thus reproducing the sound. Other companies further improved Edison's invention, and by 1900 three phonograph companies were in business.

Early models had morning-glory horns; these are especially desirable. The early cylinder players are all of special interest, because after 1910 nearly all models were made to play disk records. By 1925 the hand-cranked players were discontinued and were replaced by electric phonographs.

Our advisor for this category is Steve Oliphant; he is listed in the Directory under California.

Key:
mg — morning-glory   rpd — reproducer
NP —— nickel-plated

Busy Bee, cylinder 285.00
Cecilian, crank type, EX orig 225.00
Columbia AA, cylinder, EX 300.00
Columbia B, cylinder 325.00
Columbia BF, cylinder 400.00
Columbia BK, lyric rpd, no horn 395.00
Columbia Eagle 265.00
Columbia Graphophone, oak case, no horn, VG 250.00
Columbia QA 200.00
Edison Amberola #30, EX 275.00
Edison Amberola #75, mahog, EX 450.00
Edison Amberola AI, floor model, w/drw 1,600.00
Edison Blk Gem A 325.00
Edison Diamond Disk, floor model, EX orig 350.00
Edison Fireside A, H rpd, outside horn w/crane, EX 750.00
Edison Home B, 2/4 min, 36" horn 495.00
Edison Home C rpd, orig pk flower horn, NP crane, oak, NM ..695.00
Edison Maroon Gem, 2/4 min, EX 1,000.00
Edison Standard B 350.00
Edison Standard C 375.00
Edison Standard H rpd, 2/4 min, mg horn w/support 350.00
Edison Triumph, blk w/gold trim cygnet horn & crane, NM ...995.00
Harmony, outside horn disk, EX orig 325.00
Mignophone, disk player, outside horn, EX 285.00
Qualitiphone, front mt 175.00
Reginaphone, 20½" disk, oak horn, full rstr 6,000.00
Standard Phonograph Co, Model A, EX 350.00
Talkophone 350.00
Victor D, wood horn 1,500.00
Victor III, lg oak horn, EX 1,300.00
Victor IV, #22 blk flower horn, EX orig 800.00
Victor M, outside horn, EX orig 500.00
Victor MS, Exhibition rpd, oak case, blk metal horn, EX 1,000.00
Victor VI, mahog case, wood horn, gold trim, NM 2,950.00
Victor VV-VI, oak case, dbl doors, 8x14½x15" 125.00
Victor VV-100, floor model, EX orig 325.00
Victor VV-50, oak 150.00

Photographica

Photographic collectibles include not only the cameras and equipment used to 'freeze' special moments in time, but also the photographic images produced by a great variety of processes that have evolved since the daguerrean era of the mid-1800s.

Among the earliest cameras was the sliding box-on-a-box camera. It was focused by sliding one box in and out of the other, thus adjusting the distance of the lens to the ground glass. This was replaced on later models with leather bellows. These were the forerunners of the multi-lens cameras developed in the late 1870s, which were capable of recording many small portraits on a single plate. Double-lens cameras produced stereo images which, when viewed through a device called a stereoscope, achieved a 3-dimensional effect. In 1888 George Eastmann introduced his box camera, the first to utilize roll film. This greatly simplified the process, making it possible for the amateur to enjoy photography as a hobby. Detective cameras, those disguised as books, handbags, etc., are among the most sought after by today's collectors.

Many processes have been used to produce photographic images: daguerreotypes — the most-valued examples being the full-plate which measures 6½" x 8½"; ambrotypes, produced by an early wet-plate process whereby a faint negative image on glass is seen as positive when held against a dark background; and tintypes, contemporaries of ambrotypes, but produced on japanned iron and not as easily damaged.

Other collectible images include carte de visites, known as CDVs, which are portraits printed on paper and produced in quantity. The CDV fad of the 1800s enticed the famous and the unknown alike to pose for these cards, which were circulated among the public to the extent that they became known as 'publics.' When the popularity of CDVs began to wane, a new fascination developed for the cabinet photo, a larger version measuring about 4½" x 6½".

Stereo cards, photos viewed through a device called a stereoscope, are another popular collectible. The glass stereo plates of the mid-1800s and photo prints produced in the darkroom are among the most valuable.

For the most part, good quality images have either maintained or increased in value. Poor quality examples (regardless of rarity) are not selling well. Interest in cameras and stereo equipment is down, and dealers report that often average-priced items that were moving well are often completely overlooked. Though rare items always have a market, collectors seem to be buying only if they are bargain priced.

Our advisor for this category is Roberta Etter; she is listed in the Directory under England. See also Gutta Percha.

Albums

Celluloid w/emb Victorian lady & florals, gold clasp, 12x10" . . .90.00
Celluloid w/velvet bk, brass clasp, lg, EX 40.00
Leather, emb silver florals, Victorian, w/48 pgs, EX 85.00
Leather, silver shield & clasp, 5¼x6¼", VG 35.00
Musical, Victorian styling, EX 275.00
Velvet, red w/celluloid flowers, lg, EX 35.00

Ambrotypes

Full plate, outdoor FL view, men & women by alligator, EX . . .500.00
Half plate, group of 9 men/women/child, +gutta percha fr 150.00
Half plate, man of 1850s, Clifford, +Eichmeyer case 75.00
Half plate, man w/wht clerical collar, Brady, VG 115.00
Half plate, old man w/full beard, ruby in metal mat 65.00
4th plate, cavalry officer, bearskin hat, +gutta percha case 350.00
4th plate, Civil War Union band, oval vignette, cased 750.00
4th plate, 2 soldiers, drummer & sergeant w/sash, EX 110.00
6th plate, boot cobbler, seated at work, in full case 135.00
6th plate, boy on rocking horse, M 85.00
6th plate, father w/3 children in front of cannon on wheels 50.00
6th plate, girl on chair rests head on dog, EX 85.00
6th plate, riverboat captain & wife, 'Port 68' on hat 40.00
6th plate, sailor in blousy shirt w/lg kerchief, +case 110.00
6th plate, sheriff & deputy, badges on vests, +half case 130.00
6th plate, silversmith seated by ornate silver urn, EX 135.00
6th plate, Union officer, w/gold buttons/sword, +full case 150.00
6th plate, 2 men on beach play chess, +half case, EX 125.00
6th plate, 3 seamen in peaked caps, 1870s, +gutta percha fr 50.00
9th plate, Blk mother nursing baby, orig mat & case, EX 150.00
9th plate, Civil War soldier in homespun, pistol in belt 50.00

9th plate, Rebel in gray w/musket by side, +full case, EX 80.00
9th plate, soldier of New England militia, +full case 80.00
9th plate, 1-eyed man w/book, formally dressed, +case 55.00

Cabinet Photos

Annie Oakley stands w/4 guns, medals, Gilbert & Bacon, PA . .425.00
Auguste Bartholdi, French sculpture, Falk, NY 30.00
Blk Canyon of Gunnison, D&RGRy, canyon view, Savage, UT .30.00
Bride & groom, traditional pose, Fawlkton SD, 1870s, EX 15.00
Buddhist archways, man w/camera in lower corner, 1870s, EX . .12.50
Chief Buckskin Charlie & Band of Utes, Hook, CO, oversz 45.00
Church Near Capitol Hill CO, granite bldg w/cross, 1870s 18.00
Colby's Expo Band, 15 uniformed men, CH Colby, Ocala FL . . .25.00
Dakota Home, family by sod & tar paper home, Cross, 1880 . . . .35.00
Dakota Territy sodbuster's home, JN Templeton, 1885 . . . . .40.00
Dan Rice, circus clown, Sarony, NY, M 30.00
Edwin Booth, Sarony, NY 20.00
Elite, lady baseball player holds bat, Deming, CT, 1888 . . . . . . .45.00
Farmer & helper on steam tractor, early bromide, 1905, EX 12.00
Ferris Wheel, Brisbois, Chicago, EX .25.00
Horse-drawn merchant's buggy & Victorian house, Taylor, MA .15.00
Horvath midgets, group of 5, Wendt, EX 18.00
Indian War soldier, full length w/musket & bayonet, EX 35.00
Indian War soldiers in cavalry uniforms w/sabers, 1880s 45.00
Juneau, panoramic view w/ships, sepia, Partridge, OR, 1900 . . .45.00
Louisiana cadet, full lgth in uniform, Washburn, EX 35.00
Maggie Clark, fat lady in Barnum & Baily circus, EX 20.00
Mechanicsville NY Fire Dept w/hand pumper, Hibbard/Allen . .35.00
Nun in habit draped w/2 crosses, by crucifix, 1870s, EX 15.00
Old Spanish town, Fernandina, man w/gun by shack, Colby, FL .25.00
Oscar Wilde, bust portrait, Sarony, NY, 1882, EX 200.00
Pike's Peak w/touring group, WH Jackson, EX 35.00
Pregnant young girl, full-length pose, Wilson, Chicago IL 15.00
Sarah Bernhardt, in wht gown w/parasol, early, VG 25.00
Sarah Bernhardt, seated w/wine goblet, Nadar, Paris 60.00
Steam engine Edward T Johnson, SVRR, Baldwin, NY 30.00
Wild West Show cowboy w/Colt 1873 gun, Eisenmann, NY 60.00
12 men & 5 horses on stump of redwood tree, Horton, 1870s . . .14.00

Cameras

AH Baird, tropically-bound polished wood, half plate, EX 400.00
Aiglon, Fr sub-miniature, NP w/meniscus lens, +case, EX 275.00
Ansco Buster Brown #2, MIB 45.00
Ascot Buckeye, box type, uses plates or roll film, 1896 . . . . .60.00
Bl Beau Brownie, missing hdl, EX colors 35.00
Blair Hawk-Eye Detective, wood, ca 1893, VG 185.00
Blair Hawk-Eye Stereo, red leather bellows, ca 1904, EX 275.00
Brownie #3, 6 pat dates 1891-1902, EX 22.00
Cameradio, reflex viewer, 127 film, Universal Radio, ca 1949 . .120.00
Claudet Patient Stereoscope, red leather, brass lenses, VG 400.00
Conley Jr, folding, polished cherry interior, ca 1900 . . . . .65.00
Conley Jr, folding plate, 4x8" 40.00
Eastman Kodak NI-A Autographic Jr, folding, orig case 48.00
Eastman Kodak Premo, red bellows, brass lens, 1903, +case 65.00
Eastman Kodak Six 16, folding, M in case 45.00
Expo, pocket watch style, 1905, w/instructions & case, VG 225.00
Kodak #1-A, pocket folding, bellows type, 1909, EX 10.00
Kodak Autographic 2-C Jr, cable release & stylus, +case 45.00
Kodak Bull's Eye #3, box type, 3" film 25.00
Marvel S-16, Deco chrome & blk design on front, EX 55.00
Monroe Pocket Poco, folding, ca 1890s, 3x4" 200.00
Petie, vanity case/camera, Kunick/Frankfurt, 1958, EX 550.00

Carte De Visites

Abraham Lincoln & son Tad reading together, EX 45.00
Blk Civil War cavalry soldier in full uniform, EX 100.00
Blk Evangelist, kneeling lady in habit w/Bible, EX 10.00

C.D.V. photo of John Wilkes Booth, imprinted Silsbee, Case & Co, 229½ Washington St., Boston, rare, $110.00.

Charles Dickens, full figure, Mason, London, EX 30.00
Custer, ¾-pose, profile, Brady mk front/bk, EX 300.00
Diplomatic group, assembled for Alaska purchase, EX 45.00
Drummer boy w/sister seated ea side, Hunter, 1860s 35.00
Eli Bowen w/wife & child, man w/no arms or legs, Newman, EX .45.00
Florence Nightingale, McKilburn, London, EX 45.00
General AE Burnside, standing, Brady & Anthony, EX 35.00
General Philip Kearney, full figure, arm gone, M Brady, EX 45.00
General Sherman, hand tucked in jacket, EX 75.00
Geo A Custer, seated, long hair, M Brady, ca 1865, VG 275.00
Girl w/snake, circus performer, ca 1870s, EX 40.00
Henry W Beecher, standing, ¾-pose, Anthony & Brady, EX 20.00
Mary Lincoln, vignette, copy photo, EX 35.00
Military cadet, full length, hat at side, Johnson Bros, NY 35.00
Officer Seammons, vignette, Bradley & Rolofson, CA 10.00
Portrait of Anna Swan, 443-Pound Giant Woman, EX 25.00
Soldier w/wife, full length, Hoplins, Annapolis MD, EX 15.00
Union soldier in Hardee hat, King, Portland ME, EX 30.00

Daguerreotypes

Half plate, Blk couple, casual pose, 1840s +orig case 150.00
Half plate, family of 5, SJ Miller, Akron OH, +full case 125.00
Half plate, George Mumford, formal suit w/cravat, +case 125.00
Half plate, old man w/wooly wht hair, in suit & tie, +case 125.00
Half plate, 3 US officers of Mexican War, 1845, NM, +case .2,300.00
4th plate, Blk man/wife/3 daughters, fancy clothes, 1850s 60.00
4th plate, Navy officers, 4 in frock coats, 1850s, +case 180.00
4th plate, Theodore & Stuart F Weld, sons of Theodore Weld .300.00
4th plate, 3 children, fine clothes/toys, +gutta percha case 550.00
6th plate, Blk man w/crossed eyes, +half case 50.00
6th plate, Colonel Hyatt C Ransom, Civil War amputee, EX ..450.00
6th plate, John & Jane Morrison Willis, 1880s, +history 175.00
6th plate, lady in fancy gown, Holmes, Broadway NY, EX 50.00
6th plate, lady in lacy dress w/concertina in lap, +case 55.00
6th plate, lady weavers w/shuttles in hands, +fr/half case 325.00
6th plate, Lavinia Lee Simpson, Jonesboro ME, 1850s, EX 50.00
6th plate, MA militiaman, tall peaked cap, +full case 200.00
6th plate, post mortem, child in tartan clothes, EX 80.00
6th plate, post mortem, infant, unopened seals, NM 125.00
6th plate, post mortem, older man at rest, full case, EX 50.00

6th plate, seaman, member of Hale family of ME, 1850s, EX . . .110.00
6th plate, violinist, young man w/violin & bow, +full case 65.00
6th plate, western man of 1850s, Wm C North, Cleveland OH .50.00

Photos

Buffalo grazing, Huffman collotype, MT, 1880, 10x20", EX 40.00
Cameron Dragoons, Camp Griffin VT encampment, salt print . .75.00
Cathedral of Chihauhua, Mexico, albumen, Jackson, 13x10" . . .65.00
Civil War regiment, 60 soldiers by tents, albumen, 7x9" 50.00
Cowboys & herd on MT range, silverprint, Huffman, 11½x19" 100.00
Expo Nationale Swiss-Geneva 1896, albumen, Baud, 9x7" 35.00
Gamblers in CA casino, silverprint, 1920s, 7½x9½", EX 50.00
Horses on MT prairie, Huffman collotype, 1880s, 9x19", EX . . .55.00
Hydraulic gold mining scene, albumen, 1870s, 6½x9" 80.00
Lady in fur coat, orotone, Curtis, rare, 10x8" 175.00
Langenheim Photographic Exhibits, Watson negative, VG 60.00
Man w/3 Indian guides, 4 leopard skins, sepia, 1890s, 8x10" . . .12.00
Mohave Water Carrier, photogravure, Andrew & Son/Curtis . . .50.00
Mormon Tabernacle, Salt Lake City UT, early, EX 10.00
Mt Ranier, tinted platinum print, Curtis, 10x13", EX 100.00
Nez Perces, long hair, many beads, sepia, Curtis, 15x10½" 75.00
Niagara Falls, McPherson, Niagara Falls NY, EX 20.00
Rebel Works in Front of Atlanta, albumen, Barnard, 6½x8½" .200.00

Winfield Scott albumen print, by Brady or assistant, 1861, 12x10", $200.00

San Francisco Fire Brigade, albumen, dtd 1879, 6x8", EX 135.00
Sugar Loaf Mtn, battlefield site, albumen, M Brady, 6x9" 90.00
Watchmakers at storefront w/clock sign, 1890s, 4½x7" 25.00
Zouaves parading down NJ street, albumen, 5½x7¼" 60.00
7 Sioux Chiefs in full regalia, albumen, early, EX 95.00

Stereoscopic Views

In evaluating stereo views, the date and condition are all-important. Some views were printed over a thirty- to forty-year period — 'first generation' prices are far higher than later copies. Right now, quality stereo views are at a premium.

Abbie Gardner Sharp, at house where taken by Indians, VG . . .20.00
Antietam Battlefield view, Gardner's Gallery, Wash DC, VG . . .75.00
Blks pick cotton, Characteristic Southern Scenes, VG 30.00
Boy Scouts, groups/bands/leaders, ca 1910, 11 for 100.00

Branding Calves...Paloduro TX, Keystone, NM 15.00
CA-Yosemite Valley, Soule, Boston, 5 for 30.00
China, Keystone, complete set of 100 w/guide & atlas, rare 225.00
Clark's House, Regular Hospital for Reserve, Anthony #371 ....25.00
CO views, Denver/trolleys/Blk Hawk/etc, Chamberlain, 15 for .200.00
Custer Monument at Little Big Horn battlefield, Huffman, EX ..10.00
Dunker Church, Antietam, Sept, 1862, Taylor & Huntington ..30.00
English touring car in Derbyshire landscape, 1910, VG, 2 for ...20.00
France, HC White, set of 100 in bookcase box, M 150.00
Gen Grant's RR, City Point VA, Anthony #2516, VG 55.00
Gen Hancock, Birney, Gibbon, Garlow Near Richmond, VG ...45.00
Greece, Keystone #3700 & #3702, pr 15.00
Hanover street view, Boston, Haskell & Allen, VG 35.00
Hunting & fishing, includes buffalo herd, Ingersoll, 40 for 35.00
Major Gen Wright at Head Quarters...Near Richmond, VG 25.00
Major Gen WT Sherman & horse, Anthony #3623, VG 80.00
Maple Sugar Making in...Woods of NY, Anthony #5938 .....15.00
Memorial to...Battle of Bull Run, McCallum, 1869, VG 30.00
Mexico, Keystone, set of 100, M 225.00
Negro Village, Tripoli Africa, thatched huts, Bierstadt, NY 25.00
Officers on board the Monitor, Brady's Album Gallery #487 ....50.00
PA oil, burning tanks/gushers/etc, Detlor & Waddel, 5 for 20.00
Philippine Islands, Underwood & Underwood, 7 for 30.00
Prof Lowe Replenishing the Balloon, Anthony #2349, VG 65.00
Rocky Mountain scenery, mining sites/etc, early, 4 for 125.00
Russia, HC White, set of 100 in bookcase box, M 350.00
Sherman's Grand Army, Looking Up PA Ave, Anthony #3322 .15.00
Sioux Captured by Gen Crook, women/children in open field ..75.00
Slave Pen, Alexandria VA, Anthony #2298, VG 25.00
T Roosevelt As Rough Rider, American Steroscopic 15.00
Wounded Indians, Anthony #2342, EX 25.00
Yellowstone Park scenery, Haynes, 1880s, 36 in boxed set 145.00

Stereoviewer, collapsible, unmarked, $350.00.

Tintypes

Half plate, blacksmith shoeing horse, EX 125.00
Half plate, delivery wagon w/horse, loaded w/boxes, 1850s 75.00
Half plate, military encampment w/political delegation, EX ...175.00
Half plate, wide view of western town, early, EX 100.00
Half plate, 9 wounded soldiers w/valises & canes, walnut fr 190.00
4th plate, brothers in war, 1 Union, 1 Confederate, VG 65.00
4th plate, Civil War bugler, full length, +gutta percha fr 200.00

4th plate, early stone cutter at work on monument, EX 85.00
4th plate, ME Union cavalry soldier, tinted, EX 165.00
4th plate, mtd Union cavalry officer in full uniform, +case 275.00
4th plate, village blacksmiths, 2 men in aprons w/hammers, M ..65.00
6th plate, bearded man w/brush & pail of whtwash, VG, +case ..55.00
6th plate, Blk lady in floor-length dress, hat at side, VG 30.00
6th plate, British soldier, full length, +full case, EX 50.00
6th plate, horse & buggy in town square, ME, EX 30.00
6th plate, hunters w/shotguns in studio setting, EX 35.00
6th plate, lady doctor, instrument in hand, +half case, VG 95.00
6th plate, man w/dog & long rifle, EX, +half case 65.00
6th plate, man w/hairlip, formal attire, by table w/flowers 30.00
6th plate, Union soldier in full dress, musket at side, EX 30.00
9th plate, Blk man in fine clothes, 1860s, EX 65.00
9th plate, Civil War soldier w/sword & revolver, VG 30.00
9th plate, Infantry soldier, Hardee hat & bugle insignia 40.00
9th plate, Union soldier w/musket across lap, EX details 50.00

Viewers and Slides

Brewster, ebonized eye pcs, mirrored top flap, EX 175.00
Edison Kinetoscope w/magic lantern, +100 slides 625.00
Graphoscope, blk-enameled viewer, Souvenir of Paris, 1870 ...275.00
Graphoscope, for stereo/cabinet card photos, 1870s, EX 375.00
Graphoscope, mahog w/magnifying viewer & stereoscope, VG .215.00
Holmes-Bater Pedestal Stereo Viewer, walnut/mahog, 1850s ...75.00
Keystone Telebinocular, collapsible, book-form box 60.00
Magic lantern, Atlas support lens, red pnt w/blk/gold, 13" 175.00
Oraphoscope, hand-held viewer w/metal lens, pat 1889, EX ...45.00
Stereopticon, standard 40.00
Stereopticon, Victor #2, pat 1913, +78 slides 100.00
Viewmaster Stereoscope, +80 Viewmaster reels, 1950s, EX 75.00
Zeotrope, see movies through slots, 9½" dia, EX 475.00

Miscellaneous

Bracelet, woven hair w/dag inset of Blk lady, EX 375.00
Case, MOP, inlaid floral, 6th plate, VG 50.00
Catalog, TH McAllister, stereopticons/lanterns/etc, 1878 .....125.00
Locket, holds dags of lady & 2 children, EX 165.00
Pendant, open-faced, dag of man, lock of hair on bk 145.00
Stanhope, alabaster barrel, Niagara Falls scene 30.00
Stanhope, binoculars, bone, Statue of Liberty view 75.00
Stanhope, cross w/rosary beads, ivory, 1 religious view 55.00
Stanhope, pipe, cvd wood, 6 Port Erin views, 1" L, EX 48.00
Stanhope, scent bottle, brass, w/neck chain, 6 views, EX 150.00
Stanhope, tape measure, barrel form w/ivory finial, 1 view 65.00
Stanhope, tape measure/needle case, Queen Victoria 150.00

Piano Babies

A familiar sight in Victorian parlors, piano babies languished atop shawl-covered pianos in a variety of poses: crawling, sitting, on their tummies, or on their backs playing with their toes. Some babies were nude and some wore gowns. Sizes ranged from about 3" up to 12". The most famous manufacturer of these bisque darlings was the Heubach Brothers of Germany, who nearly always marked their product; see Heubach for more listings. Watch for reproductions.

Blk baby, crawling, Germany, 4" 75.00
Boy, nude chubby toddler, seated, 7" 85.00
Boy frowns/holds pig trying to drink from chamber pot, 8½" ...400.00

Baby in yellow gown with roses, marked Germany, 9½", $650.00.

Crying, holds plate, #14159, Germany, 4¾" 70.00
Girl, sitting, holds hairbrush, old Japan mk, 5" 35.00
Holds rabbit w/gold bell, wht gown w/pk trim, Germany, 6¼" .195.00
Lying on side, limbs up, #370, 4" 55.00
Lying on stomach, bl-gray gown, dog w/pacifier, 6¾" 70.00
Lying on stomach, flowered gown, 17" L 525.00
Reclining, playing w/kitten, Germany 100.00
Sitting, arms raised, 4½" 65.00
Sitting, holding drum, bl hat, mk Royal Rudolstadt, 8" 350.00
Sitting, leans to side, yel dress, rattle, 8" 275.00
Sitting w/cookie, Germany, 2¼" 35.00

Picasso Art Pottery

Pablo Picasso created some distinctive pottery during the 1940s, marking the ware with his signature.

Pitcher, Visage, inscribed Madoura, numbered, 13½", $13,200.00 at auction, exceeded the high estimate by $11,000.00.

Bowl, Deux Poissons, partial glaze, Madoura/Plein Feu, 10" . .1,700.00
Bowl, Merle Noir, partial glaze, 6" 825.00
Plate, Corrida, glazed, 8¾" 1,100.00
Plate, Petit Visage Solaire, partial glaze, 1969, 6¾x6½" 1,500.00

Pickard

Founded in 1897 in Chicago, Illinois, the Pickard China Company was originally a decorating studio, importing china blanks from European manufacturers. Some of these early pieces bear the name of those companies as well as Pickard's. Trained artists decorated the wares with hand-painted studies of fruit, florals, birds, and scenics, and often signed their work. In 1915 Pickard introduced a line of 23k gold over a dainty floral-etched ground design. In the 1930s, they began to experiment with the idea of making their own ware and by 1938 had succeeded in developing a formula for fine translucent china. Since 1976 they have issued an annual limited edition Christmas plate. They are now located in Antioch, Illinois.

The company has used various marks: 'Pickard' with double circles; the crown mark; 'Pickard' on a gold maple leaf; and the current mark, the lion and shield. Work signed by Challinor, Marker, and Yeschek is especially valued by today's collectors.

Our advisors for this category are Lois and Milt Steinfeld; they are listed in the Directory under New Jersey.

Basket, gold tracery on mauve, gold hdl, 4x5¼" 80.00
Bottle, scent; primroses, sgn, 1905, gold stopper, 8" 195.00
Bowl, berry; blackberry fruit & leaf, sgn J Gohlick, 7" 90.00
Bowl, gold etched int, 5-lobe, 1930-1938 mk, 3¾x9" 85.00
Bowl, vegetable; Cinderella, w/lid 55.00
Box, forget-me-nots, sgn Alex, oval, 2½x4½" 125.00
Breakfast set, Aura Argenta Linear, sgn Richter, 5-pc 550.00
Cake plate, Oriental birds, sgn Nickols, 1919, 10¾" 175.00
Card tray, florals w/gold, heart shape, 1910 mk, 5x4" 65.00
Coffeepot, allover gold etched floral 85.00

Coffeepot, creamer, and sugar bowl, Aura Argenta, ca 1908, height of pot: 8¾", $350.00 for the set.

Creamer & sugar bowl, Cinderella 25.00
Cup & saucer, Cinderella 16.00
Cup & saucer, Cinnabar 12.00
Cup & saucer, floral w/gold & silver, sgn Passony 80.00
Decanter, grapes, gold on blk, sgn Hess, +8 wines 625.00
Dish, allover gold etched floral, cartouch form w/hdls, 7" 50.00
Marmalade, dogwood w/gold, artist sgn, 6", +underplate 88.00

Mayonnaise, day liles w/gold, attached underplate 135.00
Pitcher, cherries w/gold trim, artist sgn, 7¼" 195.00
Pitcher, florals, pastel w/gold, Limoges blank, 5", +tray 95.00
Plate, calla lily, heavy gold, sgn Marker, 12½" 175.00
Plate, dinner; Cinderella 12.00
Plate, dinner; Cinnabar 10.00
Plate, garden scene, sgn Challinor, 11" 395.00
Plate, tulips, gold scalloped border, artist sgn, 8" 100.00
Plate, violets, gold border, 12" 135.00
Platter, landscape, sgn Marker, 12" 225.00
Shakers, rosebuds & forget-me-nots, pk/bl w/gold, 1905 mk 45.00
Tray, floral, gold trim, old dbl circle mk, 11x8" 65.00
Tray, vines & urns, pk/gr w/gold, gold mk, 6¼x4" 65.00
Urn, grapes & strawberries in band, allover gold, sgn, 11½" . . .525.00
Vase, deserted garden on gold, sgn Vokral, 6½" 195.00
Vase, mums, gold/rust on turq w/gold, sgn, 1905 mk, 8½" 150.00
Vase, Nouveau poinsettias, sgn Yeschek, 1905 mk, 17½" 550.00
Vase, peonies, mc on pastel w/gold, artist sgn, 15" 325.00

Pickle Castors

Pickle castors, which were both functional and decorative, became popular after the Civil War, reaching their peak about 1885. By 1900 they had virtually disappeared from factory catalogs. Numerous styles were available. They consisted of a decorated, silverplated frame that held either a fancy clear pressed-glass insert or one of decorated art glass — the latter being popular in the more affluent Victorian households and more desirable with collectors today.

In the listings below, the description prior to the semi-colon (;) refers to the jar (insert), and the remainder of the line describes the frame. Where no condition is indicated, the silverplate is assumed to be in very good to excellent condition; glass jars are assumed mint.

Alabama, gr, rare; SP fr 200.00
Albertine, wht to peach, florals, Mt WA; Pairpoint fr, +tongs .495.00
Beaded Dart, sapphire; rfn Meriden fr, +tongs 285.00
Cane, amber; birds/fountain on SP fr, +tongs 185.00
Carmen, clear, 8-sided; scrolled SP fr, +tongs 125.00
Clear; ornate Pairpoint fr w/grasshopper finial, ftd 200.00
Cranberry, HP floral, blown, ribbed; Tufts SP fr, +tongs 395.00
Cranberry, HP iris; Reed & Barton SP fr, +tongs 350.00
Cranberry, 16 blown-out columns, HP florals/dots; lg SP fr 395.00
Cranberry, 8 floral-pnt emb columns; sgn Meriden fr, +tongs . .345.00
Cranberry & vaseline spatter, satin Leaf Mold insert; ftd fr 395.00
Cupid & Venus; swans' heads on ftd Pairpoint fr, +tongs 150.00
Cut, strawberry/diamond point/fan; orig SP fr, +tongs 150.00
Daisy & Button, bl & clear; mk SP fr .145.00
Daisy & Button, canary; hallmk quadruple SP fr/lid/tongs, lg . .250.00
Daisy & Button, gr; orig SP fr, +tongs, Wilcox 295.00
Daisy & Button, sapphire bl, dbl; SP fr 350.00
Frosted Criss-Cross Diamonds; fancy fr, +tongs 150.00
Frosted pumpkin-form jar; leaf base w/pickles, Wilcox #0675 . .295.00
Invt T'print, amberina, HP florals/birds; fancy fr, +tongs 595.00
Invt T'print, cobalt, HP dots/wheat stems w/gold; Wilcox fr . . .450.00
Invt T'print, cranberry, HP decor; Middleton fr, 10", +tongs .425.00
Invt T'print, cranberry, HP decor; twig-ftd 13" fr, +tongs 395.00
Invt T'print, cranberry, HP pk rose; ornate Wilcox fr 395.00
Invt T'print, rubena, HP florals, pickle finial; SP fr 500.00
Invt T'print on Optic Diamond, HP mums; fancy SH&M fr . .595.00
King's Crown, grape etched; SP fr, VG 135.00
Peachblow, ball form, peach finial; ornate Pairpoint fr 550.00
Reverse Swirl, cranberry opal, Chrysanthemum base; fancy fr .450.00
Sculptured art glass, HP flowers; Wilcox fr w/pickles 600.00

Swirl ribs, clear & frosted; Rogers tree-bark fr, +tongs 150.00
Van Dyke, vaseline; ornate Hartford fr w/birds in bail 250.00
Vaseline opal, att Webb; ornate ftd fr .450.00
Vertical Optic, rubena; orig Pairpoint fr 450.00
Yel, HP floral; 2" cherubs hold rfn Meriden fr 395.00
Yel Dia Quilt; SP owl ornament in fr, +tongs 350.00

Mary Gregory, blue with white enamelling, marked Pairpoint frame, 12½", $650.00.

Pie Birds

Pie birds (also known as pie vents and pie funnels) have been in use since late Victorian times. Placed in the middle of a pie, they serve the dual purpose of supporting the pastry and allowing steam to escape from the pie so that it does not boil over. They come in various, interesting forms.

Our advisor for this category is Alan Pedel; he is listed in the Directory under England.

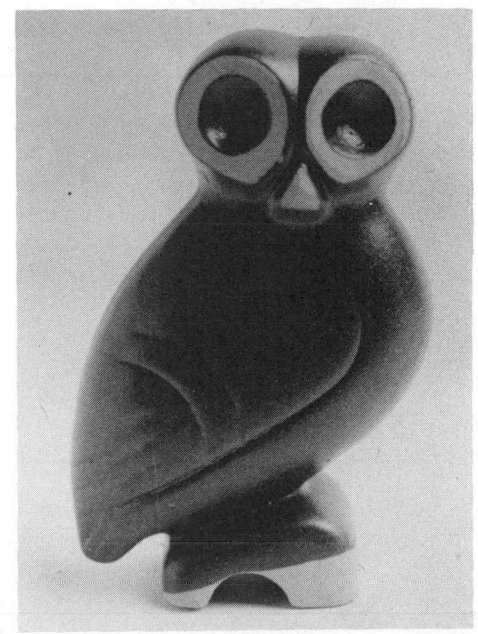

Stylized owl, pottery, $40.00.

Benny the Baker, ceramic, 5" 35.00
Bird atop funnel, ceramic, mc detail, Royal Worcester 50.00
Blackbird, ceramic, 4" 25.00
Blackbird, glass, 2-headed 40.00

Cat's head, pottery, comical, stylized, long neck, 1-eyed **40.00**
Dragon's head, pottery, long neck, lg eyes, nose is vent **40.00**
Elephant, pottery, head to left, trunk held vertically, brn **65.00**
Funnel, pottery, Improved Popular...Carries Away Steam **70.00**
Mammy, ceramic **40.00**
Rooster, ceramic, rare **24.00**
Teddy bear, pottery, standing, holding sm jar in paws **40.00**

Pierce, Howard

Howard Pierce opened a studio in Claremont, California, in the mid-1940s where he produced small ceramic models of birds and animals, figurines, and vases, making his molds and decorating his ware with no outside help except for his wife and more recently his daughter. He is best known for his skill at sculpting his models, which he decorates entirely with the airbrush. Early items were incised 'Howard Pierce, Claremont, California,' or stamped 'Howard Pierce Porcelain.' Not all of his ware is marked, however, and some may carry only his initials.

Our advisor for this category is Jack Chipman; he is listed in the Directory under California.

Figurine, bird, blk/gr, 3" **20.00**
Figurine, bobwhite, standing, stylized **20.00**
Figurine, boy & girl, standing, brn **32.00**
Figurine, eagle, blk **35.00**
Figurine, elephant, pk **18.00**
Figurine, fawn, brn **12.00**
Figurine, Hawaiian couple **35.00**
Figurine, panther, blk **18.00**
Figurine, partridge, stylized, brn **20.00**
Figurine, polar bear **15.00**
Figurine, raccoon, seated, brn, 4" **18.00**
Figurine, roadrunner, brn & wht **22.00**
Figurine, squirrel, gray **10.00**
Flower frog, quail w/2 young, 6½" **35.00**
Flower frog, St Francis, 12x7" **45.00**

Pigeon Forge

Douglas J. Ferguson and Ernest Wilson started their small pottery in Pigeon Forge, Tennessee, in 1946. Using red-brown and gray locally-dug clay and glazes which they themselves formulate, bowls, vases, and sculptures are produced there. Their primary target is the tourist trade.

Mug, pine trees, brn on gr matt, 4½" **17.50**
Vase, bl crystalline, 3½" **12.00**
Vase, dogwood blossoms, 3½" **12.00**
Vase, matt gr, ink mk, 5" **20.00**

Pigeon Blood

Pigeon blood glass, produced in the late 1800s, may be distinguished from other dark red glass by its distinctive orange tint.

Bowl, Torquay, SP rim, lg **75.00**
Celery vase, Torquay, SP rim, 6" **225.00**
Cracker jar, Beaded Drapery, ornate hdl **185.00**
Cracker jar, Torquay, SP lid, bail & hdl **295.00**
Lamp, hall; paneled shade, orig brass fr, EX **250.00**
Pickle castor, Torquay, scalloped Forbes fr w/braid hdl **325.00**
Pitcher, HP florals, clear hdl, 11½", +4 tumblers **150.00**

Pitcher, Torquay, water sz **300.00**
Shakers, Synora Lace, orig tops, scarce, pr **125.00**
Sweetmeat, Torquay, w/lid & bail **250.00**
Syrup, Scroll & Net w/Cosmos, satin, frosted hdl, orig lid ...**575.00**
Toothpick holder, Bulging Loops **125.00**
Tumbler, HP floral, ribbed **50.00**

Pin-Back Buttons

Most of the advertising buttons made until the 1920s were top-quality, full-color, celluloid-covered buttons termed 'cellos.' Many were issued in sets on related topics featuring historical people and events, animals and birds, and other themes. Several cigarette, gum, and candy companies used buttons as inserts in their products. Usually the name of the company or product was printed on a paper placed in the back of the button and held securely by the pin. Most of the back papers are still in place today, aiding in the identification of the button. Beginning in the 1920s, a large number of buttons were lithographed (printed on metal); these buttons are referred to as 'lithos.' Nearly all advertising buttons are collected today with perhaps these exceptions: common buttons picturing flags of various nations, general labor union buttons denoting the payment of dues, and similar buttons with clever sayings.

Following is a listing of some of the most popular non-political buttons. Values reflect buttons which have designs centered, colors aligned, no fading or yellowing, no spots or stains, and no cracks, splits, or dents. See also Personalities and Political Entourage.

Breyer's Ice Cream **16.00**
Chew Bull Dog, bulldog, mc, ca 1900 ....**8.00**
Colt Firearms Factory Guard, Tiffany NY, 1900 ....**45.00**
Elvis Presley, Best Wishes, portrait, mc, 1950s **20.00**
Harley-Davidson, metamorphic face, blk/wht **60.00**
JI Case, eagle **15.00**
Kar A Van Coffee, mc **17.50**
Maine Centennial, mc, 1920 ....**7.50**
Paragon Beer, E St Louis, blk/wht, 1¼" **22.50**
Phantom's Club member, phantom, mc, 1940s **65.00**
Ritz Crackers, 1936, 1" **5.00**
Santa Claus w/telescope, mc, 1¼", M **25.00**
Sherman Williams Paint, Uncle Sam, red/wht/bl **17.50**
Tri-Par Radio Co, Chicago, Master's Voice motif, w/brass **37.50**
Wear Puritan Hosiery, lady shows leg, mc, ca 1900 ....**45.00**

Pink Lustre Ware

Pink lustre was produced by nearly every potter in the Staffordshire district in the 18th and 19th centuries. The application of gold lustre on white or light-colored backgrounds produced pinks, while the same over dark colors developed copper. The wares ranged from hand-painted plaques to transfer-printed dinnerware.

Pitcher, vining resist, 4½", $175.00.

Cup & saucer, handleless; schoolhouse .35.00
Cup & saucer, resist grapes & leaves w/in wide pk band 45.00
Mug, house w/lake transfer 100.00
Pitcher, deer & dogs, emb bl vines, twig hdl, 7" 90.00
Pitcher, strawberry decor in bas-relief, 8¾" 325.00
Plaque, He That Believes Shall Be Saved, 7¾x8¾", EX 85.00
Plate, rust Adams' Rose center, 6¾" .28.00
Punch bowl, florals/house scene, scenic int, 11" 425.00

Pink Pigs

Pink Pigs on cabbage green were made in Germany around the turn of the century. They were sold as souvenirs in train depots, amusement parks, and gift shops. 'Action pigs' (those involved in some amusing activity) are the most valuable, and prices increase with the number of pigs. Though a similar type of figurine was made in white bisque, most serious collectors prefer only the pink ones. They are marked in two ways: 'Germany' in incised letters, and a black ink stamp 'Made in Germany' in a circle.

1 beside gr drum, wall mt match holder 60.00
1 beside stump, camera around neck, toothpick holder 95.00
1 by purse 65.00
1 coming out of cup 65.00
1 coming through gr fence, post at sides, open for flowers 95.00
1 in case looking through binoculars 85.00
1 in gr Dutch shoe 35.00
1 in gr suitcase bank, head 1 side, bk other, gold trim 75.00
1 in Japanese submarine, Japan imp on both sides 125.00
1 lg pig sitting behind 3" trough 75.00
1 on binoculars, gold trim 95.00
1 on gr trinket dish, leg caught in lobster claw 65.00
1 on horseshoe-shaped dish w/raised 4-leaf clover 65.00
1 on shoulder of gr ink bottle 65.00
1 reclining on horseshoe ash tray 70.00
1 riding train, 4½" 125.00
1 sits, holds orange Boston Baked Beans pot match holder 65.00
1 sitting by purse 75.00
1 sitting in bathtub 90.00
1 sitting on log, mk Germany 65.00
1 standing by toothpick holder w/camera at neck 85.00
1 standing in gr tub 75.00
1 w/attached toothpick holder 55.00
1 w/front ft in 3-part dish containing 3 dice, 1 ft on dice 75.00
1 wearing chef's costume, holds frypan, w/basket 80.00
2, mother & baby in bl blanket in tub, rabbit on board atop 70.00
2, mother at pump bathing baby in tub 115.00
2 behind trough, unmk 65.00
2 by eggshell 80.00
2 dancing, in top hat, tux & cane 95.00
2 holding hands in roadster, 4½" L 125.00
2 in bed, Good Night on footboard, 4x3x2½" 145.00
2 in love sit on lg log, 2 openings on tree stump, 7" L 67.50
2 in purse 75.00
2 on basket, head raising lid, plaque on front 80.00
2 on binoculars, gold trim 115.00
2 on bl container 40.00
2 on cotton bale, 1 peers from hole, 1 over top 90.00
2 on gr tray 50.00
2 on seesaw on top of pouch bank 75.00
2 on top hat 95.00
3, 1 on lg slipper playing banjo, 2 dancing on side 115.00
3 dressed up on edge of dish 70.00

3 sm pigs behind oval trough, mk, 2¾x2½x1¾" 35.00
3 w/baby carriage, father & 2 babies, Wheeling His Own 75.00
3 w/carriage, mother & 2 babies, Germany 85.00
3 w/coach, mama & babies, More the Merrier 85.00

Two in green car bottle, 6" long, $135.00.

Pisgah Forest

The Pisgah Forest Pottery was established in 1914 near Mount Pisgah in Arden, North Carolina, by Walter B. Stephen. Stephen is best known for his cameo ware which he decorated by hand in the pate-sur-pate style with scenes portraying covered wagons and other subjects related to the pioneer days. He also produced a turquoise crackled ware and developed a fine crystalline glaze, examples of which are highly prized by today's collectors. The ware was marked 'Pisgah Forest,' often with a potter at the wheel. Stephen died in 1961, but the work was continued by his associates.

Bowl, Cameo, wagon train, wht on gr, rose int, Stephen, 4" . . .300.00
Creamer, yel 25.00
Dish, Cameo, wagon train, wht on gr, 2½x5" W 250.00
Jar, turq, dtd 1939, w/lid, sm 45.00
Jug, turq gloss, dtd 1935, w/stopper, 8" 110.00
Match safe, potter at wheel in relief, pre-1928, 3x2½" 450.00
Mug, Cameo, dancing couple relief 290.00
Pitcher, lt gr, sgn, 1949, 3⅞" 38.00

Pitcher, purple to light blue, 8½", $75.00.

Teapot, Cameo, wagon train, wht on bl, sgn Stephen/1949, 5" . .325.00
Urn, crystalline, molded hdls, pre-1928, 11" 295.00

Vase, Cameo, dancing couples, wht on bl, 10" 700.00
Vase, crystalline, mustard flambe w/gr, waisted, 5½" 180.00
Vase, crystalline, wht w/pk & bl touches inside, 6½" 190.00
Vase, crystalline, wht w/some bl, pk int, glaze bubbles, 7" 190.00
Vase, crystalline, yel w/bl, pk int, mfg flaw, 3" 130.00
Vase, purple crackle, bulbous, 5½" 48.00

Pittsburgh

As early as 1797, utility window glass and hollowware were being produced in the Pittsburgh area. Coal had been found in abundance, and it was there that it was first used instead of wood to fuel the glass furnaces. Because of this, as many as 150 glass companies operated there at one time. However, most failed due to the economically disastrous effects of the War of 1812. By the mid-1850s, those that remained were producing a wide range of flint glass items including pattern-molded and free-blown glass, cut and engraved wares, and pressed tableware patterns.

Bottle, aqua, 16 ribs, globular, 1880s, att, 8¾", EX 125.00
Bottle, scent; pillar mold, gr, 8 ribs, orig stopper, 5" 450.00
Candlestick, cobalt, 6-sided baluster std, att, 9", EX, pr 800.00
Candlestick, flint, pewter inserts missing, 9¾", NM, pr 200.00
Canister, appl cobalt rings/lid lip/finial button, 10" 485.00
Canister, appl rings, appl finial on dome lid, 12" 160.00
Carafe, bl, pillar mold, swirl ribs, hollow hdl/stopper, 8" 145.00
Cruet, pillar mold, 15 ribs, orig stopper, 9" 165.00
Cup, lady's spittle; cobalt, appl hdl, polished pontil 225.00
Ewer, pillar mold, appl ft/collar/hdl, minor sickness, 12" 175.00
Jar, apothecary; appl bands, pressed dome lid, 11", NM 65.00
Jigger, sapphire bl, panels w/ellipses, 2¼" 35.00
Lamp, onion front, appl ft & stem, brass collar, 6" 65.00
Pitcher, flint, appl rings/ovals, sm base check, 7½" 200.00
Salt cellar, master; bl opaque, pinched, scalloped, 1⅝x3¼" 195.00
Sugar bowl, blown/cut strawberry dmn w/roundels & fans, 8¾" 790.00
Sugar bowl, gallery rim, dbl-curve dome lid, knob stem, 8" 550.00
Syrup jug, bl opaque, strap hdl, pewter lid, 1850s 550.00
Tumbler, 12-panel base, appl hollow hdl, tooled lip, 8", NM . .250.00
Vase, pillar mold bowl w/scalloped rim, baluster stem, 11" 125.00
Wine, pressed panel bowl, baluster stem, appl ft, 4", pr 75.00
Wine, Strawberry & Diamonds, wafered stem 95.00

Plastics

The term 'collectible plastics' is defined as those types produced between 1868 (when synthetic plastics were invented) and the period immediately following WWII. There are several, and we shall mention each one and attempt briefly to acquaint you with their characteristics:

1) Pyroxylin (Celluloid, French Ivory, Pyralin). Chemical name: cellulose nitrate. Earliest form, invented in 1868 by John Wesley Hyatt; highly flammable; yellows with age; much used in toiletry articles. Fairly lightweight, many articles of pyroxylin were made by heating and molding thin sheets.

2) Cellulose Acetate (Tenite, Similoid). Made in attempt to produce a product similar to cellulose nitrate but without the flammability. Had limited use in the costume jewelry trade; most often encountered as car knobs and handles of the thirties and forties. Surfaces tend to crack with age and exposure to light. Always molded, never cast. Colors varied; imitation horn and marble were most popular.

3) Casein Plastics (Ameroid, Galalith, Dorcasine, Casolith). Invented in 1904 using milk proteins. Use limited to buttons and buckles due to warping and lengthy curing time. Made in a wide range of colors; very easy to laminate or to carve from stock rods or sheets, but never molded.

4) Phenol Formaldehyde (Bakelite, Catalin, Marblette, Agatine, Gemstone, Durite, Durez, Prystal). Invented by L.H. Baekland in 1908; used extensively in the thirties. There are two major types: cast and molded. Molded types include Durez and Bakelite, dark-toned, wood-flour filled plastics that were used extensively for early telephones (still used when non-conductivity of heat and electricity is vital). The most popular name in cast phenolics was Catalin, trade name of the American Catalin Corporation of New York. Made in a wide range of colors; widely used for costume jewelry, cutlery handles, decorative boxes, lamps, desk sets, etc. Heavyweight material with a slightly 'greasy' feel; very hard, but can be carved with files, grinding tools, and abrasive cutters. Buffs to high, durable polish. Cast phenolics were used primarily from 1930 to around 1950 when they proved too labor-intensive to be economical.

5) Urea Formaldehyde (Beetleware, Plaskon, Duroware, Hemocoware, Uralite). Invented around 1929, this was lighter in color than phenol formaldehyde, thus used for injection-molded products in pastel colors. Lightweight, not strong; shiny rather than glossy. It cannot be carved and was used mainly for cheap radio and clock cases, never for jewelry.

The period between the two World Wars produced acrylic resins such as Lucite and vinyl. Polystryene made its appearance then, and furfural-phenols were in use in industrial applications. Though a great future was predicted for ethyl cellulose, by the late thirties it was still in the experimental phase. For most purposes, the field of decorative plastics from the first half of the century can be narrowed down to the five major types listed above. Of these, cellulose acetate is rarely encountered. Casein is limited to button and belt buckle manufacture; urea is easily identifiable as a cheap, brittle material. Pyroxylin is the celluloid of which so many vanity sets were made. Molded phenolics such as Bakelite were dark in color and used for utilitarian objects; cast phenolics such as Catalin were used most notably for jewelry (please don't call it Bakelite), cutlery handles, desk sets, and novelties.

Dealers and collectors should beware of reproduction Marblette animal napkin rings (they have no eye rods and no age patina) and molded acrylic bracelets in imitation of carved Catalin ones (look for a seam line or lack of definition in 'carved areas'). As prices rise, copies become more common. 1986 saw the mass-production of inlaid polka-dot bracelets using old-stock findings but without the precision fit (or patina) of the originals.

Our advisor for this category is Catherine Yronwode, who also publishes an informative newsletter, *The Collectible Plastics*; she is listed in the Directory under California and again under Clubs, Newsletters, and Catalogs.

Bakelite roulette wheel, Catalin chips; see listings for specific values.

Bakelite

Cigarette box, half-cylinder, rotates open, dk brn 35.00
Clock, electric, alarm, Deco design, blk 50.00
Clock, mantel, windup alarm, Deco design, dk brn 45.00
Inkwell, streamlined, blk, w/lid 20.00
Penholder, streamlined, blk 15.00
Radio, Majestic #55, dk brn, 1939 . . . . .100.00
Radio, Silvertone Compact, Sears, dk brn, 1936-1937 . . . . . . .100.00
Radio, Stewart Warner Varsity College, dk brn, 1938-1939 . . .100.00
Roulette wheel, dk brn, 1930s 80.00
Roulette wheel, mc Catalin chips, wood rack, w/box, 1930s . . .200.00
Watch, lady's handbag; Westclox, blk, 2¾" dia 50.00

Catalin

Ash tray, marbleized lt gr, sq, 4½" 14.00
Barometer, Taylor, amber & dk gr, rectangular, 4" 30.00
Bottle opener, chrome plate, red, gr, or amber hdl 4.00
Bracelet, bangle; apple-juice clear, figural bk-cvg 100.00
Bracelet, bangle; apple-juice clear, floral bk-cvg 90.00
Bracelet, bangle; apple-juice clear, geometric bk-cvg 80.00
Bracelet, bangle; deep cvg, w/rhinestones 60.00
Bracelet, bangle; elaborate floral cvg, narrow 24.00
Bracelet, bangle; elaborate floral cvg, wide 40.00
Bracelet, bangle; lt geometric cvg, narrow 18.00
Bracelet, bangle; lt geometric cvg, wide 20.00
Bracelet, bangle; novelty, figural or animal cvg 120.00
Bracelet, bangle; scratch cvd, narrow 10.00
Bracelet, bangle; scratch cvd, w/rhinestones 25.00
Bracelet, bangle; scratch cvd, wide 15.00
Bracelet, bangle; stylized floral cvg, narrow 18.00
Bracelet, bangle; stylized floral cvg, wide 30.00
Bracelet, bangle; uncvd, narrow 3.00
Bracelet, bangle; uncvd, wide 8.00
Bracelet, bangle; 12 inlaid polka dots, wide 120.00
Bracelet, bangle; 2-color stripes 40.00
Bracelet, bangle; 3-color stripes 50.00
Bracelet, bangle; 4-color (or more) stripes 60.00
Bracelet, bangle; 6 inlaid polka dots, narrow 110.00
Bracelet, cellulose acetate chain, 7 cvd figural charms 60.00
Bracelet, clamper; figural, animal, or novelty applique 200.00
Bracelet, clamper; inlaid geometric designs 100.00
Bracelet, clamper; stylized floral cvg .40.00
Bracelet, clamper; w/inlaid rhinestones 30.00
Bracelet, curved/flat links, deeply cvd 40.00
Bracelet, curved/flat links, uncvd 30.00
Bracelet, stretch; orig elastic, Catalin & metal 25.00
Bracelet, stretch; orig elastic, deeply cvd 40.00
Bracelet, stretch; orig elastic, mc, uncvd 30.00
Buckle, latch type, mc, cvd 30.00
Buckle, latch type, mc, novelty or figural 40.00
Buckle, latch type, mc, uncvd 15.00
Buckle, latch type, 1-color, cvd 10.00
Buckle, latch type, 1-color, novelty or figural 20.00
Buckle, latch type, 1-color, uncvd 5.00
Buckle, latch type, 1-color w/rhinestones, Deco 15.00
Buckle, slide type, mc, cvd 20.00
Buckle, slide type, mc, uncvd 10.00
Buckle, slide type, 1-color, cvd 5.00
Buckle, slide type, 1-color, uncvd 3.00
Butter mold, gr/amber/brn, floral cvg, 2½" 32.00
Buttons, card of 6, red or blk laminated, 1½" rod 18.00
Buttons, card of 6, scotty, fruit, or cvd floral figural 18.00

Buttons, card of 6, uncvd octagonal, amber, 1" dia 6.00
Cake breaker, CJ Schneider, red, gr, or amber hdl 2.00
Checkers, red & blk, full set, in box .30.00
Cheese slicer, scotty hdl, wood & chrome base 10.00
Chess set, hand cvd, red & blk, leather box 150.00
Chopsticks, ivory, pr 2.00
Cigarette box, chrome inserts, cylindrical, 4½" 35.00
Cigarette box, lt gr, wood bottom, rectangular, 5½x3¾" 25.00
Cigarette holder, imitation amber, sterling tip, orig case 25.00
Cigarette holder, long, mc or w/rhinestones 18.00
Cigarette lighter, Arco-Lite devil's head, red or blk 150.00
Cigarette lighter, mc stripes or inlay .25.00
Clock, New Haven, windup alarm, amber, Deco, 3⅝" 40.00
Clock, Sessions, electric alarm, scalloped case, 4¼" dia 50.00
Clock, Seth Thomas, windup alarm, maroon case, 3½" 35.00
Clock, Westclox, Moonbeam, electric flashing light alarm 45.00
Clothesline, Jigger, red anchors, 10 pins, metal box 8.00
Cocktail recipes, Ben Hur, mtd on drunk, red w/blk base 38.00
Cocktail recipes, Ben Hur, mtd on fighting roosters 40.00
Cork, Ben Hur, w/red fighting roosters, blk base 12.00
Corkscrew, chrome, red, gr, or amber hdl 10.00
Corn holder, Kob Knobs, diamond shape or lathe trn, 8 +box . . .30.00
Crib toy, Tykie Toy, boy, girl, clown, kitten, etc, ea 50.00
Crib toy, Tykie Toy, 11 mc spools on string, 1940s 30.00
Crib toy, Tykie Toy, 12-1½" rings on 2⅞" ring, 1940s 30.00
Dice, ivory or red, 2½", pr 15.00
Dice, ivory or red, ¾", pr 2.00
Dice cage, metal/red Catalin, blk Lucite base, w/dice 75.00
Dice cup, leather or cork lined 22.00
Dominoes, ivory or blk, full set, w/wood box 25.00
Dominoes, red or gr, full set, w/wood box 40.00
Drawer pull, 1-color, w/pnt inlay stripe 1.50
Drawer pull, 2-color, octagon, w/inlaid dot 2.50
Dress clip, mc inlaid Deco design 15.00
Dress clip, novelty, figural, animal, or vegetable 25.00
Dress clip, scratch cvd 5.00
Dress clip, stylized floral cvg 8.00
Dress clip, 1-color, w/rhinestones, Deco design 10.00
Earrings, lg drop style 8.00
Earrings, novelty, figural, animal, or vegetable, pr 14.00
Earrings, stylized floral cvg, pr 6.00
Earrings, uncvd disks, pr 3.00
Egg beater, red, gr, or amber hdl 10.00
Flatware, chrome plate, 1-color hdl 1.00
Flatware, chrome plate, 3-pc matched place setting 5.00
Flatware, stainless, 1-color hdl 1.00
Flatware, stainless, 1-color hdl, leatherette box, 36-pc 50.00
Flatware, stainless, 1-color hdl, 3-pc matched place setting 5.00
Flatware, stainless, 2-color hdl 3.00
Flatware, stainless, 2-color hdl, wood box, 36-pc 200.00
Flatware, stainless, 2-color hdl, 3-pc matched place setting 10.00
Gavel, lathe turned, ivory 18.00
Gavel, lathe turned, red, blk, & ivory 25.00
Gavel, lathe turned, red, w/presentation box, dtd 1946 . . . . . . .28.00
Ice cream scoop, stainless, red hdl 12.00
Inkwell, Carvacraft Great Britain, amber, dbl well 75.00
Inkwell, Carvacraft Great Britain, amber, single well 35.00
Knife, cvd red, gr, or amber hdl 4.00
Lamp base, brass & amber, Deco design, 10" 28.00
Lamp base, red, amber, & blk, Deco design, 8" 44.00
Letter opener, blk & amber stripes, Deco design 10.00
Letter opener, chrome/Catalin, Deco design 6.00
Letter opener, marbleized gr, dagger shape 8.00
Mah-Jong set, tiles, rails, 6-color, complete, w/box 40.00

Manicure set, tube holder, pnt floral design 35.00
Manicure set, 4-mini tools in tube, Germany 22.00
Memo pad, Carvacraft Great Britain, amber 20.00
Nail brush, Ducky, duck shape, translucent eye rod 30.00
Nail brush, marbleized lt gr, 2½x1½" 6.00
Nail brush, Masso, amber octagon, 2" dia 6.00
Nail brush, turtle shape, dark amber, 3½" 12.00
Napkin ring, amber, red, or gr, 2" dia band 3.00
Napkin ring, animal or bird, no inlaid eye or ball on head 13.50
Napkin ring, elephant w/ball on head 15.00
Napkin ring, lathe turned, amber, red, or gr, 1¾" dia 4.00
Napkin ring, Mickey Mouse or Donald Duck shape w/decal ...45.00
Napkin ring, rabbit w/inlaid eye rod 15.00
Napkin ring, rocking horse or camel w/inlaid eye rod 35.00
Napkin ring, scotty, w/inlaid eye rod 18.00
Napkin ring set, 6-colors, 2" band, orig box 30.00
Necklace, cellulose acetate chain, animal figurals 110.00
Necklace, cellulose acetate chain, Deco dangling pcs 48.00
Necklace, cvd red & amber beads, 18" 35.00
Necklace, uncvd gr beads, 20" 20.00
Ozone generator, Air-Clear, dk amber, streamlined case 40.00
Pencil sharpener, Disney character decal, silhouette shape 24.00
Pencil sharpener, gun, tank, or plane shape w/decal 18.00
Pencil sharpener, orange, no decal, ¾x1" 4.00
Pencil sharpener, red, Mickey Mouse decal, ¾x1" 20.00
Pencil sharpener, scotty, red, cvd details, blk base 12.00
Pencil sharpener, scotty, yel, silhouette shape 10.00
Pencil sharpener, Trylon & Perisphere, 1939 World's Fair 32.00
Penholder, amber & blk striped, Deco design 35.00
Penholder, marbleized amber, Deco design 20.00
Penholder, scotty, red w/blk base 42.00
Picture frame, amber & red Deco design, 6x7" 32.00
Picture frame, red, gr, or amber, sq, 6" 15.00
Pin, animal, resin wash w/glass eye, lg 50.00
Pin, animal, resin wash w/glass eye, sm 38.00
Pin, animal or vegetable, inlaid or appl in several colors, lg 95.00
Pin, animal or vegetable, inlaid or appl in several colors, sm 60.00
Pin, animal or vegetable, 1-color, lg 42.00
Pin, animal or vegetable, 1-color, sm 30.00
Pin, mc Deco design, lg 40.00
Pin, mc Deco design, sm 30.00
Pin, novelty or patriotic figural, resin wash/inlay/appl, lg 150.00
Pin, novelty or patriotic figural, resin wash/inlay/appl, sm 90.00
Pin, novelty or patriotic figural, 1-color, lg 80.00
Pin, novelty or patriotic figural, 1-color, sm 50.00
Pin, stylized floral cvg, lg 25.00
Pin, stylized floral cvg, sm 18.00
Pin, w/danglers, animal or vegetable, resin wash/inlay/appl 120.00
Pin, w/danglers, animal or vegetable, 1-color 70.00
Pin, w/danglers, geometric form, mc 45.00
Pin, w/danglers, geometric form, 1-color 30.00
Pin, w/danglers, novelty or patriotic, resin wash/inlay/appl 150.00
Pin, w/danglers, novelty or patriotic, 1-color 85.00
Pipe, amber & gr, bowl lined w/clay 15.00
Pitcher, glass, red, gr, or amber hdl, syrup size 6.00
Pocket watch, Debonaire, yel Deco case, 1⅞" dia 40.00
Poker chip rack, cylindrical, w/50 chips, 2½" 50.00
Poker chip rack, rectangular, w/200 chips, 4" 90.00
Powder box, amber & blk fluted cylinder, 2½" 35.00
Powder box, amber & gr fluted cylinder, 4" 50.00
Radio, Emerson College model, amber or gr, 1938 ....350.00
Radio, Emerson College model, red, 1938 ....395.00
Radio, Fada Streamliner, amber, amber knobs/bezel, 1941 .....400.00
Radio, Fada Streamliner, amber, red knobs/bezel 425.00

Radio, Kadette Klockette, amber, gr, or maroon, 1937 ....300.00
Radio, Kadette Klockette, red, 1937 ....325.00
Ring, inlaid Deco stripe design, 2-color 25.00
Ring, stylized floral cvg, 1-color 18.00
Ring, uncvd, 1-color 5.00
Ring, uncvd, 2-color 10.00
Ring case, hinged-lid style, amber or maroon 65.00
Ring case, open-top style, amber, red, or blk, Deco design 50.00
Safety razor, Schick Injector, amber hdl 9.00
Safety razor, Schick Injector, extra blades, orig box, 1939 .....20.00
Salad servers, Chase chrome, ivory, blk, or brn, pr 28.00
Salad servers, chrome, red, gr, or amber hdls, pr 10.00
Set, cvg; knife, fork, steel 25.00
Set, cvg; 3-pc w/wood wall rack 28.00
Shakers, ball shape or half-cylinder shape, 1½", pr 22.00
Shakers, glass, in 3⅛" Catalin holder, pr 12.00
Shakers, mushroom shape, amber & ivory, 1⅞", pr 19.00
Shakers, stepped cylinder shape, 3½", pr 18.00
Shakers, Washington Monument, 3¼", pr 15.00
Shaving brush, red, gr, or amber 14.00
Shaving brush, red, gr, or amber, w/holder 21.00
Spatula, stainless, red, gr, or amber hdl 3.00
Spoon, iced tea, chrome, w/Catalin knob, 6-pc set 10.00
Spoon, slotted, stainless, red, gr, or amber hdl 3.00
Steering knob, chrome clamp 12.00
Stirrer, iced tea; Chase, chrome ball/mint leaf, 6-pc set 20.00
Stirrer, iced tea; shovel blade, Catalin hdl, 6-pc set 20.00
Strainer, red, gr, or amber hdl, 2¾" dia 4.00
Strainer, red, gr, or amber hdl, 5" dia 6.00
Swizzle stick, baseball-bat shape, amber or red 4.00
Swizzle stick holder, amber or red, Rheingold Lager decal 50.00
Thermometer, BT Co, amber & blk, 2¾" dia 25.00
Thermometer, Taylor, amber & dk gr, rectangular, 4" 40.00
Writing set, blk, amber, or gr marble, Deco, 5-pc, orig box 110.00

Celluloid

Bracelet, imitation tortoise w/inlaid rhinestones 35.00
Bracelet, snake w/inlaid rhinestones 42.00
Bridge marker, pnt ivoroid animal or figure, France 10.00
Bridge pencil holder, animal, pearlescent ivory on blk 50.00
Buttons, ivoroid or pearlescent, ¾" dia, card of 6 ....8.00
Carving set, ivoroid, knife/fork/steel, eng blade 30.00
Clock, Greek temple facade, windup alarm, ivoroid 45.00
Dresser set, amberoid & gr marbleized, 7-pc 49.00
Dresser set, ivoroid, 10-pc, w/9" bevel glass mirror 62.00
Dresser set, ivory pearlescent or amberoid, 5-pc 38.00
Flatware, gr pearl on blk hdl, 3-pc set 9.00
Flatware, ivoroid hdl, table knife, fork, or spoon, ea 1.00
Manicure set, ivoroid, pearlescent or amberoid, 10-pc, +case ...30.00
Manicure set, ivoroid, 18-pc, roll-up leather case 25.00
Mirror, dresser; ivoroid, cut-out hdl, bevel glass, 8" 14.00
Mirror, dresser; ivoroid, oval bevel glass, 13" 24.00
Mirror, dresser; pearlescent or amberoid, bevel glass, 12" 20.00
Necklace, cellulose acetate chain, Deco dangling disks 32.00
Picture frame, easel bk, ivoroid, 2" dia 10.00
Shaving stand, ivoroid, 5-pc 75.00

Lucite

Bottle, perfume; w/atomizer, rose inclusion 10.00
Bracelet, stretch, orig elastic, clear, bk-cvd 22.00
Picture frame, Deco, clear, sq, 6" 12.00
Purse, box style, clear 20.00

Purse, box style, imitation tortoise shell 20.00
Shakers, translucent red, 4", pr 5.00

Playing Cards

Playing cards can be an enjoyable way to trace the course of history. Knowledge of the art, literature, and politics of an era can be gleaned from a study of its playing cards. When royalty lost favor with the people, Kings and Queens were replaced by common people. During the periods of war, generals, officers, and soldiers were favored. In the United States, early examples had portraits of Washington and Adams as opposed to Kings, Indian chiefs instead of Jacks, and goddesses for Queens.

Tarot cards were used in Europe during the 1300s as a game of chance, but in the 18th century they were used to predict the future and were regarded with great reverence.

The backs of cards were of no particular consequence until the 1890s. The marble design used by the French during the late 1800s and the colored wood-cut patterns of the Italians in the 19th century are among the first attempts at decoration. Later the English used cards printed with portraits of royalty. Eventually cards were decorated with a broad range of subjects from reproductions of fine art to advertising.

Although playing cards are becoming a popular collectible, prices are relatively low. Complete decks printed earlier than the first postage stamp can be purchased for less than $100. Periodic auction catalogs are available from 'Full House' Antique Playing Cards and Gambling Memorabilia. See the Directory under Clubs, Newsletters and Catalogs for the address.

Key:
C — complete   OB — original box
cts — courts   sz — size
hc — hand colored   XC — extra card
J — joker

Advertising

Craddock's Soap, ea w/different stage star, 52+J, OB, EX 100.00
EMU Cigarettes, USPC, Costa Rica, 1935, 52+J+2XC, OB, M .10.00
Herpicide, Going, Going, Gone, ca 1900, 52, no J, VG 15.00
Lewando's Cleaners, wide, Boston & NY, 1910s, 52, no J, EX ...12.00
Petoskey Cement, special cts, gold edges, 1935, 52+J+XC, M ...15.00
Redhead Matches, Australian Co, ltd ed, 52+JJ, OB, M 12.00
Schering Medical, medical people as cts, 1960, 52+JJ, OB, M ...20.00
Texaco, Marine Petroleum Products, Waddington, 52+JJ, OB, M .8.00
Time Magazine, lovely cts & Js, 1962, 52+J+XC, OB, M 60.00
Washburn Guitars, special cts, wide, pinochle, 48, OB, EX 40.00

France and Belgium

Bretagne, Kings play bagpipes, Gimaud, 1970, 52+JJJ+XC, M ...20.00
Catalanes, Spanish suits, Grimaud, ca 1890s, 48C, OB, M 45.00
Fijne Speelkarten, mc aces, Turnhoutoise, 1920, 33C, M 10.00
Jour, ltd ed of 100 decks, Braun #36, 1965, 32+2J, M 16.00
Napoleon, Catel & Farcy, ca 1960, 52+J+XC+blank, EX 25.00
Paris Expo, scenes on aces, Geuens-Willaert, 1900, 52C, M 45.00
Proverbes, nudes w/proverbs, Philibert, 1960, 52+JJ, OB, M ...30.00
Quadrilato, Bierman's #44, sq corners, ca 1910, 40C, M 10.00
Van Teeseling, music notes on aces, Carta Mundi, 1979, OB, M..12.00

Games, No Suit Signs

Bootleg, unusual suits, 1930s, 52+instructions, ½ OB, EX 30.00
Hoot, animals, Thornton W Burgess, OH, 1920, 52C, OB, VG .10.00

Jeu de Cart Geographique, Joey, 1806, 48+rules+map, OB, M ..200.00
Logomachy, 1889 ed w/1874 instructions, 36 mc cards, OB 50.00
Mad Magazine, 1980, 76+photo J+instructions, OB, M 10.00
Sigs, Army/Navy/Marines, ES Cooper, '45, 62C+rules, OB, M ..16.00
Swastika, SR Beal, Adrian MI, Indians, 1907, 55C, OB, G 20.00

Germany, Austria, and Czechoslovakia

Austrian Seasons #86, Piatnik, ca 1950, 33C, OB, M 10.00
Bohemian #208, ASS Altenburgh/Thuringen, '40s, 32C, OB, M ..20.00
Cashmere, Bernhard Altmann, Piatnik, 1950, 52+JJ, EX 50.00
Dondorf #911, gr clubs, orange diamonds, 1930s, 52C, OB, M .75.00
Dondorf Club, scenic aces, rnd corners, 1895 stamp, 52C, M ...50.00
Eduard Buttner, Skat chromolith, Berlin, 1800s, 32C, EX 75.00
Prussian, scenics, Stralsunder, ca 1900 tax stamp, 32C, VG 50.00
Salon Karte #66, ca 1925 tax stamp, 52+J, OB, M 50.00
Salzburg #13, ASS Altenburg/Thuringen, 1945, 36C, OB, M ...15.00
Schwerdter Karter, Segeth #83, Wust, 1890s, 32C, VG 135.00

Great Britain

Kimberly Diamond Jubilee of 1897, flags on aces, 52C, M 110.00
Our Prince, Edw VIII on bks, Goodall, ca 1920, 52+J, OB, EX ..60.00
Picart le Coux, for 125th Anniv of De la Rue, 52+JJ+XC, M ...20.00
Queen Victoria Diamond Jubilee, beautiful cts, 52C, VG 100.00
Royal Pavilion, Rowlandson-type cartoons, 1945, 52+JJ, OB, M ..7.50
Yel Chartreuse, narrow named, Barribal, 52+J, G 20.00

Italy, Spain, and Latin America

Argentine, gaucho designs, Rodero, Buenos Aires, '50, 40C, M ..40.00
Cartubria Porcelanizoda, Productos Leo, Mexico, '65, 40C, M ..15.00
Cauhtemoc, Aztecs, Jacques, 1950, 52+JJ+20-pg booklet, M 28.00
Chocolate inserts, cartoon bks, Boparull, 1932, 48C, M 100.00
Dante & Beatrice, Piatnik, ca 1920, 52+JJ+title card, VG 75.00
Political Satire, 104 caricatures, Munoz, 1973, 106C, OB, M ...32.00
Venete, Armanino, Rome, 1940, 52+JJ, OB, M 20.00

Miniatures and Patience

Baroness, from Dondorf plates, 1940, 52+JJ, 43x65mm, M 12.00
Disney, cartoon characters, Union, 52+Dopey J+XC, OB, M ...35.00
Elephant, on ace/JJ, Shanghai, 1960, 52+JJ, 43x57mm, OB, M ...5.00
Grimaud, 6-color 2-way cts, 1890 stamp, 52C, 37x55mm, VG ..10.00
Jeu Louis XV, Grimaud, 52C, 44x65mm, OB, EX 12.00
Movie Stars, ea bk different, Universal, 52C, 31x44mm, EX 50.00
Naipes Miniatura, Jacques, ca 1940, 40C, 41x62mm, sealed/M ...7.00
Patience, Australia, ca 1930, 52+J+3 blanks, 43x61mm, VG 7.00
Rococo Patience #96, Muller, dbl deck, 28x42mm, sealed/M ...10.00

Souvenir and Expositions

Alaska-Yukon-Pacific, 1909, 52+Chief Seattle J, OB, M 110.00
Chicago World's Fair, red ground, 1933, sealed, M 20.00
Columbia Expo, 1st deck, 52+J, OB, EX 60.00
Cuba, orig version, Romo & Kredi, ca 1905, 52C, OB, EX 50.00
Kylushu, color island scenes, Nintendo, 52+JJ, OB, M 7.00
Lake McDonald, Glacier Nat'l Park, standard faces, sealed, M ...5.00
Montreal/Quebec, wide scenic, 52+Indian J+map C, OB, VG ..25.00
Panama Canal, 1st wide scenic, 52+J+map+XC, VG 25.00
Rocky Mountains, scenic w/gold edges, 1940, OB, M 22.00
Vermont, gold edges, Chisholm, 1900, 52+J+XC, OB, M 40.00
Washington & Pacific Northwest, wide scenic, 52+J, OB, M ...60.00

Tarot and Fortune Telling

Carreras, Dondorf type, ca 1926, 36C, EX 15.00
Fortune Telling, Jan Eric, 1934, 44C, no instructions, EX 22.00
Nile, USPC #68X, gold edges, 1897-1904, 52+Life C, OB, EX ..16.00
Palmistry, McLoughlin, 1900, 40C+instructions, OB, EX 50.00
Sheridan-Douglas, Mandragora Press, '72, 78C+booklet, OB, M .16.00
Teuila, USPC, 1923, 45C+booklet, OB, NM 50.00
Vandeborre, reprint by Carta Mundi, 1974, OB, M 25.00
Wahragekunst, Mlle Le Normand, 1860s, 54+booklet, OB, EX. .200.00

Transformations

Comic Karte, Fromann & Bunt, ca 1965, 48 of 52, OB, EX 175.00
Hustling Joe II, 1895, 52+blank, ½ OB, VG 200.00
Samuel Hart, scarce, ca 1860, 50 of 52, VG 215.00
Tiffany Harlequin, bl bks, CE Carryl, 1879, 52+blank, EX 450.00

Transportation: Airline, Steamship, Railroad

American Airlines, DC7/wings/logo on gold, 1955, sealed, M ...18.00
American Steamboat #99, Am Playing Cards, 52+J, OB, EX ...40.00
At Sea, wide named, gold edges, 52+J+2XC, snap case, M 16.00
Avianca, El Colombiano, 1st issue, ca 1950, sealed, M 30.00
Canadian Pacific Ry & Royal Mail SS Line, 1900, 52+J, M 25.00
Climax #14, Tecumseh bks, Dougherty, 52C, orig case, VG 15.00
Clyde Mallory Line, Miami/Cuba/NY, 1935, 52+J+XC, OB, M .22.00
French Line, photo bks, Grimaud, ca 1920, 52C, no box, EX ...30.00
Great Northern RR, gr & silver, ca 1935, 52+JJ+XC, M 35.00
Hart's French Whist, NYCC, ca 1920, 52 w/no J, VG 9.00
Jerry Bulldog, wide named, gold edge, 52+J, OB, NM 30.00
Midway Airlines, Metrolink issue, sealed, M 10.00
Miss Budweiser, Anheuser-Busch 2-prop airliner, 1953, M 15.00
Penn RR, 3 trains & bridge, 1953, sealed, M 15.00
Pullman, logo on ace of Spades, 52+J+XC, orig case, EX 22.00
Santa Fe RR, 2 trains in mtns, 1949, sealed, M 10.00
Sitting Bull, wide named, orange border, 1901, 52C, EX 18.00
Stage #65X, stars on cts/aces/J, 52+J, ½ OB, VG 65.00
Sutherland's Circular Coon Cards, 1925, 52+J, metal box, VG .150.00

Monitor and Merrimac, 1865, complete set of
52 cards, rare, mint condition, $1,750.00.

Political

The most valuable political items are those from any period which relate to a political figure whose term was especially significant or marked by an important event or one whose personality was particularly colorful. Posters, ribbons, badges, photographs, and pin-back buttons are but a few examples of the items popular with collectors of political memorabilia.

Political campaign pin-back buttons were first mass-produced and widely distributed in 1896 for the president-to-be William McKinley and

for the first of three unsuccessful attempts by William Jennings Bryan. Pin-back buttons have been used during each presidential campaign ever since and are collected by many people. The most scarce are those used in the presidential campaigns of James Davis in 1924 and James Cox in 1920.

Our advisor for this category is Paul Longo; he is listed in the Directory under Massachusetts. See also Autographs; Broadsides; Historical Glass; Watch Fobs.

Ash tray, Willkie campaign, wht glass, 3½", EX 20.00
Badge, Alternate Nat'l Rep Convention Delegate, June 1908 ...50.00
Badge, Landon in yel/brn sunflower, 1936 ....5.00
Badge, Truman inauguration picture, 3" 12.00
Bandana, Cleveland/Stevenson, red flags on wht, 1892 ....90.00

Bandana, For President, Benj. Harrison; For Vice President Levi P. Morton; Protect Home Industry, 1888; red, white, and blue cotton, 23x23", EX, $200.00.

Bandana, T Roosevelt, red, National Progressive on 4 sides ...100.00
Banner, Repeal & Roosevelt, dk bl felt/red trim, 6x11" 90.00
Banner, Roosevelt/Garner, dk bl felt/red trim, 3x16" 60.00
Book, Authentic Life of Pres McKinley, 1901, VG 20.00
Booklet, campaign; Wilkie, 1940, 23-pg 15.00
Box, pin; JQ Adams, Be Firm For..., velvet cushion, 5" L ...550.00
Broadside, A Jackson's Inaugural Address, silk, 1829, 20x12" ..600.00
Broadside, A Lincoln, Funeral Obsequies, 10x10½", VG 110.00
Bumper sticker, George McGovern 1.00
Bust, A Lincoln, silver relief on blk velvet under glass 200.00
Button, Horatio Seymore, tintype in brass fr, 1868, 1" 200.00
Button, In Memoriam of Theodore Roosevelt, blk/wht, EX 15.00
Button, Nixon's the One, red/wht/blk, 1968, EX 4.00
Button, Washington inauguration, Long Live..., VG 200.00
Cartoon, Tammany Tiger, orig drawing, Nast, 1892, 10x9" ..1,000.00
Coffee cup, Alf Landon for President 20.00
Coin, John C Fremont, portrait, eagle on bk, 1850s 15.00
Cookie cutter, Vote Republican, tin, elephant form, orig box ...20.00
Dice cup, Don't Gamble, Elect Willkie, 2½x3" 30.00
Fan, Major Gen Zachary Taylor, paper, portrait/battle views ...500.00
Flag, silk w/embr US Seal, from Taft's office, 34x62" 300.00
Game, Watergate Darts, complete, 16" 35.00
Match safe, Grover Cleveland figural, NM 150.00
Matchbox holder, portrait of T Roosevelt, celluloid, 1941 ......35.00
Medal, Ford inaugural, Franklin, SP, M 50.00
Medal, Grant/Willkie, w/brass eagle hanger, NM 40.00
Medal, Jimmy Carter campaign, sterling, official 22.50
Medal, Kennedy inaugural, official, 1961 ....75.00
Mug, T Roosevelt, mc portrait on ceramic, 3" 75.00
Necktie, Grant/Colfax, woven portrait ea end, rare 350.00
Nutcracker, Woodrow Wilson's head figural, wood, 8" 175.00
Pamphlet, Bryan cover, Modern Woodman, 1927, EX 5.00
Paper dolls, Jackie/Caroline Kennedy, cb, complete 40.00
Paperweight, Parker/Davis jugate, Pittsburgh Glass 75.00
Pennant, campaign; Adlai, 27", NM 35.00
Penny, campaign; Lincoln/Johnson, 1864 ....45.00
Pin, Lincoln ferro, lg rnd brass fr, rim: Pat appl for, EX 850.00

Pin, Votes for Women/Victory 1915, NY State seal, EX 85.00
Pin-bk, Cox/Roosevelt, celluloid, 1920, EX 45.00
Pin-bk, Cox/Roosevelt, tin, Lynch, pat 1917, 1920 ....25.00
Pin-bk, For Persident John W Davis, celluloid, 1924 ....75.00
Pin-bk, Hoover for President, ⅞" 20.00
Pin-bk, Joe Louis World's Champion, blk/wht, 1940s, EX 16.00
Pin-bk, McKinley/Hobart, celluloid, 1896, EX 15.00
Pin-bk, McKinley/Roosevelt, Full Dinner Bucket, 1900 ....38.00
Pin-bk, Parker/Davis, celluloid, sepia, oval, 1904 ....30.00
Pin-bk, Washington & draped flag, mc, ca 1905, EX 8.00
Pin-bk, Wm J Bryan for President, 1896 ....20.00
Pin-bk, Woodrow Wilson for President 25.00
Pincushion, Teddy Roosevelt & bear figural, china, 4x3½" 150.00
Plate, JF Kennedy & Family, Cape Cod MA, ca 1961, 7" 10.00
Plate, Mr & Mrs JF Kennedy, glazed china, ca 1961, 8½" 20.00
Playing cards, Roosevelt/Wilson/Hoover/Cleveland on bks, EX .25.00
Poster, General McArthur, Salute to Victory, ca 1948, 17x21" ..75.00
Poster, Kennedy for President, leadership for '60s, 21x14" 25.00
Poster, Kennedy for President, Time for Greatness, 44x28" 30.00
Poster, McGovern for President, 1972, 21x29" 8.00
Poster, McKinley/Bryan, Real Issue, blk/wht litho, 48x35" 280.00
Poster, Nixon re-election, 22x34", M 15.00
Program, Landon/Knox cover, 1936 ....25.00
Program, Roosevelt/Garner inaugural, 1933 ....40.00
Puzzle, JF Kennedy, ca 1961, complete, 12x16", EX 30.00
Ribbon, portraits of McKinley/Hobart, 1896, 7x2¼" 40.00
Sewing kit, A Jackson, scissors/needle case/bobbins, 1829 .....250.00
Spencerian drawing, A Jackson on horsebk, in fr, 15x11½" ..1,500.00
Stamp, Wendell Wilkie, postage-like, 2 for 15.00
Stein, Dewey portrait, Ceramic Art Co, Trenton, 6" 75.00
Tapestry, JF Kennedy portrait/flag, ca 1964, 20x36" 45.00
Tie tack, Ike 56, brass w/die-cut letter/numbers 10.00
Token, Harrison campaign 1840, silvered brass, ⅞" 15.00
Token, Hayes/Wheeler campaign, wht metal, ⅞" 35.00
Tray, Garfield/Lincoln/McKinley, aluminum, blk on silver, '01 ..20.00

Tray, W.H. Taft, Grand Old Party, tin litho, 10", $175.00.

Wall clock, Spiro Agnew, celluloid, electric, 9" 35.00
Watch fob, Harding/Coolidge 1920 jugate, wht metal 50.00
Watch fob, Harrison/Morton, Protection to Industries, EX 85.00
Watch fob, Taft/Sherman, 1908 ....35.00

Pomona

Pomona glass was patented in 1885 by the New England Glass Works. Its characteristics are an etched background of crystal lead glass often decorated with simple designs painted with metallic stains of amber or blue. The etching was first achieved by hand cutting through an acid resist. This method, called first grind, resulted in an uneven feather-like frost effect. Later, to cut production costs, the hand-cut process was discontinued in favor of an acid bath which effected an even frosting. This method is called second grind.

Our advisors for this category are Betty and Clarence Maier; they are listed in the Directory under Pennsylvania.

Bowl, 1st grind, cornflowers, petaled base, 3x5¾" 350.00
Bowl, 2nd grind, fluted, 10" 175.00
Bowl, 2nd grind, Invt T'print, 8" 200.00
Butter dish, 1st grind, acanthus leaves on lid, 4x8" 600.00
Celery vase, 1st grind, cornflowers, ruffled rim, 6¼" 350.00
Celery vase, 2nd grind, cornflowers, waisted, ftd, 7" 275.00
Creamer, 1st grind, Invt T'print, 2¾" 210.00
Creamer & sugar bowl, 1st grind, cornflowers, scalloped ft 550.00
Creamer & sugar bowl, 2nd grind, cornflowers 420.00
Creamer & sugar bowl, 2nd grind, Invt T'print 250.00
Cruet, 1st grind, bl cornflowers, ball stopper, 7" 475.00
Cruet, 2nd grind, amber stain, orig stopper 245.00
Finger bowl, 1st grind, 5" 90.00
Finger bowl, 2nd grind, cornflowers, 5½" 100.00
Finger bowl, 2nd grind, pansy & butterfly, ruffled 225.00
Pickle castor, 1st grind, cornflowers, SP fr & tongs 750.00
Pitcher, lemonade; 2nd grind, bl/amber butterflies, 9" 545.00
Pitcher, water; 2nd grind, Dia Quilt, 8½" 150.00
Pitcher, 1st grind, Invt T'print, sq top, amber stain, 4½" 350.00
Pitcher, 2nd grind, cornflowers, slim form, 9", +6 mugs 1,100.00

Punch cup, second grind, blueberries on red vines with gold leaves, $135.00.

Sherbet, 2nd grind, blueberries, 2", +4" underplate 400.00
Spooner, 1st grind, 5½" 170.00
Spooner, 2nd grind, blueberries 150.00
Toothpick holder, 1st grind, amber ruffled rim, hdl, 3½" 325.00
Toothpick holder, 2nd grind, amber stain, tricorn rim 350.00
Tray, 2nd grind, cornflowers, 12½x7¾" 475.00
Tumbler, juice; 1st grind, cornflowers 175.00
Tumbler, lemonade; 2nd grind, Rivulet, amber-stained rim 185.00
Tumbler, 2nd grind, bl cornflowers, amber stain 150.00
Underplate, 1st grind, 6½" 90.00
Vase, 1st grind, amber scalloped rim/base, fan form, 2½x4" 190.00
Vase, 1st grind, cornflowers, amber rim, fan form, 3x6" 235.00
Vase, 1st grind, ovoid w/sq fluted rim, 7" 285.00
Vase, 1st grind, 5½" 150.00

Post Cards

A German by the name of Emmanuel Herrman is credited for

inventing the post card, first printed in Austria in 1869. They were eagerly accepted by the Continentals and the English alike, who saw them as a more economical way to send written messages.

Post cards, first sold here in the 1880s, were made in Germany by order of private firms. The first to be printed in the United States were on U.S. government postals. The Columbian Exposition of 1892-1893 served as the spark that ignited the post card phenomenon. Souvenir cards by the thousands were sent to folks back home — Expo scenes, transportation themes, animals, birds, and advertising messages became popular. There were patriotic themes, Black themes, and cards for every occasion and holiday. Scenics, cards with small-town railroad depots, and views of U.S. towns (especially photos) are very sought-after.

Some of the earliest post card publishers were Raphael Tuck, and Nister and Gabriel. Early 20th-century illustrators such as Brundage, Rose O'Neill, and Clapsaddle designed cards that are especially sought after today.

Although the post card rage waned at the onset of WWI, they rank today among the most sought-after paper collectibles, second only to stamps.

Even though post cards may be sixty to eighty years old, they must be in good condition. As a worth-accessing factor, condition is second only to subject matter. When no condition is indicated, the items listed below are assumed to be in excellent condition whether used or unused.

Our advisor for this category is Sally Carver; she is listed in the Directory under Massachusetts.

Key:
p/ — publisher   s/ — signed

Advertising, Wales Goodyear Bear Brand, VG 8.00
Alligator Border, Series #S647, Happy Coons, p/Langsdorf, VG .27.00
American Indian Series #8668, Sioux, p/Tuck, VG 12.00
Attwell, Keep It Dark..., p/Valentine, VG 8.00
Attwell, Scuse My Back, p/Valentine, VG 6.50
Attwell, Series #9804, Visitors, p/Tuck, EX 12.00
Aviation, Bannister, Hampden Bomber, #4851, EX 10.00
Aviation, Bristol, Beaufort Bomber, #4839, EX 10.00
Beraud, Series #9802, Bleriot Airplane, p/Tuck, EX 16.00
Boileau, Out for Fun, VG 18.00
Boileau, Watercolor Series #371, Purity, EX 25.00
Boulanger, Humorous Cats Series #122, p/Tuck, EX 9.00
Brett, M; Series #1999, Netball, fairies play, p/Faulkner 12.00
Brundage, Series #4095, Summer at the Sea, p/Tuck, VG 22.00

'Squeeze me here and listen,' cat with green glass eyes, ca 1930s, $8.00.

Christy, University Girl Series, Wisconsin, #2626, VG 16.00
Clapsaddle, A Very Merry..., dolls/teddy/toys in sock, VG 8.00
Clapsaddle, Best Christmas Wishes, Santa holding holly, VG ...10.00

Clapsaddle, Best Christmas Wishes, snow scene, VG 6.00
Clark, Rose; Officer Stout Frog, FL-379, p/Rotograph, VG 22.00
Curtis, ES; Hopi Products, children, sepia, 1904, scarce 20.00
Disney, Mad Hatter's Tea Party, #A13, EX 12.00
Disney, With Her Friends on the Sands, #A31, EX 12.00
Donaldini, Series #454, Blk man gets kicked, 6½" ball 12.00
Donaldini, Sleepchasing Series #6613, Neck & Neck, p/Tuck ..10.00
Dwig, Series #110, I Really Haven't..., p/Gabriel, VG 8.00
Dwig, What's the Use Worrying..., p/Gross, VG 10.00
Easter cutout, rabbit under umbrella w/basket of eggs, EX 25.00
Educational Series #104, Zebra, p/Tuck, EX 12.00
Educational Series #405, Chief Gunner, US Army, p/Tuck, VG .18.00
Fisher, Harrison; #771, Inspiration, VG 16.00
Fisher, Harrison; Pals, EX 16.00
Fisher, Harrison; Watercolor Series #391, My Lady Waits, VG ..20.00
Gassaway, Base-Ball Player, FL-151, p/Rotograph, VG 18.00
Gassaway, 3 Years, girl w/rake, FL-119, p/Rotograph, VG 12.00
Gibson, Detroit #14049, Plenty of Good Fish in the Sea, EX ...12.00
Halloween, A Jolly Halloween, #31, p/Wolf, VG 12.00
Halloween, Series #181, Pretty Little Girl on Broom, p/Tuck ...15.00
Halloween, Series #5, Fantasy Owl on Pedestal, p/Nash, VG ...12.00
Halloween, Series #6507, Halloween Goblins, EX 12.00
Halloween, Series #7, With a Goose Wishbone & Four..., VG ...10.00
Hartmann, E; valentine message, #3482, p/Nister, VG 12.00
Heraldic Series, Philadelphia, #5023, p/Tuck, EX 15.00
Hold-to-light, Bowery, NY, #1521L, p/Koehler, EX 30.00
Hold-to-light, D Malick, Santa in brn coat on tree stump, VG .100.00
Hold-to-light, Flat Iron Building, NY, p/Cupples, VG 25.00
Hold-to-light, Old South Church, Boston, #2310L, p/Koehler ..28.00
Hold-to-light, View from Lemon Hill, #1909L, p/Koehler, VG ..28.00
Hold-to-light/cutout, MSIB Series #58, troops on bridge, EX ...30.00
Innis, John; Forty-Niner, p/MacFarlane, 1907, VG 10.00
Innis, John; Grizzly Bear, p/MacFarlane, 1907, VG 9.00
King, Hamilton; Bathing Girl Series, Bar Harbour Girl, VG 8.00
Kris Kringle Series, Santa w/toys in chimney, p/Tuck, VG 12.00
Linen, Defend Our Country, Uncle Sam, V-10, p/Tichnor, '40s .10.00
Linen pinup, California Dish, p/Longshaw, ca 1940, EX 8.00
Linen pinup, Orchids to You, DG-9, p/Postage Stamp, '40s 8.00
Lithograph, Anheuser-Busch Brewery, p/Buxton/Skinner, EX ...30.00
Little Men & Women Series, Dolly Needs...Medicine, p/Tuck ..15.00
Little Men & Women Series, Kiss Dolly Goodbye, p/Tuck, VG .10.00
Martin, giant eggs in bk of roadster, exaggerated photo, VG 10.00
Maurice, Regent Series #2499, Wot's de Use ob Worryin?, VG ..12.00
Merte, Circus Horses Series #9946, p/Tuck, set of 6, rare, VG ...70.00
Nursery Rhyme, Little Bo Peep, p/H Milford, EX 15.00
Nursery Rhyme, Red Riding Hood, p/H Milford, EX 15.00
Oswald, Eugene; Beim Polo, monkey/zebra playing polo, VG ...12.00
Patriotic, #179, Bring Flowers, p/Tuck, uns/Brundage, VG 14.00
Patriotic, #179, Where Loyal Souls..., p/Tuck, uns/Brundage ...14.00
Patriotic, From Every Mtnside, p/Gabriel, uns/Brundage 14.00
Patriotic, July 4th Series #746, boys set barn afire, VG 9.00
Payne, Harry; Bound for Shore, #100, very early, scarce 25.00
Payne, Harry; Topman Aloft, #105, very early, scarce, VG 25.00
Payne, Harry; US Army...Through Flanders, #3159, p/Tuck 14.00
Photo, Custom Tailor & Dry Cleaner, Interior of Store 18.00
Photo, Lusitania Dining Salon, sent from ship, 1913, EX 30.00
Photo, Texaco Gas Station, Restaurant, Rooms, ca 1920, VG ..12.00
Political, Ike & Nixon, In God We Trust, p/Don Bartels, EX 12.00
Political, Mr & Mrs Wm Jennings Bryan photo, EX 8.50
Political, T Roosevelt taking inauguration oath, photo, EX 12.00
Political, Taft/Sherman campaign card, EX 18.00
Richardson, A; Golliwog, w/girl & bear, #1007, EX 18.00
Romantic Bears Series #88, baby bear sings, p/Ullman, VG 10.00
Royalty, Call of the Flag Series #8862, p/Tuck, EX 12.00

Royalty, Series #608II, Coronation, p/Tuck, EX 15.00
Russell, Indian Dog Team, Indian w/dogs pulling sled, VG 22.00
Russell, Roping a Wolf, VG 22.00
Sager, Xavier; Series #163, Paris La Nuit, outdoor scene, EX 20.00
Santa carries lamp & approaches town, #1320, p/Langsdorf, VG 15.00
Schermele, Shopping Day, mama bear/cubs, p/Salmon, ca 1950 . .6.00
Scrivner, Maude; In the Jungle, #9514, p/Tuck, VG 10.00
Ship Series #8624, HMS New Zealand, p/Tuck, VG 11.00
Silk, Clan Cameron, crest/plaids/dragons, p/Sharpe, VG 20.00
Silk, RMS Baltic, ship going left, woven silk, p/Stevens, VG . . .40.00
Slater, Types of Vessels in British Navy, #3193, p/Tuck 15.00
Steele, Pixie Market, #4967, p/Salmon, ca 1940 . . . . .7.50
Steele, Right Time, pixies, #4966, p/Salmon, ca 1940, VG 9.00
Thiele, men bowling, EX 18.00
Transparency, Gruss aus Zurich, Paris Expo, #8417, VG 28.00
Valentine, hold-to-light/cutout, cupid holding doves, EX 35.00
Wain, Louis; Lucky Day Mascot, EX 28.00
Wall, Little Coon Series #59, Deed I Didn't Steal Um, VG 14.00
Way, B; Series #3569, Southern-The Southern Belle, VG 12.00
WWI Flame Series, bombs on church, woven silk, p/Duffrene . .30.00

Posters

Advertising posters by such French artists as Cheret and Toulouse-Lautrec were used as early as the mid-1800s. Color lithography spurred their popularity. Circus posters by the Strobridge Lithograph Co. are considered to be the finest in their field, though Gibson and Co. Litho, Erie Litho, and Enquirer Job Printing Co. printed fine examples as well. Posters by noted artists such as Mucha, Parrish, and Hohlwein bring high prices. Other considerations are good color, interesting subject matter, and of course, condition. The WWII posters listed below are among the more expensive examples — 80% of those on the market bring less than $50.00.

Before 1920, 1-sheet posters measured 30" x 40"; after that they measured approximately 28" x 42". See also Fisher, Harrison; Movie Memorabilia; Political Entourage; Rockwell, Norman.

Advertising

Arbell Shoes, Blk woman's profile, Werler, ca 1955, 45x59" . . .300.00
Aubel & Fils, Goutez Lez, dog/Mousseux wine, 1920, 32x48" . .200.00
Baldwin's Bilious & Liver Pills, 1905, 26x20", EX 35.00
Belber Travelling Goods..., Blk steward, 1930s, 40x27", EX . . .450.00
Carlisle Rye, dogs gambling/drinking, fr, 1910, 12x30" 150.00
Cigno Talcum Powder, Minonzio, ca 1920, 39x27" 350.00
Citicol Clothing Dyes, LaCoholla, ca 1935, 39x53", NM 450.00
Eat More Fruit, leggy blonde w/fruit basket, ca 1938, 20x15" . . .80.00
Hajrasul Cigarettes, anon, ca 1935, 25x33", M 300.00
Hulstkamp's Liqueur, Hulstkamp on camel, 1915, 19x29", NM 300.00
Indian Motorcycle, Indian in headdress, 1913, 20½x13½" 750.00
Kyriazi Cigarette Special #34, Anton, ca 1935, 33x46", M 300.00
Le Nil Cigarette Papers, trumpeting elephant, 47x58", M 185.00
McCormick Machinery, machine/man on world, 1900, 25x35"..550.00
Mobiloil, chimp w/red cleaning cloth, 1930, 39x53", NM 425.00
Munro's 10¢ Novel #277 Clincher Jack, Indian/man, 29x21" . .750.00
New Departure Brakes, Wm Bendix as Babe Ruth, 14x20" 20.00
Old Cornelius Whiskey, girl in early plane, 1900, fr, 24x20" . . .650.00
Osborne Farm Machinery, Victorian girl, fr, 1900, 36x25" 650.00
Pettijon's CA Breadfast Food, bear on rock, 1893, 50x28" 350.00
Poggi & Astengo-Zolfi, lady/grapes, Romoli, 1947, 38x53", M .200.00
Ratty Batty Beehive Cigarettes, anon, ca 1903, 28x38", M 450.00
San Camdido Soap, Roman woman, anon, 1950, 27x39", NM .250.00
Sartori & Schiratti Silk, LaCoholla, 1928, 27x39", NM 300.00

Squibb Aspirin, mother w/child, Wilber, 1940s, 25x24" 135.00
Traveller's Companion...Tonic, mc litho, 1870s, 14x11", EX . .500.00
Union Metallic Cartridge, cowboy chased by Indians, 20x14" .350.00
US Fur Co, hunters & skunk, St Louis MO, 20x14", EX 200.00
Useful Birds of America, Arm & Hammer, 1917, EX 65.00
Vittoria Hats, spider pulls hat to web, ca 1928, 28x53", NM . . .450.00
World's Columbian Expo, Uncle Sam, fr, 1893, 16x23" 150.00
Yellow Kid, NY Journal's...McFadden's Flats, 32x45", EX 650.00
Zig-Zag Cigarette Papers, anon, ca 1903, 17x21", NM 325.00

Circus

Achile Philion, Attraction w/o Parallel, 1899, 28x48", EX 350.00
Acrobatic Monkeys, European, anon, ca 1912, 23x32", M 125.00
Alice & Rolf Arras, Friedlander, 1900, 28x37" 550.00
B&B Greatest Show on Earth, anon, 1916, 29x39", M 550.00
Circus Wulff, clown, Friedlander, 1905, 28x37" 600.00
Clown Dolly w/His. . .Family, Friedlander, 1901, 28x37", NM .500.00
Clown Zertho-6 Salto Dogs, Friedlander, 1896, 26x33" 600.00
Downey Bros Big 3-Ring Circus, Erie Litho, ca 1925, 41x27" . .150.00
Klondike-Circus Busch, Friedlander, 1904, 37x28", EX 550.00
Lewis Bros Circus, Erie Litho, ca 1925, 14x40" 135.00
Mary Gautier's Pony Boy, Friedlander, 1919, 28x19", NM 325.00
Mr Arvey-Phantaisist, Friedlander, 1893, 34x47" 900.00
New Free Street Parade, B&B, 1910, 39x29", NM 450.00
Only Riding Elephant in World, Friedlander, 1880, 25x33" . .1,500.00
PT Barnum's Greatest..., Strobridge, 26¾x36½" 1,400.00
RB B&B, Col Tim McCoy, Erie Litho, 54x19", EX 100.00
RB B&B, hippo w/baby in lake, 1945, 28x41", VG 85.00
See You at Greatest..., Coplan, RB B&B, 1944, 28x21" 75.00
Suzanne & Dagmar, European Circus, Galice, 1895, 35x49" . . .450.00
4 Blk Diamonds, Friedlander, 1908, 19x27", EX 425.00
40 Kings of Jungle, RB B&B, ca 1934, 28x21, NM 110.00

Magic

Carter, Weird & Wonderful Wizard, Otis litho, 1919, 14x22" .125.00
Carter Sweeps Secrets of the Sphinx, Otis litho, 1920, 28x40" .400.00
George, Supreme Master of Magic, Otis Litho, '20s, ½-sheet 65.00
George, Triumphant Amer Tour, Otis Litho, '20s, 1-sheet 200.00
George, Triumphant Amer Tour, Otis Litho, '20s, 20-sheet . . .300.00
Irving, An Hour in Chinatown, 1930, 14x42", M 25.00

Minstrel

Birch & Backus, San Francisco, Thomas litho, 18x22", EX 220.00
Carncross Minstrels, Blks w/banjos, 1885, 10x31" 175.00
Great Original New Orleans Minstrels, ca 1870, 28x22" 165.00
Haverly's Genuine Colored..., Strobridge, OH, 24x17½", EX . .380.00
Mastadon Minstrels, full color, 20x28", EX 160.00
Wm Murry, Eccentric Singing/Dancing. . ., 19x26" 275.00

Theatrical

Bachelor's Honeymoon, Nat'l Print, Chicago, 42x80" 50.00
Don't Tell My Wife, Erie Litho, 2-sheet, EX 35.00
Human Hearts, winter scene, Russell Morgan, 1901, 42x80" . . .125.00
Iolanthe, Buckingham guard, Gilbert/Sullivan, 1912 . . . . .150.00
Louise Liewellyn Dramatic Soprano, 42x80, 3-sheet, G 65.00
Marguerite in Prison, Faust, Calvert, 3-sheet, EX 120.00
Uncle Tom's Cabin, early, 42x28", EX .75.00
Valley Forge, cabin scene, Goes Litho, Chicago, 3-sheet, EX . . .40.00
Yeoman of the Guard, Gilbert/Sullivan, 1908 . . . . .200.00

Travel

Barcelona, bull fight scene, dtd July 9, 1948, sm, EX 30.00
British Railways, York, street scene, Buckle, 1948, 25x40" 200.00
Chicago, Am Airlines, Kauffer, ca 1940, 30x40" 185.00
D&RG Railroad, Dump Mtn Near Walsenburg, 18x24", EX 7.50
Germany Wants To See You, Axster-Heudtlass, 1935, 20x29" .175.00
Nice, people/ocean in bkground, Cappiello, 1927, 34x41" 650.00
StL&SF RR, 4th of July Cheap Excursions, 1895, 30x13" 475.00
Visit London, Queen's Guard/palace, ca 1947, 25x40" 150.00

War

Are You Playing Square?, Cornwell, 1944, 19x27", M 175.00
Arise Americans, sailor at gun, Barclay, 1941, 28x41", M 125.00
Back 'Em Up, Buy Extra Bonds; Chaliapin, 1944, 20x28", M . . .95.00
Bundles for Blue Jackets, Barclay, 1942, 14x22", M 80.00
Careless Talk Got There First, Stoops, 1944, 20x28", NM 100.00
Carelessness Helps Hitler, anon, ca 1943, 24x37", M 150.00
China...Looks to Us!, Chinese baby, Flagg, 1944, 11x14", M . . .75.00
Clear for Action, US Coast Guard; anon, 1943, 28x42", NM . .125.00
Defend. . .Country, Enlist US Army; Woodburn, 25x38", M .225.00
Do It Right, Make it Bite; Beall, 1942, 28x40", NM 150.00
Do More for Doolittle, Dolittle in photomontage, 25x33" 125.00
Enlist Now US Marine Corps, Jackson, 1945, 29x40", NM 175.00
Fly w/the Marines, eagle/bomber, HHL, 1942, 29x40", M 175.00
Give It Your Best, flag, anon, 1942, 28x40", M 60.00
Greece Fights On, face/flag, Kauffer, 1942, 24x36", NM 165.00
Help Britain Finish the Job!, Stone, ca 1943, 20x30", EX 100.00
Hip Hip Another Ship, WWI, Mengll, 61x41", EX 300.00
I Need Your Skill in a War Job!, Flagg, 1943, 22x28", M 50.00
If You Must Talk, Tell It to the Marines; '42, 30x40", NM 65.00
If You Talk Too Much, This Man May Die; Sarra, 1942, 14x20"..50.00
Join the Navy & Free the World, Privitello, 1942, 28x42" 150.00
Keep 'Em Flying!, workers/Uncle Sam, Beall, 1941, 20x28", M .125.00
Keep Him Flying!, Buy. . .Bonds; Schreiber, 1943, 28x42", NM .95.00
Leaders of the Royal Air Force, anon, 1941, 30x20", EX 75.00
Let's Go!, USA-Keep 'Em Flying!; anon, 1941, 25x38" 100.00
Let's Hit & Run Till Victory's Won!, anon, 1942, 31x41" 75.00
Navy Training Courses, sailor, Humphrey, 1939, 28x41", M 90.00
No Room for Rumors, Uncle Sam, Gee, 1943, 22x28", NM 85.00
Nurses Are Needed Now!, Army nurse, Savage, '44, 13x19", M .50.00

Ready, Join the US Marines; Sundbloom, 1942, 28x40", M 95.00
Remember, It Isn't Over Yet!; Miller, 1944, 20x27", M 50.00
Send Us More...& Fast, Vanderlaan Co, ca 1942, 17x21", M . .100.00
Smilin' Thru, Keep 'Em Rolling; engineer, anon, 19x23", NM . .80.00
Soldiers of the Red Army...Save Us!, anon, 1941, 15x22" 250.00
Someone Talked, man drowning, Siebel, 1942, 22x28", EX . . .150.00
Speed the Day w/War Bonds, Hirsch, 11x15", M 65.00
Start 'Em Flying!, Keep Fightin' Soldier; anon, 1943, 20x27" . .135.00
Thanks Please for Lost Time, Patterson, ca 1943, 18x23", M . .125.00
They Cheer When You Hedge Hop!, anon, 1943, 22x17", NM .75.00
They Cheer When You Never Use Flaps, 1943, 22x17", M 75.00
They Did Their Part, Sullivan Brothers, anon, 1943, 29x41", M .75.00
They're Closer Than You Think, anon, 1942, 28x40", EX 200.00
This Is My Fight Too!, War Bonds; anon, 1942, 22x28", M 50.00
This Is Nazi Brutality, Shahn, 1942, rare, 28x38", M 150.00
Those Overalls Are Your Uniform, Bud; anon, 1943, 20x28" . . .75.00
Too Little & Too Late, survivor at sea, 1942, 28x50", M 110.00
United We Win, Blk man, Liberman, 1942, 28x40", NM 150.00
WAAC, This Is My War Too; Smith, 1943, 25x38", M 125.00
With Your Help They'll Live Again, Vanfield, 1940, 28x43" . .110.00
Woman's Place in War, Cooper, 1944, 25x38", M 100.00
Your Scrap Can Lick..., Mohawk Beverages; anon, '43, 27x39" . .85.00

Miscellaneous

Heavyweight Champs. . .Figg 1719 to Bradock 1937, 22x35" . .100.00
Immigration, Cleveland-Many Peoples 1 Language, '17, 29x42" .95.00
Labor incentive, Strut Your Stuff, drum major, 1929, 36x44" . .200.00
Women's Suffrage, Queen Victoria as peasant, 1905, 20x30" . .350.00

Maquettes Pour L'Oeuvre Monumental, Marc Chagall illustration, signed and dated 1977, 29x20", $3,000.00.

Order Coal Now, J.C. Leyendecker illustration, extremely rare, $425.00.

Pot Lids

Pot lids were pottery covers for containers that were used for hair dressing, potted meats, etc. The most desirable were decorated with colorful transfer prints under the glaze in a variety of themes, animal and scenic. The first and probably the largest company to manufacture these lids was F & R Pratt of Fenton, Staffordshire, established in the early 1800s. The name or initials of Jesse Austin, their designer, may sometimes be found on exceptional designs. Although few pot lids were made after the 1880s, the firm continued into the 20th century.

American pot lids are very rare. Most have been dug up by collectors

Our Fighters Deserve Our Best, anon, 1942, 28x40" 100.00
Pipe Down Soldier!, Tokyo's Listening; anon, 1942, 14x20" 75.00

searching through sites of early gold rush mining towns in California. Minor rim chips are expected and normally do not detract from listed values.

American

Amandine, Chapped Hands, Phila, blk transfer, 3"	50.00
American eagle, red transfer, Kaighn's Point Soap, 3½"	300.00
Bear, blk transfer, Bear's Grease, X Bazine, 2¾", VG	525.00
Bust of Franklin, purple transfer, Jules Hauel, Phila, 3½"	275.00
Bust of Franklin, red transfer, Hauel Perfumer, 3½", M	120.00
Capitol at WA, blk transfer, Worsley Perfumer, 3½", EX	350.00
Capitol at WA, purple transfer, Worsley Perfumer, 3", EX	365.00
Cow, blk transfer, Beef Marrow, J Hauel Perfumer, 3", EX	280.00
Cure/Prevention of Chapped Hands, blk transfer, Hauel, 2¾"	200.00
Improved Cold Cream of Roses, blk transfer, Bazin, 2", NM	200.00
Man shaves/looks in mirror, purple transfer, Taylor's, 3¾"	250.00
Man shaving, blk transfer, Wright's...Compound, 3½"	500.00
Man shaving, purple transfer, Taylor's...Compound, 3½"	300.00
Map, Highest Premium Awarded...World's Fair, Hauel, 3"	220.00
Odontine or Rose Tooth Paste, blk transfer, sq, 2¾"	180.00
Odonto Oak Bark Orris Tooth Paste, purple transfer, 3⅛"	300.00
Purified Charcoal Tooth Paste, blk transfer, 2¼x3¾", EX	120.00
Rose Vegetable Tooth Paste, red transfer, Hauel, 2¾"	120.00
Washington Crossing Delaware, blk transfer, HP&WC, 3⅜"	300.00
Washington Crossing Delaware, Trylor Perfumers, Phila, early	65.00

English

Ann Hathaway's Cottage, #228, leaf & scroll border	600.00
Ann Hathaway's Cottage, #228, pearl & dot border	125.00

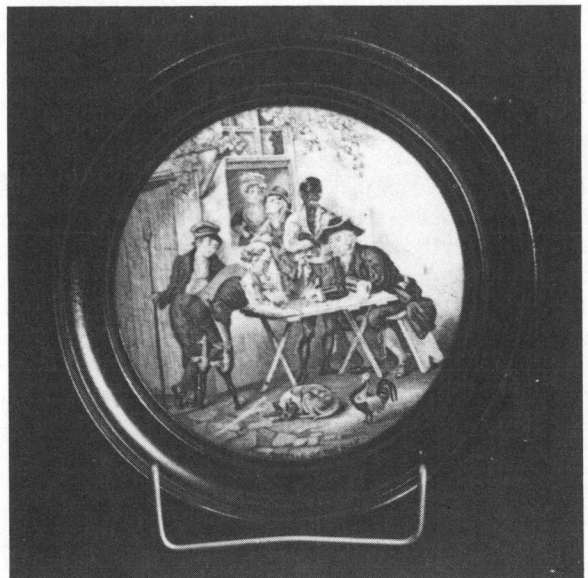

Battle of the Nile, Fenton Pratt, $250.00.

Bellevue Tavern, from the bay w/boat, Pratt, #29	375.00
Bellevue Tavern, w/carriage, Pratt, #28	200.00
Bellevue Tavern, w/Tatwell wagon, Pratt, #27	1,000.00
Dr Johnson, #175, 4"	360.00
Enthusiast, old man w/gout fishing in tub, Pratt, #245	200.00
Fishbarrow, Pratt, #58, 4" (watch for reproductions)	200.00
Garibaldi, #169	105.00
Landing the Fare, sailor carries lady through water, #38	300.00
Late Prince Consort, #153	250.00
Lobster Sauce, Pratt, #49	100.00

Race, Derby Day, Pratt, #257	125.00
Revenge, w/registry, #51	275.00
Shakespeare's Birthplace (exterior), Pratt, #226, 4"	175.00
Shakespeare's Birthplace (interior), Pratt, #227, 4"	150.00
Skewbald Horse, Pratt, #277 (2 types)	150.00
Strasberg, city scene, Pratt, #331	125.00
Strasberg, marbleized surround, +matching jar, #331	200.00
Village Wedding, Pratt, #240 (6 types)	125.00
Wimbledon 1860, line border, #223	150.00
Wimbledon 1860, marbled, #223	300.00
Wolf & Lamb, English schoolboy bully, #361	125.00

Powder Horns and Shot Flasks

Though powder horns had already been in use for hundreds of years, collectors usually focus on those made after the expansion of the United States westward in the very early 1800s. While some are basic and very simple, others were scrimshawed and highly polished. Especially nice carvings can quickly escalate the value of a horn that has survived intact to as high as $400.00. Those with detailed maps, historical scenes, etc. bring even higher prices.

Metal flasks were introduced in the 1830s; by the middle of the century they were produced in quantity and at prices low enough that they became a viable alternative to the powder horn. Today's collector regards the smaller flasks as the more desirable and valuable, and those made for specific companies bring premium prices.

Flask, brass, hunter w/whiskey, dog, & fallen deer, 9"	245.00
Flask, brass, US/eagle/clasped hands, Matthewman, EX	100.00
Flask, copper, open game bag, sitting dogs, Hawksley, 8"	325.00
Flask, copper, standing stag, violin shape, 8", EX	120.00
Flask, copper, sunburst eng, 8", VG	145.00
Flask, glass, linear relief w/beads, screw tip, 9"	40.00
Flask, wood, detailed hunt scene cvg, German, 1700s, 10"	1,200.00
Horn, checkered decor, wood plug, dtd 1861, 8"	45.00
Horn, cvd nozzle end, wood plug, 7"	60.00
Horn, detailed cvg, ca 1800, 9"	95.00
Horn, eagle/Am flag eng, late, 15"	150.00

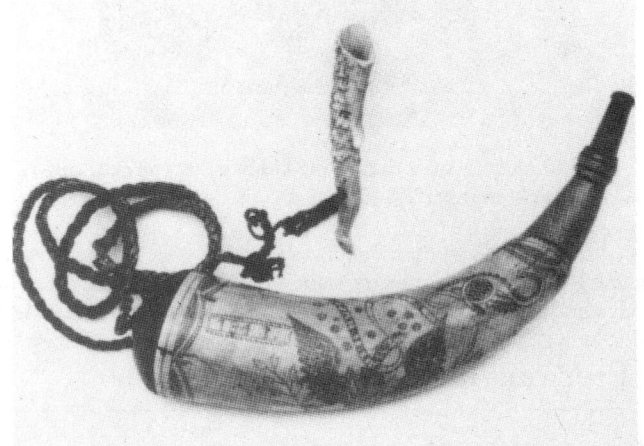

Engraved rifle horn, dated 1843, Indian, dogs and deer, inscribed Black Hawk, E Pluribus Unum on ribbon held by eagle, with carved horn tip powder measure, provenance, 10", $1,200.00.

Horn, Fr-Indian War cvd map, 1750s, 12", EX	1,650.00
Horn, heart & scallops cvgs, wood cap, 1850s, 15", VG	45.00
Horn, name/soldier/cannon/etc, allover eng, 13"	300.00
Horn, no decor, wood stopper w/sq nails, VA, 1850s, 7"	32.00

Horn, riders/lady/animals, EX details, 1700s, 8", VG 575.00
Horn, silver mts, Scottish hallmk, 13" 500.00
Horn, wildlife/name/dtd '72, allover eng, 1700s, 12½" 550.00
Horn, wood base & plug, polished, faint cvg, 1850s, 8" 20.00
Horn, 3 tooled lines at butt end, trn plug, 1820s, 9½" 75.00

Pratt

Prattware is a type of relief-molded earthenware with polychrome decoration. Scenic motifs with figures were popular; sometimes captions were added. Jugs are most common; but teapots, tableware, even figurines were made. The term 'Pratt' refers to Wm. Pratt of Lane Delph, who is credited with making the first of this type, though similar wares were made later by other Staffordshire potters.

Clock model, long case, circle dial, florals, ca 1794, 9" 385.00
Creamer, cow w/milkmaid, mc, 1810, minor rstr, 5½x6½" 750.00
Figurine, dog, blk/brn, hollow gr base, 2x2", NM 130.00
Figurine, sheep, blk/brn, hollow gr base, 2x2½", NM 130.00
Flask, putti emblematic of seasons, oval, ca 1790, 5½" 285.00
Mug, frog w/in, drinking scenes, 1850s 125.00
Pitcher, Gray Goose Nursery Rhymes, emb/mc, much rstr, 7" ..210.00
Plate, children w/dog, mc, 7" 50.00

Quill holder, goat with nursing kid in ochre, brown, and green, chip/rstr, 3", $450.00.

Tea caddy, classical figures of Summer & Autumn, 5" 185.00
Teapot, child's, HP 8-pointed mc stars, 4¼", NM 55.00
Watch stand, tall case clock, child ea side, rstr, 10½" 550.00

Precious Moments

Figurines and bells created by Samuel Butcher and produced by Enesco Co. of Chicago, a division of Stanhome Products, are becoming some of the most sought-after collectibles on today's market. Often referred to as 'America's Hummels,' these pieces endear themselves to many through the inspirational messages they portray. The first twenty-one pieces were made in 1979. These were unmarked and today are the most valuable. Since then they have been marked with a different mark for each year of production — older marks bring the higher prices. Retired figures, especially those from 1981, are also highly valued. A magazine edited by

Rosie Wells, our advisor for this category, is available if you want more information. Rosie also publishes the yearly official Secondary Price Guide for these collectibles. She is listed in the Directory under Illinois and again under Clubs, Newsletters, and Catalogs. Items listed below are assumed to be in mint condition and without box.

April Calendar Girl, girl w/umbrella, 110027, cedar tree mk 55.00
Baby's First Picture, baby posing, retired, E-2841, cross mk 65.00
Baby's First Xmas, girl w/bunny, E-5632, no mk 22.00
Bundles of Joy, girl w/packages, E-2374, hourglass mk 70.00
Come Let Us Adore Him, boy at manger, E-2011, no mk 240.00
Come Let Us Adore Him, nativity, musical, E-2810, no mk ...115.00
Dropping Over for Christmas, girl w/pie, E-2375, hourglass mk ..60.00
God Loveth a Cheerful Giver, girl w/puppies, E-1378, no mk ..580.00
I'll Play My Drum for Him, plate, dtd 1982, E-2357, no mk 55.00
Isn't He Wonderful, angel w/harp, E-5640, hourglass mk 22.00
Jesus Is the Light, girl w/doll, E-1373-G, no mk 95.00
Jesus Loves Me, boy w/teddy, bell, E-5208, no mk 40.00
Jesus Loves Me, boy w/teddy, plate, E-9275, cross mk 30.00
Let the Whole World Know, boy/girl in tub, E-7165, fish mk ...85.00
Love Beareth All Things, nurse w/bear, E-7158, hourglass mk ..50.00
Love Lifted Me, boy helping friend, E-5201, no mk 60.00
Love One Another, boy/girl sitting on stump, E-1376, no mk ...95.00
Make a Joyful Noise, girl w/goose, E-1374-G, no mk 90.00
May Calendar Girl, girl w/plant, 110035, cedar tree mk 55.00
Onward Christian Soldiers, soldier, E-0523, fish mk 45.00
Our Club Can't Be Beat, clown beating drum, B-0001, dove mk .60.00
Peace on Earth, boy on globe, musical, E-2804, no mk 75.00
Peace on Earth, choir boys, E-4725, triangle mk 45.00
Smile God Loves You, boy w/blk eye, retired, E-1373-B, no mk .75.00
Surrounded w/Joy, boy w/wreath, bell, 1983, E-0522, fish mk ...45.00
Th Purr-fect Grandma, musical, E-7184, hourglass mk 55.00
Thee I Love, boy carving tree, E-3116, no mk 90.00
Wishing You a Merry Xmas, choir girl, bell, E-5393, cross mk ...35.00

Pre-Columbian Artifacts

The term 'pre-Columbian' loosely refers to some time prior to 1492, when Columbus arrived in America. In particular, it indicates pre-1492 artifacts of Central and South America, some of which can be dated as early as 4000 B.C. Artifacts representing the cultures of the Inca, Maya, and Aztec Indians are avidly sought by the collector. These may be made of precious metals and hardstones or pottery. Some were used in rituals and religious rites; some such as bowls and other utensils, though strictly utilitarian, nevertheless convey through form and decoration the craftsmanship of these early tribes.

Key: tc —— terra cotta

Atlatl, Tiahuanaco, wood, copper weight, ca 800 AD, 14½" ...440.00
Bag, Chancay, cotton, diagonal bands, ca 1400 AD, 13x12" ...200.00
Bowl, Mayan, polychrome, monster on side, 600 AD, 5½" H ..400.00
Earrings, Sinu, gold, openwork filigree, ca 1200 AD, 3¼" 770.00
Female, Chorrera, robust body, headdress, ca 600 BC, 12½" ...935.00
Female, Valdivian, short limbs, incising, ca 2000 BC, 2½" 465.00
Mace head, Chavin, stone, 4 tapered blades, 600 AD, 5" 1,100.00
Man, Manabi, warrior w/staff, arm bands, ca 100 BC, 11" 330.00
Man, Mochica, warrior, MOP inlay shield, ca 600 BC, 7" ...1,100.00
Mask, Carchi, gold feline diety, ca 1200 AD, 4¼" 1,750.00
Mask, Chancay, wood, rectangular, lg nose, ca 1200 AD, 18" ..660.00
Mask, Mid-Mochica, copper, diamond eyes, ca 100 BC, 9¼" .1,650.00
Pectoral, Panamanian, gold, circular, pierced, ca 800 AD, 5" ..275.00
Pendant, Cost Rica, gold alloy fertility god, 1x1¾" 100.00

Pendant, Veraguas, gold eagle, wings out, ca 900 AD, 1⅜" **880.00**
Roundel, Panamanian, gold, emb beadwork, ca 900 AD, 5⅛" ..**275.00**
Textile fragment, N Coast, mc cotton, ca 600 AD, 36x22" **600.00**
Vase, Mayan, cylindrical, incised monkeys, ca 650 AD, 7" ...**440.00**
Vessel, Chavin, brnware, pumpkin form, incising, 500 BC, 10"..**440.00**
Vessel, Chavin, grayware, rnd w/slim neck, ca 400 BC, 10" ..**1,000.00**
Vessel, Mid-Mochica, drummer figural, ca 300 BC, 8½" **465.00**
Vessel, Mochica, land snail form, ca 200 BC, 7⅛" **1,750.00**
Vessel, Mochica, monkey figural, ca 200 BC, 5½" **1,200.00**
Vessel, Tairona, blkware, curled alligator, ca 1200 AD, 10" ...**275.00**
Whistle, Mayan, lady in headdress figural, ca 650 AD, 3" **440.00**

Primitives

Like the mouse that ate the grindstone, so has collectible interest in primitives increased, a little bit at a time, until demand is taking bites instead of nibbles into their availability. Although the term 'primitives' once referred to those survival essentials contrived by our American settlers, it has recently been expanded to include objects needed or desired by succeeding generations — items representing the cabin-n'-cornpatch existence as well as examples of life on larger farms and in towns. Through popular usage, it also respectfully covers what are actually 'country collectibles.'

From the 1600s into the latter 1800s, factories employed carvers, blacksmiths, and other artisans whose handwork contributed to turning out quality items. When buying, 'touchmarks' — a company's name and/ or location and maker's or owner's initials — are exciting discoveries.

Primitives are uniquely individual. Following identical forms, results more often than not show typically personal ideas. Using this as a guide (combined with circumstances of age, condition, desire to own, etc.) should lead to a reasonably accurate evaluation. For items not listed, consult comparable examples. Authority Kathryn McNerney has compiled several lovely books on primitives and related topics: *Primitives, Our American Heritage; Collectible Blue and White Stoneware;* and *Antique Tools, Our American Heritage.* You will find her address in the Directory under Florida. See also Butter Molds and Stamps; Boxes; Copper; Farm Collectibles; Fireplace Implements; Kitchen Collectibles; Molds; Tinware; Woodenware; and Wrought Iron.

Bath tub, tin w/wood trim, CI legs, EX **165.00**
Bed warmer, brass, floral emb, blk brush-decor hdl, 42" **300.00**
Bed warmer, brass, floral eng, trn wood hdl, 42½" **250.00**
Bed warmer, brass, pinwheel eng, trn hdl w/VG grpt, EX **250.00**
Bed warmer, brass, simple eng, trn hdl, 42" **170.00**
Bed warmer, copper, floral emb, 42", EX **250.00**
Bed warmer, copper, pinwheel eng, trn hdl, 40" **150.00**
Bellows, wig-powdering; orig leather, ca 1800, 2½x6½" **130.00**
Broom, made from ash log, splint brush, whittled hdl, 55" **800.00**
Cabinet, spice; pine, 8-drw, cvd knobs, 1890s, 14x24x7" **285.00**
Cabinet, spice; walnut, 6-drw, brass knobs, 7¾x11½" **250.00**
Cabinet, spice; 11-drw w/porc knobs & labels, 23x10", EX ...**300.00**
Candle mold, 1-tube, cathedral, w/braced base, 18" **295.00**
Candle mold, 1-tube, 2-pc pnt wood mold, dvtl iron band, 7" ..**150.00**
Candle mold, 12-tube, tin, 10½" **90.00**
Candle mold, 18-tube, pewter in wood fr, 16x7x21", EX **600.00**
Candle mold, 24-tube, pewter/pine, floor standing, 22" L **675.00**
Candle mold, 24-tube, redware in pine fr, 15x8½x24" **800.00**
Candle mold, 3-tube, brn japanning, tin hdl, 3x5x6½" **90.00**
Candle mold, 36-tube, tin, hdls, 9½" **440.00**
Candle mold, 4-tube, tin, crimped top, VG **80.00**
Candle mold, 48-tube, ear hdls, minor dents, 10½" **450.00**
Candle mold, 55-tube, tin in pine fr, 36" L **750.00**
Candle mold, 8-tube, tin, arched base & hdl, EX **125.00**

Candle snuffer, nickel, long shank, 11" **200.00**
Candle snuffer, scissors shape, on stenciled tin tray **75.00**
Cranberry picker, cvd hdl & wooden teeth, 6x9" **240.00**
Desk, lap; pine, brass screws, HP bear/trees, 1900, 12x10x8" **85.00**
Dipper, brass w/iron hdl, copper rivets, PA, 1850s, 16" **85.00**
Dough box, pine w/bl-gr pnt, mortised/pinned, 22x37" top **350.00**
Dough box, pine/poplar in worn red pnt, dvtl, 35" L, EX **200.00**
Dough box, poplar w/red pnt, dvtl, wear/damage, 27" L **170.00**
Dough box, red pnt, dvtl, canted sides, 1-brd lid, 10x25" L **225.00**
Dough scraper, wrought iron, short hollow hdl, 1700s **30.00**
Dryer, mitten; pierced tin, oval, 13x10x23" **130.00**
Foot warmer, cherry, pierced, wire bail, 1700s, sq **250.00**
Foot warmer, Petty's Carriage Heater, EX **85.00**
Foot warmer, punched tin in mortised fr w/trn posts, 6x9x8" ..**225.00**
Foot warmer, redware, mc mottle, prism shape, 5½x6x12" **485.00**
Foot warmer, wood, iron hdls, holes make design, ca 1820 ....**275.00**
Foot warmer, wood/punched tin, rnd w/bail hdl, charcoal pan .**325.00**
Lap robe, brn/blk crushed velvet, 62x45", EX **45.00**
Lap robe, fine quality wolf fur, furrier's label, 1890s, EX **425.00**
Lighting stand, wrought iron, tooled rod, brass finial, 45" ...**3,000.00**
Mixing stick, pewter/brass wire end, pnt wood hdl, 13½" **55.00**

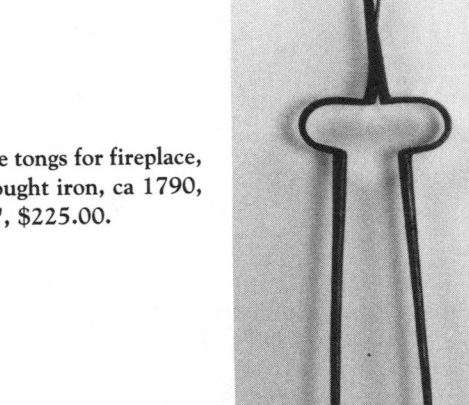

Pipe tongs for fireplace, wrought iron, ca 1790, 12", $225.00.

Powder tester, flintlock, pistol grip, brass gauge, 5½" **450.00**
Rack, candle dipping & drying; wood, 6-bar grid, 1700s, EX ...**275.00**
Rack, drying; hardwood, 4-section, folding, 66" **150.00**
Rack, drying; mahog, 3-section, 35" **100.00**
Rack, drying; pine, mortised/pinned, shoe ft, 67x34" **95.00**
Rack, drying; pine w/gr pnt, 3-bar, mortised, shoe ft, 41" **195.00**
Rack, utensil; pine, scalloped, 7 wrought hooks, 27" L **150.00**
Rack, utensil; sheet iron, crest w/birds & foliage, 27" W **1,250.00**
Roaster, coffee; sheet iron, iron shaft/wood hdl, 1800s, 50" **295.00**
Rope bed wrench, wood w/later cvd face, 13" **65.00**
Rushlight holder, iron, cvd wood base, w/candle socket **235.00**
Salt box, wood w/slant lid, ca 1760, 13x8½x8", EX **285.00**
Skimmer, tallow; hand-punched tin cone, 11½" iron hdl **85.00**
Skimmer, tinned brass, pierced, C-shape hdl, 1830s **95.00**
Spool stand, wood w/4 iron spool rods, 1700s, 3½x5" **85.00**
Stove leveler, buff clay w/brn running glaze, Bell, 3¾" **175.00**
Wafer iron, wrought iron, rnd, 17½" L **145.00**
Wafer iron, wrought iron, sq w/long hdl, 31½" L **225.00**
Wagon jack, wood/iron, mk Shaeffer/1794, rpl crank, 20" **150.00**
Washboard, curved wood, corrugated rollers on rocker fr, 24" ..**115.00**
Washboard, cvd hdl, ca 1900, 25x3¾" grooved surface **150.00**
Washboard, tin soap rack, bl/wht sponged insert, Nat'l, 25" ...**145.00**

Washing machine, Rock-A-Bye, wooden 375.00
Whisk broom, horsehair w/bone hdl, Pat Nov 16 '75, 7", EX . .135.00

Spoon rack, hard pine with chip-carved decoration, New Jersey, late 18th century, provenance, 21", $1,800.00.

Prints

The term 'print' may be defined today as almost any image printed on paper by any available method. Examples of collectible old 'prints' are Norman Rockwell magazine covers and Maxfield Parrish posters and calendars. 'Original print' refers to one achieved through the efforts of the artist or under his direct supervision. A 'reproduction' is a print produced by an accomplished print maker who reproduces another artist's print or original work. Thorough study is required on the part of the collector to recognize and appreciate the many variable factors to be considered in evaluating a print. Prices vary from one area of the country to another and are dependent upon new findings regarding the scarcity or abundance of prints as such information may arise. Although each collector of old prints may have their own varying criteria by which to judge condition, for those who deal only rarely in this area or newer collectors, a few guidelines may prove helpful. Staining, though unquestionably detrimental, is nearly always present in some degree and should be weighed against the rarity of the print. Professional cleaning should improve its appearance and at the same time help preserve it. Avoid tears that affect the image; minor margin tears are another matter, especially if the print is a rare one. Moderate 'foxing' (brown spots caused by mold or the fermentation of the rag content of old paper) and light stains from the old frames are not serious unless present in excess. Margin trimming was a common practice; but look for at least ½" to 1½" margins, depending on print size. When no condition is indicated, the items listed below are assumed to be in very good to excellent condition. See also Fisher, Harrison; Parrish, Maxfield; Rockwell, Norman.

Key: hc — hand colored

Audubon, John J.

Audubon is the best known of American and European wildlife artists.

His first series of prints 'Birds of America,' was produced by Robert Havell of London. They were printed on Whitman watermarked paper bearing dates of 1826 to 1838. The Octavo Edition of the same series was printed in three editions, the first by J.T. Bowen under Audubon's direction. There were seven volumes of prints, each 11" x 7", the first five bearing the J.J. Audubon and J.B. Chevalier mark, the last two, J.J. Audubon. They were produced from 1840 through 1871. The Bien Edition prints were full size, made under the direction of Audubon's son and daughter in the late 1850s. Due to the onset of the Civil War, only 105 plates were finished. These are considered to be the most valuable of the reprints of the 'Birds of America' Series.

In the 1950s New York Graphics reproduced the full-color prints through photolithography; and in 1971 the complete set was reprinted by Johnson Reprint Corp. of New York and Theaturm Orbis Terrarum of Amsterdam. Examples of the latter bear the watermark G. Schut and Zonen.

Although Audubon is best known for his portrayal of birds, one of his less-familiar series, 'Vivaparous Quadrupeds of North America,' portrayed various species of animals. Assembled in corroboration with John Bachman from 1839 until 1851, these prints are 28" x 22" in size.

American Beaver, #46, Bowen, 16x23¾" 550.00
American Coot, #239, Havell, unfr, 12¼x19½" 2,100.00
American Redstart, #40, Havell, unfr, 19⅜x12¼" 2,860.00
American Widgeon, #345, Havell, unfr, 15x20" 3,500.00
Baltimore Oriole, #12, Havell, ca 1830, 25¾x10⅝" 4,125.00
Barnacle Goose, #396, Havell, unfr, 25½x37½" 3,520.00
Barred Owl, #36, Bowen, ca 1850, unfr, 10½x6½" 115.00
Beswick's Wren, #18, Havell, unfr, 19½x12¼" 1,650.00
Black Tern, #280, Havell, ca 1836, 38⅛x24⅜" 990.00
Blue Bird, #113, Havell, ca 1836, unfr, 19⅜x12¼" 3,850.00
Blue Jay, #231, Bowen, ca 1850, unfr, 10½x6½" 190.00
Booby Gannet, #207, Havell, ca 1834, unfr, 26x20⅝" 1,870.00
Brown Pelican, Adult Male; #423, Bowen, orig fr, 11x7" 200.00
Buffle-headed Duck, #324, Havell, ca 1836, 14x20½" 770.00
Cedar Bird, #43, Havell, ca 1834, unfr, 19⅜x12¼" 4,950.00
Chipping Squirrel, #8, Bowen, fr, 17x21" 250.00
Common Osprey Fish Hawk, #15, Bowen, 1850, unfr, 11x7" . .100.00
Crested Titmouse, #39, Havell, ca 1834, unfr, 19½x12⅛" . . .2,750.00
Eider Duck, #405, Bowen, ca 1850, unfr, 10½x6½" 110.00

Gadwell Duck, #70, Havell edition, 23x30" (sight), $700.00.

Gray Rabbit, #22, Bowen, 20x27½" 500.00
Great Horned Owl, #61, Havell, ca 1834, unfr, 37½x25½" . .7,150.00
Herring Gull, #291, Havell, ca 1836, unfr, 37½x25½" 7,150.00
Kildeer Plover, #225, Havell, ca 1834, unfr, 12⅜x19½" 1,320.00

Long-tailed Duck, #312, Havell, ca 1836, unfr, 21x31" 3,300.00
Moose Deer, #76, Bowen, ca 1850, unfr, 10½x6½" 55.00
Noddy Tern, #275, Havell, ca 1835, unfr, 12½x19⅜" 935.00
Piping Plover, #220, Havell, ca 1834, unfr, 26¼x39⅜" 600.00
Raccoon, Bowen, ca 1845, 22x27½" 950.00
Red-breasted Merganser, #401, Havell, ca 1838, 25⅛x38⅛" .2,750.00
Roseate Tern, #240, Havell, ca 1834, unfr, 19½x12¼" 3,300.00
Sea-side Finch, #93, Havell, ca 1834, unfr, 19⅜x12¼" 4,400.00
Snowy Owl, #28, Bowen, ca 1850, unfr, 10½x6½" 150.00
Stormy Petrel, #270, Havell, ca 1834, unfr, 37½x25½" 1,100.00
Tufted Duck, #234, Havell, ca 1834, unfr, 13¾x17½" 1,760.00
Virginia Opossum, Bowen, ca 1845, 21½x27" 700.00
Whooping Crane, Male Adult; #313, Bowen, 1850, 10½x6½" .100.00
Wilson's Plover, #209, Havell, ca 1834, unfr, 12¼x19⅝" 715.00

Currier and Ives

Nathaniel Currier was in business by himself until the late 1850s when he formed a partnership with James Merrit Ives. Currier is given credit for being the first to use the medium to portray newsworthy subjects, and the Currier and Ives views of 19th-century American culture are familiar to us all. Values are given for prints in very good condition; all are colored unless indicated black and white.

Our advisors for this category are Barbara and John Rudisill; they are listed in the Directory under Massachusetts.

Abraham Lincoln, 16th President of US, blk/wht, sm folio 275.00
Agnes, NC, sm folio 95.00
American Brook Trout, sm folio 325.00
American Country Life-Summer's Evening, NC, lg folio 3,000.00
American Homestead-Winter, sm folio 800.00
American National Game of Base Ball, lg folio 30,800.00
American Scenery-Palenville NY, sm folio 295.00
American Winter Scenes-Morning, NC, lg folio 9,000.00
Apples & Plums, First Premium, sm folio 150.00
Autumn in New England-Cider Making, lg folio 18,000.00
Autumn on Lake George, sm folio 295.00
Base Hit, sm folio 250.00
Battery, NY by Moonlight, NC, sm folio 550.00
Battle of Buena Vista, NC, sm folio 125.00
Battle of Cerro Gordo, NC, sm folio 125.00
Battle of Fair Oaks VA, May 31, 1862, sm folio 175.00
Battle of Fredericksburg VA, sm folio 175.00
Battle of Pea Ridge, March 8th, 1862, sm folio 175.00
Battle of Spottsylvania VA, sm folio 175.00
Bear Hunting-Close Quarters, summer scene, sm folio 775.00
Beautiful Empress, sm folio 50.00
Benjamin Franklin, Statesman & Philosopher, NC, sm folio ...400.00
Between Two Fires, sm folio 250.00
Black-Eyed Beauty, sm folio 75.00
Blackberry Dell, med folio 400.00
Bolted, sm folio 250.00
Bombardment of Island #10 in the Mississippi River, sm folio ..300.00
Boss of the Track, sm folio 250.00
Brave Wife, sm folio 85.00
Brer Thuldy's Statue, sm folio 250.00
Bridge at the Outlet, Lake Memphremagog, sm folio 295.00
Brush for the Lead, NY Flyers on the Snow, lg folio 4,500.00
Buffalo & Chicago Steam Packet Empire State, NC, sm folio ..375.00
Bully Team, sm folio 295.00
Burning of Steamship Golden Gate, July 27, 1862, sm folio ..450.00
Bustin' a Picnic, sm folio 250.00
Butt of the Jokers, sm folio 250.00
Byron & Marianna, NC, sm folio 50.00

Cares of a Family, sm folio 500.00
Central Park-The Bridge, sm folio 450.00
Champion Stallion Directum by Director, sm folio 300.00
Champions of the Ball Racket, sm folio 250.00
Children's Picnic, sm folio 95.00
City of Mexico..., Vista de Mexico, NC, sm folio 250.00
Clearing on the American Frontier, sm folio 295.00
Clipper Ship Great Republic, NC, sm folio 425.00
Col Frank P Blair Jr, sm folio 125.00
Col Michael Corcoran, sm folio 125.00
Cork River, sm folio 65.00
Crack Shot, sm folio 195.00
Creating a Sensation, sm folio 250.00
Cross Matched Team, sm folio 250.00
Darktown Bowling Club-Bowled Out, sm folio 250.00
Darktown Law Suit-Part Second..., sm folio 250.00
Darktown Lawn Party-A Bully Time, sm folio 250.00
Darktown Opera-Serenade, sm folio 250.00
Darktown Tournament-Close Quarters, sm folio 250.00
Deacon's Mare, sm folio 250.00
Dead Game-Quail, sm folio 225.00
Death of Pope Pius IX, sm folio 50.00
Death Shot, sm folio 225.00
Declaration of Independence, NC, sm folio 295.00
Don Juan, Plate 1, NC, sm folio 30.00
Dusted & Disgusted, sm folio 250.00
Easter Flowers, sm folio 55.00
Eating Crow on a Wager, sm folio 250.00
Eliza, NC, sm folio 95.00
Emeline, NC, sm folio 95.00
English Winter Scene, sm folio 325.00
Ethan Allen & Mate to Wagon, sm folio 300.00
Evening Star, sm folio 75.00
Express Train, sm folio 2,000.00
Fall of Richmond VA, sm folio 225.00
Family Register, NC, sm folio 45.00
Feast of Roses, sm folio 150.00
Feeding the Swans, sm folio 150.00
First Ride, NC, sm folio 95.00
First Step, med folio 125.00
First Trot of the Season, lg folio 3,000.00
Fording the River, NC, med folio 600.00
Fort Sumter, Charleston Hanbon SC, sm folio 295.00
Foul Tip, sm folio 250.00
Fourth of July, sm folio 400.00
Fox Chase, Gone Away No 2, NC, sm folio 350.00
Frontier Lake, sm folio 295.00
Fruits of Temperance, sm folio 150.00
Game Dog, sm folio 250.00
Garfield Family, blk/wht, sm folio 75.00
Gen Andrew Jackson, Hero of New Orleans, NC, sm folio 150.00
Gen George Washington, Father of His Country, med folio ...300.00
Gen John C Breckenridge, blk/wht, sm folio 75.00
Gen Meagher at Battle of Fair Oaks VA, sm folio 125.00
Gen Shields at Battle of Winchester VA, sm folio 125.00
Gen Tom Thumb & Wife, sm folio 225.00
Gen US Grant, blk/wht, med folio 95.00
Getting a Hoist, sm folio 250.00
Giants Causeway, Country Antrim, Ireland, sm folio 65.00
Girl I Love, sm folio 95.00
Good Little Sisters, sm folio 95.00
Good Times on the Old Plantation, sm folio 450.00
Got 'Em Both, sm folio 250.00
Grand Nat'l Temperance Banner, NC, sm folio 160.00

Grand Pacer Flying Jib, sm folio 350.00
Grand Young Trotting Mare Nancy Hanks, sm folio 350.00
Great Fight Between Merrimac & Monitor, sm folio 650.00
Great Mississippi Steamboat Race, sm folio 500.00
Great West, sm folio 1,100.00
Grottoes of the Sea, sm folio 65.00
Harbor for the Night, sm folio 350.00
Hard Road To Travel, sm folio 250.00
Harvest Dance, NC, sm folio 95.00
Hewitt's Quick Step, NC, sm folio .75.00
Home in the Country, med folio 800.00
Home of Washington, Mt Vernon VA, med folio 300.00
Homeward Bound, NC, sm folio 1,000.00
Horse Shed Stakes Free For All, sm folio 250.00
Horse That Died on Man's Hands, sm folio 275.00
Household Treasures, sm folio 95.00
Hug Me Closer George..., sm folio 275.00
Hung Up with the Starch Out, sm folio 250.00
Husking, lg folio 10,000.00
Ice Cream Racket-Thawing Out, sm folio 250.00
Idlewild-On the Hudson, sm folio 295.00
In the Springtime, sm folio 125.00
Ingleside Winter, sm folio 850.00
Inundation, NC, sm folio 125.00
Iroquois, Winning the Derby, sm folio 425.00
Ivy Bridge, sm folio 140.00
James K Polk, 11th President of US, NC, sm folio 150.00
James Monroe, 5th President of US, NC, sm folio 150.00
John J Dwyer, Champion of America, med folio 250.00
John L Sullivan, Champion Pugilist of the World, med folio . .250.00
Jolly Jumper, sm folio 250.00
Kilkenny Castle, Ireland, sm folio .75.00
Kiss Me Quick, sm folio 95.00
Lady & Moor, NC, sm folio 50.00
Lake Memphremagog, Owl's Head, sm folio 295.00
Lake Winnepiseogee from Center Harbor NH, lg folio 5,000.00
Landing of Pilgrims at Plymouth MA, NC, sm folio 295.00
Last Ditch of Chivalry, blk/wht, med folio 150.00
Laying Back Stiff for a Brush, sm folio 250.00
Lexington of 1861, sm folio 225.00
Life in the Country, Morning, sm folio 295.00
Life of a Fireman-The Race, NC, lg folio 3,500.00
Light of the Dwelling, sm folio 95.00
Lincoln Family, blk/wht, sm folio .95.00
Little Daisy, sm folio 95.00
Little Manly, sm folio 95.00
Little Nelly, sm folio 95.00
Little Sisters, sm folio 125.00
Little White Kitties Fishing, sm folio 125.00
Little Willie, sm folio 95.00
Lord Be with You, sm folio 125.00
Loss of Steamship Arctic Off Cape Race, NC, sm folio 350.00
Lucky Escape, NC, med folio 300.00
Magic Lake, med folio 125.00
Magnificent Bldg for World's Fair 1851, NC, sm folio 475.00
Maj Gen Henry Halleck, Gen-in-Chief US Army, sm folio . . .125.00
Maj Gen John C Fremont, sm folio 125.00
Maj Gen John E Wool, sm folio 125.00
Maj Gen Winfield Hancock, sm folio 125.00
Mambrino, sm folio 425.00
Maple Sugaring, Early Spring in Northern Woods, sm folio . .1,350.00
Marriage, NC, sm folio 125.00
Martha Washington, med folio 90.00
Martin Van Buren, 8th President of US, NC, sm folio 150.00

Midnight Race on Mississippi, sm folio 650.00
Mill-Stream, med folio 425.00
Mixed at the Finish, sm folio 250.00
Moonlight in Fairyland, sm folio 95.00
Moosehead Lake, sm folio 295.00
More Free Than Welcome, sm folio 195.00
Moss Roses & Buds, 1870, sm folio 150.00
Mother's Dream, med folio 95.00
Mt Holyoke Female Seminary, blk/wht, NC, sm folio 450.00
My Little Playfellow, sm folio 95.00
My Sweetheart, sm folio 95.00
National Washington Monument, NC, sm folio 400.00
Nearest Way in Summertime, med folio 425.00
Neck & Neck to the Wire, lg folio 900.00
New England Home, sm folio 295.00
New England Winter Scene, lg folio 10,000.00
Newport Beach, sm folio 450.00
Niagara Falls from Goat Island, med folio 350.00
Niagara Falls from the Canada Side, sm folio 295.00
Night, blk/wht, sm folio 75.00
Night After the Battle, sm folio 125.00
Nip & Tuck, sm folio 250.00
Noah's Ark, N Currier, sm folio 225.00
Nova Scotia Scenery, med folio 375.00
Odd Fellows Chart, sm folio 75.00
Old Bull Dog on Right Track, med folio 225.00
Old Farm Gate, lg folio 2,500.00
Old Oaken Bucket, sm folio 250.00
Old Plantation Home, sm folio 450.00
On a Point, N Currier, med folio .950.00
Our Pasture, NC, sm folio 250.00
Pacing King Robert J, sm folio 350.00
Paddy Murphy's Jantin Car, sm folio 150.00
Part of the Battle of Shilo, sm folio 175.00
Partridge Shooting, NC, med folio 675.00
Patriot of 1776 Defending His Homestead, sm folio 250.00
Peerless Beauty, sm folio 95.00
Phebe, NC, med folio 95.00
Pioneer Cabin of the Yosemite Valley, sm folio 450.00
Point of the Joke, sm folio 250.00
Poultry Show on a Bust, sm folio .250.00
Power of Music, NC, sm folio 125.00
Prairie Fires of the Great West, sm folio 1,500.00
Presidential Reception in 1789, sm folio 325.00
Presidents of the US, sm folio 225.00
Quail on Virginia Partridge, sm folio 300.00
Rafting on the St Lawrence, med folio 600.00
Rail Shooting, NC, lg folio 8,000.00
Return from the Woods, med folio 975.00
Roadside Mill, sm folio 295.00
Rose & Lily, sm folio 95.00
Rural Lake, med folio 425.00
Sale of Blooded Stock, sm folio 375.00
Saratoga Springs, sm folio 295.00
Scenery of the Upper Mississippi-An Indian Village, sm folio . .325.00
Season of Joy, sm folio 225.00
Sheep Pasture, med folio 295.00
Shooting on the Beach, sm folio 950.00
Simply to Thy Cross I Cling, sm folio 50.00
Sisters, NC, sm folio 125.00
Snipe Shooting, sm folio 900.00
Snow Storm, med folio 2,500.00
Soldier's Adieu, NC, sm folio 125.00
Sorry Dog, sm folio 250.00

Source of the Hudson, sm folio 400.00
South Sea Whale Fishery, NC, sm folio 1,500.00
Southern Volunteers, blk/wht, sm folio 150.00
Spaniel, NC, sm folio 245.00
Spirit of the Union, sm folio 195.00
Sports Who Lost Their Tin, sm folio 250.00
Steamship Ville de Paris, sm folio 325.00
Steeple Chase Cracks, sm folio 195.00
Still Hunting on Susquehana, med folio 700.00
Straw-Yard Winter, med folio 1,000.00
Summer, sm folio 95.00
Summer Flowers, sm folio 150.00
Summer Fruits, med folio 475.00

Summer in the Country, small folio, $295.00.

Summer Morning, sm folio 295.00
Summer Night, sm folio 295.00
Summer Ramble, med folio 375.00
Surrender of Cornwallis at Yorktown VA, NC, lg folio 4,000.00
Sussex Vale, New Brunswick, sm folio 195.00
Swell Sport Stampeded, sm folio 295.00
Thistle, lg folio 4,000.00
Through to the Pacific, sm folio 1,250.00
Toll-Gate, Plank Road Jamaica, NC, sm folio 345.00
Tomb & Shade of Napoleon, NC, sm folio 125.00
Tree of Life-The Christian, NC, sm folio 125.00
Tree of Temperance, sm folio 125.00
Trenton High Falls NJ, sm folio 295.00
Trotters on Snow, sm folio 1,500.00
Trotting Gelding w/Frank & Jo Nay, lg folio 1,800.00
Tumbled to It, sm folio 250.00
Two Little Fraid Cats, sm folio 95.00
Two to Go!, sm folio 250.00
Uncle Tom & Little Eva, NC, sm folio 190.00
US Frigate Constitution, NC, sm folio 450.00
US Sloop of War Albany, NC, sm folio 525.00
US Steam Frigate Wabash, sm folio 450.00
Valley Falls, VA, sm folio 295.00
View of Bunker Hill & Monument, NC, sm folio 295.00
View of New York, sm folio 800.00
View of Park Fountain/City Hall, NY, NC, sm folio 600.00
View on Hudson, Crow's Nest, sm folio 295.00
Virginia Home in the Olden Time, sm folio 295.00
Washington, First in War..., NC, sm folio 125.00
Washington's Reception by the Ladies, NC, sm folio 125.00
Water Rail Shooting, NC, sm folio 800.00

We've Had a Healthy Time, sm folio 250.00
West Point Foundry, Cold Spring, med folio 1,500.00
Western Farmer's Home, sm folio 600.00
Who Will Love Me?, sm folio 95.00
Wild West in Darktown, sm folio 250.00
William Henry Harrison, 9th Pres of US, NC, sm folio 150.00
William R King, VP of US, NC, sm folio 90.00
Willie & Mary, sm folio 95.00
Winter Morning, med folio 2,400.00
Winter Morning in the Country, sm folio 1,600.00
Won by a Foot, sm folio 250.00
Word & the Sign, sm folio 50.00
Wreck of the Atlantic, sm folio 295.00
Yo-Semite Falls CA, sm folio 295.00
Young America, The Child of Liberty, sm folio 125.00

Fox, R. Atkinson

Clipper Ship, orig fr 65.00
Daydreams, 14x12" 75.00
English Garden, house w/thatched roof, 13½x17½" 35.00
Glorious Vista, p Master Art, 17½x29½" 45.00
Heart's Desire, ca 1927, orig fr, 12x22" 45.00
Moonlight & Roses, fr, 19x15" 45.00
Peace & Sunshine, 21x33" 85.00
Promenade 40.00
Road of Poplars 40.00
Sunset Dreams, fr, 19x15" 45.00
Sunset Dreams, p Master Art, 10½x17½" 40.00

Gutmann, Bessie Pease

An Anxious Moment, orig mat/fr, 18½x16" 45.00
Awakening, orig fr, 14" dia 60.00
Awakening, orig fr, 19x14½" 60.00
Bride, orig Nouveau fr, 10½x15½" 60.00
Butterflies & Daisies, oval, fr, 7½x6½" 20.00
Good Morning, 11x14" 65.00
Home Builders 68.00
In Port of Dreams 45.00
Mischief, orig fr 95.00
New love, orig fr, 15x11", NM 50.00
Reward, orig fr, 14x21" 50.00
Rosebud, fr 65.00
To Love & To Cherish 110.00
Wedding March, 16x21" 75.00

Icart, Louis

Louis Icart was a French artist who immortalized the French woman through his etchings, which were widely produced during the 1920s. Most of his post-1920 etchings carry a U.S. copyright notice in the margin as well as Icart's personal intaglio seal.

After the Raid, sgn, ca 1917, 15½x20" 1,750.00
Angry Steed, pencil sgn, ca 1917, 16¼x10¼" 1,800.00
Autumn Leaves, sgn/blindstamp, ca 1926, 21x16¾" 1,430.00
Basket of Apples, sgn/inscr, ca 1924, 17¾x13¼" 990.00
Blue Bandana, pencil sgn, ca 1925, 14x18" 1,100.00
Butterflies, sgn, 15x19½" 1,300.00
Casanova, pencil sgn/blindstamp, 1928, 21x14½" 1,450.00
Cat & Mouse, pencil sgn/gallery blindstamp, 1920, 8¾x11" ..1,100.00
Cinderella, pencil sgn/blindstamp, 14½x18" 935.00
Courage, My Legions; pencil sgn, ca 1917, 22x17" ...1,430.00

Cuddling, pencil sgn/blindstamp, 1926, 11½x16¾" 990.00
Dear Friends, pencil sgn/blindstamp, ca 1929, 11¼x8⅞" 1,320.00
Eve, pencil sgn/blindstamp, ca 1928, 14x19½" 1,650.00
Fair Dancer, pencil sgn/blindstamp, 1939, lt fox, 19x22" 1,400.00
Farewell, pencil sgn/blindstamp, ca 1927, 14¾x19¼" 825.00
Forsythia, sgn, ca 1926, 18½x14½" 1,200.00
Four Dears, pencil sgn/blindstamp, ca 1929, 21x15" 1,500.00
Gay Senorita, pencil sgn/blindstamp, 1939, 18½x22¼" 1,800.00

Gay Trio, ca 1936, 20x12", $3,500.00.

Girl on Windy Day, pencil sgn, 1920, 9¼x7¼" 450.00
Happy Birthday, pencil sgn, ca 1937, rstr, 13¾x18¼" 1,980.00
Illusion, sgn/blindstamp, ca 1940, 19x19" 5,500.00
Japanese Garden, pencil sgn, 1925, lt fox, 15x18" 825.00
Joan of Arc, pencil sgn/blindstamp, ca 1929, 19x14½" 1,300.00
Jug of Milk, pencil sgn, 1925, 17¾x12" 1,870.00
Lady of the Camelias, pencil sgn/blindstamp, 1927, 17x21" ..1,400.00
Lesson of Love, sgn/blindstamp, ca 1927, 10x9½" 1,200.00
Lilies, pencil sgn/blindstamp, ca 1934, 27½x19" 2,090.00
Little Prisoner, sgn, minor foxing, 15½x19¾" 900.00
Love Letters, sgn/blindstamp, ca 1926, 15x19" 1,050.00
Love's Blossom, pencil sgn/blindstamp, ca 1937, 17x25" 3,100.00
Madame Butterfly, pencil sgn/blindstamp, ca 1927, 20x13" ..1,200.00
Mardi Gras, sgn/blindstamp, 1936, 19½x19½" 4,675.00
Meditation, sgn/blindstamp, ca 1928, 12x17" 1,650.00
Milkmaid, sgn/blindstamp, ca 1928, 19½x19½" 990.00
Mimi Pinson, sgn/blindstamp, ca 1927, 21x13½" 2,860.00
Miss America, sgn/blindstamp, ca 1927, 20x13" 2,640.00
Music Lesson II, sgn, ca 1934, 15x19" 2,000.00
On the Beach, pencil sgn, ca 1925, 10½x16" 1,045.00
Orchids, pencil sgn/inscr, ca 1937, 28x19" 2,310.00

Paris Flower, pencil sgn/blindstamp, ca 1930, 15x19" 990.00
Peaches, sgn, 17½x13" 725.00
Prima Ballerina, pencil sgn/blindstamp, ca 1935, 15x19" 1,750.00
Puppies, sgn/inscr, 16½x20" 750.00
Red Gate, pencil sgn, ca 1925, 12x17" 1,650.00
Sea Gulls, pencil sgn/blindstamp, ca 1926, 20x16" 1,650.00
Singing Lesson, pencil sgn/blindstamp, ca 1926, 14x18" 1,540.00
Sleeping Beauty, pencil sgn/blindstamp, 1927, 15½x19½" ..1,320.00
Snacktime, sgn/blindstamp, ca 1941, 18x12" 2,200.00
Snow Birds, sgn, 16½x12" 1,045.00
Sofa, pencil sgn, 1927, 28x17" 1,870.00
Spanish Dancer, pencil sgn/blindstamp, ca 1929, 20½x13" ..1,045.00
Spilled Milk, pencil sgn, ca 1925, 17x11" 1,430.00
Spilled Peaches, pencil sgn, blindstamp, 1928, 20x13" 1,760.00
Storyteller, sgn/blindstamp, ca 1926, 14½x19½" 1,100.00
Sweet Mystery, pencil sgn/blindstamp, ca 1935, 20½x16" ..2,420.00
Symphony in Blue, pencil sgn/blindstamp, 1936, 23½x19" ..1,650.00
Thoroughbreds, pencil sgn/blindstamp, ca 1938, 18x35" 4,620.00
Treasures, pencil sgn, ca 1924, 9x11" 550.00
Unmasked, pencil sgn/blindstamp, ca 1933, 12x8" 1,210.00
Venus, pencil sgn/blindstamp, ca 1928, 14x19½" 1,540.00
White Underwear, sgn/inscr, 15x19" 2,200.00
Wishing Well, pencil sgn, ca 1925, 17½x12" 935.00
Woman in Wings, pencil sgn/blindstamp, 1936, 7x9½" 4,125.00
Woman playing w/cat (untitled), ca 1828, 17x12½" 715.00
Wounded Dove, sgn/blindstamp, 1929, 21x17" 990.00

Kellogg

Battle of Chattanooga TN, Nov 24, 1863 ....120.00
Brave at Home #1, 10x14" 50.00
Brave at Home #3, 13½x17½" 65.00
Children in the Wood, 13¾x16¾" 45.00
Daughters of Temperance, sm folio 65.00
Evening Prayer, 10x15" 35.00
Expectation, 10x12" 40.00
Feeding the Pigeons, 12½x16½" 25.00
John Heenan, Benencia Boy Champion of America 130.00
Pope Pius IX, 14¾x18¼" 25.00
Thomas Wildey, Father of the Order of Oddfellows 40.00
Tree of Life, color 90.00
Washington, 12½x16¼" 45.00

Kurz and Allison

Louis Kurz founded the Chicago Lithograph Company in 1833. Among his most notable works were a series of thirty-six Civil War scenes and one hundred illustrations of Chicago architecture. His company was destroyed in the Great Fire of 1871, and in 1880 Kurz formed a partnership with Alexander Allison, an engraver. Until both retired in 1903, they produced hundreds of lithographs in color as well as black and white.

Battle of Antietam, Sept 17, 1862, lg folio 200.00
Battle of Bull Run, lg folio 200.00
Battle of Lexington, med folio 38.00
Battle of New Orleans, lg folio 250.00
Battle of the Big Horn, 1889, 22x28" 485.00
Battle of Tippecanoe, 1889, 22x28" 225.00
Battle of Wilson's Creek MO, lg folio 200.00
Col Theodore Roosevelt, blk/wht, lg folio 60.00
Destruction of Battleship Maine in Havana Harbor, lg folio ...235.00
Flags of Union, sgn Kugler, 1898, lg folio 165.00
Ocelot, blk/wht, lg folio 45.00
Surrender of Admiral Cervera, July 3, 1898, lg folio 175.00

Transporting Munitions from Concord, Apr, 1775, med folio ...**35.00**
Washington Entering Trenton..., blk/wht, med folio **50.00**

McKenney and Hall

Chitte Hoholo, Seminole Chief, Greenough, 1838, 14x20" ...**225.00**
La Pa Win Soe, Delaware Chief, Biddle, 1837, 14x20" **100.00**
Meeta Koosega, Chippewa warrior, no publisher, 14x20" **160.00**
On Ge Wae, Chippewa Chief, Rice & Clark, 1843, 14x20" ...**195.00**
Paddy Carr, 14x20" **160.00**
Tish Co Hon, Delaware Chief, 14x20" **120.00**
Waa Pa Shaw, Sioux Chief, Biddle, 1836, 14x20" **180.00**

Nutting, Wallace

Born in 1862, Nutting pursued many careers. His hand-tinted photographs of landscapes and interior scenes are prized by collectors today. He was also a writer, minister, farmer, and a furniture maker, designing reproductions of early American pieces. Collectors of his prints should be aware of rosy-hued, inconsistently bright or dark examples — especially large prints of *An Elaborate Dinner* and *A Chair for John*; these have been reproduced. Prices for large interior prints have recently been on the increase. Those with animals have risen at least 25% in the past few years, and prints with men are commanding extremely high prices. Those with babies and/or adolescent children bring very high prices as well.

Our advisor for this category is Milt Steinfeld; he is listed in the Directory under New Jersey.

A Leaf Strewn Brook, flaming Autumn colors **75.00**
All Smiles, lady at mirror, interior, 7x9" fr **110.00**
Ambush of a Redcoat, red-jacketed man **385.00**
Blue Lustre Pitcher **275.00**
Hesitancy, man in red jacket **400.00**
Joy Path, fr, 11½x9½" **50.00**
Mending the Quilt, 4x6" in 12½" fr **110.00**
Mother's Day card w/sm picture, printed verse **85.00**
News in Brief, Ladies at Tea, 13" fr **145.00**
On the Way to Pasture, shepherd scene **485.00**
Pergola, Italian vista, 11" fr **110.00**
Pine Landing, fr, 10½x12¾" **60.00**
Posing, mother & child outside front door **125.00**
Sea Ledges, seascape, lg **450.00**
Swimming Pool, pond, reflections, foliage, 17" fr **65.00**
Under Old Apple Trees, weather-beaten house, exterior **85.00**

Prang, Louis

Battle of Fort Hudson, Prang's American Litho Co **170.00**
Battle of Shiloh, Prang's American Litho Co **175.00**
Cowslips, 1886, 7½x10½" **25.00**
Daisies, 1885, 9x12" **20.00**
Mock Orange or Syringa, 1885, 7½x10½" **20.00**
On the Hudson Near West Point, 1886, 6x11" **110.00**
Pansies, color, 1885, 7½x10½" **20.00**
Trespassing, 1878, 8x10" **90.00**
Windmill, Long Island, dtd 1889, 5x16", EX **40.00**

Yard Long

Famous Musicians, oak fr, EX **78.00**
Tug O' War, cats & dogs, EX **120.00**
Yard of Roses **85.00**
Yard of Burros, FW Irish, ca 1908, NM **165.00**

Yard of Kittens, orig fr **135.00**
Yard of Mixed Flowers, no fr **38.00**
Yard of Music **95.00**
Yard of Pansies, orig fr, old, EX **100.00**
Yard of Roses **85.00**

Purinton

Founded in 1936 in Wellsville, Ohio, Purinton Pottery relocated in 1941 in Shippenville, Pennsylvania, and began producing hand-painted wares that are today attracting the interest of collectors of 'country-type' dinnerware. Using bold brush strokes of vivid color, simple yet attractive patterns such as Apple, Fruits, Tea Rose, and Pennsylvania Dutch were manufactured in tableware sets as well as in many accessory pieces. The pottery closed in 1959.

Our advisor for this category is Pat Dole; she is listed in the Directory under Alabama. Pat is the editor of *The Glaze*; see Clubs, Newsletters, and Catalogs.

Bean pot or marmalade, Apple, handleless, w/lid **12.50**
Bowl, Intaglio, brn, 4" **5.00**
Bowl, Maywood, divided vegetable **35.00**
Chop plate, Apple, 12" **15.00**
Coffeepot, Intaglio, brn **35.00**
Cookie jar, Apple, oval **25.00**
Cookie jar, Apple & Pear, oval **25.00**
Cookie jar, Heather Plaid **28.00**
Creamer, Apple & Pear **5.00**
Creamer & sugar bowl, Apple **15.00**
Grease jar, Apple & Pear **20.00**
Honey jug, red flowers **8.00**
Jam & jelly dish, Normandy Plaid **15.00**
Jug, Apple, Dutch, lg, 2-pt **12.50**
Jug, Apple, Kent, 1-pt **10.00**
Jug, Apple, 5-pt **20.00**
Jug, Apple & Pear, Dutch, 2-pt **12.00**
Jug, Apple & Pear, Dutch, 5-pt **20.00**
Jug, Apple & Pear, Kent, 1-pt **7.00**
Jug, Intaglio, Kent, brn **15.00**
Mug, beer; Intaglio, brn **30.00**
Mug, beer; PA Dutch **45.00**

Oasis jug, Apple and Pear, $250.00.

Plate, Apple, 11½" **12.00**
Plate, Apple, 8½" **5.00**
Plate, Intaglio, brn, salad sz **7.00**
Saucer, Intaglio, brn **2.50**
Shakers, Apple, range type, pr **14.00**
Shakers, Apple, 4", pr **6.00**

Shakers, Apple & Pear, range type, pr	14.00
Sugar bowl, Apple, hdls, open	5.00
Teapot, Apple, 2-cup	12.00
Teapot, Maywood, 6-cup	35.00
Teapot, Normandy Plaid, 6-cup	20.00
Tray, PA Dutch, Kent	25.00
Tray, relish; Apple	20.00
Tray, relish; Intaglio, brn, 3-compartment	20.00
Tumbler, Apple, 12-oz	12.00
Tumbler, Apple, 6-oz	6.00

Purses

Beaded purses and bags represent an area of collecting interest that is very popular today. Purses from the early 1800s are often decorated with small, brightly-colored glass beads. Cut steel beads were popular in the 1840s and remained stylish until about 1930. Mesh purses are also popular. In the 1820s, mesh was woven. Chain-link mesh came into usage in the 1890s, followed by the enamel mesh bags carried by the flappers in the 1920s. Purses are divided into several categories by (a) construction techniques — whether beaded, embroidered, or a type of needlework; (b) material — fabric or metal; and (c) design and style. Condition is very important. Watch for dry, brittle leather or fragile material. For those interested in learning more, we recommend *Antique Purses, A History, Identification, and Value Guide*, Second Edition, by Richard Holiner, available at your library or local bookstore.

Key: W/D — Whiting and Davis

Alligator, paw form, gold rope hdl, 5¾x7¾"	50.00

Beaded bag, filigree frame, 6", $65.00.

Beaded, floral tapestry, jewel fr, chain hdl, 8½x12¾"	195.00
Beaded, floral w/portrait in center, rope hdl, 5¼x7¾"	100.00
Beaded, jet blk, silver fr, 6½x7"	60.00
Beaded, mc flowers on wht, chain hdl, 7x12¼"	195.00
Beaded, mc scrolling, jewel clasp, fringed, France, 7¼x12"	300.00
Beaded, peacock/flowers on blk, fringed, 7¼x10"	75.00
Beaded, scenic, fringed, chain hdl, Germany, 6½x10"	125.00
Beaded change, jet blk, German silver fr, 3¾x4"	45.00
Crochet, beige, 4-part hinged silver fr, 6½x8¼"	65.00
Leather, brn, emb, Jemco, 9x7½"	85.00
Linen, birds/floral tapestry, gold trim, 7x7¼"	85.00
Linen, floral tapestry, silver fr, 7x7¼"	85.00
Mesh, blk/red pattern, red fr, W/D, 5x7¼"	75.00
Mesh, blk/silver pattern, rust fringe, Mandalian, 4½x8¼"	85.00
Mesh, Charlie Chaplin depicted, chain hdl, W/D, 3¾x6¼"	250.00
Mesh, floral, W/D, 6x9¾"	95.00
Mesh, German silver, 4¾x6½"	65.00
Mesh, gold, chain hdl, W/D, 8¾x4¾"	75.00
Mesh, gold bead-lite style, chain hdl, W/D, 3½x5"	35.00
Mesh, pastel pattern, silver fr, W/D, 5¼x7¼"	85.00
Mesh, silver, rhinestone closure, W/D, 4x4"	50.00
Mesh, silver w/red floral center, Mandalian, 5x8¼"	115.00
Mesh, wht enamel w/chain hdl, W/D	25.00
Velvet, jet blk, silver repousse fr, chain hdl, 7¾x10"	200.00

Quezal

The Quezal Art Glass and Decorating Company of Brooklyn, New York, was founded in 1901 by Martin Bach. A former Tiffany employee, Bach's glass closely resembled that of his former employer. Most pieces were signed 'Quezal,' a name taken from a Central American bird. After Bach's death in 1920, his son-in-law, Conrad Vohlsing, continued to produce a Quezal-type glass in Elmhurst, New York, which he marked 'Lustre Art Glass.' See also that particular category. Examples listed here are signed unless noted otherwise.

Table lamp, 3-arm, floriform shades, 20", $500.00.

Chandelier, bronze w/6 feathered 7½" shades, opal rims	2,200.00
Compote, gold, sgn, 7¾"	275.00

Cup & saucer, demi; gold, sgn 250.00
Lamp, gold threads on MOP, gold int, flared 5" dia top, 8" 385.00
Salt cellar, gold, ribbed, sgn, 2½" dia .125.00
Shade, gr/gold leaves w/threads on wht irid, 5½" 175.00
Shade, zippered ribs, opal int cased w/gr irid & yel, 5" 275.00
Vase, bl irid, slim w/disk ft, 7" 350.00
Vase, bl-gold, 3 appl gold ft, 8" 375.00
Vase, brn irid, gr int, scalloped, sgn, 5½" 300.00
Vase, bud; gold, sgn, 12" 250.00
Vase, dk bl irid, classic form, 8" 350.00
Vase, feathers, gold on opal, gr swirls at top, sgn, 12" 1,200.00
Vase, feathers, gold on opal, gr zigzag band, gold neck, 5" 900.00
Vase, feathers, platinum on ivory & gr, sgn/#739, 6½" 1,100.00
Vase, gold, pinched sides, sgn/#1137, 10" 275.00
Vase, jack-in-pulpit; feathers, gold/gr, lg face, sgn, 13" 3,250.00
Vase, jack-in-pulpit; feathers, gold/opal/gr, sgn, 10" 1,900.00
Vase, jack-in-pulpit; pulled leaves on bl, sgn, 12½" 1,150.00
Vase, leaves/swirls, gr/gold, squatty, flared, 4½" 850.00
Vase, swirls, amber/gold/gr/bl on opal, gold int, 8" 500.00
Vase, swirls, bl-gr on gold, 8" 600.00
Vase, swirls/zigzags, gold/gr on gold, flared, bulb base, 5" 850.00

Quilts

Quilts, while made of necessity, nevertheless represent an art form which expresses the character and the personality of the designer. During the 17th and 18th centuries, quilts were considered a necessary part of a bride's hope chest — the traditional number required to be properly endowed for marriage was a 'baker's dozen'! Quilts were used not only for bed coverings but for curtains, extra insulation, and mattresses as well. The early quilts were made from pieces salvaged from cloth items that had outlived their original usefulness and from bits left over from sewing projects. Regardless of shape, these scraps were fitted together following no organized lines. The resulting hodge-podge design was called a crazy quilt.

In 1793 Eli Whitney developed the cotton gin; as a result, textile production in America became industrialized. Soon inexpensive fabrics were readily available, and ladies were able to choose from colorful prints and solids to add contrast to their work. Both pieced and appliqued work became popular — pieced quilts were considered utilitarian, while appliqued work was shown with pride of accomplishment at the fair. Today many collectors prize pieced quilts and their intricate geometric patterns above all other types. Many of these designs were given names: Daisy and Oak Leaf, Grandmother's Flower Garden, Log Cabin, and Ocean Wave are only a few. Appliqued quilts involved stitching one piece — carefully cut into a specific form such as a leaf, a flower, or a stylized device — onto either a large one-piece ground fabric or an individual block. Often the background fabric was quilted in a decorative pattern.

Amish women scorned printed calicos as 'worldly' and instead used colorful blocks set with black fabrics to produce a stunning pieced effect. During the Victorian era, the crazy quilt was revived, but the ladies of the 1870s used plush velvets, brocades, silks, and linen patches and embroidered along the seams with feather or chain stitches.

Another type of quilting, highly prized and rare today, is trapunto. These quilts were made by first stitching the outline of the design onto a solid sheet of fabric which was backed with a second having a much looser weave. White was often favored, but color was sometimes used for accent. The design (grapes, flowers, leaves, etc.) was padded through openings made by separating the loose weave of the underneath fabric; a backing was added and the three layers quilted as one.

Besides condition, value is judged on intricacy of pattern, color effect, and craftsmanship. In the listings that follow, examples rated excellent have minor defects.

Key:
dmn — diamond   ms — machine sewn
embr — embroidered   X — cross
hs — hand sewn

Amish

Bl center+3" maroon band+1 of bl+7" maroon border, 1949 . . .150.00
Bl stripes, faded blk ground, aqua bk, 64x82", EX 150.00
Irish Chain Variation, blk/lav, ca 1940s, 74x74", NM 450.00
Log Cabin, pk/teal gr, minor fading/sm holes/wear, 81x81" 225.00
Rolling Stone, pk/bl, bl/wht borders, 1930s, 81x69", M 675.00
Sq kite forms on sq-pcd ground, OH, 70x82", VG 350.00
Squares, blk/wht/purple, ca 1915, full sz 375.00
Star, bl shades, Holmes Co OH, 70x70", EX 200.00

Star of Bethlehem, ca 1900, 85" square, $750.00.

Stars, blk w/teal bl & beige on maroon, dtd 1905, 64x88" 500.00
Variable Star, ecru on slate bl, contemporary, 92x79" 200.00

Appliqued

Floral, stylized, red/gr/goldenrod, scroll quiltings, VG 275.00
Floral medallions, red/gr, sgn/1859, EX quilting, minor wear . . .950.00
Floral pinwheels, red/goldenrod/gr, EX quilting, 77x77" 750.00
Floral wreaths, meandering border, red/gr calicos, stains 450.00
Floral wreaths, 12 repeats, red/bl on wht, recent quilting 500.00
Grid of flowers, embr centers, scalloped, ms applique, NM 150.00
Kittens in Baskets, fine quilting, old, 56x88", EX 325.00
Lily, red & gr on wht, slave made, 1800s, full sz, EX 300.00
Medallions, 4 lg/stylized, red/goldenrod/teal, EX quilting 600.00
Pinwheels, vine border, goldenrod/calicos, EX quilting, VG . . .200.00
Poinsettias in pots ea corner/center/sides, 1950s, unused 325.00
Rose Wreath, mustard/indigo, red roses, ca 1890, lg, EX 325.00
Sqs w/cloverleaves at ea corner, gr/wht, bl ms binding 375.00
Tree of Life, bright colors, hs, new, full sz, M 350.00
Tulips, red/wht/gr, hs, 1930s, full sz, M 400.00

Pieced

Basket, triangle components, bl/goldenrod, 82x82", EX 450.00

Baskets, red/gr/gold calico, dtd 1895, 70x82", EX 450.00
Bear's Paw, burgundy & brn on wht, ca 1920, full sz, EX 285.00
Bow Tie, indigo & wht, EX quilting, 1930s, X-lg, NM 565.00
Bow Tie, mc prints, ca 1920, 69x80", EX 350.00
Bow Tie Stars, maroon/wht on navy, minor rpr/hole, 64x73" . .325.00
Butterflies, bright pk, ca 1930, full sz, NM 325.00
Cane Bottom, gr/wht, sawtooth edge, hs, 1960s, 90x100" 265.00
Crazy, Chicago Expo, Galveston TX, beadwork, 1893, 56x64". 200.00
Crazy, mc prints, embr w/'1900,' 68x80" 215.00
Crazy, pnt & embr flowers/animals/people/'1887', 65x70" 550.00
Dbl Wedding Ring, bl centers, 65x89", EX 400.00
Dbl Wedding Ring, bright colors on wht, full sz, NM 550.00
Dbl Wedding Ring, mostly bl, ca 1890, twin sz, VG 120.00
Dove in Window, rose/dk bl calicos on wht, hs, 1930s, 73x85" .365.00
Dove of Peace, cobalt & wht, recent, full sz, M 450.00
Dresden Plate, gold/orange/wht, EX quilting, old, full sz 550.00
Dresden Plate, old material, recently made, 88x105", EX 425.00
Drunkard's Path, pk calico/wht, EX quilting, ms binding, EX . .175.00
Drunkard's Path, red & wht solids, 1930s, full sz, NM 585.00
Fans, pk calicos, fine quilting, ca 1930, 65x75", EX 300.00
Flame, red & wht, center medallion, hs, sgn/1910, lg, EX 425.00
Flower Basket, brn & Turkey red, EX quilting, 1900, lg, EX . . .345.00
Flying Geese, brn & tan w/red sashing, old, 80x80", EX 425.00
Flying Geese, indigo on wht, 1900, full sz, M 800.00
Grandmother's Fan, old top, newly quilted, 85x88", EX 350.00
Hand of Friendship, bl/wht/red, blk thread, 1875, 69x82", VG .325.00
Hawaiian, red/wht/bl on wht, ca 1900, full sz, EX 550.00
Hearts, red on wht, lt yel Wedding Rings, ca 1900, lg, EX 435.00
Honeycomb, red & wht, sawtooth border, ca 1890, full sz, EX .425.00
Honeycomb, red/bl/calicos, bright, 1890s, X-lg, VG 275.00
Irish Chain, bl/wht, EX circle quilting, '30s, 72x75", VG 175.00
Jig Saw, red & wht, hs, ca 1880, ¾-sz 255.00
Lightning Bars, red/yel calicos, ms/hand quilted, 80x86" 200.00
Log Cabin, EX colors, ms binding, wear/sm holes 275.00
Log Cabin, EX detail, mc prints, red postage stamp sqs 475.00
Log Cabin, mainly red wools & silks, ca 1870s, lg, EX 245.00
Log Cabin, mc calicos & other prints, 82x28" 350.00
Log Cabin, red & bl cotton, ca 1890, lg, EX 345.00
Morning-Glory, bl print, gr leaves, 1930s, full sz, unused 175.00
Mosaic pattern, equal sz pk calico & wht triangles, rpr 180.00
N Carolina Lily, mc on wht, ca 1900, full sz, NM 350.00
NY Beauty, gr & brn on wht, EX hs, ca 1880s, full sz 345.00
Open Windows, red/bl/gr, fine sewing, ca 1910, lg, EX 245.00
Patchwork, 9 red & wht patches, diagonal, full sz, EX 350.00
Pineapple Log Cabin, red & yel on gray, ca 1900, full sz, EX . .325.00
Pinwheel, plum & indigo w/red border, ca 1890, lg, NM 265.00
Pinwheels, pastels on wht, ca 1880, full sz, EX 300.00
Poinsettias & Bows, all wht, EX work, recent, 90x108", EX . . .400.00
Postage Stamp, bright colors, hs, 1940s, 72x82", NM 150.00
Postage Stamp, pk & indigo, fancy border, 1860s, full sz 385.00
Radiant Beauty, pastels, ca 1915, queen sz, EX 425.00
Schoolhouse, mc on wht, recent, 95x108", EX 450.00
Schoolhouse, red/wht/bl, ca 1940, lg, unused 600.00
Single Irish Chain, gr calico on wht, minor wear, 76x76" 175.00
Single Star, mc prints on wht, 80x80" 200.00
Snail's Trail, red & cream, 1930s, full sz, unused 255.00
Sqs set in rows diagonally across corners, doll's, 14x14" 125.00
Star, pastel bl/wht, fine stitching, ca 1880, youth sz, EX 200.00
Star, 49 stars, ca 1860s, full sz, NM .600.00
Stars, goldenrod in cream octagons on dk bl, red grid 375.00
Stars, goldenrod on med bl, scalloped, minor wear/fading 225.00
Stars, mc on ecru w/bl grid, salmon sqs/border, ms binding 325.00
Stars, mc prints on brn & wht, 1904, rpr/wear, 72x79" 165.00
Stars, 25 in colored stripes on gray-gr calico, 74x76" 275.00

Sunbonnet Sue, EX work, old, 68x92", EX 325.00
Sunburst Medallions, goldenrod/red on wht, EX quilting 375.00
Tree of Paradise, red/wht/bl/tan/gr linens, 1800, 68x83" 475.00
Trip Around World, bright satins, matching shams, unused . . .200.00
Wedding Ring, lavenders, 1930s, full sz, unused 200.00
Windmill, soft golds/pks, hs, 1940s, 72x82", NM 185.00
Zigzag Stars, brn prints on wht, EX quilting, minor fading 375.00
12-Patch, red/burgundy/aqua, ca 1880, half-sz, EX 155.00
4-Patch Sqs, mc prints alternate w/navy, 72x87" 285.00
8-Point Star, mixed calico stars on bl, 1930s, 75x82", EX 465.00
9-Patch, intricate, rich colors, crib sz, 42x43" 375.00
9-Patch, mc prints & wht on pk calico, unused, 72x82" 225.00

Miscellaneous

Bride's, vines/flowers in urns, trapunto, 1820s, 88x90" 2,400.00
Bride's, wht cotton w/trapunto, 1820s, wear/rpr/stains 1,100.00
Chintz, EX mc floral, homespun bk, 84x93" 400.00
Lightning, red/gr, EX quilting, dtd 1899, 80x80", VG 350.00

Quimper

Quimper is a type of pottery produced in Quimper, France. A tin enamel-glazed earthenware pottery with hand-painted decoration, it was first produced in the 1600s by the Bousquet and Caussy Factories. Little of this early ware was marked. By the late 1700s, three factories were operating in the area, all manufacturing the same type of pottery. The Grande Maison de HB, a company formed as a result of a marriage joining the Hubaudiere and Bousquet families, was a major producer of Quimper pottery. They marked their wares with various forms of the 'HB' logo; but of the pottery they produced, collectors value examples marked with the 'HB' within a triangle most highly.

Francois Eloury established another pottery in Quimper in the late 1700s. Under the direction of Charles Porquier, the ware was marked simply 'P.' Adolph Porquier replaced Charles in the 1850s, marking the ware produced during that period with an 'AP' logo.

Jule HenRiot began operations in 1886, using molds he had purchased from Porquier. His mark was 'HR,' and until the twentieth century he was in competition with The Grande Maison de HB. In 1926 he began to mark his wares 'HenRiot Quimper.' In 1968 the two factories merged. They are still in operation under the name Les Faenceries de Quimper. The factory sold in the fall of 1983 to Sarah and Paul Janssens from the United States, making it the first time the owners were not French.

For those interested in learning more about Quimper pottery, we recommend *Quimper: A French Folk Art Faience* by Sandra V. Bondhus, our advisor for this category, whose address can be found in the Directory under Connecticut.

Bannette, dragonflies, decor riche, HenRiot Quimper, 12x7½" .450.00
Bell, peasant figural, ca 1930s, 5" 60.00
Bookends, boy & girl, faience, sgn Savigny, #d, pr 450.00
Bowl, peasant man, 6-sided, HB Quimper, 7½" 85.00
Bowl, serving; yel, peasant woman, oval, HB Quimper, 10½x7" .95.00
Butter pat, Eskimos, scalloped edge, gr border, HenRiot 10.00
Creamer & sugar bowl, peasants on yel, w/lid, HB, sm 95.00
Cruet set, red floral, mk HB Quimper, 1950s, 8" 65.00
Cup & saucer, berry & sponge border, HenRiot Quimper 30.00
Cup & saucer, peasants on yel, HB, jumbo sz 45.00
Egg cup, girl & boy, attached plate, HenRiot Quimper 40.00
Figurine, Joeur de Bombarde, HB Quimper, 15" 425.00
Figurine, peasant couple, HenRiot Quimper, pr 400.00
Figurine, 3 nuns w/banner, Sevellec, HenRiot Quimper, 4x6" .185.00
Inkwell, hat form 160.00

Jardiniere, swan, HenRiot Quimper, 4¼x5½" 295.00
Jug, puzzle; grapes, Buvezje le Veux Bien..., Malicorne, 6" 250.00
Knife rest, peasant, HenRiot Quimper .45.00
Pitcher, croiselle design, HenRiot Quimper, 7½" 175.00
Pitcher, geometric pattern, graceful shape, HenRiot, 7½" 145.00
Pitcher, peasant man, wide yel bands, HenRiot Quimper, 6" . . .125.00
Plate, floral, orange & bl rings, HenRiot Quimper, 7" 40.00
Plate, soup; Rouen, HenRiot Quimper, France, 9" 165.00
Platter, peasant couple/floral edge, no mk, 1800s, 14" 185.00
Porringer, woman, HenRiot Quimper, 7" 25.00
Relish dish, peasant man/floral, scalloped, 1800s, HB 255.00
Snuff bottle, bagpipe shape, lady, HenRiot 195.00
Snuff bottle, rooster, book shape, unmk, 3" 150.00

Teapot, marked HenRiot, 8", $245.00.

Teapot, geometrics, stylized peasant, HenRiot Quimper, sm . . .150.00
Tray, man & lady, HenRiot, 6½x4" .60.00
Tray, yel trim, fluted, peasant girl, HB, 9¾" 115.00
Wall pocket, bagpipes, male peasant, HR Quimper, 7x5" 295.00
Wall pocket, cone, peasant, HB Quimper, 1960s, 5½" 80.00

Vase, Art Deco nudes, marked Odetta, #1066, ca 1920, 12½", $300.00.

Radford

The Jasperware listed below was made in Zanesville, Ohio, at the A. Radford Pottery Company incorporated there in 1903. This type of ware was first designed and produced in 1896 when Albert Radford worked in Tiffin, Ohio. The Zanesville Jasper, in contrast to the original line, was decorated with Wedgwood-type cameos in relief that were not applied but were formed within the general mold. The only mark found on the ware is a two-digit shape number. The Tiffin Jasper, though not always marked, is sometimes impressed 'Radford Jasper.'

After only a few months Radford sold the plant to Arc-En-Ciel and moved his works to West Virginia. In addition to the regular line of utility wares, several artware lines were also produced there. Among them were Ruko, a standard brown underglaze decorated line; Thera, matt glazed with slip decoration; and Radura, usually done in matt green glazes.

Jardiniere and pedestal, winged creatures and foliage, green glaze, marked, $500.00.

Jasper

Mug, grape & floral relief, wht on bl, #25, 5" 225.00
Pitcher, grapes, Old Man Winter on hdl, #17, 9" 250.00
Vase, angel relief in cameo panels, wht on blk, 17" 375.00
Vase, cherubs in reserve, #14, 6¾" .175.00
Vase, lady w/flowers, bk: grapes, #59, 4" 150.00
Vase, 2 children & lion, wht/lt brn, #15, 7" 175.00

Miscellaneous

Jardiniere, Ruko, tulips, brn glaze, 8½x9" 150.00
Jardiniere & ped, winged creatures/foliage, streaky gr, 34" 500.00
Vase, Thera, floral, red on matt gr, 12½" 450.00

Radios

Vintage radios are becoming very popular. There were thousands of styles and types produced, the most popular of which today are the breadboard and the cathedral. Consoles are usually considered less saleable since their size makes them hard to display and store.

Aetna Tombstone 50.00
Atwater Kent #32, EX 100.00
Atwater Kent #40, VG 45.00
Atwater Kent #49 ....40.00
Bendix, chartreuse plastic 75.00
Coronado #908, wood cabinet 35.00
Crosley #5-50, regenerative, VG 85.00
Crosley #5-50, 1926, rare, MIB 100.00
Crosley #52, portable 80.00
Crosley #6 ....200.00
Crosley Coloradio #10-138, maroon & chrome, EX 70.00
Crosley RFL-75, rare wood front panel, rstr 95.00
Crosley Super Tridyne, regular, NM 85.00
Crosley Tombstone #148, chrome escutcheon, NM 60.00
Crosley V, EX 150.00
Detrola Super Pee Wee, 2-color brn Bakelite, cream knobs, M .155.00
Echophone S-3, cathredral model, EX 78.00
Emerson Jewelry Box, EX orig 125.00
ERLA, cathedral model w/clock, 2 knobs, rare, EX 200.00
Freed-Eisemann NR-6, EX orig 85.00
Grantline, brn Bakelite, push buttons, EX 50.00
Guthman U-17 Silver Super, w/U-44 frequency meter 75.00
Hallicrafters S-38-A, EX 50.00
Hallicrafters SX-105, government band receiver, VG 40.00
Kennedy #110, EX 500.00
Magnavox, D, pull-out drawer, table model, EX orig 95.00
Melrose, cathedral model, NM 140.00
Murdock CS-32 ....160.00
Neutidial UV-199, 5-tube, EX 85.00
Patterson PR-16, EX 150.00
Philco #20, M 150.00
Philco #20, VG 100.00
Philco #40-130, semi-tombstone, veneered table model, EX 45.00
Philco #48-482, wood cabinet, table model, EX 40.00
Philco #60, cathedral model, EX 130.00
Philco #80, cathedral model, EX orig 70.00
Radiola #26, portable, complete, EX orig 375.00
RCA #120, cathedral model 225.00
RCA #3-BX-671, VG 65.00
RCA #8-X-641, plastic case, EX orig 12.00
RCA Tombstone M-50, G 30.00
RCA X-551, brn Bakelite, table model, M 30.00
Setchell-Carlson #416, Bakelite, EX 22.00
Silvertone Neutrodyne, EX orig 75.00
Smokerette, brn, pipe stand & 3 tobacco compartments, VG ..200.00
Stewart-Warner #300, VG 65.00
Thompson #35, EX orig 95.00
Traveler, brn Bakelite, EX orig 50.00
Ward's #938-R-640-A, 1½-volt battery set, wood case 20.00
Westinghouse H-185, maroon Bakelite, portable, no cracks, EX .25.00
Westinghouse Tombstone #184, VG 45.00
Zenith #5-H-40, EX 80.00
Zenith #6-D-510, Bakelite, EX 45.00
Zenith #6-J-320, blk dial, EX 85.00
Zenith #871, sm dial, EX 85.00
Zenith #9-S-54, console, w/added 6-U5 ....225.00

Zenith F-278, beige/bl/gold cabinet, w/clock, EX 35.00
Zenith T-723, Bakelite, EX 25.00
Zenith Tombstone #807, EX 120.00
Zenith Zenette, cathedral model, 1931, EX 250.00

Sparton Model #557, three knobs, blue mirrored glass, $1,200.00.

Railroadiana

Collecting railroad-related memorabilia has become one of America's most popular hobbies. The range of collectible items available is almost endless, considering the fact that more than 175 different railroad lines are represented. Some collectors prefer to specialize in only one, while others attempt to collect at least one item from every railway line known to have existed. For the advanced collector, there is the challenge of locating rarities from short-lived railroads; for the novice, there are abundant keys, buttons, passes, and playing cards. Among the most popular specializations are dining-car collectibles — flatware, glassware, dinnerware, etc., in a wide variety of patterns and styles.

For a more thorough study, we recommend *Railroad Collectibles, Third Revised Edition*, by Stanley L. Baker, available at your local library or bookstore. Some of our listings were provided by Shrader's Antiques (see Directory, California).

Key:
BR — brass   RY — railway
BS — back stamped   SM — side marked
C — cast   ST — steel
NP — nickel plated   STMP — stamped
R&B — Reed and Barton   TM — top marked
RR — railroad

Dinnerware

Ash tray, C&O, Chessie, rnd, 3½" 58.00
Ash tray, C&O, Geo Washington, 3x7" 85.00
Ash tray, GN, pk/yel flowers, rnd, 3½" 50.00
Bowl, cereal; ATSF, Mimbreno, BS, 5¾" 75.00
Bowl, cereal; B&O, Capitol, 6½" 35.00
Bowl, cereal; CMStP&P, Traveler, 6½" 15.00
Bowl, cereal; NYC, Mercury, BS 32.00
Bowl, cereal; SP, Prairie Mountain Wildflowers, BS, 6" .58.00
Bowl, cereal; UP, Winged Streamliner, 6½" 35.00
Bowl, salad; ATSF, Mimbreno, BS, 8¾" 75.00
Bowl, salad; B&O, Sweetbriar, 6¾" 45.00
Bowl, soup; ATSF, California Poppy, 6½" 45.00
Bowl, soup; UP, Desert Flower, 6½" 26.00

Butter pat, ACL, Carolina, BS 20.00
Butter pat, ATSF, California Poppy 22.50
Butter pat, B&O, Centenary, BS 37.50
Butter pat, CB&Q, Violets & Daisies 25.00
Butter pat, D&RG, Blue Adam 18.00
Butter pat, NYNH&H, Blue Platinum, BS 95.00
Butter pat, PRR, Purple Laurel 28.00
Butter pat, UP, Harriman Blue 18.00
Butter pat, UP, Winged Streamliner 18.00
Celery dish, ACL, Flora of the South, BS, 5x10" 95.00
Celery dish, B&O, Capitol, TM, 5¾x11½" 95.00
Celery dish, C&O, Geo Washington, BS, 4½x9½" 65.00
Celery dish, CMStP&P, Traveler, 4½x10" 42.50
Celery dish, N&W, Yellowbird, 4½x10" 65.00
Compote, CP, Green Band, on ped, 6½" 75.00
Cup, bouillon; GN, Oriental, 3¾" 38.00
Cup, bouillon; SP, Prairie Mountain Wildflowers, 3¼" 72.50
Cup, bouillon; UP, Harriman Blue, 3¾" 32.50
Cup, bouillon; WP, Western Pacific, 3½" 32.50
Cup & saucer, ATSF, California Poppy 38.00
Cup & saucer, ATSF, Mimbreno, BS 80.00
Cup & saucer, B&O, Centenary, BS 68.00
Cup & saucer, demitasse; B&O, Centenary, BS 55.00
Cup & saucer, demitasse; B&O, Derby 95.00
Cup & saucer, demitasse; CMStP&P, Traveler, BS 72.00
Cup & saucer, demitasse; GN, Mountains & Flowers 95.00
Cup & saucer, demitasse; IC, Coral 95.00
Cup & saucer, demitasse; UP, Winged Streamliner, BS 39.00
Cup & saucer, GN, Mountains & Flowers, BS 95.00
Cup & saucer, NYC, Mercury, BS 80.00
Cup & saucer, PRR, Mountain Laurel 30.00
Cup & saucer, UP, Winged Streamliner 55.00
Egg cup, UP, Desert Flower, sm 35.00
Egg cup, UP, Winged Streamliner, sm 35.00
Egg cup, WP, Feather River, lg 75.00
Gravy boat, ACL, Carolina, BS 75.00
Gravy boat, ATSF, Mimbreno 85.00
Gravy boat, B&O, Chessie 35.00
Gravy boat, SRR, Peach Blossom, SM 55.00
Ice cream shell, UP, Winged Streamliner 28.00
Mustard, Coach & Four, slotted, w/lid 145.00
Mustard, D&RG, Blue Adam, slotted, w/lid 38.00
Plate, ACL, Flora of the South, 10" 145.00
Plate, ACL, Flora of the South, 7¾" 72.50
Plate, ATSF, California Poppy, 10" 50.00
Plate, ATSF, California Poppy, 7" 32.00
Plate, ATSF, Griffin, 7¾" 82.00
Plate, ATSF, Mimbreno, 10" 95.00
Plate, ATSF, Mimbreno, 7¼" 64.00
Plate, ATSF, Mimbreno, 9¾" 95.00
Plate, B&O, Centenary, 10½" 78.00
Plate, B&O, Centenary, 6¾" 38.00
Plate, B&O, Derby, 9" 54.00
Plate, C&NW, Wild Rose, 9½" 42.50
Plate, C&O, Chessie, 9" 150.00
Plate, C&O, Geo Washington, 6" 45.00
Plate, CB&Q, Violets & Daisies, 9" 42.50
Plate, CMStP&P, Galatea, 6½" 37.50
Plate, CMStP&P, Peacock, 6¼" 28.50
Plate, CMStP&P, Traveler, 5½" 15.00
Plate, CMStP&P, Traveler, 9½" 65.00
Plate, CN, Truro, 8" 27.00
Plate, CP, Tremblant, 9½" 38.00
Plate, CRI&P, Golden State (oranges), 9" 145.00

Plate, D&RGW, Prospector, 9" 98.00
Plate, FEC, Carolina, 9" 87.50
Plate, FEC, Mistic, 8½" 20.00
Plate, GM&O, Rose, 7¼" 52.00
Plate, GN, Glory of the West, 8½" 40.00
Plate, GN, Mountains & Flowers, 7" 42.50
Plate, GN, Mountains & Flowers, 9" 86.00
Plate, GN, Oriental, 8" 45.00
Plate, IC, Coral, 7½" 20.00
Plate, KCS, Roxbury, 9¼" 55.00
Plate, L&N, Green Leaf, 5½" 15.00
Plate, L&N, Regent, 7½" 18.00
Plate, MP, Eagle, 6½" 27.50
Plate, MP, Eagle, 9½" 100.00
Plate, N&W, Dogwood, 9¾" 38.00
Plate, NP, Monad, 6½" 35.00
Plate, NYC, Country Gardens, 10½" 50.00
Plate, NYC, DeWitt Clinton, 8" 25.00
Plate, NYC, DeWitt Clinton, 9" 45.00
Plate, NYC, Mercury, 9" 48.00
Plate, NYC, Mohawk, 6½" 30.00
Plate, NYNH&H, Merchants, 8½" 65.00
Plate, NYNH&H, Platinum Blue, 8½" 45.00
Plate, PRR, Broadway, 8½" 30.00
Plate, PRR, Keystone, 9" 67.50
Plate, PRR, Mountain Laurel, 6½" 18.00
Plate, PRR, Purple Laurel, 9¾" 42.00
Plate, Pullman, Indian Tree, 7½" 48.00
Plate, SAL, Orange Blossom, 7½" 65.00
Plate, SAL, Piedmont, 7" 30.00
Plate, service; IC, Pirate, 9¾" 135.00
Plate, SP, Prairie Mountain Wildflowers, divided, 9½" 95.00
Plate, SP, Prairie Mountain Wildflowers, 5½" 30.00
Plate, SP, Prairie Mountain Wildflowers, 9½" 65.00
Plate, UP, Blue & Gold, 9¾" 40.00
Plate, UP, Challenger, 9½" 88.00
Plate, UP, Desert Flower, 6½" 18.00
Plate, UP, Desert Flower, 9¾" 48.00
Plate, UP, Harriman Blue, 7" 30.00
Plate, UP, Winged Streamliner, 10½" 45.00
Plate, UP, Winged Streamliner, 6½" 24.00
Plate, WP, Feather River, 7½" 45.00
Plate, WP, Feather River, 9½" 150.00
Platter, ACL, Flora of the South, 9¼x6½" 125.00
Platter, ACL, Palmetto, 11¾x8" 95.00
Platter, ATSF, California Poppy, 9x5" 50.00
Platter, B&O, Capitol, 8x5¾" 58.00
Platter, B&O, Centenary, 11½x8¼" 78.00
Platter, C&O, Geo Washington, no portrait, 8x6½" 65.00
Platter, CMStP&P, Galatea, 10x7¼" 82.50
Platter, CMStP&P, Peacock, 8x6¼" 16.00
Platter, CMStP&P, Traveler, 8x6½" 28.00
Platter, D&RGW, Blue Adam, 15½x11" 95.00
Platter, D&RGW, Prospector, 7x5½" 32.00
Platter, Erie, Susquehanna, 8½x6" 34.00
Platter, FEC, Carolina, 9½x6½" 58.00
Platter, FEC, Mistic, 9½x6½" 38.00
Platter, GN, Hill, 10x7¼" 110.00
Platter, GN, Mountains & Flowers, 9x7½" 58.00
Platter, IC, Coral, 7x5¾" 20.00
Platter, L&N, Green Leaf, 10½x7½" 15.00
Platter, MP, Eagle, 10½x7½" 62.00
Platter, MP, St Albans, 10x7" 50.00
Platter, NP, Yellowstone, 8½x7" 62.00

Platter, NYC, DeWitt Clinton, 16x12" 145.00
Platter, NYC, Hudson, 8¾x5½" 60.00
Platter, PRR, Broadway, 8½x5½" 38.00
Platter, PRR, Purple Laurel, 9½x6½" 30.00
Platter, Pullman, Calumet, 12½x8½" 95.00
Platter, Pullman, Indian Tree, 12½x8" 140.00
Platter, Reading, Stotesbury, 10½x7" 72.50
Platter, SP, Prairie Mountain Wildflowers, 9½x7½" 58.00
Platter, SP, Sunset, 9x6½" 58.00
Platter, SRR, Peach Blossom, 9½x6½" 42.50
Platter, UP, Challenger, 9½x8¼" 27.50
Platter, UP, Harriman Blue, 10x8" .52.00
Platter, UP, Winged Streamliner, 9x7½" 28.00
Platter, WP, Feather River, 7½x5" .35.00
Sugar bowl, GN, Oriental, w/lid 65.00
Sugar bowl, N&W, Yellowbird, open 37.50
Teapot, ATSF, California Poppy 75.00
Teapot, Pullman, Verde Green 90.00
Teapot, UP, Winged Streamliner 78.00
Underplate, NP, Monad, TM, 6½" .37.50

Glassware

Ash tray, ATSF, Santa Fe in script, 3x4" 14.00
Ash tray, Erie in bl/wht w/in diamond logo, 3½" 14.00
Ash tray, GN, entwined wht letters, BS, 4" dia 17.50
Ash tray, NP, red & blk Monad logo, octagonal, BS, 5x5" 20.00
Ash tray, UP, Sun Valley Idaho, Utah Parks Co, 4¼" 12.50
Bottle, milk; Mopac, buzz saw logo, qt 20.00
Bottle, milk; MP, red buzz saw on side, 1-pt 15.00
Cordial, NP, etched Yellowstone Park logo, 3¾" 28.00
Cruet, GN, older frosted goat logo 150.00
Goblet, UP, frosted shield, 12-oz 10.00
Martini set, UP, logo in wht, shaker+2 tumblers 37.50
Mug, BN, gr name/blk slogan, 1972 . . . . .10.00
Shot glass, Pullman emb in bottom, 2½" 22.50
Shot glass, UP, frosted shield & wht stripe, 2½" 7.50
Stir stick, GN, goat cutout top, VG .2.50
Tumbler, AAR, slant sides, train around top/music, 4" 5.00
Tumbler, B&O, iced tea, set of 4 . . . . .38.00
Tumbler, B&O, oval logo w/Capitol Dome, juice sz 22.50
Tumbler, Frisco, bl bearskin, 6-oz 7.50
Tumbler, MP, eagle logo, 4¼" 18.00
Tumbler, NYC, 5" 8.50
Tumbler, SL&SF, etched Frisco Lines, 4½" 15.00
Tumbler, SR, diesel engine & Southern Serves South, 3½" 12.50
Tumbler, UP, frosted shield, 4½" 8.50
Tumbler, WP, juice sz 20.00
Wine, IC, frosted diamond logo, stemmed 15.00
Wine, NYC, 20th Century Limited, stemmed 25.00

Lamps

Berth, Pullman, aluminum, milk glass shade, 1950s, EX 47.50
Caboose wall, Handlan #180, early, rstr 75.00
Caboose wall, NW, Aladdin burner, M 85.00
Inspector's, Erie, Dietz, clear Vesta globe, sm, EX 40.00
Inspector's, Oxweld Carbide #2155, EX 87.50
Inspector's, Wolf Safety, Nat'l Carbide, NY, brass, NM 130.00
Marker, C&O, Handlan #79, fully rstr, matched set 200.00
Semaphore, GN, Adlake, oil, w/fuel pot, clear lens 125.00
Semaphore, NYC&STL, Dressel, SM, gr lens, orig pnt, EX 80.00
Switch, Adlake, oil, red/gr lenses, electrified, EX 130.00
Switch, Adlake, oil, red/wht targets, complete, EX 175.00

Switch, Adlake, rnd top, snow hoods, Pat 1909, complete, EX . .165.00
Switch, Adlake #1379, red/gr lenses, sm, rstr 78.00
Switch, W RR, cast steel, electric, all glass lenses, EX 68.00

Lanterns

B&O, Adams & Westlake, clear pear globe, drop font, EX 155.00
B&O, Adlake Kero, short amber unmk globe, dome top, EX 58.00
B&O, Dietz #39 Vulcan, red unmk globe, clip-on font/burner . .68.00
C&O, Adlake Kero, short clear unmk globe, dtd 1946, EX 37.50
CCC&StL, Handlan, clear unmk globe, rnd top, VG 60.00
CM&StP, Adlake 1913 Reliable, clear unmk globe, insert pot . .80.00
CMStP&P, Adlake Kero, amber unmk globe, Pat 1933 . . . . . . .50.00
Dietz #39 Standard, mk globe, bell bottom, Pat 1909, NM 60.00
Handlan, unmk Kero, short clear unmk globe, M 36.00
IC, Handlan, clear Corning rnd-panel globe, rnd top, early 60.00
K&IT, Handlan, red unmk globe, insert pot/burner, EX 65.00
L&N, Adlake Kero, short clear unmk globe, M 67.50
LS&MS, Adlake 1912 Reliable, clear mk globe, lacquered, EX . .150.00
LV, Adlake Kero, short red mk globe, heavy ring base, EX 50.00
MK&T, Handlan, clear unmk globe, flat top, EX 65.00
N&W, Adlake 1913 Reliable, clear mk globe, insert pot, EX 85.00
NKP, Adlake Kero, short clear unmk globe, EX 50.00
NYC, Adlake Kero, short clear unmk globe, dtd 1953 . . . . .34.00
NYNH&H, Adlake 1913 Reliable, red Dietz unmk globe, EX 60.00
P&LE, Dietz Vesta, short clear unmk globe, NM 44.00
P&LE, Dressel Arlington, short clear unmk globe, NM 48.00
Pere Marquette, Adams & Westlake 1912 Reliable, insert pot .175.00
PRR, Adlake 1923 Reliable, unmk globe, logo on dome top, EX .65.00
PRR, Adlake 3-39 Kero, short clear unmk globe, EX 45.00
PRR, Dressel Arlington, short clear unmk globe, NM 38.00
PRR, Handlan, short amber unmk globe, logo on lid, EX 50.00
Rock Island, brakeman's, clear mk 3½" globe 30.00
SR, Adams & Westlake Adams, cobalt unmk globe, Pat 1909 . .95.00
SR, Adlake Kero, short red fresnel globe, dtd 1961, EX 45.00
SR, Armspear, short clear mk globe, Pat 1925, EX 50.00
TTRR, Adlake 1923 Reliable, tall red mk globe, single guard . .125.00
WAB, Adlake #250 Kero, short clear unmk globe, EX 50.00

Linens

Blanket, Canadian Nat'l, maple leaf logo, Pendleton wool, EX . .65.00
Blanket, CPR, beaver logo, Pendleton wool, EX 60.00
Blanket, GN, brn & tan checked wool, woven logo, 55x75" . . .150.00
Blanket, Pullman, old cross-stitch pattern on cinnamon, EX 70.00
Blanket, Pullman, stamped logo, cinnamon, EX 50.00
Dish towel, BR, interwoven logo, bl on wht, 17" sq 7.50
Headrest cover, C&NW, name & 400, brn on tan, 15x20" 10.00
Napkin, D&RG, VG 5.00
Napkin, SF, interwoven logo, wht on wht, 16" sq 7.50
Napkin, SF, script letters, bl on wht, 15x16" 8.00
Napkin, UP, interwoven logo, block letters, 20x15" 8.50
Napkin, UP, sewn logo, wht on wht, 18" sq 7.00
Napkin, WAB, interwoven flag logo, 22x20" 12.00
Pillowcase, CA Zephyr, pk, reg sz .16.00
Pillowcase, CA Zephyr, wht, reg sz .7.00
Sheet, BN, wht, twin sz 12.00
Sheet, RB, Bond Hotel, twin sz 10.00
Tablecloth, CA Zephyr, interwoven logo in center, lg 12.50
Tablecloth, CN, maple leaf logo, wht, 44x48", EX 24.00
Tablecloth, D&RG, interwoven logo, wht on wht, lg 12.50
Tablecloth, Rio Grande Zephyr, wht on wht, 36x44" 22.50
Towel, Canadian Nat'l, interwoven logo in bl stripe on wht 7.50
Towel, Pullman, bl stripe, Property of..., EX 6.00

Towel, SP, interwoven logo, wht on bl stripe 8.00
Towel, UP, stmp logo, wht w/red border 6.00
Towel, UP, stmp logo, yel, lg 5.00
Towel, 19 Soo Line-Soo Line 23 on bl stripes, 16x20" 27.50

Locks

Road & bridge, UP, Adlake, BR, emb, w/chain, EX 38.00
Signal, B&O, ST, sm body, early, EX .12.00
Signal, RACO, cast BR, +screw-type key 12.00
Signal, SO RY, A&W hexagonal logo, BR, old chain, EX 88.00
Signal, SR, Adams & Westlake, BR, heart shape, EX 70.00
Signal, ST, unmk, w/unmk BR key, EX 8.00
Switch, A&BB, Adlake, BR, modern style, w/chain, EX 27.50
Switch, A&LM, Adlake Standard, ST, dtd 1975, w/chain, EX . .25.00
Switch, B&L, Bohannon, BR, dtd 1887 on hasp, EX 50.00
Switch, B&M, Bohannon #81, BR, heart shape, EX 24.00
Switch, C of GA, JHW Climax, ST, no chain, EX 50.00
Switch, C&NW, BR, heart shape, no chain, EX 37.50
Switch, C&S, ST, w/chain, EX 17.50
Switch, Canadian Nat'l, ST, w/chain & key, EX 35.00
Switch, CV, Adlake, BR, modern style, no chain, EX 32.00
Switch, D&E, Adlake, BR, modern style, NM 36.00
Switch, FJ&G, Bohannon, BR, heart shape, EX 55.00
Switch, HRY, Fraim, BR, heart shape, dtd 1916, EX 58.00
Switch, L&N, Speckmann, ST, heart shape w/hole, early 45.00
Switch, L&N, Standard Steel, EX 17.50
Switch, L&S, Hansl Mfg, BR, heart shape, NM 48.00
Switch, McCloud River, Adlake, ST, dtd 1976, EX 17.50
Switch, McCloud River, Slaymaker, ST, dtd 1963, w/chain, M . .27.50
Switch, Miller Lock, BR, heart shape, NM 32.00
Switch, N&W, Adlake, BR, late 1970s, w/mk key, EX 32.00
Switch, N&W, BR, heart shape, w/chain, w/key, EX 50.00
Switch, N&W, Standard, BR, ornate heart shape, EX 50.00
Switch, NW, American, stainless ST, heavy, EX 17.50
Switch, NYCTS, BR, heart shape, w/lt chain & ST unmk key . .60.00
Switch, OP&E, Yale, BR, ST hasp, heart shape, EX 42.50
Switch, PCSY, Ritchie & Son, BR, heart shape, no chain, EX . .42.00
Switch, SCL, Adlake Standard, ST, EX 17.00
Switch, SCL, mk Master Padlock, no chain, EX 22.00
Switch, SP, BR, serifs, incised bk panel, 1890, EX 55.00
Switch, UP, Adlake, BR, chain dtd 4-63, EX 25.00
Switch, VRY, Edwards, Virginian, no chain, undtd, early 85.00

Silverplate

Change tray, Lackawanna, 1947 BS 65.00
Change tray, SF, fluted edge, BS in English script 47.50
Coffeepot, Fred Harvey, Deco style, mushroom finial 65.00
Coffeepot, Soo Line, R&B, BS, 8-oz 88.00
Coffeepot, UP, Challenger, BS 58.00
Crumber, SP, Broadway, BS, Daylight logo, VG 65.00
Cvg set, UP, Savoy, 9¼" fork & 10½" knife, EX 80.00
Finger bowl, RI, Wallace, 1929 BS 85.00
Fork, dinner; B&M, Meriden, TM, EX 27.50
Fork, dinner; CM, Rex, 7½" 95.00
Fork, dinner; NC&StL, Sierra, R&B, BS 30.00
Fork, pickle; Fred Harvey, Albany 16.00
Fork, SP&S, Gorham, TM, 7½" 32.00
Gravy ladle, SP&S, Gorham, TM, 9" .95.00
Hot food cover, CA Zephyr, oval, BS, 1950, 9½x6½", EX 115.00
Knife, dinner; D&RG, Belmont, TM, EX 7.50
Knife, dinner; GN, intertwined logo, TM, EX 17.50
Knife, dinner; SP&S, Gorham, BS 17.50

Knife, luncheon; SF, Cromwell, TM, 7½" 17.50
Mayonnaise holder, UP, w/attached tray, 1947 . . . . .60.00
Menu holder, UP, Winged Streamliner logo, BS, 1952 . . . . . . .80.00
Spoon, grapefruit; SR, Vassar Standard, R&B, TM 17.50
Spoon, iced tea; SP&S, Gorham, BS .17.50
Spoon, iced tea; SR, Vassar Standard 32.00
Spoon, place; SP, Westfield, Meriden, BS, 1930 . . . . .17.50
Spoon, serving; SP&S, Gorham, TM, 7" 36.00
Spoon, soup; SP, Broadway, BS 17.50
Spoon, tablespoon; NP, Embassy, R&B, TM, BS, M 18.00
Sugar bowl, Atlantic Coast, w/lid, BS .90.00
Sugar bowl, CStPM&O, R&B, hdls, no lid, BS, 11-oz 125.00
Sugar bowl, Lackawanna, w/lid, BS, 8-oz 55.00
Sugar bowl, Pullman, BS, 1933, 7-oz 100.00
Syrup, CA Zephyr, acorn finial, hinged lid, w/tray, BS 200.00
Teapot, Fred Harvey, R&B, BS, ca 1925, 10-oz 115.00
Toast holder, UP, acorn finial, w/lid, BS 35.00
Toothpick holder, CStPM&O in script, ftd, R&B, BS, 3¼" 85.00

Wax Sealers and Accessories

Adams Express, BR toodstool hdl, rnd matrix, EX 85.00
Adams Express Co 8758...KY, BR, mushroom head, EX 145.00
Amer Exp Co Corygon IA, BR oval head, nickel hdl, lt wear . . .85.00
ATSF, Agent, BR head & hdl, mushroom knob, EX 135.00
ATSF, Agent, Gauge OK, tall iron hdl 100.00
C&G, New Hampton IA, hollow BR hdl 130.00
C&S, rnd, bulbous BR head, nickel hdl 150.00
For Public Use, Cheraw CO, oval BR head, hollow BR hdl 45.00
KCS, freight station, Joplin MO, wood hdl 100.00
PW&B, pewter toadstool hdl 90.00
RY Express Agency Inc, BR w/blk wood hdl, EX 45.00

Miscellaneous

Airhorn, Westinghouse, C ST, single chime, bell shape, rpt . . .155.00
Badge, hat; D&RG Conductor, BR, Main Line...Rockies, 4" 88.00
Badge, hat; NYC Transit Conductor, metal, NM 17.50
Badge, hat; OSL, Freight Brakeman, EX 65.00
Bell, Baldwin Diesel Locomotive, C ST, no yoke, 1943, rpt . . .200.00
Booklet, SP, America's Bicentennial Queen, 1975, 52-pg 6.00
Bottle, soda pop; Fred Harvey Newton Kansas emb on gr 25.00
Builder's plate, Baldwin...Works, ST, 1943, 9½" dia 75.00
Button, uniform; RI, silver color, for coat, EX 3.00
Calendar, MP, Diesel, perpetual, metal wall style, NM 140.00
Call card, Railway Express Agency, cb, logo ea side, EX 88.00
Can, oil; N&W, emb tin, EX pnt, 1-gal 30.00
Can, water; Burlington Rte, galvanized, bail hdl, 10", VG 28.00
Cookbook, B&O, What's Cooking on the..., EX 20.00
Fan, parlor car; Pullman, General Electric, wall mt, 1926 . . . . .165.00
Fire extinguisher, SP, copper & brass, 26½" 65.00
Funnel, D&RG, heavy metal, 4", EX 6.00
Guide, shipper's, WM, hardcover, illus, 1920s, EX 22.00
Key, PC, Adlake, lg, NM 9.00
Key, switch; LV, Fraim, BR, some wear, VG 17.00
Ledger, D&RG, CO depot, 1898, 10x17", 50-pg, EX 55.00
Menu, CA Zephyr, children's blocks cover, 4½x5½", EX 22.00
Menu, NYC, special dinner, single card, 1969, 5x6½" 3.50
Menu, UP, Los Angeles, photo cover, 1954, EX 6.00
Money sack, Am Ry Express, wht canvas, pre-1918, EX 30.00
Money sack, CNS&M, cotton, name in blk on wht, 8½x14" . . .17.50
Oiler, engineer's, Johnson-Urbana mk, long spout, EX 38.00
Paperweight, SR, Best friend of Charleston, metal, 1927 . . . . . .88.00
Pass, PRR, military, handwritten, 1865, sm, EX 27.50

Pass, Pullman, plain, 1902 . . . . .18.00
Pass, SR, all stations, 1901 . . . . .18.00
Payroll sheet, B&P, 50+names w/wages, 1860, 17x20", EX 7.50
Pencil, NYC, general office, medium, set of 6, M 5.00
Pin, lapel; RI, silver RI on blk, enamel, 1x¾" 36.00
Pin, lapel; Seaboard System, yel/orange on gold, M 5.00
Pin, lapel; SR, 20-year service, M 16.00
Playing cards, C&O, dbl deck, Chessie & Peake, MIB 22.00
Playing cards, MP, Eagle bks, dbl deck, M 22.00
Receipt, C&S, for apples/meat/etc, 1900, 7x9", EX 5.00
Reward notice, Western Union Telegraph, early, fr, EX 66.00
Rug, Pullman, oval ends, lav & wht on blk, 82x25", EX 60.00
Seal, boxcar; VGN, w/serial # & heavy ST fastener, EX 8.00
Shovel, coal scuttle, Burlington Rte, emb hdl, 4½" 22.50
Sign, Railway Express, porc, cream/red on gr, 2-pc, 6x20" 95.00
Sign, REA Express, rolled ST, wht/gr, 3¾x60" 50.00
Sign, Telegrams, tin, wht/maroon, flanged, 4-sides, 18x31" 80.00
Spittoon, Burlington Rte, CI, 3" flange, 6x8½" 62.50
Spittoon, Dayton Nickeline, BR, fancy, early, NM 48.00
Spittoon, Pullman, nickeled BR, BM, EX 60.00
Step box, Safety Instruction Car, ST, unmk, sm, EX 90.00
Step box, SR, conductor's, ST, 14x16" dimpled top, 25-lb, M . .150.00

Passenger step stool, Northern Pacific, $135.00.

Stickpin, N&W, Safety, enamel on gilt, NM 22.00
Tallow pot, N&W, Eagle, mk on welded ST plate, rpt, EX 27.50
Tie tack, BN, blk & gr, lg 5.00
Timetable, Richmond & Danville, NC employee, 1874, EX 45.00
Timetable, TStL&KC, Clover Leaf Route, public, 1891, EX 25.00
Token, WAB, Century of Service to Decatur IL, 1854-1954 . . . . .8.00
Torch, Burlington Rte, mk, long 9" hdl, EX 16.00
Trust plate, ACL, emb ST, EX orig 17.50
Trust plate, CNO&TP, emb ST, silver rpt, EX 28.00
Whistle, brass dome type, 3-chime, 15" 375.00
Whistle, caboose bk-up; Sherburne, Pat 1910, EX 36.00
Wrench, C&O, ST, open, dbl ends, SM, sm, EX 8.00
Wrench, N&W, machinist's, adjustable, ST, 20", EX 26.00

Razors

As straight razors gain in popularity, prices increase. And with the lure of investment appreciation, the novice or the speculator sometimes find themselves making purchases that later prove to be unwise. It is important to be able to recognize the material of which the handle is made. This has

a great bearing on value, and imitations abound. Learn to distinguish between celluloid and genuine ivory. Razors with plain celluloid handles are practically worthless unless the blade carries a desirable trademark. Those with decorations of scrollwork, leaves and vines, or decorative metal on each end fall into the $8 to $12 price range. Even plain ivory-handled razors are not especially valuable unless the blade is well marked and from a good manufacturer. On a more positive note, celluloid-handled razors with designs such as castles, windmills, nudes, deer, alligators, automobiles, horses, cowboys, peacocks, and various kinds of birds, etc., are very desirable — some more than others — and are usually worth from $25 to $50 to collectors. Those with a figural handle such as a fish, shotgun, eagle, or a barber pole might be worth in excess of $100 for an especially nice example. Ivory, on the other hand, is rarely found; if the carvings are well done, clean, undamaged specimens should start at about $100 and escalate according to the intricacy of the design.

Buffalo horn is sometimes mistakenly called bone. It is usually black, translucent tan, or gray. Though plain handles are worth very little, the early heat-molded examples with a motif such as mentioned above often sell for more than $100. In the same range are mother-of-pearl and stag (deer horn) handles; very elaborate designs go even higher, but watch for imitations.

There is one imitation, however, that is highly desirable. That is jigged bone made to look like stag. This material is rough textured and dyed a handsome tan or brown; usually examples with these handles sell in the $40 to $75 range. Razors with wooden handles are very rare, but even those from the 1800s are worth only about $35, since they are usually very plain. Twentieth-century examples are only valued at around $15. Don't be fooled by buffalo horn colored in imitation of tortoise — and you'll find celluloid imitations, too. Genuine tortoise handles are worth from $25 to $100 depending on age, condition, and workmanship. Sterling razors are valued at $75 and up, but make sure they are marked 'sterling.' Even if you were to mistake aluminum for silver, those with relief-cast designs are worth $50 to $75 — only $20 or so if the design is incised.

Corn razors were made to pare troublesome corns on the feet. They are a bit smaller and if plain worth a little more than full-size razors. Fancy examples are generally not worth as much as their full-size couterparts.

The older blades are wedge-shaped (flat-sided) in cross-section; hollow-ground blades (made after 1880) are concave. Generally speaking, those etched with words are only worth a little more than a plain, common blade. Try to find those with people, places, and things — the more famous, the better.

Key:
cell — celluloid   bd — blade

Benito, faux ivory hdl: Mussolini bust inlay, EX 40.00
Canton Cutlery, photographic picture hdl: dancing girl, EX 50.00
Case Brothers, etched bd, tang stamped Tested, bl hdl, EX 30.00
Cattaraugus, etched bd, faux ivory hdl: goddess, EX 30.00
Clauss Fremont, faux ivory hdl w/Gunstock pattern, EX 32.00
Crawick, Piccadilly, hollow-ground bd, ivory hdl, +case 85.00
E&M Aboussleman, faux ivory hdl: German silver butterfly 36.00
Ern, etched bd: Blue Steel, faux ivory hdl: elk on ridge 40.00
Ern, etched bd: Mignon, MOP hdl: 11 panels ea side, EX 150.00
Ern, etched bd: Rattler, faux ivory hdl: peacock, EX 40.00
G Wostenholm, Sheffield, Nouveau-style silver hdl, EX 275.00
H Boker, faux ivory hdl: German silver butterfly inlay, EX 45.00
Hamilton, etch hollow-ground bd, cell hdl: semi-nude w/rope . .40.00
Imperial Warranted, blk cell hdl: silver wire & MOP inlay 50.00
Imperial Warranted, hollow-ground bd, cell hdl: florals, EX 40.00
John Primble, etched bd: Belnap's...Patent, faux ivory hdl 30.00
Jones, ivory scales, folding pocket, early, 4" closed, EX 66.00
Joseph Elliot Fine Indian Steel, wedge bd, blk horn hdl 30.00
JR Torry, faux ivory hdl: German silver cowboy inlay, EX 65.00

Gold letters pressed into handle, ca 1850s, $35.00.

Lafayette Cutlery, Germany, faux ivory hdl: nude on man's bk . . **40.00**
Melchior, Solingen, mk tang, faux ivory hdl: Adolf Hitler **65.00**
Mooney & Moyer, blk hard rubber hdl: lady w/flowing hair **25.00**
Norvell Shapleigh Hdwe, etched bd, hdl: nude on lily pad **40.00**
Oxford, etched bd, faux ivory hdl: windmill scene, EX colors . . . **50.00**
Oxford, Germany, blk cell hdl: 3 deer in relief, EX **40.00**
Parker, etched bd: Union...Preserved, MOP & brass hdl, EX **80.00**
Parker Cutlery, etched bd: Improved Eagle, bone/silver hdl **25.00**
Pep, faux tortoise shell hdl: MOP escutcheon & brass trim **17.50**
Robeson Shuredge, etched bd, faux ivory hdl: fishscales, EX . . . **36.00**
Rudolf Schmidt Solingen, faux tortoise shell hdl, etched bd . . . **22.00**
Shumade, ground bd, faux ivory hdl: flowers & scrolls, EX **32.00**
Smith, Lyon & Field, etched bd, faux ivory hdl: ear of corn **45.00**
Superfine, mk tang, blk cell hdl: MOP inlay, EX **35.00**
Unmk, faux ivory hdl: castle scene, EX colors **32.00**
Van Camp Hdwe & Iron Co, etched bd: Eversharp, blk cell hdl . **40.00**
Wade & Butcher, ground bd, 3-pc MOP cvd hdl w/brass liners . **150.00**
Wade & Butcher, Sheffield, etched wedge bd: eagle, horn hdl . **25.00**
Wade & Butcher, Sheffield, framebk bd, mk blk horn hdl **20.00**
Wadsworth, clean bd, faux ivory cell hdl: geometrics, EX **17.50**
Washington, hollow-ground bd, aluminum hdl: Nouveau lady . **110.00**
Waterville Cutlery, faux ivory hdl: owl in relief, rare, EX **35.00**
WH Morley & Son, etched bd: Barber's Friend, faux ivory hdl . **40.00**
Wilbert Cutlery, etched bd: elk, yel & brn cell hdl, EX **15.00**
Winchester, hollow-ground bd, transparent orange hdl **50.00**
Wm Elliot, faux ivory hdl: windmill scene, clean bd, EX **12.50**
Worcester, faux ivory hdl: peacock w/EX colors, EX bd **45.00**
Worthington, Cleveland, faux ivory hdl: German silver inlay . . . **30.00**

Reamers

Reamers have been made in hundreds of styles and colors and by as many manufacturers. Their purpose is to extract the juices from lemons, oranges, and grapefruits. The largest producer of glass reamers was McKee, who pressed their products from many types of glass — custard; delphite and Chalaine blue; opaque white; Skokie green; black; caramel and white opalescent; Seville yellow; and transparent pink, green, and clear. Among these, the black and the caramel opalescents are the most valuable.

The Fry Glass Company also made reamers that are today very collectible. Their vaseline glass juicers with embossed lettering, both the straight-sided and ruffled-top models, are valued at well over $200. The Hazel Atlas Crisscross orange reamer in pink often brings in excess of $175; the same in blue, $150. Hocking produced a light blue orange reamer and, in the same soft hue, a two-piece reamer and measuring cup combination. Both are considered rare and very valuable with currently-quoted estimates at $350 and up for the former and $400 and up for the latter. In addition to the colors mentioned, red glass examples — transparent or slag — are rare and costly.

Among the most valuable ceramic reamers are those made by Ameri-

can potteries. The Spongeband reamer by Red Wing is valued in excess of $350; Coorsite reamers with gold or silver trim are worth $200 and up. Figurals are popular — Mickey Mouse and John Bull may bring $200 to $300. Others range from $45 to $150. Fine china one- and two-piece reamers are also very desirable and command very respectable prices.

A word about reproductions: A series of limited edition reamers is being made by Edna Barnes of Uniontown, Ohio. These are all marked with a 'B' in a circle. Other repoductions have been made from old molds. The most important of these are: Anchor Hocking 2-piece, 2-cup measure and top; Westmoreland 4-cup measure embossed with orange and lemons; Duboe; Easley's diamonds 1-piece; and spiral 1-piece #202.

Our advisor for this category is Dee Long; she is listed in the Directory under Illinois. For more information concerning reamers and reproductions, contact our advisor or the National Reamer Collectors Association (see Clubs, Newsletters, and Catalogs).

Reference numbers in the ceramic reamer listings correspond with *200 Years of Reamers* by Mary Walker, available at your local library or bookstore.

Ceramic

Bees, Japan, 2-pc **50.00**
Bl Willow, Japan, 2-pc **100.00**
Clown figural, C-25, 6½" **38.00**
Clown figural, C-29, 7½" **40.00**
Duck figural, Japan **35.00**
Floral, mc on wht, Japan, T-89, 3¾" **40.00**
Germany, china, 2-pc **60.00**
Japan, 2-pc **35.00**
Mexican face, paper label, F-49 . . . . **45.00**
Mexican w/cactus figural, Japan **105.00**
Monkey face figural, Japan **95.00**
Nippon, china, 2-pc **110.00**
Pitcher form w/florals, P-29, 8" **24.00**
Royal Rudolstadt, china, 2-pc **150.00**
RS Germany, china, 2-pc **150.00**
Shelly, china, 2-pc **95.00**
Sourpuss, Japan, 1-pc **100.00**
Tan w/gr leaves, brn hdl, D-40, 4¼" **30.00**
Tomato shape, Japan, 2-pc **45.00**
Yel w/gr leaves, L-39, 4½" **42.00**

Glass

Cambridge, crystal **10.00**
Cambridge, crystal, Easley Pat July 10, 1888; Sept 10, 1889 . . . . . **15.00**
Easley, Pat July 10, 1888 . . . . **20.00**
Federal, amber, tab hdl, ribbed, seed dam, amber **25.00**
Federal, loop hdl, ribbed, pk **35.00**
Federal, lt turq **45.00**
Federal, ruffled top, opal **45.00**
Federal, ruffled top, vaseline **125.00**
Federal, tab hdl, plain side, amber **250.00**
Fenton, baby, sun-colored amethyst **60.00**
Fenton, pitcher+reamer, red **600.00**
Fleur, opal amberina **350.00**
Fry, emerald gr **28.00**
Fry, Re-Go, gr **400.00**
Fry, Re-Go, opal wht **400.00**
Hazel Atlas, pitcher+reamer, cobalt bl, 2-cup **225.00**
Hazel Atlas, pitcher+reamer, wht w/trim, 2-cup **25.00**
Hazel Atlas, pitcher+reamer, wht w/trim, 4-cup **35.00**
Hazel Atlas, tab hdl, lemon reamer, gr **7.00**
Hazel Atlas, tab hdl, lemon reamer, wht w/red trim **20.00**

Hazel Atlas Crisscross, orange reamer, pk 200.00
Hocking, pk, 2-cup, 2-pc 150.00
Indiana, amber 100.00
Jeannette, Jennyware, Delphite bl 70.00
Jeannette, Jennyware, pk 65.00
Jeannette, Jennyware, ultra-marine 75.00
Jeannette, loop hdl, gr, lg 15.00
Jeannette, loop hdl, yellowish jadite, lg 25.00
Jeannette, pitcher+reamer, lt jadite, 2-cup 20.00
MacBeth-Evans Glass Co 300.00
McKee, grapegruit, jadite 100.00
McKee, unemb, pointed cone, custard, 5¼" 25.00

Party Line by Paden City, with 4-cup pitcher, in amber: $250.00; in turquoise: $200.00.

Silver & Co, NY, Little Handy Lemon Squeezer, 6½" 85.00
Sunkist, emb letters, chocolate 400.00
Sunkist, emb letters, dk Chalaine bl .125.00
Sunkist, emb letters, dk jadite 250.00
Sunkist, emb letters, Seville yel 50.00
Sunkist, ultramarine, rare 800.00
Sunkist, unemb, clear 85.00
US Glass, orange juice extractor, wht 25.00
US Glass, slick hdl, amber 500.00
Valencia, unemb, pk-amber 150.00
Westmoreland, baby, gr, 2-pc 150.00
Westmoreland, boat shaped, clambroth, N-391 . . . . .225.00
Westmoreland, flattened loop hdl, amber 220.00
Westmoreland, flattened loop hdl, crystal w/decor 75.00
Westmoreland, Jenkins, baby, gr 95.00

Records

Records of interest to collectors are generally not the million-selling hits by 'superstars.' Very few records by Bing Crosby, for example, are of any more than nominal value, and those that are valuable usually don't even have his name on the label! Collectors today are most interested in records that were made in limited quantities, early works of a performer who later became famous, and those issued in special series or aimed at a limited market. These are bringing prices well in excess of their original cost. The most widely-collected categories are Jazz, Dance Bands, Celebrity, Blues, Rhythm and Blues, Country and Western, Hillbilly, Rockabilly, and Rock 'N Roll.

Note: LPs and EPs (Extended Play 45 rpm) must be in their original jackets, without which they are often unsaleable at any price.

Our advisor for this category is L.R. Docks, author of *American Premium Record Guide*, which lists 50,000 records by over 6,000 artists; you will find his address in the Directory under Texas.

Key:
Bru — Brunswick   Para — Paramount
Ch — Champion   Orch—Orchestra
Col — Columbia   Vi — Victor
Edi — Edison   Vo — Vocalion

Edison long-playing (24 minutes at 80 rpm), ca 1927, $25.00.

Blues, Rhythm and Blues, Rock 'N Roll, Rockabilly

Ace, Johnny; Pledging My Love, Duke 136, 45 rpm 6.00
Albert, Mel; Sugar Plum, Apollo 530, 45 rpm 10.00
Alexander, Ora; Sweetest Daddy in. . . , Col 14626-D, 78 rpm . .25.00
Ames, Tessie; Rider Blues, Silvertone 3565, 78 rpm 20.00
Anderson, Billy; Adam & Eve, Col 14216-D, 78 rpm 20.00
Andrews, Mose; Ten Pound Hammer, Decca 7338, 78 rpm 20.00
Archibald, Great Big Eyes, Imperial 5212, 45 rpm 18.00
Armstrong, May; Joe Boy Blues, Bru 7010, 78 rpm 30.00
Atcher, Bob; Early American Folksongs, Col 9006, LP 12.00
Autry, Gene; Western Classics, Col 9001, LP 10.00
Bailey, Kid; Rowdy Blues, Bru 7114, 78 rpm 200.00
Baker, Katherine; Chicago Fire Blues, Gennett 6157, 78 rpm . .40.00
Baker, Willie; Bad Luck Moan, Gennett 6812, 78 rpm 100.00
Barnes, Fay; Good-Bye Blues, Para 12099, 78 rpm 12.00
Barnes, Willie; My Gal Treats Me Mean, Ch 15378, 78 rpm 50.00
Beach Boys, Surfin', Candix 301, 45 rpm 50.00
Beatles, Ain't She Sweet, Atco 169, LP 20.00
Beatty, EC; Little Blue Eyes, Colonial 7009, 45 rpm 7.00
Big Oscar, Mistreatment Blues, Decca 7067, 78 rpm 12.00
Bigeou, Esther; Stingaree Blues, Okeh 8025, 78 rpm 10.00
Bill, Georgia; Georgia Rag, Okeh 8924, 78 rpm 125.00
Billy & Lilly, La Dee Dah, Swan 4002, 78 rpm 7.00
Blendtones, Lilly, MGM 12782, 45 rpm 12.00
Blue Angels, Deserie, Edsel 781, 45 rpm 12.00
Bogan, Lucille; Coffee Grindin' Blues, Bru 7083, 78 rpm 30.00
Boyd, Ernie; I Gotta Find My Baby, Regal 3305, 78 rpm 11.00
Brady, Jean; My Mellow Man, Okeh 06254, 78 rpm 6.00
Brown, Gene; Big Door, Dot 15709, 45 rpm 9.00
Brown, Roy; Deep Sea Diver, Gold Star 636, 78 rpm 9.00
Burleson, Hattie; Dead Lover Blues, Para 13050, 78 rpm 75.00
Cadillacs, White Gardenia, Capitol 4825, 45 rpm 8.00
Cagle, Aubrey; Be Bop Blues, Glee 100, 45 rpm 25.00
Calicott, Joe; Fare Thee Well Blues, Bru 7166, 78 rpm 110.00

Carter, George; Hot Jelly Roll Blues, Para 12750, 78 rpm 90.00
Carver Boys, No One To Welcome Me..., Para 3182, 78 rpm ..35.00
Chandler, Wayland; Little Lover, 4 Star 1716, 45 rpm 7.00
Chiles, Buddy; Jet Black Woman, Gold Star 660, 78 rpm 12.00
Cline, Patsy; Patsy Cline, Decca 8611, LP 12.00
Cochran, Eddie; Skinny Jim, Crest 1026, 45 rpm 25.00
Coleman, Walter; Smack That Thing, Decca 7157, 78 rpm 25.00
Collins Kids, Party, Col 41012, 45 rpm 12.50
Craig, Pee Wee; Rambling Man, Choice 1000, 45 rpm 13.00
Curry, Ben; Fat Mouth Blues, Para 13118, 78 rpm 125.00
Darty, Chuck; My Steady Girl, Chart 642, 45 rpm 18.00
Davis, Genevieve; I've Got Something, Victor 20648, 78 rpm ..35.00
Day, Ruth; Painful Blues, Col 14642-D, 78 rpm 25.00
Dells, Tell the World, Vee Vays 134, 45 rpm 250.00
Demar, Jerry; Cross-Eyed Alley Cat, Ford 501, 45 rpm 25.00
Dexter, Al; Songs of the Southwest, Col 9005, LP 17.50
Diadems, Why Don't You Believe Me, Star 514, 45 rpm 9.00
Domino, Fats; Cheatin', Imperial 5220, 45 rpm 14.00
Douglass, Glenn; Heartbreak, Decca 8748, LP 17.00
Dylan, Bob; Corrina Corrina, Col 42656, 45 rpm 40.00
Erby, Jack; Hot Peter, Col 14570-D, 78 rpm 17.00
Everett, Bracey; The Lover's Curse, Atlantic 2013, 45 rpm 10.00
Felts, Derrell; Lookie Lookie Lookie, Okeh 7118, 45 rpm 10.00
Gibson, Clifford; Jive Me Blues, Bluebird 5110, 78 rpm 25.00
Grandpa Jones, Greatest Hits, King 554, LP 10.00
Gray, Billy; Tennessee Toddy, Decca 29800, 45 rpm 7.00
Gray, Geneva; Fortune Teller Blues, Okeh 8449, 78 rpm 25.00
Hawkins, Buddy Boy; Number Three Blues, Para 12475, 78 rpm .65.00
Henderson, Katherine; If You Like Me, Para 12840, 78 rpm 85.00
Hinton, Otis; Walkin' Down the Hill, Timely 1003, 45 rpm 18.00
Houston, Emerson; Hard Luck Blues, Bluebird 5791, 78 rpm 35.00
Hunter, Lee; Lee's Boogie, Gold Star 651, 78 rpm 15.00
Johnson, Lil; Keep On Knocking, Bluebird 6112, 78 rpm 8.00
Johnson, Louise; All Night Long Blues, Para 12992, 78 rpm ...100.00
Jones, Jake; Monkeyin' Around, Bru 7130, 78 rpm 35.00
Jordan, Jimmy; Jelly Killed Old Sam, Col 14622-D, 78 rpm 25.00
Largos, I Wonder Why, Dot 16292, 45 rpm 8.50
Little Brother, Sorrowful Blues, Bluebird 7277, 78 rpm 25.00
Mack, Mary; You Drink Too Much, Vo 03462, 78 rpm 8.00
Maphis, Joe; Guitar Rock & Roll, Col 21518, 45 rpm 8.50
McCravy, James; Shove It Up There, Col 14641-D, 78 rpm 14.00
McDonald, Skeets; Goin' Steady, Capitol 1040, LP 30.00
Miles, Josie; Lovin' Henry Blues, Ajax 17057, 78 rpm 30.00
Moroccans, Believe in Tomorrow, Salem 1014, 45 rpm 60.00
Nettles, Bill; Wine-O-Boogie, Starday 174, 45 rpm 12.00
Porter, Sonny; Deck Hand Blues, Col 14366-D, 78 rpm 12.00
Self, Ronnie; Big Fool, Col 40875, 45 rpm 10.00
Smith, Ethel; Jelly Roll Mill, Ch 16613, 78 rpm 50.00
Tampa Kid, Keep On Trying, Decca 7278, 78 rpm 10.00
Taylor, Vernon; I've Got the Blues, Dot 15632, 45 rpm 6.50
The Evergreens, Very Truly Yours, Chart 605, 45 rpm 25.00
The Five Jades, Without Your Love, Duke 188, 45 rpm 10.00
Walker, Willie; South Carolina Rag, Col 14578-D, 78 rpm 35.00

Country and Western

Alabama Four, Looking This Way, Broadway 8209, 78 rpm 7.00
Allen Brothers, New Salty Dog, Vi 23514, 78 rpm 20.00
Arkansas Charlie, Goodbye Old Paint, Vo 5270, 78 rpm 9.00
Baker, Buddy; Box Car Blues, Vi 21549, 78 rpm 12.00
Baker, Charles; Just Plain Folks, Ch 16614, 78 rpm 10.00
Banjo Joe, Engineer Joe, Col 15238-D, 78 rpm 12.00
Barlow, Jerry; Just Thinking of You, Lyric 703, 78 rpm 5.00
Bently Boys, Henhouse Blues, Col 15565-D, 78 rpm 25.00

Bishop, Billy; Medley of Old Favorites, Ch 15331, 78 rpm 6.00
Blankenship Family, Jack & Me, Vi 23583, 78 rpm 25.00
Blue, Bud; Blind Mother's Prayer, Okeh 45254, 78 rpm 7.00
Boone, Jimmy; The Cowboy Song, Superior 2831, 78 rpm 25.00
Brown, Oscar; You're a Little Too Small, Ch 15523, 78 rpm 12.00
Carter, Floyd; Flemington Kidnap Trial, Oriole 8847, 78 rpm 6.00
Carter Family, My Dixie Darling, Decca 5240, 78 rpm 8.50
Chase, Chezz; Log Cabin Blues, Para 3178, 78 rpm 6.50
Childre, Lew; Moonshine Blues, Gennett 7183, 78 rpm 25.00
Cross, Ballard; My Poodle Dog, Vo 5359, 78 rpm 8.00
Dandurand, Tommy; Buffalo Gal, Gennett 6273, 78 rpm 14.00
Davis, Stan; The Body in the Bag, Okeh 45401, 78 rpm 12.00
Davis Trio, Sleepy Hollow, Para 3238, 78 rpm 20.00
Dixie Crackers, The Old Bell Cow, Para 3151, 78 rpm 15.00
Elmer & Jud, Turkey in the Straw, Oriole 1414, 78 rpm 6.50
Ferguson, John; Railroad Daddy, Challenge 159, 78 rpm 12.00
Georgia Crackers, Diamond Joe, Okeh 40598, 78 rpm 12.00
Godwin, Shorty; Turnip Greens, Col 15411-D, 78 rpm 8.00
Golden, Dan; Good Old Turnip Greens, Ch 15525, 78 rpm 12.00
Hammond, John; Little Birdie, Supertone 9249, 78 rpm 8.00
Happy Jack, I'm Only Suggesting This, Col 15720-D, 78 rpm ...9.00
Harkins & Owens, A Mother's Plea, Broadway 8214, 78 rpm ..10.00
Harris, Earl; Gene, The Fighting Marine, Okeh 45566, 78 rpm ...7.00
Harris, JD; Cackling Hen, Okeh 45024, 78 rpm 12.00
Hobbs Brothers, Devil's Dream, Para 3219, 78 rpm 9.00
Jackson, Jack; I'm Just a Black Sheep, Col 15497-D, 78 rpm ...10.00
Kentucky Ramblers, Some Mother's Boy, Para 3300, 78 rpm 30.00
Kincaid, Bradley; House Carpenter, Bluebird 5255, 78 rpm 6.00
Kutter, Don; Two Little Orphans, Challenge 326, 78 rpm 9.00
Marlow, Andy; My Little Lady, Ch 15875, 78 rpm 18.00
Martin, Dan; The Cross-Eyed Butcher, Superior 2824, 78 rpm ..10.00
McGee, Dennis; Myself, Vo 5348, 78 rpm 20.00
Montana Slim, Yodeling Cowgirl, Bluebird 6827, 78 rpm 6.00
Moore, Byrd; Hobo's Paradise, Gennett 6549, 78 rpm 40.00
Newman, Fred; San Antonio, Para 3177, 78 rpm 12.00
Noack, Eddie; Triflin' Mama Blues, Gold Star 1352, 78 rpm 10.00
Oakley, Jesse; Aged Mother, Supertone 9243, 78 rpm 10.00
Peterson's Hobo Orch, Submarine Waltz, Vi 20677, 78 rpm 7.00
Pickard, Obed; Kitty Wells, Col 15141-D, 78 rpm 9.00
Pickett, Will; It Can't Be Done, Bell 1169, 78 rpm 12.00
Prairie Ramblers, Blue River, Bluebird 5302, 78 rpm 8.00
Pyle, Pete; Talking the Blues, Bullet 602, 78 rpm 5.00
Red Headed Fiddlers, The Steely Rag, Bru 526, 78 rpm 25.00
Reeves & Moody, Sweet Evelina, Vi 21188, 78 rpm 7.00
Ritter, Tex; Bill the Bar Fly, Decca 5305, 78 rpm 7.00
Salem Highballers, Going On to Town, Okeh 45455, 78 rpm ...12.00
Sisson, Allen; Walking Water, Edison 51559, 78 rpm 9.00
Steve's Hot Shots, The Press, Vi 40308, 78 rpm 25.00
Sweet Brother, I Got a Bull Dog, Gennett 6620, 78 rpm 25.00
Thompson, Ernest; Are You From Dixie, Col 130-D, 78 rpm 8.00
Toombs, Jack; Pin Ball Fever, Speed 111, 78 rpm 10.00
Turner, Lemuel; Jake Bottle Blues, Vi 40052, 78 rpm 18.00
Wanner, Enos; Strawberry Roan, Superior 2722, 78 rpm 25.00
Ward, Tommy; Mississippi River Blues, Superior 2689, 78 rpm ..30.00
Watson, Harvey; A Mother's Advice, Ch 15299, 78 rpm 9.00
Watson, Tom; Georgia Railroad, Silvertone 3262, 78 rpm 8.00
Weaver Brothers, Prison Sorrows, Col 15487-D, 78 rpm 12.00
Weber, Dan; Fair Florella, Superior 2527, 78 rpm 25.00
West, CA; Oh Willie Come Back, Supertone 9650, 78 rpm 7.00
White, Reuben; Old Sefus Brown, Challenge 336, 78 rpm 8.00
Wilkins, Frank; The Last Mile, Broadway 8205, 78 rpm 10.00
Williams, Marc; Willie the Weeper, Bru 240, 78 rpm 10.00
Wyatt & Brandon, Evalina, Col 15523-D, 78 rpm 12.00
Yates, Ira & Eugene; Sarah Jane, Col 15581-D, 78 rpm 15.00

Young, Clarence; That's a Plenty, Ch 15991, 78 rpm 12.00

Jazz, Dance Bands, Personalities

Abrams, Irwin; & Orch, The Co-Ed, Edi 51633, 78 rpm 10.00

Addison, Bernard; Toledo Shuffle, Bluebird 6174, 78 rpm 8.00

Alabama Fuzzy Wuzzies, Congo Stomp, Ch 15415, 78 rpm 100.00

Albert, Don; & Orch, True Blue Lou, Vo 3401, 78 rpm 10.00

All-Star Orch, Chloe, Vi 21149, 78 rpm 6.00

Ambassadors, You've Never Been Blue, Vo 15793, 78 rpm 6.00

Arnheim, Gus; & Orch, The Image of You, Bru 7900, 78 rpm 8.50

Astaire, Fred; A Fine Romance, Bru 7716, 78 rpm 7.00

Atlanta Syncopators, Lead Pipe Blues, Madison 50015, 78 rpm . .9.00

Austin, Gene; I Cried for You, Decca 926, 78 rpm 7.00

Austin, Lovie; Heebie Jeebies, Para 12283, 78 rpm 35.00

Babs & Her Brothers, Double Trouble, Decca 518, 78 rpm 9.00

Baby Mack, What Kind of Man Is You, Okeh 8313, 78 rpm 25.00

Bailey, William; Squeeze Me, Banner 1563, 78 rpm 20.00

Barbecue Pete, Avenue Strut, Ch 15904, 78 rpm 40.00

Barrel House Five Orch, Hot Lovin', Para 12851, 78 rpm 60.00

Beasley, Irene; Choo Choo Train, Vi 21467, 78 rpm 8.00

Booker Orch, Salty Dog, Gennett 6375, 78 rpm 50.00

Broadway Pickers, Salty Dog, Broadway 5069, 78 rpm 85.00

Brown, Les; & Orch, Swamp Fire, Decca 1231, 78 rpm 5.00

Call, Bob; Thirty-One Blues, Bru 7137, 78 rpm 60.00

Candy & Coco, Kingfish Blues, Vo 2833, 78 rpm 18.00

Casa Loma Orch, Lazy Day, Bru 6311, 78 rpm 8.50

Chicago Stompers, Wild Man Stomp, Ch 16297, 78 rpm 50.00

Coleman, EL; Steel String Blues, Okeh 8216, 78 rpm 18.00

Cooper, Robert; West Dallas Drag, Bluebird 5459, 78 rpm 12.00

Crosstown Ramblers, River Bottom Glide, Ch 15030, 78 rpm . . .18.00

Davis, Julia; Black Hand Blues, Para 12248, 78 rpm 25.00

Dixie Jazz Hounds, Waitin' Around, Domino 329, 78 rpm 18.00

Drew, George; & Orch, Hard Luck, Superior 2829, 78 rpm 25.00

Effros, Bob; Tin Ear, Bru 4620, 78 rpm 12.00

Etting, Ruth; Close You Eyes, Bru 6657, 78 rpm 6.00

Finnie, Ethel; Hula Blues, Ajax 17027, 78 rpm 18.00

Five Rythm Kings, Minnie the Moocher, Vi 23269, 78 rpm 25.00

Garland, Judy; Sleep, My Baby, Sleep; Decca 1796, 78 rpm 6.00

Gibson, Cleo; Nothing But Blues, Okeh 8700, 78 rpm 30.00

Goodman, Benny; & Orch, Jungle Blues, Bru 4013, 78 rpm 12.00

Grainger, Porter; In Harlem's Araby, Ajax 17039, 78 rpm 25.00

Green Parrot Inn Orch, At Sundown, Ch 15322, 78 rpm 10.00

Gulf Coast Trio, Grand Opera Blues, Buddy 8041, 78 rpm 30.00

Harmaniac Five, Harmaniac Blues, Para 20476, 78 rpm 30.00

Hawley, Bill; Delores, Vi 21383, 78 rpm 8.00

Herwin Hot Shots, Salty Dog, Herwin 93015, 78 rpm 85.00

Hines, Earl; Blue Drag, Bru 6345, 78 rpm 10.00

Howell, Bert; You're Driving Me Crazy, Para 13063, 78 rpm 18.00

Ipana Troubadours, Glorianna, Col 1638-D, 78 rpm 19.00

James, Madelyn; Long Time Blues, Bru 7155, 78 rpm 30.00

King, Frances; She's Got It, Okeh 40854, 78 rpm 8.00

KXYZ Novelty Band, Indiana, Bluebird 5868, 78 rpm 12.00

Langford, Frances; Moon Song, Bluebird 5016, 78 rpm 6.00

Lanin, Sam; & Orch, My Pet, Cameo 8225, 78 rpm 7.00

Leroy's Dallas Band, Tampa Shout, Col 14402-D, 78 rpm 35.00

Lewis, Alfred; Friday Moan Blues, Vo 1498, 78 rpm 40.00

Lill's Hot Shots, Drop That Sack, Vo 1037, 78 rpm 85.00

Louisiana Stompers, Hop Off, Para 12550, 78 rpm 40.00

Mariners, Happy Feet, Okeh 41433, 78 rpm 8.00

Mater, Frank; Doin' the Raccoon, Harmony 759-H, 78 rpm 7.00

Metomkin Inn Orch, So Long, Ch 15458, 78 rpm 9.00

Miller, Emmett; Lovin' Sam, Okeh 41305, 78 rpm 8.00

Mississippi Maulers, My Angeline, Col 1545-D, 78 rpm 10.00

Morse, Lee; It's the Girl!, Col 2497-D, 78 rpm 10.00

Musical Trio, Beale Street Blues, Madison 1920, 78 rpm 7.00

New Orleans Owls, The Owls' Hoot, Col 605-D, 78 rpm 18.00

Noble, Ray; & Orch, Crazy Rhythm, Bru 8098, 78 rpm 7.00

Nowlin, Sam; So What, Ch 16828, 78 rpm 20.00

Olsen, Ole; & Orch, Take Your Time, Perfect 14691, 78 rpm . . .10.00

Original Indiana Five, Brown Sugar, Bell 463, 78 rpm 13.00

Original Memphis Five, Chinese Blues, Bru 3039, 78 rpm 10.00

Original Wolverines, Shim-Me-Sha-Wabble, Bru 3707, 78 rpm .13.00

Pendleton, Andy; Sweet Emmaline, Okeh 8625, 78 rpm 8.00

Perkins, Gertrude; Gold Daddy Blues, Col 14313-D, 78 rpm 17.00

Red Hot Syncopators, Heebie Jeebies, Bell 456, 78 rpm 18.00

Rounders, Lovable & Sweet, Regal 8831, 78 rpm 7.00

Savage, Helen; It's Bad for Your Soul, Bru 4536, 78 rpm 35.00

Seven Missing Links, Angry, Perfect 14480, 78 rpm 6.00

Sioux City Six, Flock O' Blues, Gennett 5569, 78 rpm 75.00

Six Jolly Jesters, Oklahoma Stomp, Vo 1449, 78 rpm 22.00

South Street Trio, Dallas Blues, Vi 21135, 78 rpm 25.00

Stompin' Six, Jimtown Blues, Sunset 1098, 78 rpm 125.00

Ten Black Berries, St Louis Blues, Oriole 2089, 78 rpm 10.00

Tennessee Tooters, Crazy Quilt, Vo 15487, 78 rpm 11.00

Three T's, I'se a Muggin', Vi 25273, 78 rpm 7.00

University Six, Desdemona, Harmony 37-H, 78 rpm 8.00

Wallace, Ted; & Orch, Love & Kisses, Okeh 40850, 78 rpm 8.00

Washboard Trio, Washboard Rag, Para 12682, 78 rpm 40.00

Watson, El; Bay Rum Blues, Vi 21585, 78 rpm 30.00

Jelly-Roll Morton & His Red Hot Peppers, Strokin' Away, ca 1930s, $75.00.

Red Wing

The Red Wing Stoneware Company, founded in 1878, took its name from its location in Red Wing, Minnesota. In the 1920s, the name was changed to the Red Wing Union Stoneware Company after a merger with several of the other local potteries. For the most part they produced utilitarian wares such as flowerpots, crocks, and jugs. Their early 1930s catalogs offered a line of art pottery vases in colored glazes, some of which featured handles modeled after swan's necks, snakes, or female nudes. Other examples were quite simple, often with classic styling. After the addition of their dinnerware lines in the early thirties, 'Stoneware' was dropped from the name, and the company became known as Red Wing Potteries, Inc. They closed in 1967. For further study we recommend *Red Wing Stoneware, An Identification and Value Guide*, and *Red Wing Collectibles* by Dan and Gail DePasquale and Larry Peterson, available at your local library or bookstore.

Key:
MN — Minnesota   RW — Red Wing
NS — North Star   RWUS — Red Wing Union
                                        Stoneware

Brushware

Bowl, 5"	20.00
Bread crock, sheaves of wheat, lg	400.00
Flowerpot, ribbons & berries, 10"	50.00
Mug	30.00
Pitcher, lady w/harp, gr int	105.00
Planter, daffodils	25.00
Planter, geometrics	32.00
Syrup dispenser	100.00
Umbrella stand, floral	125.00
Vase, cherub	75.00
Vase, oak leaves, rnd w/sq hdls, collar neck	40.00

Commercial Art Ware

Ash tray, wing shape, maroon	15.00
Basket, red speckled, hanging, 4½"	9.00
Bowl, console; #1620	8.00
Bowl, console; oval, 15x10", +fawn flower frog, #526, 10½"	28.00
Bowl, console; pk, +candle holder	10.00
Bowl, rose, gray int, hdls	15.00
Candle holder, #1629	5.00
Candle holder, hooded shell, ivory, #980, 8"	30.00
Candlestick, gr & tan mottle, stick style, 6", pr	10.00
Flower frog, angel fish, wht	45.00
Flower frog, deer, ivory/tan	55.00
Lamp, gr, #872, mini	10.00
Planter, hat form, bl, #670	6.00
Planter, turtle, wht, sm	3.00
Reamer, yel, tall ped, 2-pc	90.00
Teapot, chicken figural, yel, #257	32.00
Tile, Minnesota Centennial, 1858-1858, 6½"	35.00
Tray, coral, Deco style	6.00
Urn, Grecian motif, #159, 9"	45.00
Vase, Deco style, triangles, ivory, #787, 6½x6"	12.00
Vase, Egyptian, dk bl, hdls, 15x8"	60.00
Vase, fish figural, open mouth, bl, #879	38.00
Vase, gr, yel int, B-1426, 8½"	10.00
Vase, lady on swing/2 children, brn, label #776, 12"	25.00
Vase, leaves, gr, 9"	12.00
Vase, wht, gr int, #1050, 8"	10.00
Vase, 4 dancing maidens, gr, cylindrical, 9"	45.00
Vase/candle holder, yel	12.00
Wall pc, violin, blk, 13"	10.00

Cookie Jars

Bunch of Bananas, bl	32.00
Carousel	65.00
Dutch Girl, yel w/brn trim	45.00
Dutch People, mc on aqua, no mk	55.00
French Baker, tan & brn, mk	55.00
Katrina, yel	45.00
Monk, yel w/brn trim	60.00
Pineapple, cobalt	45.00

Dinnerware

Tea set, 3-piece, $37.50.

Ardennes, bowl, vegetable; 1947	7.00
Ardennes, chop plate, 1947	12.00
Ardennes, gravy boat, 1947	12.00
Ardennes, shakers, pr	8.00
Bob White, bowl, sauce; 6½"	4.00
Bob White, bread tray, long & narrow	75.00
Bob White, cup	7.50
Bob White, hors d'oeuvres, bird form	38.00
Bob White, pitcher, water; 60-oz	30.00
Bob White, plate, 10½"	7.50
Bob White, plate, 6½"	5.00
Bob White, platter, 14"	18.00
Bob White, sugar bowl	7.50
Bob White, water cooler, 2-gal	28.00
Capistrano, bowl, 6"	6.00
Capistrano, cup & saucer	12.00
Capistrano, plate, 11"	10.00
Capistrano, platter, 13½"	10.00
Capistrano, platter, 15"	12.00
Iris, pitcher	20.00
Lexington Rose, creamer & sugar bowl	15.00
Lexington Rose, plate, 10½"	7.00
Lexington Rose, plate, 6"	5.00
Lexington Rose, shakers, pr	12.50
Lotus, plate, 10½"	5.00
Lute Song, bowl, divided vegetable	20.00
Lute Song, bowl, 6"	5.50
Lute Song, platter, 13"	20.00
Morning-Glory, bowl, 7½"	4.00
Morning-Glory, creamer & sugar bowl	12.00
Morning-Glory, cup	4.00
Morning-Glory, plate, 10½"	4.00
Morning-Glory, plate, 6¼"	2.00
Morning-Glory, platter, 13"	8.00
Normandie, cup & saucer	6.00
Normandie, plate, dinner sz	6.00

Normandie, shakers, pr 6.00
Orleans, chowder, gr, w/lid 5.00
Orleans, shakers, pr 5.00
Orleans, sugar bowl 6.00
Orleans, vase, gr leaf, 9" 12.00
Pepe, bowl, cereal 4.00
Pepe, cup & saucer 4.00
Pepe, plate, dinner sz 4.00
Pepe, plate, 7½" 2.50
Pompeii, bowl, cereal; 8" 7.00
Pompeii, plate, 6" 3.00
Random Harvest, bowl, 12½" 22.50
Random Harvest, celery 8.00
Random Harvest, plate, 6½" 3.50

Stoneware

Bean pot, Albany slip, Boston style, RW, 1-gal 125.00
Bean pot, Albany slip, short neck, NS, 1-gal 75.00
Bean pot, bailed, brn/wht, RWU, 1-qt 50.00
Bean pot, Saffron, band, RWU, 1-gal 40.00
Bowl, Bl Band, 6" 35.00
Bowl, bl/wht sponge, paneled, unmk, 6" 100.00
Bowl, cap; Circles & Lines, red/bl sponging on wht, w/lid 125.00
Bowl, Greek Key, brn, 10" 75.00
Bowl, shoulder; brn, RW, 1-qt 60.00
Bowl, Sponge Band on wht, RWU, 5" 100.00
Butter crock, Albany slip, high, MN, 1-gal 50.00
Butter crock, brn, low, NS, 2-lb 70.00
Butter crock, brn, low, RW, 10-lb 50.00
Butter crock, red wing/bl #20 on wht, 20-lb 275.00
Butter crock, wht, low, RW, 5-lb 25.00
Casserole, Saffron, w/lid, RWU, smallest sz 100.00
Casserole, Sponge Band, RWU, lg 125.00
Chamber pot, bl band on wht, RW advertising, unmk 50.00
Chamber pot, brn, MN 125.00
Chamber pot, wht, fancy hdl, orig lid, RW, 7" 60.00
Christmas tree holder, 1912 advertising, no water hole 300.00
Churn, butterfly/#6 on salt galze, RW, 6-gal 600.00
Churn, leaf on salt glaze, molded, MN, 3-gal 500.00
Churn, leaf/#4 on salt glaze, RW, 4-gal 500.00
Churn, parrot on salt glaze, molded, MN, 3-gal 2,600.00
Churn, red wing/#2 on salt glaze, 2-gal 165.00
Crock, birch leaves on wht, RWUS, 2-gal 35.00
Crock, butterfly/#30 on salt glaze, RW, 30-gal 700.00
Crock, dbl 'P'/#3 on salt glaze, MN, 3-gal 250.00
Crock, dbl leaves stamped on wht, RWUS, 10-gal 175.00
Crock, elephant ear leaves/#10 on salt glaze, 10-gal 60.00
Crock, lily/#30 on salt glaze, stenciled RW MN, 30-gal 800.00
Crock, red wing/#20 on salt glaze, 20-gal 80.00
Crock, 2 birch leaves/#25 on salt glaze, MN, 25-gal 300.00
Cuspidor, bl/wht sponge, unmk, 6" dia 200.00
Cuspidor, brn/wht, wide middle mold seam, unmk 80.00
Flowerpot, Albany slip, MN, 7" 175.00
Hot water bottle, emb leaves, bl/wht, RWUS 550.00
Jar, Ball lock; red wing on wht, self-sealing, 3-gal 100.00
Jar, fruit; Mason Cap, RWUS, ½-gal 550.00
Jar, fruit; Stone Mason, bl label on wht, pat 1899, 1-gal 275.00
Jar, packing; red wing on wht, bail hdl, 3-gal 125.00
Jug, bailed, Albany slip, MN, 1-gal 100.00
Jug, bailed, bl mottle, MN, 1-gal 500.00
Jug, bailed, wht, wide mouth, MN, 1-gal 100.00
Jug, beehive threshing; wht, RWUS, 5-gal 350.00
Jug, beehive; Albany slip, etched #5, RW, 5-gal 500.00

Jug, common, Albany slip, MN, 1-gal 40.00
Jug, common, Albany slip, name decor, NS, 1-gal 800.00
Jug, common, wht, MN, 1-gal 50.00
Jug, fruit; brn, wide mouth, MN, ½-gal 35.00
Jug, shoulder; bl bands on wht, cone top, MN, 1-gal 325.00
Jug, shoulder; brn/wht, ball top, RW, 1-gal 150.00
Jug, shoulder; brn/wht, cone top, RW, 1-gal 125.00
Jug, shoulder; brn/wht, cone top, RW, ½-gal 250.00
Jug, shoulder; brn/wht, cone top, RW, 2-gal 225.00
Jug, shoulder; brn/wht, dome top, MN, 1-gal 50.00
Jug, shoulder; brn/wht, funnel top, MN, 1-gal 125.00
Jug, shoulder; brn/wht, funnel top, NS, ½-gal 250.00
Jug, shoulder; brn/wht, funnel top, NS, 2-gal 250.00
Jug, shoulder; brn/wht, pear top, NS, 1-gal 125.00
Jug, shoulder; brn/wht, red wings, standard top, 2-gal 250.00
Jug, shoulder; brn/wht, standard top, RW, 1-gal 100.00
Jug, shoulder; brn/wht, wide mouth cone top, NS, 1-gal 250.00
Jug, shoulder; wht, red wing, standard top, RWUS, 3-gal 40.00
Jug, shoulder; wht, standard top, MN, 2-gal 35.00
Jug, syrup; cone top, MN, 1-gal 50.00
Jug, syrup; wht, standard top, MN, 1-gal 40.00
Koverwate, bl stamp on wht, 6-gal 125.00
Milk pan, brn/wht, NS 60.00
Pie plate, brn/salt glaze, MN 150.00
Pie plate, wht, MN 85.00
Pitcher, barrel form, Albany slip, RWUS 75.00
Pitcher, bl/wht mottle, knob on hdl top, RWUS 150.00
Pitcher, Century of Progress themes on wht 125.00
Pitcher, Cherry Band, bl/wht 125.00
Pitcher, Dutch Boy & Girl, bl/wht, RW, sm 450.00
Pitcher, Iris, Albany slip, RWP 60.00
Pitcher, milk; Russian style, unmk, ½-gal 50.00
Pitcher, mustard; brn, NS 175.00
Pitcher, pipkin; brn/wht, MN, 4-pt 225.00
Pitcher, pipkin; wht, unmk, 1-pt 50.00
Pitcher, Saffron, RWUS, sm 85.00
Pitcher, Sponge Band, RWUS, lg 125.00
Reamer, Sponge Band, RWU 500.00
Snuff jar, Albany slip, salt glaze lid, MN, 1-gal 35.00
Snuff jar, wht, RW, 1-qt 75.00
Spittoon, bl bands on salt glaze, unmk 250.00
Spittoon, salt glaze, RW on side, rare 500.00
Spittoon, wht, German style, unmk 200.00
Umbrella stand, red & bl sponging on wht, unmk 500.00
Water cooler, butterfly/#6 on salt glaze, RW, 6-gal 1,400.00
Water cooler, daisy/#4 on salt glaze, RW, 4-gal 1,200.00
Water cooler, flower (detailed) on salt glaze, RW, 6-gal 2,500.00
Water cooler, ice water/4 leaves/#25 on salt glaze, 25-gal 200.00
Wax sealer, brn, NS, ½-gal 175.00

Redware

The term redware refers to a type of simple earthenware produced by the Colonists as early as the 1600s. The red clay used in its production was abundant throughout the country, and during the 18th and 19th centuries redware was made in great quantities. Intended for utilitarian purposes such as everyday tableware or use in the dairy, redware was simple in design and decoration. Glazes of various colors were used, and a liquid clay referred to as 'slip' was sometimes applied in patterns such as zigzag lines, daisies, or stars. In the following listings, EX (excellent condition) indicates very minor damage.

Our advisor for this category is Barbara Rosen; she is listed in the Directory under New Jersey.

Platter, yellow, brown, and green slip marbleizing, minor chips and wear, 13½", $2,600.00.

Bank, amber w/brn flecks, tooled shoulder lines, ovoid, 5¼" ...125.00
Bank, apple form, worn orig red & gr pnt, 2½" 105.00
Bank, blk stencil: Charity, tooled band, ovoid, 3⅝", NM 150.00
Bank, jug form, red pnt, rpr flake at coin slot, 4¾" 65.00
Basket, yel/gr/brn marbleized, early 1800s, 9x6", NM 350.00
Bottle, dk red-brn glaze, MD, ca 1810s, 8x4¾", EX 40.00
Bottle, hot water; brn flecks, flat circular form, 8" dia 80.00
Bowl, milk; brn sponging, tooled dot line, 3¼x7", NM 225.00
Bowl, simple yel slip decor, minor wear/chips, 2x10½" 180.00
Bowl, yel slip w/gr & brn, 3x13" dia 325.00
Charger, sgraffito flowers on cream, coggled rim/ovolo, 12½" ..275.00
Charger, yel slip monogram, coggled, 14", NM 1,000.00
Charger, 4-line yel slip, coggled rim, 11½", NM 1,050.00
Cup, amber mottle, flared lip, appl hdl, 3¾", EX 85.00
Cup, gr w/orange spots & yel slip waves, 4" EX 85.00
Cuspidor, dk brn sponged stripes, 8", NM 80.00
Dish, 3-line yel slip waves, coggled, rare size, 5½", EX 700.00
Flowerpot w/attached saucer, gr-brn, mk John Bell, 5", EX 275.00
Jar, apple butter; tooled shoulder, strap hdl, unmk, 1860s 125.00
Jar, brn splotches, cylindrical, 9½", VG 95.00
Jar, dk glaze, ovoid, mk John Bell, flakes/hairline, 5½" 200.00
Jar, gr w/orange spots, tooled str/wavy lines, 8" 140.00
Jar, gr w/red highlights, emb bands, old chips, 6" 375.00
Jar, gray-gr w/brn highlights, ovoid, 10", EX 400.00
Jar, int glaze, mk John Bell, ovoid, 7½" 120.00
Jar, marbleized wht/brn/tan slip, 6", VG 200.00
Jar, reddish w/yel slip around neck, 7", EX 120.00
Jar, shiny brn w/yel spots, ovoid, 6¾" 235.00
Jar, storage; tooled shoulder, hdls, att PA, ca 1850s 145.00
Jar, wht slip w/gr mottle, w/lid, edge chips, 3½" 230.00
Jug, dk brn, tooled lines, ribbed strap hdl, ovoid, 8¾" 85.00
Jug, puzzle; simple yel slip, minor wear/flakes, 4½" 55.00
Jug, 5-line yel slip, ribbed strap hdl, ovoid, 11", EX 2,200.00
Lion on oval base, gr-tan, tooled mane, sgn RLW, 12" L, EX ...75.00
Loaf pan, bold combing in wht, coggled edge, 15x19", EX ...3,300.00
Milk pan, glazed int, unmk, 1850s, 7½" dia 135.00
Mold, turk's head, blk sponging, scalloped, 9¼" 75.00
Mold, turk's head, brn sponging, scalloped, 7¼" 55.00
Mug, appl star, strap hdl, tooled lip, 5¼" 125.00
Pie plate, brn sunburst, glaze flakes, 8½" 165.00
Pie plate, mustard yel, coggled, 11", EX 275.00
Pie plate, 3-line yel slip band & 'arrows,' coggled, 9", EX ...200.00
Pie plate, 3-line yel slip waves/flourishes, 10", NM 550.00

Pitcher, Am eagle incised, brn/gr sponging, strap hdl, 7" 700.00
Pitcher, dk brn splotches, strap hdl, minor wear, 4½" 395.00
Pitcher, wht w/brn mottle, pinched spout, rpr, 5", EX 65.00
Plate, yel slip pinwheel, coggled, worn/chipped, 12" 325.00
Porringer, rust int, hdl & bk have dk patina, 5½", EX 185.00
Pot, dk brn, open hdls, wear/chips, 13x16" dia 130.00
Pot, ruffled basket form, unmk, ca 1890 ....65.00

Regal China

Located in Antioch, Illinois, the Regal China Company has been in business since 1938. Products of interest to collectors are James Beam decanters, cookie jars, salt and pepper shakers, and similar novelty items. The Old MacDonald Farm series listed below are becoming especially collectible. See also Cookie Jars.

Old McDonald's Farm

Butter dish, cow's head 35.00
Canister, lg 95.00
Canister, med 85.00
Canister, spice; sm 35.00

Old McDonald's Farm creamer and sugar bowl, $35.00 each.

Jar, grease; pig figural 65.00
Pitcher, milk; cow's head, gold bell, tankard form 200.00
Shakers, churn, pr 18.00
Shakers, feed sacks w/sheep's head, pr 35.00
Shakers, figural heads, pr 22.00
Teapot, duck's head 135.00

Religious Items

Altar sticks, alabaster, bronze cross at center, 7½", pr 35.00
Altar sticks, gold-plated brass, Gothic, 19", pr, EX 265.00
Censer, brass, simple style, no chain, 7½" 40.00
Chalice, gold on sterling, inscribed base, simple style, 8½" 160.00
Chalice, gold-plated sterling cup, Roman style, 7½" 90.00
Ciborium, gold-plated brass, cross finial, 5x3½" 65.00
Ciborium, sterling, Baroque cross finial, France, 12½x5" 110.00
Crucifix, wrought iron, Spanish Baroque base, 24½" 65.00
Engraving, ...Way...to Everlasting Life or...Damnation, 18" 385.00
Figure, saint in nun's habit, wood, German Baroque, 64" 880.00
Incense holder, brass lamp form, Trinity symbol, 2¾x5" 40.00
Lantern, processional; brass, decor, glass insert, 14" 35.00

Paten, gold plated, hdls, 5½", EX **25.00**
Urn, dull gold color over brass, 14", pr **25.00**

Restraints

Since the beginning of time, many things from animals to treasures have been held in bondage by hemp, bamboo, chests, chains, shackles, and other constructed devices. Many of these devices were used to hold captives who awaited further torture, as if the restraint wasn't torturous enough. The study and collecting of restraints enables one to learn much about the advancement of civilization in the country or region from which they originated. Such devices at various times in history were made of very heavy metals — so heavy that the wearer could scarcely move about. It has only been in the last sixty years that vast improvements have been made in design and construction that afford the captive some degree of comfort.

Key:
bbl — barrel	lc — lock case
d-lb — double lock button	NST — non-swing through
K — key	ST — swing through
Kd — keyed	stp — stamped

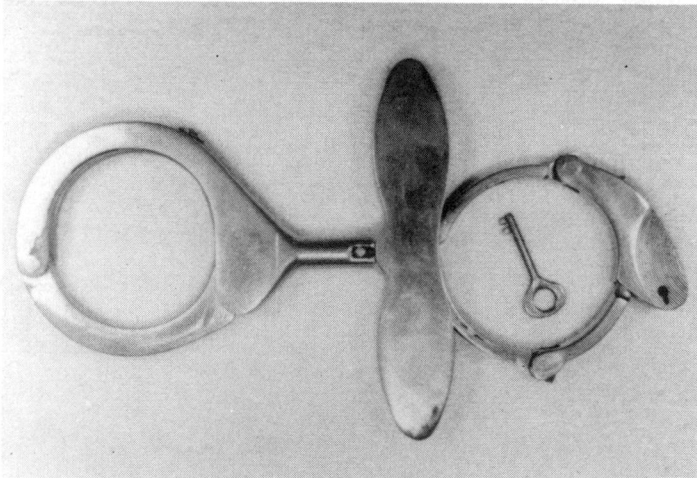

Pratt combo, one cuff connects with nipper and claw, swing through, marked Pratt, $200.00.

Foreign Handcuffs

Adams, teardrop lc, bbl Kd, NST, usually not stp **150.00**
Australian, Saf Lock, ST, takes pin-tumbler K in side, stp **110.00**
Chubb, NST, English hi-security 10-slider lock mechanism ...**200.00**
Deutsche Polizei, ST, middle hinge, folds, takes bbl-bit K **100.00**
French Lapegy, ST, alluminum alloys, takes flat bitted K **65.00**
German Clejuso, oval design, ST, dbl-cuff weight, 22-oz **90.00**
German Clejuso, oval design, ST, solid K w/lg bit, stp **80.00**
German Clejuso, sq lc, adjusts/NST, d-lb on side, bbl K **95.00**
German Darby, adjusts, well finished, sm **100.00**
German Hamburg 8, non-adjust NST, center bar/post w/K-way. **200.00**
Hiatt, English Darby, like US CW Darby, stp Hiatt & #d **55.00**
Hiatt, solid state, 2 separate cuffs joined bk to bk, stp/# **90.00**
Hiatt English non-adjust screw K Darby style, uses screw K **85.00**
Hiatt Figure 8, swings open to insert/withdraw wrists **90.00**
Italian, stp New Police, modern Peerless type, ST, sm bbl K **30.00**
Japanese, stp Chief of Police, modern Peerless type, ST **25.00**
Plug 8, remove plug before inserting external threaded K **150.00**
Spanish, stp Alcyon/Star, modern Peerless type, ST, flat K **65.00**
Spanish, stp Alcyon/Star, modern Peerless type, ST, sm bbl K ..**45.00**

Foreign Leg Shackles

German Clejuso, sq lc, adjusts/NST, d-lb on side, bbl K **105.00**
German Clejuso Darby type, adjusts/NST/plated, uses screw K .**125.00**
Hiatt English combo manacles, handcuff/leg irons w/chain **150.00**
Hiatt English non-adjust screw K Darby style uses screw K **85.00**
Hiatt Plug leg irons, same K-ing as Plug-8 cuffs, w/chain **175.00**

U.S. Handcuffs

American Munitions, modern/rnd, sm bbl Kd, ST bow, stp **45.00**
Bean Patrolman, kidney bean form, d-lb on lc, NST, stp T **90.00**
Bean-Cobb, sm rnd lc, removable cylinder, d-lb, NST, 1899 ....**80.00**
Civil War padlocking type, various designs w/loop for lock **90.00**
Colt, modern ST bow, sm bbl Kd, stp w/Colt & co name **90.00**
H&R Super, NST, shaft-hinge connector takes hollow titted K .**75.00**
Harvard, takes sm bbl K, ST, stp Harvard Lock Co **65.00**
Judd, NST, uses rnd/internally triangular K, stp Mattatuck **100.00**
Marlin Daley, NST, bottle-neck form, neck stp, dbl-titted K ..**150.00**
Mattatuck, NST, propeller-like K-way, stp Mattaluck/etc **85.00**
Peerless, ST, takes sm bbl K, stp Mfg'ered by Peerless Co **40.00**
Peerless, ST, takes sm bbl K, stp Mfg'ered by S&W Co **75.00**
Phelps, NST, twist chain between cuffs, Tower look-alike **150.00**
Pratt combo, 1 cuff connects w/nipper/claw, ST, mk Pratt **200.00**
Romer, NST, takes flat K, resembles padlock, stp Romer Co ...**200.00**
S&W 94 Maximum Security, ST, takes Ace-type K, stp S&W ..**65.00**
Strauss, ST, takes lg solid bitted K, stp Strauss Eng Co **85.00**
Tower, NST, bottom K, solid/flat fitted K goes in cuff edge **100.00**
Tower bar cuffs, cuffs separated by 10-12" steel bar **90.00**
Tower Dbl Lock, NST, takes bbl-bitted K, usually stp Tower ..**50.00**
Tower Detective Pinkerton, NST, sq lc, bbl-bitted K, no stp ..**85.00**
Tower Single Lock, NST, bbl-bit K, K-way slanted on lc, sm ..**70.00**
Tower-Bean, NST, sm rnd lc, takes tiny bbl-bitted K, stp **70.00**
Walden 'Lady Cuff,' NST, takes sm bbl K, lightweight, stp **200.00**

U.S. Leg Shackles

American Munitions, as handcuffs **55.00**
Civil War or prison ball & chain, padlocking or rivet type **175.00**
H&R Supers, as handcuffs **200.00**
Harvard, as handcuffs **75.00**
Judd, as handcuffs **110.00**
Oregon boot, break-apart shackle on above-ankle support ...**400.00**
Strauss, as handcuffs **90.00**
Tower, bottom K, as handcuffs **90.00**
Tower ball & chain, leg iron w/chain & 6-lb to 50-lb ball **150.00**
Tower Dbl-Lock, as handcuffs **75.00**
Tower Detective, as handcuffs **135.00**

Various Other Restraining Devices

African slave Darby-style cuffs, heavy iron/chain, handmade ...**95.00**
African slave Darby-style leg shackles, heavy/hand forged **150.00**
African slave padlocking or riveted forged iron shackles **125.00**
Darby neck collar, rnd steel loop opens w/screw K **135.00**
English Figure-8 nipper, claw opens by lifting top lock tab **65.00**
German Nipper, twist hdl opens/closes cuff, stp Germany/etc ..**75.00**

Reverse Painting on Glass

Verre eglomise is the technique of painting on the underside of glass. Dating back to the early 1700s, this art became popular in the 19th century when German immigrants chose historical figures and beautiful women as subjects for their reverse glass paintings. Advertising mirrors of this type came into vogue at the turn of the century.

Church/trees, EX color, beveled fr, 9½x11" 300.00
Depicting month of May, gilt-wood fr, 1800s, 19" 2,300.00
George or Martha Washington, fr, 8x5½", pr 600.00
Golden Hind, silhouette of ship, 1800s, 4x5½" 210.00
Hunting scene, hounds attack wild boar, English, 11x13½" 400.00
Napoleon, portrait in uniform, floral spandrels, 15x12" 1,000.00
Oriental beauty seated in interior, Chinese Export, 19x15" 350.00
Personification of Spring & Summer, EX color, 12x16" 375.00
Scene, bldgs/trees/etc, primitive, in walnut fr, 14x15" 250.00

Triumph of Virtue, Chinese Export allegorical, ca 1810, 27x19", $800.00.

Richard

Richard, who at one time worked for Galle, made cameo art glass in France during the 1920s. His work was often multi-layered and acid cut with florals and scenics in lovely colors. The ware was marked with his name in relief.

Our advisor for this category is Don Williams; he is listed in the Directory under Iowa.

Cameo

Goblet, river landscape, 2 cuts, knob stem & ft, 7¾" 395.00
Lamp, holly leaves/berries, 3 cuts, 9½" 2,900.00
Vase, blackberries, bl on orange, ped ft, 5½x6¼" 375.00
Vase, castle/grees/mtns, cobalt on bright orange, 15" 1,550.00
Vase, dancing girl, gr/pk on bl, 3 cuts, 10x2¾" 895.00
Vase, house by bridge, 2 cuts, bowl form w/4 ft, 8" 550.00
Vase, river landscape, rust on frost, 2 cuts, 3⅜x2" 225.00
Vase, scenic, brn to orange, 2 cuts, 8½" 475.00
Vase, trees form canopy for bldg/bridge/mtns on orange, 8" 800.00
Vase, trees/water/mtns, chartreuse on wht, 12" 450.00
Vase, village scene w/church, purple/lav on lt bl, 15" 800.00

Ridgway

As early as 1792, the Ridgway brothers, Job and George, produced fine quality earthenwares in Shelton, Staffordshire, marking their products 'Ridgway, Smith, & Ridgway,' and later, 'Job & George Ridgway.' Around 1800 the brothers split and each had his own firm, both in Shelton. They were joined in the business by various members of the Ridgway family, and in fact their descendants still operate there today.

The two firms created by the split were the Bell Works and the Cauldon Pottery. Bell produced stone china and earthenware decorated with blue transfer printing. Their mark was 'J. & W. Ridgway' or 'J. & W.R.,' until 1848 when 'William Ridgway' was used. The Cauldon Pottery made earthenware, stone china, and high-quality porcelains fine enough to win them the distinction of being appointed potters to the Queen. From 1830 their wares attest to this fact, bearing the Royal Arms mark with 'J.R.' within the crest. In 1840 '& Co.' was added. Most examples of Ridgway's wares found today are transfer-printed historical scenes. See also Staffordshire, Historical; and Flow Blue.

Ash tray, Coaching Days, metal box for matches 50.00
Bowl, Coaching Days, 6½" 40.00
Bowl, Coaching Days, 9½" 60.00
Coffeepot, Coaching Days, 8" 95.00
Compote, pk mums, gold trim, semi-porc, 3", pr 65.00
Cup & saucer, Royal Vista 20.00
Jug, Mr Pickwick, silver lustre trim, 7⅝x5⅛" 70.00
Mug, Coaching Days, 4½" 30.00

Mug, Coaching Days, 2-handled, 5", $60.00.

Mug, Polar Bear & Cat, silver lustre trim, 4½" 45.00
Pitcher, Coaching Days, 4¼" 45.00
Pitcher, Coaching Days, 5¼" 65.00
Pitcher, Coaching Days, 6" 85.00
Pitcher, stoneware, bl w/emb band, HP flowers, 1835, 11" 160.00
Pitcher, Tam O'Shanter, bl, Oct 1, 1835, 7" 120.00
Pitcher, tankard; Mr Pickwick, silver lustre trim, 9½" 100.00
Pitcher, tankard; 2 Strings to Her Box, 12½" 450.00
Plate, chop; Coaching Days, 13½" .120.00
Plate, Coaching Days, 10" 40.00
Punch bowl, flowers/birds, blk transfer w/enameling, 7x16" . . .125.00
Vase, Coaching Days, 5" 65.00

Rie, Lucie

Lucie Rie was born in Austria in 1902. She moved to London in 1938 and shared her studio with Hans Coper from 1946 to 1958. Her ceramics look modern; however, they are based on shapes from many world cultures dating back to Roman times. Lucie Rie is best known for the use of metallic oxides in her clay and glazes. She specializes in the hand throwing of thin, porcelain bowls, which is a very difficult process. Her works are in the world's best museums. All of her ceramics are impressed with a seal mark on the bottom, a cojoined 'R & L' within a rectangular reserve.

Bowl, bronze & pk, porcelain, ftd, 1980, 5" 2,400.00
Bowl, copper int/vertical blk lines, funnel form, 8½" 6,000.00
Bowl, copper/pk/wht, inlaid, 1975, 4½" 2,300.00
Bowl, gr w/bronze rim, funnel form, 7" 4,000.00
Bowl, gr w/sgraffito lines, porcelain, 1958, 6½" 3,600.00
Bowl, yel, 1975, 5" 600.00
Bowl, yel & bronze, stoneware, 1955, 10" 5,500.00
Vase, pitted gray & wht, stoneware, balaster, 1980, 14" 25,000.00
Vase, pk, pitted gray, stoneware, 4½" 1,000.00
Vase, pk w/bl spirals, stoneware, oval, 1980, 4" 1,100.00
Vase, wht w/copper rim, bottle form, 1987, 12" 5,000.00

Riviera

Riviera was a line of dinnerware introduced by the Homer Laughlin China Company in 1938. It was sold exclusively by the Murphy Company through their nationwide chain of dime stores. Riviera was unmarked, lightweight, and inexpensive. It was discontinued sometime prior to 1950. Colors are mauve blue, red, yellow, light green, and ivory. On rare occasions, dark blue pieces are found, but this was not a standard color.

Baker, oval, 9" 12.00
Batter set, complete 145.00
Bowl, fruit; 5½" 6.00
Bowl, nappy; 9¼" 13.00
Butter dish, ½-lb 50.00
Casserole, w/lid 48.00
Creamer, regular 6.00
Cup & saucer 9.00
Jug, juice; yel 45.00
Jug, w/lid 55.00

Juice set, see listing for specific values.

Plate, deep, 8" 11.00
Plate, 10" 15.00
Plate, 6" 4.50
Plate, 7" 6.50

Plate, 9" 10.00
Platter, cobalt, 12" 12.00
Platter, 11" 9.00
Sauce boat 11.00
Shakers, pr 11.00
Sugar bowl, w/lid 11.00
Syrup, w/lid 70.00
Teapot 50.00
Tumbler, hdl 40.00
Tumbler, juice 35.00

Robertson

Fred H. Robertson, clay expert for the Los Angeles Brick Company and son of Alexander Robertson of the Roblin Pottery, experimented with crystalline glazes as early as 1906. In 1934 Fred and his son George established their own works in Los Angeles, but by 1943 they had moved operations to Hollywood. Though most of their early wares were turned by hand, some were also molded in low relief. Fine crackle glazes and crystallines were developed. The ware was marked with 'Robertson,' 'F.H.R.,' or 'R.,' with the particular location of its manufacture noted. The small pottery closed in 1952.

Our advisor for this category is Jack Chipman; he is listed in the Directory under California.

Box, appl rose on lid, bl gloss, elongated/shaped form 150.00
Cigarette jar, maroon, Deco shape, sgn Robertson Hollywood .150.00
Tile, scenic w/fortress, 4-color, cloisonne technique, 8x8" ...1,300.00
Vase, Persian bl over crackle, imp FHR, 1934, 4½" 125.00
Vase, pk crackle, pillow form, 2¾x2¾" 60.00

Robj

Robj was the name of a retail store that operated in Paris for only a few years, from about 1925 to 1931. Robj solicited designs from the best French artisans of the period to produce decorative objects for the home. These objects were produced mostly in porcelain but also in glass and earthenware. The most well known are the figural bottles which were particularly popular in the United States. However, Robj also produced tea sets, perfume lamps, chess sets, ash trays, bookends, humidors, powder jars, cigarette boxes, figurines, lamps, and milk pitchers. Robj objects tend to be whimsical, and all embody the Art Deco style.

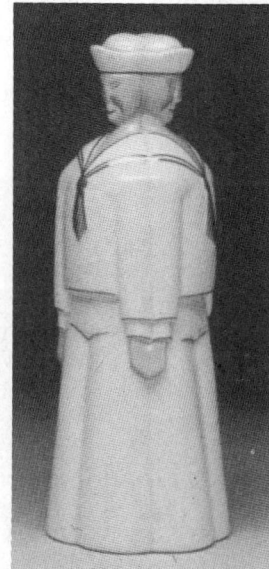

Decanter, formed as three sailors, marked, 11", $3,500.00 at auction (nearly three times the average estimated value).

Bottle, liqueur; Scotsman, mini 295.00
Cup & saucer, stylized Oriental man as hdl, ca 1925, 6 for . . .1,250.00
Decanter, 3 standing bk-to-bk sailors, hats remove, 11" 3,500.00
Figurine, bespectacled wht-haired witch w/cane, 10" 300.00
Tray, Arab figural 310.00

Roblin

In the late 1800s, Alexander W. Robertson and Linna Irelan established a pottery in San Francisco, combining parts of their respective names to coin the name Roblin. Robertson was responsible for potting and firing the ware, which often reflected his taste for classic styling. Mrs. Irelan did much of the decorating, utilizing almost every method but favoring relief modeling. Mushrooms and lizards were her favorite subjects. Vases were a large part of their production, all of which was made from native California red, buff, and white clays. The ware was well marked with the firm name or the outline of a bear. Roblin Pottery was destroyed in the earthquake of 1906.

Vase, bsk, ftd bulb body w/short neck collar, 3¼" 245.00
Vase, brn bsk, incised line, 3½" 140.00
Vase, red bsk, mk, 4" 200.00
Vase, red clay, no glaze, RAPC mk, 4x3¼" 200.00
Vase, wht bsk, cylindrical w/ridges, sgn AWR, mk, 2" 110.00

Rockingham

In the early part of the 19th century, American potters began to favor brown- and buff-burning clays over red because of their durability. The glaze favored by many was Rockingham, which varied from a dark brown mottle to a sponged effect sometimes called tortoise shell. It consisted in part of manganese and various metallic salts and was used by many potters until well into the 20th century. Over the past two years, demand and prices have risen sharply, especially in the east. See also Bennington.

Bed pan, 16¾" L, M 50.00
Bookends, young girl w/books, 7½", EX 260.00
Bottle, morning-glories emb, 8¼" 85.00
Bottle, toby form, 9½" 150.00
Bowl, fluted exterior, 2⅛x6¾" 100.00
Bowl, foliage scrolls emb, shallow, hairline, 2⅜x8¾" 125.00
Bowl, minor wear, 3x11½" 120.00
Bowl, mixing; w/spout, hairline, 16" 95.00
Bowl, mixing; 3½x8½" 85.00
Bowl, mixing; 3x9⅝" 95.00
Bowl, oval, minor wear, 12x8½" L 100.00
Bowl, oval, 9" L, M 95.00
Bowl, ped ft, 3½x4⅝" dia, NM 35.00
Bowl, str sides, 3½x12½" 100.00
Bowl, 3½x8" 55.00
Candlestick, lip rpr, 8½", pr 300.00
Figure, lion, paw on ball, tail curled, redware, 12" L, pr 500.00
Flask, morning-glory emb, 1840s, rpr, pt 125.00
Frame, emb/tooled detail, scalloped int edge, 13x15", EX 700.00
Inkwell, sleeping figure, old chips, 4" 100.00
Jar, vintage emb, hdls, 7½", EX 115.00
Miniature cuspidor, 1½" dia 110.00
Miniature jug, 1½" 50.00
Miniature pitcher, diamonds & florals incised, 2" 60.00
Mold, Turk's head, 3½x8⅛" 135.00
Mug, concave sides, 2¾" 65.00

Mug, flared lip, 3¼x3¾" 75.00
Mug, fluted panels, 3⅝" 135.00
Mug, hairline, 3⅞" 60.00
Mug, rings at base, 2⅝", EX 30.00
Mug, toby form, 5¾" 65.00
Pie plate, 11" 135.00
Pie plate, 7½" 125.00
Pitcher, Daniel Boone, bulbous, 9" 145.00
Pitcher, hunt scene emb, 8" 175.00
Pitcher, hunt scene emb, 9" 185.00
Pitcher, hunt scene/vintage emb, hound hdl, H Taylor, 10" . . .550.00
Pitcher, portrait bust emb, 7" 75.00
Pitcher, tulips emb, 8½" 225.00

Pitcher, stag and hounds, 'S.H. Russell' under spout, figural frog in bottom, made at South Amboy NJ, 1850s, 10", NM, $200.00.

Plate, Gothic arch emb, canted corners, minor wear, 8¾" 55.00
Shaker, dome top, chipped lip, 4½" 85.00
Soap dish, oval, 4¾", NM 85.00

Rockwell, Norman

Norman Rockwell began his career in 1911 at the age of seventeen doing illustrations for a children's book entitled *Tell Me Stories*. Within a few years he had produced the *Saturday Evening Post* cover that made him one of America's most-beloved artists. Though not well accepted by the professional critics of his day who did not consider his work to be art but 'merely' commercial illustration, Rockwell's popularity grew to the extent that today there is an overwhelming abundance of examples of his work or those related to the theme of one of his illustrations.

Book, Norman Rockwell's America, leather bound, ltd ed 85.00
Calendar, American Way, 1945 . . . . .55.00
Calendar, Bicentennial, M 15.00
Calendar, cover only, A Great Moment, 1965, lg 20.00
Calendar, cover only, Keep Myself Physically Strong, 1964, lg . .22.00
Calendar, Pointing the Way, 1962, 8x14½" 20.00
Figurine, First Haircut 110.00
Figurine, Lazy Bones 200.00
Figurine, Waiting for Santa 100.00
Figurine, 100th Year of Baseball, NR102 . . . . .125.00
Lithograph, Brooks Robinson, Rawlings, sgn, 24x30" 350.00
Lithograph, You Got To Be Kidden, 24x18" 500.00
Plaque, Freedom From Fear, metal, Curtis Circulation, 11x16" .280.00

Poster, Fisk Bicycle Club, boys/bike, linen bk, 37x25½", EX ...280.00
Poster, Schmidt's Beer, EX 75.00

Prints, Four Seasons, 24x18", $1,000.00 for the set. (Shown: Winter — Doing Homework.)

Sheet music, I'm Sorry I Made You Cry, Rockwell cover 5.00
Sheet music, Little French Mother, Good-Bye, Rockwell cover .30.00
Sheet music, Over...Where the Lilies Grow, Rockwell cover ...20.00
Sketch, orig, inscribed/sgn, 18x48" 2,000.00
Stein, Looking Out To Sea 225.00

Rogers, John

John Rogers (1829-1904) was a machinist from Manchester, New Hampshire, who turned his hobby of sculpting into a financially-successful venture. From the originals he meticulously fashioned of red clay, he had bronze master molds made from which plaster copies were cast. He specialized in five different categories: theatrical, Shakespeare, Civil War, everyday life, and horses. His large detailed groupings portrayed the life and times of the period between 1859 and 1892. When no condition is indicated, examples are assumed to be in very good to excellent condition.

Our advisor for this category is George Humphrey; he is listed in the Directory under Maryland.

Balcony 1,200.00
Bath 2,000.00
Bushwacker 2,000.00
Camp Life 2,000.00
Charity Patient 650.00
Checkers at the Farm 450.00
Coming to the Parson, ca 1870 ....375.00
Council of War 850.00
Elder's Daughter 800.00
Fairy's Whisper, ca 1881 ....1,400.00
Favored Scholar 425.00
Fetching the Doctor 750.00
Fighting Bob, ca 1889 ....1,100.00
First Ride 750.00
Foundling 625.00
Fugitive Story 900.00
Going for the Cows 425.00
Hide & Seek 775.00
Is It So Nominated in the Bond 375.00
Mail Day 750.00
Neighboring Pews, ca 1884 ....425.00

One More Shot 550.00
Parting Promise 400.00
Peddler at the Fair 825.00
Playing Doctor 700.00
Politics 700.00
Returned Volunteer 600.00
Rip Van Winkle at Home 325.00
Rip Van Winkle on the Mountain 400.00
Rip Van Winkle Returned 475.00
Schauchraum & Tatters 475.00
School Days 550.00
School Examination 500.00
Slave Auction 2,000.00
Speak for Yourself, John 475.00
Taking the Oath & Drawing Rations 475.00
Tap on the Window 500.00
Traveling Magician 750.00

Uncle Ned's School, 20", $750.00.

Watch on the Santa Maria 750.00
We Boys 425.00
Wounded Scout 800.00
Wrestler 1,250.00

Rookwood

The Rookwood Pottery Company was established in 1879 in Cincinnati, Ohio. Its founder was Maria Longworth Nichols Storer, daughter of a wealthy family who provided the backing necessary to make such an enterprise possible. Mrs. Storer hired competent ceramic workers who through constant experimentation developed many lines of superior art pottery. While in her employ, Laura Fry invented the airbrush-blending process for which she was issued a patent in 1884. From this, several lines were designed that utilized blended backgrounds.

One of their earlier lines, Standard, was a brown ware decorated with underglaze slip-painted nature studies, animals, portraits, etc. Iris and Sea Green were introduced in 1894 and Vellum, a transparent mat-glaze line, in 1904. Other lines followed: Ombroso in 1910 and Soft Porcelain in 1915. Many of the early artware lines were signed by the artist. Soon after the turn of the twentieth century, Rookwood manufactured 'production' pieces that relied mainly on molded designs and forms rather than freehand decoration for their esthetic appeal.

The Depression brought on financial difficulties from which the pottery never recovered. Though it continued to operate, the quality of the ware deteriorated, and the pottery was forced to close in 1967.

Unmarked Rookwood is only rarely encountered. Many marks may be found, but the most familiar is the reverse 'RP' monogram. First used in 1886, a flame point was added above it for each succeeding year until 1900. After that, a Roman numeral added below indicated the year of manufacture. Impressed letters that related to the type of clay utilized for the body were also used — G for ginger, O for olive, R for red, S for sage green, W for white, and Y for yellow.

Artware must be judged on an individual basis. Quality of the artwork is a prime factor to consider. Portraits, animals, and birds are worth more than florals; and pieces signed by a particularly renowned artist are highly prized.

Our advisors for this category are Fer-Duc, Inc.; they are listed in the Directory under New York.

Bisque

Ewer, bamboo/bird on bl/yel/gold, M Rettig, #10C, 1885, 8" . . .400.00
Ewer, butterflies, wht/blk on orange to yel, no mk, 11½" 350.00
Ewer, floral, wht on olive, tooled/gilt neck, G Young, 9x6" 400.00
Ewer, leaf/branch cvg, lt gray clay, gloss int, 1882, 12" 400.00
Ewer, mums, Rettig, no mk or date, 10¾" 375.00

Iris

Disk, Am Ceramics Society, kiln/rooks, Fechheimer, 1904, 5" .650.00
Pitcher, phlox/leaves, S Sax, #S1670F, 1900, miniature, 3¼" . .375.00
Sugar bowl, clover blossoms, F Rothenbush, #832, 1902, 4" . . .190.00
Vase, autumn leaves on cream to gray, E Diers, 1905, 7x5" 600.00
Vase, band w/trees & river, Rothenbush, 1909, 9x4¾" 2,200.00
Vase, berries/branches, bl/gr/wht, I Bishop, 1907, 7" 650.00
Vase, cherry blossoms on wht to gray, ET Hurley, 1911, 9½" . .800.00
Vase, daffodils, lg/yel on wht to gray, S Sax, 1903, 12x4" 1,400.00
Vase, dogwood, pastels, S Toohey, 1900, 12" 900.00
Vase, floral on pk to cream, Lenore Asbury, #949D, 8½" 675.00
Vase, grapes, purple on blk to violet, S Sax, 1902, 9x4½" 800.00
Vase, grapes on dk to lt gray, K VanHorn, #905E, 1907, 6½" . .475.00
Vase, holly, mc on bl to peach, S Sax, 1902, 7½", Xd/M 1,000.00
Vase, irises, lav on gr to ivory, I Bishop, 1908, 7x3½" 900.00
Vase, lg rook/full moon, CL Lindeman, #904B, 1908, 15x8" .1,500.00

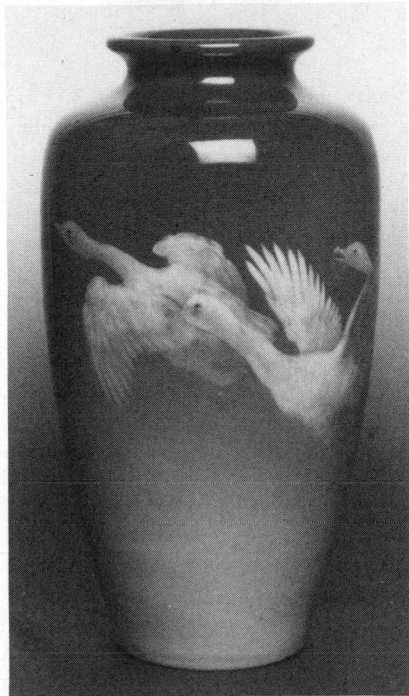

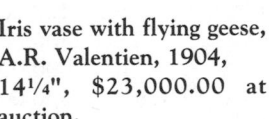

Iris vase with flying geese, A.R. Valentien, 1904, 14¼", $23,000.00 at auction.

Vase, poppies/whiplash stems, J Zettel, #922C, 1902, 8x4½" . . .850.00
Vase, swans/incised arches on blk, Shirayamadani, 1899, 10"..5,000.00
Vase, toadstools on blk to peach & gr, Schmidt, 1908, 10½" .7,500.00
Vase, tulips on peach to dk bl, S Sax, #909BB, 1906, 10x6" . .1,100.00
Vase, wild rose band, S Coyne, #30E, 1909, 7¾x3¾" 500.00
Vase, 2 lg flowers on bl to ivory, C Lindeman, waisted, 9" 700.00

Jewel Porcelain

Vase, bird/magnolia branch on dk bl, S Sax, 1917, 12x8½" . .1,350.00
Vase, dk bl w/incised collar & melon ribs, 1924, 14x12" 350.00
Vase, hollyhocks on lt bl/gold, Shirayamadani, 1946, 13x5" . . .800.00
Vase, Persian-type floral, bl/gr on turq, sgn, 1920, 18" 600.00
Vase, wild flowers/sm birds, blk on lime, A Conant, 10x5" . .2,250.00

Limoges

Creamer, reeds/sm bird, openwork rim, MA Daly, 1884, 6" L . .250.00
Jardiniere, reeds/birds, gold accents, M Rettig, 1883, 8" 950.00
Jug, bamboo/butterfly on red clay, Rettig, 1884, 4¾" 250.00
Jug, Oriental grass/clouds/butterfly, 1882, 4½" 180.00
Jug, reeds/birds, gold accents on gr tones, 1884, 5" 375.00
Vase, snow scene, sgn, pillow form, 1881, 10½", NM 900.00

Mat

Inkwell/pen tray, rook sits on rim, acorn well, dk bl, 9" 325.00
Jug, corn cvg, gr/brn, SE Coyne/Shirayamadani, 1906, 6" 500.00
Mug, emblem emb, HP flowers, red on gr, #578C, 1904, 5" 75.00
Tile, floral, gr/brn, #1977Y, Faience mk, in fr, 5½" 110.00
Tile, parrot/flowers, pk/purple on beige, in fr, 5½" 160.00
Umbrella stand, Arts & Crafts style, rust to gr, 1909, NM 325.00
Vase, berries, pk/bl, EX art, SE Coyne, #907E, 1930, 9" 750.00
Vase, daffodil/leaf emb, gr w/red streaks, 1919, #247, 8" 85.00
Vase, floral branches emb, yel/gr, Shirayamadani, 1916, 10" . . .170.00
Vase, floral cvg, bl/gr on red, S Coyne, 1905, 6", Xd/M 225.00
Vase, floral cvg, red/bl on gr, M Mitchell, 1904, 4" 300.00
Vase, irises on marine bl to mint, A Valentien, 1901, 15x5" .1,800.00
Vase, leaf/bellflower cvg, mc dripping, C Todd, 1914, 7" 190.00
Vase, leaves/flowers, brn-lined on gr, Hentschel, 1927, 8" 325.00
Vase, mums cvg, pk on gr, H Wilcox, #385Z, 1903, 9x3½" . .1,250.00
Vase, poppies/pods cvg, red/gr on wine/bl, A Pons, '07, 12¾"..1,500.00
Vase, star fish cvg, reticulated, JD Wareham, 1901, 5½" 850.00
Vase, stylized leaf cvg, gr/brn/bl, CS Todd, 1912, 9" 300.00
Vase, water lilies cvg, wht/bl/yel on gr, A Pons, 10" 850.00
Vase, waves relief at bottom, O Hicks, 1907, 6", NM 140.00
Wall pocket, gr w/touch of burgundy, Arts & Crafts, 12" 130.00

Porcelain

Candlestick, lt bl, #508, 1918, 5¾", pr 60.00
Dish, shell w/nude mermaid on edge, wht/turq gloss, 9½" L 170.00
Ink stand, dbl, mc geometrics, L Epply, 1930, 7" L 550.00
Vase, apple/leaves on wht, J Jensen, #6184E, 1945, 7½" 400.00
Vase, bird on rose branch w/butterflies, A Conant, 1921, 8" .2,900.00
Vase, blooming peach branch on copen bl, VanHorne, 9½" . . .675.00
Vase, bud; scrollwork on turq, brn int, Hentschel, 1920, 6" . . .350.00
Vase, floral band, mc on wht, E Dermott, #64I, 1919, 8½" 285.00
Vase, floral over paisley-like ground, S Sax, 1924, 6" 450.00
Vase, floral panels, J Jensen, #6314, 1946, 7½" 325.00
Vase, flowers, rose w/yel centers on pk, J Jensen, 1946, 7" 310.00
Vase, geometric/floral, mc on butterfat, S Sax, 1929, 5½" 450.00
Vase, Japanese scene, rooster/cherry tree, Conant, 25", NM .5,250.00

Vase, pansies, wax resist-type glaze, ET Hurley, 1948, 7½" 450.00
Vase, peach blossoms on bl, K VanHorne, #949D, '18, 9½x3" .. 675.00
Vase, poppies, Shirayamadani, #2782, 1946, 9½", Xd/but M ...450.00

Sea Green

Vase, bud; blk birds fly around neck, ET Hurley, 1898, 6¾" ..1,650.00
Vase, fish/seaweed, MA Daly, 4¾" 2,200.00
Vase, geese fly around neck, AR Valentien, 1895, 10½" 3,750.00
Vase, holly/berries, SE Coyne, 1901, 4¼" 500.00
Vase, leaves/long stems, blk on gr, A Valentien, rpr, 8" 600.00
Vase, mums, gr/yel on dk bl to gr, SE Coyne, 1901, 8¾" 850.00
Vase, 3 sea gulls/ocean waves/foam, SS/G/S1393, 1898, 6" ..3,000.00
Vase, 5 carp, dk bl/ivory on shaded bl/gr, M Daly, 12½" 4,800.00

Standard

Ewer, daisies, ruffled w/ribbon hdl, H Wilcox, 1897, 12x6" 475.00
Ewer, floral, J Zettel, #462D, 1893, 7" 205.00
Ewer, leaves/berries, EX art, MA Daly, ruffled, 1894, 8" 850.00

Standard honey jug, cavalier portrait, artist signed, 6½", $1,200.00.

Jug, berries, S Toohey, vertical side spout, 1893, 8" 400.00
Jug, silver overlay thistles/poppies/grapes, A Sprague, 11" ...3,000.00
Match holder, match/cigarettes, L VanBriggle, 1903, 2x3½" ...150.00
Pitcher, floral, str sides, #259C, AM Valentien/L, 1891, 6½" ..370.00
Planter, nasturtiums, A Sprague, w/orig liner, 1894, 2x8½" 450.00
Vase, acorns, ECL, #883, oval rim, 1900, 6" 200.00
Vase, berries, sgn SEC, #535E, 1894, 6¾" 350.00
Vase, cherries, SE Coyne, #611D, 1900, 8" 375.00
Vase, dogwood, Shirayamadani, long neck/sm hdls, 1890, 12" .850.00
Vase, fern fronds, EX art, LE Lindeman, 1905, 5½" 270.00
Vase, floral, AM Valentien, #556C, 1894, 11" 750.00
Vase, floral, sgn ADS, #735D, 1902, 7", Xd/but M 200.00
Vase, honeysuckle/bellflowers, ARV, pillow form, 1889, 14" .1,000.00
Vase, Irish setter, ET Hurley, pillow form, #767, 1899, 5¾" ...800.00
Vase, leaves, CF Bonsall, #352, 1902, 6" 200.00
Vase, lg poppies, M Nourse, #856, 1902, 22x8½" 3,500.00
Vase, silver overlay floral, bellflowers, M Nourse, 10" 2,700.00
Vase, silver overlay leaves, E Felton, 1892, 10¾" 1,900.00
Vase, silver overlay strapwork, tulips, CCL, 1906, 7" 1,600.00
Vase, sunflowers, EX art, MA Daly, 1891, 24x10", NM 2,500.00
Vase, 2 ears of corn, C Schmidt, #647, 1899, 7" 550.00

Tiger Eye

Jardiniere, water lilies on brn, AR Valentien, 1886, 7x8" 325.00

Vase, cherry blossoms, Shirayamadani, #604D, 1898, 6½" 775.00
Vase, frogs in slip relief, dk red clay, AR Valentien, 4" 210.00

Vellum

Bowl, roses, E Noonan, #923, 1907, 2¾x6½" 225.00
Plaque, autumn trees/lake, Ed Diers, orig fr, 1921, 4½x7½" ...850.00
Plaque, Birches, L Asbury, orig fr/EX seal, 1919, 7½x5¾" ...750.00
Plaque, Drive-Way, track-covered road, F Rothenbush, 8x6" ..700.00
Plaque, Evening, trees/hills, Rothenbush, 1899, fr, 8x4" 800.00
Plaque, harbor scene w/sailboats, Schmidt, pitted, 12x9" ...1,700.00
Plaque, Mt Rainier/lake, Rothenbush, 1921, 11x8½" 2,600.00
Plaque, Mtn Stream, many mtns, E Diers, fr, 1923, 10x12" ..4,200.00
Plaque, Northern Birches, S Sax, orig fr/factory seal, 6x8" ...1,800.00
Plaque, River, barn in bkground, Rothenbush, 1923, 4½x8" ...850.00
Plaque, scenic, pasture/mtns, F Rothenbush, 11x14" 2,900.00
Plaque, Twilight, river scene, L Epply, 1917, fr, 8x11" 2,100.00
Plaque, Venetian sailboats/3 lg posts, C Schmidt, 12x9" ...2,400.00

Vellum vase, scenic, vivid colors, L. Asbury, 1924, 15", $1,900.00.

Vase, apple blossoms on bl to gr, MH McDonald, 1913, 5½" ..350.00
Vase, apple blossoms on bl tones, pk int, L Asbury, 11" 950.00
Vase, carnations encircling, Ed Diers, bulbous, 1928, 10¾" 800.00
Vase, daisy band on flat shoulder, Rothenbush, 1931, 4" 210.00
Vase, fish on lt gr to bl, E Noonan, 1908, 7" 1,050.00
Vase, floral, dk bl top/bottom, E McDermott, 1916, 7½" 300.00
Vase, floral, EX art, SE Coyne, #166, 1904, 4¾" 200.00
Vase, floral, pastels, F Rothenbush, #904D, 1908, 8½" 400.00
Vase, harbor w/boats, C Schmidt, #2105, 1921, 5" 800.00
Vase, harbor w/Venetian boats, C Schmidt, #950, 1921, 9" ..1,500.00
Vase, harbor w/7 boats, C Schmidt, 1924, 11" 2,600.00
Vase, night scene, S Coyne, #30F, 1923, 7" 1,000.00
Vase, palm trees/shore, C Schmidt, 1926, 12x5" 2,400.00
Vase, peacock feathers, cvd/pnt, S Sax, #1126C, '13, 10x5" ..1,100.00
Vase, poppies, peach on gr to gray, E Noonan, 1907, 8" 550.00
Vase, scenic, brn-gr/purple/vivid bl, MG Denzler, 1917, 7" 650.00
Vase, scenic, brns on gr to brn, SE Coyne, 1911, 8" 1,100.00
Vase, scenic, EX art, F Rothenbush, #614C, 1929, 12½x6" ..2,000.00
Vase, scenic, pastels, F Rothenbush, slim form, 1915, 8" 750.00
Vase, scenic, sgn CGD, #950E, 1914, 7½" 550.00
Vase, scenic, snow/stream/trees, F Rothenbush, 1912, 12x6" .1,700.00
Vase, scenic, snow/sun/trees, Shirayamadani, 1912, 6½" 750.00

Vase, scenic, snow/trees, Ed Diers, #1858B, 1920, 13½" 1,100.00
Vase, scenic, snow/trees, SE Coyne, 1919, #946, 10½" 1,100.00
Vase, scenic, stream/trees, vivid colors, E Diers, 1914, 9" 900.00
Vase, scenic, trees, Ed Diers, #9097E, 1931, 9x3½" 1,200.00
Vase, scenic band, snow/trees, on bl-blk, Rothenbush, 13" ..1,700.00
Vase, silhouettes of ships on ocean, Rothenbush, 1910, 7" ...1,200.00
Vase, 3 wht geese in banded section, L Asbury, 1904, 7" 950.00

Wax Mat

Vase, berries, bl-lined on bl w/gr, SE Coyne, 1929, 8½" 325.00
Vase, cherries on blk to mustard, SE Coyne, 1925, 8" 400.00
Vase, cherries/branches, J Jensen, #604S, 1929, 7¾" 825.00
Vase, crocus, EX colors, MH McDonald, 1936, 7½" 500.00
Vase, crocus on red to yel, Shirayamadani, 1939, 7½" 800.00
Vase, deer/swirls/leaves, Deco style, Wm Hentschel, '29, 5" ...400.00
Vase, dogwood, pk on lt yel, bl neck, L Asbury, 1931, 8x6" 750.00
Vase, floral, brn-lined red & yel, E Barrett, 1926, 7½" 300.00
Vase, floral, dk bl-traced on pk & bl, SE Coyne, 1931, 4" 200.00
Vase, floral, K Jones, #939C, 1927, 9" 325.00
Vase, floral, red/bl on tan, Barrett, long neck, 1925, 16" 1,000.00
Vase, floral, SE Coyne, #1358E, 1925, 7" 250.00
Vase, floral, watercolor style, V Tischler, 1929, 11" 650.00
Vase, floral, yel/orange/gr/brn, J Jensen, #324, 1934, 18" 1,100.00
Vase, floral branches, red/brn/gr/yel, H McDonald, 1938, 5" ...400.00
Vase, fruit cvg, EX colors/workmanship, CS Todd, 1919, 8¾" ..325.00
Vase, grapes/branches, SE Coyne, #614B, 1926, 15" 950.00
Vase, irises in panels, J Jensen, #2933, 1929, 12" 420.00
Vase, leaf/flower cvg, mc on orange, C Todd, 1915, 14" 425.00
Vase, scrollwork, E Barrett, ped base, #6185, 1930, 8" 250.00

Miscellaneous

Ash tray, 1926, sm frog on rim, brn/lav mat, #2765, 6" W 65.00
Ash tray, 1930, clown, gr/brn mat, S Toohey, #6026, 4¼" 275.00
Ash tray, 1948, owl, chartreuse, #1094, 4x6" dia 125.00
Bookend, 1943, puppy, lt brn gloss, 5x5" 110.00
Bookends, 1921, rook on open book, 4-color, #2274, 6", pr 500.00
Bookends, 1924, elephant, tan, #2444D, 5", pr 225.00
Bookends, 1925, rook, brn mat, #2275, 5", pr 130.00
Bookends, 1927, ship, bl mat, sgn McDonald, 5½", pr 175.00
Bookends, 1932, pr penguins on ea, #2659, 6", pr 550.00
Bowl, 1922, flowers/animals/rooks emb, bl mat, #2177, 3x8" ...65.00
Bowl, 1936, 3 figural pelicans on sides, lt brn, #6557, 11" 190.00
Candle holder, 1924, floral, butterfat glaze, Epply, 7" 265.00
Dish, 1924, 3 joined flower forms, rose/cream, #2766, 9" 60.00
Figurine, 1932, donkey, ivory mat, W McD, 6" 175.00
Figurine, 1939, horse 'Man of War,' dk brn/gr, #6140, 6¼" 400.00
Figurine, 1944, bird on limb, natural colors, #6786, 7" 120.00
Figurine, 1955, polar bear, gr mat, #6424, 4" 250.00
Ginger jar, 1921, purple/pk gloss, #2301B, 15½", pr 800.00
Humidor, 1921, floral emb at bottom, 4 ft, bl mat, #1847 .....120.00
Jar, 1926, squeezebag, olive on bl/wht, Hentschel, lid, 19" ..1,800.00
Mug, 1906, Greek Key top, dk maroon w/bl, #587C, 4½" 50.00
Paperweight, 1917, Rookwood in block letters, purple/lav 180.00
Paperweight, 1923, elephant w/2 clowns, brn mat, 3½x4" 140.00
Paperweight, 1924, monkey on book, brn/gray/bl, #2677, 3½" .195.00
Paperweight, 1926, sitting nude, yel mat, L Abel, #2868, 4½" ..200.00
Paperweight, 1927, seal, dk brn/gray metallic, 3¼" 160.00
Paperweight, 1929, dog, open front legs, gr/bl/brn, 4¾" 100.00
Paperweight, 1929, frog, orange mat, #6097, 2½" 120.00
Paperweight, 1934, swan, yel mat, #1213, 1½x5¼" 165.00
Paperweight, 1936, pelican, lt brn gloss, #6238, 4¾" 100.00
Paperweight, 1945, duck, wht mat, #6064 ....90.00

Paperweight, 1946, bird on limb, natural colors, sgn M, 5" 150.00
Paperweight, 1946, dog, lt gr, #2777, 5" 210.00
Paperweight, 1947, bird, yel gloss, #6383, 3½" 250.00
Paperweight, 1952, goose, yel gloss, 4½" 105.00
Tile, flower, deeply molded, brn w/gr center, Faience, 4" 100.00
Tile, pine cones relief, 4-color, Faience, in fr, 6x8" 325.00
Tile, sailing ship, yel/gr/wht/lt bl, Faience, 13" 600.00
Tile, trees/mtn/river, EX color, Faience, sz w/fr: 16½" 550.00
Tile, tulips, pk on bl, 5", EX 100.00
Tile, 1910, Packard Co emblem, bl-gr, 4½", EX 75.00
Trivet, 1920, sea gull & waves, wht/gr, #2351, 5¾" 90.00
Trivet, 1928, cockatoo on branch, gr, #2043, 5½" 125.00
Trivet, 1930, Dutch woman & child, 5½" 100.00
Trivet, 1930, flower basket, mc, #3206, 5¾" 100.00
Vase, 1904, berries, OG Reed, pnt mat, unusual type, 7½" 750.00
Vase, 1918, nudes emb, porc w/wht mat, bl int, #2348, 8" 220.00
Vase, 1919, lt gr/dk bl wax mat-type gloss, w/lid, 9½" 145.00
Vase, 1920, bl w/dk pk int, hdls, #2335, 6" 80.00
Vase, 1923, bird/floral emb, dk bl mat, #2481, 9¾" 90.00
Vase, 1929, leaf band emb, bl mat, #2854, 4½" 40.00
Vase, 1930, floral emb, dk bl, #2589, 5" 35.00
Vase, 1932, red goldstone glaze, #6319D, 4¾" 200.00
Vase, 1934, leaves emb at neck, wht, hdls, #6493, 8" 80.00
Vase, 1935, Classical women, gray on rust, Barrett, 12x8" 800.00
Vase, 1935, floral, impressionistic/vivid, J Jensen, 5½" 550.00
Vase, 1936, trees/ducks emb, bl mat, #6551, 8" 90.00
Vase, 1937, 4 panels w/animals, bl, #6416, 8" 70.00
Vase, 1938, deer/trees emb, wine/aventurine, #6053, 8x6" 175.00
Vase, 1938, red goldstone, #6311, 7¼", Xd/but M 160.00
Vase, 1941, fish/flowers emb, gr mat, #6215, 7" 55.00
Vase, 1944, man/woman standing, Barrett, #6357, 6½" 550.00
Vase, 1945, birds/leaves emb, gr gloss, #6459, 4½" 40.00
Vase, 1945, horse w/grass & birds, brn on wht, W Rhem, 7½" .150.00
Vase, 1945, Mexican figures emb, turq, #6762, 5½" 50.00
Wall pocket, 1913, tulips/pointed leaves emb, pk/gr, #1391 ....90.00
Wall pocket, 1920, bug, pk/gr mat, 8½" 250.00
Wall pocket, 1921, leaf emb, bl mat, #2008, 7½" 40.00
Wall pocket, 1922, lily form, brn mat, #1036, 16" 70.00

Rorstrand

The Rorstrand Pottery was established in Sweden in 1726 and is today Sweden's oldest existing pottery. The earliest ware, now mostly displayed in Swedish museums, was much like old Delft. Later types were hard-paste porcelains that were enameled and decorated in a peasant style. Contemporary pieces are often described as Swedish Modern. Rorstrand is also famous for their Christmas plates.

Coffeepot, floral sprays emb, lav/gr, ca 1900s, 9" 500.00
Mug, irises, mauve/lav/sea gr, 1900, 6¼" 495.00
Vase, floral, purple on cream, rose-bowl form, mk, 7" dia 135.00
Vase, magnolia branches on celadon, sgn Algot Erikson, 22" .2,250.00
Vase, 5-petal flowers, lav on gr to wht, baluster form, 9½" 800.00

Rose Medallion

Rose Medallion is one of the patterns of Chinese export porcelain produced from before 1850 until the second decade of the 20th century. It is decorated in rose colors with panels of florals, birds, and butterflies that form reserves containing Chinese figures. Pre-1850s ware is unmarked and is characterized by quality workmanship and gold trim. From about 1850 until circa 1860, the kilns in Canton did not operate, and no Rose

Medallion was made. Post-1860 examples (still unmarked) can often be recognized by the poor quality of the gold trim or its absence. In the 1890s, the ware was often marked 'China'; 'Made in China' was used from 1910 through the 1930s.

See listings below for specific values.

Bowl, gilt, 1800s, 15" 900.00
Bowl, scalloped, 1800s, 2½x9" dia 370.00
Bowl, 1860-1900, 11½" 500.00
Creamer, bulbous w/hog's nose spout, 1800s, 4" 250.00
Cup & saucer, mk China, 1890s 50.00
Cup & saucer, octagonal, unmk, early 60.00
Dish, entree; canted corners, w/lid, 1800s, 9" L 350.00
Dish, tobacco leaf form, 1800s, 8½" L, EX 300.00
Jardiniere, hexagonal, rstr, late, 12x14" 225.00
Jardiniere, 1800s, 7½" 550.00
Plate, 15" 350.00
Plate, 1800s, 10" 150.00
Plate, 1825, 9½", set of 10 ....1,000.00
Platter, Made in China, 18" 275.00
Platter, mk China, 8½x11" 95.00
Platter, well & tree, 1825, worn, 16½" 350.00
Platter, 1800s, 18" 500.00
Platter, 1825, 14" 350.00
Platter, 1860s, 16½" 375.00
Platter, 1880s, 13" 300.00
Punch bowl, 13½" dia 950.00
Punch bowl, 1830s, 16" 1,650.00
Sauce boat, ovoid, 1800s, 4" 200.00
Shrimp dish, butterfly/floral center, 'A' monogram, 11", VG ...700.00
Tazza, birds/butterflies/etc, 1820s, 4x15x11" 850.00
Teapot, cord-wrapped hdl, ca 1860, rstr, 6x5½" 125.00
Teapot, wicker hdl, +2 handleless cups in wicker case 250.00
Tureen, w/lid, 1800s, 14" 1,600.00
Vase, salamander hdls, baluster form, 1800s, 17" 475.00

Roselane

From the late 1930s until 1973, Wm. and Georgia Fields operated a pottery (first in Pasadena, California; relocating later in Baldwin Park) where they produced various types of novelty items and well several lines of bowls, vases, etc. Their ware was sometimes marked with a backstamp (Roselane, Pasadena, Calif.); paper labels were also used.

Figurine, Balinese Dancers, gray/mauve, 8x10", pr 40.00
Figurine, cockatoo, head down 17.00
Figurine, East Indian Dancer, gray, 11" 25.00
Figurine, giraffe, gr, seated, #262, 7" 15.00
Planter, coolies sit on wall, gray 22.00
Teapot, Ultra '50s, blk/turq 25.00

Rosemeade

Rosemeade was the name chosen by Wahpeton Pottery Company of Wahpeton, North Dakota, to represent their product. The founders of the company were Laura Meade Taylor and R.J. Hughes, who organized the firm in 1940. It is most noted for small bird and animal figurals, either in high gloss or a Van Briggle-like matt glaze. The ware was marked 'Rosemeade' with an ink stamp or carried a 'Prairie Rose' sticker. The pottery closed in 1961.

Ash tray, horse's head emb on yel-gold, rectangular 32.00
Bowl/planter, lt bl, scalloped, 4x6" 10.00
Candle holder, scalloped, thrown, 1½x4", pr 25.00
Cotton holder, bunny, aqua 58.00
Creamer, cow's head, creamery name, pk, 4½" 38.00
Creamer, stylized horse's head, lime gr 22.00
Creamer & sugar bowl, tulips, wine, miniature 20.00
Figurine, bear, sitting, 3" 32.00
Figurine, buffalo, buff & tan, 2½x3¼" 40.00
Figurine, mouse, recumbent, gray w/pk nose, 1⅛x1¾" 17.50
Figurine, mouse on bk legs, gray, 1½" 17.50
Figurine, pheasant, 7" w/12½" wing span, M 225.00
Figurine, skunk, blk & wht, 3x3½" 22.00
Flower holder, stork, 7" 30.00
Hors d'oeuvre, pheasant, 5½x4¼" 45.00
Lamp, TV; pheasant, lg 385.00

Cock and hen pheasant, large, $275.00 for the pair.

Pitcher, rose & leaves emb on lt gr, 4¼" 20.00
Pitcher, wheat sprays emb on lt gr, 5¾" 21.00
Planter, grapes, gr, rectangular, 3½x8½x4" 28.00
Planter, grapes, gr, sq, 5½" 30.00
Rose bowl, gr shaded, 3" 17.50
Shakers, Boston terrier, bronze & wht, pr 26.00
Shakers, buffalo, 3½x2¾", pr 28.00
Shakers, cactus, yel blossom top, 1⅜", pr 22.00
Shakers, chickadee, pr 25.00
Shakers, chow-chow, rust, pr 18.00
Shakers, dalmation, blk & wht, pr 24.00
Shakers, dolphin, gr, pr 22.00
Shakers, donkey's head, pr 22.00
Shakers, ear of corn, pr 22.00
Shakers, English setter, gold & wht, pr 24.00
Shakers, fox terrier's head, pr 24.00
Shakers, greyhound, pr 22.00
Shakers, hen & rooster, blk, pr 30.00
Shakers, mallard drake & hen, pr 28.00
Shakers, Mexican chihuahua, pr 28.00
Shakers, mouse, gray w/blk & pk, 1¾", pr 24.00
Shakers, ox, brn, pr 24.00
Shakers, Paul Bunyan & Babe, pr 35.00
Shakers, pheasant w/tail down, pr 24.00

Shakers, raccoon, hands to ears, pr 24.00
Shakers, seal, lg, pr 24.00
Shakers, Siamese cats, gray & tan, 2¾", pr 24.00
Shakers, skunk, blk & wht, 2½", pr 24.00
Shakers, swan, blk, pr 24.00
Shakers, tulip, yel, pr 24.00
Shakers, turkey, pr 24.00
Tumbler, wheat, 5¼" 10.00
Vase, ball form, 2 sm wing hdls, 3¼" 22.00
Vase, blk w/incised wavy lines, ball form, 4" 28.00
Vase, bud; aqua, thrown, 5½" 27.50
Vase, bud; bronze, 7½" 18.00
Vase, bud; 4-color, 7½" 18.00
Vase, daffodil, dk bl, 4½" 18.00
Vase, Egyptian, gr, 8¼" 70.00
Wall pocket, moon form 10.00

Rosenthal

In 1879 Phillip Rosenthal established the Rosenthal Porcelain Factory in Selb, Bavaria. Its earliest products were figurines and fine tablewares. The company has continued to operate to the present decade, manufacturing limited edition plates.

Bowl, Aida, gold roses, ped ft, 11½" 85.00
Clock, figural nude/drapery atop, boy w/horn aside, 14" 3,850.00
Coffeepot, ironstone, 10" 85.00
Creamer & sugar bowl, Donatello, gold trim 35.00
Cup & saucer, Rosenthal Rose 30.00
Demitasse set, silver overlay, yel, mk, 15-pc 350.00
Dresser set, yel florals, Donatello, 4-pc 300.00
Figurine, Blackamoor w/ivory costume, 7", pr 345.00
Figurine, clown on domed column, procession of ducks, 9" 350.00
Figurine, Deco nude sits w/arm about whippet, draped, 9" 700.00
Figurine, fantail pigeons, wht on aqua base, sgn, 15" L 325.00
Figurine, girl w/braids/bouquet/hat, artist sgn, 7¾" 160.00
Figurine, Lillian Harvey, 12" 200.00
Figurine, mule, recumbent, artist sgn, dtd 1965 ....75.00
Figurine, nude boy w/wolfhound, 8" 300.00
Figurine, poodle, Selb, Germany, 8½" 200.00
Figurine, squirrel w/walnut, 7" 95.00
Plate, Delft type w/windmill, 6¾" 30.00
Plate, Wheat, 8½" 50.00

Sculpture, draped nude with Afgan hound, marked, 9", $700.00.

Tureen, etched water lilies, gold bands/hdls 65.00
Vase, bud; Oriental boy/pagoda on wht w/gold, 11" 50.00
Vase, Studio Line, stylized bird/flowers, 6" 45.00

Roseville

The Roseville Pottery Company was established in 1892 by George F. Young in Roseville, Ohio. Finding their facilities inadequate, the company moved to Zanesville in 1898, erected a new building, and installed the most modern equipment available. By 1900 Young felt ready to enter into the stiffly competitive art pottery market.

Roseville's first art line was called Rozane. Similar to Rookwood's Standard, Rozane featured dark blended backgrounds with slip-painted underglaze artwork of nature studies, portraits, birds, and animals. Azurean, developed in 1902, was a blue and white underglaze art line on a blue blended background. Egypto (1904) featured a matt glaze in a soft shade of old green and was modeled in low relief after examples of ancient Egyptian pottery. Mongol (1904) was a high-gloss oxblood red line after the fashion of the Chinese Sang de Boeuf. Mara (1904), an iridescent lustre line of magenta and rose with intricate patterns developed on the surface or in low relief, successfully duplicated Sicardo's work. These early lines were followed by many others of highest quality: Fudjiyama and Woodland (1905-06) reflected an Oriental theme; Crystalis (1906) was covered with beautiful frost-like crystals. Della Robbia, their most famous line (introduced in 1906), was decorated with designs ranging from florals, animals, and birds to scenes of Viking warriors and Roman gladiators. These designs were accomplished by sgraffito with slip-painted details. Very limited but of great importance to collectors today, Rozane Olympic (1905) was decorated with scenes of Greek mythology on a red ground. Pauleo (1914) was the last of the artware lines. It was varied — over two hundred glazes were recorded — and some pieces were decorated by hand, usually with florals.

During the second decade of the century until the plant closed forty years later, new lines were continually added. Some of the more popular of the middle-period lines were Donatello, 1915; Futura, 1928; Pine Cone, 1931; and Blackberry, 1933. The floral lines of the later years have become highly collectible. Pottery from every era of Roseville production — even its utility ware — attest to an unwavering dedication to quality and artistic merit.

Examples of the fine art pottery lines present the greatest challenge to evaluate. Scarcity is a prime consideration. The quality of artwork varied from one artist to another. Some pieces show fine detail and good color, and naturally this influences their values. Studies of animals and portraits bring higher prices than the floral designs. An artist's signature often increases the value of any item, especially if the artist is one who is well recognized. For further information, consult *The Collectors Encyclopedia of Roseville Pottery, First and Second Series*, by Sharon and Bob Huxford, available at your local library or bookstore.

Our advisors for this category are Janet and Marvin Stofft; they are listed in the Directory under Indiana.

Advertising sign, pk matt, Deco design, 2x6" 550.00
Apple Blossom, basket, #309, 8" 80.00
Apple Blossom, bowl, #326-6, 2½x6½" 35.00
Apple Blossom, ewer, #316, 8" 50.00
Apple Blossom, hanging basket 65.00
Apple Blossom, jardiniere, hdls, #342-6, 6" 50.00
Apple Blossom, vase, hdls, #387, 9" 55.00
Artcraft, candlestick, dbl, bl, 5" 45.00
Artcraft, console bowl, bl, 13" 90.00
Artwood, planter, #1055-9, 9½x7" 40.00
Autumn, jardiniere, 9½" 600.00
Autumn, pitcher, 8½" 400.00

Autumn, shaving mug, 4" 225.00
Aztec, lamp base, 11" 275.00
Aztec, pitcher, sgn, 5½" 250.00
Aztec, vase, bl, flared rim, 11½" 300.00
Azurean, mug, floral, 5" 450.00
Azurean, tankard, berries/leaves, ornate hdl, 12¼" . . .1,250.00
Azurean, vase, floral, Leffler, #822-7, 15½" 1,000.00
Bank, beehive, 3" 200.00
Bank, eagle, 2½" 175.00
Bank, monkey, 6" 150.00
Bank, pig, St Louis 1904 commemorative, 3x4" 100.00
Bittersweet, basket, #809, 8" 70.00
Bittersweet, bud vase, dbl, #873, 6" .40.00
Bittersweet, console bowl, #829-12, 12½" 45.00
Bittersweet, cornucopia, #882, 8" 45.00
Bittersweet, ewer, #816, 8" 60.00
Bittersweet, vase, #972, 5" 35.00
Bittersweet, vase, dbl, #858, 4" 40.00
Bittersweet, vase, sm hdls, #842-7, 7" 60.00
Blackberry, console bowl, 13" 150.00
Blackberry, jardiniere, sm hdls, 6" 150.00
Blackberry, jardiniere & pedestal 1,400.00
Blackberry, jug, 5" 125.00
Blackberry, vase, bulbous w/ear hdls, 5" 125.00
Blackberry, vase, hdls, 8" 175.00
Blackberry, wall pocket, paper label, 8¾" 210.00
Bleeding Heart, basket, #360-10, 9½" 110.00
Bleeding Heart, ewer, #963, 6" 60.00
Bleeding Heart, plate, #381-10, 10½" 50.00
Bleeding Heart, pot, #651-3, 3½" 35.00
Bleeding Heart, vase, hdls, #138, 4" .40.00
Bleeding Heart, wall pocket, #1287-8, 8½" 110.00
Blended, umbrella stand, floral, #609, 20" 225.00

Burmese candle holders, 7", $125.00 for the pair.

Burmese, candle holders/bookends, #70B, blk, pr 150.00
Burmese, candlestick, #75-B, pr 30.00
Burmese, wall pocket, #82-B, wht, 7½" 175.00
Bushberry, basket, #372, 12" 135.00
Bushberry, cider pitcher, #1325, 8½" 125.00
Bushberry, cornucopia, #153, 6" 35.00
Bushberry, cornucopia, dbl, #155-8, 6" 45.00
Bushberry, ewer, #1, 6" 50.00
Bushberry, mug, #1-3½, 3½" 45.00
Bushberry, vase, flared twig hdls, #39, 14" 165.00
Bushberry, vase, hdls, #411-6, 6" 50.00

Bushberry, wall pocket, #1291, 8" 125.00
Capri, basket, #510-10, gr, 9" 75.00
Capri, bowl, #527-7, red mottle, 7" 25.00
Capri, cornucopia, #556-6, 6" 45.00
Capri, window box, #569-10, red mottle, 10x3" 45.00
Carnelian I, fan vase, 6" 28.00
Carnelian I, vase, 8" 52.00
Carnelian II, bowl, 4x10" 60.00
Carnelian II, ewer, 12½" 125.00
Carnelian II, fan vase, 6½" 30.00
Carnelian II, planter, 8x3" 30.00
Carnelian II, vase, 8" 60.00
Cherry Blossom, hanging basket, 8" 300.00
Cherry Blossom, jardiniere, hdls, 10" 300.00
Cherry Blossom, jardiniere & pedestal, 25½" 1,100.00
Cherry Blossom, jug vase, hdls, 7" .165.00
Cherry Blossom, vase, 5" 115.00
Chloron, wall pocket, boy or girl, 9½", ea 450.00
Chloron, wall pocket, nude, 8½" 400.00
Clemana, candle holders, 4½", pr 95.00
Clemana, vase, narrow neck/bulbous bottom, #756-9, 9½" 150.00
Clemana, vase, sm angle hdls. #754-8, 8½" 110.00
Clematis, basket, #387, 7" 45.00
Clematis, bowl, hdls, gr, #445, 4" 20.00
Clematis, bud vase, hdls, #187, 7" 30.00
Clematis, cookie jar, #3, 10" 125.00
Clematis, cornucopia, #140, 6" 20.00
Clematis, flower pot, #668-5, 5½" 55.00
Clematis, vase, #187, 7" 52.00
Clematis, vase, hdls, #103-6, 6" 30.00
Clematis, wall pocket, #1295, 8" 80.00
Columbine, basket, #365, 7" 60.00
Columbine, bowl, hdls, #655, 3" 30.00
Columbine, cornucopia, #149-6, 5½" 30.00
Columbine, vase, angle hdls, #17-7, 7½" 40.00
Corinthian, ash tray, 2" 55.00
Corinthian, bowl, ftd, 4½" 60.00
Corinthian, bud vase, dbl, 7" 35.00
Corinthian, candlestick, 10", ea 40.00
Corinthian, jardiniere, 7" 85.00
Corinthian, umbrella stand, 20" 400.00
Corinthian, wall pocket, 8" 75.00
Cornelian, cracker jar, w/lid 175.00
Cornelian, pitcher, emb corn, 5" 75.00
Cornelian, shaving mug, 4" 65.00
Cornelian, soap dish, w/lid, 4" 85.00
Cosmos, basket, 12" 140.00
Cosmos, ewer, #951, 15" 175.00
Cosmos, vase, #375-4, 4" 35.00
Cosmos, vase, hdls, 6½" 37.50
Cosmos, vase, 3" 25.00
Cremona, vase, 4" 40.00
Cremona, vase, 7" 50.00
Crocus, vase, 9" 400.00
Crystalis, vase, sm neck, wide-shouldered tapered form, 11" . .1,350.00
Dahlrose, bowl, hdls, oval, 10" L 60.00
Dahlrose, jardiniere, hdls, 6" 50.00
Dahlrose, vase, hdls, 10" 95.00
Dahlrose, vase, pillow form, 7x5" 55.00
Dahlrose, vase, sq, 6" 60.00
Dahlrose, wall pocket, 10" 125.00
Dahlrose, window box, 12½x6" 85.00
Dawn, ewer, #834-16, 16" 200.00
Dawn, vase, #827, 6" 50.00

Decorated Art, jardiniere, floral, hdls, #448, 10" 275.00
Decorated Creamware, jardiniere & pedestal, rose decal, 26" ..550.00
Decorated Utility Ware, pitcher, 6" 35.00
Della Robbia, bowl, serpents, sgn, 8x2½" 1,400.00
Della Robbia, mug, little Dutch girls, sgn, 4" 500.00
Della Robbia, pitcher, centurion in chariot, sgn, 8" 3,500.00
Della Robbia, teapot, bell shape, 6½" 1,275.00
Della Robbia, vase, medieval cavalier/trees, sgn, 18x5½" 7,750.00
Dogwood I, bowl, 2½" 45.00
Dogwood I, jardiniere, 8" 100.00
Dogwood I, jardiniere & pedestal, 30" 600.00
Dogwood II, boat planter, 6" 50.00
Dogwood II, jardiniere, 8" 90.00
Dogwood II, tub, 7x4" 50.00
Dogwood II, vase, 14½" 150.00
Dogwood II, vase, 9" 60.00
Donatella, creamer, landscape, creamware, 3" 55.00
Donatella, tea set, Gibson Girls, creamware, 3-pc 400.00
Donatella, teapot, cherries, creamware, 8½" 300.00
Donatello, basket, 15" 300.00
Donatello, basket, 7½" 125.00
Donatello, bowl, rolled rim, 9½" 50.00
Donatello, bowl, 6" 45.00
Donatello, bud vase, dbl, 7" 225.00
Donatello, compote, 5" 60.00
Donatello, compote, 9½" 150.00
Donatello, cuspidor, 5½" 165.00
Donatello, jardiniere, 6" 85.00
Donatello, pitcher, 6½" 200.00
Donatello, plate, 8" 250.00
Donatello, vase, gray/beige, 10" 175.00
Donatello, vase, trumpet shape, 10" 62.00
Dutch, pin tray, 4" 50.00
Dutch, pitcher, milk; 4½" 150.00
Dutch, pitcher, 11" 250.00
Dutch, powder box, w/lid, 3" 200.00
Dutch, tankard, 11½" 150.00
Dutch, tobacco jar, w/lid, 5" 200.00
Earlam, bowl, hdls, 11½x3" 40.00
Earlam, planter, hdls, 10½x5½" 45.00
Earlam, vase, hdls, 6" 60.00
Early Pitchers, Boy, 7½" 200.00
Early Pitchers, Bridge, blended, 6" 50.00
Early Pitchers, Bridge, 6" 55.00
Early Pitchers, Cow, rare, 6½" 200.00
Early Pitchers, Cow, 7½" 175.00
Early Pitchers, Goldenrod, 9½" 85.00
Early Pitchers, Grape, 6" 60.00
Early Pitchers, Iris, 7" 175.00
Early Pitchers, Landscape, 7½" 55.00
Early Pitchers, Mill, 8" 175.00
Early Pitchers, Poppy, #141, 9" 100.00
Early Pitchers, Tulip, 7½" 50.00
Early Pitchers, Wild Rose, 9½" 85.00
Egypto, circle jug, 11" 500.00
Egypto, compote, 9" 300.00
Egypto, oil lamp, 5" 275.00
Egypto, pitcher, 7" 200.00
Elsie the Cow, mug, #B1 ....110.00
Falline, vase, hdls, gr, 6" 175.00
Falline, vase, hdls, 8" 200.00
Ferella, bowl, on ped, red, 12" 225.00
Ferella, vase, red, 8½" 325.00
Ferella, wall pocket, brn, 6½" 425.00

Florane, basket, 8½" 80.00
Florane, bowl, hdls, 5" 50.00
Florane, vase, 3½" 35.00
Florentine, bowl, 9" 35.00
Florentine, bud vase, dbl, 4½" 30.00
Florentine, compote, ftd, 10" 45.00
Florentine, jardiniere, 5" 45.00
Florentine, vase, 6½" 40.00
Florentine, window box, 11½" 125.00
Forget-Me-Not, dresser set, creamware w/lav or lt bl decal 300.00
Foxglove, basket, #373, 8" 60.00
Foxglove, bud vase, dbl, #160, 4½" 35.00
Foxglove, candle holders, #1150, 4½", pr 45.00
Foxglove, conch shell, #426, 6" 35.00
Foxglove, cornucopia, #166-6, 6" 40.00
Foxglove, tray, 11" 45.00
Foxglove, vase, hdls, #52-12, 12½" 80.00
Freesia, basket, #390-7, 7" 50.00
Freesia, bowl, hdls, #464-6, 8½" 30.00
Freesia, candle holder, hdls, #1161, 4½", ea 25.00
Freesia, cookie jar, #4, 10" 125.00
Freesia, cornucopia, #198, 8" 30.00
Freesia, ewer, #21, 15" 200.00
Freesia, jardiniere & pedestal 375.00
Freesia, vase, #127, 12" 130.00
Freesia, vase, hdls, #196, 8" 50.00
Freesia, vase, hdls, #463-5, 5" 40.00
Freesia, wall pocket, hdls, #1296-8, 8½" 70.00
Freesia, window box, hdls, #1392-8, 10½" 30.00
Fuchsia, basket, w/frog, #350, 8" 125.00
Fuchsia, candlestick, #1132, 2", ea 20.00
Fuchsia, pitcher, ice lip, #1322, 8" 150.00
Fuchsia, vase, floral, #893-6, 6" 50.00
Fudji, vase, stylized florals, 10" 1,350.00
Fudji, vase, typical squeezebag decor, gourd form, 8½x5½" 900.00
Fudjiyama, jardiniere, butterflies, 9" 1,200.00
Futura, bl/brn fan form w/sq opening, 6x9" 165.00
Futura, bud vase/candlestick, stacked cones, 10", pr 250.00
Futura, jard, pk/purple leaves on gr & pk, hdls, 6x8½" 375.00
Futura, pot, blended, tan/turq, 4 sq wafer ft, 5" 150.00
Futura, vase, ball form on pyramid base, balloons, 8½" 500.00
Futura, vase, brn cone w/stepped buttresses, 8" 200.00
Futura, vase, bulbous w/stacked neck, gr, 12½" 400.00
Futura, vase, upright trianglar cone on disk base, 9" 300.00
Futura, vase, wide w/'X' under step-bk neck, angle hdls, 9" 375.00
Futura, window box, blended, 15½x5" 200.00
Gardenia, basket, #609, gr, 10" 95.00
Gardenia, bowl, #600, 4" 30.00
Gardenia, cornucopia, #621, 6" 35.00
Gardenia, ewer, 6" 35.00
Gardenia, tray, #631-14, 15" 60.00
Gardenia, wall pocket, hdls, #666-8, 9½" 110.00
Gardenia, window box, #658-8, 8½x3" 25.00
Holland, tankard, #2, 9½" 125.00
Imperial I, basket, #8, 10" 80.00
Imperial I, basket, 6" 55.00
Imperial I, bud vase, triple, 8" 60.00
Imperial I, bud vase, 12" 80.00
Imperial I, comport, 6½" 80.00
Imperial II, bowl, 4½" 110.00
Iris, basket, #347, 10" 85.00
Iris, basket, #355-10, 9½" 125.00
Iris, bowl, hdls, #359, 5" 45.00
Iris, console bowl, #362-10, 3½x12½" 50.00

Iris, ewer, #926, 10" 110.00
Ivory II, cornucopia, #2, 12x5½" 35.00
Ivory II, ewer, #941-10, 10½" 50.00
Ivory II, jardiniere, 6" 40.00
Ivory II, sand jar, 14½" 225.00
Ivory II, wall shelf, #8, 5½" 70.00
Ixia, basket, #346, 10" 70.00
Ixia, console bowl, #330-7, 3½x10½" 25.00
Ixia, vase, #862-10, 10½" 50.00
Jonquil, basket, 9" 150.00
Jonquil, bowl, hdls, 3" 50.00
Jonquil, crocus pot, hdls, 7" .200.00
Jonquil, vase, hdls, 12" 225.00
Jonquil, vase, hdls, 4" 50.00
Jonquil, wall pocket, 8½" 250.00
Juvenile, creamer, bear, gr band, 4" 115.00
Juvenile, creamer, Santa Claus, 3½" 95.00
Juvenile, creamer, Sunbonnet Girl, 3½" 60.00
Juvenile, custard, sitting rabbit, gr band, 2½" 60.00
Juvenile, mug, dog, hdls, 3" 65.00
Juvenile, mug, fat puppy, gr band, 3½" 70.00
Juvenile, mug, rabbit, 3" 50.00
Juvenile, mug, standing rabbit, 3" 65.00
Juvenile, pitcher, milk; chicks 45.00
Juvenile, plate, duck w/hat, rolled edge, 8" 75.00
Juvenile, plate, fancy cat, divided, 8½" 250.00
Juvenile, plate, Little Bo Peep, rolled rim, 8" 75.00
Juvenile, plate, pig, 8" 175.00
La Rose, jardiniere, 6½" 60.00
Landscape, planter, windmill, 4½" 75.00
Laurel, bowl, 3½" 50.00
Laurel, vase, 10" 110.00
Laurel, vase, 6½" 50.00
Lombardy, jardiniere, ftd, 6½" 150.00
Lombardy, wall pocket, matt glaze, 8" 175.00
Lotus, bowl, #L6-9, 9x3" 60.00
Lotus, vase, pillow form, #L4-10, 10½" 100.00
Luffa, bowl, 4" 40.00
Luffa, jardiniere, hdls, 5¼" base 110.00
Luffa, jardiniere & pedestal, 24½" 550.00
Luffa, vase, 8" 100.00
Lustre, basket, 10" 150.00
Lustre, bowl, 5" 35.00
Lustre, vase, pk, 10" 75.00
Magnolia, ash tray, #28, 7" 45.00
Magnolia, basket, #385, 10" 95.00
Magnolia, cornucopia, #184-6, 6" 30.00
Magnolia, mug, #3, 3" 45.00
Magnolia, planter, hdls, #389, 8" L 30.00
Magnolia, tea set, #4, 3-pc 125.00
Mara, bowl, hdls, 4" 1,300.00
Matt Color, bowl, #15, 3" 35.00
Matt Color, hanging basket, 4½" 40.00
Matt Color, pot, hdls, 4" 30.00
Matt Green, planter, w/liner, #510, 4" 150.00
Matt Green, tobacco jar, 6" 60.00
Mayfair, bowl, #1110, 4" 25.00
Mayfair, bowl, #1119-9, 10" 40.00
Mayfair, cornucopia, #1013-6, 6½x3" 30.00
Mayfair, tankard, #1107, 12" .75.00
Mayfair, teapot, #1121, 5" 40.00
Ming Tree, basket, #508, 8" 65.00
Ming Tree, basket, #509-12, 13" 125.00
Ming Tree, conch shell, #563, 8½" 40.00

Ming Tree, ewer, #516, 10" 85.00
Ming Tree, floor vase, #586-15, 15½" 300.00
Ming Tree, planter, #568-8, 8½x4" 40.00
Ming Tree, vase, hdls, #581, 6" 35.00
Mock Orange, ewer, #916, 6" 50.00
Mock Orange, planter, #931-8, 9x3½" 35.00
Mock Orange, vase, pillow form, ftd, #930-8, 7" 45.00
Moderne, comport, hdls, #297-6, 6" 60.00
Mongol, mug, 3-hdl, 6" 850.00
Mongol, vase, cylindrical, 15" 1,000.00
Monticello, basket, 6½" 150.00
Monticello, vase, hdls, 9" 90.00
Morning-Glory, basket, 10½" 350.00
Morning-Glory, console bowl, sm angle hdls, 4½x11½" 170.00
Morning-Glory, vase, hdls, 6" 175.00
Morning-Glory, vase, pear form, hdls, wht, 10" 225.00
Moss, candle holder, triple, #1108, 7", ea 75.00
Moss, console bowl, 13" 60.00
Moss, vase, pillow form, hdls, #781-8, 8" 45.00
Moss, wall pocket, #1278-8, 8" 110.00
Mostique, bowl, 2½" 25.00
Mostique, bowl, 7" 40.00
Mostique, compote, 7" 65.00
Mostique, jardiniere, 8" 75.00
Mostique, umbrella stand 250.00
Normandy, jardiniere, 7" 175.00
Novelty Steins, ea 200.00
Old Ivory, jardiniere, 8" 150.00
Olympic, pitcher, Pandora Brought to Earth, 7" 2,150.00
Olympic, vase, man seated in chair, 2 maids, hdls, 11x9½" . .2,300.00
Orian, compote, on ped, #272-10, bl, 4½x10½" 60.00
Panel, candlestick, 8", pr 150.00
Panel, fan vase, nude, 6" 185.00
Panel, fan vase, nude, 8" 200.00
Panel, vase, 8" 85.00
Pasadena, occasional piece, #526, 7" 25.00
Pauleo, vase, cylindrical, ftd, 12" 700.00
Pauleo, vase, floral, orange on gray lustre, 14" 900.00
Peony, basket, #379-12, 11" .100.00
Peony, bowl, hdls, #661, 4" 35.00
Peony, cornucopia, dbl, #172 .40.00
Peony, ewer, #8, 10" 100.00
Peony, planter, #387-8, 10" 25.00
Peony, tea set, #3, 3-pc 125.00
Peony, wall pocket, #1293, bl, 8" 80.00
Persian, creamer & sugar bowl 125.00
Persian, jardiniere, lg 175.00
Persian, jardiniere, 5" 125.00
Pine Cone, basket, #353-11, bl, 11" 200.00
Pine Cone, basket, brn, #339, 13x9" 325.00
Pine Cone, basket, gr, #408, 6" 60.00
Pine Cone, boat dish, #427-8, bl, 9" 80.00
Pine Cone, bud vase, #479-7, Apple Blossom pk, 7½" 300.00
Pine Cone, console bowl, bl, 11" 75.00
Pine Cone, cornucopia, gr, #128, 8" 40.00
Pine Cone, jardiniere & pedestal, bl 900.00
Pine Cone, pitcher, bl, #415, 9" 250.00
Pine Cone, umbrella stand, brn 600.00
Pine Cone, vase, hdls, #908-8, bl, 8" 100.00
Pine Cone, vase, pillow form, #845-8, bl, 8" 125.00
Pine Cone, wall shelf, #1 . . . . .175.00
Poppy, basket, #347, 10" 85.00
Poppy, basket, #348-12, 12½" 225.00
Poppy, bowl, hdls, #336-10, 12" 40.00

Poppy, ewer, #876, 10" 75.00
Poppy, jardiniere, hdls, #335-6, 6½" 50.00
Poppy, wall pocket, #1281, 8½" 150.00
Raymor, bean pot, #194, blk .25.00
Raymor, bowl, salad; #161, gray, 11½" 15.00
Raymor, butter dish, w/lid, #181, brn, 7½" 30.00
Raymor, gravy boat, #190, brn, 9½" 12.00
Raymor, hot plate, #159 . . . . .15.00
Raymor, pitcher, water; #189, 10" 60.00
Rosecraft Black, wall pocket, 9" 125.00
Rosecraft Blended, jardiniere, 4" 35.00
Rosecraft Hexagon, bowl, hdls, 7½" 75.00
Rosecraft Hexagon, bud vase, dbl, 5" 75.00
Rosecraft Hexagon, vase, bowl form, 4" 80.00
Rosecraft Panel, jar, w/lid, 10" 300.00
Rosecraft Panel, window box, 12x6" 125.00
Rosecraft Vintage, vase, 10" 125.00
Rosecraft Vintage, window box, 11½x6" 125.00
Rosecraft Yellow, wall pocket, 10" 125.00
Royal Capri, vase, #583-9, 9" 275.00
Rozane, bud vase, floral, C Neff, 8" 110.00
Rozane, chocolate pot, floral, sgn, 9½" 400.00
Rozane, jardiniere, floral, ftd, 9½" 200.00
Rozane, jardiniere & pedestal, floral, #524, 31" 1,000.00
Rozane, letter holder, floral, C Neff, 3½" 200.00
Rozane, mug, ear of corn, sgn, 6" 225.00
Rozane, mug, floral, #886, sgn Harry Rhead, 4½" 200.00
Rozane, mug, floral, G Gerwick, 5" 175.00
Rozane, pitcher, floral, Mary Pierce, 7" 850.00
Rozane, tankard, ears of corn, V Adams, 15½" 450.00
Rozane, tankard, floral, sgn, 10½" 300.00
Rozane, vase, cow portrait, sgn, 14" 3,250.00
Rozane, vase, dog w/bird, hdls, pillow form, Pillsbury, 9" 2,000.00
Rozane, vase, floral, hdls, #883, sgn, 6" 225.00
Rozane, vase, floral, sgn J Imlay, 16" 1,000.00
Rozane, vase, grape clusters, sgn, 15" 425.00
Rozane Light, jardiniere, floral, ftd, 5" 130.00
Rozane Light, mug, grape cluster, Pillsbury, 5" 250.00
Rozane Light, tankard, ear of corn, J Imlay, 10" 400.00
Rozane Light, vase, sgn, 18" 900.00
Rozane 1917, basket, bl, 11" 90.00
Rozane 1917, basket, pk, 6" 60.00
Rozane 1917, compote, gr, 5" 70.00
Rozane 1917, spittoon, ivory, 5" 150.00
Rozane 1917, vase, yel, 10" .60.00
Russco, bud vase, dbl, 8½" .45.00
Russco, cornucopia, triple, 12½x8" 70.00
Russco, vase, hdls, 7" 70.00
Savona, wall pocket, 8" 250.00

Silhouette vase with nude, green, #768-8", $135.00.

Silhouette, basket, #710, 10" 50.00
Silhouette, cigarette box 35.00
Silhouette, cornucopia, #722 . . . . .32.00
Silhouette, ewer, #716-6, 6½" 40.00
Silhouette, ewer, #717, 10" 50.00
Silhouette, fan vase, nude, #783, 7" 150.00
Silhouette, planter, dbl, leaves, #757-9, 5½" 25.00
Silhouette, vase, leaves at bottom, #789-14, 14" 100.00
Smoker Sets, ash tray, Fatima, 3" 175.00
Smoker Sets, tobacco jar, 6" 250.00
Snowberry, ash tray 40.00
Snowberry, basket, #1BK-12, 12½" 75.00
Snowberry, bowl, hdls, #1RB, 5" 35.00
Snowberry, candle holders, #1CS-1, pr 25.00
Snowberry, console bowl, hdls, #1BL1, 10" L 35.00
Snowberry, ewer, #1TK-15, 16" 150.00
Snowberry, vase, pillow form, #1FH-6, 6½" 30.00
Sunflower, bowl, 4" 75.00
Sunflower, console bowl, hdls, 12½x3" 100.00
Sunflower, jardiniere, 9" 200.00
Sunflower, vase, hdls, 5" 60.00
Sunflower, wall pocket, 7½" 300.00

Sylvan jardiniere, 7½", $395.00.

Teasel, basket, #349, 10" .100.00
Teasel, bowl, #342, 4" 30.00
Teasel, ewer, #890, 18" 175.00
Teasel, vase, #881-6, 6" 35.00
Teasel, vase, hdld, 5" 30.00
Thornapple, basket, #342, 10" 95.00
Thornapple, bud vase, triple, #1120, 6" 50.00
Thornapple, cornucopia, 6" 30.00
Thornapple, vase, on ped, sm angle hdls, #820-9, 9½" 80.00
Thornapple, wall pocket, #1280-8, 8" 110.00
Topeo, bowl, red, 2½" 100.00
Topeo, vase, red, 15" 325.00
Tourist, bowl, 4x7" 1,100.00
Tourist, window box, 19x8½" 1,100.00
Tourmaline, candlestick, bl, 5" 40.00
Tourmaline, cornucopia, bl, 7" 45.00
Tourmaline, ginger jar 300.00
Tourmaline, planter, 12½x5" 85.00
Tourmaline, vase, loving-cup form, 8" 60.00

Tourmaline, vase, pillow from, hdls, bl, 6" **45.00**
Tuscany, console bowl, 11" L **40.00**
Tuscany, vase, hdls, 9" **60.00**
Velmoss, bowl, pointed hdls, 11x3" **45.00**
Velmoss II, bud vase, dbl, 8" **60.00**
Velmoss II, cornucopia, dbl, bl, 8½" **60.00**
Velmoss Scroll, bowl, 9x2½" **50.00**
Velmoss Scroll, candlestick, 11", pr **175.00**
Velmoss Scroll, vase, 10" **80.00**
Velmoss Scroll, vase, 6" **55.00**
Victorian Art Pottery, jar, w/lid, glossy, 8" **350.00**
Vista, basket, 12" **150.00**
Vista, vase, 17½" **400.00**
Water Lily, basket, #380, 8" **45.00**
Water Lily, bowl, hdls, #663, brn, 3" **25.00**
Water Lily, cookie jar, hdls, #1, brn, 10" **125.00**
Water Lily, cornucopia, #177, brn, 6" **35.00**
Water Lily, ewer, #10, 6" **35.00**
Water Lily, hanging basket, USA, 9" **120.00**
Water Lily, vase, hdls, #81, bl, 12" **70.00**
White Rose, basket, #364, bl, 12" **75.00**
White Rose, basket, floral, #362-8, 7½" **60.00**
White Rose, cornucopia, #143, 6" **25.00**
White Rose, ewer, #993, bl, 15" **150.00**
White Rose, pitcher, #1324 ....**70.00**
White Rose, vase, #147, 8" **50.00**
White Rose, vase, #978-4, 4" **25.00**
White Rose, wall pocket, #1289-8, 8½" **95.00**
Wincraft, basket, #210-12, 12" **100.00**
Wincraft, bowl, #227-10, 13½x4" **40.00**
Wincraft, circle vase, #1053, 8" **30.00**
Wincraft, cornucopia, #221-8, 9x5" **40.00**
Wincraft, cornucopia, #222, 8" **22.00**
Wincraft, ewer, #217, 6" **35.00**
Wincraft, tea set, #271, 3-pc **100.00**
Wincraft, vase, #282, 8" **35.00**
Windsor, basket, inverted heart-shape hdl, 4½" **175.00**
Windsor, vase, ferns, hdls, 7" **200.00**
Wisteria, console bowl, sm angle hdls, 12" **85.00**
Wisteria, vase, hdls, 10" **175.00**
Wisteria, vase, 9" **175.00**
Woodland, vase, fish/plants, 9" **1,900.00**
Woodland, vase, floral, 11" **700.00**
Woodland, vase, naturalistic floral, sgn, 17" **1,000.00**
Zephyr Lily, ash tray **35.00**
Zephyr Lily, basket, #394, gr, 8" **50.00**
Zephyr Lily, bud vase, #201-7, 7½" **25.00**
Zephyr Lily, console boat, #475, 10" **40.00**
Zephyr Lily, cornucopia, #203, 6" **35.00**
Zephyr Lily, ewer, #24, 15" **175.00**
Zephyr Lily, fan vase, #205-6, 6½" **30.00**
Zephyr Lily, hanging basket **60.00**
Zephyr Lily, vase, #137, bl, 10" **60.00**
Zephyr Lily, vase, hdls, #202-8, 8½" **50.00**
Zephyr Lily, vase, pillow form, #206-7, 7" **35.00**

Rowland and Marcellus

Though the impressive back stamp seems to suggest otherwise, Rowland and Marsellus Company were not Staffordshire potters but American importers who commissioned various English companies to supply them with the blue-printed historical ware that had been a popular import item since the early 1800s. Plates, cups and saucers, pitchers, and platters were

sold as souvenirs from 1890 to 1920. The mark may be in full or 'R. & M.' in a diamond.

Cup & saucer, Niagara Falls **65.00**
Plate, Capitol Washington DC, flat **45.00**
Plate, Charles Dickens, rolled rim **55.00**
Plate, Desoto, Mississippi River, 10" **45.00**
Plate, Indians **45.00**
Plate, Lewis & Clark Centennial, rolled rim **55.00**
Plate, Mt Vernon, flat **35.00**
Plate, Nat'l Monument to the Forefathers, flat **40.00**
Plate, Philadelphia PA, rolled rim **40.00**
Plate, Plymouth Rock, rolled rim **45.00**
Plate, Robert Burns **50.00**
Plate, Robert Fulton **50.00**
Plate, Souvenir of Old Albany **40.00**
Plate, Theodore Roosevelt **55.00**
Plate, Williamsport PA **40.00**
Plate, Zanesville OH, gr w/blk & gold **40.00**

Plate, Allentown, Pennsylvania, 10", $45.00.

Royal Bayreuth

Founded in 1794 in Tettau, Bavaria, the Royal Bayreuth firm originally manufactured fine dinnerwares of superior quality. In more recent times, they have produced lines of dinnerware and accessory items such as humidors, vases, ash trays, and boxes in patterns called Rose Tapestry, Sunbonnet Babies, Beach Babies, Nursery Rhymes, and Devil and Cards. These are highly sought by today's collectors. Figural pitchers, sugar bowls, and shakers in the shape of tomatoes, grapes, shells, and animals were made in abundance, and it is these figurals that command the higher prices today.

Our advisors for this category are Larry Brenner from New Hampshire and Dee Hooks from Illinois; they are listed in the Directory under their home states.

Figurals

Ash tray, chimpanzee, bl mk, rare **450.00**
Bowl, lobster, bl mk, w/lid, 4½" **85.00**
Bowl, oak leaf, MOP, bl mk, lg **280.00**
Bowl, pansy, yel, bl mk, 9" **300.00**
Bowl, rose, bl mk, 6" **195.00**
Box, tomato, gr leaf, bl mk, 3¾x4½" **50.00**
Candle holder, dachshund, bl mk, 4½" **250.00**

Candle holder, elk hdl, bl mk 225.00
Compote, poppy w/gr leaf stem, bl mk, 5¾x3½" 295.00
Cracker jar, poppy, MOP, unmk 350.00
Creamer & sugar bowl, apple, bl mk, w/lid 145.00
Creamer & sugar bowl, strawberry, bl mk 225.00
Cup & saucer, coffee; rose, pk, bl mk 265.00
Cup & saucer, coffee; tomato, bl mk 85.00
Cup & saucer, demitasse; apple, bl mk 135.00
Cup & saucer, demitasse; shell, bl mk 90.00
Hatpin holder, dachshund, bl mk 350.00
Hatpin holder, penguin, bl mk 400.00
Hatpin holder, poppy, red, bl mk 325.00
Humidor, bellringer, bl mk, rare 750.00
Humidor, clown, bl mk 425.00
Match holder, chimpanzee, wall hanging, bl mk 355.00
Match holder, clown, wall hanging, bl mk 195.00
Match holder, elk, wall hanging, bl mk 295.00
Match holder, poppy, red, wall hanging, bl mk 200.00
Mug, clown, bl mk, rare 245.00
Mustard, conch shell, bl mk 65.00
Mustard, grapes, wht MOP, bl mk, w/undertray 145.00
Mustard, grapes, yel, bl mk 110.00
Mustard, lemon, bl mk, w/lid & spoon 75.00
Pitcher, alligator, bl mk, cream sz 275.00
Pitcher, apple, bl mk, cream sz 150.00
Pitcher, apple, bl mk, lemonade sz, rare 550.00
Pitcher, apple, bl mk, milk sz 200.00
Pitcher, apple, bl mk, water sz 325.00
Pitcher, Art Nouveau, bl mk, cream sz 475.00
Pitcher, bass, bl mk, cream sz 165.00
Pitcher, bass, bl mk, milk sz 240.00
Pitcher, bass, unmk, cream sz 80.00
Pitcher, bellringer, bl mk, cream sz 235.00
Pitcher, bird of paradise, bl mk, cream sz 325.00
Pitcher, bull, blk, bl mk, cream sz 130.00
Pitcher, bull, blk, unmk, cream sz 60.00
Pitcher, bull, brn, bl mk, cream sz 150.00
Pitcher, butterfly, bl mk, closed wings, milk sz 425.00
Pitcher, butterfly, bl mk, open wing, cream sz 225.00
Pitcher, butterfly, bl mk, open wing, milk sz 340.00
Pitcher, butterfly, bl mk, open wing, water sz 425.00
Pitcher, cat, blk, bl mk, cream sz 125.00
Pitcher, cat, blk, unmk, cream sz, 5x4" 65.00
Pitcher, cat, brn w/wht spots, bl mk, cream sz 250.00
Pitcher, cat, gray & red, unmk, 4⅞" 85.00
Pitcher, chrysanthemum, pk, bl mk, cream sz 225.00
Pitcher, clown, red, bl mk, cream sz 150.00
Pitcher, clown, red, bl mk, milk sz 260.00
Pitcher, clown, yel, bl mk, milk sz 240.00
Pitcher, clown, yel, bl mk, water sz 500.00
Pitcher, coachman, red, bl mk, cream sz 225.00
Pitcher, coachman, red, bl mk, water sz 425.00
Pitcher, coachman, red, unmk, cream sz 185.00
Pitcher, cockatoo, bl mk, cream sz 325.00
Pitcher, conch shell w/lobster hdl, gr, unmk, water sz .320.00
Pitcher, conch shell w/lobster hdl, unmk, cream sz 55.00
Pitcher, crow, blk, bl mk, cream sz 120.00
Pitcher, dachshund, bl mk, cream sz 180.00
Pitcher, dachshund, unmk, cream sz 110.00
Pitcher, dachshund, unmk, water sz 410.00
Pitcher, duck, bl mk, cream sz 125.00
Pitcher, duck, bl mk, milk sz 175.00
Pitcher, duck, bl mk, water sz 360.00
Pitcher, duck, mk Deponiert, milk sz 160.00

Pitcher, duck, unmk, cream sz 95.00
Pitcher, eagle, bl mk, cream sz 195.00
Pitcher, eagle, bl mk, milk sz 230.00
Pitcher, eagle, bl mk, water sz 430.00
Pitcher, elk, bl mk, milk sz 210.00
Pitcher, elk, bl mk, water sz 325.00
Pitcher, elk, brn/tan, bl mk, cream sz, 4½x3½" 75.00
Pitcher, fish head, bl mk, cream sz 145.00
Pitcher, fish head, bl mk, milk sz 160.00
Pitcher, frog, bl mk, cream sz 160.00
Pitcher, girl w/basket on bk, bl mk, 4¼x2⅝" 175.00
Pitcher, girl w/pitcher, red, bl mk, cream sz 275.00
Pitcher, grape, wht satin, bl mk, milk sz 155.00
Pitcher, kangaroo, bl mk, cream sz 875.00
Pitcher, lamplighter, bl mk, cream sz 180.00
Pitcher, lemon, bl mk, cream sz 145.00
Pitcher, lemon, bl mk, rare, lemonade sz 490.00
Pitcher, leopard, bl mk, rare, cream sz 750.00

Pitcher, lobster, blue mark, 7", water size, $250.00.

Pitcher, milkmaid, bl mk, milk sz 285.00
Pitcher, monk, brn & tan, bl mk, cream sz 150.00
Pitcher, monk, brn & tan, bl mk, milk sz 245.00
Pitcher, monkey, gr, unmk, cream sz 245.00
Pitcher, mountain goat, bl mk, cream sz 250.00
Pitcher, mouse, bl mk, cream sz 650.00
Pitcher, murex shell, bl mk, water sz 200.00
Pitcher, murex shell, mc, bl mk, water sz 400.00
Pitcher, murex shell, MOP, bl mk, cream sz 65.00
Pitcher, murex shell, unmk, low, cream sz 45.00
Pitcher, oak leaf, bl mk, cream sz 135.00
Pitcher, oak leaf, bl mk, milk sz, 6¾" 160.00
Pitcher, oak leaf, gr, bl mk, water sz 500.00
Pitcher, Old Man of Mountain, mc, bl mk, cream sz 180.00
Pitcher, Old Man of Mountain, unmk, cream sz 95.00
Pitcher, orange, bl mk, cream sz, 4½" 95.00
Pitcher, orange, bl mk, water sz 450.00
Pitcher, owl, bl mk, cream sz 255.00
Pitcher, pansy, MOP, bl mk, cream sz 175.00
Pitcher, pansy, purple, bl mk, cream sz 150.00
Pitcher, parakeet, bk mk, cream sz 220.00
Pitcher, parakeet, unmk, cream sz 140.00

Pitcher, parrot, gr, bl mk, cream sz 225.00
Pitcher, parrot, unmk, water sz 325.00
Pitcher, platypus, bl mk, cream sz 400.00
Pitcher, poppy, lav MOP, bl mk, milk sz 445.00
Pitcher, poppy, red, bl mk, cream sz 110.00
Pitcher, poppy, red, bl mk, water sz 450.00
Pitcher, robin, bl mk, cream sz 145.00
Pitcher, robin, brn/gold w/red breast, unmk, cream sz 110.00
Pitcher, rooster, blk, bl mk, water sz 625.00
Pitcher, Santa, bl mk, milk sz 880.00
Pitcher, Santa, brn, bl mk, water sz 1,750.00
Pitcher, seal, bl mk, cream sz 225.00
Pitcher, seal, bl mk, milk sz 295.00
Pitcher, St Bernard, bl mk, cream sz 175.00
Pitcher, St Bernard, bl mk, milk sz 245.00
Pitcher, St Bernard, bl mk, water sz 400.00
Pitcher, strawberry, bl mk, cream sz 150.00
Pitcher, tomato, unmk, cream sz 45.00
Pitcher, trout, standing, bl mk, cream sz 150.00
Pitcher, turtle, bl mk, cream sz 275.00
Pitcher, water buffalo, bl mk, cream sz 145.00
Pitcher, water buffalo, gray/blk/red, unmk, cream sz, 5½" 85.00
Pitcher, watermelon, bl mk, water sz 480.00
Plate, lettuce leaf, yel flowers, ring hdl, bl mk, 7" 40.00
Plate, tomato & lettuce leaf, bl mk, 7½" 35.00
Relish, poinsettia, bl mk, 7½" 135.00
Shakers, clown, bl mk, pr 90.00
Shakers, elk, bl mk, ea 70.00
Shakers, grape, bl mk, pr 95.00
Shakers, strawberry, bl mk, pr 85.00
String holder, rooster, bl mk, wall hanging 225.00
Sugar bowl, grape, purple, w/lid, unmk 68.00
Sugar bowl, tomato, w/lid, bl mk 80.00
Sugar bowl, tomato, w/lid, unmk 40.00
Tea set, tomato, leaf base, bl mk, 3-pc 285.00
Teapot, grape, bl mk 275.00
Teapot, tomato, unmk 75.00
Toothpick holder, elk head, bl mk 95.00
Toothpick holder, murex shell, unmk 75.00
Tray, bread; oak leaf, wht satin, bl mk, rare 185.00
Tray, dresser; Art Nouveau, wht satin, bl mk 750.00
Tureen, rose, oval, w/lid, bl mk, 6" 250.00
Wall pocket, grapes, yel, bl mk 170.00

Florals, Scenics, and Series Ware

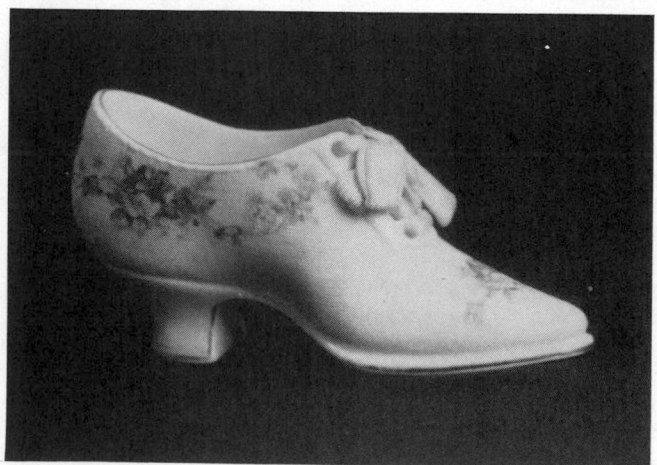

Violet tapestry shoe, green mark, 2½x5", $350.00.

Ash tray, Rose Tapestry, bl mk, sq, 4¾" 165.00
Basket, Bouquet Tapestry, bl mk, lg 350.00
Basket, Rose Tapestry, gold trim, rope hdl, 4x4½x2½" 335.00
Basket, Rose Tapestry, 3-color, bl mk, rare, 4½x3½" 265.00
Basket, Violet Tapestry, bl mk 200.00
Bell, Sunbonnet Babies, cleaning, bl mk, orig wood clapper ...595.00
Bowl, boy in barnyard, heavy gold, bl mk, 11" 225.00
Bowl, centerpc; hunt scene, flower frog lid, bl mk, 4x4" 95.00
Box, boy & girl sailing, unmk 75.00
Box, Nursery Rhymes, Jack Horner, fan shape, bl mk, 5¼" 75.00
Box, powder; lady on horse w/dog on road, unmk, 3½" dia 48.00
Cake plate, Rose Tapestry, pierced hdls, bl mk, 9¾" 235.00
Candlestick, cows, bl mk, 6" 155.00
Candlestick, Sunbonnet Babies, cleaning, bl mk, tall 175.00
Candlestick, Sunbonnet Babies, washing, bl mk, tall, pr 350.00
Candy dish, Devil & Cards, Devil Eagle, bl mk, 7" 255.00
Candy dish, Sunbonnet Babies, cleaning, club shape, bl mk ...235.00
Chamberstick, Corinthian, red/blk, bl mk 100.00
Chamberstick, Nursery Rhymes, Jack Horner, bl mk 155.00
Chamberstick, pansies & roses, shield bk, unmk 65.00
Chamberstick, Sunbonnet Babies, cleaning, ring hdl, bl mk ...295.00
Chamberstick, Sunbonnet Babies, fishing, shield bk, bl mk ..425.00
Chamberstick, Sunbonnet Babies, washing, shield bk, bl mk ..425.00
Chocolate pot, Rose Tapestry, 3-color, bl mk, 8" 975.00
Clock, dresser; Christmas Cactus Tapestry, bl mk, NM 500.00
Cup & saucer, demitasse; cattle scenic, unmk 65.00
Cup & saucer, Nursery Rhymes, Jack Horner, bl mk 150.00
Cup & saucer, Sunbonnet Babies, washing, bl mk 145.00
Fernery, Rose Tapestry, gold ring hdls, bl mk 245.00
Flowerpot, Sunbonnet Babies, ironing, bl mk, w/insert, 4" ...495.00
Hair receiver, man w/gun, bl mk 125.00
Hair receiver, Rose Tapestry, 3-color, 3-ftd, bl mk 225.00
Hair receiver, Sunbonnet Babies, cleaning, bl mk 325.00
Hair receiver, turkeys on tapestry, bl mk 195.00
Hatpin holder, farmer/2 horses scene, saucer base, bl mk 235.00
Hatpin holder, Rose Tapestry, bl mk 395.00
Hatpin holder, Rose Tapestry, unmk 300.00
Match holder, cavalier tapestry, unmk, 3¼x2½" 88.00
Match holder, hunt scene, 2-hdld bucket form, bl mk, 2½" 55.00
Match holder, Rose Tapestry, 3-color, bl mk 395.00
Match holder, storks on yel, 3-hdl, bl mk 195.00
Match holder, Sunbonnet Babies, sewing, bl mk, wall hanging .495.00
Mint dish, Rose Tapestry, bl mk, palette shape, 4½x4" 135.00
Mug, Devil & Cards, devil forms hdl, bl mk, 4¾x3¾" 195.00
Nappy, Arab horse scenic tapestry, bl mk 165.00
Nappy, hunter w/dog, clover shape, bl mk 50.00
Nappy, Sunbonnet Babies, washing/ironing, bl mk, 5x5" 295.00
Nut cup, Rose Tapestry, 3-color, gr mk, 1¾x3¼" 160.00
Pin dish, Japanese crysanthemum tapestry, bl mk, leaf form ...195.00
Pitcher, Arab on horse, jeweled, bulbous, bl mk, water sz 225.00
Pitcher, cows in pasture, bl mk, 9" 185.00
Pitcher, cows in sunset, gr at base, bl mk, milk sz 85.00
Pitcher, Devil & Cards, bl mk, cream sz 130.00
Pitcher, Devil & Cards, bl mk, water sz, 7½" 350.00
Pitcher, English coaching scene, bl mk, 5¼x2½" 60.00
Pitcher, hunt scene, bl mk, 3¼x3¼" 65.00
Pitcher, minstrels, pinched spout, bl mk, 4" 70.00
Pitcher, Nursery Rhymes, Miss Muffet & spider, bl mk, 4½" ...150.00
Pitcher, Nursery Rhymes, 3 bears, bl mk, 4¼" 95.00
Pitcher, Rose Tapestry, bl mk, pinched spout, milk sz 235.00
Pitcher, Rose Tapestry, 3-color, bl mk, cream sz 220.00
Pitcher, Sunbonnet Babies, cleaning, twisted hdl, unmk, 3¼" ..150.00
Pitcher, Sunbonnet Babies, fishing, tall, milk sz 255.00

Pitcher, Sunbonnet Babies, ironing, dbl spout, bl mk, 2½"	395.00
Pitcher, Sunbonnet Babies, sewing, bl mk, cream sz	185.00
Plate, lady w/donkey, heavy gold trim, bl mk, 10"	125.00
Plate, Rose Tapestry, 3-color, scalloped, gold rim, 7½"	225.00
Plate, salad; Nursery Rhymes, Jack & Beanstalk	135.00
Plate, Sunbonnet Babies, fishing, bl mk, 6"	135.00
Rose bowl, Rose Tapestry, 3-color, bl mk	350.00
Rose bowl, Sunbonnet Babies, cleaning, bl mk	300.00
Salt cellar, Devil & Cards, bl mk, master	200.00
Salt cellar, Sunbonnet Babies, ped ft, bl mk, master	325.00
Shakers, Nursery Rhymes, bl mk, pr	195.00
Shoe, high-laced lady's; Rose Tapestry, bl mk	395.00
Toothbrush holder, Rose Tapestry, 3-color, bl mk, 4¼x2¼"	225.00
Toothpick holder, children at play, 4-ftd, hdls, bl mk	145.00
Toothpick holder, goats grazing, bl mk	135.00
Toothpick holder, Old Man of Mountain, scuttle shape	295.00
Toothpick holder, Rose Tapestry, pk, bl mk, 2⅝"	275.00
Toothpick holder, Rose Tapestry, 3-color w/gold trim, bl mk	495.00
Toothpick holder, scenic tapestry, ftd, gold hdls, bl mk	295.00
Toothpick holder, Sunbonnet Babies, bulbous, bl mk	395.00
Toothpick holder, Sunbonnet Babies, scuttle form, bl mk	450.00
Tray, dresser; Christmas Cactus Tapestry, bl mk	450.00
Tray, dresser; Sunbonnet Babies, fishing, bl mk, 10x7½"	295.00
Tray, Sunbonnet Babies, fishing, heart shape, bl mk	135.00
Tray, Sunbonnet Babies, sewing, diamond shape, bl mk	135.00
Vase, goats on hill at sunset, gold trim, mk, 5x3"	65.00
Vase, Goose Girl, bl mk, 3¾x2½"	55.00
Vase, hunt scene, ball shape, bl mk, 2¾x2½"	48.00
Vase, hunt scene, bl mk, 5"	95.00
Vase, polar bear tapestry, gold hdls, bl mk, 4½"	250.00
Vase, Rose Tapestry, bulbous shoulder/slim neck, bl mk, 5½"	295.00
Vase, sheep scene, gr mk, 6¾x3¾"	95.00
Vase, Sunbonnet Babies, cleaning, cylindrical, bl mk, 4x1"	395.00
Vase, 3 sheep & moon on gr, hdls, SP rim, bl mk, 3¾x1½"	45.00
Wall pocket, Sunbonnet Babies, cleaning, bl mk	495.00

Royal Bonn

Royal Bonn is a fine-paste porcelain, ornately decorated with scenes, portraits, or florals. The factory was established in the mid-1800s in Bonn, Germany; however, most pieces found today are from the latter part of the century.

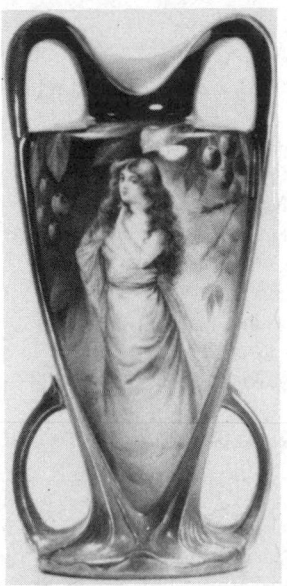

Vase, lady's portrait, signed Bode, 12", $750.00.

Biscuit jar, floral, mc on beige, brass rim/hdl/lid, 7"	100.00
Biscuit jar, floral, mc on tans w/gold, SP lid/rim/hdl, 7½"	125.00
Bone dish, flow bl	15.00
Delft, windmill in cartouch, ftd, ornate hdls, 16½"	550.00
Ewer, orchids/bird/dragonfly, gold lizard hdl, 12½"	175.00
Vase, couple & sheep on dk gr tapestry, 9½x5"	265.00
Vase, floral, gold & orange on brn & yel, 8x5"	95.00
Vase, garden scene on tapestry, pillow form, 8½x8"	425.00
Vase, iris w/gold trim, 8", pr	225.00
Vase, rooster/hen/chicks on gr, sgn Sticher, mk, 6½x3"	135.00
Vase, roses, wht on gr shaded, flared top, 8¾"	95.00

Royal Copenhagen

The Royal Copenhagen Manufactory was established in Denmark in about 1775 by Frantz Henrich Muller. When bankruptcy threatened in 1779, the Crown took charge. The fine dinnerware and objects of art produced after that time carries the familiar logo, the crown over three wavy lines.

Bowl, Flora Dancia, 10"	1,000.00
Candlestick, w/attached saucer, #2307, 2½"	54.00
Figurine, baby in nightshirt, #3208	195.00
Figurine, barn owl, #273, 8½"	375.00
Figurine, boy & girl hug w/puppy between, #707, 6x5"	280.00
Figurine, boy leading sow, #848, 7¼"	195.00
Figurine, boy w/beachball, #3542	225.00
Figurine, boy whittling stick, #905, 7¼"	300.00
Figurine, collie, #1701, lg	195.00
Figurine, dancing girl, 8¼"	275.00
Figurine, dog w/slipper, #3476, 3¾"	115.00
Figurine, elephant, #21517, wht, lg, 7"	225.00
Figurine, elephant, #22741, wht, sm, 2¼"	75.00
Figurine, February, #5424	265.00
Figurine, girl on stone, #4027	195.00
Figurine, girl sits w/doll, #1938, 5"	195.00
Figurine, girl w/doll, #3539, 5¾"	230.00
Figurine, girl w/pot cover, #3677	140.00
Figurine, goose girl, #528, 7½"	275.00
Figurine, hunter & dog, #1087, 8½"	550.00
Figurine, lovebirds	125.00
Figurine, mallard, #1934, 2¾"	240.00
Figurine, mare & foal, #4698	495.00
Figurine, mermaid on rock, #4431	900.00
Figurine, monkey, #1444, 5"	135.00
Figurine, mouse & corn cob, #512	125.00
Figurine, nude holding mirror, standing, #4639	400.00
Figurine, Pan & squirrel, #456, 8½"	450.00
Figurine, Pan on column w/flute, rabbit at base, 8½"	275.00
Figurine, Pan on tortoise, #858, 4"	195.00
Figurine, parrots on branch, #649, 7½"	215.00
Figurine, pekingese dog, #1772, 5¼"	225.00
Figurine, penguins, 2 on rock, #3118, 1930	185.00
Figurine, penguins in semi-circle, #1284, 3¾"	190.00
Figurine, polar bear, #321, 5¾"	125.00
Figurine, polar bear, #502, 13"	300.00
Figurine, polar bears, fighting, #1107, 5½"	250.00
Figurine, poodle, #4368	195.00
Figurine, Princess & Numbskull, #1473	1,750.00
Figurine, scottie dog, standing, #3161, 4"	145.00
Plate, deep; Flora Dancia, 8¾"	300.00
Plate, Flora Dancia, scene w/fox, gilt dentil rim, 10"	700.00
Plate, man w/scythe, #3614, 7"	95.00

Tray, lady & fan 45.00
Vase, fish, artist sgn, baluster form, 1900s, 12" 650.00
Vase, flowering tree design, #1434, 6½" 195.00

Vase, scenic, signed KA, 13" to top of vase, $1,500.00.

Royal Copley

Royal Copley is a decorative type of pottery made by the Spaulding China Company in Sebring, Ohio, from 1939 to 1960. In addition to the Royal Copley mark, some pieces were also marked with the company's name. Items trimmed in gold are worth from 25% to 50% more than the same item with no gold trim.

Ash tray, leaf form, pk w/yel flower, 5" 5.00
Ash tray, lily pad w/bird, turq/pk, 5" 5.00
Ash tray, mallard, sm 8.00
Creamer, chick, pk & brn, Spaulding, 4¾" 6.00
Creamer, duck, pk hat, bl wings, 4½" 10.00
Figurine, bunting, head low, tail raised, 5" 15.00
Figurine, hen, #2, 6" 9.00
Figurine, hen, Royal Windsor, 6½" 10.00
Figurine, Oriental boy, yel, 7½" 6.00
Figurine, parrot, pk/yel, 5" 8.00
Figurine, pheasant, Spaulding 15.00
Figurine, rooster, wht, lg 20.00
Figurine, skylark, bl, 5" 7.50
Figurine, spaniel, brn, 6" 15.00
Figurine, swallow, bl, 8" 15.00
Figurine, titmouse, brn, 8" 12.00
Figurine, woodpecker, red, 6¼" 8.00
Figurine, wren 10.00
Pitcher, daffodil, turq, 8" 22.00
Pitcher, floral, gray & pk, 8" 22.00
Pitcher, Pome Fruit, cream, 8" 24.00
Planter, Balinese girl, 8½" 10.00
Planter, barefoot boy, bl hat, 7½" 12.50
Planter, big blossom, gr & yel, 3" 6.00
Planter, bird in flight, bl, 7¼" 17.50
Planter, Blackamoor bust, gray, 8" 17.50
Planter, blk cat & tub 14.00
Planter, boy leaning on barrel, red & gr, 6" 9.00

Planter, Chinese boy w/big hat, pk, 7½" 9.00
Planter, cocker spaniel w/basket, 5½" 12.00
Planter, cocker spaniel's head, 5" 9.00
Planter, deer & fawn, rectangular, 6" 15.00
Planter, dog & mail box 10.00
Planter, duck & wheelbarrow 12.00
Planter, duck eating grass, 5" 8.50
Planter, Dutch girl w/bucket, 6¼" 12.00
Planter, floral arrangement, turq & red, 3¼x7" 6.00
Planter, girl leaning on barrel 12.00
Planter, Harmony, gr, 4½" 6.00
Planter, Harmony, gr, 6½" 9.00
Planter, ivy, gr on cream, ftd, 4" 4.00
Planter, kitten w/ball of yarn, 8¼" 15.00
Planter, Oriental girl leaning on vase, red & gr, 6" 9.00
Planter, Oriental lantern boy 12.00
Planter, pony, 5¼" 8.00
Planter, rooster, walking 10.00
Planter, running horse, 6" 10.00
Planter, spaniel, 7¾" 15.00
Planter, tanager, yel/peach on gr stump, 6¼" 8.00
Planter, water lily, gr, 6¼" 7.50
Vase, bow & ribbon, pk & gray, ftd, 6¼" 7.50
Vase, Carol's Corsage, aqua, 7" 8.00

Vase, deer's head relief, open center, 8", $12.00.

Vase, dragon, gray & pk, ftd, 5½" 10.00
Vase, floral decal, scroll hdls, 6¼" 7.50
Vase, Floral Elegance, cobalt, 8" 18.00
Vase, Floral Elegance, gr shaded, 8" 15.00
Vase, Oriental children, 4¾" 7.50
Vase, stylized leaf, 5½" 5.00
Wall pocket, bamboo 12.00
Wall pocket, bonnet w/flowers 35.00
Wall pocket, Tony, pirate's head 20.00

Royal Crown Derby

In the latter 1870s, a new firm, the Derby Crown Porcelain Company Ltd., began operations in Derby, England. Since 1890 when they were appointed Manufacturers of Porcelain to Her Majesty, their fine porcelain wares have been known as Royal Crown Derby. Their earliest wares were marked with a crown over 'Derby'; often a complicated dating code indicated the year of manufacture. After 1890 the 'Royal Crown Derby, England' mark was employed; in 1921 'Made In England' was substituted in the wording. 'Bone China' was added after 1945. See also Derby.

Bowl, floral, mc on wht, gold rim, w/lid, 4x5" dia 65.00
Cup & saucer, Imari 75.00
Cup & saucer, Imari, miniature, 2½" dia 240.00
Ewer, gold decor on yel, 1896, 14x6" 450.00
Ewer, gold florals & arabesques on Chinese red, 1800, 7½" 235.00
Figurine, lady & man w/beard, rnd terrain base, 1800s, 17" 225.00
Figurine, Owl 350.00
Figurine, Pouter Pigeon 350.00
Tea set, Imari, miniature, pot: 1½", 3-pc 600.00
Tray, card; Chinese pheasants, pate-sur-pate, gold trim 45.00
Vase, gilt panels on yel w/HP floral, teardrop w/hdls, 9" 150.00
Vase, mc flowers on gr, gilt relief, slim neck/ft, 12" 145.00

Royal Dux

The Duxer Porzellan Manufactur was established by E. Eichler in 1860. Located in what is now Duchcov, Czechoslovakia, the area was known as Dux, Bohemia, until WWI. The war brought about changes in both the style of the ware as well as the mark. Pre-war pieces were modeled in the Art Nouveau or Greek Classical manner and marked with 'Bohemia' and a pink triangle containing the letter 'E.' They were usually matt glazed in green, brown, and gold. Better pieces were made of porcelain, while the larger items were of pottery. After the war, the ware was marked with the small pink triangle but without the Bohemia designation; 'Made in Czechoslovakia' was added. The style became Art Deco, with cobalt blue a dominant color.

Bust, Deco lady, gold hat/bl scarf, Strubach, triangle mk, 6½" . .375.00
Bust, lady w/lyre, draped veil, pk triangle mk, 9" 500.00
Bust, nymph, orchids/leaves about face, waves at breast, 21" .2,800.00

Bust of a Victorian maid, #454, 23", $950.00.

Centerpc, maid at stern, 2nd near prow of ship-form urn, 17" . .750.00
Centerpc, maid sits on shell carried by 2 tritons, 23¼" 1,200.00
Centerpc, maid+2 cherubs support shell, gr/gold/gray, 15x20" . .950.00
Centerpc, 2 maids cavort in high waves, triangle mk, 20½" . .1,500.00
Dish, figural harem dancer w/twirling skirt aside, 14½" 800.00
Figurine, boy w/goat; girl w/sheep, 25", pr, EX 1,150.00
Figurine, camel driver, triangle mk, 17x14" 1,800.00
Figurine, cockatoo, pk/wht on brn base, mk, 16¼", pr 350.00
Figurine, couple dance, cobalt coat & dress, mk/label, 6x9" . . .350.00
Figurine, couple dance, he in red jacket; she w/rose, 9" 275.00
Figurine, couple stand in front of lg ox, 12x13" 450.00
Figurine, fisherman w/net, hat/tall boots, triangle mk, 18" 550.00
Figurine, girl, windswept dress, Strubach, triangle mk, 10" 450.00
Figurine, girl playing pipe to cobra, sgn E Kwasnitzke, 9" 575.00
Figurine, harvesters w/sickle & wheat, dk bl/gilt, 21", pr 750.00
Figurine, lady getting dressed, sgn Eli Strabach, #3396, 8" 350.00
Figurine, lady in sedan chair w/2 coachmen & dog, 16x14" 750.00
Figurine, lady w/long scarf, jug in hand, 11¼" 400.00
Figurine, man seated, works on jugs, EX details, 7½x6x4" 425.00
Figurine, mother & child w/basket, triangle mk, 8½" 395.00
Figurine, nude w/cobalt drape & 3 wht tigers, #3068/12, 17" . . .900.00
Figurine, Oriental lady, man w/fruit basket, mk, 7¼", pr 350.00
Figurine, peasant boy & girl, natural colors, 11½x4", pr 550.00
Figurine, shepherd & shepherdess, mc, triangle mk, 14", pr 850.00
Figurine, shepherdess in sheepskin robe, 2 goats, 15" 575.00
Figurine, slave boy presents box to harem girl, 13" 600.00
Figurine, Spanish couple play instruments, 10¾" 800.00
Figurine, water carrier, mc, triangle mk, 20" 1,100.00
Figurine, 2 children w/basket, pk triangle mk, 8½" 400.00
Figurine, 2 wht lions & deer, 12x16x8" 975.00
Lamps, ladies dancing, orig shades/bl finials, brass base, pr 750.00
Perfume bottle, Deco nude w/flower, triangle mk, rare, 6½" . . .650.00
Planter, high-relief maid/poppy on front, poppy hdls, 12" L . . .500.00
Vase, Deco nude ea side, cobalt w/gold, mk, 7¼x11⅝x4⅝" 495.00
Vase, figural nude astride conch shell, waves/lotus, 14½" 800.00
Vase, geisha girl, gold on wht, 12" .450.00

Royal Flemish

Royal Flemish was introduced in the late 1880s and was patented in 1894 by the Mt. Washington Glass Company. Transparent glass was enameled with one or several colors and the surface divided by a network of raised lines suggesting leaded glass work. Some pieces were further decorated with enameled florals, birds, or Roman coins.

Our advisors for this category are Betty and Clarence Maier; they are listed in the Directory under Pennsylvania.

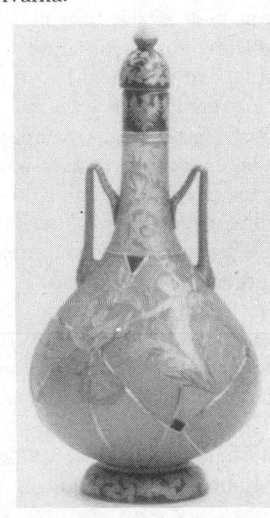

Decanter, cherubs in gold, 16", $6,500.00.

Biscuit jar, gold coins & lines on brn tones, 7½" 1,850.00
Biscuit jar, gold coins on clear satin, mk SP lid, 7½" 1,300.00
Biscuit jar, lg pk roses in scroll panels, SP mk lid, 7¾" 1,100.00
Biscuit jar, 4 gold/brn coins & mc florals, SP mts, 6½" 750.00
Ewer, floral, rampant lions around top, brn/gold, 13" 2,000.00
Pickle castor, mums, yel/wht on frost; Pairpoint fr, 9½" 1,265.00
Vase, dragon/leafy scrolls, pastels/gold, trefoil rim, 13½" 1,900.00
Vase, flock of Guba ducks, gold moon/stars, stick neck, 14" . .2,900.00
Vase, gold coins & lines, lt brn/gr panels, neck hdls, 8½" 1,985.00
Vase, mallard ducks, mc/gold, dividing lines, unmk, 7" 2,250.00
Vase, 2 flying geese, gold relief, flared base, 14x5" 1,000.00

Royal Haeger, Haeger

In 1871 David Henry Haeger, a young son of German immigrants, purchased a brick factory at Dundee, Illinois, and began an association with the ceramic industry that his descendants have pursued to the present time. Soon their production was expanded to include drainage tile. By 1914 they had ventured into the field of commerical artware. Vases, figurines, lamp bases, and gift items in a pastel matt glaze carried the logo of the company name written over the bar of an 'H.' From 1929 to 1933, they produced a line of dinnerware in solid colors — blue, rose, green, and yellow — which they marketed through Marshall Fields. Royal Haeger, their premium line designed in 1938 by Royal Hickman, and the Flower Ware line (1954 to 1963, marked 'RG' for Royal Garden) are especially desirable with collectors today. Ware produced before the mid-thirties sometimes is found with a paper label; these are also of special interest. A stylized script mark, 'Royal Haeger' in raised lettering, was used during the thirties and forties; later a paper label in the shape of a crown was used. The Macomb plant, built in 1939, primarily made ware for the florist trade. A second plant, built there in 1969, produces lamp bases.

For those interested in learning more about the subject, we recommend *Collecting Royal Haeger*, by our advisors, Lee Garmon and Doris Frizzell; both are listed in the Directory under Illinois.

Bookend, ram, standing, all colors, R-132, 9" 18.00
Bookend/planter, stallion head, all colors, R-641, 8½", pr 12.00
Bowl, console; grape clusters, ped ft, all colors, 14" L, ea 25.00
Bowl, swan, open bk, all colors, R-955, 11" L, ea 20.00
Candle holder, stalks w/grapes, all colors, R-473, 10", pr 15.00
Figurine, bull, head down, red or ebony, R-1510, 18½" L, ea 65.00
Figurine, matador w/cape, red or ebony, #6343, 11¼", ea 20.00
Figurine, panther, ebony, R-495, 24" L .30.00
Figurine, panther, ebony & colors, R-683, 18" L, ea 20.00
Figurine, panther, ebony & colors, R-733, 13" L, ea 15.00
Flower frog, dbl angelfish, all colors, R-360, 11½", ea 22.00
Flower frog, nude astride fish, all colors, R-363, 10", ea 20.00
Lamp, table; figurine, w/finial, M 50.00
Lamp, table; non-figurine, M 30.00
Lamp, TV; complete, M 25.00
Planter, girl w/basket leans over pool, 10x12½x6½" 35.00
Planter, shell, upright on waves, all colors, R-483, 11", ea 18.00
Vase, basket, floral border, all colors, R-386, 12" L, ea 22.00
Vase, bird of paradise, all colors, R-186, 12¾", ea 25.00
Vase, cock, fighting, oxblood agate, R-790 or R-791, 11½", ea . .25.00
Vase, dbl cornucopia; all colors, R-246, 16" L, ea 25.00
Vase, deer, running, all colors, R-706, 15", ea 20.00
Vase, deer, standing, all colors, R-707, 15", ea 20.00
Vase, gladiola; peacock, lg, all colors, 15½", ea 45.00
Vase, morning-glory, 3 openings, all colors, R-452, 16", ea 22.00
Vase, pouter pigeon, all colors, R-108, 7½", ea 25.00
Vase, sailfish, all colors, R-271, 9", ea .22.00
Vase, swan, head down, lg, all colors, R-36, 16", ea 35.00

Vase, swan, head down, tall, plum decor, R-856, 13" 25.00
Vase, swan, head down/wings out, all colors, R-414, 12" L, ea . . .25.00

Tiger, 11", $45.00.

Royal Rudolstadt

The hard-paste porcelain that has come to be known as Royal Rudolstadt was produced in Thuringia, Germany, in the early eighteenth century. Various names and marks have been associated with this pottery — one of the earliest was a hay fork symbol associated with Johann Frederich von Schwarzburg-Rudolstadt, one of the first founders. Variations, some that included an 'R,' were also used. In 1854 Earnst Bohne produced wares that were marked with an anchor and the letters 'EB.' Wares commonly found today are those made during the late 1800s and early twentieth century. These are usually marked with an 'RW' within a shield under a crown and the words 'Crown Rudolstadt.' Items marked 'Germany' were made after 1890.

Bust, 18th-century lady, bsk, 7" 75.00
Chocolate pot, fall foliage w/gold, mk, 11½", +4 c/s 285.00
Chocolate pot, pk roses/gold trim, 10" .150.00
Figurine, girl w/doll; boy w/basket, 15", pr 950.00
Figurine, hunchback, red cloak/bl pants, ca 1880, mk, 5½" 125.00
Pitcher, florals/leaves, gold w/bl jewels on cream, mk, 15" 325.00
Plate, maid's portrait, sgn Koller, 1900, 9½" 700.00
Smoker set, dog after cat on fence, mk, 6x6½" 165.00
Teapot, florals on beige, rose finial, mk, 6½x5" 165.00
Vase, cherub blowing bubbles figural, 6" 125.00
Vase, floral, HP w/gold beads on cobalt, gold hdls, 6½" 155.00
Vase, tapestry, bl floral on wht, brn loop hdls, 1800, 9" 160.00

Royal Vienna

In 1719 Claude Innocentius de Paquier established a hard-paste porcelain factory in Vienna where he made highly ornamental wares similar to the type produced at Meissen. Early wares were usually unmarked; but after 1744, when the factory was purchased by the Empress, the Austrian shield (often called 'beehive') was stamped on under the glaze. In the following listings, values are for hand-painted items unless noted otherwise. Decal-decorated items would be considerably lower.

Charger, Allegorie, after Titian, gold on cobalt, 24" 8,400.00
Cup & saucer, trellis/scallops/swag, mk 'k,' 1¾" 825.00
Ewer, floral, cobalt on cream w/gold, unmk, 9½x3¾" 110.00
Ewer, maid in panel on turq w/gold, ftd can base, rstr, 24" 750.00

Pitcher, tankard; maid/cupid, gilt beads/cobalt, 5" 425.00
Plate, allegorical: Mars/Venus/Bellona, sgn Knoeller, 10" 250.00
Plate, Mona Lisa, sgn Wagner, ornate gilt border, 9½" 900.00
Plate, Ruth, standing in field, sgn Wagner, 9½" 1,400.00

Urn, portrait of a lady, signed Wagner, burgundy with gilding, 19", $4,000.00.

Urn, portraits, high sq base, angle hdls, 1900, 20", pr 1,300.00
Urn, scene, 2nd on lg sq base, gilt on rose, strap hdls, 22" 425.00
Urn, titled medallions on rose w/gilt, ½-loop hdls, 15", pr . . .1,300.00
Vase, child figural between 2 egg forms, mk, 5¾x7" 145.00
Vase, girl w/bird on burgundy ground, gold trim, mk, 6¼" 150.00
Vase, Madame Lebrun portrait, gold hdls, mk, 12" 350.00
Vase, maid/dove on pk & gr lustre ea side, heavy gold, 16" . .1,500.00
Vase, Melon Boys on teal bl, cylindrical, 10½" 225.00
Vase, poppies, red on gr, beige top, folded rim, mk, 15" 200.00

Royal Worcester, Worcester

The Worcester Porcelain Company was deeded in 1751. During the first or Dr. Wall period (so called for one of its proprietors), porcelain with an Oriental influence was decorated in underglaze blue. Useful tablewares represented the largest portion of production, but figurines and decorative items were also made. Very little of the earliest wares were marked and can only be identified by a study of forms, glazes, and the porcelain body, which tends to transmit a greenish cast when held to light. Late in the fifties, a crescent mark was in general use, and rare examples bare a facsimile of the Meissen crossed swords. The first period ended in 1783, and the company went through several changes in ownership during the next eighty years. The years from 1783-1792 are referred to as the Flight period. Marks were a small crescent, a crown with 'Royal,' or an impressed 'Flight.' From 1792-1807, the company was known as Flight and Barr and used the trademark 'F&B' or 'B,' with or without a small cross. From 1807-1813, the company was under the Barr, Flight, and Barr management; this era is recognized as having produced porcelain of the highest quality of artistic decoration.

Their mark was 'B.F.B.' From 1813-1840, many marks were used, but the most usual was 'F.B.B.' under a crown to indicate Flight, Barr, and Barr. In 1840 the firm merged with Chamberlain, and in 1852 they were succeeded by Kerr and Binns. The firm became known as Royal Worcester in 1862. Since 1930 Royal Worcester has been considered one of the leaders in the field of limited edition plates and figurines.

Biscuit jar, floral on beige satin, SP lid/rim/hdl, mk, 7¼" 295.00
Biscuit jar, leaves, cobalt on wht bamboo, 7x5¾" 350.00
Candle holder, gold mouse at side, #1245, 1892 mk, 2½" 395.00
Candle snuffer, monk, 5" 75.00
Creamer & sugar bowl, leaves form body, ivory hdls 50.00
Dish, Kylin, animals/vases in panels, shell form, 8" L 700.00
Dish, still life of fruit, sgn Sebright, 1918, 11" L, pr 600.00
Ewer, duck in reeds, gilt dragon hdl, squat, 1880, 7" 300.00
Ewer, floral, gold on wht, lg gold salamander hdl, 12" 495.00
Ewer, floral, rust & yel on cream, #1136, 1889 mk, 6⅝" 225.00
Ewer, pate-sur-pate floral on dk bl, gilt hdl/leaf rim, 11" 425.00
Figurine, Amaryllis 300.00
Figurine, Anne Boleyn, bl gown/gold trim/fan, 8½" 350.00
Figurine, Apple Blossom & Bees, D Doughty, 8", pr 650.00
Figurine, Blue-Gray Gnatcatcher, D Doughty, 11½", pr 550.00
Figurine, Burmah, Doughty, #3068, 5" 160.00
Figurine, Crab apple & Butterfly, D Doughty, 10½", pr 700.00
Figurine, Dreaming, sgn Phoebe Stabler, #2875, ca 1931 . . . . .450.00
Figurine, Eastern Water Carriers, 1887, 8", pr, NM 500.00
Figurine, Egyptian w/musical instruments, 12", pr 700.00
Figurine, Goat Woman 300.00
Figurine, Grandmother's Dress, bl 125.00
Figurine, Greenwinged Teal, van Ruyckerett, 1970, 9" 200.00
Figurine, Irishman, beige satin, 1891 mk, 6⅞" 395.00
Figurine, John Bull, brn hat, gr jacket/pants, 1903 mk, 7" 395.00
Figurine, John Bull, 1891 mk, 6¼" 395.00
Figurine, lady dancing, gold base/trim, #1827, 1926 mk, 8" 375.00
Figurine, Michael, FG Doughty 85.00
Figurine, Mischief, FG Doughty, #2914, ca 1931 . . . . .265.00
Figurine, Napoleon Bonaparte, 1969, 16" 800.00
Figurine, Orange Blossoms & Butterflies, D Doughty, 8", pr . . .650.00
Figurine, Queen Ann boy w/basket, #960, 1900 mk, 9x6x7" . . .550.00
Figurine, Red-Eyed Vireo, D Doughty, 7½", pr 700.00
Figurine, Sisters 295.00
Figurine, Sorrow, semi-nude/dead bird, 1894, 10" 300.00
Figurine, Yankee, Countries of World series, 1891 mk, 7⅛" . . .395.00
Flower holder vase, roses, brass-mesh top, ftd, 1910, 5x5" 325.00
Gravy boat, butterflies/insects, mc on wht, ca 1765, 7½" 95.00
Gravy boat, Oriental landscapes, bl on wht, 1755, 7½" L 750.00
Jar, potpourri; florals w/gold, rtcl lid, ca 1917, 13" 1,275.00
Jug, owl on branch in moonlight, gold serpent hdl, 1885, 11" . .925.00
Jug, wine; floral, 5-color w/gold, bulbous, 1884 mk, 9¾" 325.00
Lamp, children/frog/tree figural, brass base, Hadley, 21" 1,500.00
Lamp, lady w/lute by tree, 2 Clarke cricklites, 1898, 25" 2,475.00
Loving cup, florals on beige, gold hdls, 7½" 215.00
Mug, floral sprays, bl on wht, ca 1775, 4¾" 175.00
Mug, Parrot & Fruit, bl on wht, ca 1770, 4½" 200.00
Mug, rose/bud cluster in cobalt, Dr Wall, 6" 275.00
Pickle dish, floral sprays, floral rim, ca 1755, 3⅛" 495.00
Pickle dish, florals, shell shape, ca 1755, 3" 245.00
Pitcher, floral, gilt on ivory, slim neck, 1861-1862 mk, 10" 250.00
Pitcher, florals, gold trim, flat bk, 5" 85.00
Pitcher, florals, gold-lined on beige, 1903 mk, 6" 125.00
Pitcher, tankard; florals/thistles w/much gold, 1884 mk, 10" . . .275.00
Plate, bl scale w/scattered florals, gilt rim, 1770, 8½" 475.00
Plate, classical ruins in blk on wht, 1765, 8¾", NM 400.00
Plate, Rococo gold/red floral, sgn Hill, 1880, 6 for 1,800.00

Plate, 3 cupids in field, heart shape, ca 1895, 6" 155.00
Platter, Japan-style birds/flowers, Chamberlain, 15", pr 550.00
Potpourri jar, HP florals w/gold, gold pierced lid, 5½" 425.00
Sauce boat, florals on pleated ground, bl/wht, oval, mk, 6" 99.00
Sugar bowl, Queen Charlotte, 1775, 4½" 320.00
Teapot, florals on herringbone, bl on wht, ca 1758, 6¾" 175.00
Teapot, foliage relief, sq body, swan neck, 1884, 6¼" 675.00
Teapot & stand, floral panels in gilt, leaf spout, FBB, 6" 400.00
Toby jug, Colonial man, bl coat/red vest, ca 1929 mk, 1¾" 85.00
Vase, crane, gold on cream, serpent hdls, 1890 mk, 8¾" 495.00
Vase, farmer/horses, sgn Davis, slim neck w/hdls, 1900, 12" 425.00
Vase, floral, gold-lined on beige, hdls, ped ft, mk, 9⅝" 325.00
Vase, floral, mc w/gold on beige, bottle form, 1897 mk, 6⅝" . . .110.00
Vase, floral, mc w/gold on beige, 1901 mk, 4¼x2⅝" 55.00
Vase, floral reserve on gilded apricot, BFB, rstr, 9", pr 800.00

Vase, gilt and bronze panels with fish and eels alternating with pierced panels of insects and flora, reticulated lid, dragon feet, ca 1883, 23", NM, $1,400.00.

Vase, ornate gilding on cream, dolphin hdls, 1880s, 11½" 475.00
Vase, poppies on cream, floral-openwork/serpent hdls, 12" 425.00
Vase, roses & lilies w/gold on bl, mk, 7x8½" 125.00
Waste bowl, Japan, exotic birds/rocks, w/gilt, F&B mk, 6¾" . . .165.00
Waste bowl, Japan, mums, mc on wht, Chamberlain, 6" 250.00

Roycroft

Near the turn of the century, Elbert Hubbard established the Roycroft Printing Shop in East Aurora, New York. Named in honor of two 17th-century printer-bookbinders, the print shop was just the beginning of a community called Roycroft, which came to be known world-wide. Hubbard became a popular personality of the early 1900s, known for his talents in a variety of areas from writing and lecturing to manufacturing. The Roycroft community became a meeting place for people of various capabilities and included shops for the production of furniture, copper, leather items, and a multitude of other wares which were marked with the Roycroft

symbol, an 'R' within a circle below a stylized cross. Hubbard lost his life on the Lusitania in 1915; production in the community continued until the Depression.

Interest is escalating in the field of Arts and Crafts in general, and Roycroft items in particular (along with Stickley, Rolfs, etc.) are rapidly appreciating in value.

Armchair, str solid arms, 2-slat bk, leather seat, 38x25" 2,000.00
Ash tray, hammered copper, strap harp/match holder, 29x8½" .300.00
Book, Gray's Ellegy, Lyric Poem, 1903, hand illuminated 95.00
Book, Last Ride, Robert Browning, #359, 1900, vellum cover . .450.00
Bookends, copper, emb poppy, ½-rnd w/rivets, 5½" 325.00
Bookends, copper on brass, stacked/grad triangles, orb mk 225.00
Bowl, geometrics, brn/gr/blk on wht, made by Buffalo, 8" 260.00
Bowl, nut; hammered copper, 3-ftd, 7", +ladle, ea die-mkd 275.00
Candlestick, brass wash, riveted 4-strap std, mk, 12", pr 750.00
Candlestick, copper, stem-like std, 4-petal cup, 14", pr 550.00
Candlestick, copper, stem-like std w/low twist, 12½", pr 650.00
Candlestick, hammered copper, petal-like disk base, 8", pr 650.00
Candlestick, hammered copper, 2-strap std, #403, 8", pr 650.00
Candlestick, hammered copper, 4-strap std/ft, mk, 12", pr . . .1,400.00
Frame, desk-top calendar; hammered copper, sm 45.00
Highchair, child's #36, 3-rung bk w/routed names, w/tray . . .1,600.00
Humidor, hammered copper, shape #635, 4x5" 290.00
Inkwell, copper, riveted at base, hand wrought, early, 2x4" 100.00
Lamp, brass on copper w/16" paneled ldgl cone shade, 20" . . .5,000.00
Lamp, desk; brass wash, mica band on shade, no mk, 13x10" . .1,300.00
Lamp, hammered copper, 7½" helmet shade; slim std, rfn, 16" . .550.00
Lamp, hammered copper dome, mica band, riveted, 14x10" . .2,800.00
Lamp, U-form base cradled in 4 reeded supports, ldgl shade . . .550.00
Lamp, 4 inset wire sections in hammered copper shade, 14" .1,750.00
Magazine stand #80, 5-shelf, logo/maple leaf ea side, 64" 550.00
Motto, hammered copper letters riveted to oak, mk, 10x40" .2,500.00
Purse, hand-tooled floral on leather, orb mk, rare, 8x6" 375.00
Spoon/ladle, hammered copper, early orig worn patina, 7" L . . .250.00
Table, library; 2-drw, copper hdw, 4-slat sides, 50" L 1,500.00

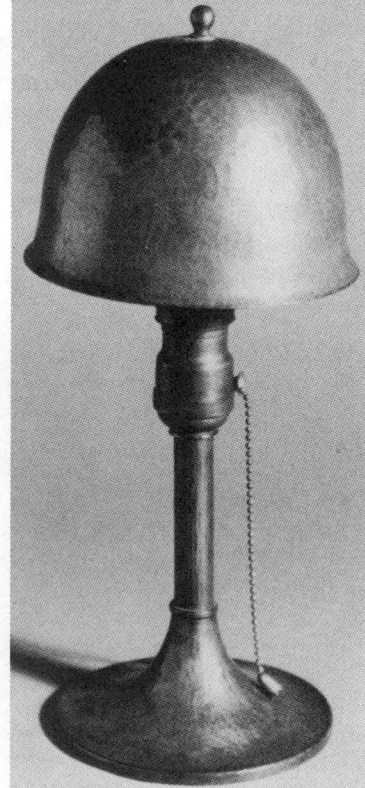

Hammered copper table lamp, stamped with an orb, cross, and R; 13½", $1,200.00.

Tray, hammered copper, worn patina, 11½x4½" 130.00
Tray, hammered copper, 2-hdl, #825, polished, 15" L 130.00
Vase, Am Beauty, hammered copper, cylinder neck, #201, 19" .750.00
Vase, bud; Am Beauty, brass wash, some exposed copper, 7" . . .200.00
Vase, copper w/pierced NP band, cylindrical, no mk, 6x3¼" . . .325.00
Vase, hammered copper, dk brn patina, ruffled, slim, 5" 185.00
Vase, hammered copper, ovoid, #223, 5" 190.00
Vase, hammered copper, tooled design at top, #236, 5" 350.00
Vase, hammered copper, wide riveted base, EX patina, 10½" . .400.00

Rozenburg

Some of the most innovative and original Art Nouveau ceramics were created by the Rozenberg factory at The Hague in The Netherlands between 1885 and 1916. Some pieces are similar to Gouda. Rozenburg also made highly-prized eggshell ware, so called because of its very thin walls; this is eagerly sought after by collectors. T.A.C. Colenbrander was their artistic leader, with J. Schelling and J. Kok designing many of the eggshell pieces.

Cup & saucer, Nouveau floral, octagonal, Van Rossum 500.00
Vase, dragonflies, eggshell, octagonal, 6" 850.00
Vase, floral branches, eggshell, paneled, Schellink, 6" 750.00
Vase, lizard ea side, olive/gray/gr on bl, bulbous, 8" 400.00
Vase, mc curvilinear abstract foliage, dbl gourd form, 12" 825.00
Vase, mushroom caps/exotic florals, eggshell, paneled, 5" 900.00
Vase, thistles in red/pk/gr, Schellink, 1907, 3¾" 1,000.00

Earthenware vase, butterflies, multicolor on dark green, ca 1901, 21½", $2,600.00.

Rubena

Rubena glass was made by several firms in the late 1800s. It is a blown art glass that shades from clear to red. See also Art Glass Baskets; Cruets; Sugar Shakers; Salts; specific manufacturers.

Basket, Hobnail, floral decor int, ruffled, clear hdl, 8x9" 210.00
Biscuit jar, T'print, shasta daisies, SP lid, 7" 350.00
Mug, floral, gold & silver trim, 8-sided, 3¾x2¼" 55.00
Mug, HP scrolls & dots, clear hdl, 3½x2¼" 45.00
Pitcher, tankard; gold-lined florals, 13", +6 5" tumblers 880.00
Rose bowl, gold florals, 4¾x5½" 120.00
Sugar shaker, Coin Spot 110.00
Syrup jug, pewter top, appl hdl, att Sandwich or NE Glass 225.00
Toothpick holder, Optic, bulbous, ring neck, Hobbs 110.00
Vase, dragons, hdls, 12½" 135.00
Vase, gold daffodils & lace, 8" 95.00

Rubena Verde

Rubena Verde glass was introduced in the late 1800s by Hobbs, Brockunier, and Company of Wheeling, West Virginia. Its transparent colors shade from red to green. See also Art Glass Baskets; Cruets; Sugar Shakers; Salts.

Bowl, Hobnail, ruffled 50.00
Creamer 40.00
Pitcher, Invt T'print, quatrelobe top, 6½" 260.00
Rose bowl 95.00
Shakers, HP florals, pewter lid, 4¼", pr 185.00
Sugar shaker, HP florals, Hobb's Coloratura series 295.00
Tumbler, floral 85.00
Vase, Drape, bowl form, ped ft, 9¼" 180.00
Vase, HP floral/bl ribbon, ribbed, cylindrical/ruffled, 11" 175.00

Ruby Stained Souvenirs

Ruby-flashed or ruby-stained glass was made through the application of a thin layer of color over clear. It was used in the manufacture of some early pressed tableware and from the Victorian era well into the twentieth century for souvenir items which were often engraved on the spot with the date, location, and buyer's name.

Bowl, master berry; Fern & Berry T'print 75.00
Cordial, dtd 1902 . . . . .35.00
Creamer, Riverside's Victoria 65.00
Creamer, T'print, miniature 30.00
Cup & saucer, T'print 40.00
Goblet, Nail 65.00
Hair receiver, Georgia Gem, metal top on glass lid 70.00
Match holder, PA 24.00
Mug, Button Arches, 2¾" 20.00
Mug, Button Arches, 3¼" 35.00
Pitcher, Button Arches, 2½" 20.00
Pitcher, tankard; Button Arches, Armourdale 75.00
Syrup, Sunk Honeycomb, orig lid, sm 175.00
Toothpick holder, Cut Block pattern, Heisey 110.00
Toothpick holder, witch's kettle, wire bail hdl 18.00
Tumbler, Button Arches, 1904 St Louis Expo 50.00
Tumbler, Lacy Medallion, 1901 . . . . .22.00

Butter dish, Punty Band, etched name and '1898,' $85.00.

Rugs

Key:
comp — complimentary   med — medallion
dmn — diamond   s/a — semi-antique
gb — guard border

Hooked

Hooked rugs are treasured today for their folk-art appeal. It was a craft that was introduced to this country in about 1830 and flourished its best in the New England states. The prime consideration is not age but artistic appeal. Scenes with animals, buildings, and people; patriotic designs; or whimsical themes are preferred. Condition is, of course, also a factor. Marked examples bearing the stamps of 'Frost and Co.,' 'Abenakee,' 'C.R.,' and 'Ouia' are highly prized. Note: the rugs listed here are rag unless noted otherwise.

Grenfell mat, polar bears and igloos, early 1900s, 36" diameter, $1,400.00.

Amish, EX geometric floral, 40x25" 225.00
Bird on branch, stylized scrolls, sgn/dtd 1920, 26x52" 150.00
Birds, 2 on blk ground, late, 22x40" .65.00
Canoes in wilderness, EX detail/color, att Grenfell, 10x12" 325.00
Collie, blk/tan on gray, red/tan border, yarn/rag, 23x38" 150.00
Deer/2 trees/2 stars/moon, stylized, EX colors, 25x40" 700.00
Dog in gr w/pk stripes on brn texture, 1800s, 56x60" 600.00
Eagle on rocks, yarn/rag, mc on beige, 38x20" 425.00
Flower vase in dmn reserve, vines in corners, 1850s, 40x40" . 1,400.00
Rabbit, yel on blk, worn, 22x33" 125.00
Rooster/hen in barnyard, 22½x37" 300.00
Sailboat, Grenfell label, minor wear, 6½x8½" 125.00
Sailboat, wht clouds/gr sea, blk/yel border, 1900s, 30x42" 500.00
Stagecoach w/passengers & driver+4 horses, 1900s, 46x55" . . .800.00
Triangles joined by strips, tape bound, 1900s, 108x120" 750.00

Oriental

The Oriental and Eastern rug market has enjoyed a renewal of interest in recent years as collectors have become aware of the fact that some of the semi-antique rugs (those sixty to one hundred years old) may be had at a price within the range of the average buyer.

Bessarabian, three birds and a human figure, multi on dark brown hand-knotted wool, 1800s, Rumania, 71x68", $2,000.00.

Afshar, 3 red/ivory med & scattered birds on blk-bl, 75x47" . . .400.00
Bidjar, bl pole med/dk bl spandrels on red, 45x67" 1,600.00
Bidjar, flowering trees on beige, gb on red, 1940, 77x43" 400.00
Bidjar, lg serrated red pole med on dk bl, herati, 42x65" 1,300.00
Caucasian, floral motif, central med on tan, wear, 144x185" .3,600.00
Chinese, 3 rows floral med, comp gb, gold/rose, 120x72" 400.00
Gorevan, intricate floral med, 121x175" 6,750.00
Hamadan, multiple med on salmon, 77x39" 425.00
Hamadan, vines/palmettes on red, red gb, 1940, 160x32" 650.00
Heriz, blk star/pendant med on red, 152x107" 2,600.00
Heriz, intricate floral med, 120x160" 5,750.00

Heriz, 8-lobed bl med on floral ground on red, 81x57" 5,600.00
Indo-Heriz, herati field/star med, salmon/wht/bl, 144x108" . .1,300.00
Indo-Kashan, tendrils/florals overall on magenta, 105x141" .6,400.00
Iranian, tree in center, 6 gb, worn, 135x150" 2,600.00
Karabagh, red med w/geometrics on cream, 1880s, 152x57" . . .600.00
Kashan, pictorial: seated sultan, red/navy, 1900, 76x50" 2,500.00
Kazvin, red/ivory med & sm spandrels on dk bl, 80x145" 2,800.00
Malayer, trellising vines on bl, rose gb, 1930, 52x39" 180.00
Mauri, Zaher Shahi pattern, 72x52" .500.00
Persian, intricate floral on bl, 80x140" 4,500.00
Persian, intricate floral on red, 120x150" 7,750.00
Persian, red med on bl w/gr & mc, 56x90" 4,400.00
Persian Heriz, semi-antique, lg med on rust, 98x141" 2,300.00
Persian runner, floral on dk red, 30x118" 750.00
Sarouk, antique, floral on cream, 6 gb, sgn, 120x142", EX . .5,900.00
Sarouk, detached florals w/in bl border on rose, 141x103" . .3,800.00
Sarouk, floral on dk red, minor wear, 120x196" 4,900.00
Tabriz, floral/birds/med on gold, bl gb, 1940, 84x50" 1,400.00
Tabriz, pictorial: trees/animals/flowers, 84x144", EX 6,300.00
Tabriz, 6 dk bl floral med on sm open orange fields, 36x20" . .1,500.00
Teheran, birds/flowers on midnight bl, 5 gb, 1920s, 106x75" .2,000.00
Tekke, 27 tekke guls in 3 rows on burgundy, 72x48" 600.00
Turkish Bergamo, geometrics/star med on red, wht gb, 86x55" .200.00
Turkoman, rows of guls on red, red gb, 120x42" 200.00

Rumrill

During the early 1930s, the Red Wing Union Stoneware Company of Red Wing, Minnesota, produced pottery for George Rumrill of Little Rock, Arkansas. Rumrill not only designed the ware but marketed it as well. In 1938 when the Shawnee Pottery Company of Zanesville, Ohio, submitted a lower bid, he awarded the contract to them, and they continued to manufacture decorative pottery for Rumrill until the early forties. His designs can be identified by the 'RumRill' mark or label.

Vase, Deco draping, wht, rnd, #601, 5¾" 30.00
Vase, leaves in relief, gr w/brn splotches, urn shape, 6", pr 30.00
Vase, nude figural hdls, 11½" 95.00
Vase, turq, H-38 . . . . .10.00
Vase, wht w/bl int, urn shape, #638, 5½" 20.00

Russel Wright Dinnerware

Russel Wright, one of America's foremost industrial engineers, also designed several lines of ceramic dinnerware, glassware, and aluminum ware that are today highly sought-after collectibles.

His most popular dinnerware, American Modern, was manufactured by the Steubenville Pottery Company from 1939 until 1959. It was produced in a variety of solid colors in assortments chosen to stay attune with the times.

Casual (his first line sturdy enough to be guaranteed against breakage for ten years from date of purchase) is relatively easy to find today — simply because it has held up so well. During the years of its production, the Casual line was constantly being restyled, some items as many as five times. Early examples were heavily mottled, while later pieces were smoothly glazed and patterned. The ware was marked with Wright's signature and 'China by Iroquois.' It was marketed in fine department stores throughout the country. After 1950 the line was marked 'Iroquois China by Russel Wright.'

To calculate values for items in American Modern, add 25% to the suggested prices in the following listings for examples in the these colors: White, Bean Brown, Black Chutney, Cantaloupe, Cedar Green, and Glacier Blue. In Casual, Brick Red and Aqua items go for around 200%

more than any other color, while those in Avocado Yellow are priced lower than suggested values.

American Modern

American Modern, see listings for specific values.

Bowl, vegetable; open 15.00
Bowl, vegetable; w/lid, 12" 25.00
Butter dish 95.00
Carafe, w/stopper, rare 95.00
Celery, 13" 22.00
Coffeepot 65.00
Creamer 8.00
Cup 5.00
Hostess set, w/cup 45.00
Pickle dish 10.00
Pitcher, w/lid, 7½" 95.00
Pitcher, water 40.00
Plate, bread & butter; 6¼" 4.00
Plate, chop 20.00
Plate, dinner 6.00
Plate, salad; 8¼" 8.00
Platter, 13¾" 25.00
Ramekin, w/lid, ind 85.00
Refrigerator jar 90.00
Relish, divided 45.00
Sauce boat, 8¼" 15.00
Saucer 3.00
Shakers, pr 10.00
Stack server 80.00
Sugar bowl, w/lid 10.00
Teapot 45.00
Tumbler, child's 45.00

Casual

Bowl, cereal; 5" 6.00
Bowl, fruit; 9½-oz, 5½" 5.00
Bowl, salad; 10" 25.00
Bowl, soup; restyled, 18-oz 15.00
Bowl, vegetable; open, 8⅛" 18.00
Butter dish, ½-lb 65.00
Casserole, 2-qt 20.00
Coffeepot, w/lid 65.00
Cup & saucer, tea; 7-oz 10.00
Gravy bowl, 12-oz, 5¼" 8.00
Mug, restyled, tall, 9-oz 35.00
Pepper mill 45.00
Plate, chop; 13⅞" 20.00
Plate, dessert & salad; 7½" 5.00
Plate, dinner; 10" 6.00

Plate, party; w/cup	35.00
Platter, oval, 10¼"	25.00
Platter, oval, 14½"	20.00
Shakers, stacking, pr	12.00
Sugar bowl, restyled	20.00
Sugar bowl, stacking, 4"	10.00
Teapot, restyled	85.00
Wine, carafe	65.00

Highlight

Bowl, cereal	15.00
Bowl, vegetable; oval	25.00
Bowl, vegetable; rnd	25.00
Creamer	15.00
Cup	15.00
Plate, dinner	15.00
Platter, oval, lg	25.00
Platter, rnd, sm	25.00

Spun Aluminum

Russel Wright's aluminum ware may not have been especially well accepted in its day — it tended to damage easily and seems to have had only limited market appeal — but today's collectors feel quite differently about it, as is apparent in the suggested values noted in the following listings.

Spun aluminum bun warmer, #333, $65.00; Lemonade pitcher, #367, and tray with lemonade tumblers, #124, $350.00 for the set.

Bowls, nested, 7", 9", 10", set	135.00
Bun warmer, sphere	65.00
Candelabrum, rare, 18x14"	95.00
Canister set, 4-pc	240.00
Casserole, pottery liner, w/lid	125.00
Casserole, walnut hdl, w/lid	95.00
Cheese board, w/cover	75.00
Coffeepot, after dinner	345.00
Coffeepot, drip; 3-pc	395.00
Cup holder, after dinner	25.00
Fruit bowl	65.00
Gravy, w/ladle & liner, 3-pc	135.00
Humidor, sandwich; w/cover	185.00
Humidor, tobacco; 12"	95.00
Humidor, tobacco; 16"	145.00
Ice bucket, in holder, w/tongs	55.00
Ice pail, rattan hdl, w/tongs, 10"	65.00
Ice pail, rattan hdl, w/tongs, 5"	35.00
Ice pail, rattan hdl, w/tongs, 6½"	45.00

Lemonade set, pitcher/tray/6 tumblers	350.00
Muffin warmer, wire insert, w/lid	85.00
Mug, beverage	35.00
Mug, ponytail hdl	35.00
Peanut scoop	38.00
Pitcher, stick hdl	185.00
Punch set, rolled edge w/8 hanging cups, rare	875.00
Punch set, w/ladle & liner, 8 cups, covered	975.00
Relish, glass insert, 13¼"	145.00
Relish rosette, lg	85.00
Relish rosette, sm	50.00
Shakers, range, pr	65.00
Tea set, on tray	425.00
Tidbit, 2-tier, rattan hdl	65.00
Tray, cork apple w/stem hdl	85.00
Tray, cork ball	55.00
Vase, sphere, 10½"	95.00
Vase, sphere, 7"	65.00

Sterling

Ash tray	65.00
Bouillon, 7-oz	8.00
Bowl, fruit; 5"	6.00
Cup & saucer	15.00
Onion soup, 10-oz	12.00
Pitcher, cream; 9-oz	12.00
Pitcher, water; 2-qt	45.00
Plate, bread & butter; 6¼"	3.00
Plate, luncheon; 9"	8.00
Plate, service; 11½"	15.00
Platter, oval, 10½"	15.00
Platter, oval, 13⅝"	20.00
Relish, 16½"	65.00

Russian Art

Before the Revolution in 1917, many jewelers and craftsmen created exquisite marvels of their arts, distinctive in the extravagant detail of their enamel work, jeweled inlays, and use of precious metals. These treasures aptly symbolized the glitter and the romance of the glorious days under the reign of the Tsars of Imperial Russia.

The most famous of these master jewelers was Peter Carl Faberge. Following the tradition of his father, he took over the Faberge workshop in 1870 at the age of twenty-four. His specialties were enamel work, clockwork automated figures, carved animal and human figures of precious or semiprecious stone and his best-known creations, the Imperial Easter Eggs — each of an entirely different design. By the turn of the century, his influence had spread to other countries, and his work was revered by royalty and the very wealthy. The onset of the war marked the end of the era.

Beaker, silver, chased town vignettes/florals, IYEZ mk, 3"	100.00
Box, gold-washed/enamel, mk ZZ/84, 2¾-oz troy	400.00
Box, gold-washed/enamel, rectangular, mk OU/84, 7-oz troy	700.00
Bronze, peasant lady w/gun/dagger sits on rocks, sgn/1882, 9"	875.00
Chalice, silver/plique-a-jour, Klingert, 1800, mk 875, 4½"	935.00
Charger, porc, florals in gilt-leaf band on rose, 1875, 15"	100.00
Cigarette box, silver, book form/eng foliage, 1900, 4¼" L	200.00
Cigarette case, silver/enamel troika scene, 1900, 4" L	200.00
Creamer, enamel silver, mk MC/84, 2-oz troy	300.00
Egg, silver gilt, chased florals, Viktor Aarne, 2½" L	375.00
Egg, silver gilt/enamel, swan vignettes/jewels/hoof ft, 4"	1,300.00
Figure, recumbent dog, rectangle base, mk PED, 1880, 16" L	1,400.00

Hand mirror, silver/enamel, mk CK St Petersburg, 7" 250.00
Icon, head of John the Baptist on dk brn, 1800s, rpr, 10x12" ..400.00
Icon, Holy Visage, inscribed, 1600s, 12½x9½", VG 475.00
Kovsh, silver gilt/enamel vines & rosettes, Ovchinnikov, 4" ...400.00
Patch box, silver, repousse/chased leafage, PT Moscow, 2" 275.00
Plate, porc, roses, floral vignette rim, Popov, 1850s, 10" 50.00
Salt dish, gold-washed enamel, kovsh form, mk, 1½-oz troy ...250.00
Shot glass, gold-washed enamel, mk AH/84, att Hollming 275.00
Vase, nephrite, gold eagle medallion mt, cylindrical, 5¾" 450.00

Vorovschikov, Moscow, 1782, 11", $6,000.00.

Sabino

Sabino art glass was produced by Marius-Ernest Sabino in France during the 1920s and '30s. It was made in opalescent, frosted, and colored glass and was designed to reflect the Art Deco style of that era. In 1960 using molds he modeled by hand, Sabino once again began to produce art glass using a special formula he himself developed that was characterized by a golden opalescence. Although the family continued to produce glassware for export after his death in 1971, they were never able to duplicate Sabino's formula.

Bird, fighting, sm 24.00
Bird, nesting, sm 24.00
Bottle, perfume; Frivolites, +atomizer, med 58.00
Bottle, perfume; Petalia 56.00
Bowl, shell form w/star center, lg 191.00
Bowl, w/Chicken La Ronde 251.00
Butterfly, wings open, sm 30.00
Chicken, drinking 52.00

Dog, Pekingese, lg 66.00
Dog, scotty 66.00
Dove, head up, sm 22.50
Fish, St George, lg 56.00
Hesitation 450.00
Knife rest, frog 23.50
Madonna, rnd base, sm 33.50
Madonna, w/halo, lg 216.00
Mirror, octagonal, 10" 25.00
Mirror, octagonal, 16" 48.00
Mirror, oval, 6x4" 15.00
Mirror, rnd, 10" 25.00
Mirror, rnd, 2" 6.50
Plate, Birth of a Star 525.00
Polar Bear 106.00
Powder box, sm 50.00
Ring box, lg 200.00
Snail shell 56.00
Statue, nude silhouette 161.50
Tray, sea urchin, lg 80.00
Tray, shell form, lg 46.00
Tray, w/hdl, rnd 64.00
Vase, Art Nouveau 225.00
Vase, Beehive 226.00
Vase, La Danse 990.00
Vase, Manta Ray 246.00

Salesman's Samples and Patent Models

Salesman's samples and patent models are often mistaken for toys or homemade folk art pieces. They are instead actual working models made by very skilled craftsmen who worked as model-makers. Patent models were made until the early 1900s. After that, the patent office no longer required a model to grant a patent. The name of the inventor or the model-maker and the date it was built is sometimes noted on the patent model. Salesman's samples were occasionally made by model-makers, but often they were assembled by an employee of the company. These usually carried advertising messages to boost the sale of the product. Though they are still in use today, the most desirable examples date from the 1800s to about 1945.

Many small stoves are incorrectly termed a 'salesman's sample'; remember that no matter how detailed one may be, it must be considered a toy unless accompanied by a carrying case — the indisputable mark of a salesman's sample.

Anchor, ship's, CI, EX 50.00
Bat, Louisville Slugger, wood, mk w/logo, 8" 15.00
Bible, 1886, EX 75.00
Bowl, CI, Griswold #72 ....65.00
Bridge, brass/steel, oak base, mechanical, 1876, 28x20x13" ..1,350.00
Carpet, 2x4" 15.00
Chair, folding lounge; pat 1927, EX 70.00
Chest, walnut, cedar lined, EX 125.00
Corsicana Grader, brass/iron/pnt w/decals, adjusts, 12" L 700.00
Dispenser, bulk oil; plated brass, detailed, w/case, 8" 2,500.00
Eyeglasses, sm nose-fitting type, folding, w/case 25.00
Fry pan, CI, Penn Stoves, EX 25.00
Hat, man's, felt, MIB 25.00
Hat, wool, snap brim, Dobbs, M in orig tin box 35.00
Kit, Royal Silver, 1895, w/catalog of same 95.00
Ladder, wood 150.00
Pan, graniteware, Stewart Ware, EX 75.00
Pitchfork, True Temper, w/cloth case & tine holder, 30", NM .650.00

Potato peeler, Nu-Way Automatic, w/case & literature, NM ..250.00
RR switch signal, CI/sheet metal/wood, Ramapo/pat 1884, 14" .375.00
Saddle, tooled leather, fully equipped, ME French, CO, 8" ..2,500.00
Saddle, tooled leather, unmk, EX 265.00
Shell, Peters Shotgun Shells, cut-away section, EX 75.00
Soap, washing machine form, Bendis soap, early 35.00
Step stool/chair, all wood construction, 10½" 400.00
Stove, Home Comfort, EX 2,900.00
Teakettle, tin, bail hdl, Germany 25.00
Toilet & sink, porc, Ariston/Made of Durock, 19", 16", VG .1,800.00
Tractor, aluminum/metal/brass, gears/clockwork, label, 27" ..2,700.00
Viles, 21 containing oil products, ca 1890 ....185.00
Waffle iron, Stover Jr, NM 115.00
Windmill, Air Charger, partial paper label, 22", VG 5,700.00
Windmill, wood, nickel gears/mechanism, w/case, 20", NM ..1,900.00

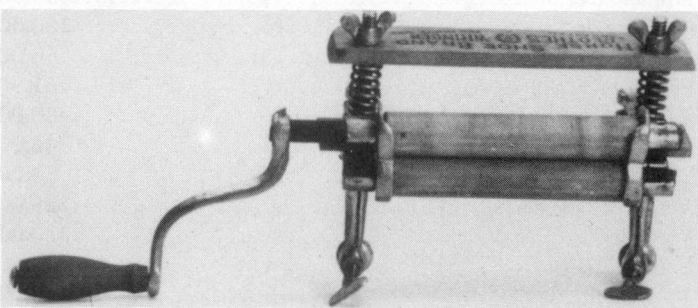

Clothes wringer, Horse Shoe Brand, 11" long, $165.00.

Salt Glaze

As early as the 1600s, potters used common salt to glaze their stoneware. This was accomplished by heating the salt and introducing it into the kiln at maximum temperature. The resulting gray-white glaze was a thin, pitted surface that resembled the peel of an orange.

Bottle, appl bird/floral, Staffordshire, 1740, 9", EX 1,500.00
Dish, leaf form w/relief currants, Staffordshire, 6½" 1,400.00
Wall pocket, Bacchus, 1700s, EX 475.00

Salt Shakers

The screw-top salt shaker was invented by John Mason in 1858. In 1871 when salt became more refined, some ceramic shakers were molded with pierced tops. 'Christmas' shakers, so called because of their December 25, 1877, patent date, were fitted with a rotary agitator designed to break up any lumps in the salt. There are four types: Christmas Barrel (rare in cranberry and amethyst); Christmas Panel (rare in colors); Christmas Pearl (opaque, pearly white with painted decor); and Octagon Waffle (clear, thick glass made in three sizes with a rotary agitator, usually having undated tops.) The dated top and patented agitator for the Christmas salt shakers were produced by Dana K. Alden of Boston; the glass bodies were made by the Boston and Sandwich Glass Co. in the late 1870s and 1880s. Identical shakers which have no agitator or dated top are the companion peppers; these fetch about 30% less than the salts on today's markets.

Today much of the interest in collecting is concentrated on art glass, Wave Crest, and custard glass examples. (See also specific categories.) If you would like to learn more about salt shakers, we recommend *The World of Salt Shakers*, by Mildred and Ralph Lechner; their address may be found in the Directory under Virginia. Those interested in novelty shakers will enjoy *Salt and Pepper Shakers*, an illustrated price guide by Helene Guarnaccia, and *The Collectors Encyclopedia of Salt and Pepper Shakers, Figural and*

Novelty, by Melva Davern. Both are available at your local library or bookstore. In the following listing, prices are for single shakers unless noted 'pair.' Values are for old, original shakers. Some of these have been reproduced, and this will be noted in the description.

Acorn, pk to wht, Hobbs, ca 1890, pr 70.00
Annie, clear 45.00
Argus Swirl, cranberry 150.00
Atterbury Twin, milk glass, combination S&P, pat 1873 ......85.00
Ball fruit jar (reproduced), pr, MIB 20.00
Basket, milk glass, HP decor 25.00
Beaded Dahlia, gr opaque, pr 32.50
Bevelled Diamond & Star 25.00
Bird, Arbor, vaseline cased, HP, bird & 2 circles, rare 150.00
Boot on Shell 20.00
Bow & Tassel, wht 22.50
Bow Tie, ca 1889, Thompson Glass Co 35.00
Bubble, opal lattice pattern, Hobbs/Brockunier, scarce 40.00
Bull's Eye & Daisy Variant, gr eyes 24.00
Burmese, ribbed barrel, no decor, Mt WA, pr 400.00
Chick head, HP roses on wht, figural metal head, Mt WA 335.00
Christmas, amber, barrel form, Sandwich, pr 175.00
Christmas, electric bl, pat dtd top, w/agitator, Sandwich 110.00
Christmas Barrel, amber, top dtd, Dana Alden 100.00
Christmas Barrel, cobalt, salt w/breaker+pepper, pr 200.00
Christmas Barrel, cranberry, salt w/breaker+pepper, pr 450.00
Christmas Barrel, gr, orig lid & agitator, pr 225.00
Christmas Barrel, peacock bl, salt w/breaker+pepper, pr 225.00
Christmas Panel, sapphire bl, top dtd, Dana Alden 140.00
Cockle Shell, satin w/HP floral, Mt WA 225.00
Corn Barrel, opaque wht & custard, rare 55.00
Cosmos, short, condiment set, 4-pc 195.00
Croesus, gr w/VG gold, pr 120.00
Currier & Ives, bl or vaseline, rare 55.00
Diamond Point & Leaf, bl opaque, rare 60.00
Diamond w/Peg, custard, pr 85.00
Egg, milk glass, flat sided, Columbian Expo, pewter top 50.00
Egg in Cup, HP, opaque, Mt WA, rare 90.00
Eureka, ruby stain, pr 48.00
Fig, violets, wht on cranberry, Mt WA, orig top 185.00
Fine Cut, yel, pr 50.00
Flower & Rain, cased, bl or yel, rare 125.00
Flower Band, pk cased, pr 85.00
Fluted Scrolls, bl opal w/decor, pr 85.00
Footed Ten Panel, opaline gr or bl, rare 60.00
Forget-Me-Not, gr, tall, Challinor 25.00
Forget-Me-Not, milk glass, tall, pr 45.00
Georgia Gem, custard, souvenir, pr 65.00
Guttate, pk cased, (reproduced), pr 75.00
Heart, bl opaque, Dithridge, 1894-1897, pr 75.00
Heart, milk glass, pr 40.00
Heart, pk opaque, pr 90.00
Herringbone MOP, pk, pewter top 290.00
Intaglio, emerald gr w/gold, Northwood, rare, pr 250.00
Invt Fan & Feather, pk slag, Northwood, 1900s, rare, pr 600.00
Jewel & Flower, bl opal w/gold 75.00
Leaf & Spear, HP opalware, Wave Crest, pr 165.00
Leaf Bracket, opaque caramel slag, Indiana Tumbler Co, rare ..175.00
Leaf Mold, cranberry cased, silver flecks, pr 145.00
Lobe Four, wht/bl floral on yel, 6-lobed, Mt WA, pr 185.00
Many Petals (Periwinkle), New Martinsville 35.00
Nail, etched, red flashed, orig top 40.00
Nestor, bl, no enamel 22.00
Optic, rubena w/floral, Hobbs, pr in Wilcox fr w/swans 190.00

Owl's head, milk glass, orig top 110.00
Panelled Scroll, gr 20.00
Panelled Sprig, milk glass w/gr decor, pr 30.00
Peachblow, Wheeling, orig tops, pr .650.00
Pillar Ribbed, glossy burmese, Mt WA, rare, pr 800.00
Pineapple & Fan, sterling lid, pr 30.00
Raindrop, bl MOP, rare, pr 410.00
Reverse Swirl, clear opal 48.00

Rib and Scroll, pigeon blood (rare color), $135.00 for the pair.

Rubena, HP butterflies & plants, pr .145.00
Rubena verde, HP floral 90.00
Sequoia, bl, in stand, pr 85.00
States, glass lid, pr 35.00
Sunset, milk glass 15.00
Swag w/Brackets, amethyst w/gold, pr 80.00
Tarentum's Victoria, custard, ca 1900, pr 110.00
Thousand Eye, amber 18.00
Wildflower, vaseline (reproduced) 45.00
Woven Neck, Wave Crest, kitten in grass decor 55.00
Wreath 12-Panel, pk roses, Mt WA, Pairpoint, pr 75.00

Novelty

African dancer, bsk, pr 20.00
Alligator, ceramic, Japan, pr 8.00
Baked potato, ceramic, pr 8.00
Bear w/garbage pail, ceramic, 5" 10.00
Bride & groom, Occupied Japan, pr .20.00
Budweiser Beer, glass bottle w/paper label, pr 10.00
Corn, ceramic, pr 9.00
Cupcake w/walnut on top, chocolate & vanilla, pr 8.00
Dice, wood, Burlington VT, pr 6.00
Dog, Bonzo, ceramic, high gloss, gold paws, pr 12.00
Fish, silvery metal, pr 8.00
Flamingo, heads down, ceramic, high gloss, pr 17.00
Foot, ceramic, wht w/red-pnt toenails, pr 8.00
Frying pan, plastic, pr 7.00
Golf bag & ball, bag is pepper/ball is salt, pr 10.00
Owl in doctor's clothing, ceramic, pr 10.00
Pig head, red/wht chalkware, pr 10.00
Popeye & Olive Oyl, ceramic, pr 25.00
Revolver, blk/brn, ceramic, high gloss, pr 9.00
Safe-T-Cup ice cream cone, ceramic, pr 14.00
Sailor, full figure, chalk-like compo, pr 10.00
Santa Claus head, hdld, ceramic, high gloss, pr 8.00
Toaster w/bread, brn is pepper/wht is salt, Starke 15.00
Tropical fish, pk & bl w/blk stripes, high gloss, 4½", pr 9.00
TV, plastic, shakers pop up when knob is turned 10.00

US Capitol Bldg/Washington Monument, wht china/gold trim . .12.00
Westinghouse washer & dryer, wht plastic, 1950, pr 20.00

Salts, Open

Before salt became refined, processed, and 'free-flowing' as we know it today, it was necessary to serve it in a 'cellar.' An innovation of the early 1800s, the master salt cellar was placed by the host and passed from person to person. Smaller 'individual' salts were a part of each place setting. A small silver spoon was used to sprinkle it onto the food. If you would like to learn more about the subject of salts, we recommend *5,000 Open Salts*, written by William Heacock and our advisor for this category, Patricia Johnson, with many full-color illustrations and current values; you will find Patricia Johnson's address in the Directory under California.

In the listings below, the numbers refer to *Open Salts* by Johnson and Heacock, and *Pressed Glass Salt Dishes* by L.W. and D.B. Neal. Lines with 'repro' within the description reflect values for reproduced salts.

Key:
EPNS — electroplated nickel silver   (+) — reproduced in
HM —— hallmarked   Italy

Animals, Figurals, and Novelties

Bird & Berry, amber, bl, or vaseline, McKee, HJ-997, M 55.00
Bird & Berry, colors, mk Degenhart, HJ-932, up from 25.00
Bird & Berry, colors, unmk Degenhart, HJ-933, up from 10.00
Chicken, covered, milk glass, Westmoreland, HJ-949, M 12.00
Pilgrim shoes, pressed, milk glass, HJ-3736 . . . . .45.00
Sleigh, clear or milk glass, Fostoria, HJ-3735, ca 1940 . . . . . . .55.00
Squirrel on stump, various colors, sgn Boyd, HJ-929, repro 6.00
Swan, Crown Tuscan, Cambridge, HJ-935 . . . . .100.00
Swan, Crown Tuscan, unsgn, repro 20.00
Swan pulling cart, carmel, HJ-941, St Clair repro 30.00
Turtle, amber, bl, or milk glass, HJ-4475, M 55.00
Turtle, clear, HJ-3758, M 45.00
Wagon, farm, pressed, amber, unmk, HJ-2084, ca 1890 . . . . . .125.00
Wheelbarrow, Greentown, bl, HJ-4669, M 125.00
Wheelbarrow, Greentown, Nile gr, M 275.00
Wheelbarrow, sgn, St Clair repro, up from 15.00

Art Glass

Burmese, rnd, ruffled, flowers, M 650.00
Crown Milano, HJ-46, M 165.00
Daum Nancy, flowers, mk, HJ-11 . . . . .600.00
Daum Nancy, winter scene, sgn 700.00
Itaglio, jeweled ormolu holder, HJ-90, M 125.00
LeGras, sterling base, sgn, HJ-12, M .550.00
Monot Stumpf, HJ-19 to HJ-22, M, ea 95.00
Monot Stumpf, jeweled ormolu holder, M 325.00
Mt Washington, decor, HJ-35 to HJ-44, M, ea 110.00
Quezal, sgn, HJ-18, 1" dia, M 175.00
Steuben, clear w/blk threading, HJ-113, M 225.00
Tiffany, ruffled, sgn LCT Favrile, HJ-32, M 125.00
Victorian, bl, rigaree, berry pontil, SP holder, HJ-96 . . . . .225.00
Webb, cranberry, acorn design, HJ-84, M 850.00
Webb, 3-color, HJ-27, M 1,200.00

China and Porcelain

Austria, HP, mk HJ-1272, M 12.00
Austria or France, HP, HJ pg 78, ind, M, ea 12.00

Boehm, lighthouse/canoe w/spoon paddle, Conta, HJ-4761, M .150.00
Egg on branches, birds, 2¾", M 150.00
Elfinware, allover florals, German, HJ-1270, M 35.00
Elfinware, basket, German, HJ-1246 to HJ-1249, M, ea 15.00
Elfinware, basket, German, HJ-1253, M 15.00
French, mk Sampson, HJ-1786, ca 1880, repro of Chinese, M ..125.00
Furstenberg, portrait, triangular, ca 1840, M 350.00
Goss, miniature ancient salt cellar, HJ-2029, M 45.00
Haviland, factory decor, HJ-1397 to HJ-1400, M, ea 35.00
KPM, dbl, boy between 2 bowls, HJ-1155 or HJ-1156, M, ea ..275.00
KPM, dbl, w/cherub, mk, HJ-1107, M 295.00
Lenox, silver overlay, HJ-1815, M 45.00
Limoges, HP, mk HJ-1275 ....12.00
Meissen, scroll ft decor, HJ-1812 to HJ-1814, M, ea 125.00
Meissen, sq, HJ-1595, ind, M 55.00
Nippon, HP, HJ-1358 to HJ-1364, ind, M, ea 12.00
Nippon, HP, ped ft, HJ-1484 or HJ-1485, M, ea 18.00
Nippon, HP buckets, HJ-1446 to HJ-1457, ind, M, ea 14.00
Pickard, sq, HJ-1569, M 55.00
Royal Bayreuth, claw, poppy, or grapes, HJ pg 89, ind 85.00
Royal Bayreuth, sheep, ped ft, HJ-1666, M 85.00
Royal Bayreuth, Sunbonnet Babies, M 150.00
Royal Copenhagen, oval, HJ-1672, ca 1920, M 25.00
Royal Worcester, HJ-1861, ca 1870, M 150.00

Cut Glass

Amber, ped ft, English, ca 1880, master, M, pr 250.00
Amber flashed, ped ft, hdls, English, HJ-2060, master, M 175.00
Amethyst, etched, Hawkes, HJ-2038, M 65.00
Bl cut to clear, ped ft, HJ-67, M 125.00
Clark, etched, ped ft, sgn, HJ-3009, M 35.00
Clear, etched, rnd, Hawkes, HJ-3268 to HJ-3269, M, ea 27.00
Clear, oval, Hawkes, HJ-3209, M 55.00
Clear, oval on ped, shell shape, French, HJ-3717, 4⅞", M 195.00
Clear, ped ft, mk Libbey, HJ-2995, M 30.00
Clear, rnd, nappy style, not salesman's sample, HJ-3170, M 65.00
Cranberry, rnd, Moser type, HJ-305, M 85.00
Cranberry, serrated top edge, rnd, HJ-304, M 65.00
Daisy & Button, oval, HJ-3214, M 20.00
Daisy & Button, rnd tub, HJ-2853, M 25.00
Fan & Diamond, HJ-3416 or HJ-3417, M, ea 15.00
Heart, club, spade, diamond, HJ-3033 to HJ-3035, M, 4 for ...250.00
Waterford, ped ft, sgn, master, HJ-3722, M 65.00
Waterford, sgn, HJ-3459, not old, ind, M 15.00
Zippered, HJ-3088-3089, M 10.00

Lacy Glass

Neal BF-1, lt opal, Basket of Flowers, Sandwich, NM 200.00
Neal BF-1F, opal, sm edge chips, underfilled, rare, 3" 145.00
Neal BS-2, opal, Beaded Scroll, Sandwich, NM 150.00
Neal BT-4D, cobalt, boat, Sandwich, EX 1,350.00
Neal BT-9, boat, New England, NM 140.00
Neal CD-2, w/lid, Sandwich, EX 525.00
Neal CN-1B, Crown, Sandwich, NM 230.00
Neal CN-1B, fiery opal, Crown, Sandwich, NM 225.00
Neal CT-1, opaque wht, Chariot, Sandwich, NM 425.00
Neal EE-1A, Eagle, Sandwich, NM 400.00
Neal EE-3, Eagle, Sandwich, NM 575.00
Neal EE-3B, opal, Eagle, Sandwich, EX 350.00
Neal EE-8, Eagle/Constitution, Sandwich, EX 525.00
Neal GA-3, Gothic Arch, Pittsburgh area, EX 90.00
Neal GA-4, med bl, Gothic Arch, Sandwich, EX 325.00

Neal HN-11, med amber, French, minor edge chips, rare, 3" ...185.00
Neal JY-2, wear/minor flakes, rare, 3" 75.00
Neal MV-1, gray-bl, Sandwich, EX 210.00
Neal NE-1, fiery opal, New England, NM 110.00
Neal NE-1A, opaque wht, New England, NM 90.00
Neal OG-10, Leaf, Providence, EX 125.00
Neal OG-4a, amethyst, extremely rare, Sandwich, NM 800.00
Neal OL-16A, opal, oval, Sandwich, EX 400.00
Neal OL-17, lt amethyst, extremely rare, Sandwich, EX 500.00
Neal OL-18A, oblong, Sandwich, EX 125.00
Neal OL-32, oval, Philadelphia, EX 425.00
Neal OL-34, Philadelphia area, NM 75.00
Neal OL-6, canary, French, NM 210.00
Neal OP-17, moonstone, Sandwich, EX 300.00
Neal OP-20, ftd/oval, Philadelphia, EX 180.00
Neal PO-6A, Peacock Eye, Sandwich, NM 170.00
Neal PP-1, Peacock Eye, ftd, Pittsburgh area, NM 325.00
Neal RD-14, peacock bl, Sandwich, extremely rare, NM 800.00
Neal RD-18, rnd/ped ft, Sandwich, NM 70.00
Neal RD-22A, purple-bl, rnd, Sandwich, EX 600.00
Neal RD-8, rnd/ped ft, Sandwich, M 260.00
Neal RP-17, med bl, slight ft bruise, Sandwich, very rare 100.00
Neal RP-25, rnd/ped ft, Sandwich 240.00
Neal RP-9, rnd/ped ft, Sandwich, NM 130.00
Neal SD-1, Strawberry Diamond, Pittsburgh area, NM 175.00
Neal SD-13, lt gr, Sandwich, NM 140.00
Neal SD-14, purple-bl, Strawberry Diamond, EX 200.00
Neal SD-4C, Strawberry Diamond, Sandwich, NM 90.00
Neal SL-1, med to dk purple-bl, shell, Sandwich, rare, NM 200.00
Neal SL-18, ped ft, Sandwich, extremely rare, EX 950.00
Neal WN-1, Wagon, Sandwich, NM 400.00

Pottery and Faience

Adams, HM, HJ-1849, ca 1902, M 140.00
Niloak, rnd, mk, HJ-1735, 1½", M 65.00
Quimper, dbl, pr of shoes, HJ-1162 ....45.00
Quimper, dbl, w/dog or pig, HJ-1134, M 85.00
Royal Doulton, HM, emb animals, HJ-1859, M 65.00
Royal Doulton, pyramid shape, HJ-1870, ca 1873, M 125.00
Satsuma, various shapes, HJ-1931 to HJ-1933, M, ea 20.00
Staffordshire, bl on tan, ped ft, ca 1850, HJ-4577, M 65.00
Staffordshire, Elfinware decor, ca 1840, M 125.00
Staffordshire, Toby, w/pepper, mc, old, (+), 5¼", M, set 350.00
Wedgewood, bl & wht, sgn HM, HJ-1871, ca 1900, M 165.00
Wedgewood, chariots, gr & wht, sgn HM, M 225.00
Wedgewood, 3-pc condiment in worn EPNS holder, HJ-4762 .225.00

Pressed Pattern Glass, Clear

Apollo, HJ-3576, master, M 20.00
Argus, HJ-2612, ind, M 10.00
Atlas, HJ-2933, ind, M 12.00
Bagware, HJ-2795, ind, M 10.00
Barberry, ped ft, HJ-3584, master, M 35.00
Barrelled Excelsior, HJ-3620, master, M 30.00
Beaded Grape Medallion, HJ-2522, ind, M 22.00
Beaded Triangle, HJ-2970, ind, M 20.00
Bigler, HJ-3620, master, M 30.00
Blackberry, HJ-3557, master, M 35.00
Bryce Bros #900, HJ-2800, ind, M 8.00
Cabbage Rose, HJ-3529, master, M 35.00
Cape Cod, HJ-2948, ind, M 15.00
Cobb, HJ-2803, ind, M 6.00

Cordova, HJ-3057, ind, M .12.00
Currier & Ives, HJ-3579, master 45.00
Diamond Quilted, HJ-3648, master, M 15.00
Duncan #72 (Flawless), etched, HJ-2887, ind 18.00
Early American Sandwich, w/saucer, Duncan, HJ-2687, M 22.00
Empress, HJ-2938, ind, M 30.00
Eureka, HJ-3611, master, M 25.00
Fancy Arch, McKee, HJ-3058, M 27.00
Fine Cut & Block, HJ-2100, M 22.00
Gallaway, HJ-2805, ind, M 22.00
Good Luck, HJ-3740, ind, M 55.00
Grasshopper, HJ-3573, master, M 45.00
Harp, Flint, HJ-3601, master 65.00
Holly, HJ-3569, master flint, M 55.00
Liberty Bell, HJ-2689, ind, M 45.00
Nevada, HJ-2624, ind, M .20.00
Oaken Bucket, HJ-2837, ind, M 25.00
Ovoid Panels, HJ-3531, master, M 25.00
Pillow, Heisey, HJ-2697, ind, M 35.00
Prismatic, HJ-2671, ind, M 8.00
Puritan, HJ-2804, ind, M .6.00
Ribbed Ivy, covered, HJ-4654, master, M 110.00
Roman Key, HJ-3582, master flint 65.00
Scroll, HJ-3538, master .35.00
Spiral Flutes, HJ-3549, master, M 12.00
Stippled Ivy Master, HJ-3593, M 40.00
Sunburst & Bar, HJ-3649, non-flint, M 25.00
Tree of Life, 'Salt,' ped ft, HJ-3581, M 95.00
Urn, Heisey, HJ-2969, ind, M 45.00
Urn, Heisey, master, M 65.00
3 Face, HJ-4428, ind, old, M 45.00
3 Face, HJ-4430 to HJ-4431, ind, repro, M, ea 12.00

Pressed Pattern Glass, Colored

Bagware, bl, amber, or vaseline, HJ-449, ind, M, ea 15.00
Beatty Rib, bl, HJ-196, ind, M 35.00
Big Pansy, gold trim, HJ-153, repro 25.00
Block & Star (Valencia Waffle), HJ-452, M 35.00
Brazilian, gr, HJ-335, ind, M 55.00
Cabinet, bl, HJ-462, ind, M 20.00
Candlewick, cranberry flashed, HJ-285, ind, M 25.00
Chippendale, vaseline or opal, English, HJ-70, M, ea 70.00
Daisy & Button, amber or bl, HJ-594, ind, M, ea 22.00
Dewdrop, amber, HJ-513, ind, M 25.00
Eyewinker, amber or gr, HJ-893, repro, ea 6.00
Fostoria #95, gr, HJ-333, M 15.00
Grape Leaf, gr, Fostoria, HJ-415, ca 1940, M 25.00
Hobnail, opal, HJ-198, ind, M 45.00
Kings Crown, ruby flashed, HJ-2776, ind, M 65.00
Lords & Ladies, vaseline or opal, English, HJ-137, M, ea 70.00
Maple Leaf (Leaf & Rib), bl or amber, HJ-435, ind, M, ea 15.00
Moon & Star, red, gr, or amber, HJ-870, repros, ea 6.00
Pattee Cross, gold trim, HJ-185, ind 20.00
Pillar, bl, vaseline, or amber, HJ-420, ind, M 15.00
Pressed Diamond, bl, amber, or vaseline, HJ-427, ind 12.00
Stippled Star, HJ-881, all colors are repros, ea 12.00
Thousand Eye Wagon, gr, HJ-860, old (repros in milk glass) 65.00
Triangle, bl, amber, or vaseline, HJ-442, ind, ea 22.00
Triangle, larger sz, all colors are repros, ea 4.00
US Rib, gr, HJ-818, ind, rare 55.00
Waffle, vaseline, HJ-559, ind, M 22.00
Wildflower, oblong, HJ-898-899, all colors are repros, ea 8.00
Wildflower, turtle base, all colors, HJ-506, M, ea 100.00

Silverplate

American, Derby, lattice holder, cranberry liner, HJ-319, M 75.00
American, flower on leaf, HJ-3977, M 35.00
American, James Tuft, flower form, HJ-4047, M 15.00
American, lattice holder, clear liner, ind, M 10.00
American, Meriden, condiment on leaves, twig hdl, HJ-4763 . .175.00
American, Meriden, Victorian, overshot insert, HJ-4215, M 5.00
American, Reed/Barton, Victoria, cranberry insert, HJ-322, M .150.00
American, rnd, emb, HJ-4017, ind, M 15.00
American, Tiffany, emb, cobalt liner, HJ-658, M 55.00
Combination w/knife rest, HJ-4245, M 12.00
English, cabbage on leaf w/spoon, HJ-4276, ind, M 45.00
English, EPNS, cobalt liner, HJ-681, M 25.00
German, oval, cobalt liner, ftd, HJ-747, M 25.00

Sterling and Continental Silver

Am, CF Rudolph, gr liners, spoons, HJ-4793, boxed set of 2 . . .225.00
Am, Indian, w/spoon, HJ-3969 to 3970, ind, M, ea 45.00
Am, Kerr, Art Nouveau, ped ft, cobalt liner, HJ-702, M 225.00
Am, Shreve & Co, Lenox insert, pepper+spoon, HJ-3853, ind. .125.00
Am, Udall & Ballow, oval, emb, ped ft, HJ-4078, M 100.00
Am, Wm Kerr, rnd, ped ft, HJ-4090, ca 1900, M 65.00
Austria, dbl, cranberry, w/hdl, HJ-4751, M 400.00
Austria, oblong, ped ft, HJ-3956, ca 1970, ind, M 25.00
Birmingham, Baroque, ftd, w/spoon, HJ-4191, ca 1899 . . . . .125.00
Equador coin, 3 llamas for legs, HJ-4070, ind 45.00
French, ornate, liner & spoon, HJ-3937, ca 1845, ind, M 125.00
French, 800, stylized lions, cobalt liner, HJ-682, M 150.00
Gorham, medallion, ped ft, HJ-3976, ca 1970 . . . . .140.00
London, A&P Bateman, oval, ped ft, HJ-3857, pr 450.00
London, oval, ped ft, heavy Baroque, HJ-4165, ca 1899 . . . . .125.00
Overlay, rnd, tab hdls, HJ-3866, ind, M 25.00
Russian, chair, HJ-4735, M 400.00
Tiffany, sq, HJ-3973, ca 1900, ind, ¾" H, M 35.00
Viking, 830, boat, enameled, w/liner & spoon, HJ-2002 . . . . .125.00
Viking, 830, boat, w/liner & spoon, HJ-4260, M 45.00

Master salt, sterling with gold wash, repousse animals, animal figural feet, 5" wide, $500.00.

Other Types

Abalone shell over copper, w/spoon, Mexico, HJ-2011, M 15.00
Celadon, silver overlay, HJ-1427, M 25.00
Celluloid, Viking salt & horn pepper, w/spoon, HJ-207, set 45.00
Cloisonne, w/pepper, HJ-1995, not old, M, set 25.00
Dbl, bl opaque, ped ft, French, HJ-144 . . . . .85.00

Dbl, pressed, bl opal, figural hdl, HJ-2088, M 65.00
Dbl, pressed, clear, hdl, HJ-3805 to HJ-3807, M, ea 18.00
Dbl, pressed, figural hdl, HJ-3777, M 45.00
Dbl, Venetian swans, cranberry or gold, M, ea 125.00
Enameled pedestal, 935 Norway, HJ-2024, M 400.00
Intaglio, bl, common variety, HJ-253, M 15.00
Intaglio, bl, kitten, HJ-223, M 35.00
Intaglio, clear, HJ-256, M 15.00
Intaglio, colors, jeweled rim, HJ-248, M, ea 35.00
Intaglio, pnt animals/etched butterfly, sgn, HJ-160, M 65.00
Millefiori, rnd, HJ-609, ind, rare, M 400.00
Stone, rose quartz, HJ-1955, M 50.00
Venetian glass, swans, cranberry w/gold flecks, M 30.00

Samplers

American samplers were made as early as the colonial days; even earlier examples from 17th-century England still exist today. Changes in style and decorative motif are evident down through the years. Verses were not added until the late 17th century. By the 18th century, samplers were used not only for sewing experience but also as an educational tool. Young ladies, who often signed and dated their work, embroidered numbers and letters of the alphabet and practiced fancy stitches as well. Fruits and flowers were added for borders; birds, animals, and Adam and Eve were popular subjects. Later, houses and other buildings were included. By the 19th century, the American Eagle and the little red schoolhouse had made their appearances.

Large house, memorial tribute, signed and dated 1816, 16x16", $3,000.00.

Alphabet, floral/birds/squirrels border, maid/sheep, 22x21" 425.00
Alphabet bands, American, sgn/ca 1810, old fr, 5x7" 320.00
Alphabet bands/crowns/numerals/verse, sgn/1726, 10x24" . . .1,300.00
Alphabets, simple detail, sgn/1836, 10x10½" 675.00
Alphabets, 2-color embr on homespun, sgn/1845, 13x14½" . . .450.00
Alphabets (9), elaborate style, linen, sgn/1724, 11x21" 1,300.00
Alphabets/house/trees/crows/flowers, sgn/1827, 15x16" 700.00
Alphabets/motto, gr embr on homespun, sgn, 11x11½" 300.00
Alphabets/stitch samples/dog/bird/etc, sgn, 11x20", VG 275.00

Alphabets/stylized trees/plants/figure, sgn/1736, 9x15", EX 825.00
Alphabets/verse, sgn/dtd 1878, 15x15½", EX 245.00
Alphabets/verse/Adam & Eve, sgn/1799, 14x18", VG 900.00
Alphabets/verse/florals, homespun, sgn/1819, 14x18½", EX . .1,100.00
Alphabets/verse/house/florals, MA, sgn/1839, 16x16", VG 600.00
Alphabets/verse/pot of flowers, data/1800, 22x23", EX 2,250.00
Alphanumerics/house/butterflies, sgn/1864, 12x15", EX 300.00
Alphanumerics/trees/fruit bowl, sgn/1796, rpr, 12x18" 350.00
Alphanumerics/verse/data, homespun, sgn/1830, 19x26", EX.. 1,200.00
Alphanumerics/verse/house scene, data/1803, 21x16", NM . .3,250.00
Brick bldg/trees/flowering plants, unsgn, 16x12½" 250.00
Family crest/people/windmill/grapes, linen, sgn/1855, 19x19" . .450.00
Family register/floral columns, RI, sgn/1832, 16x18", EX 1,800.00
Family register/floral swags & baskets, sgn/1828, 16x18" 1,450.00
Flowers in urn/birds/ribbon border, initials/ca 1830, 12x11" . . .400.00
Georgian house/animals/church, sgn/ca 1810, 17x17½", EX . . .800.00
Georgian house/turkey/trees, homespun, sgn/1810, 16x16" . .1,375.00
House/garden/animals, linen, sgn/1839, 16x20", EX 1,200.00
House/lg tree/lady in chair, 2-column verse, 1827, 20x17" . . .8,000.00
Lg weeping willow/verse/kissing birds, data/1818, 27x17" . . .1,900.00
Schoolhouse/verse/geometrics, linen, sgn/1838, 15½x16" 745.00
Sunflower/sunshine/deer/florals, England, sgn/1780, 13x17" . .1,000.00
Verse, intricate scene w/people & animals, sgn/1800, 13x13" . .1,000.00
Verse in cartouch/stag/trees, homespun, sgn/1816, 12x16" 650.00
Verse/animals/trees/flowers, silk on linen, sgn/1808, 25x20" . . .750.00
Verse/facing birds/florals, linen, sgn/1757, 13x21", EX 1,200.00
Verse/florals/birds/animals, linen, sgn/1826, 16x17", EX 375.00
Verse/giraffe/girl/2 trees, data/1837, 27x28½" 2,700.00
Verse/pots of flowers/birds in X-stitch, sgn, 16½x12" 300.00
Verse/trees/animals/gazebo, linen, sgn/1830, 15x17", EX 450.00
2-column verse, sgn/1829, linen, 25x17" 375.00
2-column verse/lg bird in tree, grapevine fr, 1819, 22x17" . . .2,200.00

Sandwich Glass

The Boston and Sandwich Glass Company was founded in 1820 by Deming Jarves in Sandwich, Massachusetts. Their first products were simple cruets, salts, half-pint jugs, and lamps. They were attributed as being one of the first to perfect a method for pressing glass, a step toward the manufacture of the 'lacy' glass which they made until about 1840. Many other types of glass were made there — cut, colored, snakeskin, hobnail, and opalescent among them.

After the Civil War, profits began to dwindle due to the keen competition of the Western factories which were situated in areas rich in natural gas and easily accessible sand and coal deposits. The end came with an unreconcilable wage dispute between the workers and the company, and the factory closed in 1888.

Our advisor for this category is Richard Marden; he is listed in the Directory under New Hampshire. See also Cup Plates; Salts, Open; specific types of glass.

Bottle, b3m, purple-bl, swirled ribs, orig stopper, 5½" 525.00
Bottle, scent; gr, circles & ovals, teardrop stopper, lg 395.00
Bottle, scent; Loop, emerald gr, orig stopper, 8", EX 800.00
Bowl, Industry, L-267, 6", EX 200.00
Bowl, Industry, L-89-2, 6", NM 225.00
Bowl, Oak Leaf, lacy, 7", NM 75.00
Bowl, opal, ftd, L-80-6, miniature, EX 110.00
Bowl, Peacock Eye, rayed, lacy, 9½" L 200.00
Bowl, Princess Feather, lacy, 1⅝x7½" 60.00
Bowl, Princess Feather, lacy, 8½", EX 100.00
Bowl, Roman Rosette, lacy, 6⅝", EX 25.00

Bowl, Tulip & Acanthus, cobalt, lacy, 6" dia, NM 550.00
Candlestick, bl opaque/wht, petal top, sandy surface, 8½" 400.00
Candlestick, canary, columnar, petal top, 8", NM, pr 700.00
Candlestick, Loop & Petal, canary, 6¾", pr 250.00
Candlestick, Loop & Petal, canary, 7", NM, pr 350.00
Candlestick, opaque powdery purple-bl, columnar, 9" 450.00
Candlestick, purple-bl opaque/wht, petal top, L 182-2, 7" 400.00
Champagne, Sandwich Star, rare 300.00
Compote, Bull's Eye, fiery opal, spiral std/rnd ft, 4½x8" 1,600.00
Compote, Loop, flint, 8¾x13", NM 450.00
Compote, Plume, lacy, matching std, underfilled, 4½x7" 175.00
Dish, eagle, octagonal, lacy, att, 7" W 600.00
Dish, Gothic Arch, oblong, lacy, 7" 110.00
Goblet, Sandwich Star, rare 475.00
Lamp, free-blown, on standard, orig burner, miniature/toy, 4" . .450.00
Lamp, Sweetheart, canary, dbl drop oil burner, late, 10" 250.00
Pitcher, L-80-4, miniature, M 80.00
Pitcher, satin w/pk swirl, leaves/flowers, ice pocket, 12" 550.00
Plate, Roman Rosette, red-amber, lacy, 5¼", NM 440.00
Plate, toddy; Oak Leaf, lacy 75.00
Relish dish, Butterfly, lacy, shaped rim, 7x10" L 400.00
Salt cellar, cobalt, hexagonal, ftd, EX 175.00
Salt cellar, peacock bl, hexagonal, ftd, M 200.00
Sauce, Peacock Eye, sapphire bl, lacy, 4¼", VG 160.00
Spill holder, Sandwich Star, clambroth (blk surface specks) . . .275.00
Spill holder, Sandwich Star, electric bl 1,300.00
Spooner, Vine, clambroth, 4½" 450.00
Sugar bowl, emb scrolled leaf/basket, 6", EX 110.00
Sugar bowl, Gothic Arch, peacock bl, L 158-4, w/lid, 5", EX . .400.00
Tureen, L-80-12, w/undertray, lacy, miniature 375.00
Vase, Circle & Ellipse, amethyst, flat rim, 7" 350.00

Circle and Ellipse vases, emerald green, 9", $2,000.00 for the pair.

Vase, Loop, canary, gauffered rim, knop base, 10" 350.00
Vase, Tulip, amethyst, 9½" 450.00
Vase, 3-Printie, canary, ftd cone form, 9", NM, pr 250.00
Vase, 3-Printie, canary, gauffered rim, 9", EX, pr 500.00
Vase, 4-Printie, canary, knop base, 11½", pr 950.00
Wash bowl & pitcher, L-80-1, miniature, EX 225.00
Whiskey taster, lt gr, hexagonal 120.00
Whiskey taster, powder bl translucent 140.00
Wine glass, Sandwich Star, rare 190.00

Sarreguemines

Sarreguemines, France, is the location of Utzschneider and Company, founded in 1770, producers of majolica, transfer-printed dinnerware, figurines, and novelties which are usually marked 'Sarreguemines.'

Invalid feeder, wht, emb flower on top 38.00

Jardiniere, allover lily pads and flowers, ca 1952, 12x15", $200.00.

Pitcher, jester holds stomach, seated on stump, mk, 13" 375.00
Plate, Cadet Rousselle, 7½" 28.00
Plate, Marlborough, 7½" 28.00
Plate, opera character from Rheingold, M 55.00
Plate, Song, 7½" 28.00
Plate, strawberries w/floral trim on aqua, 8½" 68.00
Table, coppered-bronze w/floral majolica inset, 30x28" 1,600.00
Urn, fluted, gilt/dk bl ribs on cream, pedestal base, 73" 1,700.00

Satin Glass

Satin glass is simply glassware with a velvety matt finish achieved through the application of an acid bath. This procedure has been used by many companies since the nineteenth century, both here and abroad, on many types of colored and art glass. See also Mother-of-Pearl.

Biscuit jar, pk, etched & HP birds, SP lid/bail, 7x5¼" 375.00
Bottle, scent; red to yel to amber, ball form, att Webb, 6" 250.00
Candlestick, yel w/brn roses on disk base, 8¾", pr 150.00
Cracker jar, pk, flowers/branches, SP mts, 8½" 225.00
Ewer, apricot, frosted hdl, 6½" 110.00
Ewer, bl cased, HP cream/lav/gold floral, thorn hdl, 13" 225.00
Ewer, bl w/gold floral, melon section, ruffled, 10½", pr 225.00
Finger bowl, peach shaded, florals, ruffled, 3x4⅛" 165.00
Jar, dresser; lt yel, gold floral/red leaves, att Webb, 3½" 100.00
Rose bowl, bl, 5½" 70.00
Rose bowl, bl shaded, HP floral, 8-crimp, 3⅜x3⅞" 118.00
Rose bowl, bl shaded, HP floral, 8-crimp, 6x3⅝" 135.00
Rose bowl, chartreuse shaded, emb florals, 8-crimp, 3¼x4" 118.00
Rose bowl, gr, appl flower, 8-crimp, 4⅛x3¾" 95.00
Rose bowl, lemon shaded, HP floral, 8-crimp, 4½x4¼" 125.00
Rose bowl, pk shaded, HP floral, egg shape, 5½x3¾" 135.00

Rose bowl, pk shaded, indented swirls, 8-crimp, 3½x4" 135.00
Rose bowl, rose shaded, HP floral, 8-crimp, 3¼x3⅞" 125.00
Rose bowl, Shell, lt bl, 5¼" H 140.00
Rose bowl, Shell & Seaweed, gr shaded, wht int, 5x5" 150.00
Rose bowl, yel to wht w/orchid & bl lilacs, 8-crimp, 6" H . . .70.00
Tumbler, Drapery, lt bl 50.00
Vase, apricot to wht, ruffled, 6½" .110.00
Vase, bl shaded, allover gold prunus, Webb, 5x4" 295.00
Vase, bl shaded, HP floral, jewels, frosted hdl, ribs, 10x3" 125.00
Vase, bl shaded, HP floral, ruffled, ewer form, 9¼" 100.00
Vase, brn w/gold filigree, bl/wht touches, att Webb, 9", pr 600.00
Vase, Fleurette, pk overlay, gold enamel, mk, 5¾x5½" 195.00
Vase, gr, HP gold-traced floral, bulbous, sgn Vienna, 8" 60.00
Vase, gr shaded, hydrangea/butterfly in gold, Webb, 4½" 335.00
Vase, lime, HP floral, gourd w/ring neck, att Webb, 6", pr 100.00
Vase, pk shaded, HP floral, ruffled/ribbed/hdld, 13", pr 425.00
Vase, wht, floral/leaves in gold/gr/wht, can form, Webb, 4" 75.00
Vase, wht, gold leaves/flowers, 6", pr 75.00

Satsuma

Satsuma is a type of fine cream crackle-glaze pottery or earthenware made in Japan as early as the 17th century. The earliest wares, made at the original kiln in the Satsuma province, were enameled with only simple florals. By the late 18th century, a floral brocade (or nishikide design) was favored, and similar wares were being made at other kilns under the direction of the Lord of Satsuma. In the early part of the 19th century, a diaper pattern was added to the florals. Gold and silver enamels were used for accents by the latter years of the century.

During the 1850s, as the quality of goods made for export to the western world increased and the style of decoration began to evolve toward becoming more appealing to the Westerners, human forms such as Arhats, Kannon, geisha girls, and Samurai warriors were added.

Today the most valuable pieces are those marked 'Kinkozan,' 'Shuzan,' 'Ryuzan,' and 'Kozan.' The genuine Satsuma 'mon' or mark is a cross within a circle — usually in gold on the body or on the lid, or in red on the base of the ware. Character marks may be included.

Caution: Much of what is termed 'Satsuma' comes from the Showa Period (1926 to the present); it is not true Satsuma but a simulated type, a cheaper pottery with heavy enamel.

Bowl, Millefleur (1000 Flowers), mc w/gold, 3¾" 125.00
Box, flowers & butterflies, ca 1915, 2½" dia 75.00
Box, flying birds, gold leaves, knob finial, 1840s 125.00
Box, mums, gold dragon on dbl-domed lid, 1830, 2½x4½" 225.00
Cookie jar, floral, gold & wht on tangerine, rnd, 7½x8" 150.00
Figurine, God of Fortune, 3½" 30.00
Figurine, Manjuishii sitting on lion, ca 1860, 18x19" 2,750.00
Jar, Nishikid diapering, genre scenes, bulbous, 1885, 7x5" 185.00
Jar, Nishikid diapering, paneled scenes, 1890, 5x5¼" 150.00
Plaque, lake scene, mums/peonies/etc w/gold, sgn, 1895, 10" . . .225.00
Plaque, water fowl scene, wisteria w/gold, ca 1900, 9½" 225.00
Plate, 2 samurai w/supplicant, ships at shore, sgn, 9" 175.00
Vase, chrysanthemum, jewels, scroll hdls, sgn, 1890s, 8" 115.00
Vase, cobalt w/gold florals, scene w/lady, 1910, 2¾" 58.00
Vase, dragon/rakans, mc/gilt, hexagonal baluster, Meiji, 12" . . .300.00
Vase, dragons/rakans, mc/gilt, ca 1925, 6½" 125.00
Vase, floral, mc w/gold, elephant hdls, ca 1895, 6½" 75.00
Vase, floral/butterflies, dbl gourd, serpent hdl, 11½" 275.00
Vase, floral/butterflies, Kinkozan Awata, 12" 375.00
Vase, floral/clouds, ring hdls, 1880s, 9" 250.00
Vase, haloed Arhats/Kwannon, baluster form, 1900, 12", pr 450.00
Vase, haloed Arhats/Kwannon, red/bl/gold, Taisho, 9½", pr 260.00

Vase, lady & 2 warriors, artist sgn, much gold, 1890, 14" 575.00
Vase, Nishikid diapering, genre scene, hdls, 1885, 10" 175.00
Vase, people/diapering, gilt, elephant hdls, ca 1905, 6½" 175.00
Vase, warriors/ladies/children, heavy gold, 8-sided, 7½" 275.00
Vase, wisteria on crackle, 1850s, mk, 6", pr 250.00
Vase, 2 figural reserves on brocade ground, Meiji, 18" 700.00
Vase, 2 genre scenes, 'fabric' ground, 8-sided, Meiji, 19" 700.00
Vase, 5 samurai w/gold armor on wht crackle, 13x6" 195.00

Temple vase, birds and flowers, signed, 22", $1,600.00.

Scales

In today's world of pre-measured and pre-packaged goods, it is difficult to imagine the days when such products as sugar, flour, soap, and candy first had to be weighed by the grocer. The variety of scales used at the turn of the century was highly diverse; at the Philadelphia Exposition in 1876, one company alone displayed over three hundred different weighing devices. Among those found today, brass and iron models are the most common. Those seeking additional information concerning antique scales are encouraged to contact the International Society of Antique Scale Collectors, whose address can be found in the Directory under Clubs, Newsletters, and Catalogs.

Key:
bal — balance   lb — pound
g — gram   NP — nickel plated

Acme, egg grading, pat 1924 . . . . .20.00
American Family, Art Deco, 0-25 lb by oz 30.00
Angile Dile, sm 350.00
Apothecary, brass pans, marble top, 6x19x5" 110.00
Apothecary, brass/iron, porc shelf, London, 1850, 0-7 lb 225.00
Army, gold scales, brass pans, ca 1850, EX in orig box 55.00
Balance, brass, English, 1800s 225.00
Balance, iron w/fancy scrollwork, brass pan, 0-12 lb, 21x24" . . .185.00
Bismar, wood, 1700 . . . . .150.00
Buffalo, general store, CI w/brass pan, EX 100.00
Buffalo hide peddler's, iron, oval, old, EX 75.00
Butter, cvd pine, wood pans, 1800s, EX 295.00

Butter, rnd wooden-bowl pans, hewn bar, 10x14" 340.00
Butter, wood, cvd hdl, balance type, 27" W 75.00
Butter, wood, cvd notched bar, pine tray, 1820s 350.00
Candy, blk iron w/brass scoop, 2 weights, 9½" base, EX 85.00
Chatillon's, brass faced, hanging, dtd 1891, EX 12.00
Chatillon's, brass faced, spring bal, 1892, 0-25 lb 20.00
Chatillon's, brass-plated iron, 0-50 lb 50.00
Christian Becker Chainomatic, in glass case 225.00
Dayton #166, candy store, 0-1 lb, EX orig 185.00
Detecto, brass, hanging, EX 40.00
Detecto Gram, candy store, iron w/brass pan, 1930s, 0-3 lb 75.00
Do'tchin, Chinese steelyard, bone beam, w/case, 14" L 55.00
Dodge Micrometer, CI/brass/marble, 17x17x6", VG 175.00
Druggist, walnut, brass pan, marble top, 8½x18" 125.00
Eastman, photography, orig weights, MIB 50.00
Eureka C, CI, glass face, brass pan, pat Oct 5, 1869, 18" 175.00
Excelsior, hanging, CI w/brass face, EX 12.00
Fairbanks, beam type, dismantles to store in drawer below, G . .135.00
Fairbanks, countertop, iron, brass pan/arm, pat 1859 . . . . . . .150.00
Fairbanks, floor, brass w/CI wheels, wood post, 0-500 lb 140.00
Frary's Improved Spring Bal, warranted, 0-50 lb, 2¼x8½" 40.00
Gem #6, countertop, iron base, brass pans, 8x10", VG 25.00
Gold, brass pans, wrought iron bar, ca 1850s, EX 35.00
Hanging, brass face, dtd 1892, 0-50 lb, sm 25.00
Hanson, spring bal, sq steel case w/hook, 1x5" face, 0-50 lb 25.00
Hanson, wht enamel base, metal tray, wood scoop, VG 20.00
Hone, Rutland VT, pat Aug 16, 1873, 8½x25x10", EX 38.00
IBM #167, candy store, brass scoop, orig pnt, 0-5 lb 150.00
IBM #251, fan scale, orig pnt/striping, 0-10 lb 125.00
Improved Spring Bal, 0-100 lb, EX 50.00
Jacobs, CI w/silver pnt, 14½x7" 50.00
Jiffy Way, egg grading, tin 14.00
Krups Ideal, wht porc, German, mk 0-10 kilo, 11", VG 75.00
Lander's, brass, front spring bal, 1-100 lb 35.00
Liberty Postal, flat platform, 4x5½x6" 18.00
Mancur, mk H Boker & Co Germany, 0-35/20-300 lb, 9½" L . . .75.00
Mill's, coin-op, lollypop form, 1904, EX rstr 650.00
Nat'l, candy store, ornate, sm 350.00
Nat'l, countertop, 1910, rstr, sm .350.00
Nat'l #6, candy store, w/brass tray, EX 225.00
Ohaus #1119, triple beam, 0-20 kilo 175.00
Ohaus Dial-O-Gram, grams only, orig case 60.00
Peerless Weighing Machines, NY, Honest Weight 1¢, 68", EX .635.00
Pelouze, candy store, c 1899, EX .38.00
Pharmacist's bal, brass/ceramic, 1900s, 41" 225.00
Platform, child's, CI, w/pan & graduated weights, 3½x5" 65.00
Postal, brass pans & mechanism, wood base, 1870s, EX 45.00
Prescription, beam type, oak, brass weights, 2x9½x5" 85.00
Purina Chow Chow, brass, milk weighing, 0-30 lbs, 4½x15" 75.00
RH Forchner, NY, Larrio Farm Tested, milk weighing, EX 50.00
Salters Improved Spring Bal, Warranted, 0-24 lb, M 28.00
Salters Trade Spring Bal #60T, 0-20 lb, w/knot, 4½x14½" 105.00
Standard, candy store, brass scoop, EX 150.00
Stimpson #40, candy store, fan type, 0-2 lb 175.00
Store, tin scoop hangs by 3 chains, rnd dial, old, EX 100.00
Sutler #49, household, CI front, 12½" 95.00
Toledo, brass w/porc pan, 30" 175.00
Toledo, candy store, gr metallic w/brass hdw, 1917, 3x11x8" . .155.00
Toledo Computing, gold pnt, Sept 11, 1906, 26x28x11", VG . . .35.00
Triner, brass, 0-4 lbs, EX 65.00
Triner, candy store, wht enamel, 0-1 lb 38.00
Troemner, balance, CI w/orig red pnt, NP pans, #5B, 14" L . . .105.00
Troemner, compound lever bal, iron w/5½" brass pans 85.00
Troemner, iron bal #7, w/weights, 0-11¾ lbs 250.00

Turnbulls Family, rnd brass face, 0-24 lb, 10", VG 55.00
Victor, postal, c Mar 19, 1898, VG 25.00
Voland #2220D, chain weight bal, aluminum & glass cane 350.00
Watling, drug store, red/cream, w/mirror, 58x14", EX 375.00
Weighmaster, CI, wht w/blk letters, 6x14x10", VG 25.00

Schafer and Vater

Schafer and Vater operated in Volkstadt, Germany, from the last decade of the 1800s until about 1920. They produced novelties such as figural bottles, flasks, vases, etc., marked with an 'R' within a star device.

Bottle, smiling pear figural, w/stopper 125.00
Box, powder; mother/child/angels relief, bl & wht, EX 55.00
Candlestick, lion, yel w/wht eyes, cubist shape, mk, 5¾" 95.00
Figurine, girl in lg hat, seated, pulls off socks, 5" 200.00
Figurine, girl w/2 lg Dutch shoes, mk, 4½x2¾" 95.00
Flask, A Wee Scotch 55.00
Hatpin holder, Egyptian ladies' heads, 4½" 145.00
Hatpin holder, lady w/fan, pk jasperware 100.00
Lamp, boudoir; Art Nouveau, jasperware, NM 100.00
Match holder, They will blame..., dog & puddle, 3¼x4" 130.00
Nodder, monkey grins w/outstretched hand, 4¼" 175.00
Pitcher, Blk lady figural, 4" 135.00
Pitcher, Chinaman w/howling child figural, milk sz 150.00
Pitcher, cow in dress, bl, cream sz .90.00
Pitcher, goose in bonnet, cream sz 100.00
Pitcher, Mother Goose wearing hat, 4" 160.00
Shakers, smiling apple & pear, pr .75.00

Tea set, lavender and green jasper, figural lids and handles, pot: 7", $695.00.

Teapot, smiling apple, 1-cup 125.00
Toothpick holder, sailor w/girl on knee 85.00
Tray, skeleton & coffin 180.00
Vase, cupid/musicians/birds in relief, pk jasperware, 5¼" 90.00
Vase, Grecian lady's head medallion, gold trim, mk, 4¾x3" 55.00

Scheier

Bowl, bl gloss w/brn touches, bl decor, 3¼" H 120.00
Bowl, wht/tan matt on red clay, speckled int, thin, 6" 195.00
Mug, ea w/different animal, blk on ivory, 5½", 6 for 325.00
Vase, lt to dk brn semi-gloss, U-form, hand thrown, 4½" 145.00

Schlegelmilch Porcelain

Authority Mary Frank Gaston, who is our advisor, has recently completed the second volume of *The Collector's Encyclopedia of R.S. Prussia* with full-color illustrations and current values. Mold numbers appearing in some of the listings refer to this book. You will find Mrs. Gaston's address in the Directory under Texas.

Key:
BM — blue mark   SM — steeple mark
GM — green mark   RM — red mark

E.S. Germany

Fine chinaware marked 'E.S. Germany' or 'E.S. Prov. Saxe' was produced by E.S. Schlegelmilch at his Suhl factory in the Thuringia region of Prussia from the turn of the century until about 1925.

Bowl, fox hunt scene, mk, 9⅝" 75.00
Box, trinket; Indian portrait, violin shape, Royal Saxe 125.00
Candy dish, roses, dbl-oval form, gold hdl/rim, 2 mks 45.00
Chocolate pot, fruit on cobalt to cream, mk, +4 c/s 265.00
Creamer & sugar bowl, cavalier & 2 ladies, maroon & gold 75.00
Creamer & sugar bowl, floral band, gold on purple, mk 50.00
Ewer, girl w/conch shell to ear in reserve, 7" 90.00
Hatpin holder, floral 85.00
Jar, powder; bluebird on gr & blk, 6x3½" 85.00
Pitcher, maiden w/cupid, raised florals w/gold, 7½" 180.00
Plaque, lady w/doves, mk, 10¾" 295.00
Plate, ladies & cherubs, mc/gold bands, gold trim, 6½" 65.00
Plate, 3 nymphs/cupid in chariot, sgn Kauffman, 9" 70.00
Shakers, yel roses, mk, pr 175.00
Tea strainer, floral, gold trim 155.00
Vase, Goddess of Sea medallion, gold hdls, Prov Saxe, 8½" 250.00
Vase, Goddess of Sea on turq, dbl gold hdls, mk, 10¾" 300.00
Vase, lady on bl in gold medallion, beading, hdls, mk, 6½" 165.00
Vase, lady w/peacock, urn shape, hdls, 10" 235.00
Vase, portrait, gold medallions, wht/purple, gold hdls, 9¼" 275.00
Vase, portrait, red border w/sm pk roses, hdls, mk, 11" 235.00

R.S. Germany

In 1869 Reinhold Schlegelmilch began to manufacture porcelain in Tillowitz in upper Silesia. He had formerly worked with his brother, Erdmann, in his factory in Suhl in the German province of Thuringia. Both areas were rich in resources necessary for the production of hard-paste porcelain. Wares marked with the name 'Tillowitz' and the accompanying 'R.S. Germany' phrase are attributed to Reinhold. The most common mark is a wreath and star in a solid color under the glaze. Items marked 'R.S. Germany' are usually more simply decorated than R.S. Prussia. Some reflect the Art Deco trend of the 1920s. Certain hand-painted floral decorations and themes such as 'Sheepherder,' 'Man with Horses,' and 'Cottage' are especially valued by collectors — those with a high-gloss finish or on Art Deco shapes in particular. Not all hand-painted items were painted at the factory. Those with an artist's signature but no 'Hand Painted' mark indicate that the blank was decorated outside the factory.

Basket, wht w/heavy gold hdl & rim, oval, RM 55.00
Bonbon, carnations, pk on gray w/gold, looped hdl, mk, 7¾" 32.00
Bowl, dogwood on pearly lustre, BM, 5" 20.00
Bowl, florals & geometrics, hdls, oval, 11x8½" 75.00
Bowl, ice cream; tulips, mc on bl w/gold, 2x5¼", 6 for 110.00
Bowl, mayonnaise; poppies, w/underplate & ladle, BM 68.00
Bowl, nut; roses, ruffled, ftd, RM, master+6 ind 300.00
Bowl, pheasants, 2-color on wooded bkground, 10" 195.00

Box, powder; floral, rnd, 5" 50.00
Cake plate, parrots on vine on yel, open hdls, GM 160.00
Cake plate, roses, BM 45.00
Cake set, tulips, 7-pc 135.00
Candy dish, silver decor, cloverleaf form, 6½" 45.00
Celery, swans & lily pads, unmk, 12" 165.00
Chocolate pot, sunflower in relief, scarce 98.00

Chocolate set, wild roses, blue stamped mark, pot: 8½", $365.00.

Cracker jar, floral on cream, gold trim, hdls, 6½x6" 125.00
Creamer, mc roses, corset shape, 4-ftd, mk 32.00
Creamer & sugar bowl, iris, purple on wht, mk, 2½" 48.00
Creamer & sugar bowl, poppies, wide gold band, BM 48.00
Creamer & sugar bowl, shepherd scene, no wht, ped ft, RM ...650.00
Cup & saucer, chocolate; castle & mtn, plain mold, RM 235.00
Cup & saucer, coffee; floral, BM 45.00
Hatpin holder, floral 80.00
Holder, condensed milk; floral on wht w/gold bands, mk, 5" ...145.00
Inkwell, lilies of the valley, w/lid 65.00
Mug, shaving; floral, embossings, lt moss/beige, mk 75.00
Plate, cotton plant, gold rim, 12½" 50.00
Plate, dogwood blossoms on bl/pk/ivory shaded, mk, 7" 15.00
Plate, Iris variation, RM, 10½" 245.00
Relish, carnations, pk on gray w/gold, loop hdl, mk, 7½" L ...28.00
Syrup, lilies of the valley, BM, +underplate 75.00
Tea strainer, floral, gold trim 150.00
Teapot, lilies on tan, sm 40.00
Tile, snowballs, gr-wht on peach & tan, rnd, RM 150.00
Toothpick holder, wht w/gold decor, 3-hdl 15.00
Tray, tidbit; lilies, wht on beige, 2-tiered, GM 65.00
Vase, floral, wht on gr shaded, 8½" 75.00
Vase, lady w/doves, on red/turq w/turq beads, mk, 11" 465.00
Vase, lady's portrait, medallions, gold hdls/trim, 9" 225.00

R.S. Poland

'R.S. Poland' is a mark attributed to Reinhold Schlegelmilch's factory in Tillowitz, Silesia.

Bowl, pheasants, brn shades, ped ft, brass flower frog 550.00
Cake plate, roses, moire ground, open hdls 135.00
Candlestick, violets & lilies of the valley, 6" 115.00
Creamer & sugar bowl, roses, peach on brn/gr, mk 150.00
Cup & saucer, dogwood & pine, RM 115.00
Dresser set, pk florals, tray/hair receiver/box, mk 345.00
Plate, dogwood & pine, 8" 85.00
Relish bowl, dogwood & pine, open hdl, RM 65.00
Urn, roses, pk/wht on brn, hdls, w/lid, RM, 11½" 800.00

Vase, roses, beige/wht on gold & brn, mk, 8¾x4½" 138.00
Vase, roses on brn shaded, 4¼" 105.00

R.S. Prussia

Art porcelain bearing the mark 'R.S. Prussia' was manufactured by Erdmann and Reinhold Schlegelmilch from the late 1870s to the early 1900s in a Germanic area known until the end of WWI as Prussia. The vast array of mold shapes in combination with a wide variety of decorations is the basis for R.S. Prussia's appeal. Themes can be categorized as figural (usually based on a famous artist's work), birds, florals, portraits, scenics, and animals.

Berry set, poppies, iris mold, RM, 5-pc 350.00
Bowl, centerpc; pk/yel floral, carnation mold, unmk, 14½" 285.00
Bowl, dogwood on gr lustre, RM, 3x10" 180.00
Bowl, floral, iris mold, heavy gold trim, 11¼" 225.00
Bowl, flower basket medallions, gr shadows, RM, 11" 250.00
Bowl, Hidden Image portrait, unmk, rare, 10" 325.00
Bowl, ice cream; Peacock at Urn, unmk, 6" 68.00
Bowl, lilacs on satin, 6¼" 130.00
Bowl, orchids, roses on sides, old circle mk, 10½" 90.00
Bowl, peacock & bluebirds, RM, 5½" 150.00
Bowl, pk roses & daisies, iris mold, RM, 10" 285.00
Bowl, poppies, scalloped rim, RM, 9½" 175.00
Bowl, roses, pk on wht w/gr, EX gold, mk, 3x10¾" 350.00
Bowl, roses, puffy, pk on turq, RM, 9" 150.00
Bowl, roses, yel/pk/red, gold fluted rim, RM, 10" 135.00
Bowl, roses & mums on lav, RM, 8½" 110.00
Bowl, strawberry blossoms on gr w/gold, scalloped, RM, 10" ...150.00
Bowl, Winter scene w/lake, pine trees, mtns, RM, 11" 250.00
Box, pin; roses, pk on mint gr, gold tracery, w/tray 85.00
Box, powder; flowers on water, icicle mold, RM 125.00
Butter dish, wild roses & daisies, melon ribs, unmk, +liner 275.00
Cake plate, floral, blown-out leaf border w/gold, mk, 11" 195.00
Cake plate, floral w/gold tracing on cobalt, RM, 11" 375.00
Cake plate, poppies, lacy gold, pleated/scalloped, RM, 11" ...225.00
Cake plate, poppies & daisies, icicle mold, unmk 175.00
Cake plate, rose reserves, blown-out lily border, hdls, 11" 150.00
Cake plate, roses, pk & yel, lav & pk leaves, RM, 11" 200.00
Cake plate, swans, pierced hdls, RM 450.00
Cake plate, wisteria, purple w/gold, hdls, RM 250.00
Cake plate, 2 lions, open hdls 5,400.00
Candle holder, floral on bl, hdls, unmk 100.00
Celery tray, floral, carnation mold, RM, 9" 175.00
Celery tray, floral, open hdls, RM, 12x6" 110.00
Celery tray, roses, pk/yel on gr, lily mold, unmk, 12½" 75.00
Celery tray, Sheepherder, icicle mold, unmk, 12" 195.00
Chocolate pot, calla lilies on satin, RM, 9½" 325.00
Chocolate pot, carnation mold, RM, 12", +2 c/s 600.00
Chocolate pot, Flora, pk florals w/cobalt & gold trim, mk 750.00
Chocolate pot, floral, pk on gr shaded, RM, +4 c/s 800.00
Chocolate pot, Icicle & Floral, dbl Hidden Images, RM 435.00
Chocolate pot, Melon Eaters, RM, +6 c/s (3 only EX) 2,100.00
Chocolate pot, roses, mc on gr shadows, RM 275.00
Chocolate pot, snowballs, tans/brn, RM, +5 c/s 900.00
Coffeepot, floral, pk/wht on lt gr, ftd, 8" 200.00
Coffeepot, pk roses w/gold trim, RM, 9¼" 500.00
Cracker jar, pk florals, point & clover mold, flower finial 325.00
Cracker jar, roses, red over yel/gr, RM 235.00
Creamer, castle scene, RM, 3" 185.00
Creamer, cottage scene on gr, RM 185.00
Creamer, roses, w/lid, RM, 3½" 100.00
Creamer & sugar bowl, floral, lav on mc shaded, unmk, ind ...145.00

Creamer & sugar bowl, floral on gr shaded, mk, 3¼" & 5" 165.00
Creamer & sugar bowl, mums & roses, urn form, ftd, RM 195.00
Creamer & sugar bowl, pansies & roses, clam shell tops, RM ..145.00
Creamer & sugar bowl, roses, fancy hdls, 5" 100.00
Creamer & sugar bowl, snowballs & roses, w/lid, RM, 3½" 150.00
Creamer & sugar bowl, swan scene, RM 350.00
Cup, chocolate; floral, point & clover mold, gold trim, RM 55.00
Cup, roses & holly w/gold, diagonal swirls, mk, 3½" 120.00
Cup & saucer, demitasse; poppies, pk on gr, iris mold, RM 75.00
Cup & saucer, roses, pk & wht on tan, RM 145.00
Ewer, lady's portrait, ornate gold hdl, RM, 9" 900.00
Hair receiver, roses, pk on yel & gr, unmk 125.00
Hatpin holder, floral, wht on gr shaded, bulbous, BM 195.00
Hatpin holder, roses, scalloped base, mk, 4¾" 235.00
Hatpin holder, water lilies on water, RM 175.00
Mug, fleur-de-lis/rose garlands, ftd, jeweled hdls, 2¼x3½" ...155.00
Mug, shaving; Flora, portrait, RM 285.00
Mug, shaving; floral relief, mirror on side, soap rest 300.00
Mug, shaving; poppies, pk on gr shadows, mirrored, RM 275.00
Mustache cup, poppies on pearlized lustre, ftd, +underplate ...300.00
Mustard pot, roses & daises, EX gold, RM 125.00
Nappy, florals, bud-festooned hdl, RM 75.00
Nut set, roses, ruffled, RM, master+6 ind 300.00
Pen holder, flow blue, ftd, unmk, rare, 7x2" 110.00
Pitcher, cider; Lebrun, 10" 2,300.00
Pitcher, roses, pk on gr shaded, gold trim, ftd, 6" 225.00
Pitcher, tankard; farm scene, icicle mold, RM, 11½" 850.00
Pitcher, tankard; rose & snowball, drapery mold, RM, 11" 425.00
Pitcher, tankard; roses, stippled mold, RM, 13½" 765.00
Plaque, mill scene on gr, lav/yel border, unmk, 11¼" 700.00
Plate, cottage scene, mk, 10" 695.00
Plate, Easter lily, lacy border, 11" 140.00
Plate, flower basket, icicle mold, RM, 10¼" 300.00
Plate, Melon Boys, RM, 8½" 350.00
Plate, monk, dk gr w/gold, St Kilian mk, BS, 10" 300.00

Plate, portrait of a lady, Tiffany finish, 10", $800.00.

Plate, snowbird, Winter scene, RM 600.00
Powder jar, lilies & pads on water, icicle mold, RM 125.00
Relish, roses, mc w/pk border, sawtooth mold, unmk, 9½" 175.00
Salt cellar, magnolia blossoms, boat shape, mk 45.00
Shaker, powder; scalloped skirt base, wht w/gold trim, mk 95.00
Shaker, powder; tea roses, scalloped rim & base, RM 155.00

Sugar bowl, asters, cream w/lt gr tint, RM 95.00
Sugar shaker, Colonial couple portrait on dk gr, RM 425.00
Sugar shaker, roses, scalloped base, RM, 4¾" 235.00
Sugar shaker, snowballs, wht on gr shaded, 4-ftd, unmk 145.00
Tea strainer, pk florals, w/undercup, unmk, 6" 150.00
Teapot, carnation mold, gold spout & hdl, unmk 300.00
Toothpick holder, roses, pk/wht on gr, jewels, ftd/hdls, RM . . .250.00
Tray, dresser; floral, carnation mold, hdls, RM, 11x7" 245.00
Tray, dresser; floral, iris mold, open hdls, mk, 11x7¼" 165.00
Tray, mums on gr w/gold, +hatpin holder & powder jar, BM . .175.00
Tray, Queen Louise portrait, unmk 300.00
Vase, courting couple at well, RM, 8" .800.00
Vase, florals on cobalt, SM, 5¼" 225.00
Vase, poppies & daisies reflect in water, feather mold, 8½" 175.00
Vase, roses, gold leaves, iris in relief forms hdl, mk, 7½" 325.00
Vase, roses, pk/wht w/shadow leaves on gr, hdls, RM, 6" 325.00
Vase, shepherd w/pk flowering trees, RM, 9½" 700.00

R.S. Suhl, E.S. Suhl

Porcelains marked with this designation are attributed to Schlegelmilch's Suhl factory.

Box, floral, w/beveled mirror, mk .200.00
Cup & saucer, Nightwatch, brn shaded 60.00
Jar, tapestry, w/lid, 7" 140.00
Vase, Nightwatch, brn shades, sgn Rembrandt, 7½" 750.00
Wall plaque, daisies, 10½" 60.00

R.S. Tillowitz

R.S. Tillowitz-marked porcelains are attributed to Reinhold Schlegelmilch's factory in Tillowitz, Silesia.

Bowl, dogwood on gr, oblong, open hdls, 10" 45.00
Bowl, lilacs w/bl & gold tracing, 10x8" 55.00
Cake set, fuchsia on gr w/tan shadows, open hdls, 7-pc 325.00
Creamer & sugar bowl, lilies, wht on gr shaded 175.00
Nut dish, peonies & snowballs on cream, openwork, mk, 6" 90.00
Plate, cherries, 11" 30.00
Tray, floral, bl on gr, heavy gold trim, pierced hdls, 4x8" 40.00

Schneider

The Schneider Glass Company was founded in 1914 at Epinay-sur-seine, France. They made many types of art glass, some of which sandwiched designs between layers. Other decorative devices were applique and carved work. These were marked 'Charder,' or 'Schneider.' During the twenties, commercial artware was produced with Deco motifs cut by acid through two or three layers and signed 'LeVerre Francais' in script or with a section of inlaid filigrane. See also Le Verre Francais.

Bowl, cameo, pods w/stems & thorns on red-brn, 6x11" 860.00
Bowl, orange to bl; in iron mt w/3 glass cherries, 7x14" 440.00
Charger, concave center: brn/orange mottle, Ovington, 16" . .200.00
Compote, peach/bl on amethyst base & stem, 7½x6¼" 380.00
Compote, purple/brn mottle, appl yel/brn striped ft, mk, 6¼" . .275.00
Ewer, brn mottle, leaf/berry hdl, appl Zsolnay plaque, 9" 450.00
Vase, amber/red/bl mottle, ftd ovoid, everted rim, 21" 550.00
Vase, floriform, gold irid, appl medallion/'M,' 1925, 6" 350.00
Vase, gr/brn mottle on yel, purple base, trumpet form, 9" 530.00
Vase, gray, etched, w/2 vertical glass drips, 11" 275.00
Vase, red, bl drips from top, purple base, sgn, 15", pr 1,200.00
Vase, rose/yel mottle on lav bun base, hdld amphora, 22" 800.00
Vase, smoke w/3 appl bl buttons on enameled shields, 13" 350.00

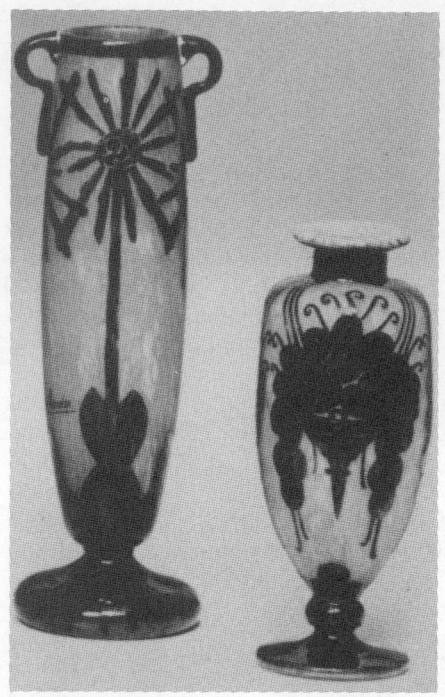

Vase, marked Charder, 13", $800.00; 9", $600.00.

Vase, thick glass w/bubbles, cylindrical on bun ft, 6" 165.00
Vase, 7 cranes in flight, cameo, brn/orange/yel, 3 cuts, 19" . .3,900.00

Schoolhouse Collectibles

Schoolhouse collectibles bring to mind memories of a bygone era when the teacher rang her bell to call the youngsters to class in a one-room schoolhouse — where often both the 'hickory stick' and an apple occupied a prominent position on her desk.

Bell, brass, mini, 5" 45.00
Bell, brass, trn maple hdl, mk #6, EX .65.00
Bell, bronze, wood hdl, 6½" 35.00
Bell, CI, arm/brackets/clapper, mk #4 Upright 1886, 18" dia . . .110.00
Book, Fun with Dick & Jane, 1940 ed, VG 10.00
Book, McGuffey's 5th Reader, VG 12.00
Book, McGuffey's 6th Reader, EX 25.00
Book, Spelling, elementary level, c 1880 to 1908, EX 25.00
Clock, Stromberg master regulator, 1915, 60" 550.00
Desk, teacher's; pine/poplar w/bl pnt Co Hplwht, VG 200.00
Helmet, football; leather, G 75.00
Ink bottle, for desk well, EX 10.00
Lunch pail, rnd, VG 20.00
Map, pull-down canvas, Universal, NY, 55x47", VG 15.00
Pencil sharpener, classroom, G 15.00
Print set, teacher's, wood, dvtl box, 1920s, EX 35.00
Slate, oval, hickory fr, 10x7", EX 55.00
Slate, wood fr, 1890s, 11½x8½", EX 25.00
Slate pencil, EX 2.00
Spelling board, wood w/movable letters, pat 1886, EX 65.00

Schoop, Hedi

Swiss-born Hedi Schoop started her ceramics business in North Hollywood in 1940. With a talented crew of about twenty decorators, she produced figurines, figure-vases, console sets, TV lamps, and other decorative housewares — much of which was accented with gold or platinum trim. Schoop's pottery closed after a fire destroyed the building in 1958. Marks are impressed or printed.

Our advisor for this category is Jack Chipman; he is listed in the Directory under California.

Bowl, formed by lady's skirt, #418, 13" dia 65.00
Cookie jar, Queen of Hearts, 12x12" 75.00
Figurine, debutante, 12½" 35.00
Figurine, flower girl w/appl flowers, 9" 24.00
Figurine, lady w/basket leads lg poodle, 10" 25.00
Figurine, Oriental man in blk & wht jacket, tall 35.00
Figurine, southern belle, 12½" 40.00

Pair of figurines, 12½", with crimped bowl, $125.00 for the set.

Flower holder, peasant woman, 12" 35.00
Flower holder, 2 girls, hands joined, rare, 8" 85.00
Planter, geisha w/umbrella, bl, #223 ....24.00

Scouting Collectibles

Scouting was founded in England in 1907 by a retired Major General, Lord Robert Baden-Powell. Its purpose is the same today as it was then — to help develop physically strong, mentally alert boys and to teach them basic fundamentals of survival and leadership. The movement soon spread to the United States, and in 1910 a Chicago publisher, William Boyce, set out to establish Scouting in America. The first World Scout Jamboree was held in 1911 in England. Baden-Powell was honored as the Chief Scout of the World. In 1926 he was awarded the Silver Buffalo Award in the United States. He was knighted in 1929 for distinguished military service and for his scouting efforts. Baden-Powell died in 1941. For further reading on the subject, we recommend *Scouting Collectibles* by R.J. Sayers; you will find his address in the Directory under Texas.

Blanket, camp; khaki, wool, stamped BSA 20.00
Book, BSA Year Book, 1915, G 15.00
Book, Handbook for Scoutmasters, Vol I, 1936, EX 10.00
Book, Scout's Test, Saalfield, 1916, EX 5.00
Book, The History of the BSA, 1937, EX 10.00
Book, The Outdoor Handy Book, 1926, EX 10.00
Book, Under the Stars & Stripes, Saalfield, 1918, EX 5.00
Booklet, Rope Knowledge for Boy Scouts, 1933, EX 5.00
Bow & arrow, BSA 25.00
Calendar, Our Heritage, Rockwell, 1950, 16x30", NM 15.00

Calendar, Pointing the Way, Rockwell, 1962, 8x14", M 12.00
Calendar, Spirit of America, Rockwell, 1929, 16x30", EX 50.00
Card, identification; BSA WWI Dispatch, 3x5", VG 10.00
Card set, BSA, compass game, VG 2.50
Coin, Nat'l Jamboree, silver metal, 1981, M 5.00
Coin, World Jamboree, emb, 1933 ....135.00
Diary, BSA, 1931, 255-pg, M 5.00
Figurine, GSA, copper/bronze 18.00
Figurine, Rockwell Cub Scout w/dog 20.00
Flag, troop; 1st issue, red/wht, 1st class emblem 17.00
Handbook, GSA, 1947, M 5.00
Knife, Camillus, 4-blade, staghorn hdl, 1946-51, G 15.00
Knife, jack; Ulster Official, 4-blade, #1996, 1977, MIB 5.00
Knife, pen; World Jamboree, 1967, VG 10.00
Knife, Remington, 4-blade, brn bone hdl, pocket sz 35.00
Knife, Remington, 4-blade, emb 1st class emblem, pocket sz 20.00
Knife, 4-blade, GSA emblem, gr plastic hdl 8.00
Magazine, Scouting, Norman Rockwell on cover, G 5.00
Map, World Jamboree, 1929, G 15.00
Medal, Eagle Scout, type 1, 1920 ....50.00
Medal, Eagle Scout, type 3, 1930 ....20.00
Medal, Liberty Loan, Ace Award, 1918 ....25.00
Medal, WWI War Savings Service, bl ribbon, 1916-1919 era ...10.00
Medallion, Liberty Bell, oval on lt bl ribbon, 1950s 5.00
Microscope, brass, 3 lenses, power 110X 20.00
Morse code signaler, MIB 10.00
Nametag, Nat'l Jamboree Trading Post, 1981, M 2.00
Neckerchief, BSA Eagle Scout 8.00
Neckerchief, Nat'l Jamboree, 1957, VG 8.00
Paperweight, GS feeding rabbit, blk case metal, 1920s 15.00
Patch, Nat'l Jamboree, 1960, used 6.00
Patch, World Jamboree, leather, 1967, M 7.00
Patch, World Jamboree USA, official, 1971, M 5.00
Pin, Gold Quill, BSA, clutch bk, 1960, M 5.00
Pin, hat; gold, M 4.00
Pin, hat; 1st class, WW II, stamped metal, G 8.00
Pin, lapel; Eagle Scout, sterling, mk, 1960s 8.00
Pin, lapel; Nat'l Jamboree, 1969, VG 4.50
Plate, A Scout Is Loyal, Rockwell, 10½" 28.00
Plate, Scoutmaster, Knowles, 1977 ....25.00
Post card, Boy Scouts First Aid, 1915, G 8.00
Post card, Camp Pow Wow, VG 5.00
Ring, sterling, 1st class emblem, BSA 10.00
Sheet music, Boy Scouts March, 1911, VG 8.00
Sign, BSA, Lawrence Wilber, 1952, NM 10.00
Uniform, complete w/pins & patches, GSA, 1929, EX 50.00
Uniform, shirt & pants, BSA, 1930s 50.00

Scrimshaw

The most desirable examples of the art of scrimshaw can be traced back to the first half of the nineteenth century to the heyday of the whaling industry. Some voyages lasted for several years, and conditions on board were often dismal. Sailors filled the long hours by carving or engraving designs in whale or walrus ivory. Using the tools of their trade, they created animal figures, boxes, pie crimpers, etc., often emphasizing the lines of their carvings with ink or berry stain. Eskimos also made scrimshaw, sometimes borrowing designs from the sailors who traded with them. See also Powder Horns.

Butter mold, cvd wood rosette w/lg whale ivory hdl, 5" 275.00
Clothespin, bone, EX trn detail, 4" L 150.00
Clothespin, bone, simple trn detail, 4¾" L 85.00

Corkscrew, 4½" sperm whale tooth hdl 125.00
Cricket cage, seascape w/man o'war, pierced-end tube 425.00
Cvg, 15 penguins on whalebone, Eskimo artist, EX details 125.00
Fid, forearm & hand holds pointed end, 5" 300.00
Fid, openwork heart-shaped hdl, 1850s, 5¾" 250.00
Fid, 3 incised rings at top, 1850s, 10" 310.00
Fishing lure, sand eel form, 1800s, 5" 150.00
Hat rack, 5 whale's teeth mtd on oak board, 1870, 28" L 450.00
Jagging wheel, fossilized ivory, EX trn detail, 5", EX 200.00
Jagging wheel, hdl: baleen inlay, bird head support, fork 1,000.00
Jagging wheel, hdl: heart/club cutouts, eng, 1850s, 6" 750.00
Jagging wheel, simple, Nantucket type, 1800s, 7" 200.00
Jagging wheel, unicorn, scroll tail, horn missing/rpr, 8" 1,300.00
Jagging wheel, 3 coin silver inlays, eng rosettes, 7" 500.00
Knife, sailor's, folding, whalebone hdls, 5½" closed 175.00
Knitting needles, coconut wood, ivory rings/tips, 15" 650.00
Letter opener, presentation dtd 1884, braided hdl, 14" 75.00
Napkin ring, inlaid bands of red wax, 1850s, EX, pr 125.00
Pipe, simple form, walrus ivory, 1800s, never used, 4" 100.00
Rolling pin, rpr knob, 1850s, 16½" .300.00
Seam rubber, letters eng on hdl facets, 1830s, 5" 650.00
Seam rubber, trn whale ivory knob w/baleen inlay, 1850s, 4¾" .375.00
Sewing box, geometric ivory & abalony inlays, 1850s, 8" 600.00
Snuff box, tooth, sailor/Free Trade..., brass collar, 4" L 600.00
Snuff box, tooth, ship/swan/etc, brass lid, late, 4" L 725.00
Tooth, bust portrait: lady in Windsor chair, mc, 6¾", pr . . .3,500.00
Tooth, Civil War-style eagle w/flags & drum, mc, 5¾" 600.00
Tooth, eagle/bird, mtd on lead base, 1850s, 4" 350.00

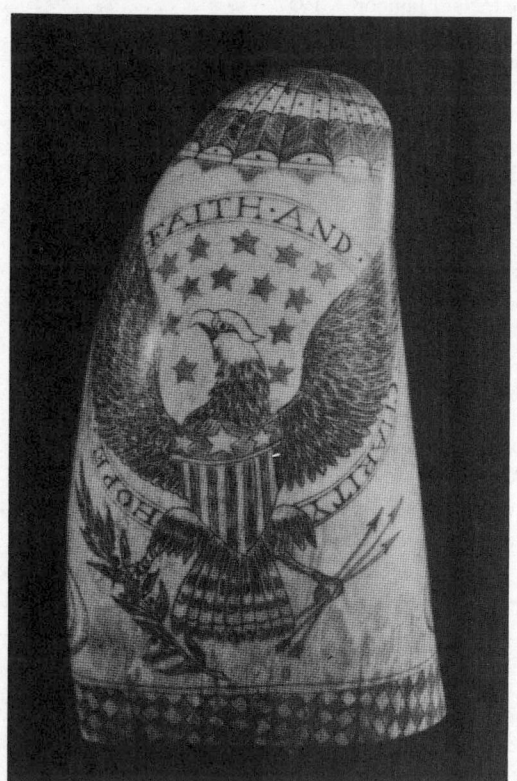

Whale's tooth, engraved on back with a whaling vessel and initials 'TW,' dated 1878, 6", $1,400.00.

Tooth, grapes, mc, sgn Frank Barcellos, contemporary, 5" 200.00
Tooth, panoramic whaling scene/lg ship below, 4", pr 1,350.00
Tooth, portrait of 'Abby,' bk: Forget Me Not, silver mt, 6" 375.00
Tooth, Ship Mercator, nude w/lyre, detailed, 3x7½" 350.00
Tooth, ship/clouds/gulls/etc, 2¼" 35.00
Tooth, shipwreck, bk: whaling scene, silver lid, 6¾" 2,000.00

Tooth, whaleboat/whale, bk: Am ship under sail, mc, 9" 6,000.00
Tooth, whaling scene, bk: Ship Chas, 1850s, 5½" 6,250.00
Tooth, whaling scene/naval battle, eng/mc, 6", EX 650.00
Tooth, 3 whaling scenes, sgn K Newman, contemporary, 6¾" .450.00
Tusk, bird/walrus/eagle/Am flag, age cracks, late, 23", EX 250.00
Tusk, group of people/man in fur cap/woman, 1875, 18" 350.00
Watch fob, eng book w/Masonic symbols, 1850s 375.00

Seals and Sealing Wax

A seal is used to affix a stamp or embossment either on an official paper or on wax such as was once used on correspondence. The sealing wax was first melted, then allowed to drip on the seam of the envelope or the writing paper. The imprint of the seal on the wax was an easily identifiable device or the writer's monogram.

Brass, Napoleon on globe, 2⅝" 55.00
Brass w/detailed ivory hdl, 2⅝", NM 200.00
Brass w/ivory hdl, 3¼" 55.00
Cherry amber, faceted, brass mts, lg .120.00
Moss agate w/gold & silver mts 120.00
Soapstone, dragon dog/pup cvg, Chinese, 2¼" 65.00
Sterling, hollow repousse hdl, French hallmk 30.00
Whalebone, trn, brass tip, sm chips, 3" 100.00

Sebastians

Sebastian miniatures were first produced in 1938 by Prescott W. Baston in Marblehead, Massachusetts. Since then more than four hundred have been modeled. These figurines have been sold through gift shops all over the country, primarily in the New England states. In 1976 Baston withdrew his Sebastians from production. Under an agreement with the Lance Corporation of Hudson, Massachusetts, one hundred designs were selected to be produced by that company under Baston's supervision. Those remaining were discontinued. In the short time since then, the older figurines have become very collectible. Price is determined by two factors: 1) in production/out of production; 2) labels — color of oval label, i.e. red, blue, green, etc.; Marblehead label, a green and silver palette-shaped label used until 1977; or no label. If there is no label and the varnish coat is quite yellowed, then it is considered to be of the Marblehead era. Dates are merely copyright dates and have no particular significance in regard to value. (Signed) 'P.W. Baston' should only have impact on price when the signature is an actual autograph — most pieces are manufactured with an imprinted 'P.W. Baston' on the base.

Abraham Lincoln, Marblehead label .60.00
Aunt Betzy Trotwood, Marblehead label 55.00
Becky Thatcher, gr label 35.00
Benjamin & Debora Franklin, Marblehead label, pr 175.00
Betsy Ross, red label 25.00
Building Days, pr 69.00
Chestnut Hill Mall, Marblehead era .225.00
Christmas Morning 45.00
Clown, bl label 95.00
Colonial Blacksmith, bl label 35.00
Colonial Kitchen, no label, Marblehead era 55.00
David Copperfield & Wife, Marblehead label 60.00
Dutchman's Pipe 200.00
Evangeline, Marblehead label 125.00
Gathering Tulips 200.00
Grocery Store, Marblehead label 60.00
Huckleberry Finn, Marblehead label, MIB 65.00

In the Candy Store (Necco) 180.00
James & Elizabeth Monroe, pr 195.00
Jell-O Giraffe 275.00
Jell-O Moose 300.00
John Smith & Pocahontas, Marblehead era, pr 215.00
Lincoln, gr label 40.00
Little Mother, Marblehead label 55.00
Madonna, chair, gr label 40.00
Minuteman, Marblehead label, MIB 65.00
Neighboring Pews 175.00
Outboard Fishers, bl label 40.00
Paul Revere, Marblehead label 55.00
Plaque, Marblehead label 200.00
Priscilla Alden, Marblehead label 90.00
Sam Houston, bl label 40.00
Shaker Man & Woman, Marblehead era, pr 125.00
Simple Simon, Howard Johnson, sgn PW Baston ...145.00
Spirit of '76, Marblehead label 65.00
Swan Boat, Boston Public Garden, Marblehead era, 2¼x3x5" .160.00
Victorian Couple, Marblehead label 55.00
Watchman, gr label, MIB 35.00
Weaver & Loom, Marblehead label 55.00
Weighing the Baby, Marblehead era 200.00

Dealer sign, ca 1938, 4",
$200.00.

Sevres

Fine-quality porcelains have been made in Sevres, France, since the early 1700s. Rich ground colors were often hand painted with portraits, scenics, and florals. Some pieces were decorated with transfer prints and decalcomania; many were embellished with heavy gold. These wares are the most respected of all French porcelains. Their style and designs have been widely copied, and some of the items listed below are Sevres-type wares.

Casket, figures by river on red w/gilt, bombe form, 7" 340.00
Charger, 3 figures in wheat field on bl, ca 1900, 20" 600.00
Compote, rtcl bowls, sm HP florals, 8½x9", pr 625.00
Cruet, scrolls/florals, gold on lt gr, ball stopper, 8½" 435.00
Cup & saucer, cupids in center panel, pk/gold rim, crown mk ...75.00
Figurine, 2 cupids, after Moreau, bsk, mk, 20" 550.00
Figurine, 3 Graces, wht bsq, #1199, 1900, 13" 325.00
Garniture, mantel; child w/flute scene, brass top/ft, 8" 135.00
Lamp, celeste bl w/HP cupids & flowers, waisted, 15", pr 550.00
Plate, couple walking in woods, gold fleur-de-lis rim, 9½" 120.00

Charger, three figures in wheat field on gilt-decorated blue ground, interlaced 'L' and Chateau Des Tuileries mark, 20", $600.00.

Plate, Louis XV or Marie Lezinska, gilt/ivory, sgn, 10", pr 150.00
Plate, Mme Lavaliere, artist sgn, gold rim, crown mk, 9½" 125.00
Platter, Letizia Bonaparte reserve on gr w/gilt, 1875, 13" 200.00
Urn, French court figures, ormolu mts, 11", pr 450.00
Urn, lady/cupid, sgn, 4 ormolu scroll ft, 1880s, 25" 1,800.00
Urn, maid/cupids reserve on gr, ormolu hdls, no lid, 26" 800.00
Urn, ormolu ram's head/floral festooning, floral finial, 9" 300.00
Urn, scene w/lady, scroll hdls, gilt ft, mk, w/lid, 9" 155.00
Vase, floral reserves on red, gold hdls/rim/base, 8x5", pr 325.00
Vase, grapes/vines, mc on wht, 1921, 15½" 1,000.00
Vase, lady, man on bench on cobalt, ormolu mts, 15", pr 850.00
Vase, lg group roses/insects on wht, gilt ft/rim, 13", pr 500.00
Vase, oxblood mottle, ormolu Deco mts, 4 loop hdls, 7" 500.00
Vase, scene w/lovers on dk bl, ornate giltwork, lid, 10" 300.00
Vase, suitor in garden on celeste bl, hdls, ormolu mt, 12", pr ...750.00
Vase, wht mums on profuse stems/leaves, Gebleux, '02, 24" ..2,700.00

Sewer Tile

Whimsies, advertising novelties, and other ornamental items were sometimes made in potteries where the primary product was simply tile.

Ash tray, standing dog at back, 5", $95.00.

Bookends, gorilla, tooled coat/open mouth, mk Superior, 15" . . .700.00
Box, ballot; incised 'C Stocker, Mar 9, 1920,' 7¾", NM 200.00
Cuspidor, tooled bark-like finish, 3x5", NM 25.00
Desk set, Universal Sewer Pipe Corp, 5½" L 65.00
Dog, sitting, head down, late, 2⅝" 60.00
Doorstop, dog w/incised details, OH, ca 1900, 10x6x5½" 170.00
Frog, hand tooled, 4¼" L 155.00
Lamb, tooled features, tan glaze, 9" L, NM 175.00
Paperweight, lion, recumbent, brn matt, 1890s, 2½x5" 55.00
Paperweight, man's head, incised features, What Cheer, 4" 85.00
Planter, stump form, inset heart w/Anna, 1945,' 6¾" 75.00
Planter, stump form, What Cheer, 5x7½" 65.00
Snail, tooled, sgn RLW, 8½", VG 65.00
Tile, lion, recumbent, brn 125.00
Water cooler, lady in relief, NM 350.00

Sewing Items

This is a field that offers much variety for both beginning and advanced collectors. Some find it interesting to assemble a broad range of the tools used in the needle arts, while others prefer to specialize in thimbles, tatting shuttles, scissors, etc. that show the diversity available in one specific group.

As needlework tools were made for daily use, their design and ornamentation reflected the history of personal fashion as well as historical events and the evolution of manufacturing processes. The various materials that were used and the methods of decorations that were employed provide the collector with exciting possibilities.

Lace bobbins of the English Midlands are an example. Lace-makers learned their craft in childhood and spent their lives working long hours under poor conditions. Their beautifully decorated bobbins, usually made of wood or bone, were embellished with dyes, inlays, intricate carvings, etc. in an effort to add beauty to an often drab existence. Inscribed with names, dates, loving messages, personal and historical events, the bobbins recorded the lives and times of the lace-maker. 'Fairings,' 'Church Windows,' 'Pewter Inlays,' 'Trolly Bobbins,' and 'Cow and Calf' are among the many types available. Although many of the more desirable examples from the 18th and 19th centuries are extremely rare, bobbin-makers of today have mastered the old techniques and are again making beautiful bobbins for comtemporary lace-makers which are eagerly sought by collectors.

There is a wide variance in the value of hand needlework tools due to materials, age, and country of origin. Prices are escalating but unsteady and tend to be regional. Gold, sterling, and enameled items are very high. Also, certain motifs (cherubs, hearts, or unique designs such as male figures and armor) bring higher prices.

Basket, wicker, gr/red/gold trim, w/lid, Victorian, 7" 28.00
Basket, wicker, HP florals, 9" dia 25.00
Bodkin, gilt, for corset 35.00
Bodkin, stork design, set of 2 . . . . .70.00
Bodkin case, wood, tubular, 4" 8.00
Box, pine w/burl grpt & gold scrolls, fitted int, 12" L 350.00
Box, rosewood, fitted interior, orig contents 2,000.00
Caddy, wood w/red & gr pnt, base+2 tiers, cushion atop, 12" . . .40.00
Chatelaine, sterling needle case/SP pencil/MOP memo, EX . . .170.00
Chatelaine, 5 sewing tools, all orig 1,500.00
Clamp, CI, blk pnt, swivel mechanism to hold fabric, 4½" 48.00
Crochet hook, cvd bone, EX 35.00
Darner, amber glass, blown ball shape w/hdl, heavy, 6¼" 95.00
Darner, bl aurene, att Steuben, ground lip, 7", M 300.00
Darner, bl glass, foot shape, molded, 5" 45.00
Darner, blk glass, blown egg form, repousse hdl, 5½" 75.00
Darner, clear w/red/wht/bl splotches, gold int, pontil, 8" 85.00

Darner, cobalt glass, blown, emb Amster 85.00
Darner, cobalt glass, ribbed hdl, ground lip, 6½", M 110.00
Darner, custard glass, sheared end, 5", M 170.00
Darner, ebony, sterling repousse hdl, mk, 4½" 65.00
Darner, glove; La Pierre Silver, NM 125.00
Darner, glove; sterling repousse florals, 4½" 110.00
Darner, gr glass, foot shape, molded, 5" 45.00
Darner, Nailsea, clear w/rose loops, wht int, Pittsburgh, 7" 350.00
Darner, Nailsea, gr w/wht loops, wht int, sheared end, 6" 550.00
Darner, pk cased in clear, mushroom shape, sheared end, 4½" . .160.00
Darner, purple glass, blown 95.00
Darner, 4-color striped glass, clear cased, sheared end, 6" 155.00
Emery, bean pod figural, gr satin, 2¼" .30.00
Emery, Blk face w/turban, 1¼" dia 45.00
Emery, dbl scallop shell w/pnt flowers on tan velvet, 1¾" 22.50
Hem gauge, sterling, Deco floral 95.00
Hem gauge, sterling, heart, Deco style 125.00
Hem gauge, sterling, Holly pattern 125.00
Lace bobbin, Midlands, bone, fairing 125.00
Lace bobbin, Midlands, ivory, fairing 165.00
Lace bobbin, Midlands, wood, leopard .67.00
Nanny pin, brass, oval goldstone top, mk, 2" 125.00
Needle case, bone, flat w/beading, ca 1850, 3½" 150.00
Needle case, celluloid, HP florals on peach, 3¾" 45.00
Needle case, celluloid, mushroom form, yel w/red cap, 2" 40.00
Needle case, celluloid, rolling pin form, bl, 4¼" 60.00
Needle case, celluloid, umbrella form, 4" 50.00
Needle case, cvd bone, fish form, steel rivet dots 150.00
Needle case, cvd walnut & bone, umbrella form, 4" L 95.00
Needle case, gold-washed sterling, eng grooves, 2¼" 160.00
Needle case, gold-washed sterling, repousse florals, 2¼" 160.00
Needle case, Indian beadwork & embr, folds, 1840s, 2½x4" 95.00
Needle case, ivory, fish form, screw knob in mouth, 4" 175.00
Needle case, vegetable ivory, acorn ends, 2¾" 75.00
Needle case, vegetable ivory, EX cvg, 2" 65.00
Needle holder, Avery, book, accordion fold 200.00
Needle holder, Avery, butterfly 650.00
Needle holder, Avery, Royal Commemorative, shield 350.00
Pincushion, barrel, ivory, cushion ea end, 1¼" H 65.00
Pincushion, beaded, dtd 1938, 2" dia 45.00
Pincushion, Dutch doll, compo head, felt clothes, 5½" 30.00
Pincushion, leather shoe, stacked heel, plush cushion, 4¼" 28.00
Pincushion, MOP, overall decor w/gr silk cushion, 1" dia 65.00
Pincushion, scallop shell, dbl; w/tan velvet cushion, 1¼" 22.00

Sterling pincushions, fish, 1½", $110.00; chick in egg, 1", 95.00. (Chick in egg is being reproduced.)

Punch, eyelet; eng florals w/gauge, mk sterling hdl, 5½" L 75.00
Punch, eyelet; slide gauge, blk wood hdl, dtd Oct 1909, 5½" . . .35.00
Ribbon threader, gilt, scroll design 65.00
Ribbon threader, sterling, fish shape 65.00
Ribbon threader, sterling, floral, 3 in case 135.00
Scissors, embroidery; sterling, daisies emb, 3½", EX 135.00

Scissors, embroidery; sterling, stork figural **75.00**
Scissors, metal, folding, 2", +storage pouch **25.00**
Scissors, steel, Expo souvenir, 6" **135.00**
Scissors, steel, medallion souvenir, 6", EX **75.00**
Sewing bird, brass, clamp-on, dtd 1856 on wings, EX **175.00**
Sewing bird, brass, 1980s repro, unmk **75.00**
Sewing bird, SP, w/heart key/clamp, pat 1852, 1940s repro **95.00**
Sewing bird, SP, w/heart key/clamp, pat 1853, orig **250.00**
Sewing bird, SP, 2 cushion, dtd 1853 on wing, rare **300.00**
Sewing bird, SP, 2 orig cushions, Meriden, ca 1867-1871 . . . . .**225.00**
Sewing bird, SP brass w/open heart key **175.00**
Sewing bird, tin plated, velvet cushion worn, 4¾" **115.00**
Sewing kit, marbleized Catalin, advertizing **35.00**
Sewing kit, wood, acorn w/thread spool **45.00**
Silk winder, bone, snowflake **32.00**
Silk winder, MOP, snowflake **45.00**
Silk winder, sterling, 4-spoke **125.00**
Tape measure, bone, castle, rnd w/brick details, 1½" **125.00**
Tape measure, brass, pig, w/coin in mouth, pat, 1½" **200.00**
Tape measure, celluloid, bald head, pull hat, Germany, 1½" **95.00**
Tape measure, celluloid, Lydia Pinkham, lg **28.00**
Tape measure, celluloid, sailing ship, Japan, 2¼" **40.00**
Tape measure, celluloid, scotty dog form, Germany **85.00**
Tape measure, celluloid, 2 dogs on pillow form, Germany, 1¾" . .**95.00**
Tape measure, ivory, barrel shape, w/spindle **135.00**
Tape measure, metal, egg w/fly as pull **85.00**
Tape measure, metal, straw hat form, 2" **165.00**
Tape measure, metal, whiskey jug form, 2" **165.00**
Tape measure, plastic, covered wagon, 1¾" **50.00**
Tape measure, plastic, house, gray w/red roof, 1½" **40.00**
Tape measure, Tunbridge, w/pincushion top, 1½x1" **175.00**
Tatting shuttle, abalone, smoky pearl tone **45.00**
Tatting shuttle, brass, eng Mother **85.00**
Tatting shuttle, celluloid, Lydia Pinkham, EX **40.00**
Tatting shuttle, German silver, Expo souvenir **225.00**
Tatting shuttle, horn, yel, quite narrow **65.00**
Tatting shuttle, sterling, Bob-O-Link, orig box **225.00**
Tatting shuttle, sterling, script initials **110.00**
Tatting shuttle, wht MOP, EX **125.00**
Thimble, sterling, beads, dots at rim, Ketcham & McDougall . . .**35.00**
Thimble, sterling, bridge/tower scene, pat '81 . . . .**100.00**
Thimble, sterling, circles & fleur-de-lis, Simons **45.00**
Thimble, sterling, dots & diamonds, Ketcham & McDougall . . .**45.00**
Thimble, sterling, flower in cap, arrow, fleur-de-lis **40.00**
Thimble, sterling, gr enamel border, 5 rose clusters, M **85.00**
Thimble, sterling, harbor scene/scrolls, star in cap **60.00**
Thimble, sterling, mountain scenic, scroll rim, Simons **45.00**
Thimble, sterling, raised band amid scrolled borders, Simons . . .**30.00**
Thimble, sterling, sailboats/house/trees/windmill, Germany **58.00**
Thimble, sterling, scrolls & stripes in border, unmk **32.00**
Thimble, sterling, wide border w/Louis XV-style rim, Simons . . .**36.00**
Thimble, vegetable ivory, 2", in cvd holder **95.00**
Thimble case, helmet, brass **195.00**
Thimble case, SP/brass, bucket **125.00**
Thimble case, sterling, acorn **175.00**
Thimble case, wood, cowboy hat **75.00**
Thimble holder, fabric, slipper form, sole is holder, 3½" **38.00**
Thimble holder, scallop shell, brass fittings, old, EX **65.00**
Thimble holder, vegetable ivory, ornate cvg, 2½" **85.00**
Thimble stand, turtle, w/post, rectangle, SP, 1x2¼" **35.00**
Thread container, sterling, beaded rim & base, 1½x1" **85.00**
Thread spool, MOP, metal shaft w/bone base, 1½" **45.00**
Thread waxer, sterling, repousse pierced cap, unmk, 2" **75.00**
Threader, sterling, eng lines at outer edge, mk, ¾" W **35.00**

Sewing Machines

B Eldridge, automatic, Wanamaker NY, 1890?, EX **130.00**
Beckwith, pat 1872, EX **275.00**

Child's Casige, chain stitch, British Zone Germany, NM, $100.00.

Child's, Signature Jr, electric, in plastic case, EX **50.00**
Child's, Singer Model 20-10, orig case, EX **70.00**
Child's, Singer Model 50, 1962, in box w/instructions **22.00**
Child's, Stitch Mistress, EX **25.00**
Child's, Toyland/Sewette, ft treadle, battery op, Japan, NM **50.00**
CI Stitchwell, clamp on, very old, EX **105.00**
DW Clark, Patent Model, 1858, NM **345.00**
Gardner, hand crank, EX **110.00**
Lindstrom, bl florals, Made in USA, EX **48.00**
Little Modiste, Casige, German British Zone, EX **50.00**
New National, hand crank, #U110023, M **90.00**
New Remington #4, claw ft, EX **105.00**
Smith & Egge, automatic, 1901, EX **175.00**
Wilcox & Gibbs, NY, 1861, G **75.00**

Shaker Items

The Shaker community was founded in America in 1776 at Niskeyuna, New York, by a small group of English 'Shaking Quakers.' The name referred to a group dance which was part of their religious rites. Their leader was Mother Ann Lee. By 1815 their membership had grown to more than one thousand in eighteen communities as far west as Indiana and Kentucky. But in less than a decade, their numbers began to decline until today only a handful remain.

Their furniture is prized for its originality, simplicity, workmanship, and practicality. Few pieces were signed. Some were carefully finished to enhance the natural wood; a few were painted.

Although other methods were used earlier, most Shaker boxes were of oval construction with overlapping 'fingers' at the seams to prevent buckling as the wood aged. Boxes with original paint fetch double the price of an unpainted box; number of fingers and size should also be considered.

Although the Shakers were responsible for weaving a great number of baskets, their methods are not easily distinguished from those of their outside neighbors, and it is nearly impossible without first-hand knowledge to specifically attribute a specific example to their manufacture. They were involved in various commercial efforts other than woodworking — among them sheep and dairy farming, sawmills, and pipe and brick making. They were the first to raise crops specifically for seed and to market their product commercially. They perfected a method to recycle paper and were able to produce wrinkle-free fabrics. Prices realized for Shaker artifacts at today's large auctions are very erratic.

Standard two-letter state abbreviations have been used throughout the following listings.

Key:
bj — bootjack   ML — Mt. Lebanon
CB — Canterbury   SDL — Sabbathday Lake
EF — Enfield   WV — Watervliet
NL — New Lebanon

Apple peeler, maple/poplar, cvd/trn/pegged, 1820s, 15x9½x7" .250.00
Basket, ash, single-wrapped rim, hickory hdls, 9x15½" 600.00
Basket, berry; maple splint, sgn, 5½x5¼" 600.00
Basket, berry; tin-banded rim/base, sgn/dtd 1859 . . . . .125.00
Basket, feather; maple splint, sgn, WV, ca 1872, 12x12½" 600.00
Basket, gathering; ash splint, hoop hdl, 13½x11½" 350.00
Basket, laundry; maple/blk ash splint, 4-hdld, EF, 15x23" . . .2,900.00
Basket, maple splint, hoop hdl, CB, 12¾x11" 600.00
Basket, maple splint, orig gray pnt, cvd hdls, 6½x12" 150.00
Basket, maple splint, sq, 4 cvd hdls, 8x11x11" 2,600.00
Basket, openwork raffia, swing hdl, elongated oval, 11" L 110.00
Basket, orchard; maple/ash splint, pine base, EF, 15½x22" 800.00
Basket, sewing; maple/ash, slide lid, star decor, 8x11½" 700.00
Basket, sewing; pine bottom, oval, attached lid, hdl, 6x5x3" . . .300.00
Basket, utility; spruce w/dbl cherry bands, swing hdl, 12" 750.00
Basket, wool; splint, orig gr-gray pnt, cvd hdls, 10½x22" 650.00
Bed, pine/ash, stain, orig rollers, 31x74" 800.00
Bench, apple; pine/maple, 1-board top, NL, 1840s, 15x9x16" . .650.00
Book, Portraiture of Shakerism, anti-Shaker, Dyer, 1822, EX . .175.00
Booklet, Manifests, United Soc, New Hampshire, 1884, 6x9" . . .35.00
Bowl, blk ash, cvd hand grips, WV, 1840s, 5¾x29x20½" 1,400.00
Bowl, bread; maple, inset hdls, sq base, WV, 1840s, 6x22x19" .600.00
Box, apple; pine, orig pnt, dvtl, canted, ML, 5½x10x9" 600.00
Box, blanket; pine, rfn, dvtl, 6-board, EF, 1860s, 25x48x24" .1,100.00
Box, blanket; poplar, orig pnt, bj ends, 22x39x15" 800.00
Box, card; pine, natural, dvtl, initialed, 1840s, 2½x5x3" 200.00
Box, comb; poplar, gr pnt, dvtl, hanging, 5x9x3⅜" 250.00
Box, document; walnut, natural, dvtl, MA, 1840s, 5¼x12x6¾"..300.00
Box, glove; poplar, brn stain, dvtl, MA, 1820s, 4¾x12x6" 350.00
Box, herb; pine, orig red pnt, labels, NL, 6½x10x7½" 1,100.00
Box, knife; maple, varnish, dvtl, 3½x15½x9" 300.00

Box, umber graining on yellow-ochre, scalloped freehand border, and painted initials in red, 2x6x4½", $3,300.00.

Box, maple/cherry, 3-finger, oval, 1½x3⅜" 1,200.00
Box, pine, brn stain, dvtl, MA, 1860, 18x24x17½" 650.00

Box, pine, orig red pnt, dvtl, papered int, 9x21x13" 1,200.00
Box, pine, orig stain, 2 drws, dvtl, SDL, 1830s, 8x15x9" 1,200.00
Box, pine/maple, orig bl pnt, 4-finger, oval, 3x4¾" 7,000.00
Box, pine/maple, wood pegs/copper nails, hdl, w/lid, 5x4¾" . . .175.00
Box, pine/maple, 4-finger, oval, ME, 4⅜x12¾" 200.00
Box, poplar/pressboard, orig pnt, half-rnd, nailed, 4x10x5" 100.00
Box, seed; pine, orig red pnt, label, ML, 3¼x23x11½", pr . . .1,000.00
Box, sewing; maple, pegs/copper tacks, lined, 6x6¾" dia 125.00
Box, sewing; maple/pine, w/contents, dtd 1851, 4½x6" 400.00
Box, storage; poplar, dvtl, iron straps, 1940s, 9½x22x22" 400.00
Box, tin, HP winter scene, sgn, CB, 3½" L 150.00
Box, walnut, stained, 4-finger, pine/maple bottom, 2¼x5¼" . . .300.00
Brush, horsehair bristle, trn maple, pk velvet ribbon, 8" 60.00
Bucket, berry; pine, orig red pnt, blk iron bands, 4½x5½" 325.00
Bucket, grain; ash/maple/pine, swing hdl, NL, 1850s, 10x8½" . .200.00
Bucket, pine, bl-gray pnt, blk bands, EF, 1850s, 9x9¾" 500.00
Bucket, pine, natural, brass wraps/bail plate, w/lid, 6x5½" 425.00
Bucket, pine, orig bl pnt, bail hdl, CB, 1820s, 14x11½" 550.00
Bucket, pine, orig bl pnt, iron hoops/hdls, 5x10" 500.00
Bucket, pine, orig gr pnt, blk iron bands, w/lid, CB, 9½x9" 400.00
Bucket, pine, orig yel pnt, stencil, CB, 1850s, 9¼x12" 175.00
Bucket, pine, yel wash, diamond bail plates, 9x12" 225.00
Candle mold, tin, 12-tube, Alfred ME, 10x7" 175.00
Candlestand, birch/cherry, orig stain, 1820s, 27x17" dia . . .2,500.00
Carrier, cherry/maple, nailed, swing hdl, 7¼x8x4¾" 250.00
Carrier, knife; oak/maple, bentwood, MA, 4½x13x8½" 150.00
Carrier, pine, hickory hdl, sq, ML, 1870s, 11¾x10¼" 800.00
Carrier, pine, natural, dvtl, swing hdl, ML, 10x10¾x7¼" 225.00
Case, medicine bottle; blk walnut, EF, 1820s, 3½x12x8½" 300.00
Chair, child's rocker; #0, splint seat, outstanding, rare 2,000.00
Chair, hickory/pine/maple, 7-spindle, revolves, 1850s, 28" . . .3,500.00
Chair, rocker; maple, splint seat/scroll arm, NL, 1820, 44" . . .8,600.00

Rocking chair, maple, possibly North Union or Union Village, Ohio, ca 1850, refinished, 45", $3,300.00.

Chair, rocker; maple, taped seat, shawl bar, #7, ML, 41½" . . .1,500.00
Chair, rocker; maple, varnish, 2-slat, CB, 1820s, 32" 4,250.00
Chair, side; birch, cane seat, tilters, EF, 1830s, 41" 3,000.00
Chair, side; maple, tape seat, 3-slat, shawl bar, ML, 33" 850.00
Chair, side; maple, tape seat/bk, shawl bar, ML, 40" 1,600.00
Chest, poplar, stain, 3 grad drws, 1840s, 37x29x20" 1,800.00
Chest, poplar/birch, stain, 8 dvtl drws, 41x54x20" 3,800.00

Chest, work; butternut, 8 dvtl drws, 1840s, 24x55x13" **3,000.00**
Chromolithograph, God Is Our Hope, walnut fr, CB, 9x20½" . **200.00**
Counter, tailor's, pine/poplar, orig pnt, 3-drw, 32x42x31" . . . **1,250.00**
Cupboard, pine, old pnt, 1 dbl-panel door, 1840s, 60x29x9" . **1,200.00**
Cupboard, pine, paneled door, mortise/tenon, hangs, EF, 30" . . **110.00**
Cupboard, pine/butternut, dvtl, hangs, EF, 1840s **550.00**
Cupboard, wash; poplar/butternut, NL, 1840s, 37x20x16" . . **2,500.00**
Desk, sewing; pine/birch, stain, 6 drws, CB, 1830s, 39" **31,000.00**
Dipper, pine/maple, stamped mk, NL, 3x11½x4⅝" **600.00**
Dipper, wood, rnd measure form w/well-shaped side hdl **145.00**
Feed sack, label: Lewis Colby, EF #23, coarse weave, 40x20" . . **100.00**
Flax wheel, birch/maple/hickory/oak, EF, 60x76½" **600.00**
Flax wheel, maple/oak, stamped mk, CB, 1820 . . . . **600.00**
Footstool, maple, varnish, ML decal, 7x12x11" **300.00**
Footstool, pine, orig pnt, arched legs, ML, 6x9½x7½" **450.00**
Grain seeder, wooden, shoulder strap, crank shaker, 7" L **175.00**
Hanger, pine, initialed, 13" **35.00**
Ironing board, pine, wool covered, leather bound, ML, 56x12" . **175.00**
Mortar & pestle, maple, orig yel wash, CB, 1840s **800.00**
Niddy-noddy, hickory/maple, cvd/trn, EF, ca 1820, 19" **150.00**
Pie lifter, curved, 2-tine, wood hdl, brass ferrule **55.00**
Pitcher, floral sprays/'Shakers ML,' Union Porcelain, 8¾" . . . **1,100.00**
Rack, drying; pine, 4 folding arms, 3 bars, 1860s, 41x37" **400.00**
Rack, towel; pine, gray pnt, trestle ft, 36x28½" **450.00**
Rail, pine, 9 cherry pegs, sgn, WV, 1820s, 34½" L **450.00**
Rolling pin, tiger/bird's eye maple, 20" **165.00**
Rug, cotton/wool, mc w/red border, hooked/cut, 35x18½" **425.00**
Rug, wool, sheared, cross & circles, mc on bl, 68x36" **550.00**
Scoop, flour; cvd & hewn, 1-pc, trn hdl, cvd finger grip **150.00**
Scoop, maple, 1-pc, ML, ca 1850, 14x6½" **525.00**
Shovel, grain; maple, 1-pc, MA, 1820s, 35½" **550.00**
Spitbox, pine, orig brn pnt, EF, 3x8x6½" **100.00**
Spool, maple, orig red pnt, silk thread, 1", pr **400.00**
Stand, cherry, 1-drw, dvtl, sq legs, MA, 29x18x17½" **2,600.00**
Stand, pine, pnt traces, dvtl gallery, ML, 1930s, 32x31x21" . . **2,200.00**
Stand, tiger maple, 1-drw, dvtl, WV, 1830s, 28x18x18" **1,600.00**
Stand, wash; pine, 1-drw, dvtl, NL, 1820s, 33x26x17" **2,300.00**
Stool, butternut, arch base, 2-step, NL, 10x15x13" **700.00**
Stool, maple, varnish, trn legs, 2-step, 9½x12x10" **400.00**
Stool, poplar, varnish, dvtl brace, 2-step, 9x12x7½" **500.00**
Stove, CI, tapered legs, rnd lid, 20½x33" **800.00**
Swift, maple, orig mustard pnt, 27" **300.00**
Swift, maple/poplar, natural, wood thumb screws, MA, 27½" . . **300.00**
Table, cherry/pine, orig pnt, 1-brd top, 1830s, 29x36x23" . . . **7,750.00**
Table, pine/birch, stain, 2-brd top, CB, 1820, 28x50x38" . . . **1,500.00**
Table, sewing; tiger maple/birch, 1-drw, CB, 1830s **8,500.00**
Table, work; butternut/pine, 1-brd top, EF, 1820, 28x37x22" **1,750.00**
Table, work; maple/pine, pegged, EF, 1830s, 24x27x22" **500.00**
Tailoring stick, cherry, natural, hand #d, ML, 1830s, 38" **700.00**
Trunk, leather covered, brass studs, CB, 1820s, 9x20x10½" . . . **500.00**
Wool wheel, chestnut/maple, natural, sgn, 35½x34½" **575.00**

Shaving Mugs

In the 1860s it became a popular practice for every man who shaved to have his own special shaving mug. Mugs belonging to men who frequented the barber shop for their tonsorial services were often personalized with their owner's name and kept on display on the barber's shelf. Occupational shaving mugs became the high point of individualism during this period. China mugs, mostly made in France, Germany, and Austria, were imported by American barber-supply companies where artists hand painted the occupation or the fraternal or sports affiliation of its customer on the mug. Often his name was added in gold. Because of sanitary rules and restrictions imposed around 1915, these personalized mugs were eventually taken off the barbers' shelves. Today, occupational shaving mugs are the most valuable. Although some are valued by the excellence of the artist, most are priced by the rarity of the subject matter.

Advertising, Antiseptic Shaving, red/gr letters, pat 1907 . . . . . **100.00**
Advertising, Artistry for Fashionable Gentlemen, VG **55.00**
Advertising, Congress Barber Chair, Rosenfield Bros **110.00**
Black cat, floral sprigs, name **350.00**
Blk man's head, open mouth for brush, big hat, EX **195.00**
Close Shave, novelty **275.00**
Dog, standing, floral sprigs, name, EX **325.00**
Fraternal, Brotherhood of RR Trainmen, caboose, Limoges, EX . **95.00**
Fraternal, FOE, emblem & name **185.00**
Fraternal, IOOF, detailed eye, Bible, & sword, EX **125.00**
Fraternal, Odd Fellows, bl eye w/eyebrow, EX gold **45.00**
Fraternal, OUAM, shield w/stars & stripes, 1926, Germany . . . **60.00**
Frog on toadstool, name **225.00**
Lithophane, flowers & butterfly, couple/kids dance in base **80.00**
Occupational, baker, 2 men at work, name **350.00**
Occupational, baker, 3 men w/loaves of bread, T&V Limoges . **225.00**
Occupational, barber in shop **800.00**
Occupational, barber w/customer, mug rack on wall **1,100.00**
Occupational, bartender at ornate bar w/2 customers, EX **450.00**
Occupational, bartender between 2 customers **300.00**
Occupational, blacksmith, man shoes horse, EX details, T&V . **225.00**
Occupational, blacksmith framed by horsehoe **400.00**
Occupational, bootmaker, red/blk boots, gold trim, Austria . . . **215.00**
Occupational, bricklayer, man working, gold trim, #d, EX **375.00**
Occupational, butcher, hog's head w/sausage around neck, EX . **275.00**
Occupational, butcher, steer's head & saws **200.00**
Occupational, butcher in shop w/female customer, hairline . . . **425.00**
Occupational, carpenter, tools w/name, gold trim, T&V, EX . . **185.00**
Occupational, carpenter, 5 men framing a house **1,700.00**
Occupational, clock merchant w/male customer **1,100.00**
Occupational, cowboy, man w/lasso on horse, gold trim, EX . . . **400.00**
Occupational, cowboy on horsebk roping steer, pnt loss **450.00**
Occupational, delivery man, wagon of watermelons, EX **275.00**
Occupational, dry goods merchant w/female customer **725.00**
Occupational, farmer, farm scene w/EX gold trim, NM **300.00**
Occupational, football player kicking ball, minor pnt loss **900.00**

Occupational, saloon keeper, interior view with two customers, 4", $550.00.

Occupational, gambler, 3 men at cards, gold trim, NM 1,150.00
Occupational, grocery delivery, horse-drawn wagon, Limoges ..345.00
Occupational, machine operator at metal-working machine ...900.00
Occupational, musician, woodwind instrument, Germany, EX .475.00
Occupational, paper hanger, man on ladder 450.00
Occupational, pig farmer, pig in pen, gold trim, Limoges 885.00
Occupational, seamstress at sewing machine, unusual 475.00
Occupational, sewing machine repairman, treadle machine ...325.00
Occupational, slaughter house, men butcher steer, EX 400.00
Occupational, sportsman, hunter w/dogs, Limoges, EX 150.00
Occupational, telegrapher w/hand on telegraph key 275.00
Occupational, tinsmith, man at bench w/tools, VG 155.00
Occupational, trainman, locomotive, name 375.00
Occupational, 10th Dragoons musician, flags/bugle/drum, EX ..300.00
Open touring car, bright colors, rare subject 1,600.00
Photographic, Blk lady, gold scrolls, Germany, EX 250.00
Photographic, man in horse-drawn carriage 600.00
Pk lustre, holly berries & leaves 45.00
Redware, brn-amber, minor wear, 4¼x5" 165.00
Slot machine, upright, Thomas Watling 2,600.00
Top hat, name 400.00

Shawnee

The Shawnee Pottery Company operated in Zanesville, Ohio, from 1937 to 1961. They produced inexpensive novelty ware — vases, flower-pots, and figurines — as well as a very successful line of figural cookie jars. These cookie jars and their dinnerware, the Corn Line, are very popular with today's collectors.

For those wanting more information, we recommend *Collecting Shawnee Pottery, A Pictorial Reference and Price Guide*, by Mark Supnick, updated in 1989. His address may be found in the Directory under Florida. In the listings that follow, gold trim may add from 50% to 100% on small items.

Cookie Jars

Add 30% to 50% to listed values for cookie jars with gold trim.

Clown, #12 ....70.00
Dutch Girl or Dutch Boy, #1025 or #1026 ....120.00
Elephant, #60 ....45.00
Jug, #75 ....80.00
Lucky Elephant 60.00

Mugsy, exceptional decoration, $150.00.

Octagon 25.00
Owl 90.00
Puss-N-Boots 60.00
Smiley the Pig 70.00
Winnie the Pig 70.00

Corn Line

The utility jar in the Corn Line doubled as a sugar bowl, the small jug, as a creamer. A three-piece range set combination comprised of a pair of shakers and the utility jar (used in this instance as a drip jar) was also available.

Bowl, mixing; 5" 22.00
Bowl, mixing; 6½" 25.00
Bowl, mixing; 8" 35.00
Bowl, soup/cereal 30.00
Casserole, ind 35.00
Casserole, 1½-qt 50.00
Cookie jar 100.00
Cup 20.00
Dish, 6" 7.00
Jug, 1-qt 50.00
Mug 30.00
Plate, 10" 30.00
Platter, 12" 40.00
Relish tray 22.00
Shaker, lg 20.00
Shaker, sm 12.00
Teapot, 30-oz 50.00
Utility jar 30.00

Miscellaneous

Bank, bulldog 50.00
Bookends, flying geese, #4000, pr 26.00
Candlestick holder, #3026 ....14.00
Cookie jar/bank, Winnie, #61 ....135.00
Creamer, elephant 16.00
Creamer, Puss-N-Boots, #85 ....20.00
Creamer, Smiley the Pig, #86 ....22.00
Darner, woman 20.00
Figurine, gazelle, #614 ....40.00
Figurine, Oriental, #602 ....5.00
Figurine, Oriental w/parasol, #601 ....8.00
Figurine, Pekingese 22.00
Figurine, puppy 22.00
Figurine, rabbit 22.00
Figurine, teddy bear 22.00
Figurine, tumbling bear 22.00
Pitcher, Little Bo-Peep, #47 ....35.00
Pitcher, Little Boy Blue, #46 ....45.00
Pitcher, Smiley Pig 45.00
Planter, boy at fence 6.00
Planter, boy at stump, #532 ....5.00
Planter, boy at stump, leaning, #533 ....5.00
Planter, boy w/chicken, #645 ....12.00
Planter, boy w/dog, #582 ....4.00
Planter, boy w/wheelbarrow, #750 ....12.00
Planter, bridge, #756 ....8.00
Planter, Buddha, #524 ....14.00
Planter, bull, #668 ....14.00
Planter, bull w/leaf 40.00
Planter, butterfly, #524 ....5.00

Planter, canopy bed, #734 . . . . .30.00
Planter, cat playing saxophone, #729 . . . . .20.00
Planter, chick w/cart, #720 . . . . .12.00
Planter, circus cage 18.00
Planter, donkey w/basket, head down, #671 . . . . .14.00
Planter, donkey w/basket, head up, #722 . . . . .14.00
Planter, donkey w/cart, #538, sm 5.00
Planter, donkey w/cart, #709, lg 14.00
Planter, duck, #720 . . . . .14.00
Planter, duck w/cart, #752 . . . . .12.00
Planter, Dutch kids at well, #710 .12.00
Planter, elephant, #759, sm 5.00
Planter, elephant & leaf 40.00
Planter, elf shoe, #765 . . . . .8.00
Planter, highchair, #727 . . . . .35.00
Planter, tractor trailer, #681 . . . . .30.00
Planter, tractor trailer cab, #680 . . . . .30.00
Planter, train set, 4-pc 100.00
Planter, 4 birds on perch, #502 . . . . .35.00
Shakers, Bo-Peep, pr 8.00
Shakers, Chanticleer, sm, pr 14.00
Shakers, duck, pr 20.00
Shakers, Dutch boy, pr 16.00
Shakers, Dutch girl, pr 16.00
Shakers, Dutch kids, pr 18.00
Shakers, flowerpot, pr 10.00
Shakers, milk can 8.00
Shakers, Mugsey, lg, pr 20.00
Shakers, owl, pr 8.00
Shakers, Puss-N-Boots, pr 8.00
Shakers, Sailor Boy, pr 8.00
Shakers, Smiley Pig, lg, pr 25.00
Shakers, Swiss kids, pr 22.00
Shakers, watering can, pr 10.00
Shakers, wheelbarrow, pr 10.00
Shakers, Winnie Pig, lg, pr 25.00
Teapot, elephant 70.00
Teapot, Tom Tom, #44 . . . . .35.00
Vase, Bow Knot, #819 . . . . .14.00
Vase, cornucopia, #835 . . . . .8.00
Vase, doe in shadow box, #850 . . . . .16.00
Vase, doves, #829 . . . . .18.00
Vase, gazelle w/baby, #841 . . . . .60.00
Vase, leaf, #821 . . . . .18.00
Vase, leaf, #823 . . . . .20.00
Vase, swan, #806 . . . . .12.00
Wall pocket, birdhouse, #830 . . . . .14.00
Wall pocket, bow 8.00
Wall pocket, girl w/rag doll, #810 . . . . .16.00
Wall pocket, Little Jack Horner, #585 . . . . .16.00
Wall pocket, mantel clock, #530 .16.00
Wall pocket, telephone, #529 . . . . .16.00

Shearwater

Since 1928 generations of the Peter, Walter, and James McConnell Anderson families have been producing figurines and artwares in their studio at Ocean Springs, Mississippi. Their work is difficult to date. Figures from the twenties and thirties won critical acclaim and have continued to be made to the present time. Early marks include a die-stamped 'Shearwater' in a dime-sized circle, a similar ink stamp, and a half-circle mark. Any older item may still be ordered in the same glazes as it was originally produced, so many pieces on the market today may be relatively new.

However, the older marks are not currently in use. Retail sales are available at the pottery or by mail order.

Black figures and pirates are usually valued at $35.00 to $50.00.

Bowl, bl w/rings, 3½x6½" base, 3½" opening 60.00
Figurine, fox, mk 35.00
Pitcher, lt bl gloss, 5" 25.00
Vase, birds/deer/leafy scrolls emb, gr/metallic gray, 6" 100.00
Vase, Ming gr, early mk, 8x5¼" 75.00
Vase, olive gr w/creamy bl flambe, funnel form, 5" 45.00
Vase, pelicans emb, Deco style, lav/brn flecks, 7" 475.00

Sheet Music

Sheet music is often collected more for the colorful lithographed covers rather than for the music itself. Transportation songs which have pictures or illustrations of trains, ships, and planes; ragtime tunes which feature popular entertainers such as Al Jolson; or those with Disney characters are among the most valuable. Much of the sheet music on the market today is valued at under $5.00; some of the better examples are listed here.

Alcoholic Blues, prohibition tune, owl on moon cover, 1916 . . .12.00
America, I Love You, patriotic views, 1915, EX 4.50
America Forever, ET Paul, 1898, VG 40.00
American Wedding March, full color litho, ET Paull, EX 55.00
As Time Goes By, from Casablanca, Bogart/Bergman cover 35.00
Black & White Rag, Botsford, 1908, VG 8.00
Boy Scouts on Trail, scout cover, 1929, EX 15.00
Caesar & Cleopatra theme, Taylor/Burton/Harrison cover, 1963 10.00
Carnival King, party scene color litho cover, ET Paull, 1911 . . . .20.00
Chasing Shadows, Sid Cary cover, 1835, EX 2.50
Comrades, I Am Going Home, W Irving Hartshorn, 1866, 5-pg .25.00
Cotton States Rag, Blk cover, 1910 .20.00
Dance of the Brownies 15.00
Dem Bones for Me, Blk man at curtains/dice, Jenkins, 1922 . . . .20.00
Don't Cry Dolly Grey, WWI soldiers march on cover, Remick . . .25.00
Embraceable You, from Girl Crazy, Rooney/Garland on cover . . .8.00
Fairy of the Wildwood, Henry A Brown, 1866, 5-pg, VG 15.00
Gone w/the Wind, rare, 1937, NM 50.00
Halifax Rag, Blk cover, 1910 . . . . .25.00
Heartbreak Hotel, Elvis cover, 1956, EX 20.00
Home Coming March, ET Paull, 1918, EX 25.00
I Did Not Know I'd Miss You As I Do, ET Paull, 1901, M 65.00
I Remember When I Try To Forget, 1934, VG 3.00
June in January, from Here Is My Heart, Crosby Carlisle 5.00
Just in Time, Judy Holliday cover, 1956, NM 4.00
Kaiser Jubilee March, ET Paull, 1913, G 27.50
Kiss Papa Goodnight, MH McChesney, 1866, 5-pg, VG 16.00
Lottie Lee, CT Lockwood, 1868, 5-pg, VG 16.50
Love's Fascination Waltz, Prang repro cover, ET Paull, 1920 . . .90.00
Mexicali Rose, Bing Crosby insert, 1935, VG 5.00
Midnight Flyer, Colorado Express train litho, 1903, EX 25.00
Modern Honeymoon, early airplane scene 15.00
My Black Bess, ET Paull, scarce, 1899, VG 50.00
My Wishing Song, Jack Benny cover, 1932, EX 2.50
Over the Rainbow, Wizard of Oz, 1939 . . . . .15.00
Over There, Norman Rockwell cover 35.00
Pinywoods Rag, Blk cover, Cocroft Music Co, 1909 . . . . .20.00
Polar Bear Polka, Albert W Berg, blk/wht litho, 1856, EX 36.00
Sam's Song, Judy Canova, by Elliot & Quadling, 1950, EX 3.00
Santa Baby, Eartha Kitt cover, 1953 .5.00
Signal from Mars, man in straight robe, ET Paull, 1901, VG 20.00

Porgy and Bess Summertime, Gershwin Publishing Corp., ca 1935, $10.00.

Summer Widowers, drinking/card playing on cover, Field, 1910 . 10.00
Sweet Memories of Thee, Welby, litho cover, 1849, VG 20.00
Tipperary Guards, soldiers fight, Starmer cover, 1915, VG 12.00
Titanic-In the Shadows of the Deep, Corry PA, 1912, VG 30.00
Vanity, Starmer cover of winged woman, ET Paull, 1919, EX . . . 55.00
Woman Forever March, ET Paull, 1916, EX 55.00
Your Lips Are No Man's Land But Mine, 1918 . . . . 5.00

Shelley

In 1872 Joseph Shelley became partners with James Wileman, owner of Foley China Works, thus creating Wileman & Co., in Stoke-on-Trent. Twelve years later James Wileman withdrew from the company, though the firm continued to use his name until 1925 when it became known as Shelley Potteries, Ltd. Like many successful 19th-century English potteries, this firm continued to produce useful household wares as well as dinnerware of considerable note. In 1896 the beautiful Dainty White shape was introduced, and it is regarded by many as synonymous with the name Shelley. In addition to the original Dainty 6-Flute design, other lovely and dainty shapes were produced: 12-Flute, 14-Flute, Leaf, Shell, Queen Anne, and the more modern shapes of Vogue, Regent, and Eve.

Though often overlooked, striking earthenware was produced under the direction of Frederick Rhead and later Walter Slater and his son Eric. Many notable artists contributed their talents in designing unusual, attractive wares: Rowland Morris, Mabel Lucie Attwell, and Hilda Cowham, to name but a few.

In 1966 Allied English Potteries acquired control of the Shelley Company, and by 1967 the last of the exquisite Shelley China had been produced to honor remaining overseas orders. In 1971 Allied English Potteries merged with the Doulton group. The name Shelley China Ltd. still exists, and it has been reported that Royal Doulton has produced trial wares bearing the Shelley backstamp.

Our advisors for this category are Lila and Fred Shrader; they are listed in the Directory under California.

Ash tray, Blue Daisy, gold trim, 3½" 22.50
Ash tray, Blue Rock, 6-flute, 5" 29.50
Ash tray, Dainty Pink, 6-flute, 5" 31.50
Ash tray, shell shape, 5" 15.00
Bowl, vegetable; Blue Rock, 6-flute, open, 5x7" 55.00
Bowl, vegetable; Bridal Rose, 6-flute, open, 6x8½" 65.00
Bowl, vegetable; Dainty Blue, 6-flute, w/lid, 6x8½" 85.00
Bowl, vegetable; Harebell, leaf shape, open, 6x8½" 55.00
Bowl, vegetable; Heavenly Pink, rnd, 7" 55.00

Butter dish, Dainty Blue, 6-flute, rnd 72.50
Butter dish, Sheraton, rnd 55.00
Butter dish, Sunray, Vogue shape 45.00
Butter dish, yel dots on Dainty White, 6-flute 65.00
Butter pat, Blue Rock, leaf shape 22.00
Butter pat, Blue Rock, rnd 18.00
Butter pat, Dainty Blue, 6-flute 35.00
Butter pat, Maytime, rnd w/gold trim 25.00
Butter pat, Rose & Red Daisy, 6-flute 27.50
Butter pat, yel dots on Dainty White, 6-flute 32.00
Cake plate, Begonia, 6-flute, tab hdls, 8" sq 45.00
Cake plate, Bridal Rose, ftd, 6-flute, 8" 89.00
Cake plate, Dainty Pink, ftd, 6-flute, 8" 95.00
Cake plate, Hedgerow, 6-flute, tab hdls, 8" sq 75.00
Cake plate, pk dots on Dainty White, 6-flute, tab hdls 75.00
Cake plate, Regency, ftd, 6-flute, 8" 88.00
Candle holder, Green Daisy, 2½", pr 65.00
Candy dish, Bridal Rose, 10-flute, 4¾" 21.00
Candy dish, Dainty Blue, 10-flute, 4¾" 24.50
Candy dish, Heather, rnd, 6" 22.50
Candy dish, Wildflower, 10-flute, 4¾" 22.00
Chamberstick, Indian Peony, brass holder, 6½" 25.00
Chamberstick, Pansy, 6-flute, brass holder, 6" 32.00
Chamberstick, Rose & Red Daisy, 6-flute, brass holder 30.00
Chocolate pot, Blue Rock, 6-flute, 8" 160.00
Chocolate pot, Harebell, leaf shape, 8" 145.00
Chocolate pot, Lily of the Valley, 6-flute, 6" 95.00
Chocolate pot, Sheraton, 6-cup 75.00
Cigarette holder, Maytime, gold trim, 2½" 25.00
Cigarette holder, Regency, 6-flute, 3" 22.50
Cigarette holder, Rose & Red Daisy, 6-flute, 3" 24.50
Coffeepot, Campanula, 6-flute, 6½" 135.00
Coffeepot, Dainty Blue, 6-flute, 6½" 140.00
Coffeepot, heraldic design, pear shape, 8½" 95.00
Coffeepot, Rosebud, bl trim, 6-flute, 6½" 125.00
Cream pot, Regency, 6-flute, 6" 45.00
Cream soup, Bridal Rose, 6-flute, w/underplate 45.00
Cream soup, Sheraton, w/underplate 28.50
Creamer, Dainty Pink, 6-flute, miniature 50.00
Creamer & sugar bowl, Blue Rock, 6-flute, w/lid 65.00
Creamer & sugar bowl, Bridal Rose, 14-flute 47.00
Creamer & sugar bowl, Bridal Rose, 6-flute, open, sm 45.00
Creamer & sugar bowl, Celandine, 6-flute, +tray 80.00
Creamer & sugar bowl, Celandine, 6-flute, lg 50.00
Creamer & sugar bowl, Dainty Blue, 6-flute, w/lid, lg 69.00
Creamer & sugar bowl, Indian Peony 45.00
Creamer & sugar bowl, Maytime, gold trim, w/lid 75.00
Creamer & sugar bowl, Regency, 6-flute, +tray 72.00
Creamer & sugar bowl, Sheraton, +tray 55.00
Creamer & sugar bowl, Sheraton, lg 38.00
Creamer & sugar bowl, Sunrise, Queen Anne shape, w/lid 65.00
Creamer & sugar bowl, Wild Anemone, 6-flute 49.50
Creamer & sugar bowl, Wild Anemone, 6-flute, w/lid 64.00
Cup & saucer, aqua & wht panels, Queen Anne shape 27.50
Cup & saucer, Archway of Roses, Queen Anne shape 40.00
Cup & saucer, Blue Rock, 14-flute 42.00
Cup & saucer, Bridal Rose, 6-flute 45.00
Cup & saucer, Celandine, lavender exterior, 12-flute 40.00
Cup & saucer, Daffodil, 14-flute 38.00
Cup & saucer, Dainty Blue, farmer-sz 55.00
Cup & saucer, Dainty Blue, 6-flute 48.00
Cup & saucer, Daisy, Queen Anne shape 40.00
Cup & saucer, Daisy, 6-flute 42.00
Cup & saucer, demitasse; Blue Rock, 6-flute 45.00

Cup & saucer, demitasse; Charm 25.00
Cup & saucer, demitasse; Dainty Blue, 6-flute 45.00
Cup & saucer, demitasse; Indian Peony 42.50
Cup & saucer, demitasse; Regency, 6-flute 40.00
Cup & saucer, gold & blk, 14-flute 42.00
Cup & saucer, Harebell, bl exterior, leaf shape 35.00
Cup & saucer, Harebell, 14-flute 40.00
Cup & saucer, Indian Peony, ped ft 44.00
Cup & saucer, Lily of the Valley, 6-flute 42.00
Cup & saucer, Maytime, gold ft 42.00
Cup & saucer, Meissenette, 6-flute 44.00
Cup & saucer, Morning-Glory, 6-flute 42.00
Cup & saucer, pk dots on Dainty White, 6-flute 47.50
Cup & saucer, Primrose, 14-flute 40.00
Cup & saucer, Shamrock, 6-flute 40.00

Windflower cup and saucer, $45.00.

Cup & saucer, yel dots on Dainty White, 6-flute 44.00
Egg cup, Bridal Rose, 6-flute, sm 42.00
Egg cup, Dainty Blue, 6-flute, lg 54.00
Egg cup, Harebell, leaf shape, sm 35.00
Egg cup, Mabel Lucie Attwell, mushroom shape 58.00
Egg cup, orange & blk Deco design, Vogue shape 27.50
Egg cup, pk w/gold pinstripe, 6-flute, sm 25.00
Egg cup, Regency, 6-flute, lg .45.00
Gravy boat, Blue Rock, 6-flute, w/underplate 60.00
Gravy boat, Sheraton, w/attached underplate 45.00
Jam jar, Bridal Rose, 6-flute, w/lid & underplate 58.00
Jam jar, Meissenette, w/lid & underplate 45.00
Jam jar, Stocks, 6-flute, w/lid 45.00
Lamp base, Indian Peony, 11" 65.00
Mug, Harmony, 5" 21.00
Mug, Primrose Chintz, 5" 30.00
Mug, Rosebud, 6-flute, 5" 35.00
Mustard jar, Georgian, w/lid .35.00
Mustard jar, Stocks, w/lid & underplate 45.00
Mustard jar, Stocks, 6-flute, w/lid & underplate 55.00
Pitcher, Dainty Pink, 6-flute, 7" 70.00
Pitcher, Mabel Lucie Attwell, 7" 70.00
Plate, Archway of Roses, Queen Anne shape, 8" 30.00
Plate, Begonia, 6-flute, 6" 10.00
Plate, Blue Daisy, 6-flute, 8" .30.00
Plate, Blue Rock, 6-flute, 10¾" 45.00
Plate, Blue Rock, 6-flute, 6" .12.00
Plate, Blue Rock, 6-flute, 8" .28.00
Plate, Blue Willow, 8" 18.00
Plate, Dainty Blue, 6-flute, 10¾" 50.00
Plate, Dainty Blue, 6-flute, 6" 15.00

Plate, English Lakes, 10¾" 50.00
Plate, English Lakes, 8" 28.00
Plate, Harebell, 6-flute, 8" 28.00
Plate, Heather, 8" 27.00
Plate, heraldic design, Chalmsley, 1836-1936, 6" 22.00
Plate, heraldic design, Prince of Wales, 1936, 8" 50.00
Plate, Indian Peony, gr & blk, 8" 30.00
Plate, Lily of the Valley, 10¾" 42.00
Plate, Lily of the Valley, 6-flute, 8" 27.50
Plate, Melody, notched, gr trim, 7" 18.00
Plate, Old Sevres, 10½" in ¾" sterling fr 150.00
Plate, Old Sevres, 8" 27.50
Plate, pk w/gold trim, 6-flute, 7" 25.00
Plate, Primrose Chintz, gold trim, 8" 28.50
Plate, Regency, 6-flute, 10¾" 45.00
Plate, Regency, 6-flute, 6" 12.00
Plate, Rose Pansy Forget-Me-Not, 8" 29.00
Plate, Rose Spray, 6-flute, 8" .29.00
Plate, Sheraton, 10½" 25.00
Plate, Sheraton, 7" 10.00
Plate, Violets, 6-flute, 8" 28.00
Plate, Wild Anemone, 6-flute, 8" 28.00
Platter, Bridal Rose, 6-flute, oval, 10" 65.00
Platter, Dainty Blue, 6-flute, oval, 8" 57.00
Platter, Georgian, oval, 10" 45.00
Platter, Regency, 6-flute, oval, 12" 75.00
Platter, Sheraton, rnd, 12" 45.00
Pudding mold, geometric shape, 7" 35.00
Pudding mold, star shape, 5" .28.50
Sauce boat, Dainty Blue, 6-flute, w/underplate 58.00
Snack set, Regency, 6-flute, cup w/indented 8" sq plate 52.00
Snack set, Violet, 6-flute, cup w/indented 8" sq plate 55.00
Snack set, Woodland, cup w/indented 7½" sq plate 52.00
Soup plate, Blue Rock, 6-flute, 8½" 38.50
Soup plate, Bridal Rose, 6-flute, 8½" 38.00
Soup plate, Sheraton, 7½" 15.00
Tea & toast, bl w/gold 8-pointed stars, 6-flute, 6x9" 55.00
Tea & toast, gr w/dk gr dots, 6-flute, 6x9" 52.50
Tea & toast, Rosebud, bl trim, 6-flute, 6x9" tray 52.00
Teapot, Archway of Roses, Queen Anne shape, 7" 75.00
Teapot, Begonia, 6-flute, 6" .100.00
Teapot, Blue Rock, 6-flute, 6" 150.00
Teapot, Dainty Blue, 6-flute, 5" 140.00
Teapot, Mabel Lucie Attwell, mushroom style 95.00
Teapot, Maytime, gold trim, 7" 100.00
Teapot, Rosebud, 6 scallops, 6" 140.00
Teapot, Sheraton, 8-cup 85.00
Teapot, yel dots on Dainty White, 6-flute, 4" 80.00
Toast rack, Dainty Blue, 3¼x7½" 55.00
Toast rack, Regency, 3¼x7½" 50.00
Toothpick holder, bl dots on Dainty White, 6-flute 24.00
Toothpick holder, Dainty Blue, 6-flute 28.00
Toothpick holder, DuBarry 21.00
Tray, pk w/gold trim, HP, 6-flute, 8x12" 75.00
Tray, Regency, 3-compartment, 6-flute, 13" 75.00
Tray, tea; Regency, 6-flute, 18" 185.00
Vase, birds & foliage, Deco style, 8" 48.00
Vase, orange/gr/blk geometric, 8" 55.00
Vase, Rosebud, 6-flute, 7" 57.00

Shenandoah

The Shenandoah Valley, extending from Virginia to Pennsylvania, is well known for the fine pottery made there from the early 1800s until the turn of the century. It is characterized by bright, clear glazes in a variety of colors used alone or in combination. Many small potteries were involved. Items marked 'Bell' indicate one of the large companies.

Flowerpot, redware, gr 'commas' on wht bsk, mk Bell, 8", EX ..350.00
Jar, brn-blk spots, appl hdl, 5⅜", NM 275.00
Jug, gr w/orange & brn spots, ovoid, strap hdl, 9", EX 800.00
Pitcher, redware, yel slip w/gr & brn splotches, 6½", EX 500.00

Silhouettes

Silhouette portraits were made by positioning the subject between a bright light and a sheet of white drawing paper. The resulting shadow was then traced and cut out, the paper mounted over a contrasting color and framed. The hollow-cut process was simplified by an invention called the Physiognotrace, a device that allowed tracing and cutting to be done in one operation. Experienced silhouette artists could do full-length figures, scenics, ships, or trains free hand. Some of the most famous of these artists were Charles Peale Polk, Charles Wilson Peale, William Bache, Doyle, Edouart, Chaimberlain, Brown, and William King. Though not often seen, some silhouettes were drawn or executed in wax. Examples listed here are hollow-cut unless noted.

Key:
bk — backing   p — profile
c/p — cut and pasted   wc — watercolor
fl —— full length

Boy, fl, ink wash/gilt detail, label/1847, 12x15" 205.00
Boy, p, blk cloth bk, blk molded fr, 3⅝x4¾", EX 70.00
Boy, standing w/cap in hand, gilt detail/ink wash, 10x13" 145.00
Boy w/whip, fl, in pencil landscape, English, 1820s, 7x6" 300.00
Child in long dress, primitive, cloth bk, pine fr, 5x7" 195.00
Cleric in pulpit, ink-wash ground, att Edouart, 11x14" 235.00

Free-cut of identified family by Edouart, in a landscape, signed and dated, ca 1841, 14x18", $2,800.00.

Girl, p, hair in pen/ink, brass fr, info on bk, 5x4½" 135.00
JG Sutton w/whip & hat, wc bg, Edouart, c/p, 9x7" 2,500.00
Lady, full dress, pencil detail w/gilt on pnt, 12x14" 145.00
Lady, p, HP bonnet/lace collar, fr, 1811, 6x4" 145.00
Lady, p, ink w/gilt detail, mk Hubbard, gilt fr, 5x6" 195.00
Lady, stylish dress/bonnet, gilt detail, reeded fr, 5x4" 105.00
Lady, stylish dress/bonnet, ink gilt detail, rvpt, fr, 7x8" 200.00
Lady in bonnet, bust length, identified in ink, KY, 4x4" 330.00
Lady in bonnet, p, pencil detail, name/1829, paper bk, 6x5" ...225.00
Man, fl, on litho ground, att Edouart, 14x11" 250.00

Man, p, blk-pnt glass bk, trn fr, 4⅝" dia 100.00
Man, p, ink detail, inked paper bk, emb brass fr, 4½x5" 110.00
Man, p, ink w/gilt detail, lacquer/gilt fr, 5x6" 195.00
Man in chair, ink ground, name/1838, att Edouart, 10x14" 200.00
Man w/eyeglass, p, blk paper on litho, Edouart/1830, 14x11" ..550.00
Woman, p, blk cloth bk/ink detail, shadow box fr, 6x7½" 150.00

Silver

Coin Silver

The mark 'Coin Silver' was used after the 1830s to indicate items made with 900 parts of silver to every 1000 parts of content.

A Miller, tongs, bright cut both sides, shell ends, 6" 130.00
A Sanborn, dessert spoon, plain, 7", pr 50.00
AG Storm, Albany NY; sauce ladle, flower basket eng hdl 75.00
Anthony Rasch, tea service, inscribed names, 1807, 3-pc 4,700.00
BC Frobisher, tongs, plain, spoon ends, 6" 65.00
Braverman & Levy, soup ladle, shell bowl, eng decor, 13½" ...135.00

Coin silver pitcher, repousse florals, marked Canfield Bros. & Co., G&W maker, Baltimore, ca 1850, $950.00.

DT, att David Tyleer, Boston; tablespoon, bright cut, 8½" 85.00
E Gifford, Fall River; salt spoon, shovel form, pr 35.00
G Boyce, NY; cup, ftd, chased band w/farm/mill/etc, 3.3-oz 300.00
G Sharp Jr, Danville KY; julep, minor dents, 5.17-oz, 4" 525.00
Geo B Hoyt, NY; tablespoon, eng name on hdl, 1840, set of 7 .160.00
Hyde & Goodrich, New Orleans; butter tub, 1850s 600.00
Hyde & Goodrich, New Orleans; ewer, swags/medallion, 16" ..5,750.00
Hyde & Goodrich, New Orleans; julep, eng name, 4-oz, 3⅜" .700.00
Hyde & Goodrich, New Orleans; ladle, decorative, 1850 .....500.00
J Boutier, NY, tablespoon, coffin-end hdl eng,'JM,' 9", pr 70.00
Knoles & Ladd, preserve spoon, Queen pattern, bright cut 58.00
Kuchler & Himmel for Hyde & Goodrich, cup, eng floral 850.00
Muhme & Co, teaspoon, name eng on hdl, 6", set of 6 ....60.00
N Harding & Co, sugar shell, scalloped bowl, fiddle-top hdl 28.00
NL Hazen, julep cup 275.00
P Dickenson, dessert spoon, 7" 22.00
PR&Co (Pelletreau Bennett/Cooke), teaspoon, floral hdl, 6" ...65.00
Stebbins & Howe, tongs, Basket of Flowers, shell ends, 6" 135.00
TC Garrett & Co, salt spoon, shovel bowl, eng 'M,' 4", pr 100.00
Wood & Hughes, NY; sugar basket, urn form/dome base, 6½" .135.00
Wood & Hughes, NY; vegetable server/tongs 175.00

Flatware

Silver flatware is being collected today either to replace missing pieces of heirloom sets or, in lieu of buying new patterns, by those who admire and appreciate the style and quality of the older ware. Prices vary from dealer to dealer; some pieces are harder to find and are therefore more expensive. Items such as olive spoons, cream ladles, lemon forks, etc., once thought a necessary part of a silver service, may today be slow to sell; as a result, dealers may price them low and make up the difference on items that sell more readily. Many factors enter into evaluation. Popular patterns may be high due to demand though easily found, while scarce patterns may be passed over by collectors who find them difficult to reassemble. See also Tiffany, Silver.

Key:
FH — flat handle   HH — hollow handle

Antique Hammered, berry spoon, Shreve 85.00
Antique Hammered, cream ladle, Shreve 50.00
Antique Hammered, gravy ladle, Shreve 70.00
Antique Hammered, ice cream fork, Shreve 25.00
Antique Hammered, tablespoon, Shreve 60.00
Bridal Rose, bouillon spoon, Alvin 35.00
Bridal Rose, butter spreader, Alvin 35.00
Bridal Rose, cocktail fork, Alvin 35.00
Bridal Rose, cold meat fork, Alvin 95.00
Bridal Rose, dessert spoon, Alvin 40.00
Bridal Rose, dinner fork, Alvin 55.00
Bridal Rose, gravy ladle, Alvin 125.00
Bridal Rose, jelly spoon, Alvin 85.00
Bridal Rose, luncheon knife, Alvin 50.00
Bridal Rose, olive spoon, Alvin 95.00
Bridal Rose, pickle fork, Alvin 95.00
Bridal Rose, pickle fork, long hdl, Alvin 110.00
Bridal Rose, pie server, Alvin, 1-pc 275.00
Bridal Rose, preserve spoon, Alvin 135.00
Bridal Rose, salad fork, Alvin 75.00
Bridal Rose, sugar spoon, Alvin 45.00
Bridal Rose, sugar tongs, Alvin, lg 95.00
Bridal Rose, teaspoon, Alvin 50.00
Bridal Rose, tomato server, Alvin 275.00
Candlelight, butter spreader, flat hdl, Towle 16.00
Candlelight, cocktail fork, Towle 15.00
Candlelight, cream soup, Towle 23.00
Candlelight, tablespoon, Towle 39.00
Chrysanthemum, berry spoon, kidney shape, Tiffany 550.00
Chrysanthemum, cocktail fork, Tiffany 49.00
Chrysanthemum, dinner set, Tiffany, 5-pc 460.00
Chrysanthemum, luncheon fork, Tiffany 75.00
Edgewood, butter knife, Internat'l 45.00
Edgewood, dinner fork, Internat'l 45.00
Edgewood, dinner knife, blunt plated, Internat'l 40.00
Edgewood, dinner knife, French SS, Internat'l 35.00
Edgewood, luncheon fork, Internat'l 37.50
Edgewood, rnd soup spoon, Internat'l 40.00
Edgewood, sugar spoon, Internat'l 37.50
Edgewood, tablespoon, Internat'l 50.00
Edgewood, teaspoon, Internat'l 30.00
Frontenac, butter spreader, Internat'l 35.00
Frontenac, fish fork, Internat'l 95.00
Frontenac, pie server, Internat'l, 1-pc 325.00
Frontenac, salad set, Internat'l 450.00
Frontenac, sugar spoon, Internat'l 35.00
Frontenac, sugar tongs, Internat'l 75.00
Frontenac, sugar tongs, Internat'l, lg 95.00
Grande Baroque, berry fork, Wallace 23.00
Grande Baroque, butter spreader, HH, Wallace 33.00
Grande Baroque, carving set, Wallace, 2-pc 130.00
Grande Baroque, cocktail fork, Wallace 40.00

Grande Baroque, cream soup, Wallace 45.00
Grande Baroque, demitasse spoon, Wallace 30.00
Grande Baroque, ice cream fork, Wallace 38.00
Grande Baroque, iced teaspoon, Wallace 45.00
Grande Baroque, pie server, HH, Wallace 45.00
Grande Baroque, salad set, Wallace, 2-pc 395.00
Grande Baroque, salt spoon, Wallace 9.00
Grande Baroque, server, flat, Wallace 46.00
Grande Baroque, serving spoon, HH, Wallace 69.00
Grande Baroque, steak knife, HH, Wallace 50.00
Grande Baroque, strawberry fork, Wallace 25.00
Irian, berry spoon, Wallace 195.00
Irian, butter knife, Wallace 48.00
Irian, cocktail fork, Wallace 35.00
Irian, soup ladle, Wallace 495.00
Irian, sugar tongs, Wallace 80.00
Irian, teaspoon, Wallace 35.00
Joan of Arc, butter spreader, flat hdl, Internat'l 18.00
Joan of Arc, cocktail fork, Internat'l 18.00
Joan of Arc, cream soup, Internat'l 25.00
Joan of Arc, gravy ladle, Internat'l 69.00
Joan of Arc, pie server, hollow hdl, Internat'l 39.00
Joan of Arc, tablespoon, Internat'l 49.00
King Richard, cream soup, Towle 37.00
King Richard, gravy ladle, Towle 79.00
King Richard, place setting, Towle, 4-pc 130.00
King Richard, sugar tongs, Towle 50.00
King Richard, tomato server, Towle 120.00

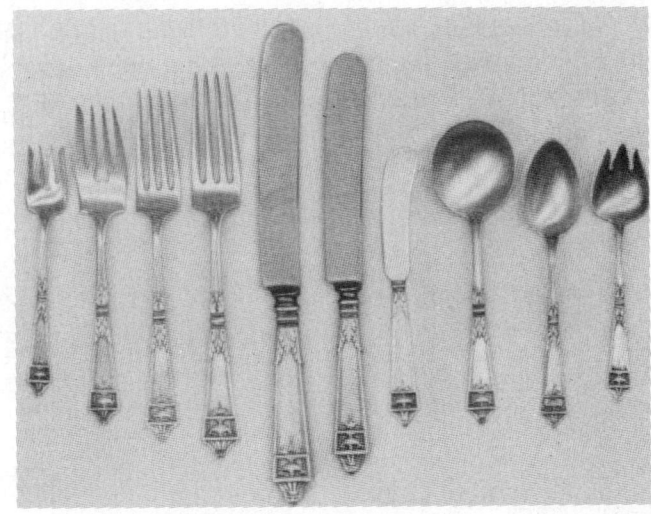

Landsdowne by Gorham, lot of 101 pieces, total weight of silver: 80.6-oz., $1,700.00.

Lily, berry spoon, Whiting 260.00
Lily, bouillon spoon, Whiting 55.00
Lily, butter pick, Whiting 115.00
Lily, cocktail fork, Whiting 45.00
Lily, cream ladle, Whiting 97.50
Lily, demitasse spoon, gold-washed bowl, Whiting 20.00
Lily, lettuce fork, Whiting 150.00
Lily, luncheon fork, Whiting 65.00
Lily, olive fork, Whiting 60.00
Lily, preserve spoon, Whiting 175.00
Lily, sugar tongs, Whiting 95.00
Louis XV, cucumber server, Whiting 70.00
Louis XV, flat pie server, Whiting 90.00
Louis XV, ice cream fork, Whiting 28.00
Louis XV, pea spoon, Whiting 165.00

Louis XV, salad fork, long, Whiting 46.00
Louis XV, sugar sifter, Whiting 79.00
Lucerne, claret ladle, Wallace 275.00
Lucerne, jelly knife, Wallace 98.00
Lucerne, pickle fork, Wallace 27.50
Lucerne, salad fork, Wallace 35.00
Lucerne, soup ladle, Wallace 275.00
Madame Jumel, berry spoon 175.00
Madame Jumel, flat butter spreader 30.00
Mary Chilton, asparagus server, Towle 250.00
Mary Chilton, bonbon, Towle 30.00
Mary Chilton, cocktail fork, Towle 15.00
Mary Chilton, cream ladle, Towle 30.00
Mary Chilton, demitasse spoon, Towle 12.00
Mary Chilton, jelly server, Towle 30.00
Mary Chilton, lemon fork, Towle 28.00
Mary Chilton, sugar spoon, Towle 28.00
Mary Chilton, sugar tongs, Towle 32.50
Mary Chilton, toast fork, Towle 55.00
Mary Chilton, tomato server, Towle 85.00
Normandie, jelly server, Wallace 27.00
Normandie, tablespoon, Wallace 39.00
Old English, butter knife, Towle 20.00
Old English, butter spreader, Towle 15.00
Old English, cold meat fork, Towle 35.00
Old English, cream ladle, Towle 25.00
Old English, dessert spoon, Towle 25.00
Old English, dinner fork, Towle 25.00
Old English, dinner knife, Towle 20.00
Old English, gravy ladle, Towle 35.00
Old English, pie server, Towle 30.00
Old English, sugar spoon, Towle 20.00
Old English, 5 o'clock spoon, Towle 10.00
Old Master, demitasse spoon 28.00
Old Master, iced teaspoon 33.00
Old Master, pie server, HH 47.00
Old Master, place setting, 4-pc 115.00
Old Master, tomato server 70.00
Orange Blossom, bonbon, Alvin 115.00
Orange Blossom, bouillon, Alvin 42.50
Orange Blossom, butter spreader, Alvin, lg 44.00
Orange Blossom, butter spreader, Alvin, sm 42.00
Orange Blossom, carving set, Alvin, sm 97.50
Orange Blossom, cream ladle, Alvin 97.50
Orange Blossom, dessert spoon, Alvin 50.00
Orange Blossom, dinner knife, Alvin 65.00
Orange Blossom, lettuce fork, Alvin 175.00
Orange Blossom, tablespoon, Alvin 55.00
Orange Blossom, tea strainer, Alvin 175.00
Pansy, butter spreader, Internat'l 30.00
Pansy, cocktail fork, Internat'l 20.00
Pansy, dessert spoon, Internat'l 40.00
Pansy, dinner knife, Internat'l 45.00
Pansy, salad fork, Internat'l 40.00
Pansy, teaspoon, Internat'l 30.00
Paul Revere, berry fork, Towle 25.00
Paul Revere, berry spoon, Towle, sm 75.00
Paul Revere, bouillon spoon, Towle 20.00
Paul Revere, butter spreader, FH, Towle 20.00
Paul Revere, butter spreader, Towle, lg 30.00
Paul Revere, cocktail fork, Towle 18.00
Paul Revere, demitasse spoon, Towle 15.00
Paul Revere, dessert spoon, Towle 30.00
Paul Revere, grapefruit, Towle 35.00

Paul Revere, lemonade spoon, Towle 25.00
Paul Revere, luncheon fork 30.00
Paul Revere, pie server, 1-pc, Towle 125.00
Paul Revere, tablespoon, Towle 30.00
Paul Revere, teaspoon, Towle 12.50
Polly Lawton, butter spreader, FH, Manchester 12.50
Polly Lawton, cocktail fork, Manchester 12.50
Polly Lawton, cream soup spoon, Manchester 20.00
Polly Lawton, demitasse spoon, Manchester 75.00
Polly Lawton, dessert spoon, Manchester 20.00
Polly Lawton, dinner fork, Manchester 25.00
Polly Lawton, dinner knife, Manchester 15.00
Polly Lawton, iced teaspoon, Manchester 15.00
Polly Lawton, salad fork, Manchester 20.00
Polly Lawton, teaspoon, Manchester 12.50
Prelude, cocktail fork, Internat'l 28.00
Prelude, cream soup, Internat'l 29.00
Prelude, flat butter spreader, Internat'l 21.00
Prelude, iced teaspoon, Internat'l 29.00
Prelude, steak knife, HH, Internat'l 45.00
Prelude, teaspoon, HH, Internat'l 55.00
Rose Point, goblet, Wallace 200.00
Rose Point, gravy ladle, Wallace 70.00
Rose Point, pierced tablespoon, Wallace 65.00
Royal Danish, carving set, 2-pc 129.00
Royal Danish, cocktail fork 28.50
Royal Danish, demitasse spoon 28.00
Royal Danish, lemon fork 28.00
Royal Danish, pickle fork 30.00
Royal Danish, steak knife 49.00
Vine, berry spoon, Tiffany 400.00
Vine, fish serving set, Tiffany 650.00
Vine, serving spoon, Tiffany 195.00
Vine, sugar sifter, Tiffany 195.00
Wave Edge, sugar sifter, Tiffany 195.00
Wave Edge, sugar spoon, Tiffany 85.00
Wave Edge, waffle server, Tiffany 395.00

Hollow Ware

Until the middle of the 19th century, the silverware produced in America was custom made on order of the buyer directly from the silversmith. With the rise of industrialization, factories sprung up that manufactured silverware for retailers who often added their trademark to the ware. Silver ore was mined in abundance, and demand spurred production. Changes in style occurred at the whim of fashion. Repousse decoration (relief work) became popular about 1885, reflecting the ostentatious taste of the Victorian era. Later in the century, Greek, Etruscan, and several classic styles found favor. Today the Art Deco styles of this century are very popular with collectors. In the listings that follow, manufacturer's name or trademark is noted first; in lieu of that information, listings are by item. Weight is given in troy ounces. See also Tiffany, Silver.

A Michelsen, carafe, collar continues to strap hdl, 11" 385.00
Abraham Petersen, coffeepot, Geo III, emb/eng florals, 10" 600.00
AG Tucker, julep cup, inscription/1853, 4.75-oz, 3½" 400.00
American, center bowl, lobed rim, 11½", 25-oz 300.00
American, coffeepot, chased w/neoclassic motifs, 14", 26-oz .1,000.00
American, dish, Victorian, floral repousse border, 12" L 200.00
Andrei Kovalski, champagne, allover eng foliage, gilt, 7½" .325.00
Arthur Dunhill, cigarette case, engine trn, gold thumb pc 160.00
Arthur Stone, bowl, fine-lobed, triple-rib band, 8" dia 225.00
Arthur Stone, bowl, rnded sq lid w/ivory finial, 4x7" dia 1,400.00
Atkin Bros, vase, eng scroll flutes/foliage, 11" 320.00

American silver coffee-pot, repousse grapes, monogrammed, 13", $600.00.

Benjamin Burt, mug, acanthus-cap scroll hdl, monogram, 6" .3,000.00
Benjamin Smith, cruet fr, beaded, crested, 5½" 375.00
Benjamin Smith, tea urn, lobed, winged paw ft, 16" 4,400.00
Canadian, center bowl, lobed, ftd, 9", 29-oz 325.00
Chas Boyton, beaker, ½-fluted body, laurel swags, 4", pr 220.00
Chas Boyton & Son, comport, gilded, pierced, 8½" dia 440.00
Chas Boyton & Son, tray, scroll hdls, crest, 23" 1,500.00
Chas Fox, teapot, Geo IV, floral finial/acanthus hdl, 6" 600.00
Chas Stuart Harris, salver, Geo manner, plain, sq, 8" 340.00
Coffee urn, moose-head hdls, stag finial, 20", EX 350.00
Cohr, compote, oblong bowl/openwork std, 5½" 200.00
Continental, champagne cooler, acanthus hdls, 37.5-oz 650.00
Crichton, pitcher, w/crest, multi-scroll hdl, 8½" 400.00
Crichton, salver, eng crest/monogram, shaped sq, 6½" 135.00
Crichton, salver, eng crest/monogram, 4-ftd, 10½" 300.00
Crichton, tray, chased foliage, cartouch form, 1922, 26" 2,400.00
Crouch-Hannam, chamberstick, plain, extinguisher, 4", pr ..2,100.00
CS Harris & Son, coffeepot, Geo manner, plain, 7", 10-oz 230.00
Daniel Pontifex, goblet, Geo III, vine border, fluted, 8½" ..1,000.00
Dominick & Haff, cake plate, basket of flowers emb rim, 14" ..440.00
Dominick & Haff, compote, pierced/eng florals, 8" 385.00
Dominick & Haff, plate, monogram, 6½", set of 12 ....200.00
Duhme Co, punch bowl, eng/pierced floral rim/ft, 14" 2,750.00
Durgin, pitcher, octagonal helmet form w/harp hdl, 8" 250.00
Dutch, fan case w/chatelaine clip, reticulated/emb, 7" L 145.00
Dutch, pitcher, eng/emb scrolls & flowers, figural hdl, 5" 135.00
E Viner, salver, raised/shaped rim, 3 scroll ft, 12" 600.00
E&Co Ltd, coffeepot, lighthouse form, urn finial, 1900, 9½" ...350.00
ED, London; sauce boat, 3 hoof ft, leaf-capped hdl, 7" L 220.00
Edward Kinsey, pitcher, cast vintage hdl/eng rose, 8" 800.00
Edward Kinsey, pitcher, classic style, S-hdl, 42.9-oz, 14" 5,100.00
Elkington & Co, sugar caster, plain, stepped ft, 6¾" 250.00
Emes & Barnard, tea set, gadrooned bands, stag masks, 3-pc .2,250.00
English, basket, Geo III style, reticulated, 11", 14-oz 550.00
English, candlestick, Corinthian columns, 7½", pr 350.00
Exeter, Geo I, cann, scroll hdl, 1723, 4" 400.00
Fordham-Faulkner, sweetmeat basket, pierced/eng, 8" 440.00
Frank M Whiting, fruit bowl, hexagonal, gilt, 12" 300.00
Frank M Whiting, vegetable dish w/lid, scroll/shell border 400.00
Frank Smith, tray, scalloped, flower garlands, 12" dia 150.00
Frederick Kandler, att; platter, Geo III, emb fruit, 13" 700.00
Gebelein, bowl, ribbed band on concave rim, 3¾x4¾" 150.00

Gebelein, shakers, urn form, tapered neck, hammered, 5", pr ..225.00
Gebelein, sugar bowl, ribbed band/scroll hdls/bud finial, 6" 250.00
Geo Angell, standish, 3 candle-socket lids on wells, 12" 1,200.00
Geo Unite, tobacco box, plain rnd oval form, 3½" 140.00
Georg Jensen, bonbon, hammered, palmette ftd base, 5" 300.00
Georg Jensen, box & stand, amber bud terminal, bud ft, 5x7". 3,000.00
Georg Jensen, coffee set, hammered, wood hdls/finials, 3-pc .1,200.00
Georg Jensen, condiment set, Blossom, 3-pc on tray, 12-oz ..2,400.00
Georg Jensen, pitcher, hammered, flared rim extends to hdl .1,900.00
Georg Jensen, pitcher w/lid, ft w/openwork band, 8" 1,200.00
Georg Jensen, sauce boat, Blossom, ivory hdl, 13-oz 2,200.00
Georg Jensen, tea service, hammered, ebony hdl, 30-oz 4,600.00
Georg Jensen, tea service, ivory mtd, 8" pot+sug/cr, 29-oz ...1,000.00
Georg Jensen, tray, hammered, chased lappet border, 23" ...3,900.00
Georg Jensen, tray, hammered, ropework rim, hdls, 22½" ...3,500.00
German, basket, Rococo reticulation/floral swags, ftd, 8" 475.00
German, berry set, scroll relief, ca 1900, mk 800, 16-pc 175.00
German, cake basket, chased/emb florals & pheasant, 10½" 465.00
German, cigarette case, appl nude/fruiting vines, 3" L 100.00
German, soap box, trio in floral fr, domed, 1700s, 2x3½x3" ...135.00
German, vinaigrette, scrolled openwork, gilt lined, 1600s 325.00
Goldsmiths-Silversmiths, comport, pierced/eng florals, 4" 230.00
Goldsmiths-Silversmiths, soup tureen/ladle/tray, 68.8-oz 1,800.00
Goodnow & Jenks, candlesticks, 4-lobed baluster, 11", pr 550.00
Gorham, asparagus tray & fork, King Geo, w/strainer, 13" 600.00
Gorham, bowl, open scrollwork, heart shape, 9" L 275.00
Gorham, butter server, pierced sterling liner, dome top 275.00
Gorham, center bowl, Martele, repousse mums, 17" L 6,000.00
Gorham, center bowl, Martele, shaped rim, anemones, 11" ..2,750.00
Gorham, center bowl, shaped rim w/floral repousse, 8½" 250.00
Gorham, chocolate pot, Martele, violets/buds, long spout ...3,500.00
Gorham, fruit bowl, openwork flared sides, disk base, 10" 330.00
Gorham, inkwell, Martele, poppies/leaves, 11½" L 3,100.00
Gorham, loving cup, Martele, repousse/eng foliage, 8" 3,000.00
Gorham, nut dish, pierced sides, ball ft, set of 6 ....90.00
Gorham, platter, Martele, repousse/eng pine cones, 15" 3,000.00
Gorham, salver, cartouch/scroll border, monogram, 1897, 13" .465.00
Gorham, sauce tureen, Chantilly, 8" L 350.00
Gorham, vase, chased Rococo motif, weighted, 30" 1,800.00
Gosen, vase, floral chasing w/appl tassels, ftd, 6¾" 150.00
Harrison Bros-Howson, grape shears, eng foliage/crest, 3-oz ...320.00
Hawksworth-Eyre & Co, candlestick, emb leaves, 11", pr ...1,250.00
Henricus Boelen, bowl, emb/chased chevron panels, hdls, 4" .1,300.00
Hessenberg, tray, eng armorials, molded rim, 22" 1,300.00
Hester Bateman, cream jug, floral repousse, 3-ftd, 5½" 250.00
Howard & Co, tray, reticulated gallery, 26" L 1,700.00
Humbert, coffee urn, animal spout/acanthus-cap legs, 16" ...3,800.00
International, center bowl, Silver Iris, 11½" 150.00
International Wedgwood, bowl, open scroll hdls, 11½" 360.00
J&J Angell, tea/coffee, Wm IV, floral eng, 4-pc, 76-oz 2,700.00
James Dixon & Sons, toast rack, Victorian, 7-bar, 6" 340.00
James Woolley, pitcher, hammered, eng monogram, 6½" 450.00
Japanese, center bowl, repousse peonies, 6½", 11-oz 450.00
Jarvie, bowl, hammered, ped base, initialed, 2¾x6½" 750.00
Jay McKay, pitcher, armorial, floral repousse, 1822, 9½" ...2,100.00
JB Jones, pitcher, leafy garland on neck, crest, 11" 600.00
JB Jones, sauce boat, gadrooned, shell knees, dtd, 8" 1,300.00
JE Terry & Co, coffeepot, fluted lower body, wood hdl, 8" 950.00
JE Terry & Co, coffeepot, fluted lower body, wood hdl, 9" ...1,200.00
Jean Puiforcat, tea/coffee, Deco, paneled, wood hdls, 4-pc ...3,800.00
JGP, Mexico; fruit bowl, fluted, handmade, 27-oz, 6x9" 175.00
John & Peter Targee, porringer, plain, pierced hdl, 7½" L ...1,400.00
John B Akin, pitcher, classic form, ped ft, 1850, 13" 1,300.00
John B Akin, pitcher, classic style, S-hdl, 14-oz, 10" 1,300.00

Joseph Ward, chocolate pot, lighthouse form, later eng, 10" ...850.00
Kalo, candy dish, ftd, hand wrought, #15, 3x4" 170.00
Kalo, centerpc bowl, ped ft, hand wrought, 4x12" 1,000.00
Kalo, pitcher, hand wrought, #9309, 5½" 1,000.00
Kalo, tray, crimped edge, hand wrought, orig bag, 12" dia 550.00
Kalo, tumbler, appl monogram, 3½" 75.00
Lebolt, cake plate, 4 spaced ribs, appl initials, 10½" 175.00
Levi-Salaman, basket, mask-eng rim, pierced florals, 8" L 325.00
LL, Dutch; cruet fr, emb vine borders, 4 ball ft, 3-bottle 240.00
London, Geo I style, trn std on rnd base, weighted, 7", pr ...400.00
M Fred Hirsch Co, pitcher, chased/monogram, 9" 330.00
M&K, Vienna; hot water kettle on stand, plain, 1862, 67-oz .1,200.00
Martin-Hall & Co, basket, pierced panels, 12" L, 23-oz 2,000.00
Martin-Hall & Co, tea set, alternate emb/plain panels, 3-pc .1,200.00
McDannold-Premium, julep cup, set of 6, ea 4.95-oz, 3⅝" ...2,850.00
Michelsen, compote, circles/scrolls eng on base, 1851, 12" 700.00
Mulford-Wendell, kettle+lampstand, grayhound finial, 13" 700.00
Mullholland, pitcher, hammered, bulbous mid-section, 9" 600.00
Novic, sugar & creamer, hammered, angle hdls, 2¼x5½" 425.00
P California, Taxco; tray, hammered, hdls, 22" L 935.00
Peruvian, bowl, hammered, scalloped rim, 14" dia 250.00
Peter & Wm Bateman, cann, scroll hdl, 1810, 5½", 11-oz 600.00
Peter & Wm Bateman, entree w/lid, dragon/hand eng, 11" L .1,200.00
Pierre Gillois, tea caddy, bombe form, shell aprons, 6" 1,200.00
R&H Farnam, teapot, Fed, eng shoulder band, rpr, 12" 500.00
R&W Sorley, bowl, appl vines issue from eng hdls, 6" 500.00
R&W Wilson, muffineer, lower body eng w/leaf tips, 8" 100.00
Redlich, bowl, foliate shape, reticulated border, 12" 400.00
Reed & Barton, center bowl, Francis I, 12" 600.00
Reed & Barton, roll tray, Francis I, 11¾" L 350.00
Reed & Barton, vase, eng/enamel stylized foliage, 11" 1,250.00
Reilly & Storer, travelling chalice, sun reserve, gilt, 3" 175.00
Richard Dimes, pitcher, Revere style, 6½" 250.00
Richard Sibley, salver, Geo III, eng leafy scrolls, ftd, 9" 650.00
Robert Garrard, salver, Geo IV, scroll border, 4-ftd, 9" 365.00
Robert Gray & Son, salver, Wm IV, eng repousse rim, 14" ..2,300.00

Robert Hennell George IV fruit basket, ca 1820, 15" wide, $4,950.00.

Robert Pilkington, salver, crest, diaper band, hoof ft, 6" 1,050.00
Russian, kovsh, boat form w/Nouveau geometric florals, 11" ...900.00
S Kirk & Son, bowl, repousse, shell/scroll border, 12" 300.00
S Kirk & Son, mayonnaise bowl+ladle, repousse, 5" 135.00
S&C, London; coffeepot, wood hdl/finial, 1955, 9", 21-oz 250.00
Samuel Wood, att; tankard, Geo III, plain, scroll hdl, 7½" ...3,000.00

Schofield, coaster, Baltimore Rose, set of 12 ....775.00
Schofield, goblet, Baltimore Rose, 6½", set of 12 ....2,700.00
Shreve & Co, bowl, appl fleur-de-lis/rivets, scalloped, 9" 175.00
Shreve & Co, bread tray, strapwork edge, hammered, 14" L ...450.00
Shreve & Co, cake plate, Bontonee Xs/rivets, #1139, 14½" ...650.00
Shreve & Co, cake plate, strapwork edge, dome base, 10" 300.00
Shreve & Co, compote base, San Francisco, monogram, 15" ...825.00
Shreve & Co, fruit bowl, row of appl silver balls, 5x9" 1,200.00
Shreve & Co, pitcher, bulbous, ped ft, 10x9" 1,360.00
Shreve & Co, place card holder, San Francisco, 16 for 660.00
Shreve & Co, plate, shaped strapwork border, 6" 85.00
Shreve & Co, teapot, undulating vine hdl/ft, 9½" 385.00
Shreve & Co, tray, peened surface, w/inscription/1915, 17" ...375.00
Shreve & Co, trophy, ftd basket, chased/stop-fluted, 43-oz 800.00
Spanish, sauce boat on undertray, dbl-lipped oval, 10" L 275.00
Spaulding Co, dish, grape leaf w/tendril hdl, 11", +shears 425.00
ST Crosby, creamer, baluster w/leaf-cap scroll hdl, 5¾" 150.00
Stalkes & Mitchison, sauce boat, scalloped edge, 7" L 375.00
TB, London; muffineer, spiral-fluted baluster, dented, 9" 165.00
Tetard Freres, soup tureen, Deco, faceted shoulders, 11" ...9,000.00
Thomas Millner, cann, bulbous, acanthus hdl, crest, 5" 950.00
Thos Powell, centerpc basket, reticulated, open base, 7½" ...2,500.00
Towle, Louis XIV, 11", set of 12 ....3,100.00
Vanderslice & Co, butter dish, dome lid w/cow finial, 5" 400.00
Wallace, comport, lobed rim, 12" dia 300.00
WH, London; coffeepot, eng foliate bands, 4 shell ft, 9½" 250.00
WH & Sons Ltd, cake basket, ribs, leaves/birds, 1919, 10" 300.00
Whiting, vase, appl trailing vines, scroll hdls, 17" 4,800.00
Wm Bond, Dublin; sweetmeat basket, fluted lower body, 7½". 1,800.00
Wm Burwash-R Sibley, coffee biggin+burner, Geo III, 10" ..1,200.00
Wm Kidney, tankard, Geo II, dbl scroll hdl, 1742, 4¾" 700.00
Wm Kingdon, cup, ftd, floral C-hdl, ribbed bowl, 1840, 5-oz ..175.00
Wm Thomson, waste bowl, lobed, c/b ft w/leaves & masks, 8" .330.00
Wood & Hughes, sauce boat & ladle on tray, acanthus hdls .1,100.00

Wordley & Mayer of Liverpool, William IV salver, 12", $1,200.00.

Silver Lustre Ware

Much of the ware known as silver luster was produced in the early 1800s in Staffordshire, England. This type of earthenware was entirely covered with the metallic silver glaze. It was most popular prior to 1840, when the technique of electroplating was developed, and silverplated wares came into vogue. Later in the century, artisans used silver lustre to develop designs on vases and other decorative ware.

Creamer, Loop Rib base, gadroon top border, 4x5" 60.00
Shaker, ribbed, ftd, 4" 45.00
Teapot, ribbed, 7½x6" 165.00

Vase, leopards and trees on green ground, attributed to De Morgan, ca 1885, 8½", $900.00.

Silver Overlay

The silver overlay glass made during the 1800s was decorated with a cut-out pattern of sterling silver applied to the surface of the ware.

Banana boat, clear, floral & scroll overlay, ftd, 12½" L 75.00
Bottle, clear, thistles overlay, sterling top, Hawkes, 12" 235.00
Bottle, scent; floral overlay, mk silver stopper, 5" 145.00
Bowl, console; gr, Nouveau overlay, rolled rim, 2½x12½" 75.00
Console set, blk glass, lg ftd bowl+2 candlesticks 225.00
Creamer & sugar bowl, clear, simple overlay, Sandland Ware ...75.00
Loving cup, cranberry, Nouveau overlay, 3-hdld, lg 495.00
Vase, gr, allover floral overlay, #207, 4" 175.00
Vase, gr, Diamond Optic, wide floral band overlay, 9" 135.00

Silverplate

Silverplated hollowware is fast becoming the focus of attention for many of today's collectors. See also Pairpoint, Silverplate; Railroadiana, Silverplate.
    Key:
    gw — gold wash   SH&M — Simpson, Hall, & Miller

Hollow Ware

Biscuit box, folding shell form in twig framework, 8½" 200.00
Book cover, pierced/repousse, brackets of angels, 1896, 10" 240.00
Candelabra, 5-arm, leafy sockets, Elkington & Co, 21", pr ...2,800.00
Candlestick, Corinthian column, sq dome base, 1880s, 8", pr ..125.00
Coffee/tea service, Aesthetic Movement, Meriden B, 6-pc 325.00
Entree dish, emb leaf/flower/berry border, dome lid, 12" 150.00
Epergne, 3 rtcl baskets, rtcl rim, mk Knickerbocker, 16" 50.00
Hot water urn on burner, Geo style, urn finial, 21" 150.00
Meat cover, armorial, gadrooned border, leaf hdl, 14" 250.00
Meat cover, emb leaves, monogram, C-scroll hdl, English, 20" .300.00
Pitcher, cvd ebony hdls, mk Cailar Bayard, water sz 120.00
Platter, emb leaf/flower/berry border, English, 19" 300.00
Platter w/dome lid, plain, sphinx hdl, Wm Wilson & Son, 18" ..55.00

Rose bowl, gadroon rim, ped ft, Ellis Barker, 6½x10" 80.00
Rose bowl, wavy rim, ped ft, IFS LTD, 6½x10½" 90.00
Tea urn, neoclassic, lion mask/rings hdls, mk/1780s, 20" 400.00
Tea urn, putti/centaur pick grapes emb, mk, 1800s, 15½" 600.00
Tray, C-scroll/leaf emb border, chased, scroll ft, 25" 200.00
Tray, scrolling foliage borders, hdls, Victorian, 34" L 165.00
Umbrella stand, floral branches, trumpet form, Wilkinson Co .220.00
Warming stand, revolves, pierced tray/pan, scroll legs, 12" 350.00
Wine cooler, leaf-cap rim, dbl-eagle crest, hdls, 9½" 700.00

Tea service, heavy silver on copper, 6-piece, $350.00.

Sheffield

Biscuit box, fruit/flowers eng, attached tray, c/b ft, 7" 100.00
Bisquit barrel, c/b ft, Jas Dixon & Sons, ca 1835 ....180.00
Bowl, sweetmeat; Edwardian, boat form, pierced sides, 8" 85.00
Candlestick, Adams style, telescoping, Boulton, 8"-10", pr 550.00
Candlestick, faceted baluster, +3-light attachment, 15", pr ...145.00
Cann, tapered, molded rim, strap hdl, 1790, 6" 225.00
Chamberstick, snuffer w/acanthus finial, S-hdl, Boulton, 4½" ..350.00
Coaster, fluted sides, gadroon/shell rim, Boulton, 7" 75.00
Coaster, scroll/floral rim, wood base w/silver bosses, 7" 170.00
Coasters, gadrooned edge, wood base, mk Boulton, 6¾", pr 550.00
Coffee jug, gadrooned border, ring foot, mk Boulton, 8" 500.00
Cream boat, gadrooned w/florals, emb C-hdl, Boulton, 4x6" ...225.00
Dish, w/lid, ornate hdls detach, mk Boulton, 11½" L, pr 2,200.00
Dish, warming; scroll hdls/ft, mk Boutlon, 9½" dia, pr 1,500.00
Dish cross, sliding scroll/shell supports, 13" L 280.00
Entree dish, plain w/eng armorials, removable hdls, sgn, 12" ...350.00
Hot plate, hinged/reeded hdls, eng crest, Boulton, 8¾" 200.00
Plate, reeded border, mk, 10¾", set of 12 ....165.00
Spoon, mk J Prime, ca 1840, 12½" 125.00
Tea urn, attached underplate, paw ft, mask/ring hdls, 16" 250.00
Tea urn, classical fluted urn form, dome lid, rpl ft, 11" 250.00
Teapot, strawberry leaf & flower finial, Boulton, 4x10½" 525.00
Teapot, ½-fluted, wood finial/C-scroll hdl, rpr, 5½" 110.00
Toast caddy, holds 6 slices, 1907 ....115.00
Tray, egg/dart border, foliate band, hdls, Dixon-Sons, 29" 465.00
Tray, eng crest, scroll band/diaper panels, sgn, 1830, 29" 600.00
Tray, molded/gadrooned border, 16" dia 200.00
Tureen, swimming turtle form, hinged lid, no mk, 20" L 1,750.00
Urn, campana form w/biforcated twist vine hdls, mk HA, 3" ..195.00
Warmer, fluted columnar supports w/paw ft, Adkin Bros, 14" ..200.00
Wine cooler, ½-fluted urn form, lion mask/ring hdls, 9" 500.00

Wine cooler, 4 acanthus/paw ft, mask/vine bands, 11", pr ...**1,300.00**

Silver Resist

The process for decorating pottery with the silver-resist method involved first coating the design or that portion of the pattern that was to be left unsilvered with a water-soluble solution. The lustre was applied to the entire surface of the vessel and allowed to dry. Before the final firing, the surface was washed, removing only the silver from the coated areas. This type of ware was produced early in the 1800s by many English potteries, Wedgwood included.

Mug, floral resist band on canary, lustre hdl, 2", NM **80.00**
Mustard pot, ribbed, ftd **75.00**
Pitcher, allover birds/flowers, 5" **200.00**
Pitcher, allover floral resist on wht w/bl highlights, 7" **400.00**
Pitcher, wide band: leaves/tendrils on wht, minor wear, 6" **175.00**

Sinclaire

In 1904 H.P. Sinclaire and Company was founded in Corning, New York. For the first sixteen years of production, Sinclaire used blanks from other glassworks for his cut and engraved designs. In 1920 he established his own glass-blowing factory in Bath, New York. His most popular designs utilize fruits, flowers, and other forms from nature. Most of Sinclaire's glass is unmarked; those that are carry his logo: an 'S' within a wreath with two shields.

Our advisors for this category are Janet and Marvin Stofft; they are listed in the Directory under Indiana.

Bowl, amber, diamonds & stars in sqs, shallow, flared, 13" **160.00**
Candlesticks, blk, pierced bobeches, baluster, 9", pr **345.00**
Finger bowl, w/underplate **75.00**
Plate, star center w/radiant threads & 4 floral panels, 10" **325.00**
Tray, Intaglio, salesman's sample, 5" dia **75.00**
Vase, blk/wht, Deco style, mk, 8" **195.00**
Vase, eng decor, trumpet form, mk, 10" **195.00**
Vase, peach, eng florals/swags/geometrics, 9½" **145.00**

Sitzendorf

The Sitzendorf factory began operations in East Germany in the mid 1800s, adopting the name of the city as the name of their company. They produced fine porcelain groups, figurines, etc. in much the same style and quality as Meissen and the Dresden factories. Much of their ware was marked with a crown over the letter 'S.'

Candelabrum, 3-arm, lady & child, appl roses, mk, 20" **495.00**
Candelabrum, 4-arm, appl florals, maid/cherub std, 19", pr **475.00**
Candelabrum, 4-arm, 2 cherubs seated at base, Voigt, 15" **325.00**
Candlestick, cherub w/dolphin, appl florals, Voigt, 15" **350.00**
Candlestick, draped child w/flower basket, mk, 8" **110.00**
Figurine, girl on bridge, suitor retrieves shoe, 8½x9" **760.00**
Figurine, King Henry VIII+6 wives, ea w/name, 8", set of 7 ..**1,850.00**
Figurine, man w/watering can; lady w/flower basket, 9", pr **280.00**
Figurine, monkey band, conductor+12 musicians, 4"-5", 13-pc .**400.00**
Figurine, monkey band, mc costumes/instruments, 6", 9-pc **850.00**
Figurine, monkey band, 1900, 4"-4½", 3-pc **375.00**
Figurine, Napoleon at Cherbourg, bl crown S mk, 11" **300.00**
Figurine, parrot on floral-encrusted tree, Voigt, 12", pr **500.00**
Figurine, slave trader, seated noble, +2 waiting girls/dogs **1,250.00**

Vase, Kauffman scene/floral panels, 3-hdl, paw ft, 8x7" **175.00**

Slag Glass

Slag glass is a marbleized opaque glassware made by several companies from about 1870 until the turn of the century. It is usually found in purple or caramel (see Chocolate Glass), though other colors were also made. Pink is rare and very expensive.

Blue, basket, cherries/leaves relief, crimped/ruffled, 9" **60.00**
Blue, humidor, drum shape, cap-shaped finial, 6½x5¼" **245.00**
Pink, Inverted Fan & Feather, bowl, fruit; 5½x9" **750.00**
Pink, Inverted Fan & Feather, cruet, 6½" **1,500.00**
Pink, Inverted Fan & Feather, jelly compote, 5" **500.00**
Pink, Inverted Fan & Feather, punch cup **250.00**
Pink, Inverted Fan & Feather, salt shaker **300.00**
Pink, Inverted Fan & Feather, sauce dish, 2½x4½" **275.00**
Pink, Inverted Fan & Feather, sugar bowl, w/lid **600.00**
Pink, Inverted Fan & Feather, tumbler **375.00**
Purple, Beaded Cable, rose bowl **27.50**
Purple, bowl, cherries, Baroque swags, w/lid, 5½x7½" **75.00**
Purple, Daily Block, celery dish, boat form, 2½x12x4⅛" **135.00**
Purple, Fluted Shell, bowl, pie crust rim, 8½" **65.00**
Purple, obelisk, novelty ornament, 8x3½" **95.00**
Purple, pitcher, emb strawberries & leaves, 6¼x3½" **95.00**

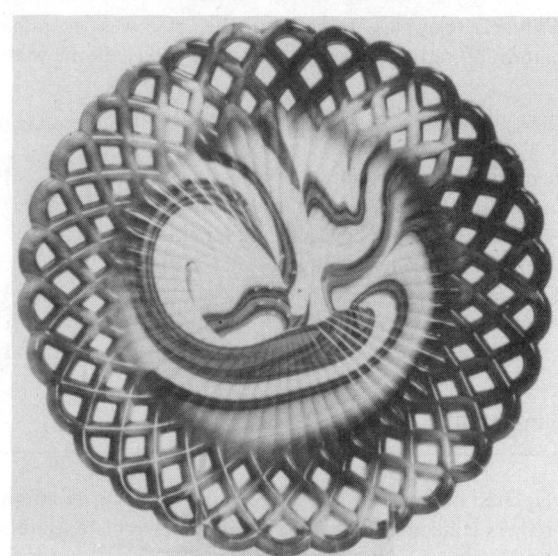

Plate, purple, lattice edge, 13", $80.00.

Purple, Rooster, butter dish **145.00**
Purple, salt cellar, urn form, 2 hdls, 2¼x3½" **55.00**

Smith Bros.

Alfred and Harry Smith founded their glassmaking firm in New Bedford, Massachusetts. They had been formerly associated with the Mt. Washington Glass Works, working there from 1871 to 1875 to aid in establishing a decorating department. Smith glass is valued for its excellent enameled decoration on satin or opalescent glass. Pieces were often marked with a lion in a red shield.

Our advisors for this category are Betty and Clarence Maier; they are listed in the Directory under Pennsylvania.

Biscuit jar, carnations, pk/gold-traced, SP mts, 5½" dia **375.00**

Bowl, gold-traced oak leaves/acorns, ribbed, lion mk, 6½" 250.00
Creamer, roses in gold on wht opaque, ornate SP mts, 3¾" 200.00
Creamer & sugar bowl, floral on wht, SP lid, ind 400.00
Creamer & sugar bowl, pansies in bl, SP mts, lion mk 300.00
Jar, dresser; floral on lt yel, lion mk, 4" dia 300.00
Jar, pansies, melon ribbed, rampant lion mk, 5½" dia 395.00
Lamp, oil; 10" shade w/HP floral & butterflies; B&H base 250.00
Mustard, Columned Ribs, florals, pk on wht w/bl dots, 3" 155.00
Powder box, iris/leaves, gold/gr on cream, melon ribs, 3x4" 335.00
Rose bowl, wild roses w/jewel stamens, gold leaves, 5½" 250.00
Sweetmeat, wild roses, gold-traced leaves, lid, lion mk, 4" 600.00
Syrup, prunus flowers in gold, ribbed, conical, lion mk, 5" 375.00
Vase, bl scrolls/gold flowers, ribbed, lion mk, 8½" 425.00
Vase, dbl pilgrim; lav wisteria w/gold, unmk, 7¼x8x2" 800.00
Vase, dbl pilgrim; wild roses, paper label, 7x8" 785.00
Vase, heron, gray/wht on pk w/gold, rings, unmk, 6x2¼" 165.00
Vase, home/winter scene, gold trim, rings, unmk, 6x2¼" 165.00
Vase, leaves/gold/lt bl scrollwork, bulbous emb top, 9x7" 585.00

Snow Babies

During the last quarter of the 19th century, snow babies — little figurals in white snowsuits — originated in Germany. They were made of sugar candy and were often used as decorations for Christmas trees. Later on, they were made of marzipan, a confection of crushed almonds, sugar, and egg whites. Eventually porcelain manufacturers began making them in bisque. They were popular until WWII. These tiny china figures range in size from just over 1" to the very rare jointed babies sometimes nearly 7" tall. Any example brings a very respectable price on the market today. Beware of reproductions.

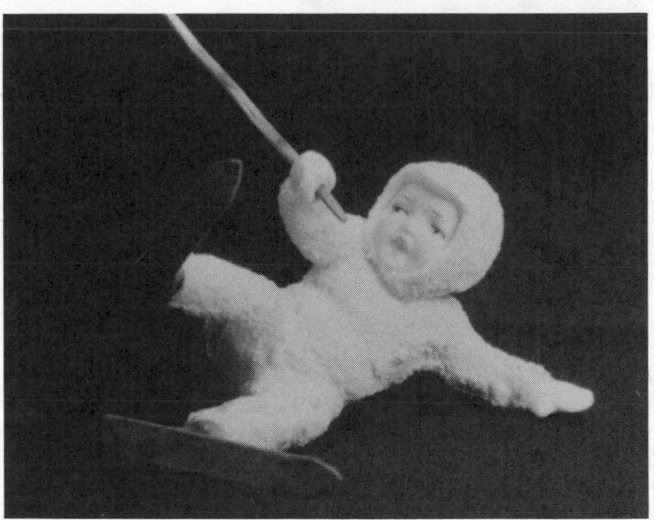

Tumbling baby on skis, wooden ski and pole, 4", $225.00.

Angel, sitting, arms outstretched, 1¾" 200.00
Babies, 1 rides/2nd pulls sled, #5209, 1⅝x2½" 100.00
Babies, 2 on sled, Germany 150.00
Babies slide down brick wall, #6602, 1⅝x2½" 125.00
Baby, jtd, good pnt, impish features, 4" 250.00
Baby, sitting, Germany, 2" 95.00
Baby, sitting, Germany, 3½" 175.00
Baby, sitting, ⅞" 35.00
Baby holds camera, 1¾" 125.00
Baby in shell, lg 25.00
Baby on red airplane, Germany, 2¼" 130.00
Baby on sled, Germany, 1¾" 45.00
Baby on sled pulled by 2 dogs, #7153, 1⅜x3" 60.00

Baby on snowball, Japan, 2" 40.00
Baby on stomach, googly-eyed, Hertivig & Co, 1915, 2¾" 175.00
Baby playing tuba, mk Germany, 1½" 75.00
Baby slides down hill on champagne bottle, tree in bkground . .145.00
Bear, Germany, 1½" 40.00
Bear on sled, mk Germany 65.00
Boy & girl skaters, 2", pr 70.00
Igloo, baby inside, Santa on roof, Germany 85.00
Man skating on 1 leg 48.00
Penguin, Germany, 4" 65.00
Santa sits in gr sleigh, w/reindeer, Germany, 3½" 225.00
Seal & red ball, Germany, 2" 35.00
Snowman, 1½" 50.00

Snuff Boxes

As early as the 17th century, the Chinese began using snuff. By the early 19th century, the practice had spread to Europe and America. It was used by both the gentlemen and the ladies alike, and expensive snuff boxes and bottles were the earmark of the genteel. Some were of silver or gold set with precious stones or pearls, while others contained music boxes. In the following listings, the dimension noted is length. See also Orientalia, Snuff Bottles.

Cow horn, oval, brass fish finial, 2x3" 165.00
Enamel, figures in landscape, 1700s, 2⅝" 400.00
Ivory, HP scene on lid, gold-pnt geometrics, 2½" dia 150.00
Papier-mache, HP girl w/mirror on lid, 2¾" dia, EX 150.00
Papier-mache, motto, 'Gen Zachs Taylor,' 1848, 3" dia, EX . . .425.00
Rvpt, family scene, frosted, jade stopper, 3x2½" 185.00
Silver, eng floral/scrollwork, engine-trn panels, 1850, 3½" 260.00
Silver, eng foliage, shaped rectangle, Birmingham, 1897, 2" . . .300.00
Tortoise shell, portrait on ivory, 1800, 2¾" dia 300.00
Walnut, trn, name/1859 in ink on inlaid cherry disk, 3¾" dia . .125.00
18k book form w/bloodstone panel, Joseph Angell, 3¼" L . . .8,000.00

Soapstone

Soapstone is a soft talc in rock form with a smooth, greasy feel from whence comes its name. In colonial times, it was extracted from outcroppings in large sections with hand saws, carted by oxen to mills, and fashioned into useful domestic articles such as footwarmers, cooking utensils, inkwells, etc. During the early 1800s, it was used to make heating stoves and kitchen sinks. Most familiar today are the carved vases, bookends, and boxes made in China during the Victorian era.

Cvg, Buddha seated on lotus throne, gr w/flecking, 10" 65.00
Cvg, Oriental girl, arms up, holds tray, on plinth, 13" 90.00
Cvg, ram, beige, EX details, ca 1900, 2½x3" 65.00
Cvg, 9 immortals on scroll base, 14" L 290.00
Inkwell, concave, beveled sides, 1½x1¾" 50.00
Inkwell, dome top, geometrics, 4 quill holders, 2½" sq 150.00
Match/card holder, pot of flowers, gray-brn, mk China, 4x5" . . .15.00
Plaque, birds/trees/flowers/rocks, 9½" on soapstone stand 100.00
Screen, 5-color floral cvg, oblong base, 5x7½" 40.00
Toothpick holder, 3 monkeys 18.50
Vase, bird/floral cvgs, wht/gray/red, 6", EX 35.00
Vase, dbl, floral cvgs, 3-color, 8½x5" .65.00
Vase, dbl, floral/birds cvgs, 3-color, 7x9" 125.00
Vase, floral cvg, mottled gray, attached blk base, 5" 30.00
Vase, floral cvg, pk/gray, mk China, 5" 30.00
Vase, floral vine cvg, 9" 48.00

Figure of a lion, 6" long, $95.00.

Vase, floral/bird cvgs, attached cvd red base, 13¾" 125.00
Vase, foliage cvg, 6" 45.00
Vase, monkey/floral cvgs, 11" 145.00
Vase, monkey/pig/bird, deep cvgs, dk brn, China, 1800s, 8½" . .145.00

Soda Fountain Collectibles

As the neighborhood ice cream parlor becomes a thing of the past, soda fountain memorabilia from fancy backbars to ice cream advertising is becoming a popular field of collecting. One area of interest is the glassware used to serve the more elaborate ice cream concoctions. A sundae glass is familiar to us all, but there was also a 'lucky mondae' glass, narrow at the bottom and flaring to a top dimension equal to one scoop. There are footed banana split dishes and soda pop glasses with the name or logo of the beverage company painted on them.

Syrup dispensers, especially those from the teens, are very popular with today's collectors. These had spherical or urn-shaped dispensers and carried names such as Jersey Creme, Buckeye, Cherry Smash, etc.

It is estimated that ice cream dippers may be found in more than 125 different sizes and styles — some bowl shaped or cylindrical, some for making ice cream sandwiches, and even a very rare heart-shaped dipper. (This one was used along with matching heart-shaped ice cream dishes.)

Glass straw holders are very collectible. Clear is the most common color, but they are also found in green and pink; some are made of frosted glass. Early examples were pattern molded; some had matching glass lids — these are the most desirable.

Our advisors for this category are Joyce and Harold Screen; they are listed in the Directory under Maryland. See also Advertising.

Ash tray, Breyer's Ice Cream, 85th Anniversary, 1866-1951 . . . .10.00
Back bar, quarter-sawn oak, shades/panels/mirror, 72x93" . . .2,800.00
Bottle, Howell's Cherry Julep Syrup, fancy top, M 175.00
Bowl, crushed fruit; paneled hexagon, ped base, w/lid 250.00
Bowl, crushed fruit; 10-sided, mk Heisey, orig lid 275.00
Cone holder, glass, orig lid, 13" 300.00
Cone holder, glass & nickel-plated metal, 15" 300.00
Cup, hot soda; Armour's Bouillon Cubes, china 20.00
Dipper, banana split; Gilchrist 400.00
Dipper, banana split; United Products .550.00
Dipper, Clipper Fountain Supply, VG 300.00
Dipper, Cold Dog cylinder 400.00
Dipper, curved sq, VG 275.00
Dipper, Dover Mfg, 2-way action 125.00

Dipper, Geer Mfg Co A-21, VG 300.00
Dipper, Gem, sz 20 . . . . .45.00
Dipper, Gilchrist #30, squeeze hdl 50.00
Dipper, Gilchrist #31, sz 10 . . . . .40.00
Dipper, Gilchrist #33, cone shape 125.00
Dipper, Gilchrist Automatic #31, in orig box, NM 100.00
Dipper, heart shaped, rare 2,000.00
Dipper, Icy-Pi, wood hdl, EX 150.00

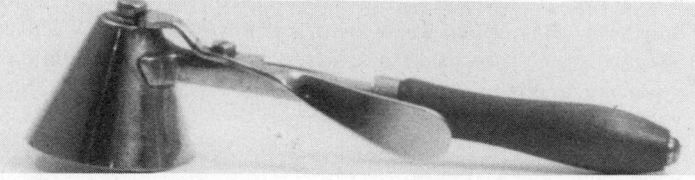

Dipper, Indestructo #3, 10", $135.00.

Dipper, Indestructo #4 . . . . .40.00
Dipper, Kingery, brass w/squeeze hdls, pat 1894 . . . . .150.00
Dipper, Philcone & MD Baking Co, rnd bowl 60.00
Dipper, sandwich, Polar Pak 300.00
Dipper, sandwich, Sanitary, thumb push 250.00
Dish, banana split; crystal, fluted sides, holding tab 7.00

Cardinal Cherry dispenser, original pump, M, $1,500.00.

Dispenser, Dad's Old Fashioned Root Beer, barrel form, NM . .250.00
Dispenser, Hires, hourglass form, w/pump, EX 450.00
Dispenser, Johnson Cold Fudge, stoneware 150.00
Dispenser, Lash's Orangeade Soda, 1920s, EX 250.00
Dispenser, Magnus CA Concordia Punch, ca 1920s, EX 195.00
Dispenser, sugar; glass body w/tin bottom, 5¾x3" dia 50.00
Dispenser, syrup; Wards Lemon Crush, w/o pump 350.00
Display, cb diecut, sundaes/sodas/etc, 12", 4 for 15.00
Display, Eat It All, papier-mache ice cream cone, 21", EX 100.00
Flavor board, tin, ca 1900 . . . . .400.00
Fountain glass, Canada Dry, crest, w/syrup line 15.00
Fountain glass, Dr Pepper, ACL label, sq 15.00
Fountain glass, Hires, Enjoy Natures..., w/syrup line 25.00
Fountain glass, Julep, yel, w/syrup line .10.00
Fountain glass, Moar, w/syrup line 10.00
Fountain glass, Richardson's Liberty Drinks 20.00
Fountain glass, Voegels ice cream cone, gold diamond 15.00
Fountain glass, 7-Up, gr 15.00
Juicer, Arnold Electric 45.00
Milk shake mixer, AC Gilbert 70.00

Milk shake mixer, Arnold, pat Apr 15, 1919 . . . . .75.00
Milk shake mixer, Hamilton Beach, gr pnt finish, 2-speed 60.00
Milk shake mixer, Hamilton Beach, marble base, as found 100.00
Milk shake mixer, Hamilton Beach, repolished to brass 225.00
Milk shake mixer, hand-cranked floor model 900.00
Mug, Armour's Veribest, crockery 40.00
Mug, Berry's Famous Root Beer, bl salt glaze 90.00
Mug, Hires, gray, lg 30.00
Mug, Hires, Mettlach, #3012 . . . . .100.00
Mug, Rochester Root Beer, emb glass, lg 20.00
Mug, Schuester Root Beer 40.00
Mug, Zipp's, dbl bl band, lg 40.00
Slicer, Dover Mfg 400.00
Soda fountain, marble, Victorian back bar style, EX 3,500.00
Straw holder, clear, brass base, 2-pc top 350.00
Straw holder, clear, Green River in Bottles 500.00
Straw holder, clear, Heisey, open side 500.00
Straw holder, clear, Jersey Cream 500.00
Straw holder, clear, paneled, metal top/bottom, pat 1918 . . . .175.00
Straw holder, clear, slim cylinder w/flared base 200.00
Straw holder, Depression glass, gr, w/NP base 350.00
Straw holder, Depression glass, pk .400.00
Straw holder, pattern glass, Bakelite finial, NP base 300.00
Straw holder, pattern glass w/glass lid 500.00
Straw holder, Sweet Heart Straws, heart shaped, eng top 600.00
Syrup bottle, vanilla, w/cup 40.00
Syrup dispenser, Birchola 1,200.00
Syrup dispenser, Buckeye Root Beer, pump mk CFJ Co, EX . .1,400.00
Syrup dispenser, Buckeye Root Beer 5¢, Root Beer on pump .1,700.00
Syrup dispenser, Cherri Bon, colored porc knob on pump . . .3,200.00
Syrup dispenser, Cherri-Chic, Hungerford Smith, w/pump . .1,500.00
Syrup dispenser, Fowler's Root Beer, porc pump knob, EX . . .1,200.00
Syrup dispenser, Grape Kola, ceramic w/grapes, 3-pc, 24" . . .1,600.00
Syrup dispenser, Howel's Cherry Julep, porc pump knob 900.00
Syrup dispenser, Jersey Creme, orig incised pump, EX 1,100.00
Syrup dispenser, Jim Dandy Orangeade, orig pump, EX 3,000.00
Syrup dispenser, Lemon Crush, porc pump knob, EX 600.00
Syrup dispenser, Stein's Famous Root Beer, porc pump knob .3,200.00
Syrup dispenser, Treet, orange lustre glass, incised pump 700.00
Tin container, Runkel's Chocolate, early graphics, NM 350.00
Wafer holder, Reliance 250.00
Window, ldgl, 'Ice Cream,' ca 1900, 20x29" 425.00

Soft Paste

Soft paste is a low-fired, granular type of porcelain that must be glazed to retain water.

Potpourri, Chantilly, minus lid, minor losses, ca 1745, 5x9", $650.00.

Creamer, steamship/Am flag, red transfer/lustre rim, 4", EX . . .150.00
Dish, gr edge, leaf form, 5¼" L, VG .65.00
Pitcher, hunting dogs/trees/vintage emb, mc/lustre, 5", EX . . .125.00
Plate, emb floral rim, blk floral transfer w/mc, 8" 75.00
Plate, emb floral rim, blk transfer w/poem, 7⅜" 150.00
Shaker, bl feather band, dome top, sm chips, 4½" 90.00
Sugar bowl, floral, Gaudy Dutch type w/lustre, 6", EX 125.00
Teapot, emb Am eagle/etc, Castleford, rpr, 7" 275.00
Teapot, floral, Gaudy Dutch type w/purple lustre, 7", EX 275.00

Spangle Glass

Spangle glass, also known as Vasa Murrhina, is cased art glass characterized by the metallic flakes embedded in its top layer. It was made both abroad and in the United States during the latter years of the 19th century, and it was reproduced in the 1960s by the Fenton Art Glass Company.

Vasa Murrhina was a New England distributor who sold glassware of this type manufactured by a Dr. Flower of Sandwich, Massachusetts. Flower had purchased the defunct Cape Cod Glassworks in 1885 and used the facilities to operate his own company. Since none of the ware was marked, it is very difficult to attribute specific examples to his manufacture. See also Art Glass Baskets; Fenton.

Basket, bl shaded w/mica, wht int, ruffled, 6½x4½x6" 120.00
Basket, bl w/mica, wht int, 8-crimp, thorn hdl, 7½x4¾" 175.00
Basket, lt gr w/mica, ribbon candy rim, looped hdl, 7½" 100.00
Basket, orange/variegated brn w/silver mica, clear hdl, 11" 110.00
Basket, pk shaded overlay w/mica, clear hdl, 5½x4x6" 118.00
Basket, tortoise-shell coloring, thorn hdl, 6" dia 125.00
Basket, turq w/wht casing & clear hdl, 6½" 100.00
Cruet, clear to bl, silver mica, Hobbs & Brockunier 435.00
Epergne, bl w/silver mica, dragon hdl, ormolu mts, 12¾" 295.00
Epergne, rose, ormolu dragon supports lily vase, 19x11" 495.00
Ewer, rose cased, mica forms coralene-like motif, 8", pr 225.00
Pitcher, red/gr/yel w/gr aventurine, 5¾" 140.00
Pitcher, rose w/silver mica, wht int, sq top, 5½" 150.00
Rose bowl, bl w/mica, wht int, appl ft, 8-crimp, 3¾x2⅝" 85.00
Rose bowl, rose shaded w/mica, 8-crimp, 5x5½" 145.00
Rose bowl, rose w/much mica, wht int, 8-crimp, 3¾x3¾" 125.00

Sweetmeat, silverplated lid and plate, 5" diameter, $295.00.

Vase, apricot cased, appl daisy hdls, ruffled, 8", pr 195.00
Vase, apricot w/mica, clear thorn hdl, ewer form, 8⅜" 125.00

Vase, bl shaded, clear thorn hdl, ewer form, 7½x3" 125.00
Vase, pk cased, appl cherries/rigaree/ruffle, 9", pr 550.00
Vase, pk w/mica, vaseline shell trim, loop hdls, 9¾" 130.00
Vase, rose w/mica, wht int, clear thorn hdls, 7¼x3½" 110.00
Vase, rust w/mica, ruffled, melon ribs, 9½" 75.00

Spatter Glass

Spatter glass, characterized by its multicolor 'spatters,' has been made from the late 19th century to the present by American glass houses as well as those abroad. Although it was once thought to have been made entirely by workers at the 'end of the day' from bits and pieces of leftover scrap, it is now known that it was a standard line of production. See also Art Glass Baskets.

Basket, bl/lt bl opaque swirls, bl thorn hdl, sq top, 8x4½" 175.00
Basket, bl/maroon/yel, melon ribbed, clear hdl, 6½x4" 110.00
Basket, pk/rose/tan/wht, ruffled, clear thorn hdl, 6x5x7" 145.00
Basket, yel opaque w/wht, gold trim, clear hdl, 5¾x4⅜" 95.00
Bottle, scent; yel/wht cased, HP flowers w/gold, w/top, 5½" 95.00
Conch shell, 2 appl amber ft, 4½" 115.00
Pitcher, brn/bl/wht, swirled ribs, clear hdl, 9" 275.00
Pitcher, brn/wht, ground pontil, 8½" .145.00
Pitcher, yel/wht appl floral spray at center, 2¾" 95.00
Rolling pin, maroon/cobalt on wht, 15x2" 110.00
Vase, mc on clear, clear hdls, 11" 90.00
Vase, red/gr/bl swirl, pear form, 10" 85.00
Vase, yel/pk/wht, flared, 8¾" 75.00
Water set, pk/wht/maroon/gr/yel, 7" pitcher+4 4" tumblers 325.00

Spatterware

Spatterware is a general term referring to a type of decoration used by English potters beginning in the late 1700s. Using a brush or a stick, brightly-colored paint was dabbed onto the soft-paste earthenware items, achieving a spattered effect which was often used as a border. Because much of this type of ware was made for export to the United States, some of the subjects in the central design—the schoolhouse and the eagle patterns, for instance — reflect American tastes. Yellow, green, and black spatterware is scarce and highly valued by collectors.

In the descriptions that follow, the color listed after the item indicates the color of the spatter. The central design is identified next, and the color description that follows that refers to the design.

Creamer, bl, peafowl, 4-color, paneled, 5½", NM 550.00
Creamer, brn, floral, 3-color, 5¼", VG 325.00
Cup & saucer, red, peafowl, 4-color, stains/flakes 150.00
Pitcher, bl, paneled, 6¾", VG 100.00
Pitcher, bl, peacock/fountain transfer, paneled, 6¼", EX 200.00
Pitcher, rainbow, red/bl, hairlines, 12" 275.00
Plate, bl, eagle/shield transfer in bl, minor stains, 8¼" 100.00
Plate, bl, peafowl, 4-color, 9½", EX 300.00
Plate, bl, peafowl in tree, 5-color, minor wear, 9" 200.00
Plate, bl, single rose, 3-color, 9¼" 225.00
Plate, bl, tulip, 4-color, minor stains, 9⅜" 275.00
Plate, bl, tulip, 4-color, wear/stains/hairlines, 8½" 85.00
Plate, bl, tulip, 4-color, 8", NM 225.00
Plate, gr, wild horses, brn transfer, 1830s, 9½" 275.00
Plate, lt bl, eagle & shield transfer, 7" .225.00
Plate, purple, eagle transfer, rpr, 9", VG 250.00
Plate, rainbow, red/bl/gr, 9½", VG 300.00
Plate, red, castle bldg, minor pinpoints, 8⅜" 400.00

Plate, toddy; gr, peafowl, 4-color, hairline, 5" 200.00
Platter, bl, horses/cowboys transfer, 12", EX 350.00
Platter, bl, single rose, red/gr/blk, stains/sm flake, 13" 215.00
Platter, bl at edge, octagonal, 13½", EX 85.00
Platter, rainbow, bl/purple, 16", VG 450.00
Soup plate, red, peafowl, 4-color, mk Adams, 9½", pr 100.00
Sugar bowl, bl, peafowl, 4-color, paneled, 7½", NM 500.00
Sugar bowl, bl/gr, wear/sm chips/stains/crow's ft, 4¾" 100.00
Sugar bowl, rainbow, red/gr, oversz matching lid, 5", VG 125.00
Tea bowl & saucer, bl, dove, 4-color, minor wear 750.00
Tea bowl & saucer, bl, fort, hairline/pinpoints 225.00
Tea bowl & saucer, bl, 4-part bud, red/gr, stains 175.00
Tea bowl & saucer, gr, peafowl, 4-color, EX 375.00
Tea bowl & saucer, purple, acorn, 4-color, stained 750.00
Tea bowl & saucer, purple, VG, miniature 95.00
Tea bowl & saucer, rainbow, red/gr, stain/sm edge chips 70.00
Tea bowl & saucer, rainbow, red/gr/bl 325.00
Tea bowl & saucer, red, dove, 4-color, EX 750.00
Tea bowl & saucer, red, stains/pinpoint flakes on ft of cup 60.00
Tea bowl & saucer, red, star, 3-color, sm table-ring flake 750.00
Tea bowl & saucer, red, teepee, stains .250.00
Tea bowl & saucer, red, thistle, red/gr .375.00
Tea bowl & saucer, red/gr, bull's eye, EX 125.00
Teapot, bl, peafowl, 4-color, paneled, 9", VG 525.00
Toddy, bl, bull's eye, 5¼" 85.00
Toddy plate, red, open tulip, 3-color, 5", M 350.00
Wash bowl, purple, holly berries, paneled, 14", EX 450.00
Wash bowl, rainbow, 12-sided, 12", M 500.00
Wash bowl & pitcher, bl, peafowl, 4-color, VG, pr 800.00

Spelter

Spelter figurines are cast from commercial zinc and coated with a metallic patina. The result is a product very similar to bronze in appearance, yet much less expensive.

Civil War bugler, ca 1860, 21", $400.00.

Bookends, Indian w/bow kneels on rocks, teepee, 8x7½", pr . . .195.00
Bust, Atalia, silver patina, 14½" 95.00
Bust, Mozart, bronze patina, 11" 65.00
Candlestick, Dutch farm scenes, silver patina, 10½" 20.00
Candlestick, ornate, gold trim, ca 1900, 9¾", pr 45.00
Condiment set, peasant lady w/basket & baby holds shakers, 7"..125.00
Figurine, English setter, opener in base, 3½x6½" 60.00
Figurine, girl feeds cat, marble base, sgn Pilet, 11½" 225.00
Figurine, horse, standing, blk/gr marbled base, 10¾" L 150.00
Figurine, Indian on horsebk, on base, 7½" 50.00
Figurine, man leads horse, blk pnt, wood base, 16½" 100.00
Incense burner, Egyptian nude holds duck, lies on stomach 110.00
Lamp, peasant girl, flower basket on head, oil burner, 13" 45.00

Spode-Copeland

The Spode Works was established in 1770 and continued to operate under that title until 1843. Their earliest products were typical underglaze blue-printed patterns, though basalt was also made. After 1790 a translucent porcelain body was the basis for a line of fine enamel-decorated dinnerware. Stone china was introduced in 1805, often in patterns reflecting an Oriental influence.

In 1833 Wm. Taylor Copeland purchased the company, continuing business in much the same tradition. During the last half of the nineteenth century, Copeland produced excellent parian figures and groups with such success that many other companies attempted to reproduce his work. He employed famous painters to decorate plaques, vases, and tablewares, many examples of which were signed by the artist. Most of the Copeland wares are marked with one of several variations that incorporate the firm name. Today the company is owned by Royal Worcester Ltd. and operates under the name of Royal Worcester Spode Ltd.

Bottle, scent; birds/shrubs in gilt on claret, 1815, 4", EX 100.00
Bowl, vegetable; Tower, bl/wht, w/lid, Copeland 185.00
Creamer & sugar bowl, Cowslip, lg 50.00
Cup, demitasse; Sorrento 15.00
Cup & saucer, Tower, Copeland 45.00
Figurine, bird on stump, blk w/yel, Spode, 4½" 25.00

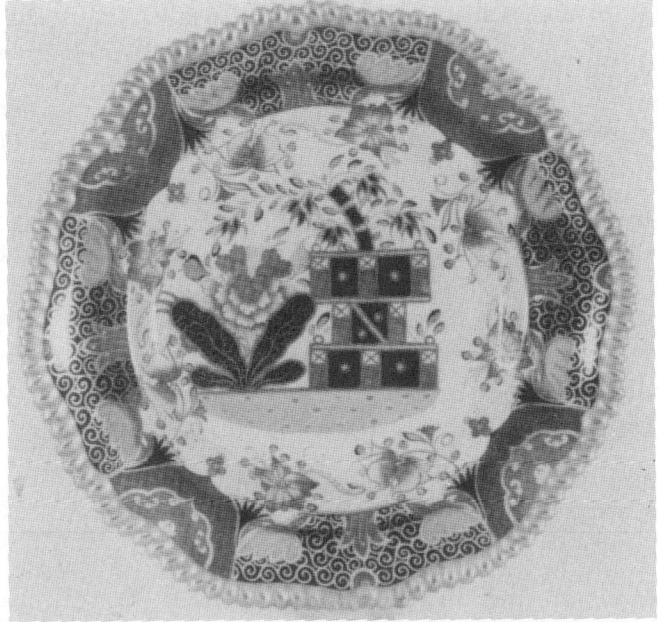

Copeland 'New Stone' Imari pattern plates, 10½", set of 12: $600.00.

Plate, bird's nest & flowers, blk on wht, Copeland, 7" 15.00
Plate, dessert; floral cartouch, sgn Worrau, set of 12 . . . . .900.00
Plate, dinner; Cowslip 20.00
Plate, dinner; Wickerlane 18.00
Plate, Royal Jasmine, Copeland, 1925, 10½", 12 for 145.00
Plate, Tower, Copeland, 10½" 25.00
Platter, exotic florals in bl & gr, mk New Stone, 21" L 300.00
Platter, Tower, Copeland, 14¾" 90.00
Tureen, river/ruins, med bl transfer, Spode, 14" L, +tray 550.00
Vase, Italiana, dk/med bl transfer, Copeland, 1900, 11" 60.00
Wash set, paraquet/fauna on pebbled ground, Copeland, 4-pc . .250.00

Spongeware

Spongeware is a type of factory-made earthenware that was popular during the last quarter of the 19th century. It was decorated by dabbing color onto the drying ware with a sponge, leaving a splotched design at random or in simple patterns. Sometimes a solid band of color was added. The vessel was then covered with a clear glaze and fired at a high temperature. Blue on white is the most preferred combination, but green on ivory, orange on white, or those colors in combination may also occasionally be found.

Bowl, bl/wht, bl stripes, hairline, 4x10½" 145.00
Bowl, bl/wht, minor rim wear, shallow ft flake, 2¼x7¾" 155.00
Bowl, brn/bl on cream, 4x7" dia 135.00
Bowl, brn/gr on yel, sm edge chips, 3½x8¼" dia 35.00
Bowl, mixing; bl/wht, stains/flakes, 5¾x11" dia 185.00
Jar, bl/wht, w/lid, missing bail, 6", EX 140.00
Pitcher, bl/wht, pattern sponging, str sides, 8¾", EX 350.00
Pitcher, bl/wht, tankard form, rpr/hairlines, 6¾" 150.00
Pitcher, gr/wht, 5⅞", VG 65.00

Syrup pitcher, spiral ribbing, 6", $475.00.

Plate, bl/wht, scalloped, ironstone, 8⅝", NM 125.00
Plate, bl/wht, scalloped rim w/emb scrolls, 10" 150.00
Platter, bl/wht, Trenton NJ, 12x8" 200.00
Tray, bl/wht, minor stains/pinpoints, 14" L 210.00
Tray, bl/wht, scalloped, 11¼" L 175.00

Spoons

Souvenir spoons have been popular remembrances since the 1890s.

The early hand-wrought examples of the silversmith's art are especially sought and appreciated for their fine craftsmanship. Commemorative, personality-related, advertising, and those with Indian busts or floral designs are only a few of the many types of collectible spoons. In the following listing, spoons are entered by city, character, or occasion.

Key:
B — bowl   FF — full figure
BR — bowl reverse   GW — gold wash
emb — embossed   H — handle
eng — engraved   HR — handle reverse

Los Angeles; Salt Lake City; Lexington, KY; $25.00 each.

Atlantic City NJ on fancy H; lighthouse eng in B 17.50
Bar Harbor, sky view emb in B; FF fish H; Shepard 45.00
Butte MT, Anaconda Mine in B; Indian head on H; copper, 5" .. 16.00
Calla lily FF H; plain B; Watson 27.50
Canada-Brocks Monument on H; Last Sacrifice Niagara in B . . .30.00
Catalina Island, Old Abe at top of H; plain B 24.00
Chicago emb in GW B; vine-like H; mk, demi 27.50
Chicago in gold & silver in B; floral H; Reed & Barton 30.00
Chicago/Indian in headdress on H; Masonic Temple in B 40.00
Cincinnati & Soldiers Monument in B; scroll H; Wallace 20.00
Colorado Springs, cowboy roping steer emb on BR; flower H . . .28.00
Detroit city seal in B; coat of arms on H; G 135.00
Drew University emb in B; gates w/torch & books on H 28.00
Floral H; plain B; Howard, demi 17.50
Fort Pitt & crown in B; fort cutout at top of twist H; 5½" 35.00
Gallipolis OH 1792 eng in GW B; scroll H; Towle, 5⅜" 16.00
Golden Gate emb in B; state seal & miner on HR; 5½" 18.00
Green Bay WI eng in GW B; bead-edged H; demi 28.00
Holly around star on H; plain B; Gorham, 1971 . . . . .30.00
Holly leaves & berries emb in B; plant on H; Whiting, bonbon .95.00
Honolulu, beach cutout in fr on H; plain B; 5⅞" 22.00
Honolulu w/beach view emb in B; FF palm tree H; 4⅜" 22.00
Hope & anchor on finial of twist H; shell forms B; mk 27.50
Idaho seal & scenes on H & HR; plain B; sugar shell 20.00
IL State Prison, Joliet in B; corn cutout on H; 5¾" 110.00

IN w/ears of corn on H; Soldiers & Sailors monument in B 20.00
Independence Hall & Liberty Bell on H; plain B 20.00
Indian head w/1 feather on H; Ladawga eng in B 35.00
Jackson bust at end of H; Hermitage emb in B; Gorham, 6⅛" . . .95.00
Jacksonville eng in B; oranges/leaves/blossoms emb on H; 6" . .22.00
Liberty NY, Hotel Wawonda etched in B; scrolled H; mk 28.00
Lick Observatory, Mt Hamilton in GW B; Mr Lick emb on H . .25.00
Lorain OH, Blast Furnaces in B; water lilies on H; Shepard 27.50
Los Angeles emb on H; plain B; demi .25.00
Louisiana, oil well emb in B; pelican on nest on H; Watson 22.00
Louisiana, pelican/bales/cane on wavy H; view in B; Shepard . . .28.00
Mexico on shank; HP fort on tip of H; plain B; demi 20.00
Mt Vernon view emb in B; George & Martha busts on H 20.00
New Orleans on HR; Mother eng in B; pelican/bale on H 28.00
New Orleans/capitol/monument HR; Old Hickory on H; demi . .32.00
Niagara Falls emb in B; Indian maid & canoe FF H; 5½" 55.00
Niagara Falls view emb in B; FF Indian maid H; 5¾" 165.00
NJ seal on H; Soldiers/Sailors Monument eng in B; Gorham 27.50
Ohio & scene on H; Indian items on HR; plain B; Watson 24.00
Old City Gate/St Augustine in B; Indian bust on H; demi 24.00
Old State House etched in B; Paul Revere emb on H; Webster . .37.50
Peoria IL, Mohammed Temple eng in B; plain H; 5½" 15.00
Petoskey MI in B; Indian chief's head on H; artifacts on HR 17.50
Pittsburgh seal, Wm Pitt on H; plain B; Watson 20.00
Portland OR, Mt Hood etched in B; floral emb H; demi 28.00
Potsville PA eng in B; wavy H; Shepard, 5½" 17.50
Ravenna OH courthouse view eng in GW B; roses on H; Towle .20.00
Recuerdo de Mexico, scenes on H; scene emb in B; mk sterling .18.00
Roses cutout on H; plain B; 5¼" 17.00
Salt Lake City, Temple Sq B; state seal on H; 5⅛" 25.00
Salt Lake City & temple emb on H; plain B; demi 25.00
Santa at chimney on H; fireplace emb in B; Gorham, 4¼" 35.00
Santa Cruz, Sea Beach Hotel in B; flower cutout on H; demi . . .28.00
Seattle World's Fair scene on H; plain B; 4⅛" 12.00
Sioux City eng in B; corn cutout on H; Watson, 6" 22.00
St Louis emb in B; cornucopia w/trailing vine on H; Gorham . . .20.00
St Louis eng in B; lilies of valley on H; demi 34.00
Sumter SC eng in B; holly cutout on H; Alvin, 5⅝" 27.50
Trenton NJ emb on scrolled H; Battle Monument view in B; 4" .14.00
Utah seal & 1896 emb on H; plain B; demi 17.50
Watson OH on H; Indian artifacts on HR; plain B; 5⅜" 20.00
Wesleyan University w/laurel wreath on H; plain B; 4⅜" 14.00
West VA, Hospital for Insane, Weston in B; wavy H; 5½" 32.00
Westerly RI, men's head emb on H; plain B; 4¼" 17.50
Yale Boat House eng in B; FF oar H; Towle, 4⅝" 17.50
Yellowstone, bear emb on H; plain B; Watson 24.00
Yellowstone, eagle shield/buffalo head H; Old Faithful in B 35.00
Yellowstone, FF bear on H; plain B; Robbins 27.50
1000 Isles eng in B; FF fish H; Watson .37.00

Sporting Goods

Our advisor for this category is Paul Longo; he is listed in the Directory under Massachusetts. See also Target Balls.

Album, Gene Tunney exercise program, 78 rpm 35.00
Baseball, 1937 World Series, autographed by NY Yankees 800.00
Bat, signed by members of the 1969 New York Mets 300.00
Bicycle, Columbia #65, NM 600.00
Bicycle, high wheel, Penny Farthing type, light/horn, 1900 ..1,700.00
Booklet, Phillips 66 Nat'l AAU Champions, 1940-1941, EX 8.00
Cuff links, sterling, plaque emb w/2 racquets & balls, pr 80.00
Cup, chrome-plated brass, collapsible, mk Cyclist Cup, 3½" 48.00

Andirons, cast iron, marked RBS/09, 20",
$2,400.00.

Game, Roger Maris Baseball, Pressman, 1962, NM 75.00
Magazine, Baseball, articles on Babe Ruth, Jan 1928 .... 40.00
Menu, Yankee Stadium Club, stadium cover, 1960s, M 15.00
Movie cartridge, Johnny Unitas passing techniques, 1971 ... 35.00
Mug, Yale/Harvard ftball game 1901, stoneware, poem, 3½" ... 275.00
Pennant, Philadelphia Phillies, pre 1950 .... 35.00
Pennant, Texas Longhorns, early 15.00
Photograph, Babe Ruth at bat, 1932 World Series, sgn, 9x7" . 1,400.00
Photograph, Mickey Mantle in tuxedo, autographed, 9¼x7½" .. 50.00
Pin, 1936 Berlin Olympiad, EX 75.00
Pin-bk button, Washington Nationals, baseball, rare 20.00
Poster, boxing, Jack Johnson, Brandt/Scheible, 1909, 19x15" ... 280.00
Program, Harlem Globetrotters, 1958, autographed by team 60.00
Program, KY Derby, 1942 .... 15.00
Program, World Series 1943 .... 200.00
Scrapbook, Boston Red Sox clippings, 100+ items, 1960s 25.00
Sheet music, Babe Ruth cover, 1928 .... 50.00
Skates, wood, high curved acorn-tip blades, 1820s 110.00
Stevengraph, John L Sullivan in boxing pose, 4x2½" 150.00
Ticket, World Series, 1948 .... 70.00
Tumbler, Toast the Champs, Baltimore Orioles, 1966, 6 MIB ... 25.00

St. Clair

The St. Clair Glass Company began as a small family-oriented operation in Elwood, Indiana, in 1941. Most famous for their lamps, the family made numerous small items of carnival, pink and caramel slag, and custard glass as well. Later, paperweights became popular production pieces; many command considerably high prices on today's market. Weights are stamped and usually dated, while small production pieces are often unmarked.

Animal dish w/cover, robin on nest, bl carnival, sgn, 5" 35.00
Ash tray, mc floral 35.00
Bird, clear, sm 45.00
Bottle, pwt base & stopper w/red flowers & mercury bubbles 40.00
Candle holder, red & wht floral, lg 35.00
Kewpie, carnival, sgn Joe St Clair 20.00
Marble, sulfide, baseball player, 2" 150.00
Novelty, Liberty Bell, bl carnival, sgn Joe St Clair 15.00
Novelty, wheelbarrow, caramel slag, sgn Joe St Clair 28.00

Paperweight, bell form, 3 mc lilies/bubbles, sgn, 4" 30.00
Paperweight, fish, bl sulfide, sgn Joe St Clair 100.00
Paperweight, frog in crystal, lg 45.00
Paperweight, pear w/leaf, clear w/gr mass bubbles 20.00
Paperweight, pitcher, 5 lilies, mercury bubbles, unsgn 20.00
Paperweight, sulfide, Dutch boy, mk, dtd 1976 .... 35.00
Paperweight, sulfide, Martha WA, wht on rose base, ltd 40.00
Paperweight, sulfide, Red Riding Hood & wolf, 3½" 320.00
Paperweight, 5 dk bl lilies w/mercury bubble & wht mound 30.00
Ring holder, teapot form, Greentown chips, sm 45.00
Ring holder, teapot form, 5 mc lilies/bubbles, sgn, 4½" 30.00
Salt cellar, swan figural, caramel slag, sgn Joe St Clair 35.00
Toothpick holder, cherry form, cobalt or wht carnival, mk, ea .. 40.00
Toothpick holder, Inverted Fan & Feather, caramel slag 75.00
Toothpick holder, sheaf of wheat, red carnival 30.00
Tumbler, Grape & Cable, bl carnival 40.00

Staffordshire

Scores of potteries sprang up in England's Staffordshire district in the early 18th century; several remain to the present time. (See also specific companies.) Figurines and groups were made in great numbers; dogs were favorite subjects. Often they were made in pairs, each a mirror image of the other. They varied in heights from 3" or 4" to the largest, measuring 16" to 18". From 1840 until about 1900, portrait figures were produced to represent particular characters, both real and fictional. As a rule, these were never marked.

The Historical ware listed here was made throughout the district; some collectors refer to it as Staffordshire Blue Ware. It was produced as early as 1820; and, because much was exported to America, it was very often decorated with transfers depicting scenic views of well-known American landmarks. Early examples were printed in a deep cobalt. By 1830 a softer blue was favored, and within the next decade black, pink, red, and green prints were used. Although sometimes careless about adding their trademark, many companies used their own border designs that were as individual as their names.

Our advisor for the Historical Blue Ware is Richard Marden; he is listed in the Directory under New Hampshire. See also specific manufacturers.

Key:
blk — black   l/b — light blue
gr — green   m/b — medium blue
d/b — dark blue   m-d/b — medium dark blue

Historical

Bowl, Battery, NY, d/b, shallow, 6½" 950.00
Bowl, Bird's Nest, att Riley, 3¼x6¼" 110.00
Bowl, Eddistone Lighthouse, d/b, shell border, Wood, 9" 575.00
Bowl, Ft Miller, Hudson & Sacandaga Rivers, red, 10¾" 165.00
Bowl, Lake, Regents Park, d/b, beaded rim, Wood, 10½" 350.00
Bowl, Landing of Lafayette, d/b, ftd/sq, Clews, 4¾x10", EX ... 650.00
Bowl, Landing of Lafayette, prof rpr in base, 3⅝x7¼" 425.00
Bowl, Ruins, d/b, w/lid, lion-form finial, EX 125.00
Coffeepot, Fruit & Floral, d/b, high dome 550.00
Coffeepot, Lafayette at Franklin's Tomb, d/b, 12" 1,250.00
Coffeepot, Wadsworth Tower, Hartford, d/b, Wood, 11½" .. 1,500.00
Creamer, Crows Nest from Bull Hill, blk transfer, Ridgway 95.00
Creamer, man, boy, horses, & bldgs, d/b 150.00
Creamer, Wadsworth Tower, d/b, Wood, EX 375.00
Cup & saucer, Basket, d/b, Stubbs/Kent 100.00
Cup & saucer, handleless; birds in flowering tree, d/b, EX 105.00
Cup & saucer, handleless; Wadsworth Tower, d/b, Wood 300.00

Cup & saucer, Urn & Flowers, d/b, Stubbs 100.00
Cup & saucer, Washington at Tomb, d/b, Wood, EX 325.00
Cup plate, Arched Stone Bridge, d/b, Wood, 3¾" 150.00
Cup plate, Castle Garden, Battery, NY, d/b, 3⅝", EX 180.00
Cup plate, country house, d/b, Adams, 3⅞", NM, pr 190.00
Cup plate, couple w/horse, pk, 3¾", EX 45.00
Cup plate, Fort Edwards NY, l/b, Clews, 4⅛", EX 85.00
Cup plate, Lafayette/Washington, red, Wood, 3¾", NM 425.00
Cup plate, Landing of Gen Lafayette, d/b, Clews, 3½" 375.00
Cup plate, Oriental scene, gr, Adams, 4" 40.00
Cup plate, Scudder's American Museum, d/b, RS&W, 4¼" ...775.00
Cup plate, sheep, d/b, Adams, minor hairline, 4" 115.00
Cup plate, Ship Anchored, 3¾" 325.00
Cup plate, View Near Conway NH, l/b, Jackson, 4⅛" 175.00
Cup plate, View of Newburgh NY, l/b, 4⅛", EX 160.00

Fruit basket and undertray, Battle of Bunker Hill in progress, reticulated, length of tray: 10", $11,000.00.

Ladle, gravy; Eagle & Shield, l/b, scrolled hdl, EX 160.00
Pitcher, Boston State House & City Hall, NY, d/b, rpr, 6¾" ...200.00
Pitcher, Castle w/Flag, d/b, Clew's State Series, 10" 1,500.00
Pitcher, Columbus, red transfer, sm lip rpr, 10½" 110.00
Pitcher, Erie Canal Inscription, Utica Tribute, d/b, 6" 800.00
Pitcher, Lake Scenery, pk, EW&S, 11" 85.00
Pitcher, Landing of Gen Lafayette, d/b, blurred, 8", EX 700.00
Plate, America & Independence, d/b, Clews, 10½", NM 300.00
Plate, America & Independence, d/b, Clews, 8", NM 250.00
Plate, Arms of South Carolina, d/b, Mayer, rare, 7¼", EX 550.00
Plate, Baltimore & Ohio RR, level, d/b, Wood, 10", NM 500.00
Plate, Columbia College, NY, d/b, RS&W, 6⅜", M 475.00
Plate, Constitution & Guerriere, d/b, 10" 900.00
Plate, Dartmouth, d/b, shell border, Wood, 9" 250.00
Plate, Drury Lane Theatre, London, d/b, foliage border, 9" ...125.00
Plate, Eashing Park, Surrey, d/b, Hall's Select Views, 7⅜" 75.00
Plate, Erie Canal at Buffalo, blk, Stevenson, 10¼" 200.00
Plate, Fairmount Near Philadelphia, d/b, Stubbs, 10", NM ...275.00
Plate, Falls of Montmorenci Near Quebec, d/b, Wood, 8½" ...275.00
Plate, Fisherman w/Net, d/b, Clew's States Series, 10⅝" 300.00
Plate, Fulham Church, d/b, Hall, 8½" 95.00
Plate, Gen Jackson, Hero of New Orleans, rust transfer, 8¾" ..400.00
Plate, Ghaut of Cutwa, d/b, Hall's Oriental Scenery, 8" 95.00
Plate, Gilpin's Mill, Brandywine Creek, d/b, Wood, 9" 375.00
Plate, Harvard, d/b, acorn/oak leaf border, Stevenson, 10" ...375.00
Plate, Hoboken in New Jersey, d/b, 7", EX 300.00
Plate, Hollywell Cottage Cavan, d/b, Riley, 10" 125.00
Plate, hunter shooting ducks, Wood's Zoological Series, 10" ...125.00
Plate, La Grange, Residence of Marquis Lafayette, d/b, 10" ...145.00
Plate, Lake, Regents Park, London Views, d/b, 9¼", EX 125.00

Plate, Landing of Gen Lafayette, d/b, Clews, 10" 325.00
Plate, Landing of Gen Lafayette, d/b, Clews, 8¾" 300.00
Plate, MacDonnough's Victory, d/b, Wood, 9¼", EX 325.00
Plate, Marine Hospital, Louisville, d/b, shell border, 8½" 300.00
Plate, Nahant Hotel Near Boston, d/b, minor scratches, 9" ...325.00
Plate, Near Fishkill, d/b, Clews, 7¾" 250.00
Plate, Near Fishkill, Hudson River, sepia, Clews, 10½" 85.00
Plate, NY City Hall, blk, Stevenson, 10" 90.00
Plate, NY from Brooklyn Heights, d/b, Stevenson, 10¼" 1,200.00
Plate, overall floral, d/b, 7" 70.00
Plate, Pains Hill, Surrey, d/b, 10" 125.00
Plate, Park Theatre, d/b, RS&W's acorn/oak leaf border, 10" ..265.00
Plate, Peace & Plenty, d/b, Clews, 9", EX 300.00
Plate, Philadelphia, d/b, Clew's Cities Series, rare, 5⅜" 350.00
Plate, Pittsfield Elm, d/b, 10⅝", EX 325.00
Plate, Quebec, d/b, Clew's Cities Series, prof rpr, 9" 125.00
Plate, Rural Cottage Scene, d/b, Wood, 7½" 75.00
Plate, Sheep on Lawn, d/b, States Series, 8¾" 225.00
Plate, Southampton, d/b, Wood's irreg shell border, 7½" 225.00
Plate, State House Boston, l/b, Wood's floral border, 8¼" 150.00
Plate, State House Boston, m/b, Rogers, 10" 150.00
Plate, Sulpher Springs, Delaware OH, blk transfer, 9⅜" 220.00
Plate, Trenton Falls, 3 people, d/b, Wood, 7¾" 275.00
Plate, Union Line, d/b, shell border, Wood, 10" 500.00
Plate, Utica NY, Meigh, 7¼" 70.00
Plate, View Near Fishkill, l/b, Clews, 10" 85.00
Plate, Warleigh House, Somersetshire, d/b, Hall, 8½" 85.00
Plate, Warwick Castle, d/b, Clew's bluebell border, 8⅛" 95.00
Plate, West Point, Hudson River, blk, Clews, 8" 75.00
Plate, Zebra, floral border, mb, Rogers, 10" 80.00
Platter, Albany, steamer on river, l/b, 13" 275.00
Platter, American Marine, brn, Ashworth, 10" 100.00
Platter, Boston from Dorchester Heights, m/b, Meigh, sm 175.00
Platter, Capitol at WA, well & tree, d/b, Ridgeway, 20½" 800.00

Platter, Castle Garden Battery, NY, dark blue, 18½", $1,000.00.

Platter, Christianburg, Africa, d/b, Wood, 18½" 1,150.00
Platter, Cromwell Dismissing Parliament, m/b, Jones, 17" 300.00
Platter, English country scene, d/b, Clews, 19" L, EX 400.00
Platter, Fairmount Near Philadelphia, d/b, eagle border, 21" ..1,500.00
Platter, Hermetage en Dauphine, d/b, Wood, 14¾", EX 500.00
Platter, Highlands, Hudson River, d/b, Wood, 12⅞" 850.00
Platter, Hudson River, blk, Clews, 13½", M 235.00
Platter, Kidbrook Sussex, d/b, Stevenson, 10½" 250.00

Platter, Lake George, pk, Adams, 13½" 225.00
Platter, Landing of Gen Lafayette, d/b, Clews, 12½" 650.00
Platter, Landing of Gen lafayette, d/b, Clews, 15", EX 800.00
Platter, Landing of Gen Lafayette, d/b, Clews, 19", NM 1,250.00
Platter, Louisville KY, d/b, Clews, 12½" 2,000.00
Platter, Niagara from the Am Side, d/b, Wood, 14¾", EX . . .1,000.00
Platter, Norwich Cathedral, d/b, Hall's Scenery Series, 10¾" . .275.00
Platter, NY. . .Heights Near Brooklyn, m/b, Stevenson, 16" .2,250.00
Platter, Tappan Bay, d/b, shell border, Wood, 9¾", EX 950.00
Platter, Theatre Printing House, d/b, 18¾" 475.00
Platter, Troy from Mt Ida, d/b, Stevenson, 10⅛", EX 2,000.00
Platter, View of Richmond, Wood's grapevine border, 13" 275.00
Platter, well & tree; Upper Ferry Bridge...Shuylkill, 19" 950.00
Sauce boat, American Villa, d/b, EX .200.00
Sauce boat, Caribou, d/b, Wood's Zoological Series, EX 225.00
Sauce boat, State House, Boston, d/b, Ridgeway 225.00
Saucer, New York City Hall, d/b, Stubbs 50.00
Saucer, Wadsworth Tower, d/b, Wood, 6¾" 150.00
Soup, Baltimore & Ohio RR, level, d/b, Wood, 10" 550.00
Soup, Beach at Brighton, d/b, shell border, Wood, 10" 275.00
Soup, Columbus, lav, Adams, 10½" 50.00
Soup, Hartford, pk, Jackson, 10½" 75.00
Soup, Palestine, d/b, Stevenson, 10" 95.00
Soup, Staughton's Church, Philadelphia, d/b, Ridgeway, 8¼" . .240.00
Soup, Wistow Hall, Leicestershire, d/b, Hall, 8½" 90.00
Sugar bowl, Boston Harbor, d/b, Rogers 650.00
Sugar bowl, Floral & Urn, d/b 165.00
Sugar bowl, Oriental Mosque, d/b, Wood 135.00
Teapot, City Hall, NY, m-d/b, Stubbs' rose border, EX 200.00
Teapot, floral, d/b, dome top, old spout flakes, 10" 225.00
Teapot, Oriental bldgs & river, d/b, minor flakes, 8" 425.00
Toddy plate, Ft Edward, Hudson River, brn, Clews, 5" 65.00
Toddy plate, Kenilworth Castle, m-d/b, Wood, 5⅛" 95.00
Tray, Floral & Urn, d/b, openwork, Riley, 10½" 150.00
Tray, Hall's Select Views, d/b, 8½" 165.00
Tray, soup tureen; Rochester Castle, m-d/b, Wood, 13⅞" 165.00
Tureen, gravy; Rabbit & Dog, d/b, Hall, complete, EX 465.00
Tureen, sauce; l/b, Wood's Cathedral City Series, complete . . .300.00
Tureen, soup; Quadruped, rose finial, d/b, Hall, w/lid 850.00
Tureen, soup; View of Palace of Delhi, d/b, Hall, complete . .1,700.00
Wash bowl, Baltimore, l/b, Meigh 325.00
Wash bowl, Upper Ferry Bridge, d/b, Stubbs, 12½", EX 375.00

Miscellaneous

Bank, single story, brn, 1840, 4" 150.00
Bank, 2-story brick house, 1850, 5" 200.00
Bust, Baron Clive of Plassey, pearlware, 1800-15, 10" 775.00
Bust, Geo Washington, blk coat, mc details, 8⅜", NM 575.00
Bust, Geo Washington, pearlware, after E Wood, 1818, 8" . .2,400.00
Bust, John Wesley, inscr: WL, Oct 26, 1822, E Wood 385.00
Bust, King George IV, outlined in gilt, ca 1820, rare, 6½" 286.00
Creamer, cow figural, copper lustre trim, ca 1830, 4¾x6¼" . . .250.00
Creamer, cow figural, pk lustre/iron-red, ca 1820, 7" 200.00
Creamer, cow w/milkmaid figural, spotted colors, 1800, 5½" .1,500.00
Creamer, creamware, gaudy floral, hairline in hdl, 5" 300.00
Cup, Admiral Hood's head form, creamware/mc, 1830, 4½" . . .550.00
Cup & saucer, handleless; Moral Maxims, blk transfer, EX 60.00
Dog, dalmation, ca 1850, 6½", facing pr 425.00
Dog, dalmation, gilt-lined bl oval base, 1850s, 5", pr 250.00
Dog, greyhound, 1850, 4", pr 350.00
Dog, greyhound seated on grassy knoll, 8¾", NM 300.00
Dog, pekingese on cushion, splashed pnt, ca 1790, 3½" 250.00
Dog, poodle, seated, d/b base, ball ft, ca 1880, 4½", pr 150.00

Dog, poodle, wht, ca 1840, 2" 100.00
Dog, recumbent, pk/gilt scroll base, ca 1840, 3½" 150.00
Dog, setter on tasseled cushion, Ralph Wood, 7", EX 4,000.00
Dog, spaniel, copper lustre spots, blk muzzle, 1850, 6", pr 250.00
Dog, spaniel, EX details, gilt collar, 1860s, 15½", pr 300.00
Dog, spaniel, pnt in gilt, 1880, 9", pr .110.00
Dog, spaniel, pups at ft, oval base, ca 1850, 6", pr 350.00
Figurine, Apollo, long pk/yel robes, ca 1795, 6" 300.00

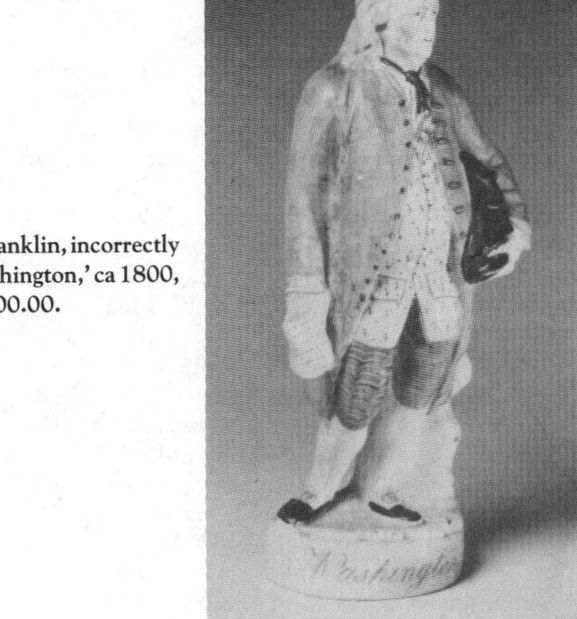

Benjamin Franklin, incorrectly labeled 'Washington,' ca 1800, 15½", $1,000.00.

Figurine, bagpiper in Highland costume, EX pnt, 1860s, 10" . . .135.00
Figurine, bear, sponged manganese w/gr, 1780, 2¾" 1,300.00
Figurine, boy on bk of lg dog, ca 1860, 10¼" 200.00
Figurine, boy w/bird's nest & bird, ca 1850, 7¾" 150.00
Figurine, cat, blk/wht, on cushion, 1850, 5½" L, pr 700.00
Figurine, cat, seated, blk/wht, ochre ribbon, 1850, 3¾", EX 195.00
Figurine, Christ, hands bound, at pillar, ca 1880, 15½" 190.00
Figurine, Christ's Agony, pearlware, Sherratt, 1830, 9½", EX . .650.00
Figurine, cobbler & his wife, ca 1860, 12½", pr 500.00
Figurine, cockerel, bl on wht, ca 1770, 5½" 385.00
Figurine, cockerel, gaudy decor, 1835, 6" 300.00
Figurine, Death of Nelson, 1845, 9" .300.00
Figurine, Dick Turpin on horse, 1850, 9" 200.00
Figurine, Duke of Wellington, ca 1840s, 7" 175.00
Figurine, flag dancers, arm in arm, oval base, 1850s, 10" 175.00
Figurine, Florence Nightingale, 1850, 15" 250.00
Figurine, Garibaldi w/horse, 14" 450.00
Figurine, girl on bk of leaping horse by fence, 1850s, 9½" 220.00
Figurine, Jumbo the elephant, ca 1890, rare, 10" 400.00
Figurine, lion, facing left, brn/wht w/blk, 1860, 3¼", EX 165.00
Figurine, lion, glass eyes, 14" L, pr 350.00
Figurine, Lost Sheep Found, boy holds sheep, ca 1775, 8¾" . . .990.00
Figurine, M Alboni as Cinderella in carriage, 1850s, 8¾" 550.00
Figurine, man dancing, orange hat/bl jacket, ca 1850, 7½" 100.00
Figurine, man playing French horn, ca 1800, 9" 250.00
Figurine, man w/lute & girl w/tambourine, 1880s, 9" 150.00
Figurine, monkey holding gr branch, ca 1880, 3½" 95.00
Figurine, Napoleon, 1845, 8" 150.00
Figurine, Napoleon III, 1856, 8" 150.00
Figurine, New Marriage Act, ca 1823, 7½", NM 1,200.00

Figurine, Peace, torching weapons, ca 1800, 8¼" 300.00
Figurine, Prince & Princess of Prussia, 1800s, 16" 200.00
Figurine, Prince & Princess of Wales, oval vase, 1845, 7½" 200.00
Figurine, Prince & Princess Royal, arm-in-arm, 1865, 12" 190.00
Figurine, Prince Albert & Queen Victoria, 1850s, 11", pr 400.00
Figurine, Prince Albert in Order of Garter robes, 1845, 12" 200.00
Figurine, rabbit eats lettuce leaf, oval base, 1860s, 3½" 200.00
Figurine, rabbits by flower-filled bocage, w/hdl, 1850, 7" 375.00
Figurine, ram/ewe, relief texture/sponged bl, Walton, 5", pr . . .600.00
Figurine, Royal Children, 1850, 12" 250.00
Figurine, Sailor, wife, & child, 1860, 13" 400.00
Figurine, Sailor leaning on barrel, 1850, 12" 200.00
Figurine, Sampson & the Lion, 1850, 10" 225.00
Figurine, Scotch couple in serpent-form boat, 8½", NM 250.00
Figurine, Scotland's Pride, soldier resting, 1860s, 10½" 200.00
Figurine, Scotsman/lady sit beneath grape arbor, 1840, 14" 250.00
Figurine, Shakespeare beside pedestal holding script, 8¾" 150.00
Figurine, Sir Robt Peel on brn horse, ca 1850, 11½" 400.00
Figurine, St Geo & dragon, bl/gr/brn/yel, R Wood, 10", EX . .5,000.00
Figurine, St Mark & St John, on base, ca 1840, 9", pr 600.00
Figurine, stag, recumbent, yel on gr base, ca 1775, 7¼" 175.00
Figurine, Tyrolean couple w/dog & lamb, ca 1865, 15¾", pr . . .200.00
Figurine, Uncle Tom & Eva, 1850, 10" 250.00
Figurine, Virgin & Child, pearlware, after E Wood, rpr, 13" . . .385.00
Figurine, Washington as Roman Emperor, horse, Wood, 15" .2,200.00
Figurine, Wellington by cannon, gold trim, ca 1860, 10" 200.00
Figurine, Winter, woman in cloak, mc, ca 1780, 9", EX 350.00
Flask, Brougham Cordial, dk brn & salt glaze, ca 1835, 7" 175.00
Flask, buildings/figures on flattened form, salt glaze, 7" 100.00
Flask, fish form, dk brn & salt glaze, 8½" W 200.00
Flask, flintlock pistol form, salt glaze, 1800s, 8¼" 300.00
Flask, house form, dk brn & salt glaze, ca 1840, 8½" 200.00
Inkwell, bird nest & snake, 1850, 3" 150.00
Inkwell, dog & pup on pillow, scroll-leg base, rpr, 4" L 130.00
Inkwell, greyhound, recumbent on cobalt base, 4" 250.00
Inkwell, old lady's head w/mouth open, 1850 . . . . .200.00
Inkwell, stag & doe, salmon & gray w/gilt, 4⅝", pr 250.00
Mug, HP drinking/dancing scene, 3½", EX 90.00
Mug, train, brn transfer w/red & gr enamel, 4", EX 150.00
Pastille burner, cottage, appl flowers, ca 1860, 5" 185.00
Pastille burner, cottage, orange/gilt walls & windows, 1840 . . . .150.00
Pastille burner, house w/flowers on base, 1850, 4" 225.00
Pastille burner, Trinity College, oval base, 8½" 175.00
Pastille burner, 2-story house, moss, 1850, 6" 200.00
Pitcher, Bacchus mask/florals, monkey hdl, 1830, 7½" 165.00
Pitcher, Byron's Illus, gr transfer, 11", EX 165.00
Pitcher, child's; child/dog in relief, copper lustre, 2¼" 75.00
Pitcher, Chinese scene, mc on wht, 7" 85.00
Pitcher, country house/garden, lt bl transfer, 12", NM 110.00
Pitcher, floral/heraldic eagle transfer, silver lustre, 7½" 460.00
Pitcher, presentation; scene, bk: inscribed/1873, w/trivet 200.00
Pitcher, silver lustre on wht, 5½", EX .50.00
Pitcher, 2 women at fountain, red transfer, 10¾", NM 80.00
Plaque, Joseph Lowndes portrait, sgn/dtd 1811, 7¼" 385.00
Plate, beggar/figures, brn on wht, octagonal, ca 1840, 6" 30.00
Plate, bird w/grapes & roses, d/b, 2 copper lustre bands, 7" 85.00
Plate, cup; Only Son, red transfer, emb mc floral trim 65.00
Plate, girl feeds chickens, blk on wht, ca 1840, 5¼" 30.00
Plate, Japan-type pattern on ironstone, F Morley & Co, 10" . . .130.00
Plate, Present for John-Independence, mother & child, 8" 120.00
Plate, toddy; temperance meeting transfer w/mc, 5", EX 115.00
Platter, bl feather edge, pearlware, Hall, 1820s, 15" 100.00
Platter, Floral, d/b, 1825, 17" 160.00
Punch bowl, hunt scene medallions, pk lustre, 5½x11½" 350.00

Saucer, portrait of Alexander & Platoff, ca 1820, pr 150.00
Spaniel, red/wht w/gilt & mc trim, facing pr, 12½", EX 370.00
Spaniel, wht w/gilt trim, minor wear, facing pr, 12" 300.00
Spill vase, Red Riding Hood & wolf, 10" 200.00
Teapot, creamware, gaudy floral, minor flakes, 7" 280.00
Teapot, floral, salt glaze, branch spout/hdl, 1760s, 6" dia 300.00
Teapot, redware, cylindrical w/combed decor, ca 1770, 9" 200.00
Tipstaff, Royal Garter, dk brn & salt glaze, 1840, 11" 198.00
Tureen, duck form, emb feathers, mc, 1770, 4x8", NM 1,300.00
Tureen, hen on nest figural, w/lid, ca 1870, 8½" 175.00
Tureen, turtle dove figural, w/lid, red/gr/brn, 1860s, 8" 525.00
Vase, Chinese scene/scroll reserves, mc/pearlware, 8", EX 400.00
Vase, spill; cow drinks by stream figural, 10½x8½", EX 220.00
Vase, spill; sheaf of wheat figural, lady beside, 1840, 14" 150.00
Vase, spill; 2 swans by tree, wht/mc foliage, 1850, 4¾", pr 125.00
Wall pocket, windmill scene, cornucopia form, 1760s, 8" 575.00
Wash set, tulips in mc on pearlware, 1830, bowl & pitcher 800.00
Waste bowl, RR scene, blk transfer w/red & gr, 6", VG 145.00

Stained Glass

There are many factors to consider in evaluating a window or panel of stained glass art. Besides the obvious factor of condition, intricacy, jeweling, beveling, and the amount of selenium (red, orange, and yellow) present should all be taken into account. Remember, repair work is itself an art and can be very expensive.

Box, HP flowers & gold, decor on base, 2½x4" 110.00
Shade, Dutch landscape, 1920s, rprs, 24" dia 450.00
Window, clear w/simple geometric floral, 52x22" 950.00

Window, Eastlake geometrics, painted panels of holly and birds, signed W.J. McPherson, Tremont St., Boston, Mass., top half: (shown) 43x44", $800.00.

Window, Prairie School, 2 floral panels, mc on slag, 27x40" . . .600.00
Window, Prairie School, 39x18", pr 850.00
Window, Prairie School, 4 floral panels, textured, 25x40" 550.00
Window, stylized floral, red/yel on vaseline, 44x23" 475.00

Lamps

Duffner & Kimberly, 22" shade w/poppy border; 64" std 4,400.00
Floral/leaf 18" dome shade; reed std/lily pad base, 23" 800.00
Grape leaf 30" shade; 66" brn-patina floor std, no mk 1,300.00
Opposing dolphin base, base/shade studded w/jewels, 18" 880.00

Stanford

The Stanford Company produced a Corn Line, similar to that of the Shawnee Company, that is today becoming very collectible. Most examples are marked, so there should be no difficulty in distinguishing one from the other.

Corn Line, butter dish 18.00
Corn Line, cookie jar, #512 ....65.00
Corn Line, creamer & sugar bowl 18.00
Corn Line, shakers, pr 12.00
Corn Line, teapot 20.00

Stangl

In 1910 Johann Martin Stangl joined the Fulper Pottery Company, working there as ceramic chemist and superintendent of the plant. After a brief absence from 1914 until 1919 when he was employed by the Haeger Pottery, Stangl returned to Fulper. He developed glazes for a new line of cigarette boxes, ash trays, vases, figurines, etc. In 1926 J.M. Stangl became president of the company, and by 1946 he and a partner gained total ownership. The Stangl name first appeared on solid-color dinnerware and novelites in 1926. By 1942 a higher grade of hand-decorated and hand-colored dinnerware was made — Fruit, Yellow Tulip, etc. — which was sold in great abundance. During the war years (1940-1946), bird figures were in great demand, since imports were restricted at that time. Stangl created its famous line of birds; these are very collectible today. Stangl ware continued to be produced after J.M. Stangl died in 1972; soon after 1978 the factory closed. Reference: *The Collector's Handbook of Stangl Pottery* by Norma Rehl, published in 1979.

Birds

Allen Hummingbird, #3634 ....55.00
Bird of Paradise, #3408, sm 70.00
Black-Throated Green Warbler, #3814 ....70.00
Blue-Headed Vireo, #3448 ....60.00
Bluebird, #3276 ....80.00
Broadtail Hummingbird, #3626 ....115.00
Cardinal, #3596, gray 60.00
Cerulean Warbler, #3456 ....60.00
Chickadees, #3581 ....160.00
Cliff Swallow, #3852 ....65.00
Cockatoo, #3405, 6" 40.00
Cockatoo, #3584 ....200.00
Cockatoo, wht glossy, #3405, 6" 55.00
Cockatoos, #3405D, pr 85.00
Duck, Drinking; purple, Terra Rose, #3250E 45.00
Duck, Flying; #3443 ....300.00
Duck, Gazing; purple, Terra Rose, #3250D 45.00
Duck, Preening; purple, Terra Rose, #3250B 45.00
Golden-Crowned Kinglet, #3848 ....65.00
Goldfinches, #3635, group 200.00
Hummingbirds, #3599D, pr 255.00
Indigo Bunting, #3589 ....55.00
Kentucky Warbler, #3598 ....50.00
Key West Quail Dove, #3454 ....250.00
Lovebird, #3400 ....50.00
Lovebirds, #3404D, pr 90.00
Oriole, #3402 ....60.00
Painted Bunting, #3452 ....100.00
Parakeet, #3449 ....145.00

Parakeets, gr, #3582D, pr 165.00
Parula Warbler, #3583, 4¼" 50.00
Pheasant hen, #3491 ....200.00
Red-Headed Woodpecker, #3752D, pr 250.00
Redstarts, #3490D, pr 125.00
Warbler, #3850, yel 60.00
Wren, #3401, w/orig tag 50.00

Western Tanagers, #3750D, $350.00.

Miscellaneous

Ash tray, Antique Gold, #1954 ....3.50
Ash tray, Antique Gold, #3942, 8" 5.00
Ash tray, Colonial Silver, #5174 ....10.00
Ash tray, gr, low, 6" 8.00
Bowl, Antique Gold, #4062 ....15.00
Bowl, Antique Gold, lacy rim, #5061 ....10.00
Bowl, Antique Gold, scalloped, #5163, 7" 12.00
Bowl, Antique Gold, single pear, #3783 ....7.50
Bowl, divided vegetable; Stardust, 10½x7" 15.00
Bowl, fruit; Starflower, 5½" 10.00
Bowl, fruit; Thistle 10.00
Bowl, Granada Gold, dbl pear hdls, #3782 ....15.00
Bowl, Holly, 9¾" 25.00
Bowl, Rhythmic Yellow, #2092 ....18.00
Bowl, Thistle, 10" 25.00
Butter dish, Thistle 20.00
Candle holder, Granada Gold, #5138 ....7.00
Candy dish, Blossom Ring, stainless hdl, 6" 4.00
Candy dish, Caribbean, bl 10.00
Casserole, Blueberry, ind, w/lid 12.00
Casserole, Thistle, w/hdls, lg 40.00
Casserole, Thistle, w/hdls, sm 10.00
Chop plate, Starflower, 12½" 20.00
Chop plate, Thistle 20.00
Coffee warmer, Blue Daisy 15.00
Coffeepot, Blueberry 35.00
Cornucopia, Terra Rose, bl, 6½" 18.00
Cosmos, Antique Gold, #5134 ....20.00
Creamer, Golden Blossom 6.50
Creamer, Golden Harvest 8.50
Creamer & sugar bowl, Golden Harvest 17.50
Creamer & sugar bowl, Sculptured Fruit 10.00
Creamer & sugar bowl, Thistle 15.00
Cup, Amber Glo 4.00
Cup, Country Garden 10.00
Cup, Starflower 10.00

Cup & saucer, Bittersweet	14.00
Cup & saucer, Thistle	11.00
Flower bowl, Granada Gold, #3410-9, 10¼"	15.00
Gravy boat, Golden Harvest	10.00
Gravy boat, Thistle, +liner	20.00
Lug soup, Magnolia	10.00
Lug soup, Thistle	10.00
Pitcher, Aztec, A-4053, 12"	15.00
Pitcher, Fruit, 1-qt	25.00
Pitcher, Golden Harvest, 2-qt	25.00
Pitcher, Town & Country Green, 3-pt	35.00
Plate, Blue Daisy, 10"	12.00
Plate, Country Garden, 10"	15.00
Plate, Jonquil, 6"	5.00
Plate, Little Boy Blue	30.00
Plate, Magnolia, 10"	10.00
Plate, Magnolia, 6"	4.00
Plate, Rooster, 9¾"	12.00
Plate, sandwich; Orchard Song, center metal hdl	6.00
Plate, Starflower, 10"	12.00
Plate, Thistle, 10"	12.00
Plate, Thistle, 6"	4.00
Plate, Thistle, 9"	8.00
Saucer, Water Lily, 6"	2.00
Shakers, Golden Harvest, pr	15.00
Shakers, Thistle, pr	15.00
Sherbet, Tulip, yel	15.00
Sugar bowl, Colonial, w/lid	8.00
Sugar bowl, Garden Flower, ind, sm	10.00
Sugar bowl, Golden Harvest	6.00
Sugar bowl, Starflower, w/lid	12.00
Teapot, Colonial	24.00
Tray, celery; Thistle	18.00
Tray, relish; Country Garden, 11¼"	20.00
Vase, Antique Gold, #2067, 7"	10.00
Vase, Antique Gold, #3413, 7"	10.00
Vase, Caribbean, #5190, 6x5½"	6.00
Vase, Colonial Silver, #5023, 9¾"	20.00
Wig stand, blonde, 14"	175.00
Wig stand, brunette, 14"	125.00
Wig stand, man, 14"	250.00

Steamship Collectibles

For centuries, ocean-going vessels with their venturesome officers and crews were the catalyst that changed the unknown aspects of our world to the known. Changing economic conditions, unfortunately, have now placed the North American shipping industry in the same jeopardy as the American passenger train. They are becoming a memory. The surge of interest in railroad collectibles and the railroad-related steamship lines has lead collectors to examine the whole spectrum of steamship collectibles.

Our advisors for this category are Lila and Fred Shrader; they are listed in the Directory under California.

Ash tray, French Line, milk glass, CGT logo, 2½x3"	9.00
Banner, Queen Elizabeth portrait in gold leaf, leather	11.00
Book, Queen Mary-A Record in Pictures, hardcover, '30-'36	40.00
Book, Titanic, A Night To Remember, Walter Lord, 232-pg	12.00
Booklet, Cunard, Conquest of the N Atlantic, 28-pg, 1950, M	13.00
Bookmark, Cunard Adventurer, red leather w/gold portrait	5.00
Candy tin, Queen Elizabeth I, Benson's, portrait lid	30.00
Cigarette box, Queen Mary, plastic, portrait lid, 3x3¾", M	25.00
Cookbook, Princess Cruises, Island Princess cover, 58-recipes	10.00

Cup, bouillon; American Mail Line	38.00
Deck plan, Antilles/Flandre, 1952, opens to 29x41"	18.00
Deck plan, Franconia III, portrait on cover, opens to 15x21"	5.50
Folder, Caronia II, World Cruise 1958, portrait cover	4.00
Folder, Lamport/Holt, Barbados travel text/photos	3.00
Hudson Bay, calender, 1 sheet, 1932, 29x16", EX	37.50
Lantern, brass, oil burner, Davey & Co London, 14x7", pr	350.00
Lantern, signal; brass, oil burner, bull's eye lens, NM	125.00
Menu, breakfast; Bremen IV, color portrait, May 1938	8.00
Menu, dinner; De Grasse, 1st class, 1951	3.50
Passenger list, Bermuda Cruise, sea gulls/logo in gold leaf	9.00
Passenger list, Constitution, Sunlane Cruise, Aug 1962	6.50
Passport cover, Frederik VIII portrait	11.00
Pin-bk button, Majestic, color portrait, 1896, ¾", M	11.00
Pin-bk button, Normandie, blk/wht photo, 1¼" dia	10.00
Program, music; Cristoforo Colombo, floral cover	3.00
Schedule, United States, pre-maiden voyage, Mar 1952, M	10.00
Sign, La Provence, French Line Flyer, tin litho, 32x28", EX	165.00
Sign, Scandinavian-American Lines, sf tin, steamship, EX	225.00
Stationery, Britannic, name/house flag, 6 sheets, M	24.00
Sugar bowl, Farrell Lines, Internat'l Silver, SP, hdls, M	9.00
Tambourine, Leonardo Da Vinci, plastic, portrait/name, 6", M	7.00
Tie bar, Mauretania II, brass w/portrait in center	16.00
Timetable & map, Pacific Coast Steamships, 1890, EX	12.50
Towel, Queen Elizabeth I, Irish linen, orig folds, 20x30", M	28.00
Tray, France III, portrait, fiberglass, 13½x18"	10.00
Wall plaque, Queen Mary, blk plastic w/gold trim, 6¼x13¼"	12.00

Steins

Steins have been made from pottery, pewter, glass, stoneware, and porcelain, from very small up to the four-liter size. They are decorated by etching, in-mold relief, decals, and occasionally they may be hand painted. Some porcelain steins have lithophane bases. Collectors often specialize in a particular type — faience, regimental, or figural — while others limit themselves to the products of only one manufacturer.

Our advisor for this category is Ron Fox; he is listed in the Directory under New York. See also Mettlach.

Key:
L — liter   PUG — print under glaze
litho — lithophane   tl — thumb lift
POG — print over glaze

Brass, relief: draped nudes, brass lid, 1-L, 9", VG	100.00
Character, barrel, pottery, inlaid lid, ½-L, M	160.00
Character, Bismarck, full color, ca 1950, ½-L, M	250.00
Character, bowling pin, lithophane, ½-L, M	200.00
Character, bowling pin, pottery, ½-L, M	160.00
Character, Drunken Monkey, Musterschutz, ½-L, M	525.00
Character, fox, stoneware, bl, minor flakes, ½-L	300.00
Character, goat, Musterschutz, ½-L, M	500.00
Character, Happy Radish, Musterschutz, rpr finial, ½-L	250.00
Character, Hops Lady, pottery, pewter lid w/dents, ½-L	120.00
Character, judge, Musterschutz, ½-L, M	800.00
Character, man in minstrel show, pottery, flakes, ½-L	160.00
Character, Monk, pottery, chip rpr on base, ½-L	250.00
Character, monkey in top hat, sitting, German verse, pottery	245.00
Character, Munich Child, M Pauson, lithophane, ¼-L, EX	250.00
Character, Munich Child, pottery, MRM #209, sm chip, ½-L	120.00
Character, Munich Child, pottery, Reinemann, hairline, ¼-L	150.00
Character, Munich Child, pottery, Reinemann, ½-L, M	250.00
Character, Munich Child, stoneware, bl, ½-L, M	250.00

Character, Munich Child on barrel, Musterschutz, ½-L, EX ...800.00
Character, Nurnerger Trichter, porc, lithophane, chip, ½-L ...475.00
Character, owl, stoneware, ½-L, M 300.00
Character, Richard Wagner, pottery, post-WWI, flake, ½-L ...160.00
Character, Sad Radish, Musterschutz, .3-L, M 375.00
Character, Sad Radish, Musterschutz, rpr flakes, ½-L 300.00
Character, Singing Pig, Musterschutz, .3-L, M 375.00
Character, skull, pottery, ¼-L, M 350.00
Character, student, porc, hash mks, minor wear, ½-L 300.00

Musterschutz character steins, porcelain, full color, .5L, Stag, $3,850.00; Boar, $3,500.00.

Glass, blown, amber, HP bowling scene, rpl lid, ½-L 150.00
Glass, blown, amber, HP wht trumpeter, gr glass inlay, ½-L ...250.00
Glass, blown, bl, HP wht florals, prism lid, ½-L, M 300.00
Glass, blown, bl opaline, inlaid bl opaline lid, ½-L, M 300.00
Glass, blown, clear, carpenter occupational inlay, ½-L 250.00
Glass, blown, clear, cut oval & line design, ¼-L, M 125.00
Glass, blown, clear, HP barmaid holding glass steins, ½-L 150.00
Glass, blown, clear, HP farmer occupational, ½-L, NM 250.00
Glass, blown, clear, HP floral & verse, 1850s, ½-L, M 400.00
Glass, blown, cobalt, HP florals, inlaid porc lid, ½-L 160.00
Glass, blown, cranberry flashed, porc inlay, ½-L, M 250.00
Glass, blown, HP Saxony crest, ½-L, M 150.00
Glass, blown, lustered, HP wht bike rider, .3-L, M 250.00
Glass, mold blown, inlay lid of Christ & angel, ½-L, M 100.00
Glass, pressed, clear, copper wheel-cut florals, ½-L, M 100.00
Glass, pressed, clear, Hotel Reuter Wash DC on lid, ½-L, M 50.00
Glass, pressed, clear, porc inlay: couples shake hands, ½-L 60.00
Pewter, eng crest, dtd 1825, minor dents & scratches, ½-L 300.00
Pewter, relief: floral & faces, ¼-L, M 120.00
Pewter, relief: hunter, minor base roughness, ½-L 160.00
Pewter, relief: Munich, minor roughness, ½-L 160.00
Pewter, relief: Nurnberg scenes, .3-L, M 120.00
Pewter, relief: suit of armor, ca 1880, 2-L, 10½", VG 400.00
Porc, HP dancers, some wear, ½-L 125.00
Porc, HP fraternal crest, ½-L 250.00
Porc, HP tavern scene, minor wear, 1-L 200.00
Porc, SMS Von Der Tann 1909-12, 4 scenes, roster, 1-L, M .1,600.00
Pottery, etched: cavaliers drinking, ½-L, M 150.00
Pottery, etched: guitar player, mk TP, #1291, ½-L, M 150.00
Pottery, etched: guitar player, rough pewter rim, ½-L 100.00
Pottery, etched: student parade, rpl lid, ½-L 100.00
Pottery, etched: zither player, flake, ½-L 150.00
Pottery, POG, Franziskaner Priest Brau, Munchen, ½-L 125.00
Pottery, relief: cavaliers drinking, base flake, 1-L 100.00

Pottery, relief: couple, post-war, ½-L, M 20.00
Pottery, relief: dice game, 1-L, M 100.00
Pottery, relief: dwarfs, DRGM, dent in lid, 1-L 100.00
Pottery, relief: fox hunt scene, fox family on lid, 1-L, M 125.00
Pottery, relief: man & 2 women, man is lid, KB, 1-L, M 165.00
Pottery, relief: monks, pewter lid, music box, 1-L, M 120.00
Pottery, relief: royal figure, barmaid on lid, sgn KB, 1-L 125.00
Pottery, relief: women & sleeping man, ½-L, M 80.00
Pottery, SMS Thuringen 1910-12, ship scenes, roster, 1-L, M ..900.00
Regimental, 123 Inft ULM 1912-14, roster, porc, ½-L, M 350.00
Regimental, 13 Saxon Jager Dresden 1906-08, ½-L, EX 800.00
Regimental, 158 Inft Paderborn 1901-03, porc, relief, ½-L 350.00
Regimental, 2 Bayr Schw Reiter Landshut 1909-12, porc, ½-L .400.00
Regimental, 2 Garde Foot Berlin 1910-12, roster, porc, ½-L ...350.00
Regimental, 25 Field Art Darmstadt 1894-96, porc, ½-L, EX ..400.00
Regimental, 58 Field Art Minden 1910-12, roster, porc, ½-L ..500.00
Stoneware, POG: barmaid, ½-L, M 125.00
Stoneware, POG: Brauhaus Nurnberg, ½-L, M 200.00
Stoneware, POG: drunken soldiers, ½-L, M 150.00
Stoneware, POG: fireman occupational, ½-L, M 250.00
Stoneware, POG: floral & verse, ½-L, M 125.00
Stoneware, relief: fireman occupational, strap rpr, ½-L 100.00
Stoneware, relief: floral & verse, ½-L, EX 100.00
Stoneware, relief: trumpeter & horse, mk, porc lid, 1-L, EX ...125.00
Stoneware, relief: 2 women, JWR, base flakes, 1½-L 125.00

Westerwald, cut design, with sacrifical lamb, dtd 1792, 10", VG, $1,000.00; Porcelain, Venus and Adonis in reserve, marked with beehive, 1-L, $2,000.00.

Steuben

The Steuben Glass Works of Corning, New York, was founded in 1903 by Frederick Carder and Thomas Hawkes. They made art glass of high quality similar to some of Tiffany's. One of their earliest types of art glass was aurene, a lustrous metallic gold or blue. They also made verre de soie, rosaline, and silverene. In 1918 Steuben became a branch of Corning Glass Works.

In the listings that follow, examples are signed unless noted otherwise. See also Aurene; Cluthra.

Key: ACB — acid cut back

Bottle, scent; verre de soie, wisteria stopper, #1445, 4" 275.00
Bowl, ACB, floral, plum jade, 3-layer, #1700, 7" H 2,750.00

Bowl, acid-cut-back Chinese motif, plum jade, signed with fleur-de-lis, 4x8", $2,400.00.

Bowl, ACB, Matzu, gr jade, globular, paper label, #1700, 6½" . .800.00
Bowl, ACB, Nedra, blk on alabaster, #1700, 7½" 1,000.00
Bowl, amethyst to clear, elaborate eng w/lion's heads, 4½" 300.00
Bowl, bl aurene on calcite, no mk, 3¼x8" 250.00
Bowl, bl aurene on calcite, scalloped, sgn Carder/Aurene, 6" . .500.00
Bowl, blk jade, #7023 . . . . .250.00
Bowl, cerise ruby shading to clear, #7171 . . . . .175.00
Bowl, Florentia, frosted border, gr leaf center, 12" 1,500.00
Bowl, gold aurene on calcite, 12" 400.00
Bowl, gold aurene on calcite, 2½x10" 350.00
Bowl, grotesque, ivory, 5¾x9½" 375.00
Bowl, rosaline, #2687, lg 350.00
Box, appl gr threading, gr faceted knob, 4½" dia 125.00
Candlestick, gr body & base, bl ring hdl, 3¾", pr 300.00
Candlestick, lt amber twist on clear hollow stem, 10", pr 425.00
Champagne, opal base/cup, twisted lav stem 250.00
Champagne, opal w/Cintra stem 150.00
Champagne, Oriental Poppy, gr stem 700.00
Champagne, swirled gold, ruby top, clear stem, 6¼" 85.00
Cocktail set, crystal w/blk reeding, jug #7056+6 cordials 600.00
Cocktail shaker, wht w/blk bosses & stopper, #7463, 9" 175.00
Compote, gold aurene on calcite, 4x6" 250.00
Compote, gold aurene on calcite, 8x8" 400.00
Compote, gr jade, alabaster ring hdls/ped ft, #2942, 8½x10" . .425.00
Compote, hollow amber & mica stem w/prunts, clear bowl, 8" .350.00
Compote, hollow bl & mica stem, swirled amber base/bowl, 8" .495.00
Compote, verre de soie, ribbed, fleur-de-lis mk, 4x7" 300.00
Compote, yel jade, alabaster base, #6252, 4½" 300.00
Console bowl, verre de soie, 16", +2 4" candlesticks 675.00
Figurine, duckling, Lloyd Atkins, 1964, 8" 250.00
Figurine, elephant, head bk, trunk upraised, script mk, 8" 300.00
Figurine, Great Dolphin, Lloyd Atkins, 1968, 11½" 800.00
Figurine, koala baby, 5¾" 1,150.00
Figurine, owl, Donald Pollard, 1955, 5" 300.00
Figurine, Trout & Fly, 18k gold fly, James Houston, 9½" 1,100.00
Goblet, gold ruby, clear stem/base, #8506, 7" 85.00
Goblet, rosaline, alabaster stem/base, etched grapes, 9" 250.00
Goblet, rosaline, alabaster twist stem, sgn Carder, 7" 325.00
Goblet, selenium red, etched grapes .400.00
Jar, ACB, leaves & flowers, gr on wht, w/lid, 5½" 800.00
Lamp, table; ACB, poppies, gold on alabaster, 12" base, EX . .1,500.00
Lamp base, ACB, wide leaves/pods, gr, 14" 750.00
Mug, etched fern, red threading at top, fleur-de-lis mk, 5" 200.00
Paperweight, yel-amber, cut/etched fish, chamfered rectangle . .275.00
Plaque, girl's profile, cire perdue, sgn Carder, 7x9" 1,000.00

Plate, amethyst, 8½" 100.00
Plate, floral/fleur-de-lis etched on blk-cased crystal, 8½" 175.00
Plate, gold ruby, swirled, no mk, 8½" .90.00
Plate, gr jade, 8½", set of 12 . . . . .300.00
Plate, Oriental Poppy, 8½" 400.00
Salt cellar, gold on calcite, ftd, mk/#3067, 1½" H 250.00
Shade, gold, sgn w/fleur-de-lis, 2¼" fitting, 6½" dia 175.00
Sherbet, bl aurene w/calcite, +underplate 200.00
Sherbet, rosaline w/alabaster ft, 5", +underplate 300.00
Tazza, gr jade w/alabaster stem & base, 3½x6" 250.00
Toddy glass, yel jade, #7711 . . . . .150.00
Vase, ACB, butterfly, pk on alabaster, teakwood lid, 8" 750.00
Vase, ACB, floral, blk on amethyst, mk, 19" 3,500.00
Vase, ACB, Matzu, jade gr on alabaster, 8" 700.00
Vase, ACB, Matzu, rose on alabaster, #6034, 12" 625.00
Vase, ACB, vintage blk on bl, mk/#2687, 10½x9" 2,300.00
Vase, bl aurene on calcite, flared/scalloped, 5¾x6" 650.00
Vase, bl jade, fleur-de-lis mk, 4¾" 400.00
Vase, clear w/blk ft, Art Deco etching, paneled, 6½" 100.00
Vase, controlled airtraps, threaded stem, flared, 7½" 170.00
Vase, Dia Quilt, Bristol yel, wht threads on top, mk, 7½" 300.00
Vase, dk bl jade, ribbed, #7430, 5½" 2,000.00
Vase, eng decor, sgn, #7307, 12" 575.00
Vase, gold aurene on calcite, scalloped rim, 6" 450.00
Vase, gold aurene on calcite, trumpet form, #346, 8" 400.00
Vase, gr jade, alabaster base, #938, 7" 180.00
Vase, gr jade w/alabaster, fan form, mk, 8" 400.00
Vase, gr jade w/alabaster 'M' hdls, sgn Carder, 12" 600.00
Vase, gr jade w/gold-threaded top, fleur-de-lis mk, 10" 1,000.00
Vase, gr threads, airtraps, cylindrical w/flared rim, 9½" 165.00
Vase, Grotesque, Flemish bl to clear, block-letter mk, 9" 300.00
Vase, intaglio flowers/leaves, ftd, mk/#7564, 6" 250.00
Vase, ivorene, flared, mk, 4½" 225.00
Vase, ivorene, flared, no mk, 7½" 225.00
Vase, ivorene, trumpet form w/sm lily form ea side, mk, 12" . . .900.00
Vase, jack-in-the-pulpit; ivorene, mk, 6" 500.00
Vase, millefiori, wht/gr on gold, no mk, 4½" 2,600.00
Vase, Oriental Poppy, #6500, 4½" .1,200.00
Vase, rosaline, alabaster base, 8" 300.00
Vase, rosaline, alabaster ring hdls & base, #2909, 10" 375.00
Vase, ruby, ribbed, #7372, 12" 300.00
Vase, topaz, ribbed, flared ped ft, mk, 12" 110.00
Vase, topaz, 3-prong, tree trunk form, mk 125.00
Vase, Tyrian, gold aurene leaves/vines on gr to purple, 9" . .10,000.00
Vase, verre de soie, ftd, paper label, 7" 250.00

Stevengraph

A Stevengraph is a small picture made of woven silk resembling an elaborate ribbon, created by Thomas Stevens in England in the latter half of the 1800s. They were matted and framed by Stevens, usually with his name appearing on the mat or, more commonly, the trade announcement on the back of the mat. He also produced silk post cards and bookmarks, all of which have 'Stevens' woven in silk on one of the mitered corners.

Anyone wishing to learn more about Stevengraphs is encouraged to contact the Stevengraph Collectors' Association, whose address can be found in the Directory under Clubs, Newsletters, and Catalogs.

Bookmark, Christmas, tassled, 12x2¾", M in wrapper 175.00
Bookmark, Gen Washington Centennial 110.00
Declaration of Independence, fr, 7¼" 160.00
First Set, tennis match, orig mat, 2x6" 325.00
For Life or Death-Heroism on Land, matted & orig fr 350.00

H.R.H., The Prince of Wales, $150.00.

Vase, fishscales in gold/red MOP, bl-gr liner, 12½" 600.00
Vase, gr, clear rigaree, gold rim, trumpet form, mk, 18" 155.00
Vase, gr to clear intaglio scrolls, stick form, 17" 550.00
Vase, gray, pk int, appl florals, ruffled egg form, 4½", pr 245.00
Vase, maroon, wht int, mk, 11" 275.00
Vase, peachblow, appl amber hdl/leaves, opal flowers, 9¾" 450.00
Vase, pk, wht int, appl florals/branches, 6⅜x4" 175.00
Vase, pk, wht int, 3 amber leaf ft/3 opal flowers, 8" 375.00
Vase, pk/wht intaglio florals, sq form, 4 snail ft, 4" 195.00
Vase, Swirl MOP, amber w/red in recesses, turq int, 17x5" . . .995.00
Vase, Swirl MOP, bl & dk rose, 10" .525.00
Vase, Swirl MOP, purple w/lav, bulbous w/stick neck, 7" 895.00
Vase, Swirl MOP, tangerine, 11x4½" 650.00
Vase, wht, rose int, appl amber chestnut/etc, 13½x6" 275.00
Vase, yel, wht int, 2 appl red cherries/branches, 9½" 165.00
Vase, yel/tan/bl swirl, enamel-relief neck, pear form, 13" 280.00
Vase, zigzags in orange/yel/wht, 9½" 375.00
Vase/toothpick holder, crimped, egg form, ftd, 4" 75.00

Last Lap, bicycles 225.00
Post card, Shakespeare's Birthplace 45.00
Start, The; horse race 160.00
Struggle, The; horse race 160.00

Stevens and Williams

Stevens and Williams glass was produced at the Brierly Hill Glassworks in Stourbridge, England, for nearly a century, beginning in the 1830s. They were credited with being among the first to develop a method of manufacturing a more affordable type of cameo glass. Other lines were also made — silver deposit, alexandrite, and engraved rock crystal, to name but a few.

Our advisor for this category is Don Williams; he is listed in the Directory under Iowa.

Basket, opal, appl amber flowers/leaves, twist hdl, 8½" 375.00
Basket, pk cased, appl amber leaves/acorns, thorn hdl, 12" 475.00
Bottle, scent; gr & crystal swirls, mk silver collar, 9" 165.00
Bowl, cameo, bamboo/floral, pk on yel int, 8-crimp, 3½x5⅝" . .750.00
Bowl, wht w/HP floral, bl int, appl amber rim/ft, 6x7" 325.00
Cornucopia, rose cased, appl apple/blooms, amber ft, 9" 1,150.00
Cruet, Arboresque, amber w/wht opaque, amber stopper, 9½" . .145.00
Cruet, florals on pk opaque, reed hdl, clear stopper, 1890 . . . . .175.00
Epergne, vaseline opal, 3-lily, appl rigaree, 24" 425.00
Jam dish, bl/wht stripes, ruffled rose bowl shape, 6x4" 110.00
Lamp, fairy; Swirl, rose MOP, mk Clarke cup, 4½x4" 550.00
Lamp, student; acid-cut yel shade, brass, 12½" 1,250.00
Liqueur set, floral intaglio, gr to clear, 7-pc on tray 750.00
Rose bowl, basketweave, pk overlay, egg shape/pleated, 6x4½" .395.00
Rose bowl, cranberry opal, upright box-pleated top, 3½" 175.00
Rose bowl, gold prunus on shaded brn, egg shape/pleated, 5" . .475.00
Rose bowl, Matsu-No-Ke frosted/appl on bl satin, 4½" H 750.00
Rose bowl, pk latticinio, mk, 4" H 275.00
Sweetmeat jar, cameo, bamboo stalks/gilt metal lid/hdl, 3x5" . .865.00
Tumbler, amber, appl amber pear/apple/branch, 3¾x3¾" 225.00
Vase, amethyst/opal stripes, trumpet form, in SP holder, 8" 160.00
Vase, cameo, bl, wht int, florals/dragonfly, unmk, 9½x3½" . .3,000.00
Vase, cameo, wht on rose, prunus, unmk, 11½" 3,500.00
Vase, cameo, 3 geese/palm trees, amber/clear on frost, 3½" 750.00
Vase, cream, pk int, appl leaf, 8-crimp top, mk, 6½x4" 145.00
Vase, cream, pk int, appl mc florals, scalloped, 7¼", pr 325.00

Cameo vase, white leafy boughs on red, attributed to Joshua Hodgetts, ca 1886, 12", $5,000.00.

Stiegel

Baron Henry Stiegel produced glassware in Pennsylvania as early as 1760, very similar to glass being made concurrently in Germany and England. Without substantiating evidence, it is impossible to positively attribute a specific article to his manufacture. Although he made other types of glass, today the term Stiegel generally refers to any very early ware made in shapes and colors similar to those he is known to have produced — especially that with etched or enameled decoration. It is generally conceded, however, that most glass of this type is of European origin.

Bottle, bride's; flowering plants/man & Fr horn, 7" 175.00
Bottle, pocket; daisy in hexagon, clear w/lt lav tone, 6" 650.00
Bottle, sapphire bl, right swirl, pontil, pocket type, 5½" 1,050.00
Bottle, scent; amethyst, swirled ribs, lay-down, no lid, 3" 100.00
Bottle, scent; cobalt, swirled, flat-sided ogee form, 2¾" 150.00
Bowl, dk cobalt, expanded diamond, appl ft, 2x3" dia 1,150.00
Creamer, dk cobalt, expanded diamond, appl hdl, 3¾" 1,150.00
Decanter, tulip plant eng, NM stopper, 12" 475.00
Flip, eng rim, eng squiggles on lid, 7½" 550.00

Flip, eng rim, fluted, tooled rim, pontil, 6" 190.00
Flip, floral/deer, mc enamel, 4" 150.00
Flip, panel molded, eng upper rim, 4½" 75.00
Mug, berries, mc enamel, appl strap hdl, 3¾" 225.00
Mug, tulip plant eng, appl strap hdl, 6½" 250.00
Salt cellar, clear w/appl bl rim, expanded diamond 325.00
Salt cellar, cobalt, blown, swirled/ftd 750.00
Salt cellar, cobalt, rnd w/scalloped ft, M 600.00
Whiskey tumbler, birds w/in sunburst eng, 3⅛" 575.00

Stocks and Bonds

   Scripophily (scrip-awfully), the collecting of 'worthless' old stocks and bonds, gained recognition as a serious collectible around the mid-1970s. Today there are an estimated 5,000 collectors in the United States and 15,000 world-wide. Collectors who come from numerous business fields mainly enjoy the hobby aspect, though there are those who consider scripophily an investment. Some collectors like the historical significance that certain certificates have. Others prefer the beauty of older stocks and bonds that were printed in various colors with fancy artwork and ornate engravings. Even autograph collectors are found in this field, on the lookout for signed certificates.

   Many factors help determine the collector value: autograph value, age of the certificate, the industry represented, whether it is issued or not, its attractiveness, condition, and collector demand. Certificates from the mining, energy, and railroad industries are the most popular with collectors. Other industries or special collecting fields include banking, automobiles, aircraft, and territorials.

   In many of the following listings, two-letter state abbreviations immediately follow company name. All are 'issued' and in near-mint condition unless noted otherwise.

   Our advisor for this category is Warren Anderson; he is listed in the Directory under Utah.

Key:
cp — coupon	U — unissued
I/C — issued/cancelled	vgn — vignette
I/U —— issued/uncancelled	

American Coal, PA/1869, train vgn, Latmer Bros print, I/C 45.00
American Coal, PA/1869, train vgn, red tax stamp on bk, I/C . .45.00
Belt RR, IN/1882, train/town vgn, blk/gold, scarce, EX 55.00
Blanca Mutual Mining & Milling, CO/1901, miner vgn, I/U . . .45.00
Blk Range Mining & Milling, IL/1881, vgn, fancy title, I/U 75.00
Burlington & MO River RR, NB/1878, farm vgn, ABNCo, I/C .40.00
Cleveland Gas Light & Coke, OH/1887, vgn, blk/wht, I/C 40.00
Confederate, 1863, vgn, blk ink, for $500 w/coupons, NM 150.00
Consolidated Wilshire Mining, AZ/1917, gr border, 5x8", I/U . .10.00
Continental Oil & Gas, TX/1921, train/gusher vgn, I/U 16.00
Corpus Christi Railway & Light, TX/1916, SBNCo print, I/U . .15.00
Cuba RR, 1910, train vgn, brn/blk ink, EX 12.50
Curtis Consolidated Mining, NV/1880, ornate artwork, I/U 50.00
Elizabeth Gold Mines, AZ/1904, 3 vgns, gr border/seal, I/U 20.00
Ely Consolidated Copper, NV/1917, goddess vgn, RBNCo, I/U .18.00
Fisk Ophir Mining, UT/1929, miner vgn, brn seal, I/U 12.00
Gold Fount Consolidated Mines, NV/1919, gold seal, I/C 16.00
Goldfield Rex Mining, AZ/1905, vgn, fancy artwork, I/U 25.00
Henrietta Mining & Milling, CO/1909, eagle vgn, I/U 20.00
Joy Prairie Mining & Developing, MO/1925, MO seal vgn, I/U .10.00
Kansas City, Mexico & Orient Railway, MO/1909, vgn, I/C 18.00
Kirwin Telephone Co, Kirwin KS, 1887 . . . . .30.00
Korinek Veterinary Remedy, OR/1914, buffalo vgn, I/U 22.00
Marcellus Farmers Elevator, WA/1925, 6" eagle vgn, I/C 14.00

Meadow Mtn Mining, CO/1904, fancy title, bl border, I/U 30.00
Moulton Mining, MT Territory/1887, 2 vgns, sgn W Clark, I/C .75.00
Nacimiento Copper, NY/1881, vgn, bold title, +coupons, I/U .125.00
Nat'l Consolidated Oil, WV/1902, oilfield vgn, I/U 25.00
Nat'l Marine Bank of Baltimore, MA/1890, ship vgn, EX 25.00
Olympic Mining, WA/1905, fine vgn, gold seal, I/U 25.00
Oregon Branch Pacific RR, OR/1860s, scenic train vgn, U 30.00
Park City Mining/Smelting, CO/'25, vgn, ABNCo, I/C 25.00
Potsdam Gold Mining, CO/1895, cavern vgn, gold seal, I/U 30.00
Raymond Mining Co, UT/1903, eagle vgn, blk/wht, I/C 18.00
Red Arrow Oil & Gas, AZ/1917, gusher vgn, gold seal, I/U 14.00
Red Indian Gold Mines Ltd, Canada/1939, brn border, I/U 10.00
Rockford Gold Mining, Cripple Creek CO, vgn, 1900 . . . . .35.00
School board, RI/1907, Indian vgn, fancy border, 10x12", EX . . .50.00
Silver Hill Mining, Dakota Territory/1885, 3-color, I/U 75.00
Smith Motor Truck Corp, VA/1917, gr ABNCo print, lg, I/U . .25.00
Tonopah Divide Mining, NV/1919, vgn, orange print, I/C 14.00
Treasure Hill Coalition Mining, AZ/1918, miner vgn, I/U 15.00
Union Mutual Ins, 1874, ship/eagle/sailor vgn, EX 25.00
United Smelters, Railway & Copper, WY/1909, 2 vgns, I/U 45.00
Wabash Oil & Gas, CO/1901, gladiator vgn, gold seal, I/U 22.00
Wagoner Refining, OK/1922, 2 refinery vgns, gr seal, I/U 15.00
Ziegler Bullfrog Mines, SD/1907, gr bullfrog vgn, I/U 40.00

Stockton

   The Stockton Terra Cotta Company was established in 1891 in Stockton, California. In 1879 the name was changed to Stockton Art Pottery Company, and several lines of art pottery, the Rekston line among them, were introduced. Their wares included vases, pitchers, jardinieres, umbrella stands, and teapots — many of which were styled with scrolling ornate handles and graceful shapes. Some examples bear the 'Rekston' mark. The pottery closed in 1902 after a third devastating fire that destroyed their buildings.

Ewer, floral on dk brn, branch hdl, 7" .145.00
Lamp base, floral on dk brn, w/fittings, 11" 150.00
Sugar bowl, ivy leaves emb, gold on cobalt, w/lid 30.00
Vase, floral on dk brn, mk, 8" 175.00
Vase, lt to dk brn gloss, ruffled, imp mk, 2x4¾" 210.00

Mug, hand-painted floral on brown glaze, three-handled, 5", $450.00.

Stoneware

   There are three broad periods of time that collectors of American pottery can look to in evaluating and dating the stoneware and earthenware in their collections. Among the first permanent settlers in America were English and German potters who found a great demand for their individually-turned wares. The early pottery was produced from red and yellow clays scraped from the ground at surface levels. The earthenware made in these potteries was fragile and coated with lead glazes that periodically created health problems for the people who ate or drank from it. There was little stoneware available for sale until the early 1800s, because the clays used in its production were not readily available in many areas and transportation was prohibitively expensive. The opening of the Erie Canal and improved roads brought about a dramatic increase in the accessibility of stoneware clay, and many new potteries began to open in New York and New England.

Collectors have difficulty today locating earthenware and stoneware jugs produced prior to 1840, because few have survived intact. These ovoid or pear-shaped jugs were designed to be used on a daily basis. When cracked or severely chipped, they were quickly discarded.

The value of hand-crafted pottery is often determined by the cobalt decoration it carries. Pieces with elaborate scenes (a chicken pecking corn, a bluebird on a branch, a stag standing near a pine tree, a sailing ship, or people) may easily bring $1,000 to $12,000 at auction.

After the Civil War, there was a need and a national demand for stoneware jugs, crocks, canning jars, churns, spittoons, and a wide variety of other pottery items. The competition among the many potteries reached the point where only the largest could survive. To cut costs, most potteries did away with all but the simplest kinds of decoration on their wares. Time-consuming brush-painted birds or flowers quickly gave way to more simply-executed swirls or numbers and stenciled designs. The coming of home refrigeration and Prohibition in 1919 effectively destroyed the American stoneware industry.

Investment possibilities: 1) Early 19th-century stoneware with elaborate decorations and a potter's mark is expensive and will continue to rise in price. 2) Late 19th-century hand-thrown stoneware with simple cobalt swirls or numbers is still reasonably priced and a good investment. 3) Mass-produced stoneware (ca. 1890-1920) is available in large quantities, inexpensive, and has been slowly increasing in price over the last ten years.

Due to the steadily increasing values of decorated stoneware, fakes are more frequently appearing in the market place. Newly-designed cobalt birds, florals, and deer are being applied to old crocks and jugs. Some reproduction stoneware is dated on the bottom of the piece. The Beaumont Pottery of York, Maine, which produced the 'finest reproduction stoneware of the 20th century,' scratched the date into each piece.

Many skillfully repaired pieces are also surfacing, and prices should reflect that condition. Look for a slight change in color and texture. The use of a black light is also useful in exposing some repairs. Buyer beware! Hint: Buy only from reputable dealers who will guarantee their merchandise.

In the following listings, 'c/s' means 'cobalt on salt glaze'; all decoration described before this abbreviation is in cobalt. See also Bennington.

Bank, tiered top highlighted w/bl, ovoid, incised name, 7" 600.00
Bottle, gray salt glaze, doughnut form, 9" 145.00
Bowl, milk; floral, brushed, c/s, hdls, imp #1, 12", EX 650.00
Bowl, milk; foliage devices at rim, c/s, spout, hdls, 11½" 550.00
Churn, bird (long-tailed), quilled, c/s, Whites Utica, rpr 625.00
Churn, bird on flower stem, c/s, Whites Utica, 3-gal 1,200.00
Churn, floral, brushed, c/s, ovoid, unmk, ca 1850 ....450.00
Churn, floral (heavy slip), c/s, unmk, ca 1850, 4-gal 450.00
Churn, shield/rampant lion & beaver, c/s, prof rpr, 18" 850.00
Churn, tulip, brushed, c/s, IM Mead, 17", EX 600.00
Crock, #6/flourish, quilled, c/s, 13" 70.00
Crock, bird, c/s, Ottman Bros & Co Ft Edward NY, 3-gal, EX .395.00
Crock, bird (long-tailed), slip cup, c/s, NA White, 11", EX 425.00
Crock, bird on branch, c/s, FT Wright & Son, MA, 1-gal 375.00
Crock, bird on floral branch, c/s, Ottman Bros, NY, 4-gal 350.00

Crock, bird/flourish, quilled, c/s, C Hart & Son, 12", VG 300.00
Crock, bird/flowers, c/s, NA White & Son Utica, 4-gal, EX ...450.00
Crock, brushwork, c/s, appl hdls, 6x10", EX 260.00
Crock, butter; leaves, c/s, hdls, no lid, 6x10", VG 260.00
Crock, dragonfly, c/s, NY Stoneware Ft Edward NY, 1-gal 250.00
Crock, floral, brushed, c/s, unmk, 1870s, 2-gal 120.00
Crock, floral, c/s, unmk, late 1870s, 5-gal 240.00
Crock, floral (bold), quilled, c/s, NA White & Son, 12", EX ...475.00
Crock, floral (extensive), c/s, J Shepard Jr, 1860s, 6-gal 1,200.00
Crock, floral (stylized), quilled, c/s, 11", VG 95.00
Crock, flower & leaf, c/s, NA White & Son Utica NY, 1-gal ...135.00
Crock, flower cornucopia, c/s, J Burger NY, ca 1860, 5-gal ...3,500.00
Crock, hen pecking corn, c/s, Haxstun-Ottman, 1860s, 4-gal ..600.00
Crock, lily & leaf, c/s, John Burger, ca 1855-1866, 2-gal 275.00
Crock, parrot on branch, c/s, FB Norton Worcester MA, 4-gal .675.00
Crock, partridge in pear tree, c/s, unmk, 1870s, 6-gal 550.00
Crock, stencil: AP Donaghho, c/s, 17½" 75.00
Crock, stencil: floral, c/s, A Conrad New Geneva PA, 3-gal ...145.00
Crock, tornadoes/#2, brushed, c/s, 8x10" 85.00
Crock, tulip/#2, c/s, 10", EX 105.00

Butter churn, dated 1876, Whites Utica, N.Y., VG, 18", $850.00.

Ewer, snake (brn w/wht dots) as hdl coils about neck, 8" 1,125.00
Figurine, dog, seated, bl face/ears, 7¾" 1,800.00
Figurine, spaniel, Staffordshire type, tan w/orange dots, 7½" ...200.00
Footwarmer, Dorchester Pottery 45.00
Jar, Albany slip w/brushed ochre florals, ca 1880, 3-gal 345.00
Jar, canning; gray w/gr-yel highlights, imp John Bell, 6½" 195.00
Jar, canning; squiggles/drips, c/s, 7½" 175.00
Jar, floral, brushed, c/s, Lyons, 1850s, inset lid, 2-gal 185.00
Jar, floral, brushed, c/s, stenciled mk, ca 1880, 12-gal 300.00
Jar, floral, c/s, ovoid, open hdls, sm edge chip, 8" 70.00
Jar, floral (covers front), c/s, unmk, 1860s, 16-gal 325.00
Jar, floral (simple), c/s, 12½" 135.00
Jar, floral (stylized), c/s, att NY State, ca 1870s, 2-gal 175.00
Jar, floral (vining), brushed, c/s, Hamilton & Jones, 4-gal 225.00
Jar, floral/#2, brushed, c/s, 10¾", NM 175.00
Jar, snuff; stencil: Maccoboy & wreath, c/s, 1880s 130.00
Jar, stencil: Demuth's Snuff, Lancaster PA, unmk, 1890s 60.00
Jar, stencil: ES&B New Brighton PA, 1890s, 2-gal 65.00
Jar, stencil: Hamilton & Jones, c/s, rim chips, 12" 165.00
Jar, stencil: Hamilton & Jones PA, brushed swirls, 5-gal 350.00
Jar, stencil: James Hamilton Greensboro PA, c/s, 2-gal 115.00
Jar, swirls/1860, c/s, semi-ovoid, unmk, 3-gal 325.00

Jar, tobacco; deer/birds/cherubs appl on bark, dog atop 375.00
Jar, tulip & leaf, c/s, Burger & Lang NY, 1870s, 3-gal 300.00
Jug, #2/2 sm hearts, brushed, c/s, DW Graves, 14", EX 175.00
Jug, Albany slip, pear shaped, 3-gal 65.00
Jug, Albany slip w/resist label: Chas Hogg, appl hdl, 3¾" 125.00
Jug, batter; brushed at spout & drop hdls, c/s, unmk, 1850s 250.00
Jug, batter; snowflake stencil+brushwork, c/s, Cowden, 1-gal . .575.00
Jug, bird, c/s, EJ Gately 83 Kneeland St Boston, 5-gal, EX 360.00
Jug, bird, c/s, Whites Utica, 2-gal 310.00
Jug, bird on branch, c/s, Haxstun-Ottman & Co, 12", NM 350.00
Jug, bird on branch, c/s, NY Stoneware Co, 14", EX 450.00
Jug, bird on branch, c/s, Poland Spring Mineral Water, 5-gal . .375.00
Jug, bird on branch, c/s, Thompson & Tyler, 1850s, 1-gal 675.00
Jug, chicken standing on table, c/s, Wm Warner, rpr, 13" 675.00
Jug, floral, brushed, c/s, Penn Yan, 1860s, 2-gal 150.00
Jug, floral, c/s, N Clark Jr Athens NY, ovoid, 2-gal 150.00
Jug, floral, c/s, Thompson & Tyler, ca 1858-1859, 2-gal 400.00
Jug, floral, c/s, unmk, 1850s, 2-gal .135.00
Jug, floral (elaborate), slip cup, c/s, NA White & Son, 14" 375.00
Jug, floral (squiggle line), c/s, NA White & Son, 1-gal 110.00
Jug, floral (stylized), c/s, C Hart & Co Odensburgh, 2-gal 230.00
Jug, grapes & leaves, c/s, Edmonds & Co, MA, 2-gal 475.00
Jug, leaf (triangular), c/s, ovoid, 1-gal 90.00
Jug, premium; Albany slip, incising, WG Ginder, 1900, 5½" . .115.00
Jug, splash, c/s, J Bennage 1837 mk, ovoid, 2-gal 240.00
Jug, stencil: A Hale...Communion Wine, c/s, 1-gal 100.00
Jug, stencil: Ferraud Williams...Detroit, c/s, 1890s, 2-gal 110.00
Jug, waves, brushed, c/s, att Greensboro PA, 1870s, 2-gal 145.00
Measure, no decor, unmk, ca 1890s 75.00
Mug, bands/simple brushed motif, c/s, sgn GNF, brn int, 3¾" . . .45.00
Pitcher, bird on branch, brushed, c/s, Chelsea #2, 13", EX 500.00
Pitcher, emb bust of girl/ivy leaves/etc, c/s, bbl form, 8" 135.00
Pitcher, emb roses/people on treebark, c/s, bbl form, 8" 95.00
Pitcher, Flat Iron bldg/wind-swept lady, c/s, Robinson, 9" 200.00
Pitcher, floral (heavy), brushed, c/s, unmk PA, 1850s 450.00
Pitcher, floral (simple), c/s, unmk NY State, 1860s 300.00
Pitcher, floral (stylized), brushed, c/s, unmk PA, 1850s, lg 450.00
Pitcher, tobacco spit, unmk, late 1800s 400.00
Pitcher, tree, c/s, att NY State, 1850s 325.00
Spittoon, leaf, brushed, c/s, ca 1850s, 7" dia 325.00
Spittoon, leaf (stylized), c/s, unmk, 12" dia 345.00
Tumbler, ftd, die stamped: W Bane/1857, bl highlights, 4" 800.00
Water cooler, floral, brushed, c/s, midwest, 1860s, 4-gal 220.00
Water cooler, floral, quilled, c/s, Whites Utica #5, EX 475.00
Water cooler, floral vines (heavy), c/s, German, ca 1900 . . . . .275.00
Water cooler, sunflower, c/s, Albany NY, ca 1880, 2-gal 1,200.00

Crock, fantail bird on branch, N.W. White & Son, Utica, N.Y., 9½", $650.00.

Store

Perhaps more more than any other yester-year establishment, the country store evokes the most nostalgic feelings for folks old enough to remember its charms — barrels for coffee, crackers, and big green pickles; candy in a jar for the grocer to weigh on shiny brass scales; beheaded chickens in the meat case outwardly devoid of nothing but feathers. Today, mementos from this segment of Americana are being collected by those who 'lived it' as well as those less fortunate! See also Advertising.

Cabinet, ribbon; w/racks, maker's name plate, 48x26" 900.00
Cabinet, screw; revolving, 72-drw, complete/orig, 31x23" 900.00
Cabinet, 30-compartment, red pnt, 1890s, 16x28x7" 200.00
Candy jar, glass, ped base, swirl collar/stopper, 30", NM 850.00
Case, collar; IL Showcase Co, ca 1910, 48x6x7" 225.00
Cash drawer, under-counter; oak, combination lock, Tucker . .125.00
Cheese/meat slicer, wood w/steel blade, Gem, pat 1908 . . . . . .120.00
Coffee bin, tin litho house form, Chicago, 1890s, 16x15x12" . .325.00
Display case, walnut, dvtl, 6 glass panes in lid, 9x26x22" 130.00
Fly chaser, CI base, windup, pat 1894, 40", NM 325.00
Hand stamp, mechanical, brass, Arvin, pat 1891 . . . . .10.00
Mannequin, cloth/cb/wood, no head/arms, CI shoes, 1900, 33"..275.00
Scoop, candy; brass, ca 1880, 9½" L 26.00
Scoop, cheese sampling; maple, long/narrow, 1850s, 12" 35.00

Stoves

Antique stoves' desirability is based on two criteria: their utility and their decorative value. It's the latter that adds an 'antique' premium to the basic functional value that could be served just as well by a modern stove. Sheer age is usually irrelevant. Decorative features that enhance desirability include fancy, embossed ornamentation, nickel-plated trim, mica windows, ceramic tiles, and (in cooking stoves) water reservoirs and high warming closets rather than mere high shelves. The less sheet metal and the more cast iron, the better. Look for crisp, sharp designs in preference to those made from worn or damaged and repaired foundry patterns. Stoves with pastel porcelain finish can be very attractive; blue is a favorite, white is least desirable. Chrome trim, rather than nickel, is the mark of a stove too recent to be interesting. Among stove types, base burners (with self-feeding coal magazines) are the most desirable. Then come the upright, cylindrical 'oak' stoves, kitchen ranges, and wood parlors. Potbellies approach the margin of undesirability; laundries and gasoline stoves plunge through it.

In judging condition, look out for deep rust pits, warped or burnt-out parts, unsound firebricks, poorly-fitting parts, poor repairs, and empty mounting holes indicating missing trim. Search meticulously for cracks in the cast iron. Our listings reflect auction prices of completely restored, safe, and functional stoves, unless indicated otherwise.

There's a thin but continuing stream of desirable antique stoves going to the high-priced Pacific Coast market. Interest in antique stoves is least in the Deep South. Demand for wood/coal stoves is strongest in areas where firewood is affordable and storage of it is practical. Demand for antique gas ranges has recently surged, especially in metropolitan markets.

The market for antique stoves is so thin and the variety so bewildering that a consensus on a going price can hardly emerge. They are only worth something to the right individual, and prices realized depend very greatly on who happens to be in the auction crowd. Even an expert's appraisal will usually miss the realized price by a substantial percent. See also Toys, Miscellaneous.

Box Stoves

A Belanger, Barge #14, parlor type, scrollwork, sm 150.00

BF&M Co #1, heater, front load, early 1800s, 17x24" 100.00
E Eaton #23, parlor, schoolhouse type, cathedral panels 350.00

Franklin Stoves

Air Tight, SH Ransom, CI fireplace, pat 1850 ....225.00
C Newcomb, CI, unique grate/legs, 1800, 28x24" 1,250.00
Corner-type fireplace, #214, CI, 1915, 31x24" 50.00
FWC #4, Fuller-Warren, 7 tiles, 10" urn, 38" 250.00
Wyer & Noble, CI/brass-trim fireplace, old 1,600.00

Parlor

AJ Coffin #4, 4-column CI, 10" urn, 1840s, 47x24" 1,200.00
Albany #2, CI 2-column, ornate, urn atop, 40x32" 200.00
Cycle #12, Cooperative, rnd, coal burner, mica door, ornate ...100.00

De Soto Parlor No. 1, cast iron parlor stove, patented 1854, 42x26x21", $550.00.

Floral #2, Fuller-Warren-Morrison 1,000.00
Iris #3, CI, pat 1859, patriotic emb, 27"+9" urn 200.00
Lady Washington, Anthony/Davy, CI, emb floral vase 225.00
Newberry, Filley #4, ornate CI, urn atop, 1856, 26" 300.00
Peerless, Pratt & Wentworth, tip-up top, 1840s, 37" 90.00
Peruvian, SH Ransom, CI, pat 1853, 27"+13" urn 225.00
Somersworth #20, CI, tip-up cooking area, 39x29" 225.00
Sylvan Red Cross #31, Co-op, CI, tiles, gargoyle legs 225.00
Tropic Crawford #114, rnd, coal burner, nickel/mica 150.00

Ranges

Detroit Jewel, cabinet, gas, glass door, 1916 ....400.00
Glenwood E, Glenwood #508 Fancy, CI, 1890s 650.00
Home Comfort CB, porc steel, 1934, 62x55", NM 1,225.00
Ideal Atlantic, #8-20, Portland, CI, ornate, rare 1,250.00
Imperial Clarion #8-20, CI, w/high shelf, fancy, 1898 ......1,500.00
Modern Glenwood Home Grand #280, CI, 2-shelf, nickel 600.00
Quaker Standard #8-20, Taunton, CI, high shelf, nickel 700.00
Queen Atlantic, Portland, simple lines, 20x20" 500.00

Universal, bl porc, Cribben-Sexton, 1923 ....2,200.00

Stove Manufacturers' Toy Stoves

Buck's Jr range, St Louis MO, 1910-1925, rfn, 23x21x11" 750.00
Dainty, Reading Stove Works, PA, 1886-1894, 7x13x8", VG ..150.00
Dolly's Favorite, Piqua OH, 1910, renickeled, 22½x19x11½" ..650.00
Estate gas range, wht porc w/nickel, Hamilton OH, '23, EX ..2,600.00
Little Eva, T Southard, NYC, 1886-1913, 8½x14x11", G ...350.00
Little Fanny, Phila Stove Works, PA, ca 1880, 7x11½x8", VG .520.00
Mascot range, gray porc, Chattanooga TN, '16, 16x19x13" ..1,700.00
Qualified, bl porc w/nickel, Karr, Belleville IL, 1925, EX 2,500.00
Qualified, bl porc w/nickel, 1960s repro, EX 2,500.00

Toy Manufacturers' Toy Stoves

Eagle, Hubley, Lancaster PA, ca 1920, 13x15x7", G 85.00
Eagle, Hubley, Lancaster PA, ca 1920, 17½x22½x9½", EX 800.00
Fireplace, unsgn, unidentified, nickeled, 7½x7½x2½" 50.00
Prize, J&E Stevens, Cromwell CT, 1913, 11½x11x6", G 60.00
Queen, The; unsgn, unidentified, 19x26x12½", EX 675.00
Rival, J&E Stevens, Cromwell CT, 1895, 13x18½x7½", G 240.00
Rose, unsgn, unidentified, early, 9x10½x9", G 155.00
Spark, Grey Iron Casting, Mount Joy PA, 13½x8x9", VG 90.00
Triumph, Kenton Hdwe, OH, 1902-1928, 14x8½x19", G 195.00

Strawberry Soft Paste and Lustre Ware

Strawberry lustre is a general term for pearlware and semi-porcelain decorated with hand-painted strawberries, vines, tendrils, and pink lustre trim. Strawberry soft paste is decorated creamware without the pink lustre trim. Both were made by many manufactures in England in the 19th century, most of whom never marked their ware.

Bowl, soft paste, rstr, 6" 325.00
Coffeepot, dome lid, soft paste, 12", NM 1,750.00
Cup & saucer, handleless; early, lustre, NM 200.00
Plate, Wood, lustre, 9" 135.00
Platter, lustre, 11" 195.00
Sauce boat, lustre, 6" 165.00
Sugar bowl, soft paste, w/lid, rstr 145.00
Teapot, soft paste, rstr, 11" 525.00
Teapot, squat, 1820s, 6", VG 450.00
Waste bowl, soft paste, mk Wood 575.00

Stretch Glass

Stretch glass, produced from the early 1900s until after 1930, was made in an effort to emulate the fine art glass of Tiffany and Carder. The glassware was sprayed with a special finish while still hot, and a reheating process caused the coating to contract, leaving a striated, crepe-like iridescence. Northwood, Imperial, Fenton, and the United States Glass Company were the largest manufacturers of this type of glass. See also specific companies.

Bobeche, vaseline, scalloped, pr 45.00
Bowl, clear, paneled, rolled rim, 1½x8¾" 22.00
Bowl, purple, 7" 25.00
Candle holder, gr, 9¾", pr 32.00
Candy jar, bl, w/lid, Fenton, #636 ....55.00
Compote, 4x5½" 20.00

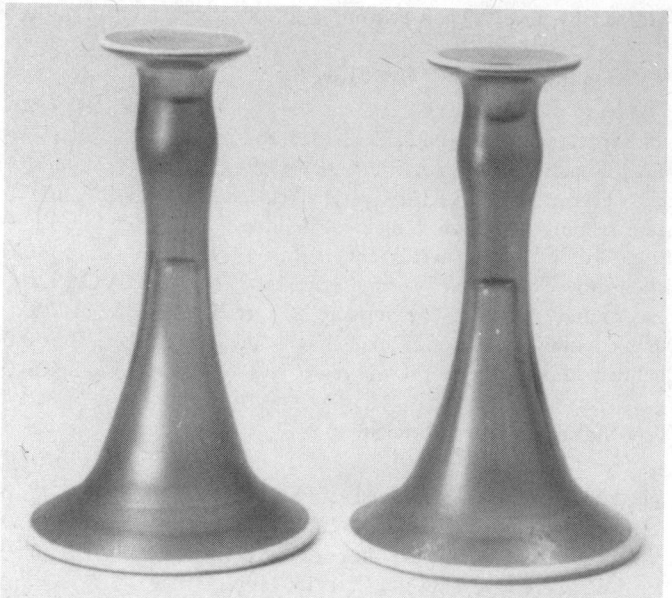

Candle holders, blue with white top and base bands, 8½", $40.00 for the pair.

Plate, gr, 12"	18.00
Rose bowl, pk, ribbed, 5"	48.00
Vase, bl, fan form, Fenton, 6"	50.00
Vase, pk, dolphin hdls, fan form, 6"	60.00
Vase, wht, fluted top, 5"	40.00

String Holders

Today, if you want to wrap and secure a package, you have a variety of products to choose from: cellophane tape, staples, etc. But in the 1800s, string was about the only available binder; thus the string holder, either the hanging or counter type, was a common and practical item found in most homes and businesses. Chalkware and ceramic figurals from the 1930s and 1940s contrast with the cast and wrought iron examples from the 1800s to make for an interesting collection.

Mammy, chalkware, 6", $125.00.

Ball, CI, 1890, EX	45.00
Barrister face atop ftd sphere, opening in mouth, pnt CI, 8"	550.00
Beehive, CI, counter style, 5x6½"	65.00

Cat, ceramic	15.00
Chef's face, ceramic, gold trim, lg	55.00
Colonial boy, mc pnt on CI, holder at bk, 7"	400.00
Girl ice skates behind gate, CI w/worn mc pnt, 7"	375.00
Grotesque face, ceramic, lg features, sgn/1900, 6x6x3"	85.00
Lacy, CI, 2-part	35.00
Lady knitting, cat playing w/string ball, tin	15.00
Lady's head, CI, string comes from mouth, rpt	350.00
Nickel-plated CI, pull string, ball moves on geared track	300.00
Sensible, 1885, w/full cone spool, EX	35.00
Smiling Buddha, wht ceramic	10.00
Spanish lady, chalkware, lg, EX	65.00
SSS for the Blood, CI, orig lid, 5", VG	130.00

Sugar Shakers

Sugar shakers (or muffineers, as they were also called) were used during the Victorian era to sprinkle sugar and spice onto breakfast muffins, toast, etc. They were made of art glass, in pressed patterns, and in china. See also specific types and manufacturers.

Acorn, pk opal w/gold florals	115.00
Acorn, sapphire bl	145.00
Apollo, etched, orig top	75.00
Apple Blossom, Northwood	125.00
Argus Swirl, peach bloom	175.00
Baby Thumbprint, amberina	200.00
Brass, boy on dolphin atop, England, 8½"	85.00
Bulging Loops, bl cased	215.00
China, cream w/pk & red roses, gold trim, Nippon, 5x3"	65.00
China, floral spray, pk/wht on wht, no mk	42.00
Chrysanthemum Base Swirl, cranberry opal	95.00
Coin Spot, bl opal, 9-panel	115.00
Cranberry, molded panels, SP lid, English, 5¾x2⅜"	95.00
Diamond Optic, clear w/gr ft, metal lid, 6"	35.00
Egg shape, pansies on peach to wht, Mt WA	225.00
Flower & Pleat, clear/frosted	115.00
Forget-Me-Not, chartreuse	115.00
Invt Fan & Feather, custard	150.00
Jumbo & Barnum	145.00
Leaf Mold, cranberry/wht spatter, orig lid	225.00

Leaf Mold, pink and white with gold fleck, $200.00.

Leaf Umbrella, bl cased, scarce	225.00
Leaf Umbrella, cranberry	225.00
Leaf Umbrella, yel cased, orig lid	165.00
Medallion Sprig, rubena	235.00

Melligo, bl opaque 80.00
Pk & wht spatter, Hobbs Coloratura series 125.00
Quilted Phlox, bl opaque 125.00
Reverse Swirl, canary opal 135.00
Reverse Swirl, cranberry opal 195.00
Ribbed Pillar, cranberry spatter, frosted 195.00
Tomato figural, ornate top, Mt WA 235.00
Wht satin w/gr shamrocks & bl dots, Dithridge 115.00

Sunderland Lustre

Sunderland lustre was made by various potters in the Sunderland district of England during the 18th and 19th centuries. It is characterized by a splashed-on application of the pink lustre, which results in an effect sometimes referred to as the 'cloud' pattern. Some pieces are transfer printed with scenes, ships, florals, or portraits.

Creamer, Sailor's Tear/ship/May Peace & Plenty, 1800s, 5" ...250.00
Humidor, parliament buildings transfer, pewter lock 195.00

Jug, East View of the Lion Bridge and view of the ship Trident, 8½", $600.00.

Jug, Mariner's Compass/Iron Bridge, polychrome, 8", NM 400.00
Jug, ship/'John Chipman 1830,' 2 verses, 9½", EX 400.00
Mug, seashells on pk, hdls 65.00
Pepper pot, cloud pattern, 4½" 85.00
Plaque, Thou God Seest Me, copper lustre trim, Dixon, 8½" ..150.00
Salt cellar, ped ft, fine mottling, soft paste 75.00
Sauce boat, Mariner's Compass, blk transfer, w/tray, 7½" 400.00
Teapot, cloud pattern, pear form, 6" 250.00

Syracuse

Syracuse was a line of fine dinnerware which was made for nearly a century by the Onondaga Pottery Company of Syracuse, New York. Collectors of American dinnerware are focusing their attention on reassembling some of their many lovely patterns. In 1966 the firm became officially known as the Syracuse China Company in order to better identify with the name of their popular chinaware. By 1971 dinnerware geared for use in the home was discontinued, and the company turned to the manufacture of hotel, restaurant, and other types of commercial tableware.

Arcadia, cup & saucer 20.00

Arcadia, plate, salad 14.00
Bombay, chop plate 95.00
Bombay, platter, lg 85.00
Bombay, soup, rimmed 25.00
Brantley, bowl, vegetable; w/lid 45.00
Brantley, gravy boat 20.00
Briarcliff, bowl, vegetable; oval 38.00
Briarcliff, cup & saucer 25.00
Briarcliff, plate, dinner 18.00
Jefferson, bowl, vegetable; oval 45.00
Jefferson, bowl, vegetable; w/lid 95.00
Jefferson, chop plate 85.00
Jefferson, coffeepot 95.00
Jefferson, creamer & sugar bowl 65.00
Jefferson, cup & saucer 25.00
Jefferson, gravy boat 45.00
Jefferson, plate, dinner 20.00
Madame Butterfly, bowl, vegetable; oval 25.00
Madame Butterfly, cup & saucer 22.00
Madame Butterfly, plate, bread & butter 9.00
Madame Butterfly, platter, med 25.00
Monticello, cake plate 25.00
Monticello, creamer 20.00
Monticello, cup & saucer 20.00
Rose Marie, bowl, salad 7.50
Rose Marie, cup & saucer 24.00
Rose Marie, plate, bread & butter 6.00
Suzanne, bowl, fruit 20.00
Suzanne, cup & saucer 25.00
Suzanne, plate, dinner 20.00
Suzanne, plate, salad 15.00
Suzanne, plate, soup 20.00
Westvale, creamer & sugar bowl, gold trim, w/lid 35.00
Westvale, platter, gold trim, 14" 22.00

Syrups

Values are for old, original syrups. Beware of reproductions! See also various manufacturers and specific types of glass.

Cone, cased yellow, clear handle, 6", $175.00.

Alba Blossoms, milk glass, HP floral, Dithridge, ca 1895 ......95.00
Apple Blossom, milk glass 175.00
Banded Portland 75.00
Banded Portland, rose flashed, very scarce 285.00

Beaded Swag, ruby stained, etched scrolls, Heisey 195.00
Block Band, George Duncan, 1880s .70.00
Bull's Eye, scalloped, pewter lid, lg .50.00
Button & Band, 6¾" 75.00
Button Arches, red flashed, glass hdl, pewter lid 225.00
Challinor's Forget-Me-Not, chartreuse 165.00
Coin Spot, bl opal, ring neck, lid dtd 175.00
Coin Spot, gr, bulbous 125.00
Columbian Coin, frosted, very scarce 225.00
Cone, bl 150.00
Coreopsis, EX decor 145.00
Empress, clear w/gold 125.00
Eyewinker 120.00
Florida (Herringbone), gr, orig spring lid 225.00
Flower & Pleat, frosted, EX gold 100.00
Grape & Leaf, gr opaque 200.00
Hobnail, bl, pewter lid, dtd 235.00
Jacob's Ladder, appl hdl, pewter lid 80.00
Lacy Dewdrop (Beaded Jewel) 125.00
Lincoln Drape, flint, eagle emb on tin lid 195.00
Locket on Chain 235.00
Locket on Chain, ruby stained 1,350.00
Moon & Star, orig tin lid, rare 125.00
Paneled Sunflower, rpl SP lid 50.00
Pilgrims Bottle, bl, orig pewter lid .145.00
Priscilla 110.00
Reverse Swirl, bl opal, collared 165.00
Ribbed Pillar, pk spatter 195.00
States 65.00
Sunflower, majolica, pk bkground, pewter lid, sgn Etruscan . . .295.00
Swan 150.00
Torpedo, pewter lid 80.00
Utah, tin lid 75.00
Venetia, cranberry 295.00
Wildflower, amber, scarce 195.00
X-Ray, gr w/EX gold 315.00

Target Balls

Prior to 1880 when the clay pigeon was invented, blown glass target balls were used extensively for shotgun competitions. Approximately 2¾" in diameter, these balls were hand-blown into a three-piece mold. All have a ragged hole where the blowpipe was twisted free. Target balls date from approximately 1840 (English) to World War I, although they were most widely used in the 1870-1880 period. Common examples are unmarked except for the blower's code — dots, crude numerals, etc. Some balls are embossed in a dot or diamond pattern so they were more likely to shatter when struck by shot, and some have names and/or patent dates. When evaluating condition, bubbles and other minor manufacturing imperfections are acceptable; cracks are not. The prices below are for mint condition examples.

Black Pitch, CTB Co 250.00
Bogardus' Glass Ball Pat'd April 10 1877, amber 250.00
Bogardus' Glass Ball Pat'd April 10 1877, other than amber . . .500.00
Emb ribs, amber 150.00
English, shooter emb in 2 rnd panels, clear 300.00
English, shooter emb in 2 rnd panels, gr 300.00
English, shooter emb in 2 rnd panels, purple 300.00
For Hockey's Patent Trap, gr 500.00
Great Western Gun Works, amber .600.00
Gurd & Son, London, Ontario, amber 400.00
Ira Paine's Filled Ball Pat Oct 23 1877, amber 250.00

Ira Paine's Filled Ball Pat Oct 23 1877, amber, set of 10 . . . . . .950.00
Ira Paine's Filled Ball Pat Oct 23 1877, other than amber 500.00
NB Glass Works Perth, other than pale gr 300.00
NB Glass Works Perth, pale gr, almost clear 200.00
Plain, amber 65.00
Plain, clear, w/mold marks 1,000.00
Plain, cobalt 100.00
Plain, purple 100.00
WW Greener St Mary's Works Birm/68 Haymarket London . .250.00

Related Memorabilia

Clay birds, Winchester, Pat May 29 1917, 1 flight in box 100.00
Pitch bird, blk, DUVROCK 1.00
Shell, dummy, w/single window, any brand 25.00
Shell, dummy shotgun, Winchester, window w/powder, 6" 100.00
Shell set, dummy, Gamble Stores, 2 window shells, 3 cut out . .125.00
Shell set, dummy, Winchester, 5 window shells 125.00
Shell set, dummy shotgun, Peters, 6 window shells+full box . . .125.00
Shotshell loader, rosewood/brass, Parker Bros, Pat 1884 . . . . . .50.00
Target, Am sheet metal, rod ends mk Pat Feb 8 '21, set 25.00
Target, blk japanned sheet metal, Bussy Patentee...London 50.00
Target, BUST-O, blk or wht breakable wafer 20.00
Trap, DUVROCK, w/blk pitch birds 150.00
Trap, MO-SKEET-O, w/birds 150.00

Tea Caddies

Because tea was once regarded as a precious commodity, special boxes called caddies were used to store the tea leaves. They were made from various materials: porcelain, carved and inlaid woods, and metals ranging from painted tin or tole to engraved silver.

Bird's eye veneer/ebonized stringing, 1800s, 6½x9½" 660.00
Mahog Empire, brass ball ft, rectangular, 5½x4¾x4¾" 140.00
Mahog veneer, 4-panel hinged dome lid, 2 caddies w/in, 15" . .265.00
Mahog w/inlaid stringing, Hplwht style, 4 ball ft 145.00
MOP inlay scrolls/vines, 4-part sloping lid, knob hdls, 14" 350.00
Papier-mache w/MOP inlay & gilt dome top, ca 1870, 8" L . . .175.00
Satinwood w/acorn & oak leaf medallion inlay, Geo III, 8" 440.00
Silverplate, people/scenes/etc repousse, 6-sided, Derby 68.00
Sterling, chinoisserie eng/branch hdl, J Mitchell, 1851, 8" . . .2,500.00
Tortoise shell, coffer form, English, 1830, 6x7" 400.00
Tunbridge, burl inlay, ca 1810 . . . . .185.00
Veneer, figured/tiger striped w/inlay edge, oval, 4½", VG 175.00

Tea Leaf Ironstone

Tea Leaf Ironstone became popular in the 1880s when middle-class American housewives became bored with the plain white stone china that English potters had been exporting to this country for nearly a century. The original design has been credited to Anthony Shaw of Longport, who decorated the plain ironstone with a hand-painted copper lustre design of bands and leaves. Originally known as Lustre Band and Sprig, the pattern has since come to be known as Tea Leaf Lustre. It was produced with minor variations by many different firms both in England and the United States. By the early 1900s, it had become so commonplace that it had lost much of its appeal.

Our advisors for this category are the owners of Hospice House Antiques; their address is listed in the Directory under Illinois.

Bowl, fruit; scalloped, H Burgess, 10" 75.00

Bowl, vegetable; Fish Hook, w/lid, Meakin 125.00
Bowl, vegetable; Pepper Leaf, w/lid 165.00
Bowl, vegetable; sq, open, Mellor Taylor, 7¼" 40.00
Butter pat, rnd, Meakin 15.00
Butter pat, rnd, unmk, 3" 15.00
Butter pat, scalloped, rnd, Meakin 15.00
Butter pat, sq, Meakin, 2¾" 15.00
Coffeepot, Bamboo, Meakin 165.00
Coffeepot, Fish Hook, Meakin, lg 150.00
Creamer, Bamboo, Meakin, 5¼" 95.00
Creamer, beaded hdl, rectangular, East End Pottery, 4¾" 85.00
Cup & saucer, Chinese shape, Shaw 95.00
Cup & saucer, cone shape, Shaw 75.00
Cup & saucer, handleless; Pepper Leaf Variant 75.00
Cup & saucer, ribbed, Adams, ca 1970 . . . . .35.00
Dish, bone, crescent shape, scalloped, Meakin 75.00
Egg cup, unmk, 3½" 395.00
Ewer & basin, Meakin, Bamboo 375.00
Gravy boat, elongated spout, Alfred Meakin 50.00
Gravy boat, Fish Hook, Meakin 50.00
Gravy boat, plain, Wedgwood 50.00

Gravy boat and underplate, Alfred Meakin, $95.00.

Nappy, Chinese shape, Shaw 22.00
Nappy, plain, sq, Meakin 20.00
Nappy, Wedgwood, 4¼" 20.00
Nappy, Wilkinson, 4½" 20.00
Pitcher, milk; Dolphin, Victory shape, Edwards, 8⅛" 195.00
Pitcher, milk; Fish Hook, Meakin, 7" 175.00
Plate, bread & butter; Wedgwood 10.00
Plate, dessert; Wilkinson 12.00
Plate, luncheon; Meakin 10.00
Plate, luncheon; Pepper Leaf, Elsmore & Forster 20.00
Plate, Meakin, 8¾", NM 12.50
Plate, Mellor Taylor, 7⅝" 10.00
Plate, Mellor Taylor, 9¾" 25.00
Plate, Wedgwood, 7⅝" 10.00
Plate, Wedgwood, 9¾" 25.00
Platter, Meakin, 16x12" 45.00
Platter, rectangular, ribbed flange, Wedgwood, 15¾x11½" 45.00
Platter, Shaw, oval, lg 45.00
Relish dish, oval w/reticulated hdl, Wilkinson 45.00
Saucer, deep, Meakin, 6" 8.00
Shaving mug, Chinese shape, Shaw, 3¼" 165.00
Shaving mug, plain, Meakin 145.00
Sugar bowl, Bamboo, w/lid, Meakin 60.00
Sugar bowl, bulbous, w/lid, Wilkinson 65.00
Sugar bowl, Cable, w/lid 65.00
Sugar bowl, Fish Hook, Meakin, w/lid, lg 65.00
Sugar bowl, Pepper Leaf, w/lid, Elsmore & Forster, 7" 100.00
Teapot, Bamboo, Meakin 110.00

Teapot, Chinese shape, paneled, Shaw, late 1850s 225.00
Teapot, ribbed spout & hdl, scalloped top, Mellor Taylor 175.00
Toothbrush holder, Bamboo, vertical, Meakin 155.00
Tureen, soup; oval, w/lid, ladel, & underplate, Davenport 995.00
Waste bowl, Pepper Leaf Variant, Elsmore & Forster 75.00

Teapots

The custom of drinking tea has resulted in the production of many tea-related collectibles; the most popular is the teapot. The first teapots were manufactured in the Chinese village of Vi-Hsing during the late 16th century and were no bigger than the tiny cups previously used for tea drinking. Amazingly, these same tiny teapots are still being used today.

A wide range of teapots can be found by the avid searcher; those most readily available today were produced from about 1870 to the present. Several books have been written solely devoted to teapots, although most are out of print. *An Anthology of British Teapots* by Philip Miller and Michael Berthoud is an extensive work with over 2,000 photographs; it is currently available from Micawber Publications, The Lawns, Church Street, Brosely, Stropshire TF12 5DG for L.24.95.

Almost every pottery and porcelain manufacturer in Europe as well as in America have produced teapots. Some are purely functional, others decorative and whimsical. Refer to various manufacturers' names for further listings.

Austria Victoria Carlsbad, fine china w/florals 30.00
Barge, S Derbyshire, England, brn, emb name, lg 75.00
Charles & Diana, mk Wales CM, brn pottery, 2½" 75.00
Dbl spout, earthenware, slip decor, ca 1890 . . . . .80.00
Dragon, Japanese coralene, mk DM, 6-cup 20.00
Ellgreave, Wood & Sons, England, ironstone, floral 35.00
Grimwades, Royal Winton, England, cozy set, floral hdls 55.00
Ming Tea Co, made in Japan, w/label, 1½-cup 15.00
Monterey, made in CA, pk spatter, lg 20.00
Noritake, mk M HP Japan, yel w/flowers, tall, 2-cup 25.00
Old English Sampler, mk H&K England, 6-cup, EX 45.00
Pyrex, mk, blown glass, etched flowers, 6-cup 45.00
Sadler, pk oval w/sm flowers, mk, 6-cup 35.00
Snow White w/Dwarfs, Walt Disney Productions, musical 50.00
Spode's Tower, England, bl/wht transfer, London shape, VG . . .45.00
Sutherland, England, silver lustre, mk, 6-cup 60.00
SYP, 'Simple yet Perfect,' brn earthenware, ca 1905 . . . . .95.00
SYP, Wedgwood, bone china, bl/wht gold, ca 1905-1906 . . . . .110.00
Wade, Scotty, mk, 1953-1955, 9" 45.00
Wedgwood, Jasperware, bl/wht, ca 1784, 2-cup 210.00
WS George, yel w/gold, rnd, mk, 6-cup, EX 18.00

Teco

Teco artware was made by the American Terra Cotta and Ceramic Company, located near Chicago, Illinois. The firm was established in 1886 and until 1901 produced only brick, sewer tile, and other redware. Their early glaze was inspired by the matt green made popular by Grueby. 'Teco Green' was made for nearly ten years. It was similar to Grueby's yet with a subtle silver-gray cast. The company was one of the first in the United States to perfect a true crystalline glaze. The only decoration used was through the modeling and glazing techniques; no hand painting was attempted. Favored motifs were naturalistic leaves and flowers.

The company broadened their lines to include garden pottery and faience tiles and panels. New matt glazes (browns, yellows, blue, and rose) were added to the green in 1910. By 1922 the artware lines were discontinued; the company was sold in 1930.

Values are dictated by size and color of glaze, with examples in colors other than green bringing the higher prices. High-gloss glaze is seldom seen and expensive.

Teco is usually marked with a vertical impressed device comprised of a large 'T' to the left of the remaining three letters.

Ash tray, X-leg frog ea side, oatmeal matt, Faience, 4½" 300.00
Ash tray/match holder, dk gr matt, imp geometrics, 4x5" 185.00
Bookends, 2 books w/owl, lt brn, 6", pr 350.00
Bowl, cream w/dk brn touches, diagonal buttresses, 9½" 280.00
Bowl, gr, protruding swirls, elephant-ft form, 2½x8½" 260.00
Bowl, gr, 4 high-relief curls at tiny rim, mk, 6x10" 1,500.00
Candlestick, gr, lily pad emerges from hdl/wraps pc, 10½" 350.00
Candlestick, wht matt, #258, 2¼x4½" 160.00
Ewer, gr/gray, curved lip & spout, #58, 4" 175.00
Lamp, gr, 4 buttressed ft, orig floral ldgl shade, 18x10" 6,000.00
Pitcher, bl-gr, 4-rib slim form w/sm hdl, label, 12x4" 550.00
Pitcher, gr/blk, ruffled spout, integral hdl, 4x5½" 175.00
Pitcher, gun metal/gr texture, concave w/wishbone hdl, 8¾" ...150.00
Tile, crouching gnome in full relief, gr, 9" 1,850.00
Tile, gr, incised geometric in ea corner, mk, 4" 150.00
Tray, Chicago Cubs logo, 3-color, rnd 150.00
Vase, aventurine, sm akimbo hdls at rim, rare glaze, 10½" 650.00
Vase, bl, concave w/4 upright buttresses canted at rim, 7½" ..1,000.00
Vase, bl, 2 rim-to-base buttresses, 5½" 550.00

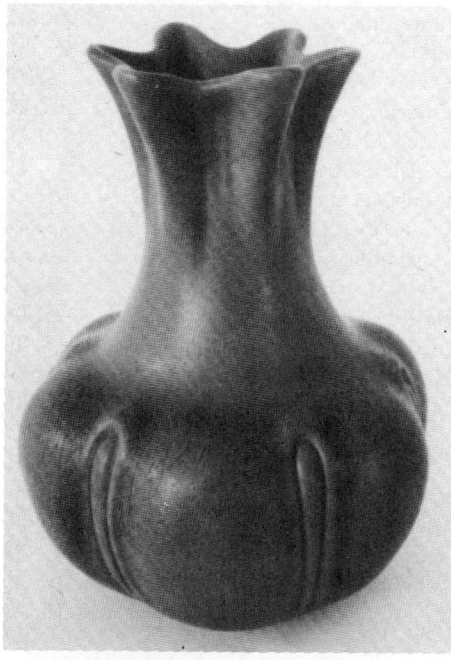

Vase, veined green glaze, impressed mark, 10½", $1,450.00.

Vase, gr, bulbous, mk, 3½" 210.00
Vase, gr, bulbous/lobed bottom, 3-ftd, tall neck, 16" 850.00
Vase, gr, closed collar rim, 7¾x5¼" 475.00
Vase, gr, cylinder w/3 8" high-relief curved straps, 9" 1,500.00
Vase, gr, flared rim, narrow neck, 4½" 295.00
Vase, gr, flared top, 2 sq closed neck hdls, 6¾" 350.00
Vase, gr, gourd form, 7" 495.00
Vase, gr, gourd form w/undulating rim, 5" 285.00
Vase, gr, long neck w/rim-to-shoulder integral hdls, 9x5" 400.00
Vase, gr, slim/waisted w/4 upright buttress hdls, 7½" 1,300.00
Vase, gr, tall/cylindrical, 4 cut-out hdls at top, 12" 2,000.00
Vase, gr, 2 rim-to-base buttresses, 6½" 550.00
Vase, gr, 2 sm neck hdls, 6" 225.00
Vase, gr, 4 str buttresses on elongated ovoid, 6¾" 700.00
Vase, gr w/blk, 4 rim-to-base buttresses, open hdls, 7" 650.00

Vase, gr w/gray, clay showing through, #165, 8" 170.00
Vase, gr w/gray, lotus flower form, 4 curving hdls, 11½" 3,000.00
Vase, gr w/gray, sm opening, 4½" 115.00
Vase, gr/blk, horizontal rings, hand thrown, 8" 350.00
Vase, lt gr, bulbous w/sm opening, #52, 4¾" 150.00
Vase, yel, cylindrical w/2 rim-to-base buttresses, 6½" 550.00

Teddy Bear Collectibles

The story of Teddy Roosevelt's encounter with the bear cub has been oft recounted with varying degrees of accuracy, so it will suffice to say that it was as a result of this incident in 1902 that the teddy bear got his name. These appealing little creatures are enjoying renewed popularity with collectors today. To one who has not yet succumbed to their obvious charms, one bear seems to look very much like another. How to tell the older ones? Look for long snouts, jointed limbs, large feet and felt paws, long curving arms, and glass or shoe-button eyes. Most old bears have a humped back and are made of mohair stuffed with straw or excelsior. Cute expressions, original clothes, a nice personality, and, of course, good condition add to their value. Some Steiff bears in mint condition may go as high as $100 per inch. These are easily recognized by the trademark button within the ear. See also Toys, Steiff.

Bears

Steiff bear, fully jointed, center seam, ca 1905-1910, 14", $2,750.00.

Chad Valley, fully jtd, mohair, vest/bow tie, 1930s, 15" 295.00
Clemens, fully jtd, mohair, straw filled, w/tag, 9" 150.00
Clemens, fully jtd, squeaker, straw filled, standing, 11" 115.00
Fully jtd, gold mohair, glass eyes, skinny, 7½" 150.00
Fully jtd, growler, gold mohair, straw filled, 21", VG 450.00
Fully jtd, long mohair, straw filled, glass eyes, 11" 275.00
Fully jtd, mohair, straw filled, glass eyes, 16" 290.00
Fully jtd, mohair, straw filled, hump, glass eyes, skinny, 14" ...300.00
Fully jtd, mohair, straw filled, w/hump, stick-pin eyes, 20" ...525.00
Fully jtd, mohair, straw filled, w/hump, 7" 150.00
Fully jtd, musical, pk/beige mohair, oversize eyes, 1920, 12" ...450.00
Fully jtd, red mohair, w/hump, glass eyes, 4" 175.00
Fully jtd, squeaker, mohair, floss nose/mouth, 1920, 12" 450.00
Fully jtd, wht mohair, straw filled, glass eyes, 8" 275.00
German, fully jtd, reddish brn mohair, open mouth, 15" 150.00
German, growler, fully jtd, sm hump, straw filled, 16½" 200.00
German, musical, jtd, mohair, straw filled, ca 1920, 24" 1,000.00
Growler on wheels, brn mohair, glass eyes, 1950s, 26" 250.00

Hermann, Floppy Zotty, not jtd, mohair, glass eyes, 1960, 8" ..150.00
Hermann, fully jtd, gray frosted fur, 11" 95.00
Hermann, fully jtd, squeaker, mohair, glass eyes, 7½" 80.00
Hermann, not jtd, squeaker, long mohair, w/tag, 11" 150.00
Hermann, Zotty, fully jtd, squeaker, long mohair, 1955, 12" ...150.00
Hueneg, growler, fully jtd, straw filled, w/tag, 17" 200.00
Jtd legs, curved arms, mohair, hump, celluloid eyes, 1940s, 8" ...75.00
Reuge, musical, fully jtd, long mohair, open felt mouth, 11½" .250.00
Schuco, fully jtd, gold mohair over metal fr, 1935, 3½" 195.00
Schuco, fully jtd, mohair, metal eyes, 2¾" 250.00
Steiff, fully jtd, gold mohair, straw filled, 1959, 7", M 150.00
Steiff, fully jtd, long gold mohair, w/button, 1905, 13", M 900.00
Steiff, fully jtd, mohair, straw filled, w/button, 9½" 500.00
Steiff, fully jtd, tan mohair, squeaker, w/tag, 1959, 10", M 200.00
Steiff, growler, jtd, tan mohair, glass eyes, 1965, 15", M 250.00
Steiff, polar bear, not jtd, mohair, w/button, 1960, 5", EX 125.00

Miscellaneous

Book, Mother Goose's Teddy Bears, Cavally, 1907, EX 325.00
Bottle warmer, wht, straw head, glass eyes, 12" 150.00
Puppet, mohair, straw-filled head, embr nose, glass eyes, 9" 150.00
Puppet, teddy w/blk ears, embr nose, Chad Valley, 10" 95.00
Tea set, teddy bears play soccer, Japan, 1920s, 16-pc 550.00
Tip tray, Roosevelt bears, dress shop ad, 1906, EX 350.00

Teddy Bear Moving Picture Book, 1907, 11", $150.00.

Telephones

Since Alexander Graham Bell's first successful telephone communication, the phone itself has undergone a complete evolution in style as well as efficiency. Early models, especially those wall types with ornately carved oak boxes, are of special interest to collectors. Also of value are the candlestick phones from the early part of the century and any related memorabilia.

American Electric, 2-box, oak 450.00
Automatic Electric, dial, 1950s 20.00
Automatic Electric, model #40 ....45.00
Century Telephone Mfg, fiddlebk, oak 375.00
Chicago Telephone Supply, Elkhart IN, magneto box 45.00
Kellogg, candlestick, brass, 1907, VG 85.00
North Electric, desk set, 1937 ....50.00
Railroad dispatcher, candlestick 75.00
RR, portable, in leather case, w/4-part connecting pole, EX ...70.00

Stromberg-Carlson Mfg, stick style 85.00
Stromberg-Carlson Special, #1534, WWII era 25.00
Sumter Mfg, oak, wall crank, sm 235.00
Western Electric, brass & blk metal candlestick, pat 1904, EX .135.00
Western Electric, candlestick, pat 1915 ....95.00
Western Electric 'Spacesaver,' w/dial 75.00

Related Memorabilia

Booklet, How to Build Rural Telephone Lines, ca 1900 ....15.00
Catalog, Western Electric Magneto Telephones & Supplies, '10 .50.00
Service pin, NW Bell, 10k gold 20.00
Shade, cased glass, Bell System on cobalt 600.00
Sign, Local & Long Distance, porc over steel, flange, 17x18" ..120.00
Sign, Public telephone, early bell, rnd, EX 165.00
Test box, portable, oak, w/carrying strap, all orig 45.00

Telescopes

Old telescopes are still appreciated for the quality of the workmanship and materials that went into their production. Some of the more elaborate styles were covered in leather or ebony and the 'draws' or extensions were often brass.

Brass, 4-draw, 37", VG 200.00
Brass & leather, 3-draw, 29", VG 125.00
Brass & wood, 3-draw, ca 1850, 34", VG 200.00
France, brass, 2-draw, 29", EX 225.00
Gilbert Astronomical, 26", +orig case, EX 45.00
J Watson, refracting table top-style tripod, ca 1800, VG 1,150.00
JJ Messer, London, brass, 1-draw, ca 1850, VG 225.00
SIB Solomons, London, cased tripod, ca 1840, EX 800.00
T Mason, Dublin, w/floor tripod, closed: 49", NM 1,850.00

Televisions

Collectible TV's are a quickly-moving group of saleable items. TV's made before WWII (circa 1920s — 1940) now sell at $1,000.00 to $10,000.00! Unusual and/or attractive wood and Bakelite sets from 1946 to 1950 usually are worth $20.00 to $200.00; metal mid-1950s televisions sell for $10.00 to $60.00. Old TV's need not work in order to attract a buyer!

Our advisor for this category is Harry Poster; he is listed in the Directory under New Jersey.

RCA, 630T5, wood case, table model, first to be mass produced, 1946, EX condition, $250.00.

Emerson portable, ca 1947, 7" 140.00

Predicta, floor model, ca 1959, EX 875.00
RCA, #630T5, wood case, table model, 1946, EX 250.00
RCA, #9-PC-41, 20" projection, 1950, EX 500.00
RCA, CT-100, 1st color TV, ca 1953 . . . . .400.00
RCA Field Test, color set, 1953, rare 3,500.00
Stromberg Carlson, Deco table model, 1940s, EX 250.00
Zenith, early 1950s, 16" porthole screen, EX 110.00

Teplitz

Teplitz, in Bohemia, was an active art pottery center at the turn of the century. The Amphora Pottery Works was only one of the firms that operated there. (See Amphora.) Art Nouveau and Art Deco styles were favored, and much of the ware was hand decorated with the primary emphasis on vases and figurines. Items listed here are marked 'Teplitz' or 'Turn,' a nearby city.

Our advisor for this category is Jack Gunsaulus; he is listed in the Directory under Michigan.

Box, turtle form w/2 children on lid, Ernst Wahliss, 7¾" L 365.00

Bust of young woman, gold-colored dress, floral-encrusted socle, ca 1900, 26", $2,800.00.

Ewer, beaded floral on beige, mk, 9" 235.00
Ewer, gold-flecked w/lg gold & mc floral, turq hdl, 10" 125.00
Ewer, grapes, red on mottle, bulbous, Stellmacher, 10" 85.00
Vase, appl flower w/man's face, HP flowers, bulbous, hdl, 11" . .225.00
Vase, bird/bee/gold leaves on tan/yel, reticulated lid, 16" 425.00
Vase, Deco floral, mc on tan, cylindrical, dbl hdls, 15½" 325.00
Vase, floral, cobalt & wht on bl, gargoyle on neck, mk, 17" . . .675.00
Vase, floral, gold & wht on gr, bulbous, dbl hdls, ftd, 13" 295.00
Vase, floral/insects, gold w/cobalt tree, bulbous, 10", pr 700.00
Vase, gold relief on cobalt, gold snake at neck, 17" 625.00
Vase, poppies, orange on gr-gold, ewer form, Wahliss mk, 17" .425.00

Terra Cotta

Terra cotta is a type of earthenware or clay used for statuary, architec-

tural facings, or domestic articles. It is unglazed, baked to durable hardness, and characterized by the color of the body which may range from brick red to buff.

Bust, man/lady clown, beige/brn, mk Repro/WP Wien, 18", pr .600.00
Bust of Salome, HP, sgn F Hartmann, 1900, 19½" 1,200.00
Figurine, cougar on tree stump, E Oehme, 1915, 6x8" 300.00
Figurine, Flora, wheat in hand, vase on head, 58" 935.00
Figurine, putto, pnt details, 25" 125.00
Figurine, 2 children w/bird's nest, on stand, French, 11" 90.00
Jardiniere, Oriental dragon relief, 14¼x12¼x7¼" 45.00
Plaque, Victorian lady w/lute, artist sgn, Athens 1870 . . . . .350.00

Sevres allegorical group, in the Clodion manner, 19th century, 15x18", $650.00.

Thermometers

Though the collecting of advertising thermometers has been popular for years, only recently have decorative thermometers come into their own as bona fide items of interest and value. Indoor and outdoor decorative models have been manufactured for hundreds of years, yet their relative scarcity enhances their value and interest for the collector. Most American thermometers manufactured early in the 20th century were produced by Taylor (Tycos), and today their thermometers remain the most plentiful on the market. They also serve as the price standards for most historical thermometers.

Insofar as sheer beauty, uniqueness, and scientific accuracy, decorative thermometers are far superior to the ordinary and inexpensive versions which carry advertising. Decorative thermometers run the gamut from plain tin household varieties to the highly ornate creations of Tiffany and Bradley and Hubbard. They have been manufactured from nearly every conceivable material—oak, sterling, brass, and glass being the favorites—and have tested the artistry and technical skills of some of America's finest craftsmen. Ornamental models can be found in free-hanging, wall-mounted, or desk/mantel versions.

Thermometer prices are based on age, ornateness, and whether mercury or alcohol is used as the filler in the tube. Thermometers with damaged, missing, or substitute parts bring greatly reduced prices. Paper scales indicate either replacement of a broken metal scale or a device of lower quality.

Virtually all American-made thermometers available today as collectors' items were made between 1875 and 1940. The Golden Age of decoratives ended in the early 1940s as modern manufacturing processes and materials robbed them of their natural distinctiveness. European thermometers, while of comparable beauty and craftsmanship, have not yet migrated to this country in any great numbers; those produced in America still dominate the buy/sell market.

Our advisor for this category is Warren Harris; he is listed in the Directory under California.

Key:
br — brass	pmc — permacolor
F & C — Farhenheit and Celsius	sc — scales
F & R — Farhenheit and Reamur	stl — stainless
mrc — mercury	

Adam Kilt, desk; br portico/scallop roof, F&R sc/mrc, 4½" 42.00
Alexandre, folding; F&R sc, mrc, 1850s 85.00
Bargess Reversible Box, br sc, oak case, mrc, 5½" 30.00
BLT-Luce, desk; figural, flared base, br w/br sc, mrc, 6" 75.00
Bradley & Hubbard, desk; br/ornate lion, br sc/mrc, 9", VG 70.00
Bradley & Hubbard, scroll bk, steel/cb, Mensh, mrc, 8" 250.00
Brown Penzance, desk; brn marble, ivory sc, mrc, 6" 75.00
C Wilder Co, bear & billboard br figural, mrc, 6½" 45.00
Casella London, wall; maxi/mini, 2 units, wood, plastic sc 235.00
CE Lange, kitchen; The Modern Thermometer, tin, pmc 150.00
Chester, desk; stl sc, sterling bezel, mrc, 2x6" 95.00
Clark, desk; ivory ped, crown, mrc, 1904, 7" 48.00
Cloister, inkwell, stl bk & base w/side angels, 1901 ....975.00
Creswel, travel; ivory case/mirror, removable sc, mrc, 2½" ..1,750.00
Desk, cvd walrus tusk, 2-tier disk base, inlay sc, 1860, 9" 220.00
Dr Dan'l Draper's Self-Recording, metal/glass, 1887, 20" 25.00
E Berman Co, desk; br/filigree/top scrollwork, mrc, 8" 55.00
Freeborn, desk; bronze w/lead decor/br sc, mrc, 8" 39.00
G Barnes, oak fold-out box, plastic sc, mrc, 2½" 75.00
G Cooper, desk; bell shape w/cupola, sterling, dial, 2x3" 50.00
Gloucester Scientific, stl case, glass front, pmc, 42" 1,050.00
Golub, hanging; mahog/br bulb cap, lg sc/red spirit, 9x2" 65.00
H Lauramark, hanging; gold stipple on boxwood, 0-120, mrc ...60.00
Harcatlib Ltd, desk; br ped on griffin, mrc, 9" 32.00
Hiergelsell Bros, indoor; cabinet/oak bk, bl liquid, #159 ....40.00
Hohmann Maurer Co, steel F&C sc & bk, mrc, 12" 27.00
J Needle, desk; figural, calendar, br w/porc sc, mrc, 6" 95.00
Jed Sirrah, hanging; silver, umbrella, mrc, 8" 70.00
Jedseth Ltd, desk; Mercury figure w/base filigree, mrc, 7" 63.00
Jockomo IN, desk; sterling face/br sc, mrc, 1904, 6" 65.00
Nova Products, desk; glass cover over bronze sc, 4" 35.00
Nova Products, desk; rnd, glass encased, dial sc, pat 1923 ......52.00
Orchard, iron case, br face, w/glass intact, 14" 35.00
Pairpoint, desk; sterling picture fr, mrc, 1907, 5" 110.00
Pairpoint, mantel; br, w/angel, sterling sc/mrc, 1904 ....115.00
Phila Therm Co, hygrometer; br sc, rotating bezel, 1928 ....40.00
Reau, desk; ornate blk bronze, wood F&C sc, mrc 57.00
S Mitzutani, alabaster ped, candle figural atop, mrc, 15" 100.00
Short & Mason, recording drum; copper case, 1910 ....78.00
Slouche, desk; alabaster ped, paper sc inset, mrc, 8x2½" 75.00
Standard, for Fairbanks & Co, rnd, br case, 1886, 7" 70.00
Standard, hanging; rnd, br rim, -40 to 150, dial 40.00
Standard, wall; br case, dial counter balance, 1885, 9" 78.00
Taylor, hanging; ornate wood bk, br sc, 10x7" 21.00
Taylor, hanging; pnt wood, red spirit, 6x24" 30.00
Taylor, lady's profile, cvd wood, emb Art Deco, 20½", EX 95.00
Taylor, wall; blk enameled case, F&R sc on stl, mrc, 12" 35.00
Taylor, wall; octagonal wood fr/metal sc, red liquid, 5" 25.00
Tiffany, desk; horoscope, bronze, mrc, 1907, 4x7" 86.00
Tycos, incubator hygrometer; glass reservoir, 4x4" 16.00
Tycos, maxi/minimum, japanned tin/br, mrc, T-5452, 8" 25.00

Tycos-Taylor, outdoor wall; wood fr, red liquid, 27x5" 70.00
Vogue, desk; Victorian, dial, gr, 1931 ....25.00
W Pratt, desk; wood inlays, ivory sc, mrc, 1900, 6" 63.00
Warren Foundries, wall; umbrella w/dragon hdl, br sc, mrc, 12" .60.00
Wise, desk; Tunbridge, twin columns, mrc, 1870, 5" 825.00
Zeradatha, desk; cast metal, dial w/rotate sc, 1926, 7" 43.00

Tiffany

Louis Comfort Tiffany was born in 1848 to Charles Lewis and Harriet Young Tiffany of New York. By the time he was eighteen, his father's small dry goods and stationery store had grown and developed into the world-renowned Tiffany and Company.

Preferring the study of art to joining his father in the family business, Louis spent the next six years under the tutelage of noted artists. He returned to America in 1870 and until 1875 painted canvases that focused on European and North African scenes. Deciding the more lucrative approach was in the application of industrial arts and crafts, he opened a decorating studio called Louis C. Tiffany and Co., Associated Artists. He began seriously experimenting with glass, and eschewing traditionally painted-on details, he instead learned to produce glass with qualities that could suggest natural textures and effects. His experiments broadened, and he soon concentrated his efforts on vases, bowls, etc. that came to be considered the highest achievements of the art. Peacock feathers, leaves and vines, flowers, and abstracts were developed within the plane of the glass as it was blown. Opalescent and metallic lustres were combined with transparent color to produce stunning effects. Tiffany called his glass Favrile, meaning handmade.

In 1900 he established Tiffany Studios and turned his attention full time to producing art glass, leaded-glass lamp shades, and household wares with metal components. He also designed a complete line of jewelry which was sold through his father's store. He became proficiently accomplished in silverwork and produced such articles as hand mirrors embellished with peacock feather designs set with gems and candlesticks with Favrile glass inserts.

Tiffany's work exemplified the Art Nouveau style of design and decoration, and through his own flamboyant personality and business acumen he perpetrated his tastes onto the American market to the extent that his name became a household word. Tiffany Studios continued to prosper until the second decade of this century when due to changing tastes his influence began to diminish. By 1920 the company had closed.

Serial numbers were assigned to much of Tiffany's work, and letter prefixes indicated the year of manufacture: A-N for 1896-1900, P-Z for 1901-1905. After that, the letter followed the numbers with A-N in use from 1906-1912; P-Z from 1913-1920. O-marked pieces were made especially for friends of relatives; X indicated pieces not made for sale.

Our listings are primarily from the auction houses in the East where Tiffany sells at a premium; our advisor tells us that in other areas of the country many examples may command prices of as much as 50% less. All items are signed unless noted otherwise.

Bronze

Box, cigar; gilt/enamel, wood lined, 6" L, EX 450.00
Box, dore, dolphins relief, cedar lined, #1680, 5x3¼" 325.00
Candelabrum, 2-arm, ea w/3 cups, central stem snuffer/hdl ..2,300.00
Candelabrum, 4-arm, glass studs, blown bobeches, 12" 1,300.00
Candelabrum, 6-arm, central flame finial, #1290-S748, 14" ...1,900.00
Candlestick, bamboo mold, flared/split base, 9¾" 400.00
Candlestick, gr glass-lined cup, slender stem, #11483, 20" ...1,800.00
Candlestick, Queen Anne's Lace, #881, 18" 1,100.00
Candlestick, rnd base, sgn/#1043, 5¾", pr 250.00
Charger, bl enamel 'tile' border/7 grad 'tile' bands, 12" 250.00

Desk calender, Grapevine, gr slag insert, #11, 4¼x6" 200.00
Desk set, Adam, letter rack/calendar/rocker blotter+2 pcs . . .1,000.00
Desk set, Am Indian, stamp box/inkwell/letter rack+3 pcs . . .1,500.00
Desk set, Grapevine, gilt/onyx accents, ea pc mk, 10-pc 3,800.00
Desk set, Grapevine, gilt/onyx accents, ea pc mk, 7-pc 2,000.00
Epergne, branch form, 10 sm recepticals, acorn base, 9" 550.00
Ferner, Grapevine, gr patina, mk, 10½" 650.00
Ferner, 5-ftd, w/12 amber irid turtlebk tiles, #386, 9½" 4,900.00
Figurine, Boston bulldog, sgn, 2" L 325.00
Frame, scrolled floral border, gilt/pastel enamels, 12x8" 1,300.00
Inkstand, Bookmark, gold dore, 8-sided, glass insert, 3x4" 625.00
Inkstand, Chinese, sqd octagon, #1752, 4½" 1,200.00
Inkwell, crab holds well, hinged shell lid, 8½" L 4,000.00
Inkwell, dome lid, 2 rows rectangles w/blown-in glass, 7" 1,500.00
Inkwell, Grapevine, etched/gr patina, opal panels, 4" sq 400.00
Inkwell, squat conical form w/rnd top, linear designs, 3½" 440.00
Letter holder, Abalone, MOP accents, 2 letter slots, 5½" 1,500.00
Planter, 8-sided/4-ftd, w/8 irid glass panels, 4" H 3,500.00
Stamp box, Am Indian, red patina, #1184, 5" L 275.00
Tray, eng stylized floral border, gilded, #1747, 14" dia 300.00
Tray, Greek Key, rnd on short ped, 8" 195.00

Glass

Basket, bl-gold, intaglio leaves, enamel insets in hdl, 10" 1,150.00
Bottle, scent; bl-gold, grooved sides, tricorn, #d, 3¾" 675.00
Bottle, scent; feathers on mustard gold, bulbous, 5¾" 650.00
Bowl, bl, ribbed/dimpled/scalloped, #1103-2248N, 4x5" 650.00
Bowl, bl-gold, #1132-485M, 3¼x5½" 500.00
Bowl, cut crystal, repousse sterling rim w/monogram, 11" 550.00
Bowl, gold, ribbed, #1216, 2½x7" 250.00
Bowl, gold irid leaf/vine eng on herringbone, 2¼x5¾" 350.00
Bowl, lily pads, gr-gold, dbl flower frog, #1177, 12" 900.00
Bowl, Rice, brn pastel, ped base, B-608, 6" 400.00
Bowl, Rice, lt gr, flared, #1925, 6" 220.00
Bowl, yel flashed on opal, stretched rim, ped ft, 4½" H 175.00
Candlestick, bl lustre, paneled knop, label/#1817, 4", pr 500.00
Candlestick, Damascene, bl irid w/silver, 10" 850.00
Candlestick, fiery opal w/aqua scalloped edge, 1x4", pr 275.00
Compote, gr flashed on amber/opal Dia Optic, 2x5¾" dia 350.00
Compote, lav flashed on opal Optic, stretch edge, 4x16" 1,200.00
Compote, morning-glories, red w/gr centers in opal, 3x7" 1,400.00
Compote, pk irid flashed on opal Optic, 2x5¼" dia 400.00
Finger bowl, bl-gold, ribbed, scalloped rim, 4½" 275.00
Finger bowl & underplate, gold, stretched/ruffled, #8918 . . . . .350.00
Loving cup, amber irid w/floral intaglio, 3 scroll hdls, 6" 1,000.00
Loving cup, bl-gold, gr intaglio leaves, #3127-H, 7½" 1,500.00
Punch cup, lily pads, gr on gold, #7421 . . . . .200.00
Rose bowl, swirls, red/gr/gold on ribbing, sgn/label, 4" H 850.00
Sherbet, bl pastel, #4294 . . . . .175.00
Sherbet, panels/leaves intaglio, gold, low ft, 4" 350.00
Sherbet, pk pastel, label, 3½" 250.00
Sherbet & underplate, bl-gold, intaglio floral 400.00
Tile, bl, gold ftd mt mk LCT/#550, 4" 250.00
Toothpick holder, bl-gold, w/prunts, 2" 375.00
Tumbler, Vintage, gold irid, 3" 185.00
Vase, bl, bulbous w/stick neck, #1065-984M, 12½" 2,250.00
Vase, bl, ribbed w/stretched flared top, ped ft, #1881, 7" 800.00
Vase, bl irid, #1812, 6" 325.00
Vase, bl to amber irid w/drag loops, slightly lobed, 5½" 1,500.00
Vase, bl-gold, herringbone decor, grooved rim, #6385, 6½" 700.00
Vase, blood red w/gold int, classic form, #1080-K, 8" 3,000.00
Vase, bud; amber irid, light ribbing, elongated ovoid, 15" 800.00
Vase, bud; gold irid, 5" 425.00

Vase, bud; pk pastel w/clear base, ribbed, #1873, 6½" 400.00
Vase, cameo, poppies, orange/gr on wht frost, #4530C, 7" . . .5,500.00
Vase, clear to gr tube form in bronze floriform ft, 21" 600.00
Vase, Cypriote, irid spots on amber, 4½" 3,000.00
Vase, dogwood intaglio, wht on cobalt irid, #2461, 17½" 4,750.00
Vase, feathers, gold on lt gold, N-5364, 5" 900.00
Vase, feathers at top, bl/gold on teal, #1252, 7" 1,600.00
Vase, feathers on bl, #8461, 8" 800.00
Vase, floriform; bl-gold, ribbed ped ft, Y-5513, 10" 1,550.00
Vase, floriform; bl-gold, ribbed/scalloped, ped ft, 11" 2,750.00
Vase, floriform; feathers, gr on wht, gr/amber ft, 13" 2,200.00
Vase, floriform; feathers, gr-bl on opal, gold ped, #d, 5" 1,300.00
Vase, floriform; feathers, ruffled, elongated ovoid, 9½" 1,800.00
Vase, floriform; gold crackle, raised base, W-7376, 15¾" 2,800.00
Vase, floriform; gr on opal, elongated cup, #2095A, 11½" 1,800.00
Vase, floriform; leaves, gr on gr/opal, gold base, #d, 13½" 5,750.00
Vase, floriform; leaves, gr on opal, gr stem w/leaves, 12" 3,300.00
Vase, floriform; leaves, gr on opal, tricorn, dome ft, 14" 2,700.00
Vase, floriform; leaves in gr, gold stretch/ruffle top, 11" 2,800.00
Vase, floriform; pulled petals, gr on amber, gr ft, 13" 1,950.00
Vase, freeform leaves, gr on gold, baluster, #5323-C, 8" 3,500.00
Vase, gold, classic urn form w/scroll hdls, #384-H, 4¾" 100.00
Vase, gold, ribbed, gold emb band near base, #351-J, 16" 650.00
Vase, gold, ribbed, hdls, #2330-B, paper label, 3¾" 400.00
Vase, gold, ribbed, in ornate bronze leaf base, 17" 400.00
Vase, gold, ribbed, ped ft, #1526-223N, 13" 950.00
Vase, gold, ribbed, ped ft, trumpet form, label, #1822, 10" 700.00
Vase, gold, ribbed scalloped top, ribbed ped ft, #d, 9" 700.00
Vase, gold, ribbed trumpet form, slim stem, #1066-177, 18" . .2,000.00
Vase, gold, swirled mold, waisted w/stick neck, W-9364, 17" .2,400.00
Vase, gold cylinder in mc enamel base, #151, 13" 600.00
Vase, gold w/abstract veining, paneled, H-1283, 4" 475.00
Vase, gr-gold w/dk gr bottom, silver swirls at middle, 7" 1,500.00

**Vase, gold with green trails and intaglio leaves, #7151, 12",
$2,100.00; Vase, gold with green vines, #1535, 13½",
$1,100.00.**

Vase, heart leaves/stems, gr on gold, #576-M, 12" 2,800.00
Vase, heart leaves/stems, gr on gold, rnd w/slim neck, 6" 1,200.00
Vase, jack-in-pulpit; gold crackle, bulbous ft, Y-5306, 19" . . .7,000.00
Vase, lappets, gr/gold on orange, onion form, tricorn, 16½" . .4,500.00
Vase, lily pads/vines, gr on gold, #2984-H, 9" 1,500.00

Vase, lily pads/vines, gr on gold translucent, Q-9831, 4" 800.00
Vase, ovals/lines, gold on brn irid, long neck, #3077, 14" 2,900.00
Vase, paperweight; flowers, lav/clear, Exhibit Pc, 8" dia 3,000.00
Vase, paperweight; lily of the valley, #2508-G, 9" 5,200.00
Vase, pulled loops, gr on gold-amber, mk LCT Q-911, 6" 795.00
Vase, pulled loops on irid gr & bl, wide shoulder, 3½" 950.00
Vase, red, delicate freeform hdls, #6656-K, 4½" 3,400.00
Vase, red w/yel int, dbl gourd form, P-328, 8" 1,800.00
Vase, swirls, bl irid on blk, #0541, 3¾" 1,600.00
Vase, swirls, yel on gold, baluster form, 8½" 875.00
Vase, tan w/gold decor, #1883-H, 4" 350.00
Vase, wavy stems/leaves, bl on bl-gray irid, baluster, 6½" 2,800.00
Wine, aqua-gr pastel, opal-edged ped ft, 4", set of 6 ....850.00
Wine, intaglio festoons, 5¾" 325.00

Lamps

Base, bronze, allover iris relief, sqd cylinder, #669, 26" 1,870.00
Base, bronze, paneled std on dished base, #534, 23" 800.00
Base, bronze, stem std w/3 stalk-like branching arms, #426 ....350.00
Base, bronze, 2-section std w/central knop, #26 ....350.00
Base, floor lamp; bronze, shaped 3-sided/3-leg base #688 ......220.00
Base, hammered copper w/enamel dandelion puffs/etc, 15" .3,700.00
Base, lily; 3-light, overlapping petals/foliate knop, #320 ......935.00
Base, oil lamp; gilt-bronze, lion's masks/strapwork, 11" 550.00
Base, spiral tendrils on std, pineapple base, #366, 24" 5,500.00
Base, vine/petal relief, 4 raised petal ft, D-805, 18½" 3,800.00
Bridge, silver strings on bl irid shade, harp support, 57" 7,100.00
Candle, gold 6-sided shade; bamboo base #1205, electric, pr .2,600.00
Candle, gr/gold crackle shade; swirl rib stick base, 11" 1,900.00
Chandelier, ldgl acorn shade w/turtle-bk tile, 18" dia, EX ...4,750.00
Chandelier, ldgl acorn shade; orig brass mts, 14x23" dia 8,500.00
Chandelier, ldgl acorn shade; unsgn, 21¾" dia 8,000.00
Desk, bl feathered inverted dome in harp support #424, 18" .5,000.00
Desk, damascene inverted bell shade in arched fr #448-S224 .5,000.00
Desk, gold damascene 7" shade; bronze base #2972-C 3,100.00
Desk, gr waves on gr irid bell shade; tray base #449, 14½" ...8,000.00
Desk, gr waves on gr irid dome shade; base #436, 18" 6,000.00
Desk, ldgl 9" brickwork shade; enameled base #369 ....850.00
Desk, opal & gr ribbed/cased 4x7" dia shade; harp std, 13" .2,400.00
Desk, shade w/2 turtlebk tiles; glass inset in base #28632 ....6,000.00
Desk, 2-arm w/gold pendant shades; stem std, #304, 20" 2,800.00
Floor, gold damascene 10" unsgn shade; #423 base, 55½" 1,900.00
Floor, ldgl 24½" geometric shade; #377 std, 80" 17,500.00
Hanging, ldgl 24" dragonfly sculpture, 3 pendants, unsgn 3,000.00
Lily, 10-light, assembled shades; #381 std, 20½" 12,000.00
Lily, 12-light, mixed colors; #382 std, 19½" 16,500.00
Lily, 3-light, gold shades (2 sgn); #319 std 3,300.00
Linenfold, amber insets; paneled bronze base #612, 16" 7,100.00
Nautilus, gr/wht shade; leaf-relief #28628 base, 13" 6,800.00
Nautilus, ldgl shell-form shade; base A-400, 14½" 3,800.00
Piano, 3-lily, mixed colors (1 sgn); #320 base, 8" 3,000.00
Sconce, sm ldgl 3-part shades ea side bronze vasiform, unsgn .1,000.00
Sconce, 2 scroll arms w/leafy terminals, 1 w/shade, 16", pr ...4,400.00
Sconce, 3-arm, amber lily shades, rnd wall plate, 15", pr 4,800.00
Shade, amber glass w/bronze lace overlay, conical, 19" dia ...3,300.00
Table, feathers, silver on brn, on base/10" shade, 15" 5,500.00
Table, feathers, 13" shade; blown-in-metal pineapple base .15,400.00
Table, ldgl brickwork 18" shade; gold dore base, #533, 22" ...6,500.00
Table, ldgl 15" spider web w/spider-cap shade; #337 std ...12,000.00
Table, ldgl 16" acorn shade; Colonial std #534, 21½" 5,100.00
Table, ldgl 17" dragonfly shade; pumpkin/pond lily base ..49,500.00
Table, ldgl 18" brickwork shade; simple #533 std, 22" 6,500.00
Table, ldgl 18" clematis shade; turtlebk tile 3-prong font ...30,000.00

Table, ldgl 18" lemon leaf shade; turtlebk #1670 base, 25" ..12,500.00
Table, ldgl 18" peony shade; leaf-mold base #368, 25" 38,000.00
Table, ldgl 20" brickwork/turtlebk tile shade; #528 std 14,000.00
Table, ldgl 20" daffodil shade; bronze base #532, 26" 19,000.00
Table, ldgl 20" lily pad shade; #9947 std, 26½" 14,000.00
Table, ldgl 20½" arrowroot shade; #370 std, 24" 20,000.00
Table, ldgl 21" 12-sided 3-row panel shade; #543 std 6,050.00
Table, ldgl 21½" laburnum shade; pierced std #397, 28" ...57,750.00
Table, ldgl 21½" peony shade; #500 6-leg base w/paw ft 53,000.00
Table, ldgl 22" Zodiac shade; Roman column std, 32" 33,000.00
Table, ldgl 26" lotus flattened cone shade; #28622 std 37,000.00
Table, ldlg 10½" ball form shade w/branches, #438 std 35,750.00
Table, lgdl 22" turtlebk tile/brickwork shade; D-794 std 14,300.00
Table, linenfold 14" unsgn shade; base #586, 23" 11,000.00

16" daffodil shade; glass and bronze signed/#d base (cracked), $6,500.00.

Pottery

Vase, honeysuckle, wht bsk, gr int, sm rpr, 10½" 475.00
Vase, leaves emb, gr w/tiny gold crystals, P-932, 6x2½" 800.00
Vase, leaves/stems emb at neck, bronzed, baluster, 13½" 2,200.00
Vase, maple leaves emb, brn on ivory, canister form, 7½" ...1,400.00
Vase, molded as bouquet of Queen Anne's Lace, gr matt, 8" .1,100.00
Vase, thick tan gloss drip, bulbous, collared rim/ft, 7x9" 350.00

Silver

Bowl, center; Georgian style, wide everted lip, 12" 575.00
Bowl, center; Marquise, 4 bun ft, 13" 400.00
Bowl, Chrysanthemum, openwork vines, monogram, 8" 400.00
Bowl, extended grapevine rim, scroll-pierced sides, 14" L 2,750.00
Bowl, spun, w/enamel detail, low flared ft, 8" dia 300.00
Candlestick, Georgian, weighted, 10", set of 4 ....1,800.00
Cigarette case, plain, gilt int, ca 1930, 3½" L 120.00

Coffee set, repousse berries/foliage, ivory hdls, 3 pc+tray 4,000.00
Creamer, leaf-cap strap hdl, scalloped, shell-cap legs, 4" 175.00
Creamer & sugar, repousse foliage, dbl ring hdls, 11-oz 300.00
Demitasse pot, Chrysanthemum, monogram, 9½", 21-oz 1,900.00
Dresser set, chased foliage centering monogram, 3-pc 200.00
Entree dish, plain w/removable cannon & fruit finial, 11" ...2,900.00
Flask, bicycle race etching on base, leather-on-glass body ...2,000.00
Flask, camel on front, bl enameling, shaped to hip, 6" 225.00
Pitcher, female head on hdl, putto on lid, chased, 12" 2,200.00
Platter, Marquise, w/monogram, 22" 800.00

Platter, repousse daisies & leaves, 20" long, $3,700.00.

Salt cellar, gold-washed fish form, +fish-hdl spoon, 4 for 450.00
Salt cellar, 3 winged griffin ft, inscribed, set of 4 ....1,900.00
Salver, Children at Play emb rim, 8" 350.00
Salver, Japanese Style, scrolling monogram, triangular, 10" 700.00
Sauce ladle, English King, monogram, pr 350.00
Tazza, emb/eng palmettes, monogram, dome base, 7" dia, pr ...400.00
Teapot, Moorish Style, allover strapwork/foliage, 5½" 3,500.00
Tray, Chrysanthemum, monogram, ftd/hdls, 16" L, pr 6,600.00
Tray, Japanese Style, bleeding hearts/beetle on rim, 7" 1,000.00
Tray, roll; lobed/foliate border, oval, 10½" L 300.00
Tray, scrolls/foliage/flower-emb border, hdls, 26", 188-oz 6,600.00
Tureen, bud finial on dome lid, leaf-cap loop hdls, 15" L 2,500.00
Vase, eng rosettes, tapered panel body, ped base, 11" 550.00

Miscellaneous

Box, enamel on copper, striated lappets, glass int, 5" dia 2,000.00
Necklace, gr/lav woven cord set w/9 irid glass scarabs, 16" ...3,300.00
Pendant, dragonfly, glass/bronze, w/chain, 20" 2,000.00
Wax seal, gold scarab w/initial, 1½" 250.00

Tiffin Glass

The Tiffin Glass Company was founded in 1887 in Tiffin, Ohio, one of the many factories composing the U.S. Glass Company. Its early wares consisted of tablewares and decorative items such as lamps and globes. Among the most popular of all Tiffin products was the black satin glass produced there during the 1920s. In 1959 U.S. Glass was sold, and in 1962 the factories closed. The plant was re-opened in 1963 as the Tiffin Art Glass Company. Products from this period were tableware, hand-blown stemware, and other decorative items.

Those interested in learning more about Tiffin glass are encouraged to contact the Tiffin Collectors' Club, whose address can be found in the Directory under Clubs, Newsletters, and Catalogs.

Advertising sign, lt bl 20.00
Ash tray, Empress, gr & crystal, #6590 ....65.00
Basket, bl satin 80.00
Basket, Empress, banana, #6553 ....150.00
Basket, Empress, red & crystal, #5556 ....145.00
Bowl, bonbon; Fuchsia, hdls 30.00
Bowl, celery; Cherokee Rose, oblong, 10½" 20.00
Bowl, Cherokee Rose, crimped, 12" 25.00
Bowl, console; Flanders, pk, flanged rim, 12" 27.50
Bowl, Empress, red & crystal, #6561 ....165.00
Bowl, grapefruit; Cadena, yel, ftd 30.00
Bowl, June Night, 10¼" 50.00
Candlestick, bl, pr 30.00

Candlestick, black glass stylized frog, 5½", $65.00.

Candlestick, blk satin, frog form, #72, pr 125.00
Candlestick, Cadena, yel 30.00
Candlestick, Flanders, pk, blown 75.00
Candlestick, Modern, crystal, #6326, pr 75.00
Candlestick, Modern, crystal, #6460, pr 175.00
Candy box, Modern, bl, #6455 ....85.00
Candy box, Modern, cut/bl, #6455 ....130.00
Candy dish, heart shape, canary yel, no pattern 85.00
Candy jar, Modern, cut/crystal, #17423 ....165.00
Cellini bowl, Modern, bl & crystal, #6067 ....150.00
Cellini bowl, Modern, citron & crystal, #6067 ....115.00
Cellini bowl, Modern, crystal, #6067 ....65.00
Champagne, Cerice etch, #071 ....15.00
Champagne, Classic Shawl Dancer 22.00
Champagne, Flanders 15.00
Champagne, Flanders, pk 25.00
Champagne, Flanders, topaz, saucer type 22.00
Champagne, June Night 22.00
Champagne, Persian Pheasant, #17399 ....25.00
Champagne, Rambler Rose, platinum trim, #42, saucer type 15.00
Claret, Cherokee Rose, #17403 ....32.50
Claret, Flanders, pk 55.00
Claret, Persian Pheasant, #17399 ....30.00
Cocktail, Byzantine 22.00
Cocktail, Cherokee Rose, #17399 ....24.00
Cocktail, Flanders 20.00
Cocktail, June Night 15.00

Cocktail, oyster; Cherokee Rose, crystal, #14196 . . . . .20.00
Cocktail, oyster; Fuchsia 20.00
Cocktail, Persian Pheasant 25.00
Console set, blk satin, 4-pc 75.00
Cordial, Flanders 55.00
Cordial, Flanders, pk 75.00
Cordial, June Night 30.00
Cornucopia, Modern, upright, Twilight, #5983 . . . . .300.00
Cornucopia, wisteria 135.00
Creamer, Fontaine, bl, tall 45.00
Creamer & sugar bowl, Flanders 32.00
Cup, Cadena 15.00
Cup & saucer, Flanders, ftd 35.00
Cup & saucer, Flanders, pk, blown 60.00
Decanter, Flanders, pk, w/stopper 285.00
Decanter, Modern, crystal, #13624 . . . . .75.00
Figurine, female pheasant, cobalt, 13½" 200.00
Goblet, Byzantine 22.00
Goblet, Classic Shawl Dancer, pulled stem 20.00
Goblet, cordial; Fuchsia, 1-oz 20.00
Goblet, ice tea; June Night 24.00
Goblet, Paulina, topaz, 6-oz, 5½" 7.00
Goblet, Paulina, topaz, 7¼" 8.00
Goblet, sherbet; Cadena, 4¾" 20.00
Goblet, water; Cadena, yel, 7½" 27.50
Goblet, water; Cherokee Rose 25.00
Goblet, water; Flanders 17.50
Goblet, water; Flanders, pk 25.00
Goblet, water; Fuchsia 18.00
Goblet, water; June Night 22.50
Goblet, water; Persian Pheasant 32.00
Lamp, hurricane; crystal, #6408, 2-pc .60.00
Lamp, hurricane; Modern, bl, #6408, 2-pc 100.00
Mayonnaise, Flanders, pk, w/liner 37.50
Parfait, June Night 35.00
Pitcher, Empress, Twilight & Kilarney 250.00
Pitcher, Flanders, pk, w/lid, #194 . . . . .275.00
Pitcher, Modern, crystal, #5691 . . . . .40.00
Pitcher, Modern, cut/Parkwood, #5691 . . . . .100.00
Pitcher, Modern, sand carved, #5961 .100.00
Pitcher, water; Classic Shawl Dancer .175.00
Pitcher, water; Flanders, pk 225.00
Pitcher, water; Fuchsia 295.00
Pitcher, water; La Fleur, gr spiral, #15003, 80-oz 55.00
Pitcher, water; La Fleur, topaz 225.00
Plate, Cherokee Rose, 6" 15.00
Plate, Flanders, pk, 6" 12.50
Plate, Flanders, pk, 8" 17.50
Plate, Flanders, 8" 9.00
Plate, sherbet; Cherokee Rose, 6" 4.50
Platter, Cameo, yel 37.50
Ram bowl, Empress, Twilight, #6609 . . . . .130.00
Rose bowl, Kilarney 75.00
Sherbet, Cherokee Rose, #17403 . . . . .12.00
Sugar bowl, Cadena 15.00
Sugar bowl, Fuchsia, ind 35.00
Sundae, Cerice etch, #071, 6-oz 15.00
Towl, Empress, Twilight & Smoke, #6561 . . . . .185.00
Tray, Birch Tree/Deerwood, pk, center hdl 45.00
Tumbler, Flanders, topaz, ftd, 9-oz 22.00
Tumbler, ice tea; Byzantine, crystal w/blk base 22.00
Tumbler, ice tea; Flanders 20.00
Tumbler, ice tea; Flanders, topaz 22.50
Tumbler, ice tea; June Night, ftd, 6½" .18.00

Tumbler, juice; June Night, ftd, 5" 16.00
Tumbler, Persian Pheasant, ftd, 5-oz 22.00
Tumbler, water; June Night, ftd 15.00
Vase, bud; Cherokee Rose, 6" 15.00
Vase, bud; Modern, Twilight, #85 . . . . .95.00
Vase, Cherokee Rose, flared, 12" 40.00
Vase, Empress, bl & crystal, #6551 . . . . .165.00
Vase, Empress, gr & Twilight, #6560 .195.00
Vase, Fuchsia, crystal, beaded, 11" 65.00
Vase, iris emb, bl satin 65.00
Vase, iris emb, citron satin 45.00
Vase, iris emb, pk satin 45.00
Vase, Modern, crystal, cornucopia, #6301 . . . . .150.00
Vase, Optic, citron, pulled ft, 12" 75.00
Vase, poppies in relief, bl velvet, 8½" .48.00
Vase, tub; Modern, sand carved w/roses, crystal, #17350 . . . . .150.00
Vase, tub; sand carved w/roses, bl, #17350 . . . . .225.00
Whiskey, La Fleur, Mandarin Yel, 2¾" 20.00
Whiskey, La Fleur, topaz, ftd 12.50
Wine, Cherokee Rose, #17403 . . . . .22.00
Wine, Classic Reed, pk, stemmed 30.00
Wine, Flanders, pk 45.00
Wine, Fuchsia 35.00
Wine, June Night, #17403 . . . . .20.00
Wine, Persian Pheasant 35.00

Tiles

Though originally strictly functional, tiles were being produced in various colors and used as architectural highlights as early as the Ancient Roman Empire. By the 18th century, Dutch tiles were decorated with polychrome landscapes and figures. During the 19th century, there were over a hundred companies in England involved in the manufacture of tile. By the Victorian era, the use of decorative tiles had reached its peak. Special souvenir editions, campaign and portrait tiles, and Art Nouveau motifs with lovely ladies and stylized examples from nature were popular. Today all of these are very collectible. See also specific manufacturers.

Minton, black transfer of cattle in stream, Wm. Wise, ca 1879, $85.00.

Advertising, Fairbanks-Standard, globe transfer, 10x10" 60.00
Architectural, Cheshire cat in tree, 4-color, 4" 250.00

CA Art, peacock in grape arbor w/fountain, bl tones, 8x12" 80.00
Calendar, advertising, octagonal, 1929, 6¼" 45.00
Calendar, Jones, McDuffie & Stratton, Boston Custom House ..48.00
Claycraft, scene: trees/house, 24-tile frieze, att, 35x23" 2,100.00
Columbia Encaustic, floral, cream/brn gloss, 4½" 24.00
Englecraft, Good Sip, bl 100.00
Head of Liberty in reserve, lt gr, 6" 50.00
IT Co/BNY, child's head relief, brn, 6" 25.00
Kensington, classic female head, brn, 6" 40.00
Little Bo Peep, Nursery Rhymes, dtd 7/31/26 ....85.00
Low, Annie Sussel portrait, olive, c 1881, 6" 350.00
Low, child's head in rnd reserve, bl, 6" 50.00
Low, geometric florals, yel-gr, 6" 25.00
Low, portraits: Industria; Religievse, orig fr, 9" dia, pr 175.00
Mercer, Indian kneeling at river, 5¼" 50.00
Minton, geometric floral, 3-color, 6", EX 30.00
Minton, King Henry, 6" 65.00
Minton, Taming of the Shrew, 6" 65.00
Rosen Den Haag, windmills by sea, sgn 250.00
Stoke on Trent Morton's China Works, horse scene, blk/wht ...50.00
Wheeling, kittens, calendar bk, 1948 ....20.00
Woman entitled 'Esmeralda'/Madison Sq Theatre 1882, gr, 8" ..75.00

Tinware

In the American household of the 17th and 18th centuries, tinware items could be found in abundance, from food containers to foot warmers and mirror frames. Although the first settlers brought much of their tinware with them from Europe, by 1798 sheets of tin plate were being imported from England for use by the growing number of American tinsmiths. Tinwares were often decorated either by piercing or painted designs which were both free-hand and stenciled. (See Toleware.) By the early 1900s, many homes had replaced their old tinware with the more attractive aluminum and graniteware.

In the 19th century, tenth wedding anniversaries were traditionally celebrated by gifts of tin. Couples gave big parties, dressed in their wedding clothes, and reaffirmed their vows before their friends and family who arrived bearing (and often wearing) tin gifts, most of which were quite humorous. Anniversary tin items may include hats, cradles, slippers and shoes, rolling pins, etc. See also Primitives and Kitchen Collectibles.

Coffeepot, 4-piece, 1-cup, attributed to the Shakers, $85.00.

Bank, can shape, emb flowers & hearts, child's 50.00
Box, spice; rectangular, mc stencils, ca 1900, 9½x7x5" 70.00

Cabinet, spice; 8-drawer, orig blk pnt/stencils, hanging 195.00
Candle box, blk finish, rnd, tab hangers at bk, 13" L 235.00
Candle holder, cup shape, stoneware drip cup, ring hdl, pr 125.00
Candle lantern, pierced, Paul Revere type 145.00
Candle lantern, whirling swastika piercing, gilt pnt, 17" 220.00
Candle snuffer, cone shape, twisted wire hdl, 1860s, 4½" 45.00
Candle stand, weighted cone base, 2-socket, 1880s, 28", VG ...80.00
Chandelier, dbl cone w/6 curved arms, 1800s, 30" dia 400.00
Cheese drainer, loop side hdls, 3 rnd ft, side/bottom holes 110.00
Colander, pierced, 2 open curved hdls, 3 ft, mk, 2x11" 130.00
Container, pierced star decor, dtd 1776-1876, 3½x7½x6½" ...175.00
Cracker pricker, scalloped edge, 8 sharp points, top hdl 85.00
Dust pan, 2" hood, flat ring hdl, 1860s, 7½x5", EX 28.00
Egg coddler, ornate base, burner, complete, 4-pc 225.00
Flour sifter, handmade, scoop shape, crank hdl, bk hdl 95.00
Food carrier, metal rack, top hdl, +3 stacked containers 55.00
Lamp, bk reflector fixed to rnd base, ring hdl, hanging 75.00
Measure, 2 compartments, side hdl, 2¾x1½" 45.00
Mirror, hired man's, decorated comb pocket, 9½x12" 75.00
Oil lamp filler, brass cap, dtd Apr 2, 1861 ....65.00
Pastry sheet, w/shelf, w/dk tin rolling pin 350.00
Roaster, 11x7" plus hdls, w/lid, EX 295.00
Sconce, crimp-edge oval, scroll arm, 9½", +snuffer 285.00
Sconce, crimped shell top, rnd base, 1820s, 13", pr 440.00
Sconce, fluted cup, beaded bk, crimped top, 1800s, 15x4½" ...295.00
Sconce, single, crimped bobeche & reflector, 1830, 10½" 550.00
Sconce, star-form mirror w/face-centered sunburst, 15", pr ...3,800.00
Sconce, 3-arm, bk fan of 9 mirrored panels, 1800s, 9" 350.00
Sconce, 3-arm, half-cylinder, crimped drips/reflectors, 11" ...1,600.00
Sieve, cottage cheese; heart form, ring ft & hdls, 4½" 200.00
Soap saver, screen wire top/bottom, pat Sept 14, 1875 ....25.00
Spatula, fish slice; rnded blade, punchwork, wood hdl 65.00
Teakettle, slant spout, movable bail, ring finial, ca 1840 ......55.00
Tinderbox, candle socket on top, hdl, +striker/flint/snuffer 225.00
Toddy warmer, funnel shape, pouring lip, side hdl 95.00

Tobacciana

Tobacciana is the generally accepted term used to cover a field of collecting that includes smoking pipes, cigar molds, cigarette lighters, humidors — in short, any article having to do with the practice of using tobacco in any form.

Perhaps the most valuable variety of pipes is the meerschaum — hand carved from hydrous magnesium, an opaque white-gray or cream-colored mineral of the soapstone family. (Much of this is today mined in Turkey which has the largest meerschaum deposit in the world, though there are other deposits of lesser significance around the globe.) These figural bowls often portray an elaborately carved mythological character, an animal, or a historical scene. Amber is often used for the stem. Other collectible pipes are corn cob (Missouri Meerschaum) and Indian peace pipes of clay or catlinite. (See American Indian Art.)

Chosen because it was the Indians who first introduced the white man to smoking, the cigar store Indian was a symbol used to identify tobacco stores in the 19th century. The majority of them were hand carved between 1830 and 1900 and are today recognized as some of the finest examples of early wood sculptures. When found they command very high prices.

Our advisor for this category is Chuck Thompson; he is listed in the Directory under Texas. See also Advertising; Snuff Boxes.

Ash tray, bronze, LaFendrich 100th Anniv, 1850-1950 ....20.00
Ash tray/pipe holder, CI, hat form, gold pnt, 6½x6x3" 60.00
Cigar box, Little Casino Cigars 20.00
Cigar case, brass, scrolling dragon appl on lid, 5¼x2½" 60.00

Log cabin Tampello cigar box, ca 1900, $225.00.

Cigarette holder, sterling, eng thistle, amber stem, England, 2" . .48.00
Cigarette urn, monkey w/top hat, wrought iron, tail cutter 85.00
Cutter, cigar; Bashful Trick Lock 65.00
Cutter, cigar; Boston Trade, clockwork, nickel w/glass, 8" 275.00
Cutter, cigar; Brunhoff, ornate, dtd 1902, EX 295.00
Cutter, cigar; El Roi-Tan Perfect Cigars 29.00
Cutter, cigar; gold filled, w/bottle opener, pocket sz 20.00
Cutter, cigar; Nouveau lady ea side, sterling 85.00
Cutter, cigar; Pico Grande 5¢ Cigars, dtd 1902 . . . . .250.00
Cutter, cigar; Sheffield blade mk Birmingham 9.375 gold 1898 . .85.00
Cutter, cigar; Smoke El Gusto Cigars, pump-hdl shape, early . .295.00
Cutter, cigar; Tom Benton Cigars, early, EX 295.00
Cutter, cigar; 3-hole, countertop, NP w/Arab paper label 165.00
Cutter, plug; Brown's Mule, Reynolds, EX 60.00
Cutter, plug; Griswold, CI 80.00
Cutter, plug; John Finzer Bros, Louisville 55.00
Cutter, plug; Sprague & Warner 75.00
Cutter, plug; wrought iron on block in sq pine box, 13" L 105.00
Dispenser, lighter fluid; Fill-Ur-Up gas pump, CI, 11" 275.00
Humidor, baby, bl/wht German porc, 1890, 9" 125.00
Humidor, figure of a lady taking snuff, German porc, 10" 150.00
Humidor, head of baby w/smiling & crying faces, pottery, 6" . . .100.00
Humidor, head of blackamoor in turban, pottery, 9" 175.00
Humidor, head of lady in hat w/veil, German bsq, 1910, 6½" . .225.00
Humidor, Huck Finn, stoneware, 1910, 10" 175.00
Humidor, hunting scene on bl, Adam's Tunstall 200.00
Humidor, lady takes tea, German stoneware, 1900, 8½" 200.00
Humidor, monkey w/pipe, pottery, 1910, 6" 100.00
Humidor, schoolmaster behind desk, pottery, 1900, 9½" 200.00
Humidor, seaman's portrait, mc on orange, porc, 7½x5½" 120.00
Humidor, Sir Walter Raleigh, stoneware, 1910, 11" 200.00
Humidor, skull figural, Carlsbad Austria 150.00
Humidor, sterling, rtcl/scrolled w/blown-in gr glass liner 850.00
Humidor, Toby, Staffordshire, 1890, 4½" 150.00
Humidor, 1-eyed pirate, pottery, 1910, 6½" 125.00
Humidor, 2 bears w/pipe, pottery, 1900, 6" 125.00
Indian chief, cvd/pnt, detailed, att J Melchers, 64" 40,000.00
Indian squaw, cvd/pnt, att Chas Robb, 58", EX 14,000.00
Knife, tobacco; CI, IZ Meriam, Whitewater WI, straps to leg . . .60.00
Lamp, newsboy/street lamp, 'Extra/J Anderson,' metal, 22" 650.00
Lighter, cigar; Sun Vapor, CI/brass/tin, Romeo figure, 28" 250.00
Lighter, Lektrolite Flameless, Deco style, 5x15" 195.00
Lighter, The Perfect, metal/wood, countertop, w/cutter, 20" . . .950.00
Mold, cigar; wooden, makes 10, EX .25.00
Opener, cigar box; Elverso Cigars 9.00

Pipe, Caminetto, brn/blk, wine pearl stem, mk 124 Business 85.00
Pipe, Castello, Sea Rock, blk, diamond logo, mk KK 100.00
Pipe, Charatan, Belvedere 'Zulu,' #461, bent billiard 40.00
Pipe, Charatan, Distinction, Dublin, extra long 135.00
Pipe, Charatan, Perfection 'Winston,' #323 DC 50.00

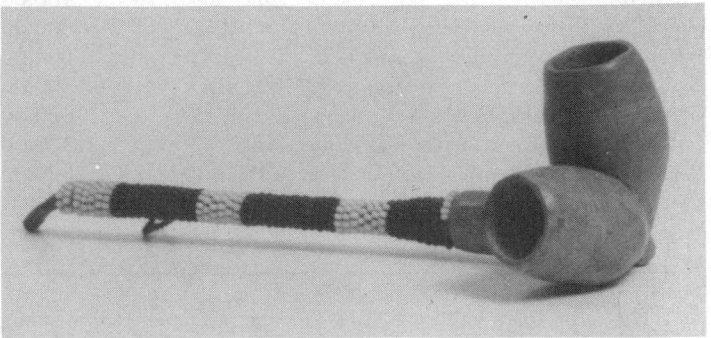

Pipe, double stoneware bowl, beaded handle, 9½", $170.00.

Pipe, Dunhill, Bruyere 'Yacht,' #596, 1971 . . . . .140.00
Pipe, Dunhill, Tanshell, #51122, tall billiard, 1978 . . . . .95.00
Pipe, elk horn, cvd quail decor, 1930s, 3½x6" 55.00
Pipe, meerschaum, lady's hand at bowl, silver ferrule, 5¾" 85.00
Pipe, meerschaum, longhorn mtn goat, full figure, 6", VG 50.00
Pipe, meerschaum, rosettes/swirls, amber stem, 4½", +case 65.00
Pipe, Stanwell, Deluxe, #44, oval shank 25.00
Press, plug; Brown's Mule, emb metal, 1920s, 12" sq 10.00
Spittoon, bl/wht stoneware, emb scroll, sponging 95.00
Spittoon, CI, bl-gray pnt, traditional shape 55.00

Toby Jugs

The delightful jug known as the Toby dates back to the 18th century, when factories in England produced them for export to the American colonies. Named for the character Toby Philpots in the song *The Little Brown Jug*, the Toby was fashioned in the form of a jolly fellow, usually holding a jug of beer and a glass. The earlier examples were made with strict attention to details such as fingernails and teeth. Originally representing only a non-entity, a trend developed to portray well-known individuals such as George II, Napoleon, and Ben Franklin. Among the most-valued Tobies are those produced by Ralph Wood I in the late 1700s. By the mid-1830s, Tobies were being made in America. See also Doulton, Lenox, and Occupied Japan.

Sailor on sea chest with embossed ship, stump handle, no lid, 12", EX, $200.00; Man, standing, hat lid, 'T Burnell' on base, 1800s, 10", $400.00.

Man, seated w/full jug, ca 1780s, rstr, 9¼" 800.00
Man, seated w/jug, mc clothes, ca 1780s, 9⅞", EX 1,000.00
Man w/jug, barrel at ft, pipe at side, 1780s, 10", EX 1,000.00
Portobello, man w/jug, mc sponging, ca 1840, rstr, 9½" 200.00
Pratt, man seated w/jug, sponging, w/lid, ca 1800, rstr, 10" 400.00
Pratt type, man seated w/jug/pipe, mc sponging, 1800s, 10" 500.00
Ralph Wood, man w/beaker/jug/pipe, ca 1780, 10", EX 1,600.00
Ralph Wood type, man w/jug, cask at ft, 1780s, 10", EX 800.00
Sailor on chest, 'dollars' ea side, ca 1820, 10½", EX 300.00
Sailor seated, beaker to lips, holds jug, 1800, rstr, 11" 800.00
Salt-glazed stoneware, man w/jug, w/lid, ca 1840, 10", VG 200.00
Walton, man seated w/jug, spots on face, ca 1820, 10½", EX . . .600.00

Toleware

The term 'toleware' originally came from a French term meaning 'sheet iron.' Today it is used to refer to paint-decorated tin items. The earliest toleware was hand painted; by the 1820s, much of it was decorated by means of a stencil. Among the most collectible today are those items painted by the Pennsylvania Dutch in the 1800s. This type of toleware has a very distinctive look. The surface is dull and unvarnished; background colors range from black to cream. Geometrics are quite common, but florals and fruits were also popular motifs. Often gold-stenciled borders were added.

American toleware is usually found in practical, everyday forms — trays, pails, jugs, boxes, and tankards, for instance — while French examples might include candlesticks, wine coolers, jardinieres, etc. Be sure to note color, design, and condition when determining date and value. In the listings that follow, the dimension given for boxes and trays indicates length.

Box, deed; floral, 2-color on blk, brass bail, worn, 11" L 250.00
Box, deed; floral, 3-color on brn, dome top, 9", EX 350.00
Box, deed; floral (stenciled), minor wear/damage, 10" L 195.00
Box, deed; floral spray, 3-color, sq panels, 9" L 300.00
Cache pot, vases/floral sprigs on blk, gilt twig hdls, 8" 425.00
Coal bin, HP floral, 25" 500.00
Coffeepot, brushstrokes, 3-color on blk, cylinder spout, 9" . . .1,100.00
Coffeepot, floral, 3-color on blk, side spout, 8", NM 1,050.00
Coffeepot, floral, 3-color on blk, str sides/gooseneck, 11" 1,760.00
Coffeepot, floral, 3-color on dk brn, worn but intact, 11" 570.00
Coffeepot, floral, 5-color on brn, long spout w/damage, 11" . . .650.00
Creamer, brushstrokes, red/yel/gr on dk brn, 4", VG 90.00

Victorian fuel bin, barnyard scene, animal paw feet, 16" long, $825.00.

Mug, floral, red/yel on dk brn, minor wear, 4¼" 275.00
Sugar bowl, brushstrokes, yel/bl/blk/wht/brn, w/lid, 4", EX 500.00
Tea caddy, leaves, gold on blk, pewter ft, brass bail, 1800 . . . . .165.00
Tea caddy, mc HP florals, oval, w/lid, 2½x3½x5¼" 135.00
Teapot, floral, red/gr on brn, oval w/str spout, 5½" 185.00
Tray, bread; Oriental scenes, 6-color on blk, 1875, 14" 250.00
Tray, bread; petal border, 4-color on blk, arched sides, 11" 600.00
Tray, floral band in red/gr, 8-sided, 12" L 250.00
Tray, fruit/leaf band, crystalized center, 8-sided, 9x13" 500.00
Tray, peaches/berries, yel borders, PA, ca 1840, 13" L 1,900.00
Tumbler, gold stenciled flowers & birds, 1850s, 3x3" 50.00

Tools

Before the Civil War, tools for the most part were handmade. Some were primitive to the point of crudeness, while others reflected the skill of those who took pride in their trade. Increasing demand for quality tools and the dawning of the age of industrialization resulted in tools that were mass-produced.

Factors important in evaluating antique tools are scarcity, usefulness, and portability. Those with a manufacturer's mark are worth more than unmarked items. When no condition is indicated, the items listed below are assumed to be in excellent condition. See also Winchester and Keen Kutter. If you would like more information, contact Jim Calison, who is listed in the Directory under New York.

Adze, bowl; Dufour, 7" blade, rpl hdl, EX 185.00
Adze, shipbuilder's, lipped 50.00
Angle divider, Stanley #30, VG 35.00
Axe, American Goose Wing, 3X mk, 13" blade, early, EX 275.00
Beader, hand; Windsor, w/brass head 100.00
Cabinet, tool; Stanley #850, oak, ca 1929, EX 255.00
Calipers, blacksmith's, dbl 45.00
Calipers, bow; SMF Bingham, steel, tapered, 10", EX 12.00
Calipers, brass, dbl, 3¼" 35.00
Carriage spring lubricator, CI, EX 18.00
Chest, cabinetmaker's, pine, blk w/red & bl panels, 41" W . .2,200.00
Chisel, corner; Humphreysville Mfg, rpl hdl, 16", VG 28.00
Chisel, corner; unmk, rpl hdl, 14", VG 25.00
Chisel, pocket; Stanley Everlasting, 8", EX 18.00
Chisel, ⅛" socket; Wetherby, rpl hdl, VG 10.00
Combination tool, Thomas Patent, bevel/square/plane, VG . . .750.00
Drill, bow; rosewood & brass, English, 10½" 145.00
Gauge, Bausch & Lomb, stainless steel/brass, 9", EX 20.00
Gauge, bevel; Hold Fast, pat 1914, 10", VG 12.00
Gauge, butt; Stanley #95, EX 15.00
Gauge, chisel; Stanley #96 repro, brass screw cap, England 22.00
Gauge, marking; Stanley #60, CI, EX 75.00
Gauge, mortise; rosewood, brass-faced fence, unmk, 8½" 45.00
Gauge, pattern maker's, Ward, crank neck, blade: 1½" W 25.00
Gauge, Stanley #92, rosewood, mk pat pen'g, EX 85.00
Glue pot, dbl, Marietta, CI, 6" dia 17.50
Hoopsetter, cooper's, walnut/iron grooved base, 1830s, 10" 125.00
Ice hammer/shaver/tongs, wrought & CI, pat June 1878, 13½" . .85.00
Jack, Conestoga wagon; dtd 1809 . . . . .195.00
Jointer, Stanley #7, pat 1910, rosewood knob & hdl 50.00
Leather cutter, steel/brass, rosewood pistol hdl, adjusts 20.00
Level, pocket; Stanley #39½, iron, japanned, 6", VG 24.00
Level, pocket; Stanley #40, japanned top, VG 15.00
Level, Stanley #36, CI, japanned Eclipse covers, 24", EX 22.00
Level, Starret, dbl plumb, CI, EX japanning, 9", EX 30.00
Level, Starret, dbl plumb, grooved bottom, 6", VG 15.00
Level, Stratton Bros, brass-bound rosewood, pat 1870, 12" 245.00

Level sight, Stanley #1, for wood level, 2 in orig box 24.00
Lumber stick, brass ends, 36" 18.00
Mallet, carpenter's, mk S Coss, burl, well made, 11" 45.00
Mallet, ship's caulking; oak w/brass bands, head: 13" L 65.00
Mortise tool, Waller Tool Co, Chicago, hinged butt 65.00
Plane, A Howland & Co NY, wood w/adjustable fence, 9", EX . .60.00
Plane, Bailey #4 . . . . .25.00
Plane, Bailey #5 . . . . .20.00
Plane, block; cabinetmaker's, Stanley #9, ca 1908, EX 1,100.00
Plane, block; Millers Falls #5, EX 30.00
Plane, block; Ohio Tool #09½, adjustable, 6½", EX 32.00
Plane, block; squirrel tailed, japanned, 8", EX 30.00
Plane, block; Stanley #103, orig blade, split knob, rare, VG 95.00
Plane, block; Stanley 4-Square, scarce, EX 32.00
Plane, circular; Stanley #13, VG japanning, ca 1907-1910, EX . .80.00
Plane, dbl end; Fulton, japanning 25.00
Plane, EC Ring, beech, compass bottom, MA, 1843-1855, 8" . . .22.50
Plane, edge block; Stanley #95, NM 100.00
Plane, jack; Stanley #5, ca 1910-1920, VG 25.00
Plane, jack; Steer's Patent #305, Jennings blade, EX 185.00
Plane, joiner; blade: Jowett Extra, mahog/steel infill, 21" 180.00
Plane, jointer; Stanley #132, 1876 US Centennial model, NM .115.00
Plane, Keen Kutter 130, metal body w/logo, japanning 25.00
Plane, molding; Mathieson, 2 blades, 9½x3¾", EX 185.00
Plane, plow; L Tyler, beech, captive-wedge arm, 1800, 7½", EX .60.00
Plane, plow; R Wells, Yankee style, rpl wedge, 8", EX 78.00
Plane, plow; unmk, boxwood, 7¾", VG 145.00
Plane, plow; WF Dominick #104, rosewood, EX 235.00
Plane, rabbet side; J Stevens, 1821-1822, VG, pr 55.00
Plane, rabbet; carriage maker's, gun metal, 7¼", EX 100.00
Plane, rabbet; Stanley #10, EX 110.00
Plane, rabbet; Stanley #10½, 1892 pat blade, EX 145.00
Plane, rabbet; Stanley #190, EX 30.00
Plane, reverse ogee molding; Lindenberger, 1700s, EX 185.00
Plane, rnd; Hunt & Wiseman, beech, 1½", EX 25.00
Plane, Stanley #21, mk 1892 blade, japanning, pre-1904, EX . .120.00
Plane, Stanley #35 . . . . .20.00
Plane, Stanley #35, transitional, eagle imprint, 1871, VG 100.00
Plane, Stanley #45, w/18 cutters in wood box 150.00
Plane, Stanley #98 & #99, pr 125.00
Plane, Stanley Bedrock #605-C, mk 1892 blade, VG 50.00
Plane, Stanley Bedrock 607-C, japanning, aluminum hdl, G 95.00
Plane, Stanley Universal #55, complete in box 325.00
Plane, surfacing; Franklin's Patent, 2-pc blade, 17½", EX 155.00
Plane, Vaughn & Bushnell #904, rare, EX 75.00
Rule, EA Stearns #53, ivory w/nickeled fittings, w/pullout 200.00
Rule, eng TM Nelson, ivory w/nickeled fittings, 24" 175.00
Rule, folding, ivory w/brass fittings, 12" 125.00
Rule, shrinkage; SR&L #30½, boxwood & brass, EX 24.00
Rule, Stanley #40 1/1, ivory 225.00
Rule, Stanley #62 . . . . .20.00
Rule, Stanley #94, 4-fold, 48", VG 65.00
Rule w/protractor & level, Stevens, brass bound, 1-ft 65.00
Saw, scroll; AH Pomeroy, Fuller's Pat 1875 fr, 28½", EX 135.00
Saw, stair; Atkins, beech, brass blade nuts, 15", VG 36.00
Scraper, Stanley #12½, rosewood sole 40.00
Scraper, Stanley #80, EX 20.00
Splitting wedge, wood top, iron ring & punch, diamond decor . .20.00
Spoke shave, Miller Falls #1, circular, rosewood hdls, VG 22.00
Square, takedown; Stanley #100-B, EX 50.00
Tack puller, emb Barcale mk, wrought iron 4.00
Wallpaper-trimming machine, 1901, lg 85.00
Wrench, Cochran Speed Nut Chicago, 1916, 9" 12.00
Wrench, crescent; Hong Kong, blk metal, 3¼", EX 4.00

Wrench, Trimo, adjustable, 18" 15.00
Wrench, windmill; Internat'l Harvester, EX 30.00
Yardstick, Stanley, oak w/brass tips 12.00

Surveyor's transit, marked 'J. Potter, Brookfield,' early 19th century, 8" diameter, $1,400.00.

Toothpick Holders

    Once common on every table, the toothpick holder was relegated to the china cabinet near the turn of the century. Fortunately, this contributed to their survival; as a result, many are available to collectors today. Because they are small and easily displayed, they are a very popular collectible; and they come in a wide range of prices to fit every budget. The rare ones have been reproduced and, unfortunately, are being offered for sale right along with the originals. (These 'repros' should be priced in the $10.00 to $15.00 range.) So unless you're sure of what you're buying, choose a reputable dealer.

    In addition to pattern glass, you'll find examples in china, bisque, art glass, and silverplate. In the listings that follow, items are glass unless noted otherwise.

Acorn, pk, w/decor 80.00
Amberina, tricorn top 225.00
Argonaut Shell, custard 275.00
Baby T'print, amberina, 2½" 175.00
Banded Portland, maiden's blush 50.00
Beaded Panel & Sunburst, Heisey 115.00
Beaded Swirl & Disk, amber 50.00
Beatty Honeycomb, bl opal, 2½x2" 45.00
Beatty Waffle, bl opal 35.00
Bees on Basket, custard 48.00
Bees on Basket, custard w/VG gold & decor 55.00
Beggar's Hand, vaseline 25.00
Bubble Lattice, vaseline satin 150.00
Bull's Eye & Fan, clear w/gold 40.00
Burmese, acorns/leaves, bulbous/pinched, sq top, 2¾" 295.00
Bxk, Teddy & the Bear, man w/bear up stump figural 135.00
Cactus, chocolate, Greentown (beware of repros) 65.00
Champion 28.00
Champion, gr 45.00

China, roses, HP, gold rim, Nippon 35.00
Chrysanthemum Sprig, bl opaque 350.00
Clover & Horseshoe, milk glass 30.00
Colonial Stairsteps, bl opal 120.00
Columbian Coin, gold coins, rare 165.00
Cordova, ruby stain 55.00
Corset, amber 75.00
Cranberry, wht florals 30.00
Criss Cross, wht opal, Consolidated 135.00
Daisy & Button, amber, top hat form 21.00
Daisy & Button, amberina 185.00
Daisy & Button w/V Ornament, vaseline 45.00
Delaware, gr w/gold 80.00
Dia Quilt MOP, wht to raspberry, ruffled, sgn Webb 325.00
Dia Quilt MOP, yel shaded, bulbous w/sqd top, 2½" 350.00
Diamond Spearhead, gr opal 28.00
Diamond Spearhead, sapphire opal 85.00
Double Arches, red stain 110.00
Empress, gr 175.00
Feather, Cambridge 35.00
Fleur-de-lis, custard w/EX gold .110.00
Florette, pk gloss 55.00
Fruit Panels 30.00
Gaelic, clear w/gold 22.00
Georgia Gem, pk 55.00
Gonterman Swirl, frosted w/amber rim 155.00
Harvard, gr opaque 35.00
Hobnail, vaseline opal 55.00
Horseshoe & Clover, milk glass 30.00
Invt T'print, amber, HP daisies, pie crust rim 145.00
Iowa 20.00
Iris w/Meander, bl opal 75.00
Iris w/Meander, clear opal 40.00
Iris w/Meander, sapphire bl w/gold 55.00
Jefferson Optic, custard 35.00
Kansas 55.00
Klondike 85.00
Lacy Medallion, gr w/gold, souvenir 27.50
Little Lobe, wht 80.00
Maine, pk stain, rare 95.00
Michigan, single floral decor, clear w/amber 75.00
Millard, ruby stain 195.00
Moire MOP, robin's egg bl, frosted leaf ft 235.00

Pansy, milk glass, 3-hdl, Kemple .20.00
Pineapple, pk satin 75.00
Pineapple & Fan, gr w/EX gold, Heisey 195.00
Pomona, 1st grind, rigaree collar 265.00
Portland 25.00
Prince of Wales Plume, clear w/gold, Heisey 120.00
Quartered Block 25.00
Reverse Swirl, bl, speckled, rare 67.00
Rib & Bead, ruby stain 55.00
Ribbed Spiral, canary 60.00
Ribbed Spiral, vaseline opal 60.00
Ring & Beads, amethyst 38.00
Royal Oak, rubena frost 125.00
Ruby Thumbprint, ruby stain 35.00
Scalloped 6-Point, clear w/gold 24.00
Scroll w/Cane Band, amber 60.00
Shell & Seaweed, pk cased, rare .145.00
Shoshone, clear w/gold 25.00
Silverplate, barrel w/spigot/fireman's helmet, Pairpoint 165.00
Silverplate, Greenaway boy filling cannon, Reed & Barton . . .150.00
Silverplate, man carries barrel on bk, Tufts #2643 . . . . . .150.00
Silverplate, pig, glass eyes, pot eng Boston...Beans, Acme 85.00
Silverplate, sailboat on waves, gold-washed int, EX 55.00
Simplicity Scroll, gold covered 30.00
Spiral Rib, vaseline 60.00
Stars & Bars, bl, rare 220.00
Statue of Liberty, lt bl, hand form, Lindsey-529 . . . . .65.00
Stippled Drawers, Findlay 110.00
Sunbeam, cobalt 60.00
Sunflower, majolica 95.00
Sunset 55.00
Swirl & Panel 18.00
Tarentum's Tiny Thumbprint, custard 55.00
Texas 25.00
Thousand Eye 35.00
Tree in Meadow 80.00
Venetian Diamond, amberina 195.00
Vermont, gr w/gold 35.00
Wild Bouquet, wht opal w/pastel decor 135.00
Windows, clear opal 80.00
Windows, cranberry opal 115.00
Winged Scroll, gr 100.00
Wreath & Shell, vaseline opal w/HP decor 195.00
Zippered Swirl & Diamond 25.00

**Mt. Washington Crown Milano type with berries and leaves,
$350.00; Empress, green with gold trim, $200.00.**

One-O-One, milk glass 45.00
Paddle Wheel 22.00
Paddle Wheel & Star 22.00

Torquay 'Devon Motto' Ware

Torquay is a unique type of pottery made in the South Devon area of England from 1867. At the height of productivity, at least a dozen companies flourished there, producing simple folk pottery from the area's natural red clay. The ware was both wheel-turned and molded and decorated under the glaze with heavy slip resulting in low-relief nature subjects or simple scrollwork.

Three of the best-known of these potteries were: Watcombe (1867-1962); Aller Vale (in operation from the mid-1800s, producing domestic ware and architectural products); and Longpark (1890 until 1957). Watcombe and Aller Vale merged in 1901 and operated until 1962 under the name of Royal Aller Vale and Watcombe Art Pottery.

Perhaps the most famous type of ware potted in this area was Motto Ware, so called because of the verses, proverbs, and quotations that decorated it. This decor was achieved by the sgraffito technique — scratching the letters through the slip to expose the red clay underneath. The most popular decorative devices were cottages, black cockerel, multi-cockerel, and a scrollwork pattern called Scandy. Other popular patterns were Kerswell Daisy, ships, kingfishers, and many other birds on blue ground.

Aller Vale ware may sometimes be found marked 'H.H. and Company,' a firm who assumed ownership from 1897 to 1901. 'Watcombe Torquay' was an impressed mark used from 1884 to 1927.

Those interested in learning more about Torquay are encouraged to contact The Torquay Pottery Collectors' Society, Publicity Chairmen, or Coordinator, whose addresses can be found in the Directory under Clubs, Newsletters, and Catalogs.

Ash tray, Cottage, Watcombe, 'Who burnt the...,' ¾x4" 25.00
Basket, Iris, Lemon, & Crute, no motto, 3¾" 45.00
Bowl, Cottage, 'We live in deeds not years,' 2¼x4" 35.00
Butter dish, Cottage, Watcombe, 'Time & tide...,' 4½" 35.00
Butter dish, Scandy, Watcombe, motto, 3x5¼x3½" 50.00
Candlestick, Multi-Cockerel, Longpark, 'Last in bed,' 6" 75.00
Candlestick, Scandy, Aller Vale, 'Let's to bed,' 6" 65.00
Chamberstick, Cockerel, Longpark, 'Don't burn...,' 5½" 85.00
Cheese dish, Cottage, rectangular top, motto, 5¼x6½" 85.00
Coffeepot, Cockerel, Longpark, 'If you can't be...,' 6½" 79.00
Coffeepot, Cottage, Watcombe, motto, 5" 75.00
Condiment holder, w/s&p, egg cup, & mustard, 3½" 100.00
Creamer, Cockerel, 'Help yerzel ter cream,' 2¼" 35.00
Creamer, Cottage, Watcombe, bulbous base, 3¾x4" 32.00
Creamer, Scandy, Longpark, tadpoles, 'Elp yerzel ...,' 2½" 30.00
Creamer, Watcombe, 'Fresh from the cow' 22.00
Cruet, Cottage, unmk, 5¼" 50.00
Cup, demitasse; Sailboat, 'Duee drink a cup a tay' 15.00
Cup & saucer, Cockerel 38.00
Cup & saucer, Cottage, 'Be like the sundial...,' very lg 65.00
Cup & saucer, Cottage, Watcombe, 'Take a cup of tea' 35.00
Cup & saucer, demitasse; Watcombe, 'Have a cup of coffee' 25.00
Dish, Scandy, 3-compartment, 'Cheese, Biscuits, Butter' 80.00
Figurine, classical, terra cotta, Watcombe, 11½" 350.00
Jam dish, Cockerel, 'Du ee ave zum uney...,' 3¾x3¼" 40.00
Jam dish, Cottage, Dartmouth, 'Aisy on the jam,' 2x5¼" 20.00
Jam dish, Cottage, Watcombe, 'Enough's as good as ...,' 3¼" . . .48.00
Jam dish, Scandy, 'Elp yerzel tu jam,' unmk, 1½x5¼" 30.00
Jam dish, Scandy, Watcombe, 'Take a little jam,' 5¼" 40.00
Jam dish, Watcombe, 'Action speaks louder than words,' 1¾x5" .30.00
Jardiniere, Orchids, gr bkground, 9x7½" 225.00
Jardiniere, Parrot, ruffled edge, 7⅜" 150.00
Jug, 'Hope on hope ever,' 3¼x2¾" .28.00
Jug, Cottage/Cheddar, Watcombe, 'Help yourself...,' 3½x4¾" . . .30.00

Match striker, Cockerel, 'A match for any man,' lg 55.00
Mug, Cottage, 'Here's to me & my wife's...,' unmk, 3¼" 30.00
Mug, shaving; Multi-Cockerel, 4x5½" hdl to spout 95.00
Mug, toby; MIE, sm, 2" 32.00
Mug, toby; Royal Torquay, lg 85.00
Mug, toby; Royal Torquay, med 60.00
Pitcher, Cockerel, 'Better do one thing,' 4¼" 45.00
Pitcher, Cottage, Dartmouth, 'Daun'ee be fraid...,' 4" 40.00
Pitcher, Desert scene, 'May you find,' unmk, 6½" 95.00
Plate, Cockerel, 'Dawntee vall bevare yum pushed,' 6" 45.00
Plate, Cockerel, Longpark, 'Guide things be...,' 5½" 38.00
Platter, Multi-Cockerel, oval, 'A place for,' 7⅜x10½" 95.00
Pot, cache; Scandy, 'One good turn deserves...,' unmk, 4x3" . . .28.00
Pot, gypsy; Cottage, 3-leg, 3¾" 45.00
Pot, hot water; Cottage, Watcombe, 'Gude thing be...,' 4x5" . . .60.00
Shakers, Cottage, Watcombe, 'No road is long...,' pr 35.00
Sugar bowl, Cottage, 'A thing of beauty is a joy forever' 24.00
Sugar bowl, Cottage, 'Be aisy w/the sugar,' sm 25.00
Sugar bowl, Cottage, Watcombe, 'Take a little sugar,' 1½x4" . . .25.00
Sugar bowl, Sailboat, Watcombe, 'Due ave zum sugar,' 1½" 20.00
Sugar bowl, sailboat/sunset, unmk, 4¼x4" 25.00
Sugar bowl, Scandy, 'Sweeten to your liking,' unmk 25.00
Sugar bowl, Scandy, Aller Vale, 'Take a little sugar,' sm 25.00
Sugar bowl, Scandy, Watcombe, 'Be canny w' th' sugar,' sm 25.00
Sugar bowl, Scandy, Watcombe, 'Sweeten to your liking,' sm . . .25.00
Teapot, Cockerel, 'Du'll make youzels at 'ome,' 3¼" 60.00
Teapot, Cockerel, Longpark, 'Du'ee ave,' 4" 85.00
Teapot, Cottage, 'Daunee Be...,' mk, 4½x4¾" 70.00
Teapot, Cottage, Watcombe, 'If yu want a cup a tay...,' 5" 85.00
Tile, 'O list to me ye ladies fair...,' 5x7½" 100.00
Tray, pen; Multi-Cockerel, 2⅞x9¼" 48.00
Vase, Kingfisher, bl glazed, stamped England, 4½x4" 38.00
Vase, Scandy, 'Were...pebbles...beach,' Aller Vale, 3⅛" 45.00
Vase, Windmill scene, Watcombe, no motto, 6" 70.00

Tortoise Shell Glass

By combining several shades of glass — brown, clear, and yellow — glass manufacturers of the 19th century were able to produce an art glass that closely resembled the shell of the tortoise. Some of this type of glassware was manufactured in Germany. In America it was made by several firms, the most prominent of which was the Boston and Sandwich Glass Works.

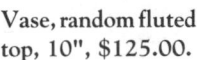

Puzzle jug, rooster motif, 4½", $75.00.

Vase, random fluted top, 10", $125.00.

Basket, wide hdl w/gold prunt & prunus flowers, 8" 185.00
Bowl, 3-ftd, 4" 100.00
Butter dish 175.00
Pitcher, tankard; decorated, 8", +pr 4½" tumblers 165.00
Pitcher, water; 7½" 80.00

Toys

Toys, obviously, are fun to collect, and those made before WWII also have special investment potential. Lithograph-printed mechanical toys, for instance, are especially popular with today's collectors and steadily continue to increase in value year after year. Condition of any type of toy is critical. They were made for children to play with, and many that have survived to the present are in a well-played-with state, which only serves to enhance the value of those that yet may be found in excellent condition. Authority Richard O'Brien has compiled an informative book, *Collecting Toys*, available at your local library or favorite bookstore. In the listings below, toys are listed by manufacturer's name when at all possible, otherwise by type. Condition is assumed excellent unless noted otherwise. The dimension listed is the greater one — height if the toy is vertical, length if that measurement is larger than height. See also Children's Things; Personalities.

Key:
b/o — battery operated   w/up — windup
NP — nickel plated

Cast Iron

Cast iron toys were made from shortly before the Civil War until the beginning of the 20th century. They are evaluated to a large extent by scarcity, complexity, design, and detail. See next section for examples of cast iron toys listed by company name.

Cast iron Andy Gump car with driver, deluxe edition with 2 license plates, crank shaft, ca 1925, 7" long, $1,500.00.

Aerial wagon, 3-horse, worn orig pnt, 44", VG 650.00
Am Oil Co truck, gr/silver w/gold trim, 10½" 375.00
Cart, 2-wheeled, pulled by lion, 8", VG 200.00
Chrysler Airflow car, 1930s, 4½", M .100.00
Convertible w/rumble seat, red pnt, 10½", EX 450.00
Fire pumper, 2-horse, w/driver, mc rpt, 19½" 400.00

Gasoline Mack truck, 7¼", G 325.00
Ox cart, bl/yel pnt, w/oxen, 11½", EX 225.00
Panel truck, Champion, worn bl pnt, rpl rubber wheel, 8" 350.00
Sleigh, fine details, ca 1880, 7" 90.00
Steam engine, orig finish, 10", EX 60.00
Train car, PA RR, #60, 12", EX 60.00
Wagon, 2-wheeled, w/mule & driver, 9½", M 200.00
Wagon w/driver, horse drawn, some orig pnt, 12" 150.00

Company or Country of Manufacturer

Alps, Bruno, bear raises glasses, tin w/up, Japan, 7", MIB 95.00
Alps, canary, hops/sings, celluloid w/up, 3½", MIB 50.00
Alps, Over the Hill, cars/ramps, tin w/up, Japan, MIB 95.00
Alps, Sambo, minstrel, celluloid w/up, Japan, 7½" 100.00
Amico, Space Scooter, tin w/plastic, b/o, 9", MIB 97.50
Arcade, Andy Gump #348 car, orig NP version, EX 1,500.00
Arcade, Andy Gump #348 DeLuxe car, mc version, 7", EX . .1,500.00
Arcade, Bulldog Mack dump truck, bl w/orig decals, 12", EX .1,100.00
Arcade, Coupe w/rumble seat, red pnt, rubber tires, 6¾", VG . .225.00
Arcade, Fageol Safety Coach, pnt CI, 12", EX 1,200.00
Arcade, Hathaway Bread truck, pnt/decal worn, 9½" 600.00
Arcade, Internat'l dump truck, gr/red pnt, 11", EX 800.00
Arcade, Mack dump truck, total rpt, 12" 500.00
Arcade, Mack Ice truck, bl pnt, 7", EX 275.00
Arcade, Reo coupe w/rumble seat, yel/blk/red, 9", VG 2,500.00
Arcade, White Moving van, red/gr w/gold letters, 13", EX . . .7,000.00
Arcade, Yel Cab, w/decal, orig driver, 9", VG 800.00
Arcade, Yel Cab bank, metal tires, orig trap/driver, 8", VG 950.00
Arcade, Yel Cab bank, rubber tires, orig trap/driver, 8", VG . . .950.00
Bandai, Cadillac, tin, friction, 1959, 11¼", MIB 300.00
Bandai, Opel Rekord Sedan, tin, friction, Japan, 8½", MIB 75.00
Bremer, Whirlwing auto race car model, 1900s, 18", NM 550.00
Buddy L, City Dray truck, pnt steel, 19", EX 145.00
Buddy L, dump truck, pnt steel, 24" .185.00
Buddy L, dump truck, sheet metal, 25", NM 550.00
Buddy L, dump truck, sheet steel, rubber tires, '33, 24", EX . . .275.00
Buddy L, Express Line truck, sheet metal, 24", VG 550.00
Buddy L, Fast Freight truck, 1940s, 20", EX 105.00
Buddy L, fire truck, extension ladder, 30" 125.00
Buddy L, Ford Flivver coupe, sheet metal, all orig, 11" EX 850.00
Buddy L, Ford Flivver delivery truck, sheet metal, 12", EX . .1,000.00
Buddy L, Ford Flivver roadster, sheet metal, orig, 11", EX 700.00
Buddy L, Ice Delivery truck, sheet metal, rstr, 25" 800.00
Buddy L, Model T, pnt steel, 11", EX 325.00
Buddy L, Model T dump truck, pnt steel, orig labels, 11", EX . .600.00
Buddy L, Robotoy truck, sheet metal, electric, 21", NM 1,800.00
Buddy L, steam shovel, sheet steel, #220, 1930, 20", EX 175.00
Buddy L, wrecking truck, sheet steel, 1st series, 28", VG 300.00
Chad Valley, Burnett model bus, tin w/up, pre-war, 12", EX . . .375.00
Chein, Aero Swing, carnival toy, tin litho, 10", MIB 195.00
Chein, Barnacle Bill, tin litho, keywind walker, 6", EX 200.00
Chein, Disneyland Mickey Mouse ferris wheel, tin w/up, 17" . .350.00
Chein, Happy Hooligan, tin litho w/up walker, 6", EX 650.00
Chein, merry-go-round, swan carts, tin w/up, 11", MIB 200.00
Chein, roller coaster, tin w/up, 20", EX 100.00
Chein, Sea Plane, tin litho w/up, EX .135.00
Chein, trolly, 270 Broadway 270, early 1900s, 8¼", EX 75.00
Chein, WWI Army Sergeant, tin w/up, 5½" 90.00
China, hen w/chicks in pram, b/o, 10", MIB 50.00
Converse, ice wagon, tin litho & wood, 18", EX 370.00
Converse, menagerie cage wagon, tin litho & wood, 13½", EX .250.00
Cragstan, cowboy, tin litho b/o, 7¾" .75.00
Cragstan, Knight in Armor, tin w/plastic bow, b/o, 12", MIB . .150.00

Cragstan, Trumpet Monkey, tin/plush, b/o, 10", MIB 188.00

Crandall, blocks, ABC litho on wood, nesting, 1881, complete .950.00

Crandall, blocks, Marriage of Jenny Wren, nesting, EX 175.00

Dent, dump truck, CI, red/gr pnt, 15", VG 850.00

Elastolin, farm set, compo/wood, 37-pc, EX 850.00

Elastolin, safari set, compo, complete, VG 650.00

Fisher-Price, Amusement Park, 1963, VG 60.00

Fisher-Price, Boom-Boom Popeye, pull toy, 1937, VG 200.00

Fisher-Price, Bunny Cart, #10, EX 55.00

Fisher-Price, Bunny Cart, #401, EX .40.00

Fisher-Price, Cackling Hen, #120, EX 25.00

Fisher-Price, Cash Register, w/crank, 1960, EX 35.00

Fisher-Price, Chatter Telephone, 1962, EX 10.00

Fisher-Price, Circus Parade Wagon, 9 jtd animals, #250, EX 75.00

Fisher-Price, Circus Wagon, pull toy, 1942, EX 175.00

Fisher-Price, Ding Dong Ducky, pull toy, 1949, G 120.00

Fisher-Price, Donald Duck Xylophone, 1938, EX 200.00

Fisher-Price, Drummer Bear, on wheels, 1932, EX 300.00

Fisher-Price, Fred Flintstone Xylophone, pull toy, 1962, VG . .130.00

Fisher-Price, Howdy Bunny, pull toy, 1939, VG 175.00

Fisher-Price, Humpty Dump Truck, 1963, EX 35.00

Fisher-Price, Ice Cream Wagon, 1940, VG 225.00

Fisher-Price, Katy Kackler, #140, EX 55.00

Fisher-Price, Merry Mutt, #473, EX .40.00

Fisher-Price, Molly Moo-Moo, pull toy, 1956, VG 140.00

Fisher-Price, Musical Push Chime, 1950, EX 35.00

Fisher-Price, Performing Circus, 1932, complete, EX 300.00

Fisher-Price, Quacky Family, pull toy, 1949, EX 48.00

Fisher-Price, Streamline Express, 1935, VG 300.00

Fisher-Price, Struttin' Donald Duck, w/stick, 1940 . . . . .180.00

Fisher-Price, Super Jet, 1952, M 130.00

Fisher-Price, Tailspin Tabby, 1948, VG 40.00

Flare, bear cyclist in turning hoop, tin w/up, Japan, 6" 115.00

Flare, tight rope walker, string balance, Japan, 8", MIB 75.00

Germany, auxillary speedboat, tin litho w/up, early, 9½" 250.00

Germany, Blk mammy w/basket, HP clockwork, 6⅝", EX 550.00

Germany, bulldog, tin litho w/up walker, 7¾", EX 100.00

Germany, Busy Lizzie, tin litho w/up, early, 6½" 500.00

**Germany, cardboard diecut with wooden base, tin wheels, 7",
$395.00.**

Germany, Charlie Chaplin, tin litho w/up w/iron ft, 7¾", EX . .950.00

Germany, clown, pnt tin/cloth w/up, 9", EX 575.00

Germany, clown drummer, pnt tin litho/cloth clothes, 6", VG .375.00

Germany, clown rides tricycle, pnt tin w/up, 8½", EX 325.00

Germany, couple, HP figures, tin w/up dancers, 8", EX 1,000.00

Germany, horse & carriage, tin litho w/up, early, 10" 190.00

Germany, Indian on horsebk, tin litho clicker, 6½" 120.00

Germany, limousine, tin litho w/up, 9", EX rstr 250.00

Germany, pool player, tin litho w/up, 1920s, 6", EX 450.00

Germany, sailor, climbing, string pull toy, 9", VG 150.00

Germany, taxi, tin litho w/up, spare tire, '20s, 8¼", EX 800.00

Germany, Toonerville Trolley, tin litho w/up, 6½", EX 900.00

Germany, Vis-A-Vis Auto, tin litho w/up, 5" 200.00

Gibbs, Bicyclist, Uncle Sam, 8", VG 250.00

Gibbs, Wagon, 2-horse, pull toy, 20" 300.00

Gilbert, erector set, #10½", EX 250.00

Gilbert, erector set, #1081, 1959, complete, w/book 35.00

Gilbert, erector set, #4½, 1954, NM in box 165.00

Gilbert, erector set, #6½, +box/instructions/motor 45.00

Gilbert, erector set, rocket launcher & extras, 1938, EX 45.00

Gunthermann, trolley car, tin litho w/up, 12½" 140.00

Hausser, Prime Mover w/searchlight, camouflage, b/o, 12", EX .600.00

Hausser, staff car, olive drab, 1 passenger, keywind, 8" 425.00

Hausser, truck, 6-wheel military, keywind, 10", VG 225.00

Hess, race car, tin litho w/up, working, 8" 225.00

Hillclimber, ambulance, 10½", M 800.00

Hillclimber, horseless carriage, lady driver, CI/wood, M 400.00

Hillclimber, racer, w/track, 7½", M 380.00

Hong Kong, Lunar Spaceman, plastic, b/o, 12", MIB 125.00

Hong Kong, Mr Flash, plastic, b/o, 9", MIB 55.00

Hubley, Auto Express, CI, gray w/red, orig driver, 9", VG 550.00

Hubley, Fire Pumper, red w/silver trim, orig driver, 10", VG . . .250.00

Hubley, Holmes Coal truck, sheet steel, 1930s, 17½", EX . . .1,200.00

Hubley, motorcycle, policeman rider, iron, rubber tires, VG . . .225.00

Hubley, Panama Digger truck, 10", EX 1,000.00

Hubley, Rocket Racer, CI, NP driver, rubber tires, #2233, 6" . .135.00

Hubley, Royal Circus bear cage, 9", VG 150.00

Hubley, sleigh, horse drawn, CI/gr & gold pnt, 1921, 15½" 550.00

Hubley, sleigh, Santa Claus, 17", M 1,000.00

Ideal, Steve Canyon's Glider Bomb Truck, MIB 50.00

Illco, Minnie Mouse Shopping Cart, b/o, 11½", MIB 48.00

Illco, Pluto, plastic, jumps/barks, b/o, 10½", MIB 88.00

Japan, Am League baseball player whistle, tin litho, 1940s 20.00

Japan, boy on trapeze, celluloid/metal, 8x6", NM 70.00

Japan, Buick, tin litho, b/o, rstr, 15" 180.00

Japan, Cary the Crow, hopping, tin litho w/up, 3x4", MIB 50.00

Japan, clown whistle, tin litho, 3½", EX 20.00

Japan, dog dressed as cowboy, tin w/up, 1930s, 6", EX 60.00

Japan, dog w/shoe, tin litho & celluloid w/up, 8", EX 30.00

Japan, Donald Duck Carousel, celluloid w/up, 10" 5,000.00

Japan, Frankenstein monster, tin litho/cloth b/o, 12", EX 120.00

Japan, Hawaiian dancer, celluloid & tin w/up, 1930s, 9", EX 90.00

Japan, Louie Armstrong Trumpet Player, tin w/up, 10", EX 350.00

Japan, Mickey Mouse, celluloid, mechanical, rare, 7", EX . . .2,500.00

Japan, monkees on monkey-mobile, tin litho/plastic b/o, NM . .195.00

Japan, monkey riding stick horse, cloth/celluloid, 4x6", MIB . . .40.00

Japan, penguin, tin litho w/up, 6", EX 65.00

Japan, planet robot, tin litho/rubber/plastic, b/o, 12¾" 800.00

Japan, Poochie Peddler, dog pushing cart, tin w/up, 6½", EX 55.00

Jones & Bixler, Express truck, CI, cream pnt, 15", VG 800.00

Joustra, trolly/bus, tin litho, keywind, #80, 12", EX 375.00

Kenton, bakery wagon, 'Bakery,' 1941, M 450.00

Kenton, cement mixer, Jaeger, iron wheels, 6½", VG 172.50

Kenton, cement mixer truck, CI, 8", VG 1,000.00

Kenton, Express #548, CI, orange pnt, orig driver, VG 600.00

Kenton, fire pumper, CI, 1920s, 14½", M 400.00

Kenton, Overland Circus band wagon, all orig, 18", NM 350.00

Kenton, Overland Circus cage wagon, all orig, 14", NM 425.00
Kenton, Phaeton touring car, 12", M 850.00
Kenton, sand & gravel wagon, CI, 10½", EX 145.00
Kenton, Yellow Cab, 1950s, 6⅜", M 290.00
Keystone, Packard overhead ladder fire truck, steel, 30" 425.00
Kilgore, Stutz roadster, rare purple/red pnt, 10½", EX 1,600.00
Kingsbury, Cadillac, steel, rubber tires, 1930s, 13", EX 225.00

Kingsberry coupe, rubber tires, ca 1925, 10" long, $525.00.

Knickerbocker, Happy, compo, jtd arms, clothes, Disney, 9" 90.00
Kohner, Donald Duck Maxi-puppet, Disney 50.00
Kohner, Mickey Mouse Tricky Trapeze, Disney 50.00
Lehmann, Autobus, red & wht, #590, pat 1907, 8⅜", EX 1,150.00
Lehmann, Dare Devil, tin litho w/up, EX 500.00
Lehmann, Express wagon, tin litho, friction, #140, 5½", EX ...325.00
Lehmann, Lila, cab & driver, pat 1903, 8⅜", EX 1,250.00
Lehmann, motorcar, carriage type, tin litho w/up, #420, NM ..650.00
Lehmann, Naughty Boy, tin litho, pat 1904, 5", EX 750.00
Lehmann, New Century Cycle, tin litho w/up, 1905, 5", EX ...750.00
Lehmann, Paddy on Pig, tin litho/cloth, rstr leg, 6" 1,000.00
Lehmann, Quack-Quack, tin litho w/up, EX 1,000.00
Lehmann, Tut-Tut Auto, red/beige tin litho w/up, 7" 850.00
Lehmann, UHU Racer & Driver, tin w/up, early, 9¼", EX ...1,700.00
Linemar, Donald Duck Acrobat, b/o 385.00
Linemar, Figaro cat, tin litho w/up, 3", NM 200.00
Linemar, Goofy Unicyclist, tin w/up, rpl rubber ears 425.00
Linemar, Ludwig Von Drake, tin w/up, 6", EX 325.00
Linemar, Mickey's Delivery truck, tin litho, friction, 6" 200.00
Linemar, Minnie Mouse rocks/knits, tin litho, 6½" 600.00
Linemar, Pluto Drum Major, tin w/up, 6½", NM 385.00
Linemar, Robotrac Bulldozer, tin b/o, 9½", MIB 150.00
Linemar, Superman Tank, hero lifts tank, tin b/o, 8½", EX ..1,000.00
Linemar, Television truck, 2 cameramen at top, tin b/o, 14" ...350.00

Lionel, trolley car with people original box, 7" long, $300.00.

Marcrest, Livestock Lines truck, 17", EX 38.00
Martin, Drunkard, tin litho & cloth w/up, 7¾", MIB 750.00

Martin, piano player, mechanical, tin/cloth, 5", VG 550.00
Martin, piano player, tin litho w/up w/sound mechanism, 6" ...900.00
Marx, ambulance, steel w/up, 14", EX 300.00
Marx, Amos & Andy Taxicab, tin w/up, 7½" 850.00
Marx, Auto Transport Truck, 23" 18.50
Marx, Balky Mule, w/up 125.00
Marx, BO Plenty, tin litho w/up, 8½", EX in box 250.00
Marx, Buck Rogers Spaceship, tin litho w/up, 11½", VG 300.00
Marx, Busy Bridge, tin w/up, all orig, 23½", EX 300.00
Marx, Busy Delivery Wagon, 3-wheeled, tin litho, 8¾" 500.00
Marx, Crazy Dancer, Donald/Goofy, tin w/up, British, 9" 550.00
Marx, Dapper Dan Coon Jigger, tin litho w/up, 10½" 350.00
Marx, Dick Tracy Siren Squad Car, tin litho, friction, 11" 125.00
Marx, Dick Tracy Squad Car, tin litho/plastic, friction, 20" ...125.00
Marx, Donald Duck Pushing Wheelbarrow, w/up 50.00
Marx, Ferdinand the Bull, tin litho w/up, 5½", EX 130.00
Marx, Fred Flintstone on Dino, tin litho b/o, 20" EX 160.00
Marx, Hey Hey Chicken Snatcher, tin litho w/up, 8¾", EX ..1,000.00
Marx, Jolly Joe Jeep, tin litho w/up, 6", EX 75.00
Marx, Jumpin' Jeep, tin litho w/up, 5½", EX 85.00
Marx, Lone Ranger Dbl Target, tin, 1939, NM in box 65.00
Marx, Merrymakers Band, musical mice, tin w/up, 9" 850.00
Marx, Mickey Mouse, whirling tail, plastic w/up, 7", MIB 210.00
Marx, Mortimer Snerd, tin litho w/up walker, 7¾", EX 200.00
Marx, Pathe News Car, camera on roof, steel, rubber tires, 10" .200.00
Marx, Pete the Talking Parrot, tin litho, b/o, 1950s, 18" 400.00
Marx, police motorcycle w/rider, tin litho w/up, siren, 8¼" 200.00
Marx, police motorcycle w/sidecar, tin litho w/up, 8", EX 130.00
Marx, Popeye Express, 2 airplanes/Olive/Popeye, tin w/up 800.00
Marx, Ride 'Em Cowboy, tin litho & celluloid w/up, 6", EX 35.00
Marx, Ring-A-Ling Circus, tin litho w/up, 7½" dia, EX 350.00
Marx, Sandy dog, tin w/up, 1930s, 7", EX in box 375.00
Marx, sedan, sheet steel, red pnt, rubber wheels, 15", EX 100.00
Marx, Sheriff Sam car, plastic w/up, EX 125.00
Marx, Siren Police car, steel w/up, rubber tires, 14", VG 225.00
Marx, Smoky Joe, fireman climbs ladder, tin w/up, 8", MIB ...400.00
Marx, Somstepa, Blk man dances, tin litho w/up, 9" 400.00
Marx, Speed Delivery motorcycle/wagon, tin litho w/up, 9" ...175.00
Marx, Superman on airplane, w/up, NM 225.00
Marx, Superman Rollover Tank, tin litho w/up, 4", EX 350.00
Marx, Tidy Tim w/cart, tin litho w/up walker, 7½", EX 250.00
Marx, Uncle Wiggly Car, litho/clockwork, ca 1935, 7", EX 500.00
Marx, Whoopie Car, tin litho w/up, 1930s, 8", EX 250.00
Matchbox, Dinkum Rear Dumper, yel 55.00
Matchbox, Prince Henry Vauxhall, 1914, red/silver 15.00
Mavco, Mickey Mouse on scooter 175.00
Metalcraft, Coca-Cola truck, pressed steel, 11", EX 475.00
Mysto, erector set, 1915, in oak box w/instructions, rare 150.00
Ohio Art, fire ladder truck, 1920s, 13½", M 350.00
Ohio Art, Mickey Mouse top, tin, 1950s 145.00
Ohio Art, sand sifter, w/Horace, Clarebell, Mickey, Pluto 200.00
Schoenhut, see Toys, Schoenhut
Schuco, Bigo-Bell Cat, gr pants, orange blouse, 11", EX 125.00
Schuco, Blk tumbler, felt/silk, tin w/up, Germany, 9½" 450.00
Schuco, clown w/suitcase, tin w/up, Germany, 5" 175.00
Schuco, Jaq, bendable mouse, tagged, 10" 115.00
Schuco, panda, 3½" 225.00
Schuco, Radio car #4012, music movement, 6", MIB 140.00
Schuco, Yes/No Monkey, 13" 195.00
Schuco, Yes/No Panda, 5", EX 450.00
Steelcraft, Graf Zeppelin, 24" 400.00
Steelcraft, Zeppelin Akron, 24" 400.00
Steiff, see Toys, Steiff
Strauss, Alabama Coon Jigger, tin litho w/up, 10", EX 400.00

Strauss, Leaping Lena sedan, tin litho w/up, '20s, 7½", EX 275.00
Structo, dump truck, tin litho, 18", EX 75.00
Tonka, Carnation Milk truck, decal on steel, 1950, 12" 62.00
Tonka, Mobile Dragline, 1950, 27", M 24.00
Tonka, Rescue Vehicle truck, 19", MIB 65.00
Tootsie Toy, Buick roadster, #6001, 1926, M 100.00
Tootsie Toy, Cadillac coupe, #6102, 1926, M 100.00
Tootsie Toy, Graham wrecker, #806, 1932, M 75.00
Tootsie Toy, milk truck, wht rubber tires, EX 60.00
Tootsie Toy, Mosquito Fleet, cast metal, 1940s, 5" 150.00
Unique Art, Artie Clown in Crazy Car, tin w/up 185.00
Unique Art, Cowboy Crazy Car, tin litho w/up, EX 135.00
Unique Art, Dandy Jim, tin litho w/up dancer, 10", VG 200.00
Unique Art, Dandy Jim, tin litho w/up dancer, 8¾", EX 250.00
Unique Art, GI Joe & His Jeep, tin litho w/up, EX 160.00
Unique Art, GI Joe & His K-9 Pups, tin litho w/up, 9", EX 125.00
Unique Art, Jazzbo Jim, tin litho w/up dancer, EX 350.00
Unique Art, Joe Penner, tin litho w/up walker, 7½", EX 350.00
Unique Art, Kiddy Cyclist, tin litho w/up, 8½" 150.00
Unique Art, Lil Abner & Band, tin w/up, 6½", EX in box 525.00
Unique Art, Popeye w/parrot cage, tin litho, w/up walker, 7½" .275.00
Unique Art, Rodeo Joe in Crazy Car, tin litho w/up, 7", G ...140.00
Wells, Green Line bus, single deck, tin litho w/up, 7" 140.00
Wolverine, Express Bus, tin litho, friction, #26A, 1950, 14" 75.00
Wolverine, merry-go-round, 5 litho horses & rider, w/up, 13" ..300.00
Wolverine, Street Railway Car, Sunny Andy, metal, 13" 45.00
Woodette, Tornado Racer, pressed steel, 1930s, 12¼", MIB ...400.00
Wyandotte, Circus Truck, +wagon & orig compo lions, #503 ..400.00
Wyandotte, Cord Roadster, steel, rubber tires, w/up, 13" 175.00
Wyandotte, Humphrey Mobile, tin litho w/up, 8½" 350.00

Farm Toys

Bulldozer, Auburn, 1960s, 10", MIB 15.00
Cattle truck, CI, Kenton, ca 1938, 8", M 100.00
Combine, John Deere #30, VG 150.00
Combine, Massey Harris Self Propelled, metal/wood, 10", G ...375.00

Oliver combine, marked SLIK 1952, 12" wide, $125.00.

Corn planter, rubber wheels, Arcade 25.00
Dump hay rake, Arcade, 7", VG 80.00
Dump truck, Internat'l Harvester, ca 1929, Arcade 150.00
Dump truck, Tonka, 11½", VG 36.00
Dump truck, 1920s, Sturditoy, 25", M 200.00
Hay loader, Vindex, M 500.00
Manure spreader, John Deere, VG 38.00
Thresher, McCormick-Deering, CI, Arcade, 10" 165.00
Tractor, Allis Chalmers, Model AC-6, decal, Arcade 175.00

Tractor, Caterpillar, CI driver, Structo, 8½", M 140.00
Tractor, Caterpillar #198, Tootsie Toy, M 20.00
Tractor, Caterpillar #269, Arcade, M 400.00
Tractor, Cockshutt, 7¾", w/wagon mk Advance Products, 8" ..395.00
Tractor, Farmall M, plastic, w/trailer, EX 110.00
Tractor, Ford FW60, 4-wheel drive, NM 20.00
Tractor, Hubley, steam boiler in front, early 1920s, 4¾" 60.00
Tractor, John Deere, 7½", w/manure spreader, 8" 150.00
Tractor, John Deere #3010, metal hubs/rubber tires, EX 85.00
Tractor, Minneapolis-Moline G-1000, wht wheels, MIB 450.00
Tractor, Oliver, blk rubber wheels, Arcade, 7" 125.00
Tractor, Oliver, w/driver, 8½", w/7" drill 250.00
Tractor, Oliver Super #55, M 550.00
Tractor/trailer, Allis Chalmers, Arcade, 1937, 12", G 65.00
Tractor/trailer, Internat'l, die-cast/steel, EX 40.00
Truck, pick-up; Internat'l Harvester, plastic/metal 100.00
Wagon, Arcade, 3½" 37.00

Guns and Cap Bombs

Though toy guns were patented as early as the 1850s, the cap pistol was not invented until 1870, when paper caps that were primarily developed to detonate muzzleloaders became available. Some of the earlier models were very ornate and were occasionally decorated with figural heads. Most are marked with the name of their manufacturer — Ace, Daisy, Bulldog, Victor, and Excelsior are the most common.

Airfire machine gun, Newell, 1940s, M 50.00
Bang-O, cap gun, CI, Stevens, 1938, 7", M 70.00
Big Bill, cap gun, CI, Kilgore, 1950s, 5½", EX 40.00
Buc-A-Roo, cap gun, CI, Kilgore, 7½", NM in box 55.00
Bull's Eye, cap gun, CI, MIB 65.00
Cowboy King, cast metal, plastic grips, Stevens, 1950s, 9" 42.00
Dick, cap gun, Hubley, 1930, VG 35.00
Dog's head, cap bomb, CI, M 80.00
Flintlock Jr, cast metal, plastic grips, Hubley, '50s, 7½" 28.00
Jax, cap gun, Kenton, 1930, VG 30.00
Lawmaker, CI, Kenton, 1939, MIB 65.00
Lightning Express, CI, train on top moves, ca 1890, 5x3x1½" ..265.00
Long Tom, CI, Kilgore, 1950s, 10", MIB 110.00
Marshall, cast metal, plastic grips, Hubley, 1950s, 10" 12.00
Pioneer, cap gun, CI, Stevens, 7½", MIB 30.00
Pirate, cap gun, metal, 9½" 25.00
Pony, cap gun, Kenton, 1930, VG 35.00
Powder keg, cap bomb, CI, M 65.00
Red Rider, lever action, Daisy, 1950s, pr 45.00
Rodeo, cap gun, Hubley, 1938, NM 45.00
Rodeo, cast metal, plastic grips, Hubley, 1950s, 7½" 20.00
Sambo, cap gun, NPCI, 4⅜", EX 400.00
Say I, cap bomb, CI, M 60.00
Scout, CI, Stevens, 7", VG 30.00
Shootin' Shell Buckle gun, CI, Mattell, 1958, NM 55.00
Smoking Tex, cast metal, plastic grips, Hubley, '50s, 7½" 23.00
Star, cap gun, NP CI, Stevens, EX 85.00
Sure-Shot, cast metal, plastic grips, Hubley, '50s, 7½" 22.00
Texan Jr, cast metal, plastic grips, Hubley, '50s, 8", EX 8.00
Trooper, cast metal, plastic grips, Hubley, 1950s, 6½" 25.00
US Secret Service, cast metal, Kilgore, '50s, 6½", +holster 24.00
Wyatt Earp, cast metal, Coyote, '50s, 2 w/holster, 8", MIB 65.00
Zooka, pop gun, metal, mc litho, bl/wht hdl, Daisy, '50s, EX 60.00

Pedal Cars and Ride-On Toys

Air Mail Plane, Streetcraft, ca 1930, 44" 700.00

Airplane, sheet metal, rubber tires, Steelcraft, 46" 700.00
Austin, hood lifts, 4-cylinder, balloon tires, trunk, 1949 . . . . . .650.00
Battleship, pnt/stencil wood, ride-on, ca 1895, 43½" 2,250.00
Cadillac, orig pnt, spare tire, 1952 model 950.00
Cadillac, sheet metal, orig pnt, Steelcraft, 36", EX 225.00
Cannonball Express, red, pedal car, 27", M 300.00
Car, red w/wht racing stripe, rstr, 16x13x34" 125.00
Car, wood spoke wheels, chain drive, pedal car, ca 1905, VG . .225.00
Coupe, open, pedal car, 1920s, 36", VG 400.00
Delivery truck, oak rack, Roledo, rstr, M 775.00
Express wagon, lg rear wheels, wood spokes/iron tires, 49" . . .1,700.00
Fire truck, pedal car, Mack, VG 300.00
Gendron Cole-8, pedal car, litho dashboard, 49", EX rstr 4,500.00
Good Humor Ice Cream truck 175.00
Henley Roll-About Scooter, swivel axle, 1913, 33x30", NM . . .550.00
Horse, hide-covered wood, glass eyes, mane/tail, 36x45" 1,300.00
Horse, wood platform, lever action stirrups, ride-on, 27" 1,500.00
Packard Dual Cowl Phaeton, pedal car, Am Nat'l, 72", VG . .3,300.00
Piedmont farm wagon, highly detailed, all orig, 31" L 1,150.00
Pioneer coaster wagon, wood artillery wheels, 1900, 43", EX . . .450.00
Pullman car, ride-on, Keystone 175.00
Roadster, gr/yel w/blk, pedal car, Am Nat'l, 47", EX 3,750.00

Red Roadster, repainted pressed steel, rubber tires, upholstered seat, windshield, 30", EX, $225.00.

Rolling Peanut Car, wood/sheet metal, wire wheels, 48" 2,750.00
Scooter, Special Delivery, gong bell, wood, ride-on 100.00
Scout Master pedal airplane, pnt wood/sheet metal, 44", VG . .750.00
Station wagon, pnt pressed steel pedal car, 44" 150.00
Supersonic Jet Plane, Murray Mfg 275.00
Tractor, John Deere, aluminum, EX .225.00
Tricycle, Thunderbolt, pulley type, wood seat, 20x34" 200.00
Van, metal, ride-on, Dugan Bros, M .175.00
Wagon, Hibbard Playmate, wood, 31" 120.00

Penny Toys

Ambulance, tin litho, red cross on door, Germany, oversz, EX . .150.00
Bird in cage, tin litho, Germany 140.00
Boxers, blk/wht litho, animated arms, Germany, 5¾", VG 250.00
Boy on sled w/curled runners, feet up, tin litho, Germany 150.00
Bus, tin litho, Germany, 1920s, oversz, EX 125.00
Camel, pack on bk opens for candy, wheeled base, Germany . .185.00
Cow w/horns & bell, wheeled base, Germany 175.00
Dbl-decker bus w/driver, steps at bk, Germany, EX 325.00
Express Parcels Delivery, truck/driver, tin litho, 4", EX 440.00
Fire truck, fireman/ladder/bell, litho w/up, Germany, 4½" 200.00

Goat, bucking, Germany 150.00
Horses pull dray wagon, candy box on bk, tin litho, 4⅜" 225.00
Jockey on race horse, wheeled base, Germany 185.00
Man in rowboat, wheeled base, Germany 250.00
Ocean liner, tin litho, rpl wheels, 4½", VG 125.00
Sailor navigating boat, tin litho, wheel missing, 4½", VG 150.00
Touring car w/driver, top down, EX .135.00
Train engine, litho engineer in window, Germany 150.00
Trolly, litho passengers, Germany, EX 250.00
Truck w/driver, open bed, Germany .125.00

Penny toy, boy on sled, 3" long, $150.00.

Pipsqueaks

Pipsqueak toys were popular among the Pennsylvania Germans. The earliest had bellows made from sheepskin. Later, cloth replaced the sheepskin, and finally paper bellows were used.

Baboon, papier-mache, flocked natural coat, silent, 6½" 220.00
Baby in cradle, wood/cb/cloth/papier-mache, 5½", EX 300.00
Baby in crib, wood/cloth/papier-mache, rpr/rpl, 5" 200.00
Bird feeding young, animated wings, papier-mache/mc, 5", EX .350.00
Chicken, papier-mache, orig pnt, silent, 4¾" 200.00
Chicken coop, feather rooster pops out, hen sits, 5¾", VG 75.00
Clown head, squeaks, papier-mache, bas relief face/torso, 5" . . .180.00
Dog, seated, papier-mache/mc pnt, silent, 5", EX 150.00
Duck w/young, bright mc pnt, glass eyes, faint squeak, 6" 300.00
Elephant, gray flocking, paper blanket, silent, 3¼", VG 150.00
Hen on nest, papier-mache/mc pnt, faint squeak, 5", EX 150.00
Husky dog, papier-mache, orig wht/gr pnt, silent, 7", EX 200.00
Lion, papier-mache, orig pnt, minor wear, silent, 5⅜" 200.00
Parrot in top hat, papier-mache w/mc pnt, squeaks 225.00
Parrot on stump, papier-mache w/EX color, faint squeak, 4" . . .120.00
Rabbit, animated ears, flocked pnt, silent, 5¼" L, EX 225.00
Rabbit, animated ears, papier-mache, flocking, squeaks, 4½" . .200.00
Rabbit, papier-mache w/yel flocking, silent, 4¾" 90.00
Rooster, papier-mache, jtd neck, cast metal legs, 7⅝" 375.00
Rooster, papier-mache, mc pnt, silent, 6", EX 175.00
Rooster, papier-mache, spring legs, mc pnt, silent, 5", EX 145.00
Turkey, papier-mache, mc pnt, silent, 3½", EX 275.00

Pull Toys

Clown in self-propelled wagon, cloth/papier-mache, 13", VG . .175.00
Cow, hide covered, glass eyes, wood base, 1880s, 12½", VG . . .250.00
Dog, stuffed gold cloth w/traces of hair, CI wheels, 8" 150.00
Dog on platform, wood/papier-mache, blk/wht, 23", VG 750.00

Horse, cvd wood w/orig pnt, EX detail, fur tail, 12" L 325.00	Rabbit, pnt eyes, regular, EX 550.00
Horse, cvd wood/dapple pnt, horsehair mane/tail, 14x16" 425.00	Reindeer, leather antlers/tail, rare, VG 575.00
Horse, fur/mane/tail, leatherette tack, metal wheels, 11" 150.00	Rhino, pnt eyes, regular 250.00
Horse, wood/papier-mache, traces of mane & tail, 10" H, EX ..300.00	Ringmaster, reduced, EX 160.00
Horse, wood/papier-mache/mc pnt, leather saddle, 9", VG 230.00	Ringmaster, regular, EX 185.00
Horse, wood/papier-mache/mc pnt, sm red wheels, 9", EX 225.00	Ringmaster, regular, rpl clothes, VG 120.00
Horse & wagon, tin, 2 wheels, 9¼", M 80.00	Rolly Poly, clown, musical, papier-mache, 15", EX 225.00
Mule, wood/papier-mache/blk flocking, wood wheels, 5¼" H ..105.00	Rolly Poly, Dutch girl, papier-mache, jtd head, 9¾", VG 650.00
Sheep, wood/papier-mache, wooly coat, glass eyes, 9x10", EX .450.00	Rolly Poly, policeman, bl outfit, 8", VG 150.00
Tiger, pnt cloth over papier-mache, glass eyes, 16", VG 90.00	Rolly Poly, Santa w/bag of toys, papier-mache, 6¾", VG 525.00
	Skier, EX in orig box 295.00
	Tent, reduced, EX 650.00
	Tiger, pnt eyes, regular, EX 200.00
	Xylophone, paper litho on wood, NM 125.00

Schoenhut

Schoenhut Rolly Polys, Foxy Grandpa, EX, 9½", $475.00; Santa Claus, EX, 9", $600.00; Negro Dude, EX, 10½", $475.00.

Bear, pnt eyes, regular, EX 250.00
Bear, pnt eyes, regular, NM 350.00
Big Game Hunter, shooting gallery, cardboard, 12x13", EX 250.00
Billy goat, 9", NM 300.00
Buffalo, pnt eyes, regular, EX 200.00
Bulldog, wht w/blk eye, leather tail/ears, regular, VG 475.00
Cow, pnt eyes, regular, EX 375.00
Donkey, pnt eyes, reduced, EX 55.00
Donkey, pnt eyes, regular, EX 65.00
Elephant, baby, oilcloth ears, string tail, VG 350.00
Elephant, pnt eyes, reduced, EX 55.00
Farmer, molded/pnt head, orig clothes/hat, minor wear, 8⅜" ..180.00
Felix, Sullivan decal, 9½" 300.00
Felix, tail missing, 1922, 4" 150.00
Gazelle, glass eyes, NM 875.00
Giraffe, pnt eyes, regular, 11" 275.00
Goat, pnt eyes, regular, EX 175.00
Goose, pnt eyes, regular 350.00
Hippo, pnt eyes, regular, EX 245.00
Horse, Apaloosa, 11", NM 75.00
Horse, brn, reduced 135.00
Humpty Dumpty Circus, complete, VG 4,200.00
Kangaroo, pnt eyes, regular, NM 500.00
Lady acrobat, reduced, EX 160.00
Lady acrobat, regular, EX 225.00
Lady circus rider, regular, EX 225.00
Lamb, pnt eyes, regular, EX 325.00
Leopard, pnt eyes, regular, EX 200.00
Lion, pnt eyes, regular, EX 200.00
Lion tamer, regular, EX 185.00
Piano, 10x10x8", VG 70.00
Pig, pk/blk, glass eyes, EX 375.00
Poodle, glass eyes, cloth mane, regular, EX 200.00
Poodle, pnt eyes, regular, EX 165.00

Steiff

Margaret Steiff began making her felt stuffed toys in Germany in the late 1800s. The animals she made were tagged with an elephant in a circle. Her first teddy bear, made in 1903, became such a popular seller that she changed her tag to a bear. Felt stuffing was replaced with excelsior and wool; when it became available, foam was used. In addition to the tag, look for the 'Steiff' ribbon and the button inside the ear. For further information we recommend *Teddy Bears and Steiff Animals*, a full-color identification and value guide by Margaret Fox Mandel, available at your local bookstore or public library. See also Teddy Bears.

Bear, Petsy, jtd, beige dralon, orig tag/button, 1965, 12" 150.00
Bear, Teddy Clown, jtd, mohair, glass eyes, 1928, 18", M 1,200.00
Bear, Zotty, squeaker, long curly mohair, 1955, 8", M 175.00
Bird, Finch, standing, plastic feet, w/button, 3½", EX 55.00
Cat, Cosy Siam, dralon, w/tag & button, ca 1970s, 9", M 75.00
Cat, Fluffy, mohair, gr glass eyes, w/button, 1930s, 4½" 65.00
Cat, musical, mohair, red calico dress, tagged, 1945-52, 9½" ...250.00
Cat, Susi, cotton plush, tag/button/orig ribbon, 1930s, 7" 95.00
Cat, Susi, mohair, gr glass eyes, w/bell & tag, 4" 55.00
Chimpanzee in Irish mail cart, metal fr, silent, 10⅜", VG 245.00
Dog, Afghan, Corso, script button, EX color, NM 175.00
Dog, Basset Hound, sitting, orig gr collar, w/chest tag, NM 75.00
Dog, Collie, reclining, w/tag & button, 5½", NM 90.00
Dog, Dachshund, felt, glass eyes, wood wheels, 1900s, 8" 175.00
Dog, Fox Terrier, velour, w/tag & button, 1900s, 10x13" 150.00
Dog, Molly, sitting, tag & button, orig ribbon, 3½", EX 75.00
Dog, St Bernard, mohair, bronze/CI wheels, 1907, 18" 750.00
Dog, Waldi, dralon fur, barking squeaker, 1971-77, life-size ...150.00
Donkey, felt, red saddle, w/button, wood wheels, 1900s, 16" ...400.00
Fox, Fred & Minnie, mohair/cloth, w/tag & button, 9", pr 500.00
Hen, mohair, metal feet, w/tag, 3", EX 60.00
Humpty Dumpty, jtd, felt w/pnt features, 1913, 10", M 1,200.00
Lion, King Leo, yel/wht mohair, CI wheels, ca 1920, EX 550.00
Lion, Papa, jtd, red nose, chest tag, 8½", NM 225.00
Mickey Mouse, velvet, felt ears, pnt mouth, 1930s, 7" 600.00
Minnie Mouse, felt, orig tag/button, 1930s, 5¼" 500.00
Pony, standing, brn/wht, w/tag & button, 4½", EX 55.00
Rabbit, puppet, w/ribbon & tag, 12", EX 55.00
Rooster, standing, metal feet, w/tag, 3", EX 65.00
Skunk, velvet mohair, w/button, 2½", EX 130.00
Tiger, standing, squeaker, w/chest tag, 5½", EX 95.00
Tiger cub, sitting, chest tag, 4", NM 90.00
Zebra, squeaker, mohair, 8", NM 65.00

Toy Soldiers

Toy soldiers were popular playthings with children of the nineteenth century. They were made by many European manufacturers in various sizes until 1848 when a standard size of approximately 1⅓" was established. The most collectible of all toy soldiers were made in England by Britains Ltd. from 1893 to 1966. In America some of the important manufacturers were Barclay, Manoil, Grey, and All-Nu.

Barclay, Boy Scout saluting, #183, NM .30.00
Barclay, bugler, #29, prof rstr 17.50
Barclay, conductor, #353, NM 7.50
Barclay, cowboy w/lasso, #95, NM 9.00
Barclay, cowboy w/upraised pistol, #250, blk clothes, NM 11.00
Barclay, doughboy charging, sm, EX 12.00
Barclay, fireman w/axe, #187, prof rstr 14.00
Barclay, grenade thrower, #76, prof rstr 12.00
Barclay, groom, #174, brn hair, EX 15.00
Barclay, Indian kneeling w/bow & arrow, #98, NM 10.00
Barclay, little boy in gray jacket, #163, NM 10.00
Barclay, mailman, #189, EX 11.00
Barclay, man on skis, #190, NM 13.00
Barclay, old man in lt gray coat, #166, NM 12.00
Barclay, Santa on skis, #195, rpt skis/poles, NM 45.00
Barclay, scout frying eggs, #185, NM 30.00
Barclay, soldier eating, #112, NM 34.00
Barclay, soldier kneeling w/gun, #145, NM 25.00
Barclay, standing at searchlight, #121, prof rstr 13.50
Barclay, tommy gunner, #72, rpl helmet, EX 12.00
Barclay, train conductor, #161, NM 9.00
Barclay, woman w/dog, #157, NM 12.00
Britains, American Indians, #208, mounted, 11-pc, EX 115.00
Britains, Arabs, #187, 8-pc, EX 75.00
Britains, Blk Watch charging w/piper, #8, 6-pc, M 160.00
Britains, cowboy w/pistol, VG 7.50
Britains, Gordon Highlanders, 6-pc, EX 60.00
Britains, Indian w/tomahawk, #208, gr tunic, EX 15.00
Britains, motorcycle w/machine gun, #199, EX 30.00
Britains, RAF fire fighters in asbestos suits, #1758, 8-pc, EX . . .550.00
Britains, Royal Air Force fire fighter, #587, wht suit, MIB 25.00
Elastolin, marching bugler, arm rpr, 3½", EX 22.00
Elastolin, marching drummer, 3½", NM 28.00
French, farmer w/pitchfork, #205, NM 10.00

Britains, Royal Field Artillery Gun Team, mounted at the walk, #1440, EX in VG box, $1,000.00.

French, lady raking, NM 10.00
Grey Iron, boy scout saluting, #72, early, EX 12.50
Grey Iron, bucking bronco, #R008, sm, NM 12.50
Grey Iron, doughboy officer, #27, NM 10.00
Grey Iron, legion bugler, #82, NM 14.50
Grey Iron, legion drum major, #80, NM 18.00
Grey Iron, US infantry officer, #12, early, EX 12.00
Grey Iron, US machine gunner, #60, early, VG 9.50
Manoil, bicycle dispatch rider, #79, NM 18.50

Manoil, blacksmith making horseshoes, #135, NM 15.00
Manoil, cannon loader, #42, NM 16.00
Manoil, nurse, #36, NM 10.00
Manoil, parachute jumper, #88, EX 17.00
Manoil, scarecrow w/straw hat, #143, NM 15.00
Manoil, sniper, #48, prof rstr 12.00
Manoil, soldier boxing, #100, prof rstr 45.00
Manoil, stretcher bearer, medical kit, #58, EX 15.00
Manoil, woman w/child, #157, NM 18.00
Manoil, young girl, for bench, #130, NM 8.00
Mignot, charging knight, mounted, NM 40.00
Tommy Toy, Little Bo Peep, NM 78.00
Tommy Toy, Old Mother Hubbard, NM 80.00

Trains

Electric trains were produced as early as the late 19th century. Names to look for are Lionel, Ives, and American Flyer.

The following listings were prepared by Bruce C. Greenberg and are taken from his comprehensive publications on Lionel, American Flyer, and Ives trains. The prices presented are the most common versions of each item. In many cases, there are several other variations often having a substantially higher value. Identification numbers given in the listings below actually appear on the item.

Our advisor for this category is Bruce Greenberg; he is listed in the Directory under Maryland.

Key: Std Gauge — Standard Gauge

American Flyer 283, S Gauge engine w/tender, EX 45.00
American Flyer 332DC, S Gauge engine w/tender, EX 350.00
American Flyer 332DC, S Gauge engine w/tender, G 100.00
American Flyer 360, 361 S Gauge diesels, EX 175.00
American Flyer 360, 361 S Gauge diesels, G 50.00
Ives 11, 0 Gauge steam engine w/tender, EX 135.00
Ives 11, 0 Gauge steam engine w/tender, G 75.00
Ives 1118, 0 Gauge steam engine w/tender, EX 135.00
Ives 1118, 0 Gauge steam engine w/tender, G 65.00
Ives 1132, Wide Gauge steam engine w/tender, 1921-26, EX . .850.00
Ives 1132, Wide Gauge steam engine w/tender, 1921-26, G . . .325.00
Ives 3240, 1 Gauge electric engine, 1912-20, EX 750.00
Ives 3240, 1 Gauge electric engine, 1912-20, G 350.00
Ives 3241, Wide Gauge electric engine, 1921-25, EX 225.00
Ives 3241, Wide Gauge electric engine, 1921-25, G 85.00
Ives 3243, Wide Gauge electric engine, 1921-28, EX 550.00
Ives 3243, Wide Gauge electric engine, 1921-28, G 200.00
Lionel 1668, 0 Gauge steam engine w/tender, 1937-41, EX . . .100.00
Lionel 1668, 0 Gauge steam engine w/tender, 1937-41, G 60.00
Lionel 2037, 0 Gauge steam engine/tender, 1954-55, 57-58, EX .85.00
Lionel 2037, 0 Gauge steam engine/tender, 1954-55, 57-58, G . .50.00
Lionel 224, 0 Gauge steam engine w/tender, 1938-42, EX 150.00
Lionel 224, 0 Gauge steam engine w/tender, 1938-42, G 60.00
Lionel 2343, 0 Gauge diesels, 2 units, EX 250.00
Lionel 2343, 0 Gauge diesels, 2 units, G 250.00
Lionel 252, 0 Gauge electric engine, 1926-32, EX 125.00
Lionel 252, 0 Gauge electric engine, 1926-32, G 75.00
Lionel 380, Std Gauge electric engine, 1923-27, EX 400.00
Lionel 380, Std Gauge electric engine, 1923-27, G 250.00
Lionel 408E, Std Gauge electric engine, 1927-36, EX 1,200.00
Lionel 408E, Std Gauge electric engine, 1927-36, G 600.00
Lionel 42, Std Gauge electric engine, 1913-23, rnd hood, EX . .450.00
Lionel 42, Std Gauge electric engine, 1913-23, rnd hood, G . . .200.00
Lionel 50, 027 Gauge gang car, 1955-64, EX 55.00
Lionel 50, 027 Gauge gang car, 1955-64, G 15.00

Lionel 58, 027 Gauge rotary snowplow, 1959-61, EX 400.00
Lionel 58, 027 Gauge rotary snowplow, 1959-61, G 160.00
Lionel 60, 0 Gauge trolley, 1955-58, EX 275.00
Lionel 60, 0 Gauge trolley, 1955-58, G 100.00
Lionel 675, 0 Gauge steam engine w/tender, 1947, EX 115.00
Lionel 700E, 0 Gauge steam engine w/tender, 1937-42, G ...1,700.00
Lionel 726, 0 Gauge steam engine w/tender, 1946-49, EX 375.00
Lionel 726, 0 Gauge steam engine w/tender, 1946-49, G 200.00
Lionel 773, 0 Gauge steam engine w/tender, 1950, EX 1,100.00
Lionel 773, 0 Gauge steam engine w/tender, 1950, G 400.00
Lionel 8, Std Gauge electric engine, 1925-32, EX 160.00
Lionel 8, Std Gauge electric engine, 1925-32, G 80.00

Trade Signs

Trade signs were popular during the 1800s. They were usually made in an easily recognizable shape that one could mentally associate with the particular type of business it was to represent, especially appropriate in the days when many customers could not read!

Allcock's Tackle, emb tin fish w/red lettering, 26" L 305.00
Baseball bat, wood, half relief, orig pnt on hdl, 80" 1,100.00
Bell foundry, wooden bell on iron rod, 3-D, 14x13", EX 325.00
Blacksmith, handwrought horseshoe w/nails & tools, 21" 350.00
Butcher, CI, implements, bull finial, 17x15", EX 325.00
Butcher, molded copper full-bodied pig, 1800s, 30" L 5,200.00
Dentist, name/# in gold/blk on blk-pnt wood, fr, 17x22" 140.00
Dr BF Barker's Tonic Bitters, HP on sheet metal, 24x36", VG .325.00
Dressmaking, pnt letters on brd, alligatored surface, 6x35" 195.00
Fishing lure figural, wood w/metal hooks, 54" L 850.00
Fountain pen, wood, shaped & trn, brass point, ca 1890, 40" L .395.00
Fur Coats, cb in orig wood fr, mc pnt, 23x17", EX 65.00
Glasses Fitted, rvpt plate glass, CI bridge/nose rest, 29" 3,200.00
Gunsmith, wooden dbl-bbl shotgun w/ramrod, 1800s, 100" ..1,000.00

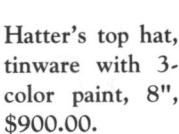
Hatter's top hat, tinware with 3-color paint, 8", $900.00.

Hawkes...Lenses, wood/blk smaltz, pnt ½-eye glasses, 13x27" .2,500.00
Ingersoll Dollar Watch, dbl-sided zinc watch form, 24", VG .1,100.00
Magazine, slide rule, brass & wood, 84x12½", EX 225.00
Mortar & pestle, trn wood, sheet zinc lid, rpt, mortar: 11" 250.00
Pocket watch, wood, iron stem, gold-pnt numerals, 16" dia 875.00
RE Bruner, rvpt name, gold/blk/bl w/abalone inlay, 47" L 575.00
Restaurant, dinner fork figural, CI, 22" L 295.00
Spectacles w/appl eyes, copper, lg, EX 395.00
Tattooing, plywood, 4 HP tattoo patterns, ca 1940, 11x32" ...125.00
Walden Knife Co, open jackknife form, wood/mc pnt, 42" L .2,400.00

Tramp Art

Today considered a type of American folk art, tramp art was made from the late 1800s until after the turn of the century. Often produced by 'tramps' and 'hobos' from wooden materials which could be scavenged (crates and cigar boxes, for instance), articles such as jewelry boxes and picture frames were usually decorated by chip carving and then stained.

Box, allover chip cvg, knob ft, EX detail, natural, 13" L 150.00
Box, chip cvd, tiered, brass hdls, dtd 1904, 9x7½x13" 165.00
Box, chip-cvd diamonds, orig pnt, paper label, 9½x4½x3¼" 60.00
Chest of drws, step-bk w/2 drws, 2 in base, +mirror, 9" 125.00
Cradle, chip cvd, leaf designs, orig pnt, ca 1900, doll sz 45.00
Frame, layered w/angle cuts, bow ties on sides, 14½x12½" 125.00
Frame, pnt traces, 1¾" W, 19" sq, VG 25.00
Frame, 3 chip-cvd tiers, scalloped, varnish, 11x8½" 65.00
Galleon model, canvas sails, mc pnt, 24x25" 275.00

Frame, holds 3 post card-sized photos, marked 'North Dakota,' 12½x8", $135.00.

Magazine rack, brass tack decor, simple crest, rpr, 15" W 40.00
Rocker, lyre splat, scalloped sides, appl chip cvg, pnt, VG 175.00
Sewing table, chip-cvd rectangles & ogee legs 850.00
Shelf, pine, chip cvd, peaked top, sgn/dtd 1924, 4½x14x12" ...155.00
Shelf, pine, scalloped, chip cvd, appl cvd flowers, 9x16x7" 135.00

Traps

Though of interest to collectors for many years, trap collecting has gained in popularity over the past ten years in particular, causing prices to appreciate rapidly. Traps are usually marked on the pan as to manufacturer, and the condition of these trademarks are important when determining their value. Grading is as follows:

Good: one-half of pan legible.
Very Good: legible in entirety, but light.
Fine: legible in entirety, with strong lettering.
Mint: in like-new, shiny condition.

Our advisor for this category is Boyd Nedry; he is listed in the Directory under Michigan. Prices listed here are for traps in fine condition.

Allsteel #0, single long spring 45.00
Auto Sented-Rev-o-Noc, snap-type mousetrap, wood 8.00
Black Hole, throw-away mousetrap, plastic 8.00

Blake & Lamb, #2 Milk pattern, dbl under spring 28.00
Blizzard, snap-type rattrap, wood 10.00
Canada Killer, unmk, beaver sz 35.00
Champion Multitrigger, Los Angeles CA, single long spring ...150.00
Cinch, mole trap 15.00
Clayton Killer 300.00
Cleaning Day, snap-type mousetrap, wood 8.00
CM Coghill, mousetrap, screws on fruit jar 15.00
Crago #4, clutch trap 185.00
Crescent #3, dbl long spring 300.00
Dahlgren 'Sur-pelt' Killer 17.00
Davenport Killer, full circles 85.00
Diamond #1, Animal Trap Co, single under spring 7.00
Diamond #15, dbl coil spring 95.00
Diamond #51 Walloper 65.00
Dodd Safe Set, snap-type mousetrap, wood 8.00
Duke #1, single long spring 3.50
Easy-setting choker, 4-hole, rnd, wood 8.00
Eclipse #1, horse-shoe shaped, dbl under spring 40.00
Economy #1, single long spring 22.00
Elgin, mousetrap, steel 8.00
Epp, chain leghold trap, Henderson Nebraska 575.00
Evans, mousetrap, brass 150.00
Funsten Submarine, float-type trap 225.00
Gabriel automatic setting, fish & game trap 85.00
Gibbs Hawk, dbl coil spring 185.00
Gibbs 2-Trigger, w/teeth, 1927 model 18.00
Hanson Killer, Canada 40.00
Hart #3, wrought, dbl long spring, stamped Chauncy Hart ...1,500.00
Hector #0, single long spring 25.00
Herters #0, single long spring 75.00
Herters Kodiak, bear trap 285.00
Iron Cat, choker-style mousetrap, metal, 1906 ....20.00
Jack Frost, Never Lose, coil spring 19.00
JVJ, gopher trap, Crete Nebraska 30.00
Kliflock #1 Killer 20.00
Little Jimmy, live rattrap, wood & tin 20.00
Little Samson, rattrap, iron w/teeth 150.00
Master Killer, by WW Stout 150.00
Mighty Mouse, snap-type mousetrap 12.00
Nash, mole trap, Kalamazoo MI, CI 15.00
Nebraska, trail trap 395.00
Newhouse #144, Oneida Community NY 95.00
Newhouse #15, bear trap, Animal Trap Co 345.00
Newhouse #150, Animal Trap Co 285.00
Newhouse #2½, single long spring, w/breastplate 35.00
Nip-It, sq 4-hole choker, wood 25.00
Oberto #400, dbl under spring 50.00
Official Weasel, snap-type weasel trap, wood, Animal Trap Co ...8.00
Old Tom, mousetrap, fits on fruit jar 10.00
Pendelum Trigger #3 Killer 160.00
Piggot, snap-type mousetrap, wood w/mirror in bk 80.00
Pines, fly trap, metal 15.00
PS&W #1 Good Luck, single long spring 65.00
Quigley, Van Camp Hwd Co, snap-type mousetrap, wood 8.00
Renkens, gopher trap 10.00
Rev-o-Noc #101, single long spring 35.00
Rexall Store Official, snap-type mousetrap, wood 8.00
Safe Set, mousetrap, metal, pat 1905-06 ....22.50
Sargent #14, rnd pan, dbl long spring 70.00
Sav-A-Leg #210, coil spring 40.00
Schuler Folding Killer, metal, mouse sz 18.00
Simplex, self-set gopher trap 18.00
Snap Shot Improved, choker-type mousetrap 12.00

Snappy, thumb-set mousetrap, metal 10.00
Star #3, dbl under spring 45.00
Streeter, snap-type mousetrap, iron, pat 1897 ....90.00
Sure Hold, cone trap, wood, sm 45.00
Taylor #1, single long spring 14.00
Trailzend #3, dbl long spring, Nelson Boode Co 150.00
Trailzend #7, dbl long spring, Nelson Boode Co 550.00
Triumph #0, single long spring, w/T cut in pan 100.00
Up To Date, mousetrap, metal, catches from either end ...20.00
Victor #1, single long spring, Kenwood NY 6.00
Wiggington, mousetrap, glass 20.00
Woodward Death Clamp, 4½" 22.00
WR Feemster, mousetrap, aluminum, Brooklyn Michigan 15.00
Zip, snap-type mousetrap, metal 8.00

Trivets

Although strictly a decorative item today, the original purpose of the trivet was much more practical. They were used to protect table tops from hot serving dishes, and irons heated on the kitchen range were placed on trivets during use to protect work surfaces. The first patent date was 1869; many of the earliest trivets bore portraits of famous people or patriotic designs. Florals, birds, animals, and fruit were other favored motifs.

Watch for remakes of early original designs. These are marked Wilton, Emig, Wright, and Iron Art.

Brass

Anchor, sm heart & cross cutouts, 9" 110.00
Horse in center, 3-legged, 3½x6" 65.00
Horse/foliage in pierced top, 3¾x6" dia 115.00
Lyre detail, 11" 35.00
Outer ring contains lg star, 6" 80.00

Peace and Plenty, 6½" diameter, $65.00.

Reticulated top, trn wood hdl, 12" wrought iron ft, 15" L 130.00
Solid triangle, hanging hole in hdl, rpl ft, 8¾" 30.00
Tilt-top tea table form, 6 heart cutouts in center, 12" 350.00

Cast Iron

God Bless Our Home around horseshoe, dtd 1892 ....45.00
Heart figural center, heart figural hdl, for sadiron, old 65.00
Star & Fan, for sadiron, Cleveland Foundry 15.00
Starflower center, compass circles/arches, 6" dia 45.00
Triangular, 1890s, 2¾" legs, 8¾x8" 30.00

Wrought Iron

Adjustable pot rest, rnd w/3 legs, 6x25x9" dia	150.00
Christmas tree form, ring hdl, sgn	125.00
Heart form, 3-ftd, 1700s, PA	300.00
Heart form, 3-ftd, 1800s, 7x5½"	125.00
Heart w/heart cutout, short legs/drake ft, 1775	650.00
Sliding rest for pan hdl, ca 1850, 22"	190.00
3-legged, w/hdl rest, 1700s, 5x25" +8" rest, EX	110.00

Trolls

The modern-day version of the troll was designed in 1952 by Helena and Marti Kuuskoski of Tampere, Finland. Those made by Dam and those marked with a horseshoe are among the most valuable, since both are made from the original Kuuskoski design. Many copies have been produced, the best of which are the Wishniks, made by the Uneeda Doll Company. These were first marketed in 1979 and are currently still available. Troll animals are scarce, and values are rising.

Bank, Dam, 7"	14.00
Bank, unmk, 7"	8.00

Bank, girl in purple and gold dress, 8", $8.00.

Caveman, sm, M	35.00
Caveman, 11"	69.00
Donkey, 1964, 9"	55.00
Giraffe, 13"	50.00
Playboy, 3"	12.00
Playboy Bunny, rare, 13"	75.00
Santa, bank	25.00
Tiny Tim, sitting	15.00

Trunks

In the the days of steamboat voyages, stagecoach journeys, and railroad travel, trunks were used to transport clothing and personal belongings. Some, called 'dome top' or 'turtle backs'; were rounded on top to better accommodate milady's finery. Today, some of the more interesting examples are used in various ways in home decorating. For instance, a flat-topped trunk may become a coffee table, while a smaller dome style may be 'home' for antique dolls or a teddy bear collection.

Hide w/leather & brass tack trim, wallpaper int, 12" L	50.00
Leather covered, gr/tan w/brass-tack trim, 15½" L	350.00
Leather-covered camphor wood, brass bound, Chinese, 42" ...	200.00
Oak, cvd, wrought iron hinges/hdls, Spanish, 1700s, 32x77" .	2,000.00
Pine, dome top, dvtl, rfn, 39" L	65.00
Pine, leather trim w/brass tacks, 17½x9½x8½"	95.00
Tooled leather, brass bound, dome top, 20" L, EX	175.00
Tooled leather, dome top, iron lock/hdl, dtd 1650, 11"	235.00
Tooled leather, dome top, wrought hdls, Spanish, 1700s, 41" ..	500.00

Yellow grain-painted dome-top trunk, ca 1830s, 42" long, $2,200.00.

Tuthill

The Tuthill Glass Company operated in Middletown, New York, from 1902 to 1923.

Bowl, hobstar in base/ea corner, nailhead/X-hatch, sgn, 8"	250.00
Bowl, hobstars/pinwheels, sgn, 8"	200.00
Bowl, Primrose, 8"	250.00
Bowl, wild roses, att, 9"	150.00
Jug, whiskey; intaglio thistles, sgn	350.00
Pitcher, water; poppy intaglio, split vesicas, +6 tumblers	1,100.00
Plate, Rosaceae, lg hobstar center w/floral intaglio, 10"	700.00
Tray, celery; Vintage intaglio bottom, hobstar bands, 11"	600.00

Tumblers, star cutting, signed, 3¾", $75.00 each.

Typewriters

The first commercially successful typewriter was the Sholes and Glidden, introduced in 1874. By 1882 other models appeared, and by the 1890s dozens were on the market. At the time of the First World War, the ranks of typewriter-makers thinned, and by the 1920s only a few survived.

Collectors informally divide typewriter history into the pioneering period, up to about 1890; the classic period, from 1890 to 1920; and the modern period, since 1920. There are two broad classifications of early typewriters: (1) Keyboard machines, in which depression of a key prints a character and via a shift key prints up to three different characters per key. (2) Index machines, in which a chart of all the characters appears on the typewriter; the character is selected by a pointer or dial and is printed by operation of a lever or other device. Even though index typewriters were simpler and more primitive than keyboard machines, they were none-the-less a later development, designed to provide a cheaper alternative to the standard keyboard models that were selling for upwards of $100. Eventually second-hand keyboard typewriters supplied the low-price customer, and index typewriters vanished except as toys. Both classes of typewriters appeared in a great many designs.

It is difficult, if not impossible, to assign standard market prices to early typewriters. Unlike collectors of postage stamps, carnival glass, etc. few people collect typewriters — so there is no active marketplace from which to establish prices. Also, condition is a very important factor, and typewriters can vary infinitely in condition. A third factor to consider is that an early typewriter achieves its value mainly through the skill, effort, and patience of the collector who restores it to its original condition, in which case its purchase price is insignificant. Some unusual-looking early typewriters are not at all rare or valuable, while some very ordinary-looking ones are scarce and could be quite valuable. No general rules apply. When no condition is indicated, the items listed below are assumed to be in excellent, unrestored condition.

American, indicator type, M 85.00
Berwin, tin, 1950s, MIB 15.00
Blickensderfer #5, dtd 1892, VG 60.00
Blickensderfer #7, oak case, EX 60.00
Blickensderfer Electric 2,000.00
Brooks 500.00
Corona, folding 20.00
Crandall 500.00
Crown, index 300.00
Fitch 600.00
Hall, index 150.00
Hammond Multiplex, folding, for all nations, M 100.00
Merritt, index, wood cover, instruction label in lid, EX ...375.00
O'Dell #2 ....250.00
Oliver Standard Visible Writer, old upright keys, M 80.00
Practical #4, oak base 110.00
Royal #10, 1922, EX 45.00
Royal #5, gold trim, VG 150.00
Sholes & Glidden, w/decor 2,500.00
Simplex Model D, red/wht/bl, index type, EX 45.00
Smith-Corona #4, portable, 1920s, EX in case 35.00
Underwood Standard, dtd 1912, EX 25.00
Victor, index 200.00
World, index 100.00

Uhl Pottery

Founded in Evansville, Indiana, in 1849 by German immigrants, the Uhl Pottery was moved to Huntingburg, Indiana, in 1908 because of the more suitable clay available there. They produced stoneware—Acorn Ware jugs, crocks, and bowls—which were marked with the acorn logo and 'Uhl Pottery.' They also made mugs, pitchers, and vases in simple shapes and solid glazes marked with a circular ink stamp containing the name of the pottery and 'Huntingburg, Indiana.' The pottery closed in the mid-1940s. Those seeking additional information about Uhl pottery are encouraged to contact the Uhl Collectors' Society, whose address is listed in the Directory under Clubs, Newsletters, and Catalogs.

Ash tray, acorn, brn, mk 70.00
Ash tray, dog at fire hydrant, brn 140.00
Ash tray, Shell service station ad, brn 60.00
Bowl, batter; pk, mk, 10" 90.00
Bowl, bulb, tulips, bl, mk, #120 ....50.00
Bowl, chili; bl, mk, 12-oz 35.00
Bowl, dog's feeding; dog emb, mk, #130, 7" 90.00
Candle holder, bl, mk 75.00
Casserole, pk, w/lid, mk, 5-pt 28.00
Churn, Acorn Ware, w/bails, mk, 3-gal 80.00
Churn, Evansville mk, 3-gal 95.00
Cookie jar, brn, mk, #522 ....65.00
Cookie jar, globe, bl, mk 120.00
Jar, Acorn Ware, wht, 30-gal 285.00
Jug, Acorn Ware, brn/wht, squat, bail hdl 150.00
Jug, Acorn Ware, 5-gal 45.00
Jug, baseball, 2½" 70.00

Jug, blue glaze, 9", $125.00.

Jug, canteen, bl, miniature 60.00
Jug, Evansville, wht, 3-gal 70.00
Jug, football figural, brn, 4" 30.00
Jug, Merry Christmas, 1937, 2½" 200.00
Jug, Merry Christmas, 1939, 2½" 145.00
Jug, polar bear, bl/wht, ½-gal, 10" 625.00
Jug, ring, tan, 2½" 125.00
Jug, softball, 3½" 210.00
Miniature, baby shoes, bl, mk, pr 145.00
Miniature, cowboy boots, bl, mk, pr 120.00
Mug, coffee; bl, mk 60.00
Mug, tan, mk, 14-oz 12.00
Pitcher, bl, bulbous, mk, #124, 8½" 125.00
Pitcher, flagon, tan, mk, 5-pt 75.00

Pitcher, grape, bl, bellied, #181 . . . . .80.00
Pitcher, grape, bl, str sides, mk, 6-pt 95.00
Pitcher, Lincoln, bl, mk, ½-pt .200.00
Pitcher, Lincoln, bl, mk, 4-pt, 10" 300.00
Roaster, bl, w/lid, mk, 11" 180.00
Vase, cemetery; bl, 5" 45.00
Vase, cut flower; bl, #117, mk .45.00

Unger Brothers

The Art Nouveau silver produced by Unger Brothers, who operated in Newark, New Jersey, from the early 1880s until 1909, is fast becoming very popular on today's collectibles market. In addition to tableware, they also made brushes, mirrors, powder boxes, and the like for milady's dressing table as well as jewelry and small personal accessories such as match safes and flasks. They often marked their products with a circle seal containing an intertwined 'UB.'

Bottle, scent; Cane, sq, reticulated sterling top, mk, 5" 125.00
Buckle, belt; lady's, Nouveau cherubs, low V-form, sterling 150.00
Cane hdl, lady smoker, sterling, mk, 2¼" 275.00
Dresser set, Love's Voyage, sterling, 10-pc 1,250.00
Jar, Prism & Cane, repousse sterling lid, 1¾x1¾" 75.00
Mirror, hand; Love's Dream 165.00
Mirror & brush set, repousse w/cupids 300.00
Rattle, Mother Goose motif 250.00
Teether, figural boy w/overalls & cap, MOP hdl, 4", EX 185.00

Universal

Universal Potteries Incorporated operated in Cambridge, Ohio, from 1934 to 1956. Many lines of dinnerware and kitchen items were produced in both earthenware and semi-porcelain. In 1956 the emphasis was shifted to the manufacture of floor and wall tiles, and the name was changed to the Oxford Tile Company, Division of Universal Potteries. The plant closed in 1976.

Ballerina, bowl, vegetable; wine, hdl, 9" 8.50
Ballerina, bowl, wine, 5" H 6.00
Ballerina, cup & saucer, wine 4.00
Ballerina, plate, wine, 12" 7.50
Ballerina, plate, wine, 9" 4.00
Ballerina, shakers, wine, pr 6.00
Cattail, bottle, water; canteen form w/stopper 15.00
Cattail, bowl, w/lid 12.50
Cattail, casserole, w/lid 18.00
Cattail, plate, 9" 5.00
Cattail, platter, 11½" 9.00
Hollyhock, pitcher, milk sz 10.00
Woodvine, shakers, pr 8.00

Val St. Lambert

Since its inception in Belgium at the turn of the 19th century, the Val St. Lambert Cristalleries has been involved in the production of high quality glass, specializing in cameo.

Our advisor for this category is Don Williams; he is listed in the Directory under Iowa. See also Animal Dishes with Covers.

Candlestick, griffins on base, frosted, mk, 11", pr 195.00
Coaster, floral base, mk, set of 6, MIB 38.00

Goblet, cobalt cut to clear, gold band w/dancing figures 120.00
Stemmed crystal, fluted/T'print banding, 24 pcs 300.00
Vase, bl over clear, Deco style, mk, 7¼" 225.00

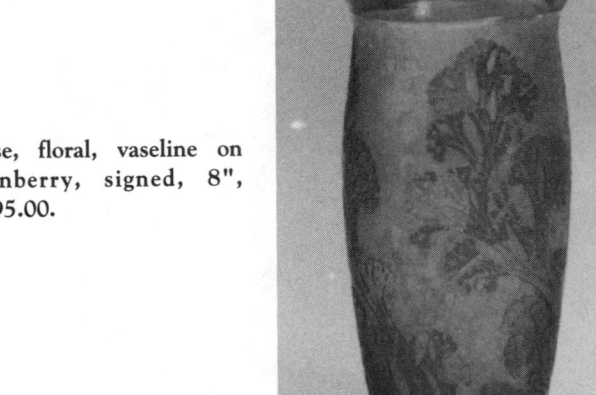

Vase, floral, vaseline on cranberry, signed, 8", $295.00.

Cameo

Basket, leaves/branches, gr on frost, emb SP rim/hdl, 4¼" 350.00
Box, 3-color on gold frost, sgn, 2⅜x4⅜" 350.00
Vase, floral/vines, turq on mottled frost, 6½" 425.00
Vase, landscape w/lg trees, red on yel, slim form, 23" 1,500.00
Vase, thistles, bl-gr on clear, strapwork ft, slim, 16" 900.00

Valentines

Pagan ritual once held that on Valentine's Day the birds of the air elected to choose their mates; and, as this premise was eagerly adopted by the homo sapien species, romantic poems became a familiar expression of one's intentions. By the mid-1800s, comical hand-colored lithographic and wood-block prints were mass-produced both here and abroad. At the turn of the century, the more romantic, often mechanical German imports forced many American companies out of business. Today's collectors often specialize — comics, post cards, mechanicals, Victorian, Kewpies, Greenaway characters, or those signed by a specific artist are among many well-established categories.

If you're interested in learning more about valentines, we recommend *Tokens of Love* by Roberta Etter; her address is in the Directory under England.

Key
hc — hand colored   p — publisher

Bank note, Bank of Love, Promise...heart & hand, 1840, 5x8" . .180.00
Cherub holds heart, ca 1918, 3" 2.00
Edwardian cherubs/children, Germany, ca 1918, 14x10" sheet . . .5.00
Emb/gilt chromolitho sachet w/addressed envelope, dtd '63 . . .120.00
Foldout, boy w/concertina, girl on swing, 3-D, Germany, EX . . .15.00
Foldout, cut-out children in front of Victorian house, NM 30.00
Foldout, cutout, basket w/heart-shaped hdl, flowers inside, 10" . .20.00
Foldout, cutout, cherub plays mandolin, cupid w/message, 7" . . .15.00
Foldout, cutout, die-emb, tulips/lady/cherubs, 9¼x11½" 20.00
Foldout, cutout, early die-emb touring car, 10½" L, M 45.00
Foldout, Kewpies, fancy 6.00
Foldout, To My Fond Love, children at water pump, 5" 6.00

Gilt lace w/silk flowers, chromolitho scraps/feathers, 1850s **200.00**
Handmade, hearts/circles/see verses as it unfolds, 1800s, 17" ... **385.00**
Ladies Polite...Writer, p Dean & Co, hc fronticepc, 1840s **160.00**
Mechanical, huge celluloid heart, old **35.00**

Mechanical, ca 1915, 9½", $12.00.

Open cut, To My Valentine, pk/red roses on bl w/gold, 8x12" ... **15.00**
Printed summons, for theft of...heart, 1880, 7¾x10" **95.00**
Shell-emb/lacy, hc fruit, opens to litho of girl, 1870, lg **75.00**

Van Briggle

The Van Briggle Pottery of Colorado Springs, Colorado, was established in 1901 by Artus Van Briggle, whose early career had been shaped by such notables as Karl Langenbeck and Maria Nichols Storer. His quest for several years had been to perfect a completely flat matt glaze; and, upon accomplishing his goal, he opened his pottery. His wife, Anne, worked with him, and they, along with George Young, were responsible for the modeling of the wares. Their work typified the flow and form of the Art Nouveau movement, and the shapes they designed played as important a part in their success as their glazes. Some of their most famous pieces were Despondency, Lorelei, and Toast Cup.

Increasing demand for their work soon made it necessary to add to their quarters as well as their staff. Although much of the ware was eventually made from molds, each piece was carefully trimmed and refined before the glaze was sprayed on. Their most popular colors were rose, blue, green, yellow, and gray.

Van Briggle died in 1904, but the work was continued by his wife. New facilities were built and by 1908, in addition to their artware, tiles, gardenware, and commercial lines were added. By the twenties, the emphasis had shifted from art pottery to novelties and commercial wares. As late as 1970, reproductions of some of the early designs continued to be made. Until about 1920, most pieces were marked with the date and shape number; after that the AA mark was used.

Ash tray, Hopi Indian, turq, pre-1922, 6" **65.00**
Bookends, bear on stump, bl/blk, 8", pr **250.00**
Bookends, peacock, turq, no mk, 5", pr **75.00**
Bowl, mermaid at rim, emb fish, bl, pre-1932, +frog **350.00**
Bowl, Nouveau swirls/florals, lt bl, 4-ftd, 1907, 11", EX **550.00**
Bowl, spade leaves, maroon/bl, mk USA, 10" **125.00**
Bowl vase, dragonflies, bl over red, exposed clay, 3x5" **500.00**

Bowl vase, peacock feathers, olive gr, dtd 1904, 5½x6½" **1,600.00**
Candle holder, dbl; plum, dtd 1931, 6x5", pr **95.00**
Ewer, med gr w/red at top, #435, 1905, 7" **205.00**
Flower frog, duck, gr/brn **35.00**
Lamp, Damsel of Damascus, Persian Rose, orig shade **200.00**
Lamp, Grecian urn, orig shade, turq, 11½" **55.00**
Lamp, Maiden at the Well, ca 1930 .... **150.00**
Lamp, 2 racing deer, Ming Bl, 11" **125.00**

Lamp, owl figural, blue-green matt tones, 10", $200.00.

Mug, gr, dtd 1905, 5" **175.00**
Shakers, floral, Persian Rose, pr **42.00**
Soap dish, shell girl, turq, IX Colo Springs G, pre-1922 .... **125.00**
Teapot, turq w/purple, bamboo reeded hdl, w/lid **135.00**
Vase, Arts & Crafts-style flowers, gr, #382, 1906, 5" **425.00**
Vase, bell flowers, med bl, #197, dtd 1903, 6x3" **900.00**
Vase, bl on dk brn clay, #522, bulbous, 1905, 4½" **375.00**
Vase, bud; maroon, dtd 1914, 8", pr **150.00**
Vase, bud; 4 heart leaves, khaki, bulbous bottom, 1904, 4" **450.00**
Vase, copper clad, emb collar, bulbous, 1907-12, 5x4" **900.00**
Vase, dbl row leaves, Persian Rose, mk III, dtd 1903, 10" **1,500.00**
Vase, Despondency, maroon w/gr, ca 1925, 12" **575.00**
Vase, dk brn gloss, #676, slim form, 1908-11, 7" **425.00**
Vase, dk brn to med brn speckles, #310, 1915, 3½" **310.00**
Vase, dk gr, suspended glaze, #325, 1908-11, 5¾" **250.00**
Vase, Dos Cabezos, 2 women at rim, bl-gray, dtd 1914, 8" ... **2,250.00**
Vase, floral, Persian Rose, 4½" **48.00**
Vase, floral w/bulbs at bottom, brn/yel, dtd 1906, 7½x4" **600.00**
Vase, floral/leaves top to base, dk bl w/red, CO Spgs, 11" **170.00**
Vase, geometric disks/bird's head, gr, #15, dtd 1902, 4¾" **950.00**
Vase, gr, cream-brn body, #734, '08-11, 7½" **350.00**
Vase, gr/bl texture, #343, date illegible, ca 1905, 5" **230.00**
Vase, iris, turq, 6" **40.00**
Vase, leaves, brn w/gr, dtd 1920, #859, 5" **110.00**
Vase, leaves, brn/med gr, wide at base, #793, dtd 1920, 5" **140.00**
Vase, leaves, dk on lt bl, #848, 7½" **60.00**
Vase, leaves encircle top, gr, cream body, #652, 1908-11, 7" ... **475.00**
Vase, lines/bows in sqs at base, gr w/red touches, 1906, 6" **400.00**
Vase, Lorelai, bl, EX mold, ca 1920s, USA, 10" **850.00**
Vase, Lorelai, lt gr to cream to gr, EX mold, dtd 1902, 10" **900.00**
Vase, Lorelai, maroon/bl, no mk, ca 1925, 9½x4½" **350.00**
Vase, maroon, Ned Curtis mks, #793, 1914, 5½" **225.00**
Vase, Nouveau floral, gr on cream body, #652, 1908-11, 6½" .. **475.00**
Vase, Nouveau floral, lt bl w/dk bl specks, #849, 4½" **75.00**
Vase, papyrus blooms, dk gr, bulbous top, #639, 1907-12, 8" ... **400.00**

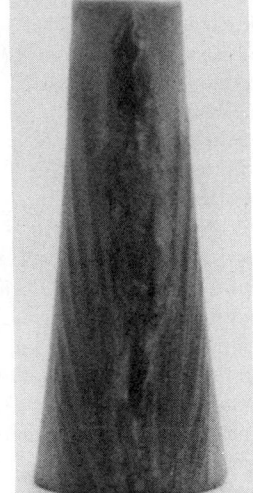

Vase, floral spire, four-color glaze, dated 1903, 14", $3,750.00.

Vase, peacock feathers emb on bl-gr, #62, dtd 1903, 12½x4" .1,750.00
Vase, poppies w/long stems, gr w/purple, #803, 1908-11, 7" 850.00
Vase, poppy buds/leaves, gr tones, #173, dtd 1904, rstr, 9¾" ...900.00
Vase, purple/dk bl mottle, step-bk neck/sm rim, 1906, 11" ...1,100.00
Vase, rose w/bl, triple cornucopia w/candle holder, 4x5" 65.00
Vase, slim leaves, mustard yel, 1907, 5" 500.00
Vase, slim leaves, purple on dk gr, #801, 1907-12, 8x3½" 800.00
Vase, stylized flower/long stems, dk gr/brn, '07-12, 8x4" 375.00
Vase, tulips at top, wht w/purple, #372, dtd 1906, 7" 475.00
Vase, vertical spikes, bl w/dk bl overglaze, 1907-12, 5x4" 300.00
Vase, whiplash stems/blossoms at top, dk bl, dtd 1906, 8x5" ...550.00
Vase, yel/gr over dk brn clay, #295, dtd 1905, 7½" 700.00
Vase, 3 Indian heads, turq, pre-1922, 11" 200.00
Vase, 3 slim floral panels, purple/gr/bl, #753, 1907-12, 10" ..1,500.00
Vase, 4 upright flowers, violet/yel/gr on khaki, 1903, 7x4" 850.00
Vase/planter, conch shell, bl, 6x16" 45.00

Vance Avon

Although pottery had been made in Tiltonville, Ohio, since about 1880, the ware manufactured there was of little significance until after the turn of the century when the Vance Faience Company was organized for the purpose of producing quality artware. By 1902 the name had been changed to the Avon Faience Company, and late in the same year it and three other West Virginia potteries incorporated to form the Wheeling Potteries Company. The Avon branch operated in Tiltonville until 1905 when production was moved to Wheeling. Art pottery was discontinued.

From the start, only skilled craftsmen and trained engineers were hired. Wm. P. Jervis and Frederick Hurten Rhead were among the notable artists responsible for some of the early artware. Some of the ware was slip decorated under glaze, other pieces were molded with high-relief designs. Examples with squeeze-bag decoration by Rhead are obviously forerunners of the Jap Birdimal line he later developed for Weller. Ware was marked 'Vance F. Co.'; 'Avon F. Co., Tiltonville'; or 'Avon W. Pts. Co.'

Pitcher, gr, hound hdl, emb animals/grapevines, 12¾", EX 500.00
Vase, clouds/stylized trees/band w/inscription, Rhead, 6" 250.00
Vase, garlands emb, yel/brn, 4 sm openings at shoulder, 11" ...125.00
Vase, nudes/fish relief, yel/brn, bulbous, 12½" 750.00

Vaseline

Vaseline, a greenish-yellow colored glass produced by adding uranium

oxide to the batch, was made in large quantities during the Victorian era. It was used for pressed glass tablewares, vases, and souvenir items.

Bowl, Daisy & Button panels, raised/scalloped base, 8" dia 80.00
Bowl, master berry; Maple Leaf 245.00
Butter dish, Daisy & Button, faceted finial, 6½" dia 125.00
Goblet, hexagonal, miniature 180.00
Jug, claret; opal, SP top & hdl, 10x5" 210.00
Marmalade, Daisy & Button, faceted finial, 5" 125.00
Plate, Horn of Plenty, 6", NM 325.00
Vase, cranberry threads, rigaree around center, 4½x3" 55.00
Vase, Waffle & T'print, 10" 550.00

Venetian Glass

Venetian glass is a thin, fragile ware usually made in colors, often with internal gold or silver flecks. It was produced on the island of Murano, near Venice, from the thirteenth century to the early 1900s. Murano-type glassware is always heavier and thicker than the older ware.

Bottle, clear w/wht loopings, amethyst rim/rigaree, 2" L 95.00
Bowl, latticinio, bl/gold/wht, sq 4½" top, 2¾" base 58.00
Candy dish, gr, clear stem & rigaree, high std 45.00
Carafe, aventurine fish stopper, mk Murano/Luxardo, 1909 ....75.00
Cigarette lighter, fish form, 12" L 95.00
Cigarette lighter, gold flecks, wht HP ribbons, 12" 45.00
Compote, gr, aventurine, appl prunts, 6½" 75.00
Figurine, bird, wht latticinio w/gold-flecked beak, 3¼x4" 100.00
Figurine, fish, ruby, gold flecks, 5½x9¾" 125.00
Figurine, parrot, ruby w/amber head/tail/ped, gold wings, 6" ...125.00
Figurine, rooster, amber, gold dusted, 9¾x6½x5" 135.00
Figurine, rooster crowing, pk to clear w/gold flecks, 9" 135.00
Figurine, tuba player, 6½" 135.00
Goblet, coin spots on mauve frost, amber stem 45.00
Top hat, wht swirled ribs, aqua int, gold flecks, 8" 70.00

Vase, green with gold aventurine, Murano paper label, 13", $95.00.

Vase, amber drops on mauve frost, ruffled bottle form, 1895 ...195.00
Vase, feathers, mauve & bl, pontil, 5" 85.00
Vase, gilt-flecked clear cased w/wht & bl, 1950s, 6½" 180.00
Vase, gr/gold latticinio in clear, ribbed cone, 1930, 12" 350.00
Vase, ruby, swan figural hdls, gilt flecks/rigaree, ftd, 12" 135.00
Vase, swans, gold-flecked on red, twist neck, ftd, 12" 115.00
Wine, latticinio stripes in cranberry/clear/opal/goldstone 75.00

Verlys

Verlys art glass, produced in France after 1931 by the Holophane Company of Verlys, was made in crystal with acid-finished relief work in the Art Deco style. Colored and opalescent glass was also used. In 1935 an American branch was opened in Newark, Ohio. Wares manufactured there were very similar, but less expensive. Both factories signed their wares 'Verlys' — the American branch by etching, the French with a molded signature.

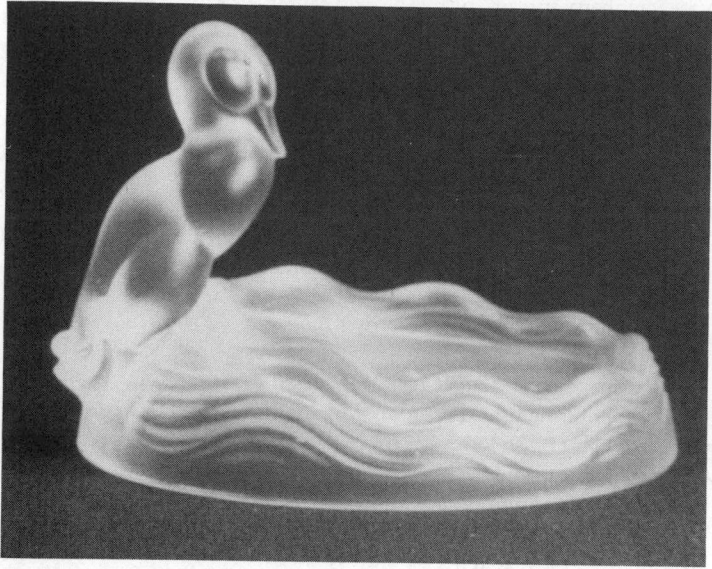

Ash tray, pelican figure on waves, 6" long, $45.00.

Bonbon, floral, smoked or amber, 7½", ea	185.00
Bowl, Chrysanthemum, frosted, 10"	125.00
Bowl, Pine Cone, bl, mk, 6"	95.00
Bowl, Pine Cone, frosted, 1¾x6"	60.00
Bowl, Poppy, mk, 14"	175.00
Bowl, sculptured bluebirds & dragonflies, 12"	135.00
Box, mum on lid, topaz, 2-pc, 5½" dia	325.00
Charger, Water Lily, 13"	150.00
Charger, Wild Duck, Directorie Bl, mk, 13½"	245.00
Figurine, pigeon, frosted, rare, 4¼"	285.00
Shade, birds & fish in relief, lav, 5¾x3⅝"	275.00
Vase, mermaids, amber, 8"	1,200.00
Vase, Seasons, artist sgn, dtd 1940, 8½"	375.00
Vase, Thistle, dk olive gr, ovoid, 9½"	375.00

Vernon Kilns

Vernon Potteries Ltd. was established by Faye G. Bennison in Vernon, California, in 1931. The name was later changed to Vernon Kilns; until it closed in 1958, dinnerware and figurines were their primary products. Among its wares most sought after by collectors today are items designed by such famous artists as Rockwell Kent, Walt Disney, and Don Blanding. Authority Maxine Nelson has compiled a lovely book, *Versatile Vernon Kilns*, with full-color photos and current prices; you will find her address in the Directory under California.

Ash tray, Kentucky, red	12.00
Brown-Eyed Susan, bowl, 7"	8.00
Brown-Eyed Susan, bowl, 8¾"	9.00
Brown-Eyed Susan, chop plate, 12½"	12.00
Brown-Eyed Susan, creamer & sugar bowl	12.50
Brown-Eyed Susan, cup & saucer	8.00
Brown-Eyed Susan, plate, dinner; 10½"	8.00
Brown-Eyed Susan, plate, 6½"	2.50
Brown-Eyed Susan, plate, 9½"	5.00
Brown-Eyed Susan, shakers, pr	8.00
Fantasia, bowl, Satyr, #124	115.00
Fantasia, bowl, Sprite, hand decor, 3x10½"	175.00
Fantasia, bowl, Sprite, pk, #125, 1940	125.00
Fantasia, bowl, Winged Nymph, pk, #122, 2½x12"	125.00
Fantasia, figurine, Baby Pegasus, 1940	175.00
Fantasia, figurine, Centaurette, recumbent, #17	300.00
Fantasia, figurine, Donkey Unicorn, #16	250.00
Fantasia, figurine, Elephant, #25, 1940	250.00
Fantasia, figurine, Hippo in Tutu, #32	250.00
Fantasia, figurine, Nubian Centaurette, #23	300.00
Fantasia, figurine, Ostrich Ballerina, #28 or #29	600.00
Fantasia, figurine, Unicorn, sitting, #14	250.00
Fantasia, plate, 10½"	50.00
Fantasia, shakers, Mushrooms, 1941, pr	100.00
Fantasia, sugar bowl, w/lid, ind	25.00
Fantasia, vase, Goddess, wht goddess w/lt gr, #126	200.00
Fantasia, vase, Pegasus, bl, #127, 12x7½" dia	200.00
Gingham, bowl, chowder; tab hdls	7.00
Gingham, casserole, w/lid	30.00
Gingham, coffee decanter	17.50
Gingham, creamer & sugar bowl	12.00
Gingham, cup & saucer	7.00
Gingham, plate, 7½"	4.00
Gingham, plate, 9¾"	5.00
Gingham, platter, 14"	12.00
Gingham, tumbler	15.00
Homespun, bowl, chowder	7.00
Homespun, creamer	5.00
Homespun, cup & saucer	8.00
Homespun, pitcher, 2-qt	20.00
Homespun, plate, 6½"	2.50
Homespun, plate, 9¾"	5.00
Homespun, platter, 12½"	12.50
Homespun, saucer, demitasse	12.00

Lei Lani, chop plate, San Marino shape, Don Blanding, 14", $60.00.

Monterey, creamer & sugar bowl 12.00
Monterey, shakers, pr 10.00
Organdie, bowl, chowder; tab hdls 5.00
Organdie, bowl, vegetable; rnd, 8" 8.00
Organdie, bowl, vegetable; w/lid 25.00
Organdie, chop plate, 12" 10.00
Organdie, chop plate, 14" 11.00
Organdie, coffee carafe 18.00
Organdie, cup & saucer 6.00
Organdie, egg cup 7.50
Organdie, mug 10.00
Organdie, pitcher, iced beverage 18.00
Organdie, plate, bread & butter 2.00
Organdie, plate, dinner 6.00
Organdie, shakers, pr 6.00
Organdie, teapot, 6-cup 18.00
Plate, Bit of Old England 28.00
Plate, Eastern Star 12.00
Plate, Eisenhower 12.50
Plate, General MacArthur, bl 10.00

Plate, 'Memento from the President,' $50.00.

Plate, Music Master, 8½" 12.00
Plate, Santa Claus, Austin TX 20.00
Plate, Will Rogers 12.50
Salamina, plate, in pewter fr, 9½" 125.00
Salamina, plate, 10½" 95.00
Salamina, plate, 14" 150.00
Salamina, sugar bowl, w/lid, regular sz 35.00
Tam O'Shanter, bowl, vegetable; divided, oval 12.00
Tam O'Shanter, casserole, w/lid 25.00
Tam O'Shanter, creamer & sugar bowl 12.00
Tam O'Shanter, pitcher, water 25.00
Tam O'Shanter, platter, 12½" 10.00
Tam O'Shanter, soup, flat 8.00
Ultra California, bowl, bl/gr, 5¾" 6.00
Ultra California, sugar bowl, yel 6.00
Ultra California, tumbler, gr, 5¼" 12.50

Viennese Enameled Ware

Bottle, scent; bulbous top w/satyr masks, scenic frieze, 4" 550.00

Cup, cupid finial, courting scenes in lid/bow/ft, Bohm, 6" . . .1,200.00
Flask, perfume; mythological figures/cupids, dome lid, 2½" 400.00
Furniture, ladies/men in landscape, settee: 6" L, 6-pc set 800.00
Tankard, winged caryatid hdl, pineapple finial, scenic, 4" . . .1,200.00
Vase, gr top w/Nouveau florals, pk center, wht bottom, 5½" . . .195.00

Windmill music box, ca 1900, 7½", $500.00.

Villeroy and Boch

The firm of Villeroy and Boch, located in Mettlach, Germany, was brought into being by the 1841 merger of three German factories — the Wallerfangen factory, founded by Nicholas Villeroy in 1787; the Mettlach factory, founded by Jean Francis Boch 1809; and Boch's father's factory in Septfontaines, established in 1767. Villeroy and Boch produced many varieties of wares, including earthenware with printed underglaze designs which carried the well-known castle mark with the name 'Mettlach.' See also Mettlach.

Bowl, mixing; Bl Willow pattern, stack set, 4-pc, 4x8½" 350.00
Bust, Mozart, bsk, rare, 12" 525.00
Charger, Meissen castle on Elbe, 12" .175.00

Cup and saucer, Oriental motif, $50.00.

Plate, child's, 3-section, boy & sailboat, mk Saxony #6823 . . . . .55.00
Plate, old touring car w/passengers, 8½" 45.00
Tile, Oriental fish, 6" 40.00
Tureen, Nimrod, w/lid 65.00
Vase, floral, bl/gr on wht, #2964, 11" .65.00

Vistosa

Vistosa was produced from about 1938 through the early forties. It was Taylor, Smith, and Taylor's answer to the very successful Fiesta line of their nearby competitor, Homer Laughlin. Vistosa was made in four solid colors —mango red, cobalt blue, light green, and deep yellow. 'Pie crust' edges and a dainty five-petal flower molded into handles and lid finials made for a very attractive yet nevertheless commercially unsuccessful product.

Bowl, salad 95.00
Creamer & sugar bowl, w/lid 25.00
Cup & saucer 15.00
Gravy boat 75.00
Pitcher, red 35.00
Plate, gr, 6" 3.00
Plate, serving, yel, 11" 12.50
Plate, 9" 8.00
Shakers, pr 15.00

Teapot, red, $95.00.

Volkmar

Charles Volkmar established a workshop in Tremont, New York, in 1882. He produced artware decorated under the glaze in the manner of the early barbotine work done at the Haviland factory in Limoges, France. He relocated in 1888 in Menlo Park, New Jersey, and together with J.T. Smith established the Menlo Park Ceramic Company for the production of art tile. The partnership was dissolved in 1893. From 1895 until 1902, Volkmar located in Corona, New York, first under the name Volkmar Ceramic Company, later as Volkmar and Cory, and for the final six years as Crown Point. During the latter period he made art tile, blue underglaze Delft-type wares, colorful polychrome vases, etc. The Volkmar Kilns were established in 1903 in Metuchen, New Jersey, by Volkmar and his son. Wares were marked with various devices consisting of the Volkmar name, initials, or 'Crown Point Ware.'

Pitcher, gr matt w/brn flecks, hand thrown, 8½", +2 mugs 175.00

Plaque, Washington's headquarters, bl/wht, hanging, 11" 175.00
Vase, dk gr w/lt gr striations at rim, 4", EX 135.00
Vase, wht/brn/gray-bl/red thick drip, Oriental style, 12" 325.00

Volkstadt

The Volkstadt Porcelain Factory was established in Thuringia, Germany, about 1760. They continue to operate to the present, often marking their wares with the 'crossed hayfork' device used since the late 1700s.

Our advisor for this category is Jack Gunsualus; he is listed in the Directory under Michigan.

Figurine, classical maiden & lion, prof rpr, 5½" 175.00
Figurine, group of Serment d'Amour, bl mk, 12" 150.00
Figurine, Introduction, lady in chair+3 others, rpr, 29" 650.00
Figurine, man offers flowers to girl on plinth, 1870s, 6½" 275.00
Vase, boy & girl w/instruments, Baroque-shape top, mk, 10" . . .160.00

Wade

The Wade Group of Potteries originated in 1810 with a small pottery located in Burslem, England. This pottery, first owned by a Henry Hallen, was eventually taken over by George Wade who opened his own pottery (also in Burslem) in 1867.

Both the Hallen pottery and the original George Wade pottery specialized in ceramic and pottery items for the textile industry, then blooming in northern England. By the early 20th century, the two potteries amalgamated, taking the name of the George Wade Pottery, which in turn became George Wade & Son, Ltd., in 1919.

George Wade's brother, Albert, had interests in two potteries, A.J. Wade, Ltd., and Wade Heath & Co., Ltd., which manufactured decorative tiles, teapots, and other related dinnerware. In 1938 Wade Heath took over the Royal Victoria Pottery in Burslem and began producing a wide range of figurines and other decorative items.

In 1947 a new pottery was opened in Portadown, Northern Ireland, to produce both industrial ceramics and Irish porcelain giftware. In 1958 all the Wade potteries amalgamated, becoming the Wade Group of Potteries. The most recent addition to the group is Wade (PDM) Limited, a marketing arm for the advertising ware made by Wade Heath at the Royal Victoria Pottery. Wade (PDM) Limited was incorporated in 1969.

For those interested in learning more about Wade pottery, we recommend *The World of Wade* by Ian Warner and Mike Posgay; Mr. Warner is listed in the Directory under Canada.

Beefeater Gin, water jug, Wade (PDM) Ltd 22.00
Biscuit barrel, Lattice pattern, ca early 1960s 40.00
Blynkyn, figurine, 1951, 2¼" 28.00
Captain Morgan Rum boat, ash tray, Wade Regicor 35.00
Carnival, figurine, ca 1929, 8" 120.00
Championship dogs, ca 1975-1981, ea 20.00
Charles & Diana wedding, trinket box, 1981 . . . . .20.00
Dog, pipe rest, ca 1973-1981, ea 18.00
Dr Foster, Red Rose Tea, ca 1971-1979 . . . . .6.00
Gingerbread Man, Red Rose Tea, ca 1971-1979 . . . . .18.00
Leprechaun, pin tray, ca 1956-1986, ea 12.00
Mother Goose, Red Rose Tea, ca 1971-1979 . . . . .5.00
Nod, figurine, 1951, 2½" 28.00
Queen's jubilee, Bell's whiskey decanter, 1986 . . . . .95.00
Romance plates, ca 1951-1960, ea 24.00
Snow White & the Seven Dwarfs, ca 1981-1986, set 180.00
Tankard, Wade (Ireland) Ltd, 1-pt 28.00
Teapot, Bramble pattern, ca 1950+ 35.00

Tom & Jerry, figurine, ca 1973-1979, pr 95.00
Viking Boat, posy bowl, ca 1959-1965 ....18.00
Wynkyn, figurine, 1951, 2¾" 28.00

Springtime, George Wade & Son, Ltd., 11", circa 1929, $145.00.

Walrath

Frederick Walrath was a studio potter who worked from around the turn of the century until his death in 1920. He was located in Rochester, New York, until 1918 when he became associated with the Newcomb Pottery in New Orleans, Louisiana.

Bowl, crouched figural nude in center, pea gr matt, 6x7" 300.00
Flower frog, 2 nude girls, lt gr, 8"; +flat brn bowl, 8" 550.00
Mug, brn, unmk, 3" 75.00
Plate, abstract trees, rust on brn matt, 6" 200.00
Vase, buds & leaves HP on gr, cylindrical, 4¾" 750.00
Vase, floral, muted colors, crystalline on gr, 6½" 650.00

Walter, A.

Almaric Walter was employed from 1904 through 1914 at Verreries Artistiques des Freres Daum in Nancy, France. After 1919 he opened his own business where he continued to make the same type of quality objects d'art in pate-de-verre glass as he had earlier. His pieces are signed A. Walter, Nancy H. Berge Sc.

Atomizer, berries & leaves, red on rose 1,000.00
Bird, beak aloft, on pine cone branch, yel/mustard, 3" 800.00
Bird, head cocked to side, ice bl/azure on gr base, 3¾" 900.00
Bookends, squirrel w/nut in paws, H Berge, 5", pr, NM 5,500.00
Bowl, beetles on base/lid, rust/gr/yel, H Berge, rstr, 7" 1,500.00
Clock case, reclining nude on stepped base, rnd top, 5½" 3,500.00
Dish, pine cones on sides/as lid finial, turq/bl, 3¼" dia 2,250.00
Figure, Buddha, sitting X-legged, molded sgn, 3" 770.00
Figure, cupid seated, flower-strewn ground, yel/gr/rust, 4" ...1,900.00
Figure, woman in cloak, lime/emerald, 8", NM 4,000.00
Paperweight, crayfish on wavy mound, rust/blk on yel, 4½" ..3,000.00
Paperweight, lizard relief, rust/blk on gr/bl, 1¾" dia 900.00
Paperweight, snail on hex base, amber/yel/gr/brn, 3" L, NM .2,500.00
Pendant, beetle relief, mottled rose on ochre/gold, sgn, 2½" .1,500.00
Pendant, bumblebee relief on gray, sgn AW/N & B, 1¾" 800.00

Pendant, locust, brn/blk on streaky gray oval, Berge, 1½" 600.00
Plaque, head of girl, hands in praying position, 4x3" 900.00
Plate, striated amber w/bl bell rim, 9½" 850.00
Tile, hermit crab/shells on hexagon, gray/purple/yel, 6" 2,250.00
Tray, beetle, bl/gr on gray, H Berge, 3¾" L 1,300.00
Tray, bumblebee in 1 of 3 corners, H Berge, 4½" 2,750.00
Tray, conch at side, gr/yel/brn, 9½" L 4,900.00
Tray, frog on leafy ground, olive/bl, 7" L 5,500.00
Tray, frog on lily pad, gr/turq/yel, 6¼" L 4,950.00
Tray, lg butterfly on stylized waves, H Berge, 8" dia 7,000.00
Tray, lg hermit crab on yel elongated oval, 11½" 11,000.00
Tray, lg lizard aside orange/yel tray, 6¾" L 4,900.00
Vase, floriform, shaded olive on salmon ft, H Berge, 6½" 4,000.00

Figure of a duck, turquoise and green, 7" long, $5,000.00.

Warwick

The Warwick China Company operated in Wheeling, West Virginia, from 1887 until 1951. They produced both hand-painted and decaled plates, vases, teapots, coffeepots, pitchers, bowls, and jardinieres featuring lovely florals or portraits of beautiful ladies done in luscious colors. Backgrounds were usually blendings of brown and beige, but ivory was also used (and on rare occasion, pink).

Various marks were employed, all of which incorporate the Warwick name. For a more thorough study of the subject, we recommend *Why Not Warwick* and *Warwick China Guide*, both by our advisor, Donald C. Hoffmann; his address can be found in the Directory under Illinois.

Mug, Dickens character, $80.00.

Decorative Plates

Bulldog, circle in brn, Champion Ambassador, IOGA, 9½" ...135.00
Bulldog, circle in brn, Champion Bromley Crib, IOGA, 9½" ..120.00
Bulldog, circle in brn, Champion Katerfelldo, IOGA, 9½" 145.00
Bulldog, circle in brn, Champion Rodney Stone, IOGA, 9½" ..125.00
Elk, crescent in brn, BPOE, IOGA, 9½" 100.00
Fisherman, circle in brn, pipe left side, IOGA, 9½" 125.00

Fisherman, circle in brn, pipe right side, IOGA, 9½" 130.00
Friar, circle in brn, w/wine bottle, IOGA, 9½" 120.00
Friar, crescent in brn, w/flowers, IOGA, 9½" 115.00
Friar, crescent in brn, w/glass or violin, IOGA, 9½", ea 120.00
Friar, crescent in brn, w/newspaper or mug, IOGA, 9½", ea . . .125.00
Friar, crescent in red, w/newspaper, IOGA, 9½" 130.00
Indian, crescent in brn, IOGA, 9½" .135.00
Indian, crescent in brn, w/full war paint, IOGA, 9½" 145.00
Monk, circle in brn, w/red cap looking left, IOGA, 9½" 125.00

Spirit Jugs

Brn, Blk boy w/banjo, IOGA, 6" 195.00
Brn, Dickens character w/guitar, IOGA, 6" 185.00
Brn, friar w/wine glass, IOGA, 6" 190.00
Brn, Indian w/braid, IOGA, 6" 195.00
Brn, Indian w/full headdress, IOGA, 6" 190.00
Brn, monk w/red cap, IOGA, 6" 160.00

Vase, Albany, brn w/floral, 7" 130.00
Vase, Albany, matt w/beechnuts, 7" 150.00
Vase, Alexandria, brn w/floral, 12½" 285.00
Vase, Carnation, brn w/poppies, 10½" 85.00
Vase, Carnation, brn w/roses, 10½" .95.00
Vase, Carnation, gr w/floral, 10½" .115.00
Vase, Carnation, pk w/portrait, 10½" 225.00
Vase, Clytie, red w/poinsettia, 6¾" 230.00
Vase, Clytie, red w/portrait, 6¾" 250.00
Vase, Cuba, brn w/floral, 7¼" 215.00
Vase, Dahlia, brn w/pine cones, 8¼" 135.00
Vase, Dahlia, red w/portrait, 8¼" 165.00
Vase, Dainty, red w/portrait, 4¼" 200.00
Vase, Gem, brn w/floral, 12" 110.00
Vase, Gem, matt w/beechnut, 12" .120.00
Vase, Grecian, brn w/floral, 8" 115.00
Vase, Grecian, red w/portrait, 8" 130.00
Vase, Helene, brn w/floral, 12" 125.00
Vase, Hyacinth, brn w/floral, 11½" .95.00
Vase, Hyacinth, brn w/portrait, 11½" 155.00
Vase, Hyacinth, red w/poinsettia, 11½" 120.00
Vase, Iris, brn w/floral, 9¾" 125.00
Vase, Iris, charcoal w/floral, 9¾" 135.00
Vase, Iris, matt w/beechnuts, 9¾" .130.00
Vase, Iris, red w/poinsettia, 9¾" 135.00
Vase, Lily, brn w/florals, 9½" 140.00
Vase, Lily, charcoal w/floral, 9½" .185.00
Vase, Louise, brn w/floral, rare, 9" 215.00
Vase, Magnolia, brn w/floral, 10½" 130.00
Vase, Magnolia, brn w/portrait, 10½" 105.00
Vase, Magnolia, charcoal w/nude, 10½" 195.00
Vase, Magnolia, wht w/birds, 10½" 185.00
Vase, Maria, brn w/floral, 10½" 185.00
Vase, Maria, brn w/portrait, 10½" .215.00
Vase, Maria, charcoal w/nude, 10½" 300.00
Vase, Maria, pk w/portrait, 10½" 300.00
Vase, Narcis, brn w/pine cones, 8½" 175.00
Vase, Narcis, brn w/portrait, 8½" .195.00
Vase, Narcis, charcoal w/nude, 6¾" 295.00
Vase, Narcis, charcoal w/portrait, 6¾" 295.00
Vase, Narcis, matt w/portrait, 8½" 270.00
Vase, Narcis, wht w/ducks, 6¾" 265.00
Vase, Narcis, wht w/sea gulls, 8½" 255.00
Vase, Oriental, brn w/floral, rare, 11" 165.00
Vase, Pansy, brn w/floral, 4" 85.00

Vase, Pansy, red w/poinsettia, 4" 100.00
Vase, Peerless, brn w/portrait, 9½" 150.00
Vase, Peerless, gr matt w/portrait, 9½" 165.00
Vase, Peerless, pk w/portrait, 9½" .295.00
Vase, Penn, brn w/floral, 9½" 125.00
Vase, Penn, matt w/no decor, very rare, 9½" 210.00
Vase, Penn, pk w/portrait, 9½" 295.00
Vase, Queen, charcoal w/semi-nude, 12" 200.00
Vase, Queen, wht w/birds, 12" 185.00
Vase, Regency, brn w/floral, 11½" .185.00
Vase, Regency, charcoal w/floral, 11½" 175.00
Vase, Roberta, brn w/monk, 10" 175.00
Vase, Roberta, red w/fisherman, 10" 200.00
Vase, Roman, wht w/floral, 11" 170.00
Vase, Rosalie, brn w/floral, 9¾" 175.00
Vase, Rosalie, charcoal w/floral, 9¾" 185.00
Vase, Rosalie, pk w/portrait, 9¾" .320.00
Vase, Rosalie, red w/portrait, 9¾" .220.00
Vase, Rose, brn w/floral, 8" 95.00
Vase, Rose, brn w/poinsettia, 8" 135.00
Vase, Rose, brn w/portrait, 8" 145.00
Vase, Rose, red w/poinsettia, 8" 135.00
Vase, Royal I, brn w/floral, rare, 10" 195.00
Vase, Senator I, brn w/floral, 13½" 190.00
Vase, Senator I, brn w/portrait, 13½" 220.00
Vase, Senator II, brn w/floral, 11½" 140.00
Vase, Senator II, brn w/portrait, 11½" 180.00
Vase, Senator II, gr matt w/beechnuts, 11½" 155.00
Vase, Thelma, brn w/floral, 9¼" 135.00
Vase, Thelma, red w/portrait, 9¼" .155.00
Vase, Victoria, brn w/floral, 8¼" 125.00
Vase, Victoria, pk w/portrait, 8¼" .285.00
Vase, Violet, brn w/floral, 4" 100.00
Vase, Violet, matt w/beechnut, 4" .185.00
Vase, Violet, red w/poinsettia, 4" 120.00
Vase, Windsor, pk w/portrait, 9¼" .230.00

Wash Sets

Before the days of running water, bedrooms were standardly equipped with a wash bowl and pitcher as a matter of necessity. A 'toilet set' was comprised of the pitcher and bowl, toothbrush holder, covered commode, soap dish, shaving dish, and mug. Some sets were even more elaborate. Through everyday usage, the smaller items were often broken, and today it is unusual to find a complete set.

Porcelain sets decorated with florals, fruits, or scenics were produced abroad by Limoges in France; some were imported from Germany and England. During the last quarter of the 1800s and until after the turn of the century, American-made toilet sets were manufactured in abundance. Tin and graniteware sets were also made.

Bl Willow, Wedgwood, ca 1800, 12" pitcher & bowl, NM 800.00
Festoon, med bl transfer, Wedgwood, bowl+pitcher, EX 125.00
Homer Laughlin, pk & yel roses on bl, gold trim, 2-pc 160.00
Knowles-Taylor-Knowles, wht w/gold, child's, bowl+pitcher 50.00
Old Paris, floral & scrollwork panels on wht, bowl+pitcher 550.00
Peacocks w/gold on cream, 7-pc 425.00
Rosetti, Royal Doulton, bowl+pitcher 210.00

Watch Fobs

Watch fobs have been popular since the last quarter of the 19th century. They were often made by retail companies to advertise their products. Souvenir, commemorative, and political fobs were also produced. All are popular collectibles today. Beware of modern restrikes and reproductions.

Adams Road machinery, road grader	45.00
Allis Chalmers, bronze	16.00
Alpha Cement, silver w/red letters	32.00
American Legion, Akron OH, tire/Indian, bronze, 1939	15.00
American Racing Pigeon Union, Milwaukee, 1928	35.00
Armour, cow's head, silver color	30.00
Atkins Saws, silver color	20.00
Avery, bulldog, brass	65.00
Babe Ruth, scorekeeper on bk	110.00
Baltimore MD, Yacht Club, brass, 1927	30.00
Bartlett, Shots & Wilson Millwork, Pittsburgh, mc enamel	18.00
Be Wise, owl form, silver color	15.00
Boy Scout, boy w/bugle, oval	45.00
Broderick & Bascom Ropes	45.00
Buffalo Pitts, pin/clicker, EX	40.00
Buick Motor Cars, NM	80.00
Business Assoc, Chicago, bronze w/bl & red enamel	15.00
Cambria Spring Co	40.00
Carborundum, Niagara Falls, Indian face, bronze	4.00
Case Centennial, tractor & plow	38.00
Case Threshing Machines, eagle on globe	65.00
Caterpillar, brass	80.00
Caterpillar D-7	20.00
Cherry Smash	140.00
Chew White's Yucatan Gum, celluloid, EX	40.00
Chi-Nomel Paint, Chinese boy	40.00
Clark's Pure Rye Whiskey, SP brass	4.00
Columbia Brewing, Detroit	38.00
Dayton 1935, airplane, gold color	17.00
DeLaval, porc	85.00
Drovers Bank, steer head	28.00
Dry Farming Soil Expo, silver, 1913	22.00
Dupont Workers, celluloid photo, #5391	24.00
Euclid Earth Moving Equipment	22.00
Fairmont Creamery, brass, 40 Yrs of Service in center, 1924	13.00
FC Ayers Mercantile, Denver CO, ears of corn	40.00
Florida Summerland, oranges, silver w/bl enamel ring	13.00
George Washington Bicentennial, 1732-1932, lead type	15.00
Golden Sheaf Baking Powder, silver color w/bl/gold celluloid	14.00
Good Whiskey, dog in center, silver	8.00
Goodyear Tire, bl/gr enamel on silver, NM	75.00
Gun in holster figural, USA emblem, 2½"	45.00
Gyro-Flow, Ingersoll-Rand, wht metal	45.00
Harris Pump Co, brass, very worn, rare	25.00
Heinz Pure Foods Products, '57' in center	28.00
Hercules Buggy, IN presentation	275.00
Home of Northwestern Business College, blk/wht celluloid	12.00
Howald's Cigar Cutter, silver w/floral design, 1909	12.00
Hunter-Trader-Trapper	140.00
Hupmobile, bl & wht porc	200.00
Ice Man, bronze, convex shape	11.00
IHC, flat letters, advertising on bk	40.00
Internat'l Harvester, bronze w/red & blk enamel	15.00
Internat'l Harvester, bucking bronco	100.00
Internat'l Harvester, dbl globe	100.00
Iowa State Seal	12.00
John Deere, deer & plow, brass, EX	90.00
John Deere 450 Crawler	60.00
Kellogg's Corn Flakes, box form, brass	50.00

King Booster, bronze w/blk & wht celluloid woman/trumpet	24.00
LaPlant Chocolate, earth mover	45.00
Leisy Brewing, porc & brass	100.00
Lexington, Heart of the Blue Grass, 1946, bronze	15.00
Lima 1933, pnt gold letters on gr	18.00
Lookout Mountain	35.00
Lycoming Foundry & Machine Co, brass, blk/bl enamel center	25.00
Mack, bulldog in center, gold color	10.00
Main Belting, grain elevator	35.00
Marmon Automobile	35.00
Master Photo Finishers of America, silver color	25.00
National Fad 5¢ Cigars, silver color	13.00
Norse American Centennial, sailing ship, 1925	60.00
NY to Paris, w/compass	65.00
Ohio Wool Grower's Co-op Assoc, sheep's head, brass	16.00
Pepsi Cola	150.00
Phoenix Brewery, Buffalo NY, fancy w/eagle, NM	115.00
Polarine Oil, polar bear, wht metal	65.00
Poll Parrot Shoes, color	35.00
Pyott Foundry Co, pulleys, brass	10.00
Read Fertilizers, porc, EX	22.00
Red Diamond Overalls, celluloid on fiber, M	65.00
Red Man, coal bucket form, bronze w/blk enamel coal, 1914	15.00
Red Man Tobacco, worn pnt on brass	35.00
Red Owl Coal, 50th Year	40.00
Reed Roller Bits, bulldog & bit	55.00
Sanico Stoves, brass	65.00
Sawyer Tools, silver color	30.00
Schotten's Cab-E-Log	45.00
Scoop Mobile, Model LD-8, bronze	20.00
Smith Oil & Gas Separator	85.00
Starrett Tools, silver color	20.00
Statue of Liberty	30.00
Sun Insurance	30.00
Theodore Roosevelt, brass, rectangular, 1904	45.00
Tiger Brand Wire Rope, silver color, USS logo, M	25.00
Trinity Portland Cement, red enamel	45.00
Union of Mine, Mill & Melter Workers, brass, 1916	20.00
United Hatters of N America, hat form, gold color	12.00
University of IA, brass	45.00
US Horseshoe Co, Erie PA, horseshoe form, gold	16.00
Utica NY, Trust Deposit Bank, 1927	24.00
Wallis Tractor	60.00
Washburn-Crosby Foods, Gold Medal, celluloid in shield	60.00
WD Horard, Hoard's Dairyman, wht metal	35.00
Western Union Life, hand holding woman/child, gold color	18.00
Wolf Milling & Flour Machinery	28.00
Worcester Salt	45.00

Watch Stands

Watch stands were decorative articles designed with a hook from which to hang a watch. Some displayed the watch as the face of a grandfather clock or as part of an interior scene with figures in period costumes and contemporary furnishings. They were popular products of Staffordshire potters and silver companies as well.

Bl overlay dish w/in Fr ormolu fr, hanger at top, 7¾"	145.00
Chalkware, alcove w/bird, arched top, twist columns, 12"	1,300.00
Cherry, box w/heart cutout, urn atop, 1800s, 9½"	700.00
Prisoner of War, bone gazebo w/arch roof, 1820s, 10x7"	950.00
Silverplate, owl, Hartford	135.00
Wood, wall mt, cvd from 1 pc, crest/rnd glass panel, 6x4"	500.00

Pink lustre and enamel, tall-case clock with allegorical figures, ca 1820, EX, $700.00.

Watches

First made in the 1500s in Germany, early watches were actually small clocks, suspended from the wrist or belt. By 1700 they had become the approximate shape and size we know today. The first watches produced in America were made in 1810. The well-known Waltham Watch Company was established in 1850, and their inexpensive 'Waterbury' models were produced by the thousands.

Open-face and hunting-case watches of the 1890s were solid gold or gold-filled and were often elaborately decorated in several colors of gold. Gold watches became a status symbol in this decade and were worn by both men and women on chains with fobs or jeweled slides. Ladies sometimes fastened them to their clothing with pins often set with jewels. The chatelaine watch was worn at the waist, only one of several items such as scissors, coin purses, or needle cases, each attached by small chains. During this period, movements and cases could be purchased separately, so inexpensive cases may sometimes be found containing well-jeweled movements, or the contrary may be true.

Most turn-of-the-century watch cases were gold-filled, and these are plentiful today. 18k cases are rare, and 22k cases are very valuable. Sterling cases, though interest in them is on the increase, are not in great demand. For character-related watches, see Personalities.

Key:

adj — adjusted	k/s — key set
brg — bridge plate design	k/w — key wind
d/s — double sunk dial	l/s — lever set
fbd — finger bridge design	mvt — movement
g/f — gold-filled	o/f — open face
g/j/s — gold jewel setting	p/s — pendant set
h/c — hunter case	r/g/p — rolled gold plate
HCI#P — heat, cold,	s — size
isochronism & position	s/s — single sunk dial
adjusted	s/w — stem wind
j — jewel	w/g/f— white gold filled
k — karat	y/g/f — yellow gold-fill

Am Watch Co, 10s, 15j, 20-yr, y/g/f, h/c, s/s 155.00
Am Watch Co, 12s, 15j, #1894, 14k, h/c, Colonial 325.00
Am Watch Co, 14s, 13j, #1884, 14k, h/c 1,150.00
Am Watch Co, 16s, 11-15j, #1872, p/s, Park Road 135.00
Am Watch Co, 16s, 15-16j, #1899, h/c 175.00
Am Watch Co, 16s, 15j, #1899, s/w, silveroid 70.00
Am Watch Co, 16s, 16j, #1872, 5-min, coin silver, Repeater ..3,000.00
Am Watch Co, 16s, 17j, #1888, Railroader, rare, NM 450.00
Am Watch Co, 16s, 17j, #1899, s/w .100.00
Am Watch Co, 16s, 17j, royal nickel case, d/s 80.00
Am Watch Co, 16s, 17j, 2-tone, Railroad King 325.00
Am Watch Co, 16s, 19j, #1899, l/s, o/f, HCI5P, Crescent St . .135.00
Am Watch Co, 16s, 19j, #1908, o/f, adj, s/s, RR, Vanguard 175.00
Am Watch Co, 16s, 21j, #1872, 14k, ¾-mvt, rare 1,950.00
Am Watch Co, 16s, 23j, g/j/s, brg, HCI5P, gold train 1,000.00
Am Watch Co, 18s, #1877, k/w, Excelsior 140.00
Am Watch Co, 18s, #1887, k/w, Excelsior 140.00
Am Watch Co, 18s, 11j, #1857, h/c, k/w, y/g/f, s/s, Ellery, EX . .150.00
Am Watch Co, 18s, 11j, #1857, k/w, 1st run, PS Barlett 575.00
Am Watch Co, 18s, 15j, #1877, k/w, RE Robbins 275.00
Am Watch Co, 18s, 15j, silverine, o/f, k/w, Fogg's Pat 125.00
Am Watch Co, 18s, 17j, #1892, HCI5P, Canadian Railway . . .400.00
Am Watch Co, 18s, 17j, #1892, o/f, y/g/f, Railroader, rare 850.00
Am Watch Co, 18s, 17j, #1892, s/w, h/c, PS Bartlett 120.00
Am Watch Co, 18s, 17j, 25-yr, o/f, y/g/f, s/s, PS Bartlett 185.00
Am Watch Co, 18s, 19j, #1883, Crescent Street 350.00
Am Watch Co, 18s, 21j, #1892, o/f, y/g/f, d/s, Crescent Str 150.00
Am Watch Co, 18s, 21j, #1892, s/w, Appleton, Tracy & Co . . .225.00
Am Watch Co, 18s, 7j, #1857, k/w, CT Parker, scarce 1,400.00
Am Watch Co, 18s, 7j, #1877, s/w, Franklin 100.00
Am Watch Co, 18s, 7j, #1883, Pioneer 80.00
Auburndale Watch Co, 18s, 7j, k/w, l/s, Lincoln 600.00
Aurora Watch Co, 18s, k/w, h/c 375.00
Aurora Watch Co, 18s, 11j, o/f, k/w, h/c 350.00
Ball (Elgin), 18s, 16j, o/f, Commercial Standard 500.00
Ball (Hamilton), 16s, 17j, #974, o/f, l/s, g/f, nickel plates 200.00
Ball (Hamilton), 18s, 19j, #999, o/f, l/s, g/f, HCI5P 475.00
Ball (Hampden), 18s, 17j, o/f, adj, RR, Superior Grade 1,500.00
Ball (Seth Thomas), 18s, 17j, #3, o/f, l/s, g/j/s, scarce 3,400.00
Ball (Waltham), 16s, 19j, o/f, Offical Standard 250.00
Ball (Waltham), 16s, 19j, 14k, o/f, l/s 600.00
Columbus Watch Co, 18s, 11-15j, k/w, k/s 425.00
Columbus Watch Co, 18s, 11j, o/f, silveroid case 100.00
Columbus Watch Co, 18s, 15j, o/f, l/s 160.00
Columbus Watch Co, 18s, 15j, 18k, k/w, k/s 1,300.00
Columbus Watch Co, 18s, 19j, g/j/s, h/c, 2-tone, grade #105 .1,750.00
Columbus Watch Co, 6s, 15j, 18k, g/j/s, nickel plate 575.00
Cornell, 18s, 15j, s/w, CM Cady 450.00
Dudley, 12s, #3, 14k, o/f, display case, Mason's 2,400.00
Elgin, 10s, g/f, h/c, mc case 325.00
Elgin, 10s, h/c, k/w, k/s, s/s, Gail Borden 150.00
Elgin, 12s, 15j, 14k, h/c 425.00
Elgin, 12s, 17j, g/f, h/c, Lord Elgin 90.00
Elgin, 12s, 17j, 14k, GM Wheeler 350.00
Elgin, 12s, 21j, g/f, h/c, Lord Elgin 175.00
Elgin, 12s, 7j, 14k, EX 200.00
Elgin, 16s, 10k, y/g/f, g/j/s, Raymond 225.00
Elgin, 16s, 11j, g/f, h/c 125.00
Elgin, 16s, 15j, doctor's, 4th model, 14k, 2nd sweep hand 650.00
Elgin, 16s, 15j, 14k, h/c 600.00
Elgin, 16s, 17j, g/j/s, s/w, o/f, BW Raymond 160.00
Elgin, 16s, 17j, 14k, h/c 600.00
Elgin, 16s, 19j, g/j/s, brg, h/c, grade #145, scarce 1,300.00
Elgin, 16s, 21j, g/f, h/c 460.00

Elgin, 16s, 21j, g/f, 3 fbd, grade #72-91, scarce 600.00
Elgin, 16s, 21j, g/j/s, 3 fbd 325.00
Elgin, 16s, 21j, o/f, y/g/f, l/s, RR, Father Time 240.00
Elgin, 16s, 21j, 14k, 3 fbd, Convertible 1,400.00
Elgin, 16s, 23j, g/f, 3 fbd, Convertible 800.00
Elgin, 17s, k/w, orig case, Leader, grade #59 ....165.00
Elgin, 17s, k/w, silveroid 70.00
Elgin, 18s, 11j, g/f, h/c, k/w, gilded, MG Ogden 110.00
Elgin, 18s, 15j, g/f, mc dial, Solar W Co 150.00
Elgin, 18s, 15j, o/f, d/s, RR, silveroid case, Raymond 125.00
Elgin, 18s, 15j, y/g/f, l/s, s/w, box hinge case 425.00
Elgin, 18s, 15j, 14k, g/f, k/w, k/s, h/c, HL Culver 800.00
Elgin, 18s, 17j, silveroid, BW Raymond 125.00
Elgin, 18s, 21j, g/f, h/c, l/s, s/w 135.00
Elgin, 18s, 21j, o/f, y/g/f, Father Time 200.00
Elgin, 18s, 23j, y/g/f, 5-position, RR, Veritas 325.00
Elgin, 6s, 11j, 14k, h/c 275.00
Elgin, 6s, 15j, 20-yr, y/g/f, h/c, s/s 150.00
Elgin, 6s, 7j, 10k, h/c 210.00
Hamilton, #3992B, 16s, 22j, HCI6P 265.00
Hamilton, #904, 12s, 21j, g/j/s, brg, HCI5P, dbl roller 150.00
Hamilton, #910, 12s, 17j, 20-yr, y/g/f, o/f, s/s 125.00
Hamilton, #912, 12s, 17j, adj, dbl roller, ¾-mvt 125.00
Hamilton, #918, presentation, 14k w/20 diamonds, orig box ...450.00
Hamilton, #920, 12s, 23j, o/f, w/g/f 225.00
Hamilton, #922MP, 12s, 18k case 800.00
Hamilton, #925, 18s, 17j, w/g/f, h/c, s/s, l/s 185.00
Hamilton, #928, 18s, 15j, o/f, y/g/f, s/s 180.00
Hamilton, #933, 18s, 16j, h/c, nickel plate 825.00
Hamilton, #938, 18s, 17j, 10k, y/g/f, adj, NAW Co Case 850.00
Hamilton, #940, 18s, 21j, nickel plate, coin silver, o/f 160.00
Hamilton, #946, 18s, 23j, o/f, g/j/s, Extra 700.00
Hamilton, #947, 23j, h/c, orig/sgn, EX 5,500.00
Hamilton, #950, 16s, 23j, o/f, y/g/f, l/s, sgn d/s 400.00
Hamilton, #965, 16s, 17j, p/s, h/c, brg, scarce 825.00
Hamilton, #972, 16s, 17j, o/f, y/g/f, g/j/s, d/s, l/s, adj ..125.00
Hamilton, #974, 16s, 17j, 20-yr, y/g/f, o/f, s/s 140.00
Hamilton, #992, 16s, 21j, o/f, y/g/f, adj, d/s, dbl roller ..185.00
Hamilton, #992B, 16s, 21j, l/s, o/f, ¾-mvt 225.00

Hampden, 18s, 23-jewel, Special Railway, $275.00.

Hampden, 12s, 17j, HCI4P, thin model, Aviator 70.00
Hampden, 12s, 7j, s/w, o/f 40.00
Hampden, 16s, 17j, h/c, s/w 200.00
Hampden, 16s, 17j, o/f, adj 125.00
Hampden, 16s, 21j, g/j/s, HCI5P/nickel plate, Dueber, ¾-mvt .150.00

Hampden, 16s, 21j, o/f, adj, dbl roller, HCI5P, New Railway ..175.00
Hampden, 16s, 7j, gilded, nickel plate, ¾-mvt 80.00
Hampden, 18s, 15j, k/w, Hayward 175.00
Hampden, 18s, 15j, k/w, mk on mvt, Railway 850.00
Hampden, 18s, 15j, s/w, gilded, JC Perry 100.00
Hampden, 18s, 16j, gilded, damaskeened, Dueber 125.00
Hampden, 18s, 17j, adj, h/c, Dueber Grand 150.00
Hampden, 18s, 17j, nickel plate, Tramway Special 200.00
Hampden, 18s, 19j, g/j/s, h/c, adj, Dueber 475.00
Hampden, 18s, 21j, g/j/s, h/c, HCI5P, New Railway 300.00
Hampden, 18s, 21j, o/f, y/g/f, d/s, HCI5P, l/s, N Am Railway ..200.00
Hampden, 18s, 23j, y/g/f, d/s, adj, New Railway 300.00
Hampden, 18s, 23j, 14k, h/c, Special Railway 775.00
Hampden, 18s, 7-11j, k/w, gilded, Springfield 95.00
Howard, 12s, 23j, 14k, h/c, brg, HCI5P, Series 8 ....625.00
Howard, 18s, 17j, 25-yr, y/g/f, o/f 250.00
Illinois, 0s, 7j, 10k, l/s, h/c 250.00
Illinois, 12s, 19j, y/g/f, o/f, d/s dial, Elite 110.00
Illinois, 16s, 17j, adj, ¾-mvt 150.00
Illinois, 16s, 17j, o/f, d/s, HCI5P, Bunn, EX 225.00
Illinois, 16s, 17j, o/f, Railway King 250.00
Illinois, 16s, 19j, o/f, y/g/f, d/s, 60-hr, Sangamo Special ..660.00
Illinois, 16s, 21j, g/j/s, HCI6P, Burlington, scarce 795.00
Illinois, 16s, 21j, g/j/s, o/f, HCI6P, Ariston 600.00
Illinois, 16s, 21j, h/c, Sangamo Special 1,000.00
Illinois, 16s, 21j, o/f, d/s, Santa Fe Special 300.00
Illinois, 16s, 21j, o/f, y/g/f, s/s, Bunn Special 225.00
Illinois, 16s, 23j, o/f, d/s, RR, heavy decor, Bunn Special ..400.00
Illinois, 18s, 11j, #1, k/w, Alleghany 140.00
Illinois, 18s, 11j, #3, o/f, s/w, l/s, Comet 85.00
Illinois, 18s, 11j, Forest City 135.00
Illinois, 18s, 15j, #1, adj, k/w, k/s, Stuart 900.00
Illinois, 18s, 15j, #1, h/c, y/g/f, k/w, gilt, Bunn 750.00
Illinois, 18s, 15j, #1, k/w, h/c, Bunn 950.00
Illinois, 18s, 15j, k/w, k/s, gilt, Railway Regulator 600.00
Illinois, 18s, 15j, s/w, silveroid 70.00
Illinois, 18s, 17j, g/j/s, adj, B&O RR Special 600.00
Illinois, 18s, 17j, o/f, d/s, adj, silveroid case, Lakeshore ..135.00
Illinois, 18s, 17j, o/f, s/w, 5th pinion, Miller 300.00
Illinois, 18s, 17j, s/w, nickel plate, coin silver, Bunn ..185.00
Illinois, 18s, 21j, g/j/s, adj, B&O RR Special 800.00
Illinois, 18s, 21j, g/j/s, g/f, o/f, HCI5P, A Lincoln 325.00
Illinois, 18s, 21j, g/j/s, HCI5P, Ben Franklin USA 1,400.00
Illinois, 18s, 21j, 14k, g/j/s, h/c, HCI5P, Bunn Special ..1,000.00
Illinois, 18s, 24j, g/j/s, adj, Chesapeake & Ohio Special ..2,250.00
Illinois, 18s, 26j, Penn Special, orig case 7,000.00
Illinois, 18s, 7j, #3, Interior 110.00
Illinois, 18s, 7j, #3, silveroid, America 90.00
Illinois, 18s, 9-11j, o/f, k/w, s/s, silveroid case, Hoyt ..110.00
Illinois, 8s, 13j, ¾-mvt, Rose LeLand, scarce 240.00
Ingersoll, 16s, 7j, wht base metal, Reliance 55.00
Lancaster, 18s, 7j, o/f, k/w, k/s, eng case, New Era 125.00
Marion US, 18s, h/c, k/w, k/s, ¾-plate, Asa Fuller 375.00
Marion US, 18s, 15j, nickel plate, h/c, s/w, Henry Randel ..360.00
Melrose Watch Co, 18s, 7j, k/w, k/s 450.00
New York Watch Co, 15j, wolf's teeth wind 1,500.00
New York Watch Co, 18s, 7j, k/w, George Sam Rice 175.00
Rockford, 16s, 17j, brg, HCI3P, dbl roller 175.00
Rockford, 16s, 21j, #515, y/g/f 200.00
Rockford, 16s, 21j, o/f, g/j/s, HCI5P, grade #537, scarce ..650.00
Rockford, 18s, 15j, o/f, k/w, silver case 100.00
Rockford, 18s, 17j, silveroid w/mc dial, fancy mvt/hands ..225.00
Rockford, 18s, 21j, o/f, Railway King 550.00
Rockford, 18s, 7j, silveroid, o/f, k/w 100.00

Seth Thomas, 18s, 17j, #2, g/j/s, adj, Henry Molineux 550.00
Seth Thomas, 18s, 17j, Edgemere 125.00
Seth Thomas, 18s, 21j, g/j/s, HCI5P, dbl roller 395.00
Seth Thomas, 18s, 7j, ¾-mvt, bk: eagle/Liberty model 125.00
South Bend, 12s, 21j, HCI5P, dbl roller, grade #431 . . . . .110.00
South Bend, 12s, 21j, orig o/f, d/s, Studebaker 200.00
South Bend, 18s, 21j, g/j/s, h/c, full plate, grade #328 . . . . . . .425.00
South Bend, 18s, 21j, 14k, h/c 750.00
Swiss, h/c, 5-min, Repeater 375.00

Waterford

The Waterford Glass Company operated in Ireland from the late 1700s until 1851 when the factory closed. One hundred years later (in 1951) another Waterford glassworks was instituted that produced glass similar to the 18th century wares — crystal glass, usually with cut decoration. Today, Waterford is a generic term referring to the type of glass first produced there.

Bowl, cut floral, dmn band, scalloped, stencil mk, 8" 250.00
Bowl, waffle-cut, fine cross hatching, fan-cut rim, oval, 14" . .1,375.00
Bowl on stand, dmn cutting, fan-cut rim, 1825, 11", EX 1,050.00
Carafe, dmn cut, faceted strap hdl, ball stopper, 12" 200.00
Carafe, dmn-cut band, faceted neck, strap hdl, ftd, 12" 225.00
Carafe, dmn-cut panels, mushroom stopper, mk, 11", pr 200.00
Compote, cut crystal, early 1800s, 7½x9" 650.00
Compote, paneled fan & sawtooth designs, t'print band, 9" . .965.00
Decanter, Colleen, 13" 225.00
Decanter, dmn-cut panels, blossom stopper, sq, mk, 10" 150.00
Decanter, faceted panels, bulbous, 12" 175.00
Decanter, Lismore, 11" 200.00
Vase, Pineapple Blossom & Diamond cutting, mk, 10" 200.00

Watt Pottery

The Watt Pottery Company was incorporated on July 5, 1922, in Perry County, Crooksville, Ohio. Their products were stoneware jars, jugs, milk pans, Dutch pots, mixing bowls (white with blue bands), churns, preserve jars, and chicken waterers, all marked in cobalt with their trademark, 'Acorn.' In 1935 these items were discontinued, and the company began to make free-hand decorated kitchen and ovenware items such as 'Banded' and 'Decorated' mixing bowls, 'spaghetti' bowls, canister sets, covered casseroles, nappies, cookie jars, ice buckets, pitchers, handled French casseroles, bean pots, salad sets, and dog dishes. Bold brush strokes of red and green contrasted with the natural buff color of the glazed body. Several patterns were produced: 'Red Apple,' 'Star Flower,' 'Rooster,' 'Autumn Foliage,' 'Morning Glory,' and 'Tulip.' Other lines were 'Basket Weave' (made in solid colors), 'Wood Grain' (a brown-glazed line), and 'Royal Danish' dinnerware.

Fire destroyed the entire manufacturing plant on October 4, 1965.

Because of the country flavor of the hand-decorated yellowware pieces, Watt Pottery is fast becoming a favorite collectible. Much of the ware was made for advertising premiums and is often found stenciled with the name of a retail company.

Bean pot, Apple, #76 . . . . .65.00
Bean pot, Bleeding Heart, #76 . . . . .40.00
Bowl, Apple, #8 . . . . .40.00
Bowl, Pansy, #8 . . . . .30.00
Bowl, Pennsylvania Dutch, mixing, #65 . . . . .50.00
Bowl, Poinsettia, tab hdls, #18, w/lid 45.00
Bowl, Rooster, #5 . . . . .40.00

Bowl, Rooster, #68 . . . . .45.00
Bowl, Rooster, #73, w/advertising 38.00
Bowl, Starflower, #24 . . . . .20.00
Bowl, Starflower, #7 . . . . .25.00
Bowl, Starflower, spaghetti 55.00
Casserole, Apple, #600, w/lid 55.00
Casserole, Apple, #601, w/lid, 9½" .65.00
Casserole, French; Rooster 65.00
Casserole, Pennsylvania Dutch, w/lid 55.00
Casserole, Rooster, #66, w/lid 65.00

Starflower casserole with tab handle, $55.00; Poinsettia ash tray, 4", $30.00.

Ice bucket, Apple, w/lid 65.00
Mug, Starflower, #501 . . . . .55.00
Pie plate, Apple 95.00
Pitcher, Apple, #15 . . . . .40.00
Pitcher, Apple, #15, w/advertising 45.00
Pitcher, Apple, #16 . . . . .55.00
Pitcher, Bleeding Heart, #15 . . . . .35.00
Pitcher, Cherry, #15 . . . . .35.00
Pitcher, Leaves, #15, w/advertising .35.00
Pitcher, Leaves, #16 . . . . .40.00
Pitcher, Rooster, #15 . . . . .40.00
Pitcher, Rooster, #16 . . . . .60.00
Pitcher, Rooster, #62, w/advertising 55.00
Pitcher, Starflower, #17 . . . . .65.00
Pitcher, Tulip, #16 . . . . .65.00
Pitcher, Tulip, #17, w/ice lip 75.00
Shakers, Poinsettia, pr 65.00
Shakers, Rooster, w/advertising, pr 100.00
Sugar bowl, Apple, #98, w/lid 85.00
Sugar bowl, Rooster, #98, w/lid & advertising 75.00

Wave Crest

Wave Crest is the trademark used on a line of creamy opaque glassware manufactured by the C.F. Monroe Company of New York, who operated there from 1892 until 1916. Vases, boxes, tablewares, and humidors in swirled and blown-out shapes were either hand painted or transfer printed with florals, scenics, or portraits. Many pieces were enhanced with ornately scrolled ormolu handles, feet, or rims. Several marks were used: the black mark, 'Trade Mark Wave Crest'; the red banner mark; and the paper label, 'Wave Crest Ware, Patented Oct. 4, 1892.'

Our advisors for this category are Betty and Clarence Maier; they are listed in the Directory under Pennsylvania.

Biscuit jar, plain mold, carnations, SP rim/bail, 8" 245.00
Biscuit jar, Rococo, floral on cream, mk, 8½x6½" 195.00
Bowl, Swirl, mc pansies/gold leaves & trim, ormolu hdls, 8" . . .550.00

Box, Collars & Cuffs, Rococo, 6x7½" dia **1,200.00**
Box, cuff; Puffy, floral, ormolu band, 6¾x6" **750.00**
Box, daisies/floral branches on bl to wht, mk, 7" dia **495.00**
Box, floral, blown-out dbl shell, hinged, 3" dia **235.00**
Box, girl's portrait, flowers/scrolls, ormolu mts, 5" dia **950.00**
Box, Puffy, florals on cobalt, lav trim, cupid ft, 7x6½" **1,400.00**
Box, Puffy, lady/petit point, ormolu ft, 6" dia **1,450.00**
Box, roses, pk on dk gr, brass head-figural ft, mk, 5x8½" **875.00**
Box, Swirl, floral, rust/orange/purple, 6½" dia **575.00**
Box, Swirl, floral on pk lustre, ormolu mts, 6½" L **700.00**
Cigarette & match holder, clovers on bl, ormolu, 4" **650.00**
Cigarette urn, bl floral w/wht dots, ftd **225.00**
Creamer & sugar bowl, bird on fence, brass hdls/lid, pr **265.00**
Creamer & sugar bowl, Swirl, rosebuds, pk on tan **635.00**
Dresser dish, Puffy, floral, ormolu collar, hdls, unmk, 4" **125.00**
Hair receiver, floral, brass lid, blk mk, 5¾" **235.00**
Jardiniere, pk roses, wht dots, cherub band at rim, mk, 8x9" . . . **450.00**

Jewel dish, ormolu base, 3½x3½", $245.00.

Letter holder, Puffy, shasta daisies, ormolu top, 5½" L **300.00**
Mustard jar, floral, unmk, 3½" **295.00**
Photo holder, Rococo, floral, mc on bl, mk, 7x4" **275.00**
Pin tray, Swirl, floral, ormolu rim, red mk, 1¾x4½" dia **135.00**
Salt cellar, tulip petal emb base, rare **165.00**
Shaker, Artichoke, bl floral, spiked pewter top, pr **335.00**
Shaker, Leaf & Spear, HP, pr **155.00**
Shaker, Scroll & Leaf Hexagon, HP, ea **40.00**
Shaker, Swirl, asters, 2¾", pr **235.00**
Shaker, Swirl & Bulge, w/transfer decor, ea **35.00**
Syrup, floral/raised dots, emb ornate SP hdl/lid, 5½" **1,150.00**
Syrup, Swirl, bl florals, metal lid & hdls **495.00**
Toothpick holder, cat in a wreath of florals, dotted rim **245.00**
Tray, Swirl, daisies, #161, orig label, 6½" dia **195.00**
Tray, Swirl, hdls, #75, banner mk, 3" dia **125.00**
Vase, floral, lt lemon to pk, ormolu hdls, mk, 9" **325.00**
Vase, mums, pk on bl, lustre medallion, ormolu hdls/rim, 7" . . . **295.00**
Vase, mums on rust shaped reserve, fancy ormolu hdls, 12" **985.00**
Vase, Niagara Falls scenic & florals, brass base, 6½" **425.00**
Vase, Rococo, floral, brass ft, red banner mk, 10½" **400.00**
Vase, Rococo, floral, brass ft, unmk, 10½" **325.00**
Vase, wild roses, cylindrical, ormolu base, unmk, 6" **150.00**

Weapons

Among the varied areas of specialization within the broad category of weapons, guns are by far the most popular. Muskets are among the earliest firearms; they were large-bore shoulder arms, usually firing black powder with separate loading of powder and shot. Some ignited the charge by flintlock or caplock, while later types used a firing pin with a metallic cartridge. Side arms, referred to as such because they were worn at the side, include pistols and revolvers. Pistols range from early single-shot and multiple barrels to modern types with cartridges held in the handle. Revolvers were supplied with a cylinder that turned to feed a fresh round in front of the barrel breech. Other firearms include shotguns, which fired round or conical bullets and had a smooth inner barrel surface, and rifles, so named because the interior of the barrel contained spiral grooves (rifling) which increased accuracy. See also Militaria.

Key:
bbl — barrel   hdw — hardware
cal — caliber   h/s — half stock
conv — conversion   mag — magazine
cyl — cylinder   oct — octagon
f/l — flintlock   p/b — patch box
f/s — full stock   perc — percussion
ga — gauge

Carbine

Burnside, 54 cal, some rpl, VG **500.00**
Maynard, 50 cal, inspection mks on stock, NM **675.00**
Remington Jenks, 54 cal, w/tape primer, VG **400.00**
Remington Model 14½-R, 38-40 cal, pump action, VG **165.00**
Remington 1879, rolling block, arsenal stamp on stock, VG . . . **135.00**
Remington 1897, rolling block, VG **145.00**
Sharps New Model 1863, 52 cal, minor pitting, G **550.00**
Smith, 50 cal, Mass Arms Co, rpl screws, G **450.00**
Springfield 1873, 45-70 cal, trapdoor, inspectors mks, EX . . . **1,500.00**
Springfield 1873, 45-70 cal, trapdoor, saddle ring, VG **425.00**
Springfield 1878, trap door, inspector mks dtd 1883, VG **225.00**
Springfield 1878, 45-70 cal, metal reblued **110.00**
Springfield 1896 Krag, 30-40 cal, 1903 on stock, VG **175.00**

Musket

BSA 1862 on lock, 58 cal rifle, VG **300.00**
Harpers Ferry Tape Primer 1858, minor rprs, rfn stock, VG . . . **275.00**
Harpers Ferry 1812 f/l, dtd 1915, rpl screws, rpr stock, G **300.00**
Harpers Ferry 1819 f/l, f/l & bbl dtd 1819, VG **525.00**
Harpers Ferry 1857 f/l, w/triangular bayonet, VG **375.00**
L Pomeroy 1840, conv to perc, dtd 1843, EX **350.00**
Mid-Eastern f/l, brass bbl bands, 34½" bbl, G **125.00**
N Starr Arms perc, lock dtd 1834 (1840 contract), VG **225.00**
N Starr Arms 1829 perc, Starr Sunburst (1840 contract), VG . **295.00**
Potsdam perc, reblued metal, VG **275.00**
Remington Maynard Tape Primer 1840, lock mk US/1857, G . **150.00**
Remington 1841, 54 cal, dtd 1852, minor stock rpr, VG **475.00**
Remington 1841, 54 cal, dtd 1853, rpr stock, G **375.00**
Springfield 1812 fl, rpr stock, VG **250.00**
Springfield 1821, 69 cal, dtd 1829, minor rprs, VG **235.00**
Springfield 1845 perc, minor rprs to stock, VG **275.00**
Springfield 1864 perc, rpr stock, G **180.00**
Tower-lock 1862 perc, 58 cal, 3 bands, crown mk, VG **450.00**

Pistol

Baretta auto, 32 cal, VG **175.00**
Belgian muff perc, 44 cal, single shot w/oct bbl, G **85.00**
Colt 1902 sporting auto, 38 cal, rimless, NP, VG **155.00**
Colt 1908 hammerless auto, 25 cal, NM **125.00**

DH Hilliard, under hammer perc, Cornish NH, EX **687.00**
German pocket, 41 cal, silver mts, walnut stocks, rpl hammer . **350.00**
Graves, under hammer perc, Bangor ME, EX **960.00**
Henry Aston 1842 perc, lock & bbl dtd 1846, 8½" bbl, VG . . **450.00**
Manton Pepperbox, 38 cal, butt cap opens, eng fr/guard, 8½" . **175.00**
Mauser auto, 7.65mm, w/leather shoulder holster, M **315.00**
Remington Rider mag, 32 cal, NP fr w/G eng, EX **550.00**
Remington 1871 Army rolling block, 50 cal, VG **275.00**
Remington 1871 rolling block, 50 cal, VG **325.00**
Remington 1891 target rolling block, 22 cal, half-oct bbl, G . . **350.00**
Remington 1911 auto, 45 cal, G **275.00**
Remington-Elliot Pepperbox, 32 cal, 4-bbl, pearl grips, VG . . **500.00**
Robert Johnson 1836 f/l, 54 cal, lock dtd 1841, VG **625.00**

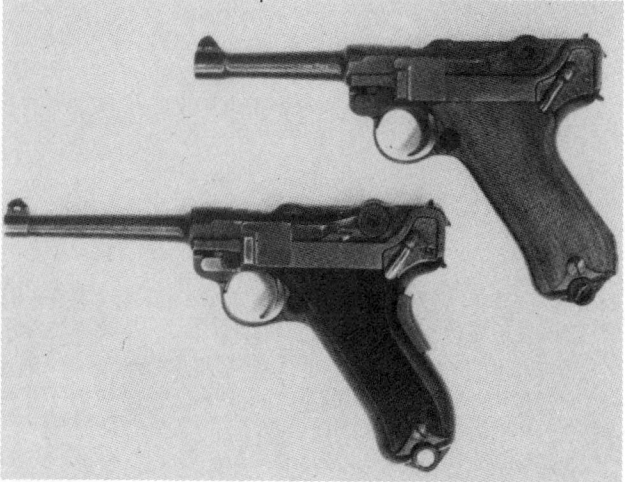

Lugars, Serial #9968, ca 1916, reworked, DWM, $500.00;
Serial #26676, ca 1924, 7.65 caliber, walnut grips, action
stamped Waffenfabrik / Bern, $800.00.

S North 1813, flintlock, poor **1,100.00**
Schneider & Co, single shot perc, Memphis TN, EX **2,860.00**
Simeon North 1819 f/l, 54 cal, lock dtd 1821, 15½", VG **950.00**
Smith & Wesson, 38 cal, lever action repeater, volcanic **4,000.00**
Spanish 1852 auto, 32 cal, gold inlay on bbl, MOP grips, VG . **200.00**
Williams f/l, 58 cal, brass bbl & hdw, rpr trigger, 13½" **225.00**

Revolver

Allen & Wheelock Navy, 36 cal, center hammer, 6" bbl **475.00**
Colt Bisley, 38 cal, factory rebuilt, NM **1,980.00**
Colt New Army & Navy dbl action, 38 cal, 4½" bbl, G **110.00**
Colt 1849 pocket, 31 cal, 5-shot, 5" bbl, G **375.00**
Colt 1861 Navy perc, 36 cal, 6-shot, cyl w/eng scene, VG . . . **425.00**
Colt 1873 single action, 45 cal, 6-shot, NP, MOP grips, EX . . **3,800.00**
Colt 1877 Lightning dbl action, 38 cal, G, +holster **145.00**
Colt 1877 Lightning dbl action, 38 cal, 3½" bbl, VG **300.00**
Colt 3rd Model Dragoon, 44 cal, 6-shot, G **1,100.00**
Joslyn Army standard perc, 44 cal, 5-shot, VG **300.00**
Manhattan, 36 cal, 5-shot, 4" bbl, G **275.00**
Remington New Army perc, 44 cal, 6-shot, G **225.00**
Whitney 2nd Model, 36 cal, eng scene on bbl, VG **550.00**
Whitney 2nd Model Navy, 36 cal, 6-shot, G **275.00**

Rifle

Adam Angstadt, over/under f/l, swivel bbl, EX **17,000.00**
Evans sporting, 44 cal, worn stock, G **155.00**
Garrell perc, curly maple stock w/silver inlay, 43" bbl **600.00**

HE Dimick perc, half stock w/eagle inlay, 36" bbl, G **325.00**
Henry, 2nd variation, 44 cal, VG **5,225.00**
Henry, 44 cal, brass fr, minor crack in stock, G **3,200.00**
J Bandle perc, half stock, NP, 32" oct bbl, VG **425.00**
Lee Enfild 1941, 30 cal, 1942 stamp on stock, G **110.00**
Leonard Reedy KY f/l, 50 cal, relief-cvd stock, EX **12,000.00**
Marlin 18, 22 cal, bolt action, VG **110.00**
Marlin 1881, deluxe factory eng, 38/55 cal, NM **12,000.00**
Martin Shell KY f/l, relief-cvd stock, unsgn, EX **20,000.00**
Morgan James, bench type, in case **4,600.00**
NY perc, curly maple f/s, 42" bbl, minor rprs, VG **300.00**
Remington American Boy Scout rolling block, 22 cal, VG **225.00**
Remington New Model revolving perc, 36 cal, 6-shot, VG **525.00**
Remington Woodsmaster 740 auto, 30-01, w/field scope, G . . . **200.00**
Remington 03-A3, bolt action, +Weaver scope, VG **375.00**
Remington 121 Field Master pump, 22 cal, VG **135.00**
Remington 34 NRA target, 22 cal, VG **75.00**
Remington-Hepburn, 22 cal, rear folding peep site, G **350.00**
Rock Island 1903, 30 cal, bolt action, EX **225.00**
Sharps New 1863, 52 cal, sm prof rpr at butt, 30" bbl, VG . . . **1,150.00**
Springfield 1873 trap door, 1883 mks, VG **235.00**
Springfield 1898 krag, 30-40 cal, 1902 on stock, VG **225.00**
Target, HM Pope, Ballard #6 action, 32/40 cal, VG, +extras . **4,895.00**
Target, Stevens Pope bbl, Ballard action **3,685.00**
US Chaffee-Reese 1882, 45/70 cal, VG **1,100.00**
Winchester 1886 Deluxe, take down, EX **1,870.00**
Winchester 71 Deluxe, 348 cal, VG **1,045.00**
Winchester 92 trapper carbine, w/registration papers, VG . . . **1,540.00**
Winchester 94 lever action, 32-40 cal, reglued metal, VG **150.00**

Shotgun

AH Fox, 12 ga, dbl bbl, Krupp bbls, VG **275.00**
Anton Sodia Ferlach, 12 ga, dbl bbl, eng receiver, NM **5,300.00**
Browning, 28 ga, dbl bbl, mk receiver, eng fr, M in case **1,000.00**
Enton Sodia Ferlach, over/under 12 ga, eng scenes/gilt, VG . **1,550.00**
I Hollis & Sons perc, 12 ga, single bbl, 28" bbl, G **65.00**
Ithaca XL900, 12 ga, ventilated rib, eng scene, M **200.00**
Ithaca 100, 20 ga, MIB **300.00**
L Bruns Nacht, 16 ga, Krupp mk, dbl bbl, VG **225.00**
Lang & Hussey Imperial Ejector, 12 ga, dbl bbl, VG **1,150.00**
LC Smith Specialty Trap, 12 ga, ventilated ribs, eng, VG . . . **1,150.00**
Marlin 19-G, 12 ga, pump action, chipped stock, G **65.00**
Mortimer Elwell perc, 10 ga, dbl bbl, London Real Twist bbl . . **85.00**
Parker Bros, 10 ga, dbl bbl, outside hammers, eng lock, VG . . **800.00**
Remington 17, 16 ga, pump action, cylinder choke, VG **145.00**
Stoeger Arms of NY, 20 ga, auto load, mk SA Luigi, Italy, M . . **85.00**
Winchester 42, 410 ga, pump action, full choke bbl, EX **1,400.00**
WW Greener, 12 ga, dbl bbl, eng receiver, gilding, VG **1,000.00**

Weathervanes

The earliest weathervanes were of handmade wrought iron and were generally simple angular silhouettes with a small hole suggesting an eye. Later, copper, zinc, and polychromed wood with features in relief were fashioned into more realistic forms. Ships, horses, fish, Indians, roosters, and angels were popular motifs. In the nineteenth century, silhouettes were often made from sheet metal. Wooden figures became highly carved and were painted in vivid colors. E.G. Washburne and Company in New York was one of the most prominent manufacturers of weathervanes during the last half of the century.

Two-dimensional sheet metal weathervanes are increasing in value due to the already heady prices of the full-bodied variety. Originality, strength of line, and patination help to determine value. When no condition is indicated, the items listed below are assumed to be in excellent condition.

Key:
fb — full-bodied   f/fb — flattened full-bodied

Angel w/trumpet & wings, pnt sheet metal, mc pnt, 44" L ...**6,300.00**
Arrow, serrated feathers on bk, sheet iron, 1890s, 35½" **95.00**
Bannerette, CI/sheet copper, arrow/scrolls, Howard, 24" L ...**1,700.00**
Convertible & driver, CI/emb zinc, on 31" arrow **200.00**
Cow, CI, ca 1900, 9x15x1", on CI 27" arrow, EX **175.00**
Cow, copper fb, cast zinc horns, Harris, rstr gilt, 28" L **7,425.00**
Cow, copper fb w/CI head & horns, on rod, 1800s, 37" L **6,600.00**
Ear of corn, CI, ca 1890s, 3x12x1", on CI 24" arrow **235.00**
Figure only, leaping stag, zinc head, fb, 1800s, 30" L **4,100.00**
Figure only, rooster, copper f/fb, 21x18" **400.00**
Figure only, running horse, hollow copper/CI head, 26", VG ..**350.00**
Fox, wrought iron, orig directionals, ca 1830, 42" L **1,500.00**
Gamecock on orb, copper/zinc f/fb, overall: 69" **2,900.00**
Horse, copper f/fb w/zinc/repousse copper, Howard, 24" L ...**4,950.00**
Horse, copper fb, emb mane/tail, gilt traces, on 33" rod **4,500.00**
Horse, running, cast copper, 6½x11x1", on 24" CI arrow **210.00**
Horse, running, cast tin, 8x10x1", on CI 25" arrow **125.00**
Horse, running, copper fb w/zinc ears, gilt, 32", +arrows **1,500.00**
Horse, running, molded tin, 11x28" **275.00**
Horse, running, molded/pnt zinc, 1800s, 31x46" **4,200.00**
Horse, running, tin, old gold pnt, 9x8x1", on CI 23" arrow **135.00**
Horse, running, tin, old wht pnt, 11x14x1, on CI 28" arrow ...**150.00**
Horse, pnt, sheet metal, molded head, Tuckerman, 31" L **3,100.00**
Horse & buggy, copper/brass fb, w/directionals, 60" **600.00**
Horse & sulky, copper/zinc f/fb, lacks reins, 1800s, 17x31" ...**3,300.00**
Horse/fire wagon, molded copper, 62" L, +directional **950.00**
Horse/sulky/driver, fb/EX detail, copper/zinc, 36", EX **6,000.00**
Indian/arrow/arm w/sword, sheet metal fb, Harris, 50x61" ..**16,000.00**
Jockey on horse, copper/zinc fb, mtd on rod, 32" L **6,000.00**
Pig, tin, gold-leaf traces, 8x14½", on CI 29" arrow **245.00**
Pig, tin, 4x9x1", on decorative CI arrow, ca 1900, EX **135.00**

Molded gilt-copper rooster, missing directionals, late 1800s, 18", $2,000.00.

Rooster, CI/zinc, James, 14x12x1" on CI 23½" arrow, EX **250.00**
Rooster, copper f/fb w/lg molded tail, on rod, 24x22" **3,300.00**
Rooster, copper fb, elaborate tail, pnt, 1800s, 25x28" **3,575.00**
Rooster, crowing, hollow copper, on 70" iron rod **300.00**
Rooster, cvd pine, orig pnt, 12", on 29" dowel arrow, EX **225.00**

Rooster, molded copper, 23x18" **350.00**
Rooster, sheet iron, 1920, mtd on 10x23" base **595.00**
Rooster, wood cutout, red pnt, 1920s, 31x46" +arrow **265.00**
Rooster, zinc fb w/repousse copper tail, Howard, 17x12" ...**3,630.00**
Rooster on orb, copper fb, sheet copper tail, 31" L +arrow ...**3,850.00**
Stag, all sheet metal, 1800s, 40x31" **3,500.00**
Stag, copper f/fb w/wrought iron antlers, yel pnt, 26x26" **7,700.00**
Tuna fish, wood w/worn pnt, metal fins, Nantucket Is, 60" ..**2,500.00**
Viking in ship, sheet metal, EX details, 1890s, 14x29" **135.00**

Weaving

Early Americans used a variety of tools and a great amount of time to produce the material from which their clothing was made. Soaked and dried flax was broken on a flax brake to remove waste material. It was then tapped and stroked with a scutching knife. Hackles further removed waste and separated the short fibers from the longer ones. Unspun fibers were placed on the distaff on the spinning wheel for processing into yarn. The yarn was then wound around a reel for measuring. Three tools used for this purpose were the niddy-noddy, the reel yarn winder, and the click reel. After it was washed and dyed, the yarn was transferred to a barrel-cage or squirrel-cage swift and fed onto a bobbin winder.

Today, flax wheels are more plentiful than the large wool wheels since they were small and could be more easily stored and preserved. The distaff, an often-discarded or misplaced part of the wheel, is very scarce. French spinners from the Quebec area painted their wheels. Many have been stripped and refinished by those unaware of this fact. Wheels may be very simple or have a great amount of detail, depending upon the owner's ethnic background and the maker's skill.

Flax wheel, orig yel pnt, 1800s, complete, EX **225.00**
Hatchel, bird/tulip/arrow-shaped iron braces, dtd 1819, 32" ...**500.00**
Hatchel, punched tin w/tulip & 1800 on wooden board, 12" **45.00**
Niddy-noddy, all wood, chip-cvd detail, minor crack, 18½" ...**195.00**
Niddy-noddy, trn shaft, wooden pins, 1700s, EX **140.00**
Reel, mixed wood w/curly maple hub, floor standing, T-base **75.00**
Tape loom, heart cutout/sunburst crest, dtd 1823, 7x21" **575.00**

William and Mary tape loom, hard pine, New England, ca 1700-1720, 10½x8", $400.00.

Yarn winder, chip-cvd edges, trn reel arms/finial, 33", EX **95.00**

Yarn winder, heart-form base, branded name/1836, EX 775.00
Yarn winder, w/counter, 1780s, EX 175.00

Webb

Thomas Webb and Sons have been making fine art glass in Stourbridge, England, since 1837. Besides their fine cameo glass, they have also made enameled ware and pieces heavily decorated with applied glass ornaments. The butterfly is a motif that has been so often featured that it tends to suggest Webb as the manufacturer.

Our advisor for this category is Don Williams; he is listed in the Directory under Iowa. See also specific types of glass such as Alexandrite, Burmese, Mother of Pearl, and Peachblow.

Bottle, scent; leaves & gold bamboo on cream, SP lid, 5¼" 250.00
Bowl, cobalt to clear, cut w/ovals/bars/florals, 15½" 400.00
Bowl, floral HP on bl shaded, chalice-type base, mk, 10x12" L .220.00
Bowl, floral/butterfly on cream, ruffled/pleated, mk, 3½x10½" .300.00
Bowl, gold prunus on brn shaded, cased, 6-crimp top, 4x6" 550.00
Jar, floral HP on wht opaque to lt bl, metal lid, mk, 6x7" 365.00
Jug, claret; palm trees, gold on wht, SP lid & hdl, #d 350.00

Perfume bottle, fuchsia, red and white on golden-yellow, signed, 5", $2,200.00.

Pitcher, floral, brn on cream to beige, appl hdl, mk, 11x5" 195.00
Pitcher, floral HP on bl, scalloped, frosted hdl, mk, 10" 145.00
Rose bowl, bl to cream, crystal applique, crimped, 3½x4⅝" 275.00
Rose bowl, floral, peachblow color, 3¼" dia 300.00
Rose bowl, Zipper MOP, brn to gr, rose lining, 3-layer 975.00
Vase, birds/flowers intaglio, rose-cased opal, 10½x3" 1,270.00
Vase, brocade, mc florals on opal, 8¾" 700.00
Vase, coral overlay, clear ruffle/leaves/ft, 6¾x5" 325.00
Vase, diamonds on wht to butterscotch, triangular top, 9½" ... 120.00
Vase, floral, mc on lt to dk bl, scalloped, ped ft, mk, 9½" 150.00
Vase, floral branches on teal gr to pk satin, dimpled, 11x5" 495.00
Vase, floral/bl bird HP on wht to butterscotch, mk, 12x5½" ... 200.00
Vase, gold floral/insect on tan to cream, propellor mk, 9" 200.00
Vase, gold hydrangea/butterfly on gr shaded satin, 4½" 335.00
Vase, gold prunus & bee on cream opaque, 8x4¾" 295.00
Vase, gold prunus & butterfly on brn shaded, stick form, 7" ... 350.00
Vase, gold prunus on lemon yel satin, 6½x3½" 325.00
Vase, gold prunus opal top, textured orange bottom, 6½" 225.00
Vase, gold prunus/butterfly on peachblow, mk, 10½", pr 1,250.00

Vase, jack-in-pulpit; Iris, gold aurene, dimpled, sgn, 4¾" 225.00
Vase, leaves, gold on amethyst overlay, mk, 9½" 190.00
Vase, MOP Swirl, amethyst/blk w/gold butterflies, att, 7" 650.00
Vase, petit point, mc on pk satin, stick neck, 7¼" 270.00
Vase, phoenix bird/chinoiserie, gold on yel shaded, mk, 8½" .. 295.00
Water set, gold prunus on pk opal, pitcher+5 glasses 700.00

Cameo

Bottle, scent; floral, wht/rose on opal, ball form, 6", NM 2,000.00
Bottle, scent; floral & butterfly, wht on amber, 5" 1,450.00
Creamer & sugar, fishscale cvg, gold ivy/butterfly, wht/pk 685.00
Punch bowl, floral/butterflies, wht/teal, silver rim, 12" 2,300.00
Vase, apple blossoms/butterfly, wht on red, 4" 1,100.00
Vase, birds & flowers on brn-stained ivory, 5¼" 850.00
Vase, Canterbury bells/butterfly, wht on red, mk, 8" 2,500.00
Vase, clover/wildflowers, wht on red, bulbous, sgn, 4½" 1,295.00
Vase, ferns/iris/butterfly, wht on pk, slim neck, 13½" 2,900.00
Vase, floral branches, red on wht, baluster, 4¾" 900.00
Vase, floral/butterfly, wht/yel, rnd w/canister neck, 4½" 700.00
Vase, leaves on brn-stained ivory, petal top, mk, 2¾x3¼" 650.00
Vase, leaves on brn-stained ivory, petal top, 5" 795.00
Vase, lilies/scrolls, lime on clear, wide rim, 6x8½" 300.00
Vase, morning-glories, wht on red frost, sgn, 8½x3¾" 2,250.00
Vase, morning-glory & butterfly, wht on red frost, 6½" 1,850.00
Vase, wild roses/thorny branches, wht on bl, squatty, 3" 1,900.00
Vase, wisteria/butterfly, wht on bl, 10" 2,300.00

Wedgwood

Josiah Wedgwood established his pottery in Burslem, England, in 1759. He produced only molded utilitarian earthenwares until 1770 when new facilities were opened at Etruria. It was there he introduced his famous Basalt and Jasperware. Jasperware, an unglazed fine stoneware decorated with classic figures in white relief, was usually produced in blues; but it was also made in ground colors of green, lilac, yellow, black, or white. Occasionally, three or more colors were used in combination. It has been in continuous production to the present day and is the most easily recognized of all the Wedgwood lines. (Jasper is a body of solid color; the term 'Jasper-Dip' refers to ware with a white body that has been dipped in an overlay color. This type, introduced in the late 1700s, is the type most often encountered on today's market.)

Though Wedgwood's Jasperware was highly acclaimed, on a more practical basis his creamware was his greatest success. Due to the ease with which it could be potted and because its lighter weight significantly reduced transportation expenses, Wedgwood was able to offer 'chinaware' at affordable prices. Queen Charlotte was so pleased with the ware that she allowed it to be called 'Queen's Ware.' Most creamware was marked simply 'Wedgwood.' ('Wedgwood & Co.' and 'Wedgewood' are marks of other potters.) From 1769 to 1780, Wedgwood was in partnership with Thomas Bently; artwares of the highest quality bear the mark indicating this partnership.

Moonlight Lustre, an allover splashed-on effect of pink intermingling with gray, brown, or yellow, was made from 1805 to 1815. Porcelain was made, though not to any great extent, from 1812 to 1822. Both of these types of wares were marked 'Wedgwood.' Stone china and Pearlware were made from about 1820 to 1875. Examples of either may be found with a mark to indicate their body type. During the late 1800s, Wedgwood produced some fine parian and majolica. Creamware, hand painted by Emile Lessore, was sold from about 1860 to 1875. From the 20th century, several lines of lustre wares — Butterfly, Dragon, and Fairyland (the latter designed by Miss Makeig-Jones) — have attracted the collector and, as their prices suggest, are highly sought-after and admired.

Nearly all of Wedgwood's wares are clearly marked. 'Wedgwood' was used before 1891, after which time 'England' was added. Most examples marked 'Made In England' were made after 1921. A detailed study of all marks is recommended for accurate dating.

Key:
WW — Wedgwood   WWE — Wedgwood England

Beaker, Jasper, dk bl, WW, 3" 120.00
Biscuit jar, Jasper, blk/gold, lion's head, SP trim, WW, 6⅜" . . .375.00
Biscuit jar, Jasper, blk/gold/wht, SP top/hdl, WW, 7x5" 695.00
Biscuit jar, Jasper, dk bl, ladies/cupids, WW, SP lid, 6" 175.00
Biscuit jar, Jasper, lav/sage gr/wht, SP lid/hdl, WW, 6x4½" . . .700.00
Biscuit jar, Jasper, lt bl, WWE, 2½x5½" 235.00
Biscuit jar, Jasper, sage gr, SP lid/hdl, WW, 6x5" 200.00
Bowl, Butterfly Lustre, gold/umber, bl/gr int, WWE, 8" 450.00
Bowl, Dragon Lustre, bl, WW, Z-4829, 2½x4½" 175.00
Bowl, Dragon Lustre, bl mottle int, flame mk WW, 3⅞x8½" . .450.00
Bowl, Dragon Lustre, gr/bl mottle w/gold, Z-4823, 4x8½" dia . .500.00
Bowl, Fairyland Lustre, firbolgs, MOP int, WW, 3x6⅜" 950.00
Bowl, Fairyland Lustre, leapfrogging elves, WW, 3⅛x4¾" 675.00
Bowl, Fairyland Lustre, leapfrogging elves, 2x4" 495.00
Bowl, Fairyland Lustre, leapfrogging fairies, WW, 2¾x5" 750.00
Bowl, Fairyland Lustre, nighttime scene w/pixies etc, 4¾" 700.00
Bowl, Fruit Lustre, mc/gold on bl, flame int, 8" 550.00
Bowl, Hummingbird Lustre, bl w/orange int, WW, MIE, 8" . . .475.00
Bowl, Hummingbird Lustre, geese borders, WW, 4½x10" 500.00
Bowl, Jasper, blk, Dancing Hours, WWE, 10" 1,225.00
Bowl, Jasper, lt bl, WWE, 2x4¾" 70.00
Bowl, nut; Fairyland Lustre, Nizami, WW, 1¼x3¾" 400.00
Bowl, vegetable; Creamware, Patrician, WWE 145.00
Box, Dragon Lustre, dragons w/in & w/o, Portland mk, 7" L . .395.00
Box, Dragon Lustre, widow finial, WW, 5¼x5½" dia 395.00
Box, Jasper, bl, heart shape, WW, 1⅝x2⅜x3⅜" 85.00
Box, Jasper, bl, Pegasus & man, WW, 1⅞x2⅝x3" 85.00
Box, Jasper, blk, WWE, 4" 155.00
Box, Jasper, dk bl, WWE, 4¾x3¾" 95.00
Box, Jasper, dk gr, heart form, WWE, 2x4½x3½" 175.00
Box, Jasper, med bl, heart form, mk, ca 1948, sm 90.00
Bust, Basalt, bearded man, WW, 4⅜x2⅛" 375.00
Bust, Basalt, Prior, WW, 11½x8" 750.00
Butter dish, Jasper, dk bl, WW, 5¾" base 225.00
Candlestick, Agate Ware, trn columnar form, WW, 9", pr 750.00
Candlestick, Jasper, dk bl, WW, 7" .130.00
Candlestick, Jasper, dk bl, WWE, 5", pr 130.00
Cheese dish, Jasper, bl, 1860, 11" dia 750.00
Clock, Jasper, lt bl, WWE, 6", EX 500.00
Creamer, Jasper, dk bl, WWE, 2¼" 80.00
Creamer, Jasper, dk gr, WWE, 2¼" 95.00
Creamer & sugar bowl, Caneware, glazed, mk, 1920s 135.00
Creamer & sugar bowl, Jasper, dk bl, SP holder, WW, 6½" . . .225.00
Creamer & sugar bowl, Jasper, lt bl, WWE 135.00
Cup, Fairyland Lustre, leapfrogging elves, WW, 3½x5" 695.00
Cup & saucer, Basalt, Niagara Falls, HP decor, WWE 90.00
Cup & saucer, demitasse; Basalt, Firnie BC, HP decor, mk 80.00
Cup & saucer, demitasse; Jasper, dk bl, WWE, 2" 75.00
Cup & saucer, Jasper, lt gr, WWE 75.00
Desk set, Jasper, sterling on bronze mts, ca 1912, 6-pc 400.00
Figurine, Basalt, cat, glass eyes, WWE, 4½" 395.00
Figurine, Basalt, elephant, blk w/yel glass eyes, WW ca 1919 . .425.00
Figurine, Erose & Euphrosyne, Basalt, WW, 16¾x4¾" 875.00
Flower arranger, Creamware, tree trunk w/holes, ca 1919 . . . . . .90.00
Flowerpot, Jasper, dk bl, WW, 3½", +stand 645.00
Garden seat, dk red w/emb birds & fans, ca 1886, 16x10" 850.00

Basalt figure of Minerva, 1875, marked Wedgwood, 18½", $1,400.00.

Hair receiver, Jasper, dk bl, WW, 3½x3¼" 145.00
Inkwell, Basalt, drum form, for plume pen, unmk, 2⅛x2¾" 95.00
Inkwell, Jasper, lt bl, dolphin supports, WW, 6" 475.00
Jar, Jasper, dk bl, SP lid, WW, 5¼" .118.00
Jar, Jasper, lt bl, WWE, 1¾x3" dia 36.00
Jardiniere, Jasper, dk bl, WWE, 6½x7" 155.00
Jardiniere, Jasper, dk gr, flared, WWE, 7½x8¼" 445.00
Jug, Jasper, yel, WWE, 6¼" 385.00
Loving cup, Jasper, lt bl, 3-hdl, WWE, 4½" 155.00
Matchbox, Jasper, dk bl, striker in lid, WWE 78.00
Matchbox holder, Jasper, lt bl, WW, 3¾x6" dia 135.00
Medallion, Jasper, lt bl, Dauphine, unmk, 1½" dia 110.00
Medallion, Jasper, lt bl, Hadrian, WW, 3" dia 130.00
Mug, Jasper, dk bl, hallmk silver rim, Elkington, WW, 5x4" . . .125.00
Mug, Shakespeare's 400th Anniversary, bone china, mk 55.00
Pitcher, Basalt, mc florals, WW, 5½x3½" 198.00
Pitcher, Basalt, Victoria BC, WWE, 3½" 80.00
Pitcher, Creamware, Vieux Rouen, WWE, 6½" 50.00
Pitcher, Jasper, dk bl, classical ladies, WW, 4x2½" 110.00
Pitcher, Jasper, dk bl, Portland, WW, 6¼" 230.00
Pitcher, Jasper, dk bl, trefoil spout, WW, 5½x4" 165.00
Pitcher, Jasper, dk bl, WWE, 4½" 130.00
Pitcher, Jasper, dk gr, Franklin & Washington, WWE, 8½" . . .420.00
Pitcher, Lustre, Fallow deer, bone china, mk, ca 1937 . . . . . . .130.00
Pitcher, syrup; Jasper, dk bl, hinged pewter top, 5¼x3" 145.00
Pitcher, tankard; Jasper, dk bl, classical ladies, WW, 6⅜" 110.00
Pitcher, tankard; Jasper, dk bl, classical ladies, WW, 7½" 145.00
Pitcher, tankard; Jasper, dk bl, WW, 5⅜x3⅜" 95.00
Pitcher, tankard; Jasper, dk bl, WWE, 4" 80.00
Plaque, Jasper, bl, portraits, 1877 mk, WW, 15" dia, pr 550.00
Plaque, Jasper, dk bl, Dancing Hours, unfr, WW, 6x12" 300.00
Plaque, Jasper, lt bl, cherubs, WW, 13½x7½" 450.00
Plaque, Jasper, sage gr, bl/wht floral border, WW, 4x9¾" 525.00
Plate, Creamware, Art Nouveau decor, mk, ca 1907 . . . . .125.00
Plate, Jasper, bl, Portland, WWE, 10" 155.00
Plate, Jasper, Cupid, lt bl, WWE, 8¾" 80.00
Plate, Jasper, dk bl, WWE, 6" 70.00
Plate, Jasper, dk bl, WWE, 7" 90.00
Ring tree, Jasper, dk bl, figures, floral border, 2¾x3⅛" 165.00

Shaker, Jasper, lt bl, lighthouse shape, WWE, 3¾" 95.00
Spittoon, Basalt, engine trn, early, 5" dia 590.00
Sugar bowl, Jasper, dk bl, w/lid, WWE, 3½" dia 75.00
Sugar bowl, Jasper, dk bl, w/lid, WWE, 5½" dia 150.00
Sweetmeat jar, Jasper, 3-color, WW, 4½" 595.00
Tea set, stoneware, WWE, 3-pc 725.00
Teapot, Basalt, Capri, HP florals, WW, 4x8" 445.00
Teapot, Basalt, HP decor, Victoria BC, WWE, 5" dia 130.00
Teapot, Basalt, HP florals, WW, 4½x6" 325.00
Teapot, Jasper, dk bl, WWE, 4½x6¼" 95.00
Teapot, Jasper, gr, WW, pre-1915, 4¼" 145.00
Teapot, Jasper, lt gr, WWE, 4x7" 120.00
Teapot, Wild Strawberry, bone china, WWE, miniature 90.00
Tile, bird & dog, Josiah Wedgwood, fr 135.00
Tray, City of London, blk decor, Rosso Antico, mk, ca 1958 . . . .80.00
Tray, Jasper, blk, mk, ca 1967, 5¾x3" 78.00
Tray, Jasper, dk bl, WW, 5" L 130.00
Urn, Jasper, lav, w/lid, WW, 9¼" 1,190.00
Vase, Annular, ribbed, lt gr, K Murray, 1940s, 9" 100.00
Vase, Basalt, Canada coat of arms, WWE, 4" 60.00
Vase, Butterfly Lustre, flame luster inside top, WW, 8½" 375.00
Vase, Butterfly Lustre, gold tracing, WW, 8⅜x4⅛" 375.00
Vase, Butterfly Lustre, MOP w/mc & gold, 8½" 375.00
Vase, Daventry, lt bl, bone china, Des Fontaines, 14" 2,000.00
Vase, Dragon Lustre, bl w/gold, gr MOP int, WW, 2-4829, 8" .265.00
Vase, Dragon Lustre, gold on bl mottle, WW, 9½x3½" 450.00
Vase, Dragon Lustre, gold on lt bl mottle, WW, 8¾x6" 475.00
Vase, Hummingbird Lustre, bl, flame int, 5x2½" 195.00
Vase, Hummingbird Lustre, bl, trumpet form, WW, 6" 225.00
Vase, Jasper, blk, cylindrical, WW, 6½x2¾" 175.00
Vase, Jasper, blk, w/lid, mk, ca 1905, 11½" 1,500.00
Vase, Jasper, blk, WW, ca 1800, 5½" 345.00
Vase, Jasper, dk bl, Cameo, WWE, 4" 55.00
Vase, Jasper, dk bl, ram's heads w/garlands, cylinder, WW, 7" . .150.00
Vase, Jasper, dk bl, sea grass at top, WW, 7" 230.00
Vase, Jasper, dk bl, WWE, 1¼" 95.00
Vase, Jasper, dk bl, WWE, 2" 95.00
Vase, Jasper, dk bl, WWE, 3x2" 85.00
Vase, Jasper, dk bl, WWE, 5" 65.00
Vase, Jasper, dk gr, Portland, mk, ca 1930, 6¼" 355.00
Vase, Jasper, lav, mk, ca 1960, 3⅜" .165.00
Vase, porc w/gold & floral, gold hdls/ft, w/lid, 1900, 9½" 425.00

Fairyland Lustre 'Jewelled Tree' vase, three scenic panels, Portland vase mark, 8", $1,000.00.

Weil Ware

Max Weil came to the United States in the 1940s, settling in California. There he began manufacturing dinnerware, figurines, cookie jars, and wall pockets. American clays were used, and the dinnerware was all hand decorated. Weil died in 1954; the company closed two years later. The last backstamp to be used was the outline of a burro with the words 'Weil Ware — Made in California.'

Casserole, floral on gr, sq, w/lid 25.00
Compote, floral, ftd 14.00
Cup & saucer, Bamboo 5.00
Dish, Dogwood, divided, sq, 10½" 7.50

Figure of girl with bowl, 11", $22.00.

Planter, boy w/bouquet, 11" 20.00
Planter, bust of lady, HP fan in hand, 8" 25.00
Plate, Bamboo, dinner sz 5.00
Plate, floral, 5" 3.00
Plate, Rose, sq, 10" 4.50
Vase, bonsai pines, 6½x4½" 25.00
Vase, bud; bonsai pines, w/coralene, #946, 6" 18.00
Wall pocket, Oriental girl 22.50

Weller

The Weller Pottery Company was established in Zanesville, Ohio, in 1882, the outgrowth of a small one-kiln log cabin works Sam Weller had operated in Fultonham. Through an association with Wm. Long, he entered the art pottery field in 1895, producing the Lonhuda Ware Long had perfected in Steubenville six years earlier. His famous Louwelsa line was merely a continuation of Lonhuda and was made in at least five hundred different shapes until 1924.

Many fine lines of artware followed under the direction of Charles Babcock Upjohn, Art Director from 1895 to 1904: Dickens Ware (1st Line), underglaze slip decorations on dark backgrounds; Turada, featuring applied ivory bands of delicate openwork on solid dark brown backgrounds; and Aurelian, similar to Louwelsa, but with a brushed-on rather than blended ground.

One of their most famous lines was 2nd Line Dickens, introduced in 1900. Backgrounds, characteristically caramel shading to turquoise matt, were decorated by sgraffito with animals, golfers, monks, Indians, and scenes from Dickens novels. The work is often artist signed. Sicardo, 1903, was a metallic lustre line in tones of rose, blue, green, or purple with flowing Art Nouveau patterns developed within the glaze.

Frederick Hurten Rhead, who worked for Weller in 1903 to 1904, created the prestigious Jap Birdimal line decorated with geisha girls, landscapes, storks, etc., accomplished through application of heavy slip forced through the tiny nozzle of a squeeze bag. Other lines to his credit are L'Art Nouveau, produced both in high-gloss brown and matt pastels, and 3rd Line Dickens, often decorated with Cruikshank's illustrations in relief.

Other early artware lines were Eocean, Floretta, Hunter, Perfecto, Dresden, Etched Matt, and Etna.

In 1920 John Lessel was hired as Art Director, and under his supervision several new lines were created. LaSa, LaMar, Marengo, and Besline attest to his expertise with metallic lustres.

The last of the artware lines and one of the most sought-after by collectors today is Hudson, first made during the early 1920s. Hudson, a semi-matt glazed ware, was beautifully artist decorated on shaded backgrounds with florals, animals, birds, and scenics. Notable artists often signed their work, among them Hester Pillsbury, Dorothy England Laughead, Ruth Axline, Claude Leffler, Sarah Reid McLaughlin, E.L. Pickens, and Mae Timberlake.

During the thirties, Weller produced a line of gardenware and naturalistic life-sized figures of dogs, cats, swans, geese, and playful gnomes.

The depression brought a slow, steady decline in sales, and by 1948 the pottery was closed. For a more thorough study, we recommend *The Collectors Encyclopedia of Weller Pottery* by Sharon and Bob Huxford, available at your local library or bookstore.

Ansonia, batter jug, 14½"	100.00
Arcadia, bud vase, 7½"	20.00
Arcadia, fan vase, 15x8"	35.00
Ardsley, candle holders, 3", pr	40.00
Ardsley, console bowl, 3½x16½"; +9½" kingfisher	265.00
Ardsley, fan vase, 8"	55.00
Atlas, bowl, #C-3, 4"	45.00
Atlas, dish, w/lid, #C-2, 3½"	80.00
Atlas, star dish, 2"	25.00
Aurelian, clock, floral, DJ Dibowski, rstr works, 13x11"	950.00
Aurelian, ewer, cavalier, sgn Fouts, 16½"	1,500.00
Aurelian, ewer, stag, by Abel, mk, 12"	1,000.00
Aurelian, jardiniere & pedestal, floral, sgn Ferrell, 45½"	2,000.00
Aurelian, jardiniere & pedestal, floral, 38"	1,200.00
Aurelian, mug, berries, artist sgn, 6"	110.00
Aurelian, mug, dog, silver lid, sgn K, 7"	1,400.00
Aurelian, mug, ear of corn, silver overlay, mk, 6"	4,000.00
Aurelian, oil banquet lamp, floral, sgn Schnieder, 27"	1,200.00
Aurelian, tankard, ear of corn, 12½"	750.00
Aurelian, vase, roses, artist sgn, squat w/integral hdl, 3"	150.00
Auroro, vase, goldfish by Hattie Mitchell, 9"	800.00
Baldin, bowl, bl, 4"	60.00
Barcelona, ewer, 9½"	150.00
Barcelona, oil jar, hdls, 25½"	850.00
Barcelona, vase, hdls, 14½"	230.00
Barcelona, vase, 7"	55.00
Blossom, cornucopia, floral on bl, 8½"	35.00
Blue Drapery, jardiniere, 5½"	40.00
Blue Drapery, planter, 4"	30.00
Blue Louwelsa, vase, berries, crimped, 3-ftd, sgn, 4½"	375.00
Blue Louwelsa, vase, floral, sgn LM, 10"	650.00
Blue Ware, jardiniere, w/2 angels, 8½"	200.00
Blue Ware, lamp base, 9"	100.00
Bonito, bowl, w/flower frog, sgn DE, 3"	75.00
Bonito, vase, floral, hdls, sgn HP, 11"	140.00
Bonito, vase, sgn NW, 7"	75.00
Bouquet, bowl, #B-8, 4"	30.00

Bouquet, console bowl, #B-12, 5x12½"	35.00
Bouquet, urn vase, #B-6, 5"	30.00
Brighton, canaries, 4"	110.00
Brighton, cardinal, sgn MH, 5½"	100.00
Brighton, chicks, 5"	110.00
Brighton, flamingo, 6"	150.00
Brighton, hanging parrot, spread wings, 15"	600.00
Brighton, parakeets, 9"	325.00
Brighton, woodpecker, 6½"	150.00
Burntwood, vase, floral, 8"	130.00
Burntwood, vase, ftd, 6½"	125.00

Blue and Decorated vase, WWI doughboy, 12", $2,750.00.

Cactus, camel, 3½"	60.00
Cactus, monkey, 4"	60.00
Cactus, snail, 3½"	60.00
Cameo, basket, 7½"	30.00
Cameo, bowl, ftd, 4"	25.00
Cameo, ewer, 10"	40.00
Cameo Jewell, jardiniere, 11"	195.00
Cameo Jewell, jardiniere, 7½"	75.00
Cameo Jewell, jardiniere & pedestal, 34"	800.00
Candis, ewer, 11"	45.00
Chengtu, covered jar, 8"	80.00
Chengtu, vase, 9"	60.00
Clarmont, bowl, hdls, 3"	45.00
Clarmont, candle holder, 8", pr	175.00
Classic, bowl, 14½"; +9" goose boy frog	80.00
Classic, fan vase, 5"	30.00
Classic, plate, wht, 11½"	30.00
Classic, wall pocket, wide, 6"	30.00
Classic, wall pocket, 7½"	30.00
Claywood, candle holder, 5"	35.00
Claywood, mug, 5"	50.00
Claywood, spittoon, 4½"	100.00
Claywood, vase, 6½"	50.00
Cloudburst, wall pocket, 5½"	35.00
Coppertone, basket, 8½"	70.00
Coppertone, console bowl, 12x3"; +frog, 4½"	225.00
Coppertone, fan vase, frogs on base, 8"	200.00
Coppertone, floor vase, 26½"	450.00
Coppertone, garden frog, 6x6"	250.00
Coppertone, owl, mottled gr w/bl, 9"	200.00
Coppertone, pillow vase, 7"	50.00
Coppertone, pitcher, fish hdl, 7½"	250.00
Coppertone, vase, frogs on base, 12"	165.00
Coppertone, vase, hdls, 15½"	165.00

Copra, basket, floral on brn bkground, 11" 125.00
Cornish, bowl, 4" 35.00
Cornish, bowl, 7½" 25.00
Cornish, jardiniere, 7" 55.00
Creamware, ash tray, HP nude putting on stockings, 4½" 190.00
Darsie, flowerpot, 5½" 30.00
Darsie, pot, 3" 25.00
Darsie, vase, 7½" 35.00
Decorated Creamware, jug, grape cluster, 5" 75.00
Decorated Creamware, teapot, floral, 5½" 125.00
Decorated Creamware, vase, grape cluster, HP, 11½" 275.00
Delsa, basket, 7" 35.00
Dickens I, jardiniere, floral, 8" 200.00
Dickens I, jug, ear of corn, 6½" 260.00
Dickens I, mug, Admiral portrait, 5" .800.00
Dickens II, advertising plate, Pickwick Papers, 12½" 1,750.00
Dickens II, ewer, mermaid, 10½" 500.00
Dickens II, jug, male golfer, 5¾" 265.00
Dickens II, mug, Black Bird, sgn UJ, 6" 450.00
Dickens II, mug, cavalier portrait, 5" 200.00
Dickens II, mug, grape cluster, mk, 5" 125.00
Dickens II, tankard, nude, sgn EL Pickens, dtd 1902, 12" 2,800.00
Dickens II, tobacco jar, The Irishman, sgn RD, 6½" 600.00
Dickens II, vase, Bald Eagle, sgn Anna Dautherty, 9" 750.00
Dickens II, vase, bunny, 17" 1,200.00
Dickens II, vase, Chief Hollowhorn Bear, sgn AD, 13" 950.00
Dickens II, vase, couple on path, cow/calf, Smith/Oshe, 16" .1,100.00
Dickens II, vase, Dickens couple in room, bulbous, 10½" 325.00
Dickens II, vase, Dombey & Son, sgn W Gibson, 10½" 700.00
Dickens II, vase, kitten, 9" 900.00
Dickens II, vase, knights on horses, sgn Upjohn, 14" 800.00
Dickens II, vase, lady playing harp, EL Pickens, 16" 1,100.00
Dickens II, vase, lady smelling flower, sgn Dusenbury, 12" . . .675.00
Dickens II, vase, serpent, sgn EL Pickens, mk, 15½" 750.00
Dickens II, vase, shepherd/sheep/dog, 15" 1,100.00
Dickens II, vase, stag & trees, twisted form, 11" 300.00
Dickens II, vase, swirling flowers/leaves, pnt/cvd, 10x6" 425.00
Dickens II, vase, White Tail, Indian/headdress, ELM, 7½" 475.00
Dickens III, carafe, w/cup, David Copperfield, sgn R, 14½" . .1,100.00
Dickens III, ewer, Squeers, sgn LM, 12½" 600.00
Dickens III, ink well, sgn R, 2½" 500.00
Dickens III, mug, Master Belling, 5" 375.00
Dickens III, teapot, Capt Cuttle, Florence Dombey, 7" 825.00
Dickens III, vase, character, Corker in circle on bk, 13" 300.00
Dickens III, vase, Charles Dickens on disk, 4" 350.00
Dickens III, vase, inscr Bailey, 9½" .450.00

Dresden, vase, windmill, sgn LJB, 10½" 500.00
Dupont, jardiniere, 7½" 80.00
Elberta, bowl vase, 3½" 30.00
Elberta, cornucopia, 8" 45.00
Elberta, jardiniere, 5½" 50.00
Eocean, flask vase, dog, sgn L Blake, 7½" 1,000.00
Eocean, vase, owl on limb, sgn EB, mk, 10½" 1,200.00
Eocean, vase, pk floral, sgn AH, 13½" 400.00
Etched Matt, vase, portrait of lady w/flower in hair, 11" 150.00
Etched Matt, vase, sailboats/6 fishermen, A Wilson, 14" 600.00
Ethel, vase, 11" 200.00
Etna, bowl, mouse, 2½" 185.00
Etna, pitcher, floral, 6½" 100.00
Etna, vase, Beethoven, 12" 350.00
Etna, vase, frog & snake, 6½" 200.00
Evergreen, candle holder, triple, 7½" 65.00
Evergreen, console bowl, 14x7½" 35.00
Fairfield, bowl, 4½" 50.00
Flemish, comport, w/cover, 8½" 150.00
Flemish, jardiniere, floral, 8" 100.00
Flemish, jardiniere, ftd, 6" 95.00
Flemish, tub, hdls, mk, 4½" 55.00
Fleron, batter pitcher, 11½" 80.00
Fleron, bowl, flared rim, 4" 25.00
Fleron, bowl, 4" 25.00
Fleron, vase, flared rim, 9" 30.00
Florala, candlestick, 11" 35.00
Florala, wall pocket, 10" 55.00
Florenzo, basket, 5½" 55.00
Florenzo, pillow vase, 4" 30.00
Florenzo, window box, 3" 35.00
Floretta, ewer, grape cluster, 10½" .135.00
Floretta, vase, grape clusters, 17" 225.00
Forest, jardiniere, 7" 70.00
Forest, jardiniere & pedestal, 26" 485.00
Forest, pitcher, glossy, 5½" 145.00
Forest, teapot, glossy, 4½" 125.00
Forest, tub planter, hdls, 6" 65.00
Fruitone, wall pocket, 5½" 80.00
Fudji, vase, squeezebag Alhambre motif, sm bulb top, 11x4" . . .800.00
Garden ornament, frog w/banjo, 13½" 1,000.00
Garden ornament, gnomes on toadstool, 17" 1,100.00
Garden ornament, goose, preening, lg 750.00
Garden ornament, rabbit, crouching, lg 700.00
Glendale, vase, 12" 325.00

Second-Line Dickensware vase, lady golfer, 9", $750.00.

Glendale vase, 8", $250.00.

Glendale, wall bud vase, dbl, 7" .135.00
Glendale, wall pocket, mother+4 baby birds, 9" 130.00
Glendale, wall pocket, 2 birds on branch, 7x7" 75.00
Gloria, ewer, #G-12, 9" 40.00
Gloria, vase, dbl, 4½" 25.00
Gloria, vase, 12½" 85.00
Goldenglow, bowl, 16x3½" 60.00
Goldenglow, bowl vase, ftd, 5½" 45.00
Goldenglow, bud vase, 8½" 35.00
Goldenglow, ginger jar, hdls, 8" .90.00
Goldenglow, wall pocket, 11" 55.00
Graystone Garden Ware, Sunray, birdbath, w/fountain, 33½" . .175.00
Greenbriar, ewer, 11½" 90.00
Greenbriar, pitcher, 10" 80.00
Greenbriar, vase, 8" 70.00
Greora, strawberry pot, 8½" 115.00
Greora, vase, ftd, 4½" 50.00
Greora, vase, 11½" 70.00
Hobart, bowl, 9½x3" 30.00
Hudson, lamp base, bluebird, 14" 250.00
Hudson, vase, berries, 10¾" 150.00
Hudson, vase, dogwood, S Timberlake, hdls, 6½" 180.00
Hudson, vase, floral, hdls, sgn Pillsbury, 13½" 650.00
Hudson, vase, floral, sgn HP, 6" 230.00
Hudson, vase, floral, sgn Pillsbury, 15" 700.00
Hudson, vase, gnarled tree exposed roots, M Timberlake, 10" . .700.00
Hudson, vase, iris, EX art, loop hdls, bulbous, 10" 300.00
Hudson, vase, parrot, hdls, sgn Timberlake, 14" 2,000.00
Hudson, vase, roses w/long stems, sgn HP, 10½" 250.00
Hudson, vase, scenic, sgn Timberlake, 8½" 625.00
Hudson, vase, scenic w/swans, sgn Pillsbury, 14½" 1,600.00
Hudson, vase, scenic w/trees & pond, sgn McLaughlin, 9½" .1,100.00
Hudson, vase, snow scene, sgn Pillsbury, 9½" 1,300.00
Hudson, vase, snow-covered mtns & pine trees, Pillsbury, 7" . .700.00
Hudson, vase, tiger, 8" 1,100.00
Hudson-Perfecto, vase, pine cones, sgn Leffler, 10" 450.00
Hunter, mug, ducks in flight, incised fish, fish hdl, 5" 200.00
Hunter, pillow vase, butterflies, sgn UJ, 5x3½" 400.00
Hunter, pillow vase, duck, 4¾" .400.00
Ivoris, pitcher, 6" 45.00
Ivoris, vase, 7" 35.00
Ivory, bottle vase, 9" 45.00
Ivory, jardiniere, squirrels in tree/leaves, 6½" 45.00
Ivory, pillow vase, 5" 15.00
Ivory, sand jar, 16" 250.00
Ivory, wall pocket, ram, 10½" .225.00
Ivory, window planter, 15½x6" .60.00
Jap Birdimal, bowl vase, birds in 3 of 6 panels, sm rim, 4¾" 185.00
Jap Birdimal, ink well, trees/windmill/house, 2x4" 145.00
Jap Birdimal, oil pitcher, sgn HMR, 10½" 900.00
Jap Birdimal, umbrella stand, trees in bl w/yel moon, 20" 525.00
Jap Birdimal, vase, bl trees, 9" .300.00
Jap Birdimal, vase, fish, narrow neck, 4½" 450.00
Jap Birdimal, vase, geisha, sgn VMH, 13" 1,600.00
Jap Birdimal, vase, geisha/trees, sgn Rhead, 7" 600.00
Juneau, bud vase, 6" 40.00
Juneau, vase, hdls, 8" 85.00
Kenova, vase, floral, hdls, 6½" .85.00
Klyro, fan vase, 6" 45.00
Klyro, planter, 3½" 30.00
Klyro, wall pocket, 7½" 60.00
Knifewood, urn, 8" 125.00
L'Art Nouveau, corn bank, 8" .140.00
L'Art Nouveau, umbrella stand, glossy, 26" 500.00

L'Art Nouveau, vase, lady standing holds flower, 17½" 300.00
LaMar, vase, scenic w/trees, 11½" 295.00
LaSa, bud vase, mk, 5½" 125.00
LaSa, lamp, sgn, 8" 230.00
LaSa, vase, biplane decor, 9" .1,800.00
Lavonia, vase, 10" 40.00
Lido, basket, 8½" 45.00
Lido, cornucopia, 5" 20.00
Lido, ewer, 10½" 45.00
Lorbeek, bowl vase, 5"; +frog, 2" 60.00
Lorber, vase, satyrs, sgn DE, 13" 950.00
Loru, vase, 8" 50.00
Louella, bowl, 3" 20.00
Louella, hair receiver, 3" 55.00
Louwelsa, bowl, floral, 2½" 50.00
Louwelsa, clock, floral, 10½x12½" 600.00
Louwelsa, ewer, bird, sgn RGT, 14" 750.00
Louwelsa, ewer, floral, mk, 10" 255.00
Louwelsa, ewer, floral, sgn Burgess, 6" 175.00
Louwelsa, ewer, floral w/silver overlay, 9" 1,800.00
Louwelsa, jug, dbl, 6" 165.00
Louwelsa, mug, floral, sgn EA, 6" 275.00
Louwelsa, mug, monk portrait, 7" 800.00
Louwelsa, mug, squire portrait, sgn Ferrell, 6½" 1,200.00
Louwelsa, pillow vase, floral, sgn M, 4" 90.00
Louwelsa, pitcher, ftd, sgn MT, 5" 150.00
Louwelsa, plaque, Indian in headdress, LJ Burgess, 12½" dia .1,250.00
Louwelsa, tankard, grape cluster, sgn, 11" 250.00
Louwelsa, tobacco jar, floral, sgn CA, 5½" 380.00
Louwelsa, vase, chicks, sgn Minnie Mitchell, 11½" 1,800.00
Louwelsa, vase, dog, sgn A Wilson, 10½" 1,500.00
Louwelsa, vase, grape clusters & leaves, sgn Lybarger, 17" 700.00
Louwelsa, vase, grizzly bear, 13", NM 525.00
Louwelsa, vase, Indian, feather headdress, Kappas, 11" 950.00
Louwelsa, vase, pansies w/silver overlay, 6½" 2,000.00
Louwelsa, vase, thistles, sgn ML, 13" 300.00
Lustre, bowl, 4x2" 18.00
Lustre, bud vase, 6" 25.00
Lustre, candlestick, 9" 15.00
Lustre, comport, 4" 50.00
Luxor, bud vase, 7½" 20.00
Malverne, boat bowl, leaves, 11x5½" 40.00
Malverne, bud vase, 8½" 30.00
Malverne, console bowl, 14½x2"; +6" frog 60.00
Malverne, pillow vase, leaves, 8½" 45.00
Malverne, wall pocket, 11" 65.00
Mammy, cookie jar, 11" 250.00
Mammy, pitcher, syrup, 6" 250.00
Manhattan, pitcher, gr floral, 10" 60.00
Marbleized, comport, 8" 70.00
Marengo, wall pocket, 8½" 100.00
Marvo, bud vase, 9" 30.00
Marvo, console bowl, 10x2½"; +3" frog 60.00
Marvo, wall vase, 8½" 40.00
Matt Floretta, tankard, pears, mk, 10½" 280.00
Melrose, basket, 10" 180.00
Mi-Flo, bowl, floral, 4" 30.00
Minerva, planter, dancing satyrs, 12x16" 500.00
Minerva, vase, flamingos, 8½" .395.00
Mirror Black, strawberry jar, 6½" 65.00
Mirror Black, wall pocket, 8" 55.00
Monochrome, candlestick, 7" 30.00
Monochrome, comport, 10" 75.00
Muskota, bowl w/goose, 4½" .110.00

Muskota, elephant, 12½x7½" 700.00
Muskota, fishing boy, 6½" 110.00
Muskota, gate w/pots & cats, 7" 400.00
Muskota, girl w/doll, 8" 135.00
Muskota, girl w/flowers & hat, 9" 150.00
Muskota, nude on rock, 8" 130.00
Muskota, turtle bowl, 9½x4½" 150.00
Neiska, bowl, ftd, 4" 30.00
Noval, comport, 9½" 120.00
Novelty Line, dachshund, 8½x4½" 65.00
Novelty Line, monkey on peanut, 8x5" 45.00
Novelty Line, tray, fox, 7x3" 135.00
Novelty Line, tray, seal, 5½x3" 50.00
Novelty Line, wall pocket, man's face, dk gr/brn, 10½" ..140.00
Oak Leaf, wall pocket, 8½" 40.00
Orris, wall pocket, 9" 35.00
Panella, bowl, ftd, 3½" 25.00
Paragon, candle holders, 2", pr 30.00
Parian, vase, 13" 100.00
Parian, wall pocket, 10" 80.00
Pastel, ewer, 10" 50.00
Pastel, planter, #P-10, 6" 40.00
Patra, basket, 5½" 75.00
Patra, jardiniere, 6" 40.00
Patricia, bowl, 13" 80.00
Patricia, pelican planter, 5" 50.00
Patricia, swan planter, 3½" 40.00
Patricia, vase, ftd, 4½" 50.00
Patricia, vase, w/geese, 8" 125.00
Pearl, bowl, 3" 45.00
Pearl, bud vase, 7" 40.00
Pearl, wall vase, 7" 85.00
Perfecto, ewer, ear of corn, sgn A Haubrich, 12" 725.00
Perfecto, pillow vase, horse's head, sgn H Pillsbury, 10½" ...3,000.00
Pierre, pitcher, 5" 30.00
Pierre, teapot, pk, 8½" 60.00
Pumila, bowl, 4" 35.00
Pumila, wall pocket, 7" 60.00
Ragenda, vase, burgundy, 12" 65.00
Raydance, vase, wht, 7½" 35.00
Roba, cornucopia, 5½" 25.00
Roba, ewer, 11" 70.00
Rochelle, vase, floral, sgn HP, 13" 325.00
Rochelle, vase, floral, sgn TF, 6" 200.00
Roma, bowl, hdls, 3" 35.00
Roma, bud vase, triple, 6½" 40.00
Roma, candle holder, 10½" 35.00
Roma, comport, 11x4½" 145.00
Roma, console bowl, 4½x10½" 50.00
Roma, jardiniere, 5" 22.00
Roma, letter pocket, 7½x4½" 125.00
Roma, log planter, 3x10½" 40.00
Roma, wall pocket, 7" 50.00
Rosemont, jardiniere, 7" 150.00
Rosemont, vase, 10" 300.00
Rudlor, console bowl, floral, 4½x17½" 30.00
Sabrinian, basket, 7" 80.00
Sabrinian, bowl, ftd, 3½" 50.00
Sabrinian, bud vase, 7" 35.00
Sabrinian, ewer, 9" 165.00
Sabrinian, window box, 9x3½" 50.00
Senic, pillow vase, #S-11, 7½" 40.00
Senic, planter, #S-17, 5½" 55.00
Senic, vase, hdls, #S-16, 12½" 85.00

Sicard, bowl, 5" 525.00
Sicard, floor vase, blown-out grapevines, 22½x9" 5,000.00
Sicard, mug, 3½" 600.00
Sicard, pillow vase, 6½x10" 585.00
Sicard, vase, berries/leaves, purple/red, unmk, 3½" 250.00
Sicard, vase, blown-out cloverleaf top, 5¼" 400.00
Sicard, vase, floral, bl/rose irid, 4-lobed, bulb top, 11" ...1,400.00
Sicard, vase, floral, gold-gr w/pk & purple, sgn, 5½" ...400.00
Sicard, vase, florals, waisted w/lg integral hdls, 7¾" ..900.00

Sicard vase, lilies, signed, 6½", $500.00.

Sicard, vase, swirling floral, bl/gr/red, hdls, 9½x10" ...1,300.00
Silvertone, basket, grapes, 13" 185.00
Silvertone, vase, 9" 125.00
Silvertone, wall pocket, wild roses, 10½" 85.00
Softone, cornucopia, pk, 8½" 30.00
Softone, ewer, pk, 9½" 35.00
Softone, planter, bl, 8x4" 35.00
Souevo, tobacco jar, 6" 200.00
Souevo, vase, ftd, 6½x8" 80.00
Stellar, vase, 6" 120.00
Sydonia, bud vase, triple, 8½" 50.00
Sydonia, candle holder, dbl, w/bud vase, 11½" 90.00
Sydonia, cornucopia, 8½" 30.00
Sydonia, planter, 4" 35.00
Tivoli, bowl, 2½" 65.00
Trellis, wall shelf, 10½" 55.00
Turada, umbrella stand, 21" 750.00
Turkis, vase, hdls, 14" 80.00
Turkis, vase, sgn DE, 8½" 40.00
Tutone, basket, 7½" 85.00
Tutone, planter, 5½" 55.00
Tutone, vase, w/candle holder, 7" 50.00
Tutone, vase, 7½" 50.00
Tutone, wall pocket, 10½" 60.00
Velva, bowl, 3½x12½" 30.00
Velvetone, pitcher, 10" 80.00
Voile, jardiniere, 6" 85.00
Warwick, basket, 9" 80.00
Warwick, circle vase, 7" 65.00
Warwick, jardiniere, 7" 60.00
Warwick, pillow vase, 7" 40.00
Warwick, wall vase, 11½" 60.00
Wild Rose, basket, floral, 5½" 25.00
Wild Rose, candle holder, triple, 6" 50.00

Wild Rose, vase, floral, hdls, 8" 20.00
Woodcraft, basket, 9½" 125.00
Woodcraft, bowl, squirrel on branch, 3½" 75.00
Woodcraft, fan vase, 8" 30.00
Woodcraft, hanging basket, 6" 60.00
Woodcraft, mug, w/baby foxes, 6" 120.00
Woodcraft, owl vase, 16" 400.00
Woodcraft, planter, w/baby foxes, 6"; +flower frog 150.00
Woodcraft, vase, 9" 65.00
Woodcraft, wall pocket, w/owl, 10" 100.00
Woodrose, jardiniere, 3½" 35.00
Woodrose, wall pocket, 6" 65.00
Zona, baby plate, rolled edge, strutting duck, 7" 40.00
Zona, comport, floral, 5½" 50.00
Zona, mug, strutting duck, 3" 30.00
Zona, pitcher, floral, 7½" 135.00
Zona, plate, dinner; apples, 10" 25.00
Zona, umbrella stand, ladies holding flowers, glossy, 20½" 600.00

West Coast Pottery

Founded in Burbank, California, West Coast Pottery has become known for finely decorated artware and novelties.

Bowl, Dutch couple, coupe style, 14" 30.00
Bowl, pk, sq, low, 8" 6.00
Flower bowl, pk shell form, rectangular, 1½x7¼x5½" 8.00
Vase, aqua/pk swirl, abstract hdls 32.00
Vase, beige, sq, 14" 18.00
Vase, Dutch girl 25.00
Vase, pk/gray, #430, 8½" 10.00
Vase, shell, turq, #201 . . . . .7.50

Western Americana

The collecting of Western American a encompasses a broad spectrum of memorabilia and collectibles. Examples of various areas within the main stream would include the following fields: weapons, bottles, photographs, mining/railroad artifacts, cowboy paraphernalia, farm and ranch implements, maps, barbed wire, tokens, Indian relics, saloon/gambling items, and branding irons. Some of these areas have their own separate listings in this book.

Western Americana is not only a collecting field but is also a collecting *era* with specific boundries. Depending upon which field the collector decides to specialize in, prices can start at a few dollars and run into the hundreds.

There has been an increased amount of focus on Western Americana collectibles in recent years, and there are several books that explore this field. For additional reading, we recommend *Treasury of Frontier Relics* by Les Beitz and *Western Memorabilia* by William Ketchum, Jr. To better understand the complexities of pricing various types of collectibles, read as much as possible concerning the field you prefer. While one strand of barbed wire may be worth $5.00, another may be worth $50.00; the same holds true in all fields.

Our advisor for this category is Warren Anderson; he is listed in the Directory under Utah.

Branding iron, Lazy JW 15.00
Bridle, English work type, heavy brass 45.00
Bull whip, leather w/trn wood hdl, 108", EX 65.00
Bust, plaster, 'Genl Custer,' Civil War uniform 220.00
Chaps, Miles City Saddlery, buffalo fur, EX 300.00

Chaps, RT Frazier, Pueblo CO, leather, handmade, 1900, lg . . .100.00
Dietz Lantern, rustic, globe missing, not usable 20.00
Gauntlets, studded leather, old, EX 50.00
Horse bit, Texas model, used, complete .10.00
Miner's pan, rustic, pre-1900 vintage, usable 30.00
Pick head, rustic, hdl missing, shows wear 10.00
Railroad lock, brass, railroad initials, rustic 25.00

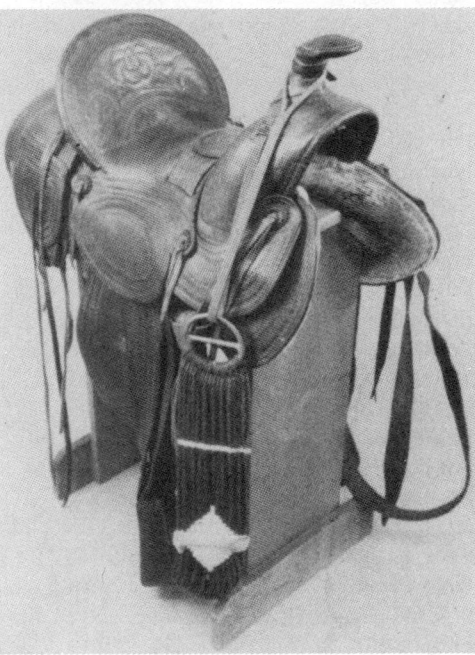

Saddle, F. G. Eldred, Sheridan WY, handmade, profuse hand tooling, built-in saddle bags, $300.00.

Saddle, McClellan 1904 US Cavalry, russet leather, 11½" . . .1,200.00
Saddle, RT Frazier, Pueblo CO, hand tooled, sq skirts, 1900 . . .500.00
Skull, buffalo, w/horns, old 100.00
Spur, rustic, sawtooth rowel 15.00
Spurs, bull rider's, Kelly, straps, pr 125.00
Spurs, Renalde, lady's legs, straps, pr 135.00
Spurs, Ricardo, eng on heel band, pr 165.00
Stirrup, lady's side saddle; Colonial Spanish silver, ornate 750.00
Tethering weight, CI, horse's head form, 1880s, 8x7x4½" 225.00
Varmit trap, rustic, complete, not usable 15.00

Westmoreland

Originally titled the Specialty Glass Company, Westmoreland began operations in East Liverpool, Ohio, producing utility items as well as tableware in milk glass and crystal. When the company moved to Grapeville, PA, in 1890, lamps, vases, covered animal dishes, and decorative plates were introduced. Prior to the 1920s, Westmoreland was a major manufacturer of carnival glass and soon thereafter added a line of lovely reproduction art glass items. High-quality milk glass became their speciality, accounting for about 90% of their production. Black glass was introduced in the 1940s, and later in the decade ruby-stained pieces and items decorated in the Mary Gregory style became popular. By the 1960s, colored glassware was being produced, examples of which are very popular with collectors today.

Early pieces were marked with a paper label; by the 1960s the ware was embossed with a superimposed 'WG.' The last mark was a circle containing 'Westmoreland' around the perimeter and a large 'W' in the center. The company closed in 1985.

The symbol (+) at the end of some of the following listings indicates items that have been reproduced. See also Animal Dishes with Covers and Carnival Glass.

Ash tray, Beaded Grape, milk glass, HP roses/bows, 4" 18.00
Ash tray, Beaded Grape, milk glass, 5" .11.00
Ash tray, English Hobnail, milk glass, hat form 10.00
Ash tray, Old Quilt, milk glass, rare, 6½" 24.00
Ash tray, Old Quilt, milk glass, 4" 20.00
Banana bowl, Old Quilt, milk glass, rare 60.00
Banana bowl, Wildflower & Lace, bl 17.00
Basket, English Hobnail, ruby 35.00
Basket, Panelled Grape, milk glass, split hdl, oval 28.00
Basket, Panelled Grape, purple slag, oval, 6½" 35.00
Basket, Pansy, pk & amethyst, #757, 4½" dia 18.00
Basket, Roses & Trellis, flared, lg 45.00
Bonbon, Panelled Grape, milk glass, ruffled, ftd 22.50
Bowl, Beaded Grape, milk glass, HP roses/bows, w/lid, ftd, 9" . .58.00
Bowl, Beaded Grape, milk glass, sq, w/lid, ftd, 7" (+) 32.00
Bowl, Beaded Grape, milk glass, sq, w/lid, ftd, 9" (+) 40.00
Bowl, Della Robbia, flared, plain, 12" .35.00
Bowl, Della Robbia, flared, pnt 58.00
Bowl, English Hobnail, milk glass, ped ft, hdls, 7¾" 35.00
Bowl, fruit; Della Robbia, plain, ftd, 6½x11¾" 42.00
Bowl, fruit; Della Robbia, pnt, ftd, 6½x11¾" 85.00
Bowl, fruit; Wildflower & Lace, pk, 10" 22.00
Bowl, Old Quilt, milk glass, bell shape, ftd, 9" 50.00
Bowl, Old Quilt, milk glass, flared, ftd, 7½" 30.00
Bowl, Old Quilt, milk glass, flared, rare, 13" 95.00
Bowl, Panelled Grape, milk glass, lace edge, ftd, 10" 38.00
Bowl, Panelled Grape, milk glass, oval, 6½" 20.00
Bowl, Panelled Grape, milk glass, w/lid, ftd, rare, 9" 50.00
Box, bl opaque, HP decor, egg form 22.00
Butter dish, Old Quilt, milk glass, ¼-lb 30.00
Butter dish, Panelled Grape, ¼-lb 25.00
Cake plate, Panelled Grape, milk glass, skirted 60.00
Cake plate, Ring & Petal, milk glass 45.00
Candle holder, Panelled Grape, milk glass, octagon, 4", pr 20.00
Candlestick, Dolphin, milk glass, 9¼" (+) 35.00
Candlestick, Ring & Petal, milk glass, pr 30.00
Candlestick, Spiral, purple slag, 6½" 40.00
Candy dish, Argonaut Shell, ruby, dolphin hdls 45.00
Candy dish, English Hobnail, milk glass, 3-ftd 28.00

Candy dish, green
satin, $32.50.

Candy dish, Old Quilt, milk glass, w/lid, low ftd 20.00
Candy dish, Panelled Grape, milk glass, 3-ftd, w/lid 32.00
Card receiver, hand form, milk glass, pnt roses & bows 28.00
Catalog, hardbk loose-leaf notebook, EX 38.00
Celery vase, Old Quilt, milk glass, 6½" 28.00

Cheese dish, Panelled Grape, milk glass 38.00
Cigar holder, clear, etched, #352 . . . . .15.00
Compote, Della Robbia 18.00
Compote, Della Robbia, pnt 32.00
Compote, Dolphin, pk, #1049, 6x8" 45.00
Compote, English Hobnail, milk glass, dbl crimp, 5" 20.00
Compote, Panelled Grape, milk glass, crimped, ftd, 9" 35.00
Compote, Panelled Grape, milk glass, HP roses/bows, ftd, 7" . .42.00
Compote, Panelled Grape, milk glass, w/lid, ftd, 7" 35.00
Cordial, Wakefield, crystal 8.00
Creamer, Panelled Grape, milk glass, 5" 15.00
Creamer & sugar bowl, Old Quilt, milk glass, w/lid 50.00
Creamer & sugar bowl, owl, cobalt, glass eyes (+) 10.00
Creamer & sugar bowl, Panelled Grape, milk glass, lg, pr 40.00
Creamer & sugar bowl, Panelled Grape, milk glass, sm 22.50
Creamer & sugar bowl, peacock, deep bl w/opal trim, 5½" 125.00
Creamer & sugar bowl, swan, cobalt carnival, w/lid (+) 40.00
Cruet, English Hobnail, milk glass, 4" .17.50
Cruet, Old Quilt, milk glass 35.00
Cruet, Panelled Grape, milk glass, w/stopper, 2-oz 20.00
Cup & saucer, Old Quilt, milk glass 25.00
Cup & saucer, Panelled Grape, milk glass 15.00
Dish, covered; camel, milk glass 100.00
Dish, covered; cat on ribbed base, bl 95.00
Dish, covered; fox, lacy base, milk glass, lg 125.00
Dish, covered; hen on basket base, milk glass 45.00
Dish, covered; swan, wings up, bl opaque 125.00
Goblet, Ashburton, gr, orig label 8.00
Goblet, Della Robbia, plain, 6" 12.00
Goblet, Della Robbia, pnt, 6" 20.00
Goblet, Panelled Grape, milk glass, 8-oz 16.00
Honey box, Panelled Grape, blk, rnd, experimental 1984 pc 35.00
Ivy ball, English Hobnail, milk glass, 5½" 18.00
Jardiniere, Old Quilt, milk glass, cupped, rare, 6½" 40.00
Jardiniere, Panelled Grape, milk glass, ftd, 5" 20.00
Jardiniere, Panelled Grape, milk glass, ftd, 6½" 30.00
Mayonnaise, Old Quilt, bell form 16.00
Mayonnaise, Panelled Grape, milk glass, ftd 20.00
Nappy, Beaded Grape, milk glass, bell shape, 8" 18.00
Nappy, Panelled Grape, milk glass, hdls, 5" 22.00
Pitcher, Old Quilt, milk glass, water sz 40.00
Pitcher, Panelled Grape, milk glass, 1-pt 35.00
Pitcher, Panelled Grape, milk glass, 1-qt 38.00
Pitcher, syrup; Old Quilt, milk glass 22.00
Planter, Panelled Grape, milk glass, 5x9" 35.00
Plate, Old Quilt, milk glass, 10½" 35.00
Plate, Panelled Grape, milk glass, #73198, 14½" 75.00
Plate, Panelled Grape, milk glass, 6" 7.00
Plate, Panelled Grape, milk glass, 8" 15.00
Plate, sandwich; Old Quilt, milk glass, 8½" 32.00
Plate, Zodiac signs, wht on bl mist, 5½" 20.00
Platter, Panelled Grape, milk glass, 14" 75.00
Puff box, Beaded Grape, milk glass, HP roses/bows, w/lid 28.00
Puff box, Old Quilt, milk glass, w/lid, 4½" 25.00
Punch set, 3 Fruits, ice bl carnival, mc fruits, 15-pc 250.00
Relish, Old Quilt, milk glass, 9" 22.00
Rose bowl, Panelled Grape, milk glass, ftd, 4" 15.00
Sauce boat, Panelled Grape, w/tray, milk glass 48.00
Shakers, Della Robbia, pr 35.00
Shakers, Old Quilt, milk glass 15.00
Shakers, Old Quilt, milk glass, pr 25.00
Shakers, Panelled Grape, milk glass, ftd, pr 20.00
Sherbet, Della Robbia, plain, 4¾" 8.00
Sherbet, Della Robbia, pnt, 4¾" 14.00

Sherbet, Old Quilt, milk glass 20.00
Sherbet, Panelled Grape, milk glass, high or low ft, rare 16.00
Slipper, bl mist, HP decor 18.00
Soap dish, Panelled Grape, milk glass, rare 45.00
Sweetmeat, Della Robbia, milk glass, 8" 38.00
Sweetmeat, Old Quilt, milk glass, w/lid, ftd 30.00
Toothpick holder, milk glass, 3 swan hdls 18.00
Tumbler, juice; Old Quilt, milk glass, rare 15.00
Tumbler, Panelled Grape, milk glass .15.00
Vase, Old Quilt, aqua ice carnival, ruffle top, ftd, 7" 35.00
Vase, Old Quilt, milk glass, bell shape, rare, 9" 48.00
Vase, Panelled Grape, milk glass, bell shape, 9" 28.00
Wine, Panelled Grape, milk glass 15.00

Wheatley, T. J.

In 1880 after a brief association with the Coultry Works, Thomas J. Wheatley opened his own studio in Cincinnati, Ohio, claiming to have been the first to discover the secret of underglaze slip decoration on an unbaked clay vessel. He applied for and was granted a patent for his process. Demand for his ware increased to the point that several artists were hired to decorate the ware. The company incorporated in 1880 as the Cincinnati Art Pottery, but until 1882 it continued to operate under Wheatley's name. Ware from this period is marked 'T.J. Wheatley' or 'T.J.W. and Co.,' and it may be dated.

Vase, applied blossoms and leaves on green ground, marked 'No. 53 Pat Sep 1880,' 18", $825.00.

Vase, floral, Limoges style, sgn/July 1880, 8¾", EX 150.00
Vase, gr, buds/broad leaves, 4 flared buttress ft, 7x9½" 750.00
Vase, gr, pk dogwood in slip relief, sq form, 9x7x3½" 150.00
Vase, gr, 8 emb buds/alternating leaves, mk W, 11x11" 600.00
Vase, gr/EX feathering, gourd form, 4 vertical str hdls, 9½" 500.00

Whieldon

Thomas Whieldon was regarded as the finest of the Staffordshire potters of the mid-1700s. He produced marbled and black Egyptian wares, as well as tortoise shell, a mottled brown-glazed earthenware accented with touches of blue and yellow. In 1754 he became a partner of Josiah Wedgwood. Other potters produced similar wares, and today the term Whieldon is used generically.

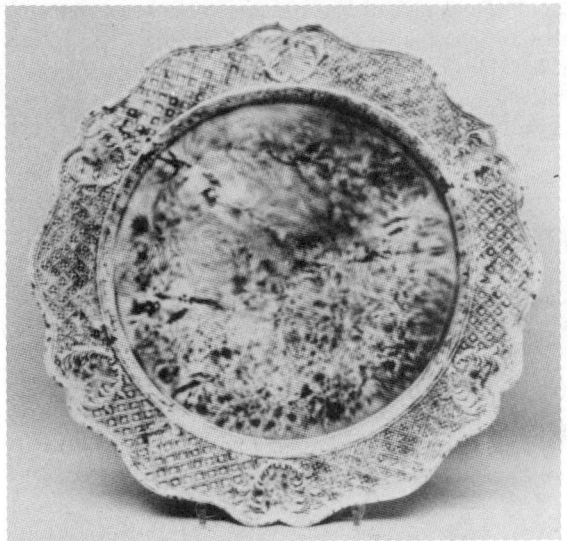

Charger, gray, green, and brown mottle; diapered rim with leafy cartouches, 1760s, 14", $1,200.00.

Coffeepot, gr/yel/brn streaky glaze, rpr, 9" 800.00
Pitcher, tankard; flint enamel glaze, 12", M 160.00
Tea caddy, Apollo/sprigs relief, dtd 1779, rpr, 6" 700.00
Teapot, cauliflower, deep gr, ca 1760, lg, NM 1,100.00
Tray, gray-gr mottle, yel/brn daubs, gadrooned, hdls, 9" L . . .2,000.00

Wicker

Wicker is the basket-like material used in many types of furniture and accessories. It may be made from bamboo cane, rattan, reed, or artificial fibers. It is airy, lightweight, and very popular in hot regions.

Imported from the Orient in the 18th century, it was first manufactured in the United States in about 1850. The elaborate, closely-woven Victorian designs belong to the mid-to-late 1800s, and the simple styles with coarse reedings usually indicate a post-1900 production. Art Deco styles followed in the twenties and thirties.

The most important consideration in buying wicker is condition — it can be restored, but only by a professional. Age is an important factor, but be aware that 'Victorian-style' furniture is being manufactured today.

Armchair, Nouveau style, Heywood-Wakefield, #6213, tall . . .500.00
Baby buggy, ornate, Victorian 600.00
Baby cradle, swings in fr, 1900 . . . . .1,100.00
Basket, arched hdl, early 1900s, 7½x9x5¾" 45.00
Basket, long cone shape, hdls, hanging, old 40.00
Chair, basketweave & lattice, Wakefield, child's sz 300.00
Chair, butterfly bk rest, cabriole legs, Wakefield, lady's 300.00
Chair, reception; heart-shaped bk, cabriole legs, natural 200.00
Chair, side; ornate fan bk, pressed seat, fancy apron 175.00
Chair, spiral stiles w/crest, tall bk, Heywood-Wakefield 800.00
Conversation bench, early 1900s 425.00
Daybed, scrolled headrest, att Heywood-Wakefield, 158" 425.00
Daybed, scrolled headrest, natural, Wakefield, 75", EX 2,200.00
Doll carriage, windowed hood, brakes, ca 1930, EX 250.00
Doll cradle, tight weave, w/hood, ca 1920s, lg 250.00
Go-cart, elaborate scrolls, uphl seat, w/parasol, 1890s 1,000.00
Highchair, Victorian, woven braid trim, simple design 150.00
Lamp, table; pyramid shade w/lattice decor, tall 375.00
Lamp, table; simple, w/shade, 24" 75.00
Loveseat, rolled bk & arm rests, caned seat, natural, 34½" 500.00
Plant stand, circular top, cabriole legs, fancy apron 350.00

Plant stand w/hanging birdcage in center, loose weave, 64" ...375.00
Potty chair, w/graniteware pot, removable tray, ca 1900, 16" 90.00
Rocker, high bk, arms & apron very elaborate, 1890s, 38" 675.00
Rocker, loose weave, sq bk w/high arm rest 240.00
Rocker, platform; arched & rolled fr, basketweave seat, pr ...1,900.00

Platform rocker, late 19th century, 47", $700.00.

Rocker, platform; Nouveau style, Heywood-Wakefield, sm 325.00
Rocker, platform; rolled serpentine fr, crown headrest 325.00
Rug beater, old orig varnish, 32" 28.00
Rug beater, orange/gr woven hdl, 9x29½" 26.00
Settee, loose weave, half-cushioned bk & cushioned seat 280.00
Sofa & lounge chair, geometric design, str apron, 70" sofa ...1,200.00
Stroller, lg rear rubber tires, Haywood-Wakefield, 38x43" 425.00
Table, occasional; sunburst apron, out-swept legs, 29x22x18" ..400.00
Table, scrollwork, curved legs, 20x16x16" 95.00
Table, tight weave, rnd, w/2 shelves 180.00
Tea cart, 2-tier, simple weave, wood fr, 30x36" L 350.00
Tray, breakfast; w/cup holder, paper rack on side, 1920s 110.00

Willets

The Willets Manufacturing Company of Trenton, New Jersey, produced a type of belleek porcelain during the late 1880s and 1890s. Examples were often marked with a coiled snake that formed a 'W' with 'Willets' below and 'Belleek' above.

Not all Willet's is factory decorated. Items painted by amateurs outside the factory are worth considerably less. In the listings below, all items are belleek unless noted otherwise. For more information, we recommend *American Belleek* with full-color photos and current market values, by Mary Frank Gaston. You will find her address in the Directory under Texas.

Bowl, floral swags & inscription dtd 1901, hdls, 7½" 155.00
Bowl, gold spray, pk buds, coral-shape hdls, pk mk, 2½x4¼" ...175.00
Bowl, silver & blk decor, 8" 95.00
Centerpiece, 5 pcs joined by shell ft, gold trim, 12½" L 90.00
Chalice, red berries/gr leaves/gold trim, mk, 11½" 450.00
Chocolate pot, gilt decor, mk, 8½" 95.00
Cigar/match holder, tree-trunk form, gold trim, mk, 4" 245.00
Creamer & sugar bowl, gold Nouveau decor, ped ft, #105 ......85.00
Cup & saucer, demi; bl geometrics w/mauve/rust/gold, mk 120.00

Cup & saucer, demi; emb veining traced in gold, pk mk 50.00
Cup & saucer, fleur-de-lis & floral w/gold, mk 80.00
Cup & saucer, gold paste floral, mk 110.00
Egg cup, petal design, gold trim, mk, 2¾" 175.00
Hatpin holder, gold paste decor 55.00
Mug, portraits of lady/cherub, artist sgn/mk, 5¼" 900.00
Pitcher, gold paste floral, bamboo shape, 5" 155.00
Pitcher, nautilus shell mold, ivory/pk/gold, coral hdl, 8" 495.00
Pitcher, pk/bl garlands, gold trim, slender, mk, 9½" 325.00
Pitcher, seashell, wht/rose, gold coral hdl, 7½x8½" 995.00
Pitcher, tankard; grapes, dragon hdl, sgn 1910, 15" 350.00
Plate, portrait, scalloped, sgn Bower 225.00
Salt cellar, bl florals, gold tracery, ruffled 36.00
Vase, birds of paradise, gold on pk lustre, gr mk, 17" 225.00

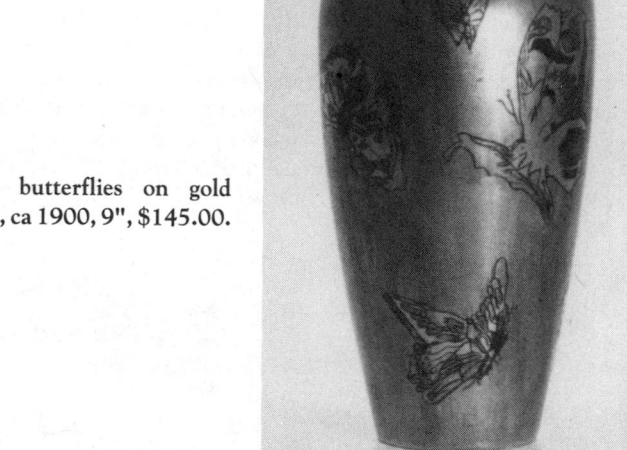

Vase, butterflies on gold lustre, ca 1900, 9", $145.00.

Vase, chrysanthemums, Deco-style hdls/neck, mk, 20½" 375.00
Vase, red geraniums, mk, 15" 275.00
Vase, roses on gr-yel mottle, sgn Aulieck, 14" 350.00
Vase, sterling overlay, Deco-style hdls/neck, mk, 12¾" 325.00
Vase, 16 birds, blk on orange, mk, 11½" 295.00

Willow Ware

Willow Ware, inspired no doubt by the numerous patterns of the blue and white Nanking imports, has been popular since the late eighteenth century and has been made in as many variations as there were manufacturers. English transfer wares by such notable firms as Allerton and Ridgway are the most sought-after and the most expensive. Japanese potters have been producing Willow-patterned dinnerware since the late 1800s, and American manufacturers have followed suit. Although blue is the color most commonly used, mauve, black, and even multicolor Willow Ware may be found. Complementary glassware, tinware, and linens have also been made.

In addition to 'Allerton' and 'Ridgway,' both companies used the possessive forms of their names in marking their wares (i.e. Allerton's, Ridgway's). For further study, we recommend the book *Blue Willow*, with full-color photos and current prices, by Mary Frank Gaston. You will find her address in the Directory under Texas. In the following listings, if no manufacturer is noted, the ware is unmarked.

Ash tray, Royal Doulton, sq, 6" 28.00
Baking dish, Hall China, 3x8" 16.00
Baking dish, Japan, oven proof, 2½x5" 16.00

Bone dish, Minton, dagger border, 8¼" 48.00
Bowl, Gibson & Sons, w/lid 50.00
Bowl, Japan, w/lid, old, EX 60.00
Bowl, salad; Ridgway's, sq, ca 1927, 4x9" 60.00
Bowl, sauce; Ridgway's, mc, HP, butterfly border, 5" 30.00
Bowl, soup; Homer laughlin, 1930s, 8" .12.50
Bowl, vegetable; Allerton, rectangular, ca 1890, 9" 150.00
Bowl, vegetable; Allerton, w/lid, 6x12" .95.00
Bowl, vegetable; Allerton, w/lid, 8½x10" 90.00
Butter dish, Buffalo, 8" 80.00
Butter dish, Myott & Son, rnd, ca 1936 .75.00
Butter dish, unmk Japan, 4½x7" 30.00
Butter pat, Grindley 22.00
Cake plate, Balmoral China, Flow Blue, sq, 10" 65.00
Cake plate, Cook, flat, 12" 36.00
Cake plate, Japan, red 30.00
Cake stand, unmk English, 2½x8½" 175.00
Candle holder, Doulton, Flow Blue, ca 1891-1902, 7½", pr 335.00
Candle lamp, Japan, 11½" 20.00
Canister set, unmk Japan, sq, w/lids, 3-pc 150.00
Chamber pot, Doulton, Flow Blue, 5½x9¼" 240.00

Cheese keeper, numbered, 8" long, $100.00.

Clock, Smith's, rnd, tin 85.00
Coffeepot, Burgess & Leigh, scroll & floral border, 7½" 90.00
Coffeepot, Josiah Wedgwood, 8" 80.00
Compote, Coalport, gold trim, ca 1960, 5x9½" 170.00
Compote, Doulton, Flow Blue, w/stand, 3x9" 165.00
Compote, unmk, mc, 3x9½" 65.00
Creamer & sugar bowl, Booth's, gold trim 120.00
Cruet, unmk Japan, pr 48.00
Cup, coffee; unmk, red, ca 1900 . . . . .30.00
Cup & saucer, Arklow, gold trim 20.00
Cup & saucer, demitasse; Burgess & Leigh, gold trim, 1930s 20.00
Cup & saucer, Japan, int decor 17.50
Cup & saucer, unmk English, blk 40.00
Dish, honey; Staffordshire, 4" 24.00
Dish, vegetable; Allerton, rnd, scalloped edge, ca 1890, 10" 60.00
Drainer, meat; dagger border, 16" 225.00
Gravy boat, Booth's, w/attached underplate, 4x8½" 70.00
Jar, coffee; unmk Japan 30.00
Jar, ginger; Mason's, pk, scenic w/scroll & floral border, 9" 70.00
Jug, batter; Hazel Atlas, frosted glass, 8½" 50.00
Jug, toby; Staffordshire, 5½" 400.00
Lamp, kerosene; Japan, w/reflector, 8" .65.00
Lamp, teapot form, 3 figures & bridge, butterfly border 50.00
Pitcher, milk; Mason's, mc, scroll/floral border, 5" 65.00
Pitcher, milk; McCoy, 9" 25.00

Place setting, Booth's, bow knot border, 3-pc 65.00
Plate, Allerton, butterfly border, 7½" 25.00
Plate, Allerton, 10" 25.00
Plate, Buffalo, Gaudy Willow, HP, 7" 90.00
Plate, Buffalo, pk, 9½" 35.00
Plate, Doulton, brn, 8½" 50.00
Plate, fish-form, scenic, dagger border, 7x10" 115.00
Plate, Gibson & Sons, 10" 14.00
Plate, grill; Occupied Japan, 10" 24.00
Plate, grill; Wallace Co, pk, 9½" 25.00
Plate, Imperial Royale, gr, 9½" 25.00
Plate, Japan, HP, 8½" 65.00
Plate, Mason's, scroll/floral border, 10" 25.00
Plate, Old Gustavsberg, red, 8½" 27.00
Plate, Staffordshire, mc, butterfly border, 9" 55.00
Plate, Wood & Sons, HP, 9" 28.00
Platter, Allerton, ca 1929-1942, 5½x7" 38.00
Platter, Booth's, bow knot border w/gold trim, oval, 16x14" . . .125.00
Platter, Burgess & Leigh, scroll/floral border, oval, 11x8½" 75.00
Platter, Japan, birds, 12" 30.00
Platter, Meakin, 14" 70.00
Platter, oval, scalloped ftd base, 19x15½" 200.00
Platter, Ridgway's, mc, HP, oval, 6½x5" 70.00
Platter, Royal, 12" 35.00
Platter, unmk, 14x11½" 135.00
Platter, unmk, 18" 115.00
Platter, W&SE, 15½x12" 210.00
Punch bowl, 6x9¼" 165.00
Salt box, Japan, wooden lid, 5x5" 65.00
Shakers, Japan, hdld, 3", pr 30.00
Shakers, unmk, 3½", pr 12.50
Shakers, unmk, 5½" 14.00
Spice set, Japan, 6-pc 60.00
Spoon, soup; Japan, 5½" 7.00
Spoon & fork, salad; Willow hdls, pr 12.50
Spoon rest, dbl, Japan, 9" 25.00
Sugar bowl, Booth's, gold trim, ca 1912, 3" 50.00
Teapot, Ashworth, ca 1880, 6" 95.00
Teapot, Booth's, 7" 125.00
Teapot, Maling, ca 1875-1908 . . . . .90.00
Teapot, Wedgwood, gold trim, ca 1908, 5½x6¼" 95.00
Toaster, American, Pan Electrical Mfg, 7x7" 400.00
Toothpick holder, Buffalo, 2¼" 35.00
Tray, bread; Booth's, scenic, scalloped edge, ca 1912, 12" L 90.00
Wall plaque, England, brass plate in oak fr, 7" dia 90.00
Wash bowl & pitcher, Doulton, ca 1891-1902 . . . . .750.00

Winchester

The Winchester Repeating Arms Company lost their important government contract after WWI and of necessity turned to the manufacture of sporting goods, hardware items, tools, etc. to augment their gun production. Between 1920 and 1931, over 7,500 different items, each marked 'Winchester Trademark U.S.A.,' were offered for sale by thousands of Winchester Hardware stores throughout the country. After 1931 the firm became Winchester-Western. See also Knives.

Our advisor for this category is James Anderson; he is listed in the Directory under Minnesota.

Calendar, store sz, EX 235.00
Calendar, 1919, M 165.00
Calendar, 1927, EX 210.00
Calendar, 1927, VG 180.00

Chisel, wood; ½" 25.00
Compass, sun; 1944 Army Corp Engineers 200.00
Envelope, hunting scene, 4 for 185.00
Fishing lure, June Bug spinner, #9716 ....65.00
Fishing plug, EX 275.00
Fly reel, #1236 ....75.00
Golf ball 165.00
Hammer, claw 65.00
Hatchet, 4⅝" wide, M 65.00
Ice skates, clamp-on style, EX 30.00
Knife, electrician's, VG 75.00
Knife, pocket; #3031, NM 100.00
Padlock 80.00
Pants, hunting; NM 50.00
Paperweight, 1910 ....60.00
Poster, tools, 3-part, early 225.00
Razor, safety; MIB 45.00
Razor strop 75.00
Receipt 10.00
Rod & reel, #5510 & #4350, EX 150.00
Rule, folding, boxwood 75.00
Ruler, brass, mk Winchester Western, NM 40.00
Screwdriver, 10" 20.00
Screwdriver, 14" 35.00
Shot bag 15.00
Sign, antler gunrack w/guns/mallards, tin, 1913, 30x36" 1,450.00
Spinner, #9632 ....40.00
Spinner, #9649, w/feather 50.00
Split shot holder, #9114 ....40.00
Tackle box, EX 85.00
Thermos, 1-qt 125.00
Umpire's chest protector 145.00
Wrench, #1131, open end 28.00
Wrench, #1213, open end 25.00
Wrench, pipe; 10" 45.00
Wrench, pipe; 6" 45.00

Windmill Weights

Windmill weights were used to protect the windmill's plunger rod from damage during high winds by adding weight that slowed down the speed of the blades.

Hummer rooster, marked 'E-184,' no paint, $350.00; With original colored paint, $450.00.

Bull, Fairbury NE, no pnt, 58-lb, 18¼x24½x1⅛" 650.00
Bull, full bodied, CI, no pnt, 13x14" 525.00
Horse, bob-tailed, CI, free-standing, #58, 17x18" 350.00
Horse, Dempster, bob-tailed, old rpt, 15½" 300.00
Horse, Dempster, long tailed, VG pnt, 57-lb, 17¼x21½x2¼" 650.00
Moon crescent, Fairbanks Morse, 1900, 22-lb, 11x6⅝" 150.00
Moon crescent, Fairbanks Morse, 1900, 27-lb, 10x6½x3½" 135.00
Rooster, CI, full bodied, EX detail, pnt traces, 19" 625.00
Rooster, CI, no pnt, 19" 525.00
Rooster, Elgin, rainbow tail, VG pnt, 60-lb, 18x16x3" 825.00
Rooster, Elgin, U-form base, EX pnt, 63-lb, 19½x18x1¾" 750.00
Rooster, Elgin #2, no pnt, 34-lb, 16½x15½x4½" 725.00
Rooster, Hummer, worn pnt, 1900, 8⅞x9⅞x1¾" 285.00
Star, US Wind Engine, no pnt, ca 1890s, 14½x14½x3" 400.00
W form, Althouse Wheeler, WI, ca 1900, 22-lb, 19½x9x2½" ..265.00

Wire Ware

Two thousand years B.C. wire was made by cutting sheet metal into strips which were shaped with mallet and file. By the late 13th century, craftsmen in Europe had developed a method of pulling these strips through progressively smaller holes until the desired gauge was obtained. During the Industrial Revolution of the late 1800s, machinery was developed that could produce wire cheaply and easily; and it became a popular commercial commodity. It was used to produce large items such as garden benches and fencing as well as innumerable small pieces for use in the kitchen or on the farm. Beware of reproductions.

Our advisor for this category is Rosella Tinsley; she is listed in the Directory under Kansas.

Basket, calling card; twisted wire, oval, ftd, hdl atop 85.00
Basket, coiled/wrapped iron hdls, 14x24", EX 110.00
Basket, diamond weave, wavy wire, 2¾x11x7" 48.00
Basket, egg; hexagonal, wire in circles, top hdl 50.00
Basket, egg; rnd bottom, heavy wire, folding, old, sm 25.00
Basket, fruit; rnd, openwork designs, ca 1900, 5x14" 80.00
Basket, miner's, oblong w/higher wire bk, 8½x8x5" 30.00
Basket, potato; bushel basket shape, wire bail hdl, old 45.00
Basket, tulip shape, folding 42.00
Basket, vegetable; fine wire, bail hdl, ca 1870, sm 35.00
Basket, washing; ball shape, 2-pc w/diamond design, hdls 48.00
Bowl, centerpc; w/3 arms supporting sm wire bowls, 23" H 95.00
Card holder, twisted wire w/row of 12 rnd loops 35.00
Compote, twisted wire, looped edge, 2 loop hdls, ftd 95.00
Door mat, ½" thick wire in wavy pattern, 32x20" 36.00
Drainer, rnd holder for silverware, ca 1900, 4x15" dia 50.00

Egg carrier, ca 1870-1890, $65.00.

Egg tongs, heavy, 2 oval cups, 11½" L 35.00
Napkin ring, twisted wire, fancy design, pr 95.00
Pen rack, horseshoe shape, easel bk, 3 prongs ea side 65.00
Pie lifter, 2-tine, wood hdl 40.00
Plant stand, semicircular, 3-tier, pnt, 36x32" 195.00
Rack, skewer; 6 skewers in 3 szs, ca 1860 ....195.00
Trivet, hexagonal, 6-ftd, 7½" dia 35.00
Trivet, ornately twisted wire, curved edge, ftd, 9" dia 60.00

Witch Balls

Witch balls were a Victorian fad touted to be meritorious toward ridding the house of evil spirits, thus warding off sickness and bad luck. Folklore would have it that by wiping the dust and soot from the ball, the spirits were exorcised. It is much more probable, however, considering the fact that such beautiful art glass was used in their making, that the ostensive Victorians perpetrated the myth rather tongue-in-cheek while enjoying them as lovely decorations for their homes.

Amethyst w/wht loops, +matching 9¾" ftd stand 1,400.00
Aqua w/lg red spots, filled w/plaster of Paris, +vase, 11" 350.00
Aquamarine w/bl/wht/purple diagonally swirled stripes, 3" 300.00
Clear, cranberry/wht loops, +trumpet-shaped stand, 12½" 650.00
Cobalt, +stand w/rnd rim & smooth base, 1870s, 8" 260.00
Cobalt w/wht loops, +ftd vase, att Pittsburgh, 10" 2,400.00
Dk amber, +matching stand w/folded rim, 12" 440.00
Med bl opaque, 5½" 45.00
Tortoise shell, lt amber w/red splotches, ca 1860, 4" 100.00
Yel-gr, wht opal stripes, ground mouth, Am, ca 1900, 5" 120.00

Woodcarvings

Wood sculptures represent an important section of American folk art. Wood carvings were made not only by skilled woodworkers such as cabinetmakers, carpenters, etc. but by amateur 'whittlers' as well. They take the form of circus-wagon figures, carousel animals, decoys, busts, figurines, and cigar store Indians. Oriental artists show themselves to have been as proficient with the medium of wood as they were with ivory or hardstone. See also Carousel Animals; Decoys; Tobacciana.

Adolf Hitler, articulated arms & legs, WWII, 9" 135.00
Airplane, single engine, EX pnt, 1930s, 4x11x7½" 35.00
Airplane, Spirit of St Louis, EX pnt, 1920s, 19x14" 175.00
Alligator, many teeth, 1-pc, sgn/dtd 1931, 2½x12x2" 125.00
Bird, pine, stylized, lg head, short tail, ca 1900, 2¼x5x1¾" 65.00
Cigar store Indian, cigar in hand, EX pnt, 1900, 9x3½x1¼" ...145.00
Eagle, full wing spread, flat bk, ca 1870, 9x16" 260.00
Elephant, pine, old mc pnt, ca 1900, 2½x4½x3½" 45.00
Fan/rosettes, owl center, cherry, Victorian, 14x15x5" 450.00
Farmer, bib overalls, movable arm w/bucket, 5½" 185.00
Flapper lady, curly hair, short skirt, HP, 1920s, 14" 125.00
Girl w/lunch box & book, EX pnt & details, 5" 125.00
Indian, primitive, worn mc pnt, age cracks, 1900s, 74" 600.00
Indian chief, EX pnt, ca 1930, 8x2x1" 25.00
Man w/lg hat, MOP inlay eyes, EX details, 1930s, 10x5½" 125.00
Parrot, perched on bar in handmade tin cage, mc pnt, 1900 ...250.00
Parrot, perched on wire ring, mc, ca 1910, 22x7½" 440.00
Plaque, bull's head mtd on oval, EX detailing, 27x15" 700.00
Snake, articulated, 16 segments, orig gr w/mc spots, 35" 170.00
Soldier, Army WWII, pnt features, cloth uniform & cap, 11½" .85.00
Sow, leather ears, glass eyes, worn pk/wht pnt, 18" L 475.00
Stove, potbellied, EX details & pnt, 9x2" 38.00

Sword, swordfish blade, ornate cvg, gold-pnt hdl, 1903, 38" ...165.00
Uncle Sam, articulated arms, EX pnt/details, 1910s, 35" ...175.00
Wagon pulled by 2 oxen, 1930s, 12x24x10" 250.00
Wall pocket, arched bk w/fish & bird w/prey relief, 12" W 160.00

Eagle podium, ca 1880, 61", $2,500.00.

Woodenware

Woodenware (or treenware, as it is sometimes called) generally refers to those wooden items such as spoons, bowls, food molds, etc. that were used in the preparation of food. Common during the 18th and 19th centuries, these wares were designed from a strictly functional viewpoint and were used on a day-to-day basis. With the advent of the Industrial Revolution which brought it new materials and products, many of the old woodenwares were simply discarded. Today, original hand-crafted American woodenwares are extremely difficult to find.

Barrel, staved, wood bands & lid, red pnt, 23x19" dia 250.00
Barrel, 6 lock-lapped hoops, old pnt, open top, 1700s, sm 85.00
Bowl, ash, scrubbed patina, 6x19x20½" 90.00
Bowl, ash w/some burl, egg shape, hanging hole, 6x13½x16" ..400.00
Bowl, burl, ash w/EX figure/color, rim crack, 2¼x5½" 130.00
Bowl, burl, EX figure, filled-in age crack, 5x18", VG 425.00
Bowl, burl, EX figure, trn int detailing, 5x15", VG 700.00
Bowl, burl, EX figure, worn finish, 2⅝x6" 450.00
Bowl, burl, EX figure, worn patina, minor cracks, 4¾x13" 900.00
Bowl, burl, EX figure & patina, minor cracks, 6½x15½" 2,000.00
Bowl, burl, EX figure/color, cut-out raised hdls, 4x11x17" ...2,200.00
Bowl, burl, EX figure/color, w/lid, 3x4¼", EX 850.00
Bowl, burl, EX figure/G color, protruding hdls, 6x16x19" 2,400.00
Bowl, burl, protruding rim hdls, varnished, 5½x13½" 950.00
Bowl, burl, VG figure, crack/rpr, 5x12x16" 750.00
Bowl, curly maple, EX patina, age crack, 1⅞x12x13" 800.00
Bowl, maple sugar; trn, bulbous, w/lid, 4½x5" 195.00
Bowl, maple w/old red, initialed/1872, 4x10x14", VG 140.00
Bowl, poplar, 1-pc, EX patina, wear/cracks, 8x24" 95.00
Bowl, rnd, worn orig bl exterior pnt, 14" dia 135.00
Bowl, traces of red, scrubbed int, age cracks, 17x26" L 250.00
Bowl, trn pine, feather-pnt seaweed, w/lid, NY, 1780s, 7" 900.00
Bowl, worn yel pnt w/scrubbed int, 4x14x20" 175.00

Bread board, BREAD on rim, 11" dia 35.00
Bucket, brn flame grpt on yel, staved, bail hdl, 6x7" 165.00
Bucket, maple sap; tin banded, old bl pnt 95.00
Bucket, metal bands/wire hdl, red pnt, att Shakers, 10½" 150.00
Bucket, sap; lap banded, old dk gr pnt 85.00
Bucket, staved, wood ears, bentwood hdl, red pnt, 11" 90.00
Bucket, staved w/bands, bail w/wood hdl, red pnt, 4½" 225.00
Bucket, staved w/buttonhole-lapped hoops, red pnt, 11¾x9" . .350.00
Bucket, sugar; staved, gr w/wht pnt label: SUGAR, 12" 235.00
Bucket, sugar; staved, hdl stenciled 18XX, 10" 55.00
Bucket, sugar; staved, wire bail/wood hdl, gray pnt, 6" 235.00
Bucket, sugar; wire bail w/wood hdl, lapped lid, 6x9" 95.00
Busk, flat cvd geometrics & sunbursts, PA, 1700s 220.00
Busk, hex signs/hearts/diamonds, chip cvg, 13½" L 250.00
Butter dish, BUTTER cvd at edge, Bl Willow dish in center 65.00
Butter paddle, bird's-eye maple, 10" .55.00
Butter paddle, bird's-eye maple, 9¼x4" 35.00
Butter paddle, burl, EX figure & form, hook hdl, 10" dia 350.00
Butter paddle, burl, EX hook hdl, old chips, 9" 175.00
Butter paddle, burl, primitive, age cracks, 9" 95.00
Butter paddle, EX burl, cut-out hdl, NY, 1700s, 6½x11" 600.00
Butter paddle, maple, primitive, tool mks/age cracks, 8" 130.00
Butter roller, cvd cow & flowers, pinned-in wood yoke, 5½" . . .225.00
Butter roller, cvd floral designs, hdl, age crack, 4¼" 95.00
Canteen, chip-cvd decor, lap-banded, 7¼" dia 265.00
Canteen, staved, hickory bands, orig red pnt, stopper, 8½" 275.00
Cheese ladder, mortised/pinned/beveled, 1700s, 28x44", EX . . .150.00
Cheese ladder, 2 rungs pegged in sides, tapered ends, 25x11" . .120.00
Cheese mold, bentwood, lap-banded, int staves, w/lid, 8x13" . .175.00
Cheese mold, grooved diamonds, pegged, ca 1800, 4x11x6" . . .175.00
Cookie board, bicycle w/rider, bk: 2 horse & wagons, 9x14" . . .480.00
Cookie board, hex signs/hearts/initials, octagonal, 7x9" 65.00
Cookie board, horse & rider, 5½x5½" .95.00
Cookie board, horse & wagon, EX patina, 3¾x7" 155.00
Cookie board, open truck filled w/people & animals, 9x23" . . .470.00
Cookie board, woman w/lamb; bk: man w/dog, rpr, 8x23" 150.00
Cookie board, 4 bunches of grapes, maple w/come curl, 4x19" . .230.00
Cookie/cutting board, short hdl w/hanging hole, 16½" dia 135.00
Cranberry scoop, fishtail hdl, natural patina, 17" L 135.00
Crimping board & roller, grooved, EX 150.00
Cutting board, curly maple, worn, 9x15¾" 95.00
Cutting board, maple burl, 13x12½" .295.00
Dipper, burl oval bowl, 18⅜" 350.00
Dipper, grain forms concentric circles in bowl, 6½" 80.00
Dipper, maple w/some burl, worn/edge damage, 9" 115.00
Dryer form, lady's long stockings, tiger maple, 36" L 60.00
Egg cup, trn maple, ped base, ca 1800s 30.00
Firkin, flat bail, fingers w/copper fastener, 9¾x9½" 95.00
Firkin, old yel pnt, copper tacks, 1800s, 10" 85.00
Firkin, orig bl pnt, copper tacks, 1800s, 11½" 235.00
Firkin, staved, interlaced wood bands, rfn/hdl crack, 8x9" 65.00
Firkin, staved, wood pegs, flat bail, old pnt, 10x9½" 150.00
Funnel, keg; hand scorped, 1-pc 75.00
Funnel, maple syrup; 1-pc, ca 1800, 8½x4½" 95.00
Funnel, maple syrup; 1-pc, 7x3½" 130.00
Grinder, herb; burl, trn mortar w/pestle, dtd 1805, 7", EX 675.00
Inkwell, orig brn grpt/stencil, label: S Silliman, 3½" 125.00
Jar, poplar, trn, edge damage/age cracks/rfn, 11½x9½" 235.00
Jar, traces of old finish, Pease, 3½" 120.00
Jar, trn, wire bail/wood hdl, worn varnish, Pease, 7", VG 425.00
Jar, trn poplar w/dk finish, minor age crack in lid, 10" 200.00
Jar, trn poplar w/dk red sponging on yel, wear/cracks, 13" 375.00
Jug, 2½x3½" 150.00
Ladle, butter; striped tiger maple, EX patina 120.00

Ladle, butter; tiger maple, ca 1800, EX 130.00
Lard press, walnut, 18" 30.00
Lemon squeezer, tiger maple, 2-part, hinged 75.00
Mallet, burl, trn hdl, 1700s, 13" 60.00
Mallet, burl w/hickory hdl, trn rings, 10½" 35.00
Measure, bentwood, iron reinforcement & hdl, 1816, 9x14" . . .125.00
Measure, maple, dbl-ended, hourglass form, 1-pc, trn, 3¾" 50.00
Measure, orig red pnt, heavy band at top, 15" dia 85.00
Mortar, burl, +trn beech pestle, 6½" 350.00
Oatmeal board, corrugated w/hdld roller, ca 1800, 8x14" 90.00
Pie peel, pine, rnd tapered paddle, 13" dia, 28" L 125.00
Pie peel, pine, short hdl, tapered end, oblong, 20½x7¾" 65.00
Pie peel, walnut, 2-pc, Amish, 1800s, 8½x7", 4" hdl 50.00
Pitcher, noggin; maple, 1-pc, beveled sides, 8" 260.00
Pitcher, noggin; maple, 1-pc, trn, 6¼" 260.00
Plate, burl, EX figure, detailed rim, worn/irreg, 7" 350.00
Plate, poplar, 7"-8", lot of 6 . . . . .450.00
Porringer, maple, scrubbed to natural, 1700s, 7" 400.00
Reamer, mushroom knob hdl, ca 1870 . . . . .75.00
Rolling pin, springerle; 6 cvd designs, roller: 3¼x1¾" 125.00

Salt box, two-color wood, ca 1840, 10½", $140.00.

Sander, holly wood w/EX trn, Crosby label, base cracks, 4" 75.00
Sander, trn, minor age crack, 3⅛" 50.00
Scoop, burl, maple w/some curl, bird's head hdl, dtd 1790 . . . .400.00
Scoop, cvd, slant sides, hook hdl, sm 55.00
Scoop, sugar; ca 1800, 7½" 130.00
Scoop, sugar; hewn, EX patina, ca 1850, 4" hdl, 8" L 130.00
Skimmer, cream; short hdl, early, EX .175.00
Skimmer, pierced, ladle shape, ca 1830 . . . . .60.00
Smoothing board, chip-cvd hex motif, simple horse hdl, VG . .800.00
Smoothing board, cvd vines/'P'/1696, girl's head hdl, 25" . . .1,600.00
Smoothing board, EX chip cvg/sgn/dtd 1787, horse hdl, 24" .1,200.00
Smoothing board, horse hdl w/rein & tail detail, 24" 875.00
Smoothing board, some curl, scratched-cvd sgn hdl, 15" 85.00
Soap dish, cvd pine, 1-pc, lollipop shape, tab hdl, 1700s 200.00
Spoon, apple butter; 3" dia hdl 25.00
Spoon, maple, ca 1850, 3½" bowl, 11" .50.00
Spoon, maple w/curl, thick wide bowl, 14½" 125.00
Spoon, smooth knob hook hdl, ca 1700s, 7", EX 150.00
Sugar tub, lap-banded, staved, w/lid, sgn/dtd 1888 . . . . .150.00
Tankard, staved, bl rpt w/mc decor, sgn/1858, lid, 12" 75.00
Tray, burl, EX figure, flat w/trn ¾" lip, 18" dia 550.00
Tray, knife; pine, dvtl, heart cutout in divide, 12x15½" 225.00
Trencher, cvd-in end hdls, 6x46x14½" 225.00

Trencher, oval, worn orig dk red pnt, early, 17x9½" 185.00
Trencher, pine, hewn rectangle, 5x15x9" 130.00
Trencher, pine w/EX orig red pnt, 1700s, 12½" L 600.00
Water carrier, staved, hickory bands, oval, orig red pnt 195.00

World's Fairs and Expos

Since 1851 and the Crystal Palace Exhibition in London, World's Fairs and Expositions have taken place at a steady pace. Many of them commemorate historical events. The 1904 Louisiana Purchase Exposition, commonly known as the St. Louis World's Fair, celebrated the 100th anniversary of the Louisiana Purchase agreement between Thomas Jefferson and Napoleon in 1803. The 1893 Columbian Exposition, known as The Chicago World's Fair, commemorated the 400th anniversary of the discovery of America by Columbus in 1492. (Both of these fairs were held one year later than originally scheduled.) The multitude of souvenirs from these and similar events have become a growing area of interest to collectors in recent years. Many items have a 'cross-over' interest into other fields: i.e., collectors of post cards and souvenir spoons eagerly search for those from various fairs and expositions.

For additional information, collectors may contact Expo Collectors and Historians Organization (ECHO), whose address is in the Directory under Clubs, Newsletters, and Catalogs; or our advisor, D.D. Woollard, Jr. His address is listed in the Directory under Missouri.

Key: T&P — Trylon & Perisphere

1876 Centennial, Philadelphia

Cloth, Memorial Hall/Art Gallery, stars & stripes, 19x25" 75.00
Fan, paper, main exhibition building, bk Oriental scene 130.00
Medallion, wood, Gen JR Hawley in relief, 2½" 75.00
Purse, leather, 4-compartment, emb metal strip, 2½x4" 30.00
Standish, w/inkwell in form of Memorial Hall, 6½" L, EX 180.00
Stud, brass, Main Building 1876, 1" dia 27.50
Towel, red & wht, woven center design, 17x29", EX 60.00

1893 Columbian, Chicago

Atlas, views/99 maps, dtd, VG 75.00
Award medal, bronze, mk Am Bronze Co, 3" dia, EX 100.00
Bone dish, Lagoon Look-South World's Fair, 6½x3", EX 22.50
Book, Chicago/World's Fair, Whitemann photogravures, 11x9" .30.00
Book, Week at Fair, soft red cover, 268-pg, 6x9", EX 35.00
Coin purse, leather, metal fr & snap, emb scene, France, EX 40.00
Fork, Souvenir...1893/Eat Wichert Pickles on porc hdl, 6½" 65.00
Paperweight, rvpt Ferris Wheel, minor pnt chips, 2½x4" 75.00
Photograph, Ferris Wheel, bk: Columbus bust, cb stock, 9x8" ...20.00
Pitcher, syrup; Fisheries Building, ironstone, metal lid 200.00
Plate, Electrical Building in brn, Wedgwood, 8½" 45.00
Plate, wht satin glass, Machinery Hall, Mt WA, 11½" 350.00
Razor, etched buildings on blade, blk hdl, 6½" closed, EX 85.00
Ribbon, Manhattan Day, bl letters/design on beige, 2¼x5½" ...45.00
Spoon, Isabella figural hdl, Women's Building in bowl, 4½" 35.00
Steroscopic view card, Statue of the Republic, EX 5.00
Tray, SP, Columbus bust, Expo buildings, 7½" dia 65.00

1898 Omaha

Badge, brass, 2-part pin-bk, US Gov't Building, EX 30.00
Medallion, brass, Nebraska building, heart shape, 1x1¼" 22.50
Pin-bk button, celluloid, Pennsylvania Day, Oct 5 1898 ....40.00

Poster, Milwaukee Litho Co, panoramic view, some wear 175.00
Trade card, boy in Storm King Rubber Boots, mc, 3½x5½" 7.50

1901 Pan American

Book, Enterprising Housekeeper, soft cover, 4½x6½" 15.00
Cent, elongated or rolled, Electric Tower 15.00
Cup, aluminum, collapsible, Pan-Am 1901, eng leaves, 2x2½" ..20.00
Frying pan, milk glass, eng name, 7" L 100.00
Lamp, ladies as N&S America, 4" globe, clear chimney, 9" 195.00
Paperweight, glass, Temple of Music, Empire Art, 4x2½x1" 27.50

1904 St. Louis

Book, Singer Sewing Machines, panoramic cover, 20-pg, 7x5" ..15.00
Bracelet, child's; clear & aqua beads, mk heart medallion 30.00
Medal, brass, 1¼" busts of Jefferson & Napoleon 30.00
Nut shell, World's Fair, nut halves w/accordion-like views 35.00
Plate, porc, 3 scenes, openwork border, Carlsbad, 9" 75.00
Spoon, brass, World's Fair in scalloped bowl, 6" 30.00
Stein, St Louis 1904, Festival Hall, Germany, 3½" dia 150.00
Watch fob, brass, 3-part, Gov't Building, state seal 70.00

1905 Lewis and Clark

Card, Henry E Dosch, Commissioner General..., 1905, EX 17.50
Folder, holds 24 post cards, folding, Wolff & O'Brien, EX 17.50
Pin-bk button, celluloid, Sighting Pacific 1805, 1½" 35.00
Post card, Oriental building, mc, unused, EX 4.00
Post card, park fairgrounds scene, Thayer, mc, unused, EX 5.00
Poster seals, complete sheet of 12, mc, 4½x6½" 15.00

1907 Jamestown

Cigar case, aluminum, emb cigar design/lettering, 3x5", EX 25.00
Mirror, pocket; celluloid, Model Post Office, 2x3", EX 30.00
Paperweight, glass, States Exhibit Building, 4x2½" 30.00
Post card, John Smith & Pocahontas, AC Bosselman 5.00
Seashell, w/Expo decal, lg, 8x5" 15.00

1915 Panama Pacific

Book, Architecture & Landscape Gardening of Expo, 202-pg ...35.00
Book, view; official souvenir, soft cover, 40-pg, 9½x12½" 22.50
Box, metal, emb Service Building on lid, 2x4½x2¼" 17.50
Cloth, silk, Tower of Jewels on orange, 12x14", EX 15.00
Folder, Painted Desert Exhibit, illus, 3x6", EX 6.00
Medal, brass, emb wreath, Business Men's League, 3" dia 50.00
Pin-bk button, celluloid, lady/2 bears, 1½" dia, EX 20.00
Table cover, bl felt, bird's-eye view of Expo, 16x25" 35.00
Tip tray, Buffalo Brewing Co 75.00

1926 Sesquicentennial

Book, cb cover Liberty Bell in oval on front, 8x5" 25.00
Case, pencil; leather, Liberty Bell/calendar, 3x8" 30.00
Key, metal, Liberty Bell-shaped head, emb ea side, 2¼" 15.00
Lamp, table; glass, Liberty Bell figural 50.00
Medallion, brass, Washington/Liberty Bell, 1¼" 12.50

1933 Chicago

Ash tray, copper, Chrysler Building emb, 3x3", EX 5.00

Ash tray, Firestone rubber tire, glass insert, EX 40.00
Book, Chicago & Her 2 World's Fairs, 100-pg, 11x7½", EX 35.00
Book, Official Guide, 176-pg, 6x9", EX 17.50
Book, Official Pictures, soft cover, 60+ pgs, 7x10", EX 22.50
Booklet, Live Power Show of Standard Oil, 5½x8", EX 7.50
Bookmark/letter opener, metal, Federal building, 4½" 7.50
Bracelet, metal, comet logo, 6 scenes, dtd 1933, EX 15.00
Brochure, Canada from Sea to Sea, colorful, 3½x7", EX 2.50
Cent, Skyway & Observation Towers, elongated, EX 10.00
Compote, silver-colored metal, paper label, 2½x6" dia 10.00
Foto-Reel, 30 fair views, in 5¼x2¼x3" cb mailing box 25.00
Letter, official stationery, sgn LR Lohr, Expo Gen Manager 20.00
Mailer, Romance of Steel..., foldout, US Steel Corp, 4x36" 4.00
Mailing folder, Official View Book, mc scenes, 20-pg, 4x6" 12.50
Map, made especially for Expo, opens to 20x30", EX 7.50
Napkin ring, gr- & copper-colored metal, scenes, 1¼x1½" 17.50
Needle folder, mc buildings ea side, 6½x4½", +needles 10.00
Photograph, panoramic view, c H Koss 1933, 10x60", EX 40.00
Playing cards, comet logo, fair scenes, complete, NM 30.00
Puzzle, fair overview, over 350 pcs in 1½x8½x8½" box 37.50
Ring, brass, comet logo, Century...., adjusts, minor wear 12.50
Seal or stamp, gummed & perforated, locomotive, 1¼x1¾" 5.00
Spoon, lady on hdl, building in bowl, Wm Rogers, EX 10.00
Spoon/bottle opener, metal, Federal building in bowl, mk 17.50
Thermometer, metal under glass, Electric Group by Night, 7½" .17.50
Ticket, lady & buildings, blk print on gr & wht, EX 10.00
Tray, metal, buildings & scenes, worn, oblong, 6½x3½" 7.50

1939 California Golden Gate

Cloth, silk or rayon, fair scenes on rose, 20" sq, EX 20.00
Folder, MO Pacific Lines, 24-pg, opens to 8x9", EX 12.50
Ice pick, wood hdl, mk World's Fair-1939/San Francisco, 8" . . .25.00
Map, AZ Roads, 1939, opens to 19x20", EX 12.50
Medal, aluminum, Golden Gate Bridge/locomotives, 1¼" 10.00
Medal, brass, Golden Gate Bridge design, 1¼" 10.00
Towel, terry cloth, Golden Gate Bridge, wht/gr, 27x15", EX . . .25.00

Plate, Golden Gate Expo, Homer Laughlin, $60.00.

1939 New York

Ash tray, Firestone rubber tire, clear glass insert, EX 40.00

Book, American Jubilee, Chesterfield ad on bk, 8½x12" 12.50
Book, NY Fair Illustrated by Camera, 66-pg 20.00
Book, Official Guide, 1st Edition, 256-pg, 5x8", 1939, EX 17.50
Book, Railroads on Parade, soft cover, 20-pg, 10x13" 15.00
Booklet, City of Light, foldout of Diorama, 24-pg, 14x10" 10.00
Booklet, NYWF in Pictures, 9½x12", 48-pc, M in envelope . . .32.50
Bottle, milk glass, T&P shape, emb decor & letters, 9" 15.00
Bowl, china, T&P/buildings/flags, maroon border w/gold, 10" . . .70.00
Box, powder; musical, T&P/dtd 1939 on top, 3½x5" 40.00
Brochure, Coronation Scot...Britain's Luxury Train, 5½x8½" . . .5.00
Brochure, General Motors Exhibit Building, illus, 4½x9" 5.00
Bulletin, NYWF, 1937 Construction Edition, 20-pg, 12½x9¼" . .20.00
Case, cigarette; sm medallion: T&P in center, 2½x3½" 25.00
Catalog, Masterpieces of Art, illus, 215-pg, 5½x8½" 22.50
Certificate, T&P at top, issued by Hotel Weston, 9½x14" 15.00
Coaster, beer; cb, Ballentine Inn, limerick, 1939, 4½" dia 10.00
Compact, mc T&P on lid, metal fr, 2¾" dia 25.00
Folder, fair scenes, T&P cover, Trichnor Bros, 4½x6", EX 12.50
Folder, Home Building Center, exhibitor's info, 11x15½" 5.00
Kan-O-Seat, cane opens to make chair, T/P, Greyhound label . .30.00
Key, brass, bl/gold enameled T&P, mk NYWF 1939/Key to NY .15.00
Key, locker; American Locker Co M-Ten, EX 5.00
Knife, New Vitex-Glas, lt bl glass, 9", M in NYWF & T&P box .25.00
Knife, pocket; faux pearl hdl w/T&P, 2-blade, 1939, 3" 30.00
Letter, official stationery, exhibit concerns, dtd 1938 . . . . .10.00
Letter opener, General Electric, T&P figural 20.00
Map, NYWF, bk shows transit map of NY, opens to 19x25", EX .12.50
Medal, brass, T&P/NYWF, Metropolitan...Ins Tower on bk, 1¼" .7.50
Penny, elongated or rolled, emb T&P, mk NYWF 1939, EX 10.00
Pin-bk, celluloid, T&P design, bl/orange/wht, less than 1" 15.00
Pin-bk button, brass, emb Hall of Communications, EX 15.00
Poster, Railroads on Parade, mc, 1940, 27x40", EX 100.00
Puzzle, T&P, Helenhart Novelty, rare, 2" 35.00
Spoon, demitasse; sterling, emb T&P on hdl, plain bowl 25.00
Spoon, T&P/1939 at finial, NYWF on hdl, scenic bowl, Rogers .10.00
Sticker, baggage; T&P, Greyhound to...NYWF 1939, 3x3½" 5.00
Tag, cb, I Was There at World's Fair of 1940 in NY, 3½" dia . . .10.00
Ticket stub, rain check to RRs on Parade, EX 2.50
Tie bar, T&P suspended on chain, enameling on metal, EX 12.50
Tumbler, glass, fair scene, ea different, 4½", 6 for 55.00
Vase, bud; ruby glass w/gold trim 25.00
Views, 16 Colored Miniature; ea 2½x3½", in mailer, NM 12.50

1962 Seattle

Booklet, Earth-Orbiting Flight of Astronaut Carpenter 7.50
Coaster, space needle, wht on bl glass insert, 4 in SP box 30.00
Dish, china, mc space needle, heart shape, 5" 10.00
Key chain, attached viewer w/design of Space Needle, EX 10.00
Medal, official, 1¼", in orig cb holder, M 10.00
Tumbler, glass, Space Needle in red & wht w/gold rim, 5½" 12.50

1964 New York

Bank, ceramic, emb unisphere/children, 4½" dia on 5" base 30.00
Car sticker, I've Seen NY State..., Theaterama, bl/orange, EX 7.50
Game, Milton Bradley, game sheet/markers/cards, 20x24", EX . .30.00
Map, offical fair map, courtesy of Esso, opens to 16x24", EX 5.00
Official Guide Book, Time-Life editors, 312-pg, EX 15.00
Puzzle, NY World's Fair, Milton Bradley, mc, complete, EX 15.00
Ticket, special admission; GM employees/stockholders, EX 5.00
Tray, metal, Heliport & Top of the Fair Restaurant, mc, 5x7" 5.00
Tumbler, frosted glass, Federal Pavilion, 3x7" 10.00

Wrought Iron

Until the middle of the 19th century, almost all the metal hand forged in America was made from a material called wrought iron. When wrought iron rusts it appears grainy, while the mild steel that was used later shows no grain but pits to an orange-peel surface. This is an important aid in determining the age of an ironwork piece.

Bird roaster, ½-moon form w/long hdl, 3 delicate ft, 1700s 700.00
Candle snuffer, scissors shape, w/wick pick 55.00
Curling iron, scissors shape, ball finials on hdls, 1700s 65.00
Firedog, dog's head w/3 legs, ca 1700s, 6½x17" 65.00
Fork, EX detail, 17" 85.00
Fork, marriage; eng initials/1827, punchwork, sgn WI, 21" 500.00
Fork, swivel rest, primitive, 14½" 65.00
Fork, toasting; rattail hanger, 3 simple ft, 1700s, 15" 350.00
Fry pan, pouring spout, hole for hanging, 12" 245.00
Hinge, C-form w/bird-head ends, 14x15", pr 200.00
Hook, lg bird silhouette w/brass eyes, spike end, 4½", pr 230.00

Lighting device, made for rush and taper, acorn-form pan, beautifully scrolled decoration, early 1700s, 14", $1,100.00.

Yellowware

Yellowware is an inexpensive, plain type of earthenware, so called because of the color of the clay used in its manufacture. Pieces may vary from buff to yellow to nearly brown; the glaze itself is clear. Some yellowware was decorated with blue, white, brown, or black bands; only seldom was it relief molded. Yellowware was made to a large extent in East Liverpool, Ohio, but other Ohio potteries as well as some in Pennsylvania and Vermont also produced it. Because it was not often marked, it is almost impossible to identify the manufacturer. English yellowware has a harder body composition. There is a growing interest in this type of pottery, and consequently prices are continually increasing.

Bank, pig; daubs of gr/amber, hairlines/chips, 5" L 45.00
Bowl, mixing; brn, gr sponging 35.00
Bowl, mixing; brn band, RRP Co, Roseville Ohio, 7" 27.50
Bowl, mixing; seaweed, bl on wht band, 12", EX 375.00
Bowl, 3 brn stripes, 10" 38.00
Casserole, ribs, knob finial, 6x10" 70.00

Chamber pot, wht band, ca 1850s 65.00
Custard cup, brn sponging decor, early 1900s, 2½x3¼" 14.00
House, bungalow style, open windows/door, IA, 6½x5½x6" ...200.00
Humidor, unmk, ca 1900 ....150.00
Inkwell, dbl, dog-head lids 200.00
Inkwell, dbl, shell-form pen holder, dog aside, rpr 175.00
Jar, bl/gr/brn running glaze, barrel form w/lid, 8" 200.00
Jar, brn running glaze, lid chipped, 12", EX 85.00
Jar, seaweed, wht band/dk brn stripes, w/lid, 6x7", NM 700.00
Jar, spice; bl bands, 'Spices,' mk H in circle, 3¾" 175.00
Milk pan, ca 1870s, 7x10" 75.00
Milk pan, mk Jeffords, 3x10½" dia 100.00
Mold, bunch of grapes, 3½x6x7" 85.00
Mold, ear of corn, 6" 65.00
Mold, rabbit form, 4x7x10" 150.00
Mug, bl bands, minor wear, 5" 65.00
Mug, bl bands, unmk, ca 1850s 50.00
Mug, seaweed, bl on wht band w/brn stripe, Ohio, 4" 325.00
Mug, wht band w/brn stripes, 4" 95.00
Mug, wht bands, unmk, ca 1850s 50.00
Pitcher, bl bands, 8", EX 85.00
Pitcher, brn bands, ca 1890s 70.00
Pitcher, HP stylized floral band, 6" 30.00
Pitcher, seaweed, gr on wht band, bl stripes, 5½", EX 400.00
Pitcher, wht bands, unmk, 8½" 75.00
Plate, unmk, ca 1900, 8" 60.00
Rolling pin, pine hdls, ca 1900 ....325.00
Salt box, 3 wht bands, 'Salt' in blk lettering, 6¾" 175.00
Shaker, bl/wht stripes, chips on dome top, 4⅛" 200.00
Shaker, seaweed, bl on wht band, chips on dome top, 4⅜" 250.00
Soap dish, rectangular, unmk, ca 1890s 125.00
Teapot, tapered hexagon, 6" 195.00

Tea bowl, mocha seaweed decoration, $275.00; Pitcher, green mocha seaweed with brown stripe, 4", $385.00.

Zanesville Art Pottery

Prior to 1900, this company was known as The Zanesville Roofing Tile Company; then it was reorganized, and production shifted to the manufacture of art pottery. Their most familiar line, La Mora, was made in the standard brown glaze as well as in a matt version very similar to Owens' Matt Utopia.

La Moro, vase, cloverleaves, hdls, 7" 100.00
La Moro, vase, floral, 2x4" 65.00
La Moro, vase, leaves, ruffled top, hdls, #825, 4½" 115.00
La Moro, vase, woman in bl drape, semi-gloss, 14½" 1,900.00

Zanesville Glass

Glassware was produced in Zanesville, Ohio from as early as 1815 until 1851. Two companies produced clear and colored hollowware pieces in five characteristic patterns: 1) diamond faceted, 2) broken swirls, 3) vertical swirls, 4) perpendicular fluting, 5) plain, with scalloped or fluted rims and strap handles. The most readily-identified product is perhaps the whiskey bottles made in the vertical swirl pattern, often called globular swirls because of their full, round body. Their necks vary in width; some have a ringed rim and some are collared. They were made in several colors — amber, light green, and light aquamarine are the most common.

Bottle, aqua, 24 swirled ribs, globular, minor sickness, 7½" 225.00
Bottle, aqua, 24 verical ribs, club shape, 7", NM 165.00
Bottle, gold-amber, 24 swirl ribs, globular, 8" 425.00
Bottle, nursing; aqua, 24 vertical ribs, 7", NM 95.00
Compote, gold amber, appl ft, baluster stem, 4x5½" 450.00
Flask, chestnut; amber, 24 vertical ribs, 5", EX 150.00
Flask, chestnut; gold-amber, 24 vertical ribs, 4¾" 425.00

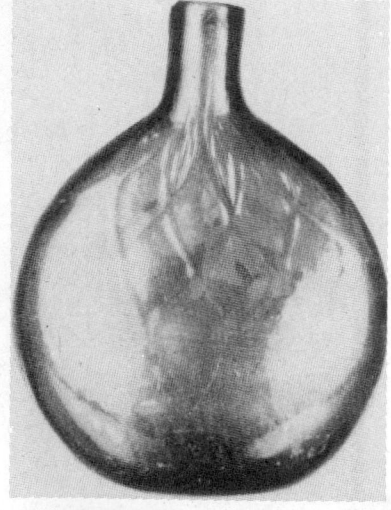

Chestnut flask, ten-diamond pattern, yellow-amber, sheared lip, 4¾", $280.00.

Inkwell, gr-aqua, 24 vertical ribs, funnel well, 2½" 120.00
Mug, dk red-amber, appl hdl, 4¼" 800.00
Pan, gold amber, 24 ribs, folded rim, 1½x5⅜" 650.00
Tumbler, lt gr, 24 vertical ribs, wear, 3¾" 275.00

Zsolnay

Zsolnay pottery has been made at Pecs in Hungary since the mid-1800s. The factory received international attention in 1878 by winning the Grand Prix gold medal at the Paris World Exhibition for their technological innovations and high artistic level. Zsolnay used lead-free high-temperature glazes on his unique 'porcelain-faience' material. The Hungarian, Persian, Turkish, Japanese, and Renaissance motifs were applied with colored glazes which after firing resulted in rich ornamentation almost in relief. In the 1890s Zsolnay introduced iridescent 'eosine' glazes in nearly every color and subsequently adopted the Art Nouveau style. The unique eosine glazes and special application techniques allowed striking artistic designs which brought the factory world-wide fame and recognition. Presently the factory produces porcelain wares and various decorative items such as the red or green iridescent-glazed figurines that are frequently seen on the market today.

Bowl, floral, pk/gold on beige, rtcl, 8½" 160.00
Centerpiece, floral/gilt, rtcl crescent form, 5x16x4" 285.00

Ewer, iridescent, raised steeple mark, impressed '5986,' 1899, 16¼", $2,650.00.

Ewer, bl floral w/trees & red sun, irid, 1900, 8¾" 485.00
Ewer, floral on beige w/gold, steeple mk, 11½" 198.00
Ewer, volcano w/trees, irid, raised steeple mk, 1901, 10" 860.00
Figurine, boxer dog, reclining, gr/gold irid, 5" L 40.00
Figurine, girl feeding bird 22.00
Figurine, polar bears, gr/gold irid, 7½" L 40.00
Pitcher, bird/floral/gilt on brn, steeple mk, 1884, 10" 295.00
Pitcher, bulbous, bl/gr gilt floral on pk, 1882, 12" 345.00
Pitcher, duck, rtcl, dbl wall, 9" 165.00
Pitcher, floral on brn, dragon hdl, steeple mk, 1880, 10" 320.00
Plaque, iris, pk/yel on cobalt, steeple mk, 1885, 14" dia 285.00
Vase, bl irid, bulbous w/4 spurs, flared neck, 1900s, 6" 225.00
Vase, bl/gr gilt peacock in relief, steeple mk, 1883, 15" 680.00
Vase, bl/red floral on beige, steeple mk, 1878, 9½" 280.00
Vase, bulbous w/figural long-haired maid aside, gr irid, 9" 160.00
Vase, flagstone red, ovoid, gold mk, 5½" 85.00
Vase, floral, irid, flared neck, looped hdls, 1900, 10" 1,250.00
Vase, floral on cream, filigree hdls/top/ft, steeple mk, 11" 220.00
Vase, honeycomb rtcl, pk/gilt, steeple mk, 1887, 8" 290.00
Vase, modeled as coiled cobra, head is spout, 9" 1,800.00
Vase, orchids relief w/gold, bulbous, baluster neck, 7¾" 185.00
Vase, trees & river w/boat, mc irid, #5282, 1900, 12" 2,400.00
Vase, tulip shape, red/gr irid, steeple mk, 1898, 7½" 750.00

Vase, blue steeple mark with 'T.J.M.,' impressed 'Z.W.PECS, 869,' 13½", $1,200.00.

The editors and staff take this opportunity to express our sincere gratitude and appreciation to each person who has in any way contributed to the preparation of this guide. We believe the credibility of our book is greatly enhanced through their efforts. See each advisor's Directory listing for information concerning their specific areas of expertise.

You will notice that at the conclusion of some of the narratives, the advisor's name is given. This is optional and up to the discretion of each individual. Simply because no name is mentioned does not indicate that we have no advisor for that subject. Our board has grown with this issue and now numbers 240; if you care to correspond with any of them or anyone listed in our Directory, please send a SASE with your letter.

Charles & Barbara Adams
Middleboro, Massachusetts

Geneva D. Addy
Winterset, Iowa

James Anderson
New Brighton, Minnesota

Tim Anderson
Provo, Utah

Warren R. Anderson
Cedar City, Utah

John Apple
Racine, Wisconsin

Dick & Ellie Archer
St. Augustine, Florida

Una Arnbal
Ames, Iowa

Mrs. Lillian Baker, Fellow IBA, Cambridge, England
Gardena, California

Roger Baker
Woodside, California

Robert Banks
Brookeville, Maryland

J. Allen Barker
Hawley, Pennsylvania

Nadine Barnett
Bowling Green, Ohio

Kit Barry
Brattleboro, Vermont

Daniel J. Batchelor
Oswego, New York

Scott Benjamin
Los Angeles, California

Phyllis & Tom Bess
Tulsa, Oklahoma

Robert Bettinger
Monterey, California

John E. Bilane
Union, New Jersey

Sandra V. Bondhus
Unionville, Connecticut

Clifford Boram
Monticello, Indiana

Dick & Waunita Bosworth
Kansas City, Missouri

Rick Botts
Des Moines, Iowa

Jeff Bradfield
Dayton, Virginia

Larry Brenner
Manchester, New Hampshire

Wm. J. Brinkley
McLeansboro, Illinois

Mike Brooks
Oakland, California

Jim Broom
Effingham, Illinois

Rick Brown
Newspaper Collector's Society of America
Lansing, Michigan

Nicki Budin
Mansfield, Ohio

Leroy F. Bruggink
Cedar Grove, Wisconsin

Jim Calison
Wallkill, New York

Donald Calkins
Lakewood, Ohio

Tod Carley
V.P., International Society of Antique Scale Collectors
Arlington Heights, Illinois

Tina M. Carter
El Cajon, California

Sally S. Carver
Chestnut Hill, Massachusetts

Jackie Chamberlain
La Canada, California

Jack Chipman
Redondo Beach, California

Joe R. & Wilma Clark
Reynoldsburg, Ohio

W. L. (Tony) Coburn
Miami, Florida

Bea Cohen
Easton, Pennsylvania

Bob Cook
Baltimore, Maryland

J.W. Courter
Simpson, Illinois

Jim Cummings
Knightstown, Indiana

Robert L. Daly
Fenton, Michigan

John Danis
Rockford, Illinois

Patricia M. Davis
Wilmington, Delaware

Gael deCourtivron
Sarasota, Florida

Mary A. De Luca
Port Clinton, Ohio

Ginny Distel
Tiffin, Ohio

DLK Nostalgia & Collectibles
Johnstown, Pennsylvania

L.R. 'Les' Docks
San Antonio, Texas

Rebecca Dodds
Ft. Lauderdale, Florida

Pat Dole
Birmingham, Alabama

Ron Donnelly
Panama City Beach, Florida

Robert A. Doyle, CAI, ISA
Fishkill, New York

Louise Dumont
Coventry, Rhode Island

Ken & Jackie Durham
Washington, DC

William Durham
Belvidere, Illinois

Rita & John Ebner
Columbus, Ohio

Bill Edwards
Rushville, Indiana

Delleen Enge
Ojai, California

Roberta Etter
London, England

Joseph Ferrara
Newburgh, New York

Vicki Flanigan
Winchester, Virginia

Gene Florence
Lexington, Kentucky

Pamela Ekey Ford
Ballwin, Missouri

Ruth Forsythe
Galena, Ohio

Daniel Fortney
Milwaukee, Wisconsin

Fostoria Glass Society of America, Inc.
Moundsville, West Virginia

Ron Fox
North Babylon, New York

Madeleine France
Plantation, Florida

James Fred
Cutler, Indiana

Terry Friend
Galax, Virginia

William Galaway
Belvidere, Illinois

Lee Garmon
Springfield, Illinois

Mary Frank Gaston
Bryan, Texas

Marjorie Geddes
Beaverton, Oregon

Tony George
El Toro, California

Steve Geppi
Baltimore, Maryland

Walter Glenn
Atlanta, Georgia

George Goehring
Baltimore, Maryland

Bruce C. Greenberg, Ph. D.
Sykesville, Maryland

Helen Greguire
Hilton, New York

Woody Griffith
Crystal Lake, Illinois

Everett Grist
Charleston, Illinois

Tom Guenin
Chardon, Ohio

Jack Gunsaulus
Plymouth, Michigan

Dr. Laszlo Gyugyi
Pittsburgh, Pennsylvania

Norman Haas
Quincy, Michigan

Doris & Burdell Hall
Morton, Illinois

Auction Houses

We wish to thank the following auction houses whose catalogs have been used as sources for pricing information. Many have granted us permission to reproduce their photographs as well.

A-1 Auction Service
P.O. Box 540672, Orlando, Florida 32854; 407-841-6681
Specializing in American antique sales

American West Archives
Anderson, Warren
P.O. Box 100, Cedar City, Utah 84720
18-page illustrated catalog issued every two months includes an auction section featuring scarce and historical early western documents, letters, autographs, stock certificates, and other important ephemera. A one-year subscription is $8.00.

Arman Absentee Auctions
P.O. Box 174, Woodstock, CT 06281; 203-928-5838
Specializing in American glass, Historical Staffordshire, English soft paste, paperweights

Barrett/Bertoia Auctions & Appraisals
1217 Glenwood Drive, Vineland, NJ 18630; 609-692-4092
Specializing in antique toys & collectibles

C.E. Guarino
Box 49, Denmark, ME 04022

Col. Doug Allard
P.O. Box 460, St. Ignatius, MT 59865

David Rago
P.O. Box 3592, Station E, Trenton, NJ 08629; 609-585-2546
Specializing in American art pottery and Arts & Crafts

Doyle, Auctioneers & Appraisers
R.D. 3, Box 137, Osborne Hill Road, Fishkill, NY 12524; 914-896-9492

Du Mouchelles
409 Jefferson Ave., Detroit, MI 48226

Early Auction Co.
123 Main St., Milford, OH 45150

F.T.S. Inc.
416 Throop St., North Babylon, NY 11704; 516-669-7232
Specializing in stein auctions with illustrated catalogs

Garths Auctions Inc.
2690 Stratford Road, Box 369, Delaware, OH 43015; 614-362-4771

Greenberg Auctions
7566 Main Street
Sykesville, MD 21784

Guernsey's
136 East 73rd Street, New York, NY 10021; 212-794-2280
Specializing in carousel figures

Hake's Americana & Collectibles
Specializing in character and personality collectibles along with all artifacts of popular culture for over 20 years. To receive a catalog for their next 3,000-item mail/phone bid auction, send $3.00 to Hake's Americana, P.O. Box 1444M, York, PA 17405

Jack Sellner Auctioneer
P.O. Box 113, Scottsdale, AZ 85252

James D. Julia
P.O. Box 210, Showhegan Rd., Fairfield, ME 04937

Lloyd Ralston Toys
447 Stratford Rd., Fairfield, CT 06432

Manion's International Auction House, Inc.
P.O. Box 12214, Kansas City, KS 66112

Maritime Auctions
R.R. 2, Box 45A, York, ME 03909; 207-363-4247

Milwaukee Auction Galleries, Ltd.
4747 W. Bradley Rd., Milwaukee, WI 53223; 414-355-5054

Nostalgia Co.
21 S. Lake Dr., Hackensack, NJ 07601; 201-488-4536

Phillips
406 E. 79th St., New York City, NY 10021

Rex Stark Auctions
49 Wethersfield Rd., Bellingham, MA 02019

Riba-Mobley Auctions Inc.
894 Main St., P.O. Box 53, South Glastonbury, CT 06073; 203-633-3076
Specializing in historical items, ephemera, autographs, photographs

Richard A. Bourne Co. Inc.
Estate Auctioneers & Appraisers
Box 141, Hyannis Port, MA 02647; 617-775-0797

Roan Inc.
Box 118, R.D. 3, Cogan Station, PA 17728

Robert W. Skinner Inc.
Auctioneers & Appraisers
Route 117, Bolton, MA 01740; 617-779-5528

Sally S. Carver Postcard Mail Auctions
179 South Street, Chestnut Hill, MA 02167; 617-469-9175
Specializing in all better quality pre-1930 postcards; SASE for information; Does not take auction consignments

Sotheby Parke Bernet Inc.
980 Madison Ave., New York City, NY 10021

Weschler's, Adam A. Weschler & Son
905 E. St. N.W., Washington, DC 20004

Willis Henry Auctions
22 Main St., Marshfield, MA 02050

Alabama

Dole, Pat
Editor of *The Glaze*
P.O. Box 4782 Birmingham, 35206
205-833-9853
Specializing in Purinton pottery

Luckey, Carl
Carl F. Luckey Communications
R.R. 4, Box 301
Lingerlost Tr., Killen, 35645
Freelance writer specializing in art antiques and collectibles

Arizona

Heberlee, Ron
7th St. Galleria
5828 N. 7th Street
Phoenix, 85012

Arkansas

Hall, Doris & Burdell
B&B Antiques
P.O. Box 1501, Fairfield Bay, 72088 or
210 W. Sassafras Dr., Morton, IL 61550
Authors of *Morton's Potteries: 99 Years*
Specializing in Morton pottery, American dinnerware, early American pattern Arkansas glass, historical items, small primitives

Musgrave, Marge
Look Nook Antiques
R.R. 3, Box 352, Mountain Home, 72653
501-499-5283
Specializing in art glass and colored Victorian glass

Yohe, Darlene, Timberview Antiques
P.O. Box 343, Stuttgart, 72160
501-673-3437
Specializing in American pattern glass, historical glass, Victorian pattern glass, carnival glass, and custard glass

California

Baker, Mrs. Lillian
15237 Chanera Ave., Gardena, 90249
213-329-2619
Author Collector Books on antique, collectible, and high-fashion costume jewelry, hatpins and hatpin holders, miniatures

Baker, Roger
Baker's Lady Luck Emporium
Box 620417, Woodside, 94062
415-851-7188
Specializing in Saloon Americana — advertising, gambling, bar bottles, cigar lighters, match safes, bowie knives, dirks, daggers, barber items: bottles, shaving mugs, razors

Benjamin, Scott
7250 Franklin Ave. #216, Los Angeles, 90046

213-876-2056
Specializing in gasoline pump globes

Bettinger, Robert
N.P.S. Box 8611, Monterey, 93943
408-443-5554
Specializing in American art pottery

Brooks, Mike
7355 Skyline, Oakland, 94611
415-339-1751
Specializing in typewriters, early televisions

Carter, Tina M.
Hot Tea
882 S. Mollison, El Cajon, 92020
619-440-5043
Specializing in teapots, tea-related items, tea tins, children's and toy tea sets, coffeepots, etc.

Chamberlain, Jackie
1520 Foothill Blvd., La Canada, 91011
818-790-5416
Specializing in holiday collectibles, antique reference books, teddy bears, pewter ice cream molds

Chipman, Jack
California Spectrum
Box 1429, Redondo Beach, 90278
Author of *California Pottery*, a reference guide to thirty-six commercial potteries located in Southern California
Specializing in California and other American ceramics

Enge, Delleen
912 N. Signal, Ojai, 93023
Author of *Franciscan Ware*, book available
Specializing in Catalina Island pottery, Franciscan pottery, matching service by mail

George, Tony
22941 Briarcroft, El Toro, 92630
714-951-1310
Specializing in watch fobs

Harris, Warren D.
4555 Auburn Blvd., Suite #11
Sacramento, 95841
Specializing in thermometers

Johnson, Patricia A.
Box 1221, Torrance, 90505
Specializing in open salts

Long's Americana
Long, Earnest & Ida
P.O. Box 90, Mokelumne Hill, 95245
209-286-1348
Specializing in children's items: toys, banks, games, etc.; publishers of *Dictionary of Toys, Vol. I & II*, *Dictionary of Still Banks*, and *Penny Lane*, a history of antique mechanical toy banks

Nelson, Maxine
873 Marigold Ct
Carlsbad, 92009
Specializing in Vernon Kilns

Oliphant, Steve
5255 Allott Ave., Van Nuys, 91401
818-789-2339
Specializing in phonographs

Pardini, Dick
3107 N. El Dorado St., Dept. SAPG, Stockton, 95204
209-466-5550
Specializing in California Perfume Company items: buyer and information center
Inquiries should be accompanied by SASE; not necessary if offering items for sale

Shrader, Fred & Lila
Shrader Antiques
2025 Hwy. 199, Crescent City, 95531
707-458-3525
Specializing in railroad, steamship & other transportation memorabilia; Shelley and select Americana

Stella's Collectibles
Memory Lanes Antique Mall
2451 Frampton St.
Harbor City, 90710
213-316-7198
Specializing in quality glass and china, paperweights, figurines, plates, jewelry

Yronwode, Catherine
6632 Covey Rd., Forestville, 95436
707-887-2424
Specializing in pre-1950 collectible plastic

Zeder, Audrey
6755 Coralite, Long Beach, 90808 (By appointment only)
Specializing in British Royal Commemorative Souvenirs (mail-order catalog available)
Author of *British Royal Commemoratives* (Wallace Homestead)

Canada

Warner, Ian
P.O. Box 44, Brampton, Ontario L6V2K7
Specializing in Wade porcelain and Swankyswigs, author of *The World of Wade*, Co-author: Mike Posgay

Colorado

Heck, Carl
Carl Heck Antiques
Box 8416, Aspen, 81612
303-925-8011
Specializing in antique stained and beveled glass and Tiffany windows; leaded and reverse-painted lamps

Connecticut

Bondhus, Sandra V.
Box 100, Unionville, 06085
203-678-1808
Author of *Quimper: A French Folk Art Faience*
Specializing in Quimper pottery

Kilbride, Richard J.
81 Willard Terrace, Stamford, 0690
203-322-0568
Author of *Art Deco Chrome, The Chase Era*

Mayer, Fran
Mechanical Music Center
18 Marshall St., Box 1078
S. Norwalk, 06854
203-852-1780
Specializing in mechanical musical instruments; illustrated catalogs of items for sale, $5 annual subscription

Rivera, Ted
Box 163, Torrington, 06790
203-489-4325
Specializing in inkwells and inkstands; Co-author of *Inkstands and Inkwells: a Collector's Guide*

Vuono, Mark
306 Mill Road, Stamford, 06903
203-329-8744
Specializing in historical flasks, blown-3-mold glass, blown American glass

Delaware

Davis, Patricia M.
700 Greenhill Ave. Wilmington, 19805 302-658-2992

District of Columbia

Durham, Ken & Jackie
By appointment
909 26 St. N.W.,
Washington, DC 20037
202-338-1342
Specializing in countertop arcade machines, trade stimulators, and vending machines; publish *Coin-Op Newsletter*, 16-page illustrated list: $2

England

Etter, Roberta
Flat 11, Hilton House, 22 Craven Hill Gardens, London, W2 3EE
01/262-8728

Pedel, Alan
Collectibles from England
Scurfield House, Braunton
Devonshire, EX331HQ
Specializing in pie birds, open salts, cat post cards, most other collectibles

Florida

Archer, Dick & Ellie
Artiques
419 Sevilla Dr., St.
Augustine, 32086 904-797-4678
Specializing in Victorian silverplate: figurals, fancy hollowware, and collectibles

Coburn, W. L. (Tony)
Coburn's Antique Mall
22405 S. Dixie Hwy.
Miami, 33170
305-258-1444
Specializing in furniture and collectibles

deCourtivron, Gael
Cocaholics
4811 Remington Dr., Sarasota, 34234
813-351-1560
Specializing in Coca-Cola memorabilia
Cocaholics hot line: 813-355-COLA

Dodds, Rebecca
Silver Flute
Box 39644, Ft. Lauderdale, 33339
Specializing in jewelry

Donnelly, Ron
Saturday Matinee
Box 7047, Panama City Beach, 32413
Specializing in Big Little Books, movie
posters, premiums, western heroes, char-
acter collectibles

France, Madeleine
P.O. Box 15555, Plantation, 33318
305-584-0009
Specializing in top quality perfume
bottles: Lalique, Steuben, Czechoslovakian

Hochman, Gene
Full House
9320 Laurel Green Drive, Boynton
Beach, 33437
407-734-8690
Mail auctions; specializing in antique
playing cards, gambling memorabilia

Hudson, Hardy
108 Green Leaf Lane
Altamonte Springs, 32714
Specializing in majolica, American art
pottery

Lawrence, Judy and Cliff
1169 Overcash Dr., Dunedin, 34698
813-734-4742
Specializing in fountain pens and mechanical pencils

Linscott, Len
Line Jewels
3557 Nicklaus Dr., Titusville, 32780
Specializing in glass insulators, Blue
Bell paperweights and other telephone
items, rare Ball fruit jars and Ball items
(SASE required)

McNearny, Kathryn
502 Kettering Way
Orange Park, 32073
Author Collector Books on blue and
white stoneware, primitives, tools

Sourbeer, Daniel M.
Daniel M. Sourbeer Antiques
Box 10614, St. Petersburg, 33733
813-866-3873
Specializing in goblets, fairings, pot lids

Supnick, Mark
8524 N.W. 2 St., Coral Springs, 33065
305-755-3448
Author of *Collecting Hull Pottery's Little
Red Riding Hood*
Specializing in American pottery

White, Douglass
Classic Interiors & Antiques
2144 Edgewater Dr., Orlando, 32804
407-841-6681
Specializing in Fulper, other American
art pottery

Georgia

Glenn, Walter
Geode Ltd.
3393 Peachtree Rd., Atlanta, 30326
404-261-9346
Specializing in Frankart

Joiner, John R.
245 Ashland Trail, Tyrone, 30290
404-487-3732
Specializing in commercial aviation
collectibles

Illinois

Antiques from Frank & Caryl
5477 Milwaukee, Chicago, 60630
312-736-2326
Specializing in Royal Doulton (tobies,
figurines, seriesware), flow blue,
Torquay, coronation, Kayserzinn, ice
cream molds, and sewing

Bean Town Antiques
Hilst, Randy
1401 Catherine, Pekin, 61554
309-347-8535; general line

Briggerman, Lawrence
Briggerman Antiques
1309 E. St. Charleston, 61920
217-345-2543
Specializing in Fiesta, Jewel Tea, Heisey, Cambridge Pottery, etc.

Brinkley, Wm. J.
Brinkley Interiors & Galleries 401 S.
Washington Ave., McLeansboro, 62859
Specializing in Meissen, Dresden, Eu-
ropean porcelains, American porcelains
(Cybis)

Broom, Jim
Box 65, Effingham, 62401
Specializing in opalescent pattern glass-
ware

Carley, Tod
Vice President — International Soci-
ety of Antique Scale Collectors
811 E. Central Road, Apt. 304
Arlington Heights, 60005
Specializing in scales

Courter, J.W.
R.R. 1, Simpson, 62985
618-949-3884
Specializing in Aladdin lamps

Danis, John
11028 Raleigh Ct., Rockford, 61111
815-877-6098
Specializing in R. Lalique

Garmon, Lee
1529 Whittier St., Springfield, 62704
217-789-9574
Specializing in Royal Haeger, Royal
Hickman, glass animals

Geissler, Carl
Geissler's Antiques
510 Buchanan, Carthage, 62321
217-357-2632
Specialing in glass, china, general line

Griffith, Woody
4107 White Ash Rd.
Crystal Lake, 60014
815-459-7808
Specializing in Jewel-T, Noritake, Hall

Grist, Everett
734 12th St., Charleston, 61920
Specializing in marbles

Hall, Doris & Burdell
B&B Antiques
210 W. Sassafras Dr., Morton, 61550 or
P.O. Box 1501, Fairfield Bay, Arkansas
72088; Authors of *Morton's Potteries:
99 Years*
Specializing in Morton pottery, American dinnerware, early American pattern glass, historical items, small primitives

Haussmann, Richard A.
Past President, Aurora Historical Soci-
ety
Aurora, 60507

Hilst, Randy
1221 Florence #4, Pekin, 61554
309-346-2710
Specializing in old fishing tackle

Hoffmann, Pat & Don, Sr.
1291 N. Elmwood Dr,.Aurora, 60506
312-859-3435
Authors of *Why Not Warwick; China
Collectors Guide*
Specializing in Warwick, china

Hooks, Dee
Dee's China Shop
Box 142, Lawrenceville, 62439
Specializing in R.S. Prussia, Royal
Bayreuth, Haviland, other fine china

Hospice House Antiques
Durham, William; Galaway, William
9633 Beaver Valley Rd
Belvidere, 61008
815-547-5128
Specializing in Tea Leaf and white ironstone

Long, Dee
112 S. Center, Lacon, 61540
Specializing in reamers

Owen, Larry & Sally
Specializing in Morten Studio Dogs

Weldi-Skinner, Mary
1656 W. Farragut Ave.
Chicago, 60640
312-271-0236
Specializing in American and European art pottery, fine glass

Wells, Rosalie J. 'Rosie'
R.R. 1, Canton, 61520
309-668-2565
Publishes magazines & other periodi-
cals for Precious Moments and Hallmark ornament collectors, write for free
literature

Indiana

Boram, Clifford
Antique Stove Information Clearing-
house

417 N. Main St., Monticello, 47960
Inquiries should be accompanied by
SASE

Cummings, Jim
2822 Mariposa, Terre Haute, 47803

Edwards, Bill
423 N. Main, Rushville, 46173
Author Collector Books on carnival
glass

Fred, James A.
Antique Radio Labs.
R.R. 1, Box 41, Cutler, 46920
317-268-2214
Specializing in radios made between
1922 and 1950

Harris, Dave
Hoosier Peddler
5400 S. Webster St.
Kokomo, 46902 317-453-6172
Specializing in advertising, toys

Haun, Ted
2426 N. 700 East, Kokomo, 46901
317-628-3640
Specializing in American pottery and
china, '50s items

Heiss, Virginia
7777 North Alton Ave., Indianapolis,
46268; 317-875-6797
Specializing in Muncie, AMACO,
Brandt Steele, Ransburg

Mary's Antiques
317-861-6878
Specializing in jewelry, glass, china

Miller, Susan
606 East Wabash Ave.
Crawfordsville, 47933
317-362-0352
Specializing in trolls

Scowden, Virgil
303 Lincoln, Williamsport, 47993
317-762-3408 or 317-762-3178
Antiques museum, general line, tours

Stapp, Charles Dennis
R.R. 2, #10 Haynes Rd.
New Albany, 47150
Specializing in knives, straight razors,
safety razors

Stofft, Marvin & Jeanette
Marnette Antiques
Tell City, 47586; 812-547-5707
Specializing in Ohio art pottery, cut
glass, R.S. Prussia — buy and sell

Iowa

Addy, Geneva D.
Winterset, 50273; 515-462-3027

Arnbal, Una
Woodland Antiques
236 Trail Ridge Rd., Ames, 50010
515-292-1005
Specializing in china, glass

Botts, Rick
2545 S.E. 60th Court
Des Moines, 50317-5099
Publisher of *Jukebox Collector* magazine

Collector of Wurlitzer jukeboxes, sales of jukebox books, service manuals, etc.

DeGood, Hal & Meredith
THE BAGGAGE CAR
513 Elm St., West Des Moines, IA
50265 515-225-3070
Specializing in Hallmark collectibles; publishers of Hallmark newsletter

Hinrichs, VerNelda & Max
Hinrichs' Antiques (shows only)
621 W. 11th St., Spencer, 51301
712-262-3680

Jaarsma, Ralph
De Pelikaan Antieks
627 Franklin St., Pella, 50219
Specializing in Dutch antiques

Main Street Antiques
110 W. Main St., Box 340
West Branch, 52358
Specializing in folk art, country Americana, the unusual

Nichols, Harold J.
Nichols Art Pottery
632 Agg Ave., Ames, 50010
515-292-9167
Specializing in American art pottery, Roseville, Weller; author of book on McCoy cookie jars

St. John, Virgil, Betty, & Martha
St. John Antiques
Box 400, Le Grand, 50142
515-479-2952
Specializing in carnival glass, Victorian colored glass, toys, Maxwell Parrish prints

Williams, Don
Ottumwa, 52501
Specializing in art glass

Kansas

Garton, Wesley
Wes-Jan Antiques
P.O. Box 780985, Wichita, 67278
316-778-1948
Specializing in American art pottery, early American flint glass

Robison, Joleen A.
502 Lindley Dr., Lawrence, 66044
Collector Books author on advertising dolls

Tinsley, Rosella
105 15th St., Osawatomie, 66064
Specializing in primitives, kitchen, farm, woodenware, miscellaneous

Kentucky

Florence, Gene
Box 7186H, Lexington, 40522
Author Collector Books on Depression Glass, Occupied Japan

Johnson, Wes
1725 Dixie Hwy., Box 169001
Louisville, 40216-9001
Specializing in Cracker Jack: toys, point of sale, packages, etc.; Checkers Confection, Schoenhut toys, Victor Toy Oats, Universal Theatre (Chicago)

Willis, Roy M.
Heartland of Kentucky Specialties
Box 428, Lebanon Jct., 40150
502-833-2827 after 6 p.m. EST
Specializing in most brands of decanters, domestic beer steins, and advertising; Open showroom

Maine

Hathaway, John
Hathaway's Antiques
Upper Main St., Bryant Pond, 04219
207-665-2124
Specializing in fruit jars — mail order a specialty

Maryland

Banks, Robert
Stars and Stripes
18901 Gold Mine Court
Brookeville, 20833
Specializing in American flags of historical significance and exceptional design. Bought and sold

Cook, Bob
Geppi's Comic World Inc.
7019/20 Security Blvd., Baltimore, 21207; or 1718 Belmont Ave. Bay G, Baltimore, 21207
Specializing in comic books, original art, and related items

Dennis & George Collectables
O'Brien, Dennis; and Goehring, George
3407 Lake Montebello Drive
Baltimore, 21218
301-889-3964
Specializing in advertising items, personalities, unusual items

Greenberg, Bruce C., Ph. D.
Greenberg Publishing Company
7566 Main St., Sykesville, 21784
Specializing in toy trains; author and publisher of comprehensive publications on Lionel, American Flyer, and Ives trains

Humphrey, George C.
4392 Prince George Ave., Beltsville, 20705
301-937-7899
Specializing in John Rogers groups

Screen, Harold & Joyce
2804 Munster Rd. Baltimore, 21234
Specializing in soda fountain 'tools of the trade' and paper: catalogs, soda fountain magazines, etc.

Massachusetts

Adams, Charles & Barbara
Middleboro, 02346; 508-947-7277
Specializing in Bennington (brown only)

Carver, Sally S.
179 South St., Chestnut Hill, 02167
617-469-9175
Author of *The American Postcard Guide to Tuck*; columnist for *Hobbies*; Collec-

tor's News; Postcard Collector; Antique Trader Price Guide; specializing in all better quality antique pre-1930 postcards; yearly postcard mail auctions with illustrated catalogs; SASE for information

Longo, Paul J.
Paul Longo Americana
Box 490, Chatham Rd., South Orleans, Cape Cod, 02662; 617-255-5482
Specializing in political pins, ribbons, banners, autographs, old stocks and bonds, baseball memorabilia of all types

Morin, Albert
668 Robbins Ave. #23
Dracut, 01826
508-454-7907
Specializing in miscellaneous Akro Agate and Westite

Owings, K.C., Jr.
Antiques Americana
Box 19, N. Abington 02351
617-857-1655
Specializing in Civil War, Revolutionary War, autographs, documents, books, antiques

Rudisill, John & Barbara
Rudisill's Alt Print Haus
3 Lakewood, Medfield, 02052
508-359-2261
Specializing in Currier and Ives

Vigue, Norm & Cathy
62 Bailey St., Stoughton, 02072
617-344-5441
Buying and selling comic character, TV and western character collectibles

Wellman, BA
#9 Cottage St., Southboro, 01772
Specializing in Ceramic Arts Studio and Pennsbury Pottery: price guide and video-tape identification guides available

Michigan

Brown, Rick
Newspaper Collectors Society of America
Box 9134-S, Lansing, 48901
517-372-8381
Specializing in newspapers

Daly, Robert L.
10341 Jewell Lake Ct., Fenton, 48430
Collector of early American bottles and flasks, specializing in bitters bottles and historical whiskey flasks

Gunsaulus, Jack
Gray's Gallery
583 W. Ann Arbor Trail
Plymouth, 48170
313-455-2373
Specializing in porcelain, glass, jewelry

Haas, Norman
264 Clizbe Rd., Quincy, 49082
517-639-8537
Specializing in American art pottery

Luttig, Pamela & Allan
Blue Boar Antiques
P.O. Box 423, Grand Ledge, 48837
Specializing in Victorian tiles, graniteware, jewelry

Nedry, Boyd W.
728 Buth Dr., Comstock Park, 49321
616-784-1513
Specializing in traps and trap-related items

Newbound, Betty
4567 Chadsworth, Union Lake, 48085
Author Collector Books on Blue Ridge dinnerware; specializing in collectible china and glass

Minnesota

Anderson, James
Box 12704, New Brighton, 55112
612-484-3198
Specializing in old fishing lures and reels, also tackle catalogs, posters, calendars

Heimstead, Doug
1349 Hillcrest Dr., Fridley, 55432
612-571-1387
Specializing in radios: Art Deco, mirrored, Bakelite, novelty

Hoppe, Gordon
10120 32nd Ave. N., Plymouth, 55441;
612-546-7461
Specializing in Roseville

Ketcham, Steve
Steve Ketcham Antiques (shows and mail order only)
Box 24114, Edina, 55424
612-920-4205
Specializing in early American bottles, stoneware, advertising

Schoneck, Steve
P.O. Box 56, Newport, 55055
612-459-2980
Specializing in Handicraft Guild of Minneapolis, American art pottery, Arts & Crafts

Missouri

Bine, John & Judy
32 San Carlos, St. Charles, 63303
314-724-1568
Specializing in Depression-era and elegant glassware
Bosworth, Dick & Waunita
Kansas City Trade Winds
7307 N.W. 75th St., Kansas City, 64152
Specializing in Fenton glass, American art pottery, Parrish prints

Ford, Pamela Ekey
1104 Holgate Drive
Ballwin, 63021
314-225-6723
Specializing in Black Cats

Old World Antiques
1715 Summit, Kansas City, 64108
Specializing in 18th- and 19th-century furniture, paintings, accessories, clocks, medical and scientific instruments, chandeliers, sconces, Sabino

Roberts, Brenda
R.R. 2, Marshall, 65340
Specializing in Hull pottery and general line
Author Collector Books on Hull pottery; please enclose SASE when requesting information

Smith, Pat
Independence
Author Collector Books doll book series

Stratton, Bill
Blue Buds Antiques
Box 8711; 417-862-4212
Specializing in Akro, pottery, etc.

Wiesehan, Doug
D&R Farm Antiques
R.R. 3, Box 202, St. Charles, 63301
Specializing in salesman's samples and patent models, antique toys, farm toys, metal farm signs

Woollard, D.D., Jr.
11614 Old St. Charles Rd.
Bridgeton, 63044
Specializing in World's Fair & Exposition memorabilia

Montana

Tanner, Joseph & Pamela
Wheeler-Tanner ESCAPES
P.O. Box 349, Great Falls, 59403
406-453-4961
Specializing in handcuffs, leg shackles, balls and chains, restraints and padlocks of all kinds (including railroad), locking and non-locking devices

Nebraska

Larsen, Robert V.
3214 19th St., Columbus, 68601
Specializing in old hatpins and hatpin holders

New Hampshire

Brenner, Larry
L. Brenner Antiques
1005 Chestnut St., Manchester, 03104
603-625-8203
Specializing in Royal Bayreuth

Marden, Richard G.
Box 524, Elm St., Wolfeboro, 03894
603-569-3209

New Jersey

Bilane, John E. (mail order only, no shop)
2065 Morris Ave., Apt. 109
Union, 07083
Specializing in antique glass cup plates

Perzel, Robert & Nancy
Popkorn
20 Spring St., P.O. Box 1057
Flemington, 08822
201-782-9631

Specializing in Stangl dinnerware, birds, and artware; Depression glass

Poster, Harry
Vintage TVs
Box 1883, S. Hackensack, 07606
201-794-9606
Specializing in vintage TVs, unusual radios, 1950s items, view master

Rago, David
Box 3592, Station E, Trenton, 08629
609-585-2546
Specializing in Arts & Crafts, American art pottery

Rosen, Barbara
6 Shoshone Trail, Wayne, 07470
Specializing in figural bottle openers and antique dollhouses

Sight Sound Style
Box 2224, S. Hackensack, 07606
Quarterly newsletter of vintage TVs and collectible radios

Steinfeld, Lois & Milt
633 Westfield Ave., Box 457
Westfield, 07091
Specializing in collectible glass and china, Victorian silverplate, and other small collectibles

New York

Batchelor, Daniel J.
R.D. #3, Box 10, Oswego, 13126
315-342-1511
Specializing in Pairpoint, Handel, and Bradley and Hubbard Lamps

Calison, Jim
Tools of Distinction
Wallkill, 12589
914-895-8035
Specializing in antique and collectible tools, buying and selling

Doyle, Robert A.
Doyle Auctioneers & Appraisers
R.D. 3, Box 137, Osborne Hill Rd., Fishkill, 12524
914-896-9492
Thousands of collectibles offered: call for free calendar of upcoming auctions.

Fer-Duc Inc.
Ferrara, Joseph; Leduc, Gerard
Box 1303, Newburgh, 12550
914-565-5990
Specializing in American art pottery (Ohr, Rookwood, Zanesville), 19th- and 20th-century American paintings

Fox, Ron
F.T.S. Inc.
416 Throop St., N. Babylon, 11704
516-669-7232
Specializing in steins; auctions with illustrated catalogs and video tapes

Greguire, Helen
Helen's Antiques
103 Trimmer Rd., Hilton, 14468
716-392-2704
Specializing in graniteware, carnival

glass lamps and shades, carnival glass lighting of all kinds

Laun, H. Thomas & Patricia
Little Century
215 Paul Ave., Syracuse, 13206
315-437-4156 or 315-654-3244
Summer Residence: Box 69-A, Cape Vincent, 13618
Specializing in fire fighting collectibles

Meisel, Louis K. & Susan P.
Meisel Primavera Gallery
133 Prince St., New York City, 10012
Specializing in Clarice Cliff and all 20th-century designs in furniture, jewelry, and objects d'art

Owens, Lowell
Owens' Collectibles
12 Bonnie Ave., New Hartford, 13413
Specializing in beer advertising

Pierce, David
85 Main St., Almond, 14804
607-276-6118
Specializing in Glidden pottery

Pisello, Faye
577 Lake St., Wilson, 14172
Specializing in Brownies by Palmer Cox

Rifken, Blume J.
Author of *Silhouettes in America — 1790-1840 — a Collector's Guide*
Specializing in American antique silhouettes from 1790 to 1840

Van Kuren, Ruth & Dale
Ruth & Dale Van Kuren Antiques
5990 Goodrich Rd.
Clarence Center, 14032
716-741-2606
Specializing in Buffalo pottery, general line

Van Patten, Joan F.
Box 102, Rexford, 12148
Author Collector Books on Nippon and Noritake

van Zwanenberg, Vincent
P.O. Box 793, Olean, 14760
716-373-3312
Specializing in Glidden pottery

North Carolina

Ricketts, Bill
Pepper's Deli
126 Cherry St., Black Mountain, 28711
Specializing in items advertising Dr. Pepper

Ohio

Bettinger, Lewis & Alice
Canton, 44708
216-478-5475
Specializing in American art pottery

Blair, Betty
Golden Apple Antiques

216 Bridge St., Jackson, 45640
614-286-4817
Specializing in art pottery, Watt, cookie jars, chocolate molds, general line

Budin, Nicki
Gourmet Antiques Inc.
703 S. Main St., Mansfield, 44907
419-756-1619 and (800)-331-8543
Specializing in Royal Doulton

Calkins, Donald
Calkins Antiques Company
The Antique Mall, 7474 Avon, Beldon Rd., Rt. #83, N. Ridgeville, 44039
216-226-0752
Specializing in American art pottery; interested in buying Cowan and Clewell

Clark, Joe R. & Wilma
Olde Time Antiques
2088 Creekview Ct.
Reynoldsburg, 40368
614-863-2637
Specializing in clocks and watches

De Luca, Mary A.
Red Barn Antiques
5510 W. Lakeshore Dr.
Port Clinton, 43452
419-635-2045
General line

Distel, Ginny
Distel's Antiques
4041 S.C.R. 22, Tiffin, 44883
419-447-5832
Specializing in Tiffin glass

Ebner, Rita & John
Cracker Barrel Antiques
4540 Helen Road, Columbus, 43232
Specializing in door knockers, cast iron bottle openers, doorstops, toy tractors, general line

Ellington, Gregg
Upper Left Antiques
47 Columbus St., Wilmington, 4517
513-382-4311
Specializing in graniteware, mocha, blue and white spongeware, yellowware, Bennington, blue and white stoneware

Ferguson, Maxine
Wayside Antiques
2290 E. Pike, Zanesville, 43701
General line, furniture, dolls, pottery, glass

Forsythe, Ruth A.
Box 327, Galena, 43021
Author of *Made in Czechoslovakia*

Guenin, Tom
Phone-Tiques
Box 454, Chardon, 44024
Specializing in antique telephones and antique telephone restoration

Hothem, Lar
Hothem House
Box 458, Lancaster, 43130
Specializing in books about Indians and artifacts

Kao, Fern
Lustre Pitcher Antiques
Box 312, Bowling Green, 43402
419-352-5928
Specializing in Shelley china, small antiques

Ketterling, Linda & Ken
3202 E. Lincolnshire Blvd.
Toledo, 43606
419-536-5531
Specializing in Victorian linens, lace, majolica

Kitchen, Lorrie
Toledo, 43612
419-478-3815
Specializing in Depression-era glass, Hall china, Fiesta, Blue Ridge, Shawnee

Kline, Mr. & Mrs. Jerry & Gerry
604 Orchard View Dr., Maumee, 43537
419-893-1226
Specializing in collecting Torquay pottery; Publicity Chairmen of the Torquay Pottery Collectors Society

Messenger, Patty
Bowling Green, 43402

Moore, Carolyn
445 N. Prospect, Bowling Green, 43402
Specializing in primitives, yellowware, graniteware

National Cambridge Collectors Inc.
Box 416, Cambridge, 43725
Specializing in Cambridge glass

National Heisey Glass Museum
Heisey Collectors of America Inc.
6th & Church Streets, P.O. Box 4367, Newark, 43055; 614-345-2932

Osborne, Ruth
Box 85, Higginsport, 45131
513-375-6605
Specializing in vintage clothing, lamps, jewelry

Penrose, Donald M. (mail order only)
6351 Garber Rd., Dayton, 45415
513-890-3728
Specializing in continental porcelains and art glass

Peters, Jeannie L.
Mt. Washington Antiques
3742 Kellogg, Cincinnati, 45226
513-231-6584
Specializing in sheet music

Rees, Debbie & Bill
631 Dryden Rd., Zanesville, 43701
614-454-2788
Buying and selling: Watt, blue and white stoneware, Steiff, cookie jars, Roseville pottery

Toohey, Marlena
c/o Antique Publications, P.O. Box 553, Marietta, 45750
Specializing in black glass

Tucker, Dan
Toledo, 43612
419-478-3815

Specializing in Depression-era glass, Hall china, Fiesta, Blue Ridge, Shawnee

Van Aman, Mildred E.
C&M Antiques
254 Newark Rd., Mt. Vernon, 43050
614-392-7708
Specializing in fine glass and china

Walczak, Mary Jo
5312 Brophy Dr., Toledo, 43611
Specializing in dolls and snow babies

Visckovich, Tony
Tony & Jenny Antiques (no shop)
109 Cullman Rd., Columbus
614-491-2023
Specializing in fine china and art glass

Walker, Bunny
Box 502, Bucyrus, 44820
419-562-8355
Specializing in Steiff teddy bears, penny toys, pottery

Whitmyer, Margaret & Kenn
Box 30806, Gahanna, 43230
Author Collector Books on children's dishes
Specializing in Depression-era collectibles

Wilkins, Juanita
The Bird of Paradise
P.O. Box 1884, Lima, 45802
419-227-2163
Specializing in R.S. China, Old Ivory, colored pattern glass, lamps, jewelry

Wise Choice Antiques
Wise, Ruth & Gil
4380 Allen Dr., Whitehall, 43213
614-239-8485
Specializing in art glass, photographica, general antiques

Young, Mary
1040 Greenridge Dr., Kettering, 45429
Author Collector Books *Collector's Guide to Paper Dolls*

Oklahoma

Bess, Phyllis & Tom
Authors of *Frankoma Treasures*
14535 E. 13th St., Tulsa, 74108
918-437-7776
Specializing in Frankoma pottery

Colonial Antiques
Gunter, A.W.; Cox, David; Dutcher, Phil
1325-1329 E. 15th St., Tulsa, 74120
918-582-5645
Specializing in early Americana, Indian rugs, oil paintings, 18th- and 19th-century furniture

Moore, Shirley Suber
2161 S. Owasso Place, Tulsa, 74114
918-747-4164
Specializing in Lu Ray Pastels

Willis, Ron L.
2110 Fox Ave., Moore, 73160
Specializing in militaria

Oregon

Bartsch, Henry
Antique Registers
2050 N. Hwy. 101, Rockaway Beach, 97136; 503-355-2932
Specializing in antique cash registers. Co-author of *Antique Cash Registers 1880-1920*

Geddes, Marjorie
Beaverton, 503-649-1041

Morris, Thomas G.
Prize Publishers
49 Monterey Drive, Medford, 97504;
Author of *The Carnival Chalk Prize*, a pictorial price guide on carnival chalkware figures with brief histories and values for each.

The Sterling Shop
Box 595, Silverton, 97381
503-873-6315
Specializing in silver

Pennsylvania

Barker, J. Allen
Toastermaster Antique Appliances
P.O. Box 592, Hawley, 18428
717-253-1951
Specializing in electric toasters and appliances

Cohen, Bea
Box 825, Easton, 18044-0825
215-252-1098
Specializing in spatterware, Gaudy Dutch, mocha, chalkware, Dedham, spongeware, Canton, textiles

DLK Nostalgia & Collectibles
P.O. Box 5112, Johnstown, 15904
Specializing in corkscrews and openers, Art Deco, clocks, toys, breweriana, miscellaneous

Gyugyi, Dr. Laszlo
P.O. 17329, Pittsburgh, 15235
Specializing in Zsolnay art pottery

Kelly, Kathy
The Kelly Collection
1621 Princess Ave., Pittsburgh, 15216
412-561-3379
Buying Phoenix glass and related items, glass company catalogs, trade journals, Monaca PA post cards

Krause, Gail
994 Jefferson Ave., Washington, 15301
Author book on Duncan Glass

Lindsay, Ralph
P.O. Box 21, New Holland, 17557
Specializing in target balls

Maier, Clarence & Betty
Mail order: The Burmese Cruet
Box 432, Montgomeryville, 18936
215-855-5388
Specializing in Victorian art glass

Posner, Judy
R.D.1, Box 273, Effort, 18330
717-629-6583

Specializing in figural pottery, cookie jars, salt and peppers, Black memorabilia, Disneyana

Rosso, Philip J. & Philip Jr.
Wholesale Glass Dealers
1815 Trimble Avenue, Port Vue, 15133
412-678-7352
Specializing in Westmoreland Glass

Theofiles, George
Miscellaneous Man
Box 1776, New Freedom, 17349
717-235-4766 from 10 a.m. to 6 p.m.
Specializing in vintage posters and graphics

Weiser, Pastor Frederick S.
New Oxford, 17350
717-624-4106
Specializing in frakturs

Rhode Island

Dumont, Louise
579 Old Main St., Coventry, 02816;
401-828-2799
Specializing in cookie jars, pottery: Hull and Shawnee

The Occupied Japan Club
c/o Florence Archambault
29 Freeborn St., Newport, 02840
Publishes monthly newsletter, *The Upside Down World of an O.J. Collector*. Please send SASE when requesting information

Tennessee

Price, Gene
Railroad Antiques
Box 278, Erwin, 37650
Specializing in railroadiana

Texas

Docks, L.R. 'Les'
Shellac Shack; Discollector
Box 32924, San Antonio, 78216; 512-492-6021
Author of *American Premium Record Guide*
Specializing in vintage records

Gaston, Mary Frank
Box 342, Bryan, 77806
Author Collector Books on china & metals

Norris, Kenn
Schoolmaster Auctions
Box 476, 110 Avenue C,
Grandfalls, 79742
915-547-2421
Specializing in school-related items and barbed wire

Sayers, R.J.
Southeastern Antiques & Appraisers
Box 246, Andrews, 79714; Author of *Scouting Collectibles*, specializing in Boy Scout collectibles, English furniture; 30 years experience

Smith, Allan
1806 Shields Dr., Sherman, 75090
214-893-3626
Specializing in children's lunch boxes
and all types of advertising, especially
Coca-Cola, Dr. Pepper, Pepsi Cola, RC
Cola, Red Goose, Buster Brown Shoes,
and western stars items

Thompson, Chuck
Chuck Thompson & Associates
P.O. Box 11652, Houston, 77293
Specializing in advertising pocket mir-
rors, writes syndicated column, *Collect-
ing for Fun*

Tunks, Greg
150 Hohldale, Houston, 77022
Publisher of *Credit Card Collector* newsletter

Utah

Anderson, Tim
Box 461, Provo, 84603
801-226-1787
Specializing in autographs: buys single
items or collections—historical, movie
stars, Mormons, sports figures, etc.

Anderson, Warren R.
American West Archives
P.O. Box 100, Cedar City, 84720
Specializing in old stock certificates

and bonds, western documents and
books, financial ephemera, autographs,
maps, prints

Vermont

Barry, Kit
86 High St., Brattleboro, 05301
Author of *The Advertising Trade Card*
Specializing in advertising trade cards
and ephemera in general

Virginia

Bradfield, Jeff
Jeff's Antiques
Corner of Rt. 42 & Rt. 257, Dayton,
22821; 703-879-9961
Specializing in post cards, candy containers, toys, pottery, furniture, lamps,
and advertising items

Cocktails & Laughter Antiques
Monsen, Randall; Baer, Rod
P.O. Box 1503, Arlington, 22210; 703-
938-2129
Specializing in perfume bottles

Flanigan, Vicki
Flanigan's Antiques
P.O. Box 1662, Winchester, 22601
Specializing in antique dolls and hand
fans

Friend, Terry
R.R. 4, Box 152-D, Galax, 24333; 703-
236-9027 after 9:30 p.m. EST
Specializing in coffee mills
All inquiries please send SASE

Lechner, Mildred & Ralph
Box 554, Mechanicsville, 23111
Author Collector Books on salt shakers
Specializing in art and pattern glass salt
shakers circa 1870-1940

Reynolds, Charles
REYNOLDS TOYS
2836 Monroe St., Falls Church, 22042;
703-533-1322
Specializing in limited edition mechanical and still banks, figural bottle openers

Washington

Rothe, Linda
Box 1551, Bellevue, 98009
Specializing in Black Americana

West Virginia

Fostoria Glass Society of America
Inc.
Box 826, Moundsville, 26041
Specializing in Fostoria glass

Wisconsin

Apple, John
John Apple Antiques
1720 College Ave., Racine, 53403; 414-
633-3086
Specializing in brass cash registers and
parts

Bruggink, LeRoy F.
313 Ramaker Ave., Cedar Grove, 53013
Specializing in Tea Leaf ironstone,
kerosene lamps

Fortney, Daniel
Suite 713 Chalet at the River, 823 N.
2nd St., Milwaukee, 53203
Specializing in china and glass

Matzke, Gene
Gene's Badges & Emblems
2345 S. 28th St., Milwaukee, 53215;
414-383-8995
Specializing in police badges, patches,
and memorabilia

Rice, Ferill J.
302 Pheasant Run, Kaukauna, 54130
Specializing in Fenton art glass

Clubs, Newsletters, and Catalogs

American Clay Exchange
800 Murray Dr., El Cajon, CA 92020

American West Archives
Anderson, Warren
P.O. Box 100, Cedar City, Utah, 84720
18-page illustrated catalogs issued every two months. Has both fixed-price
and auction sections offering early
western documents, letters, stock certificates, autographs, and other ephemera. 1-year subscription: $8

Antique and Art Glass Salt Shaker
Collectors' Society
c/o Albert Mills, Secretary/Treasurer
348 N. Hamilton St., Painted Post,
New York, 14870

Antique Radio Club of America
81 Steeplechase Rd., Devon, PA 19333

Antique Stove Association
Clifford Boram, Secretary
417 N. Main St., Monticello, IN 47960
Inquiries should be accompanied by
SASE

Antique Wireless Association
Ormiston Rd., Breesport, NY 14816

Ark Antiques
Box 3133, New Haven, CT 06515; 203-
387-3754
Specializing in hand-wrought early
20th-century silver, jewelry, metalwork;
catalog available for $10

Arts & Crafts Quarterly
P.O. Box 3592, Station E
Trenton, NJ 08629
1-800-541-5787

Avon Collectors Club
For information contact Dick Pardini
3107 North El Dorado St., Dept. SAPG,
Stockton, CA 95204
Inquiries should be accompanied by
SASE

Black Americana Catalogs
Linda Rothe
Box 1551, Bellevue, WA 98009

British Royal Commemorative Souvenirs Mail Order Catalog
Audrey Zeder
6755 Coralite St., Long Beach, CA
90808

California Perfume Company
For information contact Dick Pardini
3107 North El Dorado St., Dept. SAPG,
Stockton, CA 95204
Inquiries should be accompanied by
SASE; not necessary when offering
items for sale

Candy Container Collectors of Amer-
ica
P.O. Box 1088
Washington, PA 15301

Central Florida Insulator Collectors
3557 Nicklaus Dr., Titusville, FL 32780

*Chicagoland Antique Advertizing
Slot Machine & Jukebox Gazette*
Ken Durham, Editor
P.O. Box 2426, Dept. S, Rockville, MD
20852
20-page newspaper published twice a
year, subscription: 4 issues for $10;
sample $5

Coin-Op Newsletter
Ken Durham, Publisher
909 26th St. NW, Washington, DC
20037
Subscription (10 issues) $24, sample
issue $5

The Cola Clan
Alice Fisher, Treasurer
2084 Continental Drive, N.E., Atlanta,
GA 30345

The Coleman Lite
Herb W. Ebendorf, Editor
The Coleman Co. Inc.
History Dept., Box 1762, Wichita, KS
67201
Once-in-awhile newsletter for collec-
tors of Coleman lamps, lanterns, irons,
and related items
Collectible Plastics Newsletter
P.O. Box 1099, Forestville, CA 95436
$4 for 6 issues, sample copy 75¢

Credit Card Collector newsletter
Greg Tunks, Publisher
150 Hohldale, Houston, TX 77022

Depression Glass Daze
12135 N. State St., Otisville, MI 48463

Doyle Auctioneers & Appraisers
Doyle, Robert A.
R.D. 3, Box 137, Osborne Hill Rd.,
Fishkill, NY 12524; 914-896-9492
Thousands of collectibles offered: call
for free calendar of upcoming auctions

Expo Collectors & Historians Organization (ECHO)
c/o Ed Orth, 1436 Killarney Ave., Los
Angeles, CA 90065; 213-221-9789
Newsletter published monthly

Fenton Art Glass Collectors of America Inc.
Williamstown, WV 26187

Figural Bottle Opener Collectors
c/o Barbara Rosen
6 Shoshone Trail, Wayne, NJ 07470

Fostoria Glass Society of America Inc.
P.O. Box 826, Moundsville, WV 26041

F.T.S. Inc.
416 Throop St., North Babylon, NY,
11704; 516-669-7232
Specializing in stein auctions with illustrated catalogs

Full House Antique Playing Cards &
Gambling Memorabilia
9320 Laurel Green Dr., Boynton Beach,
FL, 33437; 407-734-8690
Mail auction catalogs; will date and
price cards–include SASE

The Glaze, Pottery Collectors Newsletter
P.O. Box 4782, Birmingham, AL 35706

Glidden Collectors
P.O. Box 793, Olean, NY 14760; 716-373-3312
Publishing first newsletter September 1988

Hake's Americana & Collectibles
Specializing in character and personality collectibles along with artifacts of popular culture for over 20 years. To receive a catalog for their next 3,000-item mail/phone bid auction, send $3.00 to Hake's Americana, P.O. Box 1444M, York, PA, 17405

The Harrison Fisher Society
c/o Deena Zachritz
Rocking Chair Emporium
123 N. Glassell, Orange, CA 92666; 714-633-5206
Or (correspondence address) P.O. Box 8188, Redlands, CA 92373
Information and research on Harrison Fisher and network of collectors and dealers; publishes annual exchange newsletter

Heisey Collectors of America Inc.
National Heisey Glass Museum
169 W. Church St., Newark, OH 43055; 614-345-2932

Hot Tea, a bi-monthly magazine for teapot collectors
Tina M. Carter, Editor
822 S. Mollison, El Cajon, CA 92020
Annual subscription rate is $10.50; sample: $1.00

Ice Screamer
c/o Ed Marks, Publisher
P.O. Box 5387, Lancaster, PA 17601
Published bi-monthly, $15 for 1 year's dues

Indiana Historical Radio Society
245 N. Oakland Ave. Indianapolis, IN 46201

International Club for Collectors of Hatpins & Hatpin Holders (ICC of H&HH)
Lillian Baker, Founder
15237 Chanera Ave., Gardena, CA 90249; 213-329-2619
Monthly *Points* newsletter and *Pictorial Journal*

International Society of Antique Scale Collectors
Bob Stein, President
111 North Canal St., Suite 380, Chicago, IL 60606
Publishes quarterly magazine

Jukebox Collector magazine
Rick Botts, Publisher
2545 S.E. 60th Ct. Des Moines, IA 50317-5099

Loose Change Magazine
Jackie Durham, Agent
909 26th St. NW, Washington, DC, 20037; Monthly magazine, subscription: $39 (payable to Jackie Durham)

Mechanical Music Center
Mayer, Fran

18 Marshall St., Box 1078, S. Norwalk, CT 06854; 203-852-1780
Illustrated catalogs of mechanical musical instruments for sale, $5 annual subscription

National Association of Miniature Enthusiasts (N.A.M.E.)
Box 2621, Anaheim, CA 92804-0621; (714) 871-NAME

National Blue Ridge Newsletter
Norma Lilly
Highland Dr., Rt. 5, Box 62, Blountville, TN 37617
$9 per year (6 issues)

National Cambridge Collectors Inc.
P.O. Box 416, Cambridge, OH 43725

National Graniteware Society
4848 Reamer Rd., Center Point, IA 52213

National Insulator Association #256
3557 Nicklaus Dr., Titusville, FL 32780

National Reamer Association
c/o Dee Long, 112 S. Center, Lacon, IL 61540

New England Society of Open Salt Collectors
Mrs. Ruth Arch, Treasurer
Stoneridge Estates, 9 Casey Circle, Waltham, MA 02154; dues $5

Newspaper Collectors Society of America
Rick Brown
Box 19134-S, Lansing, MI 48901; 517-372-8381

North American Trap Collectors Association
21419 NE 212th Ave., Battle Ground, WA 98064
Dues: $7.50 per year; Newsletter published 6 times a year

The Occupied Japan Club
c/o Florence Archambault
29 Freeborn St., Newport, RI 02840
Publishes *The Upside Down World of an O.J. Collector,* a monthly newsletter. Please include SASE when requesting information.

The Occupied Japan Club
c/o Mark Bodenhofer
412 N. Olive
Maquoketa, IA 52060

Open Salt Collectors of the Atlantic Regions (O.S.C.A.R.)
Ed & Kay Berg, Newark, DE 19711; dues are $5

Open Salt Seekers of the West, Northern California Chapter
Shirley Thompson, Treasurer, 71 Del Vista Ct., Pleasant Hill, CA 94523; dues $5

Open Salt Seekers of the West, Southern California Chapter
Marie Smith, Treasurer, 4208 Country Club Dr., Bakersville, CA 93306; dues $5

Paperweight Collectors Association
120 Old Broadway, Garden City Park, NY 11040; 516-741-3090
Chapters in many states and Canada, England, New Zealand, and West Germany.

Pen Fancier's Club
1169 Overcash Dr., Dunedin, FL 34698
Publishes monthly magazine of pens and mechanical pencils

Postcard Mail Auctions
Run by Sally S. Carver, 179 South St., Chestnut Hill, MA 02167; 617-469-9175
Specializing in all better quality pre-1930 postcards; large illustrated auction published yearly

Precious Collectibles, for Precious Moments figurine collectors, *The Ornament Collector,* for Hallmark ornaments and other ornament collectors
Rosie Wells
R.R. 1, Canton, IL 61520
Write for free literature; publishes *The Secondary Market Price Guide for Precious Moments Collectibles,* and an annual guide for Hallmark ornaments

R. Lalique—listings of items for sale
John Danis
11028 Raleigh Ct., Rockford, IL 61111; 815-877-6098

Table Toppers
1340 West Irving Park Road, P.O. Box 161, Chicago, 60613; 312-769-3184
Individual membership is $18 per year, which includes *Table Topics,* a bi-monthly newsletter for those who appreciate and enjoy spreading information about table-top collectibles and the multiple ways in which they can be used and enjoyed.

Tea Leaf Club International
P.O. Box 904, Mt. Prospect, IL 60056
Publishes *Tea Leaf Reading* newsletter, sent to all members as part of membership fee
$20 for single membership, $25 for double membership per year

Thermometer Collectors Club of America
Warren D. Harris, President
4555 Auburn Blvd., Suite #11, Sacramento, CA 95841

Thimble Collectors International
6411 Montego Road
Louisville, KY 40228
Three Rivers Depression Era Glass Society
Meetings held 1st Monday of each month at Holiday Inn, Oakdale, PA; for more information contact Nancy Zamborsky (current Corresponding Secretary), 4038 Willett Road, Pittsburgh, PA 15227; 412-882-1989

Tiffin Glass Collectors
Meetings at Seneca Cty. Museum on 2nd Tuesday of each month
P.O. Box 554, Tiffin, OH 44883

Tops & Bottoms Club
(Rene Lalique perfumes only)
c/o Madeleine France
P.O. Box 15555, Plantation, FL 33318

The Torquay Pottery Collectors Society
c/o Jerry & Gerry Kline, Publicity Chairmen
604 Orchard View Dr., Maumee, OH 43537; for membership application forms, please send SASE

The Torquay Pottery Collectors Society
c/o Mrs. Barbara Treat, Coordinator
479 Burley, Collierville, TN 38017; for membership application forms, please send SASE

The Trade Card Journal
Barry, Kit
A quarterly publication on the social and historical use of trade cards

Uhl Collectors Society
2822 Mariposa Dr., Terre Haute, IN 47803

Vernon Views newsletter
P.O. Box 945, Scottsdale, AZ 85252
Published quarterly beginning with the spring issue, $5 per year

Wheeler-Tanner ESCAPES
P.O. Box 349, Great Falls, Montana 59403
40-page catalog of magician/escape artist equipment from trick and regulation handcuffs, padlocks, leg shackles, straight jackets to picks, and pick sets. Books on all of the above and much more. Catalog: $3

World's Fair Collectors Society Inc
P.O. Box 20806, Sarasota, FL 33583; 813-923-2590
Publishes monthly *Fair News* newsletter
Michael R. Pender, Editor
Dues: (Including subscription to *Fair News*) $10 per year in U.S.A. and Canada; $16 per year overseas

Books on Antiques and Collectibles

Most of the following books are available from your local book seller or antique dealer, or on loan from your public library. If you are unable to locate certain titles in your area you may order by mail from COLLECTOR BOOKS, P.O. Box 3009, Paducah, KY 42002-3009. Add $2.00 for postage for the first book ordered and $.25 for each additional book. Include item number, title and price when ordering. Allow 14 to 21 days for delivery. All books are well illustrated and contain current values.

Books on Glass and Pottery

1810	American Art Glass, Shuman	$29.95
1517	American Belleek, Gaston	$19.95
2016	Bedroom & Bathroom Glassware of the Depression Years	$19.95
1312	Blue & White Stoneware, McNerney	$9.95
1959	Blue Willow, 2nd Ed., Gaston	$14.95
1627	Children's Glass Dishes, China & Furniture II, Lechler	$19.95
1892	Collecting Royal Haeger, Garmon	$19.95
2017	Collector's Ency. of Depression Glass, Florence, 9th Ed.	$19.95
1373	Collector's Ency of Amercian Dinnerware, Cunningham	$24.95
1812	Collector's Ency. of Fiesta, Huxford	$19.95
1439	Collector's Ency. of Flow Blue China, Gaston	$19.95
1961	Collector's Ency of Fry Glass, Fry Glass Society	$24.95
1813	Collector's Encyclopedia of Geisha Girl Porcelain, Litts	$19.95
1664	Collector's Ency. of Heisey Glass, Bredehoft	$24.95
1915	Collector's Ency. of Hall China, 2nd Ed., Whitmyer	$19.95
1358	Collector's Ency. of McCoy Pottery, Huxford	$19.95
1039	Collector's Ency. of Nippon Porcelain I, Van Patten	$19.95
1350	Collector's Ency. of Nippon Porcelain II, Van Patten	$19.95
1665	Collector's Ency. of Nippon Porcelain III, Van Patten	$24.95
1447	Collector's Ency. of Noritake, Van Patten	$19.95
1038	Collector's Ency. of Occupied Japan, 2nd Ed., Florence	$14.95
1719	Collector's Ency. of Occupied Japan III, Florence	$19.95
2019	Collector's Ency. of Occupied Japan IV, Florence	$14.95
1715	Collector's Ency. of R.S. Prussia II, Gaston	$24.95
1034	Collector's Ency. of Roseville Pottery, Huxford	$19.95
1035	Collector's Ency. of Roseville Pottery, 2nd Ed., Huxford	$19.95
1623	Coll. Guide to Country Stoneware & Pottery, Raycraft	$9.95
1523	Colors in Cambridge, National Cambridge Society	$19.95
1425	Cookie Jars, Westfall	$9.95
1843	Covered Animal Dishes, Grist	$14.95
1844	Elegant Glassware of the Depression Era, 3rd Ed., Florence	$19.95
2024	Kitchen Glassware of the Depression Years, 4th Florence	$19.95
1465	Haviland Collectibles & Art Objects, Gaston	$19.95
1917	Head Vases Id & Value Guide, Cole	$14.95
1392	Majolica Pottery, Katz-Marks	$9.95
1669	Majolica Pottery, 2nd Series, Katz-Marks	$9.95
1919	Pocket Guide to Depression Glass, 6th Ed., Florence	$9.95
1438	Oil Lamps II, Thuro	$19.95
1670	Red Wing Collectibles, DePasquale	$9.95
1440	Red Wing Stoneware, DePasquale	$9.95
1958	So. Potteries Blue Ridge Dinnerware, 3rd Ed., Newbound	$14.95
1889	Standard Carnival Glass, 2nd Ed., Edwards	$24.95
1941	Standard Carnival Glass Price Guide, Edwards	$7.95
1814	Wave Crest, Glass of C.F. Monroe, Cohen	$29.95
1848	Very Rare Glassware of the Depression Years, Florence	$24.95

Books on Dolls & Toys

1887	American Rag Dolls, Patino	$14.95
1749	Black Dolls, Gibbs	$14.95
1514	Character Toys & Collectibles 1st Series, Longest	$19.95
1750	Character Toys & Collectibles, 2nd Series, Longest	$19.95
2021	Collectible Male Action Figures, Manos	$14.95
1529	Collector's Ency. of Barbie Dolls, DeWein	$19.95
1066	Collector's Ency. of Half Dolls, Marion	$29.95
1891	French Dolls in Color, 3rd Series, Smith	$14.95
1631	German Dolls, Smith	$9.95
1635	Horsman Dolls, Gibbs	$19.95
1067	Madame Alexander Collector's Dolls, Smith	$19.95
2025	Madame Alexander Price Guide #15, Smith	$7.95
1995	Modern Collectors Dolls, Vol. I, Smith	$19.95

1516	Modern Collector's Dolls V, Smith	$19.95
1540	Modern Toys, 1930-1980, Baker	$19.95
2033	Patricia Smith Doll Values, Antique to Modern, 6th ed.,	$9.95
1886	Stern's Guide to Disney	$14.95
1513	Teddy Bears & Steiff Animals, Mandel	$9.95
1817	Teddy Bears & Steiff Animals, 2nd, Mandel	$19.95
2028	Toys, Antique & Collectible, Longest	$14.95
1630	Vogue, Ginny Dolls, Smith	$19.95
1648	World of Alexander-Kins, Smith	$19.95
1808	Wonder of Barbie, Manos	$9.95
1430	World of Barbie Dolls, Manos	$9.95

Other Collectibles

1457	American Oak Furniture, McNerney	$9.95
1846	Antique & Collectible Marbles, Grist, 2nd Ed.	$9.95
1712	Antique & Collectible Thimbles, Mathis	$19.95
1880	Antique Iron, McNerney	$9.95
1748	Antique Purses, Holiner	$19.95
1868	Antique Tools, Our American Heritage, McNerney	$9.95
2015	Archaic Indian Points & Knives, Edler	$14.95
1426	Arrowheads & Projectile Points, Hothem	$7.95
1278	Art Nouveau & Art Deco Jewelry, Baker	$9.95
1714	Black Collectibles, Gibbs	$19.95
1666	Book of Country, Raycraft	$19.95
1960	Book of Country Vol II, Raycraft	$19.95
1811	Book of Moxie, Potter	$29.95
1128	Bottle Pricing Guide, 3rd Ed., Cleveland	$7.95
1751	Christmas Collectibles, Whitmyer	$19.95
1752	Christmas Ornaments, Johnston	$19.95
1713	Collecting Barber Bottles, Holiner	$24.95
2018	Collector's Ency. of Graniteware, Greguire	$24.95
1634	Coll. Ency. of Salt & Pepper Shakers, Davern	$19.95
2020	Collector's Ency. of Salt & Pepper Shakers II, Davern	$19.95
1916	Collector's Guide to Art Deco, Gaston	$14.95
1753	Collector's Guide to Baseball Memorabilia, Raycraft	$14.95
1537	Collector's Guide to Country Baskets, Raycraft	$9.95
1437	Collector's Guide to Country Furniture, Raycraft	$9.95
1842	Collector's Guide to Country Furniture II, Raycraft	$14.95
1962	Collector's Guide to Decoys, Huxford	$14.95
1441	Collector's Guide to Post Cards, Wood	$9.95
1716	Fifty Years of Fashion Jewelry, Baker	$19.95
2022	Flea Market Trader, 6th Ed., Huxford	$9.95
1668	Flint Blades & Proj. Points of the No. Am. Indian, Tully	$24.95
1755	Furniture of the Depression Era, Swedberg	$19.95
1424	Hatpins & Hatpin Holders, Baker	$9.95
1964	Indian Axes & Related Stone Artifacts, Hothem	$14.95
2023	Keen Kutter Collectibles, 2nd Ed., Heuring	$14.95
1212	Marketplace Guide to Oak Furniture, Blundell	$17.95
1918	Modern Guns, Id. & Values, 7th Ed., Quertermous	$12.95
1181	100 Years of Collectible Jewelry, Baker	$9.95
1965	Pine Furniture, Our Am. Heritage, McNerney	$14.95
1124	Primitives, Our American Heritage, McNerney	$8.95
1759	Primitives, Our American Heritage, 2nd Series, McNerney	$14.95
2026	Railroad Collectibles, 4th Ed., Baker	$14.95
1632	Salt & Pepper Shakers, Guarnaccia	$9.95
1888	Salt & Pepper Shakers II, Guarnaccia	$14.95
1816	Silverplated Flatware, 3rd Ed., Hagan	$14.95
2027	Standard Baseball Card Pr. Gd., Florence	$9.95
1922	Standard Bottle Pr. Gd., Sellari	$14.95
1966	Standard Fine Art Value Guide, Huxford	$29.95
1890	The Old Book Value Guide	$19.95
1923	Wanted to Buy	$9.95
1885	Victorian Furniture, McNerney	$9.95